The *RHS Plant Finder* and much more ...on CD-ROM

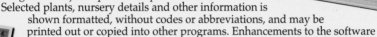

Combining an electronic version of *The RHS Plant Finder 1998/99* with other useful gardening publications and databases, this Windows CD-ROM offers a unique and remarkable resource for serious gardeners, horticultural professionals and botanists.

Based on the same data as the best-selling book, you can browse the CD-ROM or quickly find particular plants by searching on all or just a part of the plant name.

Selected plants, nursery details and other information is shown formatted, without codes or abbreviations, and may be printed out or copied into other programs. Enhancements to the software on this third edition of the CD allow you to view all the plants listed for a particular supplier and to make a 'pick list' of chosen suppliers as well as a particular choice of plants.

Also in *The Plant Finder Reference Library* are databases of the new 1998 editions of *The Seed Search* and *The Fruit & Veg Finder*, an invaluable *Dictionary of Common Names*, a *Latin Lexicon*, *Brummit's Authors & Genera* and other related information. This year, the disc is also available in an extended 'professional' edition with additional material intended for trade and scientific users, including international plant finders, wholesale suppliers, cultivar registers and the plant directory from the acclaimed *Hillier Gardener's Guide to Trees & Shrubs*.

Further information & credit card orders ☎ (01273) 476151
Website http://www.plantfinder.co.uk

The Plant Finder Reference Library *1998/99*

▶ **ORDER DIRECT FROM THE PUBLISHER**

Please supply ..... copies of Standard CD-ROM @ £25 inc VAT

..... copies of Professional CD-ROM @ £75 inc VAT

plus p&p £1 UK, £2 Europe, £3 Rest of world

I enclose a cheque for £ .... to The Plant Finder)

or ple................................ ....ican Express card (delete as appropriate)

☐☐ ☐☐☐☐ ☐☐

expiry ....er ☐☐

▶ O.... ....COUPON FOR MORE INFORMATION

Name ....

Organis..

Address ....

.... **Post code** ....

Phone number .... **E-mail** ....

Please post orders in an envelope to The Plant Finder, FREEPOST, Lewes, BN7 2ZZ. No stamp is necessary if posted in the UK.

A wealth of gardening information at your fingertips

Standard CD-ROM just £25 plus p&p...
- **The RHS Plant Finder 1998/99**
- *The Seed Search 1998*
- *The Fruit & Veg Finder 1998*
- *Arboreta & Gardens Guide*
- *National Plant Collections 1998*
- *Dictionary of Common Names*
- *Lexicon of Latin Names*
- *Brummit Authors & Genera*
- *Flora-for-Fauna*
- *UK & International Garden Societies*
- *National Trust and NT for Scotland Gardens*
- *Internet Directory for Botany*

Professional version just £75 plus p&p includes all of the above and...
- *The PPP Index 3rd edition*
- *Plantenvinder 1997/98*
- *Gardening by Mail 1998*
- *Wholesale suppliers*
- *Hillier Gardener's Guide to Trees & Shrubs*
- *NCCPG National Collections Plant Finder*
- *Cultivar registers*
- *Parks & Gardens*

CD-ROM for Windows 3.x, 95 or NT. 386 or faster PC

The Plant Finder, 10 Market Street, Lewes, BN7 2NB
Tel (01273) 476151 Fax (01273) 480871 E-mail jstockdale@compuserve.com
Illustrations & quotes from previous editions.
Contents correct at press time but subject to revision for final disc.

No stamp necessary if posted in UK

The Plant Finder
FREEPOST
Lewes
BN7 2ZZ

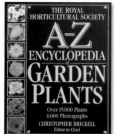
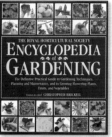
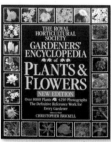
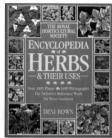
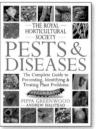

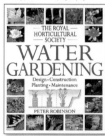
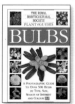

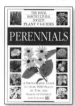

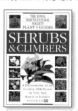

ONLY
£9.99

Every Gardener's best buy

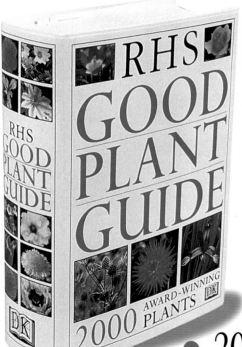

- 2000 plants -
- 1000 colour photographs -

Published 26 March 1998 • ISBN 07513 0532 4

THE
RHS
PLANT FINDER
1998-99

THE
RHS
PLANT
FINDER
1998-99

DEVISED BY CHRIS PHILIP

COMPILED BY THE
ROYAL HORTICULTURAL SOCIETY

EDITED BY TONY LORD
WITH THE BOTANISTS
OF THE RHS GARDEN, WISLEY

DORLING KINDERSLEY
LONDON • NEW YORK • SYDNEY • MOSCOW

A DORLING KINDERSLEY BOOK

Published by
Dorling Kindersley Ltd
9 Henrietta Street
LONDON WC2E 8PS
Visit us on the World Wide Web at http://www.dk.com

British Library Cataloguing Publication Data.
A Catalogue record for this book is available from the British Library.

ISBN 0 7513 0512-X
ISSN 0961-2599

Compiled by
The Royal Horticultural Society
80 Vincent Square
London
SW1P 2PE
Registered charity no: 222879
Visit us on the World Wide Web at http://www.rhs.org.uk

Maps by Alan Cooper

Printed by Unwin Brothers, Woking, Surrey
A member of the Martins Printing Group

Front cover photographs clockwise from top right: *Eryngium* × *oliverianum*, *Erythronium revolutum*,
Hakonechloa macra 'Aureola', *Euonymus oxyphyllus*, *Thunbergia grandiflora*, *Primula* Gold-laced
Group, *Rosa* 'Gloire de Dijon', *Tulbaghia simmleri*, *Dahlia* 'Bishop of Llandaff', *Daphne cneorum*

Back cover photographs clockwise from top right: *Enkianthus campanulatus*, *Salvia guaranitica*
'Blue Enigma', *Protea cynaroides*, *Griselinia littoralis* 'Dixon's Cream', *Passiflora* × *violacea*,
Cardiocrinum giganteum, *Viola sororia* 'Freckles', *Verbascum chaixii* (Cotswold Group)
'Cotswold Queen', *Iris* 'Carnaby', *Fritillaria camschatcensis*

CONTENTS

SYMBOLS AND ABBREVIATIONS

Symbols appearing to the left of the name

*	Name not validated. Not listed in the appropriate International Registration Authority checklist nor in works cited in the Bibliography. For fuller discussion see Plant Names on page 12
I	Invalid name. See *International Code of Botanical Nomenclature* 1994 and *International Code of Nomenclature for Cultivated Plants* 1995. For fuller discussion see Plant Names on page 12
N	Refer to Nomenclature Notes on page 17
¶	New plant entry in this year's Edition (or reinstated from list of previously deleted plants)
◆	New or amended synonym or cross-reference included for the first time this year
§	Plant listed elsewhere in the PLANT DIRECTORY under a synonym
×	Hybrid genus
+	Graft hybrid genus

Symbols appearing to the right of the name

†	National Council for the Conservation of Plants and Gardens (NCCPG) Collection exists for all or part of this genus
♀	The Royal Horticultural Society's Award of Garden Merit
®	Registered Trade Mark
™	Trade Mark
(d)	double-flowered
F	Fruit
(f)	female
(m)	male
(v)	variegated plant

For abbreviations relating to individual genera see **Classification of Genera** page 23.

For **Collectors' References** see page 28.

Symbols and Abbreviations used as part of the name

×	hybrid species
aff.	affinis (allied to)
cl.	clone
cv(s)	cultivar(s)
f.	forma (botanical form)
g.	grex
sp.	species
subsp.	subspecies
subvar.	subvarietas (botanical subvariety)
var.	varietas (botanical variety)

IMPORTANT NOTE TO USERS

To avoid disappointment, we suggest that you always:

> *Check with the nursery before visiting or ordering and always use the current edition of the book.*

The RHS Plant Finder exists to put gardeners in touch with nurserymen. It does *not* offer value judgements on the nurseries or the plants it lists nor intend any reflection on any other nursery or plant *not* listed.

In addition *The RHS Plant Finder* tries to cross-reference plant names to their correct *valid* name, although in some cases it is all too easy to understand why British nurserymen have preferred a more immediately comprehensible English name! *Every* name, apart from 'common' names, that has been shown in a catalogue has been listed, which is why there are so many cross-references. It is, clearly, the nursery's responsibility to ensure that its stock is accurately named both in its catalogue and on the plant when it is sold.

Plant Deletions
In this edition the **Plant Deletions Index** contains plant names that were listed in one or other of the three previous editions of *The RHS Plant Finder*, but are now no longer represented. A supplementary list of the 10,000 or so earlier deletions (only listed in an edition prior to 1995) is available on request. Please send three £1 stamps to:
The Administrator, The RHS Plant Finder, RHS Garden, Wisley, Woking, Surrey GU23 6QB.

Bibliography
The Bibliography has been omitted from this edition because of space constraints due to the increased size of the Plant Directory. To obtain a copy of the Bibliography please send a £1 stamp to:
The Administrator, The RHS Plant Finder, RHS Garden, Wisley, Woking, Surrey GU23 6QB.
The full list of Plant Deletions and the Bibliography are also available on the CD-ROM *The Plant Finder Reference Library.*

The Compiler and Editors of *The RHS Plant Finder* have taken every care, in the time available, to check all the information supplied to them by the nurseries concerned. Nevertheless, in a work of this kind, containing as it does hundreds of thousands of separate computer encodings, errors and omissions will, inevitably, occur. Neither the RHS, the Publisher nor the Editors can accept responsibility for any consequences that may arise from such errors.

If you find mistakes we hope that you will let us know so that the matter can be corrected in the next edition.

PREFACE

This year the publication of *The RHS Plant Finder* is touched with sadness. Chris Philip, originator of the idea and compiler of the book from 1987 to 1996, died on 10 January 1998. Unable to find particular plants he wanted for a new garden, Chris dreamed up the idea of a plant finder and compiled the first edition in April 1987. It sold 10,000 copies. Since then sales have increased each year and the Plant Finder has established itself as an integral part of the gardening year. In 1996 Chris received a special award from the Garden Writers Guild for devising and compiling *The Plant Finder* and in November 1997 he was awarded the Gold Veitch Memorial Medal by the RHS for his help in the advancement and improvement of the practice of horticulture. Both awards are fitting tributes to a remarkable man of vision and determination.

Due to demand, last year's edition was reprinted for the first time during the year and we look forward to this 12th edition being even more successful. While in part this is due to Dorling Kindersley, who handle the marketing and distribution of the book for the RHS, we are well aware that without the cooperation of all the nurseries there would be no *RHS Plant Finder* and we are very grateful to the nursery owners for the amount of work they put into the preparation of their entries. This year more than 900 plants have come back into the main list from the wilderness of the Plant Deletions section – very good news indeed for those gardeners who are trying to source a rare individual.

In parallel with the compilation of the nursery lists, a great deal of work goes on behind the scenes at Wisley and elsewhere checking plant names for accuracy and cross-referencing synonyms. All the botanists and horticulturists involved with this are working towards a common goal of achieving an accurate and stable source of plant names. Research continues as an essential part of the Society's work and all the resulting information is constantly input into our horticultural database. This is used as a resource for *The RHS Plant Finder* and other publications, including the new handbook of AGM plants which will be published by the RHS later this year.

The Award of Garden Merit (AGM) is the Society's highest accolade for plants of excellence for garden use, and encompasses all plant groups whether grown in the open or under glass. *The RHS Plant Finder* marks such plants with the AGM logo, a trophy symbol ♀.

Every year many comments and queries concerning nomenclature are received. Regretfully it is impossible for Dr Tony Lord or the Society to reply to these individually, but we do assure nurseries that all their queries are considered.

As in the previous two years, an electronic version of *The RHS Plant Finder* is included in *The Plant Finder Reference Library* on CD-ROM. Details of this are given at the end of the book. The Society is also active on the internet and can be reached at our web site http://www.rhs.org.uk. This includes details of all RHS shows, events, membership, publications, examinations and scientific work, including a database catalogue of the plants growing in the RHS Garden, Wisley.

Gordon Rae
Director General
The Royal Horticultural Society

HOW TO USE THE DIRECTORY

HOW TO FIND YOUR PLANT

Look up the plant you require in the alphabetical **Plant Directory**. Against each plant you will find one or more four-letter Codes, for example SLan, each Code representing one nursery offering that plant. The first letter of each Code indicates the main area of the country in which the nursery is situated, based on their county:

Geographical Key to Nursery Codes

[C] = **South West England**
Avon, Devon, Dorset, Channel Isles, Cornwall, Isles of Scilly, Somerset & Wiltshire.

[E] = **Eastern England**
Cambridgeshire, Essex, Lincolnshire, Norfolk & Suffolk.

[G] = **Scotland**
Borders, Central, Dumfries & Galloway, Fife, Grampian, Highlands, Inverness, Strathclyde.

[I] = **Northern Ireland & Republic of Ireland**.

[L] = **London area**
Bedfordshire, Berkshire, Buckinghamshire, Hertfordshire, London, Middlesex, Surrey.

[M] = **Midlands**
Cheshire, Derbyshire, Isle of Man, Leicestershire, Northamptonshire, Nottinghamshire, Oxfordshire, Staffordshire, Warwickshire, West Midlands.

[N] = **Northern England**
Cleveland, Cumbria, Durham, East Yorkshire, Greater Manchester, Humberside, Lancashire, Merseyside, Northumberland, North Yorkshire, South Yorkshire, Tyne & Wear, West Yorkshire.

[S] = **Southern England**
East Sussex, Hampshire, Isle of Wight, Kent, West Sussex.

[W] = **Wales and Western England**
All Welsh counties, Gloucestershire, Herefordshire, Shropshire and Worcestershire.

[X] = **Abroad**

Turn to the **Code-Nursery Index** on page 739 where, in alphabetical order of Codes, you will find details of each nursery which offers the plant in question. If you wish to visit any of these nurseries you can find its *approximate* location on one of the maps at the back. Those few nurseries which sell *only* by Mail Order are not shown on the maps. *Always check that the nursery you select has the plant in stock before you set out.*

Widely Available Plants
In some cases, against the plant name you will see the term 'Widely available' instead of a Nursery Code. Clearly, if we were to include every plant listed by all nurseries, *The RHS Plant Finder* would become unmanageably bulky. We have therefore had to ask nurseries to restrict their entries to only those plants that are not already well represented. As a result, if more than 30 nurseries offer any plant the Directory gives no Code and the plant is listed as 'Widely available'. You should have little difficulty in finding these in local nurseries or garden centres. However, if any readers do have difficulty in finding such plants, we will be pleased to send them a full list of all the nurseries that we have on file as stockists. This could include anything from 31 to a maximum of 50. Please write to: **The Administrator, The RHS Plant Finder, RHS Garden, Wisley, Woking, Surrey GU23 6QB**

All such enquiries *must* include the full name of the plant being sought, as shown in *The RHS Plant Finder*, together with an *A5 size stamped addressed envelope.*

If you have difficulty finding your plant
If you cannot immediately find the plant you seek, look through the various species of the genus. **You may be using an incomplete name**. The problem is most likely to arise in very large genera such as *Phlox* where there are a number of possible species, each with a large number of cultivars. A search through the whole genus may well bring success.

In the **Plant Directory, plants are listed in alphabetical order of cultivar name,** including names with trade designations attached. Such entries may appear to be out of sequence until this explanation is taken into account.

Descriptive terms which appear after the main part of the name, are shown in a smaller font to distinguish name parts that are authors, common names, collectors' codes and other descriptive terms. For example, *Acaena anserinifolia* Druce, *Lobelia tupa* dark orange.

If the plant you seek is not listed in the **Plant Directory**, it is possible that a nursery in the **Additional Nursery Index** which specialises in similar plants may be able to offer it. In addition to the plants listed in their catalogues, many nurseries are often able to supply other plants of the same general type that they specialise in. They may not list them if they only have a few available. In some cases they can arrange to propagate special items from their stock plants.

It may be that the plant name you seek is a synonym. Our intention is to list Nursery Codes only against the correct botanical name; where you look up a synonym you will be cross-referred to the correct name. **Major new cross-references** and synonyms have been marked with a ◆. This sign has only been used when the genus, species or cultivar name has been altered, but not where there have been merely minor typographic or orthographic changes.

If a cross-reference appears to go nowhere, check if the entry appears in **Plant Deletions**. Please see the section on Plant Deletions on page 10.

Nursery-Code Index

For convenience, a reverse **Nursery-Code Index** is included on page 731. This gives the names of all nurseries listed in the book in alphabetical order of nursery name together with their relevant Codes, if they are listed in the Plant Directory, or if not, the Index in which they appear.

Additional Nursery Index

The **Additional Nursery Index**, on page 842, contains brief details of other nurseries that have not been included in the **Plant Directory**. They may be listed in this Index for a number of reasons, for example, their stock is small and changes too quickly for them to be able to issue a viable catalogue, or the major part of their stock would have to be listed as 'Widely available', or simply because their latest Catalogue was not received in time for inclusion. Again, their catalogues may either give mainly common names (and this particularly applies to herb nurseries), or Latin names which do not provide sufficient information to establish easily the genus or species of the plant concerned. The location of these nurseries on the maps is marked by their listed numbers.

SUPPORTING INFORMATION ABOUT PLANTS

Classification of Genera

Genera including a large number of species or with many cultivars are often subdivided into groups, each based on a particular characteristic or combination of characteristics. Colour of flower or fruit and shape of flower are common examples, and with fruit, whether a cultivar is grown for culinary or dessert purposes. How such groups are named differs from genus to genus.

To help users of *The RHS Plant Finder* find exactly the plants they want, the majority of classifications used within cultivated genera are listed with codes, and each species or cultivar is marked with the appropriate code in brackets after its name in the **Plant Directory**. The codes relating to edible fruits are listed with the more specialised classifications; these apply across several genera. To find the explanation of each code, simply look up the code under the genus concerned in the **Classification of Genera** on page 23.

Trade Designations (Selling Names) and Plant Breeders' Rights

Plants granted protection under Plant Breeders' Rights (PBR) legislation, and those with high-volume international sales, are often given a code or nonsense name for registration purposes. Under the rules of the *International Code of Nomenclature for Cultivated Plants 1995* (ICNCP), such a name, established by a legal process, has to be regarded as the correct cultivar name for the plant. Unfortunately, the names are often unpronounceable and usually meaningless so the plants are given other names designed to attract sales when they are released. These are often referred to as selling names but are officially termed trade designations. Also, when a cultivar name is translated into a language other than that in which it was published, the translation is regarded as a trade designation in the same way as a PBR selling name. The name in its original language is the correct cultivar name.

While PBRs remain active it is a legal requirement for both names to appear on a label at point-of-sale. The reason for this may not appear obvious until it is realised that there is potentially no limit to the number of trade designations for any one plant. In reality, most plants are sold under only one trade designation, but some, especially roses, are sold under a number of names, particularly when cultivars are introduced to other countries. Usually, the registered or original cultivar name is the only way to ensure that the same plant is not bought unwittingly under two or more different trade designations. Although the use of trade designations goes against the principle that a cultivar should have only one correct name, the ICNCP has had to accommodate them, and *The RHS Plant Finder* follows its recommendations. These are always to quote the cultivar name and trade designation together and to style the trade designation in a different typeface, without single quotation marks. In this edition, all known cultivar names have been added for roses. This will inevitably make it a little less convenient to find a variety known to the user only by its trade designation but will avoid any possibility of confusion, particularly in the regrettably increasing number of cases in which several different trade designations are used for the same cultivar.

Example in *Rosa*:

| Picasso | See *R. Picasso*='Macpic' |
| Picasso='Macpic' | EBls MAus MGan |

The first of these names will be found alphabetically under the first letter of the trade designation (Picasso); the second name by the first letter of the cultivar name ('Macpic').

In the **Plant Directory, plants are listed in alphabetical order of cultivar name,** including names with trade designations attached. Such entries may appear to be out of sequence until this explanation is taken into account.

We often receive queries as to whether certain varieties are the subject of Plant Breeders' Rights. Up to date information on all matters concerning PBR in the UK can be obtained from: Mrs J G H Lee at the Plant Variety Rights Office, White House Lane, Huntingdon Road, Cambridge CB3 0LF. Telephone (01223) 342350, Fax (01223) 342386.

For details of plants which may be covered by Community Rights contact the Community Plant Variety Office (CPVO), 102 Rue de la Loi, 1st Floor Office 1/11, B-1040, Brussels, Belgium. Telephone +32 2 299 1944, Fax +32 2 299 1946.

Variegated Plants
Following a suggestion from the Variegated Plant Group of the Hardy Plant Society, we have added a (v) to those plants which are 'variegated' although this may not be apparent from their name. The dividing line between variegation and less distinct colour marking is necessarily arbitrary and plants with light veins, pale, silver or dark zones or leaves flushed in paler colours are not shown as being variegated unless there is an absolutely sharp distinction between paler and darker zones.

For further details of the Variegated Plant Group, please write to: Stephen Taffler, 18 Hayes End Manor, South Petherton, Somerset TA13 5BE.

Following the **Plant Directory** and the **Nursery Indexes**, towards the end of the book, are several further indexes. These include:

Reverse Synonyms
It is likely that users of this book will come across names in certain genera which they did not expect to find. This may be because species have been transferred from another genus (or genera). In the list of **Reverse Synonyms** on page 866, the left-hand name of each pair is that of an accepted genus to which species have been transferred from the genus on the right. Sometimes all species will have been transferred, but in many cases only a few will be affected. Consulting **Reverse Synonyms** enables users to find the genera from which species have been transferred. If the right-hand genus is then found in the **Plant Directory**, the movements of species become clear through the cross-references in the nursery-code column.

Plant Deletions
The **Plant Deletions Index** contains plant names that were listed in one or other of the three previous editions of *The RHS Plant Finder*, but are now no longer represented. A supplementary list of the 10,000 or so earlier deletions (only listed in an edition prior to 1995) is available on request (from the address at the bottom of this section). Please send three £1 stamps. There are a few instances where a genus exists in the main **Plant Directory** but with no apparent entries for either species or cultivars. These will be found in the **Plant Deletions Index** on page 870 or the supplementary list. It is also possible that some cross-references may not apparently refer to an entry in the main Directory. Again this is because the plant in question had a supplier or suppliers but is now in the **Plant Deletions Index** or the supplementary list. These references are deliberately kept so as to provide an historic record of synonyms and plant availability and to aid those who wish to try and find any of these 'deleted' plants.

These deletions arise, not only because the nursery that supplied the plants may have gone out of business, but also because some nurseries who were included previously have not responded to our latest questionnaire and have thus had to be deleted. Such plants may well be still available but we have no current knowledge of their whereabouts. Furthermore, some items may have been misnamed by nurseries in previous editions, but are now appearing under their correct name.

For those who wish to try and find previously listed plants, back editions of *The RHS Plant Finder* are still available at £6.00 (incl. p&p) from **The Administrator, The RHS Plant Finder, RHS Garden, Wisley, Woking, Surrey GU23 6QB. Cheques should be made payable to RHS Enterprises Ltd.**

Hardy Plant Society Search List

During the last few years the Hardy Plant Society has published a search list of scarce and desirable plants that might not be available in the British Isles. As a result, numerous new plants have been brought into cultivation and many old cultivars have been reintroduced. The HPS has built up a list of about 850 plants about which it is keen to obtain further information. See page 908.

SUPPORTING INFORMATION ABOUT NURSERIES

The details given for each nursery (listed in the relevant Index at the back) have been compiled from information supplied to us in answer to a questionnaire. In some cases, because of constraints of space, the entries have been slightly abbreviated and blanks have been left where no information has been provided.

Opening Times

The word 'daily' implies every day including Sunday and Bank Holidays. Although opening times have been published as submitted and where applicable, it is *always* advisable, especially if travelling a long distance, to check with the nursery first.

Mail Order - UK & EC

Many nurseries provide a Mail Order service which, in many cases, now extends to all members of the European Community. Where it is shown that there is 'No minimum charge' (Nmc) it should be realised that to send even one plant may involve the nursery in substantial postage and packing costs. Even so, some nurseries may not be prepared to send tender or bulky plants. Nurseries that are prepared to undertake Mail Order to both UK and EC destinations are shown in **bold** type in the **Code-Nursery Index**.

Catalogue Cost

Some nurseries offer their catalogue free, or for a few stamps (the odd value quoted can usually be made up from a combination of first or second class stamps), but a *large* (at least A5) stamped addressed envelope is always appreciated as well.

Overseas customers should use an equivalent number of International Reply Coupons (IRCs) in place of stamps.

Wholesale or Retail

The main trading method is indicated, but it should be stressed that some wholesalers do have retail outlets and many retailers also have a wholesale trade and would frequently be prepared to offer discounts for large single orders.

Export - (Outside the EC)

Nurseries that are prepared to consider exporting are indicated. However, there is usually a substantial minimum charge and, in addition, all the additional costs of Phytosanitary Certificates and Customs would have to be met by the purchaser. Some nurseries export 'seed only' (S0) or 'bulbs only' (B0).

Deleted Nurseries

Every year a few nurseries ask to be deleted. This may be because they are about to move or close, or they are changing the way in which they trade. A small number do not reply so we have no current information concerning them and they are therefore deleted.

Please, never use an old edition.

New Nursery Entries

Nurseries that are appearing in *The RHS Plant Finder* for the first time this year are printed in **bold type** in the **Nursery-Code Index** starting on page 731.

If any other nursery wishes to be considered for inclusion in the next edition of *The RHS Plant Finder* (1999-2000), please write for details to:

The Administrator
The RHS Plant Finder
RHS Garden
Wisley
Woking
Surrey
GU23 6QB

The closing date for new entries will be 31 January 1999.

PLANT NAMES

'The question of nomenclature is always a vexed one. The only thing certain is, that it is impossible to please everyone.'

W.J. Bean - Preface to First Edition of
Trees & Shrubs Hardy in the British Isles.

The most significant change during the last year has been the agreement to preserve *Chrysanthemum* as the botanical generic name for florists' chrysanthemums, allowing us to once more list them here rather than under the despised *Dendranthema*. This is discussed fully in Dick Brummitt's article in *The Garden*, Volume **122(9).** The publication of *The Rhododendron Handbook 1998* has brought together a great deal of informed opinion about the taxonomy of rhododendrons, almost all of which is also adopted here. However, an exception is that *R. yakushimanum*, treated as a subspecies of *R. degronianum* in the Handbook, is retained here because it is so well known to gardeners. Some changes also arise from *The European Garden Flora* Volume 5, though I have not followed it in those cases where taxa regarded as distinct by gardeners have been 'sunk'. Though it seems likely that we will adopt some of the name changes to wisterias suggested in Peter Valder's recent book, we have decided not to include them in this edition until we are sure that there is absolute consensus that they are right and that there is no chance that conflicting views exist that will cause them to change back. We feel it is important not to make any changes until we are sure they are absolutely justified: few things annoy gardeners more than changes to plant names that are subsequently shown to be ill-founded and have to be reversed. The work co-ordinated by Mrs Margaret Easter on thymes, including DNA analysis, has already yielded some clear results that allow some long-standing muddles to be resolved, though a good deal remains to be done before we can be confident that all taxa in this troublesome genus are correctly named. Much work on roses, including the addition of all the true cultivar names that we can find, is also incorporated here for the first time.

Following the acquisition of *The Plant Finder* by the Royal Horticultural Society, the Society's Advisory Panel on Nomenclature and Taxonomy was set up to try to establish the agreed list of plant names now held on the RHS horticultural database

and used in this and other RHS publications. The panel looks at all recent and current proposals to change or correct names and strives for a balance between the stability of well-known names and botanical and taxonomic correctness according to the codes of nomenclature.

The Panel reports to the Society's Science and Horticultural Advice Committee. Unlike the independent Horticultural Taxonomy Group (Hortax), its aim is to consider individual problems of plant nomenclature rather than general principles. Chaired by Chris Brickell, the panel includes Susyn Andrews (Kew), Dr Stephen Jury (University of Reading), Sabina Knees (Edinburgh), Dr Alan Leslie (RHS), Tony Lord, Dr Simon Thornton-Wood (RHS), Piers Trehane (Index Hortensis) and Adrian Whiteley (RHS).

Many name changes proposed by nurseries and Plant Finder users over the past year have been adopted but others have yet to be considered and approved by the Panel: we hope that all those who have generously told us about wrong names will be patient if the corrections they suggest are not immediately made: all such opinions are much valued but the volume of information is great and must be thoroughly checked before we make changes.

Families and genera used in *The RHS Plant Finder* are almost always those given in Brummitt's *Vascular Plant Families and Genera.* Thus, for the fourth year, there are no major changes to genera in this edition. For spellings and genders of generic names, Greuter's *Names in Current Use for Extant Plant Genera* is being followed; there are rare cases in which this disagrees with some prominent recent publications such as its use of the spelling *Diplarrhena* as opposed to *Diplarrena* in the current *Flora of Australia.* However, the general effect will be to keep names in exactly the same form as they are already known to gardeners.

In some cases the Panel feels that the conflicting views about the naming of some groups of plants will not be easily resolved. Our policy is to wait until an absolutely clear consensus is reached, not to rush to rename plants only to have to change names a second time when opinions have shifted yet again.

As in last year's, this edition contains few major changes to plant names. Many proposals to make further changes have been resisted until the panel has had time to study them more fully. If nomenclatural arguments are finely balanced, we will retain old names in the interests of stability. This does not alter the fact that all involved in the publication of *The RHS Plant Finder* remain committed to the use of plant names that are as correct as possible. As before, gardeners and nurserymen may still choose to differ and use what names they want, many preferring a more conservative and a few a more radical approach to naming. Except for those names in which we have made corrections of a couple of letters to bring them in line with the codes of nomenclature, we are responsible for none of the name changes in this or any other edition of *The RHS Plant Finder*.

Rules of Nomenclature
Throughout *The RHS Plant Finder* we try to follow the rules of nomenclature set out in the *International Code of Botanical Nomenclature 1994* (ICBN) and the *International Code of Nomenclature for Cultivated Plants 1995* (ICNCP). Cultivar names which are clearly not permissible under the latter and for which there seems to be no valid alternative are marked **I** (for invalid). The commonest sorts of invalid names seem to be those that are wholly or partly in Latin (not permissible since 1959, e.g. 'Pixie Alba', 'Superba', 'Variegata') and those which use a Latin generic name as a cultivar name (e.g. *Rosa* 'Corylus', *Viola* 'Gazania'). If no prior valid name exists, an enterprising nurseryman may publish a new valid name for any such plant. This would be considered validly published if it appeared in a dated catalogue with a clear description of the plant; the originator, if still alive, must be willing to accept the new name.

Apart from being discourteous to the plants' originators and their countries, the translating of foreign plant names into English is a bad and insular practice that is likely to cause confusion; it is also contrary to Article 28 of the 1995 ICNCP. In this edition, this and other Articles of the new Code are applied more strictly than before. The Code requires that such translations be considered trade designations and not cultivar names and so should be presented in a different font (here sans serif) and not in quotes. It may be years yet before we make sense of the host of German names and apparent English translations for a genus such as *Coreopsis*, many of which must be synonyms. Throughout *The RHS Plant Finder,* we have tried to give preference to the original name in every case, although English translations are also given as trade designations where they are in general use.

The substitution of slick selling names by nurseries which do not like, or have not bothered to find out, the correct names of the plants they sell is sharp practice not expected of any reputable nursery; it is also a probable breach of the Trades Description Act.

The publication of the ICNCP has done a great deal to clarify nomenclature without generally introducing rules that cause destabilising name changes. However, it significantly alters the sort of plant names that are allowed since 1 January 1996: nurseries who name plants are strongly urged to check that the names they want to use are acceptable under the new Code.

One Article of the 1995 Code that affects names published since 1995, is Art. 17.13, dealing in part with the use of botanical or common generic names within a cultivar or group name. This bans names in which the last word of the cultivar name is the common or botanical name of a genus or species. Two sorts of such names are commonly found: those based on colours (ending Lilac, Lavender, Rose, Rosa, Apricot, Peach, Mauve (French for *Malva*)) and those based on personal names (Rosemary, Hazel). These will be marked **I** in *The RHS Plant Finder* if known to have been published after 1995 or marked with an asterisk if their date of publication is unknown. This rule does not preclude cultivar epithets ending with common names which apply to only part of a genus such as Cerise, Cherry, Lemon, Lime, Orange, Pink, or Violet, each of which refers to more than one species and/or their hybrids.

An Article of the new Code which the Panel has agreed it cannot implement is Art. 17.11, banning cultivar names consisting of solely adjectival words in a modern language, unless one of these words may be considered a substantive or unless the epithet is the recognized name of a colour. As this rule is retroactive, applying to all cultivar names whenever they were published, if applied strictly it could require rejection of several hundred cultivar names in *The RHS Plant Finder*, many of them very well known and widely used. Furthermore, it is difficult to apply: many adjectives also have substantive meanings, albeit sometimes obscure ones, that might or might not justify acceptance of the names; it is not easy to decide which names of colours are accepted and which are not. Our Panel's judgement is that, as currently worded, this Article is unintentionally restrictive and potentially destabilizing; a future edition of the Code is unlikely to be so proscriptive. So for the time being we will not use this Article as a basis for making changes, nor for declaring already established names unacceptable.

Orthography
The ruling on orthography (i.e. correct spelling) of commemorative names, re-stated in the 1994 *International Code of Botanical Nomenclature*, has aroused a great deal of debate at Panel meetings.

This subject is discussed in the supplement to Bean's *Trees and Shrubs Hardy in the British Isles* (1988) and is given in ICBN Article 60 and the subsequent recommendations 60C.I. The meaning of Article 60.7 Example 10 (which tells us that the epithet *billardierii*, derived from the part-Latinization Billardierius, is unacceptable and must be corrected to *billardierei*) is not absolutely clear. However, my reading of it is that except for full-scale Latinizations of names (e.g. *brunonius* for Brown, thus *Rosa brunonii*), the name of the person commemorated should remain in its original form. Names ending in -er (e.g. Solander, Faber) may be become *solandri* (as in pure Latin, because -er is a usual Latin termination) or *solanderi*, if the specific name was originally spelt in this way. If this interpretation is correct, names such as *backhousiana, catesbaei, glazoviana, manescavii* and *bureavii* are not allowed and must be corrected to *backhouseana, catesbyi, glaziouana, manescaui* and *bureaui* respectively. However, not all of the several authors of the Code share the same interpretation. I have been reluctant to make further corrections in this edition until there is greater consensus on the true meaning of all the parts of the Code relating to orthography.

If my reading of the Code's rulings on orthography is correct, botanical epithets commemorating someone whose name has been transliterated from script other than Roman (e.g. Cyrillic or Japanese) present problems. Though ICNCP tells us which system of transliteration should be used, it is sometimes difficult to apply orthographic corrections to these: botanists whose names were originally in Cyrillic often had a preferred transliteration of their own name, often based on old French systems in the case of pre-Revolutionary Russian names, and it is hard to justify rejecting these; it is therefore difficult to be dogmatic about the orthography of these. However, implementation of this rule has been assisted by another new publication from Kew, *Authors of Plant Names*, which is particularly helpful in giving acceptable transliterations of names that were originally in Cyrillic.

Verification of names

Although we find that many nurseries have greatly improved the accuracy of their plant names, plants which are new entries often appear in their catalogues under a bewildering variety of wrong names and misspellings. This is partly a reflection on the rarity of the plants and nurserymen are not to be blamed for not finding correct names for plants that do not appear in recent authoritative garden literature. Some plants are simply too new for valid names and descriptions yet to have appeared in print.

Although we try to verify every name which appears in these pages, the amount of time which can be allotted to checking each of over 70,000 entries must be limited. There is always a proportion which do not appear in any of the reference sources used and those unverified names for which there may be scope for error are marked with an asterisk. Such errors may occur with species we cannot find listed (possibly synonyms for more recent and better known names) or may include misspellings (particularly of names transliterated from Japanese or Chinese, or commemorating a person). We are especially circumspect about names not known to the International Registrar for a particular genus. We are always grateful to receive information about the naming and origin of any asterisked plant and once we feel reassured about the plant's pedigree, the asterisk will be removed. Of course, many such names will prove to be absolutely correct and buyers can be reassured if they know that the selling nursery takes great care with the naming of its plants. However, although we are able to check that names are valid, correctly styled and spelt, we have no means of checking that nurseries are applying them to the right plant; *caveat emptor!*

We have great sympathy for gardeners who want to find a particular cultivar but are not sure to which species it belongs. The problem is acute for genera such as *Juniperus* and readers must search through all the entries to find their plants; even nurseries seem uncertain of the species of 'Skyrocket'. Because gardeners generally do not know (or disagree) to which species cultivars of hostas and saxifrages should be ascribed, these have been listed by cultivar first, giving the species in parentheses.

Adjectival names

Latin adjectival names, whether for species, subspecies, cultivar etc., must agree in gender with the genus, not with the specific name if the latter is a noun (as for *Styrax obassia, Lonicera caprifolium* etc.). Thus azaleas have to agree with *Rhododendron*, their true genus (neuter), rather than *Azalea* (feminine). For French cultivar names, adjectives should agree with whatever is being described; for roses, this is almost always *la rose* (feminine) but on rare occasions *le rosier* (when describing vegetative characteristics such as climbing forms), *l'oeillet* or *le pompon* (all masculine).

It is often the case that gardeners consider two plants to be distinct but botanists, who know of a whole range of intermediates linking the two, consider them to be the same species. The most notable example is for the rhododendrons, many species of which were 'sunk' in Cullen and Chamberlain's revision. In such cases we have always tried to provide names that retain important horticultural entities, even if not botanically distinct, often by calling the sunk species by a Group name, such as *Rhododendron rubiginosum* Desquamatum Group. Group names are also used for swarms of hybrids with the same parentage. These were formerly treated as grex names, a term now only used for orchids; thus grex names for lilies, bromeliads and begonias are now styled as Groups. A single clone from the Group may be given the same cultivar name, e.g. 'Polar Bear'. In many cases nursery catalogues do not specify whether the named clone is being offered or other selections from the hybrid swarm and entries are therefore given as e.g. *Rhododendron* Polar Bear Group & cl.

One new requirement of the new ICNCP is that cultivar-group names used after 1 January 1996 must have been validly published with a description or reference to a previously published description. Such publication is beyond the scope and purpose of *The RHS Plant Finder*. As editor, I may not style the more variable taxa that appear in this and subsequent editions as cultivar-groups unless they have been published elsewhere as Groups. Nevertheless, I still feel it is helpful to gardeners and other plant users to use cultivar names only for those plants that fulfil the Code's definition of a cultivar ('distinct, uniform and stable') in its narrow sense. This applies particularly to mixtures and races of seed-raised plants that embrace significant variation, are often not distinct from similar named selections and may be changed in character from year to year: Any new entries that are of this nature are here styled neither as cultivars nor as cultivar-groups but simply as epithets or descriptions, without quotation marks and thus beyond the scope of the new Code. This applies especially to plants described as 'strains' or 'hybrids', though the latter term is sometimes merely a provenance rather than a sign of common parentage. Thus plants here appearing as cultivars with their names in quotes have, as far as I can tell, uniform and predictable characteristics. There are a few cases in which it is difficult to tell whether a 'sunk' species remains horticulturally distinct enough to merit a group name, as for many of the rhododendrons; we would be grateful if users would let us know of any plants that we have 'sunk' in synonymy but which still need to be distinguished by a separate name. In many cases, the plants gardeners grow will be the most extreme variants of a species; although one 'end' of the species will seem to be quite a different plant from the other 'end' to the gardener, the botanist will see them as the outer limits of a continuous range of variation and will give them the same species name. We often hear gardeners complain 'How can these two plants have the same name? They are different!'. In such cases, although the botanist may have to 'lump' them under the same name, we will always try to provide an acceptable name to distinguish an important horticultural entity, even if it is not botanically distinct.

Taxonomic rank

In this edition, subspecies, varietas and forma are shown as subsp., var. and f. respectively. Each of these ranks indicates a successively less significant change in the characteristics of the plant from the original type on which the species was based; in general terms, a subspecies may be expected to be more markedly different from the type of a species than a forma which may differ in only one characteristic such as flower colour, hairiness of leaf or habit.

The ICBN requires the rank of each infraspecific botanical epithet to be given. In many cases, it is not at all clear whether a colour form shown as, say, *alba* is a true botanical forma or a cultivar of garden origin. Our inclination here is not to treat such plants as cultivars if they are recorded as being naturally occurring, nor if they embrace considerable variation: forma *alba* would be preferred if a valid publication is recorded, otherwise a previously-published Group name or a simple description. In the absence of conclusive evidence we will leave such names styled as they are at present and so some ranks remain to be added in future editions. In many cases, *alba* is assumed without any proof to be the correct name for a white-flowered variant though research often shows that the validly published name is something quite different such as *albiflora*, *leucantha* or *nivea*.

Author citations

In many cases the same species name has been used by two or more authors for quite different plants. Thus *Bloomingthingia grandiflora* of Linnaeus might be an altogether different species from *B. grandiflora* of gardeners (*B. grandiflora* hort.). In such circumstances it becomes necessary to define whose *Bloomingthingia* we are considering by quoting the author of the name directly after the species name. Generally the more recent name will be invalid and may be cross-referenced to the plant's first validly published name. Author's names appear directly after the species name and if abbreviated follow Brummitt and Powell's *Authors of Plant Names;* abbreviations are also listed in e.g. Mabberley's *The Plant-Book*. Such names appear in a smaller typeface, and neither in quotes nor in sans serif font so should not be confused with cultivar names or trade designations. In this edition we have uncovered yet more muddles resulting from two or more plants being known by the same name; we have, we hoped, resolved these by clearer cross-referencing.

Hyphenation

Some items of the ICBN have been 'more honour'd in the breach than in the observance'. One such is the ruling on hyphenation (Article 60.9) which forbids the use of hyphens after a 'compounding form' (i.e. *albo, pseudo, aureo, neo*). Hyphens are still permitted to divide separate words such as *novae-angliae* or *uva-crispa* and following the Tokyo Congress, after a vowel terminating a compounding form when followed by the same vowel (e.g. *Gaultheria semi-infera, Gentiana sino-ornata*).

Terminations of commemorative names

Another item of the code which is often ignored is that covering terminations of commemorative names (Article 60.11, referring to Recommendation 60C). A botanical epithet commemorating Helena must be styled *helenae* whereas one commemorating Helen may be styled either *heleniae* or, following Helena as an established Latin form of the same name or, quite frequently, of Ellen, *helenae*; in such cases when either spelling could be legitimate, the original is followed. When there is no accepted Latin alternative, the *-iae* ending is used and this seems to be more correct for *murieliae* and *edithiae*. The genitive

form of commemorative names ending in *-a* is always *-ae*, even if a man is being commemorated (as for *Picea koyamae*). It is this same article which requires that the well known *Crocosmia* be spelt *masoniorum* and not *masonorum* and that *Rosa wichurana* be spelt thus and not *wichuraiana*.

The RHS Plant Finder is useful not only as a directory of plant sources but as a 'menu' of plants grown by British gardeners. Such a list is of great value not only to private gardeners; landscapers can use it to check the range of plants they can incorporate in designs; gardeners in countries of the European Union can check which plants they can import by Mail Order; botanists can discover the species grown in Britain, some of them from recorded natural sources; nurserymen can use it to select for propagation first-rate plants that are still not readily available; horticultural authors, who often only want to write about plants the public are able to buy, will find it invaluable. For all such users, *The RHS Plant Finder* can be recommended as a source of standard, up-to-date and reliable nomenclature.

Tony Lord
April 1998

NOMENCLATURE
NOTES

These notes refer to plants in the main PLANT DIRECTORY that are marked with a 'N'.

'Bean Supplement' refers to W.J. Bean *Trees & Shrubs Hardy in the British Isles* (Supplement to the 8th edition) edited by D L Clarke 1988.

Acer palmatum var. *coreanum*
This includes but is not synonymous with the plant sold by Hilliers as *A. palmatum* 'Koreanum', that is to be named *A. palmatum* 'Korean Gem'.

Acer palmatum 'Sango-kaku'/ 'Senkaki'
Two or more clones are offered under these names. *A. palmatum* 'Eddisbury' is similar with brighter coral stems.

Acer pseudoplatanus 'Leopoldii'
True 'Leopoldii' has leaves stained with yellowish pink and purple. Plants are often *A. pseudoplatanus* f. *variegatum*.

Acer pseudoplatanus 'Spaethii'
Has large leaves with light yellow specks.

Aconitum autumnale
A synonym of *A. napellus* and *A. carmichaelii* Wilsonii Group.

Achillea ptarmica **The Pearl Group**
Refers to variable seed-raised double-flowered plants. The cultivar names 'The Pearl' and 'Boule de Neige' apply only to plants propagated vegetatively from the originals.

Acorus gramineus 'Oborozuki' & 'Ogon'
Although these seem to be the same clone in British gardens, 'Oborozuki' is a distinct brighter yellow cultivar in the USA.

Alchemilla alpina
The true species is very rare in cultivation. Plants under this name are usually *A. plicatula* or *A. conjuncta*.

Alchemilla splendens
The true species is probably not in cultivation in the British Isles.

Alopecurus pratensis 'Aureus'
Name applies only to plants with all gold leaves, not to green and gold striped forms.

Anemone magellanica
According to *European Garden Flora*, this is a form of the very variable *A. multifida*.

Anemone nemorosa 'Alba Plena'
This name is used for several double white forms including *A. nemorosa* 'Flore Pleno' and *A. nemorosa* 'Vestal'.

Anthemis 'Grallagh Gold'
The true cultivar of this name has golden yellow flowers. Plants with orange yellow flowers are *A.* 'Beauty of Grallagh'.

Artemisia 'Faith Raven' & 'Powis Castle'
Most plants labelled 'Faith Raven' are identical with 'Powis Castle'.

Artemisia granatensis hort.
Possibly a variant of *A. absinthium*.

Artemisia ludoviciana 'Silver Queen'
Two cultivars are grown under this name, one with cut leaves, the other with entire leaves.

Artemisia ludoviciana var. *latiloba* / *A. ludoviciana* 'Valerie Finnis'
Leaves of the former are glabrous at maturity, those of the latter are not.

Artemisia stelleriana 'Boughton Silver'
This is the first validly published name for this plant. 'Silver Brocade' seems to have been published earlier but in an undated publication; it is not therefore validly published.

Aster amellus **Violet Queen**
It is probable that more than one cultivar is sold under this name.

Aster dumosus
Many of the asters listed under *A. novi-belgii* contain varying amounts of *A. dumosus* blood in their parentage. It is not possible to allocate these to one species or the other and they are therefore listed under *A. novi-belgii*.

Aster × *frikartii* 'Mönch'
The true plant is very rare in British gardens. Most plants are another form of *A.* × *frikartii*, usually 'Wunder von Stäfa'.

Aster novi-belgii
See note under *A. dumosus*. *A. laevis* is also involved in the parentage of most cultivars.

Azara paraguayensis
This is an unpublished name for what seems to be a hybrid between *A. serrata* and *A lanceolata*.

Berberis aristata
Plants so named may be either *B. chitria* or *B. floribunda*.

Berberis buxifolia 'Nana'/ 'Pygmaea'
See explanation in Bean Supplement.

Berberis × *ottawensis* f. *purpurea* / 'Superba'
'Superba' is a clonal selection from f. *purpurea*.

Berberis × *ottawensis* 'Superba'
See note in Bean Supplement, p 109.

Berberis stenophylla 'Lemon Queen'
This sport from 'Pink Pearl' was first named in 1982. The same mutation occurred again and

was named 'Cream Showers'. The older name has priority.

Bergenia Ballawley hybrids
The name 'Ballawley' refers only to plants vegetatively propagated from the original clone. Seed-raised plants, which may differ considerably, should be called Ballawley hybrids.

Betula pendula 'Dalecarlica'
The true plant of this name is rare in cultivation in the British Isles and is probably not available from nurseries.

Betula utilis var. *jacquemontii*
Plants are often the clones 'Inverleith' or 'Doorenbos'

Brachyscome
Originally published as *Brachyscome* by Cassini who later revised his spelling to *Brachycome*. The original spelling has been internationally adopted.

Brachyglottis greyi and *laxifolia*
Both these species are extremely rare in cultivation, plants under these names usually being *B*. 'Sunshine'.

Buddleja davidii Petite Indigo™, Petite Plum™, 'Nanho Blue', 'Nanho Purple'
These cultivars or hybrids of *B. davidii* var. *nanhoensis* are claimed by some to be synonyms while others claim the 'Nanho' plants were raised in Holland and the 'Petite' plants in the USA. We are not yet certain whether these names are synonyms and if so which have priority.

Calamagrostis × *acutiflora* 'Karl Foerster'
C. × *acutiflora* 'Stricta' differs in being 15cm taller, 10-15 days earlier flowering with a less fluffy inflorescence.

Caltha polypetala
This name is often applied to a large-flowered variant of *C. palustris*. The true species has more (7-10) petals.

Camassia leichtlinii 'Alba'
The true cultivar has blueish-white, not cream flowers.

Camassia leichtlinii 'Plena'
This has starry, transparent green-white flowers; creamy-white 'Semiplena' is sometimes offered under this name.

Camellia 'Campbellii'
This name is used for five cultivars including 'Margherita Coleoni' but applies correctly to Guichard's 1894 cultivar, single to semi-double full rose pink.

Camellia 'Cleopatra'
There are three cultivars with this name.

Camellia 'Perfecta'
There are three cultivars of this name. 'Perfecta' of Jury is the plant usually offered by nurseries in the British Isles.

Campanula lactiflora 'Alba'
This refers to the pure white flowered clone,

not to blueish- or greyish-white flowered plants, nor to seed-raised plants.

Campanula persicifolia
Plants under "cup and saucer white" are not definitely ascribed to a particular cultivar. 'White Cup and Saucer' is a cultivar named by Margery Fish.

Carex morrowii 'Variegata'
C. hachijoensis 'Evergold' is sometimes sold under this name.

Carya illinoinensis
The correct spelling of this name is discussed in *Baileya*, **10(1)**, 1962.

Cassinia retorta
Now included within *C. leptophylla*. A valid infra-specific epithet has yet to be published.

Cedrus deodara 'Prostrata'
The true plant is extremely rare if not lost to cultivation. Most plants under this name are *C. deodara* 'Pendula'.

Ceanothus 'Italian Skies'
Many plants under this name are not true to name.

Chamaecyparis lawsoniana 'Columnaris Glauca'
Plants under this name might be *C. lawsoniana* 'Columnaris' or a new invalidly named cultivar.

Chamaecyparis lawsoniana 'Elegantissima'
This name has been applied to two cultivars, 'Elegantissima' of Schelle and subsequently (invalidly) 'Elegantissima' of Hillier.

Chamaecyparis pisifera 'Squarrosa Argentea'
There are two plants of this name, one (valid) with variegated foliage, the other (invalid) with silvery foliage.

Cistus × *loretii*
Plants in cultivation under this name are usually forms of *C*. × *dansereaui*.

Cistus × *purpureus*
The cultivar 'Betty Taudevin' does not appear to be distinct from this hybrid.

Cistus 'Silver Pink'
Plants under this name are not usually true to type. *C*. 'Grayswood Pink', *C*. 'Peggy Sammons' and *C*. × *skanbergii* are often offered under this name.

Clematis chrysocoma
The true *C. chrysocoma* is a non-climbing erect plant with dense yellow down on the young growth, still uncommon in cultivation.

Clematis heracleifolia 'Campanile'
Might be *C*. × *bonstedtii* 'Campanile' .

Clematis heracleifolia 'Côte d'Azur'
Might be *C*. × *bonstedtii* 'Côte d'Azur'

Clematis 'Jackmanii Superba'
Plants under this name are usually *C*. 'Gipsy Queen'.

Clematis montana
This name should refer to the white-flowered form only. Pink-flowered forms are referable to *C. montana* var. *rubens*.

Clematis 'Victoria'
There is also a Latvian cultivar of this name with petals with a central white bar.

Colchicum 'Autumn Queen'
Entries here might refer to the slightly different C. 'Prinses Astrid'.

Cornus 'Norman Hadden'
See note in Bean Supplement, p 184.

Cotoneaster dammeri
Plants sold under this name are usually C. dammeri 'Major'.

Crataegus coccinea
Plants might be C. intricata, C. pedicellata or C. biltmoreana.

Crocosmia × crocosmiiflora 'Citronella'
The true plant of this name has a dark eye and grows at Wisley. The plant usually offered may be more correctly C. 'Golden Fleece'.

Crocosmia × crocosmiiflora 'Honey Angels'
Also wrongly referred to as 'Citronella'.

Crocosmia × crocosmiiflora 'James Coey'
Has large tomato-red flowers. A smaller flowered plant similar to C. × crocosmiiflora 'Carmin Brillant' is sometimes sold under this name.

Crocosmia × crocosmiiflora 'Queen Alexandra'
As many as 20 different clones are grown under this name. It is not clear which is correct.

Crocus cartwrightianus 'Albus'
The plant offered is the true cultivar and not C. hadriaticus.

Dendranthema 'Anastasia Variegated'
Despite its name, this seems to be derived from 'Mei-kyo' not 'Anastasia'.

Dianthus 'Musgrave's Pink' (p)
This is the registered name of this white-flowered cultivar.

Diascia 'Apricot'
Plants under this name are either D. barberae 'Hopleys Apricot' or D. barberae 'Blackthorn Apricot'.

Dryopteris affinis polydactyla
This name covers at least three different clones.

Elymus magellanicus
Although this is a valid name, Mr Roger Grounds has suggested that many plants might belong to a different, perhaps unnamed species.

Epilobium glabellum hort.
Plants under this name are not E. glabellum but are close to E. wilsonii Petrie or perhaps a hybrid of it.

Erigeron salsuginosus
A synonym of Aster sibiricus but plants in cultivation under this name may be E. peregrinus callianthemus

Erodium cheilanthifolium
Most plants under this name are hybrids.

Erodium glandulosum
Plants under this name are often hybrids.

Erodium guttatum
Doubtfully in commerce; plants under this name are usually E. heteradenum, E. cheilanthifolium or hybrids.

Erysimum cheiri 'Baden-Powell'
Plant of uncertain origin differing from E. cheiri 'Harpur Crewe' only in its shorter stature.

Erysimum 'Variegatum'
This name might refer to any of the variegated cultivars of Erysimum.

Eucryphia 'Penwith'
The cultivar name 'Penwith' was originally given to a hybrid of E. cordifolia × E. lucida, not E. × hillieri.

Fagus sylvatica Cuprea Group/Atropurpurea Group
It is desirable to provide a name, Cuprea Group, for less richly coloured forms, used in historic landscapes before the purple clones appeared.

Fagus sylvatica 'Pendula'
This name refers to the Knap Hill clone, the most common weeping form in English gardens. Other clones occur, particularly in Cornwall and Ireland.

Forsythia 'Beatrix Farrand'
The true plant might not be in cultivation.

Fragaria chiloensis 'Variegata', F. vesca 'Variegata'
Most, possibly all, plants under these names are F. × ananassa 'Variegata'.

Fuchsia
All names marked 'N', except the following, refer to more than one cultivar or species.

Fuchsia decussata
A hybrid of F. magellanica is also offered under this name.

Fuchsia loxensis
For a comparison of the true species with the hybrids 'Speciosa' and 'Loxensis' commonly grown under this name, see Boullemier's Check List (2nd ed.) p 268.

Fuchsia minimiflora
Some plants under this name might be F. × bacillaris.

Fuchsia 'Pumila'
Plants under this name might be F. magellanica var. pumila.

Gentiana cachemirica
Most plants sold are not true to type.

Geum 'Borisii'
This name refers to cultivars of G. coccineum Sibthorp & Smith, especially G. 'Werner Arends' and not to G. × borisii Kelleper.

Halimium alyssoides and H. halimifolium
Plants under these names are sometimes H. × pauanum or H. × santae.

Hebe 'C.P. Raffill'
See note in Bean Supplement, p 265.

Hebe 'Carl Teschner'
See note in Bean Supplement, p 264.

Hebe 'Glaucophylla'
This plant is a green reversion of the hybrid *H.* 'Glaucophylla Variegata'.

Hedera helix 'Caenwoodiana'/ 'Pedata'
Some authorities consider these to be distinct cultivars while others think them different morphological forms of the same unstable clone.

Hedera helix 'Oro di Bogliasco'
Priority between this name and 'Jubiläum Goldherz' and 'Goldheart' has yet to be finally resolved.

Helleborus orientalis hort.
Plants under this name are hybrids for which the name *H.* × *hybridus* has been coined, though this has yet to be validly published.

Hemerocallis fulva 'Kwanso', 'Kwanso Variegata', 'Flore Pleno' and 'Green Kwanso'
For a discussion of these plants see *The Plantsman*, 7(2).

Heuchera micrantha var. *diversifolia* 'Palace Purple'
This cultivar name refers only to plants with deep purple-red foliage. Seed-raised plants of inferior colouring should not be offered under this name.

Hosta 'Marginata Alba'
This name is wrongly used both for *H. crispula* and, more commonly, for *H. fortunei* 'Albomarginata'.

Hosta montana
This name refers only to plants long grown in Europe, which differ from *H. elata.*

Hypericum fragile
The true *H. fragile* is probably not available from British nurseries.

Hypericum 'Gemo'
Either a selection of *H. prolificum* or *H. prolificum* × *H. densiflorum.*

Ilex × *altaclerensis*
The argument for this spelling is given by Susyn Andrews, *The Plantsman*, 5(2) and is not superceded by the more recent comments in the Supplement to Bean's Trees and Shrubs.

Iris
Apart from those noted below, cultivar names marked 'N' are not registered. The majority of those marked 'I' have been previously used for a different cultivar.

Iris histrioides 'Major'
Two clones are offered under this name, the true one pale blue with darker spotting on the falls, the incorrect one violet-blue with almost horizontal falls.

Iris pallida 'Variegata'
The white-variegated *I. pallida* 'Argentea Variegata' is sometimes wrongly supplied under this name, which refers only to the gold-variegated cultivar.

Juniperus × *media*
This name is illegitimate if applied to hybrids of *J. chinensis* × *J. sabina*, having been previously used for a different hybrid (P.A. Schmidt, *IDS Yearbook* 1993, 47-48). Because of its importance to gardeners, a proposal to conserve its present use was tabled but subsequently rejected.

Lamium maculatum 'Chequers'
This name refers to two plants; the first, validly named, is a large and vigorous form of *L. maculatum* with a stripe down the centre of the leaf; the second is silver-leaved and very similar to *L. maculatum* 'Beacon Silver'.

Lavandula 'Alba'
Might be either *L. angustifolia* 'Alba' or *L.* × *intermedia* 'Alba'

Lavandula angustifolia 'Lavender Lady'/ *L.* 'Cambridge Lady'
Might be synonyms of *L. angustifolia* 'Lady'.

Lavandula × *intermedia* 'Arabian Night'
Plants under this name might be *L.* × *intermedia* 'Impress Purple'.

Lavandula spica
This name is classed as a name to be rejected (*nomen rejiciendum*) by the *International Code of Botanical Nomenclature.*

Lavandula 'Twickel Purple'
Two cultivars are sold under this name, one a form of *L.* × *intermedia*, the other of *L. angustifolia.*

Lavatera olbia and *L. thuringiaca*
Although *L. olbia* is usually shrubby and *L. thuringiaca* usually herbaceous, both species are very variable. Cultivars formally ascribed to one species or the other have been shown to be hybrids and are listed by cultivar name alone.

Lobelia 'Russian Princess'
This has green, not purple, leaves and rich pink, not purple, flowers.

Lonicera × *americana*
Most plants offered by nurseries under this name are correctly *L.* × *italica.* The true *L.* × *americana* is still widely grown but is slow to propagate. See *The Plantsman*, 12(2).

Lonicera × *brownii* 'Fuchsioides'
Plants under this name are usually *L.* × *brownii* 'Dropmore Scarlet'.

Lonicera × *heckrotii* 'Gold Flame'
This name applies to the original clone. Many plants under this name are a different clone for which the name 'American Beauty' has been proposed.

Lonicera periclymenum 'Serotina'
See note in Bean Supplement, p 315.

Lonicera sempervirens f. *sulphurea*

Plants in the British Isles usually a yellow-flowered form of *L. periclymenum.*

Macleaya cordata
Most, if not all, plants offered are *M.* × *kewensis.*

Magnolia × **highdownensis.**
Believed to fall within the range of variation of *M. wilsonii.*

Mahonia pinnata
Most plants in cultivation under this name are believed to be *M.* × *wagneri* 'Pinnacle'.

Malus domestica 'Dumeller's Seedling'
The phonetic spelling 'Dumelow's Seedling' contravenes the ICBN ruling on orthography, i.e. that commemorative names should retain the original spelling of the person's name (Article 60.11).

Melissa officinalis 'Variegata'
The true cultivar of this name was striped with white.

Narcissus poeticus 'Plenus'
A name of uncertain application used for *N. poeticus* 'Spalding Double White' and *N. poeticus* 'Tamar Double White'.

Nemesia caerulea
The lavender blue clone 'Joan Wilder', described and illustrated in *The Hardy Plant,* **14(1)**, 11-14, does not come true from seed; it may only be propagated from cuttings.

Osmanthus heterophyllus 'Gulftide'
Probably correctly *O.* × *fortunei* 'Gulftide'.

Papaver orientale 'Flore Pleno'
P. 'Fireball' is sometimes offered under this name.

Passiflora antioquiensis
According to National Colection holder John Vanderplank, the true species is not in cultivation in the British Isles. Plants under this name are likely to be clones of *P.* × *exoniensis.*

Pelargonium 'Beauty of Eastbourne'
This should not be confused with *P.* 'Eastbourne Beauty', a different cultivar.

Pelargonium 'Lass o'Gowrie'
The American plant of this name has pointed, not rounded leaf lobes.

Pelargonium quercifolium
Plants under this name are mainly hybrids. The true species has pointed, not rounded leaf lobes.

Penstemon 'Taoensis'
This name for a small-flowered cultivar or hybrid of *P. isophyllus* originally appeared as 'Taoense' but must be corrected to agree in gender with *Penstemon* (masculine). Presumably an invalid name (published in Latin form since 1958), it is not synonymous with *P. crandallii* subsp. *glabrescens* var. *taosensis.*

Pernettya

Botanists now consider that *Pernettya* (fruit a berry) is not separable from *Gaultheria* (fruit a capsule) because in some species the fruit is intermediate between a berry and a capsule. For a fuller explanation see D Middleton *The Plantsman,* **12(3)**.

Picea pungens 'Glauca Pendula'
This name is used for several different glaucous cultivars.

Pinus ayacahuite
P. ayacahuite var. *veitchii* (syn. *P. veitchii*) is occasionally sold under this name.

Pinus montezumae
Plants propagated from mature trees in British gardens are mostly an un-named long-needled variety of *P. rudis.*

Pinus nigra 'Cebennensis Nana'
A doubtful and invalid name, probably a synonym for *P. nigra* 'Nana'.

Polemonium archibaldiae
Usually sterile with lavender-blue flowers. A self-fertile white-flowered plant is sometimes sold under this name.

Polystichum setiferum 'Wollaston'
Incomplete name which may refer to either of two cultivars.

Populus nigra var. italica
See note in Bean Supplement, p 393.

Prunus laurocerasus 'Castlewellan'
We are grateful to Dr Charles Nelson for informing us that the name 'Marbled White' is not valid because although it has priority of publication it does not have the approval of the originator who asked for it to be called 'Castlewellan'.

Prunus laurocerasus 'Variegata'
The true 'Variegata', (marginal variegation), dates from 1811 but this name is also used for the relatively recent cultivar *P. laurocerasus* 'Castlewellan'.

Prunus serrulata var. pubescens
See note in Bean Supplement, p 398.

Prunus × **subhirtella 'Rosea'**
Might be *P. pendula* var. *ascendens* 'Rosea', *P. pendula* 'Pendula Rosea', or *P.* × *subhirtella* 'Autumnalis Rosea'.

Rheum × **cultorum**
The name *R.* × *cultorum* was published without adequate description and must be abandoned in favour of the validly published *R.* × *hybridum.*

Rhododendron (azaleas)
All names marked 'N', except for the following, refer to more than one cultivar.

Rhododendron 'Hino-mayo'
This name is based on a faulty transliteration (should be 'Hinamoyo') but the spelling 'Hino-mayo' is retained in the interests of stability.

Rhus typhina

Linnaeus published both *R. typhina* and *R. hirta* as names for the same species. Though *R. hirta* has priority, it has been proposed that the name *R. typhina* should be conserved.

Robinia hispida 'Rosea'
This name is applied to *R. hispida* (young shoots with bristles), *R. elliottii* (young shoots with grey down) and *R. boyntonii* (young shoots smooth).

Rosa × damascena 'Trigintipetala'
The true cultivar of this name is probably not in cultivation in the Britsh Isles.

Rosa gentiliana
Plants might be *R. multiflora* 'Wilsonii', *R. multiflora* var. *cathayensis*, *R. henryi* or a hybrid.

Rosa 'Gros Choux de Hollande' (Bb)
It is doubtful if this name is correctly applied.

Rosa 'Maiden's Blush'
R. 'Great Maiden's Blush' may be supplied under this name.

Rosa 'Marchesa Boccella'
For a discussion on the correct identity of this rose see *Heritage Rose Foundation News*, Oct. 1989 & Jan. 1990.

Rosa 'Professeur Emile Perrot'
For a discussion on the correct identity of this rose see *Heritage Roses,* Nov. 1991.

Rosa Sweetheart
This is not the same as the Sweetheart Rose, a common name for *R.* 'Cécile Brunner'.

Rosa wichurana
This is the correct spelling according to the ICBN 1994 Article 60.11 (which enforces Recommendation 60C.1c) and not *wichuraiana* for this rose commemorating Max Wichura.

Salix alba 'Tristis'
This cultivar should not be confused with *S. tristis*, which is now correctly *S. humilis*. Although this cultivar is distinct in European gardens, most plants under this name in the British Isles are *S. × sepulcralis* var. *chrysocoma*.

Salvia microphylla var. neurepia
The type of this variety is referable to the typical variety, *S. microphylla* var. *microphylla*.

Salvia officinalis 'Aurea'
S. officinalis var. *aurea* is a rare variant of the common sage with leaves entirely of gold. It is represented in cultivation by the cultivar 'Kew Gold'. The plant usually offered as *S. officinalis* 'Aurea' is the gold variegated sage *S. officinalis* 'Icterina'.

Salvia sclarea var. turkestanica
Plants in gardens under this name are not *S. sclarea* var. *turkistaniana* of Mottet.

Sambucus nigra 'Aurea'
Plants under this name are usually not *S. nigra*.

Sedum nevii
The true species is not in cultivation. Plants under this name are usually either *S. glaucophyllum* or occasionally *S. beyrichianum*.

Senna corymbosa
Some plants sold as *S. corymbosa* are *S. × floribunda*.

Skimmia japonica 'Foremanii'
The true cultivar, which belongs to *S. japonica* Rogersii Group, is believed to be lost to cultivation. Plants offered under this name are usually *S. japonica* 'Veitchii'.

Spiraea japonica 'Shirobana'
Shirobana-shimotsuke is the common name for *S. japonica* var. *albiflora*. Shirobana means white-flowered and does not apply to the two-coloured form.

Staphylea holocarpa var. rosea
This botanical variety has woolly leaves. The cultivar 'Rosea', with which it is often confused, does not.

Stewartia ovata var. grandiflora.
Most, possibly all, plants available from British nurseries under this name are not true to name but are derived from the improved Nymans form.

Thymus serpyllum cultivars
Most cultivars are probably correctly cultivars of *T. polytrichus* or hybrids though they will remain listed under *T. serpyllum* pending further research.

Thymus 'Silver Posie'
The cultivar name 'Silver Posie' is applied to several different plants, not all of them *T. vulgaris*.

Tricyrtis Hototogisu
This is the common name applied generally to all Japanese *Tricyrtis* and specifically to *T. hirta*.

Tricyrtis macropoda
This name has been used for at least five different species.

Uncinia rubra
This name is loosely applied to *U. egmontiana* and *U. uncinata*.

Verbena 'Kemerton'
Origin unknown, not from Kemerton.

Viburnum opulus 'Fructu Luteo'
See note below.

Viburnum opulus 'Xanthocarpum'
Some entries under this name might be the less compact *V. opulus* 'Fructu Luteo'.

Viburnum plicatum
Entries may include the 'snowball' form, *V. plicatum* 'Sterile'.

Viola labradorica
See Note in *The Garden*, **110(2)**: 96.

CLASSIFICATION OF GENERA

ACTINIDIA
(s-p) Self-pollinating

BEGONIA
(C) Cane
(R) Rex
(S) Semperflorens Cultorum
(T) × *tuberhybrida* (Tuberous)

CHRYSANTHEMUM
(By the National Chrysanthemum Society)
(1) Indoor Large (Exhibition)
(2) Indoor Medium (Exhibition)
(3a) Indoor Incurved: Large-flowered
(3b) Indoor Incurved: Medium-flowered
(3c) Indoor Incurved: Small-flowered
(4a) Indoor Reflexed: Large-flowered
(4b) Indoor Reflexed: Medium-flowered
(4c) Indoor Reflexed: Small-flowered
(5a) Indoor Intermediate: Large-flowered
(5b) Indoor Intermediate: Medium-flowered
(5c) Indoor Intermediate: Small-flowered
(6a) Indoor Anemone: Large-flowered
(6b) Indoor Anemone: Medium-flowered
(6c) Indoor Anemone: Small-flowered
(7a) Indoor Single: Large-flowered
(7b) Indoor Single: Medium-flowered
(7c) Indoor Single: Small-flowered
(8a) Indoor True Pompon
(8b) Indoor Semi-pompon
(9a) Indoor Spray: Anemone
(9b) Indoor Spray: Pompon
(9c) Indoor Spray: Reflexed
(9d) Indoor Spray: Single
(9e) Indoor Spray: Intermediate
(9f) Indoor Spray: Spider, Quill, Spoon or Any Other Type
(10a) Indoor, Spider
(10b) Indoor, Quill
(10c) Indoor, Spoon
(11) Any Other Indoor Type
(12a) Indoor, Charm
(12b) Indoor, Cascade
(13a) October-flowering Incurved: Large-flowered
(13b) October-flowering Incurved: Medium-flowered
(13c) October-flowering Incurved: Small-flowered
(14a) October-flowering Reflexed: Large-flowered
(14b) October-flowering Reflexed:
(14c) October-flowering Reflexed: Small-flowered
(15a) October-flowering Intermediate: Large-flowered
(15b) October-flowering Intermediate: Medium-flowered
(15c) October-flowering Intermediate: Small-flowered
(16) October-flowering Large
(17a) October-flowering Single: Large-flowered
(17b) October-flowering Single: Medium-flowered
(17c) October-flowering Single: Small-flowered
(18a) October-flowering Pompon: True Pompon
(18b) October-flowering Pompon: Semi-pompon
(19a) October-flowering Spray: Anemone
(19b) October-flowering Spray: Pompon
(19c) October-flowering Spray: Reflexed
(19d) October-flowering Spray: Single
(19e) October-flowering Spray: Intermediate
(19f) October-flowering Spray: Spider, Quill, Spoon or Any Other Type
(20) Any Other October-flowering Type
(22) Charm
(23a) Early flowering Outdoor Incurved: Large-flowered
(23b) Early flowering Outdoor Incurved: Medium-flowered
(23c) Early flowering Outdoor Incurved: Small-flowered
(24a) Early flowering Outdoor Reflexed: Large-flowered
(24b) Early flowering Outdoor Reflexed: Medium-flowered
(24c) Early flowering Outdoor Reflexed: Small-flowered
(25a) Early flowering Outdoor Intermediate: Large-flowered
(25b) Early flowering Outdoor Intermediate: Medium-flowered
(25c) Early flowering Outdoor Intermediate: Small-flowered
(26a) Early flowering Outdoor Anemone: Large-flowered
(26b) Early flowering Outdoor Anemone: Medium-flowered
(27a) Early-flowering Outdoor Single:

	Large-flowered
(27b)	Early-flowering Outdoor Single: Medium-flowered
(28a)	Early-flowering Outdoor Pompon: True Pompon
(28b)	Early-flowering Outdoor Pompon: Semi-pompon
(29a)	Early-flowering Outdoor Spray: Anemone
(29b)	Early-flowering Outdoor Spray: Pompon
(29c)	Early-flowering Outdoor Spray: Reflexed
(29d)	Early-flowering Outdoor Spray: Single
(29e)	Early-flowering Outdoor Spray: Intermediate
(29f)	Early-flowering Outdoor Spray: Spider, Quill, Spoon or Any Other Type
(29K)	Early-flowering Outdoor Spray: Korean
(29Rub)	Early-flowering Outdoor Spray: Rubellum
(30)	Any Other Early-flowering Outdoor Type

CLEMATIS

(A)	Alpina Group (Section Atragene)
(D)	Diversifolia Group
(Fl)	Florida Group (double-flowered)
(Fo)	Forsteri Group
(I)	Integrifolia Group
(J)	Jackmanii Group
(L)	Lanuginosa Group
(P)	Patens Group
(T)	Texensis Group
(Ta)	Tangutica Group
(Vt)	Viticella Group

DAHLIA

(By The National Dahlia Society with corresponding numerical classification according to the Royal Horticultural Society's International Register)

(Sin)	1 Single
(Anem)	2 Anemone-flowered
(Col)	3 Collerette
(LWL)	4B Waterlily, Large
(MWL)	4C Waterlily, Medium
(SWL)	4D Waterlily, Small
(MinWL)	4E Waterlily, Miniature
(GD)	5A Decorative, Giant
(LD)	5B Decorative, Large
(MD)	5C Decorative, Medium
(SD)	5D Decorative, Small
(MinD)	5E Decorative, Miniature
(SBa)	6A Small Ball
(MinBa)	6B Miniature Ball
(Pom)	7 Pompon
(GC)	8A Cactus, Giant
(LC)	8B Cactus, Large
(MC)	8C Cactus, Medium
(SC)	8D Cactus, Small

(MinC)	8E Cactus, Miniature
(S-c)	9 Semi-cactus (unassigned)
(GS-c)	9A Semi-cactus, Giant
(LS-c)	9B Semi-cactus, Large
(MS-c)	9C Semi-cactus, Medium
(SS-c)	9D Semi-cactus, Small
(MinS-c)	9E Semi-cactus, Miniature
(Misc)	10 Miscellaneous
(O)	Orchid-flowering (in combination)
(B)	Botanical (in combination)
(DwB)	Dwarf Bedding (in combination)
(Fim)	Fimbriated (in combination)
(Lil)	Lilliput (in combination)

DIANTHUS

(By the Royal Horticultural Society)

(p)	Pink
(p,a)	Annual Pink
(pf)	Perpetual-flowering Carnation
(b)	Border Carnation
(M)	Malmaison Carnation

FRUIT

(B)	Black (*Vitis*)
(C)	Culinary (*Malus, Prunus, Pyrus, Ribes*)
(Cider)	Cider (*Malus*)
(D)	Dessert (*Malus, Prunus, Pyrus, Ribes*)
(F)	Fruit
(G)	Glasshouse (*Vitis*)
(O)	Outdoor (*Vitis*)
(P)	Pinkcurrant (*Ribes*)
(Perry)	Perry (*Pyrus*)
(R)	Red (*Vitis*), Redcurrant (*Ribes*)
(W)	White (*Vitis*), Whitecurrant (*Ribes*)

GLADIOLUS

(B)	Butterfly
(Colv)	Colvillei
(G)	Giant
(L)	Large
(M)	Medium
(Min)	Miniature
(N)	Nanus
(P)	Primulinus
(S)	Small
(Tub)	Tubergenii

HYDRANGEA macrophylla

| (H) | Hortensia |
| (L) | Lacecap |

IRIS

(By the American Iris Society)

(AB)	Arilbred
(BB)	Border Bearded
(Cal-Sib)	Series *Californicae* × Series *Sibiricae*
(CH)	Californian Hybrid
(DB)	Dwarf Bearded (not assigned)
(Dut)	Dutch
(IB)	Intermediate Bearded

(La)	Louisiana Hybrid
(MDB)	Miniature Dwarf Bearded
(MTB)	Miniature Tall Bearded
(SDB)	Standard Dwarf Bearded
(Sino-Sib)	Series *Sibiricae*, chromosome number 2n=40
(Sp)	Spuria
(TB)	Tall Bearded

LILIUM
(Classification according to *The International Lily Register* (ed. 3, 1982) with amendments from Supp. 10 (1992), Royal Horticultural Society)

(I)	Hybrids derived from *L. amabile, L. bulbiferum, L. cernuum, L. concolor, L. davidii, L. × hollandicum, L. lancifolium, L. leichtlinii, L. × maculatum* and *L. pumilum*
(Ia)	Early flowering with upright flowers, single or in an umbel
(Ib)	Outward-facing flowers
(Ic)	Pendant flowers
(II)	Hybrids of Martagon type, one parent having been a form of *L. hansonii* or *L. martagon*
(III)	Hybrids from *L. candidum, L. chalcedonicum* and other related European species (excluding *L. martagon*)
(IV)	Hybrids of American species
(V)	Hybrids derived from *L. formosanum* & *L. longiflorum*
(VI)	Hybrid Trumpet Lilies & Aurelian hybrids from Asiatic species, including *L. henryi* but excluding those from *L. auratum, L. japonicum, L. rubellum* and *L. speciosum.*
(VIa)	Plants with trumpet-shaped flowers
(VIb)	Plants with bowl-shaped flowers
(VIc)	Plants with flat flowers (or only the tips recurved)
(VId)	Plants with recurved flowers
(VII)	Hybrids of Far Eastern species as *L auratum, L. japonicum, L. rubellum* and *L. speciosum,*
(VIIa)	Plants with trumpet-shaped flowers
(VIIb)	Plants with bowl-shaped flowers
(VIIc)	Plants with flat flowers
(VIId)	Plants with recurved flowers
(VIII)	All hybrids not in another division
(IX)	All species and their varieties and forms

MALUS See FRUIT

NARCISSUS
(By The Royal Horticultural Society, revised 1977)

(1)	Trumpet
(2)	Large-cupped
(3)	Small-cupped
(4)	Double
(5)	Triandrus
(6)	Cyclamineus
(7)	Jonquilla
(8)	Tazetta
(9)	Poeticus
(10)	Species and wild forms and hybrids
(11)	Split-corona
(12)	Miscellaneous
(13)	Species

NYMPHAEA

(H)	Hardy
(D)	Day-blooming
(N)	Night-blooming
(T)	Tropical

PAEONIA

(S)	Shrubby

PELARGONIUM

(A)	Angel
(C)	Coloured Foliage (in combination)
(Ca)	Cactus (in combination)
(d)	Double (in combination)
(Dec)	Decorative
(Dw)	Dwarf
(DwI)	Dwarf Ivy-leaved
(Fr)	Frutetorum
(I)	Ivy-leaved
(Min)	Miniature
(MinI)	Miniature Ivy-leaved
(R)	Regal
(Sc)	Scented-leaved
(St)	Stellar (in combination)
(T)	Tulip (in combination)
(U)	Unique
(Z)	Zonal

PRIMULA
(Classification as per W.W. Smith & Forrest (1928) and W.W. Smith & Fletcher (1941-49))

(1)	Amethystina
(2)	Auricula
(3)	Bullatae
(4)	Candelabra
(5)	Capitatae
(6)	Carolinella
(7)	Cortusoides
(8)	Cuneifolia
(9)	Denticulata
(10)	Dryadifolia
(11)	Farinosae
(12)	Floribundae
(13)	Grandis
(14)	Malacoides
(15)	Malvacea
(16)	Minutissimae
(17)	Muscarioides
(18)	Nivales
(19)	Obconica

(20)	Parryi
(21)	Petiolares
(22)	Pinnatae
(23)	Pycnoloba
(24)	Reinii
(25)	Rotundifolia
(26)	Sikkimensis
(27)	Sinenses
(28)	Soldanelloideae
(29)	Souliei
(30)	Vernales
(A)	Alpine Auricula
(B)	Border Auricula
(D)	Double
(Poly)	Polyanthus
(Prim)	Primrose
(S)	Show Auricula

PRUNUS See FRUIT

PYRUS See FRUIT

RHODODENDRON

(A)	Azalea (deciduous, species or unclassified hybrid)
(Ad)	Azaleodendron
(EA)	Evergreen azalea
(G)	Ghent azalea (deciduous)
(K)	Knap Hill or Exbury azalea (deciduous)
(M)	Mollis azalea (deciduous)
(O)	Occidentalis azalea (deciduous)
(R)	Rustica azalea (deciduous)
(V)	Vireya rhododendron
(Vs)	Viscosa azalea (deciduous)

RIBES See FRUIT

ROSA

(A)	Alba
(Bb)	Bourbon
(Bs)	Boursault
(Ce)	Centifolia
(Ch)	China
(Cl)	Climbing (in combination)
(D)	Damask
(DPo)	Damask Portland
(F)	Floribunda or Cluster-flowered
(G)	Gallica
(Ga)	Garnette
(GC)	Ground Cover
(HM)	Hybrid Musk
(HP)	Hybrid Perpetual
(HT)	Hybrid Tea or Large-flowered
(Min)	Miniature
(Mo)	Moss (in combination)
(N)	Noisette
(Patio)	Patio, Miniature Floribunda or Dwarf Cluster-flowered
(Poly)	Polyantha

(PiH)	Pimpinellifolia hybrid (Hybrid Scots Briar)
(Ra)	Rambler
(RH)	Rubiginosa hybrid (Hybrid Sweet Briar)
(Ru)	Rugosa
(S)	Shrub
(T)	Tea

SAXIFRAGA
(Classification from Hegi, G. (revd. ed. 1975)
Illustrierte Flora von Mitteleuropa)

(1)	Micranthes
(2)	Hirculus
(3)	Gymnopera
(4)	Diptera
(5)	Trachyphyllum
(6)	Xanthizoon
(7)	Aizoonia
(8)	Porophyllum
(9)	Porophyrion
(10)	Miscopetalum
(11)	Saxifraga
(12)	Trachyphylloides
(13)	Cymbalaria
(14)	Discogyne

TULIPA
(Classification from *Classified List and
International Register of Tulip Names* by
Koninklijke Algemeene Vereening voor
Bloembollenculture 1996)

(1)	Single Early Group
(2)	Double Early Group
(3)	Triumph Group
(4)	Darwinhybrid Group
(5)	Single Late Group (including Darwin Group and Cottage Group)
(6)	Lily-Flowered Group
(7)	Fringed Group
(8)	Viridiflora Group
(9)	Rembrandt Group
(10)	Parrot Group
(11)	Double Late Group
(12)	Kaufmanniana Group
(13)	Fosteriana Group
(14)	Greigii Group
(15)	Miscellaneous

VIOLA

(C)	Cornuta Hybrid
(dVt)	Double Violet
(ExVa)	Exhibition Viola
(FP)	Fancy Pansy
(PVt)	Parma Violet
(SP)	Show Pansy
(T)	Tricolor
(Va)	Viola
(Vt)	Violet
(Vtta)	Violetta

VITIS See FRUIT

ACKNOWLEDGEMENTS

Generating **The RHS Plant Finder** from *BG-BASE*™ has required concentrated, steady and meticulous work throughout the last year from all involved. Plant Finder Administrator Clare Burgh, assisted by Alessandra Swan, has added many more nursery codes than in previous years and has co-ordinated the complex job of compiling nursery information and plant lists with astonishing proficiency. Our team has again benefited enormously from the efforts of Dr Kerry Walter of BG-BASE Inc. and Niki Simpson, Database Administrator. Dr Andrew Sier, Senior Database Administrator, has kept the database operational and assisted with name editing. I continue to check names in the Plant Finder, especially each year's new entries, and all our efforts are supervised by the RHS's Head of Botany, Dr Simon Thornton-Wood. I could not wish for more efficient and helpful colleagues. All who use **The RHS Plant Finder** owe them thanks and I am particularly grateful to them all for making the job of editing so much easier.

For the compilation of this edition, I am once more indebted to my colleagues on the RHS Advisory Panel on Nomenclature and Taxonomy: Chris Brickell, Susyn Andrews, Stephen Jury, Sabina Knees, Alan Leslie, Simon Thornton-Wood, Piers Trehane and Adrian Whiteley, along with Mike Grant and Diana Miller, all of whom have provided much valuable guidance during the past year. Scores of nurseries have sent helpful information about asterisked plants which has proved immensely useful in verifying some of the most obscure names. I am grateful, too, to our regular correspondents, particularly Jennifer Hewitt for so thoroughly checking iris entries and to the RHS International Registrars.

Artemisia	Dr J.D. Twibell ('94)
Bamboos	D. McClintock ('90-'94)
Bougainvillea	S. Read ('94)
Camellia	T.J. Savige, International Registrar, NSW, Australia ('93 & '96)
Cimicifuga	J. Compton ('94)
Cistus	R. Page ('97)
Conifers	J. Lewis, International Registrar, RHS Wisley ('93)
	H.J. Welch, World Conifer Data Pool ('90-'93)
	P. Trehane, International Registrar, RHS Wisley ('94)
Cotoneaster	Jeanette Fryer, NCCPG Collection Holder ('91-'92)
Cyclamen	Dr C. Grey-Wilson ('94)
Dahlia	R. Hedge, RHS Wisley ('96-'98)
Delphinium	Dr A.C. Leslie, International Registrar, RHS Wisley ('93, '97 & '98)
Dianthus	Dr A.C. Leslie, International Registrar, RHS Wisley ('91-'98)
Gesneriaceae	J.D. Dates, International Registrar ('94)
Gladiolus	F.N. Franks ('92)
Heathers	D. McClintock ('92)
Hebe	Mrs J. Hewitt ('94-'98)
Hedera	P.Q. Rose & Mrs H. Key ('91 & '93)
	Alison Rutherford ('92-'94)
Hypericum	Dr N.K.B. Robson ('94-'97)
Ilex	Ms S. Andrews ('92-'98)
Iris	Mrs J. Hewitt ('95-'98)
Jovibarba & *Sempervivum*	P.J. Mitchell, International Registrar, Sempervivum Society ('91-'93 & '98)
Juniperus	J. Lewis, International Registrar ('94)
Lavandula	Ms S. Andrews ('92-'98)
Lilium	Dr A.C. Leslie, International Registrar, RHS Wisley ('91-'98)
Narcissus	Mrs S. Kington, International Registrar, RHS ('91-'98)
Pelargonium	Mrs H. Key ('91-'95)
Pelargonium spp.	Mrs D. Miller ('93)
Polemonium	Mrs D. Allison ('94)
Rhododendron	Dr A.C. Leslie, International Registrar, RHS Wisley ('91-'98)
Salix	Dr R.D. Meikle ('93)
Salvia	J. Compton ('92 & '94)
Zauschneria	P. Trehane ('94)

To all these, as well as the many readers and nurseries who have also made comments and suggestions, we are, once again, sincerely grateful.
Tony Lord

COLLECTORS' REFERENCES

Note: Collectors' numbers which do not appear to relate to the species listed are given an asterisk after the number.

A&JW	A. & J. Watson, S America
A&L	Ala & Lancaster expedition, N Iran ,1972
AB&S	Archibald, Blanchard & Salmon, Morocco 1980's
AC&H	Apold, Cox & Hutchinson, NE Turkey, 1962
AC&W	Albury, Cheese & Watson
ACE	Alpine Garden Society expedition, China, 1994
ACL	A.C. Leslie
AGS/ES	Alpine Garden Society expedition, Sikkim, 1983
AGSJ	Alpine Garden Society expedition, Japan, 1988
Akagi	Akagi Botanical Garden
AL&JS	Leslie & Sharman, Yugoslavia, 1990
B	L. Beer, Nepal, 1975
B&L	Brickell & Leslie, China
B&M	C.D. Brickell & B. Mathew
B&S	P. Bird & M. Salmon
B&SWJ	B. & S. Wynn-Jones, Far East, 1993
BB	B. Bartholomew, Bhutan, 1974
BC	B. Chudziak, Kanchenjunga, Nepal, 1993
BC&W	Beckett, Cheese & Watson
BL&M	Beer, Lancaster & Morris, E Nepal, 1971
BM	B. Mathew
BM&W	Binns, Mason & Wright, Nepal, 1978
BS	Basil Smith
BSBE	Bowles Scholarship Botanical Expedition
Bu	S. Bubert
C&C	P.A. & K.N.E. Cox, SE Tibet, 1996
C&Cu	K.N.E. Cox & J. Cuby
C&H	P.A. Cox & P.C. Hutchison, Assam, NE Frontier & N Bengal, 1965; Sichuan & Yunnan, China, 1995
C&K	Chamberlain & Knott
C&R	Christian & Roderick, California, Oregon, Washington
C&S	A. Clark & I. Sinclair, Bhutan, 1994
C&V	K.N.E. Cox & S. Vergera, SE Tibet, China, 1995
C&W	M. Cheese & J. Watson
CC	C. Chadwell
CC&H	D.F. Chamberlain, P.A. Cox & P.C.

	Hutchison, Sichuan, China, 1989
CC&McK	Chadwell & McKelvie, Nepal, West Himalaya, 1990-92
CC&MR	C. Chadwell & M. Ramsey, Kashmir, 1985; Himachal Pradesh & W Himalaya, 1989
CD&R	J. Compton, J. D'Arcy & E.M. Rix, China, Drakensburg, Mexico & Korea
CDB	C.D. Brickell
CE&H	Christian, Elliott & Hoog, Yugoslavia & Greece, 1982
CEE	Chengdu Edinburgh Expedition, Sichuan, China, 1991
CGW	C. Grey-Wilson
CH&M	P.A. Cox, P.C. Hutchinson & D.M. McDonald, Sichuan & Yunnan, China, 1986; Bhutan, 1988
CHP&W	Chadwell, Howard, Powell & Wright, Kashmir, 1983
CL	C. Lovell
CLD	Kew, Edinburgh & RHS Expedition, Zhongdian (Chungtien), Lijiang & Dali, China, 1990
CM&W	M. Cheese, J. Mitchel & J. Watson
Cooper	R.E. Cooper (1890-1962), Bhutan, 1914 & '15; Punjab, India, 1916; NE Burma
CSE	Cyclamen Society Expedition
CT	Carla Teune
DBG	Denver Botanic Garden, Colorado
DF	Derek Fox
DM	David Millais
DS&T	Drake, Sharman & Thompson, Turkey, 1989
ECN	E. Charles Nelson
EGM	E.G. Millais, Bhutan, 1988 (with others); Sichuan & Yunnan, China, 1995
EKB	E.K. Balls
EM	East Malling Research Station clonal selection scheme
EMAK	Edinburgh Makalu Expedition, Nepal, 1991
EMR	E.M. Rix
EN	Edward Needham
ES	Euroseeds (Mojmir Pavelka), Nový Jičin, Czech Republic
ETE	Edinburgh Expedition, Taiwan, 1993
ETOT	M. Flanagan & T. Kirkham, Taiwan, 1992
F	George Forrest (1873-1932)

F&W	A. Flores & J. Watson, Chile, 1992	L&S	F. Ludlow (1885-1972) & G. Sherriff
Farrer	Reginald Farrer (1880-1920)	LA	Long Ashton Research Station clonal selection scheme.
FK	Fergus W. Kinmonth, China; Nepal; Bhutan, 1990; Vietnam, 1991	Lismore	Lismore Nursery, breeder's number
FMB	F.M. Bailey	LM&S	Leslie, Mattern & Sharman, Bulgaria, 1994
G	M.F. Gardner		
G&K	M.F. Gardner & S.G. Knees	LS&E	F. Ludlow, G. Sherriff & C. Elliott
G&P	M.F. Gardner & C. Page, Chile, 1992	LS&H	F. Ludlow, G. Sherriff & Hicks, Bhutan, 1949
GG	George Gusman		
G-W&P	Grey-Wilson & Phillips	LS&T	F. Ludlow, G. Sherriff & G. Taylor, SE Tibet, 1938
GS	George Sherriff (1898-1967)		
Guitt	G.G. Guittonneau	M&T	B. Mathew & J. Tomlinson
Guiz	J.B. Simmons, H. Fliegner & J. Russell, Guizhou, China, 1985	Mac&W	MacPhail & Watson
		McB	Ron McBeath, Nepal, 1981, '83 & '90
H	Paul Huggins. Oxford University Expedition, Tehri Garhwal, C Himalaya	McLaren	Henry McLaren, 2nd Baron Aberconway (1879-1953)
H&B	O. Hilliard & B.L. Burtt	MH	M. Heasman, Bhutan, 1992
H&M	Howick & McNamara	MS	M. Salmon
H&W	Hedge & Wendelbo, Afghanistan, 1969	MSF	M.S. Fillan, Tenerife, 1988; S Korea, 1989
Harry Smith	Karl August Harald Smith (1889-1971)	MS&CL	M. Salmon & C. Lovell
		NNS	Northwest Native Seeds (R. Ratko), Seattle.
Hartside	Hartside Nursery, breeder's number		
HH&K	S. & S. Hannay & N. Kingsbury, Bulgaria, 1995	NS	Nick Turland (Northside Seeds)
		Og	Mikinori Ogisu
HM&S	B. Halliwell, M. Mason & P. Smallcombe	P&C	D.S. Paterson & S. Clarke, Western USA, 1991
Hummel	D. Hummel, China, 1950	P&W	Polastri & Watson, Chile
HW&E	Hedge, Wendelbo & Ekberg, Afghanistan, 1982	PB	Peter Bird
		PC&H	G. Pattison, P. Catt & M. Hickson, Mexico, 1994
HWEL	J.M. Hirst & D. Webster, Lesotho		
HWJCM	Crûg Heronswood expedition, E Nepal, 1995	PD	Peter Davis
		PF	Paul Furse
J&JA	J.C. & J. Archibald	PJC	P.J. Christian
JCA	J.C. Archibald	PJC&AH	P.J. Christian & A. Hoog, Greece & Yugoslavia, 1985
JE	Jack Elliott		
JJ	John Jackson	Pras	Milan Prasil
JJ&JH	Josef J. & Jarmila Halda	PS&W	Polunin, Sykes & Williams, W Nepal, 1952
JJH	Josef J. Halda		
JLS	J.L. Sharman, USA, 1988	PW	Peter Wharton, Guizhou, China, 1994
JMT	J. Mann Taylor		
JR	J. Russell	R	J.F.C. Rock (1884-1962)
JRM	J.R. Marr, Greece & Turkey, 1975	RB	Ray Brown (Plant World, Devon), Chile, 1994
JW	J. Watson		
K	G. Kirkpatrick	RH	R. Hancock
K&E	Kew & Edinburgh Expedition, China, 1989	RMRP	Rocky Mountain Rare Plants, Denver, Colorado
K&LG	K. & L. Gillanders, Ecuador, 1994; Yunnan, China, 1993, '94, '96; Vietnam, 1992; Tibet, 1995	RS	Reinhart Suckow
		RV	Richard Valder
		S&B	M. Salmon & J. Blanchard
K&Mc	G. Kirkpatrick & R. McBeath.	S&F	Salmon & Fillan, Spain & Morocco
KEKE	Kew/Edinburgh Kanchenjunga Expedition, NE Nepal, 1989	S&L	I. Sinclair & D. Long, Bhutan, 1984
KGB	Kunming-Gothenburg Expedition, NW Yunnan, China, 1993	S&SH	Sheilah & Spencer Hannay, Lesotho, NE Cape Province, 1989 & '91; C Nepal, 1993
KR	K. Rushforth	SB&L	Salmon, Bird & Lovell, Jordan & Morocco
KRW	K.R. Wooster, breeder's number		
KW	Frank Kingdon-Ward (1885-1958)	SBEC	Sino-British Expedition, Cangshan, SW China, 1981
L	Roy Lancaster		

SBEL	Sino-British Expedition, Lijiang, Yunnan, China, 1987
SD	Sashal Dayal
Sch	A.D. Schilling, Nepal, 1975, '76, '77, '78, '83; Bhutan, 1988
SEH	Steve Hootman
SEP	Swedish Expedition to Pakistan
SF	P. Forde (Seaforde Gardens), Bhutan, 1990
SH	Spencer Hannay
Sich	Simmons, Erskine, Howick & McNamara, Sichuan, China, 1988
SS&W	Stainton, Sykes & Williams, C Nepal, 1954
SSNY	Sino-Scottish Expedition, NW Yunnan, China, 1992
T	Nigel P. Taylor
T&K	N.P. Taylor & S. Knees
TS&BC	T. Smythe & B. Cherry, Yunnan, China, 1994
TSS	T. Spring-Smyth, E Nepal, 1961-62, '70
TW	Tony Weston (with A.D. Schilling), Nepal, 1985; (with K. Rushforth) SW Yunnan, China 1993
USDAPI	US Dept of Agriculture Plant Index Number
USDAPQ	US Dept of Agriculture Plant Quarantine Number
USNA	United States National Arboretum
VHH	- Vernon H. Heywood
W	E.H. Wilson (1876-1930)
W/A	E.H. Wilson, for Arnold Arboretum, 1906-1919
W/V	E.H. Wilson, for Veitch, 1899-1905
WM	Will McLewin
Woods	Paddy Woods
Wr	David & Anke Wraight
Yu	Tse Tsun Yu (1908-1986)

PLANT DIRECTORY

ABELIA † (Caprifoliaceae)

§ *chinensis*	CB&S CPle EHic EPfP SMer SPer SSta WFar WHCG WPat WSHC WWat
§ Confetti = 'Conti' (v)	CAbP CB&S ECle LRHS MAsh SPer SPla SSta WBcn WWeb
'Edward Goucher' ♀	CB&S CDoC CPle CWit EBrP EBre ECro ELan ENot LBre LPan MAll MAsh MGos NFla SBre SEND SPer WAbe WFar WPat WPyg WWal WWat WWeb
engleriana	CPle CSam EBee EHic EPla MPla SBid SEas WWat
floribunda ♀	CB&S CDoC CFil CLan CPle CSam CTrw EBrP EBre ELan IDee LBre LHop MRav SBre SEas SPer WAbe WWat
§ × *grandiflora* ♀	Widely available
– 'Aurea'	See *A.* × *grandiflora* 'Goldsport'
– 'Compacta'	CEnd LRHS MAsh
§ – 'Francis Mason' (v) ♀	Widely available
– 'Gold Strike'	See *A.* × *grandiflora* 'Goldsport'
§ – 'Goldsport'	CB&S CBlo CDoC EBee IOrc LHop MAll MPla MWat SAga SBod SEas SOWG WPat WPyg WWat WWeb
– 'Prostrata'	EHic WWeb
I – 'Variegata'	See *A.* × *grandiflora* 'Francis Mason'
¶ 'Panash'	CLyn
rupestris hort.	See *A.* × *grandiflora*
– Lindley	See *A. chinensis*
schumannii	CAbP CB&S CBot CFil CHan CMCN CMHG CPle CSam EBrP EBre ELan ENot LBre LHop MAll MAsh SBre SDry SEas SHBN SPer SPla WAbe WFar WHCG WPat WPyg WSHC WWat
spathulata	LRHS WWat
triflora	CAbP CBot CDoC CFil CPle EHic EPla LFis LHop SPla SSta WHCG WPat WSHC WWat
zanderi	CPle CTrw GQui

ABELIOPHYLLUM (Oleaceae)

distichum	Widely available
– Roseum Group	CB&S CFil CPMA EBrP EBre EHic ELan GBuc LBre LHop MAsh MPla MUlv SAga SBre SEND SHBN SPer SSpi WPGP

ABELMOSCHUS (Malvaceae)

§ *manihot*	LChe

ABIES † (Pinaceae)

alba	LCon MBar
– 'Compacta'	CKen
– 'King's Dwarf'	CKen
– 'Microphylla'	CKen
– 'Schwarzwald'	CKen
– 'Tortuosa'	CKen
amabilis	WFro
– 'Spreading Star'	ECho
¶ *balsamea*	CAgr
– f. *balsamea*	WFro

– f. *hudsonia* ♀	CFee CKen CMac EHul GChr GDra IOrc LCon LLin MBar MGos MOne NHed NMen SLim SSmi WDin WWeb
– 'Nana'	CKen EBrP EBre EHul ELan EOrn GRei LBee LBre LCon MAsh MBri MPla SBre SRms WDin WStI
– 'Piccolo'	CKen
– 'Prostrata'	CBlo ECho
borisii-regis 'Pendula'	CKen
bornmuelleriana 'Archer'	CKen
brachyphylla dwarf	See *A. homolepis* 'Prostrata'
bracteata	ETen LCon
cephalonica	ETen LCon
§ – 'Meyer's Dwarf'	LCon LLin MAsh MBar
I – 'Nana'	See *A. cephalonica* 'Meyer's Dwarf'
¶ *cilicica*	LCon
concolor ♀	CB&S CBlo CDoC GChr GRei IOrc ISea LCon LPan MBal MBar NWea SPer WFro WMou
– 'Archer's Dwarf'	CKen LCon MGos
– 'Blue Spreader'	CKen MGos
– 'Candicans'	See *A. concolor* 'Argentea'
§ – 'Compacta' ♀	CDoC CKen EOrn LCon LLin MAsh MBar MGos NHol SLim SSta
– 'Fagerhult'	CKen
– 'Gable's Weeping'	CKen NHol
– 'Glauca'	See *A. concolor* 'Violacea'
– 'Glauca Compacta'	See *A. concolor* 'Compacta'
– 'Hillier Broom'	See *A. concolor* 'Hillier's Dwarf'
§ – 'Hillier's Dwarf'	CKen
– 'Husky Pup'	CKen
– var. *lowiana* 'Creamy'	CKen
– 'Masonic Broom'	CKen
– 'Piggelmee'	CKen
– 'Swift's Silver'	WBcn WFro
§ – 'Violacea'	LCon MAsh MBar MGos SSta
– 'Violacea Prostrata'	CBlo
– 'Wattezii'	CKen LLin
¶ – 'Wintergold'	LCon
delavayi var. *delavayi* Fabri Group	See *A. fabri*
– 'Major Neishe'	CKen
– 'Nana Headfort'	See *A. fargesii* 'Headfort'
¶ – SF 360	ISea
– SF 656	ISea
ernesti	See *A. recurvata* var. *ernestii*
§ *fabri*	LCon
§ *fargesii* 'Headfort'	CBlo LCon MBar NHol
¶ *firma*	NWea
forrestii	See *A. delavayi* var. *smithii*
fraseri	GRei LCon MBal WFro WMou
– 'Kline's Nest'	CKen
georgei SF 519	ISea
grandis ♀	CB&S ENot GAri GChr GRei IOrc LCon MBar NWea SHBN WDin WMou
– 'Compacta'	CKen
holophylla	LCon
homolepis	LCon MBlu
§ – 'Prostrata'	CKen
koreana	Widely available
– 'Aurea'	See *A. koreana* 'Flava'
– 'Blaue Zwo'	CKen
– 'Cis'	CKen
– 'Compact Dwarf'	LCon LLin MBar MGos SSta WAbe

§ – 'Flava'	CBlo CDoC CKen GAri LCon LLin MAsh MBar NHol
– 'Golden Dream'	CKen
– 'Golden Wonder'	COtt
– 'Inverleith'	CKen
– 'Luminetta'	CKen
– 'Nisbet'	ECho LCon
– 'Piccolo'	CKen
– 'Pinocchio'	CKen
I – 'Prostrata'	See *A. koreana* **'Prostrate Beauty'**
– 'Prostrate Beauty'	ECho EOrn LCon
– 'Silberkugel'	CKen
– 'Silberlocke' ♀	CBlo CDoC CKen EBrP EBre GAri IOrc LBee LBre LCon LLin LPan MAsh MBar MBlu MBri MGos NHol SBre SLim SPer SSta
– 'Silberperl'	CKen
– 'Silver Show'	CKen
– 'Starker's Dwarf'	CKen
* – 'Threave'	CKen
¶ – 'Wittboldt'	CKen
lasiocarpa var. *arizonica*	CLnd ETen LCon SSta
¶ – – 'Argentea'	NWea
– 'Arizonica Compacta'	CBlo CDoC CKen CMac EBrP EBre EHul IOrc LBee LBre LCon LLin LPan MAsh MBar MBri MGos NHol SBre SLim SMad SSta
¶ – 'Duflon'	CKen
– 'Glauca'	See *A. concolor* **'Violacea'**
– 'Green Globe'	CBlo CKen NHol
– 'Kenwith Blue'	CKen
* – 'King's Blue'	CKen
– 'Witch's Broom'	CKen
magnifica	LCon LPan WFro
I – 'Nana'	CKen
marocana	See *A. pinsapo* var. *marocana*
nobilis	See *A. procera*
nordmanniana ♀	CDoC CMCN EHul GChr LBuc LCon LPan MBal MBar MGos NWea SLim WDin WFro WTro WWal
¶ – 'Barabits' Compact'	MBar
– 'Barabits' Spreader'	CKen
– 'Golden Spreader' ♀	CBlo CDoC CKen EBrP EBre EOrn LBee LBre LCon LLin MAsh MBar MGos SBre SLim SPer SSta
¶ – 'Jakobsen'	CKen
I – 'Pendula'	LPan
numidica	LCon LPan
– 'Pendula'	CKen LCon
* – 'Prostrata'	LPan
pindrow	CDoC CLnd ETen WCoo
pinsapo	GChr LCon LPan MBar SEND WPGP
– 'Aurea'	CKen
– 'Aurea Nana'	CKen
– 'Glauca' ♀	CDoC CKen ELan IOrc LCon LPan MBar NHol WDin
– 'Hamondii'	CKen
I – 'Horstmann'	CKen NHol WAbe
– 'Kelleriis'	LCon
§ *procera* ♀	CDoC EHul GAri GChr GRei LCon MBal MBar NRoo NWea STre WDin WGwG WMou WWal
– 'Blaue Hexe'	CKen
– 'Compacta'	See *A. procera* **'Prostrata'**
– Glauca Group	CDoC CMac EBrP EBre IOrc LBre LCon LLin LPan MAsh MBar MBri MGos SBre SLim WGer WWes
– 'Glauca Prostrata'	EBrP EBre GAri IOrc LBee LBre LPan MBar MGos SBre
– 'Mount Hood'	CKen
¶ *sibirica*	LCon NWea
squamata	LCon
sutchuenensis	See *A. fargesii*
veitchii ♀	CB&S LCon MBar
– 'Hedergott'	CKen
– 'Heine'	CKen

ABROMEITIELLA (Bromeliaceae)
brevifolia ♀	CFil EOas

ABROTANELLA (Asteraceae)
sp.	ECho

ABRUS (Papilionaceae) See Plant Deletions

ABUTILON † (Malvaceae)
¶ 'Amiti'	CCan
'Amsterdam'	ERea
'Ashford Red' ♀	CCan IOrc LCns SLMG SOWG SRms WOMN WWeb
'Bloomsbury Can-can'	LBlm
'Bloomsbury Rose'	LBlm
'Boule de Neige'	CBot ERea LCns LHil MBEx MBri SLMG SOWG
'Canary Bird' ♀	CB&S CBot CGre CHal CPle ELan ERea ERom LBlm LCns LHil MBEx MBri MLan SHBN SLMG WOMN WWye
'Cannington Carol' (v) ♀	CCan ERea LBlm MBEx SBid
'Cannington Peter' (v) ♀	CCan CHal LBlm LHil MBEx
¶ 'Cannington Sally'	CCan
'Cannington Sonia' (v)	CCan ERea
'Cerise Queen'	CCan CSev
'Cloth of Gold'	LCns SOWG
Feuerglocke = 'Firebell'	CSev LHop MBEx
'Frances Elizabeth'	SOWG
'Glenroy Snowdrift'	MBal
globosum	See *A.* x *hybridum*
'Golden Fleece'	ERea GCal IBlr LCns
'Heather Bennington'	SOWG
'Henry Makepeace'	SOWG
'Hinton Seedling'	CFil EMil MBEx SBid SLMG
§ x *hybridum*	CHEx MBri
– 'Savitzii'	See *A.* **'Savitzii'**
'Kentish Belle' ♀	CAbb CB&S CFil CMHG CPle CSev CWit ECot ENot IOrc ISea MGrG NTow SBra SHBN SLMG SPer WWeb WWye
'Louis Marignac'	CCan ERea LBlm MBEx
'Marion'	LCns SOWG
'Master Michael'	CMac EMil ERea LHil SBid
megapotamicum ♀	CB&S CBot CCan CMHG CPlN CPle ECha ELan ENot ERea GCra GQui MAsh MBal MGos MGrG MRav SAxl SBra SDix SHBN SOWG WBod WHar WSHC WWat WWye
– 'Variegatum'	CAbb CB&S CBot CFil CWit ECtt ELan GQui IBlr IOrc LBlm MBEx MBri MGrG NPer SBod SBra SEas SHBN SLMG SOWG SRms WFar WHar
x *milleri* ♀	CB&S CMac CRHN ELan ERea IOrc SBra SHBN SMrm SVen WSHC

– 'Variegatum'	CB&S CCan CMHG CMac MBEx SEND SHBN SLMG
'Nabob' ♀	CCan CFil CGre CHal CWit ERea LBlm LCns LHil MBEx MBri SBid SLMG SOWG WWye
'Orange King'	CB&S
otocarpum	MSto
'Patrick Synge'	CFil CMHG CPle CWit ERav ERea GOrc LBlm LCns LGre MBEx SLMG SOWG SVen
'Peaches and Cream'	MBEx
§ *pictum*	EHol ERea LBlm MBri
– 'Thompsonii' (v)	CHal ERea LBlm LCns LHil MBEx MLLN SLMG
'Pink Lady'	CB&S ERea GQui MGrG SBra
'Red Bells'	CB&S GQui
'Red Goblin'	GCra
'Rotterdam'	LCns LHil MBEx SBid
§ 'Savitzii' (v)	CB&S CHal EPfP ERea LHil MBEx SOWG SRms SVen
sellowianum var. *marmoratum*	ERea SLMG
'Silver Belle'	LBlm
¶ 'Simcox White'	WSPU
'Souvenir de Bonn' (v) ♀	CSpe EHol ERea IBlr LBlm LCns LHil MBEx MTis NCut SBid SMrm
striatum hort.	See *A. pictum*
x *suntense*	CB&S CHEx CMHG CPle CSpe ELan ERea LHop MBal NPer SLMG SOWG SPer SSta WEas
– 'Jermyns' ♀	CB&S CDoC CEnd ECtt EPfP ERic GCra LGre MMil NEgg SMrm SSta WFar WPyg WWat
– 'Ralph Gould'	LHop
– 'Violetta'	CEnd SSpi
theophrasti	MSal
vitifolium	CB&S CBot CFil ECot ERea IOrc ISea LHop NChi NEgg SChu SPer WCFE WOMN WWat WWeb WWin WWye
– var. *album*	CAbb CB&S CHEx CMHG ECha ELan ISea LHop MAvo MGrG MLan MWhi SChu SEND SSpi SSta WFar WWat WWye
– 'Ice Blue'	CBot
– 'Tennant's White' ♀	CAbP CBot CCan CEnd EPfP ERea LGre SHBN SOWG WCru
– 'Veronica Tennant' ♀	CEnd ERea GOrc LGre SMrm WPyg

ACACIA † (Mimosaceae)

acinacea	CPle
alpina	WCel
armata	See *A. paradoxa*
baileyana ♀	CB&S CBrP CDoC CTrC ECon ECot ELan EMil ERea GQui LCns SBid SPar
– 'Purpurea' ♀	CAbb CB&S CBos CDoC CGre CWit EBee EMil EPfP ERea GQui LHop MAll MBlu SBid SPer WCot
caffra	CTrC
¶ *cardiophylla*	MFiF
catechu	MSal
cultriformis	ERea
cyanophylla	See *A. saligna*
dealbata ♀	Widely available

¶ – *prostrata*	CHEx
– *subalpina*	LPan WGer WMul
¶ *decora*	MFiF
decurrens	CBrP
¶ *dunnii*	MFiF
Exeter hybrid	CGre
farnesiana	CPle
filicifolia	WCel
¶ *floribunda*	CTrC
– 'Lisette'	ELan EPfP LCns LRHS MAll NPal WMul
frigescens	MAll WCel
¶ *galpinii*	CTrC
¶ *gerrardii*	CTrC
¶ *glaucoptera*	MFiF
julibrissin	See *Albizia julibrissin*
juniperina	See *A. ulicifolia*
karroo	CArn
kybeanensis	WCel
longifolia	CAbb CB&S CBrP CHEx CTrC EOas NPSI SRms
¶ *macradenia*	MFiF
maidenii	NGno
mearnsii	CTrC WCel WMul
melanoxylon	CB&S ISea LHil MAll WCel
motteana	ECot ERea
mucronata	CB&S
obliquinervia	WCel
obtusifolia	NGno
§ *paradoxa*	CPle EHol LHop MAll MBlu
– var. *angustifolia*	LBlm
¶ *pendula*	MFiF
podalyriifolia	CAbb CBrP CFil
polybotrya hort.	See *A. glaucocarpa*
pravissima	CAbb CB&S CDoC CFil CGre CHEx CMHG CPle CTbh CTrC CWit ERea GQui LHop LPan MAll MBal SArc SBid WCel WNor WPGP
pycnantha	CBrP
¶ *rehmanniana*	CTrC
retinodes ♀	CAbb CB&S CBrP CDoC CGre CPle ELan EPfP ERea GQui LCns MAll SEND SRms WMul
riceana	CB&S CDoC CTrC CTrG GQui
rivalis	ERea
rotundifolia	CPle
rubida	CTrC LPan MAll WMul
salicina	MAll MLan
§ *saligna*	CPle
sentis	See *A. victoriae*
sophorae	MAll
¶ *terminalis*	MFiF
* *trinervis*	ERea
§ *ulicifolia*	CGre CPle CWit
verniciflua	MAll
verticillata	CB&S CHEx CPle CTrG MAll
§ *victoriae*	ERea

ACAENA (Rosaceae)

adscendens 'Glauca'	CMdw EMan LHop MBel NBir NNor
adscendens hort.	See *A. magellanica* subsp. *magellanica*
– Margery Fish	See *A. affinis*
– Vahl	See *A. magellanica* subsp. *laevigata*
§ *affinis*	ECha SDix
§ *anserinifolia* Druce	ECha MAll MRav NHol WPer WWin
– hort.	See *A. novae-zelandiae*

buchananii   CTri EGoo ENot EPot GTou
MAll MBar MBri MLLN
MWgw NBro NMGW NNor
SIng SSmi WByw WFar WHoo
WLin WMer WPer WPyg WWhi
caerulea   See *A. caesiiglauca*
§ *caesiiglauca*   CBar CNic CRow CTri ECro
GAbr GGar GTou MAll MWat
NNor NSti SBla WEas WPer
– CC 451   MRPP
fissistipula   EHoe GAri GGar WHer WPer
glaucophylla   See *A. magellanica* subsp.
magellanica
'Greencourt Hybrid'   CLyd
inermis   CLyd EGar ELan EPot GTou
MAll MLLN SIng SSmi WPer
§ *magellanica* subsp.   EGoo EHoe GAri GGar GTou
laevigata   WWin
§ – subsp. *magellanica*   ELan GTou MAll WMer
microphylla ♀   EBrP EBre ECha ELan EMFP
ESis GGar LBee LBre MAll
MBar MBri MWat NGre NMen
NRoo SBre SHFr SPer SSmi
WByw WCer WCla WEas
WMow WPer
– Copper Carpet   See *A. microphylla*
'Kupferteppich'
– 'Glauca'   See *A. caesiiglauca*
§ – 'Kupferteppich'   CLTr CRow EGoo EHoe GAbr
GAri GGar GMaP MBri MBro
MCLN MRav NBro NCat NVic
WPat WPyg
– var. *pallideolivacea*   CRow
– 'Pewter Carpet'   EGoo EPPr SIng
– 'Pulchella'   EBrP EBre EMan LBre SBre
SChu
myriophylla   CInt EDAr GBin SGre WLin
WPer
§ *novae-zelandiae*   CRow CTri EJud GAri GTou
SDix SIng SWat WPer
ovalifolia   CLyd CNic CRow EGoo GTou
SLod WPer
¶ *pallida*   SIng
'Pewter'   See *A. saccaticupula* '**Blue
Haze**'
pinnatifida   ELan GTou NBro WPer
profundeincisa   See *A. anserinifolia* **Druce**
'Purple Carpet'   See *A. microphylla*
'**Kupferteppich**'
saccaticupula   MAll
§ – 'Blue Haze'   CGle CLTr CLyd CSam ECha
ELan EPot GCHN GTou MBar
MBro MCLN MLLN MTis
MWgw MWhi NPer SIng SPer
SRms WFar WHoo WPer WWhi
sanguisorbae Linnaeus f.   See *A. anserinifolia* **Druce**
viridior   See *A. anserinifolia* **Druce**

ACALYPHA (Euphorbiaceae)

¶ *hispaniolae*   ERea MBEx
hispida ♀   MBri
pendula   See *A. reptans*
¶ *reptans*   CGen LPVe

ACANTHOCALYX See MORINA

ACANTHOLIMON (Plumbaginaceae)

androsaceum   See *A. ulicinum*
armenum   NMen
glumaceum   MDHE MWat NMen NNrd
WPat
¶ *hilariae*   MFos

hohenackeri   SIng
§ *ulicinum*   EHyt EPot NWCA SGre

ACANTHOPANAX See ELEUTHEROCOCCUS

ACANTHUS † (Acanthaceae)

balcanicus   See *A. hungaricus*
dioscoridis var. *perringii*   CGle CHan CRDP SBla WCot
WSel WViv
hirsutus   EMar EMon SCro WCot
– JCA 109.700   SBla
– subsp. *syriacus*   CGle CLon LGre SBla
JCA 106.500
§ *hungaricus*   CArn CB&S CGle CLon ECED
ECGN EHal ELan EMan EMar
EMon EPla GCal LFis MSte
NLar SBla SPer SSoC SWat
WCot WRus
– AL&JS 90097YU   EMon
longifolius   See *A. hungaricus*
mollis   Widely available
– 'Fielding Gold'   GCal WViv
– 'Hollard's Gold'   CRDP GBin SWat WBro WCot
WViv
– Latifolius Group   EFou EGar EPla MRav MUlv
NHol SChu SPer WWal WWat
spinosus ♀   Widely available
– 'Lady Moore'   IBlr WCot WSPU
– Spinosissimus Group   CGle CMHG ECha EGar EMan
GCal SWat WCru WFar
syriacus   EBee EMan GCal NLar WViv

ACCA (Myrtaceae)

sellowiana (F)   CArn CB&S CGre CHEx CHan
CMHG CPle CSam CTrG ELan
EPla ERea ESim GQui ISea
LHop LPan LSpr MCCP MSal
SOWG SSta WPat WSHC
sellowiana 'Apollo' (F)   ERea
– 'Coolidge' (F)   ERea
– 'Mammoth' (F)   CB&S ERea
– 'Triumph' (F)   CB&S ERea
– 'Variegata' (F)   CGre

ACER † (Aceraceae)

acuminatum   CMCN WNor
albopurpurascens   CMCN
amplum   CMCN
argutum   CMCN WNor
barbinerve   CPMA EPfP WNor
buergerianum   CB&S CBlo CDoC CDul CEnd
CGre CLnd CMCN CPMA
GAri SSpi STre WCwm WDin
WNor WWat
– 'Goshiki-kaede' (v)   CPMA LNet
– 'Integrifolium'   See *A. buergerianum*
'**Subintegrum**'
– 'Naruto'   CMCN
§ – 'Subintegrum'   CMCN
– 'Tanchô'   LNet
* – 'Variegatum'   CMCN
caesium   EPfP
¶ *calcaratum*   CMCN
campbellii   CMCN LNet
§ – subsp. *flabellatum*   CGre CMCN
– – var. *yunnanense*   CMCN
– – – SF 533   ISea
– subsp. *sinense*   See *A. sinense*
– subsp. *wilsonii*   See *A. wilsonii*
campestre ♀   Widely available

– 'Carnival'	CB&S CBlo CEnd CMCN CPMA ELan LNet MAsh MBlu MBri MGos NHol SMad SSoC WMou WWeb
– 'Elsrijk'	CLnd
– 'Pendulum'	CBlo CDoC CEnd CTho
– 'Postelense'	CEnd CMCN LNet MBlu SSpi WMou
– 'Pulverulentum' (v)	CBlo CDoC CEnd CMCN LNet SMad SPer SSta
– 'Red Shine'	EBee MGos
– 'Royal Ruby'	CB&S CMCN CTho LNet MAsh SSta
* – 'Ruby Glow'	CBlo CDoC CEnd SPer
– 'Schwerinii'	CMCN
– 'William Caldwell'	CTho
capillipes ♀	CB&S CBlo CDul CMCN CSam CTho ELan ENot EPla IOrc LPan MAsh MBar MBri MGos SIgm SPer SSpi SSta WDin WGer WNor WPyg WShe WWat
¶ – 'Candy Stripe'	SSpi SSta
♦ – var. *morifolium*	See *A. morifolium*
* – 'Variegatum'	CEnd
cappadocicum	CBlo CMCN GChr MLan WCoo WDin WNor WWes
– 'Aureum' ♀	CAbP CB&S CBlo CDoC CDul CEnd CLnd CMCN CTho ELan ENot IOrc LNet LPan MAsh MBlu MBri MGos NBea SHBN SMad SPer SSpi WDin WMou WPyg
– var. *mono*	See *A. mono*
– 'Rubrum' ♀	CBlo CDoC CDul CLnd CMCN ENot IHos IOrc LPan MAsh MBlu MGos SPer SSpi WDin
– subsp. *sinicum*	CMCN EPfP WWes
carpinifolium	CDoC CLnd CMCN LNet MAsh SSpi WGer WNor WWes WWoo
catalpifolium	See *A. longipes* subsp. *catalpifolium*
§ *caudatifolium*	CMCN
¶ – B&SWJ 3531	WCru
§ aff. – CC 1744	WHCr
§ aff. – CC 1927	WHCr
caudatum subsp. *ukurunduense*	CMCN CPMA WNor
cinerascens	CMCN
cinnamomifolium	See *A. coriaceifolium*
circinatum ♀	CB&S CDul CMCN CPMA CSam CTho GChr LBuc LNet MLan SSpi SSta WDin WFro WNor WWal WWat
– 'Little Gem'	LNet
– 'Monroe'	CMCN LNet
¶ – NJM 94038	WPGP
cissifolium	CB&S CDoC CFil CMCN WNor
x *conspicuum* 'Elephant's Ear'	CPMA MBri
– 'Phoenix'	CPMA CTho LNet MBlu MBri SSpi
– 'Silver Cardinal'	See *A.* '*Silver Cardinal*'
§ – 'Silver Vein'	CMCN CPMA EBee EBrP EBre LBre LNet MBlu MBri SBre SSpi WPGP
§ *cordatum*	CMCN
§ *coriaceifolium*	CMCN WNor
crataegifolium	CMCN WNor
– 'Veitchii' (v)	CMCN CPMA EPfP LNet SSpi SSta WBcn
creticum	See *A. sempervirens*
dasycarpum	See *A. saccharinum*
davidii	CAbP CB&S CBlo CDoC CMCN CMHG ENot IOrc ISea MAsh MBal MBar MGos MRav MWat SHBN SPer WBay WDin WFro WNor WPic
– 'Ernest Wilson'	CB&S CBlo CDul CMCN COtt ELan MAsh
– 'George Forrest' ♀	CB&S CBlo CMCN CTho EBee EBrP EBre EPfP GChr LBre LPan MAsh SBre SEND SSta WDin WOrn
– 'Karmen'	MBri MGos
– 'Rosalie'	CLyn MBlu MBri
– 'Serpentine' ♀	CB&S CMCN CPMA CTho MAsh MBlu MBri NBee SSpi
♦ – 'Silver Vein'	See *A.* x *conspicuum* '**Silver Vein**'
diabolicum	CMCN
divergens	CMCN
elegantulum	CGre CMCN WFro WNor
erianthum	CDul CLnd SSpi SSta WNor
fabri	CMCN
flabellatum	See *A. campbellii* subsp. *flabellatum*
§ *forrestii*	CDul CMCN EPfP WNor
– 'Alice'	CB&S CLyn CMCN CPMA LNet MGos SSta
franchetii	CMCN
♦ x *freemanii* Autumn Blaze®	See *A.* x *freemanii* Autumn Blaze = '**Jeffersred**'
– 'Autumn Fantasy'	MBlu
§ – Autumn Blaze® = 'Jeffersred'	CDoC IOrc
fulvescens	See *A. longipes*
ginnala	See *A. tataricum* subsp. *ginnala*
giraldii	CMCN
glabrum	CLnd CMCN WNor
– subsp. *douglasii*	CLyn CMCN
globosum	See *A. platanoides* '**Globosum**'
grandidentatum	See *A. saccharum* subsp. *grandidentatum*
griseum ♀	Widely available
grosseri	CMCN CTri NEgg WFro WLRN
– var. *hersii* ♀	CBlo CDoC CDul CLnd CTho ELan ENot MAsh MBal MBri MRav NWea SPer WCwm WDin WGer WNor WOrn WPyg WWat
heldreichii	CLnd CMCN EPfP MBlu
henryi	CGre CLnd CMCN ENot LNet WNor WWes WWoo
x *hillieri*	CMCN
hookeri	CMCN
hyrcanum	CMCN
japonicum	CDul CMCN GChr LNet MBal MBar SSta WAbe WCoo WNor WWat
§ – 'Aconitifolium' ♀	CDul CEnd CMCN CPMA ELan ENot IHos IOrc LNet LPan MAsh MBar MBlu MBri MGos NPal SHBN SPer SReu SSpi SSta WDin WHar WNor WPat WWat WWeb
– 'Attaryi'	CMCN
– 'Aureum'	See *A. shirasawanum* '**Aureum**'
– 'Ezo-no-momiji'	See *A. shirasawanum* '**Ezo-no-momiji**'

- 'Filicifolium'	See *A. japonicum* **'Aconitifolium'**
- 'Green Cascade'	CEnd CMCN CPMA WPat
* - 'King Copse'	SMur
- 'Laciniatum'	See *A. japonicum* **'Aconitifolium'**
- f. *microphyllum*	See *A. shirasawanum* **'Microphyllum'**
- 'Ogurayama'	See *A. shirasawanum* **'Ogurayama'**
- 'Ô-isami'	CMCN LNet
- 'Vitifolium' ♀	CBlo CDoC CEnd CMCN CPMA ELan EPfP IOrc LNet LPan MAsh MBlu SReu SSpi SSta WWeb
kawakamii	See *A. caudatifolium*
laevigatum	CMCN
lanceolatum	CMCN
laxiflorum	CLnd CMCN SSta
lobelii Bunge	See *A. turkestanicum*
- Tenore	CLnd
§ *longipes*	CMCN
§ - subsp. *catalpifolium*	CMCN
macrophyllum	CDoC CDul CFil CMCN ISea LHyd MBlu
- 'Kimballiae'	CMCN
- NJM 94040	WPGP
- 'Seattle Sentinel'	CMCN
* - 'Variegatum'	CMCN
¶ *mandschuricum*	CPMA EPfP MBlu WWoo
§ *maximowiczianum*	CB&S CDoC CLnd CMCN CSam EBee ELan IOrc MBal SPer SPri SSta WNor WPGP WWat WWes
maximowiczii	CMCN NWea WNor
§ *metcalfii*	WNor
micranthum ♀	CMCN EPfP ESis SSpi WCoo WNor WWes
§ *mono*	CMCN EPfP
- 'Hoshiyadori' (v)	CMCN
¶ - subsp. *mono*	WNor
- 'Shufu-nishiki'	CMCN
- var. *tricuspis*	See *A. cappadocicum* subsp. *sinicum* var. *tricaudatum*
monspessulanum	CFil CMCN MAsh
§ *morifolium*	CMCN
morrisonense	See *A. caudatifolium*
negundo	CBlo CDul CLnd CMCN ENot NWea WNor WTro
- 'Argenteovariegatum'	See *A. negundo* **'Variegatum'**
- 'Auratum'	CBlo CMCN MBar WDin WPat
- 'Aureovariegatum'	CB&S MBar SHBN
¶ - subsp. *californicum*	WNor
§ - 'Elegans' (v)	CBlo CDoC CLnd CMCN COtt EBee EBrP EBre ELan ENot LBre LPan MAsh NHol SBre SHBN SPer
- 'Elegantissimum'	See *A. negundo* **'Elegans'**
- 'Flamingo' (v) ♀	Widely available
- 'Kelly's Gold'	CB&S CBlo
§ - 'Variegatum'	CB&S CBlo CLnd EBee ECrN ENot LPan MGos NBee SPer WDin
- var. *violaceum* ♀	CB&S CMCN EPla WBcn
nikoense	See *A. maximowiczianum*
oblongum	CMCN
§ *obtusifolium*	CMCN
¶ *okomotoanum*	CMCN
oliverianum	CLyn CMCN EPfP WNor
opalus	CDul CMCN
¶ - subsp. *obtusatum*	SSpi
orientale	See *A. sempervirens*
¶ Pacific Sunset®	MBri
palmatum	CDul CLan CMCN CMHG ENot ESis GAbr GChr LNet MBal MBar MBro NBee SHBN SPar SPer SSpi SSta STre WAbe WCFE WCoo WFro WHar WOrn WPat WWat
§ - 'Aka Shigitatsusawa'	CMCN CPMA LNet
- 'Akaji-nishiki'	See *A. truncatum* **'Akaji-nishiki'**
- 'Akegarasu'	CMCN
- 'Aoba-jo'	CPMA WWes
- 'Aoshime-no-uchi'	See *A. palmatum* **'Shinobugaoka'**
- 'Aoyagi'	CMCN CPMA LNet MAsh WWes
§ - 'Arakawa'	CMCN GAri LNet
- 'Aratama'	CMCN
- 'Asahi-zuru' (v)	CBlo CMCN CPMA LNet MGos SSta WWes
- 'Atrolineare'	COtt
- f. *atropurpureum*	CB&S CDul EBrP EBre ELan ENot ESis GChr GRei LBre LHyd LNet MBal MBar MGos NBee NWea SBod SBre SHBN SPer SReu WBod WDin WOrn WPat WStI WWat WWeb
- 'Atropurpureum'	WGwG WHar
- 'Atropurpureum Superbum'	CBlo CMCN MBri
- 'Aureum'	CBlo CFil CMCN CPMA ELan EPfP LNet MBri SBod SSpi WFar WPGP
- Autumn Glory Group	CPMA SSpi WWes
* - 'Autumn Red'	LPan
* - 'Autumn Showers'	CEnd
- 'Azuma-murasaki'	CMCN
- 'Beni-kagami'	CDul CEnd CMCN COtt CPMA LNet MAsh WWes
- 'Beni-kawa'	LNet
- 'Beni-komachi'	CB&S CFil CMCN CPMA LNet WPGP WPat
- 'Beni-maiko'	CBlo CFil CMCN CPMA LNet MBri WPGP WPat WWeb WWes
- 'Beni-otake'	CB&S CPMA LNet
- 'Beni-schichihenge' (v)	CB&S CBlo CEnd CMCN CPMA ELan LNet MAsh NHol SMur SSta WPat
- 'Beni-shidare Variegated'	CMCN CPMA LNet
♦ - 'Beni-shigitatsu-sawa'	See *A. palmatum* **'Aka Shigitatsusawa'**
- 'Beni-tsukasa' (v)	CBlo CEnd CPMA LNet LPan MAsh SSpi WPat WWes
- 'Bloodgood' ♀	Widely available
- 'Bonfire'	See *A. truncatum* **'Akaji-nishiki'**
- 'Brocade'	CMCN WPat
- 'Burgundy Lace' ♀	CB&S CBlo CEnd CMCN COtt CPMA IOrc LNet MAsh MBlu MGos NHol WPat WPyg
- 'Butterfly' (v) ♀	CB&S CEnd CFil CMCN CPMA EBrP EBre ELan IOrc LBre LNet LPan MAsh MBal MBar MBri MGos NHol SBod SBre SPer SReu SSta WPGP WPat WPyg WStI WWeb
- 'Carminium'	See *A. palmatum* **'Corallinum'**
- 'Chirimen-nishiki' (v)	CMCN LNet
- 'Chishio'	See *A. palmatum* **'Shishio'**
- 'Chishio Improved'	See *A. palmatum* **'Shishio Improved'**

– 'Chitoseyama' ♀ | CBlo CDul CEnd CMCN COtt CPMA CTho ELan LNet MAsh MBar MBri MGos SSpi SSta WPat WWeb
– 'Coonara Pygmy' | CMCN CPMA LNet WPat WWes
– 'Coral Pink' | CPMA
§ – 'Corallinum' | CBlo CEnd CMCN COtt CPMA LNet LPan LRHS MBri SSpi WPat
N – var. *coreanum* | CMCN CSam WNor WWeb
– 'Deshôjô' | CB&S CBlo CMCN LNet LPan MAsh MBar MBlu MGos NHol
– var. *dissectum* ♀ | CDoC CEnd CTho ENot IOrc LHyd MBar MBri MGos NBee NHol NWea SBod SHBN SReu SSoC WDin WFro WNor WPat WPyg WStI WWat
¶ – – 'Baldsmith' | CPMA
– – 'Crimson Queen' ♀ | CB&S CDoC CDul CEnd CMCN CPMA IOrc LNet LPan MAsh MBal MBri MBro MGos SPer WFar WNor WPat WPyg
– – Dissectum Atropurpureum Group | CB&S CPMA EBrP EBre ELan LBre LHyd LNet LPan MBal MGos NWea SBre SHBN SPer SReu SSpi SSta WBod WDin WFar WPat WWat WWeb
– – 'Dissectum Flavescens' | CEnd CMCN CPMA ISea
§ – – 'Dissectum Nigrum' | CBlo CMCN CTri LNet MAsh MGos NHol WLRN WPat
– – 'Dissectum Palmatifidum' | LNet
– – 'Dissectum Rubrifolium' | CMCN MBlu
§ – – 'Dissectum Variegatum' | COtt CPMA EPfP LNet MAsh SMur SSta
– – Dissectum Viride Group | CB&S CDul CMCN CPMA ELan GRei ISea LNet MAsh MBro SPer SPla SSta WBod WWeb
– – 'Green Globe' | LPan
¶ – – 'Green Mist' | CPMA
– – 'Inaba-shidare' ♀ | CB&S CDoC CEnd CMCN COtt CPMA GRei LNet LPan MAsh MBar MBri MGos NHol SBod SPer SReu SSta WPyg
* – – 'Lionheart' | CPMA WWes
– – 'Orangeola' | LNet WPat
– – 'Ornatum' | CDoC CMCN COtt CTri MGos SPer SSoC WFar WHar
¶ – – 'Sunset' | WPat
– 'Eddisbury' | CPMA SSta WPat
– 'Effegi' | See *A. palmatum* 'Fireglow'
– 'Elegans' | EPfP MAsh
– 'Ever Red' | See *A. palmatum* var. *dissectum* 'Dissectum Nigrum'
– 'Filigree' | CBlo CFil CMCN CPMA EPfP ISea LNet MAsh MBri MGos SSpi WPGP WPat
¶ – 'Fior d'Arancia' | CPMA
* – 'Fior d'Arangio' | CEnd COtt
§ – 'Fireglow' | CBlo CMCN COtt CPMA LPan WPat WWes
¶ – 'Fjellheim' | WPat
– 'Frederici Guglielmi' | See *A. palmatum* var. *dissectum* 'Dissectum Variegatum'
– 'Garnet' ♀ | Widely available
– 'Goshiki-kotohime' (v) | CMCN CPMA WPat
– 'Goshiki-shidare' (v) | CMCN LNet
– 'Green Trompenburg' | CMCN LNet
§ – 'Hagoromo' | CPMA LNet SPer

– 'Hanami-nishiki' | CMCN CPMA
– 'Harusame' (v) | CMCN LNet
– 'Hazeroino' (v) | CMCN
– var. *heptalobum* | CMCN
§ – 'Heptalobum Elegans' | CBlo CMCN CPMA LRHS SHBN SSpi
– 'Heptalobum Elegans Purpureum' | See *A. palmatum* 'Hessei'
§ – 'Hessei' | CEnd CMCN LNet WPat
– 'Higasayama' (v) | CB&S CBlo CFil CMCN COtt CPMA LNet NHol SSta WPGP WPat WWes
– 'Hôgyoku' | CMCN CPMA
– 'Ichigyôji' | CDul CEnd CMCN CPMA MAsh WWeb
– 'Improved Shishio' | See *A. palmatum* 'Shishio Improved'
– 'Inazuma' | CB&S CMCN
– 'Jirô-shidare' | LNet SMur WWeb
– 'Junihitoe' | See *A. shirasawanum* 'Junihitoe'
– 'Kagero' (v) | CPMA
§ – 'Kagiri-nishiki' (v) | CBlo CMCN CPMA LNet MAsh MGos SPer SSta WNor WWeb
– 'Kamagata' | CEnd CMCN CPMA EPfP LRHS MAsh SSta WPat WWeb
– 'Karaori-nishiki' (v) | LNet
– 'Karasugawa' (v) | CMCN CPMA LNet
– 'Kasagiyama' | CEnd CMCN COtt CPMA LRHS WPat
– 'Kasen-nishiki' | CPMA
– 'Kashima' | CDul CMCN CPMA WWes
– 'Katsura' | CB&S CEnd CFil CMCN COtt CPMA ELan ISea MAsh MBlu MBri MBro NHol SPer SSpi SSta WNor WPGP WWeb
– 'Ki-hachijô' | CMCN
– 'Kinran' | CMCN LNet LRHS MAsh WPat WWeb
– 'Kinshi' | CMCN CPMA LRHS MAsh SSta WWeb WWes
– 'Kiri-nishiki' | CMCN WPat
– 'Kiyohime' | CDoC CMCN WPat
– 'Koshibori-nishiki' | CPMA
– 'Kotohime' | CMCN CPMA
¶ – 'Koto-ito-komachi' | WPat
– 'Koto-no-ito' | CMCN
– 'Kurui-jishi' | LNet
– 'Linearilobum' ♀ | CMCN LHyd LNet MBlu NHol WNor WPat
– 'Linearilobum Atropurpureum' | WNor
– 'Little Princess' | See *A. palmatum* 'Mapi-no-machihime'
– 'Lutescens' | CMCN CPMA
– 'Maiko' | CDul CMCN
– 'Mama' | CMCN
§ – 'Mapi-no-machihime' | CMCN ELan LNet MAsh NHol SMur WPat WWat WWeb WWes
– 'Masukagami' (v) | CBlo CEnd COtt
– 'Matsukaze' | CMCN COtt CPMA WWes
– 'Mikawa-yatsubusa' | CMCN WPat
– 'Mirte' | LNet
¶ – 'Momenshide' | WPat
– 'Moonfire' | CMCN EPfP LNet LRHS MAsh WWeb
– 'Murasaki-kyohim' | CMCN CPMA WPat
– 'Mure-hibari' | CMCN
– 'Murogawa' | CMCN
– 'Nicholsonii' | CMCN CTri LPan
– 'Nigrum' | CMCN WPat

§ – 'Nishiki-gawa' CMCN CPMA
¶ – 'Nishiki-momiji' MAsh
– 'Nomurishidare' See *A. palmatum*
misapplied **'Shôjô-shidare'**
¶ – 'Nomurishidare' Wada SSpi
– 'Nuresagi' CMCN CPMA LNet
¶ – 'Ogon-sarasa' CPMA
– 'Ô-kagami' CMCN CPMA LNet MBlu
MBri SSta
– 'Okukuji-nishiki' CBlo CPMA LNet
– 'Okushimo' CFil CMCN CPMA LNet MAsh
NHol WPGP WPat
– 'Omato' LNet
– 'Omurayama' CMCN CPMA EPfP LNet
LRHS MAsh SSta WWeb
WWes
§ – 'Ô-nishiki' CMCN LNet
– 'Orange Dream' CMCN CPMA LPan MBri
WWes
¶ – 'Orido-Nishiki' (v) CBlo CEnd CMCN COtt CPMA
ELan EPfP LNet MBlu MGos
NBee NPal SCoo SSta
– 'Ôsakazuki' ♀ CB&S CDul CEnd CMCN
CPMA CSam CTho ELan GRei
IOrc LHyd LNet MBar MBri
MGos NHol NWea SBod SHBN
SPer SReu SSpi SSta WBod
WDin WPat WWat
– 'Ôshû-beni' CMCN
– 'Ôshû-shidare' CMCN CPMA
– 'Otome-zakura' CMCN
¶ – 'Peaches and Cream' (v) CPMA
– 'Pendulum Julian' CMCN
– 'Pine Bark Maple' See *A. palmatum* **'Nishiki-gawa'**
– 'Pixie' CMCN CPMA
– 'Red Dragon' CB&S CPMA LNet
– 'Red Filigree Lace' CEnd CMCN CPMA EPfP ISea
LNet MAsh MBlu
– 'Red Flash' LPan
– 'Red Pygmy' ♀ CB&S CBlo CDoC CEnd
CMCN COtt CPMA LNet MBar
MBri MGos NHol SPer SSta
WPat WWeb
– 'Reticulatum' See *A. palmatum*
'Shigitatsu-sawa'
– 'Ribesifolium' See *A. palmatum* **'Shishigashira'**
– 'Roseomarginatum' See *A. palmatum* **'Kagiri-nishiki'**
– 'Rough Bark Maple' See *A. palmatum* **'Arakawa'**
– 'Rubrum' CMCN MBal WFar
– 'Rufescens' CMCN
– 'Ryuzu' CPMA
– 'Sagara-nishiki' (v) CMCN CPMA
– 'Samidare' CMCN CPMA
N – 'Sango-kaku' ♀ Widely available
– 'Saoshika' CDul CMCN
– 'Sazanami' CMCN CPMA WNor
– 'Scolopendriifolium' WPat
– 'Seigen' CMCN
– 'Seiryû' ♀ CAbP CB&S CEnd CMCN
COtt CPMA ELan LNet LPan
MBar MBri MGos NHol SBod
SPer SSpi SSta WDin WFar
WNor WPat WWeb
– 'Sekimori' CMCN CPMA SSta WWes
– 'Sekka-yatsubusa' CMCN
– 'Senkaki' See *A. palmatum* **'Sango-kaku'**
– 'Septemlobum Elegans' See *A. palmatum* **'Heptalobum**
Elegans'
– 'Septemlobum See *A. palmatum* **'Hessei'**
Purpureum'
– 'Sessilifolium' dwarf See *A. palmatum* **'Hagoromo'**
– 'Sessilifolium' tall See *A. palmatum* **'Koshimino'**

– 'Shaina' CB&S CMCN COtt CPMA
LPan SSta WPat WWeb
– 'Sherwood Flame' CBlo CMCN CPMA LNet MBlu
MBri MGos WPat
§ – 'Shigitatsu-sawa' (v) CB&S CMCN CPMA LPan
MAsh SSta
– 'Shigure-bato' CMCN CPMA
– 'Shikageori-nishiki' MAsh
– 'Shime-no-uchi' CMCN LNet
– 'Shindeshôjô' CBlo CEnd CMCN COtt CPMA
ELan LNet LPan MAsh MBlu
MBri SBod SHBN SPer SPla
SReu SSta WFoF WNor WPGP
WPat WWeb
§ – 'Shinobugaoka' CBlo CMCN CPMA LNet
– 'Shinonome' CMCN COtt
§ – 'Shishigashira' CMCN COtt CPMA LPan
MBar MBri MGos WFar WPat
§ – 'Shishio' CBlo CMCN COtt LHyd LNet
MAsh SSpi
§ – 'Shishio Improved' CFil CMCN CPMA LNet MBlu
MGos SSta WPGP
– 'Shôjô' CMCN
– 'Shôjô-nomura' CEnd CMCN COtt
§ – 'Shôjô-shidare' CEnd COtt LRHS MAsh SSpi
¶ – 'Skeeters' WPat
– 'Stella Rossa' CBlo CMCN COtt CPMA MBlu
SBod WPat WWes
– 'Suminagashi' CDoC CMCN COtt LNet SMur
SSta
– 'Takinogawa' MAsh WWeb
– 'Tamahime' CMCN
– 'Tamukeyama' CMCN CPMA
– 'Tana' CMCN CPMA
– 'Trompenburg' CB&S CBlo CEnd CMCN COtt
CPMA CTho ELan LNet LPan
MAsh MBri MBro MGos NHol
NPal SBod SPer SPla SSpi SSta
WPat WPyg WWeb
– 'Tsuchigumo' CMCN CPMA WWes
– 'Tsukubane' CMCN
– 'Tsukushigata' CMCN
– 'Tsuma-beni' CMCN CPMA ELan EPfP LNet
LRHS MAsh WPat WWeb
– 'Tsuma-gaki' CMCN CPMA
– 'Ukigumo' (v) CB&S CEnd CMCN CPMA
ELan LNet MAsh MGos NHol
SBod SPer WPat
– 'Ukon' CMCN
– 'Umegae' CMCN CPMA
– 'Utsu-semi' CMCN CPMA LNet
– 'Versicolor' (v) CMCN CPMA LNet WWes
– 'Villa Taranto' CEnd CMCN CPMA EPfP
LNet LRHS MAsh MBlu MGos
NPal
– 'Volubile' CMCN MAsh SMur
– 'Wabito' CDul CMCN
– 'Wakehurst Pink' (v) CMCN
– 'Waterfall' CBlo CMCN CPMA LNet
MGos
– 'Wilson's Pink Dwarf' CMCN LNet
– 'Wou-nishiki' See *A. palmatum* **'O-nishiki'**
– 'Yûgure' MGos
papilio See *A. caudatum*
paxii CMCN
pectinatum subsp. *forrestii* See *A. forrestii*
– 'Sirene' CPMA MGos
¶ – 'Sparkling' MBri

pensylvanicum ♀	CB&S CBlo CMCN CSam CTho ELan EPfP LPan MGos MRav NBee NHol NWea SHBN SPer SSpi WDin WNor WOrn WWat WWeb
– 'Erythrocladum' ♀	CBlo CEnd CMCN CPMA CTho LNet MBri NHol SMad SSpi SSta
pentaphyllum	CMCN LNet SSpi
pictum	See *A. mono*
pilosum var. *stenolobum*	MBlu WWoo
platanoides ♀	CBlo CKin CLnd CMCN CPer ENot GChr GRei LBuc LHyr LPan MGos NWea SPer WDin WHar WMou WNor
– 'Cleveland'	CB&S ENot
– 'Columnare'	CDoC CMCN ECrN ENot EPfP IOrc LPan WOrn
– 'Crimson King' ♀	CB&S CBlo CDul CMCN CSam CTho EBrP EBre ELan GChr GRei LBre LBuc LHyr LNet LPan MAsh MBar MWat NBee NWea SBre SHBN SPer SSta WDin WHar WJas WOrn WWeb
– 'Crimson Sentry'	CBlo CDul CEnd CLnd CMCN COtt EBee EBrP EBre ENot IHos LBre LBuc LNet MAsh MBri MGos SBre WJas WLRN WOrn WWeb
– 'Cucullatum'	CMCN CTho
– 'Deborah'	CDul CLnd CTho LPan SHBN
– 'Dissectum'	CTho
– 'Drummondii' (v) ♀	Widely available
– 'Emerald Queen'	CDoC CLnd CMCN ENot SHBN WOrn
– 'Faassen's Black'	LPan
§ – 'Globosum'	CLnd CMCN ENot LPan MGos
– 'Goldsworth Purple'	CLnd CMCN
– 'Laciniatum'	CEnd CMCN ENot MAsh SLPl SPer
– 'Lorbergii'	See *A. platanoides* **'Palmatifidum'**
– 'Olmsted'	ENot LNet
§ – 'Palmatifidum'	CSam
§ – 'Princeton Gold = 'Prigo'	LPan
♦ – Princeton Gold	See *A. platanoides* Princeton Gold **= 'Prigo'**
– 'Pyramidale Nanum'	CTho
– 'Royal Red'	CMCN ENot MGos
– 'Schwedleri' ♀	CBlo CDul CLnd CMCN ECrN MGos NWea WDin
– 'Summershade'	CMCN
pseudoplatanus	CB&S CBlo CDul CKin CLnd CMCN CPer CTri ENot GChr GRei LBuc LHyr LPan MBar MGos NWea WDin WMou
§ – 'Atropurpureum' (v) ♀	CBlo CDoC CLnd CTho ECrN ENot IOrc MSto NBee NWea
– 'Brilliantissimum' ♀	Widely available
– 'Constant P.'	ENot
– 'Corstorphinense'	CMCN
– 'Erectum'	EBee ENot WOrn
– 'Erythrocarpum'	CMCN
N– 'Leopoldii' (v) ♀	CB&S CBlo CDoC CDul CLnd CMCN COtt CTho ELan ENot IOrc LPan MBar SHBN SPer WDin WOrn
– 'Negenia'	CMCN
– 'Nizetii' (v)	LRHS MBri
– 'Prinz Handjéry'	CB&S CBlo CDoC CDul CEnd CMCN CTri LNet LPan MAsh MBar MGos NWea SHBN SPer SSpi
– 'Simon-Louis Frères' (v)	CBar CBlo CDul CEnd CLnd CMCN GChr LNet LPan MAsh MBri MGos MWat WCFE WFoF
N– 'Spaethii' hort.	See *A. pseudoplatanus* **'Atropurpureum'**
¶ – 'Spring Gold'	MGos
– f. *variegatum*	MSto WCot
– 'Worley' ♀	CB&S CBlo CDoC CDul CLnd CMCN COtt ENot GChr IOrc NWea SHBN SPer WDin WOrn
pseudosieboldianum	CFil CMCN CPMA SSpi WFro WNor WWoo
– MSF 861	WPGP
pubipalmatum	WNor
pycnanthum	CMCN
regelii	See *A. pentapotamicum*
¶ *robustum*	WNor
rubescens	CSam
rubrum	CAgr CB&S CBlo CDoC CDul CGre CLnd CMCN CTri GCHN LHyr MAsh MGos MLan MWat NWea SPer WDin WNor WWat
– 'Bowhall'	CMCN
¶ – 'Columnare'	CMCN
– 'Morgan'	CEnd
– October Glory® ♀	CBlo CDoC CDul CEnd CMCN CMHG CSam CTho CTri GChr IOrc LPan MAsh MBlu MBri SMad SSpi SSta WCwm WWeb
– Red Sunset	CEnd CMCN CTho MBlu MBri SSpi SSta WCwm
– 'Schlesingeri'	CEnd CMCN EBee MBlu
§ *rufinerve* ♀	CB&S CBlo CDoC CDul CLnd CMCN CMHG CTho CTri ENot EPfP GChr IOrc LPan MBri NBee NWea SPer SSpi WDin WGer WNor WOrn WPyg WStI
– 'Albolimbatum'	See *A. rufinerve* **'Hatsuyuki'**
– 'Albomarginatum'	See *A. rufinerve* **'Hatsuyuki'**
§ – 'Hatsuyuki' (v)	CBlo CEnd CMCN CPMA ELan NHol SSpi
§ *saccharinum* ♀	CB&S CBlo CDul CLnd CMCN CPer ELan ENot GChr LHyr MGos MWat NWea SPer SSpi WDin WFar WNor
¶ – 'Born's Gracious'	IOrc
– 'Elegans'	See *A.* × *freemanii* **'Elegant'**
– 'Fastigiatum'	See *A. saccharinum* f. *pyramidale*
– f. *laciniatum*	CMCN ENot MBlu MGos WDin
– 'Laciniatum Wieri'	CLnd CMCN CTho NBee WWes
– f. *lutescens*	CMCN CTho ENot MBlu
§ – f. *pyramidale*	CBlo CDoC CLnd CMCN ENot IOrc LPan
saccharum	CAgr CDoC CDul CLnd CMCN NWea WCwm WNor
♦ – subsp. *barbatum*	See *A. saccharum* subsp. *floridanum*
§ – subsp. *floridanum*	CMCN
§ – subsp. *grandidentatum*	CMCN
– subsp. *leucoderme*	CMCN
– subsp. *nigrum*	CMCN
– – 'Temple's Upright'	CMCN LNet WWes
– subsp. *skutchii*	CMCN

'Scanlon' ♀	CB&S CDul CEnd CMCN CTho LPan
§ *sempervirens*	CMCN CPMA
serrulatum	CMCN
§ *shirasawanum*	CDul CMCN WCoo WNor
§ – 'Aureum' ♀	CBlo CEnd CMCN CPMA ELan ENot LHyd LNet LPan MAsh MBar MBri MGos NBee NHol SMad SPer SSpi SSta WDin WPat WPyg WStI WWat
§ – 'Ezo-no-momiji'	CMCN
§ – 'Junihitoe'	WNor
§ – 'Microphyllum'	CMCN LNet WNor
§ – 'Ogurayama'	LNet
– 'Palmatifolium'	CBlo CMCN CPMA MGos WStI
¶ – var. *tenuifolium*	CLyn WNor
sieboldianum	CLnd CMCN CTri EPfP SSpi WNor
– 'Sode-no-uchi'	CMCN
sikkimense subsp. *metcalfii*	See *A. metcalfii*
§ 'Silver Cardinal' (v)	CEnd CPMA WWes
♦ 'Silver Vein'	See *A.* × *conspicuum* 'Silver Vein'
§ *sinense*	CMCN WNor WWoo
– var. *pubinerve*	CGre
spicatum	CDul CMCN WNor
stachyophyllum	See *A. tetramerum*
§ *sterculiaceum*	CMCN
syriacum	See *A. obtusifolium*
taronense	CMCN
tataricum	CAgr CMCN MSto
§ – subsp. *ginnala* ♀	CAgr CB&S CBlo CDul CLnd CMCN CMHG CTho EBar ELan ENot IOrc MBal MGos SHBN WNor WWat
¶ – – 'Durand Dwarf'	CMCN
* – – 'Fire'	LNet
– – 'Flame'	CBlo CDul CLnd CPMA WWoo
– subsp. *semenowii*	CMCN
tegmentosum	CMCN WNor WWoo
– subsp. *glaucorufinerve*	See *A. rufinerve*
tenuifolium	CMCN
§ *tetramerum*	GQui
thomsonii	CMCN
trautvetteri	CMCN CSam WNor WTro
triflorum	CMCN EPfP SSpi SSta WWat WWes WWoo
truncatum	CAgr CMCN WNor WWoo
§ – 'Akaji-nishiki'	MAsh WWeb
– 'Akikaze-nishiki' (v)	CPMA LNet
tschonoskii	CMCN GQui WWes
– subsp. *koreanum*	CPMA WNor
§ *turkestanicum*	CMCN
velutinum	CMCN
villosum	See *A. sterculiaceum*
§ *wilsonii*	CMCN WNor
× *zoeschense*	CMCN
– 'Annae'	IOrc

ACERIPHYLLUM See MUKDENIA

× ACHICODONIA (Gesneriaceae)
§ 'Cornell Gem'	NMos

ACHILLEA † (Asteraceae)
abrotanoides	EGoo ELan EMon NGre
ageratifolia ♀	ECha LBee MBro MHig MTho NHol NLon NMen NNor SSca SSmi WByw WLRN
– subsp. *ageratifolia*	MRPP
§ – subsp. *aizoon*	EGar WPer
§ *ageratum*	CArn CSev ELau GBar GPoy LHol MChe MSal SIde WHer WJek WPer WWye
– 'W.B. Childs'	CBos CGle CSpe ECha ELan GBuc LGre MArl MAvo MCLN MNrw MSte WAbb WCot WEas
'Alabaster'	CLon CRDP EFou EMon EPPr GBuc LRHS MBel NPla
§ Anthea = 'Anblo'	CHad CWit EBee EBrP EBre EMan GSki LBre LFis MBel MBri MBro MCLN MLLN NLak NRoo SBre SMad SWat WHow
Anthea	See *A.* Anthea = **'Anblo'**
§ 'Apfelblüte'	CMGP EAst EBrP EBre ECha ECtt ELan EMan GCra LBre LFis LHop MAvo MBri MCLN MGrG MRav MTis SBre SPer SSpe SWat WMer
Appleblossom	See *A.* **'Apfelblüte'**
argentea hort.	See *A. clavennae*
– Lamarck	See *Tanacetum argenteum*
aurea	See *A. chrysocoma*
'Bahama'	GBuc MLan NBro NFai
'Bloodstone'	EGar EPPr GMac WWhi
brachyphylla	EPot
cartilaginea	EAst EFou EGar LHop MCLN MTed WCot WFar WMaN WPbr
– 'Silver Spray'	EBee NLak SRCN WWhi
chamaemelifolia	WHil
§ *chrysocoma*	ELan ESis MWat NMen NRya NTow SSmi
– 'Grandiflora'	CHad ECGN MGrG NCat WByw WLRN
§ *clavennae*	CGle EPot GCHN GMaP LBee MHig MPla MWat NMen NRoo NTow SBla SMer SRms WAbe WCot WKif
clypeolata	NFla SRms
coarctata	NBir WPer
'Coronation Gold' ♀	CDoC CWit EAst ECED EFou ELan ENot EPfP LFis MAus MBri MMil MWat MWgw SMrm SPer WEas
'Credo'	CGle CHad CMil CRDP CSev EAst EBee ECGP EFou EMan EMon EPPr GBuc MAus MBel MCLN MHlr MLLN MUlv MWgw NCat SWat WCot WElm WWhi
'Croftway'	SCro
decolorans	See *A. ageratum*
¶ *erba-rotta* subsp. *moschata*	NLar
– subsp. *rupestris*	CMea ESis MDHE MHig SMer WPer
§ 'Fanal'	CHor CMGP COtt CSpe CWit EBrP EBre ECha EHal ELan EMar GMac LBre LHop MBel MCLN MLLN MNrw MRav MWat NPla NVic SBre SChu SCro SPer SUsu SWat WMow WWin
¶ 'Faust'	EFou
'Feuerland'	CLon CWit ECha EMon EPPr GMac LFis MAvo MBro MLLN NPla SMad SPer SSpe WCot WElm WFar WHoo WPer WWhi

filipendulina MHew NSti SWat
– 'Cloth of Gold' CB&S CDoC CHor EBar ECED ECtt GCHN GMaP MBri MRav MWgw NFai NMir NNor NRoo SEas SPla WBea WByw WPer WWal
– 'Gold Plate' ♀ CDec CHad CLyd EBrP EBre ECha ECtt EFou ELan LBre MBel MCLN MLan MMil MWgw NOrc NTow SBre SCro SPer WCot WEas WHil
– 'Parker's Variety' EGar EJud GBuc MLan NOak SRCN
Flowers of Sulphur See *A.* **'Schwefelblüte'**
'Forncett Beauty' EFou NBrk SChu WWhi
¶ 'Forncett Bride' EFou
'Forncett Candy' EFou
I 'Forncett Citrus' EFou
'Forncett Fletton' EFou NBrk SCro SHel SUsu WBay WCot
'Forncett Ivory' EFou NCat NLak
fraasii SSvw WPer
glaberrima WCot WPer
grandifolia CBre CHan CPou CSam EGle EMan EMon GCal LGan LGre MSte NBro NCat NSti SMad SPer SSvw WBea WCot WHer WWye
'Great Expectations' See *A.* **'Hoffnung'**
'Hartington White' EMon GBuc MWgw
'Hella Glashoff' LGre NBrk SAga WCot
§ 'Hoffnung' CMGP EBrP EBre ECtt EFou EMan GSki LBre LHop NBrk SBre SCro SPer SSpe WBro WEas WLRN WPer WWin
holosericea NS 747 MRPP
'Huteri' CInt CLyd CMHG CNic CPea ECtt ELan EMNN EPot ESis GCHN GMaP LBee MBro MHig NCat NMen NNor NNrd SChu SSmi WAbe WEas WHil WPer WWin
'Inca Gold' EBee ECha EFou EGle EPPr SUsu SWat
x *jaborneggii* GCHN
'Jambo' CB&S
x *kellereri* ELan MBro MHig SAsh SSmi
¶ 'Kempsey Buttermilk' WBcn
x *kolbiana* EMan LHop MHig MWat NMen NRoo SDys SSmi WHoo WLin WPat WWin
§ – 'Weston' CMHG MHig NRoo NTow
§ 'Lachsschönheit' Widely available
Salmon Beauty = See *A.* **'Lachsschönheit'**
  'Lachsschönheit'
x *lewisii* NMen
– 'King Edward' ♀ CHea CMea CSam EBrP EBre ECha EFou ELan ERic ESis LBee LBre MTho NBir NMGW NRoo NTow SBla SBre SChu SSmi SUsu SWat WPer
'Libella' GBuc NFai
'Lusaka' CB&S
¶ *macrophylla* EBee
¶ 'Marmalade' SMrm
'Martina' CM&M CMGP EBee EFou EGoo EHal EMar EMon EPPr GBuc MLLN NCat NOrc NTow
* 'McVities' EFou MAvo WCot

millefolium CArn CGle EEls ELau EPar EWFC GBar GPoy LHol MGra MHew NHex NLan NMir SIde WByw WHer WOak WSel WWye
– 'Burgundy' EOrc
– 'Cerise Queen' CB&S CHor CNic ECGN ECha ECro EFou ELan ELau EMon EPar GCHN GChr LHop MHFP MWat NFai NNor NSti SPer SSoC SSpe SWat WBea WEas WGwG WOve WPer WWal WWye
– 'Colorado' CChr CM&M CPou ECGN SRCN
– 'Fire King' CHal
– 'Lansdorferglut' EPPr LRHS MBri MCLN MTed
– 'Lavender Beauty' See *A. millefolium* **'Lilac Beauty'**
§ – 'Lilac Beauty' CB&S CBlo CBos CDec CGle CSpe ECha EFou EMan EPPr GCra GLil MBel WCot WHal WMer WPbr WWhi
* – 'Lilac Queen' CMGP MArl NFai
¶ – 'Malmesbury' (v) CNat
– 'Melanie' WMer
– 'Paprika' CDec CRDP CSpe EBar EBrP EBre EPar GBuc LBre MBel MBri MCLN MCli MGrG MLLN NCat NFai NHol SBre SMad WByw WElm WMow WRus WWhi
– 'Prospero' LFis MBro MSte WMaN
– 'Red Beauty' EPar GCra MTis NCat SRms WOve
– f. *rosea* EJud MBal NRoo SRms WOMN
– 'Sammetriese' EFou ELan EMon EPPr GBuc MAvo MCLN MHFP MSte WCot WElm WHoo WMaN WPbr WPyg WRHF WWhi
¶ – 'Tickled Pink' WPer
– 'White Queen' EPfP LBuc WMer WPer
¶ 'Mondpagoda' SAga
¶ 'Moonlight' MBro WHoo
'Moonshine' ♀ Widely available
'Moonwalker' CBlo EAst MLLN SIde WFar WPer
'Nakuru' NCat
nobilis subsp. *neilreichii* CMea CRDP CSpe EGoo EMar EMon EPPr LFis MHlr MLLN MRav WCot WHal WOve
'Peter Davis' See *Hippolytia herderi*
pindicola subsp. CLyd EWes
  integrifolia
ptarmica CArn CKin ELau EWFC GBar IIve LHol MChe MHew MSal NFla NMir SIde SPer WGwy WWye
* – 'Ballerina' NCat NDov NLar WRHF
¶ – 'Boughton Beauty' NLar
– Innocence See *A. ptarmica* **'Unschuld'**
– 'Major' EFou
– 'Nana Compacta' ECha EFou EPPr MRav NNor SMrm SUsu WCot WPbr
– 'Perry's White' CBre EMon GCal GLil MBri MHlr NCat WByw WCot WMaN WMer
– 'Stephanie Cohen' WCot
– (The Pearl Group) CBlo CHal LRHS MBri MCLN
  'Boule de Neige' (clonal) NDov NPer SPer SPla WGwG
  (d) WLRN WRHF WWal

N– The Pearl Group	CB&S CGle EBrP EBre ECha
seed-raised (d)	EFou ELan GCHN LBre LHop
	MFir MWat NFai NMir NNor
	NRoo NVic SBre SHel SWat
	WBea WMaN WOld WOve
	WPer WWin
N– – 'The Pearl' (clonal) (d)	WEas
§ – 'Unschuld'	NBir
pumila	See *A. distans* subsp.
	tanacetifolia
Salmon Beauty	See *A.* **'Lachsschönheit'**
'Sandstone'	See *A.* **'Wesersandstein'**
§ 'Schwefelblüte'	ELan LFis MCLN NBir
'Schwellenburg'	EFou EGle EPPr
sibirica	WElm
– AGS 1241	CNic
– 'Kiku-san'	EMon
'Smiling Queen'	NFai
¶ 'Summer Glory'	SCro
Summer Pastels Group	CBot CM&M ECro EMan EMil
	GCHN MFir NBus NFla NMir
	NOak NOrc NRoo SEas SHel
	SRCN SRms SWat WLRN
	WMow WOve WRha
'Summerwine'	ECha EGle EGoo EMar EMon
	MBri SAga SChu SUsu SWat
	WMaN
I 'Taygetea'	CBot CGle CLyd CSam ECha
	EFou ELan EMan LBlm MAus
	MBri MWat NSti SChu SDix
	SPer SUsu SWat WByw WCot
	WFar WKif WOve WRus
	WSHC
'Terracotta'	CElw CHad CLon CRDP CSev
	CSpe EFou EMon GBuc LFis
	MAvo MBri MBro MLLN MSte
	NBir NCat NHaw SAga SChu
	SHel SOkh WBro WCot WElm
	WHal WHoo WMaN WOve
'The Beacon'	See *A.* **'Fanal'**
tomentosa ♀	CHan CTri ECha ECtt ELan
	EPfP LHop MBal NNrd SWat
	WRHF
§ – 'Aurea'	EBot ECtt ELan ELau LHol
	LPVe MLan MOne NBro NNor
	NNrd SIde SRCN WHil WPer
– 'Maynard's Gold'	See *A. tomentosa* **'Aurea'**
§ *umbellata*	NTow
– 'Weston'	See *A.* x *kolbiana* **'Weston'**
'Walther Funcke'	CHad CLon CMdw CRDP CSpe
	EGle LFis LGre MBri SAga
	SMrm WCot
§ 'Wesersandstein'	CB&S EBee EFou EMan EMon
	EPPr GMac MBri WCot WElm
	WMer WOve
'Wilczekii'	NCat NChi SBod SRms

× ACHIMENANTHA (Gesneriaceae)

'Cerulean Mink'	See × *Smithicodonia* **'Cerulean Mink'**
'Dutch Treat'	NMos
'Ginger Peachy'	NMos
'Inferno'	NMos WDib
* 'Rose Bouquet'	NMos
'Royal'	NMos

ACHIMENES (Gesneriaceae)

'Adelaide'	NMos
'Adèle Delahaute'	NMos
'Adonis Blue'	NMos
'Almandine'	NMos
'Ambleside'	NMos
'Ambroise Verschaffelt'	LAma NMos
'Ami Van Houtte'	NMos
'Ann Marie'	NMos
'Apricot Glow'	NMos
'Aquamarine'	NMos
'Bassenthwaite'	NMos
'Bea'	NMos
bella	See *Eucodonia verticillata*
'Bernice'	NMos
'Blauer Planet'	NMos
'Bloodstone'	NMos
'Blue Gown'	NMos
'Brilliant'	NMos
'Butterfield Bronze'	NMos
'Buttermere'	NMos
'Camberwell Beauty'	NMos
'Cameo Rose'	NMos
'Cameo Triumph'	NMos
'Camille Brozzoni'	NMos
candida	NMos
'Carmine Queen'	NMos
'Cascade Cockade'	NMos
'Cascade Evening Glow'	NMos
'Cascade Fairy Pink'	NMos
'Cascade Fashionable Pink'	NMos
'Cascade Rosy Red'	NMos
'Cascade Violet Night'	NMos
'Cattleya'	LAma NMos
'Chalkhill Blue'	NMos
'Charm'	LAma NMos
'Clouded Yellow'	NMos
'Compact Great Rosy Red'	NMos
'Coniston Water'	NMos
'Copeland Boy'	NMos
'Copeland Girl'	NMos
'Coral Sunset'	NMos
'Cornell Favourite 'A''	NMos
'Cornell Favourite 'B''	NMos
'Crimson Beauty'	NMos
'Crimson Glory'	NMos
'Crimson Tiger'	NMos
'Crummock Water'	NMos
'Cupido'	NMos
'Dentoniana'	NMos
'Derwentwater'	NMos
'Dorothy'	NMos
'Dot'	NMos
dulcis	NMos
'Early Arnold'	NMos
ehrenbergii	See *Eucodonia ehrenbergii*
'Elke Michelssen'	NMos
'English Waltz'	NMos
erecta	WDib
'Escheriana'	NMos
'Flamenco'	NMos
'Flamingo'	SDeJ
flava	NMos
'Fritz Michelssen'	NMos
'Gary John'	NMos
'Gary/Jennifer'	NMos
'Grape Wine'	NMos
'Grasmere'	NMos
'Harry Williams'	LAma
§ 'Harveyi'	NMos
'Haweswater'	NMos
'Hilda Michelssen'	NMos WDib
'Honey Gold'	NMos
'Ida Michelssen'	NMos
'India'	NMos
§ 'Jaureguia Maxima'	NMos

'Jennifer Goode'   NMos
'Jewell Blue'   NMos
'Johanna Michelssen'   NMos
'Jubilee Gem'   NMos
'Lakeland Lady'   NMos
'Lavender Fancy'   NMos
'Little Beauty'   LAma NMos
'Little Red Tiger'   NMos
longiflora   NMos
– 'Alba'   See *A.* **'Jaureguia Maxima'**
– 'Major'   NMos
'Magnificent'   NMos
'Marie'   NMos
'Masterpiece'   NMos
'Maxima'   LAma
'Menuett '80'   NMos
'Milton'   NMos
misera   NMos
'Moonstone'   NMos
'Old Rose Pink'   LAma NMos
'Orange Queen'   NMos
'Pally'   NMos
'Panic Pink'   NMos
'Patens Major'   NMos
'Patricia'   NMos
'Paul Arnold'   NMos
'Peach Blossom'   LAma NMos
'Peach Glow'   NMos
'Peacock'   NMos
'Pearly Queen'   NMos
'Pendant Blue'   NMos
'Pendant Purple'   NMos
'Petticoat Pink'   NMos
'Pink Beauty'   NMos
'Pinocchio'   NMos
'Prima Donna'   EOHP NMos
'Pulcherrima'   LAma
'Purple King'   NMos
'Queen of Sheba'   NMos
'Quickstep'   NMos
'Rachael'   NMos
'Red Admiral'   NMos
'Red Giant'   NMos
'Red Imp'   NMos
'Red Top Hybrid'   NMos
'Robin'   NMos
'Rosenelfe'   NMos
'Rosy Doll'   NMos
'Rosy Frost'   NMos
'Rydal Water'   NMos
'Scafell'   NMos
'Shirley Dwarf White'   NMos
'Shirley Fireglow'   See *A.* **'Harveyi'**
'Show-off'   NMos
'Silver Wedding'   NMos
'Snow Princess'   SDeJ
Snow White   See *A.* **'Schneewittchen'**
'Sparkle'   NMos
'Stan's Delight'   EOHP NMos WDib
'Sue'   NMos
'Tango'   NMos
'Tantivvy'   NMos
'Tarantella'   NMos
'Teresa'   NMos
'Tiny Blue'   NMos
'Topsy'   NMos
'Troutbeck'   NMos
'Ullswater'   NMos
'Vanessa'   NMos
'Viola Michelssen'   NMos
'Violacea Semiplena'   NMos
'Vivid'   LAma NMos

'Warren'   NMos
'Wastwater'   NMos
'Wetterflow's Triumph'   NMos
'White Admiral'   NMos
'White Rajah'   NMos
'Wilma'   NMos
'Windermere'   NMos

ACHLYS (Berberidaceae)
japonica   WCru
¶ *triphylla*   WCru

ACHNATHERUM See STIPA

ACIDANTHERA See GLADIOLUS

ACINOS (Lamiaceae)
§ *alpinus*   NMen SBla SChu
– subsp. *meridionalis*   EGle NHol NTow
§ *arvensis*   CArn MBri MSal
§ *corsicus*   ESis LFis MBro NMen SIde
                                WJek WPat WWin

ACIPHYLLA (Apiaceae)
aurea   CHEx EBee GAbr GCal ITim
                                MBal NHar SIgm SMad WAbe
                                WLin
colensoi   GAbr GCLN
dobsonii   EPot GCLN GCrs
glaucescens   MBal NHar
hectoris   EBee EPot GCLN GDra
kirkii   GCLN
'Lomond'   GCLN SIgm
lyallii   NTow
montana   EBee GCLN SIng
pinnatifida   GCLN GCrs NHar
scott-thomsonii   CHEx ETen MAll
simplex   EPot
squarrosa   EBee ECou GCal SIgm
subflabellata   ECou GCal NHar SIgm

ACNISTUS (Solanaceae)
australis   See *Dunalia australis*

ACOELORRHAPHE (Arecaceae)
¶ *wrightii*   CBrP LPal

ACOKANTHERA (Apocynaceae)
spectabilis   See *A. oblongifolia*

ACONITUM (Ranunculaceae)
alboviolaceum   GCal
anglicum   See *A. napellus* subsp. *napellus*
                                Anglicum Group
¶ *anthora*   NLar
¶ *arcuatum* B&SWJ 864   WCru
N *autumnale*   NBir
bartlettii B&SWJ 337   WCru
'Blue Sceptre'   EBrP EBre LBre NRoo SBre
                                SRms
'Bressingham Spire' ♀   CDoC CMGP EBrP EBre ECtt
                                EFou ENot GAbr GMaP LBre
                                MAus MBri MRav MWat
                                MWgw NDea NOrc NPer NRoo
                                SBre SChu SPer WOld
× *cammarum* 'Bicolor' ♀   Widely available
– 'Grandiflorum Album'   LGre NRoo

§ *carmichaelii* — CArn CBot CGle CLon EBar ECED ECro EFou EMan GAbr IBlr MAus MBro MHlr MRav NChi NFla NNor NOrc NRoo SCro SRms WBea WHoo WLin WRus

– 'Arendsii' — Widely available

– Wilsonii Group — CHad CHan CHar ECro GCra GGar MBri MSte NChi NTow SAga SChu SSoC WOve WPer WWye

§ – – 'Barker's Variety' — CPou CRow ECED EFou GBuc MFir NDea NHol NSti WMer WRus

– – 'Kelmscott' ♀ — ECGN EGle EMon MSte SAga SBla SDix WByw WFar WRHF

cilicicum — See *Eranthis hyemalis* **Cilicia Group**

compactum — See *A. napellus* subsp. *vulgare*

deflexum — MSto

'Eleonara' — EFou EPfP GBuc LRHS MBri MRav WFar

elwesii — GGar NPSI

episcopale — GCrs

aff. – CLD 1426 — GBuc WCot WFar

fischeri hort. — See *A. carmichaelii*

¶ *fukutomei* var. *formosanum* B&SWJ 3057 — WCru

§ *hemsleyanum* — CBot CGle CHan CPlN CRow ELan GAbr GCLN GCal GCra IBlr LGre LHol MFir MHlr MTho NSti NTow SAga SBla SMad SSoC SUsu WBrE WCru WEas WOld WWhi WWye

– dark blue — CMea

– *latisectum* — IBlr

heterophyllum — MSto WCot

hyemale — See *Eranthis hyemalis*

'Ivorine' — Widely available

japonicum — EBee MSto

lamarckii — See *A. lycoctonum* subsp. *neapolitanum*

lycoctonum — MAus SSoC

– 'Dark Eyes' — ECGN NBrk WBea WCot

§ – subsp. *lycoctonum* — ECED MSal SRms

– subsp. *moldavicum* — GBin

§ – subsp. *neapolitanum* — CBlo CLon ECGN ELan EMFP EPfP GCal LGan MLLN NLar NSti WRus

§ – subsp. *vulparia* — CArn ECGN ECha ECtt EFou EGar GCal GPoy LHol MAvo MSal NDea NRoo WByw WCot WEas WOld WWye

napellus — CArn CBlo CSpe ECGN ECtt EFou EWFC GAbr GPoy LBuc LGan LHol MBro MCLN MWat NFla NNor SIde SSoC SWat WHil WHoo WOld WShi WWat WWhi WWye

– 'Albiflorus' — See *A. napellus* subsp. *vulgare* **'Albidum'**

¶ – 'Bergfürst' — EBee

– 'Blue Valley' — EBee EMar EPfP

– 'Carneum' — See *A. napellus* subsp. *vulgare* **'Carneum'**

§ – subsp. *napellus* Anglicum Group — CRow CSev EBee GBuc GSki IBlr MHlr MSal MSte NSti WCot WPen WUnd

– 'Rubellum' — CHan MCli NPri

– 'Sphere's Variety' — NOrc WPyg

– subsp. *tauricum* — WCot

§ – subsp. *vulgare* 'Albidum' — CMGP CSev EBee ECGN ECGP EFou EMan EMar ETen GSki LRHS MTis NCat NFai NHol NLar NLon NPri NSti SCro SPer WByw WHow WLRN WRus

§ – – 'Carneum' — ECGN GCra GMac MLLN MRav NRoo NSti WByw WCot WEas WHal WHer WKif WWin WWye

neapolitanum — See *A. lycoctonum* subsp. *neapolitanum*

'Newry Blue' — CHad ELan GBuc GSki MBri NHol WFar WHil WMer WPer WRHF

orientale hort. — See *A. lycoctonum* subsp. *vulparia*

paniculatum 'Roseum' — EBar LRHS

pyrenaicum — See *A. lycoctonum* subsp. *neapolitanum*

ranunculifolius — See *A. lycoctonum* subsp. *neapolitanum*

sczukinii — EMon

septentrionale — See *A. lycoctonum* subsp. *lycoctonum*

¶ sp. ACE 1449 — GBuc

¶ sp. climbing from Sikkim B&SWJ 2652 — WCru

¶ sp. from Nepal B&SWJ 2954 — WCru

'Spark's Variety' ♀ — CBre CHan EAst EBar EBrP EBre ECED EFou ELan EOrc GBri GMaP GMac LBre LFis LGre MBri MCLN MHlr MRav MTis NRoo NSti SBre SChu SDix SMad SSoC WFar WOld

¶ *spicatum* — EBee

'Stainless Steel' — CChr CSpe LGre LRHS MBri SCro WCot

× *tubergenii* — See *Eranthis hyemalis* **Tubergenii Group**

¶ *variegatum* — EBee

volubile hort. — See *A. hemsleyanum*

vulparia — See *A. lycoctonum* subsp. *vulparia*

ACONOGONON See PERSICARIA

ACORUS (Araceae)

calamus — CArn CBen CRow CWat EHon ELau GPoy LPBA MCCP MHew MSal MSta NDea NGno SWat SWyc WChe WHer WMAq WWeb

¶ *calamus* 'Argenteostriatus' (v) — CB&S CBen CHan CRow CWat ECha ECtt EHon EMFW GAbr GCal LHil LPBA LWak MBal MSta NDea NOrc SWat SWyc WChe WHil WMAq WWye

– 'Purpureus' — WChe

gramineus — CRow EMFW LPBA LRot MLan SWat WHer WRHF

– 'Hakuro-nishiki' (v) — CInt COtt CSte SHBN WRHF

I – 'Licorice' — WCot

– 'Masamune' — EPla GCal WCot WLeb

N – 'Oborozuki' — CRow EGle EPla LHop

N – 'Ogon' (v) — Widely available

– 'Pusillus' — CRow EPPr EPla ESOG LHil NBro

– 'Variegatus'	CArn CBen CBrd CKel CNic CRow EHon ELan EMFW EPar EPla LHil LHop LPBA MBal MFir MSta NBro NDea NHar NMir NSti SApp SArc SWat SWyc WChe WMAq WPer WRus
– 'Yodo-no-yuki'	CRow EPla

ACRADENIA (Rutaceae)

frankliniae	CB&S CFil CMHG CPle CTrG IBlr IDee MAll SAPC SArc SBid SSpi WSHC

ACRIDOCARPUS (Malpighiaceae)

natalitius	CPlN

ACROCLADIUM See CALLIERGON

ACTAEA (Ranunculaceae)

§ *alba* ♀	CBrd CHan CLyd CPou CRow ECGN ECha GPoy GTou IBlr MFir MSal NLar NSti WMer WOMN WWat WWye
asiatica B&SWJ 616	WCru
§ *erythrocarpa* Fischer	CHan CRDP GDra GPoy MSte WEas WLin WOMN WWin
pachypoda	See A. alba
§ *rubra* ♀	CBro CLyd CMHG CRow ECGN ECGP ECha EPar GAbr GCal IBlr MLLN MSCN NHol NSti SDys SMad WByw WCru WMer WPGP WWat
– *alba*	See A. rubra f. neglecta
§ – f. *neglecta*	CHan GBuc WWat
§ *spicata*	CRDP GLil GPoy MSCN MSal MSte NLar NSti NWoo WCru WLin
– var. *alba*	See A. spicata
– var. *rubra*	See A. erythrocarpa Fischer

ACTINELLA (Asteraceae)

scaposa	See Tetraneuris scaposa

ACTINIDIA † (Actinidiaceae)

arguta	CAgr CB&S CFil CPlN MSto WPGP
– B&SWJ 569	WCru
– 'Issai' (s-p)	CB&S EBee ERea ESim LBuc MGos
– (m)	CB&S SHBN
callosa	CPlN
– var. *formosana* B&SWJ 1790	WCru
chinensis hort.	See A. deliciosa
deliciosa (f/F)	NBea SHBN SPer WDin
§ –	CGre CMac CWit ELan EMil ERom LHol MGos WSHC WShe WStI
– 'Atlas'	MBri
– 'Blake' (s-p/F)	LBuc
– 'Hayward' (f/F)	CB&S CDoC CHEx CHad COtt CPlN EBrP EBre ELan EMil EMui ERea IOrc ISea LBre MBri MGos MWat NPal SBre SDea SHBN SSta SSto WGwG WStI WWal
– 'Jenny' (s-p/F)	CMac LRHS MGos NDal SDea
– (m)	NBea SPer WDin

– 'Tomuri' (m)	CB&S CDoC CHEx CHad COtt CPlN EBrP EBre ELan EMil EMui ERea IOrc LBre MWat NPal SBre SHBN SSta SSto WStI
¶ *giraldii*	CMac
kolomikta ♀	Widely available
¶ *latifolia* B&SWJ 3563	WCru
melanandra	CAgr CPlN
pilosula	CFil CPlN GCal GOrc LRHS WCru WPGP WSHC
polygama (F)	CAgr CPlN MSto WCru
purpurea	CPlN WCru
¶ *rubricaulis* B&SWJ 3111	WCru
¶ *rufa* B&SWJ 3525	WCru
¶ sp. from China	WCru
¶ *tetramera* B&SWJ 3664	WCru

ACTINOTUS   (Apiaceae) See Plant Deletions

ADENOCARPUS   (Papilionaceae) See Plant Deletions

ADELOCARYUM See LINDELOFIA

ADENOPHORA † (Campanulaceae)

* *asiatica*	WFar
aurita	CB&S CFir MLLN MTis NSti NWoo SOkh SWat WAbe WCot WWat
bulleyana	CBrd CSev ECGN ELan EOld EPot GAbr GBuc IBlr MLLN NBro NLak NPri SSca SWat WFar WHoo WPen WPer
* *campanulata*	WPer
¶ *coelestis*	EBee SGre
¶ – ACE 2455	EPot GBuc
confusa	CMdw EBee EGar EHal GAbr GCal MLLN SMac SSca
¶ *cymerae*	EBee
forrestii	SBla WMaN
¶ – var. *handeliana* KGB 86	IDac
himalayana	ECro EGle GBri GMac MNrw WCot WHil WPer WRHF
khasiana	CBlo CFir CPea EBee GAbr NFai NSti SSca WCot WPrP WRha WWin
koreana	EBee
latifolia Fischer	GBri NBir
– hort.	See A. pereskiifolia
liliifolia	CDec CHea ECro ECtt EEls ELan EMan GAbr GCal GMac MCLN NBro NCat NPer NSti SAxl SCro SMrm SSvw SWat WCot WPer WPyg
§ *nikoensis*	MHig WAbe
* – *alba*	CGra
§ – var. *stenophylla*	EHal MHig
nipponica	See A. nikoensis var. stenophylla
§ *pereskiifolia*	EAst ECro EGar GCal LIck MHlr NBus WCot WPbr WPer
polyantha	CGen CPea EBee ECro GAbr GBuc MLLN NSti SRms SSca WByw WPic WPrP
polymorpha	See A. nikoensis
potaninii	CDoC CFir CHea ECro EGle GBuc MGrG MNrw NBro SBla SSca WPer WRHF WWhi
remotiflora	ECro
stricta	EHal MLan WSan WWeb
– subsp. *sessilifolia*	GMac

sublata — EGar WFar
takedae var. *howozana* — NSti
tashiroi — CElw CGen CHan CLyd CNic
GAbr GBri GBuc MBro MNrw
NBro SCro SHel SIgm SMac
SWat WHoo
triphylla — GAbr WFar
– var. *hakusanensis* — CPou EBee
uehatae B&SWJ 126 — WCru

ADENOSTYLES (Asteraceae)
alpina — See *Cacalia glabra*

ADIANTUM † (Adiantaceae)
¶ *aethiopicum* — WRic
§ *aleuticum* ♀ — CCuc CFil CLAP CRDP EFer
ELan IOrc NBro NHar NHol
NMar SBla WHal WPGP WRic
WWat
¶ – 'Laciniatum' — WRic
capillus-veneris — CHEx MWat SRms
– 'Banksianum' — NMar
– 'Cornubiense' — WRic
– 'Mairisii' — See *A.* × *mairisii*
– 'Pointonii' — NMar
concinnum — NMar
cuneatum — See *A. raddianum*
diaphanum — NMar
edgeworthii — NMar
formosum — NMar
henslowianum — NMar
jordanii — CFil
§ × *mairisii* ♀ — NMar WRic
* *monocolor* — MBri
pedatum ♀ — CFil CGle CHEx CLAP CRDP
EBrP EBre ECha EFer EFou
ELan EMon LBre LHil MBal
MBri MHlr NHol NOrc SApp
SBre SChu SPer SSpi SWat
WAbe WHil WPGP WRic
– var. *aleuticum* — See *A. pedatum* var. *subpumilum*
– Asiatic form — See *A. pedatum* 'Japonicum'
– 'Imbricatum' — ECha ETen NHar NHol NMar
SBla SRms
§ – 'Japonicum' — CFil CMil CRDP ELan MBri
MWgw NBir NHol SEas SRms
SSpi WCot WCru WHal WRic
– 'Laciniatum' — CFil SRms
– var. *minus* — See *A. pedatum* var. *subpumilum*
– 'Miss Sharples' — NMar SRms WRic
– 'Roseum' — See *A. pedatum* 'Japonicum'
– var. *subpumilum* f. *minimum* — NMar
◆ – – (W.H. Wagner) Lellinger — See *A. aleuticum*
peruvianum — MBri
pubescens — MBri NMar
§ *raddianum* ♀ — CFil CHal NMar
– 'Brilliantelse' ♀ — MBri NMar
– 'Crested Majus' — NMar
– 'Crested Micropinnulum' — NMar
– 'Deflexum' — NMar
¶ – 'Double Leaflet' — NMar
– 'Elegans' — NMar
– 'Feltham Beauty' — NMar
– 'Fragrans' — See *A. raddianum* 'Fragrantissimum'
§ – 'Fragrantissimum' — MBri NMar
– 'Fritz Luthi' ♀ — CHal MBri NMar
– 'Gracilis' — See *A. raddianum* 'Gracillimum'

§ – 'Gracillimum' — NMar
– 'Grandiceps' — NMar
– 'Gympie Gold' — NMar
– 'Kensington Gem' ♀ — NMar
– 'Legrand Morgan' — NMar
– 'Legrandii' — NMar
– 'Micropinnulum' — NMar
– 'Pacific Maid' — NMar
– 'Pacottii' — NMar
– 'Triumph' — NMar
– 'Tuffy Tips' — NMar
– 'Variegated Pacottii' — NMar
– 'Variegated Tessellate' — NMar
– 'Victoria's Elegans' — NMar
– 'Weigandii' — NMar
¶ *tenerum* 'Green Glory' — NMar
venustum ♀ — CDec CDoC CFil CGle CLAP
CRDP EFer ELan EMon EPot
GCal MBal NHed NMar SBla
SDix SRms SSpi SWat WAbe
WCot WEas WFib WOMN
WPGP WRic
¶ *whitei* — NMar

ADLUMIA (Papaveraceae)
fungosa — CBos CGle CPlN CSpe EBee
EHal WCru WOMN

ADONIS (Ranunculaceae)
amurensis — EPar LAma WCot
– 'Flore Pleno' (d) — EBrP EBre EPar LBre MBri
SBre SPer SRms WCot WFar
– 'Fukujukai' — EBrP EBre ECha LBre NMGW
SBre WFar
annua — EWFC MGra MHew
brevistyla — NTow SBla WAbe
¶ *multiflora* — WCru
¶ *pyrenaica* — WLin
vernalis — GPoy

ADOXA (Adoxaceae)
moschatellina — CKin EWFC MTho WGwy
WHer WShi WWye

AECHMEA (Bromeliaceae)
caerulea — See *A. lueddemanniana*
fasciata ♀ — MBri

AEGLE (Rutaceae)
sepiaria — See *Poncirus trifoliata*

AEGOPODIUM (Apiaceae)
¶ *podagraria* 'Bengt' — EMon
– 'Dangerous' (v) — CNat WCHb
– 'Variegatum' — CBre CInt CRDP CRow CWit
ECha EHoe ELan EMar EOrc
EPar EPla LHol LHop MBar
MBri MCLN NHol NSti NVic
SAxl SChu SPer WBea WHil
WOld WOve WRus WWat
WWin

AEONIUM (Crassulaceae)
arboreum ♀ — CAbb CHEx SLMG WHal
WIvy
* – 'Arnold Schwarzkopf' — CAbb CBos ERea GCra SAPC
SArc WIvy
– 'Atropurpureum' ♀ — CHEx CWit ERav EREa IBlr
LHil MBEx MBri MLan NPer
SEND SLMG WEas
* – 'Magnificum' — LBlm

– 'Variegatum' LHil NPer
balsamiferum CHEx CTbh CTrC LHil WHal
canariense CHEx LHil WHal
§ – var. **subplanum** CTrC
cuneatum CHEx CTbh CTrC SAPC SArc
* **decorum** 'Variegatum' (v) SGre
¶ 'Dinner Plate' CHEx
× **domesticum** See *Aichryson* × *domesticum*
¶ **glandulosum** SGre
haworthii ♀ CHEx CHal CTbh CTrC GAri
– 'Variegatum' CHEx
holochrysum IBlr
¶ **laxum** SGre
nobile CHEx
percarneum SLMG
simsii CHEx CTbh
¶ **spathulatum** SGre
subplanum See *A. canariense* var.
  subplanum
tabuliforme ♀ CHEx SLMG
undulatum ♀ CHEx
¶ **urbicum** CHEx
'Zwartkop' ♀ CHEx CTbh EGar EOas NPer
  WEas WHal

AESCHYNANTHUS (Gesneriaceae)
'Big Apple' WDib
Black Pagoda Group WDib
'Fire Wheel' WDib
hildebrandii WDib
'Hot Flash' WDib
lobbianus See *A. radicans*
longicalyx WDib
§ **longicaulis** ♀ MBri WDib
marmoratus See *A. longicaulis*
'Mira' MBri
'Mona' MBri
parvifolius See *A. radicans*
I 'Pulobbia' MBri
'Purple Star' MBri
§ **radicans** EBak MBri
– **lobbianus** See *A. radicans*
'Rigel' MBri
speciosus ♀ CHal
* – **rubens** MBri
'Topaz' MBri

AESCULUS † (Hippocastanaceae)
arguta See *A. glabra* var. *arguta*
× **arnoldiana** CDul CFil CMCN MAsh MBlu
  WPGP
assamica WPGP
¶ 'Autumn Splendor' CLyn
§ × **bushii** CFil EBee WPGP
californica CB&S CFil CMCN CSam CTho
  CTrw ISea SMad WPGP
× **carnea** CDul ELan GRei ISea MBal
  MBar
– 'Aureomarginata' SMad
– 'Briotii' ♀ Widely available
¶ – 'Marginata' (v) CLyn
– 'Plantierensis' CDul CTho ENot MBlu
* – 'Variegata' (v) CMCN LRHS MBlu
chinensis CEnd MBlu
'Dallimorei' EBee SMad
  (graft-chimaera)
discolor 'Koehnei' MBri
§ **flava** ♀ CFil CMCN CTho EBee ENot
  MMea SPer SSpi WCoo WPGP
– f. **vestita** CDul MBlu
georgiana See *A. sylvatica*

glabra CDul CFil CLnd CMCN CPMA
  CTho WPGP
§ – var. **arguta** CFil CMCN WPGP
– 'October Red' CFil MBlu WPGP
glaucescens CB&S CDul CMCN
¶ – 'Autumn Fire' CLyn
hippocastanum ♀ CB&S CBlo CDul CKin CLnd
  CPer CTho ELan ENot GChr
  GRei IOrc ISea LBuc LHyr
  LPan MAsh MBal MBar MBri
  MGos NBee NWea SHBN SPer
  WDin WFar WMou WOrn WStI
¶ – 'Aureomarginata' (v) SMad
§ – 'Baumannii' (d) ♀ CBlo CDoC CDul CLnd COtt
  ENot EPfP GChr LPan MAsh
  MBlu MBri MGos NWea SHBN
  SPer WDin WStI
– 'Digitata' CDul
– 'Flore Pleno' See *A. hippocastanum*
  'Baumannii'
◆ – 'Globosa' See *A. hippocastanum*
  'Umbraculifera'
– 'Hampton Court Gold' CB&S CEnd CMCN CTho
– 'Honiton Gold' CTho
– 'Laciniata' CDul CMCN IDee MBlu SMad
¶ – 'Pyramidalis' SMad
§ – 'Umbraculifera' SMad
– 'Wisselink' CDul CMCN MBlu SMad
× **hybrida** CFil WPGP
indica ♀ CDul CHEx CLnd CMCN
  CSam CTho CTrw ELan ENot
  EOas IHos IOrc ISea MAsh
  MBlu MBri SLPl SPer SSpi
  WDin WMou WPGP
– 'Sydney Pearce' CEnd CFil CMCN EBee IOrc
  MBlu MMea SMad SPer SSpi
  WPGP
× **marylandica** CPMA
× **mississippiensis** See *A.* × *bushii*
× **mutabilis** 'Harbisonii' SMad
– 'Induta' CFil MBlu MBri SMad SSpi
  WPGP WWes
§ – 'Penduliflora' CB&S CDul CEnd CFil CTho
  MBlu SMad
× **neglecta** CLnd CMCN
– 'Erythroblastos' CB&S CFil CLnd CMCN
  CPMA CTho EPfP LNet MBlu
  SHBN SMad SSpi WMou
  WPGP WPat
parviflora ♀ CB&S CBlo CDul CFil CGre
  CMCN COtt CTho ELan EMil
  ENot LNet LPan MBal MBlu
  MGos MUlv NFla SMad SPer
  SSpi WDin WPGP WWat
§ **pavia** ♀ CB&S CDul CFil CMCN CTho
  EPfP ISea WWoo
– 'Atrosanguinea' CBlo CDoC CDul CEnd CFil
  CMCN CPMA MAsh MBri
  NPal SMad SSpi WPGP
– var. **discolor** 'Koehnei' MAsh SMad
– 'Penduliflora' See *A.* × *mutabilis*
  'Penduliflora'
– 'Rosea Nana' CMCN MBlu
splendens See *A. pavia*
§ **sylvatica** CFil WPGP
turbinata CLnd CMCN ISea LBuc MBlu
  SMad WPGP
wilsonii CB&S

AETHIONEMA (Brassicaceae)
armenum ESis LIck MLan NGre SIng
  WLin

coridifolium	NBus WPer
§ *euonomioides*	NTow NWCA WLin
graecum	See *A. saxatile*
grandiflorum ♀	CMHG NBro NTow NWCA SHFr SSca WPer
– Pulchellum Group ♀	CLyd CNic EPot LHop MBro NMen NPri WAbe WWin
iberideum	MWat SRms
oppositifolium	CLyd CMea GTou MBro MWat NMen NNrd NWCA WHoo WPyg
'Warley Rose' ♀	EFou ELan EPot LHop MBro MHig MTho MWat NGre NHed NHol NMen NNor NRya SIng SRms WHoo WPat WPyg WWin
'Warley Ruber'	CLyd CNic MHig NBir WAbe

AEXTOXICON (Aextoxicaceae)
punctatum	CGre

AFROCARPUS (Podocarpaceae)
falcatus	GCal

AGAPANTHUS † (Alliaceae)
§ *africanus* ♀	EBar EPfP GSki IBlr LBlm NRog SAPC SArc SLMG SPar SWat WPer
* – 'Albus' ♀	CB&S CHEx CHad EBar EMan EPfP GSki IBlr LFis SEND SLMG SPla WPer
'Albatross'	ECha
Ardernei hybrid	CBot CFil ECha GCal IBlr LGre MTed NCat SSpi WCot WOld
¶ 'Baby Blue'	IBlr SApp
¶ 'Ballyrogan'	IBlr
'Bethlehem Star'	ERav
¶ 'Bicton Bell'	IBlr
'Blue Baby'	CB&S CDoC LRHS
¶ 'Blue Companion'	IBlr
'Blue Giant'	CBro EBrP EBre EFou IBlr LBre MTed NCut NRoo SBre SPla SWat WFar WPyg
¶ 'Blue Globe'	EBee EMan NCut SCro
'Blue Imp'	ECtt EHic GSki NHol
'Blue Moon'	CBro CHad ECha IBlr SEND SLod
¶ 'Blue Nile'	LRHS
'Blue Skies'	CB&S CTrC
'Blue Triumphator'	CBlo EPfP EWll IBlr LBow LFis MTed NCut SSte WHil WMer
'Bressingham Blue'	CBlo CBro CTri EBrP EBre EFou GCal IBlr LBre MSte SAxl SBre SSpe
'Bressingham Bounty'	EBrP EBre LBre SBre
'Bressingham White'	CGle EBrP EBre ECtt EFou GCHN LBre MBri MCLN MRav MTed MUlv NRoo SBre SSpe SWat WRus WWat
'Buckingham Palace'	IBlr WPGP
§ *campanulatus*	CGle CMon CRDP ELan ERav GDra GSki ISea MHlr SCro SWat WLRN
– var. *albidus*	CBos CRDP CSev EBee EBrP EBre ECha EFou ELan ENot GCra IBlr LBre LHop MSte NFla NHol NRoo NVic SBre SChu SPer SSpi WFar WWhi
– 'Albovittatus'	CLAP LGre
* – 'Albus Nanus'	CBlo
– bright blue	GCal
¶ – 'Buckland'	IBlr
– 'Cobalt Blue'	ECha
– 'Isis'	CBro CFir EBee EBrP EBre ECha GCHN IBlr LBre MRav NRoo SBre
¶ – 'Oxbridge'	IBlr
– Oxford blue	IBlr
– subsp. *patens* ♀	GBuc SSpi SWat
– – deep blue form	IBlr
* – 'Premier'	IBlr
– 'Profusion'	ECha IBlr LBlm SSpi
– 'Rosewarne'	CB&S GQui
– 'Slieve Donard Variety'	IBlr
* – 'Spokes'	IBlr
– variegated	ECha WOld
– Wedgwood blue	IBlr
– 'Wendy'	IBlr
– 'White Hope'	IBlr
'Castle of Mey'	CFil IBlr LGre LHyd MTho SAxl
caulescens ♀	IBlr
¶ – subsp. *angustifolius*	IBlr
– subsp. *caulescens*	SWat
* 'Cedric Morris'	ERav IBlr
¶ 'Chandra'	IBlr LBlm
¶ *coddii*	SVen
comptonii	CMon IBlr
– subsp. *comptonii*	SWat
– forms	SLMG
– subsp. *longitubus*	EBee SWat
Danube	See *A.* 'Donau'
¶ 'Delft'	IBlr
¶ 'Density'	IBlr
¶ 'Donau'	MTed
dyeri	IBlr
'Evening Star'	ERav
'Findlay's Blue'	SAxl WCot
¶ giant hybrids	LBlm
'Golden Rule' (v)	CRow IBlr LHil SSpi WCot
§ Headbourne hybrids	Widely available
'Holbrook'	CSam
'Hydon Mist'	LHyd
inapertus	CBlo CMon CRDP SBla SWat
– subsp. *hollandii*	CAvo GCal IBlr SWat
– subsp. *inapertus*	SWat
– subsp. *intermedius*	GCal IBlr LBlm SWat
– subsp. *pendulus*	CHan CRow IBlr
'Kalmthout Blue'	EBee
¶ 'Kalmthout White'	MLan
'Kingston Blue'	ECha IBlr SWas
'Lady Moore'	IBlr LBlm SWas
'Lilliput'	CAbb CB&S CBro CDoC CMHG CRow CSpe CVer EBrP EBre ECtt EFou ELan GCHN GMaP LBre MBri MGrG MRav NHol NRoo SBre WRus WWat WWin
'Loch Hope' ♀	CFil EBrP EBre LBre SApp SBre WCot
* 'Marjorie'	CLCN
'Midnight Blue'	CGle ECha ELan GCal IBlr SAxl SWas WWeb
'Midnight Star'	ERav MSte
'Molly Howick'	SAxl
¶ 'Moonstar'	LBlm
* 'Mooreanus' misapplied	GCal IBlr SAxl
'Morning Star'	ERav
'Norman Hadden'	IBlr
¶ *nutans*	EBee IBlr
– 'Albus'	GCal
Palmer's hybrids	See *A.* **Headbourne hybrids**

¶ 'Penelope Palmer' IBlr
¶ 'Penny Slade' SApp
'Peter Pan' CB&S CDoC CMil CRow CSWP CSpe CTrC EBee GBuc LHop NCut SAxl SPla WPyg WRHF WWat WWeb WWoo
'Phantom' IBlr
'Pinocchio' CAbb NHol WWoo
'Plas Merdyn Blue' IBlr
'Plas Merdyn White' IBlr
¶ 'Podge Mill' CLCN
'Polar Ice' CFir EFou EHic IBlr MCCP NCut NHol WMer WPyg
praecox CDoC CLAP ESis IBlr
¶ – 'Bangor Blue' IBlr
¶ – 'Blue Formality' IBlr
– 'Flore Pleno' (d) CLyd ECha EMon IBlr LGre WOld
– subsp. *floribundus* SWat
– – 'Saint Ivel' WHil
– subsp. *maximus* 'Albus' CPou IBlr SSpi
– 'Miniature Blue' SWat
– subsp. *minimus* GSki IBlr SWat
– – 'Adelaide' SWat
¶ – 'Supreme' IBlr
– Mount Stewart form IBlr
§ – subsp. *orientalis* CBlo CHEx CHan ERea GSki IBlr NPal SWat
– – var. *albiflorus* CBro CDoC CPou ETub GSki LBow MCLN NPal
– subsp. *praecox* IBlr
– azure SWat
– Slieve Donard form IBlr
– 'Storms River' SWat
– 'Variegatus' ♀ SLMG
– 'Vittatus' (v) CHan WCot
'Profusion' CBro
'Purple Cloud' CAbb CB&S CRos CTrC ERea GSki IBlr LRHS SPla
'Rhône' EFou IBlr
¶ 'Rosewarne' IBlr
'Royal Blue' ECtt EHic NHol SVil
'San Gabriel' (v) EMon SAxl WCot
'Sandringham' CFil IBlr WPGP
'Sapphire' CB&S IBlr
¶ 'Sky Star' LBlm
'Snowball' CB&S LRHS SApp SAxl
'Snowy Baby' CRos LRHS
'Snowy Owl' CLAP
'Streamline' CDoC EMil IBro SAxl WCot
¶ 'Sunfield' WWeb
'Tinkerbell' (v) CAbb CB&S CBro CMil CRDP CRos CSWP EMan EMil ERav LRHS MDun MTho SAxl SMad SPla SSpi WMer
'Torbay' IBlr SBla
umbellatus See *A. praecox* subsp. *orientalis*
'Underway' CMon GCal IBlr SSpi
'White Christmas' ERea
'White Dwarf' CHan ECha EFou GCra LRHS MBri WFar
'White Ice' CAbb CB&S EMil GQui SCro
'White Superior' CSpe EBee EMan NCut
'White Umbrella' WWat
'Windsor Castle' IBlr
'Windsor Grey' IBlr
'Wolga' EBee EFou
'Zella Thomas' LHyd

AGAPETES (Ericaceae)
buxifolia WBod
'Ludgvan Cross' CB&S CGre MBal

serpens ♀ CGre MBal
– 'Nepal Cream' CGre MBal
– 'Scarlet Elf' CGre SBid

AGARISTA (Ericaceae)
§ *populifolia* WWat

AGASTACHE (Lamiaceae)
anethiodora See *A. foeniculum*
anisata See *A. foeniculum*
* *astromontana* WPer
barberi LGre
* – 'Tutti-frutti' ECha EMan MRav
'Blue Fortune' EBee GBri SOkh WWeb
¶ *breviflora* EBee
¶ camphor hyssop EOHP
§ *cana* CGle ECoo EOHP LGre MUlv SDys WFar
– 'Cinnabar Rose' WFar
¶ *cusickii* EBee
'Firebird' CBot CGle CLon CMil CRDP CSev EBee EGar GCal LGre LHop MLLN MNrw NBir NHaw NPla SAga SBla SOkh SPer SUsu SWas SWat WCFE WCot WFar WWeb
§ *foeniculum* CAgr CArn CGle CHan CSev ECha EFou ELan ELau EMar EOHP EOld ERav GCHN GPoy LHol LHop MAus MChe MGra NFai NLon NNor NSti SIde SRms WGwG WPer WWye
– 'Alabaster' CGle CHan ECha ECro EFou EGoo ELau EMon WRha WWye
– 'Alba' CBlo CBot LCot MLLN SHDw SIde WFar WRha
¶ 'Globe Trotter' EFou
§ *mexicana* CDoC CGle CSam CSev ECro ELan LHop LIck MChe MHar NTow NWoo WGwG WWye
– 'Carille Carmine' CLTr MLLN WPer
– 'Champagne' CGle EGar LIck MCCP MCli MLLN SWat WPer
– 'Mauve Beauty' GBri LHop SMrm WPer
aff. – PC&H 153 CPle
– 'Rosea' See *A. cana*
nepetoides CArn MHew MSal SPil WWye
pringlei CHea EBee EMar LGre SWat WCot
rugosa CArn CFir CSev ELau EMan EOHP GBar GPoy MGra MLLN MSal NDov NPla SWat WCot WCru WJek WPer WSel WWye
¶ – 'Alba' SGre
– B&SWJ 735 EGoo EMar
rupestris CPou EBee LGre WCot
– JCA 1.025.050 CMil
scrophulariifolia EBee
urticifolia CArn CPea EPfP MSal
– 'Alba' EGar EPfP EWll SWat WEas WPer
I – 'Liquorice' CSam
– 'Liquorice Blue' CSpe EBee EMan EMar GSki LRHS MLan MWgw SChu SPer SSte SWat WPer WShe
– 'Liquorice White' CRDP CSam EBee EGar EGra EMan GSki MWgw NPla SCro SPer SPil SWat WOve
wrightii EBee

AGATHAEA See FELICIA

AGATHIS (Araucariaceae)
    australis   CFil

AGATHOSMA (Rutaceae) See Plant Deletions

AGAVE (Agavaceae)
affinis	See *A. sobria*
americana ♀	CAbb CB&S CDoC CGre
	CHEx CTrC CWSG ECha ELau
	EOas GCra GQui IBlr LCns
	LHil LPal LPan NPal SArc
	SLMG SMad
– 'Marginata'	CGre CHal CInt IBlr LHop
– 'Mediopicta' ♀	CTbh SAPC SArc SLMG WEas
¶ – 'Striata' (v)	CHEx
– 'Variegata' ♀	CAbb CB&S CDoC CHEx
	CMdw CTbh CTrC CWSG
	ECha ELau EWes GQui LCns
	NPer SAPC SArc SLMG SSoC
	SSto
angustifolia	SLMG
attenuata	SAPC SArc
avellanidens	See *A. sebastiana*
§ *celsii*	CAbb CHEx CTbh SAPC SArc
cerulata	See *A. sobria*
¶ – subsp. *nelsonii*	CTbh
chrysantha	EOas
coarctata	See *A. mitriformis*
¶ *colorata*	CHEx
ferox	CB&S CTbh
filifera ♀	CHEx EOas
gigantea	See *Furcraea foetida*
¶ *lechuguilla*	EOas
mitis	See *A. celsii*
neomexicana	SIgm
palmeri	EOas
parryi	CGre CHEx EGar EOas SIgm
– var. *couesii*	See *A. parryi* var. *parryi*
– var. *huachucensis*	CFir CHEx
§ – var. *parryi*	CTbh
potatorum var.	CTbh CTrC EOas
verschaffeltii	
salmiana var. *ferox*	CHEx SAPC SArc SLMG
schidigera	CBrP
* *shottii*	CTbh
¶ *sisalana*	CTrC
utahensis	EOas SIgm
victoriae-reginae ♀	CTbh EGar
xylonacantha	CHEx

AGERATINA See EUPATORIUM

AGLAONEMA (Araceae)
§ *crispum*	MBri
* – 'Marie'	MBri
'Malay Beauty'	MBri
roebelinii	See *A. crispum*
'Silver Queen' ♀	MBri

AGONIS (Myrtaceae)
  ¶ *marginata*   CHon

AGRIMONIA (Rosaceae)
eupatoria	CArn CKin ELau EWFC GPoy
	MChe MGra MHew NMir SIde
	SWat WCHb WCla WGwy
	WHer WOak WWye
¶ *gryposepala*	EBee
* *odorata*	WUnd

– Miller	See *A. repens*
§ *repens*	GBar MHew MSal WCHb

AGROPYRON (Poaceae)
glaucum	See *Elymus hispidus*
magellanicum	See *Elymus magellanicus*
pubiflorum	See *Elymus magellanicus*
scabrum	See *Elymus scabrus*

AGROSTEMMA (Caryophyllaceae)
coronaria	See *Lychnis coronaria*
githago	CJew EWFC MHew MMal MSal
	WCla WCot WHer WJek WOak

AGROSTIS (Poaceae)
calamagrostis	See *Calamagrostis epigejos*
canina 'Silver Needles' (v)	CBre CCuc CHor CInt CSte
	EGle EGra EHoe EJud EMan
	EMon EPPr EPot ESOG EWes
	GCal MMil MWhi
karsensis	See *A. stolonifera*
nebulosa	CInt LIck

AGROSTOCRINUM (Phormiaceae)
  ¶ *scabrum*   MFiF

AICHRYSON (Crassulaceae)
§ × *domesticum*	CHEx CHal
– 'Variegatum' ♀	CHal EBak SLMG

AILANTHUS (Simaroubaceae)
§ *altissima* ♀	CB&S CHEx CLnd CTho EBrP
	EBre EMil ENot IOrc LBre
	LPan MAsh MBlu MGos NBee
	SAPC SArc SBre SPer SRCN
	WCoo WDin WNor WStI
glandulosa	See *A. altissima*

AINSLIAEA (Asteraceae) See Plant Deletions

AJANIA (Asteraceae)
§ *pacifica*	CFis ECtt ELan EMan EMar
	ERav GCal MHar MRav
	MWgw NFai SPla SUsu WHer
	WHil WWal
tibetica JJH 9308103	NWCA
* *xylorhiza* JJH 95095	EPot

AJUGA (Lamiaceae)
'Arctic Fox'	NWes WGle
'Brockbankii'	CHal
¶ *chamaepitys*	EBee
genevensis 'Alba'	CLAP
– 'Tottenham'	MCli WMer
metallica	See *A. pyramidalis*
'Monmotaro San'	EGar
§ *pyramidalis*	CFee ECha EGar EGol LWak
	NBrk SCro WHer
– 'Metallica Crispa'	CRDP EPla EWes MBro MLLN
	NHar NPSI WHil WMer
reptans	CJew CKin ECtt ELau EWFC
	GPoy LGro LHol LPBA MChe
	MHew MSal NBrk NMir WChe
	WGwy WRHF
– 'Alba'	CArn CCot CNic CRow CTri
	ECha EFou GCal GMac MCLN
	MNrw MRav NBro NChi NPla
	NPro NSti SSvw WAlt WByw
	WCHb WFar WLin WMer
	WPer WWeb WWye

– 'Argentea'   See *A. reptans* **'Variegata'**
§ – 'Atropurpurea' ♀   CB&S CRow ECha ELan ENot
EPar LGro LPBA LSyl MBro
MWat MWgw NChi NEgg NFai
NHol NNor NRoo SMad SPer
SRCN SRms WEas WWin
– 'Braunherz' ♀   Widely available
– 'Burgundy Glow' (v) ♀   Widely available
* – 'Burgundy Red'   GDra
§ – 'Catlin's Giant' ♀   Widely available
– 'Delight' (v)   ECot ELan EMon NNrd SBod
WCHb WCer WEas
– 'Grey Lady'   EMon SUsu WBro WCot
– 'Julia'   EMon EPPr LWak
– 'Jumbo'   See *A. reptans* **'Jungle Beauty'**
§ – 'Jungle Beauty'   CRDP CRow CSev ECha ECtt
EFou EGol EOrc EPar EPla
GBar GCal LHop NHol SAxl
WCer WHen WHer WMow
– 'Macrophylla'   See *A. reptans* **'Catlin's Giant'**
§ – 'Multicolor' (v)   CArn CMCo CPri EAst ECha
EFou ELan EPar EPot GDra
LGro LPBA LWak MBar
MCLN MLLN MWat NFai
NGre NNor NNrd SBod SPer
SSmi WCer WMow WPer
– 'Palisander'   GSki MTed NSti
– 'Pink Elf'   CB&S CLyd CNic CRow CTri
EBur ELan EMan EWes LHop
NBro NNor NOak SHel SIng
SUsu SWat WBea WCer WFar
WHoo WPer WPyg
– 'Pink Splendour'   CBre CTri MGed NChi WCer
– 'Pink Surprise'   CDec CRow EBrP EBre EFou
EGol EHoe EMar EMon EPla
EPri GBar LBre LRHS MCLN
MMil NChi NGre NHol NRya
SBre SCro SSvw WCHb WEas
WPbr
¶ – 'Pink Towers'   WWeb
¶ – 'Purple Brocade'   CStr NLak WByw
– 'Purple Torch'   ECha EGar MBal MCli SLod
WCHb WCer WEas WLin
WMer
– 'Purpurea'   See *A. reptans* **'Atropurpurea'**
♦ – 'Rainbow'   See *A. reptans* **'Multicolor'**
– 'Rosea'   CHal NPro WHil
– 'Schneekerze'   EJud MCli
– 'Silver Shadow'   CBre NLak NPro WCHb
♦ – 'Tricolor'   See *A. reptans* **'Multicolor'**
§ – 'Variegata'   CB&S CPri EBrP EBre ECha
ECtt EFou EHoe ELan GDra
LBre LGan LGro LHop MBri
MCLN MHig MLLN MWgw
NEgg NRoo SBod SBre SPer
SSmi SWat WBea WHil WLin
WPbr
¶ 'Variegated Glacier' (v)   ELau

AKEBIA (Lardizabalaceae)
¶ *longeracemosa*   WCru
  B&SWJ 3606
× *pentaphylla*   CPlN EMil EPfP ERea GQui
MAsh SBra SPer
quinata   Widely available
¶ – cream form   LRHS
trifoliata   CB&S CBlo CHEx CPlN EHic
EPfP WSHC
¶ – B&SWJ 2829   WCru

ALANGIUM (Alangiaceae)
chinense   CB&S CFil CMCN WPGP

platanifolium   CBot CFil CHan CMCN EPla
MBlu WPGP

ALBIZIA (Mimosaceae)
¶ *adianthifolia*   MFiF
  distachya   See *Paraserianthes lophantha*
¶ *guachapele*   WMul
§ *julibrissin*   CArn CFil CHan CTho ISea
MLan MWat SPer WMul WPGP
– f. *rosea* ♀   CB&S CGre CHEx CMCN CPle
CTrC ELan GQui LPan MCCP
MUlv NPSI SAPC SArc SDry
SMad SOWG WBod WNor
WSHC
  lophantha   See *Paraserianthes lophantha*

ALBUCA (Hyacinthaceae)
¶ *altissima*   EBee
¶ *aurea*   EBee
  canadensis   EBee
  caudata   CMon
¶ *cooperi*   EBee
  humilis   EBee EPot ESis MSto NTow
SIng WAbe WHil WOMN
  juncifolia   CMon
  nelsonii   CAvo CMon
  shawii   EBee SBla WAbe
  tortuosa S&SH 53   CHan
  wakefieldii   CMon

ALCEA (Malvaceae)
  'Arabian Nights'   WHer
  'Blackcurrant Whirl'   WHer
  ficifolia   CGle EMFP EWes MAvo MSto
NBus NFai SSvw
  pallida   EBee EMan
– HH&K 284   CHan
§ *rosea*   CGle EJud MBri MWgw WEas
WFar
– Chater's Double Group   CHad EBrP EBre ECtt EMan
(d)   EPfP LBre MBri MTis NNor
SBre SCoo SRms WOve WRHF
– double apricot (d)   WCot
– forms   LCot SPer WLRN
– 'Lemon Light'   CMdw ECGP WLRN
– Majorette Group   ECtt
* – 'Negrite'   MRav
– 'Nigra'   CArn CGle CHad CJew CMGP
CMil EBar EGoo EMan EOrc
GCra MAus MHlr MNrw MSte
MTis MWgw NNor NPri SMad
SPer SRCN SSoC SSvw WOve
– single pink   LCot
– Summer Carnival Group   EMan SRms WGor
– yellow   LCot
§ *rugosa*   CGle CHad CMil CSam ECha
ELan EMan LGan MAvo MSte
NCut SDix WCot WEas WKif
WOMN WOld WPGP WRus

ALCHEMILLA † (Rosaceae)
§ *abyssinica*   CDoC CGle CHid CRow EHal
GAbr GBuc MBel NWes WBro
WCot WHen
N *alpina*   CBro CFee CRow ELan EPar
EWFC GMac GTou LBee
MCLN MRav MTho NBrk
NEgg NLon NMir NNor NRoo
SIng WCla WFar WMow WOld
WPbr WPer WRus WWin
¶ *aroanica*   EBee

arvensis	See *Aphanes arvensis*
conjuncta	Widely available
elisabethae	EMon EPPr MGrG NBrk WCHb
ellenbeckii	CFee CLyd CMHG EBrP EBre ELan EMon GCHN LBre LFis MBar MLLN NChi NNor NNrd NRoo NWCA SBre WByw WCHb WEas WFar WHen WPer
¶ epipsila	WPer
erythropoda ♀	Widely available
faeroensis	CHid EGle LBee NChi NNor WHil WPer WWat
– var. *pumila*	CLyd EBee LHop MSto
filicaulis 'Minima'	CNat
§ × *fulgens*	CArn CBlo CBod EPPr GAri LFis NRoo SMac WAbe WHen
glaucescens	CNat
hoppeana hort.	See *A. plicatula*
lapeyrousei	CHid EMon EPPr MSto NChi WPer
mollis ♀	Widely available
* – 'Robusta'	EBee ECha ECro EPla MTho NBrk SEND SWat
* – 'Senior'	GCal
– 'Variegata'	IBlr
¶ monticola	WPer
'Mr Poland's Variety'	See *A. venosa*
pedata	See *A. abyssinica*
pentaphylla	EBee
¶ plicatula	WPer
¶ psilomischa	EBee EMon
pumila	ECro LRHS MGrG
saxatilis	EMan WPer
* siranines	EGar ERav
speciosa	EBee LGan SHel
splendens	See *A. × fulgens*
§ venosa	SCro SLod SPer WWat
¶ aff. –	EPla
¶ vetteri	EBee
vulgaris hort.	See *A. xanthochlora*
§ xanthochlora	CAgr ECro EGol GGar GPoy MHew MSal NLar NMir WBro WHer WPer

ALECTRYON (Sapindaceae)

excelsus	CHEx

ALETRIS (Melanthiaceae) See Plant Deletions

ALISMA (Alismataceae)

lanceolatum	WChe
plantago-aquatica	CBen CKin CRow EHon EMFW GBar LPBA MHew MSta NDea SWat WChe WMAq WWeb
– var. *parviflorum*	CBen EMFW LPBA MSta NDea SRms SWat WChe WWeb

ALKANNA (Boraginaceae)

orientalis	WCru
¶ tinctoria HH&K 345	CHan

ALLAGOPTERA (Arecaceae)

¶ arenaria	LPal

ALLAMANDA (Apocynaceae)

cathartica	CPIN ECon ERea LChe MBri WMul

– 'Birthe'	MBri
* – 'Chocolate Swirl'	LChe
– 'Grandiflora'	CPIN
* – 'Hendersonii' ♀	SOWG
– 'Williamsii'	LChe
neriifolia	See *A. schottii*
§ schottii ♀	CPIN ECon SOWG
violacea	See *A. blanchetii*

ALLARDIA (Asteraceae)

glabra	See *A. tridactylites*

ALLIARIA (Brassicaceae)

petiolata	CArn CKin CSev EWFC WHer

ALLIUM † (Alliaceae)

§ acuminatum	EHyt GCHN MFos NBir WCot
aflatunense hort.	See *A. hollandicum*
akaka	ERos GCrs LBow MFos MSto
albidum	See *A. denudatum*
albopilosum	See *A. cristophii*
altissimum	LBow NRog
amabile	See *A. mairei* var. *amabile*
ambiguum	See *A. roseum* var. *carneum*
¶ amethystinum	CStr
ampeloprasum	CFil ECha WHer WPGP
– var. *babingtonii*	CNat GPoy ILis LRot MLLN WHer
amplectens	GDra NRog
§ angulosum	LLWP MMil MSto WCot
atropurpureum	ECha EMon EPar LBow MLLN NRog WCot
aucheri	CLAP
azureum	See *A. caeruleum*
'Beau Regard' ♀	LAma LBow NRog
beesianum hort.	See *A. cyaneum*
– W.W. Smith ♀	CGle CLyd EBur ESis EWes MBal MBro NBir NRya NWCA WCot
bulgaricum	See *Nectaroscordum siculum* subsp. *bulgaricum*
§ caeruleum ♀	CArn CAvo CBro CChr CHea CMil ELan EMar EMon EPot ETub LAma LBow MBri MLLN MSto MWat NBir NRog NRya NSti SUsu WBro WCHb WCot WRHF
– azureum	See *A. caeruleum*
caesium	EHyt
callimischon	CAvo CBro CMon NRog WLin
– subsp. *callimischon*	MFos
– subsp. *haemostictum*	EHyt EPot LBow NRog SBla SIng
campanulatum	MSto
cardiostemon	MBel
§ carinatum	EBee GCHN SIng
§ – subsp. *pulchellum* ♀	Widely available
– – f. *album*	CAvo CBro CMon CSWP CStr ECha EMon EPar EPot ETub GBur LBow LFis LLWP MBal MNrw NRog NSti NTow SIng SUsu WCot WPer WWin
– – 'Tubergen'	ETub
carolinianum	MSto
cepa	CJew CMil EGar GBar
– Aggregatum Group	ELau WHil
¶ – – 'Potato Onion'	GPoy
– 'Perutile'	CArn GBar GPoy ILis LHol MCoo SIde WSel

– Proliferum Group	CArn CSev EJud ELau GAbr GBar GPoy ILis LHol MChe NWoo SIde WCHb WCer WHer WOak WSel
* – 'White Flower'	WCot
cernuum	Widely available
– 'Hidcote' ♀	EMon NPla WCot
– *roseum*	CLyd
chamaemoly littorale AB&S 4387	CMon
cirrhosum	See **A. carinatum** subsp. *pulchellum*
cowanii	See **A. neapolitanum Cowanii Group**
crenulatum	MSto
§ *cristophii* ♀	Widely available
cupanii	CMon
cupuliferum	MSto
§ *cyaneum* ♀	CArn CAvo CBre CGle CGra CHan CHea CLyd EHyt GCrs LBee LBow MHig NMen NNrd NRya NTow SSca WRus
cyathophorum	CBlo GCrs NRog
§ – var. *farreri*	CArn CAvo CBro CHea CMon CNic ELan EPot ERos ESis GCHN GCrs GSki LBow LLWP MBal MBro MHig NChi NLon NMen NNor NRya WAbe WOMN
§ *denudatum*	LBow SIng
dichlamydeum	CBro LBow NRog WLin
– JCA 11765	CLAP
§ *drummondii*	ECha
elatum	See **A. macleanii**
ericetorum	EBee ERos MSto
falcifolium	NTow
– JCA 11625	CLAP
farreri	See **A. cyathophorum** var. *farreri*
'Firmament'	LBow
fistulosum	CArn CJew EJud ELan ELau EPla GBar GPoy ILis MChe MGra NBrk NNor SIde WCHb WCer WOak WPer WSel WWye
¶ – 'Welsh Red'	IIve
flavum ♀	CArn CAvo CBro CGle CHan CHea CLyd CMon ECha ELan ELau LAma LBow LGan LHop MCLN MHig NMen NRog NSti SChu SHBN SIng SUsu WCla WGor WPGP WPer
§ – 'Blue Leaf'	EPot ERos NBir
¶ – subsp. *flavum* var. *minus* HH&K 273	CHan
– 'Glaucum'	See **A. flavum 'Blue Leaf'**
– 'Golden Showers'	EBar
– var. *minus*	CNic ELan EPot MTho NWCA SSca
– var. *nanum*	EPot NTow
– subsp. *tauricum*	CMon
geyeri	EHyt WCot WLin
giganteum ♀	CArn CB&S CBot CMea ELan EMan EMon EOrc EPar EPot ETub GBur GCra LAma LBow MBri MLLN MRav NNor NOrc NRog SBod SPer SRms WFar WHoo
'Gladiator' ♀	CAvo GBur LAma LBow MLLN NRog
glaucum	See **A. senescens** subsp. *montanum* var. *glaucum*
'Globemaster' ♀	CBro CMea CMil CRDP EBee ETub GBur LAma LBow
'Globus'	EPot LBow
¶ *goodingii*	EHyt
griffithianum	See **A. rubellum**
heldreichii	EBee
hierochuntinum S&L 79	CMon
'His Excellency'	CBlo CMea LBow LRHS
§ *hollandicum* ♀	CBro CChr CGle CMon ECha EFou EMan EPfP GBur LAma LBow MLLN MSto MWat NChi NFai NOrc NRog NSti SChu WPer WRHF
– 'Purple Sensation' ♀	Widely available
– 'Purple Surprise'	LRHS
humile	MSto
hyalinum	CMon EHyt NRog
§ *insubricum* ♀	CHad CMea ERos GCrs MS&S MSto NBir SWas
jajlae	See **A. rotundum** subsp. *jajlae*
¶ *jesdianum*	LBow
* – *album*	EBee
♦ – 'Michael Hoog'	See **A. rosenbachianum 'Michael Hoog'**
¶ – 'Purple King'	LBow
kansuense	See **A. sikkimense**
karataviense ♀	Widely available
kharputense	LAma
libani	MSto WPer WWye
loratum	EPar
'Lucy Ball'	ETub LAma LBow MLLN NRog
§ *macleanii*	CArn CMil EMon EPar GBur LAma LBow MSto NBrk NRog
macranthum	CLyd EBee GCHN MSte MSto NSti SWas WLin
macrochaetum	LAma
mairei	CFee CInt EHyt ERos EWes GCHN MBar MDHE NBus NRya
§ – var. *amabile*	ERos MBal MHig NRya NTow WOMN
– – pink	NBir
'Mars'	EBee LBow LRHS MLLN
maximowiczii	EWes WThi
moly ♀	CArn CBro CGle CNic ELan ETub GBuc GBur LAma LBow MBri MHig MRav MWat NMen NRog NRya NSti SIng WCHb WCla WCot WPer WShi WWin
– 'Jeannine' ♀	CBro EBee EPot LBow WPGP
¶ 'Mont Blanc'	LBow
'Mount Everest'	CAvo CBro CMea EBee LBow LRHS
multibulbosum	See **A. nigrum**
murrayanum hort.	See **A. unifolium**
narcissiflorum hort.	See **A. insubricum**
§ – Villars	CLyd GCrs MSto NMGW NMen NSla NSti NWCA SIng
neapolitanum	CAgr CArn CGle CLTr EGar EPar LAma LBow MBri MBro NRog NSti WCot WPer
§ – Cowanii Group	CBro GBur MNrw WLin WRHF
– 'Grandiflorum'	EPla GBur MLLN NRog
§ *nigrum*	EFou EGar EMan EPar GBur LAma LBow MHlr MLLN MRav NBir NRog SChu WCot WHal
nutans	EBee LBow MSto
nuttallii	See **A. drummondii**

§ *obliquum* — CHan ECha GSki MSto WCot WPbr WTin

odorum Linnaeus — See *A. ramosum* Linnaeus

¶ *oleraceum* — WHer

olympicum — EHyt MBro

¶ – ES 13 — MRPP

§ *oreophilum* ♀ — CArn CAvo CBro ECha ECtt EHyt GBur GSki LAma LBow MFos MHig MLLN NMGW NRog NRoo SRms WBea WCla WCot WPer WWye

– 'Agalik' — LRHS

– 'Zwanenburg' ♀ — CBro CMea EPot LBow NMen NRog

orientale — EPot LAma

ostrowskianum — See *A. oreophilum*

pallens — CBre ERav LBow MTho NBir

§ *paniculatum* — CAvo CMea ECha EHic EPot MMil NRog SChu

– subsp. *fuscum* — EHic

paradoxum — LRHS NBir NRog

– var. *normale* — EHyt EMon LBow WCot

– PF 5085 — CMon

pedemontanum — See *A. narcissiflorum* Villars

perdulce — MSto

polyastrum — GCHN

porrum 'Saint Victor' — MHlr

pulchellum — See *A. carinatum* subsp. *pulchellum*

pyrenaicum — CAvo ELan EMan
Costa & Vayreda

– hort. — See *A. angulosum*

ramosum Jacquin — See *A. obliquum*

§ – Linnaeus — LAma MSto WPer

'Rien Poortvliet' — CArn LAma LBow NRog

rosenbachianum — CArn CBro EHyt EMan EPar EPot GBur LAma MLLN NCat NRog WRHF

– 'Album' — EPar EPot GBur LAma MLLN NRog WCot

§ – 'Michael Hoog' — EPot LBow

– 'Purple King' — EPot LRHS

– 'Shing' — LRHS WIvy

roseum — CArn CAvo CElw CLTr CMea EBee ECtt ELau EMon LAma LBow NRog WPer

– B&S 396 — CMon

§ – var. *bulbiferum* — GBur WCot

– 'Grandiflorum' — See *A. roseum* var. *bulbiferum*

§ *rotundum* subsp. *jajlae* — EJud EWes LLWP NMen WPer

¶ – subsp. *rotundum* — LBow

rubens — EBee

¶ *sanbornii* var. *sanbornii* — MFos

sativum — CArn EEls EJud ELau SIde WJek WOak WSel WWye

* – *aureum* — GPoy

– var. *ophioscorodon* — GPoy IIve ILis

¶ – 'Printanor' — CBod

scabriscapum — CMon

schoenoprasum — CArn CJew CSev ECha ELau GAbr GCHN GPoy LHol MBal MBar MBel MBri MBro MChe MGra MHew MRav NCat NFai NNor SIde WBea WEas WJek WMow WOak WPer WWye

– 'Black Isle Blush' ♀ — GPoy

– 'Corsican White' — EMon

– fine-leaved — ELau IIve WRha

– 'Forescate' — CBod EBee ECha EFou EJud ELau EWes GCHN GCal LHol MBal MBri MLLN NHol SSpe SSvw WCHb WCot WPbr

¶ – medium leaved — ELau

– 'Pink Perfection' ♀ — GPoy

– 'Polyphant' — CBre CJew WCHb WRha

– *roseum* — GBar

– var. *sibiricum* — EJud GBar GPoy MBri MGra SDix WSel

– 'Silver Chimes' — CMil MRav

– 'Wallington White' — EMon LHol MBro

– white — CMea CSWP ECha ELau GBar LBay LGre MBro MSte NBir SIde SSvw WBea WBon WCHb WCot WEas WHer WRha WWye

schubertii — CArn CAvo CBro CMea EMon EPar EPot ETub LAma LBow MBri MLLN MNrw NRog WCot

scorodoprasum — WCHb

– subsp. *jajlae* — See *A. rotundum* subsp. *jajlae*

scorzonerifolium var. *xericiense* — CMon

senescens — CArn CTri ECGP ECro ELan EPar ERos GCHN LBow NChi NMen SRms SSpe SSvw

§ – subsp. *montanum* — CLAP EBee EGar EGoo ELan EPot ERav MBro NMen SDix SIng WAbe WCot

§ – – var. *glaucum* — CBos CHad CHan CLyd CMea CPBP EBrP EBre ECha EMan ESis GCHN LBow LBre MBel MHig MHlr NTow SBre SIng WCot WHer WPbr WPer WWye

– subsp. *senescens* — EMon

¶ *sessiliflorum* — GCrs

sibthorpianum — See *A. paniculatum*

siculum — See *Nectaroscordum siculum*

§ *sikkimense* — CHea CMea EBee EHyt GDra LFis MBro NMen NNrd NSla NTow NWCA SBla WCot WLRN WOMN WPer

siskiyouense — MSto

sphaerocephalon — CArn CAvo CBro CHad CHea ECha ELan EPar ETub GBur LAma LBow LHop LLWP MLLN MNrw MWat NOak NRog NSti SUsu WCHb WEas WHil WOMN WPer WRHF WShi

stellatum — EHyt SSpi

stellerianum — GCHN LBow WPer

§ *stipitatum* — EBee LAma LBow NRog WCot

– 'Album' — CBro EMon ETub LAma LBow NRog

¶ *stracheyi* — WCot

szovitsii — MSto

tanguticum — GCHN

textile — MSto

thunbergii — CAvo CLTr CNic EBee LBow NBir

¶ – 'Ozawa' — SBla

tibeticum — See *A. sikkimense*

togashii — MSto

tricoccum — MSto

triquetrum — CAvo CGle CLTr ELan ERav GBar GBur GGar IBlr ILis LAma LBow NBir NMen NRog SIng WCHb WCru WHer WPer WShi WWin

tuberosum	CArn CAvo CLyd CSev ECha
	EFou EJud ELau ERos GPoy
	ILis LHol MBri MChe MGra
	MHew SIde WBea WCHb
	WCer WCot WGwG WOak
	WPer WWye
– blue-flowered	CBod IIve SHDw
¶ – purple/mauve	ELau
¶ – variegated (v)	ELau
¶ *turkestanicum*	EHyt
§ *unifolium*	CAvo CBro CGle CMon EMan
	ETub GBur LAma LBow
	LLWP MBri MLLN MRav NBir
	NCat NChi NRog NSti SSpi
	WBro WCla WPer
ursinum	CArn CKin ETub EWFC GPoy
	LAma NMir NRog WGwG
	WGwy WHen WShi WWye
validum	MSto
victorialis	MSto
vineale	CArn WHer WPer
violaceum	See *A. carinatum*
virgunculae	LBow SBla SWas WCot
wallichii	CLyd CPou EBar EMon LAma
	NBir WCot
– B 445	WLin
zaprjagaevii	EBee
zebdanense	LAma LBow MNrw MSto

ALLOCASUARINA (Casuarinaceae)

¶ *crassa*	MAll
§ *littoralis*	CGre
monilifera	ECou
¶ *nana*	MFiF
§ *verticillata*	CTrC MAll

ALNUS † (Betulaceae)

cordata ♀	CB&S CBlo CDoC CKin CLnd
	CPer ELan ENot EPfP GChr
	IOrc LBuc LHyr NBee NRog
	NWea SHBN SPer SSta WDin
	WFar WMou WOrn WStI WTro
– wild origin	CSto
crispa	See *A. viridis* subsp. *crispa*
firma	CMCN
– var. *multinervis*	See *A. pendula*
– var. *sieboldiana*	See *A. sieboldiana*
glutinosa	CB&S CBlo CDoC CKin CLnd
	CPer CSam CSto ENot GChr
	GRei IOrc LBuc LHyr MGos
	NBee NRog NRoo NWea
	SHBN SHFr SPer WDin WMou
	WOrn WStI
– 'Aurea'	CEnd CTho EBee MBlu SSpi
	WWat
– 'Imperialis' ♀	CEnd CLnd CPMA CTho EBee
	ELan ENot EPfP GChr MAsh
	MBri NBee NPSI SPer SSpi
	WDin WGer WWat
– f. *incisa*	ELan
– 'Laciniata'	CDoC CLnd CTho IOrc MBlu
– 'Pyramidalis'	CTho
hirsuta	CMCN
incana	CBlo CDoC CKin CLnd CMCN
	CPer CSto ENot GRei IOrc
	LBuc MBar NRog NWea SHBN
	WDin WMou WOrn
– 'Aurea'	CB&S CLnd COtt CTho ELan
	ENot IOrc LPan MBar MBlu
	MBri SHBN SPer WDin
– 'Laciniata'	CTho ENot WDin
– 'Pendula'	WMou

japonica	CSto
maritima	CSto
maximowiczii	CMCN CSto
– AGSJ 334	SSta
nepalensis	WFro
nitida	CGre CMCN
oregona	See *A. rubra*
rhombifolia	CSto
§ *rubra*	CBlo CDoC CKin CLnd CMCN
	CPer CSto CTho ELan ENot
	GAri GChr GRei IOrc LBuc
	NWea WDin WMou
* – 'Pinnatifida'	MBlu
§ *rugosa*	CMCN
serrulata	See *A. rugosa*
§ *sieboldiana*	CGre CSto
◆ *sinuata*	CAgr CMCN
× *spaethii* ♀	CTho IOrc MCoo
subcordata	CLnd
viridis	CAgr CMCN CPer GAri NWea
– subsp. *crispa* var. *mollis*	CMCN

ALOCASIA (Araceae)

× *amazonica* ♀	ERea MBri
¶ *cuprea* 'Blackie'	WMul
¶ – 'Greenback'	WMul
¶ *gageana*	WMul
◆ *lowii* var. *veitchii*	See *A. veitchii*
¶ *macrorrhiza*	WMul
¶ – 'Jungle Gold'	WMul
◆ *nigra*	See *A. plumbea* 'Nigra'
§ *plumbea* 'Nigra'	WMul
§ 'Uhinkii'	WMul
§ *veitchii*	WMul
I *whinkii*	See *A.* 'Uhinkii'

ALOE (Aloeaceae)

arborescens	CAbb CHEx CTrC MBro WCot
aristata ♀	CHEx EOas EWes LBlm MBri
	MBro SAPC SArc SLMG
barbadensis	See *A. vera*
brevifolia	CHEx CTbh EOas
broomii	EOas
camperi 'Maculata'	MBri
ciliaris	CHEx ERea SLMG
dichotoma	GBin
ferox	CTrC
humilis	IBlr
karasbergensis	LHil
plicatilis	CTrC
pratensis	CFir CTrC
saponaria	SLMG
striata	CHEx
striatula	CFil CHEx CTrC EOas IBlr
	SAPC SArc SBid
– var. *caesia*	IBlr
§ *vera* ♀	CArn ECon ELau EOHP EOas
	ERea GPoy ILis LBay LChe
	LHol LPJP MGra MSal NPer
	SIde SLMG WHer WOak
'Walmsley's Blue'	MBri

ALOINOPSIS (Aizoaceae) See Plant Deletions

ALONSOA (Scrophulariaceae)

¶ *acutifolia candida*	EBee
– coral	LIck
linearis	EBee LCot
meridionalis	CElw NCut
'Pink Beauty'	ELan
warscewiczii ♀	ELan ERea IBlr LGan SAga
	WWin

– pale form See *A. warscewiczii* **'Peachy-keen'**

§ – 'Peachy-keen' CSpe EMan NLak SAga

ALOPECURUS (Poaceae)

alpinus CCuc CInt EHoe EMon LRHS
– subsp. *glaucus* EHoe ETen MWhi
lanatus CInt NRya
pratensis CKin NOrc
– 'Aureovariegatus' CB&S CCuc CInt CKel CSte
 EHoe EMan EMon EPPr EPla
 ESOG GCal GMaP IBlr LHop
 MBar MCLN MSte NFai NHar
 NNor NRoo SPer SPla SSoC
 WHil WHow WLeb
N – 'Aureus' CMGP CNic ECha EFou EGra
 EPot GAbr GBin MBal MWhi
 NBro NSti NVic SCob WByw
 WLin WPer WRHF WWin
¶ – 'No Overtaking' EMon

ALOPHIA (Iridaceae)

lahue See *Herbertia lahue*

ALOYSIA (Verbenaceae)

chamaedrifolia CPle
citriodora See *A. triphylla*
§ *triphylla* ♀ CArn CBot CHad CPle CSam
 CSev CTbh CTrw ECha ELan
 ELau ENot ERea GChr GPoy
 IOrc LHol MBri NFla NNor
 NRog NWoo SDix SIde SPer
 WCHb WEas WOak WWat
 WWye

ALPINIA (Zingiberaceae)

¶ *formosana* WMul
japonica MSal
luteocarpa LChe
speciosa See *A. zerumbet*
¶ *zerumbet* 'Variegata' (v) WMul

ALSOBIA See EPISCIA

ALSTROEMERIA † (Alstroemeriaceae)

¶ 'Aimi' SBai
angustifolia P&W 6574 MSto
'Apollo' ♀ COtt LRHS MGrG SBai WViv
aurantiaca See *A. aurea*
§ *aurea* CGle CGre ELan EMar EPfP
 EWoo LBlm MHlr MRav MUlv
 NCat NFla NLar NMGW NSti
 SDys WCot
– 'Cally Fire' GCal
– 'Dover Orange' CB&S CGle CTri EBee SMrm
 WCot
– 'Orange King' CBlo CDoC EHic ENot EPfP
 MUlv NLar SCoo SDeJ
brasiliensis CGle CMil GCal NLon
'Charm' EBee LRHS SBai
¶ 'Coronet' ♀ EBee LIck SBai
'Dayspring Delight' (v) CLAP
♦ Diana, Princess of Wales See *A. Diana, Princess of Wales* = **'Stablaco'**
diluta subsp. *diluta* MSto
 Doctor Salter's hybrids EFou EHal SRms
exserens JCA 14415 MSto
'Fortune' LRHS
garaventae MSto
H.R.H. Princess See *A. H.R.H. the Princess*
 Alexandra Alexandra = **'Stablaco'**

♦ H.R.H. Princess Alice See *A. H.R.H. Princess Alice* = **'Staverpi'**
haemantha CLAP MSto
¶ *haemantha rosea* WCot
'Hawera' WCot
¶ Hawera Seedlings GCal
hookeri MSto MTho SIgm SWas
¶ 'Inca Charm' WWeb
¶ 'Inca Gold' WWeb
Inca hybrids CB&S
¶ 'Inca Salsa' WWeb
¶ 'Inca Spice' WWeb
¶ 'Inca Sunset' WWeb
ligtu hybrids ♀ CAvo CB&S CDoC CGle CHor
 CPou CTri EAst ECha ELan
 EMan EPfP ERav ETub GBur
 LHop MAus MNrw MWgw
 NNor NPer NVic SDeJ SPer
 SRms SWas WRus
'Little Eleanor' COtt EBee SBai SPla
magnifica RB 94012 MSto
Manon See *A. Princess Marie-Louise* = **'Zelanon'**
Marie-Louise See *A. Princess Marie-Louise* = **'Zelanon'**
'Marina' LRHS SBai SPla
'Mars' COtt LRHS SBai
Meyer hybrids MTho
'Orange Gem' ♀ COtt LRHS MBri SBai
'Orange Glory' ♀ COtt EBee LIck LRHS SBai
 SPla
pallida CBro SSpi
– JCA 12407 MSto
– JCA 14335 MSto
patagonica P&W 6226 MFos NTow
§ *paupercula* MSto
pelegrina CMon MTho WCot
– 'Alba' ELan
– 'Rosea' ELan
'Pink Perfection' COtt EBee LRHS MBri MGrG
 SBai SPla
¶ *presliana* subsp. *australis* CPou
– – JCA 12590 MSto SSpi
– subsp. *presliana* MSto
– RB 94103 MSto WCot
Princess Alice See *A. Princess Alice* = **'Staverpi'**
Princess Beatrix See *A. Princess Beatrix* = **'Stadoran'**
Princess Carmina See *A. Princess Carmina* = **'Stasilva'**
Princess Caroline See *A. Princess Caroline* = **'Staroko'**
♦ Princess Charlotte See *A. Princess Charlotte* = **'Staprizsa'**
Princess Elizabeth See *A. Queen Elizabeth The Queen Mother* = **'Stamoli'**
Princess Frederika See *A. Princess Frederika* = **'Stabronza'**
Princess Grace See *A. Princess Grace* = **'Starodo'**
♦ Princess Ileana See *A. Princess Ileana* = **'Stalvir'**
♦ Princess Juliana See *A. Princess Juliana* = **'Staterpa'**
Princess Marie-Louise See *A. Princess Marie-Louise* = **'Zelanon'**
Princess Mira See *A. Princess Mira* = **'Stapripur'**
♦ Princess Monica See *A. Princess Monica* = **'Staprimon'**
¶ Princess Paola LIck

◆ Princess Ragna · See *A.* Princess Stephanie = **'Stapirag'**
Princess Sarah · See *A.* Princess Sarah = **'Stalicamp'**
◆ Princess Sissi · See *A.* Princess Sissi = **'Stapripris'**
Princess Sophia · See *A.* Princess Sophia = **'Stajello'**
◆ Princess Stephanie · See *A.* Princess Stephanie = **'Stapirag'**
Princess Victoria · See *A.* Princess Victoria = **'Regina'**
◆ Princess Zsa Zsa · See *A.* Princess Charlotte = **'Staprizsa'**
pseudospathulata · MSto
  – RB 94010 · WCot
§ *psittacina* · CBos CBro CGle CHad CHan CRDP ECro ELan EPar ERav ERic ERos EWoo GCal LHil LHop MSte NTow SLMG SSoC SSpi WFar WPGP WRus WSHC
  – variegated · CRDP CSpe EGar ELan EMar EMon EPPr MGrG MRav NPla WCot
pulchella Sims · See *A. psittacina*
pulchra · SIgm
  – BC&W 4751 · CMon
  – BC&W 4762 · MSto
pygmaea · EDAr EHyt ERos MSto MTho
Queen Elizabeth The Queen Mother · See *A.* Queen Elizabeth The Queen Mother = **'Stamoli'**
'Red Beauty' · LRHS MBri MGrG NBir NCat SBai
'Red Elf' · COtt LRHS MBri SBai
§ Princess Victoria = 'Regina' · SSmt
revoluta JCA 14378 · CPou MSto
'Selina' · SBai
  short purple · WCot
¶ *simsii* · CPou
'Solent Candy' · WFar
'Solent Crest' ♀ · SBai
'Solent Haze' · SBai
'Solent Rose' ♀ · SBai
¶ sp. F&W 7975 · CPou
spathulata RB 94015 · WCot
'Spring Delight' · WCot
¶ Diana, Princess of Wales = 'Stablaco' · SSmt
§ Princess Frederika = 'Stabronza' · SSmt
§ Princess Beatrix = 'Stadoran' · SSmt
§ Princess Sophia = 'Stajello' · SSmt
§ Princess Sarah = 'Stalicamp' · SSmt
§ Princess Ileana = 'Stalvir' · SSmt
§ Queen Elizabeth The Queen Mother = 'Stamoli' ♀ · LIck SPla SSmt
§ Princess Stephanie = 'Stapirag' · SSmt
Princess Angela = 'Staprila' · SSmt
¶ Princess Emily = 'Staprimil' · SSmt
§ Princess Monica = 'Staprimon' · LIck SSmt
§ Princess Mira = 'Stapripur' ♀ · SSmt
§ Princess Sissi = 'Staprisis' · SSmt

§ Princess Charlotte = 'Staprizsa' · SSmt
§ Princess Grace = 'Starodo' ♀ · SSmt
§ Princess Caroline = 'Staroko' ♀ · SSmt
§ Princess Carmina = 'Stasilva' ♀ · SPla SSmt
§ Princess Juliana = 'Staterpa' ♀ · SSmt
§ H.R.H. Princess Alice = 'Staverpi' · SSmt
'Sunstar' · COtt SBai
umbellata F&W 8497 · SSpi
  – JCA 14348 · MSto
'Verona' · COtt EBee SBai SPla
violacea · See *A. paupercula*
'White Apollo' · EBee MBri SPla
'Yellow Friendship' ♀ · COtt EBee LIck LRHS MBri SBai SPla WLRN
Yellow King · See *A.* Princess Sophia = 'Stajello'
§ Princess Marie-Louise = 'Zelanon' · SPla SSmt
§ H.R.H. Princess Alexandra = 'Zelblanca' · SSmt

ALTERNANTHERA (Amaranthaceae)
¶ *lehmannii* · NGno

ALTHAEA (Malvaceae)
armeniaca · EEls EMon GBuc NCat
cannabina · CRDP GBri GCal MAvo MFir MHlr MUlv NNor SOkh WCot WHoo WOld WPGP WPen WRus
¶ *ficifolia* 'Golden Eye' · WElm
officinalis · CArn CHan CKin CSev ECoo ELan ELau EWFC GBar GPoy ILis LHol LHop MCLN MChe MGra MHew MMil MPEx MSal NDea NFai SIde SMad WGwy WOak WPer WWye
  – *alba* · EBee LCot MCLN WHer WWhi
§ –'Romney Marsh' · CStr GCal MRav SAxl WCot WSHC
rosea · See *Alcea rosea*
rugosostellulata · See *Alcea rugosa*

ALTINGIA (Hamamelidaceae)
chinensis · CMCN

ALYOGYNE (Malvaceae)
hakeifolia · CSpe ERea
§ *huegelii* · CAbb EDAr EMan LCns LHil LRHS MBEx
  – 'Santa Cruz' · CB&S CSpe EOrc ERea LHop SMad SMrm SOWG SSoC

ALYSSOIDES (Brassicaceae)
utriculata · CHor CMHG CNic EBar ELan LIck NPri NTow WPer WWin
  – var. *graeca* · MSte

ALYSSUM (Brassicaceae)
argenteum hort. · See *A. murale*
caespitosum · NWCA
corymbosum · See *Aurinia corymbosa*
cuneifolium · WAbe
  – var. *pirinicum* · CLyd

gemonense	See *Aurinia petraea*
idaeum	LBee
markgrafii	CLyd LFlo WCot
montanum	CArn ECha EGar ELan GAbr MWat SRms
§ – 'Berggold'	CB&S CTri EMan EPfP GChr GMaP LBee LPVe MLan NPri NRoo SIde WLRN
– Mountain Gold	See *A. montanum* 'Berggold'
§ murale	EGar
oxycarpum	EHyt EPot MFos SBla WAbe
petraeum	See *Aurinia petraea*
pulvinare	WAbe
purpureum	EHyt
pyrenaicum	NMen NWCA
saxatile	See *Aurinia saxatilis*
serpyllifolium	CLyd MOne NWCA WIvy
spinosum	CMea MBro MTho WAbe WFar
§ – 'Roseum' ♀	CMHG ECha EHyt ELan EPot ESis LBee LHop LSpr MPla MWat NMen NRoo NTow NWCA SBla WAbe WPat WPer WWin
stribrnyi	NMen WIvy
tortuosum	CLyd NMen WAbe
wulfenianum	CMHG LIck NTow NWCA

AMANA See TULIPA

× AMARCRINUM (Amaryllidaceae)

memoria-corsii	CFil
– 'Howardii'	CFil

× AMARINE (Amaryllidaceae)

'Fletcheri'	CMon
tubergenii 'Zwanenburg'	CAvo

× AMARYGIA (Amaryllidaceae)

parkeri	CFil NRog
§ – 'Alba'	CAvo NRog

AMARYLLIS (Amaryllidaceae)

§ belladonna	CB&S CBro CFil CHEx CMon CSpe EPar ERav ETub IHos LAma LBow MBri MUlv NRog SDeJ SSpi WCot
– 'Johannesburg'	CAvo EMon ETub NRog
– 'Kimberley'	EMon NRog
– 'Major'	CAvo
– 'Pallida'	See *A. belladonna* 'Elata'
– 'Parkeri Alba'	See *× Amarygia parkeri* 'Alba'
– 'Purpurea'	ETub

AMBROSIA (Asteraceae) See Plant Deletions

AMBROSINA (Araceae)

bassii S&L 315	CMon

AMELANCHIER † (Rosaceae)

alnifolia	CAgr CBlo CPle EPla ESim WWat
¶ – 'Smokey'	CBlo
arborea	WNor
bartramiana	CTho
canadensis	Widely available
– 'Micropetala'	NHol
florida	See *A. alnifolia* var. *semi-integrifolia*
× grandiflora 'Autumn Brilliance'	CEnd MAsh

– 'Ballerina' ♀	CB&S CBlo CDoC CEnd CMCN CPMA CTho ELan ENot ESim LNet LPan MAsh MBri MGos MWat NBee SHBN SPer SPla SSta WDin WHCG WPat WWat WWeb
– 'Robin Hill'	LPan SMad
– 'Rubescens'	CEnd CPMA
laevis	CB&S CBlo CTho MBal NNor SPer
lamarckii ♀	Widely available
¶ lucida	SSta
I ovalis 'Edelweiss'	CBlo CEnd COtt CPMA LRHS SBid SMur
pumila	CBlo CPle GBin GDra GSki LHop MBal MPla MSte NHol NTow SSta WAbe WNor WTin
rotundifolia 'Helvetia'	CEnd MBri
'Snowflake'	CBlo CEnd COtt CPMA LRHS SBid SSta
spicata	CBlo

AMIANTHUM (Melianthaceae)

¶ muscitoxicum	WCot

AMICIA (Papilionaceae)

zygomeris	CAbb CBot CHEx CPle GBuc GCal GCra LHil SBid SMrm SSoC SUsu WEas WWye

AMMI (Apiaceae)

majus	MSal
visnaga	MSal

AMMOBIUM (Asteraceae)

¶ alatum	WBrE

AMMOCHARIS (Amaryllidaceae) See Plant Deletions

AMMOPHILA (Poaceae)

arenaria	GQui

AMOMUM (Zingiberaceae)

cardamomum	See *A. compactum*

AMOMYRTUS (Myrtaceae)

§ luma	CGre CLan CMHG CPle CTrG CTrw EPfP ISea MAll SAPC SArc WBod WPic WWat

AMORPHA (Papilionaceae)

canescens	CB&S CBlo CFai CPle EPfP MCCP MWhi NPSI NRog NSti SBid SEND
fruticosa	CAgr CB&S CPle IOrc NRog SHFr

AMORPHOPHALLUS (Araceae)

bulbifer	LAma WCru WMul
kiusianus	CFil
¶ rivierei	LBlo WMul

AMPELODESMOS (Poaceae)

mauritanicus	EHoe EMan GBin LRHS MCCP NHol WChe WLRN

AMPELOPSIS † (Vitaceae)

aconitifolia	CPlN
arborea	CPlN

bodinieri | CPlN
brevipedunculata | See **A.** *glandulosa* var.
 | *brevipedunculata*
chaffanjonii | CPlN SMur
§ *glandulosa* var. | CB&S GAri SPer WDin
 brevipedunculata | WOMN
¶ – – B&SWJ 1094 | WCru
¶ – – f. *citrulloides* | WCru
 B&SWJ 1173
§ – – 'Elegans' (v) | Widely available
– – 'Tricolor' | See **A.** *glandulosa* var.
 | *brevipedunculata* **'Elegans'**
– var. *hancei* B&SWJ 1793 | WCru
¶ – – B&SWJ 3855 | WCru
– var. *heterophylla* | WCru
 B&SWJ 667
* – var. *maximowiczii* | CPlN
henryana | See *Parthenocissus henryana*
megalophylla | CB&S CBot CGre CHEx CPlN
 | EHal EPfP EPla ETen WBcn
 | WCru WWat
orientalis | CPlN
sempervirens hort. | See *Cissus striata*
sinica | WCru
thunbergii | CPlN
– B&SWJ 1863 | WCru
tricuspidata 'Veitchii' | See *Parthenocissus tricuspidata*
 | **'Veitchii'**

AMPHICOME See INCARVILLEA

AMSONIA (Apocynaceae)
ciliata | CFir ECGN LFis LGre SMrm
 | SSvw SWas WCot WFar WMer
 | WPer
¶ *eastwoodiana* | EBee
illustris | EBee EMon LRHS MSte SMac
¶ *jonesii* | EBee
§ *orientalis* ♥ | CDec CHad CHea CMil CVer
 | ECha EMan EPar ERea LHop
 | MAus MBri MRav SAxl SCro
 | SMrm SWas WFar WLin WOld
 | WRHF WWin
tabernaemontana | CFir CHad CHan CLyd EBar
 | ECGN ECro ELan EMan EMil
 | GBuc MMil MNrw NDov SAga
 | SHel SRms SWas WCot WFar
 | WMer
– var. *salicifolia* | ECha ECro EGar EOrc GSki
 | MSte
¶ *tomentosa* | EBee

AMYGDALUS See PRUNUS

ANACAMPTIS (Orchidaceae)
pyramidalis | SWes

ANACARDIUM (Anacardiaceae)
¶ *occidentale* (F) | LBlo

ANACYCLUS (Asteraceae)
pyrethrum | GPoy
– var. *depressus* | CGle EBrP EBre ELan EMNN
 | EMar ESis GAbr GMaP GTou
 | LBre LHop MHig NGre NMen
 | NNor NVic NWCA SBla SBre
 | SIng WAbe WFar WHoo
 | WOMN WPer WWin
– – 'Golden Gnome' | EBar

ANAGALLIS (Primulaceae)
alternifolia var. *repens* | CLyd SSca
arvensis | EWFC MHew MSal WEas
– var. *caerulea* | EWFC WAlt
foemina | MSal
linifolia | See **A.** *monellii* subsp. *linifolia*
§ *monellii* ♥ | CNic ELan EPot SBla SMrm
 | SRms SUsu WCla WOMN
 | WWin
§ – subsp. *linifolia* | EHyt
– 'Sunrise' | CPBP MHig MTho SUsu
 | WOMN
'Skylover' | EMan
tenella | EWFC NHar
– 'Studland' ♥ | EPot NMen NWCA SBla SIng
 | WAbe WFar WOMN

ANANAS (Bromeliaceae)
comosus var. *variegatus* | MBri

ANAPHALIS (Asteraceae)
alpicola | EPot NCat NMen NTow SGre
margaritacea | ECtt EFou EOld GBin GCHN
 | GMaP MBri MLLN NBro
 | NOak NSti SIde SPar SRms
 | SSca SSpe WBea WByw WFar
§ – var. *cinnamomea* | CGle CHan ECED ELan EMon
 | NHol WEas
§ – 'Neuschnee' | CTri LFis MGed NHol NMir
 | NPri NRoo SPla WBea WMaN
 | WPer WRHF
– New Snow | See **A.** *margaritacea*
 | **'Neuschnee'**
§ – var. *yedoensis* ♥ | CBre CTri EBee ECha ECot
 | EGle EPar MWat NLak SDix
 | SPer WBrE WLRN
nepalensis B&SWJ 1634 | GCra
§ – var. *monocephala* | CGle ELan EMon MAus MWat
 | NSti
nubigena | See **A.** *nepalensis* var.
 | *monocephala*
sinica subsp. *morii* | ECha LBuc
triplinervis ♥ | CBre CGle EAst EFou ELan
 | ENot GCLN GMaP MBrN
 | MLLN MRav MWgw NBro
 | NFla NHol NNor NVic SSpe
 | SWat WByw WEas WFar
 | WHoo WMow WRus WWin
– var. *intermedia* | See **A.** *nepalensis*
§ – 'Sommerschnee' ♥ | CHor EBrP EBre ECha ECot
 | ECtt EHal LBre MBri MCLN
 | MHFP MLLN MTis MWgw
 | NCat NLon NNor SAga SBre
 | SChu SPer WBea WElm WPer
 | WWal
– Summer Snow | See **A.** *triplinervis*
 | **'Sommerschnee'**
yedoensis | See **A.** *margaritacea* var.
 | *yedoensis*

ANARRHINUM (Scrophulariaceae)
bellidifolium | CMdw LIck NCut NPri WPer

ANCHUSA (Boraginaceae)
angustissima | See **A.** *leptophylla* subsp. *incana*
arvensis | EWFC MHew
§ *azurea* | NCut NOrc WPer
– 'Blue Angel' | CBlo EMan EWll
– 'Dropmore' | CBlo CMdw CTri EPfP MWgw
 | NBus NOrc NPer SIde SRms
 | SWat WOve WPer

– 'Feltham Pride' CBot GMaP MLan NPer NRoo WElm WFar WHoo WPer WPyg

¶ – 'Kingfisher Blue' MTPN
– 'Little John' COtt ECot SAga SPer SRms SWat
– 'Loddon Royalist' ♀ CB&S CDoC CGle CHea CSpe EBrP LBre ECED ECGN EFou ELan LBre LHop MAus MAvo MBri MWat MWgw NFla NPri NRoo NSti SBre SChu SPer SWat WHow WOve WRus WWin
– 'Morning Glory' CBlo LFis
– 'Opal' CBlo CGle EBee ECot EFou EMan LHop MMil MWat NRoo SChu SMrm SPla WLRN
– 'Royal Blue' CPou MLan
barrelieri WPer
caespitosa hort. See *A. leptophylla* subsp. *incana*
capensis WPer
cespitosa Lamarck ♀ ELan EPot EWes LHop SBla
italica See *A. azurea*
laxiflora See *Borago pygmaea*
§ *leptophylla* subsp. *incana* CRDP EMFP GBri WCot WRha
myosotidiflora See *Brunnera macrophylla*
officinalis CArn EJud EWFC MHew MSal SIde
sempervirens See *Pentaglottis sempervirens*
undulata SIgm

ANDROCYMBIUM (Colchicaceae)

europaeum MS 510 CMon
gramineum SB&L 26 CMon
punicum S&L 325 CMon
rechingeri CMon

ANDROMEDA (Ericaceae)

glaucophylla CMHG IOrc MBar
polifolia CMHG CSam EBrP EBre EMil EPla IOrc LBre SBre WBod WFar
– 'Alba' EBrP EBre EDen ELan GChr LBre MAsh MBal MBar MBlu MBro MDun MGos MHig MPla NHar SBod SBre SPer WAbe WLin WPat WPyg WWin
– 'Blue Ice' LRHS SSta
– 'Compacta' ♀ CHor EBrP EBre EDen EMil EPot GCHN GCrs LBre MAsh MBal MBar MBri MGos MPla NHar NHol NMen SBre SPer SReu WPat WPyg WSHC WWin
– 'Grandiflora' ELan ITim MAsh MBal MDun MGos SBod
¶ – 'Hayachine' EPot
– 'Kirigamine' ELan MAsh MBal MBri MGos MHig NHar NHol WPat WPyg
– 'Macrophylla' ♀ EPot GCrs GDra ITim MBal MBro MDun MHig NHar NHed NHol SIng SSta WAbe WLin WPat WPyg
– 'Major' MBal
– 'Minima' MBal
– 'Nana' ELan EPot LNet MAsh MGos MHig NMen STre WLRN WStI WWat WWeb
– 'Nikko' CBlo GBuc MAsh MBal MGos MHig NHar NHol WPat WPyg
– 'Red Winter' CBlo CRos

– 'Shibutsu' GAri MGos MPla SSta

ANDROPOGON (Poaceae)

gerardii EBee ECGN EHoe EMon EPPr ESOG GBin LGre LRHS WPer
ischaemum See *Bothriochloa ischaemum*
scoparius See *Schizachyrium scoparium*

ANDROSACE (Primulaceae)

albana CLyd EWes NWCA
armeniaca var. *macrantha* NWCA
¶ *axillaris* ACE 1060 EHyt
barbulata CMea CNic EHyt GCHN
¶ *bulleyana* WLin
¶ – ACE 2198 EHyt EPot
cantabrica EHyt
carnea CLyd GCHN GCrs MTho NHar NMen WCla
– *alba* LBee MBro NGre NHar WLin
– 'Andorra' EHyt WAbe
– subsp. *brigantiaca* CLyd EHyt GTou MBro NGre NHar NMen NRoo NRya NSla WAbe WHoo
– var. *halleri* See *A. carnea* subsp. *rosea*
– subsp. *laggeri* ♀ EPot GCrs GTou NHar NSla WPat
– × *pyrenaica* CGra EHyt EPot GCHN GCrs NHar NMen WAbe WPat
§ – subsp. *rosea* ♀ CPBP GDra NTow NWCA SIng WCla
ciliata CGra GTou NTow WAbe
cylindrica CGra GCHN GCrs GTou NGre NHar NMen SBla WFar
– × *hirtella* GTou NGre NHar NWCA SIng WAbe
delavayi EPot NWCA
geraniifolia ECha GCHN WAbe WCru
¶ – ex CC&McK 109 MRPP
globifera EHyt NHar WAbe
hausmannii GCHN GTou NGre
hedraeantha EPot MWat NGre WAbe
× *heeri* 'Alba' EHyt GCHN GCLN ITim
himalaica EHyt
hirtella CGra CPBP GCHN GTou MRPP NGre NHar NTow WLin
jacquemontii See *A. villosa* var. *jacquemontii*
lactea CNic GCHN GTou NGre
§ *lactiflora* CPea
§ *laevigata* NRya WAbe
– var. *ciliolata* GCrs GTou NWCA SIng
– – NNS 94-38 MRPP
¶ – 'Gothenburg' AM CGra
§ – var. *laevigata* CGra
  'Packwood'
lanuginosa ♀ CLyd CMHG CPBP EHyt ELan EPot GCrs LBee MBro MHig MWat NGre NMen NWCA SBla SDys WAbe WWin
– compact form EPot
– 'Leichtlinii' EHic
– 'Wisley Variety' SIgm
limprichtii See *A. sarmentosa* var. *watkinsii*
¶ × *marpensis* EHyt EPot
mathildae CGra GTou NNrd NTow NWCA
– × *carnea* NMen
microphylla See *A. mucronifolia* Watt
mollis See *A. sarmentosa* var. *yunnanensis*
§ *montana* CGra EHyt MFos NWCA
mucronifolia hort. See *A. sempervivoides*
¶ – Schacht's form EHyt

¶ – SEP 284 — EHyt
§ *mucronifolia* Watt — EPot GTou ITim NGre
– CHP&W 296 — NWCA
– × *sempervivoides* — EHyt EPot MRPP
muscoidea — EPot MRPP NWCA WAbe
– C&R 188 — GTou
– f. *longiscapa* — NWCA
– Schacht's form — CGra CPBP EHyt
– SEP 132 — EHyt
§ *nivalis* — MFos NTow
♦ *primuloides* Duby — See *A. studiosorum*
primuloides hort. — See *A. sarmentosa*
¶ – white form — WAbe
pubescens — EPot GCHN SBla SIng WAbe
pyrenaica — EHyt GCHN GTou ITim NGre NHar NTow SBla WAbe
rigida ACE 2336 — EPot
– KGB 168 — EPot
¶ *robusta* — EHyt
– var. *breviscapa* — NWCA
rotundifolia — GCHN GTou WCru
salicifolia — See *A. lactiflora*
§ *sarmentosa* ♀ — EHyt ELan GTou ITim LBee MBro MFir MHig MWat NGre NMen NNrd SOkh SSmi WAbe WCla WEas WHoo WPyg
– CC 407 — MRPP
– 'Chumbyi' — ESis MBro MOne MRPP NHol NTow NWCA SBla SIng SRms WHil WPat WPer
§ – 'Salmon's Variety' — CMea CTri SIgm
– 'Sherriff's' — CFee CMHG CTri GCHN GCrs MBro NHar NTow SBla SIgm SIng SRms WLin
§ – var. *watkinsii* — EPot MBro NHar NHol NMen NNrd WLin
§ – var. *yunnanensis* — CPBP MBro SIgm SIng
§ *sempervivoides* ♀ — CHea CLyd ECha EHyt ELan EPot GCHN GCrs GDra LBee MBro MHig NGre NHar NHed NHol NMen NWCA SBod SIgm SIng WAbe WHil WHoo WLin WOMN WPat WPyg WWin
– scented form — MBro
¶ – 'Susan Jane' — WAbe
sericea — NWCA
¶ sp. CD&R 2477 — WCru
§ *studiosorum* — GCHN NCat
* – *album* — EHyt
¶ – 'Doksa' — EPot
¶ *tapete* — WAbe
¶ – ACE 1725 — EPot
vandellii — CGra EHyt GBin GCHN GTou NGre NWCA WAbe
villosa — MHig WAbe
¶ – var. *arachnoidea* — WLin
– – 'Superba' — NMen
§ – var. *jacquemontii* — EHyt NHar NMen NTow SBla SIgm
– – lilac form — EPot
– – pink — EPot
– subsp. *taurica* — CLyd EHyt EPot
¶ – var. *taurica* — MRPP
'Palandoken'
vitaliana — See *Vitaliana primuliflora*
watkinsii — See *A. sarmentosa* var. *watkinsii*
yargongensis ACE 1722 — EPot

ANDRYALA (Asteraceae)
agardhii — NMen NNrd NTow NWCA SSca WPat
lanata — See *Hieracium lanatum*

ANEMARRHENA (Asphodelaceae)
asphodeloides — EBee MSal WCot

ANEMIA (Schizaeaceae)
phyllitidis — NMar

ANEMONE † (Ranunculaceae)
altaica — MSal SRms
'Andrea Atkinson' — EBee EGar MBro NPri NSti SChu WHoo WLRN
apennina ♀ — CLAP EPar SCro SWas WTin
– var. *albiflora* — ERos
¶ – double form — SWas
– 'Petrovac' CE&H 538 — EPot
baicalensis — EHic NSti
baldensis — CGle LBee LHop NMen NOak SRms WOMN
biarmiensis — See *A. narcissiflora* subsp. *biarmiensis*
blanda ♀ — EOrc LAma LHop MBri MBro MCLN MHig NChi NFla NRog SChu WCot WFar WPat WPer
– blue — CAvo CBro CMea CTri ELan EMar EPfP EPot ETub GAbr LAma MBri MBro MHlr MNFA NRoo SRms WPat
¶ – 'Blue Shades' — WPGP
– 'Charmer' — EBar EPar EPot GBur NMen NNrd WPat
– 'Ingramii' ♀ — EMan EPar LAma MBal MBro NRog WPat WRHF
– 'Pink Star' — CBro EBar EPot LAma NBir NRog
– 'Radar' ♀ — CBro CLAP EPar EPot LAma MNrw NBir NRog
– var. *rosea* ♀ — CAvo ELan LAma MLLN WPer
– 'Violet Star' — CBro EPot MNFA
– 'White Splendour' ♀ — CAvo CBro CGle CMea ECha ELan EMar EOrc EPar EPot ETub GAbr LAma LFis MBro MCLN MNFA MNrw NChi NMen NRog SChu WHil WPGP WPat WPer WRus
'Bodnant Burgundy' — LRHS
canadensis — CElw CNic CSpe ECGP MNrw NWoo WCot WElm WSan
caroliniana — CGle EBrP EBre EPot ESis GBuc GCrs LBre NOak NRoo SBre
coronaria — EPot
– De Caen Group — CSut GBur LAma WFar
§ – – 'Die Braut' — CGle MNrw NRog
– – forms — NRog
– – 'His Excellency' — See *A. coronaria* (De Caen Group) 'Hollandia'
§ – – 'Hollandia' — EPot ETub GBur SAga SUsu
– – 'Mister Fokker' — EPot ETub LAma NRog
– – The Bride — See *A. coronaria* (De Caen Group) 'Die Braut'
– – 'The Governor' — GBur GSki NCat NRog SAga
– (Mona Lisa Group) 'Sylphide' — EPot MGed MNrw NRog WCot
– MS 783 — CMon
– MS&CL 613 — CMon
– Saint Brigid Group (d) — ETub LAma MBri NRog SDeJ
– – 'Lord Lieutenant' (d) — GBur NBir NOak NRog SUsu
– – 'Mount Everest' (d) — NBir SUsu WCot
– – 'The Admiral' (d) — ETub MNrw NBir NCat NRog
– Saint Piran Group — SDeJ
crinita — NChi SMrm WLin

cylindrica	CFir CGle CMHG CSWP EMon MNrw
decapetala	GCal
drummondii	CHar MCli NPri WCla
elongata B&SWJ 2975	WCru
fasciculata	See *A. narcissiflora*
flaccida	CBro CRDP LGre LHop SIng WCot WCru WFar
× *fulgens*	ECha NWCA
– 'Annulata Grandiflora'	CMon
– 'Multipetala'	NRog
– Saint Bavo Group	CBro ECGP
globosa	See *A. multifida*
'Guernica'	GBuc
hepatica	See *Hepatica nobilis*
§ *hortensis*	CMon SBla SMad WCot WWat
– *alba*	CMon
– subsp. *heldreichii*	WIvy WThi
– MS 958	CMon
§ *hupehensis*	CBlo CBot LFis NOrc WCot WLin
§ – 'Bowles' Pink'	CBlo CMil CRDP LGan MBri MBro MWat SAxl SSca SWas WCot WCru WHoo WPGP
– 'Crispa'	CAvo CBos CRDP EBee NHol NSti WPbr
– 'Eugenie'	CGle CMil NHol
– 'Hadspen Abundance' ♀	Widely available
§ – var. *japonica*	CBos CGle CPou EAst EGar GCal NNor NPla SPer SSpi WCru WEas
§ – – 'Bressingham Glow'	CMHG EBrP EBre ECtt ELan EOrc EPot LBre LHop MBri MLLN MNFA MRav NHol NOrc NRoo NVic SBre SPer SUsu WAbb WFar WOld WWal
– – Prince Henry	See *A. hupehensis* var. *japonica* 'Prinz Heinrich'
§ – – 'Prinz Heinrich' ♀	CAvo CB&S CHad CMil EBar ECha EOld EPfP LGre LHop MAus MAvo MBel MBri MCLN MRav MTis NCut NHol NRoo SAxl SPer SPla SSpi WFar WHal WHoo WOld
– 'Praecox'	CMea EBar EFou EGol GBri LHop MBri MCLN NHol NRoo NSti SChu SCro SLod WAbb WCru WHal WHow WWal WWin
– 'Rosenschale'	GCal MBal MBri NRoo WFar
– 'September Charm' ♀	CB&S CDoC ECha EFou ELan EOrc EPfP LHop MAus MBel MBri MNFA MNrw MWgw NLar NOak NSti NTow SPer SSoC SWat WCru WPyg WWal
– 'Splendens'	CBlo EAst EBee EFou EMan LSyl MBri NCut NPla WAbb WBro WFar WHal WPyg WRHF
§ × *hybrida*	CAvo CBos CGle IHos MBro NOak SChu SPla WCru WFar WHil WHoo WOld WRHF
– 'Alba' hort. (UK)	See *A.* × *hybrida* 'Honorine Jobert'
– 'Alba' hort. (USA)	See *A.* × *hybrida* 'Lady Ardilaun'
– 'Bowles' Pink'	See *A. hupehensis* 'Bowles' Pink'
– 'Bressingham Glow'	See *A. hupehensis* var. *japonica* 'Bressingham Glow'
– 'Coupe d'Argent'	EGar NRoo
– 'Elegans'	EFou EGar LBuc MRav SWat
§ – 'Géante des Blanches' ♀	CBlo CLon ECtt EGar GCal GMac MBro NRoo WHoo WHow
§ – 'Honorine Jobert' ♀	Widely available
§ – 'Königin Charlotte' ♀	Widely available
– 'Kriemhilde'	GCal
– 'Lady Gilmour'	See *A.* × *hybrida* 'Margarete'
– 'Loreley'	CBlo CMea EBar GCal MWat NTow SPer WCot
– 'Luise Uhink'	CBlo CDoC CGle CHor CPou NBir SSpi WEas
§ – 'Margarete'	CBlo CBos CDec CPou ECtt EGol EHol MWat NBir SChu SCro SLod WHoo
– 'Max Vogel'	MTed SDys WBcn WCot
– 'Monterosa'	CGle CMil CPou CSpe EBrP EBre ELan EWes GCal LBre MBal NBir NCut SBre WCot WCru WKif
– 'Pamina'	Widely available
– Prince Henry	See *A. hupehensis* var. *japonica* 'Prinz Heinrich'
– 'Prinz Heinrich'	See *A. hupehensis* var. *japonica* 'Prinz Heinrich'
– 'Profusion'	MHlr NCut SHBN WCot WOld WPyg WRus
– Queen Charlotte	See *A.* × *hybrida* 'Königin Charlotte'
– 'Richard Ahrends'	CBos EBee EGle EGol EMan LHop MAus MBel MBri MMil MNFA NCat NHol NOrc NRoo SAxl SCro SMad SMrm SSpe SWas SWat WAbe WCru WHow WWal
– 'Rosenschale'	CBos MBri WCru WOld
– 'Rotkäppchen'	CLon GCal LBuc NBrk SAxl
¶ – 'Serenade'	EBee EFou MBri
§ – 'Superba'	SBla WKif
◆ – 'Tourbillon'	See *A.* × *hybrida* 'Whirlwind'
– 'Whirlwind'	Widely available
– 'White Queen'	See *A.* × *hybrida* 'Géante des Blanches'
– Wirbelwind	See *A.* × *hybrida* 'Whirlwind'
japonica	See *A.* × *hybrida*
¶ – 'Bressingham Spire'	WHow
× *lesseri*	CGle CLyd CNic ECha ELan EPri GCrs GMac LHop MBri MBro NNrd NSti NWoo SBla SPer WAbe WCru WHoo WPat WWin
leveillei	CBos CRDP ELan MFir MHar SIgm WCot WCru WSan
§ × *lipsiensis*	CAvo CBos CBro CHad CLon CRDP ECha EHyt EPar EPot GCHN LGre MHig MNFA MRav MTho NTow NWCA SSvw SUsu SWas WAbe WCru WHal WLin
– 'Pallida'	CRDP MNFA SSvw WAbe WCot WRus
N *magellanica* hort.	See *A. multifida*
§ *multifida*	Widely available
– var. *globosa*	WWhi
– 'Major'	CFir CLyd CMGP CNic CRDP LGan MBro NHol NWCA SBla EBee
¶ – f. *polysepala*	EBee
– red	CFir NLon NNor NRoo NSla WHil
§ *narcissiflora*	EMFP GSki LSyl NHar WCot
¶ – *citrina*	LBuc
¶ *nemerosa* 'Flore Pleno Blue Eyes'	IBlr

nemorosa ♀	CAvo CBro CElw CGle CKin EPar EPot ETub EWFC LAma LBow LGan LSyl MBal MSal NHar NHol SIng SSpi WFar WHil WMer WShi	– 'Wilks' White'	CLAP EBee EGle EPar EPot MBal
		– 'Wyatt's Pink'	CAvo CLAP LGre WAbe
N– 'Alba Plena' (d)	CAvo CBos CBro CHea CSWP ECha EPot ERos ETub GMac MHig MTho NMGW NTow SIng SUsu WAbb WCru WEas WRus	*obtusiloba*	CRDP GCrs GDra GTou MTho NHar SBla WAbe
		– *alba*	CRDP GDra LSyl NHar NHol NMen SBla WAbe
		palmata	EBee NSla WCru
– 'Allenii' ♀	CBro CHea CLAP ECha EHyt EPot ERos LGre LSyl MBal MNFA MRav NHar NMen NRya NTow SIng SSpi SWas WAbe WCot WCru WLin WPGP	– 'Alba'	CMon
		– MS 413	CMon
		parviflora	CHea EHal
		patens	See *Pulsatilla patens*
		pavonina	ERos MTho SSca SWas
		polyanthes	EBee GTou WThi
– 'Amy Doncaster'	WCot	*pulsatilla*	See *Pulsatilla vulgaris*
– 'Atrocaerulea'	EPar EPot GBuc IBlr MNFA NHol	*ranunculoides* ♀	CAvo CBro CElw CMHG CMon CRDP EHyt EPar EPot ERos ETub LAma MHig MNFA MTho NHar NHol NMen NRya NSti NTow SIng SSpi SUsu SWas WCru WEas WOMN
– 'Blue Beauty'	CLAP EPot GBuc IBlr MBal NHol NMen WAbe WCru		
– 'Blue Bonnet'	CElw GBuc WCot		
¶ – 'Blue Eyes'	CLAP CRDP EGle SUsu	– 'Pleniflora' (d)	CAvo CHea CLAP CRDP ECha EPar EPot MHlr WCot
– 'Blue Queen'	EPot		WIvy
– 'Bowles' Purple'	EPar EPot IBlr NHar NRya NTow WAbe WCot WCru WFar WIvy	¶ *riparia*	MHar
		rivularis	CAvo CBro CElw CGle CHan CHea ECha EMon EPot GCrs GMac LBee LHop LSyl MBro MNrw NChi NHar NNor NOak NRoo NSti SAxl SSpi SUsu WAbe WHoo WKif WOld WThi
– 'Bracteata Pleniflora' (d)	ECha EPot GBuc IBlr LHop MBal MBro NWoo WAbe		
¶ – 'Buckland'	IBlr		
– 'Caerulea'	EPot		
– 'Cedric's Pink'	EGle IBlr		
♦ – 'Currey's Pink'	See *A. nemorosa* 'Lismore Pink'	– CLD 573	WLin
– 'Danica'	MBal WAbe	*rupicola*	GCra MHar NBir
– 'Dee Day'	CLAP GBuc SWas WAbe	× *seemannii*	See *A.* × *lipsiensis*
– 'Flore Pleno' (d)	EBrP EBre EHic EHyt EOrc EPar LBre MBal MBro SBre WAbe WMaN WPGP	¶ sp.from China PLW12/93	WCot
		stellata	See *A. hortensis*
– forms	CMon	*sulphurea*	See *Pulsatilla alpina* subsp. *apiifolia*
– 'Green Fingers'	EPot GBuc LGre MTho WCru		
– 'Hannah Gubbay'	CLAP CRDP EBee EPar IBlr MBal WAbe	*sylvestris*	CGle CHan CNic CSpe EBrP EBre ECha GAbr LBre LFis LGan MBri MHew MNFA MSal NBir NOrc NRoo NSti NWoo SBre SPer WAbb WBea WHal WHil WOMN WRus WWin
– 'Hilda'	CLAP EPar EPot GBuc MBal NRya NTow WAbe		
– 'Knightshayes Vestal' (d)	MRav WCot WIvy		
– 'Lady Doneraile'	CLAP ECha NTow		
– 'Leeds' Variety' ♀	CRDP EGle EPot LGre MTho NHar NHol	§ – 'Elise Fellmann' (d)	CLAP CRDP WCot
		– 'Flore Pleno'	See *A. sylvestris* 'Elise Fellmann'
– 'Lychette'	CAvo EGle EPar EPot IBlr LGre MBal NTow WAbe	– 'Macrantha'	CLAP CRDP CSpe EBee MHlr SAga SWas
– 'Monstrosa'	EBee EPar EPot WCot	*tetrasepala*	GCra SSca
¶ – 'Parlez Vous'	SWas	§ *tomentosa*	CGle CMGP ECha EOld GMac NHol NRoo SCro SMrm SRms SWat WBea WCot WEas WGwG WRha WWal WWhi
– 'Pentre Pink'	EGle IBlr MTho WAbe WIvy		
– pink	LGre		
– × *ranunculoides*	See *A.* × *lipsiensis*		
– 'Robinsoniana' ♀	Widely available	– 'Robustissima'	CBos CDoC CGle EFou EGra EHic ENot LHop MBri MRav MTis MWgw NSti SHBN SPer SPla WAbb WMer
– 'Rosea'	CGle EPot LAma NHol		
– 'Royal Blue'	CBos CLAP CNic CRDP ECha EPot GBuc LAma NHol WAbe WCru WFar WTin		
		¶ – 'Serenade'	NBir NHol
		trifolia	CRDP ECha EPot ERos MBal NMen SUsu
– 'Vestal' ♀	CElw CGle CLAP CRDP EBrP EBre EHyt EPot ERos GBuc IBlr LBre LGre MNFA NFla NMGW NMen NRya SBre WBon	*trullifolia*	CRDP GCrs NHar SBla
		– *alba*	GTou WAbe
		– blue form	GTou
		– SBEC 797	NTow
– 'Virescens'	CHan SWas WAbe WIvy	*vernalis*	See *Pulsatilla vernalis*
– 'Viridiflora'	CBos CMil CRDP LGre MBri MRav MTho WBon WCot WCru	*virginiana*	CFir EBee EHal GBin MSte NChi WCot
		§ *vitifolia* De Candolle	CBos
– 'Wilks' Giant'	WCot	* – B&SWJ 1452	WCru

– B&SWJ 2320	WCru
– CC&McK 43	CGle
vitifolia hort.	See *A. tomentosa*

ANEMONELLA (Ranunculaceae)

thalictroides	CFir CGra CLAP CRDP CSpe EBee EFEx EPar LAma NHar NMen NTow SBla SWas WAbe WFar WIvy WLin
thalictroides 'Alba Plena' (d)	NHar
¶ – 'Amelia'	GCrs
¶ – 'Betty Blake'	GCrs
– 'Cameo'	EFEx GCrs MFos MS&S
– 'Double Green'	EFEx
– double pink (d)	NHar
– 'Full Double White'	EFEx
– 'Green Hurricane'	EFEx
– 'Oscar Schoaf' (d)	NHar
– pink	CLAP CRDP EHyt GBuc
– semi-double white (d)	CLAP CRDP EHyt NRya SBla WIvy

ANEMONOPSIS (Ranunculaceae)

macrophylla	CBro CMdw CPou CRDP ECha GCra ITim LGre MNrw MTho NTow SBla SHel WCot WCru WEas WOMN WOld

ANEMOPAEGMA (Bignoniaceae)

chamberlaynii	CPlN

ANEMOPSIS (Saururaceae)

californica	CRDP

ANETHUM (Apiaceae)

graveolens	CArn EOHP GPoy LHol MChe MGra MHew MMal SIde WCer WPer WSel WWye
– 'Dukat'	CJew CSev ELau GPoy MChe WShe
– 'Fern Leaved'	CBod WJek
– 'Sowa'	EOHP

ANGELICA (Apiaceae)

acutiloba	SIgm
¶ – JCA via P.Kelaidis	IDac
archangelica	CArn CGle CHid CSev ECha EEls EFou ELan ELau EMar GAbr GPoy LHol MBri MChe MGra MHew NBro NFai SChu SIde SWat WOak WOve WPer WWye
– 'Corinne Tremaine'	WHer
atropurpurea	CBot EBee EGar EWll LGre MLLN MNrw MSal NLar SWat WCHb
curtisii	See *A. triquinata*
gigas	Widely available
* *hispanica*	LLew WSan
montana	See *A. sylvestris*
pachycarpa	CRDP SDix SIgm SWat WCot
¶ *saxatilis*	EBee
§ *sylvestris*	CAgr CArn CKin EWFC GBar LHol MSal SWat WGwy WHer
* – 'Purpurea'	CBos CMea LHol SApp
taiwaniana	LHol SWat
'Vicar's Mead'	IBlr

ANGELONIA (Scrophulariaceae)

¶ *gardneri*	CSpe

¶ sp.	LHil
¶ 'Stella Gem'	LRHS

ANIGOZANTHOS (Haemodoraceae)

'Bushranger'	CB&S
flavidus	CB&S CHan EOHP MBri SOWG WCot
– red	SSoC
– yellow	LHil WBrE
humilis ♀	MSto
manglesii ♀	CTrC MLan WBrE WPer
– 'Bush Dawn'	CB&S

ANISACANTHUS (Acanthaceae)

¶ *wrightii*	EBee

ANISODONTEA (Malvaceae)

§ *capensis*	CB&S CBar EBar ELan ERea IBlr LHil LHop MAsh MBEx NBir NBrk SChu SMrm SOWG SVen WBod WEas
elegans	CSpe LHil
huegelii	See *Alyogyne huegelii*
x *hypomadara* hort.	See *A. capensis*
§ – (Sprague) Bates	CMHG CSev ECtt LBlm LPan NPer SEas SMad SRms WOMN WPer WRus
julii	LHil MCCP SMad WSan
malvastroides	CSev LHil LHop MBEx
scabrosa	CAbb CChe EMil SAga SBid

ANISOTOME (Apiaceae)

¶ *cauticola*	ITim WLin
haastii	SIgm
imbricata	GDra
¶ *pilifera*	WLin

ANNONA (Annonaceae)

¶ *cherimola*	CTrG
muricata (F)	LBlo
squamosa (F)	LBlo

ANODA (Malvaceae)

cristata 'Opal Cup'	EBar EMon

ANOIGANTHUS See CYRTANTHUS

ANOMATHECA (Iridaceae)

cruenta	See *A. laxa*
§ *laxa*	CInt CMHG CSpe CVer ECha ELan EPot ERos ETub GBur LBee LGre MNrw MTho NMen SDix SHel SSca SSpi WAbe WCla WFar WHil WOMN WPat WPer WWin
– var. *alba*	CSpe ELan EPot ERos LBee LBlm LGre MHar MTho NMen SSpi WAbe WHoo WOMN WWeb
– alba-maculata	CMHG CPea
– 'Joan Evans'	CElw EPot ERos SRms WAbe
– redspot	SSpi
viridis	CAvo CMon CPou LBow MNrw NMGW

ANOPTERUS (Escalloniaceae)

glandulosus	CHEx IBlr WCru

ANREDERA (Basellaceae)

§ *cordifolia*	CPlN LBow WCot WPer

ANTENNARIA (Asteraceae)

aprica	See *A. parvifolia*
dioica	CTri ECro ELan GCHN GPoy LHol MBro NBus SRms WCla WFar WPyg WWye
– 'Alba'	EHoe GAbr NRya WFar
– 'Alex Duguid'	GCrs LBee SBla
– 'Aprica'	See *A. parvifolia*
§ – var. *hyperborea*	LGro SSmi WAbe
– 'Minima'	EPot GCrs GDra MBro MHig MPla MWat NBro NHar NMen NNrd SIng WAbe
– 'Nyewoods Variety'	CNic EPot GDra MHig NTow
– red	SIng WLin
– var. *rosea*	See *A. microphylla*
* – 'Rubra'	CTri ECha EPPr GAri GLil MBro NMen NNrd SBla SHel SSmi WAbe WHen
– *tomentosa*	See *A. dioica* var. *hyperborea*
macrophylla hort.	See *A. microphylla*
§ *microphylla*	CMHG EHoe ELan EMNN ESis LGro MBar NHar NMen NRya NWCA SBod SDys SIng SRms SSmi WBea WEas WPat WPer
– 'Plena' (d)	SRms
neglecta var. *gaspensis*	SIng
§ *parvifolia*	CLyd CNic CTri ESis GCHN GDra LFis MBar MPla NHar SBod SIng WAbe WCla WPer WWin
– var. *rosea*	See *A. microphylla*
plantaginifolia	WCot
rosea ⚲	NVic

ANTHEMIS (Asteraceae)

aizoon	See *Achillea ageratifolia* subsp. *aizoon*
biebersteinii	See *A. marschalliana*
§ Susanna Mitchell = 'Blomit'	EBrP EBre LBre MArl NHaw SAga SBre
carpatica	CGle GCHN NBro NWoo SIgm
– 'Karpatenschnee'	MCli
cretica	CBlo
– subsp. *cretica* NS 754	NWCA
'Eva'	LGan NDov WEas WOld
frutescens	See *Argyranthemum frutescens*
N'Grallagh Gold'	CGle CHea CLon CMil EBee ECha EGar EMon EOrc EWes LHop MBri MWat NCat NFla NHol NPer SMrm WBea WEas WFar WMer WOld
§ *marschalliana*	ECha EPot ESis LBee NOak SSmi WAbe WPer
¶ – subsp. *biebersteiniana*	CHea
montana	See *A. cretica* subsp. *cretica*
nobilis	See *Chamaemelum nobile*
N'Pride of Grallagh'	GCal GCra GMac LFis MAvo MHlr NCat NRoo SHel WCot WMow
punctata subsp. *cupaniana* ⚲	CArn CB&S CGle CHad CMea ECha EFou ELan ESis GCHN LGre LHol LHop NBro NEgg NFai NHol NNor NPer NSti SAxl SDix SPer WAbe WEas WFar WMaN WOld WWin NPer
– – 'Nana'	NPer
rudolphiana	See *A. marschalliana*
¶ *sachokiana*	EBee WLin
sancti-johannis	CGle EGar EMar EMon GCra MBri MGed NOak NPer NVic SMad SPer WBea WPer

◆ Susanna Mitchell	See *A.* Susanna Mitchell = 'Blomit'
'Tetworth'	CStr EBee ECha ELan EMar EMon EPPr GBuc LHop MAvo MCLN MHlr MMil MSte NLak SChu WFar WMaN
tinctoria	CArn CGle ECED ELan ELau EMon EWFC GMac GPoy LHol MChe MGra MHew NEgg NLon NNor NPer SIde WAbe WBea WByw WJek WOak WWin WWye
– 'Alba'	CGle EAst EBee ECGN ECha EMar EMon ERic GCal LFis LGre MAvo NRoo NWoo SChu SHar WAbe WFar WHen WLRN WPer
* – 'Compacta'	EFou EWes SMrm
¶ – dwarf form	LRHS SUsu
– 'E.C. Buxton'	Widely available
◆ – 'Grallagh Gold'	See *A.* 'Grallagh Gold'
– 'Kelwayi'	CGle CHor EAst EBar ECtt EMar GCHN MCLN MTis NBro NChi NFai NPer SHel SPer SPla WBea WHen WOve WPer
¶ – 'Lemon Maid'	SChu
◆ – 'Pride of Grallagh'	See *A.* 'Pride of Grallagh'
– 'Sauce Hollandaise'	Widely available
– 'Wargrave Variety'	Widely available
triumfettii	NPer
tuberculata	NChi NRoo SBla SIng

ANTHERICUM (Anthericaceae)

algeriense	See *A. liliago* var. *major*
baeticum	CMon EBee ERos
* *bovei*	ERos SSpi
liliago	CBro CFil CGle CRDP EBrP EBre ECED ELan EMan EPot ERos ESis GCal GDra LBee LBre LGan LHop MCli MLLN MSte MTis NLak NRoo NTow SBre WCla WHow WPGP WPer
§ – var. *major* ⚲	CAvo ECha GDra IBlr LGre MWgw WCot
ramosum	CAvo CMon EBee ECGN ECha ELan EPot ERos EWes GBin GDra LGre MBro MLLN NBir NWCA SHel SMrm SWas WAbe WCla WPbr WPer
– JCA 166.300	CAvo WLin
– *plumosum*	See *Trichopetalum plumosum*

ANTHOCERCIS (Solanaceae)

¶ *littorea*	MFiF

ANTHOLYZA (Iridaceae)

coccinea	See *Crocosmia paniculata*
crocosmioides	See *Crocosmia latifolia*
paniculata	See *Crocosmia paniculata*

ANTHOXANTHUM (Poaceae)

odoratum	CArn CJew CKin GBar GBin GPoy

ANTHRISCUS (Apiaceae)

cerefolium	CArn CJew CSev EOHP GPoy ILis LHol MChe MGra MHew MMal SIde WGwG WJek WOak WPer WSel WWye

¶ *cerefolium* 'D'Hiver de   EOHP
   Bruxelles'
sylvestris 'Hullavington'   CNat
   (v)
– 'Moonlit Night'   EHoe
– 'Ravenswing'   CElw CGle CHad CHea ECoo
   EMar EMon GBri GCal LBlm
   LGre LRHS MBri MNrw MRav
   MSCN MUlv NBir NPer NSti
   SMad SUsu WByw WCHb
   WCot WEas WFar WPbr

ANTHURIUM (Araceae)

amazonicum   MBri
andraeanum   MBri
– 'Acropolis'   MBri
– 'Rose'   See *A.* × *ferrierense* 'Roseum'
cordatum   See *A. leuconeurum*
'Flamingo'   MBri
scherzerianum   MBri
– 'Rosemarie'   MBri

ANTHYLLIS (Papilionaceae)

¶ *cytisoides*   MAll
hermanniae   CHan CMHG MAll WAbe
   WFar
– 'Compacta'   See *A. hermanniae* 'Minor'
§ – 'Minor'   EPot LBee NMen NSla
montana   ELan
– subsp. *atropurpurea*   LRHS
– 'Rubra' ♀   CInt ECho EGle EPot LBee
   NMen NNor WWin
vulneraria   CFee CGen CKin EWFC GTou
   MChe MHew MWat NMir NPri
   SSpi SUsu WBea WCla WHer
   WPer
– var. *coccinea*   CLyd CMHG CNic CSpe EGar
   MBro MNrw MSte MSto MTho
   NGre NSla NTow NWCA SUsu
   WAbe WHil
– var. *iberica*   CHan
* – 'Peach'   CSpe

ANTIGONON (Polygonaceae)

leptopus   CPlN LChe
– 'Album'   CPlN

ANTIRRHINUM (Scrophulariaceae)

asarina   See *Asarina procumbens*
braun-blanquetii   CNic CPea ECro ELan EMan
   EMar GGar LRot MAus MLLN
   MOne SAga WWin
¶ 'Bridesmaid'   MBEx
¶ 'Deep Pink'   MBEx
glutinosum   See *A. hispanicum* subsp.
   hispanicum
§ *hispanicum*   CGle EBee NBir SBla WCla
   WPen
– 'Avalanche'   CHal EMan MBEx MLan SCoo
   WLRN
§ – subsp. *hispanicum*   CMea CSam CSpe CVer EDAr
   roseum   ELan NTow WKif WOld
majus 'Black Prince'   CHad MRav SAga
– subsp. *linkianum*   ECro LHop MSto WOMN
   WOld
– subsp. *majus*   SSpi
– 'Taff's White' (v)   CPou CSpe EHol LGre MTho
   SAga WLRN WRus

molle   CHan CSpe EHyt ELan EOrc
   GCal MSte MTho NBir NPer
   NWCA SUsu WCru WHoo
   WOMN WPyg
– pink   CLyd CSWP EMar EOrc GCal
   MSte MTho SOkh WCru
'Powys Pride' (v)   CSpe MHlr SAga WElm WHer
   WSan
pulverulentum   CSam ESis LGre LHop MArl
   MSto WKif
sempervirens   ESis MSto SOkh WOMN WPat
siculum   MSto
¶ 'Starlight'   MBEx
¶ 'Sugar Buttons'   MBEx
¶ 'Summer Eyes'   MBEx

APHANES (Rosaceae)

§ *arvensis*   MSal NHex WWye

APHELANDRA (Acanthaceae)

squarrosa   CHal MBri
– 'Dania' (v)   MBri

APHYLLANTHES (Aphyllanthaceae)

monspeliensis   CFee SBla

APIOS (Papilionaceae)

§ *americana*   CHan CPlN EMon WCru
   WSHC
tuberosa   See *A. americana*

APIUM (Apiaceae)

graveolens   CArn CBod EJud ELau EOHP
   EWFC GPoy IIve MSal SIde
   WJek

APOCYNUM (Apocynaceae)

androsaemifolium   MSal
cannabinum   CArn GPoy MSal WWye

APONOGETON (Aponogetonaceae)

distachyos   CBen CHEx CRDP CRow
   CWat EHon ELan EMFW
   LPBA MBal MSta NDea SWat
   SWyc WChe WWeb
krausseanus   See *A. desertorum*

APTENIA (Aizoaceae)

cordifolia   CHEx CSev NPer SHFr
– 'Variegata'   LHil MRav SHFr

AQUILEGIA † (Ranunculaceae)

akitensis hort.   See *A. flabellata* var. *pumila*
* *alba variegata*   WEas
alpina   CBot CMea ECtt ELan ELau
   GAbr GCHN GTou LSyl MAus
   MLan MSCN NNor SHel SPer
   WCla WFar WHen WOve WPer
   WSan WStI WWin
– 'Alba'   CBlo ELan MLLN NOak
– 'Hensol Harebell'   See *A.* 'Hensol Harebell'
'Alpine Blue'   SIde
amaliae   See *A. ottonis* subsp. *amaliae*
* *anemoniflora*   NEgg
aragonensis   See *A. pyrenaica*
§ *atrata*   CGle CMea CPou EMan GCHN
   GSki LHop MHig NOak WHal
   WPer
¶ *atrovinosa*   LLew
aurea   CLTr MSto NChi

baicalensis	See *A. vulgaris* **Baicalensis Group**
'Ballerina'	CMil EBee MLLN NCut NFai WHer WSan
barnebyi	CMea CMil CPou GAbr GBin GCra MLLN NSti NWCA SIgm WSan
bernardii	NOak
bertolonii ♀	CFee CGle EHyt EMNN EPot GCrs GTou LHop MBro NHar NMen NNrd NOak NRoo SBla SRms SSmi WHoo WLin WPat WPyg
– *alba*	EWes NWCA
Biedermeier Group	CM&M EBar GAbr LPVe NOrc WPer
'Blue Berry'	CLyd MBro NHar WLin WOMN WPat
'Blue Bonnet'	CMGP MTis
¶ 'Blue Jay' (Songbird Series)	CFai NPri
¶ 'Blue Jewel'	SVil
§ 'Blue Star' (Star Series)	ECtt EFou GCHN GCal WPer
brevicalcarata	CMil EBee NPri
buergeriana	CLTr CPou EBee GAbr GBin GCra WBea WPer
– f. *flavescens*	NLak
– var. *oxysepala*	See *A. oxysepala*
caerulea ♀	CGle EMan GAbr GCHN GDra NCat SIgm SRms WPen
– 'Mrs Nicholls'	EPar MBri WMer
– var. *ochroleuca*	GCHN
canadensis ♀	CChr CGle EBar ECGN ELan GSki MBal MLLN NBir NBro NGre NOak WBea WOMN WOve WPer
– 'Corbett'	GBuc
– 'Nana'	CInt CSam EPot GAri MHar MSte MSto
¶ 'Cardinal' (Songbird Series)	CFai NPri
cazorlensis	See *A. pyrenaica* subsp. *cazorlensis*
'Celestial Blue'	ELan
chaplinei	NGre
chrysantha	CChr CHea EBrP EBre ECGN GBin GCHN GCra LBre LFis MHlr MLLN NBus NHar NOak NPri SBla SBre SChu SPla SRms WBea WBrE WCot WCru WOve WPbr WPer WRus WWeb
– var. *chaplinei*	CBot NBir
– 'Yellow Queen'	CHid EFou EPfP MAvo WElm WHil
clematiflora	See *A. vulgaris* var. *stellata*
¶ 'Cream Edge'	NBir
'Crimson Star'	CBlo CHea CLTr EBrP EBre EOld EPfP LBre MLLN NBus NPla SBre SPer SVil
desertorum	ESis NHar NHol NTow
discolor	CMea GDra GSki GTou LHop MBro MHar NGre NHed NMen NRoo NWCA WOMN WPat
'Dorothy'	LHop
¶ 'Double Chocolate'	SCoo
'Double Quilled Purple'	CMil
Double Rubies (d)	SCro
§ 'Dove' (Songbird Series)	CFai EWll MRav NRoo SWat
I 'Dragonfly'	CB&S CM&M EPfP GAbr GAri GBur GMaP LWak MBri NFla NMir NOak SPer WFar WPer
'Eastgrove'	WEas
ecalcarata	See *Semiaquilegia ecalcarata*
einseleana	CBot GSki WHer
elegantula	GAbr GDra MSto NGre NRoo WHal WOMN
– JJA 11390	SIgm
¶ *eximia*	SBla
'Firewheel'	CMil EBee LRot NFai
§ *flabellata* ♀	CGle CMil CTri GAri GCHN MBro NMen WPat WPer
§ – f. *alba*	CBot CTri ELan GCHN GGar NGre NWCA WEas
– 'Blue Angel'	CB&S WPer WSan WWeb
¶ – Cameo Series mixed	EWll
– 'Jewel'	ECho LFis WHil
– 'Ministar'	CHor CM&M CNic EBar ESis GSki MBro MRav NBro NMir NOak NRoo NVic SSpe WBea WFar WHil WHoo WPer WPyg WWin
– 'Nana Alba'	See *A. flabellata* var. *pumila* f. *alba*
§ – var. *pumila* ♀	ECha GAbr GDra GTou LBee LHop MBal MHig MTho NNrd NOak NRoo SBla SIng WAbe WCla WCru WHil WPer
§ – – f. *alba* ♀	CBot CGle CMHG CSpe EBar EBrP EBre ECha ESis GAbr GDra LBee LBre LHop MBal MHig MSte NBus NChi NRoo SBre SIng SMac WCru WRus WWin
– – f. *kurilensis*	CGle EHyt GDra LBlm MSte WCla
– – 'Silver Edge'	CMil CPla CSpe NFai NPro WBea WCot
– soft pink	WHil
* – 'White Angel'	CSev MLan NHol NPro WPer WWeb
flavescens	WPer
¶ – var. *miniana* NNS 94-5	IDac
formosa	CBot CLon GCHN GGar NBro NChi NPri NRoo NWCA SBla SIng SUsu WBea WCru WHal WHoo WOMN WPer
– var. *truncata*	CGle CRDP GBuc GCra MLLN WCru
¶ – var. *wawawensis* RMRP 950136	IDac
§ *fragrans*	CArn CChr CGle CHar CInt CNic CPou ECGN GAbr GBin GCHN GCrs LGan LSyl MBro MCLN MLLN MTho NLak NOak NWes SBla SIng WHoo WMaN WOMN WRha WSan WPat
* – 'Alba'	CSam EBee GCra ITim NRoo WEas
glandulosa	
glauca	See *A. fragrans*
§ 'Goldfinch' (Songbird Series)	CBot EWll NPri NRoo
'Graeme's Green'	NFai
grata	EWll GCHN LGre SChu WCot WPGP
§ 'Hensol Harebell' ♀	CGle CHan CPou CSWP EBee LGan MBro NBus NWoo SSpe WBea WHoo WPyg WRus
hinckleyana	See *A. chrysantha* var. *hinckleyana*
hirsutissima	See *A. viscosa* subsp. *hirsutissima*
'Irish Elegance'	CMHG EGoo WRHF
japonica	See *A. flabellata* var. *pumila*

Jewel hybrids	CSpe EMNN NRoo WPer
jonesii	CGra WAbe
– × *saximontana*	MFos
¶ *kitaibelii*	EBee
'Koralle'	CFai CLTr
'Kristall'	EPri NOak WHil WMer
¶ *kuhistanica*	ECou
laramiensis	CGra CLyd CPBP MFos NTow
	NWCA WAbe WOMN
longissima	CGle CHar CMea CMil CSam
	ECGN EHic GAbr GBri GBuc
	LSyl MBro MCLN MLLN
	MTho NMir NSti SBla WBea
	WCla WEas WHal WHil WHoo
	WLin WWeb
– 'Alba'	WEas
'Magpie'	CLTr CM&M EWll NBir NOak
	SChu SIng
McKana Group	EBrP EBre ECED ELan ENot
	GAbr GCHN GMaP LBre
	LHop MAvo MWat NLon NNor
	NOak NRoo NVic SBre SPer
	SRms WBea WMow WPer
* 'Mellow Yellow'	CHan CKel CPla EBar ECGP
	GBuc MLLN MSCN NCut
	WBea WPer WViv
micrantha	ESis GCHN NSti
aff. – JCA 1.061.350	WPGP
moorcroftiana	CPBP CPou EBee NLak
– CC 1371	MRPP
Mrs Scott-Elliot hybrids	CBlo EHol EMan GAbr LIck
	LWak MBri MLan SPer WFar
Music Series ♀	CHor NOak NPri NRoo SMrm
	SRms WByw
nevadensis	See *A. vulgaris* subsp.
	nevadensis
nigricans	See *A. atrata*
nivalis	CPBP NGre SBla WOMN
§ *olympica*	CPou EBee EMan EWes GAbr
	LGre MLLN WCot WPer
'Orange Flaming Red'	LHop
ottonis	LHop
§ – subsp. *amaliae*	WAbe
§ *oxysepala*	CGle CMil EWll GCal GCra
	GMac MSto NBus SAga WHal
	WLin
¶ 'Petticoats'	NFla
'Phyll's Bonnet'	GCal
'Pink Bonnet'	GCal
¶ 'Pink Jewel'	SVil
pubescens	EBee MSto
pubiflora	GCHN GCra
– CC&MR 96	WLin
§ *pyrenaica*	CLTr CTri NHar NTow WCla
	WOMN
§ – subsp. *cazorlensis*	CMea GCHN GCLN
'Quilled Violets'	CMil EBee NWes
'Red Hobbit'	CB&S CSpe GBin NOrc NPla
	WSan WWeb
§ 'Red Star' (Star Series)	ECtt EFou GCHN NBus NOak
	WHil WPer WRus
§ 'Robin' (Songbird Series)	CBot CFai CHea NPri NRoo
	SWat
¶ *rockii*	GAbr
'Roman Bronze'	CPla GBin MCCP MLLN NCut
	WSan WWhi
saximontana	EHyt GCHN GTou LBee MHar
	MSto NHol NMen NTow
	NWCA WOMN
§ 'Schneekönigin'	ELan GCHN NOak NWes
	WEas WHen WHil WPer
scopulorum	CLyd MFos MSto NWCA
– subsp. *perplexans*	MSto
* *secundiflora*	MSto
shockleyi	CPou EBee GBuc MLan NTow
	NWCA SIng WHil
sibirica	WPer
'Silver Queen'	WRus
skinneri	CBos CMil GAbr GBin GSki
	LGre MCLN NBro NBus NLak
	SCro WBea WCru WHal WLin
Snow Queen	See *A.* 'Schneekönigin'
Songbird Series	MLLN NPri SWat WLRN
stellata	See *A. vulgaris* var. *stellata*
¶ 'Stoulton Blue'	EBee WSPU
¶ 'Sunburst-Ruby'	CPla
'Sweet Lemon Drops'	CMil CPla
thalictrifolia	CLTr GBuc LGre SBla WCot
– JCA 174.400	NHol WLin
transsilvanica	EBar
triternata	CMil NCut NTow NWCA SIgm
¶ *turczaninovii*	EBee
viridiflora	CBot CElw CGle CHad CMea
	CRDP EHyt ELan GBuc
	GCHN GCra GDra MTho
	NGre NHar NHol NRoo NTow
	SBla SMad WEas WHal
	WOMN WPat WPer
vulgaris	CArn GAbr GPoy LHol LLWP
	MAus MChe MHew NBro NMir
	SIde WBon WGwG WMow
	WOak WPer WShi WUnd
	WWye
– 'Adelaide Addison'	CGle ECha ELan GBri GBuc
	MAvo NFai NWes SWas WEas
	WFar WLin WMer WRha
	WRus WViv WWeb
– var. *alba*	CArn CLTr CMea EMan LLWP
	MAus SEND WByw
– 'Aureovariegata'	See *A. vulgaris* Vervaeneana
	Group
§ – Baicalensis Group	GCHN
♦ – 'Blue Star'	See *A.* (Star Series) 'Blue Star'
* – 'Cap de Rossiter'	CRow
– 'Christa Barlow'	CB&S
– *clematiflora*	See *A. vulgaris* var. *stellata*
¶ – 'Double Pleat' (d)	WHer
¶ – 'Double Pleat' blue/white	EWll WHil
¶ – 'Double Pleat' pink/white	WHil
♦ – 'Dove'	See *A.* (Songbird Series) 'Dove'
– var. *flore-pleno* (d)	CLTr EHic LLWP WByw
	WHen WPer
– – black (d)	WCot
– – blue	SWas WCot
– – 'Burgundy' (d)	CMil
¶ – – pale blue	WLin
– – pink	EBee
¶ – – 'Powder Blue'	CFis
– – red (d)	GCra
– – white (d)	GAbr LGre NOak SWas
♦ – 'Gold Finch'	See *A.* (Songbird Series)
	'Goldfinch'
– golden-leaved	CMea ECho EFou
– 'Grandmother's Garden'	EWll WHil
– 'Granny's Gold'	LRHS MBri
– 'Heidi'	CBot EBee EWll NEgg SVil
	WPer
¶ – 'Iceberg'	CMil EBee
– f. *inversa*	WBea
– 'Jane Hollow'	CMil CPou CRow MLLN NCut
	WLin WPrP
¶ – 'Magda'	WRha
♦ – 'Magpie'	See *A. vulgaris* 'William
	Guiness'

– 'Michael Stromminger'	WPer
– Munstead White	See *A. vulgaris* 'Nivea'
§ – 'Nivea' ♀	CBot CGle CHad CHan CMil
	CPou ECha ELan GAbr LBlm
	LFis MCLN MNrw NChi NFai
	NRoo SBla WBea WCla WHil
	WHoo WRus
– Olympica Group	See *A. olympica*
– 'Patricia Zavros'	CLTr
– 'Pink Spurless'	See *A. vulgaris* var. *stellata* pink
– 'Pom Pom Crimson'	NBro WPrP
(Pom Pom Series)	
* – 'Pom Pom Rose'	WWhi
(Pom Pom Series)	
– Pom Pom Series	CMil MCCP
¶ – 'Pom Pom Violet'	CMil NCut
(Pom Pom Series)	
¶ – 'Pom Pom White'	CLTr
(Pom Pom Series)	
¶ – 'Primivera'	CChr
♦ – 'Red Star'	See *A.* (Star Series) 'Red Star'
♦ – 'Robin'	See *A.* (Songbird Series) 'Robin'
– 'Rose Barlow'	GCal SVil WHen WViv
– 'Silver Edge'	CMil ELan GBri WBea
¶ – 'Slaty Grey'	WHil
– 'Snowdust'	EHoe
§ – var. *stellata*	CBot CGle EBar ELan GCHN
	GCra GMaP LBay NBro NFai
	NRoo WBea WHal WPer WWhi
	WWin
¶ – – 'Bicolor Barlow'	GCal WViv
– – 'Black Barlow'	EWll GCal LRot MAus NOrc
	SCro SMac WViv WWeb
– – 'Blue Barlow'	GCal SVil WViv
¶ – – double	WLin
¶ – – double blue	CMil
– – 'Greenapples'	CChr CLTr CMil EBee MAvo
	MCCP MLLN NSti WCot WHal
	WHen WHer WPrP WSan
¶ – – 'Melton Rapids'	EWll WBea
– – 'Nora Barlow' ♀	Widely available
§ – – pink	GBin
– – red	LLWP
¶ – – 'Royal Purple'	CMil NBro
– – 'Ruby Port'	CMGP EHic GCal GMaP GMac
	MTis NBus NChi NVic SLod
	SPla SRCN WHen WPbr WWhi
– – 'Sunlight White'	EWll SWat WMaN WPer WSan
§ – – white	CGle CLTr CMil GCHN LHop
	NBro WFar WHal
¶ – 'Strawberry Ice Cream'	EBee GBri NBro
– 'The Bride'	CBlo EBee MBro
– variegated foliage	See *A. vulgaris* Vervaeneana Group
N – Vervaeneana Group (v)	Widely available
– Vervaeneana Group	CHad EMon
double white (d)	
– – 'Graeme Iddon'	GBuc GCra LGre MAvo MBri
	MLLN NBrk NFai NMGW
	WPbr WRus
– – 'Woodside'	See *A. vulgaris* Vervaeneana Group
– – 'Woodside Blue'	EGoo WWhi
– 'Westfaeld'	NOak
– 'White Barlow'	GCal SCro WViv
* – 'White Bonnets'	EBrP EBre LBre SBre SRos
– 'White Spurless'	See *A. vulgaris* var. *stellata* white
♦ – 'White Star'	See *A.* (Star Series) 'White Star'
§ – 'William Guiness'	Widely available
– 'Wishy Washy'	NChi
¶ white	WLin

§ 'White Star' (Star Series)	ECtt EFou GAbr GCHN LSyl
	MTis NBus SPer WHil WPer
yabeana	EBee GBin
§ 'Yellow Star' (Star Series)	CM&M EWll

ARABIS † (Brassicaceae)

albida	See *A. alpina* subsp. *caucasica*
alpina	CB&S
§ – subsp. *caucasica*	MBar
§ – – 'Flore Pleno' (d) ♀	CHad CHan CNic CTri ECha
	ECtt ELan EOrc GAbr LGro
	LHop MFir MTho NFla NRoo
	NVic SBod WByw WEas WFar
	WOMN WWin
– – 'Goldsplash' (v)	NPro
– – 'Pink Pearl'	NPri
– – 'Pinkie'	EMNN NTay
* – subsp. *caucasica rosea*	CHal MRav NBir SRms WFar
§ – subsp. *caucasica*	CHor EBar ECtt EMNN GBur
'Schneehaube' ♀	MBar NMir NOrc NRoo SIde
	SRms WLRN WPer
– – Snowcap	See *A. alpina* subsp. *caucasica* 'Schneehaube'
– – 'Snowdrop'	MRav NPri SMer WFar
– – 'Variegata'	CBot ECha EGoo EHoe ELan
	EPot ERic LBee LHop MBri
	MRav MTho NNor NRoo NVic
	WByw WEas WFar WPat WPbr
	WWin
androsacea	EPot GTou MHig MPla MRPP
	NHed NMen NTow WLRN
x *arendsii* 'Compinkie'	ECtt NRoo SRms WLRN
– 'Rosabella' (v)	ECha LHop
aubrietoides	CLyd
blepharophylla	EPfP GAbr MWat NTow WCot
	WOMN
§ – 'Frühlingszauber' ♀	CB&S CInt CPea CTri GDra
	LPVe MOne MWat NNrd NRoo
	SIde SRms WFar WGor WOve
– Spring Charm	See *A. blepharophylla* 'Frühlingszauber'
bryoides	EPot GTou LBee MDHE NTow
caucasica	See *A. alpina* subsp. *caucasica*
¶ *cypria*	WOMN
ferdinandi-coburgi	EGar EPot MGed MPla NBro
	NBus SBod SRms WCla WEas
	WWin
– 'Aureovariegata'	CHea CMHG CTri EHoe LGro
	NGre NLon
– 'Old Gold'	CNic ECGP EPot ESis GBur
	LBee LHop MBar MHig MPla
	NEgg NHar NNrd NRoo NVic
	SBla SBod SChu SHel SIng
	SSmi WCla WEas WHoo WPat
	WPbr WWin
– 'Variegata'	See *A. procurrens* 'Variegata'
glabra	WPer
x *kellereri*	ITim NMen
muralis	See *A. collina*
§ *procurrens* 'Variegata' ♀	ECGP ECha ELan ESis EWes
	GBur GTou LBee LHop MBal
	MBar MHig MTho MWat NGre
	NHar NHol NNor NRoo
	NWCA SBla SHFr SHel SIng
	SSmi WCla
rosea	See *A. collina*
§ *scabra*	CNat
Snow Cap	See *A. alpina* subsp. *caucasica* 'Schneehaube'
soyeri subsp. *jacquinii*	See *A. soyeri* subsp. *coriacea*
stricta	See *A. scabra*
x *sturii*	NTow

× *suendermannii* MPla

ARACHNIODES (Dryopteridaceae)
¶ *aristata* WRic
simplicior NMar WCot

ARAIOSTEGIA (Davalliaceae)
pseudocystopteris CFil SSpi

ARALIA † (Araliaceae)
¶ *armata* B&SWJ 3137 WCru
bipinnata CDoC CFil WPGP
cachemirica CHad GCal MBro NLar SDix
WHoo WTin
californica GCal GPoy LGre MSal NLar
SIgm SMrm
chinensis CB&S CMCN CSam EBar MSal
NHol
– hort. See *A. elata*
continentalis CHan EBee GCal
cordata CPle GCal NLar
¶ *decaisneana* B&SWJ 3588 WCru
§ *elata* ♀ CHEx CHad CLnd CPle ELan
ENot EOas GChr IOrc LNet
LPan MBal MBlu NBee NFla
NNor SArc SEas SMad SPer
SSpi WDin WNor WPGP
– 'Albomarginata' See *A. elata* 'Variegata'
– 'Aureovariegata' CB&S CDoC ELan ENot IOrc
LNet MAsh MBri NPal WDin
WPyg
§ – 'Variegata' ♀ CB&S CBot CDoC ELan EMil
ENot IOrc LNet MBlu MBri
NFla NPal SHBN SMad WDin
WPat WPyg
racemosa EBee GCal GPoy MLLN MSal
MSte NLar SRms
sieboldii de Vriese See *Fatsia japonica*
spinosa WHer

ARAUCARIA (Araucariaceae)
angustifolia CHEx
§ *araucana* Widely available
cookii See *A. columnaris*
excelsa See *A. heterophylla*
§ *heterophylla* ♀ MBri WNor
imbricata See *A. araucana*

ARAUJIA (Asclepiadaceae)
grandiflora SLMG
graveolens CPlN
sericifera CB&S CChr CHEx CMHG
CMac CPlN CRHN EMil ERea
GQui LHop MGos SSpi

ARBUTUS † (Ericaceae)
andrachne CFil
× *andrachnoides* ♀ CAbP CB&S CDoC CFil CGre
CMHG CPMA ELan IOrc
LHop LNet LPan MBal SArc
SBid SHBN SReu SSpi SSta
WHCG WPat WWat WWeb
¶ *canariensis* CHEx
glandulosa See *Arctostaphylos glandulosa*
marina CAbP CFil CPMA CRos ELan
MAll MAsh MBri SBid SMad
SReu SSpi SSta WWeb
menziesii ♀ CFil CMCN CPMA CPle EPfP
LNet MBal SMad WCru WWat
¶ – NJM 94046 WPGP
unedo ♀ Widely available

– 'Compacta' CB&S CBlo CDoC EBrP EBre
LBre LPan MAsh MGos SBre
SHBN
– 'Elfin King' ELan LRHS SSpi
– 'Quercifolia' MBal SSta WPat WPyg
– f. *rubra* ♀ CB&S CBlo CDoC CMHG
CTrC EBrP EBre EHal ELan
IOrc LBre LHop LNet MAll
MBal MBri MGos MHlr SBre
SPar SPer SReu SSpi SSta WFar
WPat WPyg WRHF

ARCHONTOPHOENIX (Arecaceae)
¶ *alexandrae* LPal MFiF
¶ *cunninghamiana* ♀ CBrP LPal MFiF

ARCTANTHEMUM (Asteraceae)
§ *arcticum* EFou MSte NBrk
– 'Schwefelglanz' ECha EFou WCot

ARCTERICA See PIERIS

ARCTIUM (Asteraceae)
lappa CArn CKin EJud EWFC GPoy
MChe MGra MSal NHex SIde
WHer
minus CKin EWFC MHew MSal
pubens CKin

ARCTOSTAPHYLOS (Ericaceae)
* *californica* MBal
§ *glandulosa* SAPC SArc
¶ *manzanita* SMad
× *media* 'Snow Camp' MBal
– 'Wood's Red' MAll MBal MBar MGos SBrw
WFar
myrtifolia GAri MBar
nevadensis MBal MBar SReu SSta
nummularia MBal
¶ *patula* SMad
stanfordiana C&H 105 GGGa
uva-ursi CArn CBlo ENot GPoy IOrc
MBal MBar MGos MPla NNor
SBod SEas SHBN SSta
– 'Massachusetts' ELan GQui MAsh SMur SReu
SSta
¶ – 'Point Reyes' SBrw SSto
– 'Snowcap' MAsh
– 'Vancouver Jade' CEnd EDen EPfP GChr MAsh
MBar MGos NHol SBrw SPer
SReu SSta
* – 'Variegata' GCLN

ARCTOTIS (Asteraceae)
× *hybrida* 'African MBEx
Sunrise'
– 'Apricot' LHop MBEx MSte SAxl SMer
SMrm WEas
– 'Bacchus' MBEx
– 'China Rose' SAxl SMrm
– 'Flame' CBar CHad CSpe LHop MBEx
MLan MSte NPla SAga SChu
SMrm SUsu WEas
* – 'Mahogany' MSte SAxl SUsu
– 'Pink' SChu
* – 'Raspberry' LBlm
– 'Red Devil' SMrm WLRN
– 'Rosita' MBEx
– 'Terracotta' MSte
– 'Torch' MBEx

– 'Wine'	CBar CHad LHop MBEx MSte WEas WLRN
– 'Yellow'	MBEx
'Red Magic'	MBEx

ARDISIA (Myrsinaceae)
crenata CHan MBri

ARECA (Arecaceae)
catechu MBri
¶ *concinna* LPal

ARECASTRUM See SYAGRUS

ARENARIA (Caryophyllaceae)
¶ *aggregata* subsp. *erinacea*	SIng
alfacarensis	See *A. lithops*
balearica	CInt CLyd CNic ELan EPar GCHN LBee MFir MRPP MTho NGre SBod SIng SRms
bertolonii	LBee
caespitosa	See *Minuartia verna* subsp. *caespitosa*
festucoides	GCLN GTou WLRN
grandiflora	ESis
hookeri	NWCA
¶ – subsp. *desertorum*	WLin
ledebouriana	MWat NWCA WAbe
magellanica	See *Colobanthus quitensis*
montana ♀	CGle ECha ECtt EHyt ELan EMNN GCHN GMaP MArl MHar MHig MHlr MTho NMen NNor NVic SRCN SRms WAbe WEas WFar WHil WPat WPbr WPer WWeb WWhi WWin
nevadensis	WAbe
norvegica	CNat
– subsp. *anglica*	WOMN
obtusiloba	See *Minuartia obtusiloba*
pinifolia	See *Minuartia circassica*
procera subsp. *glabra*	NMen
pseudacantholimon	NGre
pulvinata	See *A. lithops*
pungens	WLin
purpurascens	CInt CLyd EHyt ELan EMNN EPot ESis MHig NMen NRoo NSla NWCA SRms WHoo WPat
– 'Elliott's Variety'	WPat
recurva	See *Minuartia recurva*
¶ *roseiflora* ACE 1526	EHyt
rubella	NTow
¶ sp. ex CC 1363	MRPP
tetraquetra	EGle GCrs GDra MTho NMen NWCA
§ – subsp. *amabilis*	CLyd EHyt EPot LBee MRPP NGre NHar NNrd NSla NTow SIng
– var. *granatensis*	See *A. tetraquetra* subsp. *amabilis*
tmolea	LHop NMen
verna	See *Minuartia verna*

ARENGA (Arecaceae)
¶ *engleri* LPal

ARGEMONE (Papaveraceae)
grandiflora	EJud ELan
mexicana	ELan WHer WOMN WWin
¶ *ochroleuca*	SUsu

ARGYLIA   (Bignoniaceae) See Plant Deletions

ARGYRANTHEMUM †   (Asteraceae)
¶ 'Anastasia'	CCan MBEx
'Apricot Surprise'	See *A.* **'Peach Cheeks'**
'Beauty of Nice'	WEas
§ 'Blizzard' (d)	CB&S CCan CLit EPri LIck LLWP MBEx SMer WLRN
'Bofinger'	LIck
♦ Boston Yellow daisy	See *A. callichrysum*
¶ 'Brides Maid'	CCan
broussonetii	CCan LIck NSty
'Butterfly'	LIck SVil
§ *callichrysum*	CCan
§ – 'Etoile d'Or'	IHos LHop LIck MBEx
– 'Penny'	MBEx
– 'Prado'	CB&S ECtt GCal LIck WLRN
– Yellow Star	See *A. callichrysum* **'Etoile d'Or'**
¶ 'Camilla Ponticella'	CCan
canariense hort.	See *A. frutescens* subsp. *canariae*
¶ 'Champagne'	CCan MBEx
'Cheek's Peach'	See *A.* **'Peach Cheeks'**
'Comtesse de Chambord'	LHil
'Cornish Gold' ♀	LFis LIck
coronopifolium	CCan LIck MBEx
¶ 'Donington Hero' ♀	LIck
double cream (d)	CCan LHil LIck
double white (d)	CHal LIck NHaw SCro
'Edelweiss' (d)	CCan CSev EBar ECtt GCal LHil LIck MBEx WEas WHen
'Flamingo'	See *Rhodanthemum gayanum*
§ *foeniculaceum* hort.	CTri ELan GMac LBlm MRav NSty SIgm WEas WHen WKif WOMN
– pink	See *A.* **'Petite Pink'**
§ *foeniculaceum* Webb	CCan CLTr CSev EBar GCal
'Royal Haze'♀	LIck NPer SMer SUsu
¶ 'Frosty'	CCan
§ *frutescens*	CDoC CHEx CLit ECtt ELan EMan LBlm LHil NFai NLon WEas
* – 'Album Plenum' (d)	SEND
§ – subsp. *canariae* ♀	CCan CHal MBEx
¶ – x *maderense*	LHil
– subsp. *succulentum* 'Margaret Lynch'	CCan LIck MBEx
¶ 'Fuji Sundance'	CCan
'George'	CLit
'Gill's Pink'	CElw CHid ECtt LHil LLWP MBEx
¶ 'Golden Treasure'	CCan
§ *gracile*	CSev LHil WEas
– 'Chelsea Girl' ♀	CB&S CCan CInt CLTr CLit ECtt EMan LIck MArl MBEx MSte SIgm SRms
'Hopleys Double Yellow' (d)	LHil NSty
§ 'Jamaica Primrose' ♀	CB&S CBar CBot CCan CHEx CLit CSev ELan ERic GMac IHos LHop LIck MBEx NHaw NSty SCro SDys SHFr WEas WOMN WPnn
♦ 'Jamaica Snowstorm'	See *A.* **'Snow Storm'**
¶ 'Lemon Chiffon'	CCan
* 'Lemon Meringue'	ECtt LIck MBEx NHaw SMer
'Levada Cream' ♀	LIck
'Leyton Treasure'	MBEx
'Lilliput'	LIck

§ *maderense* ♀   CCan CLTr CLit GCal IBlr LBlm LHil LHop LIck MBEx MSte NSty SUsu WEas WOMN WPer
– pale form   LIck
'Mary Cheek' (d) ♀   CCan EBar LHil LIck MBEx
'Mary Wootton' (d)   CCan CLit CSev ECtt ELan LIck MBEx NSty
mawii   See *Rhodanthemum gayanum*
¶ 'Mike's Pink'   CCan MBEx
'Mini-snowflake'   See *A.* **'Blizzard'**
'Mrs F. Sander' (d)   ECtt MBEx NSty
'Nevada Cream'   See *A.* **'Qinta White'**
ochroleucum   See *A. maderense*
§ 'Peach Cheeks' (d)   CB&S EMan LIck MBEx MSte NFai NHaw SAga SRms
§ 'Petite Pink' ♀   CB&S EAst ECtt EMan EPri GCal GMac LIck MBEx MSte NHaw NPer SIgm SMer SRms WEas WHen
'Pink Australian'   CLTr EBar LHil LIck MBEx
'Pink Break'   CCan CHal
I 'Pink Dahlia'   CCan
'Pink Delight'   See *A.* **'Petite Pink'**
¶ 'Pink Pixie'   CCan
'Powder Puff' (d)   CCan CLTr CLit ECtt LIck MBEx MRav NFai NHaw SCro
§ 'Qinta White' (d) ♀   CCan CLit ECtt LHil LHop LIck MBEx NSty WEas
¶ 'Rising Sun'   CCan
'Rollason's Red'   ECtt LIck MBEx
'Royal Haze'   See *A. foeniculaceum* 'Royal Haze' Webb
'Royal Yellow'   LIck
¶ 'Saute'   CCan
'Silver Leaf'   WLRN
'Silver Queen'   See *A. foeniculaceum* hort.
single pink   CLTr CLit LHil LIck NSty
§ 'Snow Storm' ♀   CB&S CBar CLit EAst EBar LIck NFai NHaw WHer
'Snowflake' (d)   CHEx CSev ECtt IHos LHil MBEx MSte NPer WHen
¶ 'Starlight'   CCan
'Sugar Baby'   CHal WLRN
'Sugar 'n' Ice'   MBEx
'Summer Pink'   MBEx WLRN
'Tenerife'   LIck MSte
'Tony Holmes'   CCan LIck
'Vancouver' (d) ♀   CB&S CBot CCan CInt CSpe EBar ELan GCal GMac IHos LHil LHop LIck MBEx NHaw NSty SChu SRms WEas WOMN
* 'Vera'   IHos LIck
'Wellwood Park'   CCan CLit ECtt LIck MBEx
¶ 'Weymouth Surprise'   CCan
'White Spider'   LIck
'Yellow Australia'   LIck

ARGYREIA (Convolvulaceae)

nervosa   CPlN

ARGYROCYTISUS See CYTISUS

ARISAEMA (Araceae)

amurense   CFil CFir CLAP EPot GCal GDra NHar NHol SSpi WCot WFar WPGP
¶ *amurense* B&SWJ 762   WCru
¶ – B&SWJ 947   WCru
¶ *angustatum* var.   WCru
   peninsulae B&SWJ 841
¶ *brevipes*   WCru

candidissimum ♀   CAvo CBro CFil CFir CLAP CRDP EPar EPot GCal GCrs LAma NHar NHol SBla SRms SSpi SWas WCot WCru WFox WHal WIvy
ciliatum   CRDP LAma MHlr SBla SSpi WCot
– CT 369   SWas WCru
concinnum   EPot LAma WCot WCru
consanguineum   CBro CFil CGle EPot LAma WCru WPGP
¶ – B&SWJ 071   WCru
costatum   CFil GBuc LAma WCru WPGP
dracontium   CArn CLAP EBot EPot LAma MSal NRog WCru
¶ *elephas*   LAma
erubescens   EPot LAma WCru
exappendiculatum   CFil CMon EPar WCot WCru WPGP
flavum   CBro CFil CHEx CLAP EHyt EPot GCal GCrs LAma NRog WCot WCru WPGP
– CC 1782   LFis
¶ *formosanum*   LAma
– B&SWJ 280   WCru
– B&SWJ 390   CPou
¶ – var. *bicolorifolium*   WCru
   B&SWJ 3528
– f. *stenophyllum*   WCru
   B&SWJ 1477
galeatum   EPot LAma WCru
griffithii   EBee EPot GCra LAma NHol NRog SMad SSON SSpi WCru
helleborifolium   See *A. tortuosum*
¶ *heterophyllum* B&SWJ 2028   WCru
– B&SWJ 280   WCru
intermedium   EPot LAma NRog WCru
– var. *biflagellatum*   CMon
– HWJCM 161   WCru
¶ *iyoanum*   WThi
jacquemontii   CAvo CBro CLAP EHyt EPot GBuc GCLN GDra LAma NRog WCru
¶ – B&SWJ 2719   WCru
– form   WCru
japonicum   See *A. serratum*
kiushianum   EFEx WCru WThi
¶ *lingyunense*   LAma WCru
§ *nepenthoides*   CBro EPot GCra LAma NHol WCot WCru
ochraceum   See *A. nepenthoides*
polyphyllum B&SWJ 3904   WCru
propinquum   EPot LAma WCru
¶ *rhizomatum*   LAma
¶ *rhombiforme*   WCru
¶ *ringens*   WPGP WThi
¶ – f. *glaucescens*   WThi
– hort.   See *A. robustum*
¶ – f. *praecox* B&SWJ 1515   WCru
¶ – f. *sieboldii* B&SWJ 551   WCru
– (Thunberg) Schott   EFEx LAma NHol WCot WCru
§ *robustum*   CFil WPGP
¶ – B&SWJ 711   WCru
§ *saxatile*   LAma
sazensoo   See *A. sikokianum*
§ *serratum*   CFil LAma WCru
– GG 89394   NHol
– GG 89399   NHol
– GG 89404   NHol
§ *sikokianum*   CFil EFEx EPot LAma WCru WPGP WThi
sp. CLD 12482*   EEls

speciosum	EPot LAma NHol WCru
¶ – B&SWJ 2403	WCru
¶ – var. *mirabile*	WCru
B&SWJ 2712	
taiwanense	CFil
– B&SWJ 269	WCru
– B&SWJ 356	CPou
¶ – var. *brevipedunculatum*	WCru
B&SWJ 1859	
¶ – f. *cinereum* B&SWJ 1912	WCru
ternatipartitum	WCru WThi
thunbergii	EFEx WThi
– subsp. *urashima*	CLAP EFEx LAma WCru
	WThi
* *tiliatum*	MHlr
§ *tortuosum*	CBro CFil CLAP CMon ECha
	EPar EPot LAma MBal NHol
	NRog NTow WCot WCru
¶ – CC 1452	CPou
¶ – (high alt.form) B&SWJ 2386	WCru
¶ – (low alt. form) B&SWJ 2298	WCru
¶ *tosaense*	WThi
triphyllum	CFil CHEx CLAP EBot EPar
	EPfP EPot LAma MSal NRog
	SAxl SLod SWas WCru WPGP
¶ – var. *atrorubens*	WPGP
♦ *utile*	See *A. verrucosum* var. *utile*
verrucosum	LAma WCru
§ – var. *utile*	EPot LAma
¶ – – HWJCM 161	WCru
* *vulgare* var. *typicum*	WCot
¶ *zanlanscianense*	WCru

ARISARUM (Araceae)

proboscideum	CB&S CBro CFee CFil CNic
	CRDP CRow ECha EHyt ELan
	EPot GCal GDra LBow
	MBal MHig MTho NBro NGre
	NHol NRog NSti SIng SPer SSpi
	WRus WWye
proboscideum MS 958	CMon EMar
vulgare	CRDP
– subsp. *simorrhinum*	CMon
SF 396/347	
– subsp. *vulgare* JRM 1396	CMon

ARISTEA (Iridaceae)

africana	SWat
confusa	SWat
ecklonii	CFil CHan CPou GSki LFis
	SLod SWat WCot WPer
ensifolia	ELan EMon SWat
– S&SH 88	CHan
grandis	WCot
lugens	SWat
macrocarpa	SWat
major	ELan GSki SWat
– pink	CGre
spiralis	SWat
woodii	SWat

ARISTIDA   (Poaceae) See Plant Deletions

ARISTOLOCHIA (Aristolochiaceae)

baetica	CPlN WCru
californica	CPlN MSto
chrysops	CPlN
clematitis	CArn CPlN GPoy MHew MSal
	NHex WCru WWye
debilis	CPlN
durior	See *A. macrophylla*
elegans	See *A. littoralis*

fimbriata	CPlN MSto
gigantea	CPlN LChe WMul
grandiflora	CPlN
¶ *heterophylla* B&SWJ 3109	WCru
kaempferi	CPlN
– B&SWJ 293	WCru
§ *labiata*	CPlN
§ *littoralis* ♀	CPlN MSto SOWG
§ *macrophylla*	CB&S CBot CHEx CPlN EBee
	ELan EPla ETen GOrc NFla
	NPal SBra SHBN SSoC WCru
manshuriensis	CPlN
– B&SWJ 962	WCru
paucinervis SF 235	MSto
peruviana	CPlN
pistolochia	CPlN
ringens Link & Otto	See *A. labiata*
– Vahl	CPlN
rotunda	CPlN
sempervirens	CPlN
sipho	See *A. macrophylla*
tagala	CPlN WMul
tomentosa	CFil CPlN SSta
trilobata	CPlN
watsonii	CPlN

ARISTOTELIA (Elaeocarpaceae)

§ *chilensis*	MAll MNes
– 'Variegata'	CAbb CB&S CHan CPle EMil
	EPla MAll MMil WEas WLRN
	WPat WPyg
fruticosa	CPle
– (f)	ECou MAll
– (m)	ECou MAll
macqui	See *A. chilensis*
serrata	ECou

ARMERIA (Plumbaginaceae)

§ *alliacea*	ECha GBar WPer
– f. *leucantha*	NBro
§ *alpina*	MWat
¶ Bee's hybrids	WMoo WUnu
'Bee's Ruby' ♀	ECED MBri MTed WMer WPer
	WWye
caespitosa	See *A. juniperifolia*
formosa hybrids	CTri ELan EMan IBlr LFis
	MNrw NCat NMir SIde WRha
§ *girardii*	EPot LBuc NHed
§ *juniperifolia* ♀	CMHG EBrP EBre ECtt ELan
	EMNN ESis LBee LBre LHop
	MPla MTho NGre NMen NNrd
	NRoo NTow NVic NWCA SBla
	SBre WCla WWin
– 'Alba'	CMea ELan EPot MHig MPla
	NGre NHar NMen NPri NRoo
	NRya WWin
– 'Beechwood'	LBee SBla SSmi
– 'Bevan's Variety' ♀	CMHG CNic EBrP EBre ECha
	ELan GCrs LBre MBro MHig
	MNrw MWat NHar NHol NMen
	NNrd NRoo NRya SBre SIng
	SSmi WAbe WHoo WPat WPyg
– dark form	EWes GDra WAbe
– rose	EPot
– spiny dwarf form	EPot
§ *maritima*	CArn CKin CMHG CRow
	EBrP EBre EPPr LBee LBre
	LHol MBar MRav NCat NMen
	NNor SBre SIde WBea WCFE
	WMow WOak

– 'Alba'	CArn CB&S CLTr ECha ELan EPot ESis LBee LPVe MBal MBar MBri NMir NNor NRya NVic SHel WAbe WBea WHen WPer WWin WWye
– subsp. *alpina*	See *A. alpina*
– 'Bloodstone'	CB&S CTri ECot ELan LBee MWat
– 'Corsica'	CMea CTri ECha MHar MOne NBir NRya SMer
– Düsseldorf Pride	See *A. maritima* **'Düsseldorfer Stolz'**
§ – 'Düsseldorfer Stolz'	CMHG CPBP EBrP EBre ECha ELan LBre LWak MBri MBro NHar NHol NMen NNrd NPro NRoo SBre WBea WHen WPat WWye
– 'Glory of Holland'	EPot
– 'Laucheana'	CBod NOak WHoo WPyg
* – 'Pink Lusitanica'	WPer
– 'Ruby Glow'	CTri GAri LBuc NMen
– 'Snowball'	NOak
– 'Splendens'	EMNN EMil EPfP ESis GCHN LFis MLan MOne MPla MWgw NHar NMir NRya NVic WFar WPer WWin
– 'Vindictive' ♀	CB&S CMea CTri EPfP LGro MBal SRms
'Nifty Thrifty' (v)	EWes NPro SCoo WCot WSPU WWeb
'Ornament'	ECtt LFis NRoo WCot WFar WHen
plantaginea	See *A. alliacea*
pseudarmeria	EBee ELan MLan MNrw WEas
rumelica	EWes
setacea	See *A. girardii*
tweedyi	CLyd EWes GTou NGre NNor NRoo NWCA
¶ *variegata* 'Stephen Taffler'	LFis
vulgaris	See *A. maritima*
welwitschii	CMHG SRms

ARMORACIA (Brassicaceae)

§ *rusticana*	CArn CSev ELau GPoy ILis LHol MBri MGra MSal NPri SIde WCer WGwy WHer WJek WMow WOak WSel WWye
¶ – 'Horwood'	WCHb
– 'Variegata'	CSev EGoo ELau EMar EMon EOrc GBar GCal LFis LHol LHop NSti NWes SMad SPla WCHb WCot WLRN WPbr

ARNEBIA (Boraginaceae)

echioides	See *A. pulchra*
◆ *longiflora*	See *A. pulchra*
§ *pulchra*	EBee ECED

ARNICA (Asteraceae)

¶ *angustifolia* subsp. *alpina*	EBee SRms
– subsp. *iljinii*	NBir
chamissonis	CSev EBee ELau GBar LHol MHew MNrw MSal SIde WJek WPer WRha WWye
¶ *frigida*	EBee
¶ *lessingii*	EBee
¶ *longifolia*	EBee
montana	CArn EOHP GPoy GTou MChe MGra MSal NSti SWat WJek WPer WRHF WWye
– yellow	MLan

nevadensis	EBee
sachalinensis	EBee

ARONIA (Rosaceae)

arbutifolia	CB&S CGre CPle CTri EPfP EPla GBin IOrc MBal MBlu MWhi SBid SHBN SMac WAbe WDin WWat
– 'Erecta'	EBrP EBre EHic ELan EPfP GChr LBre LHop MBlu MUlv SAga SBre SRms SSpi WWat SOWG
* *flexuosa*	
melanocarpa	CB&S CMCN CMHG CSam EBrP EBre EHic ELan EPla LBre MBar MBlu MRav NHol SBid SBre WCwm WDin WHCG WWat
– 'Autumn Magic'	CBlo CFai CSam EBee LRHS MBlu WRHF
– 'Viking'	EBee EHal LBuc MUlv WLRN WShe WWes
× *prunifolia*	CAgr CB&S CDoC CMHG CPle EPla NHol SBid SPer WHCG WWat
– 'Brilliant'	CDoC COtt MAsh MCoo MUlv SPer WBcn WWat

ARRHENATHERUM (Poaceae)

elatius subsp. *bulbosum*	CCuc CNic EAst EGoo EHoe
'Variegatum'	ELan EMon EPla EPot ESOG GBin LRHS MWhi NCat NChi NEgg NHol NOrc NSti NVic SAxl SCob SVil WEas WPat WPer WRus

ARTEMISIA † (Asteraceae)

§ *abrotanum* ♀	Widely available
* – 'Variegata'	WCot
absinthium	CArn CSev EEls ELau EWFC GPoy LHol MBar MChe MGra MLLN MWgw NNor NSti SIde SPer SWat WCer WOak WPer WWye
¶ – 'Corinne Tremaine' (v)	WHer
– 'Huntingdon'	CHad
– 'Lambrook Giant'	EEls EMan
– 'Lambrook Mist' ♀	COtt CSev EEls ELan ELau EMar EPPr EPfP GBri MAus MAvo MBel NPla NRoo NSti NWoo SWat WHow WJek WLRN WRus WWeb
– 'Lambrook Silver' ♀	Widely available
– 'Silver Ghost'	EEls
* – 'Variegata'	WJek
afra	EEls
§ *alba*	CSWP CSev EEls EMan EMon GBar GPoy ILis LHol NSti SIde SMad WCer WMow WPer
§ – 'Canescens' ♀	CGle CHan CLTr CSev CSpe EBrP EBre ECha EEls EFou EOrc LBre MBri MGra MNrw MTis NTow SBla SBre SChu SDix SEas SMrm SPer SSpe WHCG WHow WMer WPer WWat
annua	CArn EEls MSal SIde WWye
arborescens	CArn CGle CMHG CTri ECha EEls ELan ENot MGed NFai NSti SDry SPer WDin WHer
– 'Brass Band'	See *A.* **'Powis Castle'**
– 'Faith Raven'	CArn EEls EPla GBuc MBri NFai NNor WHer WMer WRus

– 'Nana'	ECha EEls EMan
– 'Prostata'	See *A. stelleriana* 'Boughton Silver'
– 'Silver Brocade'	See *A. stelleriana* 'Boughton Silver'
taurica	EEls
§ *thuscula*	EEls
tridentata	See *Seriphidium tridentatum*
§ *umbelliformis*	EEls GBar
vallesiaca	See *Seriphidium vallesiacum*
verlotiorum	EEls GBar
* *versicolor*	NLon NNor
vulgaris	CArn CJew EEls ELau EWFC GPoy LHol MChe MHew NNor SIde WHer WOak WWye
¶ – 'Byrne's Variegated'	EMon
– 'Cragg-Barber Eye' (v)	CNat EBee EGar MAvo WAlt WCHb WCot WHer WPbr WRha
– 'Crispa'	ELau EMon SIde
– 'Peddar's Gold' (v)	EPPr EWes
§ – 'Variegata'	CBre CLTr CWit EBee EEls EMon EPla ERav GBar GLil LFis LHol NSti SLod SMad WAlt WBea WCHb WFar WHer WHil WPbr WPer WRha
* × *wurzellii*	EEls

ARTHROPODIUM (Anthericaceae)

candidum	CBot CHan CMea CRow CSpe ECha ECou EPPr EPla EPot GBin MHlr NCat NWCA SHBN SUsu WAbe WEas WHal CInt
– *maculatum*	CAbb CMea ELan EPPr GCal LHil LRot SSoC WCot WCru WFar WWin
cirratum	CAbb CAvo CHan CTbh CTrC ECou EPPr ERea LHil MLan SVen WHal WMul
– 'Matapouri Bay'	CB&S
milleflorum	ECou NWoo

ARUM (Araceae)

§ *besserianum*	EPot
§ *concinnatum*	CFil CLAP CMon EPot EWes LAma SSpi WCot WPGP
conophalloides	See *A. rupicola* var. *rupicola*
cornutum	See *Sauromatum venosum*
creticum	CBot CBro CFil CFir CHan CMon ECha EHyt EMan EPar EPot IBlr MMil MTho NLar NRog NTow SAga SSpi SWas WPGP
– FCC form	CLAP SBla WCot
– yellow	NBir WIvy
cyrenaicum	CMon GCra
detruncatum var. *detruncatum*	See *A. rupicola* var. *rupicola*
§ *dioscoridis*	CLAP CMon EBee MFos MTho NRog WCot
¶ – JCA 195.157	WCot
– var. *liepoldtii*	See *A. dioscoridis*
– var. *smithii*	See *A. dioscoridis*
dracunculus	See *Dracunculus vulgaris*
elongatum	EPot
idaeum	SSpi
italicum	CGle CTri ETub LAma MBri MTho NLar NNrd NRog SEND SWat WAbe WByw WFar WOMN WOak WShi

– subsp. *albispathum*	CFil CMon EFou EMon EPot LAma NRog WCot WPGP
– black spotted form	EHyt
– 'Green Marble'	SBla
– subsp. *italicum*	EPla SAWi
– – 'Bill Baker'	EMon
§ – – 'Marmoratum' ♀	Widely available
§ – – 'White Winter'	CRDP EMon GBuc WCot WRus
– 'Nancy Lindsay'	EMon
– subsp. *neglectum* 'Chameleon'	CDec CHad CRDP EBee EMon SApp SMad WCot WWeb
– NL 1234	CMon
– 'Pictum'	See *A. italicum* subsp. *italicum* 'Marmoratum'
¶ – 'Spotted Jack'	MNrw
korolkowii	EPot NRog
maculatum	CArn CKin EOld EPar EPot EWFC GPoy LAma LSyl MSal NHex WHer WShi WWye
– 'Painted Lady'	WCot
– 'Pleddel'	WCot
* – 'Variegatum'	GPoy
¶ 'Miss Janay Hall'	WCot
nickelii	See *A. concinnatum*
§ *nigrum*	EMon WCot
orientale	CLAP EPot NTow
– subsp. *alpinum*	CFil WPGP
– subsp. *besserianum*	See *A. besserianum*
palaestinum	WCot
petteri hort.	See *A. nigrum*
N *pictum*	CAvo CLAP CRDP LAma LRHS NRog WCot WIvy
– ACL 321/78	EMon
– CL 28	CMon
– 'Taff's Form'	See *A. italicum* subsp. *italicum* 'White Winter'
purpureospathum	CMon WCot
* *sintenisii*	WCot

ARUNCUS † (Rosaceae)

aethusifolius	CDoC CMHG CRow EBar ECha EFou EGol ELan EMon EPla GAbr LFis MBro MCLN MLLN MRav NChi NHar NHol NNor NOak NOrc SMac WEas WFar WHoo WPer WRus WWat WWin
¶ *asiaticus*	EBee
dioicus Child of Two Worlds	See *A. dioicus* 'Zweiweltenkind'
– 'Glasnevin'	CRow CSev ECha ECtt EGol EMan EPla LFis MBri NDov NHol SChu SMac WMer
– var. *kamtschaticus*	NHol
– – AGSJ 238	NHol
– 'Kneiffii'	Widely available
§ – (m) ♀	Widely available
§ – 'Zweiweltenkind'	ECGN EMan GSki MBro MCli WMer WPer
plumosus	See *A. dioicus* (m)
sp. AGSJ 214	NHol
sylvestris	See *A. dioicus* (m)

ARUNDINARIA † (Poaceae - Bambusoideae)

amabilis	See *Pseudosasa amabilis*
anceps	See *Yushania anceps*
angustifolia	See *Pleioblastus chino* f. *angustifolius*
auricoma	See *Pleioblastus auricomus*
chino	See *Pleioblastus chino*

disticha — See *Pleioblastus pygmaeus* var. *distichus*

falconeri — See *Himalayacalamus falconeri*

fangiana — EPla

fargesii — See *Bashania fargesii*

fastuosa — See *Semiarundinaria fastuosa*

fortunei — See *Pleioblastus variegatus*

funghomii — See *Schizostachyum funghomii*

gigantea — EPla SDry WJun

hindsii — See *Pleioblastus hindsii* hort.

hookeriana hort. — See *Himalayacalamus falconeri* 'Damarapa'

– Munro — See *Himalayacalamus hookerianus*

humilis — See *Pleioblastus humilis*

japonica — See *Pseudosasa japonica*

jaunsarensis — See *Yushania anceps*

maling — See *Yushania maling*

marmorea — See *Chimonobambusa marmorea*

murieliae — See *Fargesia murieliae*

nitida — See *Fargesia nitida*

oedogonata — See *Clavinodum oedogonatum*

palmata — See *Sasa palmata*

pumila — See *Pleioblastus humilis* var. *pumilus*

pygmaea — See *Pleioblastus pygmaeus*

quadrangularis — See *Chimonobambusa quadrangularis*

simonii — See *Pleioblastus simonii*

spathiflora — See *Thamnocalamus spathiflorus*

§ *tecta* — SDry

tessellata — See *Thamnocalamus tessellatus*

vagans — See *Sasaella ramosa*

variegata — See *Pleioblastus variegatus*

veitchii — See *Sasa veitchii*

viridistriata — See *Pleioblastus auricomus*

'Wang Tsai' — See *Bambusa multiplex* 'Fernleaf'

ARUNDO (Poaceae)

donax — CBen CFil CHEx CInt CRow ECha EFul EPla EWes LBlm LPBA LPan MBlu MUlv SAPC SArc SDix SMad SSoC WHal

– 'Macrophylla' — CRow EPla LPJP

– 'Variegata' — See *A. donax* var. *versicolor*

§ – var. *versicolor* (v) — CB&S CBen CBot CHEx CInt CRDP CRow CWit ECha EFul EPla EWes LHop LPBA LPJP LPan MBEx MSta SArc SMad SPer SSoC WCot WMul

pliniana — CRow EPla SApp

ASARINA (Scrophulariaceae)

antirrhiniflora — See *Maurandella antirrhiniflora*

barclayana — See *Maurandya barclayana*

erubescens — See *Lophospermum erubescens*

hispanica — See *Antirrhinum hispanicum*

lophantha — See *Lophospermum erubescens*

lophospermum — See *Lophospermum erubescens*

§ *procumbens* — CGle CMHG ECha ELan GAbr GDra GTou LBlm MBal MTho NHex NNor NWCA SHFr SHel SLod SSpi WCla WGwG WHer WLin WOMN WPer WWin WWye

– 'Alba' — SRms

purpusii — See *Maurandya purpusii*

scandens — See *Maurandya scandens*

'Victoria Falls' — LCns SLod

ASARUM † (Aristolochiaceae)

albomaculatum — WCru
B&SWJ 1726

arifolium — CLAP EPar

¶ *asaroides* — WThi

* *campaniforme* — LAma WCru

canadense — CArn EPot GPoy MSal WCru

caudatum — CHan CLAP CRow EBee EGar EHyt EPla LHop MBri MSal NBro NLar NSti NWCA SAxl WCru WFar

¶ *caudigerum* — LAma
– B&SWJ 1517 — WCru

¶ *caudigrellum* — LAma

caulescens — CLAP LAma WThi

¶ *chinense* — WCru

¶ *debile* — LAma WCru

¶ *epigynum* B&SWJ 3443 — WCru

europaeum — CHEx CHan CLAP CTri ECha EFou ELan EMar EMon EPla ERos GPoy LHop LSpr MFir MGrG MSal MWgw NBro NHex NSti SAxl WCru WEas WFar WHer WWye

hartwegii — CLAP CMGP CRDP EHyt EMan EPar EPot ERos WCru

¶ *heterophyllum* — WThi

¶ *hexalobum* — WThi

¶ *hirsutisepalum* — WThi

infrapurpureum — WCru
B&SWJ 1994

lemmonii — EGar

leptophyllum B&SWJ 1983 — WCru

macranthum B&SWJ 1691 — WCru

¶ *maculatum* B&SWJ 1114 — WCru

¶ *magnificum* — LAma WCru

¶ *maximum* — LAma WCru WThi

¶ *minamitanianum* — WThi

¶ *sakawanum* — WThi

shuttleworthii — CGra CLAP WCot WCru
– 'Callaway' — WCot

¶ *sieboldii* — CLAP

¶ *splendens* — LAma WCot WCru WThi

¶ *stellatum* — WThi

¶ *subglobosum* — WThi

taipingshanianum — WCru
B&SWJ 1688

¶ *takaoi* — WThi

ASCLEPIAS (Asclepiadaceae)

'Cinderella' — CSev EBee LBuc SIgm WHil WOve

curassavica — CHal CSev EBar ELan LHil SHFr SLMG WMul

§ *fascicularis* — SHFr SIgm

fasciculata — See *A. fascicularis*

fruticosa — See *Gomphocarpus fruticosus*

incarnata — CHan CInt CMea CSev EBee ECED ECro ELan GLil LFis LGan MRav MSal MUlv SPer WPer

– 'Ice Ballet' — CSev EBee EFou EMan EWll MMil MTis SIgm SWat WRus

physocarpa — See *Gomphocarpus physocarpus*

purpurascens — CArn

¶ *rotundifolia* — EBee

¶ *speciosa* — EBee

syriaca — CArn CGen EBee ECro MLLN MRav MSte SHFr WPer

tuberosa	CArn CB&S CDoC EBar ECED ECro ELau EMan GPoy MNrw MRav MSal NCut NLak WPer WWal WWin
– Gay Butterflies Group	CInt MLan

ASIMINA (Annonaceae)

triloba	CAgr LBlo WNor WWoo

ASKIDIOSPERMA (Restionaceae)

¶ *esterhuyseniae*	WNor

ASPARAGUS (Asparagaceae)

asparagoides ♀	CPlN ERea
§ – 'Myrtifolius'	CHal
¶ *cochinchinensis* B&SWJ 3425	WCru
densiflorus 'Myersii' ♀	CHal ERea LHil MBri SRms
– Sprengeri Group ♀	CHal MBri SRms
falcatus	ERea MBri SEND
officinalis	CHEx ERea
¶ – 'Backlim'	EMui
¶ – 'Franklim'	EMui
◆ *plumosus*	See *A. setaceus*
pseudoscaber 'Spitzenschleier'	WCot
§ *setaceus* ♀	CHal MBri
¶ – 'Nanus'	LPVe
– 'Pyramidalis'	MBri SRms
sp. B&SWJ 871	WCru
verticillatus	GCal MCCP SRms

ASPERULA (Rubiaceae)

§ *arcadiensis* ♀	EHyt ELan EPot MTho NWCA SIng WOMN
– JCA 210.100	CPBP NTow
aristata subsp. *scabra*	ECha ELan EMar EMon
– subsp. *thessala*	See *A. sintenisii*
cyanchica	MHew
daphneola	CPBP ECho EHyt EWes SBla
gussonei	CMea CPBP EDAr EMNN EPot ESis GDra LBee MBro MHig MWat NHed NHol NMen NWCA SBla SSmi WAbe WLin WPat
hexaphylla	ECED
hirta	CMea
§ *lilaciflora*	MHig NWCA SRms SSmi
– var. *caespitosa*	See *A. lilaciflora* subsp. *lilaciflora*
§ – subsp. *lilaciflora*	CMHG CPBP ELan EPot ESis MTho NMen NNrd WWin
nitida	ELan MTho NNrd
– subsp. *puberula*	See *A. sintenisii*
odorata	See *Galium odoratum*
§ *sintenisii* ♀	CPBP EPot LBee MBro NHar NMen NTow NWCA SBla SIng SSmi WAbe WHoo
taurina subsp. *caucasica*	EMon EOrc MBro NSti WCHb WCot WHal
taygetea NS 723	NWCA
tinctoria	CArn EJud GBar GPoy LHol MChe MHew MSal SIde WCHb

ASPHODELINE (Asphodelaceae)

liburnica	CBro CMGP CMon ECGN ECGP ECha ELan EMan EMar GAbr MBel MBro MTis MWat SAga SDix SEND SSpi WCot WPer
§ *lutea*	Widely available

§ – 'Gelbkerze'	EMan
– Yellow Candle	See *A. lutea* 'Gelbkerze'
taurica	ECGN EMan WPer

ASPHODELUS (Asphodelaceae)

acaulis	CLAP EWoo SWas WIvy WLin WOMN
– SF 37	CMon
§ *aestivus*	SWat WPer
albus	CArn CBlo CBot CMil EBee ECha LGre NPri SAxl SPla WCot WPer
brevicaulis	See *Asphodeline brevicaulis*
cerasiferus	See *A. ramosus*
fistulosus	CBlo CMil ECGN ELan NBir SAga WCot WPer WWin
lusitanicus	See *A. ramosus*
luteus	See *Asphodeline lutea*
microcarpus	See *A. aestivus*
§ *ramosus*	CMon ECGN ECGP EMan MTho WCot WPer

ASPIDISTRA (Convallariaceae)

elatior ♀	CHEx CHal EBak ERav IBlr LHil MBri MHlr NPal NRog SAPC SArc SAxl SMad SRms WCot WOak
– 'Milky Way'	WCot
– 'Variegata' ♀	CHal GCal IBlr LBlm MTho NBir SRms WCot WViv
lurida	IBlr
– 'Irish Mist'	EMon IBlr

ASPLENIUM † (Aspleniaceae)

adiantum-nigrum	NHar SRms
§ *aethiopicum*	CCuc EBee EFou
alternans	See *A. dalhousieae*
§ *australasicum* f. *robinsonii*	WRic
bulbiferum ♀	ECon LCns NMar
canariense	NMar
§ *ceterach*	SRms
dareoides	GBur GDra
flabellifolium	NMar WRic
fontanum	MBri NHar WAbe
forisiense	SMad
furcatum Thunberg	See *A. aethiopicum*
¶ *monanthes*	WRic
nidus ♀	MBri
oblongifolium	NMar
platyneuron	CFil
◆ *robinsonii*	See *A. australasicum* f. *robinsonii*
ruta-muraria	SRms
§ *scolopendrium* ♀	Widely available
– var. *americanum*	WRic
– 'Angustatum'	CBar CBlo CLAP CMil EFou LHil NHar NHol SMad SPla SSoC
¶ – 'Bolton's Nobile'	EMon
* – 'Circinatum'	CFil CRow WPGP
– 'Conglomeratum'	SRms
– Crispum Group	CCuc CFil CRDP CRow EBrP EBre ECha EFer ELan EMon EPla LBre MBri MHlr NHar NHol SBre SRms WAbe WFib WPGP
– 'Crispum Bolton's Nobile' ♀	CFil NBro NMar WEas WFib WPGP WRic
* – Crispum Cristatum Group	EMon

– Crispum Fimbriatum Group	GQui
– (Crispum Group) 'Golden Queen'	CRow WRic
– Cristatum Group	CDoC CFil CHEx CRDP CRow EBee ELan EMar EMon IOrc MBal MBri MRav NHar NHed NHol NMar SMad SPer SRms SSoC SWat WFib WGor WRic
– Fimbriatum Group	MBri WRic
– 'Furcatum'	CLAP EBee EMar
– 'Kaye's Lacerated' ♀	CRow EFer EGol ELan EMon MBri NHar NHed NHol NMar SChu WFib WRic
– Laceratum Group	SRms
– Marginatum Group	CFil NMar SWat WPGP
– – 'Irregulare'	CRDP NHar NHol SChu SRms WFib
– 'Muricatum'	CRDP NMar SChu WFib WRic
– 'Ramocristatum'	CRow NMar
– Ramomarginatum Group	EFer ELan EMon SRms WRic
– 'Sagittatocristatum'	CFil WPGP
– Undulatum Group	CBar CLAP EGol EPla GGar NHar NMar SRms SSpi SWat WRic
– Undulatum Cristatum Group	MBri NHed WRic
terrestre	SRms
trichomanes ♀	CCuc CDoC CFil CHea CTrC EBee EBrP EBre EFer EFou ELan EMon GGar LBre MBal MBri MLan MMoz NHar NHed NHol NMar SBre SRms WFib WPGP WRic
– Cristatum Group	SRms
– Incisum Group	EFer EMon IOrc NHar NHol NOrc SMad WCot WFib
¶ – 'Ramo-Cristatum'	WRic
viride	SRms

ASTARTEA (Myrtaceae)
fascicularis	CTrC SOWG

ASTELIA (Asteliaceae)
banksii	CB&S CTrC EMil
§ *chathamica* ♀	CAbb CB&S CDoC CFee CFil CHEx CSWP CSev EBee ERea GCal LHop SAPC SArc SDry WCru WRus
– 'Silver Spear'	See *A. chathamica*
cunninghamii	See *A. solandri*
fragrans	CFil ECou
graminea	ECou
◆ *graminifolia*	See *Collospermum microspermum*
grandis	IBlr
nervosa	CAbb CFil CHEx ECou IBlr LHil SAPC SArc WPGP
nivicola	IBlr SApp
– 'Red Gem'	IBlr
§ *solandri*	CFil CHEx LHil

ASTER † (Asteraceae)
acris	See *A. sedifolius*
ageratoides	See *A. trinervius* subsp. *ageratoides*
§ *albescens*	CGre CPle GOrc ISea MBal WSHC
¶ – AIC337	WCot
alpigenus	NSla WOMN

alpinus ♀	EBar EBrP EBre EHyt EMNN EMar GCHN LBre MNrw MPla NMen SBla SBre SIng SRms WFar WOMN WPer WStI WWin
– var. *albus*	GCHN MPla NPri SIng WPer
– Dark Beauty	See *A. alpinus* 'Dunkle Schöne'
¶ – var. *dolomiticus*	NSla
§ – 'Dunkle Schöne'	EFou NFai NOak WPer
– 'Happy End'	CM&M EMil MAvo NFai NOak NPri NRoo WCot
¶ – 'Märchenland'	WHil
– 'Trimix'	ESis LFis NBir NMir NRoo NVic SRms WFar
– violet	NPri WPer
– 'White Beauty'	EFou NFai
amelloides	See *Felicia amelloides*
amellus	EBot NNor
– 'Blue King'	EFou LFis LIck MAus MBri MLLN NFai SPer WCot
– 'Breslau'	MBri WOld
– 'Brilliant'	CMGP EBee EBrP EBre ECtt EFou EMan EPPr LBre LFis MBri MLLN MWat NRoo SBre SMer SMrm SPer WByw WMer WOld WWin
– 'Butzemann'	EFou
– 'Doktor Otto Petschek'	WFar WMer
– Empress	See *A. amellus* 'Glücksfund'
– 'Framfieldii' ♀	WOld
§ – 'Glücksfund'	EFou
– 'Grunder'	EFou WOld
– 'Jacqueline Genebrier' ♀	CMil EPPr SAxl SChu SMrm SPla SUsu WOld
– 'King George' ♀	CKel EBrP EBre ECED EFou ELan EPPr ERou LBre MAus MBel MWat NRoo SBre SChu SPer SPla SRms SWat WAbe WCot WEas WHoo WOld WWal
– 'Kobold'	WFar WOld
– 'Lac de Genève'	EMil LFis WFar WOld
– 'Lady Hindlip'	MRav MTed WEas
* – 'Mary Ann Neil'	LFis
– 'Moerheim Gem'	EFou WEas WOld
– 'Mrs Ralph Woods'	WOld
– 'Nocturne'	ECED EPPr ERou LFis NBrk SMrm WByw WCot WOld
– 'Peach Blossom'	CDoC MAus WCot WOld
– 'Pink Pearl'	WOld
– Pink Zenith	See *A. amellus* 'Rosa Erfüllung'
§ – 'Rosa Erfüllung'	EBrP EBre ECtt EFou ELan ERou GMaP LBre MAus MBri MLLN MRav NFla NNor NRoo SBla SBre SChu SPer SPla SSpe WAbe WEas WHoo WOld WPer WRus
– 'Rudolph Goethe'	EGra EMil EPri LIck MLLN MRav MUlv NFla NVic SHBN SSea WCot WEas WMer WOld
– 'Schöne von Ronsdorf'	LBuc
– 'September Glow'	ECha EFou EGle EHal SPla
– 'Sonia'	ECED ECha EFou EGle LFis MAus MBri NFla WMer WOld
– 'Sonora'	LGre WOld
– 'Sternkugel'	NBrk WOld
– 'Ultramarine'	EFou WFar
– 'Vanity'	GBuc WOld
§ – 'Veilchenkönigin' ♀	Widely available
N – Violet Queen	See *A. amellus* 'Veilchenkönigin'
– 'Weltfriede'	WOld

¶ 'Anja's Choice'	EMon WOld
asper	See *A. bakerianus*
¶ asperulus	LGre
§ bakerianus	CMGP NOak SUsu WFar WPer
'Barbara Worl'	SAsh
capensis 'Variegatus'	See *Felicia amelloides*
	variegata
§ carolinianus	WCot WOld
'Cha-Cha'	CB&S
'Climax'	CBre ECha GBuc GCal GMac
	LBlm MNFA MRav MUlv NSti
	SAxl SPer WOld
coelestis	See *Felicia amelloides*
¶ coloradoensis	NSla
* 'Connecticut Snow Fleure'	WHil
'Coombe Fishacre' ♀	CGle EFou ERou GCal LFis
	LGre MBel MBri MBro MMil
	MUlv NFai SAga SAxl SBla
	SHel SPla SSvw WByw WCot
	WEas WFar WOld WOve
cordifolius	WFar
– 'Aldebaran'	NBrk SAxl
– 'Chieftain' ♀	MTed WIvy WOld
– 'Elegans'	CDoC EFou EGar NSti WIvy
	WOld
– 'Ideal'	CDoC ECGP WOld WPer
– 'Little Carlow'	See *A. 'Little Carlow'*
	(*cordifolius* hybrid)
– 'Little Dorrit'	See *A. 'Little Dorrit'*
	(*cordifolius* hybrid)
– 'Photograph'	See *A. 'Photograph'*
– 'Silver Queen'	WOld
– 'Silver Spray'	CDoC EFou EHic EMan ERou
	GMaP GMac MBri MBro
	MLLN MWat NBro WEas
	WHoo WMer WOld WPer
	WPyg
– 'Sweet Lavender' ♀	ERou GMac LFis NBrk WOld
corymbosus	See *A. divaricatus*
'Deep Pink Star'	WOld
delavayi	SUsu
diffusus	See *A. lateriflorus*
diplostephioides	CMil EBee SSpi
§ divaricatus	Widely available
N dumosus	WPer
eatonii	EBee
ericoides	CGle CSam ERav SIng WWin
– 'Blue Star' ♀	EFou EGar GBuc MBel MLLN
	NBrk NFai NSti SChu SHel
	WCot WOld
– 'Blue Wonder'	CGle EOrc MNFA NBrk
– 'Brimstone' ♀	CBre EPPr MNFA MRav SHel
	WOld
– 'Cinderella'	CHor CVer EGar EHal EPPr
	GBuc GMac MNFA NFla NRoo
	NSti SPla WCot WOld
– 'Constance'	NBrk WOld
– 'Enchantress'	ERou
– 'Erlkönig'	CMGP EBee EFou EHic EPPr
	GAbr LHop MBri MMil MNFA
	MSte MWgw SChu SSpe SWat
	WOld WPer WWin
– 'Esther'	CGle CHea ECha EFou EGle
	ELan EMou EOrc EPri ERou
	LFis MNFA MSte NBrk NSti
	SDix WOld
– 'Golden Spray' ♀	EBee EFou MAus MNFA NFai
	NSti SHel WMer WOld
– 'Herbstmyrte'	GBuc
– 'Hon. Edith Gibbs'	GMac
– 'Hon. Vicary Gibbs'	See *A. 'Hon. Vicary Gibbs'*
	(*ericoides* hybrid)
– 'Kaytie Fisher'	LFis
– 'Maidenhood'	WBcn WOld
– 'Monte Cassino'	See *A. pringlei* 'Monte Cassino'
– 'Pink Cloud' ♀	CGle CHan CHor CVer EBrP
	EBre EFou ERou LBre LFis
	LGan LHop MBro MNFA
	MRav MSte MWat NFai NRoo
	SBre SChu SPer SPla SWat
	WHoo WOld WPer WPyg
	WRus WWin
– f. prostratus	EMon ERav LRHS SCro
– – 'Snowflurry'	ECha EFou EJud MAvo MHlr
	WCot WOld
– 'Rosy Veil'	CBre GMac NBrk WByw WIvy
	WOld
– 'Schneegitter'	EHic MBri MSte
– 'Sulphurea'	MWat
– 'White Heather'	CVer EGar GMac MBro MHlr
	NFai SAxl WByw WCot WEas
	WHoo WIvy WOld WPyg
– 'Yvette Richardson'	MSte SHel WOld
farreri	GCHN NBro WPbr
foliaceus	EBee NTow
× frikartii	CMea EAst EBrP EBre EFou
	ELan EPar ERou GCHN LBre
	LHop MBro MRav NFla SBla
	SBre SChu SHBN SPer SSoC
	WByw WEas WOld WPer
	WWin
– 'Eiger'	NBrk WOld
– 'Flora's Delight'	EBrP EBre EFou ERou LBre
	MRav NRoo SBre WOld
– 'Jungfrau'	MTed NCut WOld
N – 'Mönch' ♀	Widely available
– Wonder of Stafa	See *A.* × *frikartii* 'Wunder von Stäfa'
§ – 'Wunder von Stäfa' ♀	EAst EBar EBee EMan GBuc
	GMac LFis LHop MAvo MBri
	MUlv NLak NSti SChu WFar
	WLRN WOld
'Herfstweelde'	CMil EFou EGar EMon GBuc
	MBro MSte SAxl SBla SHel
	SLod SWas WOld
× herveyi	EMan EMon EPPr SAga WOld
	WPbr
himalaicus	GCHN GCra GTou
– CC&McK 145	GCHN MRPP NWCA
'Hittlemaar'	EPPr WCot
§ 'Hon. Vicary Gibbs'	CBre CHea EBee LFis MNFA
(*ericoides* hybrid)	MSte NBrk WCot WOld
hybridus luteus	See × *Solidaster luteus*
§ 'Kylie' ♀	CBre EFou EMon GBuc LFis
	MSte NBrk SCro WCot WOld
	WTin
laevis	EMon MSte SHel SWas WCot
– 'Arcturus'	CDoC CFir CLTr EGar LBlm
	MBri MLLN MMil MTed NSti
	SSvw
– 'Blauhügel'	GCal
– 'Calliope'	CHan EBar ECha GCal MBro
	MGed MLLN MMil MSte MTed
	NOak SAga SMrm SUsu SWas
	WCot WFar WIvy WKif WOld
lanceolatus 'Edwin Beckett'	CBre LFis MNFA NBrk WOld
§ lateriflorus	CGle EJud ERav MNes MWat
	WHow WMaN WOld WPer
– 'Bleke Bet'	WCot WOld
– 'Buck's Fizz'	CAbb ELan NLar SPla
¶ – 'Datschii'	WFar
– 'Delight'	MLLN WCot

– 'Horizontalis' ♀ — CBot CElw CMHG ECha EFou EMon ERou GMac LFis LGan LGre MBri MPla MRav MWat NBro NSti SAga SBla SChu SDix SHBN SPer WByw WEas WMow WOld

– 'Lady in Black' — CBot EFou LBuc MSte MTed NSti SAga SMrm WCot WOld

– 'Lovely' — LFis MBro MLLN NOak WOld

– 'Prince' — CBos CGle CHad CMea CMil EBee ECha EFou EHal ELan EMan EMon EWes LFis LGre MAus MBrN MHlr MSte MWgw NBir NSti SHel SMad SPla SSpe SWas WCot WOld WPGP

likiangensis — See A. asteroides

¶ *linariifolius* — EBee

§ *linosyris* — EHal LFis MSte SPer SUsu WCot WHer WMer WOld

– 'Goldilocks' — See A. linosyris

§ 'Little Carlow' — CBos CBre CGle CHea CVer
    (*cordifolius* hybrid) ♀ — EFou EHal EJud ERou GCal GMaP LFis LGre MBel MMil MNFA MRav MWat NFai NSti SAxl SBla SWas WCot WEas WOld WOve WPer WWat

§ 'Little Dorrit' — CBre GMac MBro MLLN
    (*cordifolius* hybrid) — NOak NWes WCot WOld

macrophyllus — CBlo CFee CPou EBee EBrP EBre ELan EMon LBre MBel NSti SBre SPer WOld

– 'Albus' — EMon EPPr WIvy WOld

– 'Twilight' — CGle CMea EBee EFou EGle EMan EOrc EPPr GCal GMac MBro MLLN MSte SHel SWas WCot WFar WIvy WOld WRHF

mongolicus — See Kalimeris mongolica

natalensis — See Felicia rosulata

novae-angliae 'Andenken an Alma Pötschke' ♀ — Widely available

– 'Andenken an Paul Gerbe' — EMon WMer

– Autumn Snow — See A. novae-angliae 'Herbstschnee'

– 'Barr's Blue' — EBar EFou EMon MAus MRav MSte MTed MWat NSti SChu WMer WOld

– 'Barr's Pink' — CBre EFou EJud EMon LFis MAus MRav MWat NFla SHel WEas WFar WMer WOld WPer WPyg

– 'Barr's Violet' — NCat NLon NNor SAxl SRms WCot WOld WPer

– 'Christopher Harbutt' — ERou WOld

– 'Crimson Beauty' — EGar GMac MWat WOld

– 'Festival' — CBlo

– 'Harrington's Pink' ♀ — CGle CHea CMea ECED EFou ELan EMon EOrc ERou LHop MAus MNFA MRav MWat NFai NNor NRoo NSti SChu SCro SHel SPer WByw WEas WFar WHil WHow WOld WPyg WWin

§ – 'Herbstschnee' — CGle EBrP EBre EFou EMon ERou GCHN GMac LBre MAus MAvo MBel MNFA MWat NFai NFla NHol NNor NRoo NSti NVic SBre SChu SEas SHel SPer SSpe WOld WPer

– 'Lachsglut' — EFou

– 'Lou Williams' — WOld

– 'Lye End Beauty' — CPou EMon MFir MNFA MRav MSte MUlv MWat NNor SChu WCot WOld

¶ – mixed — WHil

– 'Mrs S.T. Wright' — EFou EGar EGle EMon ERou MBrN WByw WOld

* – 'Mrs S.W. Stern' — WOld

– 'Pink Parfait' — WCot WOld

– 'Pink Victor' — CTri EFou EPPr NFai SEND

– 'Purple Cloud' — EMon EPPr ERou GMac LHop MWat

– 'Purple Dome' — EBrP EBre EFou ELan EMon LBre MAus MAvo MBri MBro SBre SEND SSpe WCot WFar WOld

– 'Quinton Menzies' — EMon WOld

– 'Red Cloud' — CBre EFou NFai

– 'Rosa Sieger' — EBrP EBre EMon LBre SBre SChu SUsu WMer WOld WViv

– 'Rose Williams' — WOld

– 'Roter Stern' — EFou

– 'Rubinschatz' — WOld

– 'Rudelsburg' — EMon

– 'Sayer's Croft' — EGle EMon MWat WCot WOld

– September Ruby — See A. novae-angliae 'Septemberrubin'

§ – 'Septemberrubin' — CBlo CMea ECED ECtt EMon ERou LHop MRav MSte NFai SChu WByw WCot WEas WFar WOld WPyg WWin

– 'Treasure' — CBre EFou EMon WOld

– 'Violetta' — CBre EMon MSte MTed NFai WOld

– 'W. Bowman' — EMon

novi-belgii — SEas WHer

N – 'Ada Ballard' — CBlo CVer EBee ECED EMan ENot ERou GCHN MBel SPer WLRN WOld WWal

– 'Albanian' — CElw EJud WOld

– 'Alderman Vokes' — ERou WOld

– 'Alex Norman' — ERou WOld

– 'Algar's Pride' — CBre ERou MUlv WOld

– 'Alice Haslam' — CBlo CKel CMGP ECtt EFou EOld EPPr GBri MBri MFir MRav MWgw NOrc NPri SSpe WByw WLRN WMow WOld WOve WPer WRHF

– 'Alpenglow' — WOld

– 'Anita Ballard' — WOld

– 'Anita Webb' — ERou GBri NBir NOak WOld

– 'Anneke' — EPfP WGor

– Antwerp Pearl — See A. novi-belgii 'Antwerpse Parel'

– 'Apollo' — CB&S MBri NBus NPri

– 'Apple Blossom' — SHel WOld

– 'Arctic' — ERou WBcn WOld

– 'Audrey' — CMGP EBar ECED ECtt EFou ERou GCHN GMaP MBri MLLN MWgw NBro NLak NOrc SChu SEas SMer WByw WCot WMer WOld WWal

– 'Autumn Beauty' — WOld

– 'Autumn Days' — WOld

– 'Autumn Glory' — ERou WOld

– 'Autumn Rose' — CHea WOld

– 'Baby Climax' — WOld

– 'Beauty of Colwall' — WOld

– 'Beechwood Challenger' — ERou MOne WMer WOld

– 'Beechwood Charm' — MNFA WOld

– 'Beechwood Rival' — WMer

– 'Beechwood Supreme'	ERou WOld
– 'Bewunderung'	WOld
– 'Blandie'	CBlo CDoC CHea CTri ECED EFou ERou LGan MSte MWat NBro SHel WLRN WOld
– 'Blauglut'	EFou WOld
– 'Blue Baby'	LHop MRav WPer
– 'Blue Bouquet'	CDoC ECED ERou SRms WByw WOld
– 'Blue Boy'	CHea WOld
– 'Blue Danube'	WOld
– 'Blue Eyes'	ERou LGre NOak SWas WOld
– 'Blue Gown'	EGar ERou GCal MUlv WOld
– Blaue Lagune = 'Blue Lagoon'	CBlo WOld
– 'Blue Patrol'	ERou NOak WOld
– 'Blue Radiance'	MNFA WOld
– 'Blue Whirl'	ERou WOld
– 'Bonanza'	WOld
– 'Boningale Blue'	MTed WOld
– 'Boningale White'	ERou WOld
– 'Bridesmaid'	SHel WOld
– 'Brightest and Best'	NBrk WOld
– 'Caborn Pink'	LLWP
– 'Cameo'	WOld
– 'Cantab'	WBcn WOld
* – 'Cantonese Queen'	EMon
– 'Carlingcott'	ERou MOne NOak WOld
– 'Carnival'	CBlo CKel CM&M EBee EFou ERou LFis MBri MUlv NHaw NOrc SHel SPer SSpe WHow WOld
– 'Cecily'	SGre WLin WOld
– 'Charles Wilson'	WOld
– 'Chatterbox'	CDoC ECtt MAvo MRav MWat SChu SRms WLin WOld
– 'Chelwood'	WOld
– 'Chequers'	CBlo CM&M EBee ECED ECot EMan ERou NNor WGor WHow WLRN WOld
– 'Christina'	See *A. novi-belgii* **'Kristina'**
– 'Christine Soanes'	EFou WOld
– 'Cliff Lewis'	ERou WOld
– 'Climax Albus'	See *A.* **'White Climax'**
– 'Cloudy Blue'	CElw WOld
– 'Colonel F.R. Durham'	ERou MBro WMer
– 'Coombe Delight'	ERou
– 'Coombe Gladys'	ERou WOld
– 'Coombe Joy'	ERou NOak WLRN WOld
– 'Coombe Margaret'	MLLN WOld
– 'Coombe Pink'	ERou
– 'Coombe Queen'	WOld
– 'Coombe Radiance'	ERou WOld
– 'Coombe Ronald'	ERou MWat WOld
– 'Coombe Rosemary'	CDec EBrP EBre ECtt EPPr ERou LBre MUlv NOak SBre WByw WOld WRHF
– 'Coombe Violet'	LGre MWat WOld
– 'Countess of Dudley'	WOld WPer
– 'Court Herald'	WOld
– 'Crimson Brocade'	CDoC CTri ECED ELan ENot EPfP ERou MWat SHel SPer WMer WOld WWhi
– 'Dandy'	CBlo COtt ECot ELan MBro MMil SChu SEas WByw WOld WSan WWal
– 'Daniela'	CHea EFou SGre WOld
– 'Daphne Anne'	WOld
– 'Dauerblau'	WOld
– 'Davey's True Blue'	CTri EFou EMan ERou WLRN WOld WWal
– 'David Murray'	WOld

– 'Dazzler'	WOld
– 'Destiny'	WOld
– 'Diana'	CNic ERou WOld
– 'Diana Watts'	ERou WOld
– 'Dietgard'	SGre WOld
– 'Dolly'	NBir WOld
– 'Dusky Maid'	SHel WOld
– 'Elizabeth'	CElw WOld
– 'Elizabeth Bright'	WOld
– 'Elizabeth Hutton'	WOld
– 'Elsie Dale'	SAxl WOld
– 'Elta'	WOld
– 'Erica'	CElw MWat WOld
– 'Ernest Ballard'	ERou MRav WOld
– 'Eva'	WOld
– 'Eventide'	CB&S CElw CTri ECED ENot ERou MBro NOak SPer WLRN WOld WRHF
– 'F.M. Simpson'	ERou
– 'Fair Lady'	ERou MWat WOld
– 'Faith'	WOld
– 'Farrington'	WOld
– 'Fellowship'	CB&S CElw CFir CKel CMGP CSpe EBrP EBre ECED EFou ENot ERou GCHN LBre MHlr MNFA MUlv MWat SBre SEas SPer SRms WCot WEas WOld WWal
– 'Fontaine'	WOld
– 'Freda Ballard'	EBee ECED ERou GCHN MRav MWat WBro WLRN WOld WWal
– 'Fuldatal'	EFou SHel WOld
– 'Gayborder Royal'	CFir ECED ERou MOne SHel WOld
– 'Gayborder Splendour'	WOld
– 'Glory of Colwall'	WOld
– 'Goliath'	WOld
¶ – 'Grey Lady'	WOld
– 'Guardsman'	ERou MBri MUlv WOld
– 'Gulliver'	WOld
– 'Gurney Slade'	EJud ERou MBri WOld
– 'Guy Ballard'	ERou
– 'Harrison's Blue'	ERou WOld WPer
– 'Heinz Richard'	CBlo CM&M EBee ECha EFou LHop MBri MUlv NBir SBla SChu WLRN WOld
– 'Helen'	WOld
– 'Helen Ballard'	CHea ECGN EFou ERou NBrk WOld
¶ – 'Herbstgruss von Bressherhof'	MBro
– 'Herbstpurzel'	SGre WGor WMer
– 'Hilda Ballard'	ERou WOld
– 'Ilse Brensell'	EFou WOld
– 'Irene'	WOld
– 'Isabel Allen'	WOld
– 'Janet McMullen'	EJud
– 'Janet Watts'	ERou WOld
– 'Jean'	MTed MWat SChu SHel WOld
– 'Jean Gyte'	WOld
– 'Jenny'	EBrP EBre ECED ECtt EFou GCHN GMaP LBre LHop MBri MBro MRav MWat NBir SBre SHBN SPer WByw WEas WHoo WOld
– 'Jollity'	WOld
– 'Judith'	MTed
– 'Julia'	WOld
– 'Karminkuppel'	WOld
¶ – 'Kassel'	MBro
– 'King of the Belgians'	WOld

– 'King's College'	CElw MBri WOld
§ – 'Kristina'	EBrP EBre ECha ECtt EFou
	ERou LBre LLWP MBro
	MCLN MOne MRav MUlv
	NBrk SBre SChu SSpe WCot
	WHow WLin WOld WRHF
– 'Lady Evelyn	WOld
Drummond'	
– 'Lady Frances'	WOld
– 'Lady in Blue'	Widely available
– 'Lady Paget'	WOld
– 'Lassie'	CHea ERou LFis MLLN MWat
	WOld
¶ – 'Lavanda'	WLRN
– 'Lavender Dream'	WOld
– 'Lawrence Chiswell'	SHel WOld
– 'Lilac Time'	WByw WLin WOld
– 'Lisa Dawn'	WOld
– 'Little Boy Blue'	CB&S CDoC ERou NBus
	SHBN WByw WMer WOld
– 'Little Man in Blue'	WOld
– 'Little Pink Beauty'	EBar EBrP EBre ECtt EFou
	ELan ERou GCHN GChr IHos
	LBre LHop MBri MRav NFai
	NMir NVic SAga SBre SEas
	SHel SPer SSpe SWat WHoo
	WMow WOld WWal WWin
– 'Little Pink Lady'	ECED ERou WLin WOld
– 'Little Pink Pyramid'	LLWP SRms
– 'Little Red Boy'	CB&S CBlo ERou MBel WOld
– 'Little Treasure'	WOld
– 'Lucy'	WOld
– 'Madge Cato'	MOne NOak WOld
– 'Malvern Castle'	ERou
– 'Mammoth'	WOld
– 'Margaret Rose'	NOrc NPla WLRN WOld
– 'Margery Bennett'	ERou GBri NOak WOld
– 'Marie Ballard'	CB&S CElw CHea CTri ECED
	ECGN ENot ERou GMaP
	MAvo MBri MFir MRav MWat
	NBro NNor NOrc SChu SEas
	SHBN SHel SPer SRms WEas
	WHow WOld WPer
– 'Marie's Pretty Please'	NCat WOld
– 'Marjorie'	SEas WOld
– 'Marjory Ballard'	WOld
– 'Martonie'	WOld WPer
– 'Mary Ann Neil'	WOld
– 'Mary Deane'	CHea WOld WPer
– 'Melbourne Belle'	MUlv NOak WOld
– 'Melbourne Magnet'	CHea ERou WOld
– 'Michael Watts'	ERou WOld
– 'Mistress Quickly'	CPou CTri ERou MBel NOak
	SHel WBro WOld
– 'Mount Everest'	CDoC ERou WMer WOld
	WPer
– 'Mrs Leo Hunter'	NOak WOld
– 'Newton's Pink'	CTri
– 'Niobe'	ELan WMer WOMN
– 'Nobilis'	WOld
– 'Norman's Jubilee'	ERou MTed NBir WOld
– 'Nursteed Charm'	WOld
– 'Oktoberschneekuppel'	ERou MBri
– 'Orlando'	ERou WCot WOld
– 'Pacific Amarant'	SRos
– 'Pamela'	ERou WOld
– 'Patricia Ballard'	CBlo CTri ECED ERou LFis
	MFir MRav MWat NBro NLak
	NNor SMer SPer SSpe WLRN
	WLin WOld WPer
– 'Peace'	WOld

– 'Percy Thrower'	CMGP EFou ERou WEas
	WLRN WOld
– 'Peter Chiswell'	WOld
– 'Peter Harrison'	GMaP GMac MOne NBir NBrk
	NBro WOld WPer
– 'Peter Pan'	NBus WOld
– 'Picture'	WOld
– 'Pink Gown'	WOld
– 'Pink Lace'	EBar ERou MBro MLLN
	WByw WOld WPer
– 'Pink Pyramid'	EJud WOld
– 'Plenty'	ERou MBri WOld
¶ – 'Porzellan'	CMGP SAxl
– 'Pride of Colwall'	ERou MWat
– 'Priory Blush'	CHea ERou GMac NBrk NOak
	WLRN WOld
– 'Professor Anton	CBlo EBee EFou EJud EMan
Kippenberg'	EPPr ERou GCHN GMaP
	GMac LBlm MBri MRav NFai
	NPri SPer WOld WWhi
– 'Prosperity'	ERou NOak WOld
* – 'Prunella'	ERou WOld
– 'Purple Dome'	ECha WBcn WHoo WOld
– 'Queen Mary'	ERou WMer WOld
– 'Queen of Colwall'	WOld
– 'Ralph Picton'	WOld
– 'Raspberry Ripple'	CBlo ECot ERou EWes NPla
	SEas WLRN WOld WRha
	WSan
I – 'Rector'	See *A. novi-belgii* 'The Rector'
– 'Red Robin'	MWat
– 'Red Sunset'	CB&S ERou MBro SRms WOld
– 'Remembrance'	EFou MBri WOld WWhi
– 'Reverend Vincent	WOld
Dale'	
– 'Richness'	ERou LGre NOak SHel WOld
– 'Robin Adair'	WOld
– 'Roland Smith'	WOld
– 'Rose Bonnet'	CKel CMGP EFou ENot IHos
	MMil MWat SChu SHBN
	WLRN
– 'Rose Bouquet'	WOld
– 'Rosebud'	CBlo ELan SEas WEas WOld
– 'Rosemarie Sallmann'	EFou
– 'Rosenwichtel'	EFou EMar GAri MCLN SAga
	WLRN WOld
– 'Royal Blue'	WMer
– 'Royal Ruby'	ECtt WBcn WOld
– 'Royal Velvet'	ECED ENot ERou WOld
– 'Rozika'	EFou WOld
– 'Rufus'	ERou NOak WOld
– 'Sailor Boy'	EFou ERou LFis WLRN WOld
– 'Saint Egwyn'	WOld
– 'Sam Banham'	ERou
– 'Sandford White Swan'	CVer EJud ERou LLWP MBel
	MBri WPer
– 'Sarah Ballard'	ERou MWat WOld
§ – 'Schneekissen'	ECtt EGoo EHal EMan EPla
	GMaP LHop MBri NPri NTow
	SAga SBla SEND SMer SPer
	WHil WLRN WOld WWal
– 'Schöne von Dietlikon'	CDoC EFou NOak WLRN
	WMer WOld
– 'Schoolgirl'	ERou MBri WOld
– 'Sheena'	ERou MBri MUlv WOld
– Snow Cushion	See *A. novi-belgii*
	'Schneekissen'
– 'Snowdrift'	WOld
– 'Snowsprite'	CB&S ECED ELan EMan
	MWat NBro NOrc SWat WByw
	WCot WHoo WOld WWal

– 'Sonata'	EBee EJud ERou GMaP NLon NNor NOak SHel SPer WOld
– 'Sophia'	ERou NOak WOld
– 'Starlight'	ENot ERou MBri WMow WOld WRHF
– 'Steinebrück'	EFou WOld
– 'Sterling Silver'	CElw ERou NOak WByw WOld
– 'Storm Clouds'	EFou LFis
– 'Sunset'	WOld
– 'Sweet Briar'	WOld
– 'Tapestry'	CDoC WBcn WOld
– 'Terry's Pride'	WOld
– 'The Archbishop'	WOld
– 'The Bishop'	ERou WOld
– 'The Cardinal'	ECED ERou WOld
– 'The Choristers'	CVer WOld
– 'The Dean'	ERou NHaw WOld
– 'The Rector'	WOld
– 'The Sexton'	ERou WOld
– 'Thundercloud'	SHel WOld
– 'Timsbury'	WOld
– 'Tony'	WOld
– 'Tosca'	LFis
– 'Tovarich'	GMac NBrk WOld
– 'Trudi Ann'	EFou NBir WOld
– 'Twinkle'	EFou WOld
– 'Victor'	MBal WOld
– 'Violet Lady'	ERou MBro WOld
– 'Violetta'	CB&S
– 'Waterperry'	MWat
– 'Weisse Wunder'	EFou WOld
– 'White Ladies'	CBlo EBee ECtt EFou ERou GAri GMaP LLWP MUlv MWat NNor NOrc SMer SPer WLRN WWal
– 'White Swan'	CPou EMon EPPr NOak WEas WOld
– 'White Wings'	WOld
– 'Winston S. Churchill'	CTri ECED ELan ENot ERou GMaP MHFP MNFA MWat NNor NOrc NSti SEas SHBN SHel SPer SSea SSpe WOld
¶ oblongifolius	WOld
'Ochtendgloren' (pringlei hybrid) ♀	EBee EBrP EBre EFou EGle EMon EPPr GBuc LBre MSte MTed NSti SAga SBre WCot WFar WOld
pappei	See Felicia amoena
'Pearl Star'	WOld
petiolatus	See Felicia petiolata
§ 'Photograph' ♀	CMHG EFou EGar MNFA MWat NBrk WOld
§ pilosus var. demotus ♀	EGar EPPr EWes MLLN MRav MSte SCro SHel SMrm SPla WFar
'Pink Cassino'	CB&S WRus
'Pink Star'	CMil EFou GMac MHlr MWgw NPri NRoo NSti NWoo WCot WOld
'Plowden's Pink'	WOld
'Poollicht'	EFou
§ pringlei 'Monte Cassino'	Widely available
I – 'Phoebe'	WCot
– 'Pink Cushion'	WCot
§ ptarmicoides	CBlo CFee CM&M EBee EFou EMon MBrN MLLN WCot WEas WOld WPer
pyrenaeus 'Lutetia'	CHea EBee ECha EFou EGar EMan EOrc EPPr GCal GMac MMil MNFA MSte MUlv SHel SUsu WCot WFar WOld WOve
radula	CDoC EGar EMon EPPr GCal NBrk NSti WCot WOld
'Ringdove' (ericoides hybrid) ♀	CBlo CBre CMGP EBee ECED EGar ERou MMil MNFA MWat MWgw NSti SAxl SPla WCot WEas WLRN WOld WPen
'Rosa Star'	SHel WBro WOld
rotundifolius 'Variegatus'	See Felicia amelloides variegated
* sativus atrocaeruleus	ECro
scandens	See A. carolinianus
schreberi	WCot
§ sedifolius	CHea EJud ELan EMan EMon LFis MNFA MSte MWat SDix SUsu WCot WEas WFar WOld WPer WWhi
– 'Nanus'	CBos CHan ECED ECha EFou ERou LFis MBri MBro MLLN MRav NBir NFai NSti SMrm WByw WCot WFar WHow WOld
¶ – 'Snow Flurries'	MNrw NBrk
¶ sibiricus	WOld
'Snow Star'	SHel WOld
spectabilis	CLyd GAbr WOld
stracheyi	EBee NTow
subspicatus	WPer
tataricus 'Jindai'	WCot
thomsonii 'Nanus'	CGle CLyd CSam EBrP EBre ECha EFou GCHN LBre LFis LGre MBro MRav NNrd NRoo SBla SBre SPer SUsu SWas WEas WHoo WHow WOld WSHC
tibeticus	See A. flaccidus
§ tongolensis	CBlo EPfP MLLN SAga SEas SIgm WFar WOMN WWin
– 'Berggarten'	CMil EBrP EBre LBre LFis MBri MCli MMil MRav NBro NHaw NRoo SBla SBre SCro SUsu WAbe WFar WMer
– 'Dunkleviolette'	GBuc NBro
– 'Lavender Star'	CBlo EFou GBuc SRms
– 'Leuchtenburg'	ERou
– 'Napsbury'	CBlo ECha EHic ERou MCli
– 'Sternschnuppe'	MCli
– Summer Greeting	See A. tongolensis 'Sommergrüss'
– 'Wartburgstern'	CMdw EBee EGar EMan EPfP LFis MCli·NPri SHel SPla WGwG WLRN WPer WWal
tradescantii hort.	See A. pilosus var. demotus
– Linnaeus	CGle CLTr EBar EBee ECha EFou ELan EMan MFir MNFA MRav MUlv MWgw NOak NSti SCou SMad SSvw WEas WOld
tripolium	CKin WHer
turbinellus hort. ♀	EBar ECGN EFou EMon GBuc GMac MBro MHlr NBrk NTow SChu SDix SMrm WCot WFar WHer WHoo WOld
umbellatus	CBre CLTr EMon EPPr NSti SRms WCot WOld
vahlii	ECou GAbr WPer
vimineus Lamarck	See A. lateriflorus
– 'Ptarmicoides'	See A. ptarmicoides
§ 'White Climax'	EFou MTed MUlv WCot WOld
'Yvonne'	CBre

ASTERANTHERA (Gesneriaceae)
ovata CAbb CFil CGre CPlN GGGa
GGar GOrc MBal SBid WAbe
WCru WGwG WSHC WWal
WWat

ASTERISCUS (Asteraceae)
'Gold Coin' See *A. maritimus*
* 'Golden Dollar' NPri
§ *maritimus* EHic IHos LHil LIck WOMN

ASTEROMOEA (Asteraceae)
mongolica See *Kalimeris mongolica*

ASTILBE † (Saxifragaceae)
'Aphrodite' CCuc EAst EGol ENot GAbr
(*simplicifolia* hybrid) LFis MBri NFla NHol NMir
NPro SChu SPla SSpi WAbe
WGor
x *arendsii* CPea MBro NNor WPer
– 'Amethyst' CBlo CCuc CHor CMGP
CMHG CTri EBee EGol MCli
NFai NRoo SEas SMer SPer
– 'Anita Pfeifer' CMHG LBuc LRHS MBri
– 'Bergkristall' CCuc CMHG EMil
§ – 'Brautschleier' ♀ CB&S CMHG CTri ECtt EFou
EGol ENot EPfP GCHN MWat
NCut NFai SMer
– 'Bressingham Beauty' CCuc CMHG EBrP EBre ECtt
EHon ELan ENot EPar ERic
GCHN GMaP LBre LSyl MBri
MCLN MRav NFla NHol NRoo
NSti SBre SEas SPer
– Bridal Veil See *A.* x *arendsii* 'Brautschleier'
– 'Bumalda' CDoC CFir CMHG COtt
GCHN MBri MCli WWat
– 'Cattleya' CCuc CMHG EFou EPla WFar
WGor
* – 'Cattleya Dunkel' CMHG
– 'Ceres' CCuc CDoC CMHG MWat
NHol
§ – 'Diamant' CDoC CHor CMHG EAst LFis
MBri SEas WFar
– Diamond See *A.* x *arendsii* 'Diamant'
– 'Drayton Glory' See *A.* x *rosea* 'Peach Blossom'
– Elizabeth Bloom = EBrP EBre GCHN GSki LBre
'Eliblo' SBre
♦ – Elizabeth Bloom See *A.* x *arendsii* Elizabeth
Bloom = 'Eliblo'
– 'Ellie' CCuc LRHS MBri
– 'Erica' CBlo CHor CMHG CTri GGar
MBri MRav
– 'Fanal' ♀ Widely available
– 'Federsee' CB&S CMGP CMHG ECha
ELan ENot LHop SPer WFar
WLRN
§ – 'Feuer' CB&S CCuc CMGP CMHG
CSam ECha ELan EPfP GCHN
GGar NHol NVic SPer SPla
– Fire See *A.* x *arendsii* 'Feuer'
– 'Gertrud Brix' CB&S CCuc EPar WMer WRus
– 'Gladstone' CMea GCHN GHCN WGor
WWeb
– 'Gloria' CCuc CMHG CTri LPBA MBri
NCut NPla
– 'Gloria Purpurea' CBlo CCuc CHor CMHG
LRHS MBri MTed NHol
– Glow See *A.* x *arendsii* 'Glut'
§ – 'Glut' CMHG MBri NPri SRms WFar
– 'Granat' CCuc CDoC CHor CMHG
MBal MCli WLRN WWin

– 'Grete Püngel' EGol EMil LRHS MBri WMer
– 'Harmony' CMHG
– Hyacinth See *A.* x *arendsii* 'Hyazinth'
§ – 'Hyazinth' CMHG EGol ELan GAbr MCli
NFai NHol WWal
– 'Irrlicht' CB&S CCuc CGle CMHG
EHon ELan EPla LHop LPBA
MBal NDea SEas SPer SWat
– 'Kvele' CMHG MBri WFar
§ – 'Lachskönigin' CMHG MWat
– 'Mont Blanc' CMHG
– 'Obergärtner Jürgens' EBee
– 'Paul Gaärder' CMHG
– 'Pink Curtsy' EBrP EBre LBre SBre
– Pink Pearl See *A.* x *arendsii* 'Rosa Perle'
– 'Queen of Holland' CMHG MCli
– Red Light See *A.* x *arendsii* 'Rotlicht'
§ – 'Rosa Perle' CCuc CMHG ECha NHol
§ – 'Rotlicht' MBri
– Salmon Queen See *A.* x *arendsii* 'Lachskönigin'
¶ – 'Sarma' MBri
– 'Snowdrift' CCuc CMHG EBar EBrP EBre
ECha EFou EGol EPla GAri
LBre MCli NMir NNor NOak
NOrc NPro SBre SWat
– 'Solferino' CMHG
– 'Spartan' CCuc CMHG EBee ECot EHic
MBri NPro NSti WFar WGor
– 'Spinell' CBlo MWat
– 'Venus' CCuc CMHG CSam ECED
ECha ECtt EFou EGol MBel
NHol NOrc NVic SPer SSpe
SWat WFar WViv
– 'Walküre' CMHG
– 'Washington' MCli WMer
§ – 'Weisse Gloria' CCuc CMHG EBee ECha EPar
LPBA NMGW NSti SPla
– 'Weisse Perle' CMHG
– White Gloria See *A.* x *arendsii* 'Weisse
Gloria'
– 'White Queen' GChr NHol NWoo
– 'William Reeves' CCuc CMHG MFir NHol
– 'Zuster Theresa' MBri
astilboides CHan NHol WCot
'Atrorosea' ECha MBri
(*simplicifolia* hybrid)
'Betsy Cuperus' CMHG EFou MAus MCli
(*thunbergii* hybrid)
'Bonn' (*japonica* hybrid) CB&S EPar LPBA SRms WRus
¶ 'Bremen' (*japonica* hybrid) LPBA
§ 'Bronce Elegans' CB&S CMGP COtt EAst EBar
(*simplicifolia* hybrid) ♀ EBrP EBre ECha EFou EPar
GSki LBre MBal MGrG MRav
NHar NHol NMir NOrc SBre
SChu SPer WAbe WCot WFar
WMow
'Catherine Deneuve' EBrP EBre LBre SBre
'Cherry Ripe' See *A.* x *arendsii* 'Feuer'
chinensis CMHG IBlr NCut
– var. *davidii* CMHG
– 'Finale' CCuc GLil NHol SPer WEas
WFar
– 'Frankentroll' CMHG
– 'Intermezzo' GMaP
§ – var. *pumila* ♀ Widely available
– *pumila* 'Serenade' CCuc WFar
– 'Purple Glory' CMHG
– 'Spätsommer' CMHG
– var. *taquetii* Purple See *A. chinensis taquetii*
Lance 'Purpurlanze'

§ – – 'Purpurlanze'	CMHG ECha GCHN MBri MRav NBir NCat NPla NPro WCot WFar WMer WMow WWin
§ – – 'Superba' ♀	CCuc CGle CMHG CRow ECha ECoo ELan ENot GCHN MNrw MSte NCut NDea NFai NHol NNor NSti NTow NVic SDix SPer WEas WOld
– 'Veronica Klose'	CMHG LRHS MBri NPro
– 'Visions'	CCuc MBri
Cologne	See *A.* **'Köln'** (*japonica* hybrid)
* 'Crimson Feather'	ECha
× *crispa*	IBlr
– 'Gnom'	NHar
– 'Lilliput'	CB&S CMGP MBri NHar NLar
– 'Perkeo' ♀	CB&S CCuc CMHG CMea COtt CRow EBrP EBre ECha ECtt EGle GCHN GDra GGar LBre LHop MBel MBri MBro NBir NHar NHol NLar NMen NOak NRoo SBre SRms SSpi WCot
– 'Peter Pan'	NSla
– 'Snow Queen'	NHar NMen NPro WFar
'Darwin's Dream'	MBri
'Deutschland' (*japonica* hybrid)	Widely available
'Dunkellachs' (*simplicifolia* hybrid)	CBlo CCuc CM&M EBee MBri SPla WAbe WMer
'Düsseldorf' (*japonica* hybrid)	CCuc CMGP CMHG GGar MBri SPer SSea WRus
'Emden' (*japonica* hybrid)	MWat
'Etna' (*japonica* hybrid)	CB&S CCuc CDoC CMHG EGle GBri GHCN MBal NCut WRus
'Europa' (*japonica* hybrid)	CBlo CCuc EBee EMil LPBA MBal NCut NFai NOak SMad SSoC
glaberrima	EPPr EPar NGre
– var. *saxatilis* ♀	CCuc CNic CRow ELan GAri GBur GCHN MBal MBro MFos NOak NRoo NRya NSla NWoo SChu SSmi WAbe WHal WOve
– *saxosa*	See *A.* **'Saxosa'**
* – – *minor*	NNrd
'Glenroy Elf'	MBal
grandis	CMHG GBur SSca
'Hennie Graafland' (*simplicifolia* hybrid)	CB&S CMHG EBar EFou EGol
'Inshriach Pink' (*simplicifolia* hybrid)	CCuc CMHG EGol ELan EPla GCHN GChr GCrs GDra MBri NBir NHar NHol NMen NNrd NOak NPla WHal
'Jo Ophorst' (*davidii* hybrid)	CCuc CMHG ECha GCHN LPBA MBel MCLN MRav NDea SPer WLRN WWal
'Koblenz' (*japonica* hybrid)	CCuc CMHG MBri
§ 'Köln' (*japonica* hybrid)	CMHG EMil LPBA NFai
¶ *koreana*	GCal
¶ 'Koster'	LPBA
¶ 'Kriemhilde'	MSCN
¶ 'Lady Digby'	LPBA
¶ 'Maggie Daley'	EBee
'Mainz' (*japonica* hybrid)	CMHG GCHN
microphylla	CCuc CMHG NHol
– pink	CMHG NHol
'Moerheimii' (*thunbergii* hybrid)	CMHG
'Montgomery' (*pitardii* × *japonica*)	CCuc CHor ECha MBri NFai NHol

Ostrich Plume	See *A.* **'Straussfeder'** (*thunbergii* hybrid)
'Peaches and Cream'	MBri MRav
'Peter Barrow' (*glaberrima* hybrid)	SIng SRms
'Professor van der Wielen' (*thunbergii* hybrid)	CCuc CGle CMHG EFou EGle EMan GCHN GCal GGar MAus MCli MSte SAxl SMer SPer SRms SSpi WWat
pumila	See *A. chinensis* var. *pumila*
* 'Queen'	LPBA
* 'Red Admiral'	NNor
'Red Sentinel' (*japonica* hybrid)	CB&S CCuc EFou EPar GCHN MCli NHar NHol NOrc SPla
'Rheinland' (*japonica* hybrid) ♀	CCuc CMHG EGol EPfP GCHN LPBA MBri MBro SSea WEas WHoo WRus
rivularis	CFil CMHG SDix WPGP
§ × *rosea* 'Peach Blossom'	CB&S CCuc CDoC CM&M CMHG EPar GCHN MBal MBro MGrG NBir NFai NHol NSti SEas SHel WFar WHoo WMer
'Rosea' (*simplicifolia* hybrid)	CCuc NHol WFar
'Rosemary Bloom'	EBee
§ 'Saxosa'	EPot ESis NMGW
* 'Showstar'	LRHS
simplicifolia ♀	CGle CRow NHar NMen WCot WEas WFar
– 'Alba'	EFou GGar NHol
– Bronze Elegance	See *A.* **'Bronce Elegans'** (*simplicifolia* hybrid)
– 'Darwin's Snow Sprite'	LRHS MBri
– × *glaberrima*	GDra NHar
* – 'Nana Alba'	NPro
– 'Praecox Alba'	CBlo CCuc ECha MCli NFla NHol
'Sprite' (*simplicifolia* hybrid) ♀	Widely available
§ 'Straussfeder' (*thunbergii* hybrid) ♀	CCuc CM&M CMCo CMGP CTri EAst EBee EFou EPla GCHN GCal GHCN GMaP MAus MCli NHol WLRN WViv
'Superba'	See *A. chinensis* var. *taquetii* **'Superba'**
thunbergii	WWat
'Vesuvius' (*japonica* hybrid)	CB&S CBlo CCuc CHor LSyl MBel MGrG NCut NFai NSti
'W.E. Gladstone' (*japonica* hybrid)	CBlo CMHG EAst MSte NHol NPla WMer
'Willie Buchanan' (*simplicifolia* hybrid)	CBro CGle ECtt EGol EMNN GCHN GGar GHCN MBal MBar MBel MBri MHig NDea NFla NHar NHol NMen NNor NOak SChu SPer SSmi SSpi WAbe WMow WOve WWal WWat WWin
'Yakushima'	GCHN SRms
* *yakusimanum* pink	WLin

ASTILBOIDES (Saxifragaceae)

§ *tabularis*	CGle CHEx CHad CHan CRow EBrP EBre ECha EFou EGol ELan GAbr LBre MBro MCli MRav NDea NHol NSti NVic SBre SPer SSoC SWat WHoo WShe WWat WWhi

ASTRAGALUS (Papilionaceae)

alopecuroides	WCot
¶ *alpinus*	MSto
arnottii JCA 14169	CPBP MSto

¶ *centralpinus* | MSto
cicer | MSto
danicus | WUnd
¶ *detritalis* | MSto
falcatus | EBee
glycyphyllos | CAgr EMan MSal WWye
§ *massiliensis* | MSto NTow
membranaceus | ELau IIve MSal
¶ *purshii* | MSto
tragacantha hort. | See *A. massiliensis*
¶ *utahensis* | EHyt MSto
¶ *whitneyi sonneanus* | CGra

ASTRANTHIUM   (Asteraceae) See Plant Deletions

ASTRANTIA   (Apiaceae)

¶ *bavarica* | EMon GCal
¶ *carniolica* | EMon EOld
 – *major* | See *A. major*
◆ – var. *rubra* | See *A. major rubra*
 – 'Variegata' | See *A. major* 'Sunningdale Variegated'
helleborifolia hort. | See *A. maxima*
¶ 'Lars' seedlings | GCal MBel
§ *major* | Widely available
 – *alba* | CMHG CRow ECGN ECha EFou EGol EMon LLWP NBir NCat NNor NPer
 – subsp. *biebersteinii* | NBir
 – 'Buckland' | GBuc MHFP MTed MTho SAxl SSpe SSpi SWas WFar WHal WLin WPbr
 – 'Canneman' | CLon EMon WCot
 – 'Claret' | CBos CLAP CRDP EMon EOld EPPr LGre MBro MHFP SWas WCot WFar WRus
¶ – 'Elmblut' | EMon
 – 'Hadspen Blood' | Widely available
 – 'Hillview Red' | WHil WPbr
 – subsp. *involucrata* | CDec CLon GCHN MBro NHol NVic SCro SWat WFar WHow
 – – 'Barrister' | CFil CSam GBuc MUlv SSpi WPGP
 – – 'Margery Fish' | See *A. major* subsp. *involucrata* 'Shaggy'
 – – 'Moira Reid' | LGan WRus
§ – – 'Shaggy' ♀ | Widely available
 – 'Lars' | CBot CBro EAst EBee EFou EGol EMan EMon EPPr EPar MAus MAvo MBri MCLN MLLN NFai NPri NWes SMad SOkh SPer SPla SSoC WFar WRus
 – 'Maureen' | NOak
 – 'Primadonna' | CChr CSam EBee EGol MSte MTis NCut NLar NWes SCro WFar WHil WHoo WMer WPer WRha WWat
¶ – 'Roma' | EFou SWas
major rosea | Widely available
major 'Rosensinfonie' | EBee EOld GLil MCli MLLN NCut WMer WPyg WViv
§ *major rubra* | Widely available
¶ *major* 'Ruby Cloud' | MBro WHoo
 – 'Ruby Wedding' | CBlo CGle CLon EBrP EBre EMon GBuc LBre MAvo MTho NNor SBla SBre SWas WCot WLin WMer WOve WPbr WRus
§ – 'Sunningdale Variegated' ♀ | Widely available

 – 'Titoki Point' | WCot
 – 'Variegata' | See *A. major* 'Sunningdale Variegated'
§ *maxima* ♀ | Widely available
 – 'Mark Fenwick' | NBir
minor | NTow WCru
 'Rainbow' | NLar
rubra | See *A. major rubra*

ASYNEUMA   (Campanulaceae)

canescens | EMan LFis MLLN NFai SSca WCot WPen WWin
lobelioides | EHyt
pulvinatum | CPBP EHyt LBee WAbe
 – Mac&W 5880 | EPot NNrd
¶ *trichostegium* | EPot

ASYSTASIA   (Acanthaceae)

bella | See *Mackaya bella*
§ *gangetica* | CSev LHil SLMG
violacea | See *A. gangetica*

ATHAMANTA   (Apiaceae)

¶ *macedonica* subsp. *arachnoide* JCA 224105 | IDac
turbith | LGre SIgm
 – subsp. *haynaldii* | NTow
¶ *vestina* JCA 224300 | IDac

ATHEROSPERMA   (Monimiaceae)

moschatum | CB&S CGre CLan CPle WSHC WWat

ATHROTAXIS   (Taxodiaceae)

cupressoides | GAri MBar WCwm
× *laxifolia* | CDoC LCon MBar WCwm
¶ *selaginoides* | CDoC CTrG EPot MFiF WCwm

ATHYRIUM †   (Athyriaceae)

filix-femina ♀ | Widely available
* – *congestum cristatum* | WFib WRic
 – 'Corymbiferum' | GQui LSyl NHar NMar SRms
 – Cristatum Group | CCuc EFer ELan EMon NHol SCob SWat WFib WRic
§ – Cruciatum Group | CRDP CRow EGol ELan EMar EMon GAri NHar NHol SAxl SRms WFar WFib WRic
 – 'Fieldii' | CCuc CRow EFou NHar NHol SChu SRms WFib
 – 'Frizelliae' ♀ | Widely available
 – 'Frizelliae Capitatum' | CCuc CRow SRms WFib
 – 'Grandiceps' | NHar NMar SRms
 – 'Minutissimum' | CBos CCuc CDec CFil CRDP ECha EFou EGol EHon ELan EMon GCHN LPBA NMar SAxl WFib WPGP
¶ – 'Percristatum' | EMon
 – Plumosum Group | CBos CFil GQui NMar WFib
 – 'Plumosum Axminster' | CFil CRDP WRic
 – 'Plumosum Cristatum' | NMar
 – 'Plumosum Percristatum' | GQui NMar
 – Ramocristatum Group | NMar
 – 'Setigerum Cristatum' | NMar WRic
* – *superbum* 'Druery' | WFib
¶ – 'Vernoniae' ♀ | EFer ELan EMon MBri WRic
 – 'Vernoniae Cristatum' | EBee EMon GBin MBal NHar NHol NMar WFib
 – Victoriae Group & cl. | See *A. filix-femina* Cruciatum Group

goeringianum 'Pictum'   See *A. niponicum* var. *pictum*
niponicum   CCuc WAbe
– crested   ELan
– f. metallicum   See *A. niponicum* var. *pictum*
§ – var. pictum ♀   Widely available
– – crested   MBri
* – – 'Cristatoflabellatum' CLAP EMon
otophorum ♀   CRDP EBee EMon NHol NMar
                           SChu SRms WRic
– var. okanum   CBos CFil ELan EMar LHil
                           MBri NHar NHol SAxl WAbe
                           WCot
♦ proliferum   See *Diplazium proliferum*
vidalii   CFil WRic

ATRACTYLODES (Asteraceae)
japonica   EFEx
macrocephala   EFEx

ATRAGENE See CLEMATIS

ATRAPHAXIS   (Polygonaceae) See Plant
Deletions

ATRIPLEX (Chenopodiaceae)
canescens   CAgr WDin
halimus   CAgr CB&S CBot CGle CHan
                           CPle EHoe ENot GOrc LHil
                           NBir NBrk NLar SPer SSto
                           SWat WCot WDin WHCG
                           WHer WPat
hortensis   MChe WWye
– gold-leaved   MLan WCot
– var. rubra   CArn CGle CHad CRDP EGra
                           ELan EOHP LHol MChe MGed
                           MGra MHew NChi NWes SIde
                           WCHb WEas WHer WJek WKif
                           WOak WWye
portulacoides   See *Halimione portulacoides*

ATROPA (Solanaceae)
bella-donna   CArn GBar GPoy MSal WWye
– var. lutea   MSal
mandragora   See *Mandragora officinarum*

ATROPANTHE (Solanaceae)
§ sinensis   MSal

AUBRIETA † (Brassicaceae)
albomarginata   See *A.* 'Argenteovariegata'
'Alix Brett'   CPBP CTri EBrP EBre ECtt
                           EDAr ELan ESis LBee LBre
                           NEgg NPer SAga SBre
'April Joy'   CMHG ECot EDAr ELan
                           SRms
§ 'Argenteovariegata'   CSpe ELan LHop NRoo SAga
                           SBla SIgm WAbe WPyg WWeb
'Astolat' (v)   ELan GCHN LBee MOne NSla
                           SAga SBla WAbe WEas WPat
§ 'Aureovariegata'   EBrP EBre EGle ELan LBre
                           MPla NFla NNrd NPer NRoo
                           SBla SBre SIng WAbe WFar
'Belisha Beacon'   ECtt EMNN LBee MBri
 Bengal hybrids   ERic GAbr WGor
 Blaue Schönheit   See *A.* 'Blue Beauty'
'Blue Cascade'   ECtt EPfP LPVe MPla WGor
'Blue Emperor'   WMer
'Blue Gown'   NEgg
'Blue King'   WMer WUnu
§ 'Bob Saunders' (d)   CMHG CMea CTri EBrP EBre
                           ELan LBee LBre LHop SBre

'Bordeaux'   WMer
'Bressingham Pink' (d)   CMea CTri EBrP EBre ECtt
                           ELan LBre LHop MHig SBre
'Bressingham Red'   EBrP EBre LBre SBre WMer
canescens   MSto NTow
'Carnival'   See *A.* **'Hartswood Purple'**
§ columnae macrostyla   MSto
* deltoidea 'Gloria'   WPat
– 'Nana Variegata'   CPBP EPot MPla MTho WGor
– rosea   MHig
– 'Tauricola'   WMer WPyg
– Variegata Group   ECtt EPot ESis LHop MTho
                           NMen NSla SIng WFar WPat
'Doctor Mules' ♀   CDoC CTri EBrP EBre ECtt
                           IHos LBee LBre MHig NEgg
                           SBre SIng SMer SRms WPat
'Doctor Mules Variegata'   LGro MHig NEgg
'Dream'   ECtt SIng
'Elsa Lancaster'   CNic EHyt EMNN EPot EWes
                           GCrs MHig MTho NMen NSla
'Fire King'   WMer
§ 'Frühlingszauber'   SRms WGor
Spring Charm =   See *A.* **'Frühlingszauber'**
   'Frühlingszauber'
'Gloriosa'   CMHG NEgg SIng
'Godstone'   ESis EWes
'Golden Carpet'   SIng
'Golden King'   See *A.* 'Aureovariegata'
gracilis   MSto
§ – subsp. scardica   NTow SSca
'Graeca Superba'   NPri
'Greencourt Purple'   CMHG ELan EMMN GAbr
                           MHig MOne MWat SIng
'Gurgedyke'   ECho ELan MHig SIng SRms
'Hartswood'   SIng
'Hendersonii'   SRms
'Ina den Ouden'   WMer
'J.S. Baker'   SRms
'Joan Allen'   CMHG
'Joy' (d)   EMNN SIng
'Lavender Gem'   CMHG
'Leichtlinii'   NPri WPyg WUnu
'Lemon and Lime'   LBee
libanotica   See *A. columnae macrostyla*
'Little Gem'   MHig
'Lodge Crave'   SIng
macedonica   EPot MSto
'Magician'   ECtt
'Mars'   ELan SRms
'Mary Poppins'   MHig
'Maurice Prichard'   ECtt EMNN
'Mrs Lloyd Edwards'   ECtt
'Mrs Rodewald'   CMHG CMea EMNN NEgg
                           SRms
'Novalis Blue' ♀   SRms WLRN
'Oakington Lavender'   ECho ELan IHos LHop
parviflora   MSto
'Pike's Variegated'   EWes SRms
pinardii   EHyt MSto
'Prichard's A1'   WMer WPyg
'Purity'   NPri SCoo
'Purple Cascade'   ECtt EMNN EPfP GCHN
                           MOne MPla SCoo SRms WFar
                           WGor
'Purple Charm'   SRms
'Red Carpet'   CMHG EBrP EBre ELan
                           EMNN EPot IHos LBre LGro
                           MHig MPla NEgg SBre SChu
                           SIng SRms WWin
'Red Cascade'   ECtt EMNN GAbr GCHN
                           MPla SCoo
'Red Dyke'   SIng

* 'Red King' SCha
'Riverslea' SIng
'Rosanna Miles' SIng
'Rose Queen' CMea LBee SMrm
'Rosea Splendens' MPla
'Royal Blue' NNrd NRoo
'Royal Red' ESis NPri NRoo SRms WFar
WGor WUnu
'Royal Violet' NPri NRoo
¶ 'Royal Violet' WPer
(Royal Series)
♦ *scardica* subsp. *scardica* See *A. gracilis* subsp. *scardica*
'Schloss Eckberg' WMer
'Schofield's Double' See *A. 'Bob Saunders'*
'Silberrand' ECha ECtt EDAr NSla SAxl
thessala MSto
'Toby Saunders' ECho
'Triumphante' CTri
'Wanda' ECho ELan IHos SIng
'Whitewell Gem' NNrd SRms

AUCUBA † (Cornaceae)
japonica (m) CB&S CBlo CDoC CHEx ELan
SCob SReu
– 'Crassifolia' (m) CBlo CHig MBal MRav SAPC
SArc
– 'Crotonifolia' (f/v) ♀ CB&S CDoC CHEx EBrP EBre
ENot EPla LBre LPan MBal
MBar MBri MGos NWea SBre
SCob SDix SHBN SPer WDin
WHar WStI
– 'Gold Dust' (f/v) CLan WWeb
– 'Gold Splash' CBlo
– 'Golden King' (m/v) CB&S CBlo CDoC CTrw EHic
ENot EPfP LNet MGos MUlv
MWat SPla
– 'Golden Spangles' (v) CB&S CBlo ECot MBal
– 'Goldstrike' (v) CBlo CDoC EHoe LNet
– 'Hillieri' (f) CLan
¶ – 'Latiomaculata' (v) SCob
– f. *longifolia* ♀ CBlo CHig SAPC SArc SDix
– 'Maculata' See *A. japonica 'Variegata'*
* – 'Marmorata' WWeb
– 'Nana Rotundifolia' (f) EPla MUlv SCob
– 'Picturata' (m/v) CB&S CBlo ENot EPfP MBal
MBri MGos NHol SAga SBid
SCob SHBN SPer WFar
– 'Rozannie' (f/m) CB&S CBlo CDoC EAst ENot
EPla MAsh MBal MBlu MBri
MGos MLan MUlv MWat NBee
NFla SAga SCob SPer SPla
SReu WDin WStI
– 'Salicifolia' (f) CBlo ENot EPla MBri MUlv
SCob SMad SPer
– 'Speckles' GSki
– 'Sulphurea Marginata' CB&S CHEx EHic EPla MBri
(f/v) SAga SBid SPer WWal
§ – 'Variegata' (f/v) CChe CHEx ELan ENot GRei
LBuc MBal MBar MBri MGos
MRav MWat NBee NBir NFla
NNor NWea SCob SHBN SPer
SReu WAbe WBod WDin WFar
WHar WStI WWal
– Windsor form EPla LRHS MAsh
– 'Wykehurst' (v) LRHS MTed

AULAX (Proteaceae) See Plant Deletions

AURINIA (Brassicaceae)
§ *corymbosa* MLLN SSca
§ *saxatilis* ♀ EBrP EBre GAbr GDra LBre
MBar NPSI SBre SIng WFar

– 'Citrina' ♀ ECha ECtt EGar GMaP MPla
MRav MWat SDix SRms WPyg
– 'Compacta' CTri EBrP EBre ECtt ENot
LBre MBro NLon NNor SBre
WHoo
– 'Dudley Nevill' EMan GAbr MPla MSCN
MWat SBla WFar WFoF
– 'Dudley Nevill EBrP EBre ECED EGar EWes
Variegated' GAbr LBre NBir NRoo SBre
WFar
– 'Flore Pleno' (d) NRoo WEas
– Gold Ball See *A. saxatilis 'Goldkugel'*
– 'Gold Dust' ECtt LGro MOne MWat SRms
– 'Golden Queen' CDoC ECtt
§ – 'Goldkugel' ELan EMNN LBee NVic SRms
WLRN
– 'Silver Queen' ELan NRoo WEas
– 'Variegata' SIng

AUSTROCEDRUS (Cupressaceae)
§ *chilensis* CDoC CGre CKen CMCN
LCon MBal

AVENA (Poaceae)
candida See *Helictotrichon sempervirens*
¶ *sterilis* LIck

AVENULA See HELICTOTRICHON

AVERRHOA (Geraniaceae)
carambola (F) LBlo

AYAPANA See EUPATORIUM

AZARA † (Flacourtiaceae)
¶ *alpina* G&P 5015 WPGP
dentata CB&S CFil CGre CMac CPle
CTrw ERea MBal WPGP
WSHC
– 'Variegata' CMac ERea LRHS SBid
* *integerrima* GQui
integrifolia CFil WPGP
– 'Variegata' CB&S CFil
lanceolata CB&S CFil CHan CMCN CPle
CTri EPfP IOrc ISea SPer
WPGP WPic WTro WWat
microphylla ♀ CB&S CFil CGre CMCN
CMHG CPle EPla IOrc ISea
MBal NSti SArc SBra SDry
SPer SSpi WBod WPGP WSHC
WWat
– 'Variegata' CAbb CB&S CDoC CFil CGre
CMac CPle EHoe EPfP EPla
GQui IOrc ISea LHop MBal
MLan SBid SPan SSpi STre
WAbe WCru WFar WGer
WPGP WSHC WWat
N *paraguayensis* CPle GAri
petiolaris CFil CHan CPle EPfP NFla
WGer WPic
¶ – G&P 5026 WPGP
serrata CFil CHEx CHan CMCN CPle
CTrC EPla GOrc ISea NTow
SBra SDix SMad SPer SRms
WCru WDin WFar WGer WHar
WLRN WPyg WWat
¶ – 'Patagonica' ISea
sp. from Chile CGre
uruguayensis CFil CGre WPGP

AZOLLA (Azollaceae)

caroliniana	See *A. mexicana*
auct. non Willdenow	
caroliniana Willdenow	See *A. filiculoides*
§ *filiculoides*	CBen CHEx CRow ECoo EHon EMFW LPBA MSta SCoo SRms SWat SWyc WStI
§ *mexicana*	SWat WWeb

AZORELLA (Apiaceae)

filamentosa	ECou LLew
glebaria A Gray	See *Bolax gummifera*
– hort.	See *A. trifurcata*
gummifera	See *Bolax gummifera*
lycopodioides	GCHN
§ *trifurcata*	CTri ELan EPfP EPot GAbr GAri GDra GTou NRoo SDys SIng SRms SSmi WAbe WByw WPer
– 'Nana'	CNic GGar MBro MHig MTho MWat NGre NHol NMen NNrd SDys SSmi WPat

AZORINA (Campanulaceae)

§ *vidalii*	CBot CPle CSpe ERea SAPC SArc SVen WPer
vidalii 'Rosea'	EMan WOMN

BABIANA (Iridaceae)

ambigua	NRog
angustifolia	NRog
'Blue Gem'	LBow NRog
cedarbergensis	NRog
disticha	See *B. plicata*
dregei	NRog
ecklonii	NRog
hybrids	LBow
'Laura'	NRog
nana	NRog
odorata	NRog
§ *plicata*	NRog
pulchra	LBow NRog
pygmaea	NRog
rubrocyanea	NRog
scabrifolia	NRog
secunda	NRog
striata	NRog
stricta	CSut NRog
– 'Purple Star'	NRog
– 'Tubergen's Blue'	NRog
tubulosa	NRog
villosa	LBow NRog
villosula	NRog
'White King'	NRog
'Zwanenburg's Glory'	NRog

BACCHARIS (Asteraceae)

genistelloides	EPla SMad
glomeruliflora	CPle
halimifolia	CPle GBin GQui MAll SEND
– 'Twin Peaks'	SDry
magellanica	ECou
patagonica	CBlo LHop LSpr MAll SAPC SAga SArc SDys WBod WPen

BAECKEA (Myrtaceae)

¶ *camphorosmae*	MFiF
¶ *gunniana*	MAll
¶ *virgata*	CHon CTrC MAll

BAHIA (Asteraceae)

ambrosioides	SVen

BAILLONIA (Verbenaceae)

juncea	CPle WSHC

BALBISIA (Geraniaceae)

¶ *peduncularis*	WSan

BALDELLIA (Alismataceae)

ranunculoides	CRow
– f. *repens*	CRDP EMan

BALLOTA (Lamiaceae)

acetabulosa	CHan ECha EFou EGoo EHal EMan EMar MBel SDix SPar WCot WWeb
'All Hallows Green'	CGle CSam EAst EBee EBrP EBre ECtt EFou EGoo EMar GBuc LBre LHop MCLN NDov NSti SBre SChu WHen WWat
hirsuta	CGle CHan EBee
nigra	CArn MChe MHew MSal NLak NNor SIde WHer WWye
§ – 'Archer's Variegated' (v)	CHan CHar EGar EWes MBel MLLN NHol NLak SAga SIde WAlt WCot WHer WRus WSan MInt
– 'Intakes White'	MInt
– 'Variegata'	See *B. nigra* 'Archer's Variegated'
– 'Zanzibar' (v)	EMon MBel
pseudodictamnus ♀	CB&S CBot CGle CHan CHea ECha EGoo ELan LHop MAus MBal MCLN MWat NBro NFai NFla NNor NPer NSti SDix SHBN SPer SSpe WCFE WDin WEas WHen WSHC WWat WWin

BALSAMITA See TANACETUM

BALSAMORHIZA (Asteraceae)

sagittata	EMan

BAMBUSA † (Poaceae - Bambusoideae)

* *eutuldoides*	CB&S
glaucescens	See *B. multiplex*
* *gracilis*	CTrC
* *gracillima*	CB&S COtt WJun
§ *multiplex*	EFul LJus WJun
– 'Alphonse Karr'	CB&S COtt EPla ISta SCob SDry WJun
– 'Chinese Goddess'	See *B. multiplex* var. *riviereorum*
§ – 'Fernleaf'	CB&S CHEx COtt CTrC EFul EPla ISta LJus SCob SDry WJun
– 'Wang Tsai'	See *B. multiplex* 'Fernleaf'
pubescens	See *Dendrocalamus strictus*
textilis	WJun
tuldoides	WJun
ventricosa	ISta LJus SDry WJun

BANISTERIOPSIS (Malpighiaceae)

caapi	NGno

BANKSIA (Proteaceae)

aspleniifolia	MAll
¶ *coccinea*	CTrC
ericifolia	CTrC MAll SOWG

grandis	CTrC SOWG
¶ *hookeriana*	MFiF
integrifolia	CB&S CTrC GQui MAll
marginata	CTrC ECou MAll
¶ *ornata*	MFiF
quercifolia	CGre
robur	CTrC
¶ *saxicola*	MAll
serrata	SOWG
speciosa	CTrC
¶ *spinulosa*	CTrC
– var. *collina*	MAll MFiF
– var. *spinulosa*	MAll

BAPTISIA (Papilionaceae)

australis ♀	Widely available
– 'Exaltata'	EBrP EBre ELan EMan GBuc
	LBre LHop SBre
§ *bracteata*	ECro MSal SIgm
§ *lactea*	CMdw CPle EBee ECro ELan
	MAvo MSal NBir WCot
leucantha	See *B. lactea*
leucophaea	See *B. bracteata*
pendula	ECGN EMan NLar SIgm
tinctoria	CPle EMon MBro MHlr MSal
	WCot WHoo WPyg WThi

BARBAREA (Brassicaceae)

praecox	See *B. verna*
rupicola	WPer
§ *verna*	CArn GPoy SIde WHer WWye
vulgaris 'Variegata'	CGle CHal ECha ECro EHoe
	ELan GAbr MFir MSCN NBro
	NHex NOak NSti NVic SDys
	SWat WBea WByw WCHb
	WOve WPbr WSan WWin
	WWye

BARLERIA (Acanthaceae)

obtusa	ECon
repens	ECon
suberecta	See *Dicliptera suberecta*

BARTLETTINA See EUPATORIUM

BARTSIA (Scrophulariaceae) See Plant Deletions

BASHANIA (Poaceae - Bambusoideae)

§ *fargesii*	EPla ISta WJun

BASSIA (Chenopodiaceae)

scoparia	MSal
¶ – f. *trichophylla* ♀	LPVe

BASUTICA (Thymelaeaceae)

¶ aff. *aberrans* JJ&JH 940178	NWCA

BAUERA (Cunoniaceae) See Plant Deletions

BAUHINIA (Papilionaceae)

♦ *alba*	See *B. variegata*
corymbosa	CPlN LCns SOWG
galpinii	CPlN
glabra	CPlN
¶ *monandra*	WMul
natalensis	CSpe
vahlii	CPlN
§ *variegata*	MPEx WMul

BAUMEA (Cyperaceae) See Plant Deletions

BEAUFORTIA (Myrtaceae)

micrantha	SOWG
orbifolia	SOWG
sparsa	CTrC MAll SOWG

BEAUMONTIA (Apocynaceae)

grandiflora	CPlN LChe SOWG

BEAUVERDIA See LEUCOCORYNE

BECCARIOPHOENIX (Arecaceae)

¶ *madagascariensis*	LPal

BECKMANNIA (Poaceae) See Plant Deletions

BEDFORDIA (Asteraceae)

salicina	ECou MAll

BEGONIA † (Begoniaceae)

'Abel Carrière'	ER&R
acerifolia	See *B. vitifolia*
¶ *acida*	ER&R
aconitifolia	ER&R
acutifolia	ER&R
¶ 'Aladdin'	ER&R
albopicta (C)	CHal EBak ER&R
– 'Rosea'	CHal WDib
'Allan Langdon' (T)	CBla
'Alleryi' (C)	ER&R
alnifolia	ER&R
'Alto Scharff' ♀	ER&R
'Alzasco' (C)	ER&R
¶ *ampla*	ER&R
'Amy' (T)	CBla
angularis	See *B. stipulacea*
'Anita Roseanna' (C)	ER&R
'Anna Christine' (C)	ER&R
'Anniversary' (T)	CBla
'Apollo' (T)	CBla
'Apricot Delight' (T)	CBla
'Aquarius'	ER&R
'Argentea' (R)	EBak MBri
x *argenteoguttata* (C)	CHal ER&R
'Aries'	ER&R
'Arthur Mallet'	ER&R
'Aruba'	ER&R
'Autumn Glow' (T)	ER&R
'Baby Perfection'	WDib
¶ 'Bahamas'	ER&R
'Barbara Ann' (C)	ER&R
'Barclay Griffiths'	ER&R
'Beatrice Haddrell'	CHal ER&R WDib
* *benichoma*	WDib
'Bernat Klein' (T)	CBla
'Bess'	ER&R
'Bessie Buxton'	ER&R
'Bethlehem Star'	ER&R WDib
§ 'Bettina Rothschild' (R)	CHal ER&R WDib
'Beverly Jean'	ER&R
'Billie Langdon' (T)	CBla
'Black Knight'	CHal
'Bokit'	ER&R WDib
'Bonaire'	CHal
'Boomer' (C)	ER&R
'Bouton de Rose' (T)	NRog SDeJ
bowerae	CHal ER&R
§ – var. *nigramarga*	ER&R
bracteosa	ER&R
brevirimosa	ER&R

'Brown Twist' — WDib
'Bunchii' — ER&R
'Burgundy Velvet' — ER&R
'Burle Marx' ♀ — ER&R LChe WDib
'Bush Baby' — CHal
'Buttermilk' (T) — CBla
'Calico Kew' — ER&R
'Calla Queen' (S) — ER&R
'Camelliiflora' (T) — NRog
'Can-can' (R) — See *B.* **'Herzog von Sagan'**
¶ 'Can-can' (T) — CBla
'Carol Mac' — ER&R
'Carol Wilkins of Ballarat' (T) — CBla
'Carolina Moon' (R) — ER&R
carolineifolia — LHil WDib
carrieae — ER&R
'Cathedral' — ER&R WDib
'Chantilly Lace' — CHal ER&R
'Charles Jaros' — ER&R
'Charm' (S) — WDib
'Christmas Candy' — ER&R WDib
'Chumash' — ER&R
'Clara' (R) — MBri
'Cleopatra' ♀ — CHal ER&R MRav SLMG WDib
'Clifton' — ER&R
coccinea (C) — ER&R WDib
compta — See *B. stipulacea*
¶ 'Comte de Lesseps' (C) — WDib
conchifolia var. *rubrimacula* — ER&R
'Concord' — ER&R
¶ 'Connee Boswell' — WDib
convolvulacea — ER&R
¶ *cooperi* — ER&R
* 'Coppelia' — CBla
x *corallina* — EBak
§ – 'Lucerna' (C) — CHal EBak ER&R NPal
– 'Lucerna Amazon' (C) — CHal IBlr
'Corbeille de Feu' — CHal ER&R
'Cowardly Lion' (R) — ER&R
'Crestabruchii' — ER&R
'Crimson Cascade' — CBla
* 'Crystal Cascade' — CBla
cubensis — ER&R
cucullata — CHal ER&R
'Curly Locks' (S) — CHal
'Dancing Girl' — ER&R
'Dannebo' — MBri
'D'Artagnan' — ER&R
'Dawnal Meyer' (C) — ER&R WDib
'Decker's Select' — ER&R
decora — ER&R
deliciosa — ER&R
'Dewdrop' (R) — ER&R WDib
diadema — ER&R
'Di-anna' (C) — ER&R
dichotoma — ER&R
dichroa (C) — ER&R
'Di-erna' — ER&R
dietrichiana — See *B. echinosepala* **'Dietrichiana'**
– Irmsch. — ER&R
'Digswelliana' — ER&R
discolor — See *B. grandis* subsp. *evansiana*
dregei (T) — ER&R
'Druryi' — ER&R SLMG
'Dwarf Houghtonii' — ER&R
* 'Ebony' (C) — CHal ER&R
echinosepala — ER&R
'Edinburgh Brevirimosa' — ER&R

egregia — ER&R
'Elaine' — ER&R
§ 'Elaine Wilkerson' — ER&R
'Elaine's Baby' — See *B.* **'Elaine Wilkerson'**
'Elda' — ER&R
'Elda Haring' (R) — ER&R
'Elizabeth Hayden' — ER&R
'Elsie M. Frey' — ER&R
'Emerald Giant' (R) — ER&R WDib
'Emma Watson' — CHal ER&R
'Enchantment' — ER&R
'Enech' — ER&R
'English Knight' — ER&R
'English Lace' — ER&R
epipsila — ER&R
x *erythrophylla* 'Bunchii' — ER&R SLMG
§ – 'Helix' — CHal ER&R
'Essie Hunt' — ER&R
'Esther Albertine' (C) ♀ — ER&R
'Evening Star' — ER&R
'Exotica' — ER&R
'Fairy' — ER&R
'Fairylight' (T) — CBla
feastii 'Helix' — See *B.* x *erythrophylla* **'Helix'**
fernando-costae — ER&R
'Festiva' (T) — CBla
§ 'Feuerkönigin' (S) — ER&R
'Filigree' — ER&R
♦ 'Fire Flush' — See *B.* **'Bettina Rothschild'**
'Firedance' (T) — CBla
'Fireworks' (R) — ER&R WDib
'Five and Dime' — ER&R
♦ Flaming Queen — See *B.* **'Feuerkönigin'**
'Flamingo' — ER&R
'Flo'Belle Moseley' (C) — ER&R WDib
'Florence Carrell' — ER&R
'Florence Rita' (C) — ER&R
foliosa — ER&R WDib
– var. *amplifolia* — CHal ER&R
§ – var. *miniata* 'Rosea' — CHal
'Fred Bedson' — ER&R
friburgensis — ER&R
¶ 'Frosty' (T) — WDib
'Frosty Fairyland' — ER&R
'Fuchsifoliosa' — ER&R
fuchsioides ♀ — ER&R GCra LIck MArl NPri WDib WEas
– 'Rosea' — See *B. foliosa* var. *miniata* **'Rosea'**
'Full Moon' (T) — CBla
'Fuscomaculata' — ER&R
gehrtii — ER&R
glabra — ER&R
glaucophylla — See *B. radicans*
'Gloire de Sceaux' — ER&R
goegoensis — ER&R
'Gold Cascade' — CBla
'Gold Doubloon' (T) — CBla
'Goldilocks' (T) — CBla
'Good 'n' Plenty' — ER&R
§ *grandis* subsp. *evansiana* — CDec CGle CHEx CHal ELan EMon EOas ER&R GCal LHil MLLN MSte MTho NPla SDix SMad SSpi WCot WCru WHen
– – var. *alba* — CHal EMon ER&R GCal LBlm LHil MSte MTho SMad SSpi WCot
– – 'Claret Jug' — CHan EMon
– 'Maria' — EBee
– 'Simsii' — CHan WFar
* 'Great Beverly' — ER&R
'Grey Feather' — ER&R

griffithii	See *B. annulata*	¶ 'maculata' ♀	ER&R
'Gustav Lind' (S)	CHal ER&R GCra MBEx SSad	– 'Wightii' (C)	CHal CSpe ER&R
'Guy Savard' (C)	WDib	'Mad Hatter'	ER&R
'Gypsy Maiden' (T)	CBla	'Madame Butterfly' (C)	ER&R
haageana	See *B. scharffii*	'Magic Carpet'	ER&R
* 'Happy Heart'	ER&R	'Magic Lace'	ER&R
* 'Harry's Beard'	ER&R	'Majesty' (T)	CBla
hatacoa	ER&R	*manicata*	ER&R WDib
– 'Silver'	ER&R	'Maphil'	MBri
– 'Spotted'	ER&R	* 'Mardi Gras'	CBla
'Helen Teupel' (R)	ER&R WDib	'Margaritae'	ER&R
'Her Majesty' (R)	ER&R	'Marmaduke'	WDib
§ 'Herzog von Sagan' (R)	ER&R	'Marmorata' (T)	NRog
hispida var. *cucullifera*	ER&R	'Martha Floro' (C)	ER&R
'Holmes Chapel'	ER&R	'Martin's Mystery'	ER&R
homonyma (T)	ER&R	*masoniana* ♀	CHal ER&R ERea WDib
'Honeysuckle' (C)	ER&R	I 'Matador' (T)	CBla
hydrocotylifolia	ER&R	* 'Maurice Amey'	ER&R
hypolipara	ER&R	*mazae*	ER&R
incarnata (C)	ER&R	'Medora' (C)	ER&R
– 'Metallica'	SLMG	* 'Melissa' (T)	CBla
'Ingramii'	ER&R	'Merry Christmas' (R) ♀	ER&R
'Interlaken' (C)	ER&R	*metachroa*	ER&R
'Irene Nuss' (C) ♀	ER&R	*metallica* ♀	CHal ER&R
'Ivy Ever'	ER&R	'Midnight Sun'	ER&R
'Jean Blair' (T)	CBla	'Midnight Twister'	ER&R
'Jelly Roll Morton'	ER&R	'Mikado' (R)	ER&R
'Joe Hayden'	ER&R	'Mirage' ♀	ER&R
¶ 'John Tonkin' (C)	ER&R	*mollicaulis*	ER&R
'Kagaribi' (C)	ER&R	'Moon Maid'	ER&R
kellermanii (C)	ER&R	* 'Moulin Rouge'	CBla
kenworthyae	ER&R	'Mr Steve' (T)	CBla
¶ *kingiana*	WDib	'Mrs Hashimoto' (C)	ER&R
* 'Krakatoa'	CBla	*multinervia*	ER&R
'La Paloma' (C)	WDib	'Munchkin' ♀	ER&R WDib
'Lady Carol'	CHal	* 'Mystic'	ER&R
'Lady Clare'	ER&R	'Mystique'	ER&R
* 'Lady France'	ER&R MBri	*natalensis* (T)	ER&R
'Lady Snow'	CHal	'Nell Gwynne' (T)	CBla
¶ 'Lana' (C)	ER&R	'Nelly Bly'	ER&R
* 'Lancelot'	CBla	*nelumbifolia*	ER&R
'Lawrence H. Fewkes'	ER&R	*nigramarga*	See *B. bowerae* var. *nigramarga*
leathermaniae (C)	ER&R	'Nokomis' (C)	ER&R
'Lenore Olivier' (C)	ER&R	'Norah Bedson'	ER&R
'Leopard'	ER&R MBri	'Northern Lights' (S)	ER&R
'Lexington'	ER&R	*obscura*	ER&R
'Libor' (C)	ER&R	'Obsession'	ER&R
'Lime Swirl'	ER&R	'Odorata Alba'	ER&R
limmingheana	See *B. radicans*	*olbia* Kerchove	ER&R
'Linda Harley'	ER&R	'Old Gold' (T)	ER&R
'Linda Myatt'	ER&R	'Oliver Twist'	ER&R
lindeniana	CHal ER&R	'Ophelia' (T)	CBla
listada ♀	CHal ER&R MBri WDib	'Orange Cascade' (T)	CBla
'Lithuania'	ER&R	'Orange Dainty'	ER&R
'Little Brother	ER&R WDib	'Orange Rubra' (C) ♀	CHal ER&R
Montgomery'		'Orpha C. Fox' (C)	ER&R
'Little Darling'	ER&R	'Orrell' (C)	ER&R
'Lois Burks' (C)	ER&R WDib	'Panasoffkee'	ER&R
'Loma Alta'	ER&R	'Panther'	ER&R
'Looking Glass' (C)	ER&R WDib	'Papillon' (T)	ER&R
'Lospe-tu'	ER&R	* 'Parilis'	ER&R
'Lou Anne'	CBla	*partita*	ER&R
'Lubbergei' (C)	ER&R	'Passing Storm'	ER&R
'Lucerna'	See *B.* x *corallina* 'Lucerna'	'Patricia Ogdon'	ER&R
'Lulu Bower' (C)	ER&R	'Paul Harley'	ER&R
luxurians	ER&R	'Paul-bee'	ER&R
– 'Ziesenhenn'	ER&R	*paulensis*	ER&R
'Mabel Corwin'	ER&R	¶ *pearcei*	ER&R
macdougallii var.	CHal	'Peggy Stevens' (C)	ER&R
purpurea		* 'Penelope Jane'	ER&R
macrocarpa	ER&R	'Persephone' (T)	CBla
'Mac's Gold'	ER&R	'Piccolo'	ER&R

'Pickobeth' (C)   ER&R
'Picotee' (T)   CSut NRog
'Pinafore' (C) ♀   ER&R
'Pink Champagne' (R)   CBla
'Pink Nacre'   ER&R
'Pink Parade' (C)   ER&R
'Pink Spot Lucerne' (C)   ER&R
¶ *plagioneura*   ER&R
polyantha   ER&R
¶ *popenoei*   ER&R
'Président Carnot' (C)   ER&R SLMG
'Preussen'   ER&R
'Primrose' (T)   CBla
'Princess of Hanover' (R)   ER&R
procumbens   See *B. radicans*
pustulata 'Argentea'   ER&R
'Queen Olympus'   ER&R WDib
'Quinebaug'   ER&R
§ *radicans* ♀   CHal ER&R MBri
'Raquel Wood'   ER&R
'Raspberry Swirl' (R) ♀   CHal ER&R WDib
'Raymond George Nelson' ER&R
   ♀
* 'Razzmatazz'   WDib
'Red Berry' (R)   ER&R
'Red Planet'   ER&R WDib
'Red Reign'   ER&R
'Red Spider'   ER&R
'Regalia'   ER&R
rex   MBri
'Richard Robinson'   ER&R
'Richmondensis'   ER&R
'Ricinifolia'   ER&R
'Ricky Minter' ♀   ER&R
roxburghii   ER&R
'Roy Hartley' (T)   CBla
'Royal Lustre'   ER&R
'Royalty' (T)   CBla
'Saber Dance' (R)   ER&R
'Sachsen'   ER&R
salicifolia (C)   ER&R
sanguinea   ER&R
'Scarlet Pimpernel' (T)   CBla
'Scarlett O'Hara' (T)   CBla ER&R
'Sceptre' (T)   CBla
scharffiana   ER&R
§ *scharffii*   CHal EBak ER&R LChe
'Scherzo'   CHal ER&R
'Sea Coral' (T)   CBla
¶ Semperflorens Cultorum   MBri
   Group
¶ Semperflorens Cultorum   CHal
   Group double (d)
semperflorens hort.   See *B.* x *carrierei*
'Serlis'   ER&R
serratipetala   CHal EBak ER&R MBri
* *sheperdii*   WDib
'Silver Cloud'   ER&R WDib
* 'Silver Dawn'   ER&R
'Silver Jewell'   WDib
'Silver Mist' (C)   ER&R
'Silver Points'   ER&R
'Silver Sweet' (R)   ER&R
'Silver Wings'   ER&R
* 'Sir Charles'   ER&R
'Sir John Falstaff'   ER&R
Skeezar Group   ER&R
– 'Brown Lake'   ER&R
'Snowcap' (S)   ER&R
solananthera ♀   CHal ER&R LCns WDib
sonderiana   ERea
'Sophie Cecile' (C) ♀   CHal ER&R

'Speculata' (R)   ER&R
'Spellbound'   ER&R WDib
'Spindrift'   ER&R
'Spotches'   ER&R
§ *stipulacea*   CHal ER&R
§ – 'Bat Wings'   SLMG
subvillosa (S)   ER&R
'Sugar Candy' (T)   CBla
sutherlandii ♀   CAvo CHEx CHal EBak ER&R
   ERea ERos LCns LHil MBri
   NBir NPer SAxl SDix SLMG
   SMrm WCot WDib WHer
– 'Papaya'   CSpe
'Swan Song'   ER&R
'Sweet Dreams' (T)   CBla
'Sweet Magic'   CHal ER&R
'Swirly Top' (C)   ER&R
'Switzerland' (T)   LAma
'Sylvan Triumph' (C)   ER&R
'Tahiti' (T)   CBla
'Tapestry' (R)   ER&R
* *taya*   WDib
'Tea Rose'   ER&R
teuscheri (C)   ER&R
'Texastar'   ER&R WDib
¶ 'The Wiz'   ER&R
thelmae   ER&R
'Thrush' (R)   SLMG
'Thunderclap'   CHal ER&R
'Thurstonii' ♀   CHal ER&R
'Tiger Paws' ♀   CHal ER&R MBri
'Tingley Mallet' (C)   ER&R
'Tiny Bright' (R)   ER&R
'Tiny Gem'   ER&R
'Tom Ment' (C)   ER&R
'Tom Ment II' (C)   ER&R
'Tondelayo' (R)   ER&R
* 'Tribute'   ER&R
tripartita (T)   ER&R
'Two Face'   ER&R WDib
ulmifolia   ER&R
undulata (C)   ER&R
'Universe'   ER&R
venosa   ER&R
'Venus'   CHal ER&R
x *verschaffeltii*   ER&R
'Vesuvius'   WDib
'Viaudii'   ER&R
'Viau-Scharff'   ER&R
§ *vitifolia*   ER&R
'Weltoniensis'   ER&R
'Weltoniensis Alba' (T)   ER&R
* 'White Cascade'   ER&R
'Witch Craft' (R)   ER&R
'Withlacoochee'   ER&R WDib
wollnyi   ER&R
'Wood Nymph' (R)   ER&R
'Yellow Sweety' (T)   CBla
'Zuensis'   ER&R
'Zulu' (T)   CBla

BELAMCANDA (Iridaceae)

chinensis   CAbb CBot CBro CHan EBar
   EGoo EMan GPoy LHop LIck
   MHar MLLN MSal NTow
   SLMG WHal WHoo WOMN
   WPer WWye
chinensis 'Dwarf Orange'   WCot
– 'Hello Yellow'   MSte
* – 'Pumila Campbellii'   WOMN
* – 'Yellow Bird'   WCot

BELLEVALIA (Hyacinthaceae)
brevipedicellata MS 746   CMon
dubia   CMon WCot
forniculata   GTou WCot
¶ *gracilis*   WCot
hackelii MS 439   CMon
¶ *kurdistanica*   WCot
¶ *longistyla*   WCot
maura SF 387   CMon
nivalis CL 101   CMon
§ *paradoxa*   EHyt ERos NRog WCot
pycnantha hort.   See *B. paradoxa*
romana   EHyt MTho NRog
– JCA 523   CMon
sessiliflora   CMon
sp. PD 20493   WOMN

BELLIS (Asteraceae)
perennis   CKin EWFC MHew
– 'Alba Plena' (d)   ECho ELan
– 'Alice'   CGle CLTr WSan
– 'Annie'   CGle
¶ – 'Aucubifolia' (v)   WAlt
¶ – 'Capel Ulo'   WPbr
– 'Dresden China' ♀   CLTr CLyd ELan GAbr MAvo
  MTho SIng WAlt WRus WWhi
§ – 'Habanera White With   NBrk
  Red Tips'
  (Habanera Series)
– Hen and Chicken   See *B. perennis* 'Prolifera'
♦ – 'Lipstick'   See *B. perennis* '**Habanera**
  (Habanera Series)   **White With Red Tips'**
  (Habanera Series)
¶ – 'Miniskirt'   WAlt
– 'Miss Mason'   CGle GAbr NPro SIng WRus
– 'Monstrosa'   NVic
– 'Odd Bod'   WAlt
– 'Parkinson's Great   CLTr GAbr
  White'
– 'Pomponette' ♀   NVic
§ – 'Prolifera'   CElw GAbr
– 'Rob Roy' ♀   CGle
– 'Robert'   CLTr GAbr
– 'Single Blue'   See *B. rotundifolia*
  '**Caerulescens'**
– 'Stafford Pink'   GAbr
rotundifolia   CInt
§ – 'Caerulescens'   CBos CMHG CNic CSev ELan
  GAbr MTho NBir NBro
  NMGW NMen NNrd WOMN
  WPat

BELLIUM (Asteraceae)
bellidioides   NHol WAbe
crassifolium canescens   CInt WPer
minutum   CNic ESis MHig MMil MTho
  NGre NPro NTow

BELOPERONE See JUSTICIA

BENSONIELLA (Saxifragaceae)
oregona   EBee LGan LRHS

BERBERIDOPSIS (Flacourtiaceae)
corallina   Widely available

BERBERIS † (Berberidaceae)
aggregata   CAgr MBal MNrw NBir SEas
  SPer SRms WDin
amurensis 'Flamboyant'   WBcn
× *antoniana*   MBri NNor

aquifolium   See *Mahonia aquifolium*
– 'Fascicularis'   See *Mahonia* × *wagneri*
  '**Pinnacle'**
N *aristata*   CAgr CArn CMCN SMrm SMur
atrocarpa   CPle
bealei   See *Mahonia japonica* **Bealei**
  Group
bergmanniae   CPle MAll SLPl
brevipedunculata Bean   See *B. prattii*
× *bristolensis*   EPla MBri SPla SRms
buxifolia   CBlo CPle MBal SCob WCFE
– 'Nana' hort.   See *B. buxifolia* '**Pygmaea'**
N – 'Pygmaea'   CAbP CTri EBar ELan EMil
  ENot MBal MBar MBri MPla
  MRav NHol SPer STre WFar
  WPyg WStI
calliantha ♀   CBlo CChe SLPl WWat
candidula   CSam EBee EBrP EBre ENot
  IOrc LBre MBal MBar NFla
  NHol NNor SBod SBre SCob
  SPer WDin WGwG WStI WWal
  WWat
– 'Jytte'   See *B.* 'Jytte'
× *carminea* 'Barbarossa'   CBlo SPer
– 'Buccaneer'   CBlo ENot EPfP SBod SPer
– 'Pirate King'   CBlo EBee ENot MBal MRav
  SCob SEas SPer
chitria   CAgr
chrysosphaera   WWat
§ *concinna*   GCrs
congestiflora   CPle MAll SLPl
coryi   See *B. wilsoniae* var.
  subcaulialata
coxii   CPle EPla GBin MAll NTow
  WCwm
darwinii ♀   Widely available
dictyophylla ♀   CB&S CFil CPMA CPle ELan
  EPfP MBri MGos SPla SSpi
  WGer WSHC
dulcis 'Nana'   See *B. buxifolia* '**Pygmaea'**
empetrifolia   CPle NNor SIng
¶ – JCA 14165   IDac
erythroclada   See *B. concinna*
× *frikartii* 'Amstelveen' ♀   CBlo CSam EBar EBee EBrP
  EBre EHic ELan ENot EPfP
  LBre SBre SCob WFar WGor
– 'Telstar' ♀   EHic ENot LBuc MBal MBri
  MRav SCob WStI
gagnepainii 'Fernspray'   EPla MBri MRav SBod SRms
– hort.   See *B. gagnepainii* var.
  lanceifolia
§ – var. *lanceifolia*   CB&S CTri EBee ENot EPla
  IOrc MBar MGos MWat MWhi
  NHol NNor NWea SPer WFar
  WHCG WWal
– 'Purpure'   See *B.* × *interposita* 'Wallich's
  Purple'
'Georgei'   CMHG WBcn
glaucocarpa   ELan EPfP EPla LRHS SSpi
  WPat
'Goldilocks' ♀   CAbP CDoC CMHG CPMA
  EPfP MBlu MBri WBcn WGer
hookeri var. *latifolia*   See *B. manipurana*
× *hybridogagnepainii*   CBlo ELan NFla SPer
  'Chenaultii'
hypokerina   CDoC CLan
¶ *insignis* subsp. *insignis*   WCru
  var. *insignis*
  B&SWJ 2432
¶ *integerrima*   CAgr
§ × *interposita* 'Wallich's   CBlo EBee EHic ENot MBal
  Purple'   MBar SPer WGor WLRN WStI

jamesiana	CPle GAbr
julianae	CB&S CDoC ELan ENot GChr
	IOrc MBal MBar MBri MGos
	MRav NBee NFla NLon NNor
	NWea SCob SHBN SHFr SLPl
	SPer WDin WFar WHCG WHar
	WSHC
– 'Mary Poppins'	MBri
§ 'Jytte'	MWhi
kawakamii	SLPl
knightii	See *B. manipurana*
koreana	CMCN CSam ECtt EPla GBin
	NFla WWes
lempergiana	CMCN CPle
linearifolia	WPat
– 'Orange King'	CAbP CB&S ELan ENot MAsh
	MGos NBee NHol SCob SHBN
	SPer WDin WHar WPat WPyg
	WStI
'Little Favourite'	See *B. thunbergii* **'Atropurpurea Nana'**
× *lologensis*	IOrc MGos WDin WFar
– 'Apricot Queen' ♀	CAbP CB&S MAsh MBal MBri
	NBee NEgg NFla SCob SHBN
	SPer WDin WPyg WStI WWeb
– 'Mystery Fire'	CAbP CBlo CDoC COtt ECtt
	IOrc MAsh MBar MBlu MBri
	MGos NBee NEgg SCob SCoo
	SPla WFar WHar
– 'Stapehill'	CB&S ELan ENot EPfP MAsh
	MBri SSpi WFar
lycium	CAgr CPle WHCr
¶ – CC 1729	MRPP
¶ *macrosepala* var.	WCru
macrosepala	
B&SWJ 2124	
§ *manipurana*	CBlo CGre CPle EBee ENot
× *media* Park Jewel	See *B.* × *media* **'Parkjuweel'**
§ – 'Parkjuweel' ♀	CB&S CBlo EBee EHal EHic
	ENot EPfP MAsh MRav SPer
	WFar WLRN WWeb
– 'Red Jewel' ♀	CBlo CChe CDoC EBrP EBre
	EPfP EPla LBre MBri MGos
	MWat SBre SEas SPer WAbe
	WFar WWal WWeb
morrisonensis	CFil CPle WPGP
× *ottawensis*	GRei WStI
– 'Auricoma'	MAsh MGos
– 'Decora'	SPer
N – f. *purpurea*	EBee MBri NCut NFla SBod
	WDin WHar
– 'Silver Miles' (v)	COtt CPle EHoe ELan EPfP
	LHop LNet MBel MBri MCCP
	MRav WFar WPat
N – 'Superba' ♀	CB&S CBlo CChe CDoC CPle
	CTri ELan ENot GOrc LHop
	MBal MBar MGos NBee NHol
	NNor NRoo SPer SPla SRms
	SSoC WDin WFar WGwG
	WHar
§ *panlanensis*	EBee ENot MBar
patagonica	NNor
¶ *poiretii*	CAgr CPle WUnu
polyantha Hemsley	CBlo
– hort.	See *B. prattii*
§ *prattii*	CMHG MBri
pruinosa	CPle SLPl
'Red Tears'	CBlo CDoC CPMA CSam EHic
	MBlu MBri MGos MLan
	WGwG WHCG WWes
replicata	EPla
'Rubrostilla' ♀	EBee EPla MBri NNor SCob

× *rubrostilla* 'Wisley'	LRHS
sanguinea hort.	See *B. panlanensis*
sargentiana	CPle ENot NNor SLPl WTro
	WWat
sherriffii	CPle WCwm
sieboldii	WPat WPyg WWat
sp.	EPla
sp. ACE 2237	EPot
sp. C&S 1571	NMun
sp. C&S 1651	NMun
× *stenophylla* ♀	CB&S CChe ELan ENot GChr
	GRei ISea LBuc MBar MBri
	MGos MLan MWat NBee NHed
	NHol NLon NNor NWea SCob
	SPer WDin WHCG WHar
	WWin
– 'Autumnalis'	CBlo SCob
– 'Claret Cascade'	CBlo ECle EHal EHic ELan
	EPfP MAsh MBri MGos SPer
	WFar WRHF
– 'Coccinea'	EPla MGos
– 'Corallina Compacta' ♀	EHyt ELan EPot ESis LHop
	MAsh MBal MBlu MBro MGos
	MPla NHol SChu SIng SPla
	SRms WAbe WPat WPyg
– 'Cornish Cream'	See *B.* × *stenophylla* **'Lemon Queen'**
– 'Crawley Gem'	CBlo CMHG COtt LNet MAsh
	MBar MBri MGos MPla SPer
	WFar WLRN WStI
– Cream Showers™	See *B.* × *stenophylla* **'Lemon Queen'**
– 'Etna'	MAsh
– 'Irwinii'	CBlo CMHG CTri ENot EPla
	IOrc MBar MBri MGos NHol
	SCob SPer WDin WFar
N – 'Lemon Queen'	EBee NHol SPer
– 'Nana'	EPla SRms
– 'Pink Pearl'	CMHG LBuc LRHS MBri
	MGos SHBN
taliensis	CPle
temolaica	CFil CPMA CPle ELan EPfP
	MAsh MBlu MBri SPla SSpi
	WPat WWat
¶ – SF 95186	ISea
thunbergii ♀	CBlo CDoC CTri ENot GChr
	GRei LBuc MBal NWea SMer
	SPer WDin WFar WShe WStI
– f. *atropurpurea*	CB&S CPle CSam EAst EBrP
	EBre ENot GRei LBre LBuc
	MBal MBar MBri MGos MWat
	NNor NWea SBre SPer SRCN
	WBod WDin WFar WWin
§ – 'Atropurpurea Nana' ♀	CB&S EBrP EBre ECtt EHoe
	ENot ERom GRei LBre LGro
	LHop MBal MBar MGos MPla
	MWat MWhi NHol NRoo SBre
	SHBN SPer SReu SSta WDin
	WFar WPat WWat WWin
– 'Atropurpurea Superba'	See *B.* × *ottawensis* **'Superba'**
– 'Aurea'	CB&S CBot CMHG CSam
	ELan ENot EPot LGro LHop
	LNet MAsh MBal MBar MBri
	MGos MWat NHed NHol
	SHBN SIgm SPer SSpi WDin
	WFar WHCG WPat WSHC
– 'Bagatelle' ♀	CBlo COtt EBrP EBre ECtt
	ELan EMil ENot EPot ESis
	IOrc LBre MAsh MBar MBri
	MGos MPla MRav MTis NBee
	NHar SBre SPer WAbe WDin
	WPat WPyg

– 'Bonanza Gold'	CAbP CB&S ELan EPfP LRHS MAsh SMur WWeb
– 'Carpetbagger'	IOrc WHar
– 'Crimson Pygmy'	See *B. thunbergii* '**Atropurpurea Nana**'
– 'Dart's Purple'	CBlo MAsh MBri WFar
– 'Dart's Red Lady'	CBlo CBot CPMA EBrP EBre ECtt EHal ELan ENot EPla ESis IOrc LBre MAsh MBri MPla MRav NRoo SBre SPer SPla WPat
– 'Erecta'	EMil ENot MBar MGos MRav NCut SCob SPer WDin
– 'Golden Ring'	CChe EBar ECtt EHoe ELan EMil EPla GOrc LHop MBar MBri MGos NRoo SChu SEND SPer SPla WDin WHCG WHar WPat WPyg WSHC
– 'Green Carpet'	CBlo EBrP EBre EHic ENot IOrc LBre MBal MBar MBlu SBre SPer
– 'Green Mantle'	See *B. thunbergii* '**Kelleriis**'
– 'Green Marble'	See *B. thunbergii* '**Kelleriis**'
– 'Green Ornament'	MWat NCut SPer
– 'Harlequin'	CB&S CPle EBrP EBre ECtt EHoe ELan EMil ENot EPla IOrc LBre MAsh MBal MBri MGos NBee SBre SCob SPer SPla WDin WFar WHar WPat WPyg WStI WWal
– 'Helmond Pillar'	CMHG EBrP EBre EHoe ELan EMil ENot IOrc LBre MBar MBlu MBri MGos MPla MRav MTis NBee NRoo SBre SCob SMad SPer WDin WPat WPyg WSHC
§ – 'Kelleriis'	CBlo CChe CDoC EBee EHic EPfP EPla GOrc MBar SBod WRHF WStI WWeb
– 'Kobold'	CBlo CHan ENot ESis MAsh MBar MBri MGos MPla NBee NHol SEas SPer WFar WLRN WPat WPyg
– 'Pink Attraction'	CBlo
– 'Pink Queen' (v)	CBlo EBee ENot EPfP MAsh MGos WHar WPat WWeb
– 'Pow-wow'	CB&S MGos MMil MTis SMur WBcn
– 'Red Chief' ♀	CHea CMHG EBrP EBre ECtt EGra ELan ENot EPla LBre LHop MBal MGos MRav MWat NHol SBre SChu SCob SPer SPla WAbe WDin WFar WHCG WHar WPat WStI
– 'Red King'	EHol MRav WDin
– 'Red Pillar'	CB&S CBlo CLan CPle EBrP EBre EHoe ELan LBre MAsh MBal MBar MBlu MBri MGos MWat NBee NHol SBre SHBN SPla WAbe WDin WFar WPat WStI WWeb
– 'Red Rocket'	EMil MAsh MGos
– 'Rose Glow' (v) ♀	CB&S CMHG EAst ELan ENot GRei ISea LHop MBal MBar MBri MGos MPla MWat NHol NLon NNor NRoo SHBN SMad SPer SReu SSpi WAbe WBod WDin WFar WGwG WHCG WPat
– 'Silver Beauty' (v)	CB&S CBlo CMHG CPle EBee EHal ELan MGos MPla SBod WHCG WWeb

– 'Silver Mile'	See *B.* × *ottawensis* '**Silver Mile**'
* – 'Silver Queen'	CBlo CHor
– 'Somerset'	WWat
* – 'Tricolor' (v)	CBlo EHic EHoe WFar WPat WPyg WSHC
tsangpoensis	SLPl
valdiviana	CB&S CFil WPGP
veitchii	SLPl
verruculosa ♀	CB&S CLan EAst ENot GChr LHop MBal MBar MGos MPla NHol NNor NWea SCob SPer SPla SRms WBod WCFE WDin WFar WGwG WWal WWat WWeb
vulgaris	CAgr CArn GPoy MSal
– 'Atropurpurea'	CAgr
wardii	CB&S SLPl
wilsoniae ♀	CB&S CBlo CFil CLan CPle CSam EBrP EBre ELan EMon ENot GChr IOrc LBre MBar MPla MWat MWhi NWea SBre SCob SHBN SLPl SPer WDin WFar
¶ – ACE 2462	EHyt
– blue	LRHS MBri WGer
– 'Graciella'	LRHS MBri
– var. *guhtzunica*	EPla EWes
– var. *parvifolia*	CPle

BERCHEMIA (Rhamnaceae)

racemosa	CPlN SBra SPer WSHC
scandens	CPlN

BERGENIA † (Saxifragaceae)

'Abendglocken'	CMil EBee ECha EHic EPla LFis LGro LRHS MBri MTis MWat NHol NPla NSti SChu WFar WWoo
§ 'Abendglut'	Widely available
acanthifolia	See *B.* × *spathulata*
'Admiral'	ECha EGle EPla
'Apple Court White'	CDec SApp
'Baby Doll'	CDec COtt EBrP EBre ECha EFou EPla GCal GSki LBre LHop MBri MCLN MUlv NBir NHol NMir NOrc NPer NPro NRoo NTow SBre WBro WCot WRus WWeb
§ 'Ballawley' ♀	ECha EPla IBlr MAus NDea NSti SSpi SWat
N Ballawley hybrids	CMGP CMHG EBrP EBre EPar LBre LGro MUlv NHol NSti SBre SDix SPer SWat WBro WCot WHil WWoo
'Bartók'	MTed MUlv SSpi
beesiana	See *B. purpurascens*
'Beethoven'	ECha EGle EPPr EPla NBir SSpi SWas SWat WCot
Bell Tower	See *B.* '**Glockenturm**'
'Bizet'	SSpi
'Brahms'	CMil
'Bressingham Bountiful'	CBlo SPer
'Bressingham Ruby'	CDec COtt EBrP EBre EGar ENot EPla GAri LBre MHlr MTed MUlv NBir NRoo SBre SHBN WCot
'Bressingham Salmon'	CFee CMil ELan GAbr GMaP MHlr MMil MRav NHol NMir SHBN SPer WCot WMer

'Bressingham White' ♀ — CBot CMHG CTri EBrP EBre ECha ECtt ELan EOrc LBre MAus MAvo MBri MRav MUlv NDea NFai NHol NRoo SBre SPer WCot WRus WWin
'Britten' — CMil MBal
ciliata — CFee CHEx CHan CMil ECGN ECha EPla GCal GCra MBal MRav NBir NSti SDix SPer SSpi SUsu WCot WCru WEas WPGP WPer
– × *crassifolia* — See *B.* × *schmidtii*
– *ficifolia* — EPla
– f. *ligulata* — CCuc CHEx ECha EPla MWgw NBir NSti NVic SSpi WHil WPer
¶ – – B&SWJ 2693 — WCru
cordifolia — CB&S CGle CHEx CMHG EHon ELan ENot EOld GAbr GBur GCal GChr LSyl MBal MFir NDea NFai NLar NNor SHel SPer WCot WFar WMow WPer WStI
– 'Purpurea' ♀ — CB&S EBar EBrP EBre ECha ELan ENot EPla LBre LBuc LGro MBri MCLN MRav MWgw NBir SBre SDix SHBN SPer WWal
– 'Redstart' — CBlo NOak SPla
– 'Tubby Andrews' (v) — CRDP NEgg NRar
crassifolia — CB&S CGle EPla SRms SSca WByw
– 'Autumn Red' — ECha EPla
– DF 90028 — EMon
– 'Orbicularis' — See *B.* × *schmidtii*
– var. *pacifica* — CFil WPGP WWoo
¶ 'David' — EMon
delavayi — See *B. purpurascens* var. *delavayi*
'Delbees' — See *B. purpurascens* 'Ballawley'
emeiensis — SBla
'Eric Smith' — CLAP ECha EPar EPla GAbr GCal WCot
'Eric's Best' — GCra
'Evening Glow' — See *B.* 'Abendglut'
§ 'Glockenturm' — ECha EPla GCal
¶ JCA mixed red clones — CNic
'Jo Watanabe' — ECha EPla
'Lambrook' — See *B.* 'Margery Fish'
§ 'Margery Fish' — CMil ECha EPla SPer
milesii — See *B. stracheyi*
§ 'Morgenröte' ♀ — CB&S CDoC CMGP COtt EBar ECha EPla GCra MBri NDea NHol NSti SAga SHBN SPer SPla SRms SWat
Morning Red — See *B.* 'Morgenröte'
'Mrs Crawford' — ECha EPla
¶ 'Oeschberg' — MAus
'Opal' — ECha EPla
¶ 'Perfect' — LBuc
'Profusion' — MAus SPer
'Pugsley's Pink' — CBlo CMil ECha EPla GCra LHop NCat NPla SHBN WLRN
§ *purpurascens* ♀ — CDec CMHG EPla ERav GDra GSki LSyl MBal MBro NHol SDix SPer WByw WCot WHoo WPyg WWin
♦ – 'Ballawley' — See *B.* 'Ballawley'
¶ – var. *delavayi* — NVic
– – CLD 1366 — EMon SRms WPer
'Purpurglocken' — ECha EPla GCal
'Red Beauty' — CBlo

'Rosette' — NFai
'Rosi Klose' — CGle ECha EMon EPPr EPla EWes GCal MBel NRoo NTow
'Rotblum' — EAst ECtt GBin GMaP LFis LWak NCut NOrc NPri NVic WFar WPer
§ × *schmidtii* ♀ — EWll NBir NFla SDix WCot
'Schneekissen' — EGle MRav WLRN
§ 'Schneekönigin' — CGle ECha EPla WGer
§ 'Silberlicht' ♀ — Widely available
Silverlight — See *B.* 'Silberlicht'
Snow Queen — See *B.* 'Schneekönigin'
'Snowblush' — MBal SSpi
§ *stracheyi* — CBot CFee ECha EGoo EPla GCra MHig NSti SApp SDix WEas WPyg
– Alba Group — CGle CRDP ECha EMan EPfP GCal LHop NDea NGre NSti NWoo SWas WLRN
– KBE 151 — NHol
– KBE 209 — EPla NHol
'Sunningdale' — CB&S CMGP EBee EBrP EBre ECha ELan EMan EPPr EPar EPla GCra GMaP LBre MAus MLLN MRav NBir NFla NSti SBre SChu SPer SPla SSpi WMer
* 'Winter Fairy' — MUlv
'Wintermärchen' — CM&M CMGP CMHG ECha ECtt EFou ELan EPPr EPfP EPla ERav LGro MBri MCli MSte NHol NSti SAga SHel SPla SSea WRus WWeb
'Winterzauber' — MTed

BERKHEYA (Asteraceae)
¶ *cuneata* — EBee
macrocephala — EMon WCot WMer
maritima — GCra

BERLANDIERA (Asteraceae)
lyrata — GCal WCot

BERULA (Apiaceae)
erecta — EHon

BERZELIA (Bruniaceae)
lanuginosa — CTrC

BESCHORNERIA (Agavaceae)
¶ *septentrionalis* — WCot
tubiflora — CHEx EOas
yuccoides ♀ — CB&S CFil CHEx CTrC EOas IBlr IDee LHil MSte SAPC SArc SSpi

BESSERA (Alliaceae)
elegans — ETub

BESSEYA (Scrophulariaceae) See Plant Deletions

BETA (Chenopodiaceae)
trigyna — EMon
vulgaris — WHer

BETONICA See STACHYS

BETULA † (Betulaceae)
alba Linnaeus — See *B. pendula*

albosinensis ♀	CB&S CBlo CGre CMCN EBee ELan GAri GChr NWea WCoo WDin WFro WNor WOrn WWoo
– 'Bowling Green'	CTho
¶ – 'China Ruby'	MAsh
– 'Chinese Garden'	CTho
– Clone F	CTho
– 'Conyngham'	CTho
– F 19505	CEnd CSto
¶ – 'Kenneth Ashburner'	CTho
– var. *septentrionalis* ♀	CDoC CLnd CTho EBee ELan ENot LNet MAsh MBlu MBri SPer SSpi SSta WPGP WWat
– W 4106	CSto
§ *alleghaniensis*	CGre CLnd CMCN CSam CSto IOrc MBal NWea
¶ *alnoides*	WNor
apoiensis	CGre SSta
¶ *austrosinensis*	WNor
§ × *caerulea*	CTho WWat
caerulea-grandis	See *B.* × *caerulea*
celtiberica	See *B. pubescens* subsp. *celtiberica*
chichibuensis	WAbe
chinensis	SMad WNor
¶ – S016	WHCr
cordifolia	CSto
costata Trautvetter	CDoC CLnd COtt CSam CTho ELan ENot WDin WFro WOrn
davurica	CBlo CLnd CMCN WCoo WNor WWoo
– 'Maurice Foster'	CEnd CTho
¶ – 'Stone Farm'	CTho
ermanii	CB&S CDul CGre CLnd CMCN CMHG COtt CSam CSto CTho ELan ENot IOrc LPan MAsh MBal MBlu MBri MGos NWea SPer SSpi STre WDin WNor WOrn
§ – 'Grayswood Hill' ♀	CEnd CSto CTho MBal MBri MGos SPer SSpi SSta WWat
– 'Hakkoda Orange'	CTho
– var. *saitoana* subvar. *genuina*	CFil
'Fetisowii'	CDul CLnd CTho MBlu SSta
fruticosa	See *B. humilis*
glandulifera	CLnd CSto
grossa	CLnd CMCN GAri
'Hergest'	CBlo EPfP MAsh MBri MGos WHCr
§ *humilis*	CLnd
♦ 'Inverleith'	See *B. utilis* var. *jacquemontii* 'Inverleith'
jacquemontii	See *B. utilis* var. *jacquemontii*
kamtschatica	GQui
lenta	CFil CLnd CMCN MBal
luminifera	CBrd
lutea	See *B. alleghaniensis*
maximowicziana	CB&S CDoC CLnd CMCN CTho GAri MBal SSta WFro WNor WPic
medwedewii ♀	CDul CLnd CTho EPfP GAri SSta WAbe WPGP WWat
– from Winkworth	CTho
michauxii	EHyt MBro NHol WAbe WPyg
× *minor*	CSto
nana	CBlo ELan EMil ESis IOrc MBal MBar MBro MPla MWhi NSla SMac SRms SSta STre WPer
– 'Glengarry'	EPot GAri GBin WDin
nigra ♀	CB&S CBlo CDoC CDul CGre CLnd CMCN CTho ENot GChr IHos IOrc LPan MAsh MBal NWea SMad SPer SSta WDin WFro WNor
– 'Heritage'	CDul EBee ENot LPan MBlu SSta
¶ – Wakehurst form	EPfP
occidentalis	See *B. fontinalis*
papyrifera	CB&S CBlo CDul CLnd CMCN CSto ELan ENot GChr IOrc LBuc LPan MAsh MBal MBar MGos MWhi NBee NWea SHBN SPer SSta WCoo WDin WNor WOrn WWat
¶ – subsp. *humilis*	WNor
– var. *kenaica*	CDoC CTho
– 'Saint George'	CTho WWat
– 'Vancouver'	CTho
§ *pendula* ♀	Widely available
– f. *crispa*	See *B. pendula* 'Laciniata'
N – 'Dalecarlica' hort.	See *B. pendula* 'Laciniata'
– 'Fastigiata'	CBlo CDul CEnd CLnd CTho EBee EBrP EBre ELan ENot GChr LBre LPan MAsh MGos SBre SPer WOrn
– 'Golden Cloud'	CBlo CLnd IOrc MAsh
– 'Gracilis'	EMil LPan
§ – 'Laciniata' ♀	CBlo CDul CLnd CTho ENot GChr IOrc LPan MAsh MBar MBri MGos NBee NWea SHBN SPer SSpi SSta WBay WDin WMou WPyg WWes
– 'Purpurea'	CBlo CLnd CTho EBrP EBre ELan ENot IOrc LBre LPan MBal MBar MBlu MGos NBee NWea SBre SHBN SPer SSpi WDin
– 'Tristis' ♀	CB&S CBlo CDoC CDul CEnd CLnd CTho CTri EMil ENot GChr GRei IOrc LPan MBal MBar NWea SPer SSpi SSta WDin WFar WMou WOrn WPyg
– 'Youngii' ♀	CB&S CBlo CDul CEnd CLnd EBrP EBre ELan ENot GRei LBre LBuc LHyr LNet LPan MAsh MBal MBar MBri MGos MWat NBee NWea SBre SHBN SPer SSta WDin WFar WOrn
platyphylla	CMCN GAri WFro
– var. *japonica*	CLnd EBee EWes GChr WFro WWoo
– – 'Whitespire'	SBir
– – 'Whitespire Senior'	CDoC ELan MBlu
– subsp. *kamtschatica* (Regel) V.N. Voroschilov	WNor
populifolia	CMCN CSto GAri WPic
potaninii	CMHG
§ *pubescens*	CDul CKin CLnd CPer CSto GChr IOrc ISea LHyr LNet LPan MBal NWea WDin WMou
– 'Arnold Brembo'	CTho
pumila	CSto
raddeana	CFil WNor WPGP
¶ – 'Hugh McAllister'	CTho
resinifera Britton	See *B. neoalaskana*
¶ *schmidtii*	WCoo
'Snow Queen'	CBlo CDul CEnd COtt EPfP GRei LBuc MAsh MBri MGos SCoo SMer WHCr
szechuanica	CDoC CSto WAbe

– 'Liuba White'	CTho
tatewakiana	See *B. ovalifolia*
tianschanica	WNor
'Trost's Dwarf'	CB&S CBlo EHal GQui IOrc
	ISea NHar SPer WPyg
uber	CMCN
x *utahensis*	CSto
utilis	CBlo CLnd CMCN CMHG
	CTho ELan EMil ENot LNet
	MAsh MBal MBar MRav NBee
	SPer SSta WDin WFro WNor
	WOrn
– BL&M 100	CTho
– DB 319	GCra
– F 19505	CTho
¶ – 'Fascination'	SSpi
¶ – 'Forrest's Blush'	MAsh MBri
N– var. *jacquemontii*	Widely available
N– – 'Doorenbos' ♀	CLnd NBee NEgg SSta
– – 'Grayswood Ghost'	CBlo CEnd CTho EPfP SSpi
	SSta
N– – 'Inverleith'	CEnd EBee MBri SSpi WWat
– – 'Jermyns' ♀	CLnd CTho ECot LNet MBlu
	SPer SSpi SSta WWat
– – 'Silver Shadow' ♀	CLnd CTho MBri SPer SSpi
	SSta WWat
– – wild origin	CSto
– 'Knightshayes'	CTho
– McB 1257	CTho
– var. *occidentalis*	CTho
'Kyelang'	
– var. *prattii*	CEnd CGre CTho
– 'Ramdang River'	CTho
– 'Schilling'	CEnd MBri
– SF 48	ISea
– 'Silver Queen'	SSpi
verrucosa	See *B. pendula*

BIARUM (Araceae)

arundanum	CMon
bovei S&L 132	CMon
carduchorum	EPot GCrs
carratracense SF 233	CMon
davisii	CLAP EHyt EPot GCrs LAma
	LRHS MFos
– subsp. *davisii* MS 785/735	CMon
– subsp. *marmarisense*	CMon
dispar AB&S 4455	CMon
– S&L 295	CMon
ditschianum	WCot
eximium FF 1024	CMon
– PD 26644	CMon
¶ *ochridense*	WCot
– M&T 4629	CMon
pyrami PB	CMon
– S&L 584	CMon
spruneri S&L 229	CMon
tenuifolium	CLAP CMon EPot LAma SSpi
	WCot
– AB&S 4356	CMon
– subsp. *idomenaeum*	CMon
MS 758	

BIDENS (Asteraceae)

atrosanguinea	See *Cosmos atrosanguineus*
aurea	CGle ECtt EMan LIck NFai
	SAga SCoo
cernua	MHew MSal
ferulifolia ♀	CLTr CSev ECtt LHil LHop
	MBEx MFir NPer SChu SHel
	SMer SMrm WOMN
* 'Goldie'	NPri

heterophylla	CHan CMil CStr LHil SBla
	SLod SMrm SUsu SWas
– CD&R 1230	CHan
– cream	CHan
– 'Hannay's Lemon Drop'	CHan
humilis	See *B. triplinervia* var.
	macrantha
integrifolia	WCot
ostruthioides	MBEx
* *polyepis*	ELan
sp. CD&R 1515	CGle CHan CLAP
tripartita	EWFC MSal

BIGNONIA (Bignoniaceae)

capreolata	CPlN EHol EMil EPfP GOrc
	LPan SBra SSta WCru WSHC
lindleyana	See *Clytostoma callistegioides*
unguis-cati	See *Macfadyena unguis-cati*

BILDERDYKIA See FALLOPIA

BILLARDIERA (Pittosporaceae)

bicolor	CPlN
cymosa	SOWG
longiflora ♀	Widely available
– 'Cherry Berry'	CGre CPlN ECou ELan ICrw
	LHop SBra
– *fructu-albo*	CGre CPlN CPle ELan EWes
	GOrc LRHS MBal SBra SPan
	SPer
longiflora red berried	CPle CSam
scandens	CPlN ECou

BILLBERGIA (Bromeliaceae)

nutans	CHEx CHal CMdw EBak ELan
	EOas GBin IBlr LBlm LCns
	MBri SAPC SArc SLMG SRms
* *nutans* 'Variegata'	LHil
pyramidalis var. *striata*	SLMG
(v)	
saundersii	See *B. chlorosticta*
x *windii* ♀	CHEx CHal EBak ECon LCns
	SLMG SRms

BISCUTELLA (Brassicaceae)

frutescens	WWin

BISMARCKIA (Arecaceae)

¶ *nobilis*	LPal

BISTORTA See PERSICARIA

BIXA (Bixaceae)

orellana	MPEx MSal

BLANDFORDIA (Blandfordiaceae)

¶ *grandiflora*	MFiF
¶ *punicea*	MFiF

BLACKSTONIA (Gentianaceae) See Plant Deletions

BLECHNUM (Blechnaceae)

alpinum	See *B. penna-marina* subsp.
	alpinum
¶ *brasiliense*	WRic
cartilagineum	CFil CRDP
¶ *colensoi*	WRic
discolor	EOas NMar
¶ *fluviatile*	NMar

gibbum — MBri
§ *glandulosum* — NMar
¶ *indicum* — WRic
♦ *magellanicum* misapplied — See *B. chilense* AGM
minus — NMar WRic
¶ – X B.wattsii — WRic
moorei — NMar WRic
nudum — CDoC CFil CRDP CTrC EOas
occidentale nanum — See *B. glandulosum*
patersonii — WRic
penna-marina ♀ — CBro CCuc CFil EMon EPar GGar MBal MBri NHar NMar NVic SChu SDix SIng SMad SRms SSpi WAbe WEas WOMN WPGP WRic
§ – subsp. *alpinum* — CFil NMar WPGP
– 'Cristatum' — CCuc CFil EMon GDra MBal NHar WPGP WRic
spicant ♀ — Widely available
– 'Cristatum' — WRic
¶ – 'Heterophyllum' — WRic
– *incisum* — See *B. spicant* 'Rickard's Serrate'
§ – 'Rickard's Serrate' — NHar WRic
– Serratum Group — CFil
♦ *tabulare* misapplied — See *B. chilense* AGM
§ – (Thunb.) Kuhn ♀ — CCuc CFil CHEx CRow EMon IBlr LBlm LSyl MBal SAPC SArc SAxl SChu SDix SLod SSpi WPGP WRic
vulcanicum — WRic

BLETILLA † (Orchidaceae)
g. *Brigantes* — EEve EPot SWes
* – 'Moonlight' — EEve
g. *Coritani* — EEve EPot LAma SWes
formosana — EEve EPot LAma SWes
* – *alba* — EEve EPot SWes
hyacinthina — See *B. striata*
ochracea — EEve EPot LAma SWes WCot
g. *Penway Dragon* — EEve EPot SWes
* g. *Penway Imperial* — EEve EPot SWes
g. *Penway Paris* — EEve EPot SWes
g. *Penway Princess* — EEve EPot SWes
¶ g. *Penway Rainbow* — EEve EPot
* g. *Penway Rose* — EEve EPot SWes
¶ g. *Penway Starshine* — EEve EPot
g. *Penway Sunset* — EEve EPot SWes
§ *striata* — EBrP EBre ERea ERos IBlr LAma LBre LHop MBri MCli MSal NHol NRog SBre SIng SWes WCot WFar
– *alba* — See *B. striata* var. *japonica* f. *gebina*
– 'Albostriata' — ELan IBlr LAma NHol NRog SWes WCot
– var. *japonica* — EEve EPot
§ – – f. *gebina* — IBlr LAma NHol NNrd NRog SSpi SWes WCot WFar
– – – variegated — EPot SWes
szetschuanica — EEve EPot LAma SWes
'Yokohama' — EEve EPot LAma SWes

BLOOMERIA (Alliaceae)
¶ *crocea* — SSpi

BOCCONIA (Papaveraceae)
cordata — See *Macleaya cordata*
microcarpa — See *Macleaya microcarpa*

BOEHMERIA (Urticaceae)
biloba — WCot

BOENNINGHAUSENIA (Rutaceae)
¶ *albiflora* — SMac
– B&SWJ 1479 — NDov WCru
– S&SH 108 — CHan

BOISDUVALIA (Onagraceae) See Plant Deletions

BOLAX (Apiaceae)
glebaria — See *Azorella trifurcata*
§ *gummifera* — EPot GCLN ITim NWCA WAbe

BOLTONIA (Asteraceae)
asteroides — CBlo CFee CGle CHan CSev ECoo EHal EMon GMac MAus NBrk NBro NSti SWat WBea WLRN WPrP WRHF
– var. *latisquama* — CGle CHan CHea CVer ECro EFou EHic EMon GMaP GMac LRHS MBel MBrN MRav MSte MWat SMad SSvw WCot WFar WHal
– – 'Nana' — CBre CSev ECha EMan EPPr GBuc MAvo MBro MLLN MRav MWgw NBrk NBro NFai NPri WPer WPrP
¶ – 'Pink Beauty' — GMac
– 'Snowbank' — ELan MBel MCli MUlv
incisa — See *Kalimeris incisa*

BOLUSANTHUS (Papilionaceae) See Plant Deletions

BOMAREA (Alstroemeriaceae)
caldasii ♀ — CHEx CPlN CRHN ERea SBla WCot
edulis — ERea
hirtella — CPlN CRHN WIvy
ovata — ERea
patacocensis — CPle

BONGARDIA (Berberidaceae)
chrysogonum — EHyt LAma LRHS NRog

BOOPHANE (Amaryllidaceae) See Plant Deletions

BORAGO † (Boraginaceae)
alba — CJew EOHP LHol MChe WCHb
laxiflora — See *B. pygmaea*
officinalis — CArn CSev ELau EWFC GPoy LHol MBri MChe MGra MHew NFai NVic SIde WGwG WHer WOak WPer WSel WWye
– 'Alba' — CBre CGle CSev ELau EMon MGra NChi NHex WCHb WHer WJek WPer WRha
* – 'Bill Archer' (v) — CNat
¶ – 'Variegata' (v) — EMon
§ *pygmaea* — CArn CSev CSpe EBrP EBre ELan EMan EMon LBre LHop MFir MHew MTho NChi NSti NTow SBre SChu SSvw SWat WCHb WOMN WOak WPbr WPrP WWin WWye

BORINDA (Poaceae)
¶ *albocerea*   CFil

BORNMUELLERA (Brassicaceae)
tymphaea   SIgm

BORONIA (Rutaceae)
'Heaven Scent'   CB&S EMil
heterophylla   CB&S CMHG ECon ERea
                                  MAll SAga SMrm
megastigma   CB&S EMil MAll
– brown   EMil
– 'Brown Meg'   CB&S
'Southern Star'   CB&S

BOSCIA   (Capparaceae) See Plant Deletions

BOTHRIOCHLOA (Poaceae)
§ *bladhii*   CHan EPPr
caucasica   See *B. bladhii*
§ *ischaemum*   CInt EBee EGar EHoe EPPr
                                  EWes MCCP

BOTRYOSTEGE See ELLIOTTIA

BOUGAINVILLEA (Nyctaginaceae)
'Afterglow'   CWDa
'Ailsa Lambe'   See *B.* (Spectoperuviana Group)
                                  'Mary Palmer'
* 'Alabama Sunset'   CWDa
'Alexandra'   LChe MBri SLMG
'Amethyst'   ERea MBri SLMG
'Apple Blossom'   See *B.* × *buttiana* **'Audrey Grey'**
'Asia'   ERea
'Audrey Grey' (× *buttiana*)   See *B.* × *buttiana* **'Audrey Grey'**
* *aurantiaca*   CB&S
◆ 'Aussie Gold'   See *B.* **'Carson's Gold'**
'Barbara Karst'   CWDa ERea
'Begum Sikander'   CWDa
'Betty Lavers'   ERea
'Blondie'   CWDa
'Brasiliensis'   See *B. spectabilis* **'Lateritia'**
'Bridal Bouquet'   See *B.* × *buttiana* **'Mahara**
                                  Off-white'
'Brilliance'   CWDa ERea
'Brilliant'   See *B.* **'Raspberry Ice'**
§ × *buttiana* 'Audrey Grey'   CB&S ERea
§ – 'Golden Glow'   ECon ERea
§ – 'Golden McLean'   CWDa
§ – 'Jamaica Red'   ERea
§ – 'Lady Mary Baring'   EFlo ERea LCns SOWG
§ – 'Mahara Double Red'   CWDa ERea SOWG
  (d)
§ – 'Mahara Off-white' (d)   CWDa ERea LCns
§ – 'Mahara Orange' (d)   ERea LCns
§ – 'Mahara Pink' (d)   CWDa ERea
§ – 'Mardi Gras' (v)   CWDa ERea
§ – 'Mrs Butt' ♀   CWDa ERea
§ – 'Mrs Helen McLean'   ERea
§ – 'Poultonii'   ERea
§ – 'Poulton's Special' ♀   ERea LChe SLMG
§ – 'Rainbow Gold'   ERea
§ – 'Rosenka'   CWDa ERea
§ – Texas Dawn   ERea
'California Gold'   See *B.* × *buttiana* **'Golden**
                                  Glow'
§ Camarillo Fiesta℠   CWDa ERea SLMG SOWG
  (*spectabilis* hybrid)
'Captain Caisy'   CWDa ERea
'Carson's Gold' (d)   CWDa

'Cherry Blossom'   See *B.* × *buttiana* **'Mahara**
                                  Off-white'
§ 'Chiang Mai Beauty'   ERea
'Coconut Ice' (v)   CWDa EFlo LCns SOWG
'Crimson Lake'   See *B.* × *buttiana* **'Mrs Butt'**
'Dania'   MBri
'Danica Rouge'   SLMG
'Daphne Mason'   ERea
'Dauphine'   See *B.* × *buttiana* **'Mahara Pink'**
'David Lemmer'   CWDa ERea
◆ 'Delicate'   See *B.* **'Blondie'**
'Dixie'   ERea
'Doctor David Barry'   See *B. glabra* **'Doctor David**
  (*glabra*)   **Barry'**
'Donyo'   CWDa ERea LCns
◆ 'Double Yellow'   See *B.* **'Carson's Gold'**
'Durban'   See *B. glabra* **'Jane Snook'**
'Elizabeth Angus' (*glabra*)   See *B. glabra* **'Elizabeth Angus'**
'Elizabeth'   ERea
  (*spectabilis* hybrid)
* 'Elsbet'   CWDa
'Enchantment'   See *B.* **'Mary Palmer's**
                                  Enchantment'
◆ 'Fair Lady'   See *B.* **'Blondie'**
'Flamingo Pink'   See *B.* **'Chiang Mai Beauty'**
floribunda   CWDa
'Gillian Greensmith'   ERea
glabra ♀   CB&S CPlN ERea LCns MBri
– A   ERea
§ – 'Doctor David Barry'   CWDa ERea
§ – 'Elizabeth Angus'   CWDa EFlo ERea
§ – 'Harrissii' (v)   CWDa ERea MBri
§ – 'Jane Snook'   CWDa ERea
§ – 'Jennifer Fernie'   ERea SLMG
§ – 'Magnifica'   ERea
§ – 'Pride of Singapore'   ERea
§ – 'Sanderiana'   CHEx ERea LPan NRog
– 'Variegata'   See *B. glabra* **'Harrissii'**
'Gladys Hepburn'   ERea
'Gloucester Royal'   CWDa
* 'Glowing Flame'   CWDa
'Golden Dubloon'   See *B.* × *buttiana* **'Mahara**
                                  Orange'
'Golden Glow' (× *buttiana*)   See *B.* × *buttiana* **'Golden**
                                  Glow'
I 'Golden MacLean' (×   See *B.* × *buttiana* **'Golden**
  buttiana)   **McLean'**
* 'Golden Tango'   CWDa
* 'Granada'   LChe
'Harlequin'   See *B.* (Spectoperuviana Group)
                                  'Thimma'
'Harrissii' (*glabra*)   See *B. glabra* **'Harrissii'**
'Hawaiian Scarlet'   See *B.* **'Scarlett O'Hara'**
'Helen Johnson'   See *B.* **'Temple Fire'**
◆ 'Hugh Evans'   See *B.* **'Blondie'**
'Indian Flame'   See *B.* **'Partha'**
'Isobel Greensmith'   CWDa ERea LCns
* 'Jamaica Gold'   LChe
'Jamaica Orange'   CWDa ERea
'Jamaica Red' (× *buttiana*)   See *B.* × *buttiana* **'Jamaica Red'**
'James Walker'   ERea
'Jane Snook' (*glabra*)   See *B. glabra* **'Jane Snook'**
'Jennifer Fernie' (*glabra*)   See *B. glabra* **'Jennifer Fernie'**
'Juanita Hatten'   CWDa ERea
'Kauai Royal'   See *B. glabra* **'Elizabeth Angus'**
'Killie Campbell' ♀   ERea LChe MBri
'Klong Fire'   See *B.* × *buttiana* **'Mahara**
                                  Double Red'
'La Jolla'   ERea
'Lady Mary Baring' (×   See *B.* × *buttiana* **'Lady Mary**
  buttiana)   **Baring'**
'Lavender Girl'   CWDa ERea

'Lemmer's Special'   See *B.* 'Partha'
'Limberlost Beauty'   See *B.* × *buttiana* 'Mahara Off-white'
'Little Caroline'   CWDa
§ 'Lord Willingdon'   ERea
'Los Banos Beauty'   See *B.* × *buttiana* 'Mahara Pink'
§ 'Louis Wathen'   CWDa ECon LCns
'Magnifica' (*glabra*)   See *B. glabra* 'Magnifica'
'Magnifica Traillii'   See *B. glabra* 'Magnifica'
'Mahara Double Red' (× *buttiana*) See *B.* × *buttiana* 'Mahara Double Red'
'Mahara Off-white' (× *buttiana*)   See *B.* × *buttiana* 'Mahara Off-white'
'Mahara Orange' (× *buttiana*)   See *B.* × *buttiana* 'Mahara Orange'
'Mahara Pink' (× *buttiana*) See *B.* × *buttiana* 'Mahara Pink'
'Mahara White'   See *B.* × *buttiana* 'Mahara Off-white'
'Mahatma Gandhi'   See *B.* (Spectoperuviana Group) 'Mrs H.C. Buck'
'Mardi Gras' (× *buttiana*) See *B.* × *buttiana* 'Mardi Gras'
§ 'Mary Palmer's Enchantment' CWDa ERea
'Meriol Fitzpatrick'   ERea SLMG
* 'Michael Lemmer'   CWDa
'Mini-Thai'   See *B.* 'Lord Willingdon'
* 'Mischief'   CWDa
§ 'Miss Manila'   CWDa ERea
'Mrs Butt' (× *buttiana*)   See *B.* × *buttiana* 'Mrs Butt'
'Mrs Butt Variegated' (× *buttiana*) See *B.* × *buttiana* 'Mrs Butt Variegated'
'Mrs Helen McLean' (× *buttiana*) See *B.* × *buttiana* 'Mrs Helen McLean'
'Mrs McLean' (× *buttiana*) See *B.* × *buttiana* 'Mrs McClean'
Natalii Group   CWDa ERea
'Nina Mitton'   CWDa ERea
* 'Orange Cotton'   LCns
'Orange Glow'   See *B.* Camarillo Fiesta (*spectabilis* hybrid)
'Orange King'   See *B.* 'Louis Wathen'
'Orange Stripe' (v)   ERea
'Pagoda Pink'   See *B.* × *buttiana* 'Mahara Pink'
§ 'Partha'   CWDa
'Penelope'   See *B.* 'Mary Palmer's Enchantment'
¶ pink   ECon
'Pink Champagne'   See *B.* × *buttiana* 'Mahara Pink'
'Pink Clusters'   CWDa ERea
'Pink Pixie'   See *B.* 'Lord Willingdon'
'Poultonii' (× *buttiana*) See *B.* × *buttiana* 'Poultonii'
'Poultonii Special' (× *buttiana*) See *B.* × *buttiana* 'Poulton's Special'
'Pride of Singapore' (*glabra*) See *B. glabra* 'Pride of Singapore'
'Princess Mahara'   See *B.* × *buttiana* 'Mahara Double Red'
'Purple Robe'   CWDa ERea
'Rainbow Gold' (× *buttiana*) See *B.* × *buttiana* 'Rainbow Gold'
¶ 'Ralph Sander'   LCns
§ 'Raspberry Ice' (v)   ERea LCns SOWG
'Red Diamond'   ERea
'Red Glory'   CWDa ERea
* 'Reggae Gold'   CWDa
'Robyn's Glory'   See *B.* × *buttiana* Texas Dawn
'Rose Parme'   ERea
♦ 'Rosenka'   See *B.* × *buttiana* 'Rosenka'
'Royal Purple'   CWDa ERea
'Rubyana'   CWDa ERea LChe LCns SOWG
'San Diego Red'   See *B.* 'Scarlett O'Hara'

'Sanderiana' (*glabra*)   See *B. glabra* 'Sanderiana'
'Sanderiana Variegata'   See *B. glabra* 'Harrissii'
'Scarlet Glory'   ERea
§ 'Scarlett O'Hara'   CB&S ECon ERea GQui LCns SLMG SOWG
'Singapore Pink'   See *B. glabra* 'Doctor David Barry'
'Singapore White'   CWDa ERea
'Smartipants'   See *B.* 'Lord Willingdon'
'Snow Cap'   See *B.* (Spectoperuviana Group) 'Mary Palmer'
spectabilis 'Wallflower' CWDa
§ Spectoperuviana Group (v) ERea
§ – 'Mary Palmer'   CWDa
§ – 'Mrs H.C. Buck'   CWDa ERea LCns
'Summer Snow'   CWDa
Surprise   See *B.* (Spectoperuviana Group) 'Mary Palmer'
'Tango'   See *B.* 'Miss Manila'
* 'Tango Supreme'   CWDa
§ 'Temple Fire'   ERea SOWG
'Thai Gold'   See *B.* × *buttiana* 'Mahara Orange'
* 'Tom Thumb'   CWDa
* 'Tropical Bouquet'   CWDa
'Tropical Rainbow'   See *B.* 'Raspberry Ice'
* 'Turkish Delight'   CWDa ECon LChe LCns
'Variegata' (*glabra*)   See *B. glabra* 'Harrissii'
'Variegata' (*spectabilis*) See *B. spectabilis* 'Variegata'
'Vera Blakeman'   CWDa ECon ERea LCns
'Vicky'   See *B.* (Spectoperuviana Group) 'Thimma'
'Wac Campbell' (d)   CWDa
'Weeping Beauty'   ERea
* 'White Cascade'   CWDa

BOUSSINGAULTIA (Basellaceae)

baselloides Hook.   See *Anredera cordifolia*

BOUTELOUA (Poaceae)

curtipendula   CSpe EMon MAvo WHil
§ *gracilis*   CCuc CInt CSte EBee ECGN ESOG MAvo MCCP MLLN MMil NChi NSti NVic SAxl SLod SUsu WCot WPer

BOUVARDIA (Rubiaceae)

longiflora   ERea LChe LCns SOWG
triphylla   See *B. ternifolia*

BOWENIA (Boweniaceae)

serrulata   CBrP LPal
¶ *spectabilis*   CBrP

BOWIEA (Hyacinthaceae)

volubilis   CHal CPlN

BOWKERIA (Scrophulariaceae)

citrina   CGre CPle
gerrardiana   CGre CPle

BOYKINIA (Saxifragaceae)

aconitifolia   EBee ECro ELan EMon GTou LFis MGrG MLLN MRav WCot WCru
elata   See *B. occidentalis*
heucheriformis   See *B. jamesii*
§ *jamesii*   CGra CMCo LBee MHig NNrd NTow NWCA SIng WOMN
§ *occidentalis*   GGar

rotundifolia — ELan GBin GBuc NSti WCru
– JLS 86269LACA — EMon
tellimoides — See *Peltoboykinia tellimoides*

BRACHYCHILUM See HEDYCHIUM

BRACHYCHITON (Sterculiaceae)
acerifolius — CHEx

BRACHYGLOTTIS † (Asteraceae)
§ *bidwillii* — MHig SDry WAbe WCru
§ *buchananii* — SDry WCru WSHC
§ *compacta* — CSam EBee ECha ECou EPfP MAll MAsh MPla MWgw SDry SPer WEas
'Drysdale' — CPle EPfP LRHS MAll MAsh MBri MRav MTed SDry WCru
§ (Dunedin Group) 'Moira Reid' (v) — CPle EBee EGoo ELan EMon MAll MBal MUlv SDry WEas WSHC
§ – 'Sunshine' ♀ — CChe EAst EGoo ELan ENot IBlr LGro LHop MBal MBri MGos NPer SPer SPla SRms WAbe WFar WHen WTro WWat
§ *elaeagnifolia* — ISea MAll
N *greyi* — CPle CTrG EBee EHol GRei ISea MAll MBar NNor NRoo WEas WWin
§ *huntii* — CPle MAll WCru
§ *kirkii* — CSev
N *laxifolia* — NNor SIng
§ 'Leonard Cockayne' — CHEx SPer
§ *monroi* ♀ — CBar CPle CSam EAst ECou EHoe EHol ELan IBlr IOrc LHop MBal MBar MLLN MRav NNor SCoo SMer SPan SPar SPer WAbe WEas WTro WWat
– 'Clarence' — ECou
repanda — CHEx CPle CTrG
– x *greyi* — CPle LHil MAll SAPC SArc
¶ – 'Purpurea' — CHEx
§ *rotundifolia* — CDoC CPle EGoo EPfP IBlr MAll MBlu WCru WEas
§ *spedenii* — CFee GCrs GTou
I 'Sunshine Improved' — WSPU
'Sunshine Variegated' — See *B.* (Dunedin Group) 'Moira Read'

BRACHYLAENA (Asteraceae) See Plant Deletions

BRACHYPODIUM (Asteraceae)
pinnatum — EHoe EPPr ESOG
sylvaticum — CKin WPer

BRACHYSCOME (Asteraceae)
'Blue Mist' — WLRN
'Harmony' — IHos LHil
iberidifolia — ELan
'Lemon Mist' — LHop
melanocarpa — CSpe
multifida — EMan IHos MBri
nivalis var. *alpina* — See *B. tadgellii*
'Pink Mist' — LHil LHop
rigidula — ECou NMen NTow
* 'Strawberry Mousse' — EMan LHil NPri
§ *tadgellii* — MTPN
'Tinkerbell' — CBar IHos WLRN

BRACHYSTACHYUM (Poaceae - Bambusoideae)
densiflorum — SDry

BRACTEANTHA (Asteraceae)
acuminata De Candolle — See *B. subundulata*
bracteata 'Dargan Hill Monarch' — CMHG CSev LHil MBEx SRms WEas
– 'Skynet' — GMac LHil MBEx
§ 'Coco' — CMHG MHlr SMrm WCot WEas

BRAHEA (Arecaceae)
¶ *aculeata* — LPal
armata — CBrP CTbh CTrC LPal NPal SAPC SArc
brandegeei — LPal
edulis — CTrC LPal WMul

BRASSAIA See SCHEFFLERA

BRASSICA (Brassicaceae)
japonica — See *B. juncea* var. *crispifolia*
§ *juncea* var. *crispifolia* — CArn WJek
¶ *oleracea* — WHer
* *rapa* var. *japonica* — WJek
* – var. *purpurea* — WJek

BRASSIOPHOENIX (Arecaceae)
¶ *schumannii* — LPal

BRAVOA (Agavaceae)
geminiflora — See *Polianthes geminiflora*

BRAYA (Brassicaceae) See Plant Deletions

BREYNIA (Euphorbiaceae) See Plant Deletions

× BRIGANDRA (Gesneriaceae)
calliantha — NTow
¶ – 'Tinneys Rose' — GCrs

BRIGGSIA (Gesneriaceae)
¶ *aurantiaca* — GCrs

BRIMEURA (Hyacinthaceae)
§ *amethystina* — CAvo EBot ERos MHig WOMN
– 'Alba' — CAvo EBot ERos MHig NMen NRog WHil
§ *fastigiata* — CMon ERos

BRIZA (Poaceae)
maxima — CJew CRDP EJud EPla LIck NSti WByw WHal WHer WWye
¶ *maxima* from Rhodes — SApp
media — CInt CKin EBar EBrP EBre EFou EHoe ELan EMan EPla ESOG EWFC GAbr GCHN GCal LBre LHop MMal NHol NMir NSti SBre SLod SPer SPla WHal WStI
– 'Limouzi' — EMon EPPr LGre LRHS SApp SOkh
¶ sp. from Chile — EWes

BROCCHINIA (Bromeliaceae) See Plant Deletions

BRODIAEA (Alliaceae)

§ *californica*	CLAP CMon CNic
– var. *leptandra*	CLAP
capitata	See *Dichelostemma pulchellum*
coronaria subsp. *rosea*	CMon
◆ 'Corrina'	See *Triteleia* 'Corrina'
elegans	CMon
ida-maia	See *Dichelostemma ida-maia*
laxa	See *Triteleia laxa*
peduncularis	See *Triteleia peduncularis*
purdyi	See *B. minor*
stellaris	EHyt

BROMUS (Poaceae)

catharticus	See *B. unioloides*
inermis 'Skinner's Gold'	EBee EGar EHoe EMon EPPr
(v)	EPla ESOG EWes MAvo
macrostachys	See *B. lanceolatus*
morrisonensis B&SWJ 294	WCru
ramosus	CKin EHoe EPPr

BROUSSONETIA (Moraceae)

papyrifera	CB&S CFil CHEx CMCN CPle
	ELan IDee LPan MLan MPEx
	SMad WPGP WWat
– 'Laciniata'	SMad

BROWALLIA (Solanaceae)

speciosa 'Major'	MBri
– 'Silver Bells'	MBri

BRUCKENTHALIA (Ericaceae)

spiculifolia	EPot GChr ITim MBal MBar
	NHed
– 'Balkan Rose'	EDen GCal GCrs NHol

BRUGMANSIA (Solanaceae)

§ *arborea*	CArn CHEx LLew NGno NPal
	SLMG SRms
¶ *aurea*	CHEx
– 'Golden Queen'	ERea LLew MBEx
× *candida*	EBak ERea LLew
– × *aurea*	LLew
– 'Blush'	ERea
¶ – 'Ecuador Pink'	ERea
§ – 'Grand Marnier' ♀	CBot CHEx CMdw ECon ECot
	ELan ERea LLew MBri SLMG
	SOWG SSoC SVen WEas WKif
§ – 'Knightii' (d) ♀	CBot CHEx CSev EBak ECon
	ELan EPfP ERea LLew MBEx
	SOWG
– 'Plena'	See *B.* × *candida* 'Knightii'
– 'Primrose'	ERea
× *flava*	LLew
* × *insignis* 'Orange'	LBlm
§ – pink	CHEx LHil
meteloides	See *Datura inoxia*
'Panache'	CBot
* pink	LIck
rosei	See *B. sanguinea* subsp.
	sanguinea 'Flava'
§ *sanguinea* ♀	CHEx EBak ERea LHil LLew
	MBEx MBri NGno SLMG
	SOWG SSoC SVen WHer
– 'Rosea'	See *B.* × *insignis* pink
§ – subsp. *sanguinea* 'Flava'	CHEx LLew MBri
§ *suaveolens* ♀	CHEx ELan ERea ISea LLew
	NPal
* – hybrid pink	LLew
* – hybrid white	LLew
– *rosea*	See *B.* × *insignis* pink

– 'Variegata'	ERea
– × *versicolor*	See *B.* × *insignis*
* 'Variegata Sunset'	ERea
versicolor hort.	See *B. arborea*
§ – Lagerheim	ERea LBlm LPan MBEx SLMG
	SOWG
yellow	LIck

BRUNFELSIA (Solanaceae)

americana	ECon LChe SLMG
calycina	See *B. pauciflora*
eximia	See *B. pauciflora*
jamaicensis	CSpe
latifolia	ECon
§ *pauciflora* ♀	ELan MBri SLMG
– 'Floribunda'	LChe LCns SOWG
– 'Macrantha'	LCns SLMG SOWG
undulata	LChe SLMG

BRUNIA (Bruniaceae) See Plant Deletions

BRUNNERA (Boraginaceae)

§ *macrophylla* ♀	Widely available
– 'Alba'	See *B. macrophylla* 'Betty
	Bowring'
◆ – Aluminium Spot	See *B. macrophylla* Aluminium
	Spot = 'Langtrees'
§ – 'Betty Bowring'	CElw CHad CLAP CRDP
	CRow EMon GBuc SWas WFar
	WHal
§ – 'Dawson's White' (v)	CBot CGle CHEx CLAP EBrP
	EBre ECha ELan EPla GCal
	LBre LHop MAus MBri MCLN
	MRav MTho MWat NChi NLar
	NRoo NSti SBre SSpi WCot
	WHil WPbr WRus WWat
¶ – 'Gordano Gold'	EBee
– 'Hadspen Cream' (v) ♀	CElw CFee CHad CMHG CSpe
	EBrP EBre ECha EPar LBre
	LFis LHop LSpr MCLN MGrG
	MRav MTho NBir NRoo SBre
	SIgm SSpi SWat WByw WCot
	WHoo WOld WPbr
¶ – 'Langford Hewitt'	CLAP
§ – Aluminium Spot =	Widely available
'Langtrees'	
– 'Variegata'	See *B. macrophylla* 'Dawson's
	White'

× BRUNSCRINUM (Amaryllidaceae)

'Dorothy Hannibel'	CMon

BRUNSVIGIA (Amaryllidaceae)

multiflora	See *B. orientalis*
§ *orientalis*	CMon NRog
¶ *radulosa*	LLew
rosea 'Minor'	See *Amaryllis belladonna*

BRYANTHUS (Ericaceae) See Plant Deletions

BRYONIA (Cucurbitaceae)

dioica	EWFC GPoy MHew MSal

BRYOPHYLLUM See KALANCHOE

BRYUM (Sphagnaceae) See Plant Deletions

BUCHLOE (Poaceae) See Plant Deletions

BUDDLEJA (Buddlejaceae)

agathosma	CBot CFil CHan CPle WEas WHar WPen WSHC
alternifolia ♀	Widely available
– 'Argentea'	CBot CDoC CPMA CPle EBar ELan ERea MBro MHar MRav NFla NSti SHBN SPer SPla SSpi WCot WHCG WPat WSHC WWat
asiatica ♀	CBot CPIN CPle ECon ERea LCns LRHS SBid WMul
¶ – B&SWJ 2679	WCru
auriculata	CAbb CB&S CBlo CBot CGre CHan CLTr CMCN CPle CWit ERea GQui LBlm LHil NSti SBid SDix SOWG SPer WCru WHCG
australis	CPle
brevifolia	See *B. abbreviata*
* 'Butterfly Ball'	LHop WBcn WPer
caryopteridifolia	EHal EHol ENot SBid
colvilei	CAbb CB&S CDoC CFil CHEx CHan CPle CTrw CWit ENot EPfP MBal SPer WCru WEas WSpi
– C&S 1577	NMun
– 'Kewensis'	CBot CGre IBlr ISea MBlu WCru WPGP WSHC
cordata	CPle
coriacea	CPle
§ *crispa*	CB&S CBot CHad CPle ECha ELan ERav LBlm SBid SBra SDry SHBN SOWG SPer SSpi SSta WCru WHCG WKif WPGP WSHC WSpi WWat
– L 1544	NHex WPGP
crotonoides amplexicaulis	CPle
¶ *curviflora*	CPle
davidii	CArn CKin MBro NWea SHFr STre WDin
– 'African Queen'	SCob SPer
– var. *alba*	CBlo SHBN
– 'Black Knight' ♀	Widely available
– 'Blue Horizon'	CPle GCHN MHar MHlr SEND WCot WRHF
– 'Border Beauty'	EHic SEas WRHF
§ – 'Charming'	SCob WMoo
– 'Dartmoor' ♀	Widely available
– 'Dart's Blue Butterfly'	MBri
– 'Dart's Ornamental White'	CBlo EBee MBri
– 'Dart's Papillon Blue'	SLPl
– 'Dart's Purple Rain'	CBlo MBri
– 'Empire Blue' ♀	CB&S EBrP EBre ECtt ELan ENot GChr GOrc LBre MAsh MBal MRav MWat NBee NPer NWea SBre SCob SPer WDin WGwG WMow WPyg WStI WWeb
– 'Fascinating'	CBlo CTri MAsh NPer SBod WMow
– 'Flaming Violet'	CBlo
– 'Fortune'	NNor
– 'Glasnevin Blue'	CPle CTri SDix SPer
– 'Gonglepod'	ELan
– 'Harlequin' (v)	CB&S CMHG CTrw EAst EBrP EBre ELan GChr LBre LFis LHop MBal MBar MBel MBri MGos NNor NRoo SBod SBre SPer SReu WDin WEas WGwG WHCG WPbr WWat WWeb WWin

– 'Ile de France'	CB&S CBlo EHic MGos MWat NWea SCob SRms WWeb
– 'Les Kneale'	CPle MBal
◆ – Masquerade	See *B. davidii* Masquerade = 'Notbud'
§ – 'Nanho Blue'	CB&S CDoC CPle EBrP EBre ECtt ELan ENot EPla IOrc LBre LBuc LHop MAsh MBar MGos NFla NNor SBod SBre SEas SHBN SPla WDin WHCG WHar WSHC WWeb
– 'Nanho Petite Indigo'	See *B. davidii* 'Nanho Blue'
– 'Nanho Petite Purple'	See *B. davidii* 'Nanho Purple'
§ – 'Nanho Purple'	CDoC EBrP EBre ELan ENot GAri GChr LBre MAsh MBar MBel MBri NRoo SBre SPer WHar WSHC
– var. *nanhoensis*	CBlo CHan CMHG CPle GCHN MWat MWhi SEND SIde SPer WHCG
– var. *nanhoensis alba*	CBar CBlo EHal ELan EPfP LFis LHop MBar MLan MMil SPer SRms WWat
– var. *nanhoensis* blue	LHil MBri SPer WEas WMow WWat
§ – Masquerade = 'Notbud'	CBlo EHic ENot EPfP MGos MGrG NRoo WGor WLRN WStI WWes
– 'Orchid Beauty'	CBlo EBar MLan NCut SCob
– 'Peace'	CChe CTri EHic ENot EPfP NPer SPer
– Petite Indigo℗	See *B. davidii* 'Nanho Blue'
– Petite Plum℗	See *B. davidii* 'Nanho Purple'
– 'Pink Beauty'	CLTr SCob SHBN SHFr WHCG WWat
– 'Pink Charming'	See *B. davidii* 'Charming'
* – 'Pixie Blue'	MAsh NCut WWeb
– 'Pixie Red'	CLyn MAsh NCut WShe WWeb
* – 'Pixie White'	CLyn EBar MAsh NCut WWeb
– 'Purple Prince'	CB&S EHic NCut SCob WRHF
– 'Purple Rain'	SLPl
– 'Royal Red' ♀	CB&S ELan ENot GChr GOrc GRei LHop MBal MBar MBri MGos MUlv MWat NFla NNor NPer NWea SBod SHBN SPer SReu SSoC WAbe WBod WDin WGwG WHCG WWeb WWin
¶ – 'Santana' (v)	EBrP EBre LBre LRHS SBre WWeb
– 'Summer Beauty'	CBlo CPle MGos WPat WWeb
– 'Variegated Royal Red'	CBlo SCob SHBN
– 'White Bouquet'	CBlo EAst EBee GRei MBal MBel MPla MRav MWat NRoo NWea SBod SCob SEND SEas SMer SPer SReu WAbe WLRN WWeb
– 'White Cloud'	EPar GQui IOrc SRms WGwG
– 'White Harlequin' (v)	CLTr CRow LHop WCot WEas WWat
– 'White Profusion' ♀	CB&S CSam ECtt ELan GCHN GChr LFis MBal MBar MGos MHlr NBee NBrk NFla NNor NWea SCob SHBN WBea WDin WEas WFar WHCG WHar WPyg WStI WWin
§ *delavayi*	CMil CPle ERea WCru
fallowiana var. *alba* ♀	CBlo CBot CDoC CPle ELan ENot LHop MBel NNor NSti SBid SPer SPla SSpi SSta WAbe WCru WPGP WSHC WWat
– Balf. f.	CB&S CPle MSto NLon NNor SReu WPic

¶ – CLD 1109	WPGP
◆ – misapplied	See *B.* 'West Hill'
farreri	CBot CPle MSte SMrm SOWG WBod
forrestii	CBot CHEx CPle WCru
globosa ♀	Widely available
– 'Cannington Gold'	CBlo
– 'Lemon Ball'	CB&S SMad
heliophila	See *B. delavayi*
¶ *indica*	CPle
japonica	CPle
* 'Lady Curzon'	WRHF
x *lewisiana*	CPle
– 'Margaret Pike'	CBot SOWG
lindleyana	CB&S CBot CFil CGre CHan CMCN CPle ELan EPla ERea MRav NSti SBid SChu SOWG SPan SPer SPla SSpi WCru WFar WHCG WPGP WPic WSHC WWeb
'Lochinch' ♀	Widely available
loricata	CAbb CBot CGre CHan CPle ERea GQui MSte SOWG
– CD&R 190	EPla
macrostachya	CFil CPle
– SBEC 360	NHex WPGP
§ *madagascariensis*	CB&S CHEx CPlN CPle CTbh LBlm SOWG WCot WWat
myriantha	GQui
nicodemia	See *B. madagascariensis*
nivea	CBot CMCN CPle EHic ELan MHar SBid SOWG
¶ aff. – L 860	WPGP
– var. *yunnanensis*	CPle MSte
officinalis	CBot CDoC CPle ERea
paniculata	CPle
¶ *parvifolia* MPF 148	WPGP
§ x *pikei* 'Hever'	CHal CPle GQui SPer
'Pink Delight' ♀	Widely available
pterocaulis	CGre CPle
saligna	CGre CPle CTrC
salviifolia	CAbb CBot CFil CGre CPle CSWP CTbh EGar ELan GQui MAll SBid SDry SPan SPer WCot WLRN WMul WPic
¶ – Burtt 6139	WPGP
stenostachya	CPle
sterniana	See *B. crispa*
tibetica	See *B. crispa*
tubiflora	CBot CPle ERea SOWG
venenifera B&SWJ 895	WCru
x *weyeriana*	CBlo CLTr CSam CStr ECtt EOrc EPar EPla GOrc LBlm MNrw MTis MWat NBir SBod SEas WBea WEas WFar WHCG WPyg WSHC
* – 'Flight's Fancy'	EWes
– 'Golden Glow'	CB&S CBlo CChe CDoC CHan CMil CTri EAst EHic GCHN MBri MPla NNor SHel WPyg WSel WTro WWeb WWin
– 'Lady de Ramsey'	SEND WPer
– 'Moonlight'	CPle CRow EAst EHal EPla SCob WSel
– 'Sungold' ♀	CB&S CPle ELan IOrc MBal MBel MBlu MCCP MGos MLLN NFla SPer WCot WFar WHar WMow
– 'Trewithen'	CB&S

BUGLOSSOIDES (Boraginaceae)

§ *purpurocaerulea*	CKin CMHG CRDP ECha EEls ELan EMan EMar GCal MAvo MBro MHew MSal MSte SAxl SOkh WCot WEas WOld WRHF WWin WWye

BULBINE (Asphodelaceae)

bulbosa	SAga WCot
caulescens	See *B. frutescens*
§ *frutescens*	CAvo CPea CSev WCot WHal WWin
– yellow	LHil
semibarbata	EGar NBro WPer

BULBINELLA (Asphodelaceae)

angustifolia	WCot
floribunda	ETub
hookeri	CRDP ECou EPPr GAbr GCrs GDra GGar ITim LBee MFir MTho NGre NHar NHed WCot WPer
nutans var. *nutans*	EEls
rossii	GDra WLin

BULBINOPSIS See BULBINE

BULBOCODIUM (Colchicaceae)

vernum	CAvo EHyt EPot ERos ETub GCrs LAma MBri NRog WAbe WHil

BUPHTHALMUM (Asteraceae)

§ *salicifolium*	CInt CSam CSev ELan EPfP GMaP MBri MCli NBro NFla NNor NOrc NSti NTow SPer SRms SWat WBea WMer WPer
salicifolium 'Alpengold'	ECha NVic SIgm
– 'Dora'	EMan NLak SUsu WCot WWal
– Golden Beauty	See *B. salicifolium* 'Golden Wonder'
speciosum	See *Telekia speciosa*

BUPLEURUM (Apiaceae)

angulosum	CFil CLon CLyd CRDP SIgm SMrm SWas WCot WCru
angulosum copper	See *B. longifolium*
barceloi	SIgm
falcatum	CGle CLTr CLyd EBee ECGP ECha MBro MLLN NBro NFla NSti SChu SMrm WFar
fruticosum	CB&S CBos CBot CFil CHad CHan CPle ECGP ELan ICrw MAll MHar SAxl SBid SBla SChu SIgm SSpi SSta WCru WEas WKif WPGP WPat WSHC WSpi WWat
* *griffithii*	MSal
komarovianum	GCal SMrm
§ *longifolium*	CHan CRDP ECha GBin GGar NSti SWas WCot WCru
longiradiatum B&SWJ 729	WCru
¶ *multinerve*	EBee
ranunculoides	EBee MRav SMrm
rotundifolium	EWFC MSal SMrm WCot WPGP
salicifolium	SIgm
spinosum	SIgm WCru
stellatum	EBee LBee
tenue B&SWJ 2973	WCru

BURCHARDIA (Colchicaceae)
   umbellata   CMon

BURSARIA (Pittosporaceae)
   spinosa   CPle ECou GQui MAll

BUTIA (Arecaceae)
   capitata   CBrP CHEx CTbh CTrC EOas
      LPJP LPal NPal SAPC SArc
      SEND WMul

BUTOMUS (Butomaceae)
   umbellatus ♀   CBen CRow CWat ECha ECoo
      ECtt EHon EMFW LPBA
      MHew MSta NDea NVic SRms
      SWat SWyc WChe WFar
      WMAq WShi
   – 'Rosenrot'   CRow SBla SWyc
   – 'Schneeweisschen'   CRow SWyc

BUXUS † (Buxaceae)
   aurea 'Marginata'   See **B. sempervirens 'Marginata'**
   balearica   CGre CPle EPla SDry SLan
      WSHC WWat
   bodinieri   EPla SLan WWat
   * 'David's Gold'   WEas WSHC
   ¶ *glomerata*   SLan
   * 'Golden Frimley'   LHop
   'Green Gem'   EHic NHar NHol SLan
   'Green Mountain'   SLan
   'Green Velvet'   EHic NHol SLan WWeb
   harlandii hort.   EPla GAri SIng SLan
   harlandii Hance 'Richard'   SLan STre
   ¶ *henryi*   SLan
   japonica 'Nana'   See **B. microphylla**
   ¶ *jaucoensis*   SLan
   ¶ *leoni*   SLan
   macowanii   SLan
   macrophylla 'Asiatic   See **B. microphylla 'Winter**
      Winter'   **Gem'**
   § *microphylla*   CBlo CSWP EHic GDra LHol
      NHol SIde SIng SLan STre
   § – 'Compacta'   CFil SLan WCot WPGP WPat
   – 'Curly Locks'   EPla GAri NHol SLan
   – 'Faulkner'   CDoC EMil ENot ERea LHop
      MBlu MBri MUlv NFla NHol
      SLan WLRN WWeb
   – 'Grace Hendrick   SLan
      Phillips'
   – 'Green Pillow'   NHol SLan
   – 'Helen Whiting'   SLan
   – var. *insularis*   See **B. sinica** var. *insularis*
   – var. *japonica*   SLan
   ¶ – – 'Gold Dust'   SLan
   – – 'Green Jade'   SLan
   – – 'Morris Dwarf'   SLan
   – – 'Morris Midget'   EHic NHol SLan
   – – 'National'   SLan
   – – 'Variegata'   CMHG
   ¶ – – f. *yakushima*   SLan
   – 'John Baldwin'   SLan
   – var. *koreana*   See **B. sinica** var. *insularis*
   – var. *riparia*   See **B. riparia**
   – var. *sinica*   See **B. sinica**
   § – 'Winter Gem'   CLyn EHic ENot MRav NHol
      SLPl SLan
   ♦ 'Newport Blue'   See **B. sempervirens 'Newport**
      Blue'
   § *riparia*   SLan
   * *rugulosa* var. *intermedia*   SLan
   sempervirens ♀   Widely available

§ – 'Angustifolia'   NHol SLan SMad
– 'Argentea'   See **B. sempervirens**
   'Argenteovariegata'
§ – 'Argenteovariegata'   CBlo EPfP MBal MRav SLan
   WBay WFar WSHC
– 'Aurea'   See **B. sempervirens**
   'Aureovariegata'
– 'Aurea Maculata'   See **B. sempervirens**
   'Aureovariegata'
– 'Aurea Marginata'   See **B. sempervirens 'Marginata'**
– 'Aurea Pendula' (v)   EPla GAbr SLan SMad WWye
§ – 'Aureovariegata'   CArn CB&S EBee EHic EPfP
   GAbr ISea MBar MGos MRav
   MWat NCut NHol SChu SIng
   SLan SPar SPer WDin WFar
   WJek WLRN WWeb WWye
– 'Blauer Heinz'   CSev EMil MBri MTed SLan
   SPer
§ – 'Blue Cone'   EHic GBin NHol
– 'Blue Spire'   See **B. sempervirens 'Blue Cone'**
§ – 'Elegantissima' (v) ♀   Widely available
– 'Gold Tip'   See **B. sempervirens 'Notata'**
– 'Greenpeace'   EBrP EBre EHic LBre NHol
   SBre SLan
– 'Handsworthiensis'   EMil SEND SLan SPer
– 'Handsworthii'   CBlo CTri ERea NWea SRms
– subsp. *hyrcana*   SLan
– 'Ickworth Giant'   SLan
– 'Inverewe'   SLan
♦ – 'Japonica Aurea'   See **B. sempervirens 'Latifolia**
   Maculata'
– 'Kensington Gardens'   SLan
♦ – 'Kingsville'   See **B. microphylla 'Compacta'**
– 'Lace'   NHol NSti SLan
§ – 'Langley Beauty'   MHlr SLan
I – 'Langley Pendula'   See **B. sempervirens 'Langley**
   Beauty'
– 'Latifolia'   See **B. sempervirens 'Bullata'**
– 'Latifolia Macrophylla'   GAbr SEas SLan
§ – 'Latifolia Maculata' ♀   CAbP CChe CHan EPla GDra
   MBal MHlr MPla NHol NPer
   NRoo SEas SLan STre WOak
* – 'Latifolia Pendula'   SLan
– 'Longifolia'   See **B. sempervirens**
   'Angustifolia'
§ – 'Marginata'   ECtt GCHN LHop MRav NHol
   NSti SHBN SHFr SLan WHar
   WOak WStI
– 'Memorial'   EHic GAbr LGre NHol SLan
– 'Myosotidifolia'   CFil CMHG EPla NHar SLan
   WWat
– 'Myrtifolia'   CBot NHar NHol SLan
§ – 'Notata' (v)   CBlo CDec CSWP ERea GAbr
   MAsh WGor WWal
¶ – 'Parasol'   SLan
– 'Pendula'   CGre CMHG EHic SLan SMad
I – 'Pendula Esveld'   MHlr
– 'Prostrata'   EHic MHlr NHol SLan
– 'Pyramidalis'   EHic GAbr NBee SLan
– 'Rosmarinifolia'   SLan
– 'Rotundifolia'   CLnd EBee NFla SIde SLan
   WDin
– 'Salicifolia Elata'   SLan
– 'Silver Beauty' (v)   CB&S EMil MGos
– 'Silver Variegated'   See **B. sempervirens**
   'Elegantissima'
– 'Suffruticosa' ♀   Widely available
* – 'Suffruticosa Blue'   NHol
– 'Suffruticosa Variegata'   CB&S EOHP ERea SRms
– 'Vardar Valley'   EHic NHar SLan
* – 'Variegata'   EPfP
– 'Waterfall'   SLan

§ *sinica* — SLan
§ – var. **insularis** — EPla
¶ – – 'Filigree' — NHol SLan
– – 'Justin Brouwers' — CSev SLan
– – 'Pincushion' — SLan
– – 'Tide Hill' — SLan
wallichiana — CFil EPla SLan WPGP WWat

CACALIA (Asteraceae)
§ *glabra* — EBee

CAESALPINIA (Caesalpiniaceae)
gilliesii — CBot CFai CHEx EMil NPSI SOWG
pulcherrima — LChe
– f. *flava* — LChe

CAIOPHORA (Loasaceae)
acuminata — MSto
coronata — MSto
prietea — MSto

CALADENIA (Orchidaceae)
g. **Fairy Floss** — SWes
¶ *menziesii* — SWes

CALADIUM (Araceae)
§ *bicolor* (v) — MBri
× *hortulanum* — See *C. bicolor*
§ *lindenii* (v) — MBri WMul

CALAMAGROSTIS (Poaceae)
N× *acutiflora* 'Karl Foerster' — CLon EBee EBrP EBre ECGN ECha EGar EHoe EPPr EPla ESOG GAbr GCal GOrn LBre NSti SApp SAxl SBre SDix SMer SPer WChe WWye
– 'Overdam' (v) — Widely available
arundinacea — Widely available
– 'Autumn Tints' — ECou
– 'Gold Hue' — ECou ESOG
§ *brachytricha* — CHan CSte EBee ECGN ECha EGle EPPr EPla ESOG EWes GBin GOrn
§ *epigejos* — EPPr NHol
– CLD 1325 — EPla

CALAMINTHA † (Lamiaceae)
alpina — See *Acinos alpinus*
clinopodium — See *Clinopodium vulgare*
cretica — CLyd EMon GBar LHop MHew MTho WLin WPbr WPer WWye
– *variegata* — WEas
¶ 'Gottfried Klein' — MRav
§ *grandiflora* — Widely available
– 'Variegata' — CDec CGle CMil CRow EEls ELan EMan EMon LFis LHop MBro MCLN MGrG SCro SSpe SWat WByw WCHb WFar WHer WHoo WMaN WPbr WRus
§ *nepeta* — CArn CLon ECha ECoo EEls EWFC LGan LGre MAus MCLN MFir MGrG MGra MRav MSte NBir NBro SBla SWat WEas WFar WHal WOve WPbr WPer WWin WWye
– subsp. *glandulosa* — EMon MTPN WHoo
ACL 1050/90

– – 'White Cloud' — CGle CHea CSpe EBrP EBre ECGN ECha EFou GBuc GMac LBre LGre LHol MBro MCLN MSte NTow SBre SLod SSpe WHoo WMaN WPbr WRus WWye
¶ – 'Gottfried Kuehn' — MAus
§ – subsp. *nepeta* — CGle CHan CSev ECGN EFou ELan EMon GBar GMac LHol LHop MBri MPla MTho NFla NOak SHel SIde SPer SUsu WCHb WHoo WMer WRus WSHC WWat WWhi
– – 'Blue Cloud' — CGle CHan CHea CHor CMil ECGN ECha EFou LGre LHol MAus MRav NTow SHel SLod SSpe SUsu SWat WMaN WRus WWye
nepetoides — See *C. nepeta* subsp. *nepeta*
§ *sylvatica* — CAgr CNat LHol NLar SRCN WCla
– subsp. *ascendens* — MHew MLLN WPbr
¶ – HH&K 163 — CHan
vulgaris — See *Clinopodium vulgare*

CALAMOVILFA (Poaceae) See Plant Deletions

CALANDRINIA (Portulacaceae)
caespitosa — NGre
grandiflora — EBar ELan LHop MLLN SAga WWin WWye
megarhiza — See *Claytonia megarhiza*
sericea — CPBP
¶ – *alba* — WLin
sibirica — See *Claytonia sibirica*
umbellata — EBar NPri NWCA SBla WPer WWin WWye
* – *amarantha* — WOMN

CALANTHE (Orchidaceae)
amamiana — EFEx
arisanensis — EFEx
aristulifera — EFEx LAma NRog
bicolor — See *C. discolor* var. *flava*
biloba — LAma
brevicornu — LAma
caudatilabella — EFEx
chloroleuca — LAma
discolor — EFEx LAma NRog SWes
§ – var. *flava* — LAma
hamata — EFEx
herbacea — LAma
japonica — EFEx
mannii — EFEx LAma
masuca — LAma
nipponica — EFEx
puberula — LAma
reflexa — EFEx LAma NRog
§ *sieboldii* — EFEx LAma NRog SWes WCot
striata — See *C. sieboldii*
tokunoshimensis — EFEx
tricarinata — EFEx LAma SWes

CALATHEA (Marantaceae)
albertii — MBri
albicans — See *C. micans*
crocata — MBri
'Exotica' — MBri
'Greystar' — MBri
kegeljanii — See *C. bella*
lietzei — MBri
– 'Greenstar' — MBri

§ *majestica* — MBri
makoyana ♀ — CHal MBri
* 'Mavi Queen' — MBri
metallica — MBri
* 'Misto' — MBri
oppenheimiana — See *Ctenanthe oppenheimiana*
orbiculata — See *C. truncata*
ornata — See *C. majestica*
picturata 'Argentea' — MBri
– 'Vandenheckei' — MBri
roseopicta — MBri
§ *truncata* — MBri
veitchiana — MBri
warscewiczii — MBri
'Wavestar' — MBri
zebrina ♀ — MBri

CALCEOLARIA † (Scrophulariaceae)

acutifolia — See *C. polyrhiza*
alba — CPla
arachnoidea — GCra MSto NWoo WWhi
× *banksii* — EBee GQui LBlm MFir WCot
bicolor — GCal GCra WCot
§ *biflora* — CLyd CMea CPBP ELan GDra GTou MBal MMal NWoo WLin WWin
– 'Goldcrest Amber' — GCra NMen SRms WPer
'Camden Hero' — CLyn GCra MBEx WWat
chelidonioides — MTho
× *clibranii* — MBEx
crenatiflora — GCra MSto NWoo
cymbiflora — MSto
ericoides JCA 13818 — MSto
falklandica — CNic ELan NWCA SIng SRms SSca WPer WWin
¶ *fiebrigiana* — MSto
filicaulis — MSto
fothergillii — MSto NMen
'Goldcrest' — EPfP NPri
helianthemoides JCA 13911 — MSto
¶ *hirsuta* — MSto
'Hort's Variety' — MTho
hyssopifolia JCA 13648 — MSto
§ *integrifolia* ♀ — CB&S CDec ELan EMar EMon ERav LBlm MBal MFir NRog SAga SChu SPer SRms WOMN WWat
– var. *angustifolia* ♀ — SDry
– bronze — SPer WAbe
'John Innes' — EBur ELan ESis NWCA WCot
'Kentish Hero' — CB&S CElw ELan EOrc LBlm LHil MAvo MBEx NPer SChu WCot
lagunae-blancae — MSto WLin
lanigera — ELan EWes MSto
mendocina — MSto
mexicana — MSto MTPN SHFr
nivalis JCA 13888 — MSto
aff. *pavonii* — LHil
perfoliata JCA 13736 — MSto
¶ *pinifolia* — CPBP WLin
¶ – JCA 14450 — IDac
¶ *pinnata* — MSto
plantaginea — See *C. biflora*
§ *polyrhiza* — ELan MBal MSto NNrd NRoo NRya NWCA WCla
purpurea — MSto
rugosa — See *C. integrifolia*
scabiosifolia — See *C. tripartita*
sp. ex P&W 6276 — MRPP
sp. JCA 14128 — MSto
sp. JCA 14172 — MSto

'Stamford Park' — MBEx
tenella — ECtt ELan EPot ESis MSto NHar NTow WAbe WOMN
§ *tripartita* — MSto
uniflora var. *darwinii* — GCra GTou MSto NMen SIng
volckmannii — MSto
'Walter Shrimpton' — EDAr ELan EPot EWes NWCA

CALDCLUVIA (Cunoniaceae)

paniculata — ISea

CALEA (Asteraceae)

zacatechichi — NGno

CALENDULA (Asteraceae)

officinalis — CArn CJew ELau GPoy LHol MChe MGra MHew MSal SIde WHer WJek WOak WRha WSel WWye
officinalis Fiesta Gitana — WJek
– 'Prolifera' — WHer
– 'Variegata' — MSal

CALLA (Araceae)

aethiopica — See *Zantedeschia aethiopica*
palustris — CBen CHEx CRow CWat ECoo EHon GAri GGar LPBA MSta NDea SWat SWyc WChe WMAq WWeb

CALLIANDRA (Mimosaceae)

brevipes — See *C. selloi*
emarginata minima — SOWG
§ *selloi* — CTrC WMul

CALLIANTHEMUM (Ranunculaceae)

anemonoides — NHar WAbe
coriandrifolium — GDra

CALLICARPA (Verbenaceae)

bodinieri — NBir
– var. *giraldii* — CDec GBin MAsh MHlr MRav NFla SSta WDin WFar WRHF WWat WWeb
– – 'Profusion' ♀ — Widely available
dichotoma — CBlo CPle CTrG GSki MNes WSHC WWat WWin
japonica — CPle
– 'Leucocarpa' — CB&S CBlo CPle EHic EPfP LRHS MRav SBid SPer WBcn WWat

CALLICOMA (Cunoniaceae)

serratifolia — MAll

CALLIERGON (Sphagnaceae) See Plant Deletions

CALLIRHOE (Malvaceae)

¶ *digitata* — EBee
involucrata — EBee EMan MAvo NWCA SIng SMad
¶ *triangulata* — EBee

CALLISIA (Commelinaceae)

elegans ♀ — CHal
§ *navicularis* — CHal CInt
repens — CHal MBri

CALLISTEMON (Myrtaceae)

brachyandrus	MAll
'Burning Bush'	CB&S LBlm MAll SOWG
chisholmii	SOWG
citrinus	CHEx CHon CLTr CPle CTrC
	ECot ECou ERav ERom GOrc
	GSki ISea NPer SLMG SMac
	SOWG SPer WGwG WHar
	WWal WWin
– 'Albus'	See *C. citrinus* **'White Anzac'**
– 'Canberra'	SOWG
– 'Firebrand'	LRHS SMur WWeb
– 'Mauve Mist'	CB&S CTrC LBlm LRHS MAll
	NPal SOWG SSta
– 'Perth Pink'	CB&S GSki MAll
– 'Splendens' ♀	CB&S CDoC CHEx CMac
	CSam CTrC EBrP EBre ELan
	EMil GQui IOrc LBre MAll
	NPal SAga SBra SBre SDry
	SHBN SHFr SOWG SReu SSta
	WBod WStI WWat
§ – 'White Anzac'	GCHN MAll
– 'Yellow Queen'	CB&S
coccineus	CGre
comboynensis	SOWG
flavescens	SOWG
flavovirens	MAll SOWG
glaucus	See *C. speciosus*
'Kings Park Special'	EHol SOWG
* *laevis*	LHil LRHS
lanceolatus	CGre
linearifolius	CHon MAll
linearis ♀	CBlo CHan CHon CMac CTrC
	CTri ECou EHic ELan EMil
	IOrc MAll MBal SLMG SOWG
	SRms SSpi WNor
macropunctatus	CGre MAll SOWG
pachyphyllus	CGre MAll SOWG
¶ – var. *viridis*	MAll
pallidus	CB&S CGre CHon CMHG
	CMac CPle CWit ELan EPfP
	IDee MAll SOWG SPer SSta
¶ – lilac	MAll
paludosus	See *C. sieberi*
¶ – pink form	CHon
* *pearsonii*	SOWG
'Perth Pink'	CFee CTrC SBid SOWG
phoeniceus	CHon MAll SOWG
pinifolius	CGre CHon MAll SOWG SPan
– green form	CHon LLew MAll
pityoides	CGre ECou MAll SOWG
	WAbe
– alpine form	MAll
– from Brown's Swamp,	ECou MAll
Australia	
polandii	SOWG
recurvus	MAll
'Red Clusters'	CB&S ELan ERea GSki LRHS
	MAll SMur SOWG
rigidus	CB&S CBlo CChe CDoC CHEx
	CHon CLan CMHG CMac CTri
	CTrw EBrP EBre ELan EMil
	EOas GSki ISea LBre MAll
	MBlu MGos MLan SBre SLMG
	SOWG SSoC WCru WDin
	WWeb
'Royal Sceptre'	MAll
rugulosus	CHon MAll SOWG

salignus ♀	CHEx CHon CMHG CPlN
	CTrC CTri GSki IOrc ISea
	MAll MBal MCCP SAxl SLod
	SOWG SPer SSoC WGwG
	WSHC
– 'Ruber'	MAll
§ *sieberi* ♀	CGre CHon CMHG CTrC
	ECou EPfP GSki ISea MAll
	NBir SOWG
§ *speciosus*	CHon CTrC MAll SMur SOWG
	SPan WAbe WLRN
subulatus	CMHG ECou MAll MBal
	MCCP NCut SAPC SArc
	SOWG
teretifolius	SOWG
viminalis	CTrC EHic MAll SOWG
– 'Captain Cook' ♀	CB&S CTrC ECou ERea LCns
	LRHS SOWG
– 'Hannah Ray'	MAll SOWG
– 'Little John'	CB&S CWSG LRHS MAll SBid
	SOWG
– 'Malawi Giant'	SOWG
'Violaceus'	CHan CHon MAll
viridiflorus	CGre CPea CPle ECou GQui
	IBlr MAll MCCP SOWG WSan

CALLITRICHE (Callitrichaceae)

autumnalis	See *C. hermaphroditica*
§ *hermaphroditica*	EMFW SAWi
§ *palustris*	CBen ECoo EHon SWyc
verna	See *C. palustris*

CALLITRIS (Cupressaceae)

¶ *monticola*	MFiF
oblonga	CGre ECou
rhomboidea	CGre ECou

CALLUNA † (Ericaceae)

vulgaris	CKin MGos
– 'Adrie'	EDen
– 'Alba Argentea'	EDen
– 'Alba Aurea'	ECho EDen MBar
– 'Alba Carlton'	EDen
– 'Alba Dumosa'	EDen
– 'Alba Elata'	CNCN ECho EDen MBar
– 'Alba Elegans'	EDen
– 'Alba Elongata'	See *C. vulgaris* **'Mair's Variety'**
– 'Alba Erecta'	EDen
– 'Alba Jae'	EDen MBar
– 'Alba Minor'	EDen
– 'Alba Multiflora'	EDen
– 'Alba Pilosa'	EDen
– 'Alba Plena' (d)	CB&S CMac CNCN ECho
	EDen MBar SBod WStI
– 'Alba Praecox'	EDen
– 'Alba Pumila'	EDen MBar
§ – 'Alba Rigida'	CMac CNCN EDen MBar
– 'Alec Martin' (d)	EDen
– 'Alex Warwick'	EDen
– 'Alexandra'	EDen NHol NRoo SCoo
¶ – 'Alicia'	ECho EDen
– 'Alieke'	EDen
– 'Alison Yates'	EDen MBar
– 'Allegretto'	EDen
– 'Allegro' ♀	CMac CNCN EDen GAri MBar
	MOke NHol SBod WStI
– 'Alportii'	CMac EDen GDra MBar MOke
	SBod WStI
– 'Alportii Praecox'	CNCN ECho EDen MBar SBod
– 'Alys Sutcliffe'	EDen
– 'Amanda Wain'	ECho EDen
– 'Amethyst'	ECho EDen NHol

– 'Amilto'	CNCN ECho EDen NHol
– 'Amy'	EDen
– 'Andrew Proudley'	EDen MBar NRoo
– 'Anette'	ECho EDen NHol SCoo
– 'Angela Wain'	ECho EDen NRoo
– 'Anna'	EDen
– 'Annabel' (d)	EDen
– 'Anne Dobbin'	EDen
– 'Anneke'	EDen
– 'Annemarie' (d) ♀	CNCN EBrP EBre EDen ENot
	GChr LBre MGos NHol SBod
	SBre SCoo
– 'Anthony Davis' ♀	CNCN EDen MBar MGos
	MOke NHol SBod
– 'Anthony Wain'	EDen MGos
– 'Anton'	EDen
– 'Apollo'	EDen
– 'Applecross' (d)	CNCN EDen SHBN
– 'Arabella'	EDen NHol
– 'Argentea'	EDen MBar
– 'Ariadne'	EDen
– 'Arina'	CNCN ECho EDen MBri MOke
– 'Arran Gold'	CNCN EDen MBar
– 'Ashgarth Amber'	EDen
– 'Ashgarth Amethyst'	EDen
¶ – 'Ashgarth Shell Pink'	EDen
– 'Asterix'	EDen
– 'Atalanta'	EDen
¶ – 'Atholl Gold'	CMac EDen
– 'August Beauty'	CNCN ECho EDen MOke
– 'Aurea'	CNCN ECho EDen
– 'Autumn Glow'	ECho EDen
– 'Baby Ben'	CNCN EDen
– 'Barbara Fleur'	EDen SBod
– 'Barja'	EDen
– 'Barnett Anley'	CNCN ECho EDen
– 'Battle of Arnhem' ♀	CNCN EDen MBar
– 'Beechwood Crimson'	CNCN EDen
– 'Ben Nevis'	EDen
– 'Beoley Crimson'	CB&S CNCN EDen GAri GDra
	MBar MGos SBod
– 'Beoley Gold' ♀	CB&S CNCN CTri EBrP EBre
	EDen GChr LBre MBar MBri
	MGos MOke NHol NRoo SBod
	SBre SHBN WStI
– 'Beoley Silver'	CNCN EDen NRoo
– 'Bernadette'	EDen
– 'Betty Baum'	EDen
– 'Blazeaway'	CMac CNCN CTri EDen GDra
	MBar MBri NHar NHol NRoo
	SBod SHBN WStI
– 'Blueness'	EDen
– 'Bognie'	CNCN EDen
– 'Bonfire Brilliance'	CNCN EDen MBar NHar SBod
– 'Boreray'	CNCN EDen
– 'Boskoop'	CNCN EBrP EBre EDen LBre
	MBar MBri NHol NRoo SBod
	SBre
– 'Bradford'	EDen
– 'Braemar'	CNCN EDen
– 'Braeriach'	EDen
– 'Branchy Anne'	EDen
– 'Bray Head'	CNCN EDen MBar SBod
– 'Brightness'	EDen
– 'Brita Elisabeth' (d)	EDen
– 'Bud Lyle'	EDen
– 'Bunsall'	CNCN EDen
– 'Buxton Snowdrift'	EDen
– 'C.W. Nix'	CNCN ECho EDen MBar
– 'Caerketton White'	ECho EDen GChr
– 'Caleb Threlkeld'	ECho EDen NHol
– 'Calf of Man'	EDen

– 'Californian Midge'	CNCN EDen GAri MBar MGos
	NHol
– 'Carl Röders' (d)	EDen
– 'Carmen'	ECho EDen
¶ – 'Carngold'	EDen
– 'Carole Chapman'	EDen MBar MGos SBod SHBN
– 'Carolyn'	EDen
– 'Catherine Anne'	EDen
– 'Celtic Gold'	EDen
– 'Chindit'	EDen
– 'Christina'	EDen
– 'Cilcennin Common'	EDen
– 'Citronella'	EDen
– 'Clare Carpet'	EDen
– 'Coby'	EDen
– 'Coccinea'	CMac ECho EDen MBar SBod
– 'Colette'	EDen
– 'Con Brio'	CNCN EDen LRHS
– 'Copper Glow'	EDen
– 'Coral Island'	EDen MBar MGos
¶ – 'Corrie's White'	EDen
– 'Cottswood Gold'	EDen
– 'County Wicklow' (d) ♀	CNCN CTri EBrP EBre EDen
	GChr LBre MBar MBri MGos
	MOke NHar NHol NRoo SBod
	SBre SHBN
– 'Craig Rossie'	EDen
– 'Crail Orange'	EDen
– 'Cramond' (d)	CNCN ECho EDen GDra MBar
– 'Cream Steving'	ECho EDen
– 'Crimson Glory'	CNCN EDen MBar NHed WStI
– 'Crimson Sunset'	CNCN EDen SBod WStI
– 'Crowborough Beacon'	EDen
– 'Cuprea'	CNCN EDen GDra MBar MBri
	MOke NHol NRoo SBod WStI
– 'Cuprea Select'	EDen
– 'Dainty Bess'	CNCN EDen MBar NHol SBod
	WStI
– 'Dark Beauty' (d)	CNCN EBrP EBre EDen LBre
	MGos NHed NHol NRoo SBre
	WStI
– 'Dark Star' (d) ♀	CMac CNCN EBrP EBre EDen
	LBre MBar MGos MOke NHar
	NHol NRoo SBre SCoo
– 'Darkness' ♀	CB&S CNCN CTri EDen MBar
	MBri MGos MOke NHar NHol
	SBod SCoo SHBN WStI
– 'Darleyensis'	EDen
– 'Dart's Amethyst'	EDen
– 'Dart's Beauty'	EDen
– 'Dart's Brilliant'	EDen
– 'Dart's Flamboyant'	CNCN EDen
– 'Dart's Gold'	ECho EDen MBar NHar NRoo
– 'Dart's Hedgehog'	ECho EDen
– 'Dart's Parakeet'	CNCN EDen
– 'Dart's Parrot'	ECho EDen NHar
– 'Dart's Silver Rocket'	EDen NRoo
– 'Dart's Squirrel'	EDen
– 'David Eason'	CNCN ECho EDen
– 'David Hagenaars'	EDen
– 'David Hutton'	EDen MBar
– 'David Platt' (d)	EDen
– 'Denny Pratt'	EDen
– 'Desiree'	EDen
– 'Devon' (d)	EDen
– 'Diana'	EDen
– 'Dickson's Blazes'	EDen
– 'Dirry'	CNCN EDen
– 'Doctor Murray's White'	See *C. vulgaris* **'Mullardoch'**
– 'Doris Rushworth'	EDen
– 'Drum-ra'	EDen GDra MBar SBod SRms
– 'Dunkeld White'	EDen

– 'Dunnet Lime'	EDen
– 'Dunnydeer'	EDen
– 'Dunwood'	EDen MBar
§ – 'Durfordii'	ECho EDen
– 'E.F. Brown'	CNCN EDen
– 'E. Hoare'	EDen MBar
– 'Easter-bonfire'	CNCN EDen NHol
– 'Eckart Miessner'	EDen
– 'Edith Godbolt'	CNCN EDen
– 'Elaine'	ECho EDen
– 'Elegant Pearl'	EDen MBar SBod
– 'Elegantissima'	CNCN EDen MOke
– 'Elegantissima Lilac'	EDen
– 'Elegantissima Walter Ingwersen'	See *C. vulgaris* **'Walter Ingwersen'**
– 'Elkstone'	CNCN EDen MBar SBod
– 'Ellen'	EDen
– 'Else Frye' (d)	EDen
– 'Elsie Purnell' (d) ♀	CNCN EDen MBar MGos MOke NHol SBod WStI
– 'Emerald Jock'	EDen SBod
– 'Emma Louise Tuke'	ECho EDen
– 'Eric Easton'	EDen
– 'Eskdale Gold'	EDen
– 'Fairy'	CMac CNCN EDen MOke
– 'Falling Star'	EDen
– 'Feuerwerk'	EDen
§ – 'Finale' ♀	CNCN EDen MBar
– 'Findling'	EDen
– 'Fire King'	EDen MBar
– 'Firebreak'	ECho EDen MBar
– 'Firefly' ♀	CMac CNCN EBrP EBre EDen LBre MBar MBri MOke NHar NRoo SBod SBre SHBN WStI
– 'Firestar'	EDen
– 'Flamingo'	CNCN EBrP EBre EDen LBre MBar MBri MOke NHar NHol NRoo SBre
– 'Flatling'	EDen NHol
– 'Flore Pleno' (d)	EDen MBar
– 'Floriferous'	EDen
– 'Florrie Spicer'	EDen
– 'Fokko' (d)	EDen
– 'Fortyniner Gold'	EDen
– 'Foxhollow Wanderer'	CNCN EDen MBar MOke SBod
– 'Foxii'	EDen
– 'Foxii Floribunda'	ECho EDen MBar
◆ – 'Foxii Lett's Form'	See *C. vulgaris* **'Velvet Dome'**
– 'Foxii Nana'	CNCN EDen MBar NHar NHed NHol SBod
– 'Foya'	EDen
– 'Fred J. Chapple'	CNCN EDen GDra MBar MBri MOke SBod WStI
– 'Fréjus'	EDen
– 'French Grey'	CNCN EDen
– 'Fritz Kircher'	EDen NHol
– 'Gerda'	EDen
– 'Ginkels Glorie'	EDen
– 'Glasa'	EDen
– 'Glen Mashie'	EDen
– 'Glencoe' (d)	EDen MBar MBri MGos MOke NHar
– 'Glendoick Silver'	EDen
– 'Glenfiddich'	CNCN EDen MBar
– 'Glenlivet'	EDen MBar
– 'Glenmorangie'	EDen MBar
– 'Gnome Pink'	EDen
– 'Gold Charm'	EDen
– 'Gold Finch'	EDen
– 'Gold Flame'	EDen LRHS MBar SBod
– 'Gold Hamilton' (d)	ECho EDen NHol
– 'Gold Haze' ♀	CB&S CMac CNCN EBrP EBre EDen LBre MBar MBri MOke NHol NRoo SBod SBre SCoo WStI
– 'Gold Knight'	ECho EDen LRHS MBar SBod
– 'Gold Kup'	EDen MBar
– 'Gold Mist'	ECho EDen LRHS NHed
– 'Gold Spronk'	EDen
– 'Goldcarmen'	ECho EDen
¶ – 'Golden Blazeaway'	ECho EDen
– 'Golden Carpet'	CB&S CNCN EDen GDra MBar MBri MGos MOke NHar NHed NHol SRms WStI
– 'Golden Dew'	EDen
– 'Golden Dream' (d)	EDen
– 'Golden Feather'	CB&S CNCN EDen MBar MGos SBod SHBN
– 'Golden Fleece'	CNCN EDen
– 'Golden Max'	EDen NHar
– 'Golden Rivulet'	EDen LRHS MBar
– 'Golden Turret'	CNCN ECho EDen NRoo
– 'Golden Wonder' (d)	ECho EDen
– 'Goldsworth Crimson'	ECho EDen
– 'Goldsworth Crimson Variegated'	CNCN EDen MBar SBod
– 'Grasmeriensis'	EDen MBar
– 'Great Comp'	EDen MBar
– 'Grey Carpet'	CNCN EDen MBar SBod
– 'Grijsje'	EDen
– 'Grizzly'	EDen
– 'Grönsinka'	EDen
– 'Guinea Gold'	CNCN ECho EDen MBar MBri NRoo
§ – 'H.E. Beale' (d)	CB&S CNCN CTri EBrP EBre EDen GDra LBre MBar MBri MGos MOke NHar NHed NHol SBod SBre SHBN
– 'Hamlet Green'	CNCN EDen MBar
– 'Hammondii'	CNCN EDen SBod WStI
– 'Hammondii Aureifolia'	CNCN EBrP EBre EDen GAri LBre MBar MBri MOke SBre
– 'Hammondii Rubrifolia'	CNCN EDen MBar MBri MOke NHar
– 'Harlekin'	EDen
– 'Harry Gibbon' (d)	EDen
– 'Harten's Findling'	EDen
– 'Hatjes Herbstfeuer' (d)	EDen
– 'Hayesensis'	EDen
¶ – 'Heidberg'	EDen
– 'Heidepracht'	EDen
– 'Heidesinfonie'	EDen
– 'Heideteppich'	EDen
– 'Heidezwerg'	EDen
¶ – 'Helen Gill'	EDen
– 'Herbert Mitchell'	EDen
– 'Hester'	EDen
– 'Hetty'	EDen
– 'Hibernica'	EDen MBar
– 'Hiemalis'	EDen MBar
– 'Hiemalis Southcote'	See *C. vulgaris* **'Durfordii'**
– 'Highland Cream'	CNCN SDys
– 'Highland Rose'	CNCN ECho EDen
¶ – 'Highland Spring'	SDys
– 'Hilda Turberfield'	EDen
– 'Hillbrook Orange'	EDen MBar
– 'Hillbrook Sparkler'	EDen
– 'Hinton White'	EDen
– 'Hirsuta Albiflora'	EDen MBar
– 'Hirsuta Typica'	CNCN ECho EDen
– 'Hirta'	CNCN EDen MBar SBod
– 'Hollandia'	EDen
– 'Holstein'	EDen

– 'Hookstone'	EDen MBar
– 'Hoyerhagen'	EDen
§ – 'Hugh Nicholson'	CNCN EDen NHar
– 'Humpty Dumpty'	ECho EDen NHol
– 'Hypnoides'	EDen
– 'Ide's Double' (d)	EDen SBod
– 'Inchcolm'	EDen
– 'Ineke'	CNCN EDen MBar
– 'Ingrid Bouter' (d)	EDen
– 'Inshriach Bronze'	CNCN EDen GDra MBar SBod
– 'Iris van Leyen'	CNCN ECho EDen LRHS
– 'Islay Mist'	EDen
– 'Isobel Frye'	EDen MBar
– 'Isobel Hughes' (d)	EDen MBar
– 'J.H. Hamilton' (d) ♀	CNCN CTri EDen GDra MBar MBri MGos NHol SBod SRms WStI
– 'Jan'	EDen
– 'Jan Dekker'	CNCN EDen LRHS NHol SBod
– 'Janice Chapman'	ECho EDen MBar
– 'Japanese White'	EDen
– 'Jenny'	EDen
– 'Jill'	EDen
– 'Jimmy Dyce' (d) ♀	EDen SBod
– 'Joan Sparkes' (d)	CNCN EDen MBar WStI
¶ – 'Jochen'	EDen
– 'John F. Letts'	CNCN EDen MBar MGos SBod SHBN SRms WStI
– 'Johnson's Variety'	CNCN ECho EDen MBar
– 'Josefine'	EDen
– 'Joseph's Coat'	EDen
– 'Joy Vanstone' ♀	CMac CNCN EDen MBar MBri MGos MOke NHol NRoo SHBN
– 'Julia'	CNCN EDen
– 'Julie Ann Platt'	EDen
– 'Karin Blum'	EDen
– 'Kermit'	EDen
– 'Kerstin'	CNCN ECho EDen LRHS NHol
– 'Kinlochruel' (d) ♀	CMac CNCN EDen GChr GDra MBar MBri MGos MOke NHar NHol NRoo SBod SHBN SRms
– 'Kirby White'	CNCN EDen MBar MBri NHed NHol
– 'Kirsty Anderson'	EDen MOke
– 'Kit Hill'	EDen MBar
– 'Kuphaldtii'	EDen MBar
– 'Kuppendorf'	EDen
– 'Kynance'	CNCN EDen MBar
– 'Lady Maithe'	EDen
– 'Lambstails'	EDen MBar MGos
– 'L'Ancresse'	EDen
– 'Late Crimson Gold'	EDen
– 'Lemon Gem'	EDen
– 'Lemon Queen'	EDen
– 'Leprechaun'	ECho EDen
– 'Leslie Slinger'	CNCN EDen LRHS MBar
– 'Lewis Lilac'	EDen
– 'Liebestraum'	EDen
– 'Lime Glade'	CNCN ECho EDen
– 'Limelight'	EDen
– 'Llanbedrog Pride' (d)	CNCN EDen MBar
– 'Loch Turret'	CNCN EDen MBar MBri MOke NRoo
– 'Loch-na-Seil'	EDen MBar
– 'London Pride'	EDen
– 'Long White'	CNCN ECho EDen MBar
– 'Lüneberg Heath'	EDen
– 'Lyle's Late White'	CNCN EDen
– 'Lyle's Surprise'	EDen MBar
– 'Lyndon Proudley'	EDen

§ – 'Mair's Variety' ♀	CNCN EDen GDra MBar SBod
– 'Mallard'	EDen
– 'Manitoba'	EDen
– 'Marie'	EDen
– 'Marion Blum'	EDen MBar
– 'Marleen'	CNCN EDen MBar NHol SBod
– 'Marlies'	EDen NHol
– 'Martha Hermann'	EDen
– 'Masquerade'	EDen MBar
– 'Matita'	EDen
– 'Mauvelyn'	EDen
– 'Mazurka'	EDen
– 'Melanie'	ECho EDen NHol
¶ – 'Mick Jamieson' (d)	EDen
– 'Mies'	EDen
– 'Minima'	EDen MBar SBod
– 'Minima Smith's Variety'	EDen MBar
– 'Mini-öxabäck'	EDen
– 'Minty'	EDen
– 'Mirelle'	CNCN EDen
– 'Miss Muffet'	NHol
– 'Molecule'	EDen MBar
– 'Monika' (d)	EDen
– 'Moon Glow'	EDen
§ – 'Mousehole'	CNCN EDen MBar MGos MOke NHol
– 'Mousehole Compact'	See *C. vulgaris* 'Mousehole'
– 'Mrs Alf'	EDen
– 'Mrs E. Wilson' (d)	EDen
– 'Mrs Neil Collins'	EDen
– 'Mrs Pat'	CNCN EDen GAri MBar MOke NHol
– 'Mrs Ronald Gray'	CMac CNCN EDen MBar
– 'Mullach Mor'	EDen
§ – 'Mullardoch'	EDen MBar
– 'Mullion' ♀	CNCN EDen MBar MOke
– 'Multicolor'	CB&S CNCN EDen GDra MBar MOke NHed NHol SBod SRms
– 'Murielle Dobson'	EDen MBar
§ – 'My Dream' (d)	CNCN EBrP EBre EDen LBre MBar NHol NRoo SBre SCoo
– 'Nana Compacta'	CNCN EDen ESis MBar MOke SRms
– 'Natasja'	EDen
– 'Naturpark'	EDen MBar
– 'Nico'	EDen
– 'Nordlicht'	EDen
– 'October White'	CNCN EDen
– 'Oiseval'	EDen
– 'Old Rose'	EDen
– 'Olive Turner'	ECho EDen
– 'Olympic Gold'	EDen
– 'Orange and Gold'	ECho EDen
– 'Orange Carpet'	EDen
– 'Orange Max'	EDen
– 'Orange Queen' ♀	CEnd CNCN EDen MBar SBod
– 'Öxabäck'	MBar
– 'Oxshott Common'	CNCN EDen GQui MBar SBod
– 'Pallida'	ECho EDen
– 'Parsons' Gold'	EDen
– 'Parsons' Grey Selected'	EDen
– 'Pat's Gold'	EDen
– 'Peace'	EDen
– 'Pearl Drop'	EDen MBar
– 'Penhale'	EDen
– 'Penny Bun'	EDen
– 'Pepper and Salt'	See *C. vulgaris* 'Hugh Nicholson'
– 'Perestrojka'	ECho EDen NHol

– 'Summer Orange'	CNCN EDen MBar NHol
– 'Sunningdale'	See *C. vulgaris* **'Finale'**
– 'Sunrise'	CNCN EDen MBar MGos
	MOke NHol SBod WStI
– 'Sunset' ♀	CB&S CNCN EBrP EBre EDen
	GDra LBre MBar NHol SBod
	SBre SRms WStI
– 'Sunset Glow'	EDen
– 'Talisker'	ECho EDen
– 'Tenella'	EDen
– 'Tenuis'	CNCN ECho EDen MBar
– 'Terrick's Orange'	EDen
– The Pygmy'	EDen
– 'Tib' (d) ♀	CMac CNCN EDen MBar MBri
	MOke NHed NRoo SBod SRms
	WStI
– 'Tino'	EDen
– 'Tom Thumb'	EDen MBar
– 'Tomentosa Alba'	EDen
– 'Tom's Fancy'	EDen
– 'Torogay'	EDen
– 'Torulosa'	EDen
– 'Tremans'	EDen
– 'Tricolorifolia'	CNCN EDen GDra NHol SBod
– 'Underwoodii' ♀	ECho EDen MBar
§ – 'Velvet Dome'	EDen MBar SBod
– 'Velvet Fascination'	CNCN ECho EDen LRHS
	MBar NHol
– 'Violet Bamford'	EDen
– 'Visser's Fancy'	EDen
§ – 'Walter Ingwersen'	EDen
– 'Westerlee Gold'	EDen
– 'Westerlee Green'	EDen
– 'Westphalia'	EDen
– 'White Carpet'	EDen MBar
– 'White Coral' (d)	ECho EDen SDys
– 'White Gold'	EDen
– 'White Gown'	EDen GDra
– 'White Lawn' ♀	CNCN EDen MBar MGos
	NHed NHol SHBN SRms
– 'White Mite'	ECho EDen MBar
– 'White Princess'	See *C. vulgaris* **'White Queen'**
§ – 'White Queen'	EDen MBar
– 'White Star' (d)	EDen LRHS
– 'Whiteness'	CNCN EDen SDys
– 'Wickwar Flame' ♀	CB&S CMac CNCN EBrP EBre
	EDen GDra LBre MBar MBri
	MGos MOke NHar NHol NRoo
	SBod SBre WStI
– 'Wingates Gem'	EDen
– 'Wingates Gold'	EDen
– 'Winter Chocolate'	CNCN EDen MBar MBri MGos
	MOke NHed NHol NRoo SBod
	WStI
– 'Winter Fire'	EDen
– 'Winter Red'	EDen
¶ – 'Wollmers Weisse' (d)	EDen
– 'Wood Close'	EDen
– 'Yellow Basket'	EDen
– 'Yellow Dome'	CNCN
– 'Yellow One'	EDen
– 'Yvette's Gold'	EDen
– 'Yvette's Silver'	EDen
– 'Yvonne Clare'	EDen

CALOCEDRUS (Cupressaceae)

§ *decurrens* ♀	CB&S CDoC CMac EBrP EBre
	EHul ENot EPfP IOrc LBre
	LCon LPan MBal MBar MBlu
	MBri NWea SBre SLim SPer
	SSta WFro WMou WWat

– 'Aureovariegata'	CBlo CDoC CKen IOrc LCon
	LLin LNet LPan MAsh MBar
	MBlu MBri NHol SLim
– 'Berrima Gold'	CKen
§ – 'Depressa'	CKen
– 'Intricata'	CKen
– 'Nana'	See *C. decurrens* **'Depressa'**
– 'Pillar'	LRHS MBri SMad

CALOCEPHALUS (Asteraceae)

brownii	See *Leucophyta brownii*

CALOCHORTUS (Liliaceae)

albus	EPot
– var. *rubellus*	EDAr EPot GCrs LAma
amabilis	EPot
amoenus	WCot
¶ *apiculatus*	EPot
argillosus	EPot
barbatus	EHyt EPot NWCA WOMN
* *bruneaunis*	EPot
clavatus	EPot
* – *avius*	EPot
concolor	EPot
eurycarpus	See *C. nitidus*
excavatus	EPot
¶ *howellii*	EPot
leichtlinii	EPot
luteus	EHyt EPot LAma
* – 'Golden Orb'	EDAr GCrs
macrocarpus	EPot
§ *nitidus*	EPot
¶ *plummerae* JA 94-104	EHyt
pulchellus	EPot
splendens	LAma
striatus JA 93-21	EHyt
superbus	EPot GCrs
tolmiei	EPot
uniflorus	EHyt EPot WCot WOMN
venustus	EDAr EHyt EPot LAma
vestae	EHyt EPot

CALOMERIA (Asteraceae)

§ *amaranthoides*	EMon LHol WJek

CALONYCTION See IPOMOEA

CALOPHACA (Papilionaceae)

grandiflora	CB&S

CALOPOGON (Orchidaceae) See Plant Deletions

CALOSCORDUM (Alliaceae)

§ *neriniflorum*	EBur EHyt SWas WAbe

CALOTHAMNUS (Myrtaceae)

blepharospermus	SOWG
gilesii	CTrC SOWG
homolophyllus	SOWG
quadrifidus	SOWG
rupestris	SOWG
sanguineus	SOWG
validus	SOWG

CALOTROPIS (Asclepiadaceae)

gigantea	MSal

CALPURNIA (Papilionaceae) See Plant Deletions

CALTHA † (Ranunculaceae)

'Auenwald'	CLAP CRDP CRow
'Honeydew'	CLAP CRDP CRow GBuc
¶ *howellii*	WLin
introloba	SWat
laeta	See *C. palustris* var. *palustris*
leptosepala	CLAP CRow NGre WOMN
– NNS 9420	EPot
natans	CRow
palustris ♀	Widely available
– var. *alba*	Widely available
– 'Flore Pleno' (d) ♀	CBen CGle CRow EBrP EBre
	ECha EHon ELan GDra LBre
	LHop LPBA LSyl MBal MBri
	MCLN MSta NDea NFai NHar
	NNor NSti SBre SPer SRms
	SWat SWyc WByw WChe
	WWeb
– var. *himalensis*	GCrs NGre
– 'Marilyn'	CRDP
– 'Multiplex' (d)	COtt WViv
§ – var. *palustris*	CBen CBre CRDP CRow ECha
	EHon ELan EMFW EMon
	EPar GAri GGar LPBA MSta
	NDea SPer SSpi SWat WChe
– – 'Plena' (d)	CRow CSam CWat ENot EPfP
	WCot WMAq
– var. *radicans*	CRow EMFW GCrs
¶ – 'Semiplena'	EMon
– 'Stagnalis'	CRow SWyc
– 'Tyermannii'	CRow
polypetala hort.	See *C. palustris* var. *palustris*
sagittata	CRow
'Susan'	CRow

CALYCANTHUS (Calycanthaceae)

fertilis	EBee EBrP EBre EPfP LBre
	LBuc MBlu MUlv SBre SPer
	SSta WSHC
– 'Purpureus'	MBlu
floridus	CArn CB&S CBlo CMCN
	CPMA CPle EBar ELan ENot
	IOrc LHol MBlu MUlv MWhi
	WLRN WWat WWin
– var. *laevigatus*	See *C. floridus* var. *glaucus*
occidentalis	CAgr CB&S CGre CMCN CPle
	ELan EMil LLew LRHS MBlu
	SSpi WPGP

CALYDOREA (Iridaceae)

speciosa	See *C. xiphioides*

CALYPSO (Orchidaceae) See Plant Deletions

CALYPTRIDIUM (Portulacaceae)

umbellatum	See *Spraguea umbellata*

CALYSTEGIA (Convolvulaceae)

¶ *collina* subsp. *venusta*	WCot
§ *hederacea* 'Flore Pleno'	CPIN CSpe ECha ELan EMon
(d)	EOrc EPar GMac LFis LHop
	MTho NSti SMad WCot WHer
	WWin
japonica 'Flore Pleno'	See *C. hederacea* **'Flore Pleno'**
¶ *macrostegia* subsp.	WCot
cyclostegia	
pulchra	WCru
silvatica 'Incarnata'	EBee EMon EOrc MAvo

CALYTRIX (Myrtaceae) See Plant Deletions

CAMASSIA † (Hyacinthaceae)

cusickii	CAvo CBro CMea EBrP EBre
	ECha ELan EMan EMon EPar
	GBur GMaP LAma LBow LBre
	MBri MTho NBir NFai NRog
	NSti SBre WCot
esculenta	See *C. quamash*
fraseri	See *C. scilloides*
N *leichtlinii* 'Alba'	GBur
– 'Alba' hort.	See *C. leichtlinii* subsp.
	leichtlinii
* – 'Alba Plena'	CMon
– 'Blauwe Donau'	See *C. leichtlinii* subsp.
	suksdorfii **'Blauwe Donau'**
I – Blue Danube	See *C. leichtlinii* subsp.
	suksdorfii **'Blauwe Donau'**
– 'Electra'	ECha SWas WFar
– hort.	See *C. leichtlinii* subsp.
	suksdorfii
§ – subsp. *leichtlinii* ♀	CAvo CBro CHad CLAP CMea
	CMil EFou ELan EMan EMon
	EPfP GBri GMaP ISea LAma
	MGed MRav NCat WShi
N – 'Plena' (d)	ECED ECha WCot WFar
– 'Semiplena'	CAvo CBro CFai CLAP CMea
	CRDP EMon EPar
§ – subsp. *suksdorfii*	CAvo EBee ECha EFou EPar
	ETub GBuc LBow NCat NRoo
	SAga SPer
§ – – 'Blauwe Donau'	LAma LBow LRHS MGed
– – Caerulea Group	CBro CHad CMea CMil CRDP
	ELan EMan EMon EPar EPfP
	ISea LAma MUlv NRog WAbb
	WHoo WPGP
§ *quamash*	CAvo CBro CLAP CMea ECha
	ELan EMon EPar ETub GBur
	GSki LAma LBow MAvo MBri
	MRav MTho NBir NRog SPar
	SRms WByw WFar WShi
	WWeb
– 'Blue Melody'	CBro CMea EMon LRHS
– subsp. *linearis*	NHol
– 'Orion'	CBro CLAP CMea CSWP
	EMon GBuc WCot
§ *scilloides*	MBri WCot

CAMELLIA † (Theaceae)

'Auburn White'	See *C. japonica* **'Mrs Bertha A. Harms'**
'Baby Face'	See *C. reticulata* **'Tongzimian'**
'Barbara Clark' (*saluenensis* X *reticulata*)	MGos SCog
'Barbara Hillier' (*reticulata* X *japonica*)	CTre
'Barchi'	See *C. japonica* **'Contessa Samailoff'**
'Bertha Harms Blush'	See *C. japonica* **'Mrs Bertha A. Harms'**
'Black Lace' (*reticulata* X *williamsii*)	CTrh EBee MAsh MBal SCog SExb SPer WLRN
'Bonnie Marie' (hybrid)	CTre SCog
¶ 'Christmas Daffodil' (*japonica* hybrid)	CTrh
chrysantha	See *C. nitidissima* var. *nitidissima*
'Contessa Lavinia Maggi'	See *C. japonica* **'Lavinia Maggi'**
'Cornish Clay'	ISea
'Cornish Snow' (*japonica* X *cuspidata*) ♀	CB&S CGre COtt CSam CTre CTrh GGGa IOrc ISea LNet MBal SHBN SMad SPer SReu SSpi SSta WBod WWat

'Cornish Spring' (*japonica* X *cuspidata*) ♀ CB&S CDoC COtt CTre CTrh EPfP WBcn WLRN WWat
'Corsica' SHBN
crapnelliana CGre
cuspidata CGre CTre CTrh SSpi
'Czar' See *C. japonica* **'The Czar'**
'Dawn' See *C.* X *vernalis* **'Ginryû'**
'Delia Williams' See *C.* X *williamsii* **'Citation'**
'Diamond Head' (*japonica* X *reticulata*) CB&S
'Doctor Clifford Parks' (*reticulata* X *japonica*) ♀ CTre SCog
'Donckelaeri' See *C. japonica* **'Masayoshi'**
'Eclipsis' See *C. japonica* **'Press's Eclipse'**
'El Dorado' (*pitardii* X *japonica*) CTrh SCog
'Extravaganza' (*japonica* hybrid) CTrh SBod SCog
¶ 'Fairy Wand' (hybrid) CB&S
'Faustina Lechi' See *C. japonica* **'Faustina'**
'Felice Harris' (*sasanqua* X *reticulata*) SCog
– 'Forty-niner' (*reticulata* X *japonica*) ♀ CB&S SCog
'Fragrant Pink' (*rusticana* X *lutchuensis*) CTrh
'Francie L' (*saluenensis* X *reticulata*) CGre CTre CTrh SCog SSta
'Frau Minna Seidel' See *C. japonica* **'Otome'**
'Freedom Bell' ♀ CB&S CTre CTrh GGGa ISea MAsh SCog
'Gay Baby' CB&S MGos
grijsii CTrh
hiemalis 'Chansonette' SCog
– 'Dazzler' CTre CTrh SCog
'Hiemalis Hiryû' See *C. hiemalis* **'Kanjirô'**
§ *hiemalis* 'Kanjirô' CTrh SCog
– 'Shôwa-no-sakae' SCog
– 'Sparkling Burgundy' CB&S CTre LHyd SCog
'Imbricata Rubra' See *C. japonica* **'Imbricata'**
'Innovation' (X *williamsii* X *reticulata*) CB&S CTre ISea MGos
'Inspiration' (*reticulata* X *saluenensis*) ♀ CB&S CGre CMac CSam CTre CTrh EPfP GGGa ISea LHyd MAsh MBri MGos SBod SCog SHBN SSpi WBod
japonica 'Aaron's Ruby' CB&S COtt CTre
– 'Ada Pieper' CTrh
– 'Adelina Patti' CB&S CTre CTrh SCog
– 'Adolphe Audusson' ♀ CB&S CTre CTrh CTrw EBrP EBre ELan ENot EPfP GChr IOrc LBre LHyd LNet MAsh MBal MBri MGos SBod SBre SCog SHBN SMad SPer SReu SSta WBod WGwG WStI
– 'Adolphe Audusson Special' CB&S
§ – 'Akashigata' ♀ CTre CTrw ENot EPfP IHos MWat SMad SReu SSta WWat
§ – 'Akebono' CTrw
– 'Alba Plena' CGre CMac CTre CTrh ENot IHos IOrc LNet MGos SBod SCog SPer WFox
– 'Alba Simplex' CB&S CGre CMac CTre CTrh ELan EPfP IOrc LNet MBal SBod SCog SHBN SPer SSta WStI
¶ – 'Albertii' WBod
– 'Alexander Hunter' ♀ CTre MAsh SBod
– 'Alice Wood' CB&S
§ – 'Althaeiflora' CB&S CGre CTre

– 'Anemoniflora' CB&S CTre ELan IHos SBod SPer
– 'Angel' CB&S CTre SCog
¶ – 'Angela Cocchi' WBod
– 'Ann Sothern' CTrh
– 'Annie Wylam' CTrh SCog
§ – 'Apollo' CB&S CDoC CSam CTrh EPfP IHos MAsh MGos SHBN SPer WBcn WBod
§ – 'Apple Blossom' CGre CMac ELan LRHS MBal
* – 'Augustine Supreme' CMac
– 'Augusto Leal de Gouveia Pinto' CB&S CTre SCog
¶ – 'Australis' CTrh
– 'Ave Maria' CTrh SCog
– 'Azurea' CGre
– 'Baby Sis' CB&S
– 'Ballet Dancer' ♀ SCog SPla WBcn WGwG
– 'Baron Gomer' See *C. japonica* **'Comte de Gomer'**
¶ – 'Baronne Leguay' LRHS
– 'Benten' (v) CTrw LRHS
– 'Berenice Boddy' ♀ CB&S CTrh
– 'Betty Foy Sanders' CTrh
– 'Betty Sheffield' CGre COtt CTre ECle MGos SBod SCog SHBN WBod
– 'Betty Sheffield Blush' CBlo
– 'Betty Sheffield Supreme' CB&S CDoC CGre LRHS SCog SPer
– 'Blackburnia' See *C. japonica* **'Althaeiflora'**
– 'Blaze of Glory' CDoC CGre CTrh SCog
§ – 'Blood of China' CB&S CDoC COtt MAsh SBod SCog SExb SPer WBod
– 'Bob Hope' ♀ CB&S CGre CTre CTrh SCog
– 'Bob's Tinsie' ♀ CGre CTre CTrw MBri SCog
§ – 'Bokuhan' CGre CTre
¶ – 'Bonomiana' WBod
– 'Brushfield's Yellow' CB&S CDoC CGre COtt MBal MGos SPer SSta
– 'Bush Hill Beauty' See *C. japonica* **'Lady de Saumarez'**
§ – 'C.M. Hovey' ♀ CMHG CMac CTrh EPfP MAsh MBal MNes SCog SHBN WBcn WFar WGwG
– 'C.M. Wilson' ♀ CMac CTre SCog
N – 'Campbellii' WBod
– 'Campsii Alba' WStI
– 'Can Can' CB&S SCog
¶ – 'Canon Boscawen' CTrG
– 'Cara Mia' CB&S CTre
– 'Cardinal's Cap' CGre
– 'Carter's Sunburst' ♀ CB&S CDoC CTrh EPfP
– 'Cécile Brunazzi' SCog
– 'Chandleri Elegans' See *C. japonica* **'Elegans'**
– 'Charlotte de Rothschild' CTrh CTri
– 'Charming Betty' See *C. japonica* **'Funny Face Betty'**
– 'Cheryll Lynn' CTrh WBod
– 'Cinderella' CTre SCog
– 'Clarise Carleton' CTre CTrh
– 'Colonel Firey' See *C. japonica* **'C.M. Hovey'**
– 'Commander Mulroy' CTrh WBcn
– 'Compton's Brow' See *C. japonica* **'Gauntlettii'**
§ – 'Comte de Gomer' CGre ELan EPfP LRHS MBri SSta WBcn
– 'Conspicua' CB&S
§ – 'Coquettii' ♀ CB&S CTre MAsh
– 'Countess of Orkney' CTre
– 'Dainty' CB&S
– 'Daitairin' See *C. japonica* **'Dewatairin'**
– 'Dear Jenny' CB&S CTrG CTre SCog

¶ – 'Debbie' — WGwG
– 'Debutante' — CB&S CGre CMac CTre CTrh LHyd MAsh MBri SCog SHBN WBcn
– 'Desire' — CB&S CMHG CTrh SCog
– 'Devonia' — CB&S EPfP LHyd MBal MBri
§ – 'Dewatairin' — CMac WBod
– 'Dixie Knight' — SSta
– 'Dobreei' — CMac WBod WGer WWal
– 'Doctor Burnside' — CB&S CMHG CTrh SCog
– 'Doctor Tinsley' ♀ — CBlo CGre CTrh SCog WBcn
– 'Dona Herzilia de Freitas Magalhaes' — CB&S CTre SSta
– 'Donnan's Dream' — CTrh
– 'Double Rose' (d) — SCog
– 'Drama Girl' ♀ — CB&S CGre CTre CTrw IOrc MBal SBod SCog WBod
– 'Duchesse Decazes' — CB&S COtt CTre MGos
– 'Effendee' — See *C. sasanqua* 'Rosea Plena'
– 'Eleanor Hagood' — CB&S CGre WBcn
§ – 'Elegans' ♀ — CB&S CGre CHig CMac CTre ECle ENot IHos IOrc LHyd MBal MWat SBod SCog SHBN SPer SReu SSta WBcn
– 'Elegans Champagne' — CTrh MAsh SCog WBcn
– 'Elegans Splendor' — CTre WBcn
– 'Elegans Supreme' — CGre CTre SCog
– 'Elisabeth' — SCog
– 'Elizabeth Arden' — CBlo CTre
– 'Elizabeth Dowd' — CB&S SCog
– 'Elizabeth Hawkins' — CTre CTrh WLRN
– 'Ella Drayton' — SCog
¶ – 'Ellen Sampson' — MAsh
– 'Emperor of Russia' — CB&S ELan WBod
– 'Erin Farmer' — CB&S SCog
¶ – 'Eximia' — WBod
– 'Fatima' — CTre
– 'Fimbriata Alba' — See *C. japonica* 'Fimbriata'
– 'Finlandia Variegated' — SCog
– 'Fire Dance' — CTrh
– 'Fire Falls' — CMHG
– 'Flame' — CB&S
§ – 'Fleur Dipater' — WBod
– 'Forest Green' — ELan LRHS MAsh SCog
– 'Frosty Morn' — CB&S
¶ – 'Furo-an' — MAsh
§ – 'Gauntlettii' — SCog
¶ – 'Gay Chieftain' — WBod
– 'Giardino Franchetti' — CGre
§ – 'Gigantea' — SCog
§ – 'Gigantea Red' — IOrc
– 'Gladys Wannamaker' — SCog
– 'Glen 40' — See *C. japonica* 'Coquettii'
– 'Gloire de Nantes' ♀ — CB&S CGre MNes WBcn WBod
* – 'Golden Wedding' — MAsh
¶ – 'Goshoguruma' — WBod
– 'Grace Bunton' — CB&S
– 'Granada' — SCog
– 'Grand Prix' ♀ — CMHG CTrh CTrw SCog SSta
– 'Grand Slam' ♀ — CB&S CMHG CMac COtt CTre CTrh EHic ISea MAsh SCog WBcn
– 'Guest of Honor' — CB&S COtt
– 'Guilio Nuccio' ♀ — CB&S CDoC CTre MGos SCog SExb SPer WBod
– 'Gwenneth Morey' — CB&S CMHG CTre EPfP
§ – 'Hagoromo' ♀ — CBlo CGre ELan ENot EPfP IHos MBal SHBN WBcn WBod WFox WWat
– 'Hakurakuten' ♀ — CBlo CTre CTrh EHol ISea SBod SCog WBod

– 'Hanafûki' — CTre WBod
– 'Hanatachibana' — CBlo SExb WBcn
– 'Hassaku' — See *C. japonica* 'Hassaku-shibori'
– 'Hatsuzakura' — See *C. japonica* 'Dewatairin'
– 'Hawaii' — CB&S CMac CTre CTrh SCog WFox
– Herme — See *C. japonica* 'Hikarugenji'
– 'High Hat' — CB&S LHyd WBod
– 'Hinomaru' — CMac
¶ – 'Holly Bright' — CTrh
§ – 'Imbricata' — CBlo CDoC CTre ENot IHos MGos SCog SExb
– 'Imbricata Alba' — SCog SSta
– 'In the Pink' — CMHG
– 'Italiana Vera' — MAsh
– 'J.J. Whitfield' — CMac
– 'Jack Jones Scented' — CMHG
– 'Janet Waterhouse' — CB&S SCog WWat
– 'Jean Clere' — MGos WBcn
– 'Jingle Bells' — SCog
– 'Joseph Pfingstl' — CBlo CGre CMHG CTre MAsh WBod
– 'Joshua E. Youtz' — LHyd SCog
– 'Joy Sander' — See *C. japonica* 'Apple Blossom'
§ – 'Julia Drayton' — LRHS
– 'Julia France' — CB&S
– 'Juno' — CB&S
– 'Jupiter' ♀ — CB&S CDoC CMac CTre CTrh CTri CTrw EHic EPfP ISea LHyd LNet MAsh MBal MGos SCog SHBN SMad WBod
– 'Katie' — SCog
– 'Kellingtoniana' — See *C. japonica* 'Gigantea'
– 'Kenny' — CB&S
– 'Kewpie Doll' — CTrh SCog
– 'Kick-off' — CB&S CTrh SCog
– 'Kimberley' — CB&S EPfP SCog WBcn WBod WLRN
– 'King's Ransom' — CMac
§ – 'Kingyo-tsubaki' — CGre SSta WBod
– 'Kitty' — SBid SCog
¶ – 'Kitty Berry' — CTrh
§ – 'Konronkoku' ♀ — SCog WBcn
– 'Kouron-jura' — See *C. japonica* 'Konronkoku'
– 'Kramer's Beauty' — SCog
– 'Kramer's Supreme' — CB&S CGre LNet MBal MGos SBod SCog SExb WLRN
§ – 'Kumasaka' — WBod
– 'Lady Campbell' — WBcn
– Lady Clare — See *C. japonica* 'Akashigata'
§ – 'Lady de Saumarez' ♀ — LNet SBod
– 'Lady de Saumarez' white — CGre
– 'Lady Erma' — CB&S
– 'Lady Loch' — CTre CTrh MGos SCog
– 'Lady Marion' — See *C. japonica* 'Kumasaka'
– 'Lady Vansittart' — CB&S CSam CTre ELan ENot IHos ISea LHyd LNet MAsh MBal SBod SCog SPer WBcn WBod
§ – 'Lady Vansittart Pink' — MGos SBod SHBN
– 'Lady Vansittart Red' — See *C. japonica* 'Lady Vansittart Pink'
– 'Lanarth' — CTre
– 'Latifolia' — CTre
– 'Laurie Bray' — CGre
§ – 'Lavinia Maggi' ♀ — CGre CTre CTrh ELan GAri IHos IOrc LHyd MAsh MBri MGos SBod SCog SHBN SPer SReu SRms SSta

– 'Lavinia Maggi Rosea'	SCog
§ – 'Le Lys'	SCog
– 'Lemon Drop'	CTrh
– 'Lily Pons'	CTrh
¶ – 'Lipstick'	CTrh
– 'Little Bit'	CB&S CTrh SSta
– 'Little Bo Peep'	CTrh
– 'Little Red Riding Hood'	CB&S COtt
– 'Little Slam'	CB&S
I – 'Lotus'	See *C. japonica* **'Gauntlettii'**
– Lotus	See *C. japonica* **'Gauntlettii'**
– 'Lovelight'	CTrh SCog
– 'Lucy Hester'	CTre MBal
– 'Lulu Belle'	SCog
– 'Ma Belle'	CMHG SCog
– 'Madame Charles Blard'	WBod
– 'Madame de Strekaloff'	CMac
– 'Madame Lebois'	CB&S
– 'Madame Lourmand'	WBod
– 'Madame Martin Cachet'	CMHG SCog
– 'Madge Miller'	CTre ELan LRHS
– 'Magnoliiflora'	See *C. japonica* **'Hagoromo'**
– 'Magnoliiflora Alba'	See *C. japonica* **'Miyakodori'**
– 'Maiden's Blush'	CMac SCog
¶ – 'Margaret Davis'	ECle
– 'Margaret Davis Picotee'	CB&S CGre CMHG CTrh CTrw MGos SCog SPla SSta WBcn
– 'Margherita Coleoni'	CB&S SBod SHBN WBcn
– 'Marguérite Gouillon'	ISea SCog
– 'Mariana'	CTrh SSta
– 'Marie Bracey'	CB&S
– 'Marinka'	CB&S
– 'Marjorie Magnificent'	LRHS
– 'Mark Alan'	CTrh
– 'Maroon and Gold'	WBcn
– 'Mars' ♀	CB&S CTre EHic MWat WBod
– 'Mary Costa'	CB&S CGre CTrh
– 'Mary J. Wheeler'	CTrw
§ – 'Masayoshi' ♀	CMac IOrc LNet
§ – 'Mathotiana'	CTrw MBal
– 'Mathotiana Alba' ♀	CB&S CMac MBal SBid SCog SPer SReu SSta
– 'Mathotiana Purple King'	See *C. japonica* **'Julia Drayton'**
§ – 'Mathotiana Rosea'	CB&S CMac CTre LNet SBod SCog SHBN SPer WBod
– 'Mathotiana Supreme'	CDoC SCog
– 'Matterhorn'	CTrh MAsh WBcn
– 'Mattie Cole'	CGre CTre
– 'Mattie O'Reilly'	CTre
– 'Mercury' ♀	CB&S CBlo CDoC CMac COtt GGGa MWat SHBN SPer WBod
– 'Mercury Variegated'	CMHG
– 'Midnight'	CB&S CGre CMHG MAsh SCog
¶ – 'Midnight Magic'	CTrh
– 'Midnight Serenade'	CTrh
– 'Midsummer's Day'	CB&S
§ – 'Mikenjaku'	CBlo ENot LNet
– 'Miss Charleston' ♀	CB&S SCog
– 'Miss Universe'	CGre CTrh SCog
¶ – 'Mississippi Beauty'	CTrh
§ – 'Miyakodori'	EPfP
– 'Monsieur Faucillon'	CB&S
– 'Monstruosa Rubra'	See *C. japonica* **'Gigantea Red'**
– 'Monte Carlo'	SCog WBod
¶ – 'Morning Glow'	WBod
– 'Moshe Dayan'	EBee
§ – 'Mrs Bertha A. Harms'	CGre
– 'Mrs D.W. Davis' ♀	CB&S CGre CTrw
* – 'Mutabilis'	WBcn
– 'Nagasaki'	See *C. japonica* **'Mikenjaku'**
– 'Nigra'	See *C. japonica* **'Konronkoku'**
– 'Nobilissima'	CB&S CDoC CMac CTre CTrh CTri ENot IHos ISea MAsh MWat SBid SBod SCog SHBN SPer SPla SSta WBcn WBod WWeb
– 'Nuccio's Cameo'	CTrh
– 'Nuccio's Gem'	ELan MBri SCog SSta
– 'Nuccio's Jewel' ♀	COtt CTre CTrh MGos SCog SExb SPer WBcn
– 'Nuccio's Pearl'	CB&S SCog WBcn WFar
– 'Onetia Holland'	CB&S CTre CTrw SCog
§ – 'O-niji'	MBal SCog SPer
– 'Optima Rosea'	CB&S ENot
§ – 'Otome'	WBod
– 'Paolina Maggi'	SCog
– 'Patricia Ann'	CTrh
– 'Paul's Apollo'	See *C. japonica* **'Apollo'**
– 'Peachblossom'	See *C. japonica* **'Fleur Dipater'**
– 'Pensacola Red'	SCog
– 'Pink Champagne'	CTre SBod
– 'Pink Perfection'	See *C. japonica* **'Otome'**
¶ – 'Pink Star'	WBod
– 'Pope Pius IX'	See *C. japonica* **'Prince Eugène Napoléon'**
– 'Powder Puff'	CTre
– 'Preston Rose'	CB&S CTre ISea MBal WBcn WWat
– 'Pride of Descanso'	See *C. japonica* **'Yukibotan'**
– 'Primavera'	CTrh
– 'Princess Baciocchi'	CB&S
* – 'Princess du Mahe'	CMac
– 'Purity'	See *C. japonica* **'Shiragiku'**
– 'Purple Emperor'	See *C. japonica* **'Julia Drayton'**
– 'R.L. Wheeler' ♀	CB&S CDoC CGre CTre CTrw MBal SCog
– 'Rafia'	SSta
– 'Rainbow'	See *C. japonica* **'O-niji'**
– 'Red Dandy'	CDoC SCog
– 'Roger Hall'	SCog
– 'Rôgetsu'	CB&S CGre WBod
– 'Roman Soldier'	CB&S
¶ – 'Rose Dawn'	WBod
– 'Rubescens Major' ♀	CB&S CGre ISea LHyd
– 'Ruddigore'	CTrh
– 'Saint André'	CMac WLRN
– 'San Dimas'	CTrh WBcn
– 'Saturnia'	COtt
– 'Scented Red'	WWat
– 'Scentsation' ♀	CMHG COtt CTre SCog
– 'Sea Gull'	CTrh
– 'Seiji'	CMac
– 'Serenade'	CMHG
– 'Shin-akebono'	See *C. japonica* **'Akebono'**
– 'Shirobotan'	EPfP GQui SCog SPla WBod
– 'Silver Anniversary'	CB&S CMHG CTrh ELan GQui MAsh MGos SBod SCog SReu SSta
¶ – 'Snowflake'	WBod
– 'Souvenir de Bahuaud-Litou' ♀	CB&S CBlo CGre CTre SBid SCog WBod WWat
– 'Spencer's Pink'	CB&S CTre CTrw LRHS
¶ – 'Spring Formal'	CTrh
– 'Sylvia'	CMac LRHS WBod
– 'Tammia'	CB&S COtt
– 'Temple Incense'	CB&S
– 'Teringa'	CTre
§ – 'The Czar'	CB&S CTre CTrw ISea WBod

– 'The Mikado'	CGre CTre SCog
– 'Thomas Cornelius Cole'	CTre
– 'Tiffany'	CB&S CDoC CTre LHyd LNet SHBN SPla SSta
– 'Tinker Bell'	CB&S CGre
– 'Tinker Toy'	CTrh
– 'Tom Thumb'	CMHG CTrh SRms
– 'Tomorrow'	CB&S CTre CTrw MAsh SCog WBod WFox
– 'Tomorrow Park Hill'	SCog
– 'Tomorrow's Dawn'	CB&S
– 'Tregye'	CB&S
– 'Trewithen White'	CSam
§ – 'Tricolor' ♀	CB&S CDoC CGre CMac CTrh ENot IHos IOrc MAsh SCog SExb SHBN SPer WBod WGwG
– 'Tricolor Red'	See *C. japonica* **'Lady de Saumarez'**
– 'Valtevareda'	CGre
§ 'Japonica Variegata'	CGre WBcn
japonica 'Victor de Bisschop'	See *C. japonica* **'Le Lys'**
– 'Victor Emmanuel'	See *C. japonica* **'Blood of China'**
– 'Ville de Nantes'	CB&S SSta WBcn
– 'Virginia Carlyon'	CB&S CTre
¶ – 'Virginia Robinson'	WBod
– 'Vittorio Emanuele II'	CTrh
– 'Warrior'	COtt CTre MAsh
– 'White Nun'	SCog
– 'White Swan'	CB&S CMac COtt CTre MAsh
– 'White Tulip'	CGre
– 'Wilamina'	CTrh
– 'Wildfire'	SCog
– 'William Bartlett'	CTrh
– 'William Honey'	CTrh
– 'Yoibijin'	See *C. japonica* **'Suibijin'**
– 'Yours Truly'	CB&S CMac CTre CTrh LHyd SBod SCog
– 'Yukimi-guruma'	WBod
§ – 'Yukishiro'	CTrw
– 'Zoraide Vanzi'	WBod
'Jury's Charity'	See *C.* x *williamsii* **'Charity'**
kissi	CGre CTrh
'Leonard Messel' (*reticulata* x *williamsii*) ♀	CB&S CDoC CGre CMHG CTre CTrh ENot GGGa IHos ISea LHyd MBal MGos SBod SCog SExb SHBN SMad SPer SReu WBod WStI
'Lila Naff' (*reticulata* hybrid)	CTre
¶ *lutchuensis*	CTrh
'Madame Victor de Bisschop'	See *C. japonica* **'Le Lys'**
'Magnolia Queen'	See *C. japonica* **'Priscilla Brooks'**
§ *maliflora* (d)	CB&S WWat
'Nijinski' (*reticulata* hybrid)	ISea
oleifera	CSam CTre CTrh SCog WWat
'Pink Spangles'	See *C. japonica* **'Mathotiana Rosea'**
¶ 'Polar Ice' (*oleifera* hybrid)	SCog
'Portuense'	See *C.* **'Japonica Variegata'**
'Quintessence' (*japonica* x *lutchuensis*)	SCog
reticulata	CGre CTre
– 'Captain Rawes' ♀	CB&S CMac CTre
– 'Flore Pleno'	See *C. reticulata* **'Songzilin'**
– 'Ming Temple'	CTre
– 'William Hertrich'	CB&S CGre CTre
'Robert Fortune'	See *C. reticulata* **'Songzilin'**
rosiflora	CTre CTrh
'Royalty' (*japonica* x *reticulata*)	CB&S CTre
rusticana 'Arajishi'	CB&S CMac COtt CTre SCoo WBod WLRN WWal
– 'Shiro-daikagura'	WBod
'Salonica'	See *C.* x *williamsii* **'Shimna'**
saluenensis	CGre CTre CTrh
– 'Apple Blossom'	See *C.* **'Shôwa-wabisuke' (Wabisuke)**
– 'Exbury Trumpet'	CTre
– x *japonica*	See *C.* x *williamsii*
– 'Trewithen Red'	CTrw
¶ – 'William's Lavender'	WBod
'Salutation' (*saluenensis* x *reticulata*)	CB&S CGre CSam CTre ISea
sasanqua	CSam ISea
* – 'Alba'	SCog
– 'Apple Blossom'	MAsh
– 'Ben'	SCog
– 'Bettie Patricia'	SCog
– 'Crimson King' ♀	CGre GQui MBal SBod SCog SHBN WBod WStI
– 'Flamingo'	See *C. sasanqua* **'Fukuzutsumi'**
– 'Flore Pleno'	See *C. maliflora*
– 'Fuji-no-mine'	CTrh
§ – 'Fukuzutsumi'	CB&S COtt SBod SCog
– 'Gay Sue'	CTrh
– 'Hugh Evans'	CB&S CDoC COtt CTre CTrh LHyd SCog SSta WFox
– 'Jean May'	CB&S CDoC COtt CTre SBod SCog
– 'Kenkyô'	SCog SPla SSta
– 'Little Liane'	SCog
– 'Little Pearl'	CTrh
– 'Lucinda'	SCog
– 'Mignonne'	CTrh
– 'Mine-no-yuki'	SCog
– 'Narumigata' ♀	CB&S CDoC CMac COtt CTrw LHyd MAsh MBal MBlu SBod SCog SSta WSHC
¶ – 'Navajo'	CTrh
– 'Nodami-ushiro'	CTrh
– 'Nyewoods'	CMac
– 'Paradise Blush'	SCog
– 'Paradise Glow'	SCog
– 'Paradise Hilda'	SCog
– 'Paradise Pearl'	SCog
– 'Paradise Petite'	SCog
– 'Paradise Venessa'	SCog
– 'Peach Blossom'	CB&S
– 'Plantation Pink'	ECle SCog SPer
– 'Rainbow'	CTrh ISea SCog SSta
– 'Rosea'	SSta
§ – 'Rosea Plena'	CB&S CMac CTre CTrw
I 'Sasanqua Rubra'	CMac
I *sasanqua* 'Sasanqua Variegata'	SSta WWat
– 'Shishigashira'	CTrh
– 'Snowflake'	SSta
– 'Tanya'	CTrh
'Satan's Robe' (*reticulata* hybrid) ♀	CMHG CTre SCog
'Scentuous' (*japonica* x *lutchuensis*)	CTrh SCog WBcn
'Show Girl' (*sasanqua* x *reticulata*)	CTre CTrh SBod SCog WBod
§ *sinensis*	CGre CTre
¶ 'Snow Flurry' (*oleifera* hybrid)	SCog
'Splendens'	See *C. japonica* **'Coccinea'**
'Spring Festival' (*cuspidata* hybrid) ♀	CHig CMHG CTrh

'Spring Mist' (*japonica* X *lutchuensis*) — CMHG CTrh

'Stella Polare' — See *C. japonica* 'Etoile Polaire'

'Swan Lake' (hybrid) — SCog

taliensis — CGre CTre

thea — See *C. sinensis*

'Tinsie' — See *C. japonica* 'Bokuhan'

'Tôkô' — See *C. sasanqua* 'Azuma-beni'

'Tom Knudsen' (*reticulata* X *japonica*) — CMHG CTre CTrh EPfP

'Tomorrow Supreme' — See *C. japonica* 'Tomorrow Variegated'

transnokoensis — CTre CTrh

'Tricolor Sieboldii' — See *C. japonica* 'Tricolor'

'Tristrem Carlyon' (*reticulata* hybrid) — CB&S CBlo CTre LRHS MAsh WFox

¶ *tsai* ♀ — CGre CTrh

'Usu-ôtome' — See *C. japonica* 'Otome'

vernalis 'Hiryû' — SCog

– 'Kyô-nishiki' — SCog

– 'Yuletide' — SCog

'Waterloo' — See *C. japonica* 'Etherington White'

§ × *williamsii* — CGre

– 'Anemone Frill' — CTrh

– 'Anticipation' ♀ — CB&S CGre CMHG CSam CTre CTrh CTrw ENot EPfP GGGa GOrc IOrc ISea LHyd MAsh MBri MGos SBod SCog SExb SHBN SPer SSpi WBcn

– 'Anticipation Variegated' — SCog

– 'Ballet Queen' — CB&S MGos SPer

– 'Ballet Queen Variegated' — SCog SSta

– 'Bartley Number Five' — CMac

– 'Beatrice Michael' — CB&S CMac CTre

– 'Bow Bells' — CGre CMac CTre CTrh LHyd SCog WWat

– 'Bowen Bryant' ♀ — CGre CTre CTrh CTrw GGGa SCog

– 'Brigadoon' ♀ — CTre CTrh CTri CTrw EPfP GGGa IOrc LHyd MAsh MBal MGos SCog SExb WBod WWal

– 'Burncoose' — CB&S

– 'Burncoose Apple Blossom' — CB&S

– 'C.F. Coates' — CTre MNes SSta

– 'Caerhays' — CB&S CTre

– 'Carolyn Williams' — CB&S

– 'Celebration' — CB&S

§ – 'Charity' — CTrh

– 'Charles Colbert' — CTrh

– 'Charles Michael' — CB&S CGre

– 'China Clay' ♀ — CB&S CDoC CSam CTrG CTre LHyd SBod SCog WWal

§ – 'Citation' — CB&S CGre CMac CTrw WBod

– 'Clarrie Fawcett' — CTre

– 'Contribution' — CTrh

– 'Crinkles' — CGre

– 'Daintiness' ♀ — CB&S CTre CTrh SCog SPer

– 'Dark Nite' — CMHG

– 'Debbie' ♀ — CB&S CGre CHEx CMac CSam CTrG CTre CTrh CTrw EBrP EBre ELan IOrc LBre LHyd MAsh MBal MBri MGos MRav SBod SBre SCog SExb SHBN SPer SSpi SSta WBcn WBod

– 'Debbie's Carnation' — CMHG

– 'Donation' ♀ — Widely available

– 'Dream Boat' — CB&S

– 'E.G. Waterhouse' — CB&S CGre CMHG CTrh CTri CTrw EHic EPfP GChr MAsh MBal SBod SCog SSta WBcn WBod WWeb

– 'E.T.R. Carlyon' ♀ — CB&S CTre EPfP MAsh MBal WFox

– 'Elegant Beauty' — CB&S CGre CTre CTrh CTrw IHos MBal SBod SCog SExb SPer WGwG

– 'Elizabeth Anderson' — CTrh

– 'Ellamine' — CB&S

– 'Elsie Jury' ♀ — CB&S CGre CMac CSam CTri CTrw GQui IHos IOrc LHyd MAsh MBal MGos SBod SCog SExb SPer WBcn WGwG WWal

– 'Exaltation' — CB&S

– 'Francis Hanger' — CB&S CSam CTre CTrh CTrw IOrc MBal SBod SCog SSpi WWal

– 'Galaxie' ♀ — CB&S CTrh EPfP ISea

– 'Garden Glory' — CTre CTrh

– 'Gay Time' — CTre MAsh

– 'George Blandford' ♀ — CB&S CMHG CMac CTre

– 'Glenn's Orbit' ♀ — CB&S CGre CTre CTrw WBcn

– 'Golden Spangles' (v) — CB&S CGre CMac CTrG CTre CTrh ELan GOrc IOrc LHyd MBal MBri MGos MNes SPer SPla SReu SSta WBcn

– 'Grand Jury' — CB&S CTre MGos

– 'Gwavas' — CB&S CTre

– 'Hilo' — CTrw

– 'Hiraethlyn' ♀ — CTre WBod

– 'Hope' — CTrh SCog

¶ – 'Inspiration' — ISea

– 'J.C. Williams' ♀ — CB&S CGre CMac CSam CTre CTrw ENot IHos IOrc ISea LHyd MBal MRav SBod SCog SPer SSpi

– 'Jenefer Carlyon' ♀ — CB&S CTre LRHS

– 'Jill Totty' — CTrh

– 'Joan Trehane' ♀ — CMHG CTrw

– 'Jubilation' — SPer

– 'Julia Hamiter' ♀ — CB&S CGre CTrw

– 'Jury's Yellow' — CB&S CTrh CTrw ECle ELan EPfP GOrc GQui IOrc MAsh MBri MGos SBod SCog SHBN SPer SSta WBcn WWat

– 'Laura Boscawen' — CTrG CTrh

– 'Les Jury' — SCog

– 'Margaret Waterhouse' — COtt CTre

– 'Mary Christian' ♀ — CB&S COtt CTre EPfP LBuc LHyd MRav WBod

– 'Mary Jobson' — CB&S CTre WWat

– 'Mary Larcom' — CTre

– 'Mary Phoebe Taylor' — CB&S CDoC CTre CTrh CTrw SBod SCog SHBN WBod WFox

– 'Mildred Veitch' — CGre CTre

– 'Mirage' — CTrh

– 'Mona Jury' — CMHG SCog

– 'Monica Dance' — CB&S

– 'Muskoka' ♀ — CB&S CTrh ISea

– 'New Venture' — CB&S

– 'November Pink' — CB&S CTre EHol

– 'Opal Princess' — SCog

– 'Parkside' — CTre

– 'Phillippa Forward' — CMac

– 'Rendezvous' — CDoC SPla

– 'Rose Court' — WBod

– 'Rose Parade' ♀ — CTrh

¶ – 'Rose Quartz' — LRHS

– 'Rosemary Williams' — CB&S CTre CTrw

– 'Ruby Bells' — CMHG

– 'Ruby Wedding'	CTrh GQui SCog SPer
– 'Saint Ewe' ♀	CB&S CDoC CGre CTrG CTre CTrh CTri CTrw MBal MBri MGos MRav SBod SCog SHBN SPer WBod
– 'Saint Michael' ♀	CB&S
– 'Sayonara'	CTre CTrh SCog
– 'Senorita'	CTrh LHyd
– 'Taylor's Perfection'	CTrw
I – 'The Duchess of Cornwall'	CTre
– 'Tiptoe' ♀	CTrh
– 'Tregrehan'	COtt
– 'Water Lily' ♀	CB&S CDoC CTre CTrh CTrw EPfP MGos WBcn
– 'Wilber Foss'	CB&S CGre CTre CTrh CTrw
¶ – 'William Carlyon'	CB&S CTre MBal
– 'Wood Nymph'	COtt CTre ISea MBal
– 'Yesterday'	CTre MAsh SMur
¶ 'Winter's Interlude'	SCog
(oleifera X sinensis)	
* 'Winter's Touchie'	SCog
(C. ?oleifera X sasanqua)	
'Winton' (cuspidata X	CB&S
saluenensis)	
'Yukihaki'	See *C. japonica* **'Yukishiro'**

CAMPANULA † (Campanulaceae)

alaskana	See *C. rotundifolia* var. *alaskana*
§ *alliariifolia*	Widely available
– 'Ivory Bells'	See *C. alliariifolia*
allionii	See *C. alpestris*
§ *alpestris*	GCLN GTou
– 'Grandiflora'	EPot
– JCA 250500	SBla
¶ – 'Rosea'	MTPN
alpina	GAbr GDra NNrd
– subsp. *orbelica*	See *C. orbelica*
anchusiflora	MNrw NWCA
argyrotricha	SIng
– CC&McK 477	NTow
arvatica ♀	CLyd EPot GCHN LBee MBro MHig MRPP NGre NHar NNrd NRya NTow SIng SSmi WAbe WLin
– 'Alba'	CLyd EPot LBee MHig NTow
¶ – X *cochleariifolia*	WBea
aucheri	EBur EPot GCLN GDra NSla
'Avalon'	SAsh
§ 'Balchiniana' (v)	SIng WEas
barbata	ELan GCHN GDra GTou LHop MSte MSto NMen NWCA WCla WMoo WPer
– var. *alba*	ELan
bellidifolia	CMHG NBir
§ *betulifolia* ♀	CGra CSam ECtt EHyt GCHN GDra MBro MFos NGre NHar NLon MWin NNor NTow WHoo WPat
– JCA 252.005	SBla
'Birch Hybrid' ♀	CMHG ECtt ELan EMNN ESis GCHN GDra LBee MBal MBro NHar NMen NNrd NRoo SCro SIng WFar WPyg
§ *bluemelii*	WLin
bononiensis	EHal EMon NBrk SRms WOld
¶ 'Bumblebee'	CGra
'Burghaltii' ♀	Widely available
caespitosa	EHyt
calaminthifolia	EBur WOMN
§ *carnica*	MSte

carpatha	MRPP
carpatica ♀	CGle GAri GDra MBar MBri MMal NBro NChi NNor SRms SWat WWin
– f. *alba*	CGle LPVe MBro MMal NNor SIng SWat WMaN
§ – 'Blaue Clips'	CDoC EAst EBar ECtt ELan EMNN EPar ESis GTou MPla NFla NMen NRoo NVic SPer SPla SRms WFar WPer
– Blue Clips	See *C. carpatica* **'Blaue Clips'**
– 'Blue Moonlight'	EBrP EBre EBur LBre NRoo SBre SMer
– 'Bressingham White'	CBlo EBrP EBre GAri GCHN GDra LBre SBla SBre WHoo
– 'Caerulea'	CB&S
– 'Chewton Joy'	CLyd EBrP EBre EPPr GAri GCHN LBre MBro SBre WLin
– 'Ditton Blue'	GDra
– dwarf form	EPot
– 'Karpatenkrone'	EBee
– 'Kathy'	GBuc SAsh SWas
– 'Maureen Haddon'	EBrP EBre GAri GCHN GMac LBre NWCA SBre
– 'Molly Pinsent'	LBay
– 'Queen of Somerville'	NNrd NWoo
– 'Snowdrift'	ELan
– 'Suzie'	EWes SBla
– var. *turbinata*	GDra MTho NGre NSla SRms WPer
– – f. *alba*	NNrd
– – 'Georg Arends'	CLyd SAsh
– – 'Hannah'	EBrP EBre GCHN GDra LBre SBre
– – 'Isabel'	GCHN LRHS
– – 'Jewel'	LBee LRHS SIng SSmi
– – 'Karl Foerster'	CTri EBrP EBre GBuc GCHN LBre MTho NNrd NRoo SBre SMer WHoo
– – 'Pallida'	GDra SSmi
– – 'Wheatley Violet'	CLyd GCHN LBee MRPP NMen SBla
§ – 'Weisse Clips'	CPri EAst ECtt ELan EMNN EPar ERav ESis GTou LHop MPla NFla NMen NRoo NVic SPer SPla SRms WFar WPer
– White Clips	See *C. carpatica* **'Weisse Clips'**
§ *cashmeriana*	CGen CGra EBur EHyt GCHN GCra ITim NTow NWCA WOMN
cephallenica	See *C. garganica* subsp. *cephallenica*
§ *chamissonis*	EHyt GAbr GBuc NNrd NSla
§ – 'Major'	CPBP EMNN EPot EWes MBro NMGW
– 'Oyobeni'	MOne NHar SUsu WLin
§ – 'Superba' ♀	EBur EGle ELan GDra MBal MFos MTho NGre NMen NSla NTow SSmi
choruhensis	CGra EHyt EPot GCLN
§ *cochleariifolia* ♀	CLyd CPBP CPri CSpe ELan EMNN ESis GCHN GTou MBal MBro MFir MHig MTho MWat NGre NHar NRoo SIng SSvw WAbe WCla WFar WHoo WMaN WPer WWhi WWin
– var. *alba*	CMea CVer EMNN EPot GCHN MBal MBro MHig MWat NChi NGre NHar NMen NNrd NRya SBla SSmi WAbe WCla WHoo WMaN WPer
– 'Bavaria Blue'	NHar

– 'Bavaria White'	NHar
– 'Blue Tit'	EPot GBuc
– 'Cambridge Blue'	EBrP EBre GCHN LBre NMen SBre SSmi WAbe
– 'Elizabeth Oliver' (d)	Widely available
– 'Flore Pleno' (d)	ECtt NHol NMen WRHF
– 'Miss Willmott'	CBrd EBur MTho NBir NTow
– 'Oakington Blue'	CTri MBro NHol
– var. *pallida*	SRms
– – 'Miranda'	CNic MHig WIvy
– 'Silver Chimes'	MBro WMaN
– 'Temple Bells'	MBro
– 'Tubby'	CInt CLyd CMea CRDP GCHN MTho SAga SRms
– 'Warleyensis'	See *C.* × *haylodgensis* 'Warley White'
– 'White Baby'	NPri
collina	CTri GBri MBro NHar NPri WAbe WHoo WPer WPyg
'Constellation'	MDHE NCat NNrd
'Covadonga'	CLyd CPBP MBro MDHE SIng
dasyantha	See *C. chamissonis*
¶ 'E.H. Frost'	CSpe
'E.K. Toogood'	CElw CPBP ECtt EMNN GBur GMac MAvo MDHE MWat NBro NFai NHar NHol NMen SBla SCro SMac SRms WAbe WRHF
elatines	NNrd NOak
– var. *elatinoides*	MHar
– – JCA 254.300	SBla
§ 'Elizabeth'	Widely available
eriocarpa	See *C. latifolia* 'Eriocarpa'
excisa	GCLN LBee NPri
'Faichem'	GCra WPer WSan
fenestrellata	MDHE MTho NBro SRms SSmi WAbe
finitima	See *C. betulifolia*
foliosa	WCot
formanekiana ♀	CSam EBur EDAr MFos MLLN NWCA WSan
fragilis	CPBP EBur ELan WPer
– subsp. *cavolinii*	EHyt
'G.F. Wilson' ♀	EBur EGle MBal
garganica ♀	ELan ESis GAbr MBro MRav NFla NHar NMen NNor NRoo SIde WFar WHoo WMaN WPer
– 'Aurea'	See *C. garganica* 'Dickson's Gold'
– 'Blue Diamond'	ELan EMNN ESis LHop SAga SCro SIng WAbe WLRN
§ – subsp. *cephallenica*	CLyd MDHE NBro NHol NNrd
§ – 'Dickson's Gold'	CElw CGle CHea CMea EBrP EBre ECtt ELan EPot GCal LBee LBre LHop MBro MHig NEgg NHar NHed NHol NMen NRoo SAxl SBre SIng WAbe WFar WPat WPbr WPnn WWal
– 'Hirsuta'	SRms
– 'W.H. Paine' ♀	CInt CLyd EBrP EBre ECho ELan LBre NCat NSla SBre SIng WHoo
§ 'Glandore'	NCat
glomerata	CB&S CBot CKin EBar GTou MBal MFir MHew MMal NBro NFai NMir NRya NSti SOkh SSoC SUsu WBea WByw WFar WOve WWin
– var. *acaulis*	CDoC CNic EBar EMNN EOld EPot GCHN MBro NMen NOak NTow SEas SPla SSca WFar WHil WHoo WPer WPyg WWin
– var. *alba*	CB&S CSev ELan EMon GMaP LWak MBal MBri MBro MCLN MNrw MUlv MWat NBro NFai SChu SPer SPla SSvw SWat WFar WHil WHoo WMaN WPer
– 'Alba Nana'	CLyd NPro
– 'Caroline'	MGed MRav SOkh SPer WHil WPbr
– Crown of Snow	See *C. glomerata* 'Schneekrone'
– var. *dahurica*	CHan CTri LGan MCLN MOne NLar NOak WBea WEas WMoo WPer
– 'Joan Elliott'	CSev EBrP EBre ECha GBuc LBre MRav MWat NBrk NCat SBre SChu WCot WFar
– 'Purple Pixie'	EBrP EBre LBre SBre
§ – 'Schneekrone'	ECha EFou MCli MGrG MRav NBrk NLon NNor NOak NRoo WBea WFar WRHF
– 'Superba' ♀	Widely available
– 'White Barn'	ECha GCra MRav NBrk NOak
grossekii	GBuc MNrw MSto
× *hallii*	CNic ESis MBro MPla MRPP NGre NRoo NWCA WPat
hawkinsiana	CPBP
¶ – JCA 256002	IDac
× *haylodgensis*	See *C.* × *haylodgensis* 'Plena'
§ – 'Plena' (d)	CElw CSpe ELan EPot ESis GMac IHos LBee LHop MBal MBro MHig NBro NHar NRoo SBla SIng SRms SSmi WAbe WEas WHoo WKif WPyg
§ – 'Warley White' (d)	CNic EBur ELan EPot GDra NNrd
'Hemswell Starlight'	CLyd NMen NPro
hercegovina	NTow
– 'Nana'	CGra CPBP NNrd WAbe
§ *incurva*	CBot CGle CMHG CPou EBur EGar ELan GBin GBuc MMil MNrw MRPP MTho MTis NBrk NBro NHol NLak NOak NSti SMrm WBea WByw WPer WUnu
– *alba*	ELan
– 'Blue Ice'	LFis WWin
– JCA 256.800	MBro
× *innesii*	See *C.* 'John Innes'
isophylla ♀	MBri SIng SLMG WEas WOMN
– 'Alba' ♀	SIng SLMG WEas WOMN
– 'Flore Pleno' (d)	EBur WOMN
– 'Mayi' ♀	CSpe
– 'Variegata'	See *C.* 'Balchiniana'
jaubertiana	CGra EHyt
'Joe Elliott' ♀	CGra EPot EWes MHig SIng
§ 'John Innes'	CLyd MGed
kemulariae	ESis GCHN MAvo NNrd WPer
– *alba*	MAvo
'Kent Belle'	Widely available
kolenatiana	GCHN
laciniata	CFir
lactiflora	Widely available
N – 'Alba' ♀	MAvo
– *alba*	See *C. lactiflora* white
– 'Blue Avalanche'	SMrm
– 'Blue Cross'	COtt EFou NLar NRoo WCot

– 'Loddon Anna' ♀	Widely available
– 'Pouffe'	CDoC EBrP EBre ECha EFou ELan GMac LBre LGan MBro MGrG MRav NBro NFla NRoo SBre SCro SPer SPla SWat WHil WHoo WLin WOld WPyg WRus WWin
– 'Prichard's Variety' ♀	Widely available
– 'Violet'	EBee SWat WPer
§ – white	CBot EBrP EBre ECha EFou LBre MBro MCLN NBir NBrk SBre SPer SPla WHoo WOld WPer
– 'White Pouffe'	CSpe EBrP EBre EFou EHal ELan EOrc GAbr GMaP GMac LBre MBro MRav NLar SBre SMer SOkh SPer SPla SWat WByw WCot WFar WHil WHoo WLin WPyg WRus
lanata	EBar GAbr SMad SSca WBea
lasiocarpa	CPBP EBur WAbe WFar
¶ – 'Talkeetna'	CGra
§ *latifolia*	CAgr CArn CBos CKin CSev ECha EFou GAbr GMac LGan MCLN MWgw NChi NFla NMir NNor NOrc NTow NVic SPer WCer WCla WEas WFar
* – 'Amethyst'	CChr
– 'Brantwood'	CBos CGle CInt CMil COtt EBrP EBre EMan EMar GMac LBre MBel MFir MSte MWat NBrk NHol NOak NPro SBla SBre SChu SCro SMer SPer SSpe WBea WCot WWin
§ – 'Eriocarpa'	CHan
– 'Gloaming'	EBee LRHS MBri MTed WCot
– var. *macrantha*	EBrP EBre EFou GAbr GLil LBre LFis LHop MCLN MCli MNrw MRav MSCN MSte NSti SBre SIgm SSvw WCot WHil WHoo WPer WRus WWat WWye
– var. *macrantha alba*	CBos CDoC CM&M CMil ECtt EMan EPri LFis LGre LHop MAus MRav NHol SPla WCot WPer WPyg WWat
– white	CGle CHan CMHG EBrP EBre ECha LBre MBro MCLN MSte NNor NTow SBre SPer SSpi WEas WHoo WRus
– 'White Ladies'	EBrP EBre LBre NRoo SBre
§ *latiloba*	CBos CBre CGle CMHG EBrP EBre EGar EMon LBre LGro MBro MFir SBre WByw WCot WEas WHoo WRHF WWin
– 'Alba' ♀	CBre CElw CGle CSpe CVer EBee EBrP EBre EFou EHal ELan GAbr GCal GMac LBre LFis LGan LHil MRav NChi SBre WAbe WEas WLin WMaN
– 'Hidcote Amethyst' ♀	Widely available
– 'Highcliffe Variety' ♀	CMGP EBee ECGN ECha EFou EJud EMan EPfP LFis MBel MBri MCLN NLar NSti SChu SPla SSpe SSpi WCot WEas WKif WLRN WOld WPbr WRHF WRus
* – 'Highdown'	MAvo MLLN WFar

– 'Percy Piper' ♀	CHea CSam ECED EFou EHal ELan GMac MAus MBel MBri MNrw MRav MSCN NBrk NBro NNor NSti SHel WByw WFar WLin WPbr WRHF
¶ – 'Splash'	MAvo
ledebouriana pulvinata	WLin
lingulata	EBee
linifolia	See *C. carnica*
'Lynchmere'	EWes MBro NTow
makaschvilii	EBee
¶ *marchesettii*	EBee
'Marion Fisher'	MBro WEas WHoo
'Mist Maiden'	CFee CLyd CMHG CPBP LBee NTow WFar
moesiaca	NLar SGre
mollis var. *gibraltarica*	NTow
muralis	See *C. portenschlagiana*
¶ *myrtifolia*	NWCA
nitida	See *C. persicifolia* var. *planiflora*
– var. *planiflora*	See *C. persicifolia* var. *planiflora*
'Norman Grove'	CLyd EGle EPot LBee MHig
ochroleuca	CMea CRDP EAst EBrP EBre EGar GAbr GCal LBre MCLN NLak SBre SCro SWat WBea WCot WHal
olympica Boissier	GCra
– hort.	See *C. rotundifolia* '**Olympica**'
ossetica	See *Symphyandra ossetica*
pallida subsp. *tibetica*	See *C. cashmeriana*
patula	GBin LSyl MHew SGre WCla
'Paul Furse'	CMea EPPr MAvo MTed NSti WHil WLin WWin
¶ *pelviformis*	MNrw
peregrina	EBee
persicifolia	Widely available
– *alba*	Widely available
§ – 'Alba Coronata' (d)	CDec CFir CMil EBrP EBre EMon EPPr LBre MAus MBal MBro NBir NBrk NRoo SBre SPer WEas WFar WRus
– 'Alba Plena'	See *C. persicifolia* '**Alba Coronata**'
– 'Bennett's Blue'	EBee EOrc LFis
– blue	EMan EOrc NCut WEas WFar WPbr
– 'Blue Bell'	CBlo WBro
– 'Blue Bloomers' (d)	EMon EWes GBri MAvo
– blue cup-in-cup	CMil WLin WPbr WRus
– 'Boule de Neige' (d)	CDec CHan CHea CLon CMil ECha EMon GCra GMac LFis NBrk NMGW NOak NRya WCot WEas WHil WPbr
– 'Caerulea Coronata'	See *C. persicifolia* '**Coronata**'
* – 'Caerulea Plena'	EBar ELan WEas WPbr
– 'Capel Ulo' (v)	WHer WPbr
– 'Carillon'	GBri NBrk WCot
§ – 'Chettle Charm'	Widely available
§ – 'Coronata' (d)	CHea EFou MRav
N – cup & saucer white	CBlo CElw CLyd ELan MMHG NBrk WByw WHil WPbr WPer
– double blue (d)	CLon CSWP EGar EOrc MAus MBal MBel MCLN NBro NFai SUsu WBro WByw WCot WEas WFar WPbr WRHF WRus WWhi
¶ – double powder blue	WLin
– double white (d)	EBee ELan NChi SUsu WByw WMoo WRus
– 'Eastgrove Blue'	NWes

– 'Fleur de Neige' (d) ♀ CGle CMea CSam EBrP EBre LBre MBel MBri MBro MLLN NOak NPro NRoo NTow SBre SWat WHoo WLin WPyg WRus WSel

– 'Flore Pleno' (d) CHan NBir

– 'Frances' (d) CSpe EMon GBri MAvo MRav SWat WLin WMaN WPbr

– 'Frank Lawley' EBee EBrP EBre EFou LBre SBre WPbr

– 'Gawen' (d) CElw CGle GBri GMac LGre MHlr NRoo SUsu WCot WHer WLin WPen WRHF WWoo

– 'George Chiswell' See *C. persicifolia* 'Chettle Charm'

– 'Grandiflora Alba' GBuc SSca

§ – 'Hampstead White' (d) CDec CHan CLon CMil EBee ECha EEls LFis MBel MBri MCLN NBir NBro SBla SChu SUsu WCot WEas WHoo WLin WPrP WWin

– 'Hetty' See *C. persicifolia* 'Hampstead White'

– Irish double white EMon

– 'Moerheimii' (d) EOrc EPar MBel NBir WIvy WPbr WWin

– var. *nitida* See *C. persicifolia* var. *planiflora*

* – 'Peach Bells' EBar NOak

– 'Perry's Boy Blue' NPer NTow

– 'Pike's Supremo' LHop NBir

§ – var. *planiflora* CPBP CSpe EBee GTou NHar NTow WAbe WOMN

§ – – f. *alba* WAbe WOMN WSan WWin

– 'Pride of Exmouth' (d) CGle CHea CPou CSam ELan EMon GMac LHop LLWP MArl MBro NLon NNor NOak NVic WCot WFar WHil WHoo WLin WMaN WPbr

– subsp. *sessiliflora* See *C. latiloba*

– 'Telham Beauty' CDoC CHea CKel COtt ECED EFou ELan EPri LHop LRot MCLN MFir MRav SAga SMad SMer SMrm SPer SRCN WHil WMoo WPbr WPer WRus WWat

– 'Wedgwood' MBal

N – 'White Cup and Saucer' NBrk NCat WFar WIvy WRus (d) WWhi

– 'White Queen' (d) CMGP EBee EFou NCat NFai WEas

– 'Wortham Belle' (d) CGle CSev EBee EMan EPri ERic GCal GMac LFis LHop MAvo MBel MCLN MMil NCat NRoo NSti SChu SCoo SPer SSpi SWat WGle WLRN WMoo WMow WOve WRus WWal WWoo

petrophila CLyd WAbe WLin

pilosa See *C. chamissonis*

piperi CGra CPBP GCLN MFos SBla WAbe

¶ – 'Marmot Pass' CGra

– 'Townsend Ridge' CGra

planiflora See *C. persicifolia* var. *planiflora*

§ portenschlagiana ♀ CAgr CElw ELan ENot GAbr LGro MHar MHig MWat NBro NGre NRoo NRya NVic SBla SDix SPer SRms SSmi WAbe WCot WEas WMoo WPyg WWin

– 'Lieslelotte' GBuc MDHE

– 'Major' CMCo SRms WFar

– 'Resholdt's Variety' CMea CNic CSam EBrP EBre EFou ELan EPla GCHN LBee LBre NCat SBre WLRN WPer

poscharskyana CAgr CElw CPri ELan ESis GTou LBlm LBuc LGro MBal MFir NBrk NBro NFla NGre NHol NMen NOrc NRoo SMer SPer SPla SSmi WAbe WBea WByw WFar WPer WWhi

– 'Blauranke' EBee EBrP EBre EWes GAri GCHN LBre MDHE NRoo SBre

– 'Blue Gown' GMaP WWeb

– 'E.H. Frost' CBre ECtt EMNN ESis LBlm LHop LWak MBro MHig MPla MWat NBro NCat NHol NMGW NMen NNrd NRya SCro SIng SSmi WBea WLin WPer

– 'Glandore' See *C.* 'Glandore'

– 'Lilacina' EPPr SCro SHel SIng WThi

– 'Lisduggan' CBre CChr CGle CNic EBrP EBre EBur ESis EWes GAbr LBre MBal MBro MWat NBro NCat NChi SBla SBre SIng WAbe WBea WPer WPyg WWin

– 'Stella' ♀ EBrP EBre EMNN ENot EPPr ESis GCHN GChr LBre MRav NBro NCat NMen NNrd NRoo NVic SBre SChu SDix SIng WFar WPyg

– variegated EHoe IBlr

primulifolia CChr CInt CPou EBee EBrP EBre ECoo EGar ELan GBuc GCra LBre LFis MBro MMil MNrw MTis NFai SBre SSca WFar WHow WPer WPrP WPyg WSan WWeb WWin

¶ – 'Blue Spires' LRHS MBri

× pseudoraineri EBee EBur EHyt ELan EWes NGre NNrd NSla SSmi

pulla CHea CLyd CMea CRDP EBur EHyt ELan EMNN EPot ESis MBro MHig MTho NFla NGre NHar NMGW NMen NNrd SSmi WAbe WFar WPat WPer WPnn

– *alba* CHea CInt CMea CPBP CRDP EBur EHyt ELan EMNN LBee MBro NHar NMGW NNrd WAbe WPat

× pulloides CLyd EBrP EBre LBee LBre NMen SBre SSmi

punctata CBot CMHG CMil CSpe EAst ECoo ECro EFou GCHN LFis LGan LLWP MAus MBel MBro MFir MRav NBrk NBro NGre NHar NSti SBla WCla WEas WFar WHil WMoo WPer WWin

– f. *albiflora* CHan LGan LHop MBri MBro MCLN MLLN MOne NMen SCro SSvw WPbr WWin

– var. *hondoensis* CHar CPea EBee ECro MBel NLar NSti WBea WPbr WUnu

– 'Nana Alba' CLon CMil EHyt GBin GCal GMac WCot

– 'Rosea' CGle CMea MBri NNrd SRms WHil WSan

– 'Rubriflora' Widely available

¶ – 'White Hose-in-hose' SBla
¶ – wine red form CStr
* 'Purple Dwarf' NGre
pusilla See *C. cochleariifolia*
pyramidalis CBot CMGP EFou EPfP LIck
MSCN NLak NNor NOrc SSca
WByw WPer
– *alba* CM&M CMGP EFou MAus
SIde SSca WPer
raddeana CNic CRDP CTri GCHN MBro
NBus NGre NHar NMen NTow
SCro SSmi WFar
raineri ♀ CFee CGra CPBP EHyt EPot
LBee MBro NMen NOak NTow
NWCA SBla WAbe WPat WPyg
– 'Nettleton Gold' EPot
§ *rapunculoides* CAgr LRot MCLN MCli MLLN
NPri SWat WHer WPer
– 'Alba' CStr EMon
rapunculus ILis LFis MGed
* 'Rearsby Belle' WPbr
recurva See *C. incurva*
rhomboidalis Gorter See *C. rapunculoides*
rotundifolia CArn CFis CKin CNic MGra
MHew NChi NMir NNrd NRoo
NSti SIde SRms SSvw WBea
WCla WGwy WJek WOak
WOve WPer
§ – var. *alaskana* NWCA
– var. *alba* MBro NChi WHoo WPyg
– 'Caerulea Plena' See *C. rotundifolia* '**Flore
Pleno**'
– forms MBro
¶ – 'Jotunheimen' CGra EHyt
§ – 'Olympica' CInt EBar EBee EBur EPfP
GAbr GCHN LFis MHar NPri
SEas WFar
– 'Superba' SCro
rupestris CBot CPBP EBur MFos
rupicola JCA 262.400 SBla
¶ 'Sarastro' EBee EFou EMon LGre
sarmatica CGle CHan CHea GAbr GBuc
NNrd NOak NSti SRms WMaN
WPer
sartorii CPBP EBur ELan WWin
saxifraga EBur EHyt GCHN
scabrella CGra MFos NWCA
scheuchzeri NNrd
scouleri NWCA
shetleri CGra CPBP EHyt
sibirica LFis WPer
¶ sp.from Iran EMon
sp. from Morocco CGra
spathulata subsp. NNrd
spathulata
sporadum MFos
'Stansfieldii' CPBP EBur EPot
¶ *stevenii* CGra EBee
* 'Swannbles' WCot
¶ × Symphyandra GMac
takesimana Widely available
* – *alba* LSyl MAvo NFla SMad WIvy
WRus
– dark form LFis
– 'Elizabeth' See *C.* '**Elizabeth**'
¶ *teucrioides* EHyt
thessala CGra CSWP MSto SSca WCot
thyrsoides GDra GTou ITim MNrw NGre
NNrd NWCA WCla WHal
WPer
– subsp. *carniolica* NChi
tommasiniana ♀ EHyt LBee NHar SAsh WOMN

topaliana WLin
trachelium CGle CKin EBar ECoo EGar
EOrc LHop MAus MHew
MNrw MRav NHaw SCou SIde
SSca WByw WCla WFar WHer
WPbr WPer
– var. *alba* CGle CPea LFis LSyl MFir
MNrw NGre NNor SCou SSca
WCot WFar WPer WWal WWhi
– 'Alba Flore Pleno' (d) CBos CFir CGle CHea CLon
CPou ECha EFou ELan EMan
EMon LHop MBel SAxl SMac
SOkh WByw WCot WFar WGle
WHoo WMaN WPbr WRus
WSan
– 'Bernice' (d) CFil CGle CHad CHea CMil
EBrP EBre ELan EMon EOrc
GCHN GCra LBre LHop MBel
MBri MRav NSti SBla SBre
SOkh SSpi WByw WFar WGle
WHoo WPbr WPyg WRus
WWin
* – 'Faichem Lilac' EBee MTis NChi WCot
– lilac-blue CBlo NCut NOrc
tridentata NTow WLin WPer
troegerae LBee LRHS SBla
tubulosa See *C. buseri*
'Tymonsii' CPBP EBur ECho EHyt ELan
ESis LBee MHig NBir NNrd
'Van-Houttei' CElw CHan CHar CMil EMan
EMon GCal LGre MBro MSte
NBrk SUsu WCot WFar WPbr
WPer
versicolor LFis WOMN WPer
– G&K 3347 EMon
– NS 745 MRPP NWCA
vidalii See *Azorina vidalii*
waldsteiniana CPBP EPot LBee NTow SSmi
WFar WOMN WPer
– JCA 266.000 MBro
'Warley White' See *C.* × *haylodgensis* '**Warley
White**'
'Warleyensis' See *C.* × *haylodgensis* '**Warley
White**'
× *wockei* See *C.* × *wockei* '**Puck**'
§ – 'Puck' CPBP EBur EHyt EPot ESis
GDra LBee MBro NHar NMen
NSla NWCA SSmi WAbe WPat
* 'Yvonne' EDAr NNrd NPri SIng WLRN
WPer
zoysii CGra LRHS

CAMPANULA × SYMPHYANDRA
(Campanulaceae)
C. *punctata* × S. *ossetica* CPou NCat

CAMPANUMOEA See CODONOPSIS

CAMPHOROSMA (Chenopodiaceae) See Plant
Deletions

CAMPSIS (Bignoniaceae)
* *atrosanguinea* LRHS
grandiflora CB&S CHEx CPlN EBrP EBre
EHic ELan ENot EPfP EPla
GSki LBre LPan NPal SBre
WCFE
radicans CArn CB&S CBot CDoC CHEx
CMac CPlN CRHN ELan EPla
GQui LPan MGrG MHlr MNrw
MWat NBea NFla SHBN SPer
WDin

– 'Flamenco'	CB&S CBlo CPlN EBee EBrP EBre EHic GOrc GQui GSki IOrc LBre LHop NBea NPal SBra SBre WBro WCru	§ *indica*	CB&S CHEx CMon CSev EFul ERav GCra LBlm MBEx SAPC SArc SLMG
§ – f. *flava* ♀	CDoC CHEx CMac CPlN CSam EBee ELan EPla IOrc LHol LHop MBri MCCP MWat NBea NPal NSti SBra SPer SSoC SSta WBro WSHC	– 'Purpurea'	CMon ECha ERav LBlm MBEx SDix WPGP
		¶ – *variegata*	LHil
		¶ 'Ingeborg'	NCut
		¶ 'Intrigue'	MBEx
– 'Yellow Trumpet'	See *C. radicans* f. *flava*	*iridiflora*	CMon CSev CWit ECha EOas MBEx SAPC SArc SDix
* × *tagliabuana* 'Flamenco'	MAsh	'Jivago'	MBEx
– 'Madame Galen' ♀	CB&S CMac CPlN EBrP EBre EMil IOrc LBre LHol LHop LPan MAsh MBlu MBri MGos MLan MTis MWat NBea NSti SBra SBre SHBN SPer SReu SSpi SSta WWeb	'King Hakon'	MBEx
		I 'King Humbert' (blood-red)	LBlo
		King Humbert (orange-red)	See *C.* 'Roi Humbert'
		'King Midas'	CHEx MBEx SVen
		'Königin Charlotte'	MBEx
		'La Gloire'	MBEx
		¶ 'Lesotho Lill'	LHil
CAMPTOSORUS See ASPLENIUM		'Libération'	MBEx
		'Louis Cayeux'	LHil MBEx
		'Lucifer'	EOas LHil MBEx
CAMPTOTHECA (Nyssaceae)		*lutea*	LBlm WCot
¶ *acuminata*	ISea	♦ 'Malawiensis Variegata'	See *C.* 'Striata'
		¶ 'Melanie'	CHEx
		'Meyerbeer'	MBEx
CAMPYLOTROPIS (Papilionaceae) See Plant Deletions		'Mrs Tim Taylor'	MBEx
		musifolia	CHEx LBlo LHil LPJP MBEx SDix
CANANGA (Annonaceae)		§ 'Oiseau de Feu'	MBri SVen
¶ *odorata*	ERea	'Oiseau d'Or'	LHil MBEx
		'Orange Perfection'	CHEx MBEx
CANARINA (Campanulaceae)		'Orchid'	LAma MBEx MBri
canariensis ♀	CPlN CPle WOMN	'Panache'	MBEx
		'Perkeo'	CHEx MBEx
		'Picadore'	MBEx
CANDOLLEA See HIBBERTIA		'Picasso'	LAma MBEx
		* 'Pink Sunburst'	WCot
CANNA † (Cannaceae)		'President'	CHEx LAma LHil MBEx MBri SAga
¶ 'Adams Orange'	CHEx		
'Angele Martin'	MBEx	♦ 'Pretoria'	See *C.* 'Striata'
¶ 'Argentina'	LBlo	* 'Pringle Bay' (v)	LBlo
'Assaut'	CHEx MBEx SVen	'Professor Lorentz'	CFil MBEx WPGP
'Australia'	MBEx	'Ra'	LLew MBEx MSta WMAq
'Black Knight'	GBuc LAma MBEx	'Richard Wallace'	CHEx MBEx NCut
brasiliensis 'Rosea'	MBEx	§ 'Roi Humbert'	MBEx SLMG SVen
¶ 'Brilliant'	CHEx NCut	'Roi Soleil'	CHEx MBEx WPGP
'Champion'	CHEx MBEx	¶ 'Roitelet'	CHEx
'Chinese Coral'	CHEx LHil	'Rosemond Coles'	MBEx SLMG
'Cleopatra'	MBEx	'Saladin'	LHil MBEx
coccinea	MBEx SVen	'Sémaphore'	MBEx
¶ 'Creamy White'	CHEx	'Shenandoah'	MBEx
Crozy hybrids	MHlr NPal	'Singapore Girl'	MBEx
'Di Bartolo'	MBEx	'Strasbourg'	CHEx MBEx
'Durban' (v)	CSpe LBlo LHil LPJP MBEx WCot WMul WSPU	§ 'Striata' (v)	CSev CSpe EOas LBlo LHil LPJP MBEx MSta SVen WCot WMul WSPU
edulis	See *C. indica*		
× *ehemanii*	CGre CHEx SVen	'Striped Beauty' (v)	MBEx
¶ × *ehemanii* × *iridiflora*	LHil	¶ 'Stuttgart'	MBEx
'En Avant'	MBEx	'Talisman'	MBEx
'Endeavour'	CFil LLew LPJP MBEx MSta WMAq WMul WPGP	'Taney'	MSta WMAq
		¶ 'Tango'	CHEx
'Erebus'	MBEx MSta WMAq	'Taroudant'	LHil MBEx
'Etoile du Feu'	MBEx	'Tashkent Red'	LHil
'Extase'	MBEx	'Tirol'	MBEx SVen
Firebird	See *C.* 'Oiseau de Feu'	'Tropical Rose'	WMul
'General Eisenhower'	MBEx	* 'Variegata' (v)	LAma
× *generalis*	CB&S CHEx	'Verdi'	LHil MBEx
glauca	CMon MBEx SDix	*warscewiczii*	CBos LBlo MBEx SLMG
'Gnom'	MBEx	'Wyoming'	CDoC EOas LAma LHil LLew MBEx NCut
'Golden Lucifer'	LAma MBri MRav SAga		
¶ 'Heinrich Seidel'	CHEx	'Yellow Humbert'	CDoC CSev LAma
'Hercule'	MBEx		
hybrids	LBow		

CANTUA (Polemoniaceae)
buxifolia   CB&S CFee CFil CPle ERea
                          GQui LCns LHil SIgm SLMG
                          SMad SOWG

CAPPARIS   (Capparaceae) See Plant Deletions

CAPSICUM (Solanaceae)
annuum   MBri
* – 'Janne'   MBri

CARAGANA (Papilionaceae)
arborescens   CBlo ENot EPfP GChr IOrc
                          MBar MCoo MWhi SRCN
                          WDin WFro WStI WWat
– 'Lorbergii' ♀   CDoC CEnd CLnd IOrc LPan
                          MBlu SEas SPer WAbe WDin
                          WFoF
– 'Pendula'   CBlo CLnd ELan ENot EPfP
                          GRei MAsh MBar MBlu NBee
                          NEgg SPer WDin WStI
– 'Walker'   CB&S CBlo CDoC COtt EBee
                          EBrP EBre EMil IOrc LBre
                          LPan MAsh MBar MBri MGos
                          SBre SMad SPer WStI
aurantiaca   MBar SMad
brevispina   CPle SRms
franchetiana   CLnd
frutex 'Globosa'   SPer
jubata   SMad
¶ *microphylla*   SMad WNor

CARDAMINE † (Brassicaceae)
alba   WEas
asarifolia hort.   See *Pachyphragma*
                          macrophyllum
– Linnaeus   WCru
bulbifera   CHan CRDP IBlr LGan NWoo
                          SIng WCru WUnd
enneaphyllos   ECha IBlr SSpi WCru WFar
                          WRHF
¶ *glanduligera*   SWas
§ *heptaphylla*   CLAP EBee ELan EPar GBri
                          IBlr MBri MRav SWat WCru
                          WHoo
– Guincho form   CFir IBlr
– white   GMaP WCot
§ *kitaibelii*   EBee EPar IBlr NHol SIng SSpi
                          WCru
laciniata   SWat WCot
latifolia Vahl   See *C. raphanifolia*
macrophylla   CLAP COtt SWas SWat WCot
                          WCru WIvy
§ *microphylla*   EHyt GCrs
§ *pentaphyllos*   CGle ECha ELan EPar EPla
                          ERos GAbr GCrs MBri MRav
                          NSti SIgm SSpi WCot WCru
                          WFar WOMN
– bright pink form   CLAP
pratensis   CArn CKin CRow EMan EMar
                          EWFC MMal NDea NMir NOrc
                          SIde SWat WCla WGwy WHer
                          WOak WShi
– 'Edith' (d)   CGle CHid CLAP CMil CRow
                          GAri GBuc MNrw SAxl SWat
                          WHil

– 'Flore Pleno' (d) ♀   CBre CFee CGle CHid CNic
                          CRow CSpe CVer ECha GAbr
                          MCLN MNrw MSta MTho
                          NBro NChi SBla SWat WAlt
                          WChe WCla WEas WHoo
                          WMer WOMN WRus
– 'William' (d)   CGle CMea CVer EPPr GBuc
                          MNrw WFar WHil
quinquefolia   CGle EPar NCat SWas WCru
                          WFar WHal WWye
§ *raphanifolia*   CBre CGle CRow CVer EBee
                          ECha EOrc GAbr GBuc GCal
                          GGar IBlr MFir MRav NBro
                          NCat NChi NVic SWat WCru
trifolia   CGle CRDP ECha ERos GAbr
                          GCal LBay LBee LGan MBar
                          MHig MRav NBro NChi NNor
                          NRya NTow NVic SWat WCru
                          WFar WHal WHer WHil WWye
* *trifolia digitata*   MTho
waldsteinii   CLon EGle SWas WCot WCru
                          WHal WTin

CARDIANDRA (Hydrangeaceae)
formosana B&SWJ 2005   WCru

CARDIOCRINUM (Liliaceae)
cordatum   MSto
– var. *glehnii*   CFil MSto WPGP
giganteum ♀   CAvo CB&S CBot CBro CFil
                          CHEx EBot EOas EPar GGGa
                          IBlr LAma LSyl MAvo MBal
                          MBlu MGrG NRog SAga SMad
                          SPer SSoC SSpi WCot WCru
                          WHer WPGP
– var. *yunnanense*   CFil GGGa IBlr SSpi WCru

CARDIOSPERMUM (Sapindaceae)
grandiflorum   CPlN

CARDUNCELLUS   (Asteraceae) See Plant
Deletions

CARDUUS (Asteraceae)
benedictus   See *Cnicus benedictus*

CAREX (Cyperaceae)
albida   CCuc CInt EBee EGle EHoe
                          EMon EPPr EPla ESOG EWes
                          GOrn MBal
appressa   EBee
atrata   CCuc ECoo EGar EHoe EMar
                          EMon EPPr EPla ESOG ESis
                          MAvo
baccans   EPla GCal
berggrenii   Widely available
binervis   GBin
boottiana   EWes GGar
brunnea   EHoe EPPr EWes
– 'Variegata'   CCuc EHoe GGar SCob WCot
buchananii   Widely available
– 'Viridis'   CB&S CSte ELan EPPr EPla
                          ESOG EWer WPbr
caryophyllea 'The   CCuc CSte EGoo EHoe EPPr
  Beatles'   EPla ESOG MCCP MMoz
                          NBro NHar NHol

comans	CCuc CKel CMea EBee EFul EHoe ELan EMon EOld EPPr EPar EPla ESOG GCHN GCal GGar GOrn IBlr LHil MAvo MBal NBro NHol NOak SHel SIng
– bronze	CCuc CGle CLTr CRow EBar EBrP EBre ECou EHoe EMon EPla EPot ESOG ESis LBre MBri NHar NHol NMir NOrc NSti NWes SBre WHal WLin WOMN WPer WStI WWat WWye
* – 'Small Red'	GOrn LRot MAsh
§ **conica**	LHil LHop MBri SPer
– 'Hime-kan-suge'	See C. conica 'Snowline'
§ – 'Snowline' (v)	CCuc CElw CGle CSte ECha EHoe ELan EMon EPla ESOG ESis GCHN GDra LHil MBrN MBri NBro NEgg NFai NHol NMir NOak NPSI NSti NWCA WPer WRus WWye
crus-corvi	EPPr
dallii	ECou EWes
demissa	CCuc CInt EBee EHoe EPPr EPla ESOG GBin WWye
depauperata	CCuc EHoe EMon EPla ESOG WWye
digitata	WWye
dipsacea	CElw CRow CSpe ECou EHoe EMon EPla ESOG GCal GOrn MLLN MWhi NChi NHed NWCA WChe WHal WPer WWye
dissita	CInt
¶ **divulsa**	GBin
dolichostachya	EMon ESOG GBin MAvo
'Kaga-nishiki' (v)	SApp WCot
§ **elata** 'Aurea' (v) ♀	Widely available
♦ – 'Bowles' Golden'	See C. elata 'Aurea'
– 'Knightshayes' (v)	EMon WCot
* 'Everbright' (v)	CB&S
'Evergold'	See C. oshimensis 'Evergold'
¶ **ferruginea**	GBin
firma	MHig NNrd
– 'Variegata'	CLyd EHyt EPPr EPar MAsh MDHE MTho MWat NHar NMen NTow NWCA SChu SIng WRus
§ **flacca**	EHoe ESOG GBin MSCN SApp
– 'Bias' (v)	CKin CNat EMon EPPr ESOG NSti SApp
§ – subsp. **flacca**	EWes NHol SApp
¶ **flaccosperma**	SApp
* **flagellaris** 'Cyperacea'	CInt
flagellifera	Widely available
flava	EHoe ESOG
forsteri	See C. pseudocyperus
fortunei 'Variegata'	See C. morrowii 'Variegata'
¶ **fraseri**	GBin
'Frosted Curls'	Widely available
♦ **glauca**	See C. flacca subsp. flacca
– Bosc. ex Boott	ESOG
– Scopoli	See C. flacca
grayi	CElw CHan CInt EGar EHoe EMar EMon EPla ESOG GCal MCCP MSCN MTho WChe WCot WPer WWye
§ **hachijoensis**	EMon EPPr EPla ESOG LRHS
'Hime-kan-suge'	See C. conica
hirta	CKin EPPr
hispida	WWye
hordeistichos	EBee
¶ **intumescens**	EBee
kaloides	CVer EHoe EPPr EWes
'Little Red'	SApp
lurida	GBin MCCP
macloviana	EBee EPPr ESOG
montana	EPPr
¶ **morrowii**	GCHN
– Boott	IBlr MWhi NSti WPyg
– 'Evergold'	See C. oshimensis 'Evergold'
– 'Fisher's Form' (v)	CBrd CCuc CFil CHan CInt CSte CTrC EFou EGol EHoe EPPr EPla ESOG GCHN LHil LHop MBri NHar NMir SApp WCot WPGP WPer WWye
– 'Gilt'	EMon EPPr LRHS
– hort.	See C. oshimensis
– 'Nana Variegata'	NBir NWoo WPGP
N – 'Variegata'	CCuc CFil CGle CHan CMHG CRow EAst EHoe ELan EMon EPPr EPla ESOG MAvo MBal MBar MCLN MRav NEgg NHed NHol NLon NNor NSti SApp SHFr SIng SPer WBea WWat
muricata	CKin
muskingumensis	CB&S CCuc CSte CVer EBee ECGN EGar EHoe EMar EMon EPPr EPla ESOG GBin LHil MBri NBro NFai NHol NSti SApp SDix SMad SPan SUsu WPbr WPer WWye
– 'Oehme'	EMon GBin SApp WCot
¶ – 'Silberstreif'	EMon
– 'Small Red'	EMil
– 'Wachtposten'	GCal MFir
nigra	CKin EHon GAbr
– subsp. **tornata**	SIng
– variegated	EMon GBin WCot
¶ **obnupta**	EBee
ornithopoda	EPot LGan
– 'Aurea'	See C. ornithopoda 'Variegata'
§ – 'Variegata'	CCuc CKel CSpe EBrP EBre ECtt EGol EHoe EPla ESOG GCHN GOrn LBre LHil MBal MBrN MBro MWhi NBro NGre NHar NHol SBre SCob SSmi WFar WRus WWat WWye
§ **oshimensis**	IBlr
– 'Evergold' (v) ♀	Widely available
– 'Variegata'	NBir SApp SCob
otrubae	CKin
ovalis	CKin
pallescens	GBin WWye
– 'Wood's Edge' (v)	CNat
panicea	EHoe EMar EPPr ESOG SApp
¶ **pauciflora**	EPPr
pendula	Widely available
– 'Moonraker'	CBot
petriei	CCuc CSam CVer CWSG EAst EBar ECha ECoo EHoe ELan EMon EPPr EPot GAbr GAri GOrn LHil LLWP MHlr MMoz NHed NPSI NVic SPla SSoC WCot WFar WPer
¶ **phyllocephala**	EHoe WCot
– 'Sparkler' (v)	EBee NHol SApp WCot
pilulifera 'Tinney's Princess' (v)	EHoe EPPr EPot GBur IBlr LRHS MBri MCCP NHol

plantaginea	CHEx CHan EGar EHoe EMar
	EMon EPPr EPla ESOG GBin
	WCot WFar WPGP WPbr
§ *pseudocyperus*	CInt CKin ECGN EGar EHoe
	EHon EPPr EPla ESOG EWFC
	GBin GCHN MLLN MSCN
	MSta SRms SWyc WPer WWye
pulicaris	CKin
¶ *reinii*	EBee
remota	CKin EPPr ESOG GBin WWye
riparia	EMFW EPPr ESOG LPBA
	MWhi WShi WWeb
◆ – 'Bowles' Golden'	See *C. elata* **'Aurea'**
– 'Variegata'	CBen CCuc CGle CMGP CRow
	ECha ECoo EHoe EHon
	EMFW EMon EPPr EPla
	ESOG GCHN GCal LHil LPBA
	MBrN MBri MUlv NBro NFai
	SCro WAbb WByw WHal WHil
* *saxatilis* 'Variegata'	EMon
secta	ECou EHoe EPPr GOrn NLak
– var. *tenuiculmis*	CCuc EHoe EMon EOld EPPr
	ESOG GBin LRHS MAvo
	MWhi NHol SApp
siderosticha	CCuc EPot GAri WPGP WPer
¶ – 'Kisokaido'	EMon
¶ – 'Shima-nishiki'	EMon
– 'Variegata'	CGle CHEx CHan CMHG
	CRow CSte EHoe EMon EPPr
	EPla GCHN GOrn LGan LHil
	LHop MBar MBri MSCN NBro
	NFai NHol NSti NVic SUsu
	WByw WHil WRus WStI WWat
	WWye
'Silver Sceptre'	CMHG CMil CSte EBee EMon
	EPla LRHS MCCP NFai NHol
	NLak NPSI NPla NPro NSti
	SApp WCot WWat
sp. from Uganda	GCal
sp. from Wellington, New	EWes
Zealand	
¶ *spissa*	SApp
¶ *stenocarpa*	EBee
stricta Goodenough	See *C. elata*
– 'Bowles' Golden'	See *C. elata* **'Aurea'**
stricta Lamarck	EPPr EPla
sylvatica	CKin ECGN MBrN WWye
testacea	Widely available
– 'Old Gold'	LRot SMer
¶ *texensis*	SApp
trifida	CInt ECou EHoe EPla ESOG
	GAbr GCHN GCal MWhi SPla
	WChe WCot WWye
uncifolia	ECou
vulpina	CKin EPPr

CARICA (Caricaceae)

¶ *papaya* (F)	WMul

CARISSA (Apocynaceae)

bispinosa	SLMG
grandiflora	See *C. macrocarpa*
§ *macrocarpa* (F)	CSpe ECon ERea

CARLINA (Asteraceae)

acanthifolia	EHyt GCal MAvo WGle
¶ – subsp. *cyanara*	NWCA
JJA 274.101	
acaulis	CM&M ECro ELan EPfP LFis
	MBel NBro NSti NWCA SRms
	SSpi WEas WOak WPer WPyg
– bronze	ECGN EMan GCal NChi

– *caulescens*	See *C. acaulis* subsp. *simplex*
§ – subsp. *simplex*	CDec EBee ECGN ECGP ECha
	GBuc GMaP MHar MHlr NPri
	NRoo WCot WPer
– – bronze	MAvo
vulgaris	CKin EWFC MAvo WPer
¶ – 'Silver Star'	SSvw

CARMICHAELIA (Papilionaceae)

¶ *aligera*	CPle ECou MAll SVen
angustata	ECou MAll
appressa	ECou
§ *arborea*	ECou MAll WBod
arenaria	CPle MAll
astonii	ECou
australis	See *C. arborea*
¶ *corrugata*	ECou
cunninghamii	ECou
curta	ECou
enysii	CTri ITim MHig
– AGS 27	MRPP
– var. *ambigua*	ECou
– 'Pringle'	ECou
exsul	ECou
fieldii	ECou MAll
flagelliformis	CPle ECou MAll SVen
glabrata	CPle ECou MAll MBlu
grandiflora	ECou MAll
kirkii	ECou
– × *astonii*	ECou
– hybrid	SIgm
monroi	ECou MAll MHig
nigrans	ECou MAll
odorata	ECou MAll SVen
orbiculata	ECou MAll
ovata	ECou MAll
'Parson's Tiny'	ECou MAll
petriei	ECou MAll
rivulata	ECou MAll
robusta	ECou MAll
solandri	ECou
uniflora	ECou
virgata	ECou
williamsii	ECou

CARMICHAELIA × CORALLOSPARTIUM

'County Park'	ECou
'Essex'	ECou
'Havering'	ECou
Car. *kirkii* × Cor.	ECou
crassicaule	

× CARMISPARTIUM (Papilionaceae)

astens	See × *C. hutchinsii*
§ *hutchinsii*	ECou
– 'County Park'	ECou MAll

CARPENTERIA (Hydrangeaceae)

californica ♀	CBot CPMA ELan ENot EPfP
	GQui IOrc LHop LNet MAll
	MBri MGos MWhi NPal SBra
	SHBN SPer SReu SSpi SSta
	WAbe WHCG WHar WPat
	WSHC WWat
¶ *californica* 'Bodnant'	LRHS
¶ – 'Elizabeth'	CPMA LRHS SPla WWeb
– 'Ladhams' Variety'	CB&S CPMA EBee WSPU

CARPINUS † (Corylaceae)
betulus ♀ — CB&S CBlo CDoC CKin CLnd CPer EBrP EBre ELan ENot GChr GRei IHos IOrc LBre LBuc LHyr LPan MBri NBee NWea SBre SPer STre WDin WHar WMou WNor WOrn WStI
betulus 'Columnaris' — CLnd CTho
* – 'Columnaris Nana' — CMCN
§ – 'Fastigiata' ♀ — CB&S CBlo CDoC CLnd CMCN CTho EBrP EBre ELan ENot EPfP GChr IOrc LBre LHyr LPan MBar MBlu MGos NBee NWea SBre WDin WMou WOrn WPyg
– 'Frans Fontaine' — CMCN CTho IOrc MBlu SSta
– 'Horizontalis' — CMCN
– 'Incisa' — GAri
– 'Pendula' — CTho EBee EBrP EBre GAri LBre SBre
– 'Purpurea' — ENot
– 'Pyramidalis' — See *C. betulus* 'Fastigiata'
caroliniana — CLnd CMCN GAri ISea WNor WWoo
* *comptoniifolia* — CMCN
cordata — WDin
coreana — CMCN CTho ISea WNor WWoo
fargesii — See *C. laxiflora* var. *macrostachya*
henryana — WDin
japonica — CEnd CMCN EPfP LBuc MBlu SMad WWoo
laxiflora — CMCN GAri ISea SMad SSpi WNor
§ – var. *macrostachya* — CBlo CDoC CEnd WNor
mollicoma — WWoo
omeiensis — WWoo
orientalis — CMCN GAri WNor
polyneura — EPfP WNor
¶ *tschonskii* — CMCN
¶ *tschonoskii* — CMCN
turczaninowii — CMCN ISea WDin WNor WShe WWoo
viminea — EPfP WNor

CARPOBROTUS (Aizoaceae)
§ *edulis* — CAgr CHEx CTrC EOas IBlr MCCP SAPC SArc SEND SLMG WHer
muirii — CTrC
sauerae — CTrC

CARPODETUS (Escalloniaceae) See Plant Deletions

CARTHAMUS (Asteraceae)
tinctorius — MChe MSal

CARUM (Apiaceae)
carvi — CArn CJew ELau GPoy LHol MChe MHew NVic SIde WHer WJek WOak WPer WSel WWye
copticum — MSal
petroselinum — See *Petroselinum crispum*

CARYA † (Juglandaceae)
cordiformis ♀ — CMCN
glabra — CAgr
N *illinoinensis* — CMCN

myristiciformis — CMCN
ovata ♀ — CAgr CMCN MBlu SSpi

CARYOPTERIS † (Verbenaceae)
x *clandonensis* — CB&S CBot CTrw ELan ENot GRei LHop MWat NBir NNor SHel WBod WDin WFar WHCG WHar WSHC WStI WWat WWin WWye
x *clandonensis* 'Arthur Simmonds' — CBlo ECha EHal EHic EPfP LFis LHop MAsh MBal MBri SPer WGor
¶ – 'Dark Night' — MBri
– 'Ferndown' — CArn CChe CDoC EBee EBrP EBre ELan EMil LBre LFis LHop MAsh MUlv SBre SPer SPla SReu SSpi WDin WFar WSHC WWeb
– 'First Choice' — CAbP EFou ELan LRHS MAsh MWat SMrm SPer WRus
– 'Heavenly Blue' ♀ — Widely available
– 'Kew Blue' — CB&S CBot CDoC CLTr CSpe EAst EBrP EBre ELan EMil ENot LBre MGos NFla SBre SEas SHBN SPer SPla SSta WGwG WHar WOMN WPyg WSHC WWat WWeb WWye
– 'Longwood Blue' — GCal LRHS MAsh WBcn WWeb
* – 'Newleaze' — LHop
* – 'Pershore' — LRHS MBri MTis WCFE WSPU
– 'Worcester Gold' — Widely available
* 'Dark Prince' — WBcn
divaricata — CFil CPle EBee EMon WPGP
¶ – variegated (v) — EMon
§ *incana* — CPle EBrP EBre ELan ERav LBre LFis LHop MSte MUlv MWhi SBre SPer SPla WCot WSHC
– pink form — LRHS
– weeping form — EHic GBuc GCal LFis SBid SMrm SPan WPat
mastacanthus — See *C. incana*
odorata — CPle

CARYOTA (Arecaceae)
¶ 'Hymalaya' — LPal
mitis — LPal
¶ *obtusa* — LPal
¶ *ochlandra* — LPal
¶ *ophiopellis* — LPal
¶ *urens* — LPal

CASSANDRA See CHAMAEDAPHNE

CASSIA (Caesalpiniaceae)
corymbosa Lam. — See *Senna corymbosa* Lam.
obtusifolia — See *Senna obtusifolia*

CASSINIA (Asteraceae)
¶ *aculeata* — MAll
¶ *aureonitens* — MAll
leptophylla — CDoC MAll SPer
– subsp. *fulvida* — CB&S ECou EHoe EMil GOrc GTou IOrc MBar MBlu MPla NNor SAga SPer STre WTro
– subsp. *vauvilliersii* — CDoC MAll NNor
– – var. *albida* — CB&S CHan EGoo MAll SPer WBod WGer WGwG
¶ – – CC 570 — NWCA

– – 'Silberschmelze' SOWG
N *retorta* CDoC ECou MAll NLon NNor
– yellow MAll
'Ward Silver' CBot ECou EWes GSki MAll
NNor SPan

CASSINIA × HELICHRYSUM (Asteraceae)
* C. sp. × H. sp. WKif WPen WSHC

CASSIOPE † (Ericaceae)
'Askival' ITim
¶ 'Askival Arctic Fox' GCrs
¶ 'Askival Freebird' GCrs
¶ 'Askival Snowbird' GCrs
¶ 'Askival Snow-wreath' GCrs
¶ 'Askival Stormbird' GCrs
'Badenoch' EPot GAri GDra LRHS MBal
NHar
'Bearsden' GAri GDra MBal MBar NHar
NRya WPat WPyg
'Edinburgh' ♀ CMHG EPfP EPot GAbr GChr
GDra MBal MBar MBro NHar
NHol NMen WAbe WPat WPyg
'George Taylor' WAbe
'Kathleen Dryden' GDra MBal
lycopodioides ♀ EPot GCrs GDra GTou MBal
MBar MGos NHar NHol WAbe
WFar
– 'Beatrice Lilley' ELan EPot EWes GAri GChr
GTou MAsh MBal MBar MHig
NHar NHed NHol WAbe WPat
WPyg
– 'Rokujô' EPot GCrs NHol
'Medusa' GDra GTou LRHS MBal MHig
NHar NHol WPat WPyg
mertensiana GTou MBal MBar NHed NMen
– 'California Pink' MHig
– dwarf form MBal
– var. *gracilis* CMHG ELan LRHS MDun
MGos MHig NHar NHol
– – dwarf form EPot
'Muirhead' ♀ EPot GDra GTou MBal MBar
MHig NHar NHed NHol NMen
NRya SRms WAbe WPat WPyg
'Randle Cooke' ♀ ELan EPot EWes GChr GCrs
GDra GTou MBal MBar MBro
MHig NHar NHed NHol SRms
WAbe WPat WPyg
selaginoides LS&E 13284 GAri
§ *stelleriana* SSta
tetragona EPfP GTou LRHS MBal MBar
SRms
– var. *saximontana* EPot MBal NHol
wardii WAbe
– × *fastigiata* Askival Strain WAbe

CASTANEA † (Fagaceae)
'Layeroka' (F) CAgr
mollissima CMCN GAri WWoo
× *neglecta* CTho
sativa ♀ CB&S CDoC CHEx CKin CLnd
CPer ENot GChr GRei IOrc
LBuc LHyr LPan MAsh MBar
MBri MWat NBee NRog NWea
SHBN SPer WDin WFar WHar
WMou WOrn WStI WWes
§ – 'Albomarginata' CBlo CDoC CTho EBee EBrP
EBre LBre MBlu MBri MGos
NBee SBre SMad SPer WMou
WWeb WWes
– 'Anny's Red' MBlu
– 'Anny's Summer Red' CDul SMad

– 'Argenteovariegata' See *C. sativa* **'Albomarginata'**
– 'Aspleniifolia' CB&S MBlu WPGP
– 'Aureomarginata' See *C. sativa* **'Variegata'**
– 'Bournette' (F) ESim
¶ – 'Glabra' MAsh
– 'Marron de Lyon' (F) CEnd CTho EMui ESim MBlu
MCoo WMou
§ – 'Variegata' CAbP CB&S CFil CMCN COtt
CTho ELan EPfP LPan MAsh
– 'Vincent van Gogh' SMad
'Simpson' CAgr

CASTANOPSIS (Fagaceae)
cuspidata CMCN

CASUARINA (Casuarinaceae)
cunninghamiana CTrC
equisetifolia CGre CTrC
¶ *glauca* CPle
littoralis See *Allocasuarina littoralis*
stricta See *Allocasuarina verticillata*

CATALPA † (Bignoniaceae)
bignonioides ♀ CB&S CBlo CBot CDoC CHEx
CLnd CMCN CTho ELan ENot
IOrc LHyr LPan MBri MBro
MCCP MWat MWhi NBee NPal
NWea SPer WBod WDin WNor
bignonioides 'Aurea' ♀ Widely available
– 'Purpurea' See *C.* × *erubescens* **'Purpurea'**
– 'Variegata' EPfP LNet LRHS MBro SSta
WPat WPyg
bungei LPan WNor
– 'Purpurea' ELan
× *erubescens* LPan
§ – 'Purpurea' ♀ CB&S CBlo CBot CDoC CEnd
CHEx CLnd CTho EBrP EBre
EMil IOrc LBre MAsh MBlu
MBro SBre SHBN SMad SPer
SSoC WPat WPyg
fargesii CFil CLnd
¶ – f. *duclouxii* WPGP
ovata CAgr CBlo CGre CHEx CMCN
speciosa CB&S CHEx CLnd CMCN
LRHS SPer WMou
– 'Pulverulenta' CEnd CMCN

CATANANCHE (Asteraceae)
caerulea Widely available
– 'Alba' CGle CPou EAst ECha EFou
EPar LIck NBir NNor NPri
SIgm SPer SSvw WBea WFar
WMow WOld WPer WWhi
– 'Bicolor' CBre CHan CM&M CSev
EMan EMar GBur GCal LFis
MCLN MHFP NFai NNor SAxl
SOkh WElm WHer WMaN
WWal
– 'Major' ♀ ENot GCal MBri MWat SRms
WEas
* – 'Stargazer' WRHF
caespitosa SBla

CATAPODIUM (Poaceae) See Plant Deletions

CATHA (Celastraceae)
edulis NGno

CATHARANTHUS (Apocynaceae)
roseus ♀ MBri
– Ocellatus Group MBri

CATOPSIS (Bromeliaceae)
¶ *berteroana*   WMEx

CAULOPHYLLUM (Berberidaceae)
thalictroides   CArn CRDP MSal WCot WThi

CAUTLEYA (Zingiberaceae)
lutea   See *C. gracilis*
spicata   CHEx IBlr WCru
– 'Robusta'   CRDP EMan GCal SMad SSoC

CAYRATIA (Vitaceae)
japonica   CPlN
– B&SWJ 570   WCru

CEANOTHUS † (Rhamnaceae)
'A.T. Johnson'   CBlo CPle EGra ENot LNet
          MAsh NFai SHBN SPer SRms
          SSoC WAbe WGwG WWal
americanus   CArn CPle MSal
– 'Fincham'   CKno
arboreus   SAPC SArc
– 'Owlswood Blue'   LRHS
– 'Trewithen Blue' ♀   CB&S CChe CGre CHad CLan
          CMHG CMac CPle CSam CTrw
          EBrP EBre ELan EMil IOrc
          ISea LBre LHop LNet MRav
          SAga SBre SPer WAbe WFar
          WFoF WSHC WStI WWat
          WWeb
'Autumnal Blue' ♀   Widely available
azureus   See *C. coeruleus*
'Basil Fox'   LRHS
'Blue Buttons'   LRHS MAsh
* 'Blue Carpet'   ISea
'Blue Cushion'   CB&S CBlo CLan ECtt EHic
          LHop MAsh MGos MRav
          MWat WFar WWat
'Blue Jeans'   CAbP CBlo CPle EBee LRHS
          MBri SBid SPan WAbe
* 'Blue Moon'   LRHS MAsh WWeb
'Blue Mound' ♀   CDoC CGre CLan CMHG
          CTrw EBrP EBre EMil ENot
          LBre MGos MRav NHol NLon
          NNor SBre SPer SPla SReu SSpi
          WSHC WWal WWat WWeb
* 'Blue Star'   LHop
* 'Borne Again'   WBcn
'Burkwoodii' ♀   CB&S CDoC CMac CSam EBrP
          EBre GRei IOrc LBre MAsh
          MBal MBri MGos NNor SBre
          SHBN SPer SReu WFar WWal
'Cascade' ♀   CB&S CLan CMHG CSam
          EAst ELan ENot IOrc LNet
          MBri MGos MWat NFla NNor
          SPer WAbe WBod WHCG
          WSHC WStI
♦ 'Comtesse de Paris'   See *C.* × *delileanus* '**Comtesse
          de Paris**'
'Concha'   Widely available
crassifolius var. *planus*   LRHS
* – 'Plenus'   SBid
cyaneus   CGre CPle
'Cynthia Postan'   CAbP CPle CSam CWSG EBrP
          EBre EPfP GOrc ISea LBre
          LRHS MAsh MBlu MWat SBre
          SPan WAbe
'Dark Star'   CBlo CChe CTbh CWSG EPfP
          EWll GOrc MAsh SAga SOWG
          SReu SSta

'Delight' ♀   CBlo EBee ELan EPla IOrc
          NFla NNor SBid SPer SSoC
          WAbe WBod WFar WWat
§ × *delileanus* 'Comtesse de   MRav
          Paris'
– 'Gloire de Versailles' ♀   CB&S CBot CChe CKno CMac
          CPle CSam ELan ENot IOrc
          ISea MAsh MBri MGos NBee
          NBrk SHBN SPer SReu SSta
          WAbe WDin WFar WGwG
          WPyg WSHC WWeb WWin
– 'Henri Desfossé'   CBlo CKno CPle ELan SBid
          SOWG SPer WDin WFar WKif
– 'Indigo'   CKno NFla
– 'Topaze' ♀   CB&S CBlo CKno CPle ELan
          EMil ENot EPfP ISea SAga
          SBid SOWG WHar WKif
dentatus hort.   See *C.* × *lobbianus*
dentatus Torrey & A Gray   CMac CPle ELan ENot GRei
          IOrc MAsh MBal MGos NNor
          SChu SPer WPyg
– var. *floribundus*   ELan LRHS
– 'Prostratus'   MBal
* – 'Superbus'   EBee
* 'Diamond Heights'   SPer WWeb
'Dignity'   CLan WWeb
divergens   CPle MAll SBid
'Edinburgh' ♀   CBlo CMHG MAsh MBri NCut
          SBid SPan WBod WWeb
'Eleanor Taylor'   CPle LRHS
'Fallen Skies'   LRHS WWeb
foliosus   CPle
– var. *austromontanus*   CB&S CLan CPle CTrw EHic
          SPan
'Frosty Blue'   LRHS
'Gentian Plume'   SMad
gloriosus   CPle CSam EWes IOrc MAll
          SAga SBid SDry WSHC WWat
– 'Anchor Bay'   COtt ELan EPfP LRHS SCob
          SOWG SPan WWeb
– 'Emily Brown'   CB&S
griseus var. *horizontalis*   CB&S WFar
'Hurricane Point'
– – 'Yankee Point'   CB&S CBlo CChe CMHG
          CMac ECtt EMil LHop LNet
          MAsh MBel MBri MRav NFai
          SHBN SPer WAbe WDin WFar
          WWeb
hearstiorum   CPle LRHS
impressus   CB&S CBlo CLan CMHG CPle
          ELan EMil ENot GOrc MAsh
          MBal MRav SEas SPer SPla
          SSoC WAbe WEas WFar WPyg
          WWeb
integerrimus macrothyrsus   CPle
N 'Italian Skies' ♀   CB&S CBlo CDoC CLan
          CMHG CMac CSam CTbh
          EHal ELan EMil LHop MAsh
          MBri MGos MRav SAga SEas
          SPer WBod WGwG WWeb
'Joyce Coulter'   CB&S EMil ISea
'Julia Phelps'   CMHG CWSG ISea WEas
'Ken Taylor'   CRos LRHS MAsh
§ × *lobbianus*   CB&S CTri ERic WLRN
– 'Russellianus'   CAbP CBlo SHBN
× *mendocinensis*   CPle
oliganthus   CPle
× *pallidus*   WBcn
– 'Golden Elan'   CPle

– 'Marie Simon' — CB&S CBlo CBot CKno CPle ELan EMil EPfP LHop MBri MRav NFla NLon NNor SEas SMad SPer SRms WFar WKif WPyg WSHC WWeb

¶ – 'Marie Simon Variegated' (v) — CPMA

– 'Perle Rose' — CB&S CBlo CChe CKno CMac CPle CSam IOrc MTis SHBN SOWG SPer SPla WKif WSHC

papillosus — CGre CMac CPle SBid WBod

– var. *roweanus* — CMac CPle GAri WEas WWat

'Pershore Zanzibar' (v) — EBee LRHS MGos SCoo WSPU

'Pin Cushion' — CWSG EPfP LRHS SPla WFoF WPat WWat

'Point Millerton' — CBlo MAsh MBlu SPla

prostratus — GSki LBuc MAsh SDry SHBN WAbe WEas WWin

'Puget Blue' ♀ — Widely available

purpureus — CPle EHic LBuc MAll WWeb

ramulosus — LRHS

'Ray Hartman' — SMad SSoC WBcn

repens — See *C. thyrsiflorus* var. *repens*

rigidus — CPle SBid SDry SPla SRms WAbe WSHC WWeb

– 'Snowball' — ELan EPfP GSki SSto WBcn

'Sierra Blue' — WFar

'Snow Flurries' — CB&S CBlo EHal EHic EHol EMil EPfP SPan WFar WWat WWeb

sorediatus — CPle

'Southmead' ♀ — CBlo CTri EBee EHic EMil GBuc IOrc ISea MAsh MBri MGos NCut NFla WAbe WBod WHCG WPat WWat

spinosus — CPle

thyrsiflorus — CB&S CBlo CMac CTri ELan LNet MAsh MBal MBri MTis NFai NHol SArc SHBN SRms WAbe WDin WFar WHar

– 'Millerton Point' — CPle CWSG ELan EMil MBro SBid WWeb

§ – var. *repens* ♀ — Widely available

– 'Skylark' — CBlo CDoC CPle CRos CSam CTbh EBee EHic ELan LHop MAsh MBri SBid SBra SDix SReu SSta SVil WFar WWat WWeb

* 'Tilden Park' — LRHS

* 'Underway' — WWat

× *veitchianus* — CB&S CBlo CMac CSam ENot GChr LNet MAsh MBar NHol NPer SBid SEas SPer SSta WWeb

verrucosus — CPle

'White Cascade' — MAll SPan

CEDRELA (Meliaceae)

sinensis — See *Toona sinensis*

CEDRONELLA (Lamiaceae)

§ *canariensis* — CArn CGle CInt CSev GPoy IBlr ILis LHol MChe MGra MSal NHex SIde SOWG SWat WCer WHer WOMN WOak WPer WWye

mexicana — See *Agastache mexicana*

triphylla — See *C. canariensis*

CEDRUS (Pinaceae)

atlantica — See *C. libani* subsp. *atlantica*

brevifolia — See *C. libani* subsp. *brevifolia*

deodara ♀ — CDoC CMac EHul ENot GRei IOrc LBee LCon LHyr MBal MBar MBri MGos NBee NWea SHBN SLim SPer SReu STre WAbe WDin WMou WPyg WWat WWeb

– 'Argentea' — MBar MGos NHol

– 'Aurea' ♀ — CDoC EHul EOrn ISea LBee LCon LLin LPan MAsh MBar MBri SLim SReu SSta WDin WFar WFro WOrn

– 'Blue Dwarf' — CKen LCon LLin MAsh NHol

* – 'Blue Mountain Broom' — CKen

– 'Blue Triumph' — LPan

– 'Cream Puff' — LCon LLin MBar MGos

– 'Feelin' Blue' — CDoC CKen COtt EBrP EBre EPla LBee LBre LCon LLin LPan MAsh MBar MBri MGos SBre SCoo SLim WDin WWeb

– 'Gold Cone' — MGos

– 'Gold Mound' — CKen GAri

– 'Golden Horizon' — CDoC CKen CMac EBrP EBre EHul EOrn IOrc LBee LBre LCon LLin LPan MAsh MBar MBri MGos NBee NHol SBre SHBN SLim SPer SSta WDin WPyg WWeb

– 'Karl Fuchs' — EBrP EBre ETen LBre LRHS MAsh MBri SBre WGor

– 'Kashmir' — MBri

– 'Klondyke' — LCon

– 'Lime Glow' — CKen

– 'Mountain Beauty' — CKen

– 'Nana' — CKen

– 'Nivea' — CKen

– 'Pendula' — CDoC EHul LPan MBar MGos MWat WGor WStI

– 'Pygmy' — CKen

– 'Roman Candle' — EOrn ISea SHBN

– 'Scott' — CKen

– 'Silver Mist' — CKen

* 'Home Park' — CKen

libani — CMCN CTri GChr LRHS MAsh NBee SFam WPGP WWeb

§ – subsp. *atlantica* — CDoC CGre EHul LCon MBar NWea SLim SPar WDin WMou WWal

– – 'Aurea' — CDoC CMac LCon LLin LPan MAsh MBar MGos SSta WDin WHar

– – 'Fastigiata' — CDoC CMac EHul LCon LPan MBar MBri SLim

– – Glauca Group ♀ — Widely available

– – 'Glauca Fastigiata' — CKen

– – 'Glauca Pendula' — CDoC CKen EHul EOrn IOrc LCon LNet LPan MBar MBri MGos NBee SLim SMad SSta WGer WOrn WWes

– – 'Pendula' — CMac GAri NBee

§ – subsp. *brevifolia* ♀ — CDoC GAri LCon MBar MBri

– – 'Epstein' — LCon MBar

– – 'Hillier Compact' — CKen

– – 'Kenwith' — CKen

– subsp. *libani* ♀ — CDoC CMac EHul ENot IOrc LCon MBar MBri MLan NWea SHBN SPer WDin WFro WMou WNor WWat

– – 'Comte de Dijon' — EHul LCon LLin SLim

– – Nana Group — CKen LCon MAsh

– – 'Sargentii' CDoC CKen CMac EBrP EBre
  EHul EOrn ISea LBre LCon
  LLin MAsh MBal MBar MBri
  MGos SBre SLim SSta
– – 'Taurus' MBar NHol

CELASTRUS (Celastraceae)
angulatus CPIN
orbiculatus CB&S CMCN CMac CPIN
  EBee ELan EMil GBin MPla
  MRav NHol NPal NSti SPer
  SReu SSta WBod WFar WGwG
  WSHC
– 'Diana' (f) ELan NBea SSta
– 'Hercules' (m) ELan NBea
– Hermaphrodite Group CSam EHic EPla GOrc GSki
  ♀ MCCP NHol SBra SDix SPan
  WGer WTro WWat WWeb
¶ – var. *papillosus* WCru
  B&SWJ 591
¶ – var. *punctatus* WCru
  B&SWJ 1931
♦ *punctatus* See *C. orbiculatus* var.
  punctatus
scandens CB&S CMac CPIN ELan MSal
  SMur

CELMISIA † (Asteraceae)
adamsii IBlr
allanii GCLN IBlr
alpina GAbr IBlr NHol
– large form IBlr
angustifolia EPot GCLN GCrs IBlr
– silver form IBlr
argentea EPot EWes GCLN GCrs GTou
  NHar NHed
asteliifolia IBlr
  Ballyrogan hybrids IBlr
bellidioides EPot GDra IBlr NHar NHol
  NMen NWCA WAbe
bonplandii IBlr
brevifolia GCLN IBlr
coriacea GCal GCra IBlr NHar NNor
– 'Harry Bryce' IBlr
dallii IBlr
densiflora GCrs GDra GMaP IBlr
discolor IBlr
dureitzii IBlr
'Edrom' GTou
glandulosa IBlr
gracilenta GCrs IBlr NSla
– CC 563 NWCA
– forms IBlr
graminifolia IBlr
hectorii EPot IBlr ITim
holosericea IBlr
hookeri GCal
incana IBlr
  Inshriach hybrids MBal
  Jury hybrids IBlr
longifolia GCLN GDra SSpi
– large form IBlr
– small form IBlr
mackaui IBlr
monroi IBlr
morganii IBlr
prorepens IBlr
§ ramulosa var. tuberculata GTou IBlr ITim WAbe
saxifraga IBlr
semicordata GBri NHar
– 'David Shackleton' IBlr
– subsp. *stricta* GCrs IBlr

* sericifolia IBlr
sericophylla IBlr
– large form IBlr
sessiliflora EPot GAri GTou IBlr ITim
  WLin
– 'Mount Potts' IBlr
spectabilis IBlr MDun NEgg NHar
– var. *angustifolia* IBlr
– subsp. *magnifica* GAri IBlr
traversii EPot GCLN IBlr NHar
verbascifolia GCLN IBlr
viscosa IBlr
§ walkeri GCrs GTou IBlr
webbiana See *C. walkeri*

CELOSIA (Amaranthaceae)
argentea var. cristata MBri
– – Plumosa Group MBri

CELSIA See VERBASCUM

CELSIOVERBASCUM See VERBASCUM

CELTIS (Ulmaceae)
africana CGre
aurantiaca CMCN
australis CB&S LPan MFiF SRCN SSpi
  SSta
¶ julianae WNor
occidentalis CPle ELan EPfP LRHS
– var. *pumila* WNor
sinensis CMCN CPle WNor
tournefortii CMCN

CENOLOPHIUM (Apiaceae)
denudatum SDix SIgm

CENTAUREA (Asteraceae)
¶ alba HH&K 228A CHan
argentea CBot
atropurpurea ECGN EMon NLar
bella CBot CGle CHad CHea CSam
  CSev CSpe EFou EHal ELan
  EMar EOld EOrc GCal GMac
  LFis LHop MBri MGrG MHig
  NBro NChi NNor NNrd NRoo
  NSti SHel SMrm
benoistii CHad CHan ECGN EJud EMar
  MRav WCot
'Blue Dreams' EMon MAvo MGrG WPbr
cana See *C. triumfettii* subsp. *cana*
candidissima hort. See *C. cineraria*
– Lamarck See *C. rutifolia*
cheiranthifolia EBee ECha GCal WFar WPbr
§ – var. *purpurascens* EMon MAvo
§ cineraria MBEx WCot WEas
cyanus CJew EWFC MHew MMal
  WFar WJek
cynaroides See *Leuzea centauroides*
dealbata CBot CHar CKel EBar ECtt
  EOld GAbr LGan MAvo MBro
  MFir NBro NFai NMir NOak
  NOrc NRoo SCro WByw WFar
  WHoo WOve WPer WWin
– 'Steenbergii' CGle CHor CPou CRDP EBrP
  EBre ECED ELan GBur GCal
  LBre MBel MBri MCLN MRav
  NChi NMGW NOak NPer NSti
  SBre SOkh SPer SSpe WAbb
  WByw WCot WFar

debeauxii subsp. *nemoralis*	CKin
fischeri	See *C. cheiranthifolia* var. *purpurascens*
glastifolia	EMon GCal MAvo WCot WPbr
gymnocarpa	See *C. cineraria*
hypoleuca 'John Coutts'	Widely available
¶ *jacea*	CGen
¶ *kerneriana* subsp. *kerneriana* HH&K 297	CHan
macrocephala	Widely available
¶ *marschalliana* HH&K 271	CHan
¶ – HH&K 276	CHan
montana	CBre EBee ELan EWFC GAbr LBlm LGan MBro MCLN MFir NBro NLar NNor NOak NOrc NRoo NVic SHel SSvw SWat WByw WFar WHal WHen WOak WOve WPer WStI WWin WWye
– *alba*	Widely available
§ – *carnea*	CBre CElw CMea ECha MAvo NChi NFla WBon WHal WPbr WRus WWin
¶ – 'Gold Bullion'	EGar EMon WBcn
– 'Grandiflora'	GCal LRHS MBri
* – 'Lady Flora Hastings'	CBot GMac MTed
– 'Ochroleuca'	CElw EMon SOkh SWat WPbr
– 'Parham'	CMGP CPou CSev EBee EMan GCal LBlm LFis MBel MBro MCLN NPla NRoo NSti SChu SHel SMrm SOkh SPer SPla SSpe SWat WLRN WPbr
– *rosea*	See *C. montana carnea*
* – *violacea*	IBlr
– 'Violetta'	CPou NBir
◆ *nervosa*	See *C. uniflora* subsp. *nervosa*
nigra	CArn CKin EPfP EWFC MHew MOne NLan NMir WCla WJek
– var. *alba*	CArn
– subsp. *rivularis*	ECha WPbr
orientalis	ECha LGre NBro SIgm WPbr WPer WRha
ornata	CStr
¶ *pannonica* subsp. *pannonica* HH&K 259	CHan
parilica NS 699	NWCA
phrygia	EBee GBuc MGed MNrw
pulcherrima	CBot CHea ECha EGle EMon MHar MLLN NChi NOak SIgm WCot WPbr WPer
'Pulchra Major'	See *Leuzea centauroides*
rhapontica	See *Leuzea rhapontica*
rigidifolia	LFis SMer
¶ *rupestris*	LGre
ruthenica	ECha SIgm WCot WPbr
salonitana	CElw EMon MAvo WCot
scabiosa	CArn CKin CPea ECoo EHal EWFC MChe MHew MWhi NLan SIde WCla WGwy WJek WPer
scabiosa alba	CNat EFou EMan MAvo NRoo WAlt
scabiosa 'Nell Hill'	CNat WAlt
simplicicaulis	CHan CInt CMea CNic CRDP GAbr LGan MAvo MBel MBro MFir MHlr MRav MTho NChi NRoo SRms WCot WEas WHoo WOMN WPer WWhi
¶ *solstitialis* subsp. *solstitialis* HH&K 179	CHan
§ *triumfettii* subsp. *cana* 'Rosea'	CNic CPea CRDP EFou NNrd WWin
– subsp. *stricta*	ECoo EMar EMon EPPr GBuc MAvo MCCP MSte NMGW NTow WOMN WPbr
– – from Macedonia	LFis
§ *uniflora* subsp. *nervosa*	CSam EMan MSto NBro SGre WBea WPer WRha

CENTAURIUM (Gentianaceae)

chloodes	See *C. confertum*
§ *confertum*	MNrw
erythraea	CArn EWFC GPoy MChe MHew MSal SIde WCla WWye
scilloides	CInt MBro MPla MTho NGre NMen NNor NWCA SRms WCla WGwy WHoo WOMN WWin

CENTELLA (Apiaceae)

§ *asiatica*	CArn EOHP ILis MSal

CENTRADENIA (Melastomataceae)

inaequilateralis 'Cascade'	CHal CInt CLTr ECtt EMan LHil LPVe MBri NFai WCot WLRN
rosea	See *C. inaequilateralis*

CENTRANTHUS (Valerianaceae)

§ *ruber*	Widely available
§ – 'Albus'	Widely available
– *atrococcineus*	ECha SPer WPer
– var. *coccineus*	CB&S CDoC CLTr EBee ELan ENot EPfP GAbr LIck MAus MWat NFai NPri SEND SMrm WHil
* – 'Roseus'	NCut

CEPHALANTHERA (Orchidaceae)

falcata	EFEx
longibracteata	EFEx

CEPHALANTHUS (Rubiaceae)

occidentalis	CB&S CBlo CPMA CPle EBar EHic ELan EMil LFis MBlu MBro MPla SPer SSta WPat

CEPHALARIA (Dipsacaceae)

§ *alpina*	CElw CGle ECha EMan GCHN MNrw NFla NGre NHed NNrd NPri NTow SIng SMer SOkh SRms SWat WFar WLin WPer
– 'Nana'	CMil NMen NWCA WPat WPyg
ambrosioides	MLLN
flava	EFou LFis
§ *gigantea*	Widely available
leucantha	EBot EGar GAbr GBuc MBel MLLN WBea WElm WWhi
litvinovii	EMon
radiata	EBee
tatarica	See *C. gigantea*
¶ *uralensis*	EMon

CEPHALIPTERUM (Asteraceae)

¶ *drummondii*	MFiF

CEPHALOTAXUS (Cephalotaxaceae)

fortunei	CAgr CGre
harringtonia	LLin MRav SMur

– var. *drupacea* | CMCN EPla LCon WWat
– 'Fastigiata' | CB&S CDoC CKen EHul EOrn ETen LCon LPan MBar MBri SLim SSmi WGer
– 'Gimborn's Pillow' | MBar
– 'Korean Gold' | CKen

CEPHALOTUS (Cephalotaceae)

follicularis | EAnd EEls GTro MHel WMEx

CERASTIUM (Caryophyllaceae)

alpinum | CMea ELan
– var. *lanatum* | CPBP EGoo EWes MHig NGre NNrd NTow NWCA WPer
candidissimum | EWes
theophrasti | WPat
tomentosum | CHal CTri EFer EGoo ELan GBur LGro NNor NPri NVic WBea WCer WFar WLRN WPer
– var. *columnae* | CBlo EBrP EBre ECha ECho EHoe EPfP EWes LBre MHar MHlr SBre SRCN SRms WCot WHoo
– 'Silberteppich' | EGoo LFis

CERATONIA (Caesalpiniaceae)

siliqua | MSal

CERATOPHYLLUM (Ceratophyllaceae)

demersum | CBen CRow EHon EMFW NDea SAWi SWat SWyc WChe

CERATOSTIGMA † (Plumbaginaceae)

abyssinicum | ELan ERav LBlm
griffithii | Widely available
¶ – 'Album' | CPle
– SF 149/150 | ISea
§ *plumbaginoides* ♀ | Widely available
ulicinum | LHop
willmottianum ♀ | CB&S CBot CLan CPle EBrP EBre ECha ELan ENot EOrc IOrc LBre LFis LHop MBal MBri MWat NHol SBre SDix SHBN SMad SOWG SPer SReu SSta WDin WEas WOld WWat
– 'Forest Blue' | CAbP ELan ENot MAsh SCoo SPer SPla SReu SSta WWeb

CERATOTHECA (Pedaliaceae)

triloba | SUsu SWat

CERCIDIPHYLLUM † (Cercidiphyllaceae)

japonicum ♀ | CB&S CBar CBlo CGre CLnd CMCN CPMA CTho ELan ENot GOrc IOrc LHop LPan MBal MBar MBri NBee NHol NPer SHBN SPer SSpi SSta WAbe WDin WFar WHCG WWat
¶ – 'Heronswood Globe' | CPMA
– f. *pendulum* | CBlo CEnd CFil CPMA ELan MAsh MBlu MBri WWes
– 'Red Fox' | CMCN LRHS MDun WGer
– 'Rotfuchs' | CEnd CPMA MBlu SMad SSpi WPGP
– 'Ruby' | CB&S CPMA
magnificum ♀ | CEnd CFil CMCN MBlu MGos
¶ – Og 95.144 | CFil WPGP

CERCIS (Caesalpiniaceae)

canadensis | CAgr CB&S CMCN EMil MCCP MGos NPal SPer WNor WPat WWes
canadensis 'Forest Pansy' ♀ | CB&S CEnd CMCN COtt CPMA ELan EMil LHop LNet LPan MBlu MBri MGos SCoo SMad SPer SSta WDin WHar WPat WWes
¶ – 'Rubye Atkinson' | MBlu
chinensis | CLnd MCCP NPSI SPer WShe WWoo
– 'Avondale' | CEnd CPMA LNet MBlu
occidentalis | SOWG
reniformis 'Texas White' | CPMA
siliquastrum ♀ | CB&S CBot CLnd CMCN CSam CTho CTrC ELan ENot ERom IOrc LHop LNet LPan MBar MBri MGos MWat NFla SHBN SOWG SPer SReu SSta WDin WFro WPat WWat
– f. *albida* | CB&S CBlo CBot CDoC CLnd CTho EPfP LPan SPer WWeb

CERCOCARPUS (Rosaceae)

breviflorus | See *C. montanus* var. *paucidentatus*

CERINTHE (Boraginaceae)

glabra | CPea WWye
major | WEas WSan
– 'Purpurascens' | CBos CChr CElw CHad CKel CLon CMea CPea CRDP CSpe ECre EGoo EJud EMan EWoo LIck MCLN MFir MHar SMad SMrm SSoC SUsu WBea WCot WElm WOve WPen WSan WWhi

CEROPEGIA (Asclepiadaceae)

africana | CPIN
ampliata | CPIN
barklyi | CHal
lanceolata | See *C. longifolia*
linearis subsp. *woodii* ♀ | CHal IBlr MBri SLMG SRms
* – – 'Variegata' | CInt
§ *longifolia* | SLMG
pubescens B&SWJ 2531 | WCru
radicans | CPIN SLMG
stapeliiformis ♀ | SLMG

CEROXYLON (Arecaceae)

alpinum | LPJP LPal NPal
¶ *ventricosum* | LPal

CESTRUM (Solanaceae)

aurantiacum | CB&S CPIN CPle ERea IBlr IDee LHil SLMG WMul
¶ – | SOWG
¶ × *cultum* | CPle
§ *elegans* ♀ | CHal CPle IBlr LCns LHil MBEx SLMG SOWG WHar WMul
¶ – 'Penlee' | LHil
fasciculatum | CB&S CPle GQui IBlr LHil SLMG SOWG
'Newellii' ♀ | CAbb CB&S CHEx CHan CMHG CPle CSev CTbh ELan ERea ERom GQui IBlr ISea LCns MBal NPSI SCog SLMG SOWG WMul WOMN WSHC

nocturnum	CB&S CPlN CPle ECon ELan ERea LBlm LHil LLew MSal SLMG SOWG WMul
parqui ♀	CAbb CDec CGre CMHG CPle ECha ECon ELan ERea IBlr LHil LHop SDix SOWG SUsu WKif WOld WPen WSHC
¶ – hybrid	LHil
psittacinum	CGre CPle SLMG
purpureum	See *C. elegans*
¶ *roseum*	ECon
– 'Ilnacullin'	CB&S CGre CPle EHol ERea IBlr
* *splendens*	SOWG
§ *violaceum*	CB&S ERea LBlm LHil LLew
– 'Woodcote White'	LHil

CHAENACTIS (Asteraceae)
¶ *ramosa*	MRPP

CHAENOMELES (Rosaceae)
× *californica*	CAgr CPle
cathayensis	CAgr CPle CPou CTho EPla SSpi
§ *japonica*	CAgr ENot GOrc GRei MBal MBar NNor SEND WDin
– var. *alpina*	MPla
– 'Sargentii'	CB&S CBlo CFai CMac COtt EHic NBee
lagenaria	See *C. speciosa*
maulei	See *C. japonica*
sinensis	See *Pseudocydonia sinensis*
§ *speciosa*	CSam CTrC ISea MBal MBar NFla NNor NWea WNor
– 'Apple Blossom'	See *C. speciosa* 'Moerloosei'
– 'Aurora'	LRHS MBri
– 'Cardinalis'	CGre
– 'Choshan'	See *C.* × *superba* 'Yaegaki'
– 'Contorta'	CB&S EPfP
– 'Falconnet Charlet' (d)	WWal
– 'Geisha Girl'	CB&S CBlo CChe CDoC CEnd CMac EAst EBrP EBre ECtt ESis GAbr LBre LHop MAsh MBri MCCP MGos MRav NPSl SAga SBre SHBN SPer SPla WPyg WWat WWeb
¶ – 'Grayshott Salmon'	CLyn MCCP NPla SPan
– 'Knap Hill Radiance'	CBlo
§ – 'Moerloosei' ♀	CPMA CSam EAst ELan ENot MAsh MBri MPla MRav NPSl NSti SHBN SPer SPla SSta WDin WGwG WWal WWat WWeb
– 'Nivalis'	Widely available
– 'Port Eliot'	MBal WBcn WWeb
– 'Rosemoor Seedling'	GAri
– 'Rubra Grandiflora'	CBlo
– 'Simonii' (d)	CB&S CBlo EHic EHol ENot ISea MBal MBri MGos NBee NFla NWea SEND SPer WWat
– 'Snow'	CSam ISea MBal MPla MRav MWat SEas WLRN WStI
– 'Umbilicata'	ENot NHol SPer SRms WWes
¶ – 'Yukigoten'	WWeb
× *superba*	NNor
– 'Boule de Feu'	CTri ECtt SCob
– 'Cameo' (d)	CBot CChe CDec EAst EPfP MBri SEas SLPl WLRN WWat
– 'Clementine'	CBlo
– 'Coral Sea'	NNor
– 'Crimson and Gold' ♀	Widely available
– 'Elly Mossel'	CB&S CBlo CMac NHol WLRN
¶ – 'Ernst Finken'	WSPU
– 'Etna'	CBlo EHic NCut
– 'Fire Dance'	CBlo CMac ECtt ENot MAsh NHol SCob SEas SPer WLRN
– 'Hever Castle'	CBlo MPla
– 'Hollandia'	CBlo MGos NEgg WRHF
– 'Issai White'	LRHS MBri
– 'Jet Trail'	CB&S CBlo EAst EBee EHic ELan ENot MBri MCCP MGos MRav SCob SLPl
– 'Knap Hill Scarlet' ♀	CBlo EBrP EBre ECot ENot EPfP IOrc LBre LHop MAsh MHlr SBre SEND SPer SRms STre WBod WDin WStI WTro WWat
– 'Lemon and Lime'	CLyn CPMA EBee ELan ENot MRav NSti SPer WBcn WWat
– 'Nicoline' ♀	CB&S CBlo CDoC EHic ENot EPfP GRei MBri MWat SBra SCob WDin WFar WStI
– 'Ohio Red'	SCob WBod WTro
– 'Pink Lady' ♀	Widely available
¶ – 'Red Trail'	ENot
– 'Rowallane' ♀	CBlo EBee ENot EPfP GAri MBal MRav MWat NFla SEas SHBN SPer WLRN
– 'Texas Scarlet'	MBri
– 'Tortuosa'	CBlo EHic GOrc SMad SPan WWat

CHAENORHINUM (Scrophulariaceae)
glareosum	WCla
§ *origanifolium*	CNic CPBP CSpe ESis LBee LIck NWCA WCru WWin
– 'Blue Dream'	CMdw CSpe EMan GBri LRHS MDHE MGed NPri SCro WFar WLRN WPer WWal

CHAEROPHYLLUM (Apiaceae)
hirsutum	CRow ELan NBrk
– 'Roseum'	CBre CGle CHan CHar CLTr ECGP ECha ECoo EFou EMar GCal MCLN MFir MRav MUlv NChi NSti SBla SMrm SPer SSpi WAbb WByw WEas WFar WHal WPer WPrP WSHC

CHAETACANTHUS (Acanthaceae) See Plant Deletions

CHAMAEBATIARIA (Rosaceae) See Plant Deletions

CHAMAECRISTA (Caesalpiniaceae) See Plant Deletions

CHAMAECYPARIS † (Cupressaceae)
formosensis	CKen
funebris	See *Cupressus funebris*
lawsoniana	EHul GAri GChr GRei ISea MBar NWea WDin WMou
– 'Albospica' (v)	CMac EHul MBal MBar MWat SBod WFar
– 'Albospica Nana'	See *C. lawsoniana* 'Nana Albospica'
– 'Albovariegata'	ECho EHul EOrn LBee MBar SRms
– 'Albrechii'	ENot
– 'Allumii Aurea'	See *C. lawsoniana* 'Alumigold'

– 'Allumii Magnificent'	CB&S MAsh WWeb	
§ – 'Alumigold'	CB&S CDoC CKen CTri LCon MAsh MBal MBar MGos MWat SBod SLim SPer WGwG WStI WWal WWeb	
– 'Alumii'	CDoC CMac CTri EHul ENot GChr GRei MBal MBar MGos NWea SLim SMer SPer WStI	
– 'Argentea'	See *C. lawsoniana* 'Argenteovariegata'	
§ – 'Argenteovariegata'	CMac LCon SLim	
I – 'Aurea Compacta'	ECho	
– 'Aurea Densa' ♀	CBlo CKen CMac CTri EHul EOrn GAri LCon MAsh MBar MGos SBod SSmi STre	
– 'Aureovariegata'	MBal MBar	
§ – 'Barabits' Globe'	MBar MWat	
§ – 'Bleu Nantais'	CKen CMac CTri EHul EOrn LBee LCon LLin LNet MAsh MBal MBar MGos MPla MWat NBee SBod SHBN SLim SSmi WCFE WWal	
– 'Blom'	CKen EHul LRHS MAsh MBri	
– 'Blue Gem'	LBee NHol	
§ – 'Blue Gown'	CBlo CTri EHul GRei LBee MBar MGos SRms	
§ – 'Blue Jacket'	MBar	
– 'Blue Nantais'	See *C. lawsoniana* 'Bleu Nantais'	
– 'Blue Surprise'	CKen EHoe EHul EOrn EPla LCon LLin MAsh MBal MBar MOne MPla NPro WFar WWal	
– 'Bregeon'	CKen	
– 'Broomhill Gold'	CDoC CMac EBrP EBre EHul ENot LBre LCon LNet MAsh MBal MBar MBri MGos MPla MWat NHol SBod SBre SLim SPer WDin WWal WWeb	
– 'Buckland Gem'	WLRN	
* – 'Burkwood's Blue'	MBar	
– 'Caudata'	CKen MBar WBcn	
– 'Chantry Gold'	CBlo CKen EHul SLim	
§ – 'Chilworth Silver' ♀	CChe CDoC CMHG EBrP EBre EHul EOrn EPot LBee LBre MBar MBri MGos MPla MWat SBod SBre SHBN SLim SPer SRms WDin WFar WGwG WStI WWal	
– 'Chingii'	EHul	
– 'Columnaris'	CB&S CDoC CMac EBrP EBre ENot EPfP GRei IHos IOrc ISea LBee LBre MBal MBar MBri MGos MOke NBee NWea SBre SHBN SLim WFar	
– 'Columnaris Aurea'	See *C. lawsoniana* 'Golden Spire'	
N – 'Columnaris Glauca'	CTri EBrP EBre EHul EOrn GChr LBre LCon LPan MAsh MGos MPla MWat SBod SBre SPer WDin WFar WStI WWeb	
I – 'Cream Crackers'	EHul	
– 'Croftway'	EHul SRms	
– 'Delorme'	CBlo	
– 'Dik's Weeping'	SMad	
– 'Drummondii'	EHul	
– 'Duncanii'	EHul LCon MBal	
– 'Dutch Gold'	CBlo EHul GAri MAsh	
– 'Dwarf Blue'	See *C. lawsoniana* 'Pick's Dwarf Blue'	
– 'Eclipse'	CKen	
N – 'Elegantissima'	CKen CMac	
– 'Ellwoodii' ♀	CB&S CChe CMac EBrP EBre EHul ENot EPfP EPot GChr GDra GRei LBre LCon LLin MBal MBar MGos MPla MWat NEgg NRoo NWea SBod SBre SLim SPer WCFE WDin WFar MBri	
– 'Ellwood's Empire'	Widely available	
– 'Ellwood's Gold' ♀	CDoC EOrn LBee LLin MBri MGos NHol SLim SSmi SVil WGwG WLRN WPat	
– 'Ellwood's Gold Pillar'	CDoC EOrn LBee LLin MBri MGos NHol SLim SSmi SVil WGwG WLRN WPat	
§ – 'Ellwood's Nymph'	CBlo CKen CNic EOrn EPot MBar MBri SHBN SLim WGor WWeb	
– Ellwood's Pillar	CChe CDoC CKen CMac EAst EBrP EBre EHul EOrn EPot LBee LBre LCon LLin MAsh MBar MBri MGos MPla MWat NBee NHol SBod SBre SLim SSmi WDin WFar WWal	
– 'Ellwood's Pygmy'	CMac ECho EPot MBar NHol	
– 'Ellwood's Silver'	MAsh WFar WGor	
* – 'Ellwood's Treasure'	WCFE	
– 'Ellwood's Variegata'	See *C. lawsoniana* 'Ellwood's White'	
§ – 'Ellwood's White' (v)	CBlo CKen CMac EHul EOrn MBal MBar MBri SHBN WFar	
I – 'Emerald'	CKen MBar MBri NHol	
– 'Emerald Spire'	CBlo CDoC CMac CTri MAsh	
– 'Empire'	CBlo	
– 'Erecta Aurea'	ECho EHul LBee SBod	
– 'Erecta Filiformis'	MBar MBri	
§ – 'Erecta Viridis'	CB&S CDoC CMac CTrG CTri GRei LCon MBal MBar MPla MWat NEgg NWea SBod WDin WFar	
– 'Ericoides'	EHul	
– 'Erika'	MBar	
– 'Fantail'	CBlo	
– 'Filiformis Compacta'	EHul	
– 'Fleckellwood'	EHul LBee LLin MAsh MBar MGos MPla SBod SLim SMer WLRN WStI WWal	
– 'Fletcheri' ♀	CB&S CMac EHul ENot LBee LCon MAsh MBar MGos MPla NBee NWea SBod SHBN SLim SPer WDin WFar WStI	
– 'Fletcheri Aurea'	See *C. lawsoniana* 'Yellow Transparent'	
– 'Fletcheri Nana'	CBlo	
– 'Fletcher's White'	ECho EHul MBar	
– 'Forsteckensis'	CKen CMac CNic EHul EOrn ESis ISea LLin MBar MGos MOne NWea SLim SRms SSmi WFar WGwG WWal	
I – 'Forsteckensis Aurea'	CBlo	
I – 'Fraseri'	CMac LCon MBar NWea WDin	
– 'Gail's Gold'	CKen	
– 'Gilt Edge'	CKen	
– 'Gimbornii' ♀	CDoC CMac EBrP EBre EHul EOrn GChr LBee LBre LCon LLin MAsh MBar MBri MPla NBee SBod SBre SLim SRms WAbe WCFE	
– 'Glauca Spek'	See *C. lawsoniana* 'Spek'	
– 'Globus'	See *C. lawsoniana* 'Barabits' Globe'	
– 'Gnome'	CChe CDoC CMac CNic EHul EOrn EPot ESis GAri LCon MBal MBar MGos MPla NHol SBod SLim SPer	
– 'Gold Flake'	CBlo MBar MBri MGos	

– 'Gold Splash'	CBlo CKen MBar
– 'Golden Guinea'	WGor
– 'Golden King'	MBar SRms
§ – 'Golden Pot'	CDoC CKen CMac EHul EOrn LBee LCon MBar MGos MOke MPla MWat NRoo SBod SMer WAbe WFar WGwG WWal WWeb
§ – 'Golden Queen'	CKen CMHG EHul
– 'Golden Showers'	CKen EHul
§ – 'Golden Spire'	LRHS MBar SBod
– 'Golden Triumph'	CBlo EHul
– 'Golden Wonder'	CDoC CMHG CMac EHul IOrc LBee LBuc LCon LNet MBal MBar MGos NWea SRms WFar WStI
– 'Goldfinger'	CDoC CKen NHol
– 'Grant's Gold'	EHul
– 'Grayswood Feather'	CDoC CKen CMac CTri EHul LBee LCon MAsh MBar MGos MPla SLim SMer WWeb
– 'Grayswood Gold'	CBlo CDoC CKen EHul EOrn LBee MBar MPla SSto
– 'Grayswood Pillar' ♥	CBlo CKen CMac EHul EOrn LBee LCon MBal MBar MGos
– 'Green Globe'	CBlo CKen EBrP EBre EHul EOrn EPot LBee LBre LCon LLin MAsh MBar MBri MPla NHol SBod SBre WAbe WDin
§ – 'Green Hedger' ♥	CMac EHul ENot GRei LBuc MBar SBod SRms
§ – 'Green Pillar'	CKen CTri EGra GAri IOrc LBee MBal MBar MGos MWat SHBN WStI
– 'Green Spire'	See *C. lawsoniana* **'Green Pillar'**
– 'Green Wall'	EHul
– 'Grey Cone'	CKen LBee
– 'Hillieri'	MBar
– 'Hogger's Blue Gown'	See *C. lawsoniana* **'Blue Gown'**
* – 'Hogger's Gold'	CBlo EHul WGor
– 'Howarth's Gold'	GAri MBri
I – 'Imbricata Pendula'	CKen EPla SMad
– 'Intertexta' ♥	CMHG EHul WCwm
– 'Ivonne'	MGos
– 'Jackman's Green Hedger'	See *C. lawsoniana* **'Green Hedger'**
– 'Jackman's Variety'	See *C. lawsoniana* **'Green Pillar'**
– 'Kelleriis Gold'	EHul LPan
– 'Killiney Gold'	CMac
– 'Kilmacurragh' ♥	CMac ENot GRei MBal MBar MGos NWea SPer WCwm
– 'Kilworth Column'	CBlo MGos
– 'Knowefieldensis'	CMHG CMac EHul LLin
§ – 'Lane' ♥	CDoC CMHG CMac EHul ENot EPfP LCon MAsh MBal MBar MGos NWea
– 'Lanei'	See *C. lawsoniana* **'Lane'**
– 'Lanei Aurea'	See *C. lawsoniana* **'Lane'**
– 'Lemon Flame'	NHol
¶ – 'Lemon Pillar'	CBlo
– 'Lemon Queen'	CBlo EGra EHul LBee LCon LRHS NBee SSte
– 'Limelight'	CKen EHul EPot
– 'Little Spire'	CDoC CMHG CTri EBrP EBre EOrn EPla LBee LBre LCon LLin MBar MBri MGos MPla NHol SBre SLim WGor WWal
– 'Lombartsii'	CTri EHul LCon
– 'Lutea' ♥	CMac EHul LCon MBal MGos SBod SPer
§ – 'Lutea Nana' ♥	CBlo CKen CMac EHul MBar MOne WGwG WLRN
§ – 'Lutea Smithii'	CBlo CMHG EHul MBar NWea
– 'Luteocompacta'	CKen LBee LRHS SHBN
– 'Lycopodioides'	EHul MBar SSmi
* – 'MacPenny's Gold'	CMac
– 'Milford Blue Jacket'	See *C. lawsoniana* **'Blue Jacket'**
§ – 'Minima'	MBar SRms WCFE
– 'Minima Aurea' ♥	Widely available
I – 'Minima Densa'	See *C. lawsoniana* **'Minima'**
– 'Minima Glauca' ♥	CMac EBrP EBre EHul ENot EPfP EPot GChr GRei LBre LCon LLin MBal MBar MBri MGos MOke MPla NEgg NHol NWea SBod SBre SHBN SLim SPer WDin WGwG WWeb
– 'Moonlight'	CBlo MBar MGos MPla
– 'Nana'	CMac MBar
§ – 'Nana Albospica' (v)	CKen EHul EOrn LBee LCon LLin MAsh MBal MBar MGos MPla NBee NPro SLim SPla WGwG WWal
– 'Nana Argentea'	CKen ECho EHul EPfP WGor
– 'Nana Lutea'	See *C. lawsoniana* **'Lutea Nana'**
§ – 'Nana Rogersii'	EOrn MBar SRms WFar
– 'New Silver'	CBlo
– 'Nidiformis'	CBlo EHul LBee MBal MBar NWea SLim SRms
– 'Nyewoods'	See *C. lawsoniana* **'Chilworth Silver'**
– 'Nymph'	See *C. lawsoniana* **'Ellwood's Nymph'**
– 'Pearl Nova'	CBlo
§ – 'Pelt's Blue' ♥	CBlo CDoC CKen EHul LBee LCon LPan MAsh MGos NBee SCoo SHBN SLim SMer WLRN
– 'Pembury Blue' ♥	CDoC CKen CMHG CMac EBrP EBre EHul ENot EOrn EPfP GChr LBee LBre LCon MAsh MBar MGos MPla MWat NBee NWea SBod SBre SHBN SLim SPer WDin WFar WWeb
– 'Pendula'	MBar
§ – 'Pick's Dwarf Blue'	CBlo EHul MBar MBri NHol
– Pot of Gold®	See *C. lawsoniana* **'Golden Pot'**
– 'Pottenii'	CDoC CMac EHul IOrc LBee LCon MAsh MBal MBar MGos MPla MWat NBee NWea SBod SHBN SPer WDin WFar WStI
– 'Pygmaea Argentea' (v) ♥	Widely available
– 'Pygmy'	CBlo CNic EHul ESis GAri MBar MOne MPla SLim WLRN
– 'Pyramidalis Lutea'	CKen
– 'Rijnhof'	EHul GAri WBcn
– 'Roger's Gold'	CBlo
– 'Rogersii'	See *C. lawsoniana* **'Nana Rogersii'**
I – 'Romana'	ENot MBri
– 'Royal Gold'	ECho EHul EOrn
– 'Silver Queen' (v)	CKen GChr GRei MBal MBar NWea
– 'Silver Threads' (v)	CMac EBrP EBre EHul ENot EOrn EPla LBee LBre LCon LLin MAsh MBar MBri MGos MPla MWat SBod SBre SLim WStI WWeb
– 'Silver Tip'	EHul SLim
I – 'Slocockiana'	EHul SHBN
♦ – 'Smithii' Dallimore & Jackson	See *C. lawsoniana* **'Lutea Smithii'**
– 'Snow Flurry' (v)	EHul LBee

– 'Snow White' (v)	CDoC EBrP EBre EHul EOrn EPla LBee LBre LCon LLin MAsh MBar MBri MGos MPla NHol SBre SLim SPla WGor WWeb
– 'Somerset'	CBlo CMac MBar
§ – 'Spek'	CB&S
– 'Springtime'	CBlo EOrn MAsh MBri SLim WGor WWeb
– 'Stardust' ♀	CChe CDoC CMac EHul ENot GRei IHos IOrc LCon MAsh MBal MBar MBri MGos MPla MWat NHol NRoo SBod SHBN SLim SPer WDin
– 'Stewartii'	CMac CTri GChr MBal MBar MGos MPla NBee NWea SBod SHBN SMer SPer WStI
– 'Stewartii Erecta'	CBlo ENot
– 'Stilton Cheese'	MBar
* – 'Summer Cream'	EHul
– 'Summer Snow'	CB&S CChe CDoC CMHG CMac EHoe EHul ENot IOrc LBee LLin MAsh MBal MBar MBri MGos MPla SBod SLim SPla SRms WFar WGwG WStI WWal WWeb
– 'Sunkist'	CKen MAsh WFar
– 'Tamariscifolia'	CDoC EHul EOrn LCon MBal MBar SBod WDin WFar WGwG WLRN WStI WWal
– 'Temple's White'	CKen
– 'Tharandtensis Caesia'	EOrn LCon MBar WFar
– 'Tilford'	EHul
– 'Treasure' (v)	CDoC CKen EBrP EBre EHoe EHul EOrn LBee LBre LCon LLin MAsh MBar MBri MGos NHol SBre SLim WGor
– 'Triomf van Boskoop'	EHul MBar
– 'Van Pelt's Blue'	See *C. lawsoniana* 'Pelt's Blue'
– 'Versicolor' (v)	MBar
– 'Westermannii'	CMac EHul LCon MBal SBod SLim SPer
– 'White Spot' (v)	CDoC CKen EBrP EBre EHul LBee LBre LCon MBal MBar MBri SBre SLim WStI WWal
– 'Winston Churchill'	CBlo LCon MBar MGos MPla SBod SPer
– 'Wisselii' ♀	CDoC CKen CMac CTrG CTri EHul ENot EOrn GChr ISea LBee LCon LLin MAsh MBar NWea SBod SPer SRms WCFE WDin
– 'Wisselii Nana'	CKen EHul
– 'Wissel's Saguaro'	LCon LRHS MAsh
– 'Witzeliana'	CBlo ECho EOrn MBar MBri MGos WGer
– 'Wyevale Silver'	MBar WGor
– 'Yellow Cascade'	ECho EHul MOne
– 'Yellow Queen'	See *C. lawsoniana* 'Golden Queen'
– 'Yellow Success'	See *C. lawsoniana* 'Golden Queen'
§ – 'Yellow Transparent'	CMac CTri LCon MBar MGos SBod SHBN SLim SPer WGor
– 'Yvonne'	CBlo EPla LRHS MAsh MBar MBri NHol SLim SPla WWeb
leylandii	See *X Cupressocyparis leylandii*
nootkatensis	MBar SMer
¶ – 'Aurea'	MAsh
– 'Aureovariegata'	EHul
– 'Compacta'	CBlo CTri MBar
– 'Glauca'	LCon MBar
– 'Gracilis'	EHul
– 'Jubilee'	SMad
– 'Lutea'	CMHG CMac CTri LCon MBal MBar NWea
– 'Nidifera'	MBar WCwm
– 'Pendula' ♀	CDoC EBrP EBre ENot EOrn IOrc LBre LCon LLin LNet LPan MAsh MBal MBar MBri MGos NBee NWea SBre SLim SMad SPer WCwm WDin WFar WGer
I – 'Pendula Speech House'	WCwm
– 'Variegata'	MBar SLim
obtusa 'Albospica'	ECho EHul
– 'Albovariegata'	CKen
– 'Aurea'	CDoC
I – 'Aureovariegata'	See *C. obtusa* 'Opaal'
– 'Aurora'	CKen EOrn LCon
* – 'Autumn Gold'	MBar
– 'Bambi'	CKen EOrn MGos
¶ – 'Barkenny'	CKen
– 'Bartley'	CKen EPot
– 'Bassett'	CKen
– 'Bess'	CKen
– 'Caespitosa'	CKen EPot
– 'Chabo-yadori'	CBlo CDoC CMHG EHul EOrn LCon LLin MBal MBar MGos NHol SBod SLim
– 'Chilworth'	CKen LCon MBar MBri
– 'Chima-anihiba'	See *C. obtusa* 'Pygmaea Densa'
¶ – 'Chirimen'	CKen
– 'Confucius'	CBlo EHul
– 'Contorta'	EOrn EPot LCon MBar MBri
– 'Coralliformis'	ECho EOrn LLin MBal MBar NHol SMur WGwG
§ – 'Crippsii' ♀	CB&S CKen CMac EHul EOrn EPot LCon MBal MBar MGos NHol SBod SLim SPla
– 'Crippsii Aurea'	See *C. obtusa* 'Crippsii'
– 'Dainty Doll'	CKen EOrn
– 'Densa'	See *C. obtusa* 'Nana Densa'
– 'Draht'	CBlo CDoC MBar
¶ – 'Elf'	CKen
I – 'Ellie B'	CKen EOrn
– 'Ericoides'	CKen ECho EOrn
– 'Erika'	CBlo ECho MPla WBcn
– 'Fernspray Gold'	CBlo CDoC CKen CMHG CMac CTri EHul ENot EOrn LCon LLin MAsh MBar MBri MPla NHol SBod SLim WWeb
– 'Flabelliformis'	CKen EOrn
– 'Gimborn Beauty'	LCon
– 'Golden Fairy'	CKen EBrP EBre EOrn LBre SBre
– 'Golden Filament'	CKen
– 'Golden Nymph'	CKen EOrn MAsh MBri
– 'Golden Sprite'	EBrP EBre EPot LBre LCon MAsh MBri SBre
– 'Goldilocks'	ECho EHul
– 'Gracilis Aurea'	CKen
– 'Graciosa'	See *C. obtusa* 'Loenik'
– 'Hage'	CKen EOrn EPot LCon MBri MPla
– 'Hypnoides Nana'	CKen EOrn
– 'Intermedia'	CKen EOrn EPot
¶ – 'Ivan's Column'	CKen
– 'Juniperoides'	CKen EOrn WAbe
– 'Juniperoides Compacta'	CKen EPot WAbe
– 'Kamarachiba'	CKen WBcn
– 'Kanaamihiba'	MAsh MBar
– 'Konijn'	EOrn WLRN

– 'Kosteri'	CDoC CKen CMac EBrP EBre EHul EOrn EPot ESis LBee LBre LCon LLin MBar MGos MPla NHed SBre SHBN SIng SLim
– 'Laxa'	LCon
¶ – 'Leprachaun'	LCon
– 'Little Markey'	CKen EOrn
§ – 'Loenik'	MBar NHol
– 'Lycopodioides'	EOrn EPot
– 'Marian'	CKen
§ – 'Mariesii' (v)	CKen EBrP EBre EOrn EPla LBre LCon MAsh MBri SBre SHBN
– 'Minima'	CKen EPot LCon
– 'Nana' ♀	CBlo CKen CMHG CMac EPot GAri LBee LCon MBar MBri MGos MPla NHol SIng SSmi
– 'Nana Albospica'	ECho
– 'Nana Aurea' ♀	CDoC CMac EBrP EBre EHul EPot LBre LLin MBar MBri MWat NHol NPro NWea SBre SHBN SIgm SIng SMer WStI WWeb
– 'Nana Compacta'	LCon MBri
§ – 'Nana Densa'	CKen CMac
– 'Nana Gracilis' ♀	CDoC CKen EBrP EBre EHul ENot EPfP GRei ITim LBee LBre LCon LLin LNet MBal MBar MBri MGos MWat NHed NHol NWea SBod SBre SHBN SLim SPer WDin
I – 'Nana Gracilis Aurea'	EHul SMur WFar
I – 'Nana Lutea'	CBlo CKen EBrP EBre EHul EOrn EPfP EPla ESis LBee LBre LCon LLin MAsh MBar MBri MPla NHol NRoo SBod SBre SLim SPla SSmi WGer
– 'Nana Pyramidalis'	CBlo EHul
– 'Nana Rigida'	See *C. obtusa* 'Rigid Dwarf'
– 'Nana Variegata'	See *C. obtusa* 'Mariesii'
§ – 'Opaal'	LCon MBar WBcn
– 'Pygmaea'	CDoC EBrP EBre EHul ENot EOrn EPot ESis LBre LCon LLin MAsh MBal MBar MPla SBod SBre SLim SPla WWal
– 'Pygmaea Aurescens'	MBar SIng
§ – 'Pygmaea Densa'	CKen
– 'Repens'	EOrn
§ – 'Rigid Dwarf'	CKen EHul EOrn EPot LBee LCon LRHS MBar MBri WLRN
* – 'Saint Andrew'	CKen
– 'Snowflake' (v)	CKen
– 'Snowkist' (v)	CKen
– 'Spiralis'	CKen MBar
– 'Stoneham'	CKen LCon MBar
– 'Tempelhof'	CDoC CKen EHul EOrn EPot LCon LLin MAsh MBar MBri MGos MPla NHed SBod SLim SMer WWeb
– 'Tetragona Aurea' ♀	CB&S EGra EHul EOrn LCon MBar MGos SBod SLim WGer
– 'Tonia' (v)	CBlo CKen EHul EOrn ESis MBri SLim WLRN
– 'Wissel'	CKen EOrn
– 'Yellowtip' (v)	CKen EHul LCon MBar MGos GAri
pisifera	
– 'Aurea Nana'	See *C. pisifera* 'Strathmore'
– 'Avenue'	CBlo EHul LCon MPla NHol
¶ – 'Baby Blue'	LCon
– 'Blue Tower'	CBlo

– 'Boulevard' ♀	Widely available
– 'Compacta'	ECho EOrn MLan NHed WFar
– 'Compacta Variegata'	ECho EHul EOrn MBar NHed
– 'Curly Tops'	CKen LCon MGos WBcn
– 'Devon Cream'	LLin MBar MPla NHol SBod WWeb
– 'Filifera'	CBlo CMac EBrP EBre LBre MBal MBar SBod SBre SIng SLim WBod WFar
– 'Filifera Aurea' ♀	CGre CKen CMHG CMac EBrP EBre EHul EOrn LBre LCon LLin LNet MBal MBar MBri NBee NWea SBod SBre SRms WDin WFar
– 'Filifera Aureomarginata'	CMac EBrP EBre GAri LBre MBal MBar SBre SLim
– 'Filifera Nana'	CDoC EBrP EBre EHul EOrn LBre LCon MBal MBar MBri MOne MWat NHed SBre SPer STre WDin WFar
I – 'Filifera Sungold'	See *C. pisifera* 'Sungold'
I – 'Filifera Variegata'	EHul LLin
* – 'Gold Cascade'	MGos
– 'Gold Cushion'	CKen
– 'Gold Dust'	See *C. pisifera* 'Plumosa Aurea'
– 'Gold Spangle'	CMHG EHul MBar MGos SBod WFar
* – 'Golden Dwarf'	SPla
– 'Golden Mop' ♀	CKen EHul LCon MAsh
– 'Hime-himuro'	CKen
– 'Hime-sawara'	CKen EOrn
– 'Nana'	CKen EBrP EBre EHul EPfP GAri IOrc LBre LLin MAsh MBal MBar MBri MWat NHed NHol SBod SBre SMer SSmi WFar
I – 'Nana Albovariegata'	CBlo CDoC CNic LBee MBar MBri NPro SBod SSmi
– 'Nana Aurea'	See *C. pisifera* 'Strathmore'
§ – 'Nana Aureovariegata'	CDoC CMac EHul EPot ESis IOrc LCon MAsh MBal MBar MBri MPla MWat NHed NHol SBod SLim SPer SSmi WFar WWal
I – 'Nana Compacta'	CMac SRms
– 'Nana Variegata'	ECho MBar SLim
I – 'Parslorii'	CKen
– 'Pici'	CKen
– 'Repens'	MBal SRms
– 'Plumosa'	
– 'Plumosa Albopicta'	MBal MBar SBod
§ – 'Plumosa Aurea'	CKen EHul MAsh MBal MBar NWea WDin WFar
– 'Plumosa Aurea Compacta'	CBlo CKen CMHG CMac GAri LCon MPla NHed
I – 'Plumosa Aurea Compacta Variegata'	CMac
– 'Plumosa Aurea Nana'	CBlo CDoC ENot MAsh MBal MBar MGos MPla NBee NHed WGwG WWal
I – 'Plumosa Aurea Nana Compacta'	CMac SBod
– 'Plumosa Aurescens'	CBlo CMac
§ – 'Plumosa Compressa'	CDoC CKen CNic EHul ESis LBee LCon MBar MBri MGos NHed SIng SLim WGor WGwG
* – 'Plumosa Densa'	See *C. pisifera* 'Plumosa Compressa'
– 'Plumosa Flavescens'	CDoC CMac EHul LLin MBar MPla MWat NHed
I – 'Plumosa Juniperoides'	CKen EBrP EBre EHul EOrn ITim LBre LCon MAsh MBar MOne MPla SBre

– 'Plumosa Purple Dome'	See *C. pisifera* **'Purple Dome'**
I – 'Plumosa Pygmaea'	ECho MGos MLan WGor
§ – 'Plumosa Rogersii'	CDoC EHul MBar MGos MPla SBod
§ – 'Purple Dome'	EHul MBar MGos SBod WLRN
– 'Rogersii'	See *C. pisifera* **'Plumosa Rogersii'**
– 'Silver and Gold' (v)	CBlo EHul MBar MOne
– 'Silver Lode' (v)	CKen EOrn
– 'Snow' (v)	CKen CMac EOrn GAri MBal MBar MPla SBod SIng SMer WDin
– 'Snowflake'	CKen EHul
§ – 'Squarrosa'	GAri MBal MBar NWea WDin WFar WGor
N – 'Squarrosa Argentea'	MBal
I – 'Squarrosa Blue Globe'	CKen
– 'Squarrosa Dumosa'	CKen EHul MBar
– 'Squarrosa Intermedia'	EHul LLin MBar MGos
I – 'Squarrosa Lombarts'	CMac EBrP EBre EHul EOrn LBee LBre LCon LLin MAsh MBar MPla MWat NHed NPro SBod SBre SSmi WGwG
– 'Squarrosa Lutea'	CKen MAsh MBar NPro
– 'Squarrosa Sulphurea'	CMHG CMac EBrP EBre EHul EOrn EPfP LBee LBre LCon LLin MAsh MBal MBar MPla MWat NBee SBod SBre SLim SPer WDin WFar WWal
– 'Squarrosa Veitchii'	See *C. pisifera* **'Squarrosa'**
§ – 'Strathmore'	CKen EHul LLin MBar NHol WWal
§ – 'Sungold'	CDoC CKen CMHG CTri EGra EHul ENot LBee LCon LLin MAsh MBar MBri MPla SBod SLim
– 'Tama-himuro'	CKen EPot LLin MGos SLim
– 'White Beauty'	CKen
* – 'White Brocade'	CMac
– 'White Pygmy'	EOrn EPot MAsh
thyoides 'Andelyensis' ♀	CBlo CDoC CMac EHul EOrn GAri LLin MAsh MBal MBar MPla NHol WAbe
– 'Andelyensis Nana' ♀	CKen WPyg
– 'Aurea'	EHul MBar WBcn
– 'Conica'	CKen MAsh
– 'Ericoides' ♀	CBlo CDoC CKen CMac CSam CTri EHul EOrn LBee LLin MAsh MBal MBar MWat NHed SBod SPer WDin WFar WGwG WPyg WWal
§ – 'Glauca'	EOrn
– 'Kewensis'	See *C. thyoides* **'Glauca'**
– 'Purple Heather'	LRHS SMur
– 'Red Star'	See *C. thyoides* **'Rubicon'**
§ – 'Rubicon'	CBlo CDoC CKen CMac EBrP EBre EHul EOrn EPla ESis LBee LBre LCon LLin MAsh MBar MGos MPla NHed SBod SBre SLim SPla WFar WGer
– 'Schumaker's Blue Dwarf'	EPla WBcn
– 'Top Point'	CKen LCon SLim
– 'Variegata'	ECho EHul MBar

CHAMAECYTISUS (Papilionaceae)

§ *albus*	ECtt ENot GQui NNor SDix SPer WDin WStI
¶ *danubialis* HH&K 327	CHan
§ *hirsutus*	CFil CHan SBid WLin WPGP
polytrichus ♀	EPot GDra MHar MHig WLin
proliferus	MAll

§ *purpureus*	CAbP EBrP EBre ELan IOrc LBre LHop MBal MBar MBri MGos MPla SBre SHBN SPer WAbe WDin WFar WOMN WPat WWin
– f. *albus*	EPfP MBar MPla SHBN SPer WAbe WOMN
§ – 'Atropurpureus' ♀	ENot MPla NFla NHol SPer
– 'Incarnatus'	See *C. purpureus* **'Atropurpureus'**
pygmaeus C&W 3818	WOMN
§ *supinus*	EBee LHop MAll SHFr SRms

CHAMAEDAPHNE (Ericaceae)

§ *calyculata*	CB&S CPle LRHS SPer WSHC
calyculata 'Nana'	EHic MBal MBar MGos MPla SPer

CHAMAEDOREA (Arecaceae)

elegans ♀	LPal MBri
✦ *erumpens*	See *C. seifrizii*
¶ *linearis*	LPal
metallica Cook ♀	LPal
– hort.	See *C. microspadix*
§ *microspadix*	LPal
¶ *radicalis*	LPJP LPal
§ *seifrizii* ♀	LPal

CHAMAELIRIUM (Melanthiaceae)

luteum	WThi

CHAMAEMELUM (Asteraceae)

§ *nobile*	CArn CSev ELau GBar GPoy LHol MBar MBri MGra MMal NNrd NRoo SIde WJek WOak WPer WSel WWye
– 'Flore Pleno' (d)	CGle CHan CMea CSev ECha ELan ELau GPoy LHol MBri MGra NBro NCat NRoo NSti SIde SSvw WAbe WBea WEas WFar WHal WJek WOak WOve WPer WWhi
– 'Treneague'	CArn CBre CSev ELan ELau GAbr GBur GPoy LHol LMor MBri MGra NHol NNor NRoo NSti SIde SIng WAbe WFar WHal WHer WJek WOak WPer WWye

CHAMAENERION See EPILOBIUM

CHAMAEPERICLYMENUM See CORNUS

CHAMAEROPS (Arecaceae)

excelsa hort.	See *Trachycarpus fortunei*
excelsa Thunberg	See *Rhapis excelsa*
humilis ♀	CAbb CB&S CBrP CFil CHEx CTbh CTrC EOas IOrc LHil LPJP LPal NPal NRog SAPC SArc SDry SEND SPar WGer WPGP WPic
– 'Cerifera'	LPal
¶ – silver back	NPal

CHAMAESCILLA (Anthericaceae)

¶ *corymbosa*	MFiF

CHAMAESPARTIUM See GENISTA

CHAMBEYRONIA (Arecaceae)
¶ *macrocarpa*   CBrP LPal

CHAMELAUCIUM (Myrtaceae)
uncinatum   ECon LRHS

CHARA (Charophyceae)
vulgaris   SAWi

CHASMANTHE (Iridaceae)
aethiopica   CPou LHop MBel NRog
bicolor   CMon CPou SMrm
floribunda   CFee CSut LBow NRog
– var. *duckittii*   NRog

CHASMANTHIUM (Poaceae)
§ *latifolium*   EBee ECGN ECha EHoe ELan
                              EMan EPPr EPla ESOG GBin
                              LRot MBrN MLLN NPSI NSti
                              SDix SMad WFar WRus WWat
                              WWoo

CHEILANTHES (Adiantaceae)
¶ *feei*   WRic
lanosa   SRms
§ *nivea*   WRic
tomentosa   LHil WRic

CHEIRANTHUS See ERYSIMUM

CHELIDONIUM (Papaveraceae)
♦ *japonicum*   See *Hylomecon japonica*
majus   CChr CKin CRow ELau EWFC
                              GPoy MChe MHew MSal NHex
                              SIde WCHb WHer WRHF
                              WShi WWye
¶ – 'Bowles' Variety'   EBee
– 'Flore Pleno' (d)   CBre CGle CRow ECoo ELan
                              GBar GCHN GCal NBrk NBro
                              NSti WCHb WHer WOve
– var. *laciniatum*   CInt EMon GBar WCHb WRha
– 'Laciniatum Flore Pleno'   CRow EBee EJud EMar GCal
  (d)   IBlr NBro WCot WPer

CHELONE (Scrophulariaceae)
barbata   See *Penstemon barbatus*
§ *glabra*   CArn CHan CHea EBar ECha
                              ECro EFou EGol ELan GCal
                              GPoy HHop MAus MBel
                              MCLN MHew MSal NBro NHol
                              SChu SCro SPer WFar WMer
                              WMow WOld WPer WWat
                              WWye
lyonii   ETen NCut NLar SHFr WShi
obliqua   Widely available
– var. *alba*   See *C. glabra*
¶ – *rosea*   LRHS

CHELONOPSIS (Lamiaceae)
moschata   EBee ECha

CHENOPODIUM (Chenopodiaceae)
ambrosioides   CSev
bonus-henricus   CArn CSev EJud ELau GAbr
                              GBar GPoy ILis LHol MChe
                              MGra SIde WCHb WHer
                              WOak WPer WSel WWye
botrys   MSal

CHEVREULIA   (Asteraceae) See Plant
Deletions

CHIASTOPHYLLUM (Crassulaceae)
§ *oppositifolium* ♀   CGle CInt ECha ELan ESis
                              GCHN MBal MBar MBro MFir
                              MHig MWat NGre NRoo
                              NWCA SHel SMer SRms SSmi
                              WAbe WEas WFar WHoo
                              WWin WWye
– 'Frosted Jade'   See *C. oppositifolium* 'Jim's
                              Pride'
§ – 'Jim's Pride' (v)   CRow EAst ECha EMon EWes
                              LBee LBlm LHop MAvo MHig
                              MHlr MRav NGre NMGW
                              NPer NVic SHFr SLod SMad
                              SRms WAbe WCot WRHF
                              WRus WWin WWye
simplicifolium   See *C. oppositifolium*

CHILIOTRICHUM (Asteraceae)
diffusum   CPle ECou EHic GChr GDra
                              GOrc GSki IDee MAll MBlu
                              SMad SPer

CHILOPSIS (Bignoniaceae)
linearis   MSto

CHIMAPHILA   (Pyrolaceae) See Plant Deletions

CHIMONANTHUS (Calycanthaceae)
fragrans   See *C. praecox*
nitens   CMCN CPle
§ *praecox*   Widely available
– 'Grandiflorus' ♀   CEnd ENot
– var. *luteus* ♀   CB&S CBlo CEnd CPMA ENot
                              EPfP LRHS WWeb
¶ – 'Mangetsu'   SSta
– 'Trenython'   CEnd CPMA SSta
yunnanensis   CGre EPfP
¶ *zhejiangensis*   EPfP

CHIMONOBAMBUSA (Poaceae -
Bambusoideae)
falcata   See *Drepanostachyum falcatum*
hookeriana hort.   See *Himalayacalamus falconeri*
                              'Damarapa'
macrophylla f. *intermedia* EPla SDry
§ *marmorea*   CFil EPla ISta LJus SDry WJun
                              WPGP
– 'Variegata'   EFul EPla ISta LJus SCha SDry
                              WJun
§ *quadrangularis*   EFul EPla GAri ISta LJus SDry
                              WJun WPGP
– 'Svow' (v)   ISta SDry
§ *tumidissinoda*   EPla ISta NDov SDry

CHIOGENES See GAULTHERIA

CHIONANTHUS (Oleaceae)
retusus   CMCN EPfP MBlu WWat
virginicus   CB&S CBlo CEnd CFil CHEx
                              CMCN CPMA ELan EPfP IOrc
                              MBlu MPla NFla SMad SSta
                              WDin WHCG WWat

CHIONOCHLOA (Poaceae)
conspicua   CElw CFil CHan GAbr GAri
                              MBal MFir NBir WLRN WPGP
– 'Rubra'   See *C. rubra*

flavescens — EBee GBin GSki
¶ *flavicans* — MBel
§ *rubra* — CElw EBrP EBre EHoe EMon
EPPr EPla LBre SApp SBre
SHBN WCot WPGP

CHIONODOXA † (Hyacinthaceae)
cretica — See *C. nana*
§ *forbesii* — CBro CMon EPot WPer WShi
– 'Alba' — EPar LAma NRog
– 'Blue Giant' — EPot LRHS
– 'Pink Giant' — CAvo CBro ELan EPot ETub
LAma NEgg
– 'Rosea' — EPar LAma NRog
§ – Siehei Group ♀ — CBro
gigantea — See *C. luciliae* **Gigantea Group**
luciliae Boissier ♀ — CAvo CBro EPar EPot ETub
LAma MBal MBri NMen NRog
§ – Gigantea Group — ELan EPot ETub LAma NEgg
NRog
– – 'Alba' — EPot
– hort. — See *C. forbesii*
* *mariesii* — LAma
§ *nana* — CAvo CMon EHyt
sardensis ♀ — CAvo CBro EBar EPar EPot
ETub LAma MBal NEgg NRog
WPer
siehei — See *C. forbesii* **Siehei Group**
tmolusi — See *C. forbesii* 'Tmoli'

CHIONOGRAPHIS (Liliaceae)
japonica — EFEx

CHIONOHEBE (Scrophulariaceae)
armstrongii — ITim
densifolia — ECou EHyt NHed WPat
pulvinaris — CPBP EHyt EPot GCLN GCrs
ITim NHar NSla WAbe

× **CHIONOSCILLA** (Hyacinthaceae)
§ *allenii* — CMon LAma

CHIRITA (Gesneriaceae)
sinensis ♀ — CHal WDib

CHIRONIA (Gentianaceae) See Plant Deletions

CHLIDANTHUS (Amaryllidaceae)
fragrans — NRog

CHLORANTHUS (Chloranthaceae)
¶ *oldhamii* B&SWJ 2019 — WCru
¶ *serratus* — WCru

CHLOROPHYTUM (Anthericaceae)
¶ *comosum* 'Mandanum' (v) CHal
– 'Variegatum' ♀ — CHal LChe MBri SRms
– 'Vittatum' (v) ♀ — SRms
§ *laxum* 'Bichetii' (v) — WCot
♦ – 'Variegatum' — See *C. laxum* 'Bichetii'
§ *majus* — WCot
nepalense B&SWJ 2393 — WCru

CHOISYA (Rutaceae)
'Aztec Pearl' ♀ — Widely available
dumosa var. *arizonica* — SDry
ternata ♀ — Widely available
§ – Sundance = 'Lich' ♀ — Widely available
♦ – Moonshine — See *C. ternata* Moonshine =
'Walchoi'

– Moonsleeper — See *C. ternata* Sundance = 'Lich'
– Sundance — See *C. ternata* Sundance = 'Lich'
§ – Moonshine = 'Walchoi' — EBrP EBre LBre LRHS SBre

CHONDROPETALUM (Restionaceae)
tectorum — CTrC WMul WNor

CHONDROSUM (Poaceae)
gracile — See *Bouteloua gracilis*

CHORDOSPARTIUM (Papilionaceae)
muritai — ECou MAll
stevensonii — CHEx CPle ECou EPfP MAll
SBid WHer
– 'Duncan' — ECou
– 'Kiwi' — ECou
– 'Miller' — ECou

CHORISIA (Bombacaceae) See Plant Deletions

CHORIZEMA (Papilionaceae)
cordatum ♀ — CPlN CPle
¶ *dicksonii* — MFiF
diversifolium — CPlN ERea
ilicifolium — CAbb CB&S CPlN CSPN
CWSG ERea GQui SBid

CHRYSALIDOCARPUS (Arecaceae)
♦ *lutescens* — See *Dypsis lutescens*

CHRYSANTHEMOPSIS See
RHODANTHEMUM

CHRYSANTHEMUM (Asteraceae)
'Adorn' (22d) — MCol
'Agnes Ann' (29K) — MCol
'Albert Broadhurst' (24b) — NHal
'Albert's Yellow' (29Rub) MCol MMil
'Alison' (29c) — LRHS
'Alison Kirk' (23b) — NHal
'Allouise' (25b) ♀ — MCol NHal
alpinum — See *Leucanthemopsis alpina*
'American Beauty' (5b) — MCol
'Amy Shoesmith' (15a) — MCol
'Anastasia' (28) — CLTr ECtt EMan EPPr GMac
LHop MCol MMil MRav NBrk
NFai NSti SEas SPla SRms
SUsu WEas WPer WRHF
WWin
N'Anastasia Variegated' — CSam ECED EMon MBel NSti
(28) — WCot WHer WRHF
'Anastasia White' (28) — WCot WIvy
'Angelic' (28) — MCol
'Angora' (25b) ♀ — MCol
'Anja's Bouquet' — EMan
'Anna Marie' (18c) ♀ — MCol
'Anne, Lady Brocket' — CLTr CMil EFou EMon GBuc
MBel NBrk NBro WCot WMaN
'Apollo' (29K) — EFou EMon EWll LRHS SMer
'Apricot' (29Rub) — EBrP EBre ECtt EFou EPPr
LBre MFir MMil MRav SBre
SMad SSoC SSvw WCot
'Apricot Chessington' — NHal WWol
(25a)
'Apricot Chivenor' (9c) — MCol NHal
'Apricot Courtier' (24a) — NHal WWol
'Apricot Margaret' (29c) — LBut MCol
♀
¶ 'Archie Benson' (3b) — WWol
'Arctic' (9c) — MCol
arcticum Linnaeus — See *Arctanthemum arcticum*

argenteum   See *Tanacetum argenteum*
'Aunt Millicent' (29K)   MCol
'Autumn Days' (25b)   MCol NHal
'Babs' (28)   MMil
'Bagley Cream' (3b)   MCol
¶ 'Bagley Glow' (4b)   MCol
¶ 'Bagley Pink' (14b)   MCol
'Balcombe Perfection'   MCol NHal WWol
   (5a)
balsamita   See *Tanacetum balsamita*
'Barbara' (22)   MCol NHal WLRN
'Beacon' (5a) ♀   NHal WWol
'Belair' (9c)   MCol
'Belle' (29K)   LRHS
'Beppie' (29e)   MCol
¶ 'Bernadette Wade' (25b)   WWol
'Bessie Rowe' (25a)   MCol
'Betty' (29K)   MCol
'Betty Wiggins' (25b)   MCol
'Bill Bye' (1)   NHal
'Bill Wade' (25a)   MCol WWol
'Black Magic' (24b)   MCol
'Bob Dear' (25a)   MCol
'Bo-peep' (28)   EMon MCol
'Bravo' (22c) ♀   MCol
* 'Breitner's Supreme'   MAus WCot
'Brenda Rowe' (5a)   MCol
'Brietner' (24b)   MCol MNrw
'Bright Eye' (28)   MCol WPer
'Brightness' (29K)   NFai SChu SHel SUsu WEas
'Broadacre' (7a)   MCol
'Broadway Mandy' (29c)   NHal
'Bronze Belair' (9c)   MCol
'Bronze Bornholm' (14b)   MCol
'Bronze Cassandra' (5b)   NHal
   ♀
'Bronze Dee Gem' (29c)   NHal
§ 'Bronze Elegance' (28b)   CLTr CM&M CMil CSam EFou
                   ELan EMan EMon MLLN NSti
                   SIng SPer SPla SRms SUsu
                   WAbe WEas WIvy WMaN
                   WWat
'Bronze Enbee Wedding'   NHal
   (29d) ♀
'Bronze Fairy' (28a)   MCol
'Bronze Margaret' (29c)   ♀ LBut MCol NHal
'Bronze Maria' (18a)   MCol
'Bronze Matlock' (24b)   NHal WWol
'Bronze Max Riley' (23b)   NHal WWol
'Bronze Mayford   MCol NHal
   Perfection' (5a) ♀
♦ 'Bronze Mei-kyo'   See *C.* **'Bronze Elegance'**
♦ 'Bronze Pamela'   See *C.* **'Pamela'**
¶ 'Bronze Pennine Goal'   WWol
'Bronze Yvonne Arnau'   MCol
   (24b)
'Brown Eyes' (29K)   WWin
'Bruera' (24a)   NHal
'Bryan Kirk' (4b)   NHal WWol
'Buff Peter Rowe' (23b)   NHal
'Bullfinch' (12a)   WWol
'Bunty' (28)   EBee LRHS MRav
'Cameo' (28a) ♀   MCol WIvy
'Candid' (15b)   MCol
'Candylite' (14b)   MCol
'Carlene Welby' (25b)   NHal WWol
'Carmine Blush'   WCot WLin
¶ 'Caroline Barclay' (14a)   WWol
I 'Cassandra' (5b)   NHal
'Cheddar' (13a)   MCol
'Cherry Enbee Wedding'   WWol
   (29d)

'Cherry Margaret' (29c)   NHal
'Chessington' (25a)   MCol NHal WWol
'Chester Globe' (23b)   NHal
¶ 'Chesterfield' (15b)   WWol
'Chestnut Talbot Parade'   NHal
   (29c) ♀
'Chivenor' (9c)   MCol NHal
'Christine Hall' (25a)   MCol
'Christopher Lawson'   NHal WWol
   (24a)
cinerariifolium   See *Tanacetum cinerariifolium*
I 'Citrus' (29K)   EFou
'Clara Curtis' (29Rub)   CGle CKel ECha EFou ELan
                   EMon GMac LHop MAus MBel
                   MBri MCol MFir MRav NBir
                   NBrk NPer NVic SChu SEas
                   SPer SPla SUsu WEas WHoo
                   WLin WMaN WPer WRus
                   WWin
'Claudia' (24c)   MCol
clusii   See *Tanacetum corymbosum*
                   subsp. *clusii*
coccineum   See *Tanacetum coccineum*
'Colossus' (24a)   NHal WWol
'Copper Margaret' (29c)   LBut
'Cornetto' (25b)   MCol NHal WWol
'Corngold' (5b)   NHal
corymbosum   See *Tanacetum corymbosum*
'Cossack' (2)   WWol
'Cottage Apricot'   CHea EBar EWoo GMac LHop
                   SMrm WEas WRHF
'Cottage Pink'   See *D.* **'Emperor of China'**
'Courtier' (24a)   NHal
'Cream Elegance' (9c)   NHal
'Cream John Hughes' (3b)   NHal
'Cream Margaret' (29c) ♀   NHal
'Creamist' (25b)   MCol WWol
'Cricket' (25b)   MCol
'Crimson Yvonne Arnaud'   MCol
   (24b) ♀
'Dana' (25b) ♀   NHal
'Daniel Cooper' (29Rub)   MCol
'Danielle' (29d)   MCol
'Dark Triumph'   WLRN
'David Shoesmith' (25a)   MCol
'Deane Dainty' (9f) ♀   NHal
'Debonair' (22c) ♀   MCol NHal WLRN
'Dee Candy' (29c)   NHal
'Dee Crimson' (29c)   NHal
'Dee Gem' (29c) ♀   NHal
'Denise' (28) ♀   MCol WLRN
'Dennis Fletcher' (25a)   WWol
'Derek Bircumshaw' (28a)   MCol
'Deva Glow' (25a)   MCol NHal
§ 'Doctor Tom Parr' (28)   CGle EFou ELan EMon EPPr
                   LGre MBel MFir NBrk
¶ 'Domingo' (4b)   WWol
'Donna' (22f)   MCol
'Doreen Burton' (25b)   MCol
'Doreen Hall' (15a)   MCol WWol
'Doreen Statham' (4b)   NHal WWol
'Dorothy Stone' (25b)   NHal
'Dorridge Beauty' (24a)   NHal WWol
'Dorridge Bolero' (24a)   WWol
'Dorridge Celebration'   WWol
   (3b)
'Dorridge Crystal' (24a)   NHal WWol
¶ 'Dorridge Dawn' (4b)   WWol
'Dorridge Flair' (3b)   NHal
'Dorridge King' (4b)   WWol
'Dorridge Velvet' (4b)   NHal
'Dorridge Vulcan' (23b)   WWol

'Dragon' (9c) — NHal
'Duchess of Edinburgh' (29Rub) — CDec CGle CSam EBar EBrP EBre ECED ECtt ELan EMon GMac LBre LGre MBri MCol MFir MRav SBre SEas SSpe SSvw WEas WMaN WPyg WRHF WRus
'Early Bird' (24b) ♀ — MCol
'Ed Hodgson' (25a) — MCol NHal
'Edelgard' — WMaN
'Edelweiss' (29K) — EFou LHop
'Egret' (23b) — WWol
'Elegance' (9c) — MCol NHal
'Elizabeth Lawson' (3a) — NHal
'Elizabeth Shoesmith' (1) — NHal
'Ellen' (29c) — LBut NHal
'Emily' (22) ♀ — MCol
'Emma Lou' (23a) — MCol NHal
§ 'Emperor of China' (29Rub) — CDec CGle CMil ECha EFou EMar EMon GCal GCra GMac LGre MBel MCol MRav MSte NBrk NFai NLon NNor SChu SMad SSvw SUsu WEas WFar WHoo WMaN WRus
'Enbee Dell' (29d) — MCol
'Enbee Frill' (29d) — MCol
'Enbee Sunray' (29d) — EFou
'Enbee Wedding' (29d) ♀ — MCol NHal WWol
'Encore' — LFis
'Ermine' (23a) — MCol NHal
'Evelyn Bush' (25a) — MCol
'Eye Level' (5a) — NHal
'Fairway' (15a) — NHal
'Fairweather' (3b) — MCol WWol
'Fairy' (28) — MCol
'Fairy Rose' (4b) — LRHS MCol
¶ 'Felicity' (15b) — WWol
'Fellbacher Wein' (29K) — EFou
'Feu de l'Automne' — EFou
'Fieldfare' (22) — NHal
'Fiery Barbara' (22c) — WLRN
'Flame Enbee Wedding' (29d) — MCol WWol
'Flamingo' (9f) — MCol
§ 'Fleet Margaret' (29c) ♀ — LBut
'Flying Saucer' (6a) — MCol
foeniculaceum — See Argyranthemum foeniculaceum (Willd.) Webb & Sch.Bip.
'Foxdown' (25b) — MCol
'Foxy Valerie' (22c) — LFis
'Fred Shoesmith' (5a) — MCol WWol
'Fresha' (25a) — WWol
'Frolic' (25b) — MCol WLRN
frutescens — See Argyranthemum frutescens
¶ 'Fulfen' (24b) — NHal
'Galaxy' (9d) ♀ — MCol NHal
'Gambit' (24a) — MCol NHal
'Gazelle' (23a) — MCol
'Geordie' (25b) — WWol
'George Griffiths' (24b) ♀ NHal
¶ 'Gerry Tull' (29d) — NHal
'Gertrude' (19c) — MCol
'Gigantic' (1) — NHal
I 'Ginger' (22c) — WLRN
'Gingernut' (5b) — MCol NHal WWol
'Gladys' (24b) — EBee ELan EWoo WPbr
'Glowing Lynn' — WLRN
'Gold Chessington' (25a) — WWol
'Gold Enbee Wedding' (29d) ♀ — NHal WWol
'Gold Foil' (5a) — NHal WWol

'Gold Margaret' — See D. 'Golden Margaret'
'Golden Angora' (25b) — MCol
'Golden Cassandra' (5b) ♀ — NHal
'Golden Courtier' (24a) — NHal
'Golden Creamist' (25b) ♀ — MCol
'Golden Elegance' (5a) — NHal WWol
'Golden Honeyball' (15b) — MCol
'Golden Ivy Garland' (5b) — MCol
§ 'Golden Margaret' (29c) ♀ — LBut MCol NHal
'Golden Mayford Perfection' (5a) ♀ — MCol NHal
'Golden Pamela' (29c) — NHal
'Golden Pixton' (25b) — MCol
'Golden Plover' (22) — NHal
'Golden Saskia' (7b) — MCol
'Golden Seal' (7b) — EMon GBuc MAvo MCol NBrk
'Golden Treasure' (28a) — MCol WWol
'Golden Wedding' (29K) — MCol
'Goldengreenheart' — WCot
'Goodlife Sombrero' (29a) ♀ NHal
¶ 'Grace Fraser' (15b) — WWol
'Grace Riley' (24a) — MCol
'Grandchild' (29c) — LRHS MCol
§ grandiflorum — MNrw SRms
'Green Satin' (5b) — WWol
'Grenadier' (24b) — MCol
'Grenadine' (22c) ♀ — NHal
haradjanii — See Tanacetum haradjanii
¶ 'Harold Lawson' (5a) — NHal
'Harry Wilson' (3b) — NHal
'Harry Woolman' (3b) — NHal
'Harvest Emily' (22c) — MCol
'Harvey' (29K) — MCol
'Hayley Griffin' (25a) — NHal
* 'Hazel' (29K) — LRHS
'Hazel Macintosh' (5a) — NHal
'Hazy Days' (25b) — NHal
'Heather' (15a) — WLRN
'Heather James' (3b) — MCol NHal
'Hedgerow' (7b) — MCol
'Heide' (29c) ♀ — MCol NHal
'Hekla' (30) — MCol
¶ 'Hesketh Knight' (5b) — NHal
¶ 'Highland White Dream' — LRHS
'Holly' (22b) ♀ — WLRN
'Honey' (25b) — EMan LRHS SMer
'Honeyball' (25b) — MCol
'Horace Martin' — LRHS
'Horningsea Pink' (19d) — ECGP EPPr
hosmariense — See Rhodanthemum hosmariense
'Imp' (28) — MCol
'Innocence' (29Rub) — CGle CSam EBee EFou EHal ELan EMon GMac MBel MRav NFai NSti SEas SMad SPla WEas
'Irene' (29K) — CElw
'Ivy Garland' (5b) — MCol
'Janice Shreeve' (24a) — MCol
'Jante Wells' (28) — EMon MBel MCol MFir WEas
'Jennifer' (22c) — WLRN
'Jessie Cooper' — See D. 'Mrs Jessie Cooper'
'Jimmy Motram' (1) — NHal
'Joan' (5b) — LRHS
'John Cory' (3b) — NHal
'John Harrison' (25b) — MCol NHal
'John Hughes' (3b) — MCol NHal WWol
'John Wingfield' (14b) — NHal WWol

'Julia' (28) — CLTr EFou
'Julie Lagravère' (28) — EFou EMon GBuc MBel WByw
¶ 'June Buglass' (3b) — WWol
'June Rose' (24b) — NHal
¶ 'Kay Woolman' (3b) — NHal
¶ 'Ken Lyons' (7b) — MCol
'Keystone' (25b) — MCol
'Kimberley Marie' (15b) — NHal
× *koreanum* — See *D.* grandiflorum
'Lady in Pink' (29Rub) — GBuc
'Lakelanders' (3b) — NHal WWol
¶ 'Lantern' (15b) — WWol
'Laser' (24b) — NHal WWol
'Laurie' (22c) — WLRN
'Leading Lady' (25b) — WWol
'Legend' (22) — NHal
* 'Lemon Heidi' (29c) — MCol
'Lemon Margaret' (29c) ♀ NHal
leucanthemum — See *Leucanthemum vulgare*
'Lilian Hoek' (29c) — MCol
'Lilian Jackson' (7b) — MCol
'Linda' (22c) — MCol WLRN WWol
¶ 'Lindie' — EFou
'L'Innocence' (29K) — WMaN
'Lisa' (22c) — MCol
'Little Dorrit' (29K) — EBar LRHS MCol
'Liverpool Festival' (23b) — MCol
'Long Island Beauty' (6b) ♀ MCol
'Long Life' (25b) — MCol
'Lorna Wood' (13b) — NHal
'Louise' (25b) — LRHS
¶ 'Louise Park' (24a) — NHal
'Lucy Simpson' (29K) — MCol MMil WMaN
'Lundy' (2) — NHal
'Lyndale' (25b) — MCol
'Lynmal's Choice' (13b) — MCol
'Lynn' (22) — NHal WLRN
macrophyllum — See *Tanacetum macrophyllum*
'Mac's Delight' (25b) — MCol
'Madeleine' (29c) ♀ EBrP EBre LBre LBut SBre
'Malcolm Perkins' (25a) — NHal
'Mandarin' — CGle EFou
◆ *maresii* — See *Rhodanthemum hosmariense*
'Margaret' (29c) ♀ LBut MCol NHal
'Maria' (28a) — MCol
'Mariann' (12a) — WWol
'Marion' (25a) — LBut
'Martha' — EBar LRHS
'Martin Riley' (23b) — MCol
'Mary' (29K) — MCol WMaN
'Mary Stevenson' (25b) — MCol
'Mary Stoker' (29Rub) — CGle CKel CSam ECha ECtt
  EFou EHal ELan EMon GBri
  GMac MAus MBel MBri MBro
  MCol MNrw MRav NBro NFai
  NSti SEas SPer SSpe WEas
  WHoo WMaN WPyg WRus
'Mason's Bronze' (7b) — MCol
'Matlock' (24b) — MCol NHal WWol
'Mavis' (28a) ♀ MCol
mawii — See *Rhodanthemum gayanum*
'Max Riley' (23b) ♀ NHal WWol
¶ *maximowiczii* — EMon
maximum hort. — See *Leucanthemum × superbum*
− Ramond — See *Leucanthemum maximum* (Ramond) DC
'May Shoesmith' (5a) — MCol NHal
'Mayford Perfection' (5a) ♀ MCol NHal
'Megan' (22d) — WLRN

'Megan Woolman' (3b) — WWol
'Mei-kyo' (28b) — CGle CM&M CMea CMil ECtt
  EFou ELan EMon MBel MLLN
  MRav NFai SIng SPer SPla
  SRms SSea SSvw WAbe WEas
  WRus WWat
'Membury' (24b) ♀ MCol NHal
'Minaret' (3b) — WWol
'Minstrel Boy' (3b) — MCol
'Miss Prim' (24b) — WWol
'Moira' (29K) — LRHS
'Molly Lambert' (5a) — NHal
'Morning Star' (12a) — WWol
'Mottram Minstrel' (29d) — MCol
'Mottram Sentinel' (29d) — MCol
'Mottram Twotone' (29d) — MCol
§ 'Mrs Jessie Cooper' (29Rub) — ECGP EFou ELan EMon MSte
  NBir NBrk SChu SEas WCot
  WHoo WLRN WPbr
'Music' (23b) — MCol NHal
'My Love' (7a) — MCol
'Myss Madi' (29c) ♀ NHal
naktongense — See *D. zawadskii* var. *latilobum*
'Nancy Perry' (29Rub) — CElw CSam ELan EMon LGan
  MCol SChu SEas
§ *nankingense* — EMon
'Nantyderry Sunshine' (28b) ♀ CMea EFou MAvo MWgw SIng
  SMrm SPla SUsu WAbe WCot
  WEas WMaN WPen WPer
  WRus WWat
'National Celebration' (25a) — NHal WWol
'Nell Gwyn' (29Rub) — MCol
'Nicole' (22c) — MCol NHal WLRN
nipponicum — See *Nipponanthemum nipponicum*
'Nu Dazzler' (9d) — MCol
'Nu Robin' (9d) — MCol
'Nu-Rosemary' (9d) ♀ MCol NHal
'Old Cottage Yellow' — NFai
'Orange Allouise' (25b) — NHal
¶ 'Orange Corfu' — WWol
'Orange Enbee Wedding' (29d) — NHal
'Orange Fairway' (15b) — NHal
'Orange Margaret' — See *D.* 'Fleet Margaret'
'Orangeade' (24b) — MCol
pacificum — See *Ajania pacifica*
§ 'Pamela' (29c) — NHal
'Panache' (5a) — MCol
parthenium — See *Tanacetum parthenium*
¶ 'Pat Davison' (25b) — NHal
'Patricia Millar' (14b) — NHal
'Paul Boissier' (29Rub) — CGle CMil EFou ELan EMon
  LGre MBel MHlr NSti WByw
  WCot WEas WHoo
'Pauline White' (15a) — NHal WWol
'Payton Blaze' (29c) — MCol
'Payton Dale' (29c) ♀ MCol NHal
'Payton Lady' (29c) — MCol
'Payton Snow' (29c) — MCol NHal
'Payton Snow' (29c) — NHal
'Peach Allouise' (25b) ♀ NHal
¶ 'Peach Cassandra' (5b) — MCol
'Peach Courtier' (24a) — NHal
'Peach Enbee Wedding' (29d) ♀ LBut MCol
'Peach Lynn' (22c) — WLRN
'Peach Margaret' — See *D.* 'Salmon Margaret'
'Pearl Celebration' (24a) — NHal WWol
'Pelsall Imperial' (3a) — MCol
¶ 'Pennine Autumn' (29c) — MCol

¶ 'Pennine Bouquet' (29e) WWol
'Pennine Canary' (29c) ♀ LBut
¶ 'Pennine Charm' (29b) MCol
'Pennine Cheer' (29c) WWol
¶ 'Pennine Claret' (29c) WWol
¶ 'Pennine Click' (29c) WWol
'Pennine Club' (29d) ♀ NHal WWol
'Pennine Coffee' (29c) WWol
¶ 'Pennine Colt' (29d) WWol
'Pennine Crystal' (29c) MCol
'Pennine Dancer' (29d) LBut
¶ 'Pennine Dart' (29d) WWol
'Pennine Dell' (29d) MCol
'Pennine Digger' (29c) WWol
'Pennine Eagle' (29c) NHal
'Pennine Gift' (29c) MCol NHal WWol
'Pennine Ginger' (29c) ♀ NHal
'Pennine Gipsy' (29c) WWol
'Pennine Glory' (29c) MCol NHal WWol
'Pennine Goal' (29c) ♀ WWol
'Pennine Hayley' (29d) WWol
'Pennine Jade' (29d) ♀ LBut
'Pennine Jessie' (29d) NHal
'Pennine Magnet' (29a) ♀ NHal WWol
'Pennine Marie' (29a) ♀ MCol NHal
'Pennine Oriel' (29a) ♀ MCol NHal WWol
'Pennine Pageant' (29d) WWol
'Pennine Panda' (29d) NHal WWol
'Pennine Polo' (29d) MCol NHal
'Pennine Posy' (29f) WWol
'Pennine Purple' (29c) MCol
'Pennine Ranger' (29d) NHal WWol
'Pennine Romeo' (19c) WWol
'Pennine Saffron' (29c) NHal WWol
'Pennine Sally' (29c) WWol
'Pennine Ski' (29c) MCol
'Pennine Slumber' (29c) WWol
'Pennine Soldier' (29d) ♀ LBut NHal
'Pennine Splash' (29d) NHal WWol
'Pennine Swan' (29c) MCol NHal
'Pennine Swing' (29d) NHal WWol
¶ 'Pennine Wine' (29c) LBut
'Percy Salter' (24b) MCol
'Perry's Peach' MAvo NPer
'Peter Fraser' (14b) WWol
¶ 'Peter Pan' (24b) WRus
'Peter Rowe' (23b) MCol NHal
'Peter Sare' (29d) EBrP EBre GMac LBre SBre
'Peter White' (23a) MCol
'Peterkin' CHea EBrP EBre ECtt EMar
EMon GMac LBre LGre SBre
'Phil Houghton' (1) WWol
¶ 'Phillip McNamara' (3b) WWol
'Pink Duke' (1) NHal
'Pink Favorite' (5b) MCol
¶ 'Pink Honeysuckle Time' WWol
'Pink Ice' (5b) MCol WRha
'Pink John Wingfield' NHal WWol
(24b)
'Pink Margaret' (29c) ♀ NHal
'Pink Nu Rosemary' (9d) MCol
♀
'Pink Overture' (15b) MCol
'Pink Pennine Cheer' WWol
(29c)
'Pink Progression' ECED ECtt GMac NBir NBrk
'Pixton' (25b) MCol
'Playmate' (29K) MCol
'Polar Gem' (3a) MCol NHal
'Pot Black' (14b) WWol
praeteritium See *Tanacetum praeteritum*

'Primrose Alison Kirk' NHal
(23b)
'Primrose Allouise' (24b) NHal
♀
'Primrose Angora' (25b) MCol
'Primrose Bill Wade' NHal
(25a)
'Primrose Chessington' NHal WWol
(25a)
'Primrose Courtier' See *D.* **'Yellow Courtier'**
'Primrose Cricket' (25b) MCol
'Primrose Dorothy Stone' NHal
(25b)
'Primrose Enbee NHal
Wedding' (29d)
'Primrose Ermine' (23a) NHal
'Primrose John Hughes' NHal WWol
(3b)
'Primrose Margaret' See *D.* **'Buff Margaret'**
'Primrose Mayford MCol NHal
Perfection' (5a) ♀
'Primrose West NHal
Bromwich' (14a)
'Princess' (29K) LRHS
'Princess Anne' (4b) MCol
'Promise' (25a) MCol NHal
ptarmiciflorum See *Tanacetum ptarmiciflorum*
'Purleigh White' (28b) EFou MAvo SIng SPla WAbe
WMaN WRus
'Purple Fairie' (28b) MCol
'Purple Glow' (5a) NHal
'Purple Margaret' (29c) LBut NHal
'Queenswood' (5b) MCol
¶ 'Quill Elegance' (9f) MCol
'Rachel Knowles' (25a) MCol NHal WWol
'Radiant Lynn' (22c) MCol WLRN
'Raquel' (29K) MCol
'Rayonnante' (11) MCol
'Red Balcombe NHal WWol
Perfection' (5a)
'Red Carlene Welby' WWol
(25b)
'Red Early Bird' (24b) MCol
'Red Formcast' (24a) NHal
¶ 'Red Galaxy' (9d) NHal
'Red Gambit' (24a) NHal
'Red Mayford Perfection' MCol
(5a)
'Red Pamela' (29c) NHal
'Red Rosita' (29c) MCol
'Red Shirley Model' (3a) NHal
'Red Wendy' (29c) ♀ LBut MCol NHal
'Redall' (4c) MCol
'Regal Mist' (25b) MCol
'Regalia' (24b) ♀ MCol
'Remarkable' (30) MCol NHal
'Riley's Dynasty' (14a) NHal
'Robeam' (9c) ♀ WWol
'Robin' (22) NHal WLRN WWol
¶ 'Roblaze' (9c) NHal
¶ 'Roger Kirby' (15a) WWol
¶ 'Rolass' (9c) NHal
'Romantika' EFou
'Romany' (2) WEas
¶ 'Romark' (9c) MCol
'Rose Broadway Mandy' MCol
(29c)
'Rose Enbee Wedding' MCol NHal WWol
(29d)
'Rose Mayford Perfection' MCol NHal
(5a) ♀

¶ 'Rose Patricia Millar' NHal
(14b)
'Rose Pink Debonair' (22) WLRN
roseum See *Tanacetum coccineum*
'Rosita' (28b) MCol
¶ 'Roswan' (9c) NHal
'Royal Cardinal' (9c) MCol
'Royal Command' EMon NBro WCot
(29Rub)
'Royal Lynn' (22c) MCol WLRN
rubellum See *Dendranthema zawadskii*
'Ruby Enbee Wedding' NHal WWol
(29d)
'Ruby Mound' (29K) CLTr EFou LFis LGre MCol
WEas
'Ruby Raynor' (29Rub) MCol
'Rumpelstilzchen' CMea EBee EMan EMar EPPr
MAvo WPbr WPer
¶ 'Russet Gown' EBee
'Rybronze' (9d) NHal
'Ryfinch' (9d) MCol
'Ryflash' (9d) MCol
'Rylands Gem' (24b) ♀ MCol
'Rylands Victor' (23c) MCol
'Rynoon' (9d) ♀ MCol
'Rytorch' (9d) MCol
'Salmon Enbee Wedding' NHal WWol
(29d) ♀
'Salmon Fairie' (28a) ♀ MCol
§ 'Salmon Margaret' (29c) LBut MCol WWol
♀
'Salmon Rylands Gem' MCol
(24b)
'Salmon Susan Rowe' MCol
(24b)
'Sam Vinter' (5a) NHal
'Sandy' (30) MCol
'Sarah' (22f) WLRN
'Sarah's Yellow' CSam
'Saskia' (7b) MCol
'Scottie' (24b) NHal WWol
'Sea Urchin' (29c) MCol
'Seashell' (28b) MCol
¶ 'Seatons Flirt' (3b) WWol
'Setron' EBee
'Shelly' (22b) WLRN
'Shining Light' (29K) MCol
'Simon Mills' (2) NHal
'Soft Lynn' (22c) NHal WLRN
'Solarama' (9e) NHal
'Sonnenschein' LHop WHen
'Sophia' (22c) WLRN
'Southway Sanguine' (29d) NHal
¶ 'Southway Stomp' (29d) NHal
'Southway Sure' (29d) ♀ LBut NHal
¶ 'Sparta' (9c) NHal
'Spartan Glory' (25b) WWol
'Spartan Magic' (29d) WWol
'Spartan Moon' (25b) WWol
'Spartan Rose' (29c) WWol
'Spartan Torch' WWol
'Spartan White' (29c) WWol
'Spencer's Cottage' (13b) MCol
* 'Spoons' SCro SHel
'Stan's Choice' (29K) MCol
¶ 'Stardust' (24b) MCol
'Starlet' (29K) LRHS MCol
'Stockton' (3b) NHal
'Stoke Festival' (25b) MCol
'Stuart Jackson' (25a) WWol
'Stunning Lynn' WLRN

¶ 'Sunbeam' (28) EBrP EBre ECtt EFou LBre
SBre
'Sundora' (22d) NHal WLRN
'Sunflight' (25b) MCol
'Sunny Denise' WLRN
'Sunny Linda' (22c) WLRN WWol
'Susan Rowe' (24b) MCol
'Sutton White' (25a) WWol
'Suzanne Marie' (24a) WWol
'Taffeta' (9c) MCol NHal
'Talbot Bolero' (29c) MCol NHal
'Talbot Parade' (29c) ♀ NHal
'Tang' (12a) WWol
'Tapestry Rose' CGle CMil EMon GMac MMil
NBrk
'Target' (24b) MCol NHal WLRN
'The Favourite' (5b) MCol
¶ 'Thoroughbred' (24a) WWol
'Toledo' (25a) WWol
'Tom Blackshaw' (25b) NHal
'Tom Parr' See *D.* 'Doctor Tom Parr'
'Tom Snowball' (3b) NHal
'Tommy Trout' (28) MCol
'Tone Gambol' (29a) MCol
'Tone Sail' (29a) MCol
'Tracy Waller' (24b) NHal
'Triumph' (22) NHal
'Tundra' (4a) NHal
uliginosum See *Leucanthemella serotina*
'Universiade' (25a) NHal
'Vagabond Prince' CSam MBro WHoo
'Valerie' (10) LFis
'Vanity Pink' (7b) MCol
'Vanity Primrose' (7b) MCol
'Venice' (24b) NHal WWol
'Venus' (29K) CBlo LRHS MBro
'Vera Smith' (3b) MCol
¶ 'Victor Rowe' (5b) ♀ MCol
'Vrenelli' EFou
'Wedding Day' (29K) CElw CLTr EMan EMon GBuc
MAvo MBro MFir MHlr MLLN
MMil NNor SRms SSpe SUsu
WCot WHoo WMaN WOve
WRus
'Wedding Sunshine' (29K) LRHS MAvo MMil WCot
welwitschii See *C. segetum*
'Wembley' (24b) WWol
'Wendy' (29c) ♀ LBut MCol NHal
¶ 'Wessex Dawn' (29d) MCol
'Wessex Eclipse' (29c) MCol NHal
'Wessex Ivory' (29d) MCol
'Wessex Sunshine' (29d) MCol
'West Bromwich' (14a) NHal
§ *weyrichii* EBrP EBre ELan LBre LFis
LHop MHig MTho NGre NHol
NMen NNrd NWCA SBla SBod
SBre SHel SSmi WAbe WOMN
'White Allouise' (25b) ♀ NHal
'White Beppie' (29e) MCol
'White Bouquet' (28) MCol WWol
'White Cassandra' (5b) NHal
'White Fairweather' (3b) WWol
'White Gloss' (29K) LRHS SMer
'White Margaret' (29c) ♀ LBut MCol NHal WWol
'White Nu Rosemary' (9d) NHal
'White Rachel Knowles' NHal
(25a)
'White Rayonnante' (11) MCol
'White Sands' (9a) ♀ MCol
'White Skylark' (22) NHal
'White Sonja' (29c) MCol
'White Spider' (10) MCol

'White Taffeta' (9c)   MCol NHal
'White Tower'   EPPr
'Win' (9c)   NHal
'Windermere' (24a)   NHal
'Winnie Bramley' (23a)   WWol
'Winning's Red' (29Rub)   NBro SMad WWin
'Winter Queen' (5b)   NHal
'Woolley Globe' (25b)   WWol
'Woolman's Prince' (3a)   WWol
'Woolman's Star' (3a)   NHal
¶ 'Woolmans Venture' (4b) NHal
'Yellow Allison Kirk'   NHal
  (23b)
'Yellow Allouise' (25b)   NHal
'Yellow Beppie' (29e)   MCol
§ 'Yellow Courtier' (24a) NHal WWol
'Yellow Danielle' (29d)   MCol
'Yellow Ellen' (29c)   NHal
'Yellow Flying Saucer'   MCol
  (6a)
'Yellow Fred Shoesmith'   WWol
  (5a)
'Yellow Galaxy' (9d) ♀   MCol
'Yellow Gingernut' (25b)   MCol NHal WWol
'Yellow Hazy Days' (25b)   NHal
'Yellow Heather James'   MCol
  (3b)
'Yellow Heide' (29c) ♀   MCol NHal
'Yellow John Hughes'   MCol NHal WWol
  (3b) ♀
'Yellow John Wingfield'   MCol NHal WWol
  (14b)
'Yellow Lilian Hoek'   MCol
  (29c)
'Yellow Margaret' (29c) ♀ LBut MCol NHal
'Yellow May Shoesmith'   NHal
  (5a)
'Yellow Mayford   MCol NHal
  Perfection' (5a) ♀
'Yellow Megan Woolman'   WWol
  (3b)
'Yellow Pennine Oriel'   MCol NHal WWol
  (29a) ♀
'Yellow Percy Salter'   MCol
  (24b)
'Yellow Phil Houghton'   WWol
  (1)
'Yellow Plover' (22)   NHal
* 'Yellow Pom' (28)   LRHS
¶ 'Yellow Roswan' (9c)   NHal
'Yellow Sands' (9d)   MCol
'Yellow Spider' (10)   MCol
* 'Yellow Stardust' (24b) MCol
'Yellow Taffeta' (9c)   MCol
'Yellow Talbot Parade'   NHal WWol
  (29c)
'Yellow Triumph' (24a)   WLRN
'Yellow Whitby' (5b)   MCol
§ yezoense ♀   EFou ELan EMan EMon MBel
                           NFai SPla WCot WEas WRus
 – 'Roseum'   MBel WRus
'Yvonne Arnaud' (24b) ♀   MCol
§ zawadskii   WHer WPyg WRus
'Zesty Barbara' (22c)   WLRN

CHRYSOCOMA (Asteraceae)
ciliata JJH 9401633   NWCA
coma-aurea   CTrC LHil

CHRYSOGONUM (Asteraceae)
virginianum   CHal CMea CRDP ECha EMan
                           MRav SPer WFar WPbr WRHF

CHRYSOLEPIS (Fagaceae) See Plant Deletions

CHRYSOPOGON (Poaceae)
gryllus   EMon LRHS

CHRYSOPSIS (Asteraceae)
villosa   See Heterotheca villosa

CHRYSOSPLENIUM (Saxifragaceae)
¶ alternifolium   EMan
davidianum   CBre CGle EBee ECha EMan
                           EPar EPot LSpr NBir SMac
                           SOkh WCot WCru WGer
                           WGwy WWat
 – SBEC 231   NHol NWoo
oppositifolium   EMNN GAri GDra GGar WCla
                           WHer

CHRYSOTHAMNUS (Asteraceae) See Plant
Deletions

CHRYSOTHEMIS (Gesneriaceae)
pulchella ♀   CHal

CHUNIOPHOENIX (Arecaceae) See Plant
Deletions

CHUQUIRAGA (Asteraceae) See Plant
Deletions

CHUSQUEA † (Poaceae - Bambusoideae)
argentina   ISta
culeou ♀   CDoC CFil CGre CHEx EFul
                           EOas EPfP EPla IOrc ISta LJus
                           MMoz MNes SDry SSta WJun
                           WNor
 – 'Breviglumis'   See C. culeou 'Tenuis'
§ – 'Tenuis'   ERod ISta LJus SDry
liebmannii   WJun
montana   EPla ISta WPGP
nigricans   ISta
quila   EPla ISta SDry
ramosissima   CFil SDry
valdiviensis   ISta

CIBOTIUM (Dicksoniaceae) See Plant Deletions

CICERBITA (Asteraceae)
§ alpina   GAbr NHex NLar
macrorhiza B&SWJ 2970   WCru
plumieri   MAvo WCot
 – 'Blott'   WCot

CICHORIUM (Asteraceae)
intybus   Widely available
 – f. album   CGle CPou CRDP EBee ECha
                           ECoo ECro EMan EMon LHol
                           LHop MAus MAvo MRav MSte
                           NSti SChu SWat WCHb
 – 'Roseum'   CGle CJew CPou CRDP EBee
                           ECGP ECha ECoo ECot ECro
                           ELan EMan EMon GBri LHol
                           LHop MAus MAvo MRav
                           NRoo SChu SPer SWat WCHb
                           WHow WWal WWin

CICUTA (Apiaceae) See Plant Deletions

CIMICIFUGA † (Ranunculaceae)
acerina   See C. japonica

§ *americana* — MSal SRms
¶ *arizonica* — SBla
  cordifolia Pursh — See *C. americana*
  — Torrey & A Gray — See *C. rubifolia*
  dahurica — CHan CTri EBee GAbr GCal MCli MSal SWat WCru
¶ *elata* — WCru
  foetida — GPoy
¶ *frigida* B&SWJ 2657 — WCru
§ *japonica* — CHan CHid CRow EBee GAbr GCal LFis LGre NDov NPSI WCot WRus
  racemosa ♀ — CArn CRow EBrP EBre EGol ELan GCal GPoy LBre LFis LGan LHol MBal MSal NDea NPSI NRoo NSti NWoo SBre SPer WByw WFar
  — var. *cordifolia* — See *C. rubifolia*
* — 'Purple Torch' — WEas
  — 'Purpurea' — See *C. simplex* var. *simplex* **Atropururea Group**
  ramosa — See *C. simplex* var. *simplex* **'Prichard's Giant'**
§ *rubifolia* — CHan ECGN GMaP LGre MSal WCru
  simplex — CBot CFil CMea LHol MBri MHlr SPer SWat WWat
  — var. *matsumurae* 'Elstead' ♀ — CBos CFil CHan CRow ECha EPar GCal LGre MRav SSpi
  — — 'Frau Herms' — ECha LGre
  — — 'White Pearl' — CB&S CDoC CHan CRow EAst ECha EFou EGol ELan GMaP LFis LGre LHop MAus MBri NCat NDea NFla NRoo NSti NTow SCro SMrm SPer SPla SSpi WHoo WMow WPGP WPbr
¶ — 'Scimitar' — LGre
  — 'Silver Axe' — GCal
§ — var. *simplex* — Widely available
  Atropurpurea Group
  — — 'Brunette' — LGre MUlv SWat
§ — — 'Prichard's Giant' — CHan GAri GBuc GCal LGre MBri MLLN WPen
  sp. B&SWJ 343 — CPou
¶ *yunnanensis* ACE 1880 — GBuc

CINERARIA (Asteraceae)
  maritima — See *Senecio cineraria*

CINNAMOMUM (Lauraceae)
  camphora — CB&S CFil CHEx CTrG ERea GQui

CIONURA (Asclepiadaceae)
§ *erecta* — CPlN
  oreophila — CPlN GCal SMur

CIRCAEA (Onagraceae)
  lutetiana — CKin EWFC MHew MSal WHer WShi
  — 'Caveat Emptor' (v) — EMon WCot

CIRSIUM (Asteraceae)
  acaule — CKin ECro
  diacantha — See *Ptilostemon diacantha*
  dissectum — CKin
  eriophorum — CKin NMir
  helenioides — See *C. heterophyllum*
§ *heterophyllum* — CKin ECGN ECro EMon WCot

¶ *japonicum* 'Early Rose Beauty' — ECGN
* — 'Pink Beauty' — WFar
  — 'Rose Beauty' — ELan MBri NMir WFar
  oleraceum — ECro NLar
  palustre — CKin
  rivulare 'Atropurpureum' — CElw CGle CMCo CMil CSev ELan MAvo MTed NBir NTow SSpi WByw WCHb WCot WEas WHal WMer WPGP WWye
  vulgare — CKin
¶ — variegated — WAlt
¶ — white form — WAlt

CISSUS (Vitaceae)
  adenopoda — CPlN
  antarctica ♀ — CTrC MBri
  discolor — CHal
¶ *hypoglauca* — MFiF
¶ *pedata* B&SWJ 2371 — WCru
  rhombifolia ♀ — MBri
  — 'Ellen Danica' ♀ — CHal MBri
§ *striata* — CB&S CHEx CPlN CSPN CTrC EMil LRHS SBra WCot WCru WSHC WWat

CISTUS † (Cistaceae)
× *aguilarii* — CTri MAll MRav SIgm WGer WOve WSHC
  — 'Maculatus' ♀ — CB&S CBot CDoC CLTr EBrP EBre ELan LBre LGre MBri MWgw NFai SBre SDry SDys SEas SLMG SPer WAbe WGer WHCG WKif WWeb WWin
  albanicus — See *C. sintenisii*
  albidus — CArn MAll MLLN NTow SDry SSpi WHer
  algarvensis — See *Halimium ocymoides*
  'Ann Baker' — MBri SPan
  'Anne Palmer' — CHor NBrk WAbe
  atriplicifolius — See *Halimium atriplicifolium*
  'Barnsley Pink' — See *C.* 'Grayswood Pink'
  'Blanche' — LRHS WKif WPGP
¶ 'Candy Stripe' (v) — EMar MAsh MCCP MMHG NPro WRHF WWeb
  × *canescens* — WAbe
  — f. *albus* — CB&S CMHG LGre MBri NSti SIgm WAbe WGer WHCG
  (O.E. Warb) J-P Demoly
  'Chelsea Bonnet' — EBar EHic SBid SPan SUsu SVen WAbe WPen
♦ 'Chelsea Pink' — See *C.* 'Grayswood Pink'
§ *clusii* — CHar MAsh SAxl
  coeris — See *C.* × *hybridus*
  × *corbariensis* — See *C.* × *hybridus*
¶ *creticus* — MBel
§ — subsp. *creticus* — CMHG EBar EBee EGoo ELan GBin LGre MAll MBel MSte NNor SPer WAbe WGer WWin
¶ — — f. *albus* — MBel
§ — subsp. *incanus* — LGre MNrw SSte WHCG
  × *crispatus* 'Warley Rose' — CLon CSam EGoo MBri NSti SAxl SHBN SIgm WAbe
  crispus hort. — See *C.* × *pulverulentus*
§ — Linnaeus — CHan ECha EGoo GAbr GOrc LGre NNor SIgm SPan WAbe WEas WGer WWeb
  — 'Prostratus' — See *C. crispus* Linnaeus
  — 'Sunset' — See *C.* × *pulverulentus* 'Sunset'

§ × *cyprius* ♀ — CMHG CSpe CTrC EAst ECtt ELan ENot LHil LHop MAll MBel MGos MWat MWhi NBrk NSti SDix SEND SMad SRms WBod WDin WGer WPnn WWeb

– 'Albiflorus' — WBcn

§ × *dansereaui* — CHan CHar CMHG CSam EBee ELan EMan ENot IOrc NSti SHBN SLMG SPer WAbe WPat WPyg WWat

¶ – 'Albiflorus' — WAbe

– 'Decumbens' ♀ — Widely available

¶ – 'Jenkyn Place' — MBri

'Elma' ♀ — CMHG CSpe EPfP LGre MBri SDry SIgm SPan WAbe WHCG WPGP WWat

♦ × *florentinus* hort. — See × *Halimiocistus* 'Ingwersenii'

§ – Lamarck — CLTr EBee IOrc MAll MMil NCut NNor SChu WSHC

formosus — See *Halimium lasianthum*

§ 'Grayswood Pink' — CMHG ELan EPla GCal GMac GOrc MAll MAsh MBri MLLN MSte NSti SCoo SEND SIgm SMrm SOkh SRms SSoC WAbe WGer WHCG

halimifolius — See *Halimium halimifolium*

hirsutus — NWoo SDry SEND WHar

N– var. *psilosepalus* — CPle EBar EEls WAbe WHer

§ × *hybridus* ♀ — CChe CMHG ECha ELan ENot GRei IOrc LHol LHop MGos MWat NChi NFai NNor NSti SDix SHBN SLPl SPer SSta SUsu WAbe WBod WCFE WDin WEas WHCG WOMN WWat WWin

incanus — See *C. creticus* subsp. *incanus*

– subsp. *creticus* — See *C. creticus* subsp. *creticus*

– subsp. *incanus* — See *C. creticus* subsp. *incanus*

ingwerseniana — See × *Halimiocistus* 'Ingwersenii'

ladanifer hort. — See *C.* × *cyprius*

ladanifer Linnaeus ♀ — CB&S ECha ELan IOrc MBal MLan MRav NChi NLon NNor NSti SChu SPer SPla WCru WEas WFar WHar WSHC WWye

– var. *albiflorus* — CB&S SPan SSpi

– Palhinhae Group — See *C. ladanifer* var. *sulcatus*

– 'Pat' — CGre

§ – var. *sulcatus* ♀ — CLTr LGre MSte SDry SMac WAbe WCot

lasianthus — See *Halimium lasianthum*

laurifolius ♀ — ENot EPfP EPla ESis LHol MAll MBal MGos MLan MNrw NChi NSti SLPl SPer WEas WHar WPic WWal WWat

× *laxus* 'Snow Queen' — See *C.* × *laxus* 'Snow White'

§ – 'Snow White' — CAbP CBlo CDoC CHan ELan LGre LHop MBel MBri MSte NPer NSti SAga SAxl SChu SPan SPer SSpi WKif WWeb

libanotis — CSam ELan NNor

'Little Gem' — MAsh MBri SPan

♦ × *longifolius* — See *C.* × *nigricans*

× *loretii* hort. — See *C.* × *dansereaui*

N– Rouy & Fouc. — See *C.* × *stenophyllus*

× *lusitanicus* Maund. — See *C.* × *dansereaui*

'Merrist Wood Cream' — See × *Halimiocistus wintonensis* **'Merrist Wood Cream'**

monspeliensis — CHan CPle EPfP GOrc MAll MAsh SAxl SPer SPla SSpi WPGP

¶ – CMBS 62

Golden Treasure = 'Nepond' (v) — COtt ECle EPfP GChr LRHS MAsh MGos SMur SPla MAll SPan

× *nigricans* — See *C.* × *nigricans*

♦ × *obtusifolius* hort. — See *C.* × *nigricans*

– Sweet — CHan CInt EHic ELan EPfP EWes MAll MBel MBrN MWhi NLon SLPl SMer

♦ *ochreatus* — See *C. symphytifolius* subsp. *leucophyllus*

ocymoides — See *Halimium ocymoides*

osbeckiifolius — SSpi

'Paladin' — WAbe

palhinhae — See *C. ladanifer* var. *sulcatus*

parviflorus hort. — See *C.* 'Grayswood Pink'

– Lamarck — CBot ECha LGre LHol LHop MAll NSti SChu SPer WSHC

'Peggy Sammons' ♀ — CBot CDoC CLTr EBrP EBre ECha ELan IOrc LBre LHop MBri MRav NBrk NSti SBre SIgm SPer SSoC WBod WHCG WHar WPyg WSHC WWat

populifolius — CFis CMHG ECha EHic MAll SPer SSta WAbe

– var. *lasiocalyx* — See *C. populifolius* subsp. *major*

§ – subsp. *major* ♀ — CPle EPfP IOrc LGre SBid SMrm

♦ *psilosepalus* — See *C. hirsutus* var. *psilosepalus*

§ × *pulverulentus* ♀ — CHan CTri MAll MBel SChu SCro WDin WLRN WSHC

§ – 'Sunset' — CB&S EAst EBrP EBre ELan ENot IOrc LBre LHop MBri MGos MWat NBrk NSti SBre SDix SEas SHBN SPer SPla SReu SSta WAbe WBod WDin WFar WHCG WWeb

– 'Warley Rose' — See *C.* × *crispatus* **'Warley Rose'**

N× *purpureus* ♀ — Widely available

– 'Alan Fradd' — CBlo EBee EHic ENot GMac LHol MAsh MBri MGrG NBrk NHaw SAga SCoo SCro SEND SLod SMrm SPan SPla WGwG WPen WWal

– 'Betty Taudevin' — See *C.* × *purpureus*

rosmarinifolius — See *C. clusii*

sahucii — See × *Halimiocistus sahucii*

salviifolius — CB&S CHan CPle CSam EBee ISea MAll SPan SRCN SSpi WHCG WLRN WWeb

– 'Avalanche' — MAll MRav WAbe

– × *monspeliensis* — See *C.* × *florentinus*

– 'Prostratus' — CMHG ELan LGre LRHS NPro WWat

'Silver Pink' — Widely available

§ *sintenisii* — GCHN NSla

× *skanbergii* ♀ — CB&S CLTr CSam CSpe ELan ENot LFis LHop MGos MWat MWgw NBir NBrk NFai NSti SArc SAxl SDix SDys SEas SHBN SPer WEas WGwG WPGP WWal WWat WWin

§ 'Snow Fire' — LRHS MAsh MBri SLPl SPan SSpi

'Snowflake' — See *C.* **'Snow Fire'**

× *stenophyllus* — LGre WFar WKif

* 'Stripey' — SVen

symphytifolius — WFar WPic

'Tania Compton' — See *C.* × *cyprius* **'Tania Compton'**

'Thornfield White' — SAxl

tomentosus   See *Helianthemum*
                nummularium subsp.
                tomentosum
× *verguinii*   LGre LHop MBri SDix SIgm
                SPan
– var. *albiflorus*   See *C.* × *dansereaui* unblotched
villosus   See *C. incanus*
wintonensis   See × *Halimiocistus wintonensis*

CITHAREXYLUM (Verbenaceae)

quadrangulare Jacquin   See *C. spinosum*
§ *spinosum*   CPle

× CITROFORTUNELLA (Rutaceae)

¶ *floridana*   CGOG LHol
– 'Eustis' (F)   ECon ERea SCit
– 'Lakeland' (F)   ERea
Lemonquat (F)   SCit
Limequat   See × *C. floridana*
§ *microcarpa* (F) ♀   CAgr CGOG EHol EPfP ERea
                LCns LHol MBri SCit
§ – 'Tiger' (v/F)   CB&S ECon EHol EPfP ERea
                LCns SCit
– 'Variegata'   See × *C. microcarpa* 'Tiger'
mitis   See × *C. microcarpa*
Procimequat (F)   SCit
reticulata (F)   SCit
swinglei 'Tavares' (F)   ERea

× CITRONCIRUS (Rutaceae)

¶ Citremon   CAgr
¶ 'Swingle' (F)   SCit
webberi 'Benton'   SCit
¶ – 'C-32'   CAgr
¶ – 'C-35'   CAgr
– 'Carrizo'   CAgr SCit
– 'Rusk'   CAgr SCit
– 'Troyer'   CAgr

CITRONELLA (Icacinaceae)

mucronata   See *C. gongonha*

CITRUS † (Rutaceae)

¶ *amblycarpa* Djeruk Lime   ERea
  (F)
aurantiifolia (F)   SCit
– 'Indian Lime' × *limon*   ERea
  (F)
– 'La Valette' × *limon* (F)   ECon ERea
aurantium (F)   SCit
– 'Aber's Narrowleaf' (F)   SCit
– 'Bigaradier Apepu'   SCit
– 'Bittersweet' (F)   SCit
– 'Bouquet de Fleurs'   CGOG ERea LHol SCit
– 'Bouquetier de Nice'   LChe LHol
– 'Bouquetier de Nice à   SCit
  Fleurs Doubles'
– 'Gou-tou Cheng' (F)   SCit
– var. *myrtifolia*   CGOG ERea SCit
  'Chinotto' (F)
– 'Sauvage' (F)   SCit
– 'Seville' (F)   CGOG ERea
– 'Smooth Flat Seville' (F)   SCit
– 'Willowleaf' (F)   SCit
bergamia Bergamot   CGOG ERea
– 'Fantastico'   SCit
Calamondin   See × *Citrofortunella microcarpa*
deliciosa   See *C.* × *nobilis*
¶ Ichang Lemon (F)   CAgr
ichangensis (F)   SCit

jambhiri 'Milam'   SCit
– Red Rough Lemon (F)   SCit
– Rough Lemon (F)   SCit
– Schaub Rough Lemon (F)   SCit
japonica   See *Fortunella japonica*
junos   CAgr
kinokuni   SCit
Kumquat   See *Fortunella margarita*
latifolia 'Bearss' (F)   CGOG ERea
– 'Tahiti' (F)   ECon ERea LChe
limettoides (F)   SCit
limon (F)   LPan
– 'Eureka Variegated' (F)   CGOG SCit
– 'Fino' (F)   CGOG SCit
§ – 'Garey's Eureka' (F)   ERea LCns
– 'Imperial' (F)   ERea
– 'Lemonade' (F)   ERea SCit
– 'Lisbon' (F)   ERea
– 'Quatre Saisons'   See *C. limon* 'Garey's Eureka'
– × *sinensis*   See *C.* × *meyeri*
– 'Variegata' (F)   ERea
– 'Verna' (F)   CGOG SCit
– 'Villa Franca' (F)   ERea
– 'Yen Ben' (F)   SCit
× *limonia* 'Rangpur' (F)   ERea
macrophylla   SCit
♦ *madurensis*   See *Fortunella japonica*
maxima (F)   ERea SCit
medica (F)   SCit
♦ – 'Cidro Digitado'   See *C. medica* var. *sarcodactylis*
– 'Ethrog' (F)   ECon ERea SCit
§ – var. *sarcodactylis* (F)   CGOG ERea SCit
× *meyeri* 'Meyer' (F)   CAgr CB&S CGOG ECon
                EHol EPfP ERea GTwe LCns
                LHol LHop SCit SLMG SPer
♦ *microcarpa* Philippine Lime   See × *Citrofortunella*
                microcarpa
mitis   See × *Citrofortunella*
                microcarpa
natsudaidai   SCit
§ × *nobilis* (F)   LPan
– 'Blida' (F)   ERea SCit
– 'Ellendale' (F)   SCit
– 'Murcott' (F)   ERea SCit
– Ortanique Group (F)   CGOG ECon SCit
– 'Silver Hill Owari' (F)   ERea
– Tangor Group (F)   ERea
× *paradisi* (F)   LPan
– 'Foster' (F)   ERea
– 'Golden Special' (F)   CTrC ERea
– 'Navel' (F)   SCit
– 'Red Blush' (F)   CGOG
– 'Star Ruby' (F)   CGOG ECon ERea SCit
– 'Wheeny' (F)   SCit
pennivesiculata (F)   SCit
– 'Ponderosa' (F)   CGOG ERea LChe SCit
reshni Cleopatra Mandarin   SCit
  (F)
¶ *reticulata* 'Arrufatina' (F)   CGOG
– 'Dancy' (F)   SCit
– 'Fina' (F)   SCit
– 'Hernandina' (F)   CGOG SCit
– (Mandarin Group)   ERea LCns LHol
  'Clementine' (F)
– – 'Comun' (F)   CGOG
– – 'De Nules' (F)   CGOG ECon SCit
– – 'Encore' (F)   ERea
– – 'Fortune' (F)   CGOG ECon SCit
– – 'Tomatera' (F)   CGOG
– 'Marisol' (F)   CGOG SCit
– 'Nour' (F)   CGOG SCit
§ – 'Nova' (F)   CGOG SCit

¶ – 'Orogrande' — CGOG
– × *paradisi* — See *C.* × *tangelo*
– Satsuma Group — See *C. unshiu*
– – 'Clausellina' (F) — CGOG ECon ERea
– – 'Okitsu' (F) — CGOG SCit
– – 'Owari' (F) — CGOG SCit
– 'Suntina' — See *C. reticulata* 'Nova'
sinensis (F) — ERea LPan SAPC SArc
– 'Egg' (F) — ERea
– 'Embiguo' (F) — ERea
– 'Harwood Late' (F) — ERea
– 'Jaffa' — See *C. sinensis* 'Shamouti'
– 'Lane Late' (F) — CGOG SCit
– 'Malta Blood' (F) — ECon ERea
– 'Midknight' (F) — ERea
– 'Moro Blood' (F) — ERea SCit
– 'Navelate' (F) — SCit
– 'Navelina' (F) — CGOG ECon ERea SCit
– 'Newhall' (F) — CGOG LChe SCit
– 'Parson Brown' (F) — ERea
– 'Prata' (F) — ERea
– 'Ruby' (F) — ERea
– 'Saint Michael' (F) — ERea
– 'Salustiana' (F) — CGOG SCit
– 'Sanguinelli' (F) — CGOG ERea LChe SCit
§ – 'Shamouti' (F) — ERea
– 'Succari' (F) — SCit
– 'Tarocco' (F) — SCit
– 'Thomson' (F) — ERea
– 'Valencia' (F) — ECot ERea
– 'Valencia Late' (F) — CGOG ECon ERea LChe SCit
– 'Washington' (F) — CGOG CTrC ERea GTwe LHol SCit
tachibana — SCit
× *tangelo* 'Minneola' (F) — CGOG SCit
– 'Nocatee' (F) — SCit
– 'Orlando' (F) — SCit
– 'Samson' (F) — SCit
– 'Seminole' (F) — ERea
– 'Ugli' (F) — SCit
§ *unshiu* (F) — ERea
– 'Hashimoto' (F) — CGOG SCit
volkameriana — ERea SCit

CLADIUM (Cyperaceae)
mariscus — WChe

CLADOTHAMNUS (Ericaceae)
pyroliflorus — SSta

CLADRASTIS (Papilionaceae)
kentukea ♀ — CArn CB&S CLnd CMCN CPle ELan EPfP ERod LPan MBlu NPal WCoo WDin WNor WShe WWat

CLARKIA (Onagraceae)
concinna — WOMN
* *repens* — CSpe

CLAVINODUM (Poaceae - Bambusoideae)
§ *oedogonatum* — EPla SDry

CLAYTONIA (Portulacaceae)
alsinoides — See *C. sibirica*
australasica — See *Neopaxia australasica*
caroliniana — LAma NRog
§ *megarhiza* var. *nivalis* — GDra MAsh NGre NTow NWCa
§ *nevadensis* — EMar
parvifolia — See *Naiocrene parvifolia*

§ *perfoliata* — CArn EWFC GPoy ILis WCHb WHer
§ *sibirica* — CAgr CArn CNic CRow CSpe ECoo EEls EJud LGan NBus SDys WFox WHen WPer WRHF WWye
– 'Alba' — WCot
virginica — EPot LAma MBro NRog

CLEMATIS † (Ranunculaceae)
'Abundance' (Vt) — CDoC CPev CRHN CSCl CSPN EHGC ERob ESCh ETho GMac IOrc LHol LPri MBri MCad NBea NHol NTay SBra SChu SDix SHBN SPla WSHC WWeb
'Ada Sari' (L) — MCad
addisonii — CSCl MSto WOMN
aethusifolia — CB&S CPlN CSCl CSPN ETen ETho LPri MBri NTay SBra
afoliata — CB&S CPev ECou ETho MSto
'Akaishi' — ERob ESCh MCad NTay
akebioides — CHan CPlN CSCl MCad NBrk SBra SHBN SPer WFar
'Akemi' (L) — MCad
'Akeshina' — MCad
♦ Alabast® — See *C.* Alabast = 'Poulala'
'Alba Luxurians' (Vt) ♀ — Widely available
albicoma — CSCl
'Albiflora' — CBlo CSPN MCad
I 'Albina Plena' (A/d) — ESCh ETho NBrk SPla
'Alice Fisk' (P) — CBlo CSCl ESCh LPri MCad NBea NBrk NHaw NTay SBra SHBN WGor
'Aljonushka' — CSCl ELan EOrc ERob ESCh ETho MBri MCad MGos NBea NBrk NTay SBra SMur SPer SPla WSHC
'Allanah' (J) — CRHN CSCl EHGC ELan EPfP ERob ESCh ETho LPri MCad MGos NBea NTay SBra SEas WStI
§ *alpina* (A) ♀ — CMac CPev CSCl GDra GSki IOrc MBal MBar MCad NEgg NMen NPer NRoo SHBN SIng WAbe WFar WWat
– 'Burford White' (A) — CSCl LPri MCad NBrk
– 'Columbine' (A) — CPev EBee EHGC ENot EOrc ETho LPri MBar MCad NBea NTay SBra SDix WWeb
– 'Columbine White' — See *C. alpina* 'White Columbine'
– 'Constance' (A) — CBlo CSPN EHGC EPfP ESCh ETho GMac NSti NTay SBra SPer SRms WWeb
– 'Foxy' (A) — CBlo EHGC EPfP ERob ESCh ETho GMac LPri MBri NBrk NTay
– 'Frances Rivis' (A) ♀ — Widely available
– 'Frankie' (A) — CDoC CSPN EBrP EBre EHGC ELan ERob ESCh ETho LBre MBri NTay SBra SBre WGor WWeb
– 'Helsingborg' (A) ♀ — CB&S CSCl CSPN EBrP EBre EHGC ELan ENot ESCh ETho LBre LPri MBri MCad NBea NHol NSti NTay SBra SBre SPla WFar WWes
– 'Jacqueline du Pré' (A) — CHad CPev CSCl CSPN EHGC ERob ESCh ETho IHar MCad MGos NBrk SBra SPer

– 'Jan Lindmark' See *C. macropetala* **'Jan Lindmark'**
– 'Odorata' (A) ERob MGos
§ – 'Pamela Jackman' (A) CDoC CSCl CSPN EAst EBrP EBre EHGC ELan ESCh GChr IHar IOrc LBre LFis LPri MCad MGos NBea NHol NRoo NTay SBra SBre SDix SHFr SPer WFar WWeb
– 'Pink Flamingo' (A) CBlo CSPN EBee EBrP EBre EHGC ELan ENot ERob ESCh ETho GMac LBre MBri NEgg NPri NSti NTay SBra SBre SMur WWeb
– 'Rosy Pagoda' (A) CSPN EBrP EBre EHGC ELan EPfP ESCh LBre LPri MCad NBea NBir NRoo SBre SSta WWat
– 'Ruby' (A) CMac CPev CSCl EHGC ELan ESCh ETho GChr LHol LPri MBri MCad MGos NBea NEgg NHol NSti SBra SChu SDix SHBN SPer SReu WSHC WWat WWeb
§ – subsp. *sibirica* (A) CPev MCad MSto
§ – – 'White Moth' (A) CBlo CMac CSCl CSPN EBrP EBre ELan ESCh ETho IHar LBre LPri MBri MCad NBea NBrk NHol NTay SBra SBre SPer SRms WSHC
– 'Tage Lundell' See *C.* **'Tage Lundell'**
§ – 'White Columbine' (A) ♀ CBlo CRHN CSCl CSPN EPfP ERob ESCh ETho MBri MCad NBea SBra
– 'Willy' (A) Widely available
'Ametistina' (A) ERob
◆ 'André Devillers' See *C.* **'Directeur André Devillers'**
I 'Andromeda' (Fl) ERob ESCh NTay
'Anita' (Ta) EMil ERob ESCh MCad SPer WTre
'Anna' (P) CBlo CSCl CSPN ERob MCad NTay
◆ Anna Louise See *C.* Anna Louise = **'Evithree'**
'Annabel' (P) ERob MCad
'Annamieke' (Ta) CSCl ERob SBra WTre
* 'Anniversary' LPri
¶ 'Anuska' EBrP EBre LBre SBre
apiifolia CPev CSCl ERob ESCh NTay SBra
'Arabella' (D) CBar CHad CHan CLAP CPev CPou CSCl CSPN EHGC ESCh ETho MBri MCad NBea NBrk NTay SBra SMur SPla WSHC WWeb
◆ Arctic Queen See *C.* Arctic Queen = **'Evitwo'**
aristata CPlN ECou MCad MSto
armandii CB&S CBot CHad CPev CSCl CSPN EBrP EBre EHGC ELan ENot ESCh ETho IOrc LBre LHol NHol NPal NSti NTay SArc SBra SBre SDix SHBN SPar SPer SSoC WSHC
– 'Apple Blossom' CB&S CPev CPou CSCl CSPN EHGC ERob ESCh GQui IHar IOrc LPri MCad MGos NBea NHol NTay SBra SHBN SPer SReu SSoC SSta WStI
– var. *biondiana* CMac ERob MNes SBla
– 'Bowl of Beauty' ERob MCad
– 'Jeffries' CSPN LRHS
– 'Meyeniana' ERob MCad

– 'Snowdrift' CB&S CPev CSCl CSam EPfP ESCh GOrc LPri MCad MGos NTay SEas SPer SReu SRms
× *aromatica* ERob ESCh ETho GMac LFis MCad NBea SBra
'Asagasumi' (L) MCad
'Asao' (P) CLAP CRHN CSCl CSPN EAst EBrP EBre EHGC ELan ERob ESCh ETho LBre LPri MCad NBea NTay SBra SBre SPer SSoC WWat WWeb
'Ascotiensis' (J) ♀ CPev CRHN CSCl CSPN EBee EBrP EBre EHGC ESCh ETho LBre LPri MCad NBea NTay SBra SBre SDix SPer WStI
'Ashitaka' MCad
§ 'Aureolin' (Ta) ♀ CSCl EBrP EBre EHGC EPfP LBre MBar MBri MCad MGos NBrk NHol SBra SBre
'Aurora Borealis' MCad
australis MSto
'Bagatelle' (P) MCad
'Barbara Dibley' (P) CPev CSCl CTri ESCh LPri MBri MCad NBea NTay SBod SBra SDix WBod
'Barbara Jackman' (P) CPev CSCl CSPN CSam EHGC ENot ERob ETho LPri MBar MBri MCad MRav NBea NTay SBra SDix SPer WFar WStI
barbellata (A) CSCl ERob LRHS MCad
– 'Pruinina' See *C.* **'Pruinina'**
'Beata' (L) MCad
'Beauty of Richmond' (L) CBlo EBee MCad NBea NNor SDix SPer
'Beauty of Worcester' (Fl/L) CLAP CPev CSCl CSPN EAst EBrP EBre EHGC ELan ESCh ETho LBre LPri MAsh MBar MCad NBea NEgg NHaw NTay SBra SBre SDix SPer
'Bees' Jubilee' (P) ♀ Widely available
'Bella' (J) MCad
'Belle Nantaise' (L) CBlo CPev CSCl CSPN EBrP EBre EHGC EPfP ERob ESCh ETho LBre LPri MCad NBea NTay SBre
'Belle of Woking' (Fl/P) CPev CRHN CSCl CSPN EBrP EBre EHGC ELan ERob ESCh ETho GMac LBre LPri MBar MBri MCad NBea NHaw NTay SBra SBre SDix SHBN SPer WGwG
'Bessie Watkinson' MCad
'Betina' (A) ESCh MCad
'Betty Corning' (VtxT) CSCl CSPN EBrP EBre EHGC EMil EOrc EPfP ERob ESCh ETho LBre LFis LPri MBri MCad NBrk NTay SBra SBre WBay
'Betty Risdon' ERob ETho NBea
¶ 'Big Horns' MSto
§ 'Bill MacKenzie' (Ta) ♀ Widely available
¶ 'Black Madonna' (P) ERob
'Black Prince' ELan EPfP ERob ESCh
§ 'Blekitny Anioł' (J/Vt) CBlo CRHN CSCl EPfP ERob ESCh ETho LPri MCad NBrk NTay SBra
Blue Angel See *C.* **'Blekitny Anioł'**
'Blue Belle' (Vt) CBar CPou CRHN CSCl CSPN EHGC ELan ESCh LPri MBri MCad NBea NBrk NSti NTay SBra WWeb

'Blue Bird' (A/d) — CBlo CRHN CSCl EBee EHGC EOrc IOrc LPri MCad NBea NHol SBod SBra SPer SRms

♦ 'Blue Boy' (D) — See *C.* × *eriostemon* **'Blue Boy' (D)**

'Blue Boy' (L/P) — See *C.* **'Elsa Späth'**

'Blue Dancer' (A) — CAbP CBlo CSCl EHGC ESCh ETho MBal MWat NEgg NTay WWeb WWes

'Blue Gem' (L) — CBlo ERob ESCh MCad NBrk SBra

'Blue Ravine' (P) — EHGC EPfP ERob ESCh ETho MCad NTay

× **bonstedtii** — ESCh
– 'Côte d'Azur' — NCut
– 'Crépuscule' — ERob ESCh NCut SRms
'Boskoop Beauty' (PxL) — MCad NBrk
'Bracebridge Star' (L/P) — CSCl ERob ESCh SBra
brachiata — CSCl SBra
brachyura — ERob
§ **'Brunette'** (A) — ERob ESCh MCad MGos SBra WTre
¶ **buchananiana** De Candolle — CSCl
¶ – S&SH 373 — CHan
buchananiana — See *C.* **rehderiana**
   Finet & Gagnepain
'Burford Variety' (Ta) — ERob ESCh LPri MBri MCad NBea NTay
'Burma Star' (P) — CLAP CPev ESCh MCad
'C.W. Dowman' (P) — ERob
¶ 'Caddick's Cascade' — MCad
calycina — See *C.* **cirrhosa**
campaniflora — CBot CHan CPev CPlN CSCl CSPN EHGC EOrc ERob ESCh ETho MBri MCad MSto MWhi NBea NBrk NSti NWCA SBra SDix
– 'Lisboa' — ERob ETho NBrk WSHC
'Candy Stripe' — CSCl ERob
'Capitaine Thuilleaux' — See *C.* **'Souvenir du Capitaine Thuilleaux'**
'Cardinal Wyszynski' — See *C.* **'Kardynał Wyszyński'**
'Carmencita' — GMac NBrk
'Carnaby' (L) — CB&S CSCl CSPN EAst EBrP EBre EHGC ELan ENot ESCh ETho LBre LPri MBar MBri MCad MRav NBea NHaw NTay SBod SBra SBre WWeb
'Carnival Queen' — CSCl ERob NTay
'Caroline' (J) — CPev CSCl ESCh ETho MCad NBrk
× **cartmanii** (Fo) — ECou SBla
– 'Joe' (Fo) — CB&S CSCl EHyt ESCh ETho EWes GCrs GMac ITim LPri MAsh MBri MCad MGos MLan NBea NBrk NHar SAga SMad SMrm WAbe WBay
– 'Moonbeam' (Fo) — MGos NBrk SIng SMrm WCot
'Centre Attraction' — MCad
'Chalcedony' (FlxL) — CPev CSCl ERob ESCh ETho MCad MGos NBrk NTay WMer WTre
'Charissima' (P) — CPev CSCl ERob ESCh ETho IHar LPri MBri MCad WTre
chiisanensis — EMar ERob MCad MSto SBra WCwm
♦ **chinensis** hort. — See *C.* **terniflora**
– Retz — ERob MCad
'Christian Steven' (J) — MCad
chrysantha var. **paucidentata** — See *C.* **hilariae**
– B&L 12237 — NBea SWas

N **chrysocoma** Franchet — CHan CPev CSCl EBar ELan ETho LPri MBar MCad MRav NHol SBla SBra SDix WCru WWat
¶ – ACE 1093 — CPou
– hybrid — CSCl ERob
chrysocoma hort. — See *C.* **montana** var. **sericea**
¶ **chrysosoma** hybrid — NTay
¶ 'Cicciolina' (Vt) — ERob
§ **cirrhosa** — CBlo CBot CPev CSCl ELan ESCh GSki LPri MCad SPer
– var. **balearica** ♀ — Widely available
– – forms — CPev MCad WCru
– 'Freckles' ♀ — Widely available
– 'Jingle Bells' — CBlo ERob ESCh ETho LFis LPri LRHS
– 'Wisley Cream' — CB&S CSCl CSPN EBrP EBre ECtt EHGC ELan ENot EOrc ESCh ETho LBre LPri MAsh MCad MHlr NBea NHol NSti NTay SBra SBre SChu SPer SPla WBay WSHC WWeb
coactilis — CSCl
'Colette Deville' (J) — EPfP ERob MCad NBrk SBra
columbiana — CSCl LFis MSto
– var. **columbiana** — MSto
'Comtesse de Bouchaud' (J) ♀ — CMac CPev CSCl CSPN EAst EBrP EBre EHGC ELan ENot ETho GRei IHos LBre LPri MBar MBri MCad NBea NEgg NHaw NRoo SBra SBre SDix SHBN SPer
connata — CBot CPlN ERob MSto NBrk NWCA SBra WCru
¶ – HWJCM 132 — WCru
'Corona' (PxL) — CBlo CPev CSPN EAst EBee EHGC ELan ERob LPri MBar MCad NBea NHaw NTay
'Corry' (Ta) — ESCh MCad NBrk
'Countess of Lovelace' (P) — CB&S CLAP CSCl CSPN EBrP EBre EHGC ELan ESCh ETho ICrw LBre LPri MBar MCad MGos MHlr MSte NBea NTay SBod SBra SBre SDix SPer
County Park Group (Fo) — ECou
'Crimson King' (L) — CBlo CTri ESCh MAsh MCad NTay SBod SBra WGor
§ **crispa** — CPlN CPou CSCl EPfP ERob MCad MSto NBea NTay SBra WSHC
¶ – 'Burford Bell' — WTre
§ – 'Cylindrica' — CBlo CSCl MCad MSto NBrk ERob
¶ – hybrid — ERob
I – 'Rosea' — See *C.* **crispa** **'Cylindrica'**
cunninghamii — See *C.* **parviflora**
'Cyanea' — CBlo EHGC ERob ESCh ETho GMac LPri MBri NTay
× **cylindrica** — CSCl CSPN ESCh MCad NBrk SBra
'Daniel Deronda' (P) ♀ — CPev CSCl CSPN EAst EBrP EBre EHGC ELan ERob ESCh ETho LBre LPri MBri MCad NBea NTay SBod SBra SBre SDix SPer WWal WWeb
'Dawn' (L/P) — CPev CSCl CSPN EHGC ESCh ETho LPri MCad NBea NTay SBra SPer WGwG WWal
'Debutante' — ETho
'Denny's Double' (d) — ERob ESCh MCad NBrk WTre
denticulata — WCru
dioscoreifolia — See *C.* **terniflora**

¶ 'Directeur André Devillers' (P)   ERob MCad

'Doctor Ruppel' (P) ♀   CMac CPev CSCl CSPN EAst EBrP EBre EHGC ELan ESCh ETho LBre LPri MBar MBri MCad MGos NBea NNor NRoo SBod SBra SBre SDix SHBN SPer WSHC

'Dorothy Tolver'   EHGC ERob ESCh ETho

'Dorothy Walton' (J)   CBlo CRHN CSCl CSPN ESCh ETho LPri MCad NBrk NTay SBra

douglasii   See *C. hirsutissima*

'Duchess of Albany' (T) ♀   Widely available

'Duchess of Edinburgh' (Fl)   Widely available

'Duchess of Sutherland' (Vt/d)   CPev CSCl CSPN EHGC ESCh LPri MAsh MCad NBea NTay SBra SDix WSHC

× *durandii* (D) ♀   Widely available

¶ 'Early Sensation' (Fo)   MBri MCad WTre

'Ebba'   MCad

'Edith' (L) ♀   CBlo CSCl CSPN EBrP EBre EHGC ERob ESCh ETho LBre LPri MAsh MBri MCad NBea NBrk NHaw NTay SBra SBre WGor WWat

'Edomurasaki' (L)   CBlo CSCl CSPN EHGC ESCh LPri LRHS MBri NTay

'Edouard Desfossé' (P)   CBlo CSCl EHGC ESCh LRHS NTay

'Edward Prichard'   ERob ESCh NBea NBrk

§ 'Elsa Späth' (L/P) ♀   CB&S CPev CSCl CSPN EAst EBrP EBre EHGC ELan ENot ERob ESCh ETho LBre LPri MBar MBri MCad MGos MRav NBea SBra SBre SDix SPer WMer

'Elvan' (Vt)   CHan CPev CSCl ERob ESCh GMac MCad NBea NBrk NTay WSHC

'Emilia Plater' (Vt)   ERob ESCh ETho MCad SBra WTre

'Empress of India' (P)   CBlo EBrP EBre ERob ESCh LBre LPri MCad NBea NTay SBre

§ × *eriostemon* (D)   CSCl CSPN EBar EMar EPfP ESCh LFis MCad MSte NBrk NHaw NHol NSti SBra SPer

§ – 'Blue Boy' (D)   EPfP ERob ESCh LFis MBri MCad NBrk NHaw SBra

§ – 'Hendersonii' (D)   CHad CLon CPev EAst EBrP EBre EHGC ELan EOrc ERob ESCh ETho LBre LHop MCad MRav NBea NBir NHol NTay SBra SBre SCro SDix SPer SWat WLin WOMN WSHC WWal

'Ernest Markham' (J/V) ♀   CB&S CMac CPev CSCl CSPN EAst EBrP EBre EHGC ELan ENot ETho GChr LBre LPri MBar MBri MCad MGos NBea NHaw NRoo SBra SBre SDix SHBN SPer WFar

'Esperanto' (J)   MCad

¶ 'Etoile de Malicorne' (P)   NTay

'Etoile de Malicorne' (P)   CBlo EBee ESCh ETho MBri MCad NBea WGor WSHC

'Etoile de Paris' (P)   CBlo CSCl ERob ESCh ETho LRHS NTay SBra

'Etoile Rose' (T)   CHan CLAP CPev CSCl CSPN EAst EBrP EBre EHGC ELan EOrc ERob ESCh ETho IOrc LBre LFis LPri MCad NBea NTay SBra SBre SChu SMur SPer WFar WSHC

'Etoile Violette' (Vt) ♀   CBar CLAP CMac CSCl CSPN EAst EHGC ELan ENot EOrc ESCh ETho LPri MBar MBri MCad MHlr NBea NSti SBod SBra SChu SDix SHBN SPer SSta WSHC WWat WWeb

§ Liberation® = 'Evifive'   EBee EHGC ERob ESCh ETho LRHS NTay

§ Royal Velvet® = 'Evifour'   CB&S CSCl CSPN EHGC ESCh ETho MBri MCad NTay WWeb

¶ Josephine® = 'Evijohill'   ESCh ETho LRHS NPri NTay WWeb

§ Sugar Candy® = 'Evione' (P)   CB&S CBlo CSPN EBrP EBre EHGC EMil ESCh ETho LBre MAsh MBri NPri NTay SBre WWeb WWes

¶ Blue Moon® = 'Evirin'   ESCh ETho LRHS NPri

§ Petit Faucon® = 'Evisix'   CBlo CSCl EBrP EBre EHGC ETho LBre LRHS MBri NTay SBre

§ Anna Louise® = 'Evithree' (P)   CSCl CSPN EBee EHGC ERob ESCh ETho LRHS MBri MCad NTay

§ Arctic Queen® = 'Evitwo' (Fl)   CB&S CBlo CSCl CSPN EBrP EBre EHGC ESCh ETho LBre LPri MBri MCad NBea NTay SBre WBay WLRN WTre WWeb WWes

'Fair Rosamond' (L/P)   CPev CSCl CSPN EHGC EPfP ERob ESCh ETho LPri MBri MCad NBea NTay SBod SBra SDix

'Fairy Queen' (L)   CSCl ESCh ETho LPri MCad NTay SBra

fargesii   See *C. potaninii*

× *fargesioides*   See *C.* 'Paul Farges'

fasciculiflora   CBot CGre CMHG CPlN CSCl ETen MCad SSpi WCru SBla

– L 657

♦ *finetiana* hort.   See *C. indivisa*

– L.   SDix

'Firefly'   ESCh NTay

'Fireworks' (P) ♀   COtt CSCl CSPN EAst EBee EBrP EBre EHGC ENot ESCh ETho LBre MBri MCad NBea NPri NTay SBra SBre WFoF WGor WStI WWeb

'Flamingo' (L)   MCad

flammula   Widely available

* – *rotundiflora*   CSCl

– 'Rubra Marginata'   See *C.* × *triternata* **'Rubromarginata'**

florida

– 'Bicolor'   See *C. florida* **'Sieboldii'**

– 'Flore Pleno' (d)   CPev CSCl CSPN EBrP EBre ELan EOrc ESCh ETho LBre MCad NBea NHol NTay SBra SBre SHBN SMad SPer SPla SSoC

§ – 'Sieboldii'   Widely available

foetida   CB&S MSto

forrestii   See *C. napaulensis*

§ *forsteri* — CB&S CPlN CSCl CSPN CSam ESCh GSki LPri MCad NBrk NTay SBod SBra WCru WOMN WSHC WWat

– × *indivisa* — WCru

'Four Star' (L) — LPri MCad NTay

'Fuji-musume' (L) — CSCl ERob LPri MCad WMer

fusca hort. — See *C. japonica*

◆ – *koreana* — See *C. koreana*

– Turczaninow — MCad MSto

¶ – var. *coreana* f. *umbrosa* — WCru
　B&SWJ 700

– dwarf form — MSto

§ – subsp. *fusca* — CSCl ESCh

– var. *kamtschatica* — See *C. fusca* Turczaninow subsp. *fusca*

– var. *mandshurica* — CSCl

§ – var. *violacea* — CSCl EHyt EPfP ERob ESCh ETho MCad MSto NBea SBra WSHC

'G. Steffner' (A) — ESCh

'Gabriëlle' (P) — ERob ESCh MCad WMer

'Général Sikorski' (L) ♀ — CMac CSCl CSPN CSam EAst EBrP EBre EHGC ELan ESCh ETho LBre LPri MBri MCad MGos NBea NHaw NTay SBra SBre SDix SPer WWat

gentianoides — CSCl CSPN ERob GCHN MCad

'Gillian Blades' (P) ♀ — CSCl CSPN EAst EBrP EBre EHGC ELan EPfP ESCh ETho LBre MBri MCad NBea NBrk NTay SBra SBre SSoC

'Gipsy Queen' (J) ♀ — CB&S CPev CRHN CSCl CSPN EBrP EBre EHGC ELan ENot ERob ESCh ETho GChr LBre LPri MBar MBri MCad NBea NTay SBod SBra SBre SDix SHBN SPer WFar WWat

'Gladys Picard' (P) — ERob ESCh MCad

glauca hort. — See *C. intricata*

glaucophylla — CSCl

glycinoides — GSki MSto

'Glynderek' (L) — ERob ESCh MCad NTay

'Golden Harvest' (Ta) — ERob

◆ Golden Tiara® — See *C.* Golden Tiara = 'Kugotia'

gouriana — ERob ESCh NTay SBra

¶ – subsp. *lishanensis* — WCru
　B&SWJ 292

gracilifolia — ELan ERob ESCh LRHS

'Grandiflora Sanguinea' — See *C.* 'Södertälje'
　Johnson

grata CC 1895 — WHCr

– hort. — See *C.* × *jouiniana*

– Wallich — CPev MCad NBrk

'Gravetye Beauty' (T) — CHad CPev CSCl CSPN EAst EHGC ELan EOrc ESCh ETho LFis LHol LPri MBri MCad NBea NRoo SBra SDix SHBN SMad SPer SReu SSta WMer WSHC WWat

'Green Velvet' (Fo) — CSCl ECou

¶ *grewiiflora* B&SWJ 2956 — WCru

'Guernsey Cream' (P) — CBlo CSCl CSPN EBrP EBre ECle EHGC EMil ESCh ETho LBre LPri MBri MCad NBea NTay SBra SBre WLRN WTre WWeb WWes

'Guiding Star' — ERob ESCh MCad NTay SBra

'H.F. Young' (L/P) ♀ — CLAP CPev CRHN CSCl CSPN EBrP EBre EHGC ELan ESCh ETho LBre LPri MBar MBri MCad MGos NBea NTay SBod SBra SBre SChu SDix SHBN SPer SSta WStI WWin

'Hagley Hybrid' (J) — Widely available

'Haku-ôkan' (L) — CPev CSCl CSPN EBrP EBre EHGC ESCh ETho LBre LPri MAsh MCad NBea NTay SBod SBra SBre WWeb

'Hanaguruma' (P) — ESCh MCad WMer

'Haruyama' — MCad

Havering hybrids (Fo) — ECou

¶ 'Heather Herschell' — CPev

'Helen Cropper' (P) — EPfP ERob MCad NBrk

'Helios' (Ta) — CSCl EHGC ENot EPfP ERob ESCh ETho IHar MBri MCad MGos NBrk SBra WCot

hendersonii Koch — See *C.* × *eriostemon* 'Hendersonii'

– Standley — See *C.* × *eriostemon*

'Henryi' ♀ — CPev CSCl CSPN EAst EBrP EBre EHGC ELan ENot ESCh ETho IOrc LBre LPri MBar MBri MCad MLan NBea NTay SBra SBre SDix SPer SPla WSHC

henryi var. *morii* — WCru
　B&SWJ 1668

heracleifolia — CBot CPou CSCl EHGC ESCh GCra GSki MCad NLar NRoo

N – 'Campanile' — CPev CSCl ERob ESCh LPri MCad NBea NBir NTay SDix

N – 'Côte d'Azur' — ESCh MCad MTed

– var. *davidiana* — CPev CPle ELan ESCh NHol SRms WTre

– – 'Wyevale' ♀ — CHan CPev CSCl CSPN CSpe EBrP EBre ELan ERob ESCh ETho IHos LBre LHop LPri MBri MCad NBea NTay SBra SBre SCro SDix SPer SSoC WEas WFar WHil WWye

– 'Roundway Blue Bird' — CBot

'Herbert Johnson' (P) — CPev MCad NBrk SBra

hexapetala — CSCl ERob

– De Candolle — See *C. forsteri*

– hort. — See *C. recta* subsp. *recta* var. *lasiosepala*

'Hidcote Purple' (L) — MCad

'Hikarugenji' — ERob ESCh MCad NTay

§ *hilariae* — CSCl EBee ERob ESCh SBra

§ *hirsutissima* — CSCl MSto NOak

– var. *scottii* — ERob WOMN

'Honora' (P) — ESCh MCad

hookeriana — MSto

'Horn of Plenty' (L/P) ♀ — CSCl CSPN EHGC ESCh ETho MBri MCad NBea NPri NTay SBra

'Huldine' (Vt) — Widely available

§ 'Hybrida Sieboldii' (L) — CMac CRHN CSCl CSPN EHGC ERob ESCh LPri MCad NBea NBrk NTay SBra SPer

'Hythe Egret' — EHyt

ianthina — See *C. fusca* var. *violacea* Turczaninow

'Imperial' (P/d) — ERob

§ *indivisa* — CPev CSCl EHGC LPri MCad

– (f) — MCad

– 'Fairy' (Fo) — ECou

– var. *lobata* — CSCl EHGC

– (m) — MCad

integrifolia | CPou CSCl EHGC ESCh GMac
LFis LGan LHop LPri MBri
MBro MCad MGos MTho NFla
NHol NLar NPer NRoo NSti
SPer SRms SSoC WCru WFar
WPer

– 'Alba' | CBot CSCl EHGC EPfP NTay
SPer WSHC

§ – var. *albiflora* | CHad EBee ESCh ETho GBuc
LPri MBel MBri MCad NBea
NBir NBrk NRoo SBra WCru

– 'Amy' | ERob
* – 'Cascade' | CSCl
* – 'Finnis Form' | SChu
¶ – 'Floris V' | ERob
I – 'Hendersonii' hort. | ETho
– 'Hendersonii' Koch | See *C.* x *eriostemon*
| **'Hendersonii'**

– 'Lauren' | ERob
– 'Olgae' | CHad CLAP CPev CSCl CSPN
EBee ESCh ETho LPri MCad
NBea NBrk NTay SBra SDix
WTre

– 'Pangbourne Pink' | CHad CLAP EHGC ESCh
ETho GBuc MCad NBea NBrk
NHaw NTay SBra WCru WSHC

– 'Pastel Blue' | CPev ERob ESCh MCad NBea
– 'Pastel Pink' | CPev ERob ESCh ETho MCad
– 'Rosea' ♀ | CBot CLon CPev CSCl CSPN
EHGC ERob ESCh ETho LGan
LPri MBri MCad MTho NBea
NBrk NTay SPer SSoC WCru

– 'Tapestry' | CPev CSCl ERob MCad NTay
SBra

– white | See *C. integrifolia* var. *albiflora*
§ *intricata* | CSCl CSPN EPfP ETen MCad
MSto WCot WWat
'Ishobel' (P) | CSCl ERob ESCh LPri MCad
NBrk

ispahanica | See *C. orientalis* **Linnaeus**
'Ivan Olsson' (PxL) | EPfP ERob ESCh LPri
'Jackmanii' ♀ | CB&S CMac CRHN CSCl CTri
EBrP EBre EHGC ENot ERob
ESCh ETho GRei IHar IHos
LBre MCad NBea NEgg NRoo
NWea SBod SBra SBre SPer
SSoC WWeb

'Jackmanii Alba' (J) | CPev CSCl CSPN EAst EBrP
EBre EHGC ELan ESCh ETho
LBre LPri MBar MBri MCad
NBea NBrk NTay SBra SBre
SDix SPer

'Jackmanii Rubra' (J) | CPev CRHN CSCl ERob ESCh
LPri MAsh MCad NBea SBra
WLRN

N 'Jackmanii Superba' (J) | CMac CPev CSCl CSPN EAst
EBrP EBre EHGC ELan ETho
GChr LBre LPri MBar MBri
MCad MGos NBea NTay SBra
SBre SDix SHBN SPer SReu
SSta WBod

¶ 'Jacqueline' | LRHS
'James Mason' | CBlo CPev CSCl CSPN EHGC
ESCh ETho LRHS MCad NTay
WMer WTre

§ 'Jan Pawel II' (J) | CBlo CMac CSCl CSPN EBee
EBrP EBre EHGC ELan ESCh
ETho IHar LBre LPri MCad
NBea NTay SBra SBre SPer

§ *japonica* | CBlo CPev CSCl MCad MSto
NBea NBrk

♦ – var. *obvallata* | See *C. obvallata*

'Jashio' | MCad
¶ 'Jennifer Valentine' | MCad
'Jenny Caddick' | ERob MCad
'Jim Hollis' (Fl) | ERob MCad NTay
¶ 'Joan Gray' | ERob
'Joan Picton' (P) | CSCl ESCh LPri MAsh MCad
NBea NTay SBra

'John Gould Veitch' (Fl) | MCad
* 'John Gudmunsson' | ESCh
'John Huxtable' (J) | CDoC CPev CRHN CSCl
EHGC ERob ESCh ETho LPri
MCad NBea NBrk NHaw NTay
SBra SDix WGor

John Paul II | See *C.* **'Jan Pawel II'**
'John Warren' (L) | CSCl EHGC ESCh ETho LPri
MCad NBea NTay SBod SBra
SDix SPer WWeb

'Jorma' (J) | MCad
§ x *jouiniana* | EBee EHGC ERob ESCh GBuc
GOrc MBal MBlu MCad SPer
WSHC

§ – 'Mrs Robert Brydon' | ELan EPfP ERob MCad NBea
NBrk NFla NTay SBra SHel
SPer WCot

– 'Praecox' ♀ | CLAP CPev CRHN CSCl EAst
EFou EHal ELan EOrc EPla
ESCh ETho GMac LPri MAus
MBar MBri MCad NBea NBir
NHol NPro SBra SChu SDix
SPer WWeb

'Kacper' (L) | CSCl LPri MCad NTay
§ 'Kakio' (P) | CSCl EAst EBee EHGC ELan
ENot ERob ESCh ETho LPri
MCad NBea NTay SBra SPer
WLRN

'Kaleidoscope' | MCad
§ 'Kardynał Wyszyński' (J) | CBlo CRHN CSCl EBee EHGC
ESCh LPri MCad MGos NBea
NTay SBra

'Kasugayama' (L) | ERob MCad
'Katherine' | MCad WMer
'Kathleen Dunford' (Fl) | CBlo CSCl EHGC ESCh LPri
MAsh MCad NBea NTay SBra
WMer

'Kathleen Wheeler' (P) | CBlo CMac CPev EBrP EBre
EHGC ERob ESCh ETho LBre
LPri MCad NBea NTay SBra
SBre SDix

'Keith Richardson' (P) | CPev CSCl LPri MCad NBea
NBrk NTay SBra

'Ken Donson' (L) ♀ | CBlo EBee EHGC EPfP ESCh
ETho MBri MCad NBrk NTay
SBod SBra

'Kermesina' (Vt) | Widely available
'King Edward VII' (L) | CSPN EHGC EPfP ERob ESCh
ETho LPri LRHS NBea NBrk
SBra WGor WStl WTre

'King George V' (L) | ERob ESCh NBrk NTay SBra
'Kiri Te Kanawa' | CPev CSCl EPfP ERob ESCh
MCad NBrk WTre

kirilovii | CSCl ERob GSki
'Königskind' (P) | ERob ESCh MCad
koreana | CSCl ERob MCad MSto NBea
♦ – 'Brunette' | See *C.* **'Brunette'**
* – *citra* | ESCh
– var. *fragrans* | CSCl
– f. *lutea* | CSCl EHyt MCad MSto
'Kosmiczeskaja Melodija' | MCad
(J)

§ Golden Tiara® = | ESCh ETho MAsh MCad MGos
'Kugotia' (Ta) | NBea NTay WLRN WWeb

¶ 'Kyllus' (L) | NTay

ladakhiana CHan CPev CSCl EPfP ESCh
ETho GQui MCad MSto NBea
NBir NTay SBra WCru

'Lady Betty Balfour' CPev CSCl CSPN EBar EBrP
(J/Vt) EBre EHGC ELan ESCh LBre
LPri MBri MCad NHaw NTay
SBra SBre SDix WFar WWal

'Lady Caroline Nevill' (L) CPev CSCl EHGC ERob ESCh
ETho LPri MCad NBea NTay
SBra

'Lady in Red' LPri

'Lady Londesborough' (P) CPev CSCl CSPN EHGC ELan
ESCh ETho LPri MCad NBea
NBrk NTay SBra SDix WLRN

'Lady Northcliffe' (L) CPev CSCl CTri EHGC ELan
EPfP ESCh ISea LPri MAsh
MCad NBea NTay SBra SDix
SPer

'Ladybird Johnson' (T) CPev CSCl ERob ESCh ETho
MCad NBrk

¶ 'Lanuginosa Candida' MCad

lasiandra CSCl ERob

lasiantha CSCl ESCh MSto

'Lasurstern' (P) ♀ CB&S CPev CSCl CSPN EAst
EBrP EBre EHGC ELan ENot
ERob ESCh ETho LBre LPri
MBar MBri MCad MLan NBea
NHaw NTay SBod SBra SBre
SDix SPer SSoC WFar WSHC

'Laura' (L) MCad

'Laura Denny' (P) CSCl MCad NBrk

'Lavender Lace' MCad

'Lawsoniana' (L) CSCl CSPN EAst EHGC ESCh
LPri MAsh MBar MCad NBea
NBrk NTay SBra

'Lemon Chiffon' (P) CSCl EHGC ERob MCad NBrk
NTay SBra

♦ Liberation See *C.* Liberation = 'Evifive'

§ *ligusticifolia* CSCl ERob GSki MSto

'Lilacina Floribunda' (L) CSCl CSPN EBar EHGC ELan
ESCh LPri MBar MCad NBea
NBrk NHaw NTay SBra

'Lilactime' CBlo EHGC ERob ESCh LPri
NBea

'Lincoln Star' (P) CMac CPev CSCl CSPN CSam
EAst EBrP EBre EHGC ELan
ERob ESCh ETho LBre LPri
MBar MCad MRav NBea NBrk
NTay SBra SBre SDix SPer

'Lincolnshire Lady' WPen

'Little Joe' EHyt

'Little Nell' (Vt) CPev CRHN CSCl CSPN EAst
EBrP EBre EHGC ELan ESCh
ETho LBre LHol LPri MBri
MCad MHlr NBea NBrk NHol
NSti NTay SBod SBra SBre
SDix SPer SSta WFar WSHC

¶ 'Lord Herschell' CPev

'Lord Nevill' (P) ♀ CPev CSCl EBrP EBre ESCh
IHar LBre LPri MBri MCad
NTay SBod SBra SBre SDix

'Louise Rowe' (Fl) CSCl EBee EBrP EBre EHGC
ELan ESCh ETho IHar LBre
LPri MCad NBea NTay SBra
SBre SPla

'Lucie' (P) ESCh MCad

'Lunar Lass' (Fo) ECho EHyt ETho LBee MCad
WAbe

'Lunar Lass' × *foetida* EBee ECou GCHN

'Luther Burbank' (J) ERob ESCh MCad

macropetala (A/d) CB&S CPev CSCl EAst EHGC
ELan ENot EPot ERob ESCh
GChr GDra LHol LPri MBal
MBar MCad MGos MWat NBea
NEgg NHol SBod SDix WBod
WWat WWin

– 'Ballerina' (A/d) MCad

– 'Ballet Skirt' (A/d) EHGC ERob ESCh MCad
MGos WTre

– 'Blue Lagoon' See *C. macropetala* 'Lagoon'

– 'Chili' CBlo ERob ESCh NBrk NTay

♦ – 'Floralia' See *C.* 'Floralia'

– forms (A/d) CPev

♦ – 'Harry Smith' See *C. macropetala* 'Chili'

§ – 'Jan Lindmark' (A/d) CSPN EBee EBrP EBre EHGC
ESCh ETho LBre MCad MGos
NBea NBir NTay SBra SBre
SPla WFar WGor

§ – 'Lagoon' (A/d) EHGC ERob ETho LRHS
NBrk SBra SMur

* – 'Lord Neville' EHGC

– 'Maidwell Hall' CDoC CMac CSCl EBrP EBre
hort. (A/d) ♀ EHGC ERob ESCh ETho LBre
LFis LPri MCad MGos NBea
NBrk NHol NRoo SBra SBre
SChu SHBN SPer SPla WSHC

– 'Markham's Pink' (A/d) Widely available
♀

– 'Pauline' (A/d) ERob NBrk SBra

¶ – 'Pearl Rose' (A/d) ERob

¶ – 'Purple Spider' (A/d) ERob ESCh LRHS MBri WTre
WWeb

– 'Snowbird' (A/d) CBlo CPev ERob ESCh ETho
NBea NHol SBra

– 'Vicky' (A/d) CSCl

– 'Wesselton' (A/d) ERob ETho NHol

– 'White Lady' (A/d) ERob ESCh SDix

– 'White Moth' See *C. alpina* subsp. *sibirica*
'White Moth'

– 'White Swan' See *C.* 'White Swan'

¶ – 'White Wings' (A/d) ESCh

'Madame Baron Veillard' CPev CSCl CSPN EAst EBrP
(J) EBre EHGC ESCh ETho IHar
LBre LPri MBar MCad MHlr
NBrk NTay SBra SBre SDix

'Madame Edouard André' CDoC CPev CRHN CSCl CTri
(J) ♀ EHGC EPfP ERob ESCh ETho
LPri MCad NBea NTay SBra
SDix

'Madame Grangé' (J) ♀ CPev CRHN CSPN EHGC
EPfP ESCh ETho GMac LPri
MCad NBea NBrk NHaw NTay
SBod SBra SDix

'Madame Julia Correvon' Widely available
(Vt) ♀

'Madame le Coultre' See *C.* 'Marie Boisselot'

'Madame van Houtte' (L) ESCh MCad

'Majojo' (Fo) CB&S

'Mammut' (P) ERob ESCh

§ *mandschurica* CSCl ERob MCad MSto

¶ – B&SWJ 1060 WCru

marata CSCl MSto

'Marcel Moser' (P) CPev ESCh MCad NBrk NTay
SBra SDix WFar

'Margaret Hunt' (J) CBlo CSCl CSPN EBee EHGC
ELan ERob ESCh LPri MCad
NBea NBrk NTay SBra SPla

'Margaret Wood' (P) ERob ESCh MCad

'Margot Koster' (Vt) CBlo CDoC CRHN CSCl EBrP
EBre EHGC ESCh LBre LPri
MBri MCad NBea NHaw NTay
SBra SBre WSHC

§ 'Marie Boisselot' (L) ♀ — Widely available
'Marie Louise Jensen' (J) — ESCh MCad NTay
marmoraria ♀ — CPBP CSCl EPot GCLN MCad NHar SBla SWas WAbe WCot WFar
– × *cartmanii* 'Joe' — NHar
– hybrid — LBee LRHS NHar WAbe
– × *petriei* (f) — CSCl
§ 'Maskarad' (Vt) — CBlo CSPN EBee EBrP EBre EHGC ERob ESCh ETho LBre NBrk SBra SBre WLRN WWeb
¶ 'Masquerade' (P) — MBri NTay SMur
Masquerade (Vt) — See *C.* **'Maskarad' (Vt)**
§ 'Matka Teresa' — MCad
'Maureen' (L) — CPev CSCl CSPN EBee EHGC ESCh ETho LPri MCad NBea SBra SDix
¶ *mauritiana* — CSCl ERob
maximowicziana — See *C.* **terniflora**
'Meeli' (J) — MCad
§ 'Mevrouv Oud' (P) — ESCh
microphylla — ECou MCad MSto
'Miikla' (J) — ERob
'Minister' (P) — MCad
'Minuet' (Vt) ♀ — CHad CRHN CSCl CSPN EBrP EBre EHGC ELan ESCh ETho IOrc LBre LPri MBri MCad NBea NHol NRoo NTay SBra SBre SChu SDix SPer SVil WSHC WWeb
'Miriam Markham' (J) — CBlo CPev ERob ESCh MCad NBea
'Miss Bateman' (P) ♀ — CMac CPev CSCl CSPN EAst EBrP EBre EHGC ELan ERob ESCh ETho LBre LPri MBar MBri MCad MPla NBea SBod SBra SBre SDix SPer WSHC
'Miss Crawshay' (P) — CBlo CPev CSCl EBee EHGC ESCh MCad NBea NTay SBra
N *montana* — CB&S CPev CSam CTrw ENot ESCh GChr GRei IHos LPri MBal MBar MCad MGos MWat NBea NEgg NHol NRoo SBod SBra SDix SHBN SSta WWeb
– *alba* — See *C. montana*
– 'Alexander' — CBlo CDoC CPou CSCl CSPN EHGC ERob LPri MCad MGos NTay SBra WCru
* – 'Boughton Beauty' — WWeb
* – 'Broughton Star' (d) — CBlo CGre CHad CPou CRHN CSCl CSPN EHGC ESCh ETho GMac LFis LPri MBri MCad MGos NBea NHaw SBra WWeb
– 'Continuity' ♀ — EHGC MCad SBra SDix WSHC
– 'Elizabeth' ♀ — Widely available
– 'Fragrant Spring' — ERob ESCh MCad MGos NTay SBra WTre
– 'Freda' ♀ — CRHN CSCl EBrP EBre EHGC ENot ESCh ETho GMac IHar LBre LPri MBri MCad MGos NBea NHol NRoo NSti SBra SBre SDix SHBN SMad SPer WCru
– 'Gothenburg' — CBlo EBee EHGC EPfP ERob ESCh ETho SBra WWes
– f. *grandiflora* ♀ — CHad CMac EBrP EBre ECtt EHGC ELan ENot ERob ESCh ETho GOrc ISea LBre LBuc LPri MBri MCad MGos NBea NTay SBra SBre SPer SReu WSHC WWat WWeb
¶ – 'Hidcote' — ERob

¶ – 'Jackie' — WWeb
* – 'Lilacina' — CBlo
– 'Marjorie' (d) — Widely available
– 'Mayleen' — CBlo CHad CPou CSCl EBee EBrP EBre EHGC ESCh ETho GMac LBre LPri MBri MCad MGos NBea NTay SBra SBre SHBN SPer SPla WPen WWeb
– 'Mrs Margaret Jones' (d) — CSCl EHol ERob ESCh ETho NBrk SBra
– 'New Dawn' — ERob ESCh MCad SBra WTre
– 'Odorata' — CBlo CDoC CSCl ELan EPfP ERob ETho GSki MCad MGos NTay SBra WGor WWat
* – 'Olga' — ESCh
– 'Peveril' — CPev CSCl ERob ETho IHar MCad NBrk SBra
– 'Picton's Variety' — CDoC CPev CSCl ETho LPri MCad NBea NHol SBra SHBN SPer SRms
– 'Pink Perfection' — CDoC CSCl EAst EBrP EBre EHGC ELan ESCh ETho GOrc LBre LPri MCad NBea NBrk NHaw NHol NTay SBra SBre SPer WStI WWeb
– 'Pleniflora' (d) — MCad MGos SBra
– var. *rubens* ♀ — Widely available
¶ – *rubens* 'East Morning' — NBrk
– var. *rubens* 'Odorata' — EHGC ESCh
– 'Rubens Superba' — See *C. montana* **'Superba'**
§ – var. *sericea* ♀ — CBot CHan CPev CTri ESCh LPri LRHS MCad NBea NBrk NTay SBra SRms WCru WFoF WWat WWeb
– 'Spooneri' — See *C. montana* var. *sericea*
§ – 'Superba' — CBlo ECtt SHBN
– 'Tetarose' ♀ — Widely available
– 'Veitch's Form' — CBot
– 'Vera' — CSPN EBee EHGC ERob ESCh ETho GMac MCad NBea NBir NBrk NTay SBra WCru
– 'Warwickshire Rose' — CHan ETho MCad MGos NBrk NHaw NHol NPro NTay SBra WSHC WWeb
– var. *wilsonii* — CBot CLan CPev CSCl CSPN CSam EBrP EBre EHGC ELan ESCh ETho LBre LHol LPri MBar MCad MRav MWat NBea NTay SBra SBre SDix SPer WSHC WWeb
'Monte Cassino' (J) — CSCl ERob ESCh MCad
§ 'Moonlight' (P) — CPev CSCl ERob ESCh LPri MCad NBea NBrk SBra
'Moonman' (Fo) — EHyt ETho
* 'Morning Cloud' — MCad
'Mother Theresa' — See *C.* **'Matka Teresa'**
'Mrs Bush' (L) — CBlo ESCh LRHS MCad NBea NTay WWes
'Mrs Cholmondeley' (L) ♀ — CMac CPev CSCl CSPN CSam EAst EBrP EBre EHGC ELan ENot ESCh ETho LBre LPri MBar MBri MCad MGos NBea NTay SBra SBre SDix SPer WFar WSHC
'Mrs George Jackman' (P) ♀ — CPev EHGC ERob ESCh ETho LPri MCad NBea NBrk NTay SBra SDix WStI
'Mrs Hope' (L) — CPev ESCh MAsh MCad NBea NBrk NTay SBra WTre
'Mrs James Mason' — CPev CSCl ESCh ETho MCad NBea SBra

'Mrs N. Thompson' (P)	CMac CPev CSCl CSPN EAst EBrP EBre EHGC ELan ENot ERob ESCh ETho IHar LBre LPri MBar MBri MCad NBea NHaw NTay SBod SBre SDix SHBN SSoC SSta
♦'Mrs Oud'	See *C.* **'Mevrouv Oud'**
'Mrs P.B. Truax' (P)	CBlo CSCl CSPN EBee EHGC ESCh LPri MCad NBea NRoo NTay SBra SDix WLRN
'Mrs Robert Brydon'	See *C.* × *jouiniana* **'Mrs Robert Brydon'**
'Mrs Spencer Castle' (Vt)	CPev CSCl ERob ESCh LPri MAsh MCad NBea NTay
'Mrs T. Lundell'	ERob ESCh ETho MCad NBrk
'Mukle'	MCad
'Multi Blue'	CB&S CSCl CSPN CTri EBrP EBre EHGC ELan ENot ERob ESCh ETho IHar LBre LPri MBri MCad MGos NBea NTay SBra SBre SMad SSoC
'Muly'	MCad
'Musa China' (L)	MCad
'Myôjô' (P)	CSCl CSPN EHGC ESCh ETho LPri MCad NTay WMer
'Myôkô' (L)	CBlo MCad WMer
§ *napaulensis*	CB&S CPev CPIN CSCl EPot ERob ESCh IBlr LPri MCad MSto NBea SBra SHFr WCru WLRN WSHC WTre
'Natacha' (P)	ERob ESCh MCad
'Negritjanka' (J)	ERob
'Nelly Moser' (L/P) ♀	Widely available
New Zealand hybrids	ECou
'Nikolai Rubtsov'	ERob ESCh MCad NTay
'Niobe' (J) ♀	Widely available
'North Star'	See *C.* **'Pôhjanael'**
'Nuit de Chine'	MCad
obscura	CSCl
§ *obvallata*	CSCl
§ *occidentalis*	CSCl MSto
– var. *dissecta*	SSpi
– subsp. *occidentalis*	CSCl
ochotensis	CSCl MCad MSto
ochroleuca	MSto
'Olimpiada-80' (L)	ESCh SPla
* 'Opaline'	MCad
orientalis hort.	See *C. tibetana* subsp. *vernayi*
– 'Bill MacKenzie'	See *C.* **'Bill MacKenzie'**
– 'Orange Peel'	See *C. tibetana* subsp. *vernayi* **'Orange Peel'**
* – 'Rubromarginata'	CPev
– 'Sherriffii'	See *C. tibetana* subsp. *vernayi* **LS&E 13342**
§ *orientalis* Linnaeus	EHGC ELan EPfP ESCh GSki MCad MSto NChi NHol SBod SBra SReu
– var. *daurica*	CHan
– var. *orientalis*	CStr ETho
– var. *tenuifolia*	ERob
'Otto Froebel' (L)	ETho MCad NTay
'Paddington'	ETho
'Pagoda' (PxVt)	CDoC CPev CRHN CSCl CSPN EHGC EOrc ESCh ETho LFis MCad NBea NTay SBra SPla SRms WSHC WWat
'Pamela Jackman'	See *C. alpina* **'Pamela Jackman'**
paniculata Gmelin	See *C. indivisa*
¶ – 'Lobata'	CSCl WTre
– Thunberg	See *C. terniflora*
* 'Paola'	MCad NTay
'Parasol'	ERob
§ *parviflora*	MSto
– × *forsteri*	ESCh
* 'Pastel Princess'	MCad NTay
patens	CBlo CSPN EHGC WTre
– Chinese form	ERob ESCh
– Japanese form	ERob ESCh
¶ 'Patricia Ann Fretwell'	CPev EBrP EBre LBre LRHS SBre
§ 'Paul Farges'	CB&S CSPN EHGC ERob ETho LFis MBri MCad NBrk NTay SBra WWeb
'Pennell's Purity' (L)	ESCh MCad
'Percy Picton' (P)	MAsh
'Perle d'Azur' (J) ♀	Widely available
'Perrin's Pride' (Vt)	CSCl CSPN EHGC ERob ESCh ETho MCad NBrk NTay WFar WMer
¶ *peterae*	CSCl ERob
♦ Petit Faucon	See *C.* Petit Faucon = **'Evisix'**
petriei	ECou EHyt EPot ESCh NTow
– × *foetida*	ECou
– × *forsteri*	ECou
– 'Limelight' (m)	CSCl
– × *marmoraria*	GCHN
– 'Princess' (f)	CSCl ECou
¶ 'Peveril Peach'	CPev
'Peveril Pearl' (P)	CBlo CPev CSCl CSPN EBee EHGC ERob ESCh ETho LPri MCad NTay WWeb
¶ 'Peveril Pendant'	CPev
phlebantha	CPIN
I 'Phoenix' (P)	ESCh
pierotii	ERob
'Pink Champagne'	See *C.* **'Kakio'**
'Pink Fantasy' (J)	CPev CSCl CSPN CTri EBee EBrP EBre EHGC ESCh ETho IHar LBre LPri MAsh MBar MCad NBea NBrk NTay SBra SBre WWeb
'Pink Pearl'	MCad NBea NBrk
§ *pitcheri*	CHan CPev CPIN CSCl EHGC ELan ERob ESCh MBri MCad MSto NBea NBrk NTay SSpi WSHC
* – 'Phil Mason'	CSCl
* 'Pixie'	MGos
§ 'Pôhjanael' (J)	ERob ESCh MCad
'Polish Spirit' (Vt) ♀	Widely available
§ *potaninii*	CSCl ELan MBri MCad SBra
§ – var. *potaninii*	CGle CHan CPev EPfP ERob ETen MBri MCad MGed NBea SBra
– var. *souliei*	See *C. potaninii* var. *potaninii*
§ Alabast® = 'Poulala' (Fl)	CBlo EBee EHGC EMil ERob ESCh ETho MCad NTay
§ Vino® = 'Poulvo' (J)	CBlo CSCl CSPN EBee EHGC ERob ESCh ETho ICrw IHar MBri MCad NTay
¶ 'Prairie River' (A)	ERob
'Prince Charles' (J)	CHad CLAP CPou CSCl EBee EBrP EBre EHGC ELan ESCh ETho LBre LPri MCad NBea NBir NHaw NRoo NTay SBra SBre SDix SPla WSHC
'Prince Philip' (P)	ERob ESCh
§ 'Princess Diana' (T)	CBlo CPev ERob ESCh ETho NBrk
'Princess of Wales' (L)	CHan CSCl EHGC ESCh LPri LRHS MCad NBea SBra WSHC
'Prins Hendrik' (L/P)	CBlo CSCl EHGC ERob ESCh MCad WGor

'Proteus' (Fl) — CPev CSCl CSPN EAst EBar EBrP EBre EHGC ELan ESCh ETho IHar LBre LPri MCad NBea NTay SBra SBre SDix SPer SPla WSHC WWeb

¶ *psilandra* B&SWJ 3650 — WCru

quadribracteolata — ECou EHyt

'Queen Alexandra' (P) — ERob MCad

'Ramona' — See *C.* **'Hybrida Sieboldii'**

¶ *ranunculoides* CD&R 2345 — WCru

– KGB 111 — MSto

recta — CFee CHad CHan CPev CSPN LHol LPri MBel MBri MBro MCad MLLN NBea NOak NRoo NWCA SPer WByw WHil WHoo WPer WPyg WWye

– 'Grandiflora' — CSCl NHol

– 'Peveril' — CPev ERob NBrk

– 'Purpurea' — CB&S CBot CHad CHea CSCl EFou EHoe ELan EOrc ETho LFis LGan LGre LHop MCad NBea SBla SBod SBra SDix SMad SPer WByw WHoo WSHC WWye

§ – subsp. *recta* var. *lasiosepala* — WWat

* – 'Velvet Night' — CSpe MMil

'Red Cooler' — MCad

§ *rehderiana* ♀ — CBot CGre CHad CHan CPev CPlN CSCl CSPN CSam ELan ERob ESCh ETho LPri MBri MCad NBea NBrk NHol NTay SBra SChu SDix SHBN SPer SSpi WAbe WSHC WWat

'Rhapsody' — CPev CSCl EHGC EPfP ERob ETho IHar MCad NBrk NTay WSHC

'Richard Pennell' (P) ♀ — CMac CPev CSCl CSPN EBee EHGC ERob ESCh ETho LPri MBri MCad NBea NBrk NTay SBra SDix

¶ 'Roko-Kolla' (J) — ESCh

'Romantika' (J) — ESCh SBra SPer

'Rose Supreme' — MCad

'Rosie O'Grady' (A) — CSPN EHGC ELan ESCh ETho IHar LPri MBar MBri MCad MGos NBea NHol NSti SBra SPer

* 'Rosugyana' — MCad

'Rouge Cardinal' (J) — CMac CPev CRHN CSCl CSPN EAst EBrP EBre EHGC ELan ESCh ETho GMac LPri MBar MBri MCad NBea SBod SBra SBre SDix SHBN SPar SPer SSta WBod

'Royal Velours' (Vt) ♀ — Widely available

♦ Royal Velvet — See *C.* Royal Velvet = **'Evifour'**

'Royalty' (LxP) ♀ — CB&S CSCl CSPN EBrP EBre EHGC ELan ESCh ETho LBre LPri MBri MCad NBea NBir NTay SBra SBre SDix WBod

'Ruby Anniversary' — MCad

'Ruby Glow' (L) — CBlo CSPN EHGC EPfP ERob ESCh MCad NTay SBra WLRN WStI WTre WWeb

'Ruby Lady' — LPri

'Rüütel' (J) — ESCh MCad NTay

'Sally Cadge' (P) — MCad

'Samantha Denny' — ERob NBea NBrk NTay

'Saruga' — MCad

'Satsukibare' — ERob MCad

'Saturn' (Vt) — EBee ERob ESCh MCad NBea SBra SPla

'Scartho Gem' (P) — CMac CPev CSCl EBee EHGC ESCh MCad NBea NTay SBra

'Schneeglanz' (P) — MCad

'Sealand Gem' (L) — CBlo CPev CSCl CSPN EAst EBee EHGC ESCh ETho MCad NBea NHaw NTay SBod SBra

'Serebrjannyj Ruczejok' — MCad

'Serenata' (J) — CSCl EHGC ERob LPri MBri MCad NBea NTay

serratifolia — CHan CLon CPev CSCl CSPN ELan ESCh LPri MCad NBea SBra SDix SPer

'Sheila Thacker' — ETho

¶ 'Sherriffii' (Ta) — ERob

'Shogun' — EHGC MCad

¶ 'Sho-Un' (L) — ERob

¶ 'Sialia' (A/d) — ESCh

sibirica — See *C. alpina* subsp. *sibirica*

'Signe' (Vt) — ERob ESCh MCad

'Silver Lining' — MCad

'Silver Moon' (L) ♀ — CBlo CSCl CSPN ECle ESCh ETho LPri MAsh MCad NBea NPri NTay SBra WFar WMer WWeb

'Simi' — MCad

simsii Britt. & A.Br. — See *C. pitcheri*

– Sweet — See *C. crispa*

¶ Blue Rain = 'Sinij Dozhdz' (D) — MBri

'Sir Garnet Wolseley' (P) — CBlo EHGC ERob ESCh NBrk NTay SBod SBra SDix

'Sir Trevor Lawrence' (T) — CPev CSCl CSPN EBrP EBre EHGC ERob ESCh ETho LBre LFis LPri MCad NBea NTay SBod SBra SBre SDix SPer WWat

smilacifolia subsp. *andersonii* — MSto

'Snow Queen' — CB&S CBlo CLAP CSCl CSPN EBrP EBre EHGC EPfP ESCh ETho LBre LPri MBri MCad NBea NTay SBra SBre WWeb

§ 'Södertälje' (Vt) — CBlo CRHN CSCl CSPN EBrP EBre EHGC ELan ERob ESCh ETho GMac LBre LPri MCad NTay SBra SBre WLRN

songarica — CBlo CSCl CSPN LFis MCad MSto NBea NBrk NHol SBra WSHC

– var. *songarica* — ERob

¶ – 'Sundance' — WTre

'Souvenir de J.L. Delbard' (P) — ERob ESCh NBea NBrk NTay SBra

§ 'Souvenir du Capitaine Thuilleaux' (P) — CPev EAst EBee ESCh ETho LPri MBri MCad NBea SBra SPer

sp. B&SWJ 1243 — WCru

¶ sp.from China ACE 16807* — WCru

'Special Occasions' — ESCh ETho NTay WWeb

spooneri — See *C. montana* var. *sericea*

– 'Rosea' — See *C.* × *vedrariensis* **'Rosea'**

'Sputnik' (J) — EPfP ERob MGos NTay

stans — CHea CMdw CPou EPfP ERob ESCh GSki LRHS MCli SIng SSca

– 'Rusalka' — ERob

'Star Fish' (L) — ESCh

'Star of India' (P/J) ♀ | CBlo CPev CRHN CSCl EBee EBrP EBre EHGC ERob ESch ETho IHar LBre LPri MBri MCad NBea NTay SBra SBre SDix
'Strawberry Roan' (P) | NTay
♦ Sugar Candy | See C. Sugar Candy = 'Evione' (P)
Summer Snow | See C. 'Paul Farges'
'Sunset' (J) | CSPN EHGC ELan EPfP ESch ETho MAsh MBri MCad NTay SBra SMur WLRN
'Susan Allsop' (L) | CPev ESch MCad WTre
'Sylvia Denny' (Fl) | CSPN EAst EBrP EBre EHGC ELan ERob ESch ETho IHar LBre LPri MBar MBri MCad NBea NBrk NTay SBod SBra SBre SPer
'Sympathia' (L) | CSCl ERob ESch MCad
§ 'Tage Lundell' (A) | CSPN EHGC ERob MCad NBea NBrk NTay
'Tango' (T) | CSCl ERob ESch ETho MCad NBrk
tangutica | Widely available
– 'Aureolin' | See C. 'Aureolin'
– 'Bill MacKenzie' | See C. 'Bill MacKenzie'
¶ – dwarf form | MSto
– 'Gravetye Variety' | CBlo CSCl ERob ESch NHol
– 'Lambton Park' | CSCl EHGC EPfP ERob ESch ETho LPri MCad NBea NBrk NTay SBra SPla
– var. *obtusiuscula* | MSto
– 'Radar Love' | CMdw WHer
tashiroi B&SWJ 1423 | WCru
'Tateshina' (P) | MCad
tenuiloba | MSto
§ *terniflora* | CPev CSCl EHGC EHol EPfP ESch ETho LPri MCad MSto NBea NBrk NTay SBra SPer
– Caddick's form | CHan
– var. *mandshurica* | See C. *mandschurica*
– var. *robusta* | See C. *terniflora* var. *terniflora*
§ – var. *terniflora* | ERob ESch
'Teshio' (Fl) | EPfP ERob ESch LPri MCad SBra
'Tevia' | MCad
texensis | CSCl CSPN MCad MSto NBea WFar
'The Bride' (J) | CSCl ERob ESch MCad NBrk NTay
'The Comet' | LPri
* 'The First Lady' | ESch MCad
'The President' (P) ♀ | Widely available
'The Princess of Wales' | See C. 'Princess Diana'
'The Vagabond' (P) | CBlo CSCl EHGC ELan ERob ETho LPri MCad NBea NBrk NTay WLRN
thunbergii hort. | See C. *terniflora*
– Steudel | See C. *hirsuta*
§ *tibetana* | CMac CPev CSCl CSPN EHGC ELan ETho MBal MBar MCad MNrw MSto NChi NNor NTay SPer WSHC WWat
§ – subsp. *vernayi* ♀ | CMHG CNic CSCl EBee ERob MCad MPla MSte NBea SBra SPer WWat WWin
– – CC&McK 193 | NWCA
– – var. *laciniifolia* | ERob ESch NHol
§ – – LS&E 13342 | CPev CSCl EPfP ESch MBri MCad NBea NBrk NHol SBra SDix SPer

§ – – 'Orange Peel' | EAst EBar EBee EHGC ENot ERob ESch IOrc LBuc MCad MGos
'Titania' (PxL) | EPfP ERob
'Trianon' (P) | CSCl ERob MCad NBrk
§ x *triternata* | CDoC CPev CRHN CSCl CSPN
'Rubromarginata' ♀ | EAst EHGC ELan EOrc ERob ESCh ETho GMac LFis LPri MBri MCad MGed NBea NHol NRoo SBod SBra SDix SMur SPer SPla WCru WSHC
* 'Tsuzuki' | ERob ESCh
'Twilight' (J) | CSPN ECle EHGC ESCh ETho MAsh MCad NBea NTay SBra SPer
'Ulrique' (P) | ESCh LRHS NTay
uncinata | CPev
¶ – B&SWJ 1893 | WCru
'Valge Daam' (L) | MCad
'Vanilla Cream' | ECou
x *vedrariensis* | MCad NBrk SPer
– 'Dovedale' | CPev
– 'Highdown' | CBlo CSCl ERob LPri MCad NBrk NHol SBra SPer
§ – 'Rosea' | CTrw ESCh MCad NBrk WSHC
veitchiana | ERob
'Venosa Violacea' (Vt) ♀ | CRHN CSCl CSPN EHGC ELan EOrc ESCh ETho GMac LPri MBri MCad NBea NSti SBra SDix SPer WFar WSHC WWeb
♦ *vernayi* | See C. *tibetana* subsp. *vernayi*
'Veronica's Choice' (L) | CPev CRHN CSCl EBee EBrP EBre EHGC ELan ERob ESCh ETho LBre MBri MCad MGos NBea NTay SBra SBre
versicolor | CSCl ERob MSto
♦ *verticillaris* | See C. *occidentalis*
N 'Victoria' (J) | CPev CSCl EAst EBrP EBre EHGC ELan ESCh ETho LBre LPri MCad NBea NHaw NTay SBra SBre SDix
'Ville de Lyon' (Vt) | Widely available
♦ Vino℗ | See C. Vino = 'Poulvo'
* 'Viola' (J) | ERob ESCh MCad NTay
'Violet Charm' (L) | CBlo CSPN EHGC ERob ESCh NTay
'Violet Elizabeth' (P) | CSCl ESCh MCad NBrk NTay SBra
viorna | CPlN CSCl ERob LPri MSto NBea WSHC
virginiana Hooker | See C. *ligusticifolia*
– hort. | See C. *vitalba*
§ *vitalba* | CArn CJew CKin CPev CSCl ERob ESCh MBar MCad WGwy WHer
viticella | CPev CSCl EBar ERob ESCh ETho LHol LPri MCad NBea SBra SDix WOMN WSHC WStI WWat
¶ – 'Brocade' | CPev
* – 'Foxtrot' | ERob
– 'Mary Rose' (d) | CPev CSCl ERob SBra
– 'Purpurea Plena Elegans' (d) ♀ | Widely available
'Viticella Rubra' (Vt) | ETho NBrk
'Voluceau' (Vt) | CPou CRHN CSCl CSPN EAst EBee EHGC ELan ESCh MCad NBea NTay SBra SPer WStI
'Vostok' (J) | ERob
'Vyvyan Pennell' (Fl/P) ♀ | Widely available

'W.E. Gladstone' (L)	CPev CSCl EBee EHGC ENot ERob ESCh ETho LPri MCad NBea NTay SBra SDix SPer
'W.S. Callick' (P)	ERob ESCh MCad WTre
'Wada's Primrose' (P)	CDoC CSCl CSPN EAst EBrP EBre EHGC ELan ERob ESCh ETho IHar LBre LPri MBri MCad MRav NBea NEgg NRoo NTay SBra SBre SPer SPla WSHC
'Walenburg' (Vt)	SBra
'Walter Pennell' (Fl/P)	CBlo CPev ESCh ETho LPri MCad NBea NTay SBra WGor
'Warszawska Nike' (J)	CLAP CRHN CSCl EHGC ELan EPfP ESCh ETho IHar LPri MCad MGos MSte NBea NTay SBra SPer WStI
'Western Virgin'	ERob ESCh
¶ 'Westerplatte' (P)	WTre
§ 'White Swan' (A)	CBlo CSCl CSPN EHGC ESCh ETho LHol LPri MBri MCad NBea NHol NRoo NSti SBra SPer SPla SSoC WFoF WTre
'White Tokyo' (A)	MGos
'Wilhelmina Tull' (L)	CSCl ERob ESCh MCad NBrk
'Will Goodwin' (L) ♀	CB&S CSCl CSPN EAst EBrP EBre EHGC ELan EPfP ESCh ETho LBre LPri MBri MCad NBea NBrk SBra SBre WStI
'William Kennett' (L)	CPev CSCl CSPN EAst EBar EHGC ELan ESCh ETho LPri MBar MBri MCad MGos MRav NBea NTay SBod SBra SDix SPer
'Wistaria Purple' (A)	NBrk
'Wolga' (P)	MCad
'Xerxes'	See C. 'Elsa Späth'
'Yellow Queen'	See C. 'Moonlight'
'Yorkshire Pride'	MCad
'Yukikomachi' (LxJ)	MCad
'Yvette Houry' (L)	ERob ESCh MCad NTay WMer

CLEMATOPSIS (Ranunculaceae)

¶ scabiosifolia	EBee

CLEMENTSIA See RHODIOLA

CLEOME (Capparaceae)

§ hassleriana	MLan SMrm SWat
¶ sp. JCA 13931	IDac
spinosa hort.	See C. hassleriana

CLERODENDRUM (Verbenaceae)

bungei ♀	CAbb CB&S CBlo CBot CGre CHEx CHad CPle CWit ELan EPar EPla ERea MBlu NPal SDix SLMG SMad SMur SPer SSpi SSta WBod WOMN WWal WWat WWye
§ chinense 'Pleniflorum' (d)	ERea WMul
fragrans var. pleniflorum	See Clerodendron chinense 'Pleniflorum'
myricoides 'Ugandense'	CPlN CSpe ECon ELan EPfP ERea LChe LCns SLMG SOWG WMul
philippinum	See Clerodendron chinense 'Pleniflorum'
speciossissimum	LChe
X speciosum	CPlN LChe LCns
splendens ♀	SLMG SOWG
thomsoniae ♀	CPlN ELan LChe LCns MBri SOWG WMul

trichotomum	CB&S CEnd CGre CHEx CTrw CWit EBrP EBre EMil ENot EPla ERom GSki IOrc LBre LPan MWhi SBre SPer SReu SSpi SSta WBod WCoo WDin WGer
¶ – 'Carnival' (v)	EPfP LRHS MAsh SMur SSpi SSta WWeb
– var. fargesii ♀	CAbb CB&S CBlo CPMA CPle EBar ELan IOrc LHol LHop MBlu MGos NFla SHBN SPer SSpi WCot WEas WHar WPat WPyg WWat
* – – 'Variegatum'	CPMA SPer WWes

CLETHRA (Clethraceae)

acuminata	WWoo
alnifolia	CB&S CBlo CBot CGre CMHG CSam CTrG CWSG ECro ELan EMil GCHN GChr IOrc MBar SPer SRms SSpi WBod WDin WWin WWye
– 'Alba'	EMil
– 'Hummingbird'	LRHS
– 'Paniculata' ♀	CDoC EHic MUlv WWat
– 'Pink Spire'	CB&S CDoC EHic ELan EPfP MPla MRav MUlv SCoo SPer WFar WLRN WPyg WStI WWat
– 'Rosea'	CBot EMil IOrc MBal MBar MBlu MGos SHBN SPer WSHC WWat
* – 'Ruby Spice'	LRHS
arborea	CB&S CFil CHEx CMHG CPle CTre
barbinervis ♀	CB&S CFai CMCN CWSG EPfP GGGa MBel MBlu SPer WBod WCoo WSHC WWat
delavayi ♀	GGGa GQui MBal SSpi
– C&H 7067	GGGa
fargesii	MGos
monostachya	GGGa

CLEYERA (Theaceae)

fortunei	See C. japonica 'Fortunei'
– 'Variegata'	See C. japonica 'Fortunei'
§ japonica 'Fortunei' (v)	CDoC CFil WWat
– var. japonica	MBal

CLIANTHUS (Papilionaceae)

¶ formosus	MFiF
§ puniceus ♀	CAbb CB&S CHEx CHan CMac CPlN CPle CTrw ECou EMil ERea IHos LCns LHop MBal SArc SBid SHFr SLMG SOWG SPer SSoC WAbe WBrE WCru WPat
§ – 'Albus' ♀	CBot CPle CTrw ELan EMil ERea IHos IOrc LCns LHop MAll SBid SDry SLMG SOWG SPer SSoC
– 'Flamingo'	See C. puniceus 'Roseus'
– 'Red Admiral'	See C. puniceus
– 'Red Cardinal'	See C. puniceus
§ – 'Roseus'	ELan EMil ERea IHos LHop
– 'White Heron'	See C. puniceus 'Albus'

CLINOPODIUM (Lamiaceae)

acinos	See Acinos arvensis
ascendens	See Calamintha sylvatica
calamintha	See Calamintha nepeta

grandiflorum	See *Calamintha grandiflora*
§ *vulgare*	CArn CKin ECoo EOHP EWFC GBar MHew NMir SIde WCla WHer WOve

CLINTONIA (Convallariaceae)

andrewsiana	CBro GDra GGGa SSpi WCru WThi
borealis	CBro SWas WCru
udensis	WCru
umbellulata	WCru
uniflora	WCru

CLITORIA (Papilionaceae) See Plant Deletions

CLIVIA (Amaryllidaceae)

gardenii	ERea
miniata ♀	CB&S CHal SRms WCot
– var. *citrina* 'New Dawn'	ERea
– hybrids	ERea LAma LHil MBri NPal SEND
– 'Striata'	ERea
nobilis	ERea

CLUSIA (Clusiaceae)

rosea	See *C. major*

CLYTOSTOMA (Bignoniaceae)

§ *callistegioides*	CPlN ERea

CNEORUM (Cneoraceae)

tricoccon	CFil WOMN

CNICUS (Asteraceae)

§ *benedictus*	CArn GPoy MSal SIde WFar WHer WWye

COBAEA (Cobaeaceae)

pringlei	CHan
(House) Standl. CD&R 1323	
scandens ♀	CPlN IBlr NFai SMrm WPen
– f. *alba* ♀	CBos IBlr WPen
trianea	CPlN ERea

COCCOTHRINAX (Arecaceae)

¶ *crinita*	LPal

COCCULUS (Menispermaceae)

carolinus	CPlN
§ *orbiculatus*	CPlN WCru
trilobus	See *C. orbiculatus*

COCHLEARIA (Brassicaceae)

armoracia	See *Armoracia rusticana*
glastifolia	MSal
officinalis	MSal WHer

COCOS (Arecaceae)

¶ *nucifera* (F)	LPal
plumosa	See *Syagrus romanzoffiana*
weddelliana	See *Lytocaryum weddellianum*

CODIAEUM † (Euphorbiaceae)

variegatum var. *pictum* 'Gold Moon' (v)	MBri
– – 'Gold Sun' (v)	MBri
– – 'Goldfinger' (v)	MBri
– – 'Juliette' (v)	MBri
– – 'Louise' (v)	MBri
– – 'Mrs Iceton' (v)	MBri
– – 'Petra' (v)	MBri
– – 'Sunny Star' (v)	MBri

CODONANTHE (Gesneriaceae)

gracilis	EBak WDib
paula	WDib

× CODONATANTHUS (Gesneriaceae)

'Sunset'	WDib
'Tambourine'	MBri WDib

CODONOPSIS (Campanulaceae)

bhutanica	CMdw EBee GAri GCrs MHar MSto
bulleyana	EBee GCra MHar NMen
cardiophylla	GDra MHar MNrw MSto
clematidea	Widely available
convolvulacea ♀	CBlo CPlN GBuc GDra MTho NHar NSla SDix WCru WHoo
– 'Alba'	See *C. grey-wilsonii* 'Himal Snow'
– Forrest's form	See *C. forrestii* Diels
¶ *dicentrifolia* HWJCM 267	WCru
§ *forrestii* Diels	CNic EBee EHyt GCra NHar NTow WCru
– hort.	See *C. grey-wilsonii*
§ *grey-wilsonii*	CLAP NChi
§ – 'Himal Snow'	CLAP EBee EHyt EPot GCrs GDra MSto NHar SWas
handeliana	See *C. tubulosa*
§ *javanica* B&SWJ 380	WCru
kawakamii	EBee
– B&SWJ 1592	WCru
§ *lanceolata*	CPlN CRDP GAri GCra MCCP MSto NChi NHar WCru
¶ *lancifolia* B&SWJ 3835	WCru
meleagris	GCra GDra NHar
– hybrid	NChi
mollis	CBlo EBee GSki MSto NLar WCot
◆ *nepalensis* Grey-Wilson	See *C. grey-wilsonii*
obtusa	EBee MSto NChi
ovata	CBot CFir CGle ELan EPri GBuc GCra GDra LGan LHop MSto MTho NBro NChi NWCA SBla SRms SSca WEas
pilosula	EBee GAri GCra MLLN MNrw MSto MTho NChi WCru
rotundifolia	CPlN EBee
– var. *angustifolia*	MSto NChi
silvestris	EBee
subsimplex	EBee GCra MSto NChi
tangshen	CArn CGre CPlN EBee EPot GBuc GCra GPoy MCCP MNrw MSal MSto MTho NBro NChi NSti WCru
§ *tubulosa*	EBee MSto
ussuriensis	See *C. lanceolata*
vinciflora	CFir GCra GDra MSto NChi SBla WCru
viridiflora	CLyd MHar WRha
viridis	EHal
– S&L 4962	GCra

COELOGLOSSUM × DACTYLORHIZA See × DACTYLOGLOSSUM

COFFEA (Rubiaceae) See Plant Deletions

COIX (Poaceae)
lacryma-jobi MSal

COLCHICUM † (Colchicaceae)
agrippinum ♀ CAvo CBro CFee CMon EHyt
EMon EPar EPot LAma MBal
MRav NBir NMGW NRog
WAbe WTin
algeriense AB&S 4353 CMon
'Antares' LAma
atropurpureum CBro EBot EPot LAma
'Attlee' EPot LAma LRHS
'Autumn Herald' LAma LRHS
N 'Autumn Queen' ♀ CBro LAma LRHS
§ *autumnale* CArn CAvo CBro CFee EPot
ETub GPoy LAma MBal
NMGW NRya WAbe WShi
* – 'Albopilosum' NBir
§ – 'Alboplenum' CBro CSWP EPot ETub LAma
NMGW
– 'Album' CAvo CBro CSWP ECha EHyt
EPar EPot ETub GDra LAma
MBal NBir
– var. *major* See *C. byzantinum*
– var. *minor* See *C. autumnale*
– *minor album plenum* See *C. autumnale* 'Alboplenum'
– 'Nancy Lindsay' ♀ CBro EPot NMGW
§ – 'Pleniflorum' (d) CBro EPar EPot LAma
– 'Roseum Plenum' See *C. autumnale* 'Pleniflorum'
baytopiorum EHyt EPot LAma
– PB 224 CMon
§ *bivonae* CBro CLAP ECha EPot LAma
NMGW
§ *boissieri* CMon EHyt EPot
– S&L 468 CMon
bornmuelleri Freyn CAvo CBro EPar EPot LAma
– hort. See *C. speciosum* var.
bornmuelleri hort.
bowlesianum See *C. bivonae*
§ *byzantinum* ♀ CAvo CBro CMon EBot EPar
EPot LAma MBri NRog
– *album* CBro EBot EPot ETub
cilicicum CBro CMon EPot ETub LAma
WAbe
– 'Purpureum' LAma
'Conquest' See *C.* 'Glory of Heemstede'
corsicum CMon EHyt EPar LAma WLin
cupanii EHyt EPot LAma
* – var. *cousturieri* EHyt
– Glossophyllum Group CMon EPot
– MS 977 CMon
¶ – var. *pulverulentum* EPot
'Daendels' LAma LRHS
deserti-syriaci SB&L 155 CMon
'Dick Trotter' LAma LRHS
'Disraeli' CBro LRHS
doerfleri See *C. hungaricum*
'E.A. Bowles' LAma
fasciculare LAma
§ *giganteum* EPot LAma
§ 'Glory of Heemstede' ECha LAma
hierosolymitanum LAma
§ *hungaricum* CBro EPot LAma
– f. *albiflorum* EHyt
'Huxley' EPot
illyricum See *C. giganteum*
kesselringii CLAP
kotschyi LAma
laetum hort. See *C. parnassicum*
'Lilac Wonder' CBro ECha EHyt EMan EPot
ETub LAma MBri NMGW
NRog WCot

lingulatum NRog
– S&L 217 CMon
§ *longiflorum* LAma
lusitanicum LAma
– HC 2273 CMon
luteum LAma NRog
macrophyllum LAma
– S&L 578 CMon
micranthum LAma
neapolitanum See *C. longiflorum*
* – *macranthum* CMon
¶ *parlatoris* EPot
– Rix 2127 CMon
§ *parnassicum* CLAP CMon ECha EPot
¶ *peloponnesiacum* EHyt
'Pink Goblet' ♀ CBro EHyt EMon EPot LAma
polyphyllum LAma
'Prinses Astrid' CAvo LAma
procurrens See *C. boissieri*
psaridis S&L 198 CMon
¶ *pusillum* EPot
– MS 803/833 CMon
'Rosy Dawn' ♀ CBro ECha EMon EPot LAma
sibthorpii See *C. bivonae*
speciosum ♀ CAvo CBro CMon EBrP EBre
EMon EPot ETub LAma LBre
MBal MHlr NBir SBre WCot
WShi
– 'Album' ♀ CAvo CBro CFee EBrP EBre
ECha EHyt EPar LAma LBre
MBri NBir NMGW SBre
– 'Atrorubens' ECha EPot GDra LAma
§ – var. *bornmuelleri* hort. CMon EMon
– var. *illyricum* See *C. giganteum*
– 'Maximum' LAma
¶ – 'Rubrum' EPot
stevenii SB&L 120 CMon
¶ *szovitsii* EPot
tenorei ♀ LAma NBir
'The Giant' CAvo CBro ECha EPot ETub
LAma NMGW NRog
troodii ♀ CMon
umbrosum CMon
variegatum CBro LAma
– S&L 594 CMon
'Violet Queen' CBro CFee EPot LAma
'Waterlily' ♀ CAvo CBro CLyd EBrP EBre
ECha EMon EPar EPot ETub
GCLN LAma LBre MBal MBri
NBir NMGW NRog SBre
WAbe WCot
'William Dykes' EPot LAma
'Zephyr' LAma LRHS

COLEONEMA (Rutaceae)
album SAga WPat
pulchrum CSpe CTrC ECre LHop MAll

COLEUS See PLECTRANTHUS,
SOLENOSTEMON

COLLETIA (Rhamnaceae)
armata See *C. hystrix*
cruciata See *C. paradoxa*
ferox MAll
§ *hystrix* CB&S CPle GBin MAll SAPC
SArc SMad WDin
– 'Rosea' CAbb CGre CPle SAPC SArc
SMur WAbe WSHC
§ *paradoxa* CB&S CGre CHEx CPle CTri
EPla LPJP MAll SAPC SArc
SMad

¶ – × *spinosissima*   SMad

COLLINSIA (Scrophulariaceae)
bicolor Benth.   See *C. heterophylla*

COLLINSONIA (Lamiaceae)
canadensis   CArn EBee ELan MSal

COLLOMIA (Polemoniaceae)
debilis   EHyt NWCA
– var. *larsenii*   GTou
grandiflora   LCot WRHF

COLLOSPERMUM (Asteliaceae)
§ *microspermum*   IBlr

COLOBANTHUS (Caryophyllaceae)
¶ *acicularis*   EHyt
apetalus   NHol
buchananii   ECou
canaliculatus   CPBP ECou NTow
sp. CC 465   NWCA

COLOCASIA (Araceae)
antiquorum   See *C. esculenta*
§ *esculenta* ♀   CHEx EOas WMul
¶ – 'Fontanesii'   WMul
– 'Illustris'   WCot
* – 'Nigrescence'   WMul

COLQUHOUNIA (Lamiaceae)
coccinea ♀   CArn CHEx CHal CHan CTrC
          CWit EMil MAll MBal MRav
          WBod WSHC
– var. *mollis*   See *C. coccinea* var. *vestita*
§ – var. *vestita*   CB&S CFai CFil CGre CPle
          EBee EPfP NPSI SEND WPat

COLUMNEA (Gesneriaceae)
'Aladdin's Lamp'   CHal NMos WDib
'Apollo'   WDib
× *banksii*   CHal MBri WDib
'Bold Venture'   WDib
* 'Bonfire'   WDib
§ 'Broget Stavanger' (v)   WDib
'Chanticleer' ♀   CHal MBri WDib
I 'Firedragon'   WDib
'Gavin Brown'   WDib
gloriosa   EBak
'Heidi'   MBri
hirta ♀   MBri WDib
– 'Variegata'   See *C.* **'Light Prince'**
'Inferno'   WDib
'Katsura'   MBri SOWG WDib
I 'Kewensis Variegata' ♀   MBri
§ 'Light Prince' (v)   MBri WDib
'Merkur'   WDib
microphylla 'Variegata'   MBri
I 'Midnight Lantern'   WDib
'Rising Sun'   WDib
'Robin'   WDib
schiedeana   CHal MBri WDib
'Starburst'   NMos
'Stavanger' ♀   CHal EBak MBri WDib
'Stavanger Variegated'   See *C.* **'Broget Stavanger'**
'Winifred Brown'   WDib
Yellow Dragon Group   CHal

COLUTEA (Papilionaceae)
arborescens   CAgr CArn CB&S CBlo EBrP
          EBre ELan EMil ENot IBlr
          IOrc LBre MBlu MGos MPEx
          MSal MWhi NNor NWea SBre
          SHBN SIde SPer WDin WHer
          WOve WWin
× *media*   CHad EMil MBel MBlu WBcn
– 'Copper Beauty'   CB&S CHan ELan MGos SPer
          WPat
orientalis   CDoC CPle
persica   SOWG

COMARUM See POTENTILLA

COMBRETUM (Combretaceae)
erythrophyllum   CGre
paniculatum   CPlN MSto

COMMELINA (Commelinaceae)
coelestis   See *C. tuberosa* **Coelestis Group**
dianthifolia   CFee CInt CRDP EMon GBuc
          GCal GCrs MTho NTow SLMG
          SSad WCot WPer
* – 'Sapphirino'   EMon
tuberosa   CAvo CMdw EHic ELan GBuc
          MLan NSti SLod
– 'Alba'   ELan EMon GCal MLLN MSte
          NTow WHer WPer WWye
¶ – 'Axminster Lilac'   WPer
§ – Coelestis Group   CHan CInt ECha EMon ETub
          GCal MLLN NFai SLMG SUsu
          WFar WHer WOMN WPer
          WWin WWye
– 'Snowmelt'   MGrG
virginica hort.   See *C. erecta*
– Linnaeus   IBlr

COMPTONIA (Myricaceae)
¶ *peregrina*   WCru

CONANTHERA (Tecophilaeaceae)
campanulata   CMon

CONIOGRAMME (Adiantaceae)
intermedia   NMar
¶ *japonica*   WRic

CONIOSELINUM (Apiaceae)
morrisonense B&SWJ 173   WCru
¶ *schugnanicum*   EBee

CONIUM   (Apiaceae) See Plant Deletions

CONOCEPHALUM   (Conocephalaceae) See
Plant Deletions

CONOPODIUM (Apiaceae)
majus   CKin WShi

CONRADINA (Lamiaceae)
verticillata   CFee SBla

CONSOLIDA (Ranunculaceae)
§ *ajacis*   EWFC MHew MSal
ambigua   See *C. ajacis*
regalis   ECoo

CONVALLARIA † (Convallariaceae)

japonica	See *Ophiopogon jaburan*
keiskei	CLAP
majalis ♀	Widely available
§ – 'Albostriata'	CFil CHEx CLAP CRDP CRow ECha ELan EPar MRav MTho NBir NRar SAxl SDys SSvw WCHb WCot WCru WEas WFox WHer WPGP
¶ – 'Berlin Giant'	EBee WCot
– 'Flore Pleno' (d)	EBee WCot WFox
– 'Fortin's Giant'	CAvo CBro CLAP CMea CRDP CRow ECro EGar ELan EMan EPar EPla ERav LHop MRav NBrk WCot WPGP
* – 'Haldon Grange'	CBos CLAP WCot
– 'Hardwick Hall' (v)	CAvo CLAP CRDP CRow EHoe EPot NRar WCot WFox
– 'Hofheim' (v)	CRow
– 'Prolificans'	CAvo CBro CLAP CRDP CRow EMon EPar EPot ERos SIng SSvw WPbr
– var. *rosea*	CAvo CBro CGra CLAP CRDP CRow EGar ELan EMon EPar EPot ERav ERos LHol LHop MAus MTho NBir NRar NSti SIng SPer WEas WGle WHil
– 'Variegata'	CAvo CBlo CBos CRow EGar EPla ERav SMac SMad
– 'Vic Pawlowski's Gold' (v)	CRow WCHb
montana	LRHS WThi
transcaucasica	WHer

CONVOLVULUS (Convolvulaceae)

althaeoides	CBot CFil CHad CMil CPle CSam ECGP MAvo MNes MTho SAga SBla SChu SHFr SMad SWas WAbb WCru WEas WHal WOld WWin
§ – subsp. *tenuissimus*	CGle CSWP CSpe EBee EMar EWes GCal LHop MWat NTow SAsh SAxl SUsu WCot
§ *boissieri*	CFir EHyt MTho NWCA SBla WAbe
cantabricus	MSto
chilensis RB 94080	MSto
cneorum ♀	Widely available
elegantissimus	See *C. althaeoides* subsp. *tenuissimus*
incanus	WCru
lineatus	CPBP EHyt ELan ESis LBee MBro MRPP MSto MTho NHar NMen NNrd NWCA SBla WAbe
mauritanicus	See *C. sabatius*
nitidus	See *C. boissieri*
remotus	MSto
§ *sabatius* ♀	CB&S CGle CHEx CHad CHal CHan CMHG ECha ELan ERea GCHN GCal lHos LHop MBEx NHar SAxl SBla SDix WAbe WEas WOMN WOld WSHC WWat WWin
– dark form	CMHG CSpe ELan EMan GCal LFis LHil LHop LIck LLWP MBEx MSte SMrm SUsu

COOPERANTHES See ZEPHYRANTHES

COOPERIA See ZEPHYRANTHES

COPERNICIA (Arecaceae)

¶ *alba*	LPal
¶ *prunifera*	LPal

COPROSMA † (Rubiaceae)

acerosa	See *C. brunnea*
areolata	ECou
atropurpurea (m)	ECou MAll
baueri	See *C. repens*
'Beatson's Gold' (f/v)	CB&S CBlo CBot CDec CGre CHan CLTr CMHG CPle EMil ERea GOrc GQui IOrc MAll MBEx MPla NFai STre WHen WSHC
billardierei	See *C. quadrifida*
'Blue Pearls' (f)	ECou
'Brunette' (f)	ECou
§ *brunnea*	ECou MHig
– (m) X *kirkii*	ECou
cheesemanii (f)	ECou
– (m)	ECou
– 'Mack' (m)	MAll
– 'Red Mack' (f)	MAll
'Chocolate Soldier' (m)	ECou
'Coppershine'	CB&S ERea MAll MBEx
crassifolia (m) X *repens*	ECou
X *cunninghamii* (f)	ECou MAll
depressa	ECou
'Green Girl' (f)	ECou MAll
'Hinerua' (f)	ECou
'Indigo Lustre' (f)	ECou
'Jewel' (f)	ECou
X *kirkii* 'Kirkii' (f)	CFee CInt ECou ERea STre
– 'Kirkii Variegata' (f)	CB&S CGre CPle CTrC ECou EMil ERea GQui LHop MAll SEas SOWG STre WBrE WSHC
'Kiwi-gold' (v)	CB&S ECou ERea MAll
'Lemon Drops' (f)	ECou
linariifolia	ECou
lucida (f)	ECou MAll
macrocarpa (f)	ECou
– (m)	ECou
nitida (f)	ECou
– (m)	ECou
parviflora (m)	ECou
'Pearl's Sister' (f)	ECou
'Pearly Queen' (f)	ECou MAll
petriei	CLTr CNic ECou MHig SIng WAbe
¶ – AGS 50	MRPP
– 'Don' (m)	ECou
– 'Lyn' (f)	ECou
propinqua	EPla SDry WSHC
– (f)	ECou
– (m)	ECou
'Prostrata' (m)	ECou
§ *repens*	LHil
– 'Apricot Flush' (f)	ECou
– 'Brownie' (f)	ECou
– 'County Park Purple' (f)	ECou ERea MAll
– 'Exotica' (f/v)	ECou LHop
§ – (f)	CHEx ECou
– (m)	CB&S ECou SEND
– 'Marble King' (m/v)	ECou
– 'Marble Queen' (m/v)	ECou LHil LHop MAll SEND SLMG WLRN
– 'Orangeade' (f)	ECou
– 'Painter's Palette'	CB&S LHil MAll
– 'Picturata' (m/v)	ECou ERea
– 'Pink Splendour' (m/v)	CB&S CDoC ERea LHop SEND

– 'Silver Queen' (m/v)	ECou SVen
– 'Variegata' (m)	ECou LHil MAll
rigida	ECou MAll
robusta	ECou MAll SDry
– 'Williamsii Variegata' (f/m)	LHop
rotundifolia	ECou
'Roy's Red'	ECou
rugosa (f)	ECou
tenuifolia (m)	ECou
'Violet Drops' (f)	ECou MAll
virescens	ECou MAll
'Walter Brockie'	CGre CHal CLTr LHil
'White Lady' (f)	ECou MAll

COPTIS (Ranunculaceae)
quinquefolia	WCru

CORALLOSPARTIUM (Papilionaceae)
crassicaule	ECou

CORDYLINE (Agavaceae)
australis ♀	Widely available
– 'Albertii' (v) ♀	CB&S CHEx CTrC EHic ERea GQui LNet MBri SAPC SArc WCot
* – 'Atropurpurea'	CB&S
* – 'Black Tower'	CB&S MAsh WGer
* – 'Coffee Cream'	CTor CTrC EBee IOrc ISea MAsh MBlu SSto WGer
– 'Pink Strip'	CAbb CDoC ERic IOrc ISea MAsh SPla WGer WWeb
– Purpurea Group	CB&S CBot CHEx EAst EBrP EBre ENot ERea GOrc GQui IOrc ISea LBre NCut SBre SEND SHBN SMad SPer WFar WGer WStI WWeb
– 'Red Star'	CAbb CB&S CBlo CDoC COtt CSpe CBee EHic ENot MCCP MLan SMer SPar WLRN WWes
– 'Sundance'	CB&S CBlo CTor CWit EBee IOrc MBri MCCP NCut SMer SPla SSto SWat WFar WPyg WStI WWeb WWes
– 'Torbay Dazzler' (v)	CAbb CB&S CDoC CHEx COtt CTor CWit EBrP EBre ELan ENot IOrc ISea LBre LPan MAsh MBal MBri NPal SBre SEND SHBN SPer SPla SSto WGer WPat WStI WWeb
– 'Torbay Green'	CTor
* – 'Torbay Razzle Dazzle'	CTor
– 'Torbay Red'	CAbb CB&S CHEx COtt CSam CTor CTrC EBee ELan IOrc LPan MAsh MBlu MBri SPla SSto WPat WWeb
– 'Torbay Sunset'	CDoC COtt CTor ELan IOrc SSto
– 'Torbay Surprise'	CAbb CTor
– 'Variegata'	CBot CHEx
* **autumn**	NCut
banksii	CTrC ECou EWes MAll WLRN
fruticosa 'Atom'	MBri
– 'Baby Ti'	MBri
– 'Calypso Queen'	MBri
– 'Kiwi'	MBri
– 'Orange Prince'	MBri
– 'Red Edge'	MBri
– 'Yellow King'	MBri
'Green Goddess'	CB&S CTrC

§ **indivisa**	CB&S CBrP CHEx CTrC EBak MAll MBri SAPC SArc WGer WPGP
kaspar	CHEx SAPC SArc
parryi 'Purpurea'	NPal
* 'Pink Stripe'	CB&S COtt CTor CTrC SSto
'Purple Tower'	CB&S CBlo CDoC COtt CTor CTrC EHic EMil IOrc MAsh SPla SSto WFar WLRN WPat WWeb
§ **stricta**	CHEx MBri
terminalis	See *C. fruticosa*
* 'Torbay Coffee Cream'	EHic

COREOPSIS † (Asteraceae)
auriculata Cutting Gold	See *C. auriculata* '**Schnittgold**'
§ – '**Schnittgold**'	CBlo CM&M CMea CSam CWit EOld EWll LFis MWat NCut NRoo SHel WPer
– 'Superba'	EBrP EBre LBre SBre
¶ 'Baby Gold'	EPfP LRHS
Baby Sun	See *C.* '**Sonnenkind**'
'Goldfink'	EBrP EBre ECED ECha GSki LBre MNrw MRav SBre SIng SRms
grandiflora	EHal SWat WOld WWeb
– 'Astolat'	NLak
– 'Badengold'	CB&S CDoC EMil MLLN
I – 'Calypso' (v)	WWeb
– 'Domino'	NCut NOak WShe
– 'Early Sunrise'	CSam EBee ECtt GMaP NFai NMir NPer SMer WBea WHen WHoo WPer WPyg WRHF
¶ – 'Flying Saucers'	LRHS
¶ – 'Kelvin Harbutt'	CStr
– 'Mayfield Giant'	CBlo EBee EFou EMan EWll MGrG MWat NFla NPri NVic SMer SRms SWat WBea WFar
– Ruby Throat	See *C. grandiflora* '**Rotkehlchen**'
– variegated	WCot
integrifolia	EMon WCot
lanceolata	MLLN NSti
– 'Sterntaler'	CFir EFou EMil EPar NOrc NRoo NTow WHil WPer
maximilianii	See *Helianthus maximilianii*
rosea	EGar MBel NLar NPro WHil
– 'American Dream'	Widely available
¶ – f. **leucantha**	CStr
– 'Nana'	SPla
§ 'Sonnenkind'	CMea ECtt EPar GMaP MHig NBro NMen
Sun Child	See *C.* '**Sonnenkind**'
'Sunburst'	CBlo COtt ELan EOHP NFai NOak SRCN WOve WPer
'Sunray'	CB&S ECtt EPar LPVe MBri MFir MGrG MNrw NFai NNor NOak NOrc NRoo NVic SIde SRCN SSea WCot WPer WWal WWeb WWye
tinctoria	MSal SIde
– var. **atkinsoniana**	WPer
tripteris	CGen CPou EMon SMrm WCot WFar
verticillata	CMea ECha ENot LFis MBal MBrN MBro MFir MWat NFai NPer SDix SRms SSpe SWat WAbe WEas WHal WOld WPyg
¶ – 'Alba'	MBro

– 'Golden Gain' — EBee EBrP EBre EMan EPla EWll GBri GSki LBre LHop MArl MLLN MMil NCat NHol SBre WWal

– 'Golden Shower' — See *C. verticillata* **'Grandiflora'**

§ – 'Grandiflora' ♀ — CB&S CHor COtt CSev EBrP EBre EFou ELan GMaP LBre MBri MCLN NCat NHol NLon NNor NOak NVic SBre SChu SMad SPer SPla SSpe WPbr WWal WWin

– 'Moonbeam' — Widely available

¶ – 'Rosea' — CHar

– 'Zagreb' — COtt CSev EBar EBrP EBre ECtt EMil ENot EPar EPla LBre LFis MBri MCLN MLLN MSCN MUlv NHol NRoo NTay SBre SPla WFar WHil WMer WMow WOld WPbr

CORETHROGYNE (Asteraceae) See Plant Deletions

CORIANDRUM (Apiaceae)

sativum — CArn EOHP GPoy ILis LHol MChe MGra MHew SIde WOak WPer WWye

– 'Cilantro' — CJew CSev GAbr WGwG WHer

– 'Leisure' — CBod CSev MMal

– 'Santo' — ELau GPoy WJek

CORIARIA † (Coriariaceae)

intermedia B&SWJ 019 — WCru

japonica — CPle SVen WCru WWat

¶ – B&SWJ 2833 — WCru

kingiana — ECou WCru

§ *microphylla* — WCru

myrtifolia — CB&S CFil CPle GSki WCru

nepalensis — CPle GCal WCru

ruscifolia — WCru

¶ *sarmentosa* — WCru

terminalis var. — CPle CTrG GBuc GCal IBlr
xanthocarpa — MBal MNrw NHol WCot WCru

thymifolia — See *C. microphylla*

CORIS (Primulaceae) See Plant Deletions

CORNUS † (Cornaceae)

alba — CKin CLnd CPer CTri ENot GChr IHos IOrc MAsh MBar MBri NWea SRms WDin WMou WStI

* – 'Albovariegata' — ENot

– 'Argenteovariegata' — See *C. alba* **'Variegata'**

– 'Aurea' ♀ — CB&S CMCN EBrP EBre ECtt EHoe ELan EPla IOrc LBre MAsh MBar MBri MRav NBee SBre SEas SHBN SPer SSpi WAbe WDin WFar WPat WWeb

– 'Elegantissima' (v) ♀ — CB&S CLnd CMCN EAst EBrP EBre EHoe ELan ENot GRei LBre LBuc LHop MBal MBar MBri MGos MWat NNor NWea SBre SHBN SMad SPer SReu SSta WDin WGwG WWat WWeb

– 'Gouchaultii' (v) — CB&S CBlo CDoC EBee EHic LPan MBar NPla SRms WDin

¶ – 'Ivory Halo' — EBrP EBre LBre MAsh SBre

– 'Kesselringii' — CAbP CB&S EBrP EBre EHoe EMil ENot EPla GChr IOrc LBre MBar MBri MWat SBre SEas SMad SPer SPla SSta WDin WFar WLeb

– 'Siberian Pearls' — CB&S COtt EBee ELan MBlu NEgg

§ – 'Sibirica' ♀ — Widely available

– 'Sibirica Variegata' — CDoC CPMA EBee EBrP EBre EPla GOrc IOrc LBre LPan MAsh MBlu MBri MGos NBee NEgg SBre SHBN SSpi WFar WPat WPyg WWeb

– 'Spaethii' (v) ♀ — CB&S CBot EBrP EBre EHoe ELan ENot EPla GOrc GRei IOrc LBre LHop MBal MBar MGos MWat NBee NFla NNor NWea SBre SHBN SMad SPer SSta WHar WWeb WWin

§ – 'Variegata' — CB&S CBlo SPer WWal WWin

– 'Westonbirt' — See *C. alba* **'Sibirica'**

alternifolia — CBlo CMHG COtt CPMA ELan IOrc LPan SPer SSpi WWat

§ – 'Argentea' (v) ♀ — CDoC CFil CPMA CRos EBrP EBre ELan EMil ICrw LBre LHop LPan MAsh MGos MUlv MWat NBee NHol SBre SHBN SMad SPer SReu SSpi SSta WHCG WPGP WPat WWat

– 'Variegata' — See *C. alternifolia* **'Argentea'**

amomum — CB&S EPla NHol WWat

angustata — CBlo MBal SPer

angustifolia — See *C. linifolia*

§ 'Ascona' — CPMA CRos ELan MBri SPer SSpi SSta WWes

australis — EPla

baileyi — See *C. stolonifera* **'Baileyi'**

§ *canadensis* ♀ — CAgr CB&S CFee CHEx ELan ENot GChr IOrc ISea LBuc LNet LSyl MBar MBlu MBri NGre NHar NHed NHol NNor SHBN SMac SPer SReu SSta WAbe WFar WPat WRus WWat

candidissima — See *C. racemosa*

capitata — CB&S CBar CGre CHan CPMA CTbh CTrG CTri IOrc SEND SSpi WAbe WCoo

¶ – ACE — WHCr

¶ – 'Rag Doll' (v) — CPMA

controversa — CB&S CBlo CDoC CFee CMCN CPMA CSam CTho ELan EMil GChr IOrc LPan MBar MBlu NHed NWea SHBN SLPl SPer SReu SSpi SSta WCoo WDin WHar WPGP WWat

– 'Pagoda' — CBlo CEnd CPMA MBlu SMur SSpi

– 'Variegata' ♀ — CTho ECrN ENot MAsh MGos SPla WFoF WPGP

– 'Variegata' Frans type — CB&S CBot CEnd CPMA CRos EBrP EBre ELan EMil ERom IOrc LBre LNet LPan MBlu MBri MPla MSta MWat SBre SHBN SPer SReu SSta WDin WHCG WPat WSHC WWat

'Eddie's White Wonder' ♀	CB&S CEnd CFil CPMA CRos CTho ELan ICrw IOrc LNet LPan MBal MBlu MBri MGos SBid SPer SReu SSpi SSta WDin WPat WPyg
florida	CBlo EHic ELan EPfP GOrc IOrc ISea SPer SReu SSta WLRN WNor WWat
– 'Alba Plena' (d)	CBlo CPMA
– 'Apple Blossom'	CPMA
¶ – 'Cherokee Brave'	SSpi
– 'Cherokee Chief' ♀	CAbP CB&S CBlo CEnd COtt CPMA LPan MGos NBee
– 'Cherokee Princess'	CBlo CPMA CRos ELan LPan LRHS SMur SSta
– 'Clear Moon'	LPan
– 'Cloud Nine'	CB&S COtt CPMA LPan LRHS MBal SSpi
* – 'Daniela'	LPan
– 'Daybreak' (v)	CB&S CEnd COtt CPMA LPan SPer
– 'First Lady'	CB&S CBlo CEnd CPMA LPan SPer
– 'Fragrant Cloud'	LPan
– 'G.H. Ford' (v)	CPMA
– 'Golden Nugget'	CPMA
– 'Green Glow' (v)	CPMA
– 'Junior Miss Variegated' (v)	CPMA
– 'Moonglow'	CPMA
– 'Pendula'	CPMA
– 'Pink Flame' (v)	CPMA
– 'Purple Glory'	CPMA
– 'Rainbow' (v)	CAbP CB&S COtt CPMA ELan EPfP LPan MAsh MBri MGos NEgg SHBN SPer SSta WDin
– 'Red Giant'	CBlo CPMA CRos ELan EPfP LRHS SMur SSpi SSta
– 'Royal Red'	CPMA
– f. *rubra*	CB&S CBlo CDoC CTho ELan EPfP LPan LRHS MAsh MGos NEgg SSta WNor WPyg
– 'Spring Song'	CPMA MBri
– 'Stoke's Pink'	CBlo CEnd COtt CPMA LNet
– 'Sunset' (v)	CBlo CEnd COtt CPMA MGos SPer
– 'Sweetwater'	CPMA
– 'Tricolor'	See *C. florida* 'Welchii'
§ – 'Welchii' (v)	CEnd CPMA
– 'White Cloud'	CPMA LPan
foemina	See *C. stricta*
hemsleyi	EPla WCoo
§ *hessei*	ELan EPla MBro WPat WPyg
'Kelsey's Dwarf'	See *C. stolonifera* 'Kelseyi'
kousa	CB&S CDoC CHEx CMCN CTho ELan EMil ERom ISea LNet MBal MBar MWat NFla NLon NNor SHBN SPer WAbe WCoo WDin WFar WHCG WHar WStI WWat
* – *angustifolia*	SSta
¶ – 'Beni-fuji'	CPMA
– 'Bonfire' (v)	CPMA
– var. *chinensis* ♀	Widely available
– – 'Bodnant Form'	CBlo CEnd CPMA SPer
– – 'China Girl'	CAbP CBlo CEnd COtt CPMA CRos ELan LPan MAsh MBlu MBri MGos SHBN SMad SPer SSta WPyg
– – 'Milky Way'	CBlo CPMA LPan SPer
– – Spinners form	CPMA
– 'Gold Star' (v)	CAbP CB&S CBlo CEnd COtt CPMA CTho ELan IOrc LPan MAsh MBri MGos SHBN SPer SPla SSpi WWeb
– 'Greta's Gold' (v)	CPMA
– 'Madame Butterfly'	CEnd CPMA ELan SSpi
* – 'Nicole'	LPan
– 'Radiant Rose'	CPMA
– 'Rosea'	CPMA CTho
– 'Satomi' ♀	CB&S CEnd CFil COtt CPMA ELan LNet LPan MAsh MBri SPer SReu SSpi SSta WDin
– 'Snowboy' (v)	CB&S CBlo CEnd COtt CPMA LRHS NEgg SPer
¶ – 'Snowflake'	CPMA
¶ – 'Summmer Majesty'	CPMA
– 'Sunsplash' (v)	CPMA
– 'Temple Jewel' (v)	CPMA
¶ – 'Triple Crown'	CPMA
¶ – 'Tsukubanomine'	CPMA
– 'Weaver's Weeping'	CB&S COtt CPMA NEgg
macrophylla	CMCN SMad WCwm
mas ♀	CAgr CB&S CFee CPMA CPle EBrP EBre ELan ENot GChr LBre LPan MBal MBar MBri MGos MWat NHol NNor NWea SBre SHBN SPer SSta WCoo WDin WHCG WMou WWat
– 'Aurea' (v)	CAbP CPMA ELan EMil EPla MAsh MBri MCCP SPer SSpi SSta WAbe WDin WPat WWat
§ – 'Aureoelegantissima' (v)	CBlo CFil CPMA ELan LNet MAsh MBri MBro NHol SPer SSta WPGP WPat WSHC
– 'Elegantissima'	See *C. mas* 'Aureoelegantissima'
– 'Golden Glory'	CB&S CPMA
– 'Variegata' ♀	CB&S CBot CMCN CPMA ELan EMil IOrc LNet LPan MAsh MBri MGos NEgg NPal SPer SSpi WFar WPat WWat
N 'Norman Hadden' ♀	CAbP CBar CPMA CRos CSam CTho MAsh SBid SHBN SHFr SMad SPer SSpi SSta WAbe WPat WWat
nuttallii	CB&S CSam ELan EMil GOrc LPan MBal MBro SHBN SSta WDin WNor WWat
– 'Ascona'	See *C.* 'Ascona'
– 'Colrigo Giant'	CPMA SSpi
– 'Gold Spot' (v)	CB&S CBlo CPMA EPfP IOrc MGos SPer WWes
– 'Monarch'	CB&S CBlo CPMA LPan SPer WWes
– 'North Star'	CPMA CRos SPer
– 'Portlemouth'	CEnd CPMA SPer
obliqua	CFil EPla WPGP
§ *occidentalis*	EPla
officinalis	CPMA EPfP LPan WCwm WWat
'Ormonde'	CPMA SPer SSpi WWes
'Pink Blush'	CPMA
pubescens	See *C. occidentalis*
pumila	NHol WDin
§ *racemosa*	WWat
¶ *rugosa*	WNor
I × *rutgersiensis* 'Aurora'	CPMA
– 'Ruth Ellen'	CPMA
– 'Stellar Pink'	CPMA

sanguinea	CB&S CBlo CKin CLnd CPer CTri EBrP EBre ENot GChr LBre LBuc MAsh MPEx NNor NWea SBre WDin WGwG WHar WMou
– 'Compressa'	See *C. hessei*
– 'Midwinter Fire'	CB&S CBlo CDoC COtt EBee EBrP EBre ECle ENot EPla ERic EWll LBre LBuc LPan MBar MGos MWat NBee SBre SMad SRms WFar WLRN WWeb
§ – 'Winter Beauty'	CDoC EMil IOrc LHop MAsh MBro NHol SCoo SEas WPat WPyg WWat
– 'Winter Flame'	See *C. sanguinea* **'Winter Beauty'**
sp. CLD 613	EPla
stolonifera ♀	CArn MGos
– 'Flaviramea' ♀	CB&S CLnd EBrP EBre ELan ENot GChr GRei IOrc ISea LBre LBuc MBar MBri MGos MWat NBee NNor NWea SBre SHBN SPer SReu SSta WDin WHar WLeb WWat WWin
§ – 'Kelseyi'	CB&S CBlo CWit EBar EBee EPla ESis IOrc MBar NBee SBod SLPl SPer SVil WLRN WWat
§ – 'White Gold' (v)	CABP CBlo CPMA EBee ENot EPla IOrc MBri MGos WWeb
– 'White Spot'	See *C. stolonifera* **'White Gold'**
§ *stricta*	CLnd
walteri	CMCN WCwm

COROKIA (Escalloniaceae)

buddlejoides	CAbb CMHG CPle ECou MAll MGrG SOWG WBod WCru WPic WTro
– var. *linearis*	CPle
'Coppershine'	CB&S CMHG MAll
cotoneaster	CABP CHor CPle CTrw ECou ELan ENot EPot MBlu MUlv NHol SDry SPar SPer SSta WBod WBrE WFar WPat WSHC WWat WWes
– 'Little Prince'	CB&S
– 'Ohau Scarlet'	ECou
– 'Ohau Yellow'	ECou
– 'Swale Stream'	ECou
– 'Wanaka'	ECou
macrocarpa	CDoC CPle ISea MAll SDix SPer WSHC
¶ – × *buddlejoides*	MAll
× *virgata*	CABP CB&S CDec CHan CMHG CPle CTrC ECou ELan EMil IOrc ISea MAll MBlu MCCP MWhi SArc SPer WSHC WTro WWal
– 'Bronze King'	CDoC CMil CPle CWit SPer
– 'Bronze Knight'	MHar
– 'Bronze Lady'	MAll MBal
– 'Cheesemanii'	ECou
– 'County Park Lemon'	ECou MAll SOWG
– 'County Park Purple'	ECou
* – 'Dartonii'	MBlu
* – 'Frosted Chocolate'	CB&S
– 'Havering'	ECou
¶ – 'Pink Delight'	EPfP
* – *purpurea*	MAll
– 'Red Wonder'	CBlo CMHG EBee ERea MAll SAga SDry SEND SOWG

* – 'Sunsplash'	CB&S
– 'Virgata'	CChe ECou
– 'Yellow Wonder'	CB&S CMHG ECot ECou MAll SAga

CORONILLA (Papilionaceae)

cappadocica	See *C. orientalis*
comosa	See *Hippocrepis comosa*
emerus	See *Hippocrepis emerus*
glauca	See *C. valentina* subsp. *glauca*
globosa	SUsu
minima	NTow SBla
§ *orientalis*	NWCA WWin
– var. *orientalis*	EHyt
valentina	CMac CSPN CSam EMil LHop MHlr SBra SDix SVen WCot WFar WRHF
§ – subsp. *glauca* ♀	CB&S CBot CFee CGle CMac CPle CSam CTri ELan ENot ERea IOrc MBal MWhi NTow SPer SRCN SRms WAbe WHCG
– – 'Citrina' ♀	CB&S CBot CDec CDoC CHan CSam ELan LGre LHop MLan NPer SChu SPer SVil WAbe WHCG WKif WRus WSHC WSpi
* – – 'Pygmaea'	WCot
– – 'Variegata'	CB&S CBot CGle CHan CLTr CMac CPle CSPN CSam EBrP EBre ELan EMil ERea LBre LHop MAsh SBra SBre SDix SPer SSta WAbe WEas WFar WSHC
§ *varia*	SRCN WCot

CORREA (Rutaceae)

alba	CSev ECou ERea MAll SMur
– 'Pinkie'	ECou ERea LHop MAll SOWG
backhouseana ♀	CAbb CB&S CHan CPle CSam CTrG CTri ECre ERea GCal GQui IBlr IOrc LCns LHop MAll SAga SLMG SOWG WBod WSHC
¶ *baeuerlenii*	MAll SOWG
calycina	ERea
decumbens	CPle ECon ECou GSki LCns MAll SMur SOWG WSHC
'Dusky Bells'	CHan CPle CSWP CWSG ECou ERea LCns LHop MAll SOWG
'Dusky Maid'	CAbb MAll WAbe WLRN
'Harrisii'	See *C.* **'Mannii'**
lawrenceana	CAbb CB&S CWSG GQui IBlr LHil MAll SBid WAbe WLRN
– *rosea*	CMHG
§ 'Mannii' ♀	CHan CLTr CSam CSev ECou ERea IOrc LHop MAll MNes SOWG WAbe WSHC WWat
'Marian's Marvel'	CAbb CB&S CMHG ERea GQui LCns MAll SOWG SVen WAbe WLRN
pulchella	CB&S CGre CMHG CPle CTri ERea GQui LBlm MAll MNes SAga SOWG WAbe
§ *reflexa*	CMHG CPle ECou LBlm MAll SOWG
¶ – var. *reflexa*	MAll
– *virens*	WEas
– 'Yanakie'	CPle
speciosa	See *C. reflexa*
¶ *viridiflora*	GQui

CORTADERIA † (Poaceae - Bambusoideae)

argentea	See *C. selloana*
§ *fulvida*	CCuc EBrP EBre EGar EPla IBlr LBre SBre SMad
§ *richardii* (Endlicher) Zotov	CHEx CHan EFou EHoe ELan EWes GAri GGar IBlr MBal SAPC SArc
– hort.	See *C. fulvida*
§ *selloana*	CB&S CHEx CTri EBrP EBre ELan ENot EOHP EPfP LBre LNet MBar NBee NNor SAPC SArc SBre WStI
§ – 'Albolineata' (v)	CMil CSte EHoe EWes SEND SMad WLRN
§ – 'Aureolineata' (v) ♀	CB&S CMil EHoe ELan ENot IHos MAsh MBal MBri MGos SAxl SCob SEas SHBN SPer WPat
– 'Gold Band'	See *C. selloana* 'Aureolineata'
– 'Monstrosa'	SMad
– 'Pink Feather'	CBlo EBar MWat NEgg SHBN SRms WPyg WStI
– 'Pumila' ♀	CB&S CCuc CDoC CHEx EBar EBrP EBre ECtt EHoe ELan ENot EPla GAbr LBre MBal MBri MGos NEgg NFai SApp SBre SCob SDix SEas SHBN SMad SPer SPla WLeb WStI
– 'Rendatleri'	CB&S CDoC EHoe ELan MAsh MBal SCob SEND SEas SMad WLRN WShe
– 'Roi des Roses'	CBlo
– 'Rosea'	CHEx CSte GSki MBal MBar MBri
– 'Silver Comet'	WWoo
– 'Silver Fountain'	EGar ELan LRHS MAsh SPer
– 'Silver Stripe'	See *C. selloana* 'Albolineata'
– 'Sunningdale Silver' ♀	CB&S CBlo EBrP EBre ECtt EHoe ELan ENot IHos LBre MBal MBri MGos MUlv MWat SBre SCob SEas SHBN SMad SPer WLeb WPyg
– 'White Feather'	CBlo CHEx CLan ECtt WFar WHil
Toe Toe	See *C. richardii* (Endlicher) Zotov

CORTUSA (Primulaceae)

altaica	GCal
brotheri	NWCA
matthioli	CGle EPfP GTou LBee LGan MBal MFir NGre NMGW NMen NRya NTow NWCA WFar WWhi
– 'Alba'	ECGN EPPr GCal LBee MBal NHar NWCA
– var. *congesta*	EBee
– subsp. *pekinensis*	CFir EBee GCra GDra GSki LBee LSyl NDov NHar NRoo WOve
– var. *yezoensis*	EHyt

CORYBAS (Orchidaceae)

¶ *diemenicus*	SWes
¶ *incurvus*	SWes

CORYDALIS (Papaveraceae)

alexeenkoana	CLAP EPot
◆ – subsp. *vittae*	See *C. vittae*
ambigua	ETub
Chamisso & Schlecht.	

– hort.	See *C. fumariifolia*
angustifolia	EPot GCrs
¶ *blanda* subsp. *parnassica*	EPot
◆ 'Blue Panda'	See *C. flexuosa* 'Blue Panda'
bracteata	CLAP GCrs LRHS
¶ – 'Marina'	CLAP
bulbosa auct. non DC	See *C. cava*
– De Candolle	See *C. solida*
buschii	GCrs
cashmeriana	EHyt EPot GCra GCrs GTou NHar SBla WAbe WHal WIvy
– 'Kailash'	GBuc
caucasica	EPot GCrs GDra LAma
– var. *alba* misapplied	See *C. malkensis*
§ *cava* ♀	CGle EBot EPar EPot LAma
– *albiflora*	EPar EPot
¶ *chaerophylla* B&SWJ 2951	WCru
cheilanthifolia	Widely available
chionophila	MSto
conorhiza	EHyt EPot
◆ *decipiens*	See *C. solida* subsp. *incisa*
elata	CAvo CBos CLAP CMil CRDP CSev CSpe CVer EPla EPot GCrs IBlr LHop MAvo MTho NHar NHol NNrd SAga SSoC SSpi SUsu SWas SWat WAbe WCot WCru WFar WHal WLin
– 'Blue Summit'	SBla
erdelii	GCrs
firouzii	EPot
flexuosa	Widely available
§ – 'Blue Panda'	CBos EBee EHyt EPPr EPfP SHBN SSoC SSpi
– CD&R 528	CAvo CGle EHyt LGre MBro MRav NHar NRar NRya SAga SIng WCot WCru WOMN WRHF
– 'China Blue' CD&R 528c	Widely available
– 'Nightshade'	CElw GAri GBuc MAvo SAxl SHBN SWat WCot WRHF
I – 'Norman's Seedling'	EPPr WPGP
– 'Père David' CD&R 528b	Widely available
– 'Purple Leaf' CD&R 528a	CAvo CBos CBro CDec CElw CMea CMil CRow CVer ECha EPot GBuc GCal GCra IBlr MBri MDHE NHol SAxl SPer SUsu SWas WAbe WCot WCru WFar WHer WHoo WKif WWeb
§ *fumariifolia*	EPot LAma MTho NRog
glauca	See *C. sempervirens*
glaucescens	EPot GCrs
¶ – 'Medeo'	GCrs
¶ *haussknechtii*	EHyt GCrs
henrikii	EHyt EPot GCrs
integra	GCrs
intermedia	EPot
* *itacifolia*	WCot
kashgarica	EPot
linstowiana	CElw CLon CSpe EHyt EMon IBlr MSto WCot
– CD&R 605	CLAP
§ *lutea*	CB&S ECro ELan EMar GBuc IBlr LGro MTis NFai NPer NPri NRoo NVic SEND SRms WBea WBon WCot WHen WRha
§ *malkensis* ♀	CLAP EHyt EPot GCrs NBir NTow
nobilis	EPot MSto SHBN
nudicaulis	EPot GCrs
ochotensis	MSto NLar
¶ – B&SWJ 3138	WCru

§ *ochroleuca*	CAvo CRow EMan EMar EPot ESis GCra LFis MBro MCLN MTho MTis WBro WCru WFar WHal WRha
ophiocarpa	CGle CInt EHoe ELan EMar GAri GCal GGar IBlr LSyl MFos MPEx WBea WCot WFoF WOve WSan WWhi
¶ *oppositifolia* subsp. *oppositifolia*	EHyt GCrs
paczoskii	EHyt EPot LRHS WAbe
¶ *pallida* B&SWJ 395	WCru
parnassica	EHyt
paschei	EHyt
popovii	GCrs
pseudofumaria alba	See *C. ochroleuca*
pumila	EPot GCrs LRHS NTow
pumila alba	EPot
rosea	GBuc IBlr
ruksansii	EPot GCrs
§ *saxicola*	EPot MSto
◆ *scandens*	See *Dicentra scandens*
schanginii	CLAP EPot
– subsp. *ainii*	CLAP EHyt EPot GCrs
scouleri	NBir
§ *sempervirens*	CHid CInt MLLN MLan NFai WCru WHer WSan WWin
– *alba*	CHid ELan MLLN WFoF
¶ *shanginii* subsp. *shanginii*	EHyt
smithiana	WFar
– ACE 154	CPBP EHyt EPot GBuc MRPP NMen
§ *solida* ♀	CBro CElw CGle CMea CRDP EHyt EPar EPot ETub GCrs IBlr LAma MHlr MRPP NFla NHar NMen NNrd NRog NRya WAbe WCot WFar WHil WShi WWhi
– BM 8499	NHol
◆ – subsp. *densiflora*	See *C. solida* subsp. *incisa*
– forms	EPot
¶ – from Penza	GCrs
– 'Harkov'	GCrs LRHS
¶ – 'Ice Pink'	EPot
§ – subsp. *incisa*	CMea EHyt EPot GCrs LRHS MHig MTho
– MS 881	CMon
* – 'Smokey Blue'	EHyt
¶ – 'Soft Pink'	EPot
– subsp. *solida* 'Beth Evans' ♀	CBro EHyt SWas WCot
– – 'Blushing Girl'	GCrs
¶ – – 'Highland Mist'	GCrs NHar
¶ – – 'Prasil Sunset'	EHyt
– f. *transsylvanica*	CLAP CMon EHyt EPot GCrs NBir NHar NRya SWat WOMN
¶ – – 'Dieter Schacht'	GCrs
– – 'George Baker' ♀	CAvo CBro EHyt EPot GCrs MTho NHar NHol SWas WAbe WCot
– – 'Lahovice'	EPot
– – 'Nettleton Pink'	EPot
sp. ACE 2443	EPot
¶ *tauricola*	EPot
thalictrifolia Franchet	See *C. saxicola*
tomentella	EPot MSto SIng WAbe
¶ *uniflora*	GCrs
§ *vittae*	EHyt
wendelboi	EPot GCrs
¶ – subsp. *congesta* 'Abant Wine'	EPot

wilsonii	CBot CLyd GCHN GCal IBlr MTho NBro NTow NWCA SBla WEas WOMN
zetterlundii	GCrs

CORYLOPSIS † (Hamamelidaceae)

§ *glabrescens*	CPMA MBal SMur WNor
– var. *gotoana*	CPMA ELan EPfP MAsh SMur SPer SSpi WWat
himalayana KR 990	WAbe
pauciflora ♀	CB&S CPMA EBrP EBre ELan EMil ENot IOrc LBre MBal MBri MGos NBee SBre SHBN SPer SReu SSta WBod WPat WWal WWat
platypetala	See *C. sinensis* var. *calvescens*
– var. *laevis*	See *C. sinensis* var. *calvescens*
sinensis	EMil SSta WFar
§ – var. *calvescens*	CBlo CPMA MBal
§ – – f. *veitchiana* ♀	CBlo CPMA MBal SMur WWoo
¶ – – – 'Purple Selection'	CPMA
§ – var. *sinensis* ♀	CPMA CWit EAst EHic EPfP MBal MGos SReu SSta WAbe WWat
– – 'Spring Purple'	CABP CPMA EPfP LHop MAsh MBri SPer SPla SSpi SSta WWat
spicata	CB&S CBlo CPMA ELan IHos MBal MBlu MHlr MPla SCoo SPer WBay WHCG
veitchiana	See *C. sinensis* var. *calvescens* f. *veitchiana*
willmottiae	See *C. sinensis* var. *sinensis*

CORYLUS † (Corylaceae)

avellana (F)	CKin CLnd CPer EBrP EBre EMui ENot ERea GRei IOrc LBre LBuc LHyr MBal MBar MBri NBee NRog NRoo NWea SBre SKee WDin WHar WMou WStI
– 'Aurea'	CBlo CEnd COtt CTho ELan ENot EPfP LBuc MAsh MBlu MGos NHol SPer SPla SSta WDin WPyg
– 'Bollwylle'	See *C. maxima* 'Halle'sche Riesennuss'
– 'Contorta' ♀	Widely available
– 'Cosford Cob' (F)	CBlo CDoC CTho CTri EBrP EBre ERea ESim GTwe LBre LBuc MBlu MBri MGos NRog SBre SDea SKee SPer WWal
§ – 'Fuscorubra' (F)	CMac IOrc MRav
§ – 'Heterophylla'	CEnd CTho WMou WWes
– 'Laciniata'	See *C. avellana* 'Heterophylla'
– 'Merveille de Bollwyller'	See *C. maxima* 'Halle'sche Riesennuss'
– 'Nottingham Prolific'	See *C. avellana* 'Pearson's Prolific'
§ – 'Pearson's Prolific' (F)	ERea ESim GTwe LBuc SDea MBlu WMou
– 'Pendula'	See *C. avellana* 'Fuscorubra'
– 'Purpurea'	See *C. avellana* 'Fuscorubra'
§ – 'Webb's Prize Cob' (F)	ERea GTwe IOrc LHol NRog SDea WMou
colurna ♀	CBlo CFil CLnd CMCN CTho ENot GChr IOrc LHyr MGos NBee NWea SKee SLPl SMad SPer WDin WMou WOrn
– × *avellana*	See *C.* × *colurnoides*
* – 'Te Terra Red'	CEnd CMCN MBlu SMad WMou

§ x *colurnoides* ESim
maxima (F) CLnd EMui GTwe NWea SDea WDin
– 'Butler' (F) CBlo ERea GTwe SKee WPyg
– 'Ennis' (F) ERea GTwe SKee
– 'Fertile de Coutard' See *C. maxima* 'White Filbert'
– 'Frizzled Filbert' (F) ERea
– 'Frühe van Frauendorf' See *C. maxima* 'Red Filbert'
– 'Grote Lambertsnoot' See *C. maxima* 'Kentish Cob'
– 'Gunslehert' (F) CBlo ERea GChr GTwe SKee WPyg
– Halle Giant See *C. maxima* 'Halle'sche Riesennuss'
§ – 'Halle'sche Riesennuss' (F) ERea GTwe LHol SKee
§ – 'Kentish Cob' (F) CBlo CDoC CSam CTho EBrP EBre ERea ESim GTwe IOrc LBre LBuc MBlu MGos NRog SBre SFam SKee SPer SRms WHar WPyg
– 'Lambert's Filbert' See *C. maxima* 'Kentish Cob'
– 'Longue d'Espagne' See *C. maxima* 'Kentish Cob'
– 'Monsieur de Bouweller' See *C. maxima* 'Halle'sche Riesennuss'
– New Giant See *C. maxima* 'Neue Riesennuss'
– 'Purple Filbert' See *C. maxima* 'Purpurea'
§ – 'Purpurea' (F) ♀ CTho EBrP EBre ELan ENot ERea GChr LBre LBuc MBal MBar MBri MGos MWat NBee NFla NLon NWea SBre SHBN SPer SSta WDin WHar WMou WPat WStI WWat WWeb
§ – 'Red Filbert' (F) CBlo CEnd ERea GTwe IOrc MBlu NRog SKee
– 'Red Zellernut' See *C. maxima* 'Red Filbert'
– 'Spanish White' See *C. maxima* 'White Filbert'
§ – 'White Filbert' (F) ERea GTwe NRog SKee WHar
– 'White Spanish Filbert' See *C. maxima* 'White Filbert'
– 'Witpit Lambertsnoot' See *C. maxima* 'White Filbert'
x *vilmorinii* WMou

CORYMBIUM (Asteraceae) See Plant Deletions

CORYNEPHORUS (Poaceae)
canescens EBee EHoe EMan GBin MCCP MLLN

CORYNOCARPUS (Corynocarpaceae)
laevigatus CHEx ECou MBri
– 'Picturatus' CHEx
– 'Variegatus' CHEx

COSMOS (Asteraceae)
§ *atrosanguineus* Widely available

COSTUS (Zingiberaceae)
§ *cuspidatus* LChe
igneus See *C. cuspidatus*
malortieanus LChe
speciosus NRog WMul
spiralis LChe

COTINUS (Anacardiaceae)
americanus See *C. obovatus*
§ *coggygria* ♀ CB&S CDoC CMCN EAst EBrP EBre ELan ENot IOrc LBre LHop MBar MBri MWat NBee NNor SBre SDix SHBN SPer WDin WFar WGwG WHCG WHar WWat WWes

– 'Foliis Purpureis' See *C. coggygria* **Rubrifolius Group**
– 'Notcutt's Variety' CBlo EBee EBrP EBre ELan ENot LBre MAsh SBre SPer SPla WWes
– 'Pink Champagne' CPMA
– Purpureus Group ENot
– 'Red Beauty' COtt LRHS MBri
– 'Royal Purple' ♀ Widely available
§ – Rubrifolius Group CB&S MBal NNor SChu SDix SPer SPla WHCG WWeb
– 'Velvet Cloak' CBlo CPMA CSam ELan EPfP MAsh MGos SPer SPla SReu SSta WHCG WPat WPyg WWat
'Flame' ♀ CBlo CPMA IOrc MAsh SPla WPat WWeb
'Grace' ♀ Widely available
§ *obovatus* ♀ CBlo CGre CMCN CMHG CPMA CPle ENot EPfP SHBN SPer WWat WWes

COTONEASTER † (Rosaceae)
acuminatus SRms WPGP
♦ *acutifolius* var. *laetevirens* See *C. laetevirens*
adpressus ♀ CBlo EPfP EPla GDra MGos NCut NHar NNor NWea
§ – 'Little Gem' GAri MAsh MBri MPla NMen SRms WFar
– var. *praecox* See *C. nanshan*
– 'Tom Thumb' See *C. adpressus* 'Little Gem'
affinis SRms
afghanicus CC 738 WLRN
* *albokermesinus* SRms
altaicus SRms
ambiguus SRms
amoenus SLPl SRms
apiculatus CSWP SRms
armenus SRms
§ *ascendens* SRms
assadii SRms
assamensis SRms
§ *astrophoros* CBlo MBlu SIng SRms
atropurpureus SRms
§ – 'Variegatus' ♀ CBot EBar EHoe ELan ENot EPot GChr GRei IOrc LHop MBal MBar MBri MGos NBee NHol SHBN SPer SRms WAbe WRHF WSHC WWal WWat WWin
bacillaris SRms
boisianus SRms
bradyi SRms
§ *bullatus* ♀ ELan ENot GRei MGos NNor NTow SEND SPer SRms WCwm WSHC WWat
– 'Firebird' CBlo SPer SRms
– f. *floribundus* See *C. bullatus*
– var. *macrophyllus* See *C. rehderi*
buxifolius blue-leaved See *C. lidjiangensis*
¶ – 'Brno' SRms
– f. *vellaeus* See *C. astrophoros*
– Wallich ex Lindley EHic ESis SRms
calocarpus SRms
cambricus CNat SRms
canescens SRms
cashmiriensis ♀ SRms
cavei EPla SRms
chailaricus SRms
chengkangensis SRms
cinerascens SRms

§ *cochleatus*	CChe EPot ESis GAri GDra
	MBal MBar MGos MPla NFla
	NMen SReu SRms WCot WEas
	WRHF WWat
§ *congestus*	CFee EBrP EBre IOrc LBre
	MBal MBar MBri MBro MGos
	MRav NLon NNor NRoo SBre
	SPer SRms WAbe WHar WWat
	WWin
– 'Nanus'	CLyd CMHG CNic ELan EMil
	EOrn ESis MAsh MBro MOne
	MPla NHol NNrd SIng SPla
	SRms WHCG WPat WPyg
	WWat
conspicuus	CSam SRms
– 'Decorus' ♀	CMHG ELan ENot GOrc GRei
	IOrc MBar MGos MRav NHol
	NNor NRoo NWea SEas SPer
	WDin WPyg WStI WWes
– 'Flameburst'	MBal MBri SHBN
– 'Red Alert'	SRms
– 'Red Glory'	SRms
* – 'Winter Jewel'	CBlo
¶ *cooperi*	SRms
crispii	SRms
¶ aff. –	SRms
cuspidatus	SRms
N *dammeri* ♀	CBlo CChe CMHG ELan ENot
	GRei ISea LBuc MAsh MBal
	MBar MGos NBee NNor NWea
	SIng SPer SRms WDin WHCG
	WHar WWat WWin
– 'Major'	NFla WCFE
– 'Oakwood'	See *C. radicans* 'Eichholz'
– var. *radicans* hort.	CBlo SPla
– – Schneider	See *C. radicans*
– 'Streibs Findling'	See *C. procumbens*
dielsianus	NWea SRms
– 'Rubens'	SRms
discolor	SRms
distichus	See *C. nitidus*
– var. *tongolensis*	See *C. splendens*
divaricatus	ENot EPla GRei SPer SRms
	WFar WWat
duthieanus	SRms
§ – 'Boer'	MBar SRms
elegans	SRms
ellipticus	SRms
♦ 'Erlinda'	See *C. × suecicus* 'Erlinda'
¶ 'Falconeri'	SRms
fangianus	SRms
floccosus	CBlo EHal GOrc GRei MBri
	NWea SPer SRms WLRN
	WWat
forrestii	SRms
franchetii	CB&S CChe CMHG EBrP
	EBre ELan EMil ERom GCHN
	IOrc LBre LBuc LPan MBal
	MGos MRav MWat NBee
	NWea SBre SPer SPla SRms
	WDin WFar WGwG WHar
	WStI
♦ – var. *sternianus*	See *C. sternianus*
frigidus	CBlo GAri NWea SRms
§ – 'Cornubia' ♀	CBlo CLnd EBrP EBre ELan
	ENot GCHN GChr GOrc LBre
	LHop LNet LPan MAsh MBar
	MBri MGos MLan MRav MWat
	NWea SBre SEas SHBN SPer
	SRms WDin WStI WWat
– 'Fructu Luteo'	IBlr SRms
– 'Notcutt's Variety'	EBee ELan ENot WWes

– 'Saint Monica'	MBlu
froebelii	SRms
gamblei	SRms
¶ *gangmobaensis*	SRms
giraldii	SRms
glabratus	SLPl SRms
glacialis	SRms
glaucophyllus	SEND SRms
§ *glomerulatus*	ESis MBar SRms
goloskokovii	SRms
gracilis	SRms
griffithii	SRms
harrovianus	SLPl SRms
harrysmithii	SRms
hebephyllus	SRms
henryanus	SRms
– 'Anne Cornwallis'	WBcn
§ 'Herbstfeuer'	CBlo EBee ECtt EGra EHol
	MBal MGos MRav MWat NLon
	NNor SPla SRms WAbe
hessei	SRms
'Highlight' (aff. *sheriffii*)	ECtt SRms
hissaricus	SRms
§ *hjelmqvistii*	LBuc SRms WFar WRHF
– 'Robustus'	See *C. hjelmqvistii*
– 'Rotundifolius'	See *C. hjelmqvistii*
horizontalis ♀	CLan CMHG ELan ENot GChr
	GOrc GRei IOrc ISea LGro
	MBal MBar MBri MGos MWat
	NBee NFla NLon NNor NWea
	SDix SHBN SPer SReu SRms
	WAbe WDin WWat WWin
– 'Tangstedt'	ENot
– 'Variegatus'	See *C. atropurpureus*
	'Variegatus'
– var. *wilsonii*	See *C. ascendens*
¶ *hsingshangensis*	SRms
humifusus	See *C. dammeri*
hummelii	SRms
'Hybridus Pendulus'	See *C. salicifolius* 'Pendulus'
hylmoei	SLPl SRms
ignavus	EHal SLPl SRms
¶ *ignescens*	SRms
induratus	SRms
insculptus	SRms
insolitus	SRms
integerrimus	NHol SRms
§ *integrifolius*	CMHG EHic ELan EPfP EPla
	ESis LNet MAsh MBal MBar
	MBri MWhi NHol NRoo SRms
	STre WWat
juranus	SRms
¶ *kitaibelii*	SRms
kweitschoviensis	SRms
lacteus ♀	CBlo CSam CTri ELan ENot
	EPla IOrc LBuc LPan MGos
	MRav SEND SHBN SPer SPla
	SRms WDin WFar WRHF
	WWat
§ *laetevirens*	SRms
¶ *langei*	SRms
laxiflorus	SRms
§ *lidjiangensis*	EBee SRms WCot
linearifolius	EHol SRms
lucidus	SRms
ludlowii	SRms
§ *mairei*	SRms
– Yu 14144	MBal
marginatus	SRms
marquandii	EPla NNor SRms
megalocarpus	SRms
§ *meiophyllus* ♀	SRms

talgaricus	SRms
tengyuehensis	SRms
tomentellus	SRms
tomentosus	SRms
transens	SRms
tripyrenus	SRms
turbinatus	SRms
turcomanicus	SRms
veitchii	SRms
vernae	SRms
¶ *verruculosus*	SRms
vestitus	SRms
villosulus	SRms
¶ *vilmorinianus*	SRms
wardii hort.	See *C. mairei*
– W. W. Smith	CBlo IOrc NBee
× *watereri*	CBlo CLnd GChr LNet MAsh
	MGos NWea SPla WDin WWeb
◆ – 'Avonbank'	See *C. salicifolius* 'Avonbank'
– 'Cornubia'	See *C. frigidus* 'Cornubia'
– 'Goscote'	MGos
– 'John Waterer' ♀	SRms
– 'Pendulus'	See *C. salicifolius* 'Pendulus'
– 'Pink Champagne'	CAbP MAsh MBri SPer
wilsonii	SRms
zabelii	SRms
– 'Magyar'	SRms

COTULA (Asteraceae)

atrata	See *Leptinella atrata*
– var. *dendyi*	See *Leptinella dendyi*
coronopifolia	CBen CSev CWat LPBA MSta
	NDea SWat SWyc WChe WWeb
goyenii	See *Leptinella goyenii*
hispida	CInt CLyd CMHG EBar ECtt
	EPot GAbr GCHN MBar MHig
	MTho MWat NMen NNor NPer
	NRya NWCA SBla SChu SIgm
	SIng SSmi WAbe WCru WEas
	WFar WMow WPat WPer
lineariloba	CHea CPBP ECha EWes LBee
	WLRN
minor	See *Leptinella minor*
pectinata	See *Leptinella pectinata*
perpusilla	See *Leptinella pusilla*
* 'Platt's Black'	LRHS
potentilloides	See *Leptinella potentillina*
pyrethrifolia	See *Leptinella pyrethrifolia*
reptans	See *Leptinella scariosa*
rotundata	See *Leptinella rotundata*
scariosa	See *Leptinella scariosa*
sericea	See *Leptinella albida*
serrulata	See *Leptinella serrulata*
sp. C&H 452	MRPP NWCA
squalida	See *Leptinella squalida*

COTYLEDON (Crassulaceae)

chrysantha	See *Rosularia chrysantha*
gibbiflora var. *metallica*	See *Echeveria gibbiflora* var.
	metallica
oppositifolia	See *Chiastophyllum*
	oppositifolium
orbiculata	WCot
– S&SH 40	NGre
* *pomedosa*	MBri
* – 'Variegata'	MBri
simplicifolia	See *Chiastophyllum*
	oppositifolium
undulata	WEas

COWANIA (Rosaceae) See Plant Deletions

CRAIBIODENDRON (Ericaceae)

yunnanense	CPle MBal

CRAMBE (Brassicaceae)

cordifolia ♀	Widely available
koktebelica	ECha
maritima	CGle CSev ECGP ECha EMan
	EMar ERav GPoy MAus MAvo
	MLLN MSal MWgw NNor NSti
	SPer SSoC SWat WCot WCru
	WHer WHoo WMer WPer
	WWeb
– 'Lilywhite'	ILis WCot
orientalis	ECha MAvo WCot
tataria	CArn EGar EMan MAvo WCot
	WPer

CRASPEDIA (Asteraceae)

¶ *globosa*	MFiF
lanata var. *elongata*	GCLN
richea	See *C. glauca*
uniflora	GCLN

CRASSULA (Crassulaceae)

anomala	NGre
arborescens	GAri SLMG SRms STre
argentea	See *C. ovata*
coccinea	CHEx CTrC EDAr SLMG
dejecta × *coccinea*	CHEx
falcata ♀	IBlr MBri WCot
* *galanthea*	SLMG
§ *helmsii*	EHon EMFW NDea WChe
	WMAq WWeb
justi-corderoyi	CHal
§ *milfordiae*	CNic CTri ELan MBar MOne
	MRPP MWat NBir NGre SBod
	WPer
monstrosa	SLMG
muscosa	STre
§ *ovata* ♀	CHEx CHal EBak GBin MBri
	NPer SLMG
– 'Basutoland'	MPla
– 'Blue Bird'	GBin
* – 'Coral'	GBin
– 'Hummel's Sunset' (v) ♀	CHal SLMG
* – *nana*	STre
* – 'Riversii'	SLMG
– 'Variegata'	CHal EBak SLMG
pellucida subsp.	CHal
marginalis	
peploides	NGre
perforata	CHal SLMG
– 'Variegata'	CHal
portulacea	See *C. ovata*
recurva	See *C. helmsii*
rupestris ♀	MBri
rupicola	GAri
§ *sarcocaulis*	CHEx CHal CTri ELan EOas
	EPot ESis GTou MHar MPla
	MRPP MTho NGre NMen NVic
	NWCA SBod SIng SRms SSmi
	STre WAbe WEas WPat WSHC
	WWin
– *alba*	CHal ELan NGre SHFr SIng
	STre WAbe WPer
– 'Ken Aslet'	NGre SIng STre
schmidtii	CHal MBri
sedifolia	See *C. milfordiae*
sediformis	See *C. milfordiae*
socialis	CHal
tetragona	SLMG

* *tomentosa* 'Variegata' LHil

+ CRATAEGOMESPILUS (Rosaceae) See Plant Deletions

CRATAEGUS (Rosaceae)
- *arnoldiana* CEnd CLnd CTho MCoo SEND SLPl
- 'Autumn Glory' CBlo CEnd CLnd EBee EBrP EBre LBre MGos SBre
- *azarolus* CAgr WMou
- – 'White Italian' (F) ESim
- *champlainensis* CTho
- N *coccinea* NWea
- *cordata* See *C. phaenopyrum*
- *crus-galli* hort. See *C. persimilis* 'Prunifolia'
- *crus-galli* Linnaeus CB&S CBlo CDoC CLnd CTho LBuc SPer WDin WJas WMou
- – var. *pyracanthifolia* CTho
- x *durobrivensis* CLnd CTho WWat
- ¶ *ellwangeriana* MCoo
- *eriocarpa* CLnd
- *flabellata* CEnd SSpi
- *gemmosa* CEnd CTho
- x *grignonensis* CB&S CLnd ENot LBuc MCoo SPer WJas WPyg
- § *laciniata* CBlo CEnd CLnd CMCN EBee EPfP MAsh MCoo SHBN SSpi WJas WMou
- § *laevigata* CPer WMou
- – 'Coccinea Plena' See *C. laevigata* 'Paul's Scarlet'
- – 'Crimson Cloud' CBlo CEnd CLnd EBee ENot EPfP GChr MAsh MBri SCoo SPer WJas WOrn WPyg
- ◆ – 'Flore Pleno' See *C. laevigata* 'Plena'
- – 'Mutabilis' CTho SHBN
- § – 'Paul's Scarlet' (d) ♀ Widely available
- – 'Pink Corkscrew' CTho GAri MBlu
- § – 'Plena' (d) CB&S CBlo CDoC CTho EBee GChr IHos LPan MAsh MBri NWea SFam SHBN SPer WMou WOrn
- – 'Punicea' CBlo
- – 'Rosea Flore Pleno' (d) ♀ CB&S CBlo CDoC CLnd CTho EBrP EBre ELan ENot GRei LBre LBuc LPan MAsh MBar MBri MGos MWat NWea SBre SHBN SPer WDin WJas WStI
- x *lavalleei* CBlo CLnd CTri EBee ENot EPfP GChr MAsh SPer WDin WOrn
- – 'Carrierei' ♀ CBlo CDoC CSam CTho EPfP IOrc LPan MBri NWea
- x *media* 'Gireoudii' (v) CEnd CPMA CLNet MBlu MGos WMou WPat
- *mexicana* See *C. pubescens* f. *stipulacea*
- *mollis* CAgr
- *monogyna* CB&S CDoC CKin CLnd CPer EBrP EBre ELan ENot EPfP GChr GRei LBre LBuc LHyr MBar MBri MGos NBee NWea SBre SPer WDin WMou
- – 'Biflora' CBlo CEnd CTho EBee MAsh NWea WMou WSPU
- – 'Compacta' EPla MBlu
- – 'Ferox' CTho
- – 'Flexuosa' LNet
- – 'Stricta' CLnd CTho EBee ENot WOrn WSpi
- – 'Variegata' LNet WBcn WMou WSPU
- x *mordenensis* 'Toba' (d) CBlo CDoC CLnd CTho
- *orientalis* See *C. laciniata*

- *oxyacantha* See *C. laevigata*
- *pedicellata* CLnd CTho LPan MCoo
- § *persimilis* 'Prunifolia' ♀ CB&S CBlo CDoC CMCN CSam CTho CTri EBrP EBre ELan ENot GChr IHos LBre LHyr LPan MBar MBri MGos NBee NWea SBre SHBN SPer WDin WFar WMou WOrn WPyg
- § *phaenopyrum* CLnd CMCN CTho SLPl SSpi WAbe WMou WWat
- *pinnatifida* WMou
- – var. *major* CBlo CEnd ESim
- * 'Praecox' CBlo
- *prunifolia* See *C. persimilis* 'Prunifolia'
- § *pubescens* f. *stipulacea* CMCN
- *punctata* SLPl
- *schraderiana* CTho MCoo WJas
- *tanacetifolia* CLnd CTho MBlu SSpi WMou
- *wattiana* CLnd CTho

x CRATAEMESPILUS (Rosaceae)
- *grandiflora* CTho

CRAWFURDIA (Gentianaceae)
- ¶ *speciosa* B&SWJ 2102 WCru
- ¶ – HWJCM 135 WCru

CREMANTHODIUM (Asteraceae)
- ¶ *arnicoides* EBee

CRENULARIA See AETHIONEMA

CREPIS (Asteraceae)
- *aurea* ECha EPar GAbr GAri GGar IBlr
- *incana* ♀ CFee CGle EBrP EBre ECha EMFP EMan EPar GBri LBre LHop LLWP MAvo MTho NChi NHaw NSla SBre SDix WAbe WCot WFar WWin

CRINITARIA See ASTER

CRINODENDRON (Elaeocarpaceae)
- § *hookerianum* ♀ Widely available
- *patagua* CB&S CEnd CGre CLTr CPle CSam EPfP GQui LHop MAll MBal SPer WAbe WPic WSHC

CRINUM (Amaryllidaceae)
- *amoenum* WCot
- *aquaticum* See *C. campanulatum*
- § *bulbispermum* ELan
- – 'Album' ECha
- *capense* See *C. bulbispermum*
- *moorei* CAvo ETub NRog
- ¶ *pedunculatum* R.Br. MFiF
- § x *powellii* ♀ CAvo CB&S CMil CMon CSev CSpe EBak ECha ELan ETub LAma LBow LHop MAus MBal MBri MSta MUlv NRog SDix SLMG SMer SPer SSpi WCru WHow
- – 'Album' ♀ CAvo CHEx CHan CMon ECha ELan EMan ERav ETub EWes LAma LBow MAvo MUlv NRog SLMG SPar SSpi WCru WPic WViv
- – 'Longifolium' See *C. bulbispermum*
- ¶ – pink CHEx

– 'Roseum'	See *C.* × *powellii*
yemense	CMon

CRIOGENES See CYPRIPEDIUM

CRITHMUM (Apiaceae)
maritimum	CArn GPoy MGrG MSal NLar SIgm WCot WWye

CROCOSMIA † (Iridaceae)
'Amberglow'	CElw CGle EBar EWoo IBlr MBri WMer WRus
¶ *aurea*	SIng WCot
– var. *aurea*	GCal IBlr
– hort.	See *C.* × *crocosmiiflora* 'George Davison' Davison
– var. *maculata*	IBlr
– var. *pauciflora*	IBlr
* 'Baby Barnaby'	MUlv
§ Bressingham Beacon = 'Blos'	EBrP EBre LBre NHol SBre SLod SWat
♦ Bressingham Beacon	See *C.* Bressingham Beacon = 'Blos'
'Bressingham Blaze'	CMHG EBrP EBre EGar GCal IBlr LBre MBri NOak NTay SBre WCot
'Carnival'	IBlr
× *crocosmiiflora*	CLTr CTri ECha EPla IBlr MBel MCli NCut NOrc NTay SWat WCHb WCot WShi
– 'Babylon'	IBlr LRHS MAvo
¶ – 'Burford Bronze'	IBlr
– 'Canary Bird'	CBlo CBro CRow CSam GAbr GCHN GCal GMac IBlr NRoo
– 'Carmin Brillant'	CAvo CBro CFil CLTr CRos CRow CSev EBrP EBre EGar GCal IBlr IBro LAma LBre LRHS MBri NHol NSti NTay SAxl SBre SUsu WCot
¶ – 'Citronella' J.E. Fitt	CBro
– 'Comet'	GBuc IBlr IBro MBri
– 'Constance'	CBre ETub IBlr NFai WCHb WWoo
§ – 'Croesus'	EGar GBri IBlr IBro NRoo SWas WCot WHal
– 'Custard Cream'	IBlr IBro MBri WCot
– 'Dusky Maiden'	CAvo CBos CHad CMil EAst EHic IBlr MCLN MMil NDov NHol NWes SOkh SPla WCot
§ – 'E.A. Bowles'	IBlr NRoo
– 'Eastern Promise'	CBre IBlr
– 'Elegans'	CElw IBlr
§ – 'Emily McKenzie'	CBro CFee EBrP EBre ECha EFou EGol ELan EOrc GCal IBlr LAma LBlm LBow LBre LGre LHop MCCP NBir NHol NRog NWes SBre SMad SPer WCHb WEas WFar WMer
– 'Firebrand'	IBlr MBri WCot
– 'Flamethrower'	IBlr WCot
§ – 'George Davison' Davison	CDec CGle CPou CRow CSev ECha EMan ERic GCal IBlr MRav NHol WGle
§ – 'Gerbe d'Or'	CRow ECGP EGar GBri GCal GMac IBlr IBro MCLN NHol NRoo SApp SOkh SSpe SUsu WCot WViv
– 'Gloria'	IBlr
§ – 'Golden Glory'	EPar IBlr
– 'Golden Sheaf'	EGar GBri IBlr
– 'Goldfinch'	IBlr IBro
– 'Hades'	IBlr
– 'Highlight'	IBlr
– 'His Majesty'	CAvo CGle CLTr CMil CRDP CRow CSam EBrP EBre EGar IBlr IBro LBre LGre LRHS MAvo MBri NHol SAga SAxl SBre WCot WGer WPer
§ – 'Jackanapes'	CAvo CBro CMil CRDP CRow EBrP EBre EGar EPPr GCal IBlr LBre MBri NHol NRoo SBre WCot WHal WWhi
§ – 'James Coey' J.E. Fitt	CBro CFee CFil CHad CRow CTrC ECha EFou GCal IBlr LAma LHop MCLN NHol NOrc NRog SPer WCot WFar
* – 'Jesse van Dyke'	IBlr
§ – 'Jessie'	IBlr MBri WCot WPer
– 'Kiatschou'	CFil EBee ECha EGar IBlr SAxl SLod
– 'Lady Hamilton'	CAvo CBro CFee CFil CFir CMHG CRDP CRow EBrP EBre EGar GBuc GCal IBlr IBro LBre LGre LHop MBri MUlv NRoo SAga SAxl SBre SChu SWas WFar WMer WRus
– 'Lady McKenzie'	See *C.* × *crocosmiiflora* 'Emily McKenzie'
– 'Lady Oxford'	CFil ECha EGar IBlr IBro WCot
– 'Lutea'	EGar EGra IBlr
– 'Marjorie'	CAvo WCot
– 'Mephistopheles'	IBlr
¶ – 'Météore'	NOrc NPri
– 'Morning Light'	IBlr WCot
§ – 'Mrs Geoffrey Howard'	CBos CGle CSam EGar GBri IBlr IBro SUsu SWas WCot WPGP
– 'Mrs Morrison'	See *C.* × *crocosmiiflora* 'Mrs Geoffrey Howard'
– Newry seedling	See *C.* × *crocosmiiflora* 'Prometheus'
– 'Nimbus'	GBri IBlr
§ – 'Norwich Canary'	Widely available
– 'Princess'	See *C.* × *crocosmiiflora* 'Red Knight'
– 'Princess Alexandra'	IBlr WCHb WMer WWoo
– 'Prolificans'	IBlr
§ – 'Prometheus'	IBlr
N – 'Queen Alexandra' J.E. Fitt	ECha EGar EHal IBlr IBro LAma LHop MAvo MLan NCut SPla SWas SWat WCot WHal WLin
– 'Queen Charlotte'	IBlr
– 'Queen Mary II'	EBee IBlr
– 'Queen of Spain'	CRos EGar IBlr IBro LRHS MBri MLLN NTay NWes WMer
– 'Red King'	IBlr NPri
§ – 'Red Knight'	CAvo EBee IBlr IBro WCot
– 'Rheingold'	See *C.* × *crocosmiiflora* 'Golden Glory'
– 'Saracen'	EGar IBlr MBri WCot WFar WPer
– 'Sir Matthew Wilson'	EGar GBri IBlr
– 'Solfaterre' ♀	CAvo CBro CElw CMHG CRDP CRos CRow ECha EFou EGol ELan GCHN GCal IBlr LGre LHop MBel MBri MUlv NHol NRoo NSti NWes SAxl SBla SMad SPer WCot WEas WMer
– 'Solfaterre Coleton Fishacre'	See *C.* × *crocosmiiflora* 'Gerbe d'Or'
– 'Star of the East'	Widely available

§ – 'Sulphurea' CBos CPou CRos CRow CSam EBee EFou EOrc GCal GGar IBlr LAma LGre LHop MBel MBri MCLN NHol NRoo NWes SDix SOkh SPer WAbe WEas WHal WPer

– 'Sultan' CGle EGar IBlr WCot WFar WMer

* – 'Tiger' IBlr

– 'Venus' EGar EGra IBlr

– 'Vesuvius' W. Pfitzer IBlr MBri

¶ 'Culzean Peach' GCal

'Darkleaf Apricot' See *C.* × *crocosmiiflora* **'Gerbe d'Or'**

'Debutante' WCot WRus

'Eldorado' See *C.* × *crocosmiiflora* **'E.A. Bowles'**

'Emberglow' CBro CMHG CRow CSam EBrP EBre ECGN EGar GCHN GCal IBlr LAma LBre MBal MBri NHol NLon NRoo SBre SMer SPer SUsu SWat WAbb WHal WPer

* 'Feuerser' EBee NHol

'Fire King' hort. See *C.* × *crocosmiiflora* **'Jackanapes'**

'Firebird' CBlo EBrP EBre ECha GBuc IBlr LBre MUlv NHol NRoo SBre SMer

'Fireglow' IBlr WPer

'George Davison' hort. See *C.* × *crocosmiiflora* **'Golden Glory', 'Sulphurea'**

Golden Fleece Lemoine See *C.* × *crocosmiiflora* **'Gerbe d'Or'**

N 'Honey Angels' EGar MBel MLan NSti NTow SUsu WCot WPer

'Jackanapes' WWeb

'Jenny Bloom' CAvo CFil EBrP EBre EGar GCal LBre NBir NRoo NTay SBre

§ 'Jupiter' CBlo CM&M EFou EGar EMil IBlr MMil NHol WHal

'Kiaora' IBlr

'Lady Wilson' hort. See *C.* × *crocosmiiflora* **'Norwich Canary'**

'Lana de Savary' CRow EGar GBri IBlr WCot

'Late Cornish' See *C.* × *crocosmiiflora* **'Queen Alexandra' J.E. Fitt**

'Late Lucifer' SDix

§ *latifolia* IBlr

– 'Castle Ward Late' CLAP CRow EGar GCal IBlr MSte SAxl

– 'Vulcan' T.Smith IBlr

'Lucifer' ♀ Widely available

'Marcotijn' CSam EGar EWoo GCal IBlr NLon

'Mars' CMil EGar EHal GBuc GCal IBlr IBro MAus NCut NFai NHol NTay SUsu WCHb WCot WFar WGer WPer WWoo

§ *masoniorum* ♀ CB&S CHEx CHan CRow ECha EFou ELan EOld EOrc GAbr GBuc IBlr IBro LAma LFis MWat MWgw NFai NFla NHol NNor NRog SPer SRms SWat WAbb WByw WCot WPGP WPer

¶ – 'Auricorn' IBlr

– 'Dixter Flame' IBlr SDix

– 'Fern Hill' IBlr

– 'Flamenco' IBlr IBro LRHS MBri MTed MUlv WCot

* – 'Manderin' IBlr

¶ – 'Minotaur' IBlr

– red IBlr

– Rowallane orange IBlr

– 'Rowallane Yellow' EBrP EBre GBri GCHN IBlr LBre LRHS MBri NHol NRoo SBre

mathewsiana IBlr

¶ aff. – IBlr

¶ 'Merryman' WRus

'Mistral' IBlr

'Mount Stewart' See *C.* × *crocosmiiflora* **'Jessie'**

'Mount Usher' CAvo ECha EGar IBlr LRHS MBri

'Mr Bedford' See *C.* × *crocosmiiflora* **'Croesus'**

'Orangeade' GBri IBlr SAxl

* 'Orangerot' NCut

aff. *paniculata* IBlr

§ – CAvo CB&S CPou EMar GAbr IBlr MBal MUlv NHol NOrc NTow SAPC SArc SAxl SChu WHoo WPyg

– 'Major' CTri SPer

– red IBlr

* – 'Ruby Velvet' IBlr

pearsei IBlr

pottsii CAvo CFee CRow EGar EPla GBin IBlr SLod WFar

– CD&R 109 CLAP CPou

– 'Culzean Pink' GBuc IBlr

– deep pink IBlr

– 'Grandiflora' IBlr

– 'Red Star' NFai

rosea See *Tritonia disticha* subsp. *rubrolucens*

'Rowden Bronze' See *C.* × *crocosmiiflora* **'Gerbe d'Or'**

'Rowden Chrome' See *C.* × *crocosmiiflora* **'George Davison' Davison**

'Saturn' See *C.* **'Jupiter'**

'Severn Sunrise' Widely available

'Short Red' WCot

'Sonate' NCut NHol NWes WPer

'Spitfire' CAvo CBot CMil CRow CSam EBee EBrP EBre ECha EGar GBuc IBlr LBre MBri MRav MSta NRoo SBre SChu SWat WByw WEas WFar WLRN

'Tangerine Queen' IBlr

¶ 'Vic's Yellow' SSpe

* 'Voyager' CTrC NFai WWoo

I 'Vulcan' A.Bloom CMil EBrP EBre EWoo IBlr LBre MBri SBre WFar

¶ 'Walberton Red' SAxl

¶ 'Walberton Yellow' SApp WCot

'Zeal Giant' IBlr

'Zeal Tan' CElw IBlr

Zeal unnamed IBlr

CROCUS † (Iridaceae)

abantensis EHyt ERos LAma

adanensis EHyt

'Advance' CAvo CBro EPar EPot LAma NRog

§ *aerius* LAma

– 'Cambridge' EHyt

alatavicus CBro EHyt EPot LRHS

albiflorus See *C. vernus* subsp. *albiflorus*

§ *ancyrensis* CAvo CBro EPar EPot ETub LAma NRog WShi

§ *angustifolius* ♀ — CAvo CBro EBar EBot EBrP EBre EPot ERos LAma LBre NRog SBre

– 'Minor' — EPot LAma

antalyensis — EPot

asturicus — See *C. serotinus* subsp. *salzmannii*

asumaniae — EHyt EPot ERos LRHS

aureus — See *C. flavus* subsp. *flavus*

banaticus ♀ — CBro EHyt EPot ERos GCrs LAma NHol WCot

– *albus* — EHyt EPot

baytopiorum — EHyt EPot LAma

biflorus — LAma NRog

– subsp. *adamii* — CLAP ERos LAma

– subsp. *alexandri* — EPot ERos LAma MRPP NRog

§ – subsp. *biflorus* — CMon ERos LAma

– – MS 984/957 — CMon

– subsp. *crewei* — ERos LAma

– subsp. *isauricus* — EHyt LRHS

– subsp. *melantherus* S&L 226 — CMon

– 'Miss Vain' — CAvo LAma

– var. *parkinsonii* — See *C. biflorus* subsp. *biflorus*

– subsp. *pulchricolor* — LAma

– subsp. *weldenii* 'Albus' — ERos LAma LRHS

– – 'Fairy' — CAvo CBro EPot LAma

'Big Boy' (*speciosus* × *pulchellus*) — EHyt

biliottii — See *C. aerius*

boryi ♀ — CAvo EHyt EPot LRHS

– CE&H 582 — MSto

– VHH 1546 — CMon

cambessedesii — CLAP CMon EHyt

– PB 91 — CMon

§ *cancellatus* subsp. *cancellatus* — EHyt EPot ERos LAma

– var. *cilicicus* — See *C. cancellatus* subsp. *cancellatus*

– subsp. *mazziaricus* — CNic EHyt ERos LRHS MSto

– subsp. *pamphylicus* — LRHS

candidus var. *subflavus* — See *C. olivieri* subsp. *olivieri*

§ *cartwrightianus* ♀ — CAvo CBro EHyt LAma LRHS MSto

N– 'Albus' ♀ — CLAP CMon EHyt EPot ERos

– S&L 484 — CMon

¶ *caspius* — EHyt

chrysanthus 'Ard Schenk' — EBar LAma

– 'Blue Bird' — EPar EPot LAma

– 'Blue Giant' — LAma

– 'Blue Pearl' ♀ — CAvo CBro CMea EPar EPot ETub LAma MBri NBir NRog WShi

– 'Blue Peter' — CBro LAma

– 'Brass Band' — CAvo LAma LRHS

– 'Canary Bird' — NRog

– 'Cream Beauty' ♀ — CAvo CBro EBrP EBre EPar EPot ETub EWal LAma LBre MBri NBir NRog SBre WShi

– 'Dorothy' — EPot LAma NRog

– 'E.A. Bowles' ♀ — LAma

– 'E.P. Bowles' — CBro EPot LAma MBri NRog

– 'Elegance' — CBro LAma

– 'Eye-catcher' — EPot ETub LAma

– var. *fuscotinctus* — CBro ETub LAma MBri NRog WShi

– 'Gipsy Girl' — CBro EPot LAma MBri NRog

– 'Goldilocks' — CBro EPot ETub LAma

– 'Herald' — LAma

– 'Ladykiller' ♀ — CBro EBrP EBre EPar EPot LAma LBre MBri NRog SBre

– 'Moonlight' — CAvo CBro LAma NRog

– 'Prins Claus' — CAvo EPot ETub LAma WShi

– 'Prinses Beatrix' — EPot LAma NRog

– 'Romance' — EPot LAma

– 'Saturnus' — EPot LAma NRog

– 'Sky Blue' — LAma

– 'Skyline' — CAvo CBro EPot GCrs

– 'Snow Bunting' ♀ — CAvo CBro EPar EWal LAma NBir NRog

– 'Spring Pearl' — CBro LAma

– 'Warley' — NRog

– 'White Beauty' — LAma

– 'White Triumphator' — EPot ETub LAma NBir NRog

– 'Zenith' — LAma

– 'Zwanenburg Bronze' ♀ — CAvo EBrP EBre EPar EPot EWal LAma LBre NRog SBre

'Cloth of Gold' — See *C. angustifolius*

clusii — See *C. serotinus* subsp. *clusii*

corsicus ♀ — EHyt EPar EPot ERos LAma

cvijicii — EPot

dalmaticus — EPot LAma

¶ *danfordiae* — LRHS

'Dutch Yellow' — See *C.* × *luteus* 'Golden Yellow'

etruscus ♀ — CAvo ERos GCrs

– B&S 334 — CMon

* – 'Rosalind' — EPot

– 'Zwanenburg' — EPot LAma

flavus — See *C. flavus* subsp. *flavus*

§ – subsp. *flavus* ♀ — EPot LAma

– M&T 4578 — CMon

fleischeri — CMea EPot ERos LAma NMen

gargaricus — EPot ERos GCLN LRHS

'Golden Mammoth' — See *C.* × *luteus* 'Golden Yellow'

goulimyi ♀ — CAvo CBro EHyt EPar EPot ERos LAma MRPP WCot

– 'Albus' — See *C. goulimyi* 'Mani White'

– deep colour form — EHyt

– var. *leucanthus* — EHyt

§ – 'Mani White' ♀ — CAvo EHyt

– S&L 197 — CMon

'Haarlem Gem' — LAma WCot

§ *hadriaticus* ♀ — CAvo CLAP EHyt EPot LAma LRHS MSto

– BM 8124 — CMon

– var. *chrysobelonicus* — See *C. hadriaticus*

– f. *lilacinus* — EPot

hermoneus LB 1 — CMon

hyemalis S&L 50 — CMon

¶ *imperati* ♀ — CNic

¶ – subsp. *imperati* — EHyt

– – 'De Jager' — CAvo EPot ETub LAma WCot

– – MS 965 — CMon

– subsp. *suaveolens* — LRHS

– – MS 962 — CMon

karduchorum — CBro LAma NRog

korolkowii — EHyt EPar EPot ERos ETub GCrs LAma

– 'Golden Nugget' — EPot

– 'Kiss of Spring' — EPot

– 'Yellow Princess' — EPot

kosaninii — ERos MPhe

kotschyanus ♀ — EHyt MSto

– 'Albus' — EPot SRms

– subsp. *cappadocicus* ♀ — EHyt LRHS

– CM&W 2720 — CMon

§ – subsp. *kotschyanus* — CBro CLAP EPot LAma NRog WCot

– var. *leucopharynx* — CMon ECha

laevigatus ♀ — CLAP

– CE&H 612 — CMon

– 'Fontenayi' — CAvo CBro EPot ETub LAma

– form — LAma

– from Crete — EHyt LRHS

'Large Yellow'	See *C.* x *luteus* **'Golden Yellow'**	– 'Artabir'	CAvo CBro EPot MRPP
lazicus	See *C. scharojanii*	– 'Cassiope'	EPot LAma
longiflorus ♀	CAvo CBro EPot ERos	– 'Conqueror'	CBro ETub LAma WHoo
– MS 968/974/967	CMon EHyt	¶ – subsp. *ilgazensis*	EPot
§ x *luteus* 'Golden Yellow' ♀	EPot LAma MHlr	– 'Oxonian'	EMon EPot LAma
		x *stellaris*	See *C.* x *luteus* **'Stellaris'**
§ – 'Stellaris'	CMon EBot EHyt EPot ERos	*susianus*	See *C. angustifolius*
malyi ♀	CLAP CMon EPot GCrs LRHS	*suterianus*	See *C. olivieri* subsp. *olivieri*
'Mammoth Yellow'	See *C.* x *luteus* **'Golden Yellow'**	*thomasii* B&S 364	CMon
medius ♀	CBro CMon ECha EHyt EPot ERos LAma NMGW NMen NRog	– MS 978/982	CMon
		tommasinianus ♀	CAvo CBro EPar EPot ETub LAma MBri NMGW WShi
minimus	CBro CMea EHyt EPar EPot ERos LAma	– f. *albus*	CBro EHyt EPot LAma LRHS
niveus	CAvo CBro CLAP EHyt EPot ERos LAma WCot	– 'Barr's Purple'	LAma
		– 'Bobbo'	EHyt
– S&L 194	CMon	– 'Eric Smith'	CAvo CLAP
nudiflorus	CAvo CBro CLAP EHyt EPot ERos LAma NHol	– 'Lilac Beauty'	EPot LAma
		– PF 6584	CMon
– MS 872	CMon	– var. *pictus*	EHyt LAma LRHS
ochroleucus ♀	CBro EBot EBrP EBre EHyt EPot ERos LAma LBre NRog SBre	– var. *roseus*	CBro CLAP EHyt EPot LAma MRPP
		– 'Ruby Giant'	CAvo CBro CNic EPar EPot ETub LAma NRog WShi
olivieri	EHyt EPar EPot ERos LAma		
– subsp. *balansae* 'Zwanenburg'	EPot	– 'Whitewell Purple'	CAvo CBro EPot LAma MBri MHlr NMGW NRog
¶ – subsp. *istanbulensis*	EPot	*tournefortii* ♀	CAvo CBro CLAP CMon EHyt EPot ERos LAma
§ – subsp. *olivieri*	CMon LAma		
oreocreticus	EHyt MSto	*vallicola*	MSto
– PB 137	CMon	*veluchensis*	EPot
pallasii	EPot LAma	– JCA 354.002	CLAP
pelistericus	EHyt EPot	*veneris* PB 198	CMon
pestalozzae	EPot ERos	§ *vernus* subsp. *albiflorus*	EPot ERos LAma MSto
– var. *caeruleus*	EHyt EPot ERos	– 'Enchantress'	EPot ETub LAma
pulchellus ♀	EPot ETub LAma WCot	– 'Flower Record'	EPot NBir
– M&T 4584	CMon	– 'Graecus'	EHyt EPot ERos
'Purpureus'	See *C. vernus* **'Purpureus Grandiflorus'**	– 'Grand Maître'	LAma NRog
		– 'Jeanne d'Arc'	CBro EPot ETub LAma NBir NRog
reticulatus	CLAP EHyt MPhe		
– subsp. *reticulatus*	EPot	– 'King of the Blues'	LAma NRog
robertianus ♀	EHyt LRHS	– 'Paulus Potter'	NRog
sativus	CArn CAvo CBod CBro ELan EOHP EPot GPoy LAma LHol MBri MHew MSal NRog	– 'Peter Pan'	NRog
		– 'Pickwick'	EPot ETub LAma NBir NRog
		§ – 'Purpureus Grandiflorus'	CBro EPot ETub LAma NRog
– var. *cartwrightianus*	See *C. cartwrightianus*	– 'Queen of the Blues'	CBro EPot NRog
– var. *cashmirianus*	CMon ETub	– 'Remembrance'	EPot GCrs LAma NBir NRog
scardicus	EHyt EPot	– 'Sky Blue'	NRog
scepusiensis	See *C. vernus* subsp. *vernus* var. *scepusiensis*	– 'Snowstorm'	LAma
		– 'Striped Beauty'	LAma NRog
§ *scharojanii*	EHyt EPot	– 'Vanguard'	CBro EPot ETub LAma NRog
§ *serotinus* subsp. *clusii* ♀	CBro EHyt EPot LAma	– subsp. *vernus* 'Grandiflorus'	See *C. vernus* **'Purpureus Grandiflorus'**
§ – subsp. *salzmannii*	CBro ECha EHyt ERos LAma MSto	§ – – Heuffelianus Group	EHyt EPot
– – AB&S 4326	CMon	* – subsp. *vernus* napolitanus	ERos
– – MS 343	CMon		
– – SF 218	CMon	§ – subsp. *vernus* var. *scepusiensis*	EHyt EPot ERos MRPP
sibiricus	See *C. sieberi*		
§ *sieberi* ♀	EHyt EPot ERos LAma	– 'Victor Hugo'	NRog
§ – 'Albus' ♀	CAvo CBro EBar EPot LAma	– WM 9615 from E Slovenia	MPhe
– subsp. *atticus*	EPot LAma	*versicolor*	EHyt MSto
– 'Bowles' White'	See *C. sieberi* **'Albus'**	– 'Picturatus'	EBrP EBre EPot ERos ETub LAma LBre SBre
– 'Firefly'	CBro EPot LAma NRog		
– 'Hubert Edelsten' ♀	EHyt EPot ERos LAma	'Yellow Mammoth'	See *C.* x *luteus* **'Golden Yellow'**
– f. *pallidus*	CMon	'Zephyr' ♀	CBro EPot ERos ETub GCLN ITim LAma
– subsp. *sublimis* 'Tricolor' ♀	CBro EPot ERos ETub GCrs LAma		
		zonatus	See *C. kotschyanus* subsp. *kotschyanus*
– 'Violet Queen'	CBro ETub LAma MBri NRog		
speciosus ♀	CAvo CBro EBrP EBre EPar ETub GCHN LAma LBre NHol NMGW NRog SBre WShi		

CROSSANDRA (Acanthaceae)

infundibuliformis	MBri

– 'Aitchisonii'	CBro EPot LAma
– 'Albus' ♀	CBro CMon ECha EPar EPot

CROTALARIA (Papilionaceae)

¶ *cunninghamii*	MFiF

CROWEA   (Rutaceae) See Plant Deletions

CRUCIANELLA (Rubiaceae)
stylosa   See *Phuopsis stylosa*

CRUCIATA (Rubiaceae)
§ *laevipes*   CKin EWFC NMir WGwy

CRYPTANTHA   (Boraginaceae) See Plant
Deletions

CRYPTANTHUS (Bromeliaceae)
bivittatus ♀   CHal
– 'Pink Starlight' (v) ♀   MBri
– 'Roseus Pictus'   CHal
bromelioides   MBri
* 'Red Starlight' (v)   MBri
x *roseus* 'Le Rey'   MBri
– 'Marian Oppenheimer'   MBri

CRYPTBERGIA   (Bromeliaceae) See Plant
Deletions

CRYPTOCARYA (Lauraceae)
alba   CGre

CRYPTOGRAMMA (Cryptogrammaceae)
crispa   CCuc SRms

CRYPTOMERIA (Taxodiaceae)
fortunei   See *C. japonica* var. *sinensis*
japonica ♀   GAri IOrc LCon MLan STre
                           WFro WNor
§ – 'Araucarioides'   EHul
– 'Bandai-sugi' ♀   CBlo CDoC CKen CMac EHul
                           EOrn ESis LCon LLin MBar
                           MGos MOne NHed SCoo SLim
                           SSmi STre WStI
– 'Barabits Gold'   MGos
– 'Compressa'   CBlo CKen CSam EBar EHul
                           ESis LBee LCon LLin MBar
                           MBri MOne MPla SLim SSmi
                           WGwG WLRN
§ – 'Cristata'   CDoC CMac ELan LCon LLin
                           MBal MBar NPal WWeb
* – 'Cristata Compacta'   EOrn
– 'Elegans'   CB&S CDoC CHig CMac EHul
                           ELan ENot EOrn GRei IOrc
                           LCon LLin LNet LPan MBal
                           MBar MUlv MWat SBod SHBN
                           SLim SPer WDin WFar WPyg
                           WWin
– 'Elegans Aurea'   CBlo CDoC CTri EHul LCon
                           LLin MBal MBar MPla SBod
                           SRms STre WDin WPyg WTro
– 'Elegans Compacta' ♀   CB&S CBlo CDoC EBar EHul
                           LBee LCon MBar MPla SLim
                           WWeb
– 'Elegans Nana'   CBlo LBee SLim SRms
– 'Elegans Viridis'   CBlo SLim
– 'Enko-sugi'   See *C. japonica* 'Araucarioides'
– 'Globosa'   CDoC EOrn SRms
– 'Globosa Nana'   EHul LBee LCon LLin LPan
                           MBar NHed SHBN SLim WGor
– 'Jindai-sugi'   CMac MBal MBar MPla NHed
– 'Kilmacurragh'   CKen EHul MBar SLim
– 'Kohui Yatsubusa'   CKen
* – 'Konijn Yatsubusa'   CKen
– 'Koshiji-yatsubusa'   EOrn LCon MBar MBri
– 'Koshyi'   CKen
– 'Little Diamond'   CKen

♦ – 'Littleworth Dwarf'   See *C. japonica* 'Littleworth
                           Gnom'
§ – 'Littleworth Gnom'   LCon
– 'Lobbii Nana'   See *C. japonica* 'Nana'
§ – 'Mankichi-sugi'   CBlo
– 'Midare-sugi'   See *C. japonica* 'Viridis'
– 'Monstrosa'   CMHG MBar
– 'Monstrosa Nana'   See *C. japonica* 'Mankichi-sugi'
§ – 'Nana'   CDoC CMac CTri EBrP EBre
                           EGra EHul EPfP LBre LLin
                           MBal MPla SBod SBre SPer
                           WLRN
– 'Pygmaea'   CBlo LCon MBar SRms
– 'Rasen-sugi'   COtt GAri LCon NPal SLim
                           SMad
– 'Sekkan-sugi'   CB&S CBlo EBrP EBre EHul
                           EOrn EPfP GAri LBee LBre
                           LCon LLin MAsh MBar MBri
                           MGos MPla MUlv SAga SBre
                           SLim SMad WPyg
– 'Sekka-sugi'   See *C. japonica* 'Cristata'
§ – var. *sinensis*   CMCN LCon
* – – 'Vilmoriniana   EOrn
     Compacta'
§ – 'Spiralis'   CDoC CGre CKen CMHG
                           CMac EHul EOrn EPfP IOrc
                           LBee LCon LLin MBal MBar
                           MBri MGos NHed SLim SPer
                           SSmi WWeb
§ – 'Spiraliter Falcata'   CBlo CDoC MBar
– 'Tenzan-sugi'   CKen
* – 'Tilford Cream'   MAsh
– 'Tilford Gold'   EGra EHul EOrn LLin MBar
                           NHed WAbe WBcn
– 'Vilmorin Gold'   CKen EOrn
– 'Vilmoriniana' ♀   CDoC CKen CMHG EBrP
                           EBre EHul ENot EPfP IOrc
                           LBee LBre LCon LLin MAsh
                           MBal MBar MGos MWat NHed
                           NHol SBod SBre SHBN SIng
                           SLim SPer SPla SSmi SSta
                           WDin
– 'Viminalis'   NHol
– 'Winter Bronze'   CKen
– 'Wogon'   See *C. japonica* 'Aurea'
– 'Yatsubusa'   See *C. japonica* 'Tansu'
– 'Yokohama'   CBlo EHul EOrn LCon MBar
                           NHol SLim
– 'Yore-sugi'   See *C. japonica* 'Spiralis'
– 'Yoshino'   CKen
sinensis   See *C. japonica* var. *sinensis*

CRYPTOSTEGIA   (Asclepiadaceae) See Plant
Deletions

CRYPTOTAENIA (Apiaceae)
canadensis   MRav MTPN
japonica   CPou EGar LFis WHer WJek
– f. *atropurpurea*   CElw CGle CLTr CMea CPla
                           CVer EBrP EBre ECha ECoo
                           ECro EHoe EMan EMar EMon
                           GCal LBre LSpr MNrw NPer
                           NWes SBre WCHb WCot WEas

CTENANTHE (Marantaceae)
§ *amabilis* ♀   CHal MBri
* 'Greystar'   MBri
lubbersiana ♀   CHal MBri
§ *oppenheimiana*   MBri
setosa   MBri
'Stripe Star'   MBri

CTENIUM (Poaceae)
¶ *concinnum* EBee

CUCUBALUS (Caryophyllaceae)
baccifer EMon MNrw

CUCUMIS (Cucurbitaceae)
metulifer (F) MSto

CUCURBITA (Cucurbitaceae)
'Cerrano' MSto
ficifolia MSto

CUDRANIA (Moraceae)
tricuspidata CAgr

CUMINUM (Apiaceae)
cyminum CArn SIde WGwG

CUNILA (Lamiaceae) See Plant Deletions

CUNNINGHAMIA (Taxodiaceae)
§ *lanceolata* CB&S CBlo CGre CMCN ELan
LCon LLin MDun MPla MUlv
SLim SSta WNor
§ – 'Bánó' MPla
– 'Compacta' See *C. lanceolata* 'Bánó'
* – 'Coolwijn's Compact' CKen
– 'Little Leo' CKen
sinensis See *C. lanceolata*
unicaniculata See *C. lanceolata*

CUNONIA (Cunoniaceae) See Plant Deletions

CUPHEA (Lythraceae)
caeciliae CHal CLTr MBEx
cyanaea CMHG CSev ENot LHil LHop
MBEx SDix SIgm SVen
– *hirtella* CMHG EBee LHop MBEx
SDys
hyssopifolia ♀ CFee CHal CPle CTre EMil
GQui IBlr MBEx MBri SRms
STre
– 'Alba' CLTr CPle LIck MBEx MLan
NPri STre
– 'Riverdene Gold' CHal CLTr MBEx
– 'Rob's Mauve' CB&S
– 'Rosea' LIck NPri
§ *ignea* ♀ CHal CLTr ELan IBlr LCns
MBEx MBri NPri SLMG
SOWG SRms SUsu
– 'Variegata' CHal IBlr LCns LHil MBEx
SLod SOWG
llavea See *C.* × *purpurea*
macrophylla MBEx
miniata hort. See *C.* × *purpurea*
platycentra See *C. ignea*
¶ *violacea* IDee

× **CUPRESSOCYPARIS** † (Cupressaceae)
§ *leylandii* CB&S CChe CDoC CMac EBrP
EBre EGra EHul ENot IOrc
ISea LBre LBuc LCon LHyr
LPan MBal MBar MBri MGos
SBod SBre SLim SPer WHar
WMou WStI

§ – 'Castlewellan' CB&S CDoC CMac EBrP EBre
EGra EHul ENot EPot ERom
IOrc ISea LBre LBuc LCon
LHyr LPan MBal MBar MBri
MGos MWat SBod SBre SLim
SPer WAbe WHar WMou
– 'Galway Gold' See × *C. leylandii* 'Castlewellan'
– 'Gold Rider' ♀ CDoC EHul IOrc LBee LPan
MAsh MBar MBri MGos SLim
SPer WHar WLRN WStI
§ – 'Harlequin' (v) CMHG LCon MBar SLim
WHar WWeb
* – 'Herculea' WWeb
– 'Hyde Hall' CTri EOrn EPla ESis LBee
LCon SBod SSto WAbe WLRN
* – 'Medownia' WWeb
– 'Naylor's Blue' CMac
– 'Olive's Green' COtt IOrc LCon LPan SCoo
WHar
– 'Robinson's Gold' ♀ CMac EHul GAri GQui ISea
LBee LCon MBal MBar NWea
SBod SLim WHar WStI
– 'Silver Dust' (v) MBri NEgg SRms WAbe WFar
– 'Variegata' See × *C. leylandii* 'Harlequin'
¶ *notabilis* ♀ WCwm
ovensii EHul WCwm

CUPRESSUS (Cupressaceae)
¶ *abramsiana* WCwm
N *arizonica* var. *arizonica* CHEx MBal
§ – – 'Arctic' CBlo LRHS MAsh MBri WFar
– var. *bonita* See *C. arizonica* var. *arizonica*
– 'Conica Glauca' ENot MBar
– var. *glabra* 'Aurea' CBlo EHul LCon MAsh MBar
SLim
– – 'Blue Ice' CB&S CBlo CDoC CMHG
EHul LCon LLin MAsh MBar
MBri MGos SLim
– – 'Compacta' CKen
– – 'Conica' CKen SBod WWat
I – – 'Fastigiata' CB&S EHul LCon LPan MBar
MBri
– 'Pyramidalis' ♀ CBlo CMac MAsh SPer WCwm
I – 'Sulfurea' CBlo CKen
bakeri CMHG ISea
cashmeriana See *C. torulosa* 'Cashmeriana'
duclouxiana CMHG
¶ *dupreziana* WCwm
glabra See *C. arizonica* var. *glabra*
◆ – 'Arctic' See *C. arizonica* var. *arizonica*
'Arctic'
goveniana GAri MBar
guadalupensis CMHG
¶ *lusitanica* WCwm
– 'Glauca Pendula' CBlo CKen CPMA LCon MBri
WCwm
¶ – 'Knightiana' WCwm
– 'Pygmy' CKen
macrocarpa CDoC CHEx EHul GChr
SEND WHCr
– 'Barnham Gold' SBod SRms
I – 'Compacta' CKen CMac
– 'Donard Gold' ♀ CMac CTri EOrn LCon MBal
MBar
– 'Gold Cone' CKen
– 'Gold Spread' ♀ CDoC EHul EOrn LBee LCon
SLim
– 'Goldcrest' ♀ CB&S CDoC CMac EHul ENot
EOrn IOrc LBee LCon LLin
LPan MBal MBar MBri MGos
MPla SBod SLim SPer WAbe
WDin WPyg

– 'Golden Cone' CMac MBal
– 'Golden Pillar' CBlo CDoC CMac EHul LBee
LCon LLin MAsh MBar MBri
MWat SLim SPla WDin WLRN
WPyg WWeb
– 'Greenstead MAsh
Magnificent'
– 'Horizontalis Aurea' CTri EHul MBar
– 'Lohbrunner' CKen
– 'Lutea' CB&S CDoC CMac EHul
MWat
– 'Pygmaea' CKen
– 'Sulphur Cushion' CKen
– 'Sulphurea' See *C. macrocarpa* **'Crippsii'**
– 'Wilma' EHul LCon MGos SCoo WWeb
– 'Woking' CKen
sempervirens CB&S EHul GChr LLin
– 'Green Pencil' See *C. sempervirens* **'Green**
Spire'
– 'Pyramidalis' See *C. sempervirens* **'Stricta'**
– var. *sempervirens* See *C. sempervirens* **'Stricta'**
§ – 'Stricta' ♀ CArn CSWP CSam EHul EPfP
GAri LCon LPan SAPC SArc
SLPl
– 'Swane's Gold' ♀ CB&S CKen CMHG EHul
LBee LCon LLin MAsh MPla
SLim
– 'Totem Pole' CBlo EHul EPfP MGos SEND
SLim WBcn
§ *torulosa* 'Cashmeriana' ♀ CHEx ERea MBri SLim WNor

CURCUMA (Zingiberaceae)
zedoaria LAma

CURTONUS See CROCOSMIA

CUSSONIA (Araliaceae)
paniculata SIgm

CYANANTHUS (Campanulaceae)
§ *chungdienensis* WAbe
¶ *delavayi* ACE 2449 EHyt WAbe
inflatus GCra
integer hort. See *C. microphyllus*
– 'Sherriff's Variety' GDra NHar WAbe WLin
lobatus ♀ EHyt GBuc LBee NGre NSla
SBla SRms
– 'Albus' EPot EWes NHar SBla WAbe
– 'Dark Beauty' NHar SChu SRms
– dark form EWes GDra WAbe WLin
– giant form GCrs GDra GTou NHar SBla
– × *microphyllus* NWCA
¶ *macrocalyx* WAbe
§ *microphyllus* ♀ EPot GDra GMaP LBee NGre
WAbe
sherriffii EHyt
I *zhongdienensis* See *C. chungdienensis*

CYANELLA (Tecophilaeaceae)
capensis See *C. hyacinthoides*
orchidiformis CMon LBow

CYANOTIS (Commelinaceae)
somaliensis ♀ CHal

CYATHEA (Cyatheaceae)
australis CTrC EOas GQui LPal WRic
brownii EOas WRic
cooperi CB&S EOas WRic
* – 'Brentwood' WRic
dealbata CAbb CB&S CHEx GQui WRic

¶ *dregei* WRic
¶ *incisoserrata* WRic
¶ *lepifera* WRic
¶ *lunulata* WRic
* 'Marleyi' WRic
medullaris CB&S CHEx EOas MFiF WRic
smithii CHEx EOas WRic
tomentosissima WRic

CYATHODES (Epacridaceae)
§ *colensoi* CMHG ECou EPot MAll MBal
MBar MBri MPla NHar NHol
SPer SSpi WAbe WBod WPat
WWat
¶ *empetrifolia* EPot
fasciculata See *Leucopogon fasciculatus*
fraseri See *Leucopogon fraseri*
juniperina ECou
§ *parviflora* ECou

CYBISTETES (Amaryllidaceae)
longifolia NRog

CYCAS (Cycadaceae)
circinalis LPal
kennedyana See *C. papuana*
media LPal
¶ *panzihihuanensis* LPal
revoluta ♀ CAbb CBrP CHEx CTrC LCns
LPal LPan MBri NPal SAPC
SArc SEND SPar WNor
§ *rumphii* CBrP LPal
¶ *siamensis* LPal
¶ *simplicipinna* LPal
¶ *taitungensis* CBrP LPal
thouarsii See *C. rumphii*

CYCLAMEN † (Primulaceae)
africanum CBro CElm CLCN CMon EBrP
EBre EHyt EJWh EPot ITim
LAma LBre MAsh SBre STil
WAbe WIvy
balearicum CAvo CBro CElm CLCN CMon
EBrP EBre EJWh EPot LAma
LBre LCTD MAsh MBal SBre
STil WCot
cilicium ♀ Widely available
– f. *album* CAvo CBro CElm CLCN EBrP
EBre EHyt EJWh GCrs LAma
LBre LCTD MAsh SBre STil
§ *coum* ♀ Widely available
– var. *abchasicum* See *C. coum* subsp. *caucasicum*
* – Blanchard's form EJWh
pink-flowered
– 'Broadleigh Silver' LCTD
– BSBE STil
§ – subsp. *caucasicum* EPot LAma STil
– subsp. *coum* CBro MBal
– – f. *albissimum* LCTD
¶ – – – 'Golan Heights' STil
– – 'Atkinsii' CBro MBro
– – f. *coum* 'Crimson SDeJ
King'
– – – 'Dusky Maid' LCTD
– – – 'Linnett Jewel' LCTD
– – – 'Linnett Rose' LCTD
¶ – – – Nymans Group EPot LCTD SBla
– – – Pewter Group ♀ CMil ERos MAsh MTho NRoo
SSpi WIvy WPyg
– – – – bicoloured EJWh
– – – – 'Blush' LCTD STil

repandum	CAvo CBro CElm CFil CLCN EBrP EBre EHyt EJWh LAma LBre LCTD MAsh MBal NGre NRoo SBla SBre SSpi STil SWas WHer WPGP
– JCA 5157	SSpi
§ – subsp. *peloponnesiacum* ♀	EJWh MAsh
§ – – var. *peloponnesiacum*	CBro CElm CLCN LCTD NGre SSpi STil
– – var. *vividum*	STil
– 'Pelops' misapplied	See *C. repandum* subsp. *peloponnesiacum* f. *peloponnesiacum*
– subsp. *repandum* f. *album*	CLCN EHyt EJWh MAsh SBla STil
– subsp. *rhodense*	CLCN LAma LCTD MAsh SSpi STil
¶ – WM 9709	MPhe
rohlfsianum	CBro CElm CFil CLCN CMon EJWh MAsh NGre STil WPGP
× *saundersii*	CLCN EJWh STil
trochopteranthum	CAvo CBro CElm CLCN EJWh EPot LAma MAsh NRog SBla STil WAbe WIvy
× *wellensiekii*	STil

CYCLANTHERA (Cucurbitaceae)
pedata	CPlN MSto

CYCLOSORUS   (Thelypteridaceae) See Plant Deletions

CYDISTA (Bignoniaceae)
aequinoctialis	CPlN

CYDONIA (Rosaceae)
* 'Isfahan'	SKee
japonica	See *Chaenomeles speciosa*
oblonga (F)	ESim LHol
– 'Bereczcki'	See *C. oblonga* 'Vranja'
– 'Champion' (F)	GTwe WJas
– 'Le Bourgeaut' (F)	GTwe
* – 'Lescovacz'	MGos WJas
– 'Ludovic'	GTwe WJas
– Portugal = 'Lusitanica' (F)	CBlo GTwe NRog SIgm WJas
– 'Meech's Prolific' (F)	CSam CTho EMui ERea ESim GTwe MBlu MWat NDal SDea SFam SIgm SKee
– pear shaped	CBlo CTri NRog
– 'Seibosa' (F)	SKee
§ – 'Vranja' (F) ♀	CDoC CMac CTho EBrP EBre ERea GTwe LBre LBuc MBri MGos NRog SBre SDea SFam SIgm SKee SPer WDin WJas WMou

CYMBALARIA (Scrophulariaceae)
aequitriloba 'Alba'	GGar
§ *hepaticifolia*	EDAr EPot LBee NGre NNrd SRms WCot WCru WPer
– 'Alba'	CNic
§ *muralis*	CArn CKin EWFC GAbr MBar MWat NMir NPri SIde WGor WHer WMow
– 'Albiflora'	See *C. muralis* 'Pallidior'
§ – 'Globosa Alba'	CHal EDAr EPot MDHE
– 'Globosa Rosea'	WCla
– 'Nana Alba'	CPea ELan GAbr MDHE MLan NNrd NPri NWCA WPer

– 'Pallidior'	CMea ESis MAvo MBar NHar NVic WOMN WWin
§ *pallida*	CMea LBee NHar NSla SBla WByw WCla WCru WFar WPer
¶ – 'Alba'	LBee
§ *pilosa*	ECtt EMNN GAbr NGre NNrd NSti WLRN
– 'Alba'	NGre

CYMBIDIUM † (Orchidaceae)
¶ *ensifolium* 'Kwanyin Susin'	SWes
– var. *rubrigemmum*	SWes
¶ – 'Tehku Susin'	SWes
* *goeringii* var. *formosanum*	SWes
¶ – 'Tow Tow Shang'	SWes
sinense	SWes
* – var. *album*	SWes

CYMBOPOGON (Poaceae)
citratus	CArn CJew CSev ELau EOHP GPoy LHol MChe MGra MSal NPri SHDw SIde WCHb WGwG WHer WJek WOak WWye
martinii	GPoy MSal
nardus	GPoy MSal

CYMOPHYLLUS (Cyperaceae)
fraseri	EPla WCot

CYMOPTERUS   (Apiaceae) See Plant Deletions

CYNANCHUM (Asclepiadaceae)
* *acuminatifolium*	GCal
sp. B&SWJ 1924	WCru

CYNARA (Asteraceae)
§ *baetica* subsp. *maroccana*	ECha LGre SWas
§ *cardunculus* ♀	Widely available
– ACL 380/78	EMon
– 'Cardy'	CBot ECGN EMan MLLN MTed MWat SRCN WWhi
– dwarf form	SDix
¶ – 'Florist Cardy'	NLar NPSI
¶ – New House Farm Strain	MCoo
– Scolymus Group	CB&S CHEx CHad CJew EBrP EBre EPfP ERav GCal GPoy ILis LBre LHol MBri SBre SMrm WByw WHer WOak
– – 'Green Globe'	CBod CBot CSev ECoo MWat NPSI NPer
– – 'Gros Camus de Bretagne'	WCot
– – 'Gros Vert de Lâon'	WCot
¶ – – 'Large Green'	NLar
– – 'Purple Globe'	CArn NPSI
– – 'Violetto di Chioggia'	WHer
hystrix	See *C. baetica* subsp. *maroccana*

CYNOGLOSSUM (Boraginaceae)
amabile ♀	EBar ELan MGed SRms
– 'Firmament'	WCot
– f. *roseum*	WFar
dioscoridis	CBot CGle NLar WPer WRha
glochidiatum	EBee
grande	CFee SCro
♦ *imeretinum*	See *C. glochidiatum*

nervosum — CBot CGle EAst EBrP EBre
ECED ECGP ECha ECtt EFou
EMil EPar LBre MAus MRav
NMir NSti SBre SPer SRms
SWat WCHb WWhi WWin

officinale — EWFC GBar MChe MHew
MSal NMir SIde WCHb WCer
WHer

¶ *wallichii* — CFee

zeylanicum — WOMN

CYNOSURUS (Poaceae)

cristatus — CKin

CYPELLA (Iridaceae)

aquatilis — MSta

§ *coelestis* — EGar WPer

herbertii — CGle CMon LAma MHig

plumbea — See *C. coelestis*

CYPERUS (Cyperaceae)

§ *albostriatus* — CHal MBri

¶ – 'Nanus' — MMoz

alternifolius hort. — See *C. involucratus*

§ *cyperoides* — MBri

diffusus hort. — See *C. albostriatus*

§ *eragrostis* — CCuc CDec CElw CHal CRow
EBee ECha EGar EHoe EPPr
EPla SDix SWat WAbb

esculentus — IBlr

fuscus — CCuc CInt EPPr NSti WHal

¶ *glaber* — EMan

haspan hort. — See *C. papyrus* 'Nanus'

§ *involucratus* ♀ — CBen CHEx CHal EBak EHon
EMFW EOas ERea LBlm LCns
MBri MSta SApp SArc SWat
WChe WFar WWeb WWye

– 'Gracilis' — CCuc EBak MBri

longus — CBen CCuc CHan CRow CWat
EBrP EBre EHoe EHon EMFW
EPPr ESOG LBre LPBA
MHew MSta NDea NSti SApp
SBre SMad SSoC SWat SWyc
WChe WHal WMAq WWeb
WWye

nanus — CHEx

¶ *obtusiflorus* subsp. — WCot
sphaerocephalus

papyrus — CHEx CInt ERea LCns LPan
MBri MSta SSoC WMul

§ – 'Nanus' — CInt ERea

sumula hort. — See *C. cyperoides*

vegetus — See *C. eragrostis*

CYPHANTHERA (Solanaceae) See Plant Deletions

CYPHOMANDRA (Solanaceae)

betacea (F) — LBlo LHil WMul

– 'Goldmine' (F) — ERea

– 'Oratia Red' (F) — ERea

CYPRIPEDIUM (Orchidaceae)

¶ × *barbeyi* — SWes

calceolus — SWes

– var. *parviflorum* — SWes

¶ *candidum* × *macranthos* — SWes

debile — EFEx

g. *Emil* — XFro

flavum — SWes

– red unspotted form — EFEx

– yellow spotted form — EFEx

§ *formosanum* — EFEx LAma SSpi SWes

franchetii — SWes

¶ g. *Gisela* — SWes XFro

guttatum var. *guttatum* — EFEx

♦ – var. *yatabeanum* — See *C. yatabeanum*

henryi — EFEx SWes

§ *japonicum* — EFEx LAma SWes

♦ – var. *formosanum* — See *C. formosanum*

♦ – var. *japonicum* — See *C. japonicum*

macranthos — EFEx SWes

* – var. *album* — SWes

– dark pink form from — SWes
Wou-long, China

– green-flowered — EFEx

– var. *hotei-atsumorianum* — EFEx SWes

– light pink form from — SWes
Man-chou, China

– var. *rebunense* — EFEx

– var. *speciosum* — EFEx SWes

margaritaceum — EFEx SWes

¶ g. *Maria* — SWes

¶ *parviflorum* var. *makasin* — GCrs

passerinum — SWes

¶ *pubescens* — LAma SWes

reginae — LAma SWes

segawae — EFEx SWes

tibeticum — SWes

§ *yatabeanum* — EFEx

CYRILLA (Cyrillaceae)

racemiflora — CPle SSpi

CYRTANTHUS (Amaryllidaceae)

§ *brachyscyphus* — WSPU

§ *elatus* ♀ — CAvo CBro CHal CSev CSpe
EBot ERea ETub LAma LBow
MBri MCCP NChi NRog SRms
WCot WHer

– 'Delicatus' — ETub LBow

falcatus — CMon MLan

luteus — SWas

mackenii — NRog

– var. *cooperi* — LBow

parviflorus — See *C. brachyscyphus*

* 'Pink Diamond' — CBro

purpureus — See *C. elatus*

sanguineus — CMon

¶ 'Snow White' — CBro

speciosus — See *C. elatus*

CYRTOMIUM (Aspidiaceae)

§ *caryotideum* — GQui NMar SMad WRic

§ *falcatum* ♀ — CCuc CHEx CHal CHid CRDP
CTrC EBee EHic EMon MBri
NMar NOrc SAPC SArc SVen
WOMN WRic WWat

– 'Butterfieldii' — EMon

– 'Rochfordianum' — CRow LBlm WFib

§ *fortunei* ♀ — CFil CHal CHid EBee EFer
EFou EHic GBin IOrc MWgw
NHar NHed NHol NMar SChu
SRms WCot WFib WRic

– var. *clivicola* — CBar EBee NHar NHed WRic

lonchitoides — WRic

macrophyllum — NMar WRic

CYRTOSPERMA (Araceae) See Plant Deletions

CYRTOSTYLIS (Orchidaceae)

¶ *reniformis* — MFiF

¶ *robusta*   MFiF

CYSTOPTERIS † (Athyriaceae)

bulbifera	CCuc CFil EFer EPot GQui NMar NVic WEas
diaphana	WRic
dickieana	CFil GAri NHar NMar NVic SRms WFib
fragilis	CCuc CFil EFer EMon GQui MBal NBro NHed NMar SRms WFib WRic
– 'Cristata'	EMon
– var. *sempervirens*	WRic

CYTISOPHYLLUM (Papilionaceae)

§ *sessilifolium*	CBlo ESis

CYTISUS (Papilionaceae)

albus Hacq.	See *Chamaecytisus albus*
albus hort.	See *C. multiflorus*
'Andreanus'	See *C. scoparius* f. *andreanus*
ardoinoi ♀	GDra MBal MBro MHig MPla NHol NRoo WLin
battandieri ♀	Widely available
– 'Yellow Tail' ♀	CEnd LRHS MBri MGos WSPU
× *beanii* ♀	CMHG CMea ELan ENot ESis GDra MAll MAsh MBal MBar MPla MWat NNor SPer SRms WDin WWat
¶ – 'Osiris'	EPfP
'Boskoop Glory'	CBlo SPer
'Boskoop Ruby' ♀	CBlo EBee EGra GSki ISea SSoC WLRN
'Burkwoodii' ♀	CB&S EBee EHic ENot GCHN GChr MAll MWhi NFla SPla WPyg WStI
'Butterfly'	CB&S
canariensis	See *Genista canariensis*
'Compact Crimson'	EBrP EBre LBre SBre
'Cottage'	CBlo EPot GDra MAll MBro MPla NHol WAbe WBod WLin
'Cottage Gold'	EHic GSki MPla
'Criterion'	MAll NCut
'Dainty'	MAll
'Dainty Maid'	CEnd
'Daisy Hill'	CBlo
§ *decumbens*	CBlo IOrc MAsh MBro NHar NHol WLin WWin
demissus	See *Chamaecytisus hirsutus demissus*
'Dorothy Walpole'	CBlo CMHG
'Dragonfly'	CBlo ELan IOrc
'Dukaat'	EBrP EBre LBre MAsh SBre SHBN WLRN
'Firefly'	CBlo MBal
'Fulgens'	CBlo ELan EPfP MAsh MBar SPer WLRN WWeb
'Golden Cascade'	CB&S CBlo ELan GChr MWat WGwG WLRN WWeb
'Golden Showers'	MBal
'Golden Sunlight'	CBlo EBee EGra ELan ENot SHBN WStI
'Goldfinch'	CB&S CBlo CChe CDoC EGra ENot ISea MBri MWat SMer WAbe WWeb
hirsutus	See *Chamaecytisus hirsutus*
'Hollandia' ♀	CB&S CMHG EBrP EBre EGra GCHN GChr LBre MAll MBar MGos NFla SBre SHBN SPer WDin WStI WWeb WWin
× *kewensis* ♀	CSam EBrP EBre ELan ENot EPot GDra GOrc GRei LBre LGro LHop MBal MBar MBri MGos MPla MWat NBee NNor SBre SHBN SPer SReu SRms SSta WDin WPat WWat WWin
– 'Niki'	CBlo MAll MAsh MBri MGos MPla SHBN SPan WGer
'Killiney Red'	CBlo CChe EBee EGra ENot IOrc MAll MBal MBri SHBN WRHF
'Killiney Salmon'	CBlo EBee EHic ENot MAll MAsh MGos MPla SPan SSoC
'La Coquette'	CBlo CDoC CMHG MBar WLRN
'Lena' ♀	CMHG EBee EBrP EBre EGra GAri GOrc LBre MAll MAsh MBar MBri MGos MPla MTis NRoo SBre SPan WBod WFar WStI WWeb
leucanthus	See *Chamaecytisus albus*
'Lord Lambourne'	CBlo CChe NCut
maderensis	See *Genista maderensis*
'Maria Burkwood'	CBlo SHBN
'Minstead' ♀	CBlo EAst EBee EBrP EBre ECle ELan EPfP LBre MAll MBal SBre SPer WAbe
monspessulanus	See *Genista monspessulana*
'Moonlight'	MAll SPer WGwG WWal
'Moyclare Pink'	CMHG MSte
'Muldean'	WWeb
§ *multiflorus* ♀	MBal SPer SRms
– 'White Bouquet'	MBri
nigrescens	See *C. nigricans*
§ *nigricans*	CFil CPle ENot SPer WPGP
– 'Cyni'	ELan EPfP MAsh NFla SPer SSpi SSta
nubigenus	See *C. supranubius*
'Palette'	ELan SPer WRHF
'Porlock' ♀	CDoC CLan CSPN CTre CWSG CWit ELan MTis SEND SPla WBod WWeb
× *praecox*	See *C.* × *praecox* 'Warminster'
– 'Albus'	EAst EBrP EBre ELan ENot GCHN GRei IOrc LBre MAsh MBar MBri MGos MWat NRoo SBre SEND SHBN SPer SPla WAbe WCFE WHCG WWal WWat
– 'Allgold'	CB&S CChe CMHG EBrP EBre EGra ENot GRei LBre MAsh MBar MBri MPla MRav NHol NRoo SBre SHBN SPer SPla SReu SSta WAbe WBod WDin WGwG WWal
– 'Canary Bird'	See *C.* × *praecox* 'Goldspeer'
– 'Frisia'	CB&S GAri MBar NFla WBod WFar
§ – 'Goldspeer'	CBlo ENot MAll SEND
§ – 'Warminster' ♀	EAst EGra ELan ENot GCHN GChr GDra GRei LHop MBal MBar MBri MGos MPla MWat NHol NRoo NWea SHBN SPer WAbe WWin
'Princess'	MBri MPla WBcn
procumbens	EPla LHop MBal
purgans	CBlo CPle MAll MBal NLon NNor
purpureus	See *Chamaecytisus purpureus*
racemosus hort.	See *Genista* × *spachiana*
Red Favourite	See *C.* 'Roter Favorit'

'Red Wings' CBlo EGra GBur GCHN GDra
MGos SPer WAbe WStI
§ 'Roter Favorit' CBlo MBar WGor
scoparius CAgr CArn CBlo CKin ENot
EWFC GChr GRei IIve MCoo
NWea SRms WDin
§ – f. *andreanus* ♀ CBlo EBee EGra ENot GChr
GRei MAll MGos NLon NNor
SPer
– – 'Splendens' CB&S CBlo WStI
– 'Cornish Cream' ♀ CB&S CBlo ECot EPfP MBri
SPer WBod
§ – subsp. *maritimus* CBlo GSki MAll MBri MMHG
SLPl MBod WGer
– 'Pastel Delight' CB&S
– var. *prostratus* See *C. scoparius* subsp.
maritimus
sessilifolius See *Cytisophyllum sessilifolium*
§ *striatus* SSpi
supinus See *Chamaecytisus supinus*
'Windlesham Ruby' CChe EBee EGra EHic ELan
EPfP GRei MAsh MBar MPla
SHBN SMer SPer WDin WPyg
WWeb
'Zeelandia' ♀ CB&S EBee EHic ENot MBar
MPla MRav SEND SMer SPla
SSoC WAbe WRHF WWeb

DABOECIA † (Ericaceae)

§ *cantabrica* GAri MBal
§ – f. *alba* CB&S CMac CNCN COCH
EBrP EBre ENot GDra LBre
MBal MBar MBri MOke NHol
SBod SBre SHBN WStI
– 'Alba Globosa' EDen MBar
* – 'Arielle' CB&S EDen
– 'Atropurpurea' CNCN COCH EBrP EBre
EDen ENot LBre MBal MGos
MOke NHol SBre WBod WStI
– 'Barbara Phillips' EDen MBar
– 'Bicolor' ♀ CNCN COCH EDen EPfP
MBal MGos MOke NHar
– 'Blueless' COCH EDen
– f. *blumii* 'Pink Blum' EDen
– – 'White Blum' CNCN COCH ECho EDen
¶ – 'Bubbles' EDen
– 'Celtic Star' EDen SDys
– 'Charles Nelson' (d) EDen MBar MOke
– 'Cherub' EDen
– 'Cinderella' CNCN EDen MBar
– 'Cleggan' EDen
– 'Covadonga' CNCN COCH EDen MBar
– 'Creeping White' EDen
– 'Cupido' CNCN COCH EDen MGos
– 'David Moss' ♀ CNCN EDen MBal MBar SBod
– 'Donard Pink' See *D. cantabrica* 'Pink'
– 'Early Bride' COCH EDen
– 'Eskdale Baron' EDen
– 'Eskdale Blea' EDen
– 'Eskdale Blonde' EDen
– 'Glamour' EDen
– 'Globosa Pink' EDen
– 'Harlequin' EDen
– 'Heather Yates' EDen MOke
– 'Hookstone Purple' COCH EDen MBar MGos
MOke NHol
– 'Lilacina' EDen MBar
§ – 'Pink' COCH EDen MBar NMen
SRms
– 'Pink Lady' EDen MBar
– 'Polifolia' CB&S CNCN EDen GDra
MOke SBod SHBN SRms

– 'Porter's Variety' ECho EDen MBar MOke NHar
– 'Praegerae' CB&S CMac CNCN EDen EPfP
MBal MBar MGos NHol SBod
– 'Purpurea' ECho EDen MBar
– 'Rainbow' CDec CNCN EDen MBar
– 'Rodeo' EDen
– 'Rosea' EDen MBar
– subsp. *scotica* EDen MBar
'Bearsden'
– – 'Ben' EDen
– – 'Cora' CNCN EDen MBar
– – 'Goscote' EDen MGos
– – 'Jack Drake' ♀ CNCN EDen GChr GDra MBal
MBar MBri MOke
– – 'Red Imp' EDen
– – 'Robin' EDen
– – 'Silverwells' ♀ CNCN EDen EPfP GChr MBar
MBri MGos NHar
– – 'Tabramhill' CNCN EDen MBar
– – 'William Buchanan' ♀ CMac CNCN EDen GChr GDra
MBal MBar MBri MGos MOke
NHar NHol NMen SBod
– – 'William Buchanan CNCN EDen MBar MBri
Gold' MTPN
– 'Snowdrift' EDen MBar
– 'Tinkerbell' ECho
– 'Waley's Red' ♀ COCH EDen EPfP GQui MBar
SDys
– 'White Carpet' EDen
– 'Wijnie' EDen
– 'William Buchanan' See *D.* × *scotica* 'William
Buchanan'
× *scotica* See *D. cantabrica* subsp. *scotica*
cultivars

DACRYCARPUS (Podocarpaceae)

§ *dacrydioides* ECou
– 'Dark Delight' ECou

DACRYDIUM (Podocarpaceae)

bidwillii See *Halocarpus bidwillii*
cupressinum ECou
franklinii See *Lagarostrobos franklinii*
laxifolium See *Lepidothamnus laxifolius*

DACTYLIS (Poaceae)

glomerata 'Variegata' CCuc EGle EMan EMon ENot
EPPr IBlr MAvo NBro NCat
NSti

× DACTYLOGLOSSUM (Orchidaceae) See
Plant Deletions

DACTYLORHIZA (Orchidaceae)

aristata EFEx
– × *fuchsii* EFEx
* – *punctata* EFEx
× *braunii* IBlr
§ *elata* ♀ EPar GCrs IBlr LAma SSpi
¶ – 'Lydia' GCrs
* – *variegata* IBlr
§ *foliosa* ♀ CBro CEnd ERos GCLN IBlr
MBri MNrw MTho NHar WAbe
WCru WFar WOld
§ *fuchsii* EPot ERos GBuc MNrw NHar
NRya SSpi WChe WCru WHer
WShi
* – *alba* SWes
– 'Cruickshank' NHar
– × *purpurella* See *D.* × *venusta*
× *grandis* SWes

¶ hybrids — WCru
incarnata — LAma SWes
g. *Larissa* × *purpurella* — SWes
§ *maculata* — CHid EPar GCrs IBlr LAma NRog SWyc WChe WCru WHer WShi
maderensis — See *D. foliosa*
§ *majalis* — LAma SSpi SWes WCru
– subsp. *praetermissa* — See *D. praetermissa*
– × *sambucina* — See *D. 'Madonna'*
mascula — See *Orchis mascula*
§ *praetermissa* — SSpi
purpurella — SSpi
'Tinney's Spotted' — NHar

DAHLIA † (Asteraceae)

'Alloway Cottage' (MD) — LAyl NHal
'Alltami Classic' (MD) — NHal
'Alltami Corsair' (MS-c) — LAyl NHal
'Alltami Cosmic' (LD) — NHal
'Almand's Climax' (GD) ♀ — GHCN LBut
'Alstergruss' (Col) — NRog
'Alva's Doris' (SS-c) ♀ — LAyl
'Alva's Supreme' (GD) — LBut NHal
'Amaran Candyfloss' (SD) — NHal
'Amaran Relish' (LD) — NHal
'Amberglow' (MinBa) — LAyl NHal
'American Copper' (GD) — NHal
'Amgard Delicate' (LD) — NHal
¶ 'Amira' (SBa) — NHal
* 'Anatol' (LD) — CSut
'Andrew Magson' (SS-c) — NHal
'Andrew Mitchell' (MS-c) — NHal
* 'Andries Amber' (MinS-c) — LBut
'Andries' Orange' (MinS-c) — LBut
'Anglian Water' (MinD) — NHal
* 'Anniversary Ball' (MinBa) — LAyl
¶ 'Apricot Beauty' (MS-c) — NHal
'Apricot Jewel' (SD) — LAyl
'Arabian Night' (SD) — CBos CHad EBee LAma NRog SDeJ WCot WPen
'Athalie' (SC) — GHCN
'Autumn Lustre' (SWL) ♀ — LAyl
'B.J. Beauty' (MD) — LAyl NHal
'Barbarry Ball' (SBa) — NHal
'Barbarry Banker' (MinD) — LAyl NHal
¶ 'Barbarry Fern' (SD) — NHal
'Barbarry Flag' (MinD) — NHal
¶ 'Barbarry Ideal' (MinD) — LBut
'Barbarry Majestic' (SBa) — NHal
'Barbarry Snowball' (MinBa) — LAyl
¶ 'Barbarry Token' (SD) — NHal
'Baret Joy' (LS-c) — NHal
'Bednall Beauty' (DwB) — CBos CDec CGle CHad CLTr CMil CRDP CSpe EBee EWes LHil LHop MBEx MHlr NSti SMrm WCot
'Berwick Wood' (MD) — NHal
'Biddenham Fire' (SD) — SMrm
'Biddenham Strawberry' (SD) — LAyl
'Biddenham Sunset' (MS-c) — LAyl
'Bishop of Llandaff' (Misc) ♀ — Widely available
'Black Diamond' (Ba) — CHad

'Black Fire' (SD) — LAyl SMrm
'Black Monarch' (GD) — NHal
'Bloom's Amy' (MinD) — NHal
¶ 'Blue Beard' — CSut
'Bonaventure' (GD) — NHal
'Bonne Esperance' (Sin/Lil) — CInt LBut
'Border Princess' (SC) — SDeJ
'Bracken Ballerina' (SWL) — LAyl LBut NHal
'Brackenhill Flame' (SD) — NHal
'Brandaris' (MS-c) — LAyl
'Brandysnap' (SD) ♀ — LAyl
'Butterball' (MinD) ♀ — LAyl
'Cameo' (WL) — NHal
¶ 'Candy Cane' — CSut
'Candy Cupid' (MinBa) ♀ — LBut NHal
'Candy Keene' (LS-c) — NHal
'Carolina Moon' (SD) — LAyl NHal
'Carstone Cobblers' (SBa) — NHal
¶ 'Carstone Ruby' (SD) — NHal
'Charlie Two' (MD) — LAyl LBut NHal
'Cherry Wine' (SD) — LAyl
'Cheyenne' (SS-c) — NHal
'Chimborazo' (Col) — LAyl
'Christmas Carol' (Col) — NHal
'Christopher Nickerson' (MS-c) ♀ — LAyl
'Christopher Taylor' (SWL) — NHal SMrm
'Clair de Lune' (Col) ♀ — LBut NHal
'Clarion' (MS-c) — SDeJ
¶ 'Classic A1' (MC) — LAyl
coccinea — CAvo CFil CGle CMon CPou GCal GMac WCot WPGP
– hybrids — GCal
'Connie Bartlam' (MD) — NHal
'Conway' (SS-c) ♀ — LAyl
¶ 'Cornel' (SBa) — LBut
'Corona' (SS-c/DwB) — LAyl NHal
'Cream Beauty' (SWL) — LBut
'Cryfield Bryn' (SS-c) — NHal
'Cryfield Keene' (LS-c) — NHal
'Crystal Ann' (MS-c) — NHal
'Curiosity' (Col) — LBut NHal
'Czardas' — GCal
'Daddy's Choice' (SS-c) — LAyl
'Dad's Delight' (MinD) — LBut
'Daleko Jupiter' (GS-c) — NHal
'Dana Iris' (SS-c) ♀ — LAyl
'Dandy' — See *D. 'Harvest Dandy'*
'Danjo Doc' (SD) — NHal
'Dark Splendour' (MC) — LAyl
'Davenport Anita' (MinD) — LAyl
'Davenport Honey' (MinD) — NHal
'Davenport Sunlight' (MS-c) — LAyl
'David Digweed' (SD) — NHal
'David Howard' (MinD) ♀ — CGle CHad EBee EBrP EBre ECle ELan EMan GCal LBre MMil NHal NHaw SBid SBre SPla WCot WHil WLRN
¶ 'Dawn Sky' (SD) — LAyl
'Daytona' (SD) — CSut
'Dazzler' (MinD/DwB) — LAyl
'Deborah's Kiwi' (SC) — NHal
'Debra Anne Craven' (GS-c) — NHal
'Doris Day' (SC) — LAma LBut NHal NRog
'Doris Knight' (SC) — LBut

'Downham Royal' (MinBa) — CSut

'Duet' (MD) — LAma NRog

'Dusky Harmony' (SWL) — LBut

'Earl Marc' (SC) — LBut

'East Anglian' (SD) — LAyl

'East Court' (Sin) — SMrm

'Easter Sunday' (Col) — LAyl SMrm

'Eastwood Moonlight' (MS-c) — NHal

'Edinburgh' (SD) — LAma NRog WRha

'Elizabeth Hammett' (MinD) — NHal

'Ellen Huston' (Sin/DwB) ♀ — CHad LRHS MBri NHal WHil

'Elma E' (LD) — LAyl NHal

'Elmbrook Chieftain' (GD) — LAyl

'Ernie Pitt' (SD) — LAyl

¶ 'Esther' — MBri

'Eveline' (SD) — ETub SDeJ

'Evelyn Foster' (MD) — NHal

'Exotic Dwarf' (Sin/Lil) — NHal

'Explosion' (SS-c) — LBut NHal

'Ezau' (GD) — CSut

'Fascination' (SWL/DwB) ♀ — CBos LAyl MHlr NHal SChu WCot

'Fashion Monger' (Col) — LAyl NHal

'Fermain' (MinD) — NHal

* 'Fernhill Suprise' (SD) — LBut

¶ 'Fidalgo Supreme' (MD) — NHal

'Figurine' (SWL) ♀ — LAyl NHal

'Finchcocks' (SWL) ♀ — LAyl

'Fiona Stewart' (SBa) — GHCN

'Firebird' (MS-c) — See *D.* 'Vuurvogel' (MS-c)

'Firebird' (Sin) — NRog

'Flutterby' (SWL) — LAyl

'Foreman's Jubilee' (GS-c) — LAyl

'Formby Supreme' (MD) — LAyl

'Forncett Furnace' (B) — GCal

'Freya's Thalia' (Sin/Lil) — LBut

¶ 'Frigoulet' — CSut

* 'Friquolet' — LAma

'Fusion' (MD) — CSut

'Gaiety' (SD/DwB) — LAyl

¶ 'Gala Parade' (SD) — NHal

'Garden Festival' (SWL) — LAyl

'Garden Party' (MC) ♀ — LAyl

'Gateshead Festival' (SD) — LAyl NHal

'Gay Mini' (MinD) — LBut

'Gay Princess' (SWL) — LAyl

§ 'Geerling's Indian Summer' (MS-c) ♀ — NHal

'Gerrie Hoek' (SWL) ♀ — LAma LBut NRog

'Glorie van Heemstede' (SWL) ♀ — LAma LAyl LBut NHal NRog SMrm

'Go American' (GD) — NHal

'Gold Crown' (LS-c) — NRog

'Golden Emblem' (MD) — SDeJ

'Golden Impact' (MS-c) — NHal

'Good Earth' (MC) — LAma

'Grenadier' (SWL) — MHlr WCot

'Grenidor Pastelle' (MS-c) — GHCN LAyl LBut NHal

'Gypsy Boy' (LD) — LAyl

'Hamari Accord' (LS-c) ♀ — LAyl NHal

'Hamari Bride' (MS-c) ♀ — LAyl

'Hamari Girl' (GD) — NHal

'Hamari Gold' (GD) ♀ — NHal

'Hamari Katrina' (LS-c) — LAyl

'Hamari Rosé' (MinBa) ♀ — LAyl NHal

¶ 'Hamari Sunshine' (LD) ♀ — NHal

* 'Haresbrook' — WCot

* 'Hartenaas' (Col/DwB) — NRog

'Harvest Amanda' (Sin/Lil) ♀ — LBut

'Harvest Brownie' (Sin/Lil) — LBut

§ 'Harvest Dandy' (Sin/Lil) — LBut

§ 'Harvest Imp' (Sin/Lil) — LBut

§ 'Harvest Inflammation' (Sin/Lil) — LBut

§ 'Harvest Red Dwarf' (Sin/Lil) — LBut

§ 'Harvest Samantha' (Sin/DwB) ♀ — LBut

§ 'Harvest Tiny Tot' (Sin) ♀ — LBut

'Hayley Jayne' (SC) — NHal

'Hazard' (MS-c) — LAma NRog

'Henriette' (MC) — CSut

'Hillcrest Albino' (SS-c) ♀ — LAyl

'Hillcrest Desire' (SC) ♀ — NHal

'Hillcrest Hillton' (LS-c) — NHal

'Hillcrest Royal' (MC) ♀ — LAyl NHal

'Hillcrest Suffusion' (SD) — LBut NHal

'Hillcrest Ultra' (SD) — LAyl

'Hit Parade' (MS-c) — CSut LAma NRog

'Honey' (Anem/DwB) — CInt NRog

'Honeymoon Dress' (SD) — LAyl LBut NHal

'House of Orange' (MD) — SDeJ

'Hugh Mather' (MWL) — LAyl

'Imp' — See *D.* 'Harvest Imp'

imperialis — CMon GCal MBEx WCot

'Inca Dambuster' (GS-c) — LBut NHal

'Inflammation' — See *D.* 'Harvest Inflammation'

¶ 'Inglebrook Jill' (Col) — NHal

'Iris' (Pom) — LBut NHal

'Jane Horton' (Col) — LBut

'Jean Fairs' (MinWL) — LBut

'Jean McMillan' (SC) — NHal

'Jeanette Carter' (MinD) ♀ — LAyl

¶ 'Jeanne D'Arc' — CSut

'Jescot Jess' (MinD) — LBut

'Jescot Julie' (O) — LAyl LBut

¶ 'Jescot Lingold' (MinD) — CSut

'Jessica' (S-c) — CSut NHal

'Jessie G' (SBa) — NHal

'Jessie Ross' (MinD/DwB) — LAyl

'Jill Day' (SC) — LBut

'Jill's Delight' (MD) ♀ — LAyl

'Jim Branigan' (LS-c) — LAyl NHal

'Joan Beecham' (SWL) — LAyl

'Jocondo' (GD) — LAyl NHal

'Johann' (Pom) — LBut NHal

'John Prior' (SD) — LAyl NHal

'John Street' (SWL) ♀ — LAyl LBut

¶ 'Jomanda' (MinBa) — NHal

'Jo's Choice' (MinD) — LBut

'Karenglen' (MinD) ♀ — LBut NHal

'Kathleen's Alliance' (SC) ♀ — LAyl NHal

'Kathryn's Cupid' (MinBa) ♀ — GHCN LAyl NHal

'Keith's Choice' (MD) — NHal

'Kenn Emerland' (MS-c) — LAma

¶ 'Kenora Canada' (MS-c) — NHal

'Kenora Challenger' (LS-c) — LAyl NHal

'Kenora Fireball' (MinBa) — NHal

¶ 'Kenora Sunset' (MS-c) — NHal

'Kenora Superb' (GS-c) — LAyl NHal

'Ken's Coral' (SWL) — NHal
'Kidd's Climax' (GD) ♀ — GHCN LBut NHal
'Kimi' (O) — LBut
'Kim's Marc' (SC) — GHCN LBut
'Kiwi Gloria' (SC) — GHCN NHal
'Klankstad Kerkrade' (SC) — LAyl
'Kochelsee' (MinD) — LAma
¶ 'Kotare Jackpot' (SS-c) — LAyl
'Kym Willo' (Pom) — LBut
'La Cierva' (Col) — LBut NHal
'Lady Linda' (SD) — GHCN LAyl LBut NHal
'Lady Sunshine' (SS-c) — LAyl
'L'Ancresse' (MinBa) — LAyl NHal
* 'Laura's Choice' (SD) — LAyl
¶ 'Lauren's Moonlight' (MS-c) — NHal
'Lavender Athalie' (SC) — LAyl
¶ 'Lemon Cane' — CSut
'Lemon Elegans' (SS-c) ♀ — GHCN LAyl LBut NHal
* 'Life Force' — CSut
'Lilac Shadow' (S-c) — CSut
'Lilac Time' (MD) — CSut SDeJ
'Lilianne Ballego' (MinD) — NHal
'Linda's Chester' (SC) — LBut NHal
¶ 'Lismore Moonlight' (Pom) — NHal
¶ 'Lismore Sunset' (Pom) — NHal
'Lismore Willie' (SWL) — LAyl LBut
'Little Dorrit' (Sin/Lil) ♀ — LBut
'Little Dream' (S-c) — SDeJ
'Little Sally' (Pom) — LBut
'Little Tiger' — NRog
'Madame Vera' (SD) — LBut
'Maelstrom' (SD) — LAyl
'Majestic Kerkrade' (SC) — LAyl
'Majuba' (MD) — LAma NRog SDeJ
'Margaret Ann' (MinD) — LAyl LBut
'Mark Damp' (LS-c) — NHal
'Mark Hardwick' (GD) — LAyl NHal
'Marlene Joy' (MS-c) — NHal
'Martin's Yellow' (Pom) — NHal
¶ 'Mary Eveline' (Col) — NHal
'Mary Layton' (Col) — NHal
'Mary Pitt' (MinD) — LAyl NHal
merckii — CGle CHad CSpe GCal GMac MBEx MNrw MTho NBro NSti SIng SMad SUsu WPer WRus WWin
– *alba* — CFil CHad CSpe MTho WPGP WPer
– compact — CBos CFil WPGP
'Meredith's Marion Smith' (SD) — NHal
'Mi Wong' (Pom) — GHCN NHal
'Mini' (Sin/Lil) — LBut
'Minley Carol' (Pom) — NHal
'Minley Iris' (Pom) — LBut
'Minley Linda' (Pom) — LAyl LBut NHal
¶ 'Mistill Contessa' (MinD) — NHal
'Monk Marc' (SC) — LBut
'Monkstown Diane' (SC) — LAyl NHal
'Moonfire' (Misc) — CFir EBee EBrP EBre ECle GCal LAyl LBre LHop MBEx MMil MSte MTis NHal NHaw SBre SSea WCot WHer WMer
'Moonlight' (SD) — MBri SBid
'Moor Place' (Pom) — LAyl NHal WCot
'Morning Dew' (SC) — SDeJ
'Morning Kiss' (LSD) — SDeJ
'Mount Noddy' (Sin) — SMrm

'Mrs McDonald Quill' (LD) — NHal
'Murdoch' — WCot
'Murillo' — MBri NRog
'My Love' (SS-c) — LAma NRog
'Nargold' (MS-c) — NHal
'Neal Gillson' (MD) — LAyl NHal
'Nepos' (SWL) — NHal
'New Baby' (MinBa) — NRog
'Nina Chester' (SD) — LAyl NHal
'Noreen' (Pom) — LAyl NHal
'Oakwood Diamond' (SBa) — LBut
'Omo' (Sin/Lil) ♀ — LBut
'Orange Keith's Choice' (MD) — NHal
¶ 'Orange Mullett' (MinD) ♀ — LAyl
'Orfeo' (MC) — LAma NRog
I 'Orion' (MD) — CSut
'Ornamental Rays' (SC) — LBut
'Park Princess' (DwB/SC) — LAma NHal SDeJ
'Paul Chester' (SC) — NHal
'Peach Cupid' (MinBa) ♀ — LBut NHal
'Peachette' (Misc/Lil) ♀ — LBut
'Pearl of Heemstede' (SD) — LAyl NHal
'Periton' (MinBa) — LAyl NHal
'Pink Jupiter' (GS-c) — LAyl NHal
'Pink Pastelle' (MS-c) ♀ — LAyl NHal
'Pink Sensation' (SC) — LBut
'Pink Shirley Alliance' (SC) — LAyl
¶ 'Pink Suffusion' (SD) — NHal
'Pink Surprise' (LS-c) — SDeJ
'Pink Symbol' (MS-c) — LAyl
pinnata soft yellow — CDec CGle
'Piper's Pink' (SS-c/DwB) ♀ — LAyl
I 'Pippa' (MinWL) — LBut
'Plum Surprise' (Pom) — NHal
¶ 'Polventon Supreme' (SBa) — LBut
'Pomponnette' (Anem) — CSut
'Pontiac' (SC) — LAyl
'Pop Willo' (Pom) — GHCN LBut NHal
'Porcelain' (SWL) ♀ — LBut NHal
'Potgieter' (MinBa) — NRog
'Preference' (SS-c) — LAma
'Preston Park' (Sin/DwB) ♀ — LAyl NHal
'Pride of Berlin' — See *D.* 'Stolze von Berli'
'Primrose Diane' (SD) — NHal
'Promotion' (MC) — SDeJ
'Purple Gem' — NRog
* 'Quantum Leap' — WCot
'Radfo' (SS-c) — GHCN NHal
'Raffles' (SD) — LAyl
'Raiser's Pride' (MC) — NHal
'Rebecca Lynn' (MinD) — NHal
¶ 'Red Balloon' (SBa) — NHal
'Red Diamond' (MD) — NHal
'Red Dwarf' — See *D.* 'Harvest Red Dwarf'
'Red Velvet' (SWL) — LAyl LBut NHal
I 'Reedley' (SWL) — LBut
'Reginald Keene' (LS-c) — NHal
'Rhonda' (Pom) — LBut NHal
'Rhonda Suzanne' (Pom) — LBut
'Richard Marc' (SC) — LBut
'Risca Miner' (SBa) — GHCN LBut
¶ 'Rockliffe' (MinD) — NHal
'Rose Jupiter' (GS-c) — NHal

'Rothesay Herald' LAyl
(SD/DwB)
'Rothesay Reveller' (MD) LAyl
'Rotterdam' (MS-c) SDeJ
I 'Roxy' CDec CMil EBee EBrP EBre
LBre LRHS NSti SBre WCot
WWeb
'Ruby Wedding' (MinD) NHal
'Ruskin Belle' (MS-c) LAyl
'Ruskin Diane' (SD) LBut NHal
* 'Ruskin Tangerine' (SBa) LBut
'Safe Shot' (MD) NRog
'Salmon Beauty' (D) SDeJ
'Salmon Keene' (LS-c) NHal
'Salsa' (Pom) ♀ NHal
'Samantha' See D. 'Harvest Samantha'
'Satellite' (MS-c) SDeJ
'Scarlet Kokarde' (MinD) GHCN
'Scottish Rhapsody' NHal
(MS-c)
¶ 'Seattle' (SD) SCoo
'Senzoe Ursula' (SD) GHCN LAyl
'Shandy' (SS-c) LAyl NHal
sherffii CHad CHal CMon MBEx
MCCP MNrw
– × *coccinea* CHad
'Sherwood Standard' NHal
(MD)
'Sherwood Titan' (GD) LAyl
'Shirley Alliance' (SC) LAyl
'Siemen Doorenbos' NRog
(Anem)
'Silver City' (LD) NHal
¶ 'Silver Years' SCoo
'Small World' (Pom) GHCN LAyl LBut NHal
'Snowstorm' (MD) LAma SDeJ
'So Dainty' (MinS-c) ♀ LAyl
'Sonia' CSut
* 'Spacemaker' SDeJ
§ 'Stolze von Berlin' NRog
(MinBa)
'Stoneleigh Cherry' (Pom) LBut
'Suffolk Punch' (MD) CSut LAyl LBut SMrm
'Suitzus Julie' (DwB) NHal
'Summer Night' (MC) CHad CSut
'Superfine' (SC) LAyl
'Swanvale' (SD) NHal
'Sweet Sensation' (MS-c) NHal
'Sweetheart' (SD) CInt LBut
¶ 'Sylvia's Desire' (SC) NHal
¶ 'Sympathy' (SWL) NHal
'Tally-ho' (WL) LHil LRHS MBri WCot WWeb
'Thomas A. Edison' (MD) CSut LAma
'Tiny Tot' See D. 'Harvest Tiny Tot'
'Tommy Doc' (SS-c) NHal
¶ 'Tomo' (SD) NHal
'Top Choice' (GS-c) SDeJ
'Trendy' (SD) SDeJ
'Trengrove Jill' (MD) LAyl NHal
'Trengrove Tauranga' LAyl
(MD)
¶ 'Trevelyn Kiwi' (S-c) NHal
'Tui Orange' (SS-c) NHal
'Vaguely Noble' (SBa) NHal
'Vazon Bay' (MinBa) CSut
'Vera's Elma' (LD) NHal
'Veritable' (MS-c) SDeJ
'Vicky Crutchfield' (SWL) LAyl LBut
'Wanda's Capella' (GD) LAyl NHal
'White Alva's' (GD) ♀ LAyl NHal
'White Ballet' (SD) ♀ LBut NHal
'White Klankstad' (SC) LAyl

'White Linda' (SD) LAyl NHal
'White Moonlight' (MS-c) LBut NHal
'White Perfection' (GD) SDeJ
¶ 'White Polventon' (SBa) NHal
'White Swallow' (SS-c) NHal
'Willo's Surprise' (Pom) NHal
¶ 'Winkie Colonel' (GD) NHal
'Winston Churchill' LBut
(MinD)
'Wittemans Superba' LAyl NHal
(SS-c) ♀
'Wootton Cupid' (MinBa) LAyl LBut NHal
♀
'Wootton Impact' (MS-c) LBut NHal
♀
'Worton Bluestreak' LBut
(SS-c)
'Yellow Cheer' (SD/DwB) SDeJ
'Yellow Hammer' LAyl NHal SChu SMrm WHil
(Sin/DwB) ♀
'Yellow Impact' (MS-c) NHal
¶ 'Yellow Linda's Chester' LBut
(SC)
'Yellow Star' (MC) CSut
'Yellow Symbol' (MS-c) LBut
'Yelno Enchantment' LAyl
(SWL)
'Yelno Harmony' (SD) ♀ LBut
'Yelno Velvena' (SWL) LAyl
I 'Yvonne' (MWL) NHal
'Zorro' (GD) ♀ LAyl LBut NHal

DAIS (Thymelaeaceae) See Plant Deletions

DAISWA See PARIS

DALEA (Papilionaceae)
¶ *fremontii* EBee
purpurea EMan

DAMPIERA (Goodeniaceae)
diversifolia CSpe

DANAE (Ruscaceae)
§ *racemosa* ♀ CFil ECro ENot GCal IHos
MTed NRoo NTow SAPC SArc
SBid SDry SPer SRms SSpi SSta
WBay WSpi WWeb

DAPHNE † (Thymelaeaceae)
acutiloba CHan CPMA ERea LRHS
MPla SPer SSta WCru WWes
albowiana CPMA GCrs MPla WCru
WPGP WPat WWat WWes
alpina CPMA NNrd SBla WAbe
WOMN WPat
altaica CPMA
'Anton Fahndrich' SBla
arbuscula ♀ CPMA EPot SBla SIgm WPat
– subsp. *arbuscula* f. SBla
albiflora
'Beauworth' CPMA EHyt GCrs SBla
bholua ERea LHop SBid SReu SSta
WCru WSpi WWat
I – 'Alba' CB&S CPMA LRHS SBla SSta
WCru WPGP
– 'Damon Ridge' CPMA
– Darjeeling form CFil CPMA CPle CSam ELan
EPfP NPal SBid SBla SPla SSpi
WCru WPGP WPat WWat
WWeb

¶ – var. *glacialis* — WCru
– – 'Gurkha' ♀ — CPMA
– 'Jacqueline Postill' ♀ — CPMA EPot LRHS MBlu MBri SBla SMur SPer SSpi WCru WPat
– Waterhurst form — CPMA
blagayana — CBlo CFil CPMA EPot LHop MBal MGrG MPla SBla SIgm SRms WCru WPGP WWat
* – *nana* — ITim
'Bramdean' — SBla
× *burkwoodii* ♀ — CB&S CBlo CBot CSam EPot IOrc MBal MHig SHBN WCru WDin WGwG WRHF WWat
– 'Albert Burkwood' — CPMA NWea SBla
– 'Astrid' (v) — CB&S COtt CPMA ELan LHop LNet MBlu MGos SSta WDin WPyg WWeb WWes
§ – 'Carol Mackie' (v) — CBot CPMA GAbr LHop SBla SIgm SPer SSta WWat
– 'G.K. Argles' — CBlo CPMA EPfP LRHS SBid SBla SPer WCru WPat WWes
– 'Gold Strike' (v) — CPMA
– 'Lavenirei' — CPMA
* – 'Moonlight' — LRHS
– 'Somerset' — CB&S CBlo CPMA ELan ENot IOrc ITim LHop LNet MBar MBlu MGos MPla NBee SAga SBla SBod SHBN SPer SReu SSoC SSta WDin WLin WPGP WPyg WSHC WShe WWeb
§ – 'Somerset Gold Edge' (v) — CPMA SPer WCru
¶ – 'Somerset Variegated' — CFil WPGP
– 'Variegata' broad cream edge — See *D.* × *burkwoodii* **'Somerset Variegated'**
– 'Variegata' broad gold edge — See *D.* × *burkwoodii* **'Somerset Gold Edge'**
– 'Variegata' narrow gold edge — See *D.* × *burkwoodii* **'Carol Mackie'**
caucasica — CPMA SBla
'Cheriton' — CPMA GCrs SBla
cneorum — CB&S CBlo CPMA ELan ENot EPfP MBal MBar NBee NEgg SReu SSoC SSta WPat WWat WWeb WWin
– f. *alba* — SBla
– 'Eximia' ♀ — CPMA EPot GCrs IOrc LNet MGos MGrG SHBN SPla WAbe WCru
* – 'Poszta' — CPMA SBla SMrm
– var. *pygmaea* — CPMA EPot SBla WPat
– – 'Alba' — WPat
– 'Rose Glow' — CPMA
¶ – 'Rubrum' — EPot
– 'Variegata' — CPMA EPot LHop MBar MMil MPla NWCA SBla SHBN SPer SReu SSta WAbe WSHC
collina — See *D. sericea* **Collina Group**
'Fragrant Cloud' — SBla
  (aff. *acutiloba*) CD&R 626
genkwa — CPMA SPer
giraldii — CPMA EPot GCrs MGrG SIgm SSpi WCru
× *hendersonii* — CPMA
– 'Appleblossom' — SBla
– CDB 11660 — SBla
– 'Ernst Hauser' — GCrs SBla
– 'Fritz Kummert' — SBla
– 'Rosebud' — SBla
× *houtteana* — CBot CPMA LRHS MPla NBir SSta WCru

× *hybrida* — CPMA SBla
japonica 'Striata' — See *D. odora* **'Aureomarginata'**
jasminea — CPMA GCrs SBla SIng WPat
– AM form — EHyt
jezoensis — CPMA
juliae — SBla
'Kilmeston' — CPMA EHyt SBla
laureola — CPMA CSWP GPoy MBro MGos MPla NPer SPan WSpi WWat WWye
– var. *cantabrica* — SChu
¶ – 'Margaret Mathew' — EPot
– subsp. *philippi* — CBlo CPMA EPfP LHop MPla SChu SHBN SPer SSpi SSto WAbe WCru WWat
'Leila Haines' × *arbuscula* — CPMA SBla
longilobata — WCru
– 'Peter Moore' — CPMA
× *manteniana* — WPat
– 'Manten' — CPMA
'Meon' — SBla
mezereum — Widely available
– f. *alba* — GAbr IOrc LHop MBar MGrG MPla NChi NNrd SEas SHBN SReu SSta WAbe WCru WPGP WPat WPyg WTin WWat WWeb
– 'Bowles' Variety' — CBot CPMA EPot
– 'Grandiflora' — See *D. mezereum* var. *autumnalis*
– 'Rosea' — MGos SRms
– var. *rubra* — CB&S CBlo CPMA ELan EPfP IOrc LNet NBee NFla SPer SReu WAbe WCru WDin WWeb
– 'Variegata' — LHop
× *napolitana* ♀ — CHan CPMA LNet LRHS SSta WWat
odora — CBlo CPMA CPle ERea LSpr MGos SChu SRms SSta WCru WSel
§ – f. *alba* — CPMA ERea MGos
§ – 'Aureomarginata' — Widely available
– 'Banana Split' — LRHS
– 'Clotted Cream' — CPMA
– var. *leucantha* — See *D. odora* f. *alba*
– 'Marginata' — See *D. odora* **'Aureomarginata'**
– var. *rubra* — CPMA LRHS NPSI SSta
– 'Sakiwaka' — CPMA
– 'Walberton' (v) — LRHS
* – 'Zuiko-nishiki' — WCru
oleoides — CPMA GAbr GCrs LNet SBla
petraea — SBla
– 'Alba' — See *D. petraea* **'Tremalzo'**
– 'Grandiflora' ♀ — EPot GCrs SBla WAbe WPat
§ – 'Tremalzo' — SBla
pontica ♀ — CB&S CPMA CPle EHyt ELan EOHP GAbr LHop MPla SAxl SDix SMad SPer SSpi WCru WPat WWat
retusa — See *D. tangutica* **Retusa Group**
'Richard's Choice' — CPMA
¶ *rodriguezii* — WPGP
× *rollsdorfii* 'Arnold Cihlarz' — SBla
'Rosy Wave' — SBla
§ *sericea* ♀ — CFil CPMA MHig SBla WCru
§ – Collina Group — CPMA SMur SRms SSpi SSta WAbe WWat
× *suendermannii* — SBla

tangutica ♀	CB&S CEnd CHan CMHG CPle ELan EPot GCrs IOrc ITim LNet MBal MBar MGrG MHig MPla MTho NHar NHol SDix SHBN SPer SSta WHCG WPat WPyg WWal WWat WWeb
§ – Retusa Group ♀	CB&S CPMA ECha EHyt GAbr GChr GDra LHop MBri MPla NRoo SBla SHBN SMac SReu SSta WAbe WPyg
x *thauma*	SBla
– 'Aymon Correvon'	SBla
'Tichborne'	SBla

DAPHNIPHYLLUM (Daphniphyllaceae)

himalense var.	CFil CHEx CPle EPfP SAPC
macropodum	SArc SBid SPer WPGP
– – B&SWJ 581	WCru
¶ *humile* B&SWJ 2898	WCru
¶ *macropodum*	IDee MBlu
¶ sp. B&SWJ 4058	WCru

DARLINGTONIA (Sarraceniaceae)

californica ♀	CFil EEls EFEx GTro MHel WMEx WPGP

DARMERA (Saxifragaceae)

§ *peltata* ♀	Widely available
– 'Nana'	EBrP EBre ECha LBre MFir NHol SBre WOld

DASYLIRION (Dracaenaceae)

§ *acrotrichum*	CHEx SAPC SArc
gracile Planchon	See *D. acrotrichum*
longissimum	CAbb
wheeleri	CAbb CTrC EOas

DASYPHYLLUM (Asteraceae)

diacanthoides	CGre

DASYPYRUM (Poaceae) See Plant Deletions

DATISCA (Datiscaceae)

cannabina	GCal WPic

DATURA (Solanaceae)

arborea	See *Brugmansia arborea*
chlorantha	See *Brugmansia chlorantha*
cornigera	See *Brugmansia arborea*
§ *inoxia*	EBak ERea MSal MSto SOWG
¶ – 'Evening Fragrance'	SPar
¶ – subsp. *inoxia*	NGno
metel	ERea
* – 'Cherub'	GQui
meteloides	See *D. inoxia*
rosea	See *Brugmansia* X *insignis* pink
rosei	See *Brugmansia sanguinea*
sanguinea	See *Brugmansia sanguinea*
stramonium	CArn EWFC MHew MSal NGno WHer
¶ – var. *chalybaea*	MSal
suaveolens	See *Brugmansia suaveolens*
versicolor	See *Brugmansia versicolor* Lagerheim
– 'Grand Marnier'	See *Brugmansia* X *candida* 'Grand Marnier'

DAUCUS (Apiaceae)

carota	CArn CKin EWFC MHew WGwy WHer

DAVALLIA † (Davalliaceae)

bullata	See *D. mariesii*
canariensis ♀	CFil CGre
♦ *fejeenis*	See *D. solida* var. *fejeenis*
§ *mariesii* ♀	MBri WCot WRic
– var. *stenolepis*	NMar
♦ *pyxidata*	See *D. solida* var. *pyxidata*
§ *solida* var. *fejeenis* (Hook.) Noot.	MBri
§ – var. *pyxidata* (Hook.) Noot.	NMar
trichomanoides	NMar WRic
– var. *lorrainei*	NMar
tyermannii	NMar

DAVIDIA (Davidiaceae)

involucrata ♀	Widely available
– var. *vilmoriniana* ♀	CGre ELan EPfP LNet MAsh MGos MWat NBee NFla NPal SSta

DEBREGEASIA (Urticaceae)

longifolia	CPle

DECAISNEA (Lardizabalaceae)

fargesii	CBrd CMHG CPle EBar ELan EMil EPla GOrc LPan MBel MBlu MCCP MDun MGos MWhi NHol NPal NTow SMad SPar SPer SSta WCoo WDin WWat
¶ *insignis*	WNor

DECODON (Lythraceae)

verticillatus	CHan EHon

DECUMARIA (Saxifragaceae)

barbara	CFil CGre CHEx CMac CPlN EMil EPfP EPla GOrc SBra SHBN SPer SSta WCru WSHC WThi WWat
sinensis	CGre CHEx CPlN EPfP SAPC SArc SSpi SSta WSHC

DEGENIA (Brassicaceae)

velebitica	GCLN NTow WLin

DEINANTHE (Hydrangeaceae)

bifida	EBrP EBre LBre SBre WCru
caerulea	WCru

DELAIREA (Asteraceae)

§ *odorata*	CHEx WMul

DELONIX (Caesalpiniaceae)

regia	LBlo SOWG WMul

DELOSPERMA (Aizoaceae)

§ *aberdeenense*	CHEx WCot WOMN
* *album*	CHEx
ashtonii	EOas WPer
'Basutoland'	See *D. nubigenum*
congestum	MFos WCot
cooperi	CFai EOas MFos MHig NGre NTow WPat WPer WPyg WWoo

lineare	NBir
lydenburgense	IBlr
macellum	EOas NGre
§ *nubigenum*	CHEx CHMG CTrC EDAr
	ELan EOas EPot GGar LBee
	LWak MBro MFos NGre NHol
	NNrd SBod SIng SSmi WHoo
	WOMN WPer WPyg WWin
sutherlandii	EDAr NGre NMen WCot WPyg

DELPHINIUM † (Ranunculaceae)

¶ 'Abendleuchten'	LGre
'Agnes Brookes'	ERou
alabamicum	MSto
'Alice Artindale'	CBos CDec CHad CHea EGle
	LGre SMrm SWas WCot WSan
ambiguum	See *Consolida ajacis*
andesicola	MSto
'Ann Woodfield'	MWoo
'Anne Page'	ERou
Astolat Group	CB&S CBot CDoC EBrP EBre
	ECED ELan GAbr LBre LPVe
	LRot MAus MBri MRav MWat
	NFla NNor NPri NRoo SBre
	SPer SSoC SUsu WSan
¶ 'Augenweide'	EFou
Avon strain	EBar MWoo
barbeyi	MSto
'Basil Clitheroe'	EBrP EBre LBre SBre
¶ *beesianum*	MSto
Belladonna Group	ELan
– 'Andenken an August	See *D.* **(Belladonna Group)**
Koeneman'	**'Wendy'**
– 'Atlantis'	ECha EFou LGre MBri MTed
	WViv
– 'Balkleid'	EFou MBri
– 'Blue Shadow'	EFou
– 'Capri'	EFou
– 'Casa Blanca'	CBlo CGle CMdw EBrP EBre
	EFou LBre MTis SBre SPla
	WLRN
– 'Cliveden Beauty'	CBlo CGle EBrP EBre EFou
	GBri LBre SBre SMrm SPla
	WLRN WMer
I – 'Freedom'	LRHS
– 'Kleine Nachtmusik'	EFou
– 'Moerheimii'	CBlo EFou SPla WMer
– 'Peace'	EBrP EBre LBre SBre
– 'Piccolo'	ECha EFou MBri SPla
– 'Pink Sensation'	See *D.* × *ruysii* **'Pink Sensation'**
– 'Völkerfrieden'	EBrP EBre EFou LBre MBri
	MUlv NPri NPro SBre SPla
	WMer WRus
× *bellamosum*	CBlo CBot EBee EFou GBri
	MTis SMrm SPla WLRN WViv
'Berghimmel'	EFou
'Beryl Burton'	ERou
'Betty Baseley'	ERou
bicolor	MSto
Black Knight Group	CB&S CDoC EBrP EBre ECtt
	ELan EOld GAbr LBre MAus
	MBri MRav MWat MWgw NFla
	NMir NNor NPri NRoo NVic
	SBre SPer SSoC WBro WRus
'Blauwal'	EFou LGre
Blue Bird Group	CB&S ELan EPfP GAbr MAus
	MBri MRav NLon NMir NNor
	NPri NRoo NVic SPer
'Blue Butterfly'	See *D. grandiflorum* **'Blue Butterfly'**
'Blue Dawn' ♀	CBla ERou

Blue Fountains Group	ELan EMan LHop MBri NBee
	NOak SPer WStI
Blue Jade Group	CBla EFou ERou NNor
'Blue Jay'	CB&S CMGP EBrP EBre ENot
	EOld LBre MAus NBir NPri
	SBre WLRN
'Blue Lagoon'	CBla
'Blue Nile' ♀	CBla ERou MWoo
Blue Springs Group	NOrc
'Blue Tit'	CBla ERou MWat
'Blue Triumph'	WPyg
'Blue Triumphator'	EFou
'Bruce' ♀	ERou MWoo
brunonianum	CLyd MHar MSto SBla
bulleyanum	MSto
'Butterball'	CBla
californicum	MSto WWin
Cameliard Group	CB&S CMGP EBrP EBre ECtt
	ELan EMan GAbr LBre NCut
	NPri SBre SPer WLRN
'Can-can'	ERou
cardinale	CBot CGen CPou GCra MSto
	WOMN
'Carl Topping'	ERou
carolinianum	MSto
¶ – subsp. *virescens*	EBee MSto
cashmerianum	CBot CHan CPou ELan EWes
	MFos MSto MTho NTow WCot
	WOMN
– 'Gladys Hull'	EWes
'Cassius' ♀	CBla ERou MWoo
caucasicum	See *D. speciosum*
* 'Centurion Sky Blue'	CFai
ceratophorum	MSto
¶ *chamissonis*	MSto
¶ *cheilanthum*	EBee NFla
'Chelsea Star'	CBla ERou
'Cherub'	CBla ERou MWoo
chinense	See *D. grandiflorum*
'Christel'	EFou
'Circe'	ERou
'Clack's Choice'	ERou WViv
'Claire'	MWoo
* 'Clear Springs Lavender'	SVil
* 'Clear Springs Mid Blue'	SVil
* 'Clear Springs Pink'	SVil
'Clifford Lass'	MWoo
'Clifford Pink'	CBla MWoo
'Clifford Sky'	MWoo
Connecticut Yankees	CBlo CChr NNor NOak
Group	
'Conspicuous' ♀	CBla ERou MWoo
'Constance Rivett'	ERou
¶ aff. *crassifolium*	MSto
'Cressida'	ERou
'Cristella'	ERou
'Crown Jewel'	CBla EFou ERou
'Cupid'	CBla ERou
'Daily Express'	ERou
'David's Magnificent'	WEas
decorum	MSto
delavayi	MSto WLin
¶ – CLD 895	EHyt
* 'Delfy Blue'	CFai
'Demavand'	ERou
'Dolly Bird'	CBla ERou
'Dreaming Spires'	SRCN
'Duchess of Portland'	ERou
¶ dwarf dark blue	LRHS
¶ dwarf lavender	LRHS
¶ dwarf pink	LRHS
¶ dwarf sky blue	LRHS

'Eamonn Andrews' ERou
elatum CBrd GCal SRms WOMN
'Elmfreude' EBrP EBre LBre SBre
'Emily Hawkins' ♀ ERou MWoo
'Eva Gower' ERou
exaltatum CPou ECGN MSto
'F.W. Smith' EFou LBuc MTed WMer WPyg
'Fanfare' ♀ CBla ERou
'Father Thames' ERou
'Faust' ♀ CBla ECGN EFou ERou MWat
MWoo
'Fenella' ♀ CBla MWoo WCFE
'Finsteraarhorn' EFou
'Fred Yule' ERou
Galahad Group CB&S CDoC EBar EBrP EBre
ECED EFou ELan ENot GAbr
LBre LGre MAus MBri MRav
MWat NBir NFla NMir NNor
NPri NRoo NVic SBre SPer
WShe
'Garden Party' CBla
'Gemma' MWoo
geraniifolium MSto NTow
'Gillian Dallas' ♀ CBla ERou MWoo
glareosum EHyt MSto WLin
glaucum MSto
¶ 'Gletscherwasser' LGre
'Gordon Forsyth' CBla ERou MWoo
'Gossamer' EFou
§ *grandiflorum* EPot ESis MSto NChi SMrm
§ – 'Blauer Zwerg' CGle EBee EPfP WRus
§ – 'Blue Butterfly' CBot CMea CSpe EBrP EBre
EBur EFou LBre LHop MWgw
NOrc SAga SBla SBre SCoo
WWhi WWin
– Blue Dwarf See *D. grandiflorum* **'Blauer
Zwerg'**
* – 'Tom Pouce' WHil
Guinevere Group CB&S CMGP EBrP EBre ECtt
EMan EOld GAbr LBre LPVe
MBri MWat NBir NLon NNor
NPri NRoo SBre SPer WRHF
'Guy Langdon' ERou
'Harlekijn' EFou
'Harmony' ERou
himalayae MSto
hotulae EBee
hybridum MSto
Ivory Towers Group ECtt
'James Nuttall' CHea ECha
'Joyce Roffey' ERou
'Judy Knight' ERou MWat
'Kestrel' ERou
King Arthur Group CB&S CDoC EBrP EBre ECtt
ELan ENot EPfP GAbr LBre
MAus MBri MOne MRav
MWat NFla NNor NPri SBre
'Lady Guinevere' ERou WPyg
'Lady Hambleden' See *D.* **'Patricia, Lady
Hambleden'**
'Langdon's Royal Flush' CBla MWoo
♀
'Leonora' ERou
likiangense EPot MSto
* 'Lilac Arrow' EFou
'Lilian Bassett' ♀ ERou MWoo
'Loch Leven' ♀ CBla ERou MWoo
'Lord Butler' ♀ CBla
'Lorna' ERou
§ *luteum* GCra MSto NChi

Magic Fountains Series EBrP EBre GAbr LBre NCut
NPri NRoo SBre WGor WHil
WRHF
I 'Magic Fountains Sky EFou
Blue'
'Margaret Farrand' ERou
'Marie Broan' ERou
'Max Euwe' EFou
menziesii EBee MSto NWCA
'Michael Ayres' CBla ERou MWoo
'Micky' EFou
'Mighty Atom' ♀ CBla EFou ERou MWoo
'Min' ♀ ERou MWoo
'Molly Buchanan' CBla ERou MWat
montanum MSto
'Moonbeam' CBla
'Morning Cloud' ERou
'Mother Teresa' ERou
'Mrs Newton Lees' EBrP EBre EFou ERou LBre
SBre WPyg
'Mrs T. Carlile' ERou
multiplex MSto
muscosum MSto
* 'Mystique' CBla ERou
'Nar' EFou
nelsonii MSto
New Century hybrids CB&S EBrP EBre LBre SBre
'Nicholas Woodfield' MWoo
'Nimrod' CBla ERou
'Nobility' CBla ERou
nudicaule CBot CGen EBar ELan EMar
EPfP ESis GBuc GDra MSto
NRoo NWCA WLin WOMN
– var. *luteum* See *D. luteum*
nuttallianum MSto
occidentale MSto
'Olive Poppleton' CBla MWoo
'Oliver' ERou MWoo
* *orfordii* MSto NWCA
'Our Deb' ♀ MWoo
oxysepalum MSto
Pacific hybrids ENot NOak SRms WByw
* 'Pandora' CBla
* 'Parade' EFou
parryi MSto
'Patricia Johnson' ERou
¶ Percival Group LBuc LRHS
'Pericles' CBla
'Pink Ruffles' CBla ERou
pogonanthum MSto
'Polar Sun' ERou
przewalskii EPot MSto
'Purity' ERou
'Purple Ruffles' ERou
'Purple Sky' EFou
'Purple Triumph' ERou
'Purple Velvet' CBla
pylzowii CLyd EBee GCra GCrs MBro
MSto NNrd
pyramidatum MSto
'Pyramus' ERou
'Red Rocket' CB&S EFou
requienii CBot CFee ERav GCra LBay
MSto MTho NBir WCot WEas
WHer
'Rosemary Brock' ♀ ERou MWoo
'Royal Copenhagen' EBrP EBre LBre SBre
♦ 'Royal Flush' See *D.* **'Langdon's Royal Flush'**
'Ruby' CBla
§ × *ruysii* 'Pink Sensation' CBot CLAP EFou ERou GBri
MTed NPri WMer WPGP WPyg
WRus

'Sabrina'   CBla ERou
'Samantha'   ERou
scaposum   MSto
'Schildknappe'   EFou LGre
'Schönbuch'   EFou
scopulorum   EBee MSto
§ *semibarbatum*   CBot CGen NPri WOMN
'Sentinel'   ERou
'Shimmer'   CBla ERou
'Silver Jubilee'   ERou
'Silver Moon'   ERou
* 'Sky Fantasie'   EFou
'Skyline'   CBla ERou
Snow White Group   NBir NOak SRms
'Snowdon'   CStr
'Solomon'   ERou
Southern Aristocrats   MBro WGle WHoo WPyg
  Group
Southern Consort Group   CBlo WGle WHoo WPyg
Southern Countess Group   WGle
  ♀
Southern Debutante   CBlo WGle WHoo WPyg
  Group
Southern Jesters Group   CBlo WGle WHoo WPyg
Southern Ladies Group   MBro WHoo WPyg
Southern Maidens Group   WGle
  ♀
Southern Minstrels Group   WGle
Southern Royals Group   CBlo MBro WGle WHoo WPyg
  sp. ACW   EWes
  sp. CLD 349   MSto
¶ sp. from Czech Republic   CGra
* 'Space Fantasy'   WCot
§ *speciosum*   MSto
'Spindrift' ♀   EFou
¶ *stapeliosmum* B&SWJ 2954   WCru
staphisagria   EOHP MHew MSal
* – 'Variegatum'   WCot
'Strawberry Fair'   CBla EFou ERou MAus MWat
                               WViv
suave   MSto
'Summer Haze'   ERou
Summer Skies Group   CB&S CMGP ECGN ECtt
                               EMan MAus MBri MWat
                               MWgw NBir NFla NNor NPri
                               NRoo SPer SSoC WRus
'Summerfield Miranda' ♀   MWoo
'Summerfield Oberon'   WCot
'Summerfield Viking'
'Sungleam' ♀   ?ou ERou MAus MWat
'Sunkissed'   MWoo
'Swan Lake'   ERou
tatsienense   CGen CLyd CMdw EHyt GDra
                               LHop MBro MSto MTho NChi
                               NWCA SSca WHoo WLin
                               WOMN WPyg
– 'Album'   EWes MSto WOMN
'Tessa'   ERou
'Thundercloud'   ERou
'Tiddles' ♀   CBla
'Titania'   CBla
trichophorum   MSto
tricorne   MFos MSto WCot
'Turkish Delight'   CBla ERou
uliginosum   MSto
'Vespers'   CBla ERou
vestitum   GCan
virescens subsp. *wootonii* MSto
'Walton Beauty'   MWoo
'Walton Gemstone' ♀   CBla MWoo
'Watkin Samuel'   ERou
'White Ruffles'   CBla

yunnanense   GDra
'Yvonne'   EFou
zalil   See *D. semibarbatum*

DENDRANTHEMA † (Asteraceae)
cultivars   See *Chrysanthemum*
♦ *nankingense*   See *Chrysanthemum
                                 nankingense*
♦ *pacificum*   See *Ajania pacifica*

DENDRIOPOTERIUM See SANGUISORBA

DENDROBENTHAMIA See CORNUS

DENDROBIUM † (Orchidaceae)
¶ *kingianum* ♀   ERea
  moniliforme   SWes

DENDROCALAMUS (Poaceae) See Plant
Deletions

DENDROMECON (Papaveraceae)
  rigida   CB&S CFil CPle EPfP LRHS
                               SBid SMad SSoC SSta WPGP
                               WPen

DENDROSERIS (Asteraceae)
  littoralis   CHEx

DENNSTAEDTIA (Dennstaedtiaceae)
¶ *davallioides*   WRic

DENTARIA (Brassicaceae)
  californica   EPar
  digitata   See *Cardamine pentaphyllos*
  diphylla   EPar
  microphylla   See *Cardamine microphylla*
  pinnata   See *Cardamine heptaphylla*
  polyphylla   See *Cardamine kitaibelii*

DERMATOBOTRYS (Scrophulariaceae) See
Plant Deletions

DERRIS (Papilionaceae)
  elliptica   CPlN

DERWENTIA See PARAHEBE

DESCHAMPSIA (Poaceae)
  cespitosa   CKin CNat EGar EPPr GMaP
                               GOrn MBar MBrN MWhi NHol
                               WCFE WPer
  – subsp. *alpina*   EHoe EMon EPPr LRHS
  – Bronze Veil   See *D. cespitosa*
                               'Bronzeschleier'
  § – 'Bronzeschleier'   CHan EBrP EBre ECGN ECoo
                               EFou EHoe EMan EPla ESOG
                               GBri GCHN GCal IBlr LBre
                               LGre MAus MCLN MSte NDov
                               NHol NSti SBre SMrm SPer
                               SPla WCot WRus WWat
  – 'Fairy's Joke'   See *D. cespitosa* var. *vivipara*
  – Gold Dust   See *D. cespitosa* **'Goldstaub'**
  – Golden Dew   See *D. cespitosa* **'Goldtau'**
  – Golden Pendant   See *D. cespitosa* **'Goldgehänge'**
  – 'Golden Shower'   CMil ECtt EMan EPfP NHol
                               SLPl
  – Golden Veil   See *D. cespitosa* **'Goldschleier'**
  § – 'Goldgehänge'   CCuc EGar EHoe EMon EPPr
                               EPla ESOG GCal IBlr NSti

§ – 'Goldschleier'   CVer EBee EBrP EBre ECha
EFou EHoe EMon EPPr EPla
ESOG GAri GBuc GCHN
GOrn IBlr LBre MCLN NHar
NOak SApp SBre
§ – 'Goldstaub'   EFou WCot
§ – 'Goldtau'   EBrP EBre ECGN ECha EHoe
EMon EPPr EPla ESOG ESis
GCHN LBre LHil MTis NEgg
NHol NOrc SBre SPla
– subsp. *paludosa*   EMon EPPr
§ – var. *vivipara*   CVer ECtt EHoe EMon EPPr
EPla ESOG LHil NBro NHol
NSti SApp SLPl WFox
flexuosa   CCuc CPea EHoe EMon EPPr
MBri WPer
– 'Tatra Gold'   Widely available
* 'Morning Dew'   ECoo WFar

DESFONTAINIA (Loganiaceae)
§ *spinosa* ♀   Widely available
– 'Harold Comber'   MBal WBod WCru
– *hookeri*   See *D. spinosa*

DESMANTHUS (Mimosaceae)
¶ *illinoensis*   EBee
¶ *leptolobus*   NGno

DESMAZERIA (Poaceae)
rigida   See *Catapodium rigidum*

DESMOSCHOENUS (Cyperaceae) See Plant Deletions

DESMODIUM (Papilionaceae)
callianthum   CPle CSam CTrC MAll NPSl
¶ *canadense*   EBee
§ *elegans*   CFil CPle ELan MTis SPan
WBod WFar WSHC
podocarpum B&SWJ 1269   WCru
praestans   See *D. yunnanense*
tiliifolium   See *D. elegans*
§ *yunnanense*   CHEx CPle EPfP LRHS SBid
WCru WSHC

DEUTZIA † (Hydrangeaceae)
¶ *calycosa*   CFil
¶ – 'Dali' SBEC 417   SDys WPGP
chunii   See *D. ningpoensis*
compacta   CFil CHan CHar WBod WPGP
WWat
– 'Lavender Time'   CPle ECle EHic GSki MPla
NHol SEas SPan WPat WRHF
corymbosa   CFil
crenata 'Flore Pleno'   See *D. scabra* 'Plena'
– var. *nakaiana*   SIng
– – 'Nikko'   CB&S CPBP CTri EBrP EBre
EHyt EPla ESis EWes GOrc
LBre LHop MAsh MBar MGos
MHig MPla NNrd SBre SMac
WHCG WOMN WSHC WWeb
WWin
¶ – var. *pubescens*   CFil WPGP
× *elegantissima*   CBlo CMHG ENot ISea MRav
NFla SReu SRms
– 'Fasciculata'   EHic SMad SPer WWin
– 'Rosealind' ♀   CB&S CBlo EBrP EBre ECtt
ELan ENot IOrc LBre LHop
MBri MGrG MPla NBee NCut
NFla SBre SPer SPla SReu SSpi
SSta WAbe WKif WPyg WSHC

glomeruliflora   CFil
gracilis   CBlo CTri GQui MBal MBar
MBel MPla MRav MWat NBee
SEas SLod SPer WDin WGwG
WHCG WStI WWal WWat
– 'Carminea'   See *D. × rosea* 'Carminea'
§ – 'Marmorata'   CBlo CMil CPMA ECro
WHCG WWes
– 'Variegata'   See *D. gracilis* 'Marmorata'
hookeriana   GGGa ISea WWat
× *hybrida* 'Contraste'   CDoC SPer
– 'Joconde'   ECtt EHic GSki NHol SMad
WKif
– 'Magicien'   CHar CMHG CSam EBrP EBre
ECtt ELan ENot EPla LBre
MBal MBel MRav NFla SBre
SEas SHBN SPer SSta WFar
WHCG WHar WPGP WPat
– 'Mont Rose' ♀   CB&S EAst EBrP EBre ELan
ENot GRei LBre LBuc MAsh
MBal MBar MBel MGos MPla
MRav NBee NRoo SBre SEas
SPer SReu SSta WDin WHCG
WSHC WStI WWin
– 'Perle Rose'   WLRN
× *kalmiiflora*   CB&S CMil EBrP EBre EPla
GQui LBre MBar MBel MBri
MGos MGrG MRav MWhi
NNor SBre SLPl SPer SRms
WAbe WDin
× *lemoinei*   CBot
¶ *longifolia*   CFil WPGP
– 'Veitchii' ♀   CPle GQui MRav SMrm
× *magnifica*   CDoC ELan GQui IOrc MRav
NFla SPan SRms WHCG WHar
WStI WWeb WWin
– 'Rubra'   See *D.* 'Strawberry Fields'
monbeigii   ENot WWat
§ *ningpoensis*   CEnd CWSG EBee EHic NHol
NSti SLPl SPan SPer SSta
WPGP
'Pink Pompon'   See *D.* 'Rosea Plena'
pulchra   CFil CHan CHar CPle ECle
EHal EHic GOrc NPro NSti
SBid SEND SMac SPer SSpi
WHCG WPGP WWat
¶ – B&SWJ 3870   WCru
purpurascens   WPyg
× *rosea*   CTrw EBrP EBre ECro EGra
ENot GRei LBre MBar MPla
MWat NFla NLon SBre SHBN
SMer SRms WHCG WKif WStI
WWin
– 'Campanulata'   ENot GSki
§ – 'Carminea' ♀   CB&S GChr MBal MHlr MTis
SDix SEND SPer SRms SSta
WDin WPyg
§ 'Rosea Plena' (d)   CHar EHic EPfP GSki MGrG
MPla SMac SSta
scabra   NPro WCru
§ – 'Candidissima' (d)   CBlo CMHG GQui ISea MBri
MRav SMer SPer
– 'Codsall Pink'   MGos MRav
§ – 'Plena' (d)   CB&S CChe CPle ECro ECtt
ELan EPfP NFla NNor SHBN
SPer WPyg WWal
– 'Pride of Rochester' (d)   EBrP EBre EHic ENot GChr
LBre MBar MRav SBre WDin
WHar WLRN
– 'Punctata' (v)   CFai CMHG EHoe MWhi
SRms
– 'Variegata'   EPla NPro NSti WPGP

schneideriana	LRHS
setchuenensis	EPfP GGGa GQui SBid SSpi
	SSta WSHC
– var. *corymbiflora* ♀	CBot CFil EPfP WKif WPGP
	WWat
¶ *staminea*	CFil WPGP
§ 'Strawberry Fields' ♀	CEnd CLTr LRHS MAsh MBlu
	MBri MTis NPro SPan WKif
	WLRN
taiwanensis	CFil WPGP
× *wellsii*	See *D. scabra* 'Candidissima'
× *wilsonii*	SRms

DIANELLA (Phormiaceae)

caerulea	ECou ELan GBuc LHil SHel
– var. *petasmatodes*	LHil
– 'Variegata'	See *D. tasmanica* 'Variegata'
intermedia	IBlr WCot WWat
– 'Variegata'	EPPr WCot
nigra	CFil ECou LBlm
* – 'Variegata'	WCot
revoluta	ECou IBlr WCot
tasmanica	CElw CFee CFir CGle CHEx
	CHan CMon CRow ECou ECre
	GBuc GGar IBlr LBlm SAga
	SArc SIgm SLod SSpi WWat
§ – 'Variegata'	CFir CRDP CSam ECou ELan
	EPPr EWes GQui IBlr LHil
	LHop NPSI WCot WOld WWat

DIANTHUS † (Caryophyllaceae)

¶ *acicularis*	EHyt
'ACW 2116'	LBee WPer
'Ada Florence'	MWoo
'Admiral Crompton' (pf)	NPin
'Admiral Lord Anson' (b)	WKin
'Admiration' (b)	SHay
'Afton Water' (b)	SHay
'Alan Hardy' (pf)	MWoo
'Alan Titchmarsh' (p)	NSti SBai
'Albatross' (p)	SChu
'Albert Portman' (p)	NCra
'Aldridge Yellow' (b)	SAll
'Alice' (p)	EBee EMFP EPfP SAll SHay
'Alice Forbes' (b)	SAll SHay
¶ 'Alice Lever' (p)	WAbe
'Allen's Ballerina' (b)	NCra
§ 'Allen's Huntsman' (p)	CBlo
§ 'Allen's Maria' (p)	CBlo CThr EBee NCra NPla
'Alloway Star' (p)	EMFP
'Allspice' (p)	CLTr CLyd CThr EGar EMFP
	MBro NCra SChu SMrm SSvw
	WEas WHoo WPyg WWhi
	WWye
¶ 'Allspice Sport' (p)	WKin
Allwoodii Alpinus Group	CNic
(p)	
alpinus ♀	CGle CLyd EMFP GDra GTou
	LBee MBal NGre NHol NMen
	SBla SIng SRms WHen WPer
– 'Adonis'	GCLN
– 'Albus'	CPBP EHyt LBee MHig SBla
	WAbe
§ – 'Joan's Blood' ♀	CMea ECha EPot ESis GAbr
	LHop MBro NHar NMen NRoo
	SAga SBla WAbe WHoo
	WLRN WPyg
– 'Millstream Salmon'	EHyt EPot ITim
– 'Rax Alpe'	EPot NNrd
'Alyson' (p)	SAll
* 'Amalfi' (pf)	SAll
'Amarinth' (p)	EGar EMar MNrw

amurensis	CChr EBrP EBre EMon GCal
	LBre SBre WCla WPer
anatolicus	CLyd CTri EGle EHic ELan
	LBee MHig NHol SBla WLRN
	WPer
'Andrew' (p)	SHay
'Angelo' (b)	SAll
'Ann Franklin' (pf)	MWoo SBai
'Ann Unitt' (pf) ♀	MWoo
'Annabelle' (p)	CLyd EMFP GMaP LRHS
	MDHE MHig SChu
¶ 'Annette' (pf)	LIck NHol
'Annie Claybourne' (pf)	MWoo NPin
'Anniversary' (p)	NPin SBai
'Apricot Sue' (pf)	SHay
¶ 'Arctic Star' (p)	EBee LIck NHol NRoo
arenarius	CGen CMea CNic EMFP
	GCHN LPVe NPri SHel WPer
	WWin
'Argus'	CMil WKin
Arizona (pf)	SAll
* 'Arlene' (b)	SAll
armeria ♀	CKin EWFC MGra WHer WPer
– Deptford pink	ELan
'Arnhem Spirit' (pf)	MWoo
arpadianus	GCLN MPla NGre NHol
'Arthur' (p)	EMFP
'Arthur Leslie' (b)	SAll
§ × *arvernensis* (p) ♀	CLyd CNic CSam ECha GAbr
	GDra MBro MHig MPla NGre
	NRoo SAga WPat
'Ashley' (p)	SAll
atrorubens	See *D. carthusianorum*
	Atrorubens Group
'Audrey Robinson' (pf)	MWoo NPin
¶ 'Audrey's Frilly'	WKin
'Aurora' (b)	SHay
'Autumn Tints' (b)	SAll
'Auvergne'	See *D.* × *arvernensis*
'Avon Dasset'	LBuc
'Baby Treasure' (p)	CLyd NHol
'Badenia' (p)	CLyd LBee MHig SBla SChu
	SIgm
Bailey's Yellow Delight®	SBai
(p)	
'Ballerina' (p)	SHay
¶ 'Barbara Evelyn' (pf)	NPin
barbatus Nigrescens	CBre CHad CHan CSpe LBlm
Group (p,a) ♀	LFis MHlr WCot
I – 'Sooty'	SSca WHer WUnu WWhi
'Barleyfield Rose' (p)	CGra CLyd EWes MDHE NHar
	SIng WAbe
'Barlow' (pf)	SHay
basuticus	MHig
¶ – subsp. *basuticus*	CSpe
¶ 'Bath's Pink'	GMac
§ 'Bat's Double Red' (p)	CCot EGar EMFP LBlm NCra
	SSvw
'Beauty of Cambridge' (b)	SAll
'Beauty of Healey' (p)	CLTr EMFP
'Becka Falls' (p)	CThr NCra SHay SRms
'Becky Robinson' (p) ♀	CThr ELan EMFP SAga SAll
	SHay SSvw WWhi
'Bella'	CPBP
'Belle of Bookham' (b)	SAll
'Berlin Snow'	EPot ITim LBee MFos SGre
'Bet Gilroy' (b)	SHay
'Betty Buckle' (p)	SChu
'Betty Day' (b)	SHay
'Betty Dee' (pf)	NPin

'Betty Norton' (p)   CLyd CPri EBee MBro MHig
MOne NBus NCra NHaw SBla
SMrm SSvw WHoo WKif
WLRN WPyg
'Betty Tucker' (b)   SHay
'Betty's Choice' (pf)   NPin
¶ 'Betty's Delight' (pf)   NPin
'Binsey Red' (p)   EMFP SSvw WKin
¶ Black and White Minstrels WKin
   Group
* 'Blue Carpet'   WPer
'Blue Hills' (p)   CLyd ECho ELan LBee MWat
SChu SIng
'Blue Ice' (b)   SAll SHay
'Blush'   See *D.* **'Souvenir de la**
     Malmaison'
'Bobby' (p)   SAll
'Bobby Ames' (b)   SHay
'Bob's Highlight' (pf)   NPin
'Bombardier' (p)   EBrP EBre LBre NCra NRoo
SBre WIvy
'Bookham Fancy' (b)   SAll SHay
'Bookham Grand' (b)   SHay
'Bookham Lad' (b)   SAll
'Bookham Lass' (b)   SHay
'Bookham Perfume' (b)   SBai SHay
'Bookham Sprite' (b)   SAll SHay
'Bourboule'   See *D.* **'La Bourboule'**
'Bovey Belle' (p) ♀   CLTr CSam CThr EBrP EBre
ECot LBre NCra NPin NPla
SBai SBre SMer
'Boydii' (p)   CLyd NCra NRoo WOMN
WWoo
'Bransgore' (p)   MBro WHoo WPyg
§ Dona® = 'Brecas' (pf)   SAll SBai
brevicaulis   NWCA
– *brevicaulis*   CGra
– Mac&W 5849   WOMN
'Brian Tumbler' (b)   SAll
'Bridal Veil' (p)   CLon CThr EMFP GAbr NCra
SChu SSvw
'Brigadier' (p)   MHar SRms WPer WWin
♦ 'Brilliant'   See *D.* *deltoides* **'Brilliant'**
¶ 'Brilliant Star' (p)   CPBP LIck NHol NRoo
'Brimstone' (b)   SHay
'Bruce Parker' (p)   SBai
'Brympton Red' (p)   CLon CLyd CThr ECha EFou
EGar EMFP EOrc NCra NSti
SBla SChu SMrm SSvw WEas
WKif
§ 'Caesar's Mantle' (p)   SSvw WKin
caesius   See *D. gratianopolitanus*
– 'Compactus'   See *D. gratianopolitanus*
     'Compactus Eydangeri'
callizonus   CLyd CPBP ESis LBee NWCA
WOMN
'Calypso' (pf)   SHay
¶ 'Calypso Star' (p)   LIck NHol NRoo
'Camelford' (p)   NCra WKin
'Camilla' (b)   CLyd CThr EGoo EMFP SSvw
'Can-can' (pf)   SHay
'Candy' (p)   See *D.* **'Sway Candy' (p)**
'Candy Clove' (b)   SAll SHay
¶ *capitatus* subsp.   EBee
   andrzejowskianus
'Carinda' (p)   SHay
'Carlotta' (p)   SHay
'Carmen' (b)   SHay
'Carmine Letitia Wyatt'   EBee
   (p)
'Caroline Bone' (b)   SHay
'Caroline Clove' (b)   SHay

carthusianorum   CHad CHan EGar EMFP GSki
MNrw MSte SSvw WCot WPer
– subsp. *vaginatus*   GCLN
caryophyllus   CArn CJew IIve MGra SIde
WOak
* 'Casper' (pf)   SAll
'Casser's Pink' (p)   GBuc MTho
'Catherine Glover' (b)   SAll SHay
* 'Catherine Tucker'   WEas
'Catherine's Choice'   See *D.* **'Rhian's Choice'**
¶ *caucaseus*   EHyt
'Cecil Wyatt' (p)   CMea CThr
§ 'Cedric's Oldest' (p)   SChu WKin
'Champagne' (pf)   SAll
'Charity' (p)   CMHG
'Charles' (p)   SAll
'Charles Edward' (b)   SAll
'Charles Musgrave'   See *D.* **'Musgrave's Pink'**
'Charlotte'   SAll
'Charm' (b)   SHay
'Chastity' (p)   EMFP GAbr GCHN GMaP
MBro SBla SChu SSvw WHoo
WPyg
Cheddar pink   See *D. gratianopolitanus*
'Cherry Clove' (b)   SAll
¶ 'Cherry Moon'   LRHS
'Cherryripe' (p)   SHay
'Cheryl'   See *D.* **'Houndspool Cheryl'**
'Chetwyn Doris' (p)   NPin SBai
chinensis (p,a)   MBri
'Chris Crew' (b) ♀   SBai
'Christine Hough' (b)   SAll
'Christopher' (p)   CBlo EBrP EBre GCHN LBre
SAll SBre SHay
cinnabarinus   See *D. biflorus*
'Circular Saw' (p)   CInt SChu
'Clara' (pf)   MWoo NPin SHay
'Clara's Flame' (pf)   SHay
'Clara's Lass' (pf)   MWoo NPin SHay
'Clare' (p)   SAll SHay
'Claret Joy' (p) ♀   CThr EBrP EBre ELan EMFP
GBur LBre NCra NPin SBai
SBre
'Clarinda' (b)   SAll
¶ 'Clifford Pink'   WKin
'Clunie' (b)   SAll SHay
§ 'Cockenzie Pink' (p)   CLTr CThr EMFP GAbr SAll
SSvw WEas
'Cocomo Sim' (pf)   SHay
'Constance' (p)   CBlo SAll
'Constance Finnis'   See *D.* **'Fair Folly'**
'Consul' (b)   SAll
'Copperhead' (b)   SHay
'Coronation Ruby' (p) ♀   NPin SBai
'Coste Budde' (p)   CLyd ECha EMFP SMrm WEas
WIvy WKin
¶ 'Cranborne Seedling' (p)   WKin
'Cranmere Pool' (p) ♀   CMea CThr EBee EBrP EBre
ELan EMan LBre MAus MWat
NCra NPin NRoo SBai SBre
SHay SMrm
¶ 'Cream Lass' (pf)   NPin
'Cream Sue' (pf)   MWoo NPin SHay
'Crimson Ace' (p)   SHay
¶ 'Crimson Joy' (p)   EBee
Crimson Tempo® (p)   SBai
'Crimson Velvet' (b)   SHay
crinitus   SHFr
'Crompton Bride' (pf)   NPin
'Crompton Classic' (pf)   NPin
'Crompton Princess' (pf)   MWoo NPin
'Crossways' (p)   CLyd MHig NHar

¶ *cruentus* — MSte
'Dad's Choice' (p) — SBai
'Dad's Favourite' (p) — CGle CSam CThr ECha EMFP LBlm MBro NCra SAll SBai SHay SRms WEas WHoo WWhi
'Daily Mail' (p) — NCra SBai SChu SMer WWhi
'Dainty Dame' (p) — CInt CKel CMea CTri EBee EGoo ESis GBur GMaP LBee MOne NBus NCra NHol NRoo SAga SBla SChu SMrm WLRN WWoo
'Dainty Lady' (b) — SBai
'Damask Superb' (p) — CLyd EMFP MBro SSvw WKin
'Daphne' (p) — SAll
Dark Tempo® (pf) — SBai
'Darling' (b) — SAll
'Dartington Double' (p) — NHol
'Dartington Laced' — WKin
'Dartmoor Forest' (p) — SBla
'David' (p) — CPri EPfP SAll SHay
'David Saunders' (b) ♀ — SBai
'Dawlish Charm' (p) — CThr
'Dawlish Joy' (p) — CThr
'Dawn' (b) — SAll SHay
* 'Dazzler' — MPla
Delphi® (pf) — SBai
deltoides ♀ — CArn CKin CSev ECha ELan EMan EWFC LHol MGra MPla SRms WCla WJek WOak WUnd
– 'Albus' — CChr CLyd ECha GSki MBar MPla SRms SWat WCla WPer
– 'Bright Eyes' — CChr
§ – 'Brilliant' — CSev GTou LPVe MNrw SRms SWat WGor WOve
– 'Broughty Blaze' — GDra
– 'Dark Eyes' — EWes
– 'Erectus' — ELan NFla NLon SIde
– Flashing Light — See *D. deltoides* 'Leuchtfunk'
§ – 'Leuchtfunk' — CPri EBrP EBre EMNN GDra GTou LBre LGro MOne MTis NFla NHar NMir NVic SBre SHel SRms SWat WEas WHen WPer
– maiden pink — EPfP
– 'Microchip' — NHar SRms SSca
* – 'Red Eye' — MNrw
– *splendens* — EPfP
'Denis' (p) — CLyd EBrP EBre ELan LBre NCra NPla SAll SBai SBre SRms
'Desert Song' (b) — SAll
'Desmond' — WRus
'Devon Blush' (p) — EBee EBrP EBre LBre LRHS SBre WWoo
¶ 'Devon Charm' (p) — LRHS
Devon Cream® (p) — CThr EBee EBrP EBre EMFP LBre LRHS NRoo SBre SRms WLRN
Devon Dove® (p) ♀ — CMea CThr EBee EBrP EBre EMan EPfP GMaP LBre NRoo SBre SRms WWoo
Devon General® (p) ♀ — CThr CTri EBrP EBre LBre LRHS SBre WWoo
Devon Glow® (p) ♀ — CLTr CThr EBrP EBre EMFP EPfP GMaP LBre SBre WLRN WWeb WWoo
'Devon Joy' (p) — CMea CThr
'Devon Magic' (p) — CBlo NRoo SRms WWoo
Devon Maid® (p) ♀ — CThr EBrP EBre LBre LIck SBre
'Devon Pearl' (p) — CBlo CThr EBee

'Devon Pride' (p) ♀ — EBrP EBre EMFP LBre SBre
Devon Wizard® (p) ♀ — EMFP NRoo WLRN WWeb
'Dewdrop' (p) — CInt CLyd CMea CSWP CTri EBee ESis GCHN LBee MOne NBir NCra NHar NMen NRoo SAll SChu SMer SMrm SSvw WAbe WHil WLRN WPer
'Diana' — See *D. Dona* = 'Brecas'
'Diane' (p) ♀ — CLyd CThr EBrP EBre ELan EMFP LBre LHop NCra NPin SAga SAll SBai SBre SHay WEas WPer WWal
* 'Diane Cape' — SAll
'Dick Portman' (p) — SBai
'Diplomat' (b) — SAll
'Doctor Archie Cameron' (b) — SHay
'Doctor Ramsey' — CLyd MHig
Dona® — See *D. Dona* = 'Brecas'
'Dora' — LRHS MDHE
'Doris' (p) ♀ — CMea CPri CThr EBrP EBre ECha ELan EMFP ENot GCHN GMaP LBre LFis LHop MAus MWat NBro NCra NFla NPin NRoo SAll SBai SBre SHay SSvw WEas WWin
'Doris Allwood' (pf) — MWoo NPin
'Doris Elite' (p) — SAll
'Doris Galbally' (b) — SBai
'Doris Majestic' (p) — SAll
'Doris Ruby' — See *D. 'Houndspool Ruby'*
'Doris Supreme' (p) — SAll
'Double Irish' — See *D. 'Irish Pink'*
'Downs Cerise' (b) — SHay
§ 'Dubarry' (p) — CLyd CTri EWes MHig NLak SBla WGor WPer
'Duchess of Westminster' (M) — WMal
* 'Duet' — SAll
'Dunkirk' (b) — MWoo
'Dunkirk Spirit' (pf) ♀ — SBai
'Dusky' (p) — NCra WKin
¶ 'Dwarf Vienna' — CPri
'E.J. Baldry' (b) — SHay
'Earl of Essex' (p) — CCot CMil CThr EMFP NCra SAll SHay WWhi
'Ebor II' (b) — SAll
'Edenside Scarlet' (b) — SHay
'Edenside White' (b) — SAll
'Edna' (p) — SAll
* 'Eilat' — SAll
'Eileen' (p) — SAll
¶ 'Eileen Lever' (p) — WAbe
'Eileen O'Connor' (b) ♀ — SBai
¶ 'Elfin Star' (p) — NHol NRoo
'Elizabeth' (p) — CElw CFee CGle CThr LHop
'Elizabeth Jane' (p) — EMFP
'Elizabeth Pink' — SMrm
'Elizabethan' (p) — CSam
* 'Elizabethan Pink' — CNic EGar
'Ember Rose' — See *D. 'Le Rêve'*
'Emile Paré' (p) — MTho SChu SSvw
'Emperor' — See *D. 'Bat's Double Red'*
'Enid Anderson' (p) — SChu SSvw
¶ 'Enid Burgoyne' — WKin
¶ *eretmopetalus* — NSla
erinaceus — CMea EMNN EPot ESis GCHN GCrs GMaP GTou ITim LBee MBro MOne MPla NHar NMen NRoo NTow NWCA WAbe WPer WWin
– var. *alpinus* — CLyd EPot

'Erycina' (b)	SAll SHay
'Ethel Hurford'	WHoo WKin
'Eudoxia' (b)	SAll
'Eva Humphries' (b)	SAll SBai SHay
¶ 'Evening Star' (p)	NHol NRoo
'Excelsior' (p)	CBlo CThr NNor NSti
'Exquisite' (b)	SAll
§ 'Fair Folly' (p)	CThr NBus NRoo SChu SSvw WEas
'Fair Lady' (p)	CMHG
¶ 'Falcon' (pf)	SBai
'Fanal' (p)	CHea CLyd NBir
* 'Fancy Magic' (pf)	CBlo SAll
'Farnham Rose' (p)	CLTr SChu
'Fenbow Nutmeg Clove' (b)	SChu WKin
'Fettes Mount' (p)	CHid CLTr GAbr NChi NSti SSvw
'Fiery Cross' (b)	SAll SHay
'Fimbriatus' (p)	MBro WHoo WPyg
'Fingo Clove' (b)	SAll
'Fiona' (p)	SAll
'Firecrest Rose'	CCot
'First Lady' (b)	SAll
'Flame' (p)	SHay
'Flame Sim' (pf)	SHay
'Fleur' (p)	SAll
'Forest Edge' (b)	SBai
'Forest Glow' (b)	SAll
'Forest Sprite' (b)	SAll SBai
'Forest Treasure' (b)	SAll SBai
'Forest Violet' (b)	SAll
'Fortuna' (p)	SAll
'Fountain's Abbey' (p)	EMFP NChi WIvy WKin
'Fragrant Ann' (pf) ♀	MWoo NPin SHay
'Fragrant Phyllis' (pf)	NPin
'Fragrant Rose' (pf)	NPin
'Frances Isabel' (p) ♀	NCra SAll
'Frances King' (p)	MWoo
'Frances Sellars' (b)	SHay
'Frank's Frilly' (p)	CThr SSvw WKin
'Freckles' (p)	CThr SHay
'Freda' (p)	SAll
'Freeland Crimson Clove' (b)	SHay
freynii	CLyd EPPr EWes MOne NGre NHed NMen SAga WAbe
N Fringed Pink	See *D. superbus*
furcatus	MSto NWCA
'Fusilier' (p)	CLyd CMea CSpe EBrP EBre EMFP ESis GCrs LBre MBar MOne NCra NHol NPri NRoo SAga SAll SBre SChu WHoo WPat WPer
'G.J. Sim' (pf)	SHay
'Gail Tilsey' (b)	SHay
'Galil' (pf)	SAll
'Garland' (p)	CLyd CMea CTri NNrd NRoo WGor
'Garnet' (p)	SChu
¶ 'Gatekeeper' (p)	GCHN
'Gaydena' (b)	SAll
'George Allwood' (pf)	NPin
giganteus	ECGN EMFP IBlr MNrw MSto
'Gingham Gown' (p)	NBir NBrk NLak
'Gipsy Clove' (b)	SHay
glacialis	GMaP GTou NHar NHol NRya
– subsp. *gelidus*	CGra NGre NMen
'Glebe Cottage White'	CGle CLTr CVer
'Glorious' (p)	SHay
¶ 'Gold Fleck'	EBee LBee
'Golden Cross' (b) ♀	SBai
'Golden Rain' (pf)	SHay
¶ 'Golden Sceptre' (b) ♀	SBai
'Grandma Calvert' (p)	SAll
graniticus	WPer
'Gran's Favourite' (p) ♀	CKel CLTr CMea EBrP EBre ELan EMFP GMaP LBre LFis MTho MWat NPin NRoo SBai SBre SChu SHay SRms WEas WHoo WWye
§ *gratianopolitanus* ♀	CArn CLyd CTri GCHN GTou LBee LHol MGra MHig MNrw NMen NOak SIde SRms WAbe WOMN WPer WWye
– 'Corinne Tremaine'	WPbr
– 'Emmen' (p)	CInt
– 'Fellerhexe' (p)	WEas
– 'Flore Pleno' (d)	CLyd EMFP MInt SSvw
* – 'Karlik'	CLyd
§ – 'Princess Charming'	MHig
– red	GAbr
– 'Rosenfeder'	WPer
– 'Splendens'	WPer
§ – 'Tiny Rubies'	CLyd ECho WAbe WFar
'Gravetye Gem' (p)	NCra
'Gravetye Gem' (b)	CLyd NRoo SRms WPyg
'Grenadier' (p)	ECho ELan WLin
'Greytown' (b)	GCal
'Gwendolen Read' (p)	SHay
¶ 'Gypsy Star' (p)	Llck NHol NRoo
haematocalyx	EHyt NWCA WAbe WPer
– 'Alpinus'	See *D. haematocalyx* subsp. *pindicola*
§ – subsp. *pindicola*	CPBP EMFP MFos NHol NSla WOMN WPat
'Hannah Louise' (b) ♀	SBai
'Harlequin' (p)	EBee ECtt EMFP NCra NRoo WPer
'Harmony' (b)	SAll SHay
'Harry Wilcock' (pf)	MWoo NPin
Havana® (pf)	SBai
'Haytor'	See *D. 'Haytor White'*
'Haytor Rock' (p) ♀	CThr EBee EBrP EBre EPfP LBre NCra SBre SHay
§ 'Haytor White' (p) ♀	CSam CThr EBrP EBre EMFP EMan GCHN LBre MHlr NCra NPin SBai SBre SChu SHay SRms SSvw WEas WWhi
'Hazel Ruth' (b) ♀	SBai
'Heidi' (p)	EPfP SRms
'Helen' (p)	CThr SAll SHay WEas
'Helena Hitchcock' (p)	CThr
'Herbert's Pink' (p)	EMFP WKin
¶ 'Hereford Butter'	WKin
'Hidcote' (p)	CLyd CNic CTri ELan EMFP MHig MWat NBus NMen NRoo SBla WLRN WWin
'Hidcote Red'	ECho
* Highgates hybrid	CLyd
'Highland Fraser' (p)	GAbr MBro MHig SAll SRms WEas WHoo WKif WWin
'Highland Queen' (p)	WKin
'Hilda Scholes' (p)	NCra
* 'Hi-lite' (pf)	SAll
hispanicus	See *D. pungens*
'Hope' (p)	CLyd EBee EMFP SChu SSvw
'Horsa' (p)	SHay
§ 'Houndspool Cheryl' (p) ♀	CMea CPri ELan EMFP GAbr GMaP NPin WWeb
§ 'Houndspool Ruby' (p) ♀	CLyd CMea CSam CThr EMFP EPfP MGed MWat NOak NPin SBai SMer WEas WWeb
'Howard Hitchcock' (b) ♀	SBai

'Huntsman'	See *D.* **'Allen's Huntsman'**
'Ian' (p)	CLTr CThr NPin SAll SBai SHay
'Ibis' (b)	SHay
'Icomb' (p)	CLyd CSam CTri SRms WHoo WPer WPyg
'Impulse' (pf)	SBai
'Ina' (p)	GDra SRms
Incas® (pf)	SBai
'Inchmery' (p)	CCot CLTr CLyd CMil EBrP EBre ECED EMFP LBre NCra NNor NTow SAll SBre SChu SHay SSvw WEas WHoo WMaN WWhi
Indios® (pf) ♀	SBai
'Inglestone' (p)	CSam CTri NHar SBla WLin WPer
'Inshriach Dazzler' (p) ♀	CHea CInt CMea EBrP EBre GAbr GCHN GCrs GDra ITim LBee LBre LHop NCra NHar NHed NHol NPri NRoo NRya SBla SBre WHal WLin
'Inshriach Startler' (p)	CFee CMea GDra NRoo
¶ 'Ipswich Pink' (p)	LGro WElm
'Irene Della-Torré' (b) ♀	SBai
'Ivonne Orange' (pf)	SBai
'J.M. Bibby' (pf)	SHay
'Jacqueline Ann' (pf) ♀	SHay
'Jane Austen' (p)	EBee NBrk NCra SChu WKin WPer WWye
'Jane Coffey' (b)	SHay
'Janelle Welch' (pf)	MWoo
japonicus	LCot
'Jenny Wyatt' (p)	EBrP EBre LBre SBre SHay
'Jess Hewins' (pf)	NPin
'Jessica' (pf)	SAll
'Joan Randal' (pf)	SBai
¶ 'Joan Schofield' (p)	NHol NRoo
'Joan Siminson' (p)	WKin WWhi
'Joanne' (pf)	MWoo
'Joanne's Highlight' (pf)	NPin
'Joan's Blood'	See *D. alpinus* **'Joan's Blood'**
'Joe Vernon' (pf)	NPin
'John Ball' (p)	CLTr EMFP SSvw
'John Faulkner' (pf) ♀	MWoo
¶ 'John Grey' (p)	WKin
'John Partridge' (p)	SBai
'Joy' (p) ♀	CThr EBee EBrP EBre EMFP EMan EPfP LBre NCra NPin SBai SBre SHay SRms
'Judy' (p)	CLyd
'Julian' (p)	SAll
'Kathleen Hitchcock' (b)	SBai
'Kesteven Chambery' (p)	CLyd WPer
'Kesteven Chamonix' (p)	WPer
'Kesteven Kirkstead' (b) ♀	CSWP
'Kestor' (p)	NCra
'King of the Blacks' (p,a)	CHad ELan MRav
kitaibelii	See *D. petraeus* subsp. *petraeus*
'Kiwi Pretty' (p)	CThr
knappii	CGen CLyd CPou EGar ELan GCHN LGan MHar MLLN MNrw NChi NOak SAga SIde SPil SSca WCla WPer WRha WWin WWye
¶ – 'Yellow Harmony' (p,a)	MMal NPri WHer
§ Salamanca = 'Kosalamana' (pf)	SBai

§ 'La Bourboule' (p) ♀	CSam ELan EMNN EPot GAbr GDra LBee MBar MBro MHig MPla MWat NMen NRoo SBla SIng SRms WLin WPat WPer WWin
'La Bourboule Albus' (p)	CMea CTri EPot MHig NMen NRoo SBla WAbe WPer WWin
'Laced Hero' (p)	CElw SChu WKin
laced hybrids	WCla
'Laced Joy' (p)	CThr EMFP SAll SChu SHay SMer
'Laced Monarch' (p)	CThr EBee EBrP EBre EMFP GCHN LBre MBro NPin SAga SAll SBai SBre SChu SRms SSvw
'Laced Mrs Sinkins' (p)	SBai
'Laced Prudence'	See *D.* **'Prudence'**
'Laced Romeo' (p)	CCot EMFP SAll SChu SHay WEas
'Laced Treasure' (p)	CLTr CThr SAll
'Lady Granville' (p)	SSvw WKin
'Lady Salisbury' (p)	EMFP WKin
§ 'Lady Wharncliffe' (p)	CLTr CMil EMFP SSvw WKin
'L'Amour' (b)	SAll
* 'Lancing'	EGoo
'Lancing Lady' (b)	SAll
'Lancing Monarch' (b)	SAll SHay
langeanus	SIng
– NS 255	NWCA
'Laura' (p)	SAll SHay
'Lavender Clove' (b)	SAll SBai SHay
'Lavender Lady' (pf)	NPin
¶ 'Lawley's Red' (p)	WKin
'Leiden' (b)	SAll SBai
'Lemsii' (p)	EMFP GCHN MBal NMen NVic WHoo WPer WPyg WWye
'Lena Sim' (pf)	SHay
'Leslie Rennison' (b)	SAll SHay
'Letitia Wyatt' (p) ♀	CMea CThr NCra NRoo
'Leuchtkugel'	WAbe WLin
Liberty®	SBai
'Lightning' (pf)	SAll
'Lilac Clove' (b)	SHay
'Lior' (pf)	SAll
'Little Jock' (p)	EBrP EBre ELan EMNN EPot GCHN LBee LBre LHop MBal MBar MHig MWat NCra NEgg NFla NGre NHar NHol NNrd NRoo SAll SBla SBre SRms SSmi WEas WWin
'Little Miss Muffet' (p)	CLyd
'Little Old Lady'	See *D.* **'Chelsea Pink'**
'London Brocade' (p)	NBrk NCra WIvy WKin
'London Delight' (p)	CCot CThr NCra SHay
'London Glow' (p)	CLTr CThr SAll WKin
'London Lovely' (p)	CLTr CThr NCra SAll SSvw
'London Poppet' (p)	CCot CThr SAll WHoo
'Loveliness' (p)	CBre
lumnitzeri	EPot MSto WPer
'Lustre' (b)	SAll SHay
¶ 'Mab'	WKin
'Madame Dubarry'	See *D.* **'Dubarry'**
'Madonna' (p)	EBee SBai SHay WKin
Malaga® (pf) ♀	NPin SAll SBai
'Mambo' (pf)	SAll SBai
'Mandy' (p)	SAll
'Manningtree Pink'	See *D.* **'Cedric's Oldest'**
'Marcato' (pf)	SBai
'Marg's Choice' (p) ♀	EMFP
'Maria'	See *D.* **'Allen's Maria'**
'Marmion' (M)	WMal

'Petticoat Lace' (p) — EMFP SHay
'Phantom' (b) — SHay
'Pheasant's Eye' (p) — CLTr CLyd EMFP NCra SSvw WKin
'Philip Archer' (b) — SHay
* 'Picton's Propeller' (p) — GBuc
'Pike's Pink' (p) ♀ — CKel CLyd CMea CSam ELan GCHN LBee LFis LHop MBal MHig MWat NCra NEgg NHol NMen NNrd NRoo SAll SSmi SSvw WAbe WEas WLin WWin
pindicola — See *D. haematocalyx* subsp. *pindicola*
pinifolius — MSto
'Pink Bizarre' (b) — SHay
'Pink Calypso' — See *D.* 'Truly Yours'
'Pink Damask' (p) — GAbr
* 'Pink Dona' (pf) — SAll
'Pink Doris' (pf) — NPin
* 'Pink Fringe' — NSla
'Pink Jewel' (p) — CInt CLyd CMea CTri ECha ESis LBee MHig MOne NHol NMen NRoo SAll SChu SIng WEas
'Pink Monica Wyatt' (p) — CThr
'Pink Mrs Sinkins' (p) — CLTr ECha EMFP GAri SAll SBai SChu WHoo
'Pink Pearl' (p) — CBlo CThr EBee SAll WLRN
'Pink Sim' (pf) — SAll
'Pixie' (b) — CLyd EPot NHol
¶ 'Pixie Star' (p) — NHol NRoo
plumarius — EBee MGed NMir SRms SSvw WByw WGor WPer
– 'Albiflorus' — NOrc WPer
pontederae — MSto WPer
'Portsdown Fancy' (b) — SHay
'Portsdown Lass' (b) — SHay
'Portsdown Perfume' (b) — SHay
Prado® (pf) — SAll SBai
preobrazhenskii — MSto SGre
'Pretty' — EBee LHop
'Pretty Lady' (p) — MDHE NRoo
'Prince Charming' (p) — CGra CSam ELan EMNN GAbr ITim NMen NNrd NRoo SAga SBla SHel SRms WLRN WPer
'Princess Charming' — See *D. gratianopolitanus* 'Princess Charming'
'Princess of Wales' (M) — WMal
'Priory Pink' (p) — SAll
§ 'Prudence' (p) — CThr NCra SAll WHoo
'Pudsey Prize' (p) — EHyt
¶ 'Pummelchen' (p) — ITim
'Purley King' (p) — CThr
'Purple Jenny' (p) — SAll
¶ 'Purple Pacal' (pf) — SBai
'Purple Pierrot' (pf) — SBai
'Purple Rendez-vous' (pf) — SAll SBai
pygmaeus — NBro
– B&SWJ 1510 — NHol NPla WCru
¶ – B&SWJ 3533 — WCru
'Queen of Hearts' (p) — CLyd EBrP EBre ESis LBre NBus SBre SMrm WPer WWoo WWye
§ 'Queen of Henri' (p) — CHea CLyd CMea EBee GMaP LBee MMil NCra NHaw NHol NNrd NPri NRoo SBla SChu WFar
'Queen of Sheba' (p) — CThr EMFP NCra SChu SSvw WKin
'Raby Castle' — See *D.* 'Lord Chatham'
'Rachel' (p) — CLyd NRoo WAbe
'Raggio di Sole' (pf) — SAll SBai

'Rainbow Loveliness' (p,a) — NBir SAll SSca WCla WHil
'Ralph Gould' (p) — ECho
Ramona® (pf) — SBai
'Red and White' (p) — WKin
¶ 'Red Denim' (p) — SIng
'Red Penny' (p) — NBro NCat NRoo SAsh WWin
* 'Red Rimon' (pf) — SAll
'Red Velvet' — CLyd CSWP LBee LRHS SAsh SMrm
'Red-edged Skyline' (pf) — SHay
'Reiko' (pf) — SAll
'Reine de Henri' — See *D.* 'Queen of Henri'
'Rendez-vous' (pf) — SAll SBai
'Renoir' (p) — SAll SHay
'Revell's Lady Wharncliffe' — See *D.* 'Lady Wharncliffe'
'Riccardo' (b) ♀ — SBai
'Richard Gibbs' (p) — MHig NRoo WWin
'Rimon' (pf) — SAll
'Rivendell' (p) — CPBP EHyt EPot NHar NSla WAbe
'Robert' (p) — SAll
'Robert Baden-Powell' (b) — SHay
'Roberta' (p) — SAll
* 'Robin Ritchie' — WHoo WKin
'Robin Thain' (b) — SAll SBai SHay
'Rodrigo' (pf) — SBai
'Ron's Joanne' (pf) — SHay
'Roodkapje' (p) — SSvw WKin
'Rose de Mai' (p) — CBre CLTr CMil CSam CSev EBee EBrP EBre EMFP LBlm LBre LLWP NCra SAll SBre SChu SMer SSvw WEas WHoo WLin
'Rose Joy' (p) ♀ — CThr EBee EMFP NCra NPin SBai SHay SRms
'Rose Monica Wyatt' (p) — CThr
'Rose Perfection' (pf) — SHay
'Rosealie' (p) — SHay
'Royal Scot' (pf) ♀ — MWoo
'Royalty' (p) — SHay
'Roysii' (p) — CLyd MPla WPer
'Rubin' (pf) — WEas
'Ruby' — See *D.* 'Houndspool Ruby'
'Ruby Doris' — See *D.* 'Houndspool Ruby'
¶ 'Ruby Wedding' (p) — GCHN
rupicola — CNic
'Russling Robin' — See *D.* 'Fair Maid of Kent'
'Sahara' (pf) — SAll
¶ 'Saint Edith' (p) — WKin
'Saint Nicholas' (p) — EMFP NCra WKin
¶ 'Saint Winifred' — WKin
◆ Salamanca — See *D.* Salamanca = 'Kosalamana'
'Sally Anne Hayward' (b) — SHay
'Salmon Clove' (b) — SHay
'Sam Barlow' (p) — CLTr CMil CPri CThr EMFP GMaP NCra SAll SChu SHay SIng SSvw WWye
'Sandra Neal' (b) ♀ — SBai
'Santa Claus' (b) — SAll SHay
'Scania' (pf) — SHay
scardicus — EHyt
'Scarlet Fragrance' (b) — SHay
'Scarlet Joanne' (pf) — MWoo NPin SHay
scopulorum perplexans — NTow
seguieri — GCra GSki MNrw WPer
serotinus — MSto
'Shaston' (b) — SHay
'Shaston Scarletta' (b) — SHay
'Shot Silk' (pf) — NPin
'Show Aristocrat' (p) — SAll

'Show Portrait' (p)   NNor
simulans   EHyt EWes WOMN
'Sir Arthur Sim' (pf)   SHay
'Sir Cedric Morris'   See *D.* **'Cedric's Oldest'**
* 'Six Hills'   CLyd WPat
'Snow Clove' (b)   SHay
'Snowbird' (pf)   SAll
'Snowfire'   SChu
'Snowshill Manor' (p)   WPer
* 'Sofia' (pf)   SAll
'Solomon' (p)   CThr WKin
'Solway Hannah Scholes'   NPin
  (pf)
'Solway Sunset' (pf)   NPin
'Solway Surprise' (pf)   NPin
'Solway Susan' (pf)   NPin
'Solway Sweetheart' (pf)   NPin
'Sops-in-wine' (p)   CLTr CLon CSam CThr ECha
   EGar EMFP GCal GMac LWak
   MNrw NCra SAll SChu SHay
   SSvw WEas WPbr
'Southmead' (p)   MHig
§ 'Souvenir de la   CMil WMal
   Malmaison' (M)
   sp. B&SWJ 1414   GCra
   sp. J Watson   MFos
'Spangle' (b)   SAll
¶ 'Spangled Star' (p)   CMea EBee LIck NHol NRoo
'Spencer Bickham' (p)   EMFP EPot MNrw
'Spring Beauty' (p)   LPVe NBir NFla
¶ 'Spring Star' (p)   EBee LIck NHol NRoo
'Square Eyes'   See *D.* **'Old Square Eyes'**
squarrosus   EGar EPot LBee MHar MHig
   NGre NWCA
* – *alpinus*   ECho
¶ – *nanus*   CNic
– 'Nanus'   CLyd ELan EWes
'Squeeks' (p)   SChu
'Staccato' (pf)   SBai
'Stan Stroud' (b)   SHay
sternbergii   GCrs
– JJH 931078   NWCA
'Storm' (pf)   SBai
'Strathspey' (b)   SAll SHay
'Strawberries and Cream'   CThr EBee EBrP EBre EMFP
   (p)   EMan LBre LHop NOrc NPin
   SBai SBre SHay SMer
strictus var. *brachyanthus*   See *D. integer* subsp.
   minutiflorus
* – *pulchellus*   EHyt
§ *subacaulis*   EPot GAbr MMil NHar NWCA
suendermannii   See *D. petraeus*
* 'Sullom Voe'   NRoo
'Sunray' (b)   SAll SHay
'Sunstar' (b)   SAll SHay
§ *superbus*   CGen GCra MTho WCla WPer
   WWhi WWin WWye
– 'Crimsonia'   WPer
– *longicalycinus*   MNrw MSte
¶ – var. *longicalycinus*   WCru
   B&SWJ 3230
I – 'Primadonna'   WPer
* – 'Rose'   WPer
– 'Snowdonia'   WPer
'Susan' (p)   EMFP SAll
'Susannah' (p)   SAll
* 'Susan's Seedling' (p)   SAll
'Swanlake' (p)   SHay
'Swansdown' (p)   NNor
'Sway Belle' (p)   CThr NCra NPla SBai
§ 'Sway Candy' (p)   CThr NCra SBai
'Sway Gem' (p)   SBai

'Sway Joy' (p)   NCra SBai
¶ 'Sway Lass' (p)   SBai
'Sway Mist' (p)   NCra
'Sway Pearl' (p)   NCra NPin SBai
'Sway Ripple' (p)   SBai
'Sweet Sue' (b)   SAll SHay
'Sweetheart Abbey' (p)   CCot CLon CLyd CMil CThr
   EMFP NCra SChu SMer SSvw
sylvestris   EPot
– 'Uniflorus'   MHig
¶ 'Syston Beauty' (p)   WKin
¶ 'Tamsin' (p) ♀   LIck MAus SSvw
* 'Tasty' (pf)   SAll
¶ *tatsiense*   CChr
'Tayside Red' (M)   WMal
Tempo® (pf)   SBai
* *tenerifa*   MBri
'Terra' (pf)   SBai
'Terry Sutcliffe' (p)   EBee WKin
'Texas' (pf)   SAll
The Bloodie Pink   See *D.* **'Caesar's Mantle'**
'Theo' (pf)   SAll
'Thomas' (p)   EFou NBrk SAll SChu WEas
'Thomas Lee' (b)   SAll
'Thora' (M)   WMal
'Tinnington Secret   CLyd
   Garden'
'Tiny Rubies'   See *D. gratianopolitanus* **'Tiny**
   Rubies'
'Toledo' (p)   EMFP
'Torino' (pf)   SAll
'Tracy Barlow' (b)   SHay
'Tracy Jardine' (pf)   MWoo
'Treasure' (p)   SHay
'Trevor' (p)   SAll
Tundra® (p)   SBai
turkestanicus   CLyd MSto NBir SSte
§ – 'Patricia Bell'   CSam
¶ 'Tweedale Seedling'   GBuc
* 'Tyrolean Trailing   SAll
   Carnations'
'Uncle Teddy' (b) ♀   SBai
uniflorus   MHig
'Unique' (p)   CLon EMFP MBro SBla SSvw
   WHoo WIvy WKin
'Ursula Le Grove' (p)   CLTr EMFP SSvw WHoo WIvy
   WKin
'V.E. Jubilation' (pf)   MWoo
'Valda Wyatt' (p) ♀   CThr ELan EMFP EMan EPfP
   GCHN LHop MGed NCra NPin
   NRoo SAll SBai SChu SRms
   WWhi
Valencia® (pf)   SBai
'Vera Woodfield' (pf)   MWoo
'Vermeer'   WLRN
'Violet Clove' (b)   SHay
'Visa' (pf)   SAll
'W.A. Musgrave'   See *D.* **'Musgrave's Pink'**
'W.H. Brooks' (b)   SAll
'Waithman Beauty' (p)   CCot CLyd CTri ECha GAbr
   MBar MBro MHar MHig MPla
   NCra NRoo SAll SSvw WEas
   WHoo WPer WPyg WWye
'Waithman's Jubilee' (p)   CCot GCHN NBrk NCat SRms
   WLin
'Warden Hybrid' (p)   CMea CTri EMNN EPfP ESis
   GAbr LIck MHig MOne NCra
   NHol NRoo SBla WAbe WLRN
   WWoo
'Warrior' (b)   CBlo
¶ 'Wedding Bells' (pf)   NPin
'Weetwood Double' (p)   CSam WPer

'Welcome' (b)	SHay
weyrichii	NMen NNrd WOMN WPer
'Whatfield Anona' (p)	CLyd EGle ELan SAll
'Whatfield Beauty'	ECho ELan LRHS MDHE SAll
§ 'Whatfield Brilliant'	CLyd LBee
'Whatfield Can-can'	CInt CLyd CMea CPBP CPri
	EMFP ESis MDHE MOne
	NCra NHol NRoo SAll WAbe
	WWeb WWoo
'Whatfield Cyclops'	CLyd CPBP EBee ESis EWes
	MBro MOne NCra NRoo SAll
	SChu WHoo WLRN WWoo
'Whatfield Dawn'	ECho ELan MDHE NNrd SAll
'Whatfield Dorothy Mann'	CLyd ECho ELan MDHE SAll
(p)	
'Whatfield Fuchsia' (p)	SAll
'Whatfield Gem' (p)	CInt CKel CLyd EBrP EBre
	ELan EMFP ESis GCal LBre
	MBro MOne MWgw NCra
	NHol NMen NRoo SAll SBre
	WHoo WPer
'Whatfield Joy' (p)	CLyd ELan EPot ESis GAbr
	LBee MOne NCra NHol NMen
	NPri NRoo NTow SAll
'Whatfield Magenta' (p)	CLyd CPBP EGle ELan EPot
	ESis GAbr LBee LRHS MOne
	NCra NHol NNrd NRoo SAll
	SChu WAbe WEas WLin
'Whatfield Mini' (p)	CLyd SAll WPer
'Whatfield Miss' (p)	SAll
'Whatfield Misty Morn'	ECho ELan
(p)	
'Whatfield Peach' (p)	SAll
'Whatfield Pom Pom' (p)	CLyd
'Whatfield Pretty Lady'	ECho ELan MDHE SAll
(p)	
'Whatfield Rose' (p)	ECho MDHE SAll
'Whatfield Ruby' (p)	CLyd EGle EHyt ELan EMFP
	LRHS MDHE SAll WLin WPer
'Whatfield Supergem'	CLyd ECho ELan EPot MDHE
	SAll
'Whatfield White' (p)	CLyd ECho ELan LRHS
	MDHE SAll
'Whatfield White Moon'	ECho
(p)	
'Whatfield Wink'	EGle
'Whatfield Wisp' (p)	CLyd CM&M CPBP CTri EGle
	EHyt ELan NBir NMen WFar
	WLRN
'White Barn' (p)	ECha
'White Joy' (p) ♀	EMFP
'White Ladies' (p)	CLyd CThr ELan EMFP ENot
	SAll
¶ 'White Liberty' (pf)	SBai
'White Lightning' (pf)	SAll
'Whitecliff' (b)	SAll SHay
'Whitehill' (p) ♀	EPot NHol NMen NNrd NWCA
	NWoo WPat WWin
'Whitesmith' (b) ♀	SAll
¶ 'Whitford Belle' (p)	SBai
'Widecombe Fair' (p) ♀	CLTr CMea CThr CTri EBee
	EBrP EBre EMan LBre MAus
	NCra NPla SAll SBre
'William Brownhill' (p)	CMil EMFP SChu SMer SSvw
'Winsome' (p)	SHay
'Woodfield's Jewel' (p)	MWoo
¶ 'Yellow Rendez-Vous'	SBai
(pf)	
'Yorkshireman' (b)	SAll SHay
'Zebra' (b)	SAll SBai SHay
zederbaueri	NWCA SIng WLin

DIAPENSIA (Diapensiaceae)
lapponica var. *obovata*	WAbe

DIARRHENA   (Poaceae) See Plant Deletions

DIASCIA † (Scrophulariaceae)
¶ 'Alys'	WPeH
anastrepta	CVer EGar GCal MSCN WPer
	WWye
¶ – HWEL 0219	NWCA
¶ 'Andrew'	WPeH
'Appleby Appleblossom'	CMea CRDP CSam CSpe CStr
	EOrc EPot LLWP MAvo MBEx
	MLLN SChu SSoC SWas
'Appleby Apricot'	EMar EPot MAvo MBEx
	MSCN MTho WHoo
'Apricot' hort.	See *D. barberae* 'Hopley's Apricot'
'April Fool'	EOrc LLWP MAvo WCot
	WPeH
* 'Aquarius'	SChu WPeH WPen
barberae	CInt EBrP EBre EHic ELan
	GAri GCal LBre LHop SBre
	SEas WOve
§ – 'Blackthorn Apricot' ♀	Widely available
§ – 'Fisher's Flora' ♀	LFis
§ – 'Hopleys Apricot'	CLTr ELan LHop MBEx
	MLLN NBrk WPbr
¶ – HWEL 037	NWCA
§ – 'Ruby Field' ♀	CB&S CGle EBar ECha EFou
	ELan EMNN GCHN GCal
	LHop MAus MBri NEgg NHaw
	NSti SAxl SBla SIng SPer SRms
	WEas WHoo WOld WRha
	WWeb
¶ 'Belmore Beauty'	EGoo LLWP MAvo WByw
'Bloomsbury Ice'	LBlm
¶ 'Blue Bonnet'	EHic EPot MBEx WPeH
♦ 'Blush'	See *D. integerrima* 'Blush'
♦ 'Chalgrave Beauty'	EMan
♦ Coral Belle	See *D.* Coral Belle = 'Hecbel'
§ *cordata*	CGle CMHG CSpe EMon EPot
	IHos MBal NBro NHar NMen
	SHel WOve WWin WWye
– hort.	See *D. barberae* 'Fisher's Flora'
– x 'Lilac Belle'	SCoo SHFr
cordifolia	See *D. barberae* 'Fisher's Flora'
'Cotswold Beauty'	LFis
'Crûg Variegated'	EPot MAvo MLLN WCot
	WCru WPbr WPer
'Dainty Duet'	EOrc EWes MBEx MGed SChu
	SUsu WPer
'Dark Eyes' ♀	LHil SChu WPeH
elegans	See *D. fetcaniensis* , *D. vigilis*
'Elizabeth' ♀	LFis NFai NHar WPeH WPen
'Emma'	CMea EBar EOrc LHop LLWP
	NHar SChu SIng SUsu WPeH
felthamii	See *D. fetcaniensis*
§ *fetcaniensis*	CHan CLon CMHG CMea
	CSam EMon LBlm LFis LGre
	LHil LHop MAus MBEx MBal
	MHig MTho NHaw NPer SChu
	SCro SIgm SIng SPer WHal
	WMow WPbr WPer WWin
♦ *flanaganii*	See *D. stachyoides* , *D. vigilis*
'Frilly' ♀	CRDP CSpe ECtt MHig NBrk
	SChu WPeH
§ Coral Belle = 'Hecbel'	Widely available
§ Sydney Olympics =	CSpe EHic EPot LHil LLWP
'Hecsyd'	MDHE MLLN NHar NHaw
	WLRN WPer
'Hector Harrison'	See *D.* 'Salmon Supreme'

'Hector's Hardy' ♀   CSpe EOrc SUsu WPeH

¶ 'Ice Cracker'   EHic EPot MBEx MMil SIng WPeH

§ *integerrima* ♀   CHan CMHG CSam CSpe EBar ECha ELan EOrc GCal LFis LGre LHil LLWP MBEx MBro MFir SAxl SChu SHel SIgm SMrm SPla WEas

◆ – 'Alba'   See *D.* '**Blush**'

§ – 'Blush'   CSpe EGoo EMan EMar LHil NHar NLak SMrm SUsu

¶ – from Lesotho   GCal

– 'Harry Hay'   CGle

◆ – 'Ivory Angel'   See *D. integerrima* '**Blush**'

integrifolia   See *D. integerrima*

¶ 'Jac Pot'   WPeH

'Jack Elliott'   ITim WCFE

'Jackpot'   EPot MDHE

'Jacqueline's Joy'   CGle CLyd CRDP EMan GMac LLWP MBEx NHar NHaw NNrd NPer NPla SAga SChu SMrm SSoC SUsu

'Joyce's Choice' ♀   CSpe EBee EOrc EPot EWes GCal LBee LGre LHop LLWP MBEx MBri MSCN NHaw NPla NPri NWes SAga SAxl SChu SMer SUsu WAbb WLRN

'Kate'   LHil MBEx NLak SChu SIng SMrm WCru WPeH

¶ 'Katherine Sharman' (v)   EMon

'Lady Valerie' ♀   CLTr CRDP CSpe EOrc EWes GMac LHil LHop LLWP MBEx MBri MGed MLLN NHar NHaw NWes SLod SWas WPer WWin

'Lilac Belle' ♀   CB&S CBos CLTr CRDP CSam CVer ECtt ELan GCal LHil LHop LLWP MBEx MHig MMil MTho NHar NHaw NNrd NSti SChu SEas SLod SMrm SUsu WPbr WPer WWin

'Lilac Dream'   LHop LLWP WPeH WWin

'Lilac Lace' (v)   NHar WPeH

'Lilac Mist' ♀   CLTr CMil EOrc LGre LLWP MBEx MLLN NHar NPla NSti SAxl SChu SDix SLod SSoC SUsu WPen

'Lilac Queen'   WEas

lilacina   CLTr CLyd CMHG ECtt EMan GAri SUsu WPer WWye

¶ 'Little Charmer'   MBEx WPeH

¶ 'Little Emma'   WPeH

¶ 'Little Fiona'   WPeH

'Louise'   CSpe EOrc EPot GBuc MDHE NBir NHar SMrm WPeH

'Lucy'   CRDP CSpe EPot LLWP NBir NHar WPeH

¶ 'Lucy' × *mollis*   SChu WPeH

megathura   GCal

¶ 'Megavil'   EPot

mollis   CSpe GCal LLWP SIng WPeH

'Orangeade'   EOrc LLWP SUsu WPeH

'Pale Face'   CSpe NHar

patens   CLyd MBEx MTho SAga WPen

¶ 'Patio Wine'   EHic

'Paula'   LHil LHop

¶ 'Penlyn'   WPeH

personata   LLWP

'Pink Queen'   GCal

'Pink Spot'   SAga SIng WPeH

* 'Pisces'   SChu WPeH

¶ *racemulosa*   WPeH

¶ 'Red Ace'   EPot MDHE WPeH

'Red Start'   CPBP EHic EOrc LFis LHop LLWP MDHE MMil NHar NHaw NLak NPla SChu SIng SMrm SUsu SVil WLRN WPeH WWeb WWin WWoo

rigescens ♀   Widely available

– 'Anne Rennie'   CSpe

– × *integerrima*   WLRN

– × *lilacina*   EBee EHic EMan EMar MArl MCLN NCat NHaw NHol NLak SIgm WPbr

◆ – pale form   See *D. rigescens* '**Anne Rennie**'

'Ruby Field'   See *D. barberae* '**Ruby Field**'

'Ruby's Pink'   EOrc WPeH

'Rupert Lambert' ♀   CLTr EMon GBuc GCal GMac LHil LHop LLWP MBEx MBro NHar NSti SChu SLod SUsu WHoo WLin WPer WPyg

§ 'Salmon Supreme'   CB&S CBar CGle CHad CLTr CSam CSev ECha ECtt EHyt ELan GCal GMac LFis LGre LHil LHop LLWP MMil MTho NHar NHaw SChu SMrm SUsu WEas WPbr WPer WRus

'Selina's Choice'   EOrc EPot GBuc SChu WPeH

§ *stachyoides*   EBar EBrP EBre EHal ELan LBlm LBre LHop NDov NHaw NPer SBre WPer WWhi

'Stella'   LHop

* 'Strawberry Sundae'   SCoo

'Super Salmon'   EPot

◆ Sydney Olympics   See *D.* Sydney Olympics = '**Hecsyd**'

tugelensis   CGle CLon SUsu WFar

'Twinkle' ♀   CLyd CPBP CRDP CSpe EHyt EMar EPot EWes GCal GMac LHil LLWP MBEx MLLN NFai NHar NHol NNrd SAga SChu WAbe WCru WOMN WPer WWin

* 'Twins Gully'   GCal

* *variegata*   SIng

§ *vigilis* ♀   Widely available

* – × Elliott's variety   MAus

– 'Jack Elliott' ex JE 8965   CB&S CLTr CSev CSpe EBrP EBre EHic EWes LBre LHop NHaw NHol SBre SHel SIde SUsu SWas WLRN WPer WShe

'Wendy'   EOrc LHop MAvo WPeH

¶ 'White Cloud'   LLWP SChu WPeH WPen WSPU

'Woodcote'   LHil LLWP NLak

DIASCIA × LINARIA   See **NEMESIA** *caerulea*

DICENTRA † (Papaveraceae)

'Adrian Bloom'   CDoC EBar EBrP EBre LBre LRot MCLN MCli MTho NCat NOak NSti SBre SPer SPla WBro

'Bacchanal'   Widely available

'Boothman's Variety'   See *D.* '**Stuart Boothman**'

¶ 'Boothman's White'   WWeb

'Bountiful'   CGle CMHG CRow EBee ECED EGol GMaP LHop MBro MCLN MLLN MRav MTho NNor NRoo NSti SPer WLin WRHF

'Brownie'   GBuc MBel MCLN NCat NSti SOkh WEas

canadensis	EPot GBuc MSal MTho WCot WThi
'Catforth Filigree'	NCat
chrysantha	ECGN SCoo
'Coldham'	WCru WTin
cucullaria	CBos CGra CRDP CRow CSWP EHyt EPot ERos GBuc GCrs LGre MHig MRav MTho NHar NMen NRya NSti NTow NWCA SWas WAbe WCot WCru WLin WThi
– 'Pittsburg'	EBee SWas
* 'Dark Stuart Boothman'	NOak
eximia 'Alba'	See *D. eximia* **'Snowdrift'**
– hort.	See *D. formosa*
– (Ker-Gawler) Torrey	MTho MWat NSti SWat
§ – 'Snowdrift'	CLAP CLon CM&M CSpe EAst EBee ELan EPfP MBro MHFP MTho NWoo SDys SRms SSpi WLin WWat WWeb
§ *formosa*	CGle CRow ECGN ECha EGol ELan LAma MBal MBro MCLN MTho NBro NNor NOak NOrc NPri NRoo NVic SChu SIng SSea WByw WEas WHoo WWal WWin
§ – *alba*	CGle CHad CRow ECha ELan LGre MAus MCLN NBir NNor NOak NRoo NVic SChu SPer WAbe WByw WFar WPbr WRus
* – 'Aurora'	EFou
– 'Furse's Form'	NCat NOak WCot
– subsp. *oregona*	CLAP CRow EPar GCal LFlo MBal MFos NCat NChi NOak NRoo NSti NTay WAbb WAbe WByw WCru WWin
– – 'Rosea'	MBel NChi
§ Snowflakes = 'Fusd'	GAbr MUlv
'Langtrees' ♀	Widely available
'Luxuriant' ♀	CB&S CGle CRow EBrP EBre ECtt EGol ELan EOld EPar EPri GAbr GBur LBre LGan MBri MCLN MGrG MLLN NFla NOak NRoo NSti SBre SPer SWat WAbe WBea WHoo WWeb
macrantha	CAvo CFil CGle CHad CRDP CRow ECha EPfP LGre MTho SSpi SWas WCru WOMN WPGP
macrocapnos	CB&S CFir CHan CPlN CRow EBrP EBre GQui LBre LFis MSto MTho SBre SMrm WCot WCru WSHC WWeb
'Pearl Drops'	CDec CRow EBrP EBre EGol ELan EPla GBuc GBur GMaP LBre LSpr MBri MSte NOak NRoo SBre SMac SOkh SSoC WAbb WAbe WEas WHoo WMer WPyg WRus WWhi WWin
peregrina	GTou
§ *scandens*	CGle CMil CPlN CRHN CRow CSpe ELan EPfP GBin GCal MCCP MTho NLar WCru WPbr WSHC WWhi
– B&SWJ 2427	WCru
'Silver Smith'	CFil
◆ Snowflakes	See *D.* Snowflakes = **'Fusd'**
'Snowflakes'	CDoC COtt EBrP EBre EWes GCHN LBre NHaw NRoo SBre WCer
spectabilis ♀	Widely available
– 'Alba' ♀	CAvo CB&S CBot CBro CGle CHad CRow EBrP EBre ECha EFou EGol ELan GBur LAma LBre LHop MBri MGrG NBro NRoo NSti SBla SBre SMad SPer WAbe WEas WPbr WRus
– 'Goldheart'	CHad GBri LRHS MGrG SPla
'Spring Morning'	CElw CGle CMHG CMil CRow CSam EGle IBlr NSti SChu SSpi WBon WEas WRHF WRus
§ 'Stuart Boothman' ♀	Widely available
thalictrifolia	See *D. scandens*

DICHELOSTEMMA (Alliaceae)

congestum	CAvo ERos LBow MNrw WCot
§ *ida-maia*	CAvo CPou EPot WLin
§ *pulchellum*	NTow
volubile	CPlN

DICHOPOGON (Anthericaceae)

¶ *strictus*	EBee

DICHORISANDRA   (Commelinaceae) See Plant Deletions

DICHOTOMANTHES (Rosaceae)

tristaniicarpa	CFil SRms

DICHROA (Hydrangeaceae)

febrifuga	CAbb CB&S CFil CGre CHan EWes GQui LBlm LCns LHil LHop SBid SOWG WCru
versicolor	CPle

DICHROMENA (Cyperaceae)

* *colorata*	CInt CRow MCCP

DICKSONIA † (Dicksoniaceae)

antarctica ♀	CAbb CB&S CDoC CFil CHEx COtt CTbh CTrC CTre CTrw EOas EWes ISea LHil LPal LPan MLan NHol NPal SArc WFib WGer WMul WNor WRic WWeb
fibrosa ♀	CB&S CHEx EOas WRic
¶ *sellowiana*	WRic
squarrosa ♀	CB&S CHEx CTrC EOas ERea MLan SAPC SArc WRic
¶ *youngiae*	WRic

DICLIPTERA (Acanthaceae)

§ *suberecta*	CHal EHol ERea LBlm LHop SIgm SOWG

DICOMA   (Asteraceae) See Plant Deletions

DICRANOSTIGMA (Papaveraceae)

lactucoides	EBee WLin

DICTAMNUS (Rutaceae)

albus ♀	CArn EBrP EBre ECha EFou ELan GCal LBre LFis LGre LHop MAus MBel MBri MUlv NHol NLar NSti SBla SBre SChu SHFr SPer WHoo WMer WOMN WWye

§ – var. **purpureus** ♀ · CBot EBrP EBre ECha EFou
ELan ENot GCal GPoy LBre
LGre LHop MAus MBel MBri
MUlv NCut NHol NSti SAxl
SBla SBre SChu SEas SPer
WGwG WHoo WOMN WOld
fraxinella · See *D. albus* var. *purpureus*

DICTYOLIMON (Plumbaginaceae)
macrorrhabdos · NWCA

DICTYOSPERMA (Arecaceae)
album · LPal MBri

DIDYMOCHLAENA (Aspidiaceae)
lunulata · See *D. truncatula*
§ *truncatula* · CHal MBri

DIDYMOSPERMA (Arecaceae)
caudatum · See *Arenga caudata*

DIEFFENBACHIA (Araceae) See Plant
Deletions

DIERAMA (Iridaceae)
¶ *argyreum* · CPla EBee WCot WPGP WSan
'Ariel' · IBlr
¶ 'Black Knight' · IBlr
'Blush' · IBlr
¶ 'Candy Stripe' (v) · CPla CRow
cooperi · CHan IBlr
– 'White Form' S&SH 20 · CHan
* 'Donard Legacy' · IBlr
§ *dracomontanum* · CBro CFil CGle CHan CLon
CPou CRDP CRow CVer
ECGN GCal IBlr LGre MHar
NBir NLar NRoo SBla SWat
WCot WHil WHoo WOMN
– dwarf lilac · GCal
– dwarf pale pink · GCal
– dwarf pink · GCal
¶ *dubium* × *robustum* · EBee
ensifolium · See *D. pendulum*
¶ *erectum* · WCot
grandiflorum · IBlr
igneum · CFai CFir CMea CMil ECGP
ELan IBlr MLLN MNrw MTed
SIng SMad SSca WAbe WCot
WPGP
– CD&R 278 · CHan CPou CRDP
jucundum · CHan EBee GBuc MLLN
latifolium · CHan CPla IBlr WSan
medium · CLon EBee GSki MHlr WCot
WPGP
'Milkmaid' · IBlr
¶ 'Pamina' · IBlr
¶ 'Papagena' · IBlr
¶ 'Papageno' · IBlr
pauciflorum · CFil CFir CHan CHid CLon
CMil CRDP CVer LGre WAbe
WCot
§ *pendulum* · CAvo CBot CFee CMGP EBrP
EBre EFou ELan IBlr LBre
MBri MFir MHar NHol NRoo
SBre SWat WAbe WByw
WGwG WRus WWal
'Puck' · ECha GCal GCra IBlr MRav
NCat
pulcherrimum · Widely available
– var. *album* · GBuc
– 'Blackbird' · IBlr SSoC

– × *dracomontanum* · SMad
– dwarf forms · GCal GSki WWhi
– forms · CRDP CRow IBlr NRoo WSan
¶ – 'Pearly Queen' · CRow
¶ – 'Peregrine' · WPGP
– Slieve Donard hybrids · CChr GBri GCal GMac LHop
NLar
◆ *pumilum* (Baker) N.E.Br. · See *D. pendulum* var. *pumilum*
◆ – hort. · See *D. dracomontanum*
¶ 'Queen of the Night' · IBlr
reynoldsii · IBlr
robustum · CHan IBlr WCot
– S&SH 49 · CHan
– S&SH 63 · CHan
– white S&SH 18 · CHan
* 'Snowbells' · WWhi
sp. from Lesotho · GCal
sp. SH 85 · CHan
¶ 'Tamino' · IBlr
'Titania' · IBlr
trichorhizum · CHan WCot
¶ 'Tubular Bells' · IBlr
'Violet Ice' · IBlr
'Westminster Chimes' · IBlr

DIERVILLA † (Caprifoliaceae)
lonicera · CPle MTis SMac SPan WFar
WWat
middendorffiana · See *Weigela middendorffiana*
rivularis · CPle
sessilifolia · CB&S CHan CPle EPar GOrc
IOrc MBel MHlr SChu SLPl
WBod WCot WHCG WMow
WRus WSHC WWin
¶ – 'Butterfly' · MBri
× *splendens* · CDoC CMHG CPle EBar EHoe
ELan EMil EPla IOrc LHop
MBar MPla MRav MUlv NHol
SEas SLPl SPer SSta WAbe
WDin WStI WTro

DIETES (Iridaceae)
bicolor · CTrC ERea
grandiflora · CMon CTrC ERea
§ *iridioides* · CGle CSWP GBin LBow MSte
SVen WPer

DIGITALIS † (Scrophulariaceae)
ambigua · See *D. grandiflora*
apricot hybrids · See *D. purpurea* 'Sutton's
Apricot'
'Butterfingers' · WCot
* *campanulata alba* · WRHF
¶ *cariensis* · EBee
ciliata · CChr CFir EBee ECGN ELan
GCra LFlo MLLN MSto NLak
NOak SCou SSte WSel
davisiana · CBot CLon EGoo GAbr GCra
LFlo MSto NLak NOak SCou
WCot WHil WPGP WPer
dubia · CBot CMea NBir SPil WBro
WCHb WGor
eriostachya · See *D. lutea*
ferruginea · CArn CChr CFee CGle CHad
CHan CInt CSev ECha ECtt
EFou EGol ELan EOrc MBri
MCLN MGrG MTho NBro
NNor SBla SCou SPer SSvw
WCHb WEas WOMN WPer
WWye

DIONAEA (Droseraceae)

DIONYSIA (Primulaceae)

DIOON (Zamiaceae)

spinulosum   CBrP LPal

DIOSCOREA (Dioscoreaceae)
batatas   MSal
deltoidea   WCru
dregeana   CPlN
elephantipes   CPlN
quinqueloba   WCru
villosa   MSal

DIOSMA (Rutaceae)
ericoides   EDen LBuc SRms
¶ –'Pink Fountain'   WWeb
– 'Sunset Gold'   CInt LBuc SCoo WWeb

DIOSPHAERA (Campanulaceae)
asperuloides   See *Trachelium asperuloides*

DIOSPYROS (Ebenaceae)
¶ *austroafricana*   CTrC
duclouxii   CFil SBid WPGP
kaki (F)   CGre CMCN LPan SSpi
lotus   CAgr CB&S CFil CMCN LPan
    SSpi WPGP
virginiana (F)   CAgr CMCN EPfP ICrw SSpi

DIPCADI (Hyacinthaceae)
lividum SF 1   CMon

DIPELTA (Caprifoliaceae)
floribunda   CBot CFil CPMA CPle LRHS
    WPGP
ventricosa   CFil CPMA EPfP LRHS WPGP
    WWat
yunnanensis   CFil EPfP LRHS SPla WPGP

DIPHYLLEIA (Berberidaceae)
cymosa   CRDP ECha EMan EOld EPar
    MSal SAxl WCru

DIPIDAX See ONIXOTIS

DIPLACUS See MIMULUS

DIPLADENIA See MANDEVILLA

DIPLARRHENA (Iridaceae)
§ *latifolia*   CAvo LBee MHig SWas WAbe
moraea   CDoC CHan CHid ECha GCal
    GGar IBlr ILis LFis MHig
    MTho MUlv NPSI SSpi WAbe
    WHal WOld WPGP WWin
– *minor*   SWas
¶ – 'Slieve Donard'   CRDP
– West Coast form   See *D. latifolia*

DIPLAZIUM (Athyriaceae)
§ *proliferum*   WRic

DIPLOTAXIS (Brassicaceae) See Plant
Deletions

DIPOGON (Papilionaceae)
§ *lignosus*   CPlN MSto WCot

DIPSACUS (Dipsacaceae)
§ *fullonum*   CArn CHal CKin CLTr EJud
    EWFC GCHN MChe MGra
    MHew MUlv NBro NLan NMir
    SIde SSvw WBea WByw WCer
    WHer WOak WPer WWye
– subsp. *fullonum*   WJek
inermis   CHan EBee GCal GCan NPSI
    WFar
– CC&McK 567   GCHN
¶ *laciniatus*   SRCN
pilosus   CKin EWFC
sativus   NHex
sylvestris   See *D. fullonum*

DIPTERACANTHUS See RUELLIA

DIPTERONIA (Aceraceae)
sinensis   CB&S CFil CMCN CSam SSpi
    WNor

DISA (Orchidaceae)
¶ *aurata*   GCrs
¶ g. *Diores*   GCrs
× *kewensis*   GCrs SWes
'Kirstenbosch Pride'   GCrs
tripetaloides   GCrs
uniflora   GCrs

DISANTHUS (Hamamelidaceae)
cercidifolius ♀   CAbP CPMA ELan EPfP ICrw
    IDee MAsh MBel MBlu MBri
    MGos SPer SReu SSpi SSta
    WDin WWat

DISCARIA (Rhamnaceae)
¶ *toumatou*   MAll

DISELMA (Cupressaceae)
archeri   CBlo CKen CNic LCon MBar

DISPOROPSIS (Convallariaceae)
arisanensis B&SWJ 1490   WCru
¶ *aspera*   WCru
§ *pernyi*   CAvo CHid CLAP CLon CRDP
    EBee ECha EPar LGre MBel
    NHar SAxl SLod SWas WCot
    WCru WFar WHal
¶ sp. from Philippines B&SWJ   WCru
    3891

DISPORUM (Convallariaceae)
cantoniense   WCot
¶ – B&SWJ 1424   WCru
¶ – var. *kawakamii*   CAvo
flavens   CRDP EBrP EBre EPar LBre
    MUlv SAxl SBre SWas WCot
    WFar WPGP
¶ – B&SWJ 872   WCru
hookeri   WCru
– var. *oreganum*   CBro CRow GTou IBlr WCru
kawakamii B&SWJ 350   WCru
lanuginosum   CBro GCrs WCot WThi
lutescens   WCru
maculatum   CRDP LGre SMac SWas
nantauense B&SWJ 359   WCru

sessile 'Variegatum'	CAvo CBro CFil CHan CRDP CRow EBrP EBre ECha ELan EMan EPar EPla EPot LBre LGan MRav NTow SAxl SBla SBre SSpi SUsu SWas WCru WFar WHal WPbr WWin WWye
shimadae B&SWJ 399	WCru
smilacinum	WCru
* – 'Aureovariegatum'	WCru
¶ – B&SWJ 713	WCru
smithii	CFil CHan CRDP EBee EPar EPot ERos NBir NHar NMen NTow WCru WPGP WWat
sp. B&SWJ 872	WCru
taiwanense B&SWJ 1513	WCru
uniflorum	WCru
¶ – B&SWJ 651	WCru
¶ *viridescens*	NRya

DISSOTIS   (Melastomataceae) See Plant Deletions

DISTICTIS (Bignoniaceae)

buccinatoria	CPlN
'Mrs Rivers'	CPlN

DISTYLIUM (Hamamelidaceae)

myricoides	CMCN EPfP
racemosum	CB&S CTre ELan GSki SHBN SReu SSta WSHC WWat

DIURANTHERA See CHLOROPHYTUM

DIURIS (Orchidaceae)

corymbosa	SWes
from South Australia	
– from West Australia	SWes
drummondii 'Buttery'	SWes
¶ *lanceolata*	SWes
¶ 'Pioneer Big Ears'	SWes
punctata 'Old Vic'	SWes
sulphurea 'Golden Dragon'	SWes

DIZYGOTHECA See SCHEFFLERA

DOBINEA (Podoaceae)

vulgaris B&SWJ 2532	WCru

DODECADENIA   (Lauraceae) See Plant Deletions

DODECATHEON † (Primulaceae)

alpinum	CGra GCrs NHar NRya
– JCA 11744	SBla
amethystinum	See *D. pulchellum*
clevelandii	NTow NWoo
– subsp. *insulare*	CNic LRHS NWCA SBla
– subsp. *patulum*	LRHS
conjugens	NTow
– JCA 11133	CNic
cusickii	See *D. pulchellum* subsp. *cusickii*
dentatum ♀	CElw CVer EPar GLil LBee MBal MBro MPhe MTho NMen NSla NTow WAbe
– subsp. *ellisiae*	GCrs MPhe NGre NRya
frigidum	WAbe
§ *hendersonii* ♀	CBro EPar MBal MPhe SBla
¶ – subsp. *parvifolium*	GCLN

♦ *integrifolium*	See *D. hendersonii*
§ *jeffreyi*	MBro MPhe NHar NMen NWCA SBla WAbe WCla WViv
– 'Rotlicht'	NHar SRms
* × *lemoinei*	EPot
§ *meadia* ♀	CAvo CB&S CBot CBro CMea CSam ECha EFou ELan EPot ESis LAma LBee LHop MBri MBro MTho NBro NEgg NGre NHol SBla SPer WAbe WCla WEas WFar WHil WHoo WWat
– f. *album* ♀	CB&S CBro CLon CSWP CVer ECha EFou ELan EOrc EPar GDra LAma LHop MLLN MTho NHol NRoo NRya NSti NTow SPer SRms WWat
– from Cedar County	WAbe
– membranaceous	WAbe
– 'Millard's Clone'	EPar
pauciflorum (Dur.)E. Greene	See *D. meadia*
– hort.	See *D. pulchellum*
poeticum	EHic MBro NTow
§ *pulchellum* ♀	CBro CNic EPar EPot GDra LBee MBal MBro NHar NMen NRya NWCA SBla WAbe
§ – subsp. *cusickii*	LBee NWCA SRms
– subsp. *pulchellum* 'Red Wings'	CLon CMea CVer EBrP EBre EPot GDra LBre MBro NTow SBre WHoo WPyg
– *radicatum*	See *D. pulchellum*
radicatum	See *D. pulchellum*
redolens	EBee WAbe
tetrandrum	See *D. jeffreyi*

DODONAEA (Sapindaceae)

viscosa	CArn ECou IBlr LHil
– subsp. *angustifolia*	CPle CTrC
– subsp. *cuneata*	MAll
– subsp. *linearis*	MAll
– 'Purpurea'	CAbb CB&S CGre CPle CTrC ECou EHic ERea LHop MAll MUlv

DOLICHOS (Papilionaceae)

lablab	See *Lablab purpureus*
lignosus	See *Dipogon lignosus*

DOLICHOTHRIX (Asteraceae)

§ *ericoides*	WHer

DOMBEYA (Sterculiaceae)

burgessiae	IDee SOWG

DONDIA See HACQUETIA

DOODIA (Blechnaceae)

aspera	GQui NMar
§ *caudata*	NMar WRic
heterophylla	NMar
media	GQui NMar WRic
mollis	NMar
* *rubra*	NMar
♦ *squarrosa*	See *D. caudata*

DORONICUM † (Asteraceae)

austriacum	CMGP EPri MSCN NCat SSca
carpetanum	CSam EJud
caucasicum	See *D. orientale*
§ *columnae*	GDra WLin
cordatum	See *D. columnae*

§ × **excelsum** 'Harpur Crewe' — CDec CGle ECED ELan MAus MHlr NPer NTow NVic WCot WEas

'Finesse' — CBlo EBee EPfP NOak SOkh SRms WHil

§ 'Frühlingspracht' (d) — CRDP ELan ENot GDra NFla SPer SRms WFar

¶ **grandiflorum** — EBee

'Miss Mason' ♀ — CDoC MBri MCLN NBro SPer

§ **orientale** — CBlo ENot EPfP GAbr GBur MOne MSCN NPla SEND SMac SWat WByw WMow WOve

– 'Goldcut' — EWll NRoo SPla WLRN

– 'Magnificum' — EAst EBrP EBre EMan GMaP LBre LPVe MFir MWat NFai NFla NLon NMir NOak SBre SMer SRms WBea WFar WPer WPyg WWal WWin

pardalianches — CMea ECha GCra MHew MLLN SDys WByw WCot WRHF

plantagineum 'Excelsum' — See *D.* × **excelsum** 'Harpur Crewe'

'Riedels Goldkranz' — GBuc MBri NBro

Spring Beauty — See *D.* 'Frühlingspracht'

DORYANTHES (Doryanthaceae)
¶ **excelsa** — CTrC MFiF
palmeri — CHEx

DORYCNIUM See LOTUS

DORYOPTERIS (Sinopteridaceae)
pedata — MBri

DOUGLASIA (Primulaceae)
laevigata — See **Androsace laevigata**
montana — See **Androsace montana**
nivalis — See **Androsace nivalis**
vitaliana — See **Vitaliana primuliflora**

DOVYALIS (Flacourtiaceae)
¶ **caffra** — LBlo

DOXANTHA See MACFADYENA

DRABA (Brassicaceae)
acaulis — CGra WLin
aizoides — EBrP EBre ECha ELan GCHN GCrs GDra LBre MHig MOne MWat NGre NNrd NRya SBre SIng SRms WCla WWin
aizoon — See *D. lasiocarpa*
alticola JJH 119.94 — EPot
§ **aspera** — GDra
bertolonii Boissier — See *D. loeseleurii*
– Nyman — See *D. aspera*
– Thell. — See *D. brachystemon*
bruniifolia — EBrP EBre EBur EGle EWes LBre MHig MTho NWCA SBre SSmi
– subsp. **bruniifolia** — CGra
bryoides — See *D. rigida* var. *bryoides*
¶ – JJH 960858 — MRPP
cappadocica — EHyt GCLN MFos
cinerea — GBin
compacta — See *D. lasiocarpa* **Compacta Group**
cretica — NMen
cusickii — CGra CPBP
cuspidata — EPot

daurica — See *D. glabella*
dedeana — EWes GBin WWin
– subsp. **mawii** — NTow
densifolia — GCLN MFos MHig NGre NTow
– JJA 11826 — NWCA
dubia — GBin
glacialis var. **pectinata** — NTow
hispanica — GBin NMen
– subsp. **lebrunii** — MRPP
hoppeana — NWCA
imbricata — See *D. rigida* var. *imbricata*
§ **incana** — MOne WPyg WWin
§ – **Stylaris Group** — MHig
kitadakensis — GCHN
§ **lasiocarpa** — MRPP
§ **loeseleurii** — NPri
lonchocarpa — MHig
longisiliqua ♀ — CLyd EHyt ITim MHig NWCA SBla SIng
– EMR 2551 — EPot
magellanica — CPBP MDHE
mollissima — CGra CLyd EHyt EPot GTou MHig NMen NWCA WAbe WLin
oligosperma — CGra CPBP MFos NWCA
¶ – NNS 94-40 — MRPP
oreades CC&McK 804 — MRPP
¶ **ossetica** var. **racemosa** — WLin
¶ **pamirica** — ITim
parnassica — GCHN
paysonii — CLyd
– var. **treleasei** — MFos SIng WAbe
polytricha — EHyt GTou NSla WAbe
repens — See *D. sibirica*
rigida — CMea MLan MTho SIng SSmi
§ – var. **bryoides** — CGra EHyt GDra MBro NGre NHar NWCA WAbe WLin
¶ – – HZ 82-97 — EHyt
§ – var. **imbricata** — EHyt MBro NGre NHar NHol NTow SSmi WLin
– – f. **compacta** — EPot
rosularis — EPot SIng WLin
rupestris — See *D. norvegica*
sakuraii — NGre WWin
× **salomonii** — EPot
sauteri — GCHN
scardica — See *D. lasiocarpa*
¶ sp. CC 1911 — MRPP SGre
¶ **sphaeroides** — CGra
streptocarpa — MFos
stylaris — See *D. incana* **Stylaris Group**
* **thymbriphyrestus** — WLin
ussuriensis — WPer
ventosa — GTou MHig NGre NTow SIng

DRACAENA † (Dracaenaceae)
congesta — See *Cordyline stricta*
¶ **draco** — ECre WMul
fragrans — MBri
– (Compacta Group) 'Compacta Purpurea'
– – 'Compacta Variegata' — MBri
– – 'Lemon Lime' (v) — MBri
– – 'Warneckei' (v) ♀ — MBri SRms
– – 'Yellow Stripe' (v) — MBri
* – **glauca** — MBri
– 'Janet Craig' — MBri
– 'Massangeana' (v) ♀ — MBri
indivisa — See *Cordyline indivisa*
marginata (v) ♀ — MBri
– 'Colorama' (v) — MBri
sanderiana (v) ♀ — MBri

* *schrijveriana*	MBri
steudneri	MBri
stricta	See *Cordyline stricta*

DRACOCEPHALUM (Lamiaceae)

altaiense	See *D. imberbe*
argunense	CPBP CRDP EBee LBee LFis LGre NGre NMen SAxl SBla SCro SRms SSoC WPat WPen WPer WWin
* – 'Album'	EBee
botryoides	CMea CPBP EBee GCrs NWCA
calophyllum var. *smithianum*	NGre
canescens	See *Lallemantia canescens*
forrestii	CLyd ESis SBla SMac
grandiflorum	EBee NGre SUsu
hemsleyanum	WPat
§ *imberbe*	CPBP EFou
¶ *isabellae*	EBee
mairei	See *D. renatii*
moldavica	MSal SIde WWye
nutans	EBee SSvw
¶ *oblongifolium*	WLin
¶ *peregrinum*	EBee
prattii	See *Nepeta prattii*
§ *renatii*	EBee MSal
¶ *rupestre*	EPPr
ruyschianum	CPBP ELan EMan EMon EPPr LFlo MBro MLLN NWCA NWoo WCot
sibiricum	See *Nepeta sibirica*
virginicum	See *Physostegia virginiana*
wendelboi	CPea EBee GBri MLLN NBir NBus WPbr WPer WWin

DRACOPHYLLUM (Epacridaceae) See Plant Deletions

DRACUNCULUS (Araceae)

canariensis	CAvo GCra SWat
– MS 934	CMon
§ *vulgaris*	CGle CHEx EBot EMon EOas EPar EPot MCCP MRav NPSI SDix SEND SSoC SWat WCot WCru WHal

DRAPETES (Thymelaeaceae)

dieffenbachii	GDra
lyallii	GDra

DREGEA (Asclepiadaceae)

§ *sinensis*	CBot CGre CMac CPlN CSam EBee ELan ERav ERea GQui NPal SBra SHBN SOWG SPer WCot WSHC WWat WWeb

DREPANOSTACHYUM (Poaceae - Bambusoideae)

§ *falcatum*	CHEx ISta LJus WJun
falconeri hort.	See *Himalayacalamus falconeri* 'Damarapa'
hookerianum	See *Himalayacalamus hookerianus*
¶ *khasianum*	CHEx ISta
microphyllum	ISta SDry WJun
* *scandens*	CFil ISta WPGP

DRIMIOPSIS (Hyacinthaceae)

maculata	CMon

DRIMYS (Winteraceae)

aromatica	See *D. lanceolata*
colorata	See *Pseudowintera colorata*
§ *lanceolata*	CAbb CGre CHan CMHG CPle CTrC CTrG CTrw ECou ELan EMil IOrc ISea LHop MAll MBal MBel MBlu SDry SPer SSta WAbe WBod WCru WGwG WSHC WWat
– (f)	ECou
– (m)	ECou
winteri	CAbb CAgr CB&S CDoC CFil CHEx CPle CTrG CTrw EPfP IOrc ISea MAll MUlv SArc SHBN SMad SPer WBrE WCru WSHC WWat
– var. *andina*	EPfP GGGa SBid SSpi WPGP
§ – var. *chilensis*	CGre CHEx CLan ISea MBal WCru WPGP
– 'Fastigiata'	LBlm
– Latifolia Group	See *D. winteri* var. *chilensis*

DROSANTHEMUM (Aizoaceae)

floribundum	CHEx EOas WEas
hispidum	CHEx CHal EBrP EBre ELan EOas EPot LBre LHop MBro MHig MTho NGre NMen NNrd NTow NWCA SBod SBre SIng WPat WPyg
¶ *speciosum*	EOas

DROSERA (Droseraceae)

adelae	EAnd MHel WMEx
aliciae	EAnd MHel WMEx
andersoniana	EFEx
anglica	WMEx
x *badgerupii* 'Lake Badgerup'	WMEx
'Beermullah'	WMEx
binata	GTro MHel WMEx
§ – subsp. *dichotoma*	MHel
– 'Extrema'	WMEx
– 'Multifida'	MHel WMEx
¶ – T form	EAnd
browniana	EFEx
bulbigena	EFEx
bulbosa	WMEx
– subsp. *bulbosa*	EFEx
– subsp. *major*	EFEx
x *californica* 'California Sunset'	WMEx
capensis	EAnd GTro MHel WMEx
– *alba*	EAnd GTro MHel WMEx
– narrow-leaved	WMEx
capillaris	WMEx
cuneifolia	WMEx
dichotoma	See *D. binata* subsp. *dichotoma*
dielsiana	WMEx
erythrorrhiza	WMEx
– subsp. *collina*	EFEx WMEx
– subsp. *erythrorrhiza*	EFEx
– *imbecilia*	EFEx
– subsp. *magna*	EFEx
– subsp. *squamosa*	EFEx
filiformis var. *filiformis*	EAnd WMEx
gigantea	EFEx WMEx
graniticola	EFEx
hamiltonii	WMEx
heterophylla	EFEx WMEx
intermedia	WMEx
– x *rotundifolia*	See *D.* x *beleziana*
loureirii	EFEx

macrantha	EFEx WMEx
– subsp. *macrantha*	EFEx
macrophylla macrophylla	EFEx
– *prophylla*	EFEx
'Marston Dragon'	WMEx
menziesii subsp. *basifolia*	EFEx
– subsp. *menziesii*	EFEx
– subsp. *thysanosepala*	EFEx
modesta	EFEx
* *multifida*	GTro
orbiculata	EFEx WMEx
peltata	EFEx WMEx
platypoda	EFEx WMEx
pulchella	WMEx
– × *nitidula*	WMEx
ramellosa	EFEx
rosulata	EFEx WMEx
rotundifolia	GBar WMEx
salina	EFEx
slackii	MHel WMEx
¶ *spatulata*	WMEx
¶ – Kansai	WMEx
¶ – Kanto	WMEx
stolonifera	WMEx
– subsp. *compacta*	EFEx
– subsp. *humilis*	EFEx
– subsp. *porrecta*	EFEx
– subsp. *rupicola*	EFEx
– subsp. *stolonifera*	EFEx
stricticaulis	WMEx
tubaestylus	EFEx WMEx
zonaria	EFEx WMEx

DRYANDRA (Proteaceae)

¶ *armata*	MFiF
* *aromatica*	MFiF
¶ *quercifolia*	MFiF

DRYAS (Rosaceae)

drummondii	SBla WAbe
– 'Grandiflora'	GDra
* – 'Grandiflora E.B. Anderson'	NHar
§ *integrifolia*	EPot GAri GDra NHar NMGW SIng WAbe WLin WWin
¶ – 'Greenland Green'	WAbe
lanata	See *D. octopetala* var. *argentea*
octopetala ♀	CAgr CBar CGle CSam ELan ESis GCHN GDra GTou LHop MBal MBro MHig MWat NChi NFla NHar NHol NNor NNrd NVic SBla SIng WAbe WEas WFar WHoo WUnd WWin
– 'Minor' ♀	LBee MBro MHig NMen NWCA NWoo WAbe WHoo WPat WPyg
× *suendermannii* ♀	CMHG EBrP EBre ELan EPfP GAri GTou LBee LBre MBro NNrd NRoo NWCA SBre WAbe WHoo WPat WPyg
tenella	See *D. integrifolia*

DRYOPTERIS † (Aspidiaceae)

aemula	EFer SRms
§ *affinis* ♀	CCuc CFil CRow ECha EFou EHic EPar GGar LSyl MBal NFla NHol NMar SRms WFib WRic
§ – subsp. *borreri*	EFer
– 'Congesta'	WFib WWat
– 'Congesta Cristata'	EBrP EBre LBre NHar NHol SBre

– Crispa Group	GBin IOrc SCob
– 'Crispa Gracilis' ♀	CBar CCuc CDoC CLAP CMil CTrC EBee EFer ELan EMon LHil MBri NBir NLak SAxl SPer SPla SRms WAbe WRic
– 'Cristata' ♀	Widely available
– 'Cristata Angustata' ♀	EFer ELan EMon GBin IOrc NHol NLak NMar SRms WFib WPGP WRic
– 'Cristata Grandiceps Askew'	CCuc NCat NMar WFib
– 'Pinderi'	EBee EFou ELan MBri NOrc WGor WRic
N– Polydactyla Group	GQui NMar
* – 'Polydactyla Mapplebeck' ♀	CCuc CRDP CRow EMon NHol SRms
¶ – 'Revolvens'	WRic
– 'Stableri'	EFer EMon GQui WFib
¶ *aitoniana*	WRic
atrata hort.	See *D. cycadina*
austriaca hort.	See *D. dilatata*
blanfordii	CFil WPGP
borreri	See *D. affinis* subsp. *borreri*
¶ *buschiana*	CHEx
carthusiana	CBlo CFil EFer NHar SAxl SRms WPGP WRic
– 'Cristata'	NVic
clintoniana	WRic
× *complexa* 'Stablerae'	NMar WRic
* 'Corley'	WRic
crassirhizoma	WRic
¶ *cristata*	WRic
§ *cycadina* ♀	CCuc CFil CRDP CTrC EBee EFer ELan EMar EMon IOrc MHlr NHol NMar SEas SMad SPla WFib WGor WRic WWat
darjeelingensis	WCru
¶ *dickinsii*	EMon WRic
§ *dilatata* ♀	CBar CCuc CKin EBee ECha EFer ELan EMon MBal NHol NMar SCob SPer SRms WFib WRic
– 'Crispa Whiteside' ♀	CFil CLAP EFer ELan EMon MBri NHar NHol NPla SAxl WAbe WFib WPGP WRic WWoo
– 'Grandiceps'	CRDP CRow EFer EMon MBri NHar NHol NVic SChu WFib WRic
– 'Lepidota Cristata' ♀	CCuc CRDP ELan EMon IOrc NHar NHol NMar SCob SPer SRms WFib WRic
– 'Lepidota Grandiceps'	NMar
erythrosora ♀	Widely available
* – 'Prolifera' ♀	CDoC CLAP CRDP EFer EMon GCal GMaP MSte NBir NHar NHol NMar NPla WAbe WFib WRic
expansa	EMon
filix-mas ♀	EPfP LHil LPBA MGra SRCN WHil WShi
– 'Barnesii'	CBlo CCuc EFer MSte NHar NHed NMar WRic
– 'Bollandiae'	WRic
* – 'Corymbifera Crispa'	EFer
– 'Crispa'	EHon NHol SCob WFib
– 'Crispa Congesta'	See *D. affinis* 'Crispa Congesta'
– 'Crispa Cristata'	CCuc CLAP CRDP EBrP EBre EGol ELan EMon LBre LHop MBri NHed NHol NMar SBre SChu SMer SPla SRms SWat WFib WGor WRic

– 'Crispatissima'   CCuc
– Cristata Group   EFer NMar SCob SPer WFib
    WRic
– 'Cristata' ♀   CBar CCuc CFil CKin CRow
    EBrP EBre EFer EFou EHon
    ELan IOrc LBre MBal MSta
    NMar NOrc SBre SChu SCob
    SPer SWat WFib WRic WWye
– (Cristata Group) 'Fred   MLan NHol WFib
  Jackson'
* – 'Cristata Grandiceps'   EFer
– 'Cristata Martindale'   CRDP CRow GQui NHol NMar
    SRms WFib
– 'Depauperata'   CCuc CFil CRDP SChu WFib
    WPGP
– 'Fluctuosa'   SRms
– 'Grandiceps Wills' ♀   CRow EMon NHol NMar SChu
    WFib WRic
– 'Linearis'   CBar CRow EBrP EBre EFer
    EHon ELan EMar EMon IOrc
    LBre MBri SBre SCob SRms
– 'Linearis Congesta'   CFil WPGP
– 'Linearis Cristata'   EBrP EBre LBre NMar SBre
    WRic
– 'Linearis Polydactyla'   CLAP EHic NHar NLak NMar
    SPla WShe
– 'Multicristata'   NMar
– Polydactyla Group   GAri NMar SPer WFib
– 'Polydactyla Dadds'   IOrc MBri MLan WFib
¶ *fragrans*   WRic
goldieana   GMaP LSyl NHar NMar WFib
    WRic
guanchica   CFil
¶ *hawaiiensis*   WRic
hirtipes   See *D. cycadina*
hondoensis   CFil
lacera   NHar
¶ *lepidopoda*   WRic
marginalis   NMar WRic
§ *nigropaleacea*   NHar
odontoloma   See *D. nigropaleacea*
oreades   NHar SRms
paleacea   WHil
pallida   CFil
pseudomas   See *D. affinis*
× *remota*   NMar SRms WRic
sieboldii   CCuc CFil CLAP ELan EMon
    NHar NHol NMar SChu SRms
    WFib WPGP WRic
¶ sp. from Emei Shan, China   WPGP
¶ *stenolepis*   WRic
stewartii   NHar WRic
× *tavelii*   IOrc
tokyoensis   NHar WFib WRic
× *uliginosa*   WRic
uniformis   EFer
wallichiana ♀   CBar CFil CLAP ECha EFer
    EFou ELan EMar EMon GBin
    GBuc GCal LHil MBri NChi
    NFla NHar NMar NOrc SBla
    SChu SPar SRms WAbe WFib
    WHal WRic

DRYPIS   (Caryophyllaceae) See Plant Deletions

DUCHESNEA (Rosaceae)
chrysantha   See *D. indica*
§ *indica*   CAgr CSWP ECro EHic EMan
    GAbr IBlr MRav NHol NPri
    NSti SRms SSca WCer WOak

§ – 'Harlequin' (v)   EMon EPPr EPla GBar GBuc
    MCCP MNrw MTho NLar NSti
    WRha
¶ – 'Snowflakes'   CRow
¶ – 'Taff's Silverline' (v)   EMon
– 'Variegata'   See *D. indica* **'Harlequin'**

DUDLEYA (Crassulaceae)
¶ *cymosa*   NTow
– subsp. *pumila*   MFos WCot
farinosa   CHEx IBlr
¶ *lanceolata* NNS 95230   IDac

DUMORTIERA   (Weisnerellaceae) See Plant Deletions

DUNALIA (Solanaceae)
§ *australis*   CGre CHan CPlN CPle LHil
    LLew SOWG SVen
– blue   EWll WHer
– large-flowered form   LHil
– white   CBot

DURANTA (Verbenaceae)
§ *erecta*   CPle CSpe
– 'Variegata'   CPle
plumieri   See *D. erecta*
repens   See *D. erecta*
* *stenostophylla*   CSpe

DYCKIA (Bromeliaceae)
argentea   See *Hechtia argentea*

DYMONDIA (Asteraceae)
margaretae   LRHS

DYPSIS (Arecaceae)
§ *decaryi*   CBrP LPal
¶ *decipiens*   LPal
§ *leptocheilos*   LPal
§ *lutescens* ♀   LPal MBri
¶ *utilis*   LPal

DYSCHORISTE   (Acanthaceae) See Plant Deletions

EBENUS   (Papilionaceae) See Plant Deletions

ECBALLIUM (Cucurbitaceae)
elaterium   MHew MSal WHer

ECCREMOCARPUS (Bignoniaceae)
ruber   See *E. scaber* f. *carmineus*
scaber ♀   CB&S CChr CPlN CRHN CSev
    CTrC CTrG ELan EMil ENot
    GAbr GCHN LIck MBri MNrw
    NBro NChi NPer SPer WBrE
    WBro WFar WWye
– f. *aureus*   CB&S CMHG SHFr WHoo
    WOMN
§ – f. *carmineus*   CB&S CMHG CNic EBar EBee
    GCHN MHar WCru WHoo
    WPyg
– f. *roseus*   CBot CGle WBro WOMN

ECHEVERIA † (Crassulaceae)
affinis   MBri
agavoides ♀   MRav WBrE
* – 'Metallica'   MBri
* 'Black Knight'   LHil SLMG

* 'Black Prince'	CHEx NPer SGre
derenbergii ♀	CHEx SLMG
* 'Duchess of Nuremberg'	SLMG
elegans ♀	CHEx CHal EOas LHil MBri SAPC SArc
§ *gibbiflora* var. **metallica** ♀	WEas
glauca Bak.	See *E. secunda* var. *glauca*
harmsii ♀	CSWP LHil NTow WEas WOMN
* 'Harry Butterfield'	WCot
'Imbricata'	CHEx
'Paul Bunyon'	CHal
¶ 'Perle von Nürnberg' ♀	SGre
pulvinata ♀	CHal
* – 'Frosty'	SGre
§ *secunda* var. **glauca**	GBur IBlr NBir SLMG
* – – 'Gigantea'	NPer
setosa ♀	CHEx SLMG
'Warfield Wonder' ♀	WEas

ECHINACEA † (Asteraceae)

angustifolia	CArn ECGN GPoy MSal WCot WWye
¶ 'Mecklenburg Select'	EBee
pallida	CBot CMil EAst EBee EGar ELan EMan GPoy LFis LHol MSal NCut NPri SMad SOkh SSoC SUsu WCot
paradoxa	CPou EMan LFis MSal SDys
§ *purpurea*	Widely available
– Bressingham hybrids	EBrP EBre ELan LBre SBre SPer WFar
¶ – 'Green Edge'	EFou
– 'Leuchtstern'	CMdw EBee ECGN GSki LGan MBel NCut WPer
– 'Magnus'	CBot CGle EBrP EBre ECGN LBre LHop LRot MBel MBro MCLN MNrw MSCN MTis NRoo NSti NWes SBre SCro SMad SOkh WBro WHen WHil WMer WPer WPyg
– 'Robert Bloom'	ECED ENot LFis LGre LHop WCot
¶ – 'Rubinstern'	LGre
– 'White Lustre'	EBee EBrP EBre ECha EGar LBre MUlv NWoo SBre WCot WMer
– 'White Swan'	Widely available
simulata	MSal

ECHINOPS (Asteraceae)

albus	See *E. 'Nivalis'*
¶ *bannaticus*	MAus WLin
* – 'Albus'	EAst EPfP
§ – 'Blue Globe'	EBee ECGN EHic EMan GCal LFis MCli SCoo SSca WHil WLRN WPer WWal WWhi
– 'Taplow Blue' ♀	CB&S CSev EBar EBee EBrP EBre ECro EFou ELan GAbr GCal LBre LHop MCLN MUlv MWat NCut NFla NPer SBre SCro SEND SPer SPla WLRN WMer WWeb
exaltatus	EBee NBir
maracandicus	GCal
microcephalus	EGar EMon
– HH&K 285	CHan
§ 'Nivalis'	CBre EBee ECha ECro EHic ELan EPla GAbr GCal MWgw NSti SEND SPer
¶ *oxyodonta* HH&K 145	CHan

– HH&K 235	CHan
¶ *oxyodontus* HH&J 153	CHan
* *perringii*	GCal
ritro hort.	See *E. bannaticus*
¶ – 'Charlotte'	CStr
¶ – 'Moonstone'	CRow
– 'Veitch's Blue'	CDoC CM&M CMGP EBee GCal GLil MAus MBri MCLN MCli NCat NCut NLak SSpe WCot WLRN WMer WWeb
ritro Linnaeus ♀	CB&S CHan ECha ECtt ELan ENot GCHN MArl MCLN MHlr NBro NCut NFai NNor NRoo NVic SEND SPer SRms SSvw WBea WEas WFar WOve WPer WWin
– subsp. **ruthenicus** ♀	EBee ECGP ELan EMon EWll GBuc MRav NTow WBro WCot WPGP
sphaerocephalus	CHan ECha ECro ELan EMan EMon IBlr SSca WBea WByw WCot WLRN WPer
¶ – 'Arctic Glow'	CBre CMil CPou EBee GMaP GSki LBuc MBro MCLN MMHG MSte NBro NChi NCut NLar NPri SCro SGre SPla SSpe SSvw WBay WBea WElm WHil WLRN WViv WWhi
§ *strigosus*	EBee
tournefortii	EGar
¶ *tschimganicus*	EBee

ECHINOSPARTUM See GENISTA

ECHIUM (Boraginaceae)

§ *candicans*	CAbb CHEx CTbh CTrC ECre EOas ERav LHil MNrw SAPC SArc SVen
fastuosum	See *E. candicans*
¶ *italicum*	NLar
* *nebrum*	GBri NPri
¶ *nervosum*	SGre
§ *pininana*	CAbb CGre CHEx CHan CTbh CTrC ECre ELan EOas EWes ISea NPal SAPC SArc WCHb WElm WHer
pinnifolium	See *E. pininana*
russicum	CFir ECGN LGre MAvo NChi SIgm WCot
× *scilloniense*	CHEx
¶ sp. from Greece	WHer
vulgare	CArn CKin ECGN EEls ELan EOHP EWFC LHol MChe MGra MHew MSal NMir SIde WBrE WHer WJek WWye
webbii	CGre CHan
wildpretii	CAbb CBot CHEx CTrC ECre EOas SAPC SArc SIgm WHer

EDGEWORTHIA (Thymelaeaceae)

§ *chrysantha*	CB&S CPMA LBuc LPan WSHC
– B&SWJ 1048	WCru
– 'Rubra'	CPMA
papyrifera	See *E. chrysantha*

EDRAIANTHUS (Campanulaceae)

dalmaticus	SBla
dinaricus	NSla
graminifolius ♀	CHea ECtt GDra LBee NHar NMen NWCA WFar WPer WWin

– *albus*   See *E. graminifolius* subsp.
     niveus
§ *pumilio* ♀   CGra EPot GMaP NGre NHar
     NHed NMen NTow SBla SIng
     SRms WAbe WLin
serbicus   NBir
§ *serpyllifolius*   CPea
§ – 'Major'   WAbe

EGERIA (Hydrocharitaceae)
§ *densa*   CBen SWyc

EHRETIA (Boraginaceae)
§ *acuminata* var. *obovata*   CGre
¶ *dicksonii*   SSpi WPGP
ovalifolia   See *E. acuminata* var. *obovata*
thyrsiflora   See *E. acuminata* var. *obovata*

EHRHARTA (Poaceae)
¶ *thunbergii*   EBee

EICHHORNIA (Pontederiaceae)
'Azure'   MSta
crassipes   CBen CHEx CWat EMFW
     LPBA MSta NDea
– 'Major'   SAWi WWeb

ELAEAGNUS † (Elaeagnaceae)
angustifolia   CAgr CB&S CBlo CBot CPle
     ENot MBlu MCoo MRav NSti
     SHBN SLPl SPer SRms WDin
     WGer
– Caspica Group   See *E.* 'Quicksilver'
argentea   See *E. commutata*
§ *commutata*   CAgr CBot CDoC CMCN CPle
     EHoe ENot EPar IOrc LHop
     MBlu MCoo MWhi NNor SLPl
     SMad SPer SSta WHCG WRus
     WStI
× *ebbingei*   CB&S CHEx CPri EBrP EBre
     ELan ENot GOrc GRei IOrc
     LBre LBuc MBal MCoo MGos
     MWat SBre SHBN SPer SPla
     SReu SSta WBod WDin WFar
     WGwG WHCG WWat WWeb
     WWin
– 'Coastal Gold'   CAbP CBlo CDoC COtt EBee
     EMil ENot LBuc MAsh MBri
     MGos MUlv SReu SSta WPat
     WWes
– 'Forest Gold'   ELan LRHS MAsh
– 'Gilt Edge' (v) ♀   CB&S CDoC CLan CMHG
     EHoe ELan ENot IOrc LHop
     LPan MBal MBri MGos MPla
     MWat SHBN SPer SPla SReu
     SSta WAbe WHCG WHar
     WPat WStI WWeb
¶ – 'Gold Splash'   MBri
¶ – 'Golden Splash'   CWSG
– 'Limelight' (v)   Widely available
– 'Salcombe Seedling'   LHop MBri MUlv WAbe
– 'Southern Seedling'   CHEx
glabra 'Reflexa'   See *E.* × *reflexa*
macrophylla   CLan CSam ENot NNor SDry
multiflora   CAgr LBuc SPer
– 'Gigantea'   ELan
parvifolia ♀   EBee ENot SPan
pungens   CPle ERom NBir
– 'Argenteovariegata'   See *E. pungens* 'Variegata'
– 'Aureovariegata'   See *E. pungens* 'Maculata'

– 'Dicksonii' (v)   CBlo CDoC LNet SPer SPla
     SRms SSpi WBcn
¶ – 'Forest Gold'   CAbP
– 'Frederici' (v)   CB&S CBlo CDoC CMHG
     EHoe ELan ERav MAsh MBal
     MBri MPla MRav NHol SCob
     SHBN SPer SSpi WDin WHCG
     WPat WWat
– 'Goldrim' (v)   CBlo COtt CSam GOrc MAsh
     MBri MGos SCob SHBN WDin
§ – 'Maculata' (v) ♀   Widely available
§ – 'Variegata'   CB&S CBlo CDoC IOrc MBal
     MBri NBir SCob SHBN SPer
     WAbe WHCG WLRN
§ 'Quicksilver' ♀   CFil CHad CPMA CPle ECha
     ECre ELan MPla SMur SPer
     SPla SSpi SSta WCru WEas
     WHCG WPGP WSHC WWat
§ × *reflexa*   CFil CPle WWat
umbellata   CAgr CPle MBlu MCoo SPer
     WHCG WWat
– *borealis*   CFil

ELAEOCARPUS (Elaeocarpaceae) See Plant Deletions

ELATOSTEMA (Urticaceae)
daveauanum   See *E. repens* var. *repens*
repens var. *pulchrum* ♀   CHal MBri
§ – var. *repens* ♀   CHal

ELEGIA (Restionaceae)
capensis   CFee CHEx CTrC WMul
¶ *equisetacea*   CFee WNor
¶ *fenestrata*   IDac

ELEOCHARIS (Cyperaceae)
acicularis   CBen ELan EMFW NDea SWyc
     WChe WWeb
palustris   EMFW MSta SWyc

ELEPHANTOPUS (Asteraceae) See Plant Deletions

ELETTARIA (Zingiberaceae)
cardamomum   CArn CHEx CPle GPoy LBlm
     MBri MSal WCot WJek WMul

ELEUTHEROCOCCUS (Araliaceae)
pictus   See *Kalopanax septemlobus*
senticosus   GPoy
septemlobus   See *Kalopanax septemlobus*
§ *sieboldianus*   MRav
– 'Aureomarginatus'   CB&S
§ – 'Variegatus'   CBot CHan ELan EPfP ICrw
     IOrc LFis LHop MBlu MGos
     NPal SPan WCot WHer WSHC

ELINGAMITA (Myrsinaceae)
johnsonii   CHEx

ELISENA (Amaryllidaceae)
longipetala   See *Hymenocallis longipetala*

ELLIOTTIA (Ericaceae)
bracteata   See *Tripetaleia bracteata*
pyroliflorus   See *Cladothamnus pyroliflorus*
¶ *racemosa*   CTrG

ELLISIOPHYLLUM (Scrophulariaceae)
pinnatum B&SWJ 197   WCru

ELMERA (Saxifragaceae)
¶ *racemosa*   WAbe

ELODEA (Hydrocharitaceae)
canadensis   CBen EHon EMFW SAWi
     SWat SWyc WChe
crispa   See *Lagarosiphon major*
densa   See *Egeria densa*

ELSHOLTZIA (Lamiaceae)
¶ *ciliata*   EOHP
fruticosa   CArn CPle WWye
stauntonii   CArn CB&S CBot CDoC CFee
     ECha EMan EOHP EPri GPoy
     MTis SBid SEND SLPl SMad
     WSHC WWye
– 'Alba'   CBot

ELYMUS (Poaceae)
arenarius   See *Leymus arenarius*
canadensis   CCuc EHoe NPSI
– f. *glaucifolius*   GCal
¶ *cinereus*   EPPr
farctus   EPPr
giganteus   See *Leymus racemosus*
glaucus hort.   See *E. hispidus*
§ *hispidus*   CCuc CHan CInt CMil CSpe
     EBee ECoo EGoo EHoe EMan
     EPPr ESOG ESis LHop MBri
     MUlv NPSI SAxl SOkh SPer
     SUsu WHil WWye
N *magellanicus*   Widely available
§ *scabrus*   ESOG LRHS SMrm
tenuis   CCuc CInt EBee
villosus var. *arkansanus*   EPPr ESOG

ELYTROPUS (Apocynaceae) See Plant
Deletions

EMBOTHRIUM † (Proteaceae)
coccineum   CB&S CHEx CTrG ELan EMil
     EPfP GOrc IOrc SDry SReu
     WBrE WNor WPat WPyg
– Lanceolatum Group   CEnd CGre ELan EPfP GOrc
     MBal SBid SHBN SPer SSpi
     SSta WPic
– – 'Inca Flame'   CEnd CFai COtt CPMA CWSG
     ISea NHed SBrw SMur SSta
     WPat WWat
* – – 'Inca King'   LRHS MAsh
– – 'Norquinco' ♀   CB&S IOrc LRHS MBal MBri
     WBod WCru WPyg
– Longifolium Group   CB&S IBlr IOrc ISea

EMILIA (Asteraceae)
javanica hort.   See *E. coccinea*

EMINIUM (Araceae)
albertii   LAma

EMMENOPTERYS (Rubiaceae)
¶ *henryi*   CFil CLyn EPfP WPGP

EMPETRUM (Empetraceae)
luteum   MBar
nigrum   GAri GPoy MAll MBal MBar
     MHig SMur

– 'Bernstein'   EDen IDee NHol
* – 'Gold'   CMHG
– var. *japonicum*   GDra GTou
– 'Lucia'   MGos
¶ *rubrum*   MAll

ENCELIOPSIS (Asteraceae)
¶ *argophylla*   EBee
¶ *covillei*   EBee

ENCEPHALARTOS (Zamiaceae)
natalensis   LPal

ENCHYLAENA (Chenopodiaceae)
¶ *tomentosa*   MFiF

ENDYMION See HYACINTHOIDES

ENGELMANNIA (Asteraceae) See Plant
Deletions

ENKIANTHUS † (Ericaceae)
campanulatus ♀   Widely available
– var. *campanulatus* f.   CWSG ELan GGGa MAsh
  albiflorus   MBal MBri SMur SPer SSpi
– var. *palibinii*   CGre GAri GGGa LRHS MAsh
     MBal MGos SSpi SSta WBrE
     WNor WWat
– 'Red Bells'   CAbP CBlo COtt CPMA
     CWSG EPfP GOrc MBri NHed
     SSpi SSta SSto WWeb
– var. *sikokianus*   CFai CWSG GAri GGGa
* – 'Variegatus'   LRHS
cernuus var. *matsudae*   GAri
– f. *rubens* ♀   CB&S GAri GGGa MAsh MBal
     MBri SSpi SSta WNor WWat
     WWeb
chinensis   ELan EPfP GAri GGGa MAsh
     SPer SSta WNor WWat
deflexus   CFil LRHS MAsh SSta WPGP
perulatus ♀   CFil EMil EPfP GAri LRHS
     MBar SSpi WWes

ENSETE (Musaceae)
§ *ventricosum*   CAbb CBot CHEx EOas LCns
     LPal SAPC SArc WMul
¶ – 'Atropurpureum'   CHEx
¶ – 'Maurelii'   LCns

ENTELEA (Tiliaceae)
arborescens   CHEx ECou

EOMECON (Papaveraceae)
chionantha   CHEx CHid CSam CVer EBrP
     EBre ECha EMar EPla ERos
     GAbr GCal IBlr LBre MRav
     MUlv NGre NSti SBre SMad
     SSpi WCru WFar WGwy WHer
     WOld WWin WWye

EPACRIS (Epacridaceae)
paludosa   GCrs GGGa
petrophila   GCrs GGGa WPat

EPHEDRA (Ephedraceae)
alte   WCot
americana var. *andina*   SAPC SArc
distachya   GPoy NNor WWye
equisetina   EBee
– JJH 920912   EMon

– JJH 9308135	NWCA
fedtschenkoi	EBee WIvy
fragilis	EPla SDry
gerardiana	CNic NHex
– var. *sikkimensis*	EPla SDry WPer
¶ *likiangensis*	EBee
§ *major*	SDry WHer
minima	MTPN NWCA
monosperma	EBee
nebrodensis	See *E. major*
nevadensis	CArn GBin GPoy MSal
przewalskii	EBee
sinica	MSal
viridis	CArn GBin MSal

EPIDENDRUM (Orchidaceae)

radicans	See *E. ibaguense*

EPIGAEA (Ericaceae)

asiatica	MBal
gaultherioides	GGGa MBal
repens	MBal

EPILOBIUM (Onagraceae)

§ *angustifolium*	CGle CKin GBar NNrd SWat WHer
§ – var. *album*	CBot CBre CElw CGle CHad CMea CSpe ECha EEls ELan EPot GAbr GCal LBlm LHol MBri MCLN MRav NCat NHex SAxl SWat WCHb WCla WEas WHal WHer WPer WSHC WWat
– 'Isobel'	CSpe LFis MAvo MRav NHex WAbb WBay WCot
– f. *leucanthum*	See *E. angustifolium album*
– 'Stahl Rose'	CBot EMon EWes GCal LGre MAvo NHex SMrm SWat WCot WSHC
californicum Haussknecht	See *Zauschneria californica* subsp. *angustifolia*
– hort.	See *Zauschneria californica*
canum	See *Zauschneria californica* subsp. *cana*
§ *chlorifolium*	WOMN
– var. *kaikourense*	See *E. chlorifolium*
crassum	CPBP EBar GBuc NWoo WWin
§ *dodonaei*	CGle EBee EMan LFis LHol MLLN MTho WCot WRha WSHC WWin
fleischeri	CLyd EDAr MTho SAga SUsu WCot WSHC
garrettii	See *Zauschneria californica* subsp. *garrettii*
N *glabellum*	CGle CHea CMea CSpe ECha ELan EMan GMac LBee LGre LHop MWat NBir NMen SAga SPer SUsu WAbe WEas WOve WWin
– 'Sulphureum'	CNic EBee GCra GMaP NChi
hirsutum	CKin SWat WCla
– *album*	NSti WAlt
¶ – 'Caerphilly Castle' (d)	WAlt
– *roseum*	WRha
–'Well Creek' (v)	CElw ECha EMan EMar LFis MAvo MLLN SWat WCot WPbr WPer
latifolium	NGre
luteum	WCla
microphyllum	See *Zauschneria californica* subsp. *cana*
montanum	CKin
– variegated	CNat WAlt
obcordatum	CLTr LHop NWCA SBla SSca
rosmarinifolium	See *E. dodonaei*
* *spathulifolium*	LHop
tasmanicum	WHer
villosum	See *Zauschneria californica* subsp. *mexicana*
wilsonii hort.	See *E. chlorifolium*

EPIMEDIUM † (Berberidaceae)

acuminatum	CBos CElw CFil CLAP CVer EBee EFEx GLil LGre SChu WAbe WPGP
– L 575	CLon CRDP MSte SBla SSpi WAbe
¶ 'Akakage'	GLil
¶ 'Akebono'	GLil
alpinum	CMGP EMon EPar GBuc MBal NHol SAxl SMac SPer WPbr
Asiatic hybrids	SChu SWas WPbr
'Beni-chidori'	GLil
'Beni-kujaku'	GBuc GLil
¶ *brevicornu* Og 88010	SBla
¶ – f. *rotundatum* Og 82010	SBla
x *cantabrigiense*	CBlo CVer EBrP EBre ECro ECtt EOrc EPla GCHN GDra GLil LBre MBal MBri MBro MRav MUlv NHol NRoo SBre SMac SPer WAbe WCru WHow WPbr WWeb
cremeum	See *E. grandiflorum* subsp. *koreanum*
davidii	CRDP ECha GBri MBro MSte SSpi WAbe WHal WPbr
– EMR 4125	CElw CLAP SAga SBla
diphyllum	CBos CRDP EMon LGre NDov SAga SBla SWas WHal WPbr
– dwarf white	GLil
dolichostemon	CBos SBla SWas WAbe
¶ – Og 81010	SBla
elongatum	WPbr
'Enchantress'	CBos ECha GBuc NRoo SSpi SWas WHal WPbr
fangii Og 81.007	SBla
¶ *flavum* Og 92036	SBla
franchetii 'Brimstone Butterfly' Og 87.001	SBla
¶ 'Genpei'	GLil
§ *grandiflorum* ♀	CFis CHan CLTr CTri ECha EGar ELan EOrc EPar EPot GAbr GDra MBal MBri MBro NBir NHar NMen NWoo SAga SBla SMac SPer SWas WCru WFar WPbr WRus
– 'Album'	CLAP EPot
– var. *coelestre*	GLil
– 'Crimson Beauty'	CLAP ECha GBuc LGre SAga SChu WCru WHal
– 'Elfenkönigin'	LRHS WAbe
– 'Koji'	WPbr
§ – subsp. *koreanum*	CFil CLAP CLon CRDP EFEx GLil LGre MBro NDov NHar SAxl SBla WAbe WPGP
– lilac seedling	CHad CRDP LGre SAxl SWas WFar
¶ – 'Lilacinum'	SBla
– 'Lilafee'	Widely available
– 'Mount Kitadake'	GLil SSpi SWas
– 'Nanum' ♀	CGra CMil CRDP EHyt EPot LGre NHar NTow SBla SChu SWas WAbe WCru WLin

– 'Rose Queen' ♀   CBos CHan CLTr CM&M CMil
CVer EBrP EBre EHyt EPPr
EPar GBuc GGar LBre LFis
LGre NRoo SBla SBre SChu
SMac SSpi SVil SWas WWeb
§ – 'Roseum'   CLAP EBrP EBre GBri LBre
NTow SBre WWeb
¶ – 'Rubinkrone'   EBee NHol
– 'Shikinomai'   SWas WPbr
– f. *violaceum*   CFir CLAP CLTr SBla SChu
WAbe
– 'White Queen' ♀   CFir CLon CRDP CVer GLil
LGre NOak SBla SMac SSpi
SWas WAbe WPbr
'Kaguyahime'   SBla
¶ *latisepalum* Og 91002   SBla
leptorrhizum   EMon NBrk SBla WAbe
– Og Y 44   CRDP EHyt SAga SSpi SWas
¶ 'Little Shrimp'   MBro WPat
macranthum   See *E. grandiflorum*
membranaceum   GLil WAbe WPbr
ogisui Og 91.001   SBla
× *omeiense*   SBla WBcn
pauciflorum Og 92.123   SBla
× *perralchicum* ♀   CBro EMon EPot GBuc GMaP
MBal MBel NFla NRoo SChu
SLPl SSON SSpi WFox WPGP
WRus WSHC
– 'Frohnleiten'   Widely available
– 'Wisley'   MBro SBla
perralderianum   CFil CSam EBrP EBre EFou
ELan ENot LBre LGan LGro
MBal MBro MFir MRav NHar
SBla SBre SCro SOkh SPer
SRms SSpi WAbe WCru WHen
WHow WLin WPbr WWin
pinnatum   CDoC GMaP MSta WHal WOld
§ – subsp. *colchicum* ♀   Widely available
¶ – – 'Black Sea'   GLil
– – L 321   SBla
– *elegans*   See *E. pinnatum* subsp.
colchicum
¶ *platypetalum* Og 93085   SBla
pubescens Og 91.003   SBla
pubigerum   CBlo EBee ECha EGar EGle
GAbr GLil MAus MBal MWgw
NHol NPri WPbr WPrP
¶ *rhizomatosum* Og 92114   SBla
× *rubrum* ♀   Widely available
sagittatum   EFEx GLil WPbr
'Sasaki'   GBuc GLil
¶ *sempervirens*   SBla
setosum   CElw CFil ECha MSte SBla
SMac SSpi SWas WAbe WPbr
¶ 'Shiho'   GLil
¶ 'Sohayaki'   GLil
stellulatum 'Wudang Star' SBla
L 1193
'Sunset'   GLil
'Tamabotan'   GBuc GLil
× *versicolor*   CBlo MBal WFox
– 'Cupreum'   SMac SSpi
– 'Neosulphureum'   CBro CLAP EMon SMac SSpi
WHil
– 'Sulphureum' ♀   Widely available
– 'Versicolor'   LGre NHar SBla SWas
× *warleyense*   Widely available
– 'Orangekönigin'   EBee EPar GBuc LBuc MAus
MBel MMil NSti SPla SWas
WHil WPbr WWeb
¶ *wushanense* 'Caramel'   SBla
Og 92009

× *youngianum*   CB&S EGle EPot SBla
– 'Lilacinum'   See *E.* × *youngianum* 'Roseum'
– 'Merlin'   CBos CFir ECha EHyt GLil
SBla SChu SWas WAbe WSan
– 'Niveum' ♀   Widely available
§ – 'Roseum'   CLon CRDP EFou EMan EMil
EPar ERos GAbr GLil MBal
MBri MUlv NHar NPri NSti
NTow SBla SMac SMad SOkh
SPer WAbe WPbr WRHF
WRus
– 'Typicum'   CLon WAbe
– white seedling   EHyt

EPIPACTIS (Orchidaceae)

gigantea   CAvo CBos CBro CFee CFil
ECha EHyt ELan EPar EPot
ERos MBal MHig MS&S MTho
NHar SBla SWes WAbe WChe
WCru
* – 'Serpentine Night'   IBlr
helleborine   SSpi WUnd
* g. *Lowland Legacy*   SWes
'Edelstein'
* – 'Frankfurt'   SWes
palustris   EDAr EHyt NHar SWes WChe
WCot WHer
¶ 'Renate'   SWes
* g. *Sabine* 'Frankfurt'   SWes
thunbergii   EFEx

EPIPREMNUM (Araceae)

§ *aureum* ♀   CHal EBak LBlo MBri
– 'Marble Queen' (v)   CHal
§ *pinnatum*   MBri

EPISCIA (Gesneriaceae)

§ *dianthiflora*   CHal MBri SRms WDib
* 'Iris August'   MBri
* *primeria*   MBri
* 'San Miguel'   CHal MBri WDib

EQUISETUM † (Equisetaceae)

arvense   MSal
'Bandit'   EMon
¶ × *bowmanii*   CNat
camtschatcense   SMad WHil
giganteum   CNat
hyemale   CHEx CNat EBrP EBre EPla
LBre MCCP SBre WChe
§ – var. *affine*   CNat ELan EPla WPbr
– var. *robustum*   See *E. hyemale* var. *affine*
¶ *ramosissimum* var.   EMFW MCCP WChe WWeb
japonicum
scirpoides   CInt EBrP EBre EMFW LBre
MCCP SBre WMAq WWeb
sylvaticum   CNat

ERAGROSTIS (Poaceae)

♦ *abyssinica*   See *E. tef*
¶ *capensis*   EBee EWes
chloromelas   CMHG
curvula   CElw CInt CSpe ECGN ECha
EHoe EMon EPPr ESOG GBin
MAvo MCCP SUsu WCot WPic
– S&SH 10   CCuc CHan CRDP NLak
§ *tef*   LIck
trichodes   GBin WPer

ERANTHEMUM (Acanthaceae)

¶ *pulchellum*   LHil

ERANTHIS (Ranunculaceae)
§ *hyemalis* ♀   CBro CMea ELan EMon EPar
     EPot ETub EWFC LAma MBri
     MBro MHew MHlr NRog
     WMaN WOMN WRHF WShi
§ *hyemalis* Cilicica Group   CBro CMea EMon EPar EPot
     ERav LAma NRog
§ – Tubergenii Group   EPot
– – 'Guinea Gold' ♀   EHyt
¶ *pinnatifida*   EFEx

ERCILLA (Phytolaccaceae)
volubilis   CAbb CFee CGre CPlN CPle
     CSam ERav ETen GOrc LHop
     MAll WCot WCru WPic WSHC

EREMAEA (Myrtaceae)
beaufortioides   SOWG
pauciflora   SOWG

EREMURUS (Asphodelaceae)
§ *aitchisonii*   LAma
¶ – 'Albus'   WCot
* 'Brutus'   CMea LAma MMHG
bungei   See *E. stenophyllus* subsp.
     stenophyllus
elwesii   See *E. aitchisonii*
himalaicus   CBot ELan EPar ETub GBur
     LAma LBow NEgg SAga SCoo
     SMad SPer SUsu WPyg
× *isabellinus* 'Cleopatra'   CBot CMea CSWP GBur
     GCHN LAma LBow LRHS
     MCli MLLN MMHG NHol
     NPSI WCot WPGP
– 'Pinokkio'   ETub GBur LAma WPyg
– Ruiter hybrids   CBlo CSWP EBee ECot ELan
     EMan EPar EPfP GBur LAma
     MLLN NFla SCro SPer WBro
     WViv
– Shelford hybrids   CB&S CBlo ELan EPfP LAma
     LBow MLLN MMHG MNrw
     NOak SDeJ WSan
'Moneymaker'   GBur LAma
'Oase'   EBee ELan GBur LBow
'Obelisk'   CMea EHic LBow LRHS NPla
robustus   CB&S CBot CHEx EPar ETub
     LAma LBow LFis NRog SIgm
     SMad SPer WCot WPyg
¶ – pink   NPSI
¶ 'Romance'   LBow
stenophyllus   CBro NFai NHol WPGP WSan
     WWeb
– subsp. *aurantiacus*   LFis
§ – subsp. *stenophyllus*   CMea ELan EOld EPar EPfP
     ETub GBur LAma LBow
     MCLN MLLN MNrw NEgg
     NFla NNor NOak NRog SMad
     SPer WCot WPyg

ERIANTHUS See SACCHARUM

ERICA † (Ericaceae)
arborea   CNCN CTrG MBal SAPC SArc
     SHBN
§ – 'Albert's Gold' ♀   CB&S CNCN CTrC EBrP EBre
     EDen ELan EPfP GChr IOrc
     LBre MAsh MBal MBar MBri
     MOke NHol SAga SBod SBre
     SPla

– var. *alpina* ♀   CMac CNCN EDen ENot IOrc
     MBal MBar MGos NHar SBod
     SDys SPar SPer SReu SSta
     WWat
* – 'Arbora Gold'   See *E. arborea* 'Albert's Gold'
– 'Arnold's Gold'   See *E. arborea* 'Albert's Gold'
– 'Estrella Gold' ♀   CDoC CNCN EBrP EBre EDen
     ELan LBre MAsh MBal MBar
     NHar NHol SBod SBre SPer
     SPla SSta SVil WStI
¶ – 'Picos Pygmy'   SDys
– 'Spring Smile'   EDen
australis ♀   CB&S ELan MBar SHBN
– 'Castellar Blush'   CNCN EDen MAsh NHol
– 'Holehird'   EDen
– 'Mr Robert' ♀   CNCN EDen ELan EPfP LRHS
     MBar SBod
– 'Riverslea' ♀   CNCN EDen GAri IOrc MAsh
     MBal MBar MOke NHol SBod
     SPer
bauera   EDen
canaliculata ♀   CB&S CGre EDen EPfP MBal
     SBod
carnea 'Accent'   EDen
– 'Adrienne Duncan' ♀   CNCN COCH EDen MBar
     MBri MOke NHed NHol NRoo
     SBod
– 'Alan Coates'   CNCN COCH EDen MBar
– 'Alba'   COCH EDen
– 'Altadena'   CNCN COCH EDen MBar
– 'Amy Doncaster'   See *E. carnea* 'Treasure Trove'
– 'Ann Sparkes' ♀   CMac CNCN COCH EBrP
     EBre EDen GChr LBre LGro
     MBar MBri MGos MOke MWat
     NHol SBod SBre SPla
– 'Atrorubra'   CMac CNCN COCH EDen
     MBar NHol
– 'Aurea'   CB&S CMac CNCN COCH
     EDen LGro MBar MBri MOke
     MPla NHed NHol SBod
– 'Barry Sellers'   COCH EDen LRHS NHol
– 'Bell's Extra Special'   COCH ECho EDen
– 'Beoley Pink'   CNCN COCH EDen SBod
– 'C.J. Backhouse'   COCH EDen
– 'Carnea'   CNCN COCH EDen MBar
     MOke NHol
– 'Catherine'   EDen
– 'Cecilia M. Beale'   CNCN COCH EDen MBar
     NHol
– 'Challenger' ♀   CNCN COCH EBrP EBre
     EDen LBre MBar MBri MGos
     NHol NRoo SBod SBre
– 'Christine Fletcher'   COCH EDen
– 'Clare Wilkinson'   CNCN COCH EDen
– 'David's Seedling'   COCH EDen
– 'December Red'   CB&S CMac CNCN COCH
     EBrP EBre EDen LBre MBar
     MBri MOke MWat NHol SBod
     SBre SPla
– 'Dommesmoen'   EDen
– 'Early Red'   COCH EDen
– 'Eileen Porter'   CMac CNCN EDen GDra MBar
– 'Foxhollow' ♀   CNCN COCH EBrP EBre
     EDen ENot GChr GDra LBre
     LGro MBar MBri MGos MOke
     MPla MWat NHar NHol NRoo
     SBod SBre SHBN
– 'Foxhollow Fairy'   CB&S CNCN COCH EDen
     MBar SRms
¶ – 'Gelber Findling'   COCH EDen

– 'Golden Starlet' ♀	CMac CNCN COCH EBrP EBre EDen LBre LGro MBar NHol SBre SPla
– 'Gracilis'	ECho EDen MBar NHed NHol
– 'Heathwood'	CB&S CNCN COCH EDen ENot MBar NHol SBod SRms
– 'Hilletje'	CNCN COCH EDen NHol
– 'Ice Princess'	CNCN COCH EDen NHol
– 'Isabell'	CNCN EDen LRHS
– 'Jack Stitt'	COCH EDen MBar
– 'James Backhouse'	CMac CNCN ECho EDen NHed NHol
– 'January Sun'	COCH EDen NHol
– 'Jason Attwater'	EDen
– 'Jean'	CNCN EDen LRHS NHol
– 'Jennifer Anne'	CNCN COCH EDen MBar
– 'John Kampa'	CNCN COCH EDen MBar NHol NRoo
– 'John Pook'	MGos
– 'King George'	CMac CNCN COCH CTri EBrP EBre EDen GChr LBre MBar MGos MWat NHar NHol NRoo SBod SBre SHBN SPla
– 'Lake Garda'	COCH EDen NHol
– 'Late Pink'	COCH EDen
– 'Lesley Sparkes'	COCH EDen MBar
– 'Little Peter'	COCH EDen
– 'Lohse's Rubin'	COCH ECho EDen NHed
– 'Loughrigg' ♀	CMac CNCN COCH CTri EDen GDra MBar MGos MOke NHol NRoo SBod WStI
– 'March Seedling'	CB&S CNCN COCH EBrP EBre EDen GDra LBre MBar MBri MGos MOke MPla NHol SBod SBre WStI
– 'Margery Frearson'	EDen
– 'Martin'	COCH EDen
¶ – 'Moonlight'	EDen
– 'Mrs Sam Doncaster'	CNCN COCH ECho EDen MBar SBod
– 'Myretoun Ruby' ♀	CB&S CMac CNCN COCH EBrP EBre EDen ENot GDra LBre LGro MBar MBri MGos MOke MPla MWat NHar NHed NHol NRoo SBod SBre SHBN
– 'Nathalie'	CNCN ECho EDen LRHS
– 'Orient'	COCH EDen
– 'Pallida'	COCH EDen
– 'Pink Beauty'	See *E. carnea* 'Pink Pearl'
– 'Pink Cloud'	CNCN COCH EDen
– 'Pink Mist'	COCH EDen LRHS
§ – 'Pink Pearl'	CNCN COCH EDen MBar
– 'Pink Spangles' ♀	CB&S CMac CNCN COCH EBrP EBre EDen GChr GDra LBre LGro MBar MBri MGos MOke MPla NHol NRoo SBod SBre
– 'Pirbright Rose'	CNCN COCH ECho EDen MPla SBod
– 'Polden Pride'	COCH EDen
– 'Porter's Red'	COCH ECho EDen LRHS MBar
– 'Praecox Rubra' ♀	CB&S CNCN COCH EDen GDra LGro MBar MGos MOke NHol
– 'Prince of Wales'	CNCN COCH ECho EDen NHol
– 'Queen Mary'	CNCN ECho EDen SBod
– 'Queen of Spain'	CNCN COCH EDen MBri MOke
– 'R.B. Cooke' ♀	CNCN COCH EDen MBar MBri SBod

– 'Red Rover'	COCH EDen
– 'Robert Jan'	EDen
– 'Rosalie'	CNCN EDen LRHS NHol
– 'Rosalinde Schorn'	COCH EDen NHol
– 'Rosantha'	CNCN EDen NHol
– 'Rosea'	ECho EDen
– 'Rosy Gem'	CNCN ECho EDen MBar
– 'Rosy Morn'	COCH EDen
– 'Rotes Juwel'	CNCN ECho EDen LRHS
– 'Rubinteppich'	CNCN COCH EDen SBod
– 'Rubra'	EDen
– 'Ruby Glow'	CNCN COCH CTri EDen ENot MBar MOke NHed NHol
– 'Scatterley'	EDen
– 'Schatzalp'	EDen
– 'Schneekuppe'	CNCN COCH EDen NHol
– 'Schneesturm'	COCH EDen
§ – 'Sherwood Creeping'	EDen MBar
– 'Sherwoodii'	See *E. carnea* 'Sherwood Creeping'
– 'Smarts Heath'	CNCN COCH ECho EDen NHol
– 'Snow Queen'	CNCN COCH EDen MBar NRoo SBod
– 'Spring Cottage Crimson'	COCH EDen MBar
– 'Spring Day'	EDen
– 'Springwood Pink'	CMac CNCN COCH CTri EDen GDra LGro MBar MBri MGos MOke MPla MWat NHol SBod SHBN
– 'Springwood White' ♀	CB&S CMac CNCN COCH EBrP EBre EDen ENot GDra LBre LGro MBar MBri MGos MOke MPla MWat NHar NHol SBod SBre SHBN
– 'Startler'	COCH EDen LRHS MBar NHol SBod SPla
– 'Sunshine Rambler' ♀	CNCN COCH EDen MBar MGos NHol
– 'Thomas Kingscote'	CNCN COCH EDen MBar
§ – 'Treasure Trove'	CMac COCH EDen NHol
– 'Tybesta Gold'	CNCN COCH EDen NHol
– 'Urville'	See *E. carnea* 'Vivellii'
– 'Viking'	CNCN COCH EDen NHol NRoo
§ – 'Vivellii' ♀	CMac CNCN COCH CTri EBrP EBre EDen ENot GDra LBre MBar MBri MOke MPla MWat NHar NHed NHol SBod SBre
– 'Vivellii Aurea'	COCH EDen
– 'Walter Reisert'	CNCN COCH EDen
– 'Wanda'	COCH EDen MBar
– 'Wentwood Red'	COCH EDen
– 'Westwood Yellow' ♀	CMac CNCN COCH EBrP EBre EDen LBre LGro MBar MBri NHar NHol SBod SBre SPla
– 'White Glow'	CMac ECho
– 'White March Seedling'	EDen
– 'Whitehall'	EDen LRHS NHol
– 'Winter Beauty'	CNCN COCH EDen MOke MPla NHed NHol
– 'Winter Gold'	COCH EDen
– 'Winter Melody'	EDen
¶ – 'Winter Rubin'	EDen
– 'Winter Snow'	ECho EDen
¶ – 'Winterfreude'	EDen NHol
– 'Wintersonne'	ECho EDen LGro NHol
ciliaris alba	EDen
– 'Aurea'	CMac CNCN EDen MBar SRms
– 'Camla'	EDen MBar

– 'Corfe Castle' ♀	CNCN EDen MBar SBod	– 'Foxhollow Mahogany'	EDen MBal MBar
– 'David McClintock' ♀	CNCN EDen GChr MBar	– 'Frances'	EDen
	MGos	– 'Fred Corston'	EDen
– 'Globosa'	ECho EDen GChr	– 'G. Osmond'	EDen MBar MOke
– 'Maweana'	EDen	– 'Glasnevin Red'	EDen MBar NHar
– 'Mrs C.H. Gill' ♀	CMac CNCN EDen GChr	– 'Glencairn'	EDen MBar NHol
– 'Ram'	EDen	– 'Godrevy'	EDen SBod
– 'Rotundiflora'	EDen	– 'Golden Charm'	CMac CNCN ECho EDen GChr
– 'Stapehill'	EDen		NHol
– 'Stoborough' ♀	CNCN EDen MBar	– 'Golden Drop'	CNCN EDen GChr MBar MBri
– 'White Wings'	CNCN EDen		MGos MOke NHol SBod
– 'Wych'	EDen	– 'Golden Hue' ♀	CB&S CMac CNCN EDen
cinerea 'Alba Major'	CNCN ECho EDen MBar		MBar MOke NHed NHol
– 'Alba Minor' ♀	CNCN EBrP EBre EDen LBre	– 'Golden Sport'	ECho EDen MGos NHar
	MBar MBri.MOke NHar NHol	– 'Golden Tee'	EDen
	SBod SBre	– 'Graham Thomas'	See *E. cinerea* 'C.G. Best'
– 'Alette'	EDen	– 'Grandiflora'	EDen MBar
– 'Alfred Bowerman'	EDen	– 'Guernsey Lime'	EDen MBar
– 'Alice Anne Davies'	EDen	– 'Guernsey Pink'	EDen
– 'Angarrack'	EDen	– 'Guernsey Plum'	EDen
– 'Anja Blum'	EDen	– 'Guernsey Purple'	EDen
– 'Ann Berry'	CNCN EDen MBar SBod	– 'Hardwick's Rose'	CNCN EDen MBar
– 'Apple Blossom'	EDen	– 'Harry Fulcher'	CNCN EDen MBri MOke
– 'Apricot Charm'	CNCN EDen MBar SBod	– 'Heatherbank'	EDen
– 'Aquarel'	EDen	– 'Heathfield'	EDen
– 'Ashdown Forest'	EDen	– 'Heidebrand'	EDen MBar
– 'Ashgarth Garnet'	EDen MBar	– 'Hermann Dijkhuizen'	EDen
– 'Atropurpurea'	CNCN ECho EDen MBar	– 'Honeymoon'	EDen MBar
	NHed	– 'Hookstone Lavender'	EDen
– 'Atrorubens'	EDen MBar NHar SRms	– 'Hookstone White' ♀	CNCN EBrP EBre EDen GDra
– 'Atrorubens, Daisy Hill'	EDen		LBre MBar NHed SBre
– 'Atrosanguinea'	CNCN MBar MGos SBod	– 'Hutton's Seedling'	EDen
– 'Atrosanguinea Reuthe's	ECho EDen	– 'Iberian Beauty'	EDen
Variety'		– 'Jack London'	CNCN EDen
– 'Atrosanguinea Smith's	ECho EDen	– 'Janet'	ECho EDen MBar MGos
Variety'		– 'Jersey Wonder'	EDen
– 'Baylay's Variety'	EDen MBar	– 'Jim Hardy'	EDen
– 'Blossom Time'	EDen MBar	– 'John Ardron'	EDen SBod
– 'Brick'	EDen	– 'John Eason'	EDen NHol
– 'Bucklebury Red'	EDen	– 'Joseph Murphy'	CNCN EDen MBar
– 'C.D. Eason' ♀	CNCN EDen GDra MBar MBri	– 'Joseph Rock'	EDen
	MGos MOke NHol SBod	– 'Josephine Ross'	EDen MBar
§ – 'C.G. Best' ♀	CMac CNCN EDen MBar	– 'Joyce Burfitt'	CNCN EDen
– 'Cairn Valley'	EDen	¶ – 'Jubilee'	ECho
– 'Caldy Island'	EDen MBar	– 'Katinka'	CNCN EDen MBar NHol
– 'Carnea'	EDen	– 'Kerry Cherry'	EDen
– 'Carnea Underwood's	EDen	– 'Knap Hill Pink' ♀	CNCN ECho EDen MBar
Variety'		– 'Lady Skelton'	EDen MBar
– 'Celebration'	ECho EDen	– 'Lavender Lady'	EDen
– 'Cevennes' ♀	CNCN EDen MBar MGos	– 'Lilac Time'	ECho EDen MBar
	MOke SBod	– 'Lilacina'	ECho EDen MBar MOke
– 'Champs Hill'	EDen	– 'Lime Soda'	CMac CNCN EDen MBri
– 'Cindy' ♀	CNCN EDen MBar MOke	– 'Lorna Anne Hutton'	EDen
	NHol	– 'Maginess Pink'	CNCN
– 'Coccinea'	CNCN ECho EDen	– 'Marina'	EDen
– 'Colligan Bridge'	EDen MBar	– 'Michael Hugo'	CNCN EDen
– 'Constance'	EDen MBar	– 'Miss Waters'	EDen MBar
– 'Contrast'	EDen LRHS MBar	– 'Mrs Dill'	ECho EDen MBar
– 'Daphne Maginess'	CNCN	– 'Mrs E.A. Mitchell'	CNCN EDen LRHS MGos
– 'Discovery'	EDen		MOke
– 'Doctor Small's	EDen	– 'Mrs Ford'	EDen MBar
Seedling'		– 'My Love'	CNCN EDen MBar MBri MOke
– 'Domino'	CNCN EDen MBar MGos	– 'Nell'	EDen MBar
	MOke	– 'Nellie Dawson'	EDen
– 'Duncan Fraser'	CNCN ECho EDen MBar	– 'Newick Lilac'	EDen MBar MOke
– 'Eden Valley' ♀	CMac CNCN EDen MBar	– 'Next Best'	MBar
	MGos NHol SBod SRms	– 'Novar'	EDen
– 'England'	ECho EDen	– 'Old Rose'	EDen
– 'Felthorpe'	EDen	– 'P.S. Patrick' ♀	CNCN EDen MBar MGos
– 'Fiddler's Gold' ♀	CNCN EDen GAri MBar MBri	– 'Pallas'	EDen
	MOke NHar NHed NHol	– 'Pallida'	EDen
– 'Flamingo'	EDen	– 'Patricia Maginess'	CNCN

– 'Peñaz'	EDen
– 'Pentreath' 🏆	CNCN EDen MBar MBri MOke
– 'Pink Foam'	EDen MBar
– 'Pink Ice' 🏆	CB&S CMac CNCN EBrP EBre EDen GDra LBre MBar MBri MGos MOke NHar NHed NHol SBod SBre
– 'Plummer's Seedling'	EDen MBar
– 'Prostrate Lavender'	EDen
– 'Providence'	EDen LRHS
– 'Purple Beauty'	CB&S CNCN EDen MBar MGos MOke
– 'Purple Robe'	ECho EDen LRHS
– 'Purple Spreader'	EDen
– 'Purpurea'	EDen
– 'Pygmaea'	EDen MBar
– 'Red Pentreath'	EDen
– 'Rijneveld'	EDen
– 'Robert Michael'	EDen
– 'Rock Pool'	EDen MBar NHol
– 'Rock Ruth'	EDen
– 'Romiley'	EDen MBar MBri MOke
– 'Rosabella'	CNCN EDen MBar
– 'Rose Queen'	ECho EDen
– 'Rosea'	EDen
* – 'Rosea Splendens'	EDen
– 'Rozanne Waterer'	EDen
– 'Ruby'	CMac CNCN EDen MBar
– 'Sandpit Hill'	EDen MBar
– 'Schizopetala'	CNCN EDen MBar
– 'Sea Foam'	CNCN EDen MBar
– 'Sherry'	CNCN EDen MBar
– 'Smith's Lawn'	EDen
– 'Snow Cream'	EDen MBar
– 'Son of Cevennes'	MGos
– 'Spicata'	EDen
– 'Splendens'	CNCN EDen
– 'Startler'	CB&S EDen MBri MOke
– 'Stephen Davis' 🏆	CNCN EBrP EBre EDen LBre MBar MBri MOke NHol SBod SBre
¶ – 'Steven Leitch'	ECho
* – 'Strawberry'	EDen
– 'Sue Lloyd'	EDen
– 'Summer Gold'	CNCN EBrP EBre ECho EDen LBre LRHS NHed SBre
– 'Tilford'	EDen
– 'Tom Waterer'	EDen MBar
– 'Uschie Ziehmann'	EDen
– 'Velvet Night' 🏆	CB&S CMac CNCN EDen MBar MBri MOke NHar NHol SBod SRms
– 'Victoria'	EDen MBar
– 'Violetta'	CNCN EDen
– 'Vivienne Patricia'	EDen MBar
– 'W.G. Notley'	EDen
– 'West End'	EDen
– 'White Dale'	ECho EDen MBar
– 'Windlebrooke' 🏆	CNCN EDen MBar NHol SBod
– 'Wine'	EDen
– 'Yvonne'	ECho EDen
cruenta	EDen
curviflora	EDen
× *darleyensis* 'Ada S. Collings'	CNCN COCH EBrP EBre EDen LBre MBar MPla NRoo SBod SBre SHBN SPla
– 'Alba'	See *E.* × *darleyensis* 'Silberschmelze'
– 'Archie Graham'	COCH EDen
§ – 'Arthur Johnson' 🏆	CB&S CMac CNCN COCH EBrP EBre EDen LBre MBar MBri MGos MOke MPla NHol SBod SBre SHBN SPla SRms
– 'Cherry Stevens'	See *E.* × *darleyensis* 'Furzey'
§ – 'Darley Dale'	CMac CNCN COCH EBrP EBre EDen LBre MBar MBri MOke MPla NHol SBod SBre
– 'Dunreggan'	COCH EDen
– 'Dunwood Splendour'	See *E.* × *darleyensis* 'Arthur Johnson'
– 'Epe'	COCH EDen
– 'Erecta'	COCH EDen
§ – 'Furzey' 🏆	CB&S CMac CNCN COCH EDen MBar MBri MGos MOke MPla NHar NHed NHol NRoo SBod SHBN SPla SRms
– 'George Rendall'	CB&S CMac CNCN COCH CTri EDen GDra MPla NHol
– 'Ghost Hills' 🏆	CNCN COCH EBrP EBre EDen GDra LBre MBar MOke MPla NHol SBod SBre SHBN
– 'J.W. Porter' 🏆	CNCN COCH EDen MBar MOke NHed SPla
§ – 'Jack H. Brummage'	CMac CNCN COCH CTri EBrP EBre EDen LBre MBar MBri MGos MOke MPla NHar NHol SBod SBre SHBN SPla
– 'James Smith'	COCH EDen MBar
– 'Jenny Porter' 🏆	CMac CNCN COCH EDen MBar MBri MOke
– 'Kramer's Rote' 🏆	CMac CNCN COCH CTri EBrP EBre EDen LBre MBar MBri MGos MOke NHed NHol NRoo SBre SPla
– 'Margaret Porter'	CB&S CMac CNCN COCH EDen MPla SBod
– 'Mary Helen'	CNCN COCH EDen LRHS NHol
– Molten Silver	See *E.* × *darleyensis* 'Silberschmelze'
– 'Mrs Parris' Red'	EDen
– 'Norman R. Webster'	CNCN COCH EDen NRoo
– 'Pink Perfection'	See *E.* × *darleyensis* 'Darley Dale'
§ – 'Silberschmelze'	CB&S CNCN COCH CTri EBrP EBre EDen GDra LBre MBar MBri MGos MOke NHed NHol SBod SBre SHBN SPla
* – 'Silver Bells'	CMac
– 'Spring Surprise'	EDen
– 'W.G. Pine'	COCH EDen
– 'White Glow'	CNCN COCH CTri EDen NHol
– 'White Perfection' 🏆	CNCN COCH EBrP EBre EDen LBre MBar MBri NHol NRoo SBre SPla
discolor	CGre
doliiformis	EDen
§ *erigena*	SHBN
– 'Alba'	CMac COCH EDen MBar
– 'Brian Proudley' 🏆	CNCN COCH EDen MBar SBod
– 'Brightness'	CB&S CNCN COCH EBrP EBre EDen GChr LBre MBar MBri MOke NHar NHed NHol SBod SBre
– 'Coccinea'	COCH EDen
– 'Ewan Jones'	CNCN COCH EDen IOrc MBar
– 'Glauca'	COCH EDen

– 'Golden Lady' ♀	CMac CNCN COCH EBrP EBre EDen LBre MBar MBri MGos MOke NHol SBod SBre SPla
– 'Hibernica'	EDen
– 'Hibernica Alba'	EDen MBar
– 'Irish Dusk' ♀	CNCN COCH EBrP EBre EDen LBre MBar MBri MGos MOke NHar NHol SBod SBre SPla SRms
– 'Irish Salmon' ♀	CMac CNCN COCH EDen GChr MBar NHed SEND
– 'Irish Silver'	COCH EDen MBar MBri
– 'Ivory'	COCH EDen
¶ – 'Maxima'	EDen
– 'Mrs Parris' Lavender'	EDen
– 'Mrs Parris' White'	EDen
– 'Nana'	EDen
– 'Nana Alba'	CNCN COCH EDen MBar
– 'Rosea'	ECho EDen MBar
– 'Rosslare'	EDen
– 'Rubra'	ECho EDen NHed
– 'Superba'	CMac CNCN COCH EDen MBar MGos MOke SBod
– 'W.T. Rackliff' ♀	CB&S CNCN COCH EBrP EBre EDen ENot LBre MBar MBri MGos MOke NHol SBre SHBN SPla SRms
– 'W.T. Rackliff Variegated'	EDen
fontana	EDen
formosa	CGre
glomiflora	CGre
gracilis	CGre ECho EDen
¶ × *griffithsii*	NHol
¶ – 'Ashlea Gold'	EDen
§ – 'Heaven Scent' ♀	CNCN COCH EDen LRHS
§ – 'Valerie Griffiths'	COCH EDen LRHS MBar NHol
♦ 'Heaven Scent'	See *E.* × *griffithsii* **'Heaven Scent'**
hibernica	See *E. erigena*
× *hiemalis*	EDen
¶ × *krameri*	EDen SDys
lusitanica ♀	CB&S CMac CNCN COCH CTrG EDen MAsh MBar SBod
– 'George Hunt'	CDoC CNCN EDen ELan MAsh NHol SBod SPer
* – 'Sheffield Park'	SPer
mackayana subsp. *andevalensis*	EDen
– 'Ann D. Frearson' (d)	CNCN EDen
– 'Doctor Ronald Gray'	CNCN EDen MBar MBri MOke SBod
– 'Donegal'	EDen
– 'Errigal Dusk'	EDen
– 'Galicia'	CNCN EDen
– 'Lawsoniana'	EDen
– 'Maura' (d) ♀	EDen
– 'Plena' (d)	CNCN EDen MBar MOke
– 'Shining Light' ♀	EDen SDys
– 'William M'Calla'	EDen
mammosa	EDen
manipuliflora	MBar
– 'Aldeburgh'	CNCN EDen
¶ – 'Cascade'	EDen
– 'Corfu'	COCH EDen
– 'Don Richards'	COCH EDen
– 'Elegant Spike'	EDen
– 'Ian Cooper'	COCH EDen
– 'Korcula'	COCH EDen

♦ – × *vagans* 'Valerie Griffiths'	See *E.* × *griffithsii* **'Valerie Griffiths'**
♦ – 'Waterfall'	See *E. manipuliflora* **'Cascade'**
mediterranea	See *E. erigena*
¶ *multiflora* 'Formentor'	EDen
× *oldenburgensis* 'Ammerland'	EDen SDys
– 'Oldenburg'	EDen
pageana	EDen
plukenetii	CGre
× *praegeri*	See *E.* × *stuartii*
scoparia subsp. *azorica*	EDen
– subsp. *maderincola* 'Madeira Gold'	EDen
§ – subsp. *scoparia* 'Minima'	EDen MBar
– – 'Pumila'	See *E. scoparia* subsp. *scoparia* **'Minima'**
sparsa	CGre
speciosa	EDen
sphaeroidea	CGre
§ × *stuartii*	MBar SBod
– 'Charles Stuart'	See *E.* × *stuartii* **'Stuartii'**
– 'Connemara'	EDen
– 'Irish Lemon' ♀	CNCN EBrP EBre EDen GDra LBre MBar NHar NHol SBod SBre
– 'Irish Orange'	CNCN EDen MBar NHol SBod
– 'Nacung'	EDen
– 'Pat Turpin'	EDen
§ – 'Stuartii'	CNCN EDen
§ *terminalis* ♀	CNCN COCH EDen ENot IOrc MBar SBod SEND SPer SRms WPic
– *stricta*	See *E. terminalis*
– 'Thelma Woolner'	CMac CNCN COCH EDen MBar
tetralix	CKin SRms WCla
– 'Afternoon'	EDen
– 'Alba'	EDen
– 'Alba Mollis' ♀	CMac CNCN EDen ENot MBar MBri MOke NHar NHol SBod
– 'Alba Praecox'	EDen
– 'Allendale Pink'	EDen
– 'Ardy'	EDen
– 'Bala'	CNCN EDen
– 'Bartinney'	EDen MBar
– 'Con Underwood' ♀	CMac CNCN EBrP EBre EDen GChr LBre MBar MBri MOke NHol SBod SBre SRms
– 'Curled Roundstone'	EDen
– 'Dänemark'	EDen
– 'Daphne Underwood'	EDen
– 'Darleyensis'	EDen
– 'Dee'	EDen
– 'Delta'	EDen MBar
– 'Foxhome'	EDen MBar
– 'George Frazer'	EDen
– 'Hailstones'	EDen MBar
– 'Helma'	EDen
– 'Hookstone Pink'	CNCN EDen MOke NHar SBod SHBN
– 'Humoresque'	EDen
– 'Ken Underwood'	CNCN EDen MBar SHBN
– 'L.E. Underwood'	EDen MBar NHol
– 'Mary Grace'	EDen
– 'Melbury White'	CNCN EDen MBar
– 'Morning Glow'	See *E.* × *watsonii* **'F. White'**
– 'Pink Glow'	EDen
– 'Pink Pepper'	EDen
– 'Pink Star' ♀	CMac CNCN EBrP EBre EDen LBre MBar NHol SBre

– 'Rosea'	EDen
– 'Rubra'	EDen
§ – 'Ruby's Variety'	EDen MBar
– 'Ruby's Velvet'	See *E. tetralix* **'Ruby's Variety'**
– 'Ruth's Gold'	CMac CNCN EDen MBar NHol
– 'Salmon Seedling'	EDen
– 'Silver Bells'	EDen MBar
– 'Stardome'	EDen
– 'Swedish Yellow'	EDen
– 'Terschelling'	EDen
– 'Tina'	CNCN EDen
– 'Trixie'	EDen
– 'White House'	EDen
umbellata	CNCN EDen MBar WAbe
vagans 'Alba Nana'	See *E. vagans* **'Nana'**
– 'Birch Glow' ♀	CNCN EDen NRoo SBod
– 'Carnea'	EDen
– 'Charm'	EDen
¶ – 'Chittendenii'	EDen
– 'Cornish Cream' ♀	CNCN EDen GAri MBar NHol
– 'Cream'	CNCN EDen MOke NHar
– 'Diana Hornibrook'	CNCN EDen MBar MOke NHar SHBN
– 'Diana's Gold'	EDen
– 'Fiddlestone' ♀	CNCN EDen MBar SBod
– 'French White'	CNCN EDen MBar SBod
– 'George Underwood'	EDen MBar
– 'Golden Triumph'	ECho EDen MBar NHol
– 'Grandiflora'	CNCN EDen MBar
– 'Holden Pink'	CNCN EDen MOke NHar SBod
– 'Hookstone Rosea'	EDen MBar
– 'Ida M. Britten'	EDen MBar
– 'J.C. Fletcher'	EDen
– 'Kevernensis Alba' ♀	EDen MBar SBod SRms
– 'Leucantha'	EDen
– 'Lilacina'	CMac CNCN EDen MBar
– 'Lyonesse' ♀	CB&S CMac CNCN EBrP EBre EDen ENot LBre MBar MBri MGos MOke NHol NRoo SBod SBre SRms
– 'Miss Waterer'	EDen MBar
– 'Mrs D.F. Maxwell' ♀	CB&S CMac CNCN EBrP EBre EDen GChr LBre MBar MBri MGos MOke NHar NHol NRoo SBod SBre SRms
– 'Mrs Donaldson'	EDen
§ – 'Nana'	ECho EDen MBar
– 'Pallida'	CNCN EDen
– 'Peach Blossom'	EDen MBar
– 'Pyrenees Pink'	CMac CNCN EDen MBar MOke NHar
– 'Rosea'	ECho EDen
– 'Rubra'	CNCN ECho EDen MBal MBar
– 'Saint Keverne'	CB&S CMac CNCN EDen MBal MBar MGos MOke NHar NHol NRoo SBod
– 'Summertime'	CNCN EDen MBar
– 'Valerie Proudley' ♀	CB&S CMac CNCN EBrP EBre EDen GDra LBre MBar MBri MGos MOke MWat NHar NHol SBod SBre SHBN SRms
– 'Valerie Smith'	EDen
– 'Viridiflora'	CNCN EDen MBar
– 'White Giant'	EDen
– 'White Lady'	ECho EDen MBar
– 'White Rocket'	CNCN EDen MBar
– 'White Spire'	EDen
– 'Yellow John'	CNCN ECho EDen
x *veitchii*	MBal
¶ – 'Brockhill'	SDys
– 'Exeter' ♀	CNCN COCH EBee EDen EPfP GAri MAsh MBar
– 'Gold Tips' ♀	CNCN CTrC EDen MAsh MBal MBar MBri MGos MOke NHar
– 'Pink Joy'	CNCN EDen GAri MAsh MBal MBri MOke NHar
versicolor	CGre
verticillata	EDen SBod
viridescens	CGre EDen
x *watsonii* 'Cherry Turpin'	EDen
– 'Ciliaris Hybrida'	EDen
– 'Dawn' ♀	CNCN EDen GDra MBar MBri NHar NRoo SBod SHBN
– 'Dorothy Metheny'	EDen
§ – 'F. White'	EDen MBar
– 'Gwen'	CNCN EDen MBar
– 'H. Maxwell'	CNCN EDen MBal
– 'Mary'	EDen
– 'Pink Pacific'	EDen
– 'Rachel'	EDen MBal
– 'Truro'	EDen
x *williamsii* 'Cow-y-Jack'	EDen
– 'David Coombe'	EDen
– 'Gold Button'	EDen
– 'Gwavas'	CNCN EDen MBar SBod
– 'Ken Wilson'	EDen SDys
¶ – 'Lizard Downs'	EDen
– 'P.D. Williams' ♀	CNCN ECho EDen MBal MBar

ERIGERON † (Asteraceae)

acer	CKin EWFC MHew WCla WHer
– var. *debilis*	MFos
¶ – HH&K 269A	CHan
'Adria'	GBuc MAvo MMil NLak NRoo SPer WHow
§ *alpinus*	EHol GCHN GTou LBee MOne NGre
'Amity'	EBrP EBre EFou GCHN LBre MMil SBre SMer
aurantiacus	CM&M CSam EBar EHol EPfP LHop MCCP NBro NOak SEas SIng
§ *aureus*	MDHE NMen NSla WAbe WOMN
§ – 'Canary Bird' ♀	EGle EWes MSta NBir NHar SIng SWas WAbe WLin
* 'Azure Beauty'	EPfP LRHS NPro SHel
Azure Fairy	See *E.* **'Azurfee'**
§ 'Azurfee'	CSam EBar ELan ERic GAbr GMaP MCLN NFai NMir NOak NRoo SEas SMer SPer SPla WBea WHen WMer WPer WWin
¶ 'Birch Hybrid'	SIng
Black Sea	See *E.* **'Schwarzes Meer'**
bloomeri	MFos
'Blue Beauty'	SRms
borealis	CSam GCHN
'Charity'	CGle CMGP EFou EGar MMil MRav WLRN
chrysopsidis 'Grand Ridge' ♀	CPBP NWCA SIng WAbe
compactus consimilis	CGra
– NNS 93-252	MFos MRPP
compositus	CGra ELan GAbr GCHN ITim NGre NWCA SRms WPer
§ – var. *discoideus*	EBur EHyt NMen WPer
– var. *glabratus*	MFos
– 'Rocky'	NPri
Darkest of All	See *E.* **'Dunkelste Aller'**

'Dignity' — EBee EFou EJud ELan GCHN LFis MWat NTow NVic SEas SMer SPer SSpe SUsu WCot WEas WViv

'Dimity' — CGle ECha EHic EPPr GMac MBri WAbe WCot WWin

§ 'Dunkelste Aller' ♀ — CGle CSev EAst EBrP EBre ECED EFou EGar ELan EMan ENot GCHN LBre MAus MBri MRav MTis NFla NRoo SBre SHel SPer SRms WBro WMer WMow WWin

¶ *elegantulus* — NSla

* *epirocticus* NS 462 — NWCA

'Felicity' — CElw EFou MBel MMil MWgw SRms

flettii — GCHN WPer WWin

'Foersters Liebling' ♀ — CSev LFis MBri MHlr MNrw MWat NFla NPla NRoo SHel WByw WCot WMer

formosissimus — EBee

'Four Winds' — ECtt ELan EMan EMon EWes GAbr LHop MRav MUlv NMen WMer WPer

from Big Horns — CGra

glaucus — EHol EJud GMaP NCat NVic SMrm SSte WBea WBro WCot WFar WLRN

– 'Albus' — CSev LBee LHop MDHE SMad WMow WPer

– 'Elstead Pink' — CSev CTri NFai SPla WByw WEas WMow WUnu

¶ – pink — NCat

– 'Roseus' — CB&S CHal

howellii — EBee ECha

§ *karvinskianus* ♀ — Widely available

kennedyi alpigenum — MFos
  NS 93-276

leiomerus — CLyd CNic EPot GCrs LBee MHig NTow NWCA WOMN

linearis — CGra MFos NWCA WPat

'Mrs F.H. Beale' — SCro

mucronatus — See *E. karvinskianus*

multiradiatus — NLak WPer

nanus — CLyd NWCA WPat WPer WPyg

¶ *oreganus* — EBee

peregrinus — WPer

philadelphicus — CElw CGle CMil EHic EMan NBir NBro SOkh

Pink Jewel — See *E.* 'Rosa Juwel'

Pink Triumph — See *E.* 'Rosa Triumph'

pinnatisectus — NNrd NWCA WPer

polymorphus — WAbe

'Prosperity' — CGle EFou

pygmaeus — MFos

pyrenaicus hort. — See *E. alpinus*

– Rouy — See *Aster pyrenaeus*

'Quakeress' — CBos CElw CGle CSam EBrP EBre EFou EMan EMon GCHN GMac LBre LGan MAus MBel MRav MTis MUlv NBro NCat NRoo SBre SHel SMer SMrm SSpe WCot WLin WRHF

§ 'Rosa Juwel' — CM&M CSam EBar EFou ENot ERic GAbr GBur GCHN LHop LPVe NBir NBro NMir NOak NRoo SEND SEas SHel SMer SPer SPla SRms WBea WHen WMow WPbr WPer

§ 'Rosa Triumph' — EFou MBel SPla

'Rosenballett' — EBrP EBre LBre MUlv NBrk SBre WFar

'Rotes Meer' — ELan MBri NTow SEas

rotundifolius — See *Bellis rotundifolia*

  'Caerulescens' — 'Caerulescens'

N *salsuginosus* — NOak

§ 'Schneewittchen' — CGle CMGP EAst EBar EBee EFou EGar ELan EMan GMac LHop LRHS MAus MBel MMil MWat NRoo NSti NVic SCro SHel SPla WLRN WMow

'Schöne Blaue' — NBro NPri NRoo

§ 'Schwarzes Meer' — EFou EHal LHop MUlv NRoo SPla WCot WMer

scopulinis — EHyt LBee

simplex — LLew MWat NGre NMen NNrd NSla NTow WOMN

Snow White — See *E.* 'Schneewittchen'

'Sommerabend' — MTed

'Sommerneuschnee' — CDoC ECha NPri SHel

¶ sp. dwarf from Idaho, USA — CGra

sp. from Bald Mountains — NWCA

* 'Spanish Daisy' — EAst

speciosus — SMer

'Strahlenmeer' — EBee LRHS NCat WCot WLRN

trifidus — See *E. compositus* var. *discoideus*

tweedyi — NBro

¶ *unalaschkensis* — EBee

uncialis conjugans — CGra

uniflorus — GBin NNrd

'Unity' — MWat

vagus — WWin

– JCA 8911 — MFos MRPP

'White Quakeress' — CElw EJud GBuc LHil MCLN SLod SOkh WCot WHow WRHF

'Wuppertal' — CBlo CMGP EBee EGar EMan LRHS MMil WLRN

yukonensis — CLyd

ERINACEA (Papilionaceae)

§ *anthyllis* ♀ — MAll SIng

pungens — See *E. anthyllis*

ERINUS (Scrophulariaceae)

alpinus ♀ — CMea EBot ELan ESis EWFC GBur GTou MBal MBro MPla MRPP MWat NBro NGre NHol NNor NRoo SIng WAbe WCla WEas WFar WPer WPyg WWin

– var. *albus* — CBot CLyd CNic GTou MBro MPla NMen NWCA SRms WAbe WCla WHoo WPer WPyg

– 'Dr Hähnle' — CNic EBrP EBre LBre MHig NMen SBre SRms WHoo WPyg

– 'Mrs Charles Boyle' ♀ — MBro SIng WHoo WOld WPyg

* *olivana* — EWes

ERIOBOTRYA (Rosaceae)

deflexa — CHEx EMil

japonica (F) ♀ — CAbb CB&S CBot CGre CHEx CHan EMil ERea ERom GQui LPan SArc SDry SSta WHer WNor WSHC WWat

– 'Benlehr' (F) — ESim

– 'Mrs Cookson' (F) — ESim

ERIOCAPITELLA See ANEMONE

ERIOCEPHALUS (Asteraceae)
africanus　　　WJek

ERIOGONUM (Polygonaceae)
brevicaule var. *nanum*　　NWCA
caespitosum　　CPBP NTow NWCA SIgm
§ – subsp. *douglasii*　　MFos
– – NNS 95-238　　MRPP
¶ – NNS 94-44　　MRPP
douglasii　　See *E. caespitosum* subsp.
　　douglasii
flavum　　WPer
¶ *giganteum*　　MAll
heracleoides minus　　MFos WLin
jamesii　　WPat WPyg
kennedyi subsp.　　WLin
　　alpigenum
– subsp. *austromontanum*　NTow
libertini　　WLin
¶ *lobbii* subsp. *lobbii*　NHol
ochrocephalum　　NHol
ovalifolium　　GCLN NTow NWCA SIgm
¶ – var. *depressum* NNS 94-47 MFos
panguicense alpestre　NHol
rosense　　EHyt
¶ *saxatile*　　WLin
umbellatum　　CHan ECha EPot NHol NTow
　　SIng
* – *haussknechtii*　　NHol WLin
– var. *humistratum*　　CGra NHol WLin
– var. *porteri*　　NWCA WLin
– var. *torreyanum*　　CMea MBro MHig NHol WLin
　　WPat
– subsp. *umbellatum*　　LBee
ursinum　　NHol WLin

ERIOPHORUM (Cyperaceae)
angustifolium　　CBen CWat EHoe EHon
　　EMFW EPPr EPla ESOG
　　GCHN GOrn LPBA MCCP
　　MMoz MSta NDea SWat WChe
　　WHer WMAq WPer WWeb
latifolium　　LPBA MSta WChe
vaginatum　　See *Scirpus fauriei* var.
　　vaginatus

ERIOPHYLLUM (Asteraceae)
lanatum　　CSam EBar ECha EMon GAbr
　　GMaP LGan MWat NCat NGre
　　NVic SBla SChu WEas WFar
　　WWin
¶ – 'Bella'　　NLar
* – 'Pointe'　　GSki MCCP SRms SSca

ERIOSTEMON (Rutaceae)
myoporoides　　ECon LCns

ERITRICHIUM (Boraginaceae)
§ *canum*　　NHol NTow WLin
nanum　　CGra
rupestre　　See *E. canum*
– var. *pectinatum*　　NWCA
strictum　　See *E. canum*

ERODIUM † (Geraniaceae)
absinthioides var.　　EMan GCHN
　　amanum
–　　GCHN LRHS
– blue　　GCHN
§ *acaule*　　GCHN NGre NRog NRoo
　　NTow

alnifolium　　GCHN
balearicum　　See *E.* × *variabile* 'Album'
battandierianum　　GCHN
boissieri　　GCHN
botrys　　SCou
brachycarpum　　GCHN
carvifolium　　CElw CFir GBur GCHN MBri
　　MDHE MHar NChi
§ *castellanum*　　EBee ESis GCHN MTis NBro
　　NRog NRoo NSti SAxl SBla
　　SCou SCro
chamaedryoides　　See *E. reichardii*
§ *cheilanthifolium*　　CSam EPot GCHN GMaP
　　NLak SHBN WMaN
– 'Bidderi'　　MDHE NChi
chrysanthum　　CBot CGle CLyd CMea EFou
　　EHyt ELan EOrc EPot GBur
　　GCHN GCal LGre LHop MTho
　　NHed NRog NRoo NWCA
　　SAga SBla SMrm WAbe WBea
　　WEas WPer WRus WWin
– pink　　CGle EPPr LGre MDHE SMrm
　　SUsu SWas
– *sulphureum*　　WPnn WShe
ciconium　　SCou
cicutarium　　EWFC SCou
§ – subsp. *cicutarium*　GCHN
corsicum　　CGle CNic EBur ELan MDHE
　　MTho NRog WAbe
– 'Album'　　CSam GCHN MDHE MMil
　　WAbe
♦ 'County Park'　　See *E. foetidum* 'County Park'
crinitum　　GCHN
danicum　　SCou
daucoides hort.　　See *E. castellanum*
'Eileen Emmett'　　GCHN MDHE
* 'Elizabeth'　　GCHN
§ *foetidum*　　EGle GCHN LFis MDHE
　　MWat NMen NRog NSla WAbe
　　WCot WOld
§ – 'County Park'　　CElw CMea ECha ECou EDAr
　　EMan EPPr EWes GBur GCHN
　　MDHE MMil MOne NChi
　　NHed NMen NRog NRoo SAga
　　SBla SChu SHBN SIng SMrm
　　SUsu WKif WPnn WRus
– 'Pallidum'　　CHal CSam
– 'Roseum'　　EMan GCal MWat SBla WAbe
　　WPer
* 'Frans Choice'　　MDHE
¶ 'Fran's Delight'　　CMea
N *glandulosum* ♀　　CMea ELan EMan GCHN GCal
　　LBee LHop MBro MOne NRog
　　SAga SBla SIng SRms WBea
　　WEas WKif WPat WPer
gruinum　　ECoo GCHN SRCN WPnn
　　WSan
guicciardii　　EDAr
N *guttatum*　　CGle CHea EMan MPla MWat
　　NMen NTow SAga SRms WAbe
　　WHal WPer WSHC
'Helen'　　GCHN
heteradenum　　See *E. petraeum*
hirtum　　SCou
× *hybridum*　　EGle ELan EPar EWes NRoo
　　WAbe WHal
– hort.　　See *E.* 'Sara Francesca'
hymenodes hort.　　See *E. trifolium*
jahandiezianum　　GCHN
'Julie Ritchie'　　WHoo
'Katherine Joy'　　CNic MDHE NChi NHed NRog
　　SIng

x *kolbianum*	MBro MDHE NChi SWas WHoo WPnn WPyg
– 'Natasha'	ECha ELan EMan EPot EPri EWes GCHN LBee MDHE NHol NMGW NMen NRog SChu SHBN SMrm SWat WFar WKif
'Las Meninas'	CRDP GCHN
¶ x *lindavicum*	WPnn
– 'Charter House'	GCHN WPnn
¶ – pink form	WPnn
macradenum	See *E. glandulosum*
malacoides	GCHN SCou
manescaui	Widely available
– dwarf form	CSpe
◆ 'Merstham Pink'	See *E. foetidum* 'County Park'
moschatum	SCou
– Guitt 88041904	GCHN
munbyanum	GCHN
neuradifolium	GCHN
Guitt 86040601	
'Nunwood Pink'	GCHN MDHE
pelargoniiflorum	CBot CGle CRDP ESis EWes GCHN LFis MTho NBro NChi SAga SCou SRms SWas WEas WHil WOMN WPGP WPnn WPyg WRus WWeb WWin
petraeum subsp. *crispum*	See *E. cheilanthifolium*
– subsp. *glandulosum*	See *E. glandulosum*
◆ – (Gowan) Willdenow	See *E. foetidum*
'Pickering Pink'	GCHN MDHE NMen NRog SIng SWat
pimpinellifolium	GCHN
'Princesse Marion'	GCHN
'Rachel'	GCHN MDHE
recorderi	GCHN
¶ 'Red Eve'	MDHE
§ *reichardii*	CElw ESis LBee MFos MPla MTho NGre NHol NRog SBla SIng SRms SUsu SWat WBea WCla WOMN WPnn
– cultivars	See *E.* x *variabile*
– 'Derek'	ECho
– JR 961	GCHN
– JR 962	GCHN
– JR 963	GCHN
– JR 964	GCHN
* – 'Rubrum'	NHol
¶ 'Rodie'	MDHE
rodiei	GCHN MDHE
romanum	See *E. acaule*
§ *rupestre*	CBot CMea ECho ECtt GBur GCHN MDHE NHed
salzmannii	See *E. cicutarium* subsp. *cicutarium*
§ 'Sara Francesca'	MDHE NSla
saxatile	GCHN
x *sebaceum* 'Polly'	GCHN
¶ 'Spanish Eyes'	MDHE SMrm SWas
'Stephanie'	CElw CFis CInt EGle GCHN LBee MDHE NBir NChi NHol SAsh SHBN
supracanum	See *E. rupestre*
tordylioides	GCHN WHal
trichomanifolium	EWes LBee SAsh WPnn
De Candolle	
◆ – hort.	See *E. cheilanthifolium* , *E. valentinum*
§ *trifolium*	ELan MMil NChi NRoo NSti SIng SSpi SUsu WCru WHal WHoo
– Guitt 85051701	GCHN

– var. *montanum*	GCHN
§ *valentinum*	GCHN NNrd NRog
§ x *variabile*	EHyt
§ – 'Album'	CHea ELan EMNN EPot GBuc GBur GMac LBee MBar MPla MTho NCat NHar NMen NRoo NVic NWCA SBla SHBN SMrm SUsu WAbe WCla WEas WOMN WOld WPat WPer WPnn WWin
– 'Bishop's Form'	ECtt EMNN EPot ESis GBur GMac LFis MBar MBro MHig MPla NBro NGre NHar NHol NMen NNrd NRog NRoo NTow SBla SHBN SRms WHoo WPat
– 'Flore Pleno' (d)	EAst ECtt EDAr EHyt ELan EWes MHig MPla NGre NRog SHBN SHFr SIng WAbe WOld WPer WPnn
– 'Roseum' ♀	CBot ECho ELan EPar MHig NGre NRog NRoo NWCA SHBN SIng SRms WAbe WOld WPer WWin
I 'Westacre Seedling'	EWes
x *wilkommianum*	EDAr NRog

ERPETION See VIOLA

ERUCA (Brassicaceae)

vesicaria subsp. *sativa*	CArn CBod CJew ELau GPoy LHol MChe MGra SIde WHer WJek WOak WSel WWye

ERYNGIUM † (Apiaceae)

§ *agavifolium*	Widely available
alpinum ♀	CB&S CElw CGle ECha EFou ELan EPar GDra GLil GMac MBal MBro MCLN MLLN MTho NBir NChi SIng SPer SWat WEas WHoo WOve WPGP
– 'Amethyst'	CRDP ELan GBuc MBri MCli MTed NLar NTow WMer
– 'Blue Star'	CBot ECGN ELan GCal GCra GSki LGre LHop MTis NCat NRoo NWes SPla SSpi WHoo WPer
– 'Holden Blue'	GCal
– 'Opal'	LRHS MBri
– 'Slieve Donard'	EAst IBlr LFis LRHS SPer
– 'Superbum'	CBot CRDP ECGN GSki NLon NRoo SBla SMad SRms
amethystinum	CBot EBee ECGN ECGP ECha EMan EWes GSki LGre MAvo MBri NChi NLak SChu SIgm SRCN WLRN WPer
biebersteinianum Nevski	See *E. caucasicum*
bourgatii	Widely available
– 'Oxford Blue' ♀	CHan CLon CMea CMil CRDP EPar LGre NTow SSoC SWas WEas WOld
– 'Picos'	CGle LGre SMrm
bromeliifolium hort.	See *E. agavifolium*
caeruleum	EMon EWes MNrw NFai NLak SIng SMad WCot
campestre	CBot EMon NLar SIgm SMad SRCN WPer
§ *caucasicum*	EBee ECGN GBuc NLak
creticum	EHal EWes MAvo NBir NBro
decaisneanum	See *E. pandanifolium*
Delaroux	See *E. proteiflorum*
dichotomum	EMon LGre

– Caeruleum Group	ECro
ebracteatum	CLon EBee GCal SIgm WCot
– var. *poterioides*	SMad
§ *eburneum*	CBot CDoC CHan EBrP EBre
	ECha EHal EMon EWes GBuc
	LBre LFlo MSCN NBro NChi
	NLak SBre SGre WCot WFar
	WPic
¶ *foetidum*	CArn EOHP
¶ 'Forncett Ultra'	EFou EMon
§ *giganteum* ♀	CDec CGle CHad CHan CMHG
	CMea ECha EFou ELan ERav
	LGan LHil LHop MAus MBal
	MHlr MTho MWat NBro NChi
	NRoo NSti NWoo SBla SDix
	WEas WOMN WOld WPGP
	WWeb
– 'Silver Ghost'	EFou EGle EMon SDix SMrm
	SUsu WCot WHal
glaciale	CFil NLak
– JJA 461.000	NWCA SBla
* *horridulum*	CMHG
horridum	EBee EBrP EBre ELan EOas
	EWes GCra LBre MBro MFir
	MNrw NBro NChi NLak SArc
	SBre SIgm SMad WBea WHer
	WWhi WWin
¶ 'Jos Eijking'	MCLN MRav
maritimum	CArn CBot CPou CRDP ECha
	ECoo EGoy LGre SIgm SRCN
	SSpi SWas WCot WSel
Miss Willmott's Ghost	See *E. giganteum*
× *oliverianum* ♀	CMea CRDP CSam ECGN
	ECGP EFou ELan EMan GAbr
	GBuc MAus MAvo MBri MBro
	MCli NRoo SDix SMad SPer
	WByw WMer WWeb
§ *pandanifolium*	CGre CLon CMHG EFou EGle
	EOas ETen EWes GBin GCal
	IBlr LHil NLak SAPC SArc
	SAxl SDix WBrE WCot
paniculatum	See *E. eburneum*
planum	Widely available
– 'Bethlehem'	CLon GCal LBuc WMer WPyg
	WWeb
§ – 'Blauer Zwerg'	CLon EFou GLil MAus SCoo
	SMad SPla WMer WPyg
– 'Blaukappe'	CBot CFir CHar CKel ECGP
	EFou GBri LGre MBro MOne
	NCut NLar WHoo WOve
	WPGP WPyg
– Blue Dwarf	See *E. planum* 'Blauer Zwerg'
– 'Blue Ribbon'	CMGP CRDP EFou EMan
	LBuc SSte
– 'Flüela'	CGle CLon EBee ECro EMan
	EWes GCal GMaP NCat NLak
	SAxl SChu SPla SWat WWal
– 'Seven Seas'	CFir EMar GMaP LHop LRHS
	NLak NRoo SAxl SChu SPla
	SWat WCot WLRN WPer
– 'Silverstone'	EBee GCal GSki LBuc MAus
	NPla NPri
– 'Tetra Petra'	CB&S EFou MCCP WHil WPer
– violet blue	GCal
§ *proteiflorum*	CHan CRDP CSev EMan GBin
	GCal LHop NLak SRms SSpi
	SWat WBro WCot WGle
serra	EWes GBin
sp. CD&R	EWes
¶ sp. RB 94054	NSti
spinalba	CBot GCal GSki LFlo LGan
	NLak NSla WPer
tricuspidatum	CBlo EBee LRHS NLak WPer
× *tripartitum* ♀	Widely available
variifolium	Widely available
yuccifolium	CArn CHEx EBot ECoo EGar
	EMan EMon EOas EWes GCal
	LHil MSCN NChi NLak NSti
	SIgm SMad WWeb
× *zabelii*	CRDP ECGP ECha ELan GCal
	GMac MFir MHlr MLan NBir
	NTow WCot
– 'Donard Variety'	CLon EWll GCal LRHS MAvo
	WMer
– 'Jewel'	CLon
– 'Violetta'	CGle CLon ELan GBuc MBri
	SWat WHoo

ERYSIMUM † (Brassicaceae)

§ *alpestre*	NBro
¶ – J. Jurasek 222/96	MDHE
alpinum hort.	See *E. hieraciifolium*
'Anne Marie'	ELan LFlo MRav SOkh
arenicola var. *torulosum*	See *E. torulosum*
arkansanum	See *E. helveticum*
§ *asperum*	NTow
'Aunt May'	CElw SMrm
'Bowles' Mauve' ♀	Widely available
¶ 'Bowles' Purple'	ISea
'Bowles Yellow'	EHic GBuc NSti SMer
'Bredon' ♀	ECoo ELan EOld GAbr GCHN
	MAsh MRav NBro NPer NSti
	NTow SAga SAxl SUsu WFar
	WKif WRus
'Butterscotch'	CChr CElw CFee CGle CLTr
	CMHG CMil CSam MHig
	MRav NHaw SSvw SUsu WEas
	WMer WWhi
capitatum	CLyd MDHE NMen
'Cheerfulness'	EGar MArl MBri MRav SPla
cheiri	CJew EWFC IBlr LHol SIde
	WCot WEas WHer
N– 'Baden-Powell' (d)	EGar ELan
– 'Bloody Warrior' (d)	CBot CCot CElw CHan ELan
	GBuc GCal GCra MPla MTho
	NPer WEas
– 'Deben'	CBot
– 'Harpur Crewe' (d) ♀	CB&S CBot CFee CGle CMHG
	CSev ELan EPot LHop MBal
	MBri MTho NBro NPer SBla
	SChu SRms SUsu WAbe WEas
	WHoo WPat WPyg WRus
	WWin
– 'Jane's Derision'	CNat
'Chelsea Jacket' ♀	CLTr CM&M ECGP EHic
	EMar GAbr GBri MAus MRav
	NChi NLak SAga WEas WElm
	WMaN WOve WPen WRus
'Chequers'	ELan WPer WRus
concinnum	See *E. suffrutescens*
'Constant Cheer' ♀	CCot CElw CSam CSpe EGoo
	EMar GAbr GBuc GBur GMac
	NCut NFai NPer NSti SAga
	SUsu WEas WKif WOMN WPat
	WPer WRha WRus
cuspidatum	SSte
¶ 'Devon Cream'	WWoo
'Devon Gold'	See *E. 'Plant World Gold'*
'Devon Sunset'	CElw CGle CHan CLyd CPla
	CSam CSpe LFlo MSte NHaw
	SAga SLod SUsu WEas WMaN
	WOMN WPen WRus
'Dorothy Elmhirst'	See *E. 'Mrs L.K. Elmhirst'*
¶ dwarf lemon	WHoo

'Ellen Willmott' WCot WMaN
¶ 'Emm's Variety' NCat
¶ *gelidum* J. Jurasek 220/96 MDHE
* 'Gingernut' NPer
'Glowing Embers' CFis MAsh MBri SOkh SPla
SUsu
'Gold Flame' MWat
'Golden Gem' EHic MDHE NHed WLRN
WPen WPer
'Golden Jubilee' CHal ECho NTow
§ *helveticum* CNic ECoo ESis GBur GCra
GTou NPri NTow SIng SRms
§ *hieraciifolium* CSam MBal NBro WLRN
humile WCot
'Jacob's Jacket' CCot CFee CGle CLTr CMil
EBar EGoo GCHN MSCN
NChi NPer NRoo SAga SChu
WEas WMaN WRus WWin
'John Codrington' CChr CGle CHan CMHG CMil
CSam GBuc GCHN NChi NFai
NPer SAga SAxl SBla SChu
SHBN SUsu WEas WHoo WKif
WLin WPen
'Joseph's Coat' CCot WViv
'Jubilee Gold' ELan SIng
'Julian Orchard' CFis CMil LFlo SAxl SUsu
kotschyanum CLyd EPot LBee MDHE MHig
NMen NPro NRoo NSla NTow
NWCA WAbe
'Lady Roborough' CFis CMil GBuc SMrm
* 'Lewis Hart' MAvo WCot
linifolium CPea EBur ECoo LWak MDHE
SRms WGor
§ – 'Variegatum' CArn CBar CGle CSam EAst
ELan EOrc EPot LFis LHil
LHop MAsh MSCN NPer SAga
SCro SPer WAbe WEas WHil
WHoo
'Miss Hopton' CCot NPer NTow WEas WHil
WLin
'Moonlight' CCot CElw CMHG CSam GBuc
GCHN LBee LWak MRav
MSCN MTho NBrk NBro NChi
NNor NSti SChu SPer WEas
WHil WLin WMaN WOve
WPer
§ 'Mrs L.K. Elmhirst' CElw CHan MBri MGrG MRav
NPer SHel WCot WMaN WOve
mutabile CB&S CCot CInt CLTr CMHG
CTri EOrc GCHN MFir MRav
NBir NBro NSti SSvw SUsu
WEas WMaN WMow
– 'Variegatum' CBot CElw CFis WEas WHoo
'Onslow Seedling' GCHN
'Orange Flame' CMHG CNic ECha ELan EPot
GAbr LBee LHop MBar MHig
MPla MRav NBro NPer NPri
NRoo NTow SChu WPer
perofskianum WEas
Perry's hybrid NPer
'Perry's Peculiar' NPer
'Perry's Pumpkin' MGrG NPer
§ 'Plant World Gold' COtt CPla LRHS
'Plantworld Lemon' COtt CPla EPri LRHS SCoo
'Primrose' GAbr GCHN LHop MHlr
WCot WPer
§ *pulchellum* MWat SUsu WEas WPat WPyg
aff. – JJH 9309143 NWCA
– 'Variegatum' NCut NFla
pumilum De Candolle See *E. helveticum*
'Rosemoor' EGar MRav

'Rufus' CCot CMHG CMil CSam ELan
GCHN MAvo NHaw SAga
WEas WHil
rupestre See *E. pulchellum*
§ *scoparium* ECGP EHic LHop MCCP NBro
NLak NTow
'Scorpio' NCut
♦ *sintenisianum* See *E. alpestre*
'Sissinghurst Variegated' See *E. linifolium* 'Variegatum'
'Sprite' CLyd CMHG CMea CTri EPot
MPla NGre NNrd NPer
§ *suffrutescens* CPle ESis NBro NPer
'Sunbright' NCat NRoo
'Sunshine' ELan
§ *torulosum* NPer
'Valerie Finnis' EBar WMaN
N 'Variegatum' CB&S SHBN WRus WWin
¶ 'Wembdon Bravery' LFlo
'Wenlock Beauty' ♀ CCot CMHG CSam CSev ELan
GCHN MSCN MTho NChi
NFai SAga SAxl SChu SRms
SUsu WEas WMaN WMer
WPer WRus WWhi
'Wenlock Beauty CMil NChi
Variegated'
wheeleri EBee ECoo EMar NPer
WOMN

ERYTHRAEA See CENTAURIUM

ERYTHRINA (Papilionaceae)
¶ *caffra* WMul
crista-galli ♀ CAbb CB&S CBot CGre CHEx
ELan EMil ERea GQui LLew
MLan SBid SOWG SPan SSoC
WMul
– 'Compacta' SMad
¶ *fusca* WMul
§ *humeana* CGre
indica See *E. variegata*
latissima WCot
lysistemon SOWG
princeps See *E. humeana*
vespertilio SOWG

ERYTHRONIUM † (Liliaceae)
albidum CLAP EPot GBuc LAma MCli
NRog
americanum CArn CBro CLAP CRDP ECha
EPot GCrs GDra LAma LBow
MLLN MS&S MSal NRog SSpi
SWas WAbe WCru
¶ 'Blush' IBlr
californicum ♀ CLAP CWoo MS&S NRog
SWas WAbe
¶ – J&JA 13216 CLAP
§ – 'White Beauty' ♀ CAvo CBro CLAP EBrP EBre
ECha EHyt ELan EPot ETub
GBur GCrs ITim LAma LBow
LBre MBal MDun MHig MTho
NHar NHol SBre SIng SSON
SSpi WAbe WCru WKif
caucasicum CLAP LBow NRog
citrinum CWoo WAbe
¶ – J&JA 13462 CLAP
– 'Citronella' CBro CLAP EPar ERos GBuc
GBur LAma LBow NEgg NHar
NRog WCru
cliftonii See *E. multiscapoideum*
Cliftonii Group
dens-canis ♀ Widely available
– 'Charmer' EPot

– 'Frans Hals'	CBos CLAP CSpe EPar EPot ERos GBuc GBur GCrs LAma MTho NRog SSON WCru
– from Slavenia	CLAP
– JCA 470.001	CLAP
– 'Lilac Wonder'	EPar EPot LAma MTho NRog
– var. *niveum*	EPot LAma
– 'Old Aberdeen'	CLAP
– 'Pink Perfection'	EPar EPot ERos GCrs LAma MCli NHar NRog SUsu WCru
– 'Purple King'	EPot ERos LAma NHar NRog SPla WCru
– 'Rose Queen'	CAvo CBro EPar EPot ERos ETub GBuc GBur LAma MAvo MLLN MTho NHar NHol NRog WAbe WPen
– 'Snowflake'	CAvo CLAP CMea CRDP ECha EHyt EPar EPot ERos LAma MAvo MCli MLLN NHar NHol NRog SSON SSpi WAbe WCru
– 'White Splendour'	CBro NEgg
– WM 9615 from E Slovenia	MPhe
elegans	CFil WPGP
§ *grandiflorum*	GCrs MS&S NHar
◆ – subsp. *chrysandrum*	See *E. grandiflorum*
¶ – J&JA 11394	CLAP
¶ – MPS 007	CLAP EHyt
helenae	CFil CLAP IBlr WPGP
hendersonii	CLAP CWoo LAma MS&S
– J&JA 12945	CLAP SSpi
– JCA 11116	CLAP
howellii	CFil CLAP WPGP
¶ – J&JA 13441	CLAP
japonicum	CBro EBee EFEx EHyt EPar LAma LBow NFai NRog WAbe WCru
'Jeannine'	WCru
'Joanna'	CBro CLAP LAma
'Kondo'	EBee EHyt EMon EPot ERos GBur LAma MBro MHig MS&S MTho NHar NRog NRoo WAbe WCru WPat
* *moerheimii* 'Semiplena'	EPot
§ *multiscapoideum*	CLAP MPhe
§ – Cliftonii Group	CLAP MPhe
¶ – Cliftonii Group J&JA 13525	CLAP
oregonum	CLAP CWoo EPar MS&S WAbe
– subsp. *leucandrum*	CLAP MPhe MS&S
– – J&JA 13494	SSpi
'Pagoda' ♀	Widely available
purdyi	See *E. multiscapoideum*
revolutum ♀	CBro CFil CWoo GGar IBlr LBow MS&S NWoo SSpi WCru
– Johnsonii Group	CFil MBal NHar WCru WPGP
– 'Knightshayes Pink'	CLAP
– 'Pink Beauty'	WNor
– 'White Beauty'	See *E. californicum* 'White Beauty'
sibiricum	GCrs
¶ – 'Altai Snow'	GCrs
¶ – 'White Fang'	GCrs
'Sundisc'	ECha EPot MTho NRog
tuolumnense ♀	CAvo CBro EHyt EPar EPla EPot ERos GCrs LAma LBow MBal MDun NHar NRog WAbe

ESCALLONIA (Escalloniaceae)

'Alice'	SLPl SPer
§ *alpina*	CPle

'Apple Blossom' ♀	CB&S CLan CTrw EBrP EBre ELan GRei IOrc LBre LHop MBal MBri MGos MPla MWat NNor NPer SBod SBre SHBN SLPl SPer WAbe WDin WGwG WHCG WHar WWeb WWin
§ *bifida*	CDoC CGre CHan CPle CWit LRHS WSHC WWat
'C.F. Ball'	CTri ELan GCHN GChr GRei IOrc LBre MAll MGos NFla NWea SEND SRms WAbe WDin WHer WPic WStI
'Cardinalis'	MAll NCut
'Dart's Rosy Red'	CBlo MBri NHol SLPl
'Donard Beauty'	CBlo CChe SRms
'Donard Brilliance'	MGos
'Donard Radiance' ♀	CB&S CChe CDoC ELan ENot ISea LHop MAll MGos MWat NHol SBod SPer SRms WAbe WDin WGer
'Donard Rose'	WWeb
'Donard Seedling'	Widely available
'Donard Star'	EBee ENot EPfP IOrc MAll MGos NWea SBid WGwG WWeb
'Donard Surprise'	NNor
'Edinensis' ♀	CMHG ECtt EMil ENot EPfP GChr MAll MBar NFla NNor SBid SEND SRms WDin WGer WWat
'Erecta'	CBlo EPfP MAll SBid
× *exoniensis*	SRms
fonkii	See *E. alpina*
'Glory of Donard'	ENot
* *gracilis alba*	CPle
'Gwendolyn Anley'	CLTr CMHG MAsh MGos NTow SBod SLPl SPer WWat
'Hopleys Gold'	See *E. laevis* 'Gold Brian'
illinita	CPle MAll WPGP WPic
'Iveyi' ♀	Widely available
§ *laevis*	CTrw SDry
§ – 'Gold Brian'	CMHG CSam EBee EBrP EBre EHic EHoe ELan ENot IOrc LBre MGos MWat SAga SBid SBre SPer SRms WHar WStI WWeb
– 'Gold Ellen' (v)	CBlo EBrP EBre EMil LBre LHop MBri MCCP NHol NTow SAga SBre SCoo SEND SPla WStI
'Langleyensis' ♀	CB&S CTri GOrc MAll MWat MWhi NLon NNor NWea SBod WDin WFar WHar WSHC
leucantha	CGre CPle MAll
littoralis	CPle
mexicana	CBot CHan WWat
montevidensis	See *E. bifida*
¶ 'Newry'	SPer
organensis	See *E. laevis*
'Peach Blossom' ♀	CDoC CPle EBar EBee ELan EMil ENot MGos SAga SBid SHBN SLPl SPer WGwG WHCG WWal WWeb
'Pink Elf'	CBlo ECtt IOrc MBri NCut WLRN
'Pink Pearl'	SRms
'Pride of Donard' ♀	CB&S CBlo CLan IOrc LHop MAll SPla SRms WWeb
punctata	See *E. rubra*
'Rebecca'	GOrc

'Red Dream' CBlo CChe CFai EBrP EBre IOrc LBre LBuc MAll MAsh MBri MGos NFla NPSI NPro SBre SCoo SSto WGer WLRN WStI

'Red Dwarf' WAbe

'Red Elf' CMHG EBrP EBre ECtt ELan EMil ENot GOrc IOrc LBre LHop MAll MBar MBri MGos MPla MTis MWat NHol SBre SLPl SPer SRms WFar WHen

'Red Hedger' CBlo CDoC EHic EMil MTis SBid SCoo

resinosa CPle SAPC SArc SMrm

revoluta CPle SDry

rosea CPle

rubra 'Crimson Spire' ♀ CB&S CChe EBar EBrP EBre ENot GRei LBre MAll MBri MGos MRav MWat NNor SAga SBod SBre SHBN SPer SPla SRms WBod WHen WStI

– 'Ingramii' CChe CMHG MAll SBod SHBN

§ – var. *macrantha* CB&S CChe CHEx EGra EMil GChr GRei ISea MAll MAsh SPer SPla WAbe WBod WDin WGer WGwG WPic WStI WWal

– 'Pubescens' CPle

– 'Pygmaea' See *E. rubra* 'Woodside'

– var. *uniflora* SDry

§ – 'Woodside' CPle EHic EHol EPfP MAll MGos NHol NPro SBid SIng SRms WHCG

'Silver Anniversary' CB&S CBlo LHop MAll MGos MPla SBid WBcn WLRN WWeb

'Slieve Donard' CBlo ENot MAll MGos MRav SLPl SRms WWeb

tucumanensis CGre CPle

virgata CPle WWat

viscosa CPle MAll

EUCALYPTUS † (Myrtaceae)

aggregata MAll SAPC SArc SPer WCel WTro

¶ *alpina* MAll

amygdalina CMHG

approximans subsp. *approximans* WCel

archeri CTho GAri GQui ISea MAsh MBal MCCP WCel

brookeriana CMHG

caesia GCHN

¶ *cameronii* CHon

camphora WCel

cinerea CTrC GQui IOrc WCel

citriodora ELau EOHP GQui NCut SIde WCel WLRN WNor

coccifera ♀ CB&S CDoC CHEx ELan GAri IOrc ISea LPan MAll MBal MCCP SEND SPla SSpi WCel WNor

¶ – silver leaved WCel

consideniana LLew

cordata CGre CMHG LHop MBal WCel

crenulata CTrC GQui WCel

dalrympleana ♀ CB&S CDoC CMHG CSam CTho EBee EBrP EBre ELan ENot EWes IOrc LBre MAll MBal MBel MGos SBid SBre SPer SPla SRCN WCel WTro WWeb

deanei WCel

debeuzevillei See *E. pauciflora* subsp. *debeuzevillei*

delegatensis CMHG CTrC GAri IOrc MAll WCel WTro

divaricata See *E. gunnii divaricata*

* *eximia nana* WTro

ficifolia MBlu

fraxinoides WCel

glaucescens CGre CMHG EWes GQui LPan LRHS MAll SAPC SArc SBid SPer WCel WGer

globulus ♀ CHEx CMHG ELau GAri MBal MSal SBid SSoC WCel

goniocalyx WCel

§ *gregsoniana* ISea LLew WCel

gunnii ♀ Widely available

§ – *divaricata* GQui LPan WCel WGer

* –'Silver Drop' EOHP

johnstonii GAri MAll NCut SPer

kitsoniana MBal WCel

kybeanensis GQui LPan WCel

lehmannii SOWG

leucoxylon CTrC WCel

macarthurii WCel

¶ *macrandra* CHon

mannifera subsp. *elliptica* WCel

mitchelliana WCel

* *moorei nana* CBlo CPle GAri WNor

neglecta WCel

nicholii CHEx EWes GQui WBod WCel WGer

niphophila See *E. pauciflora* subsp. *niphophila*

nitens GAri LLew MBal WCel

§ *nitida* CGre CMHG WCel WNor

nova-anglica CMHG GAri

ovata CMHG

parvifolia ♀ CB&S CDoC CLnd GAri ISea LPan SAPC SArc SDry SEND SSte WCel

pauciflora CBlo CDoC CTri EBee EBrP EBre ELan EPfP GAri LBre MBal SBid SBre SEND SPar SPer WCel WNor

¶ – subsp. *acerina* WCel

§ – subsp. *debeuzevillei* GQui LRHS MCCP SAPC SArc WCel

¶ – subsp. *hedraia* WCel

– var. *nana* See *E. gregsoniana*

§ – subsp. *niphophila* ♀ Widely available

– – 'Pendula' CMHG GAri WCel

perriniana CB&S CHEx CMHG EBee ELan ENot IBlr MBal SAPC SArc SDry SPer SPla WBod WCel WNor WPat

phoenicea SOWG

¶ *preissiana* CTrC

pulverulenta CBlo CGre GAri WCel WGer

regnans GAri ISea MBal WCel

risdonii GAri WNor

rodwayi CMHG

rubida CGre CMHG EWes IOrc WCel

simmondsii See *E. nitida*

stellulata GAri MAll MCCP WCel

¶ *stricta* CHon

stuartiana	See *E. bridgesiana*
sturgissiana	GCHN
subcrenulata	CMHG GAri GQui ISea WCel
tenuiramis	CGre
urnigera	CGre GAri GChr MAll WCel
vernicosa	WCel
– subsp. *johnstonii*	CMHG GAri WCel
viminalis	CMHG GAri LLew WCel

EUCHARIDIUM See CLARKIA

EUCHARIS (Amaryllidaceae)

§ *amazonica*	LAma NRog SDeJ
grandiflora hort.	See *E. amazonica*
– Plan. & Lind.	LBow

EUCODONIA (Gesneriaceae)

'Adele'	NMos WDib
andrieuxii	NMos
– 'Naomi'	CHal NMos WDib
'Cornell Gem'	See *x Achicodonia* 'Cornell Gem'
'Tintacoma'	NMos
verticillata 'Frances'	NMos

EUCOMIS (Hyacinthaceae)

§ *autumnalis*	CAvo CBro CPou CSWP CTrC GBin GSki LAma LLew MCCP WCot
bicolor	CAvo CBro CFir CHEx EBak EBee EGoo ETub LAma LBow LHil MHlr NRog SAga SDix SMad SSoC WCru WHil
– 'Alba'	CAvo GSki
– hybrids	EFou SUsu
§ *comosa*	CAvo CB&S CBro CFir CHEx EBot EMan EMon ENot GSki LAma LBow NRog SMad WCru WLRN
¶ – purple-leaved	EBot
¶ *montana*	LLew WHil
pallidiflora	CHEx
pole-evansii	CFir CTrC GBin GCal LLew WCot WLRN
punctata	See *E. comosa*
¶ *regia*	LLew
undulata	See *E. autumnalis*
zambesiaca	CFee GBin LBow
'Zeal Bronze'	CFil CMHG GCal NSti WCot WPGP

EUCOMMIA (Eucommiaceae)

ulmoides	CFil CPle SMad WPGP

EUCROSIA (Amaryllidaceae) See Plant Deletions

EUCRYPHIA † (Eucryphiaceae)

'Castlewellan'	ISea
cordifolia	CB&S CGre CTrw ISea MBal SCog
– Crarae hardy form	GGGa
– x *lucida*	CB&S CGre IOrc ISea MBal SCog WDin WWat
glutinosa ♀	CB&S CGre ELan ICrw ISea LHyd MAsh MBal MBri NBir SHBN SPer SSpi SSta WAbe WDin WNor WPat WWat
– Plena Group (d)	ISea
x *hillieri* 'Winton'	CGre CMHG ISea MBal

x *intermedia*	CGre CSam CTrG ELan GCHN GGGa GOrc NPal SCog SHBN SPer SRms SSpi WDin WPat WWat WWeb
– 'Rostrevor' ♀	CB&S CLan CMHG CPMA ELan ICrw ISea MAsh MBal MBel SAga SCog SPer SReu SSta WBod WFar WSHC
lucida	CGre CMHG ELan EPfP GGGa GSki ISea LHyd MBal SCob WNor WPGP WWat
– 'Ballerina'	ISea
– 'Gilt Edge' (v)	ISea
– 'Leatherwood Cream' (v)	ISea
– 'Pink Cloud'	CFai CMHG CPMA ELan ISea LRHS SPer SSpi
milliganii	CB&S CDoC CFil CGre CMHG ELan GQui ISea LHop MBal MBlu MUlv NPal SCob SCog SHBN SPer SRms SSpi SSta WAbe WPGP WSHC WWat
moorei	CAbP CB&S CFil CGre ELan ISea MBal SSta
x *nymansensis*	CB&S CTrG EBrP EBre EMil ENot EPfP LBre LHop MBal SAPC SAga SArc SBre SCog SReu SRms SSpi WBay WBrE WHCG WStI
– 'George Graham'	ISea MBal
– 'Mount Usher'	IOrc ISea
– 'Nymansay' ♀	CB&S CLan CMHG CPMA CTrC ELan GGGa ISea LHyd MAsh MBal MBar MBri MGos MRav NPal SDix SHBN SPer SSta WAbe WDin WPat WPyg WSpi WWat
N 'Penwith'	CPMA ISea LBuc MBal NCut SSpi WWat

EUGENIA (Myrtaceae)

¶ *australis*	LHil
myrtifolia	CPle CSev STre

EUMORPHIA (Asteraceae)

* *canescens*	EGoo
prostrata	CSpe
sericea	CHan GOrc NNor WSHC

EUNOMIA See AETHIONEMA

EUODIA (Rutaceae)

daniellii	See *Tetradium daniellii*
hupehensis	See *Tetradium daniellii* Hupehense Group

EUONYMUS (Celastraceae)

alatus ♀	CB&S CPMA EAst ELan ENot GChr GRei IOrc LHop LNet MBal MBar MWat NBee NWea SHBN SPer SReu SSpi SSta WBod WCoo WDin WHCG WMou WPic WWal WWat WWeb
– var. *apterus*	SHBN
– 'Ciliodentatus'	See *E. alatus* 'Compactus'
§ – 'Compactus' ♀	CDoC CEnd CPMA EBrP EBre EHic EPla ESis IOrc LBre LNet MAsh MBlu MBri MGos MPla MUlv NHol SBid SBre SPan SPla SReu SSpi WDin WWat

* **atropurpureus cheatumii**	CPMA
bungeanus	CMCN EPla WWat
¶ – 'Dart's Pride'	EPfP
cornutus var.	CPMA EPfP EPla WMou
quinquecornutus	WOMN WPat
europaeus	CArn CDoC CKin CLnd CPer EBrP EBre ELan EPla EWFC GChr LBre LBuc LPan NWea SBre SRms WDin WHar WHer WMou
– f. *albus*	CBot EMil EPla
– 'Atropurpureus'	LPan
– 'Atrorubens'	CBrd CPMA
– 'Aucubifolius' (v)	CFil EPfP EPla WPGP
* – 'Aureus'	CNat
– var. *intermedius*	ENot EPla
– 'Red Cascade' ♀	Widely available
farreri	See *E. nanus*
fortunei 'Canadale Gold' (v)	EBee ENot EPla ESis MGos MWhi NBee NFai NHol SPer WWeb
– 'Coloratus'	CBlo CLan EHol ENot MBar MBlu NCut SBid SHBN SPer WDin WGwG WTro WWal
¶ – 'Country Gold'	CBlo NFla
– 'Croftway'	SCro
– 'Dart's Blanket'	CBlo EGoo ELan ENot EPla MRav MWhi SBid SLPl SSta SSto WDin
– 'Emerald Cushion'	ENot ESis NCut SPer
– 'Emerald Gaiety' (v) ♀	Widely available
– 'Emerald 'n' Gold' (v) ♀	Widely available
– 'Emerald Surprise'	MBri NHol NPro
– 'Gold Spot'	See *E. fortunei* 'Sunspot'
– 'Gold Tip'	See *E. fortunei* Golden Prince
– 'Golden Pillar' (v)	EBee EHic EHoe EHol MDHE WCot
§ – Golden Prince (v)	CB&S CWSG ENot EPla IOrc MBar NFai NHol SPer WGor WStI
– 'Harlequin' (v)	COtt CPMA CSam CWSG EHoe ELan GOrc LBuc LHop MAll MAsh MBar MBlu MGos MPla NPro SAga SHBN SIng SMad SPer SSta SSto WWal WWeb
– 'Highdown'	WWat
– Blondy = 'Interbolwi'	CAbP COtt CPMA EBrP EBre ECle ELan EMil ENot EPla LBre MAsh MBar MBri MGos MPla SBid SBre SCoo SMad SPer SPla SSta WBod WPyg WRHF WShe WWeb WWes
– 'Kewensis'	CMGP CMHG CNic CPle ENot MBar MPla MRav MWat NTow SAPC SArc SBod WCot WCru WWat
– 'Minimus'	CBlo CTri EGoo EHal EHic EPla ESis MGos NFai NHol NPro SIng SPla WFar WPer
* – 'Minimus Variegatus'	ECho
§ – var. *radicans*	CPlN
– 'Sheridan Gold'	EBee ECtt EHic EHoe EPla MPla MRav NHol SEas SHBN
– 'Silver Gem'	See *E. fortunei* 'Variegatus'
– 'Silver Pillar' (v)	EBar EHic EHoe ENot ERav ESis LRHS WFar
– 'Silver Queen' (v) ♀	CB&S CLan CPri EAst ELan ENot EPla GOrc IOrc MBal MBar MGos MWat NBir NBrk NFla SHBN SMad SPer SReu SSta WDin WGwG WHCG WSHC WWal WWat
– 'Sunshine' (v)	CAbP CBlo EHic ELan EPla MAll MAsh MGos NCut NPro SBid
§ – 'Sunspot' (v)	CMHG EBrP EBre ECtt ELan ENot EPla ESis GOrc LBre LHop MBar MGos MRav NFai NHed NHol NTow SAga SBre SEas SPla SRms SSta WBod WDin
– 'Tustin'	EPla SLPl SSto
§ – 'Variegatus'	CMHG ELan ENot MAll MBar NNor SPer SRms STre WDin WPat WPyg
– var. *vegetus*	EPla SPer
grandiflorus	CPMA
hamiltonianus	CMCN
– subsp. *hians*	See *E. hamiltonianus* subsp. *sieboldianus*
§ – subsp. *sieboldianus*	CMCN CPMA LHop MBal SLPl SMrm SPan WCoo WWat
– – 'Coral Charm'	SMrm SMur
– 'Winter Glory'	CBlo CPMA LRHS MBri WWes
– var. *yedoensis*	See *E. hamiltonianus* subsp. *sieboldianus*
* **hibarimisake**	SBla
japonicus	EBee ENot EPfP LRHS SBid SPer WDin
– 'Albomarginatus'	CB&S CBlo CTri LFis MBar MPla NBrk SBid SEND SRms WSHC WWeb
– 'Aureopictus'	See *E. japonicus* 'Aureus'
– 'Aureovariegatus'	See *E. japonicus* 'Ovatus Aureus'
§ – 'Aureus' (v)	CB&S ENot EPla GOrc LPan MAll MBal MBri SBid SDix SEas SHBN SMac SPer SPla WDin WHar WWeb
– 'Bravo'	CDoC EHic NHol
¶ – 'Chedju'	WBcn
– 'Chollipo'	CBlo ELan LRHS MAsh
* – 'Compactus'	LPan
– 'Duc d'Anjou' Carrière (v)	CB&S CLTr EBrP EBre EHoe ELan EPla ESis EWes LBre LPan MAsh SBre SDry SMad SPla
– 'Duc d'Anjou' hort.	See *E. japonicus* 'Viridivarigatus'
– 'Golden Maiden'	CBlo ELan EPfP LRHS MAsh
– 'Golden Pillar' (v)	EPla ESis
¶ – 'Harvest Moon'	WWeb
§ – 'Latifolius Albomarginatus' ♀	EBrP EBre EHic EHoe EHol EPfP EPla LBre MNrw SBid SBre SPer
– 'Luna'	See *E. japonicus* 'Aureus'
– 'Macrophyllus Albus'	See *E. japonicus* 'Latifolius Albomarginatus'
– 'Maiden's Gold'	COtt SBid WRHF
– 'Marieke'	See *E. japonicus* 'Ovatus Aureus'
– 'Mediopictus'	MBri
– 'Microphyllus'	EMil MBal MUlv STre

§ – 'Microphyllus Albovariegatus'	CLTr CMHG ELan EMil EPla EPot MBal MBar MBrN MGos MHig MRav NHol SAga SHBN SPla SSca WHCG WPat WPyg WSHC WStI WWat
– 'Microphyllus Aureovariegatus'	CBlo EMil MWhi SEas SSto WPat WPyg WWin
– 'Microphyllus Aureus'	See *E. japonicus* **'Microphyllus Pulchellus'**
§ – 'Microphyllus Pulchellus' (v)	CB&S CMHG ENot EPla EPot ESis LFis LHop MBar MNrw MRav NHed NHol SAga SBid SEas WHCG WPyg WWeb
– 'Microphyllus Variegatus'	See *E. japonicus* **'Microphyllus Albovariegatus'**
§ – 'Ovatus Albus' (v)	SBid
§ – 'Ovatus Aureus' (v) ♀	CCHe CTri ENot ESis LPan MBal MBar MGos MPla MRav SBid SEas SPer SPla SRms WDin WPat WRHF WStI
– 'Président Gauthier' (v)	CDoC EPla LPan MGos NCut WBay WGer
– 'Robustus'	CDoC EPla
¶ – 'Silver King'	CBlo
* – 'Silver Princess'	SHBN
– 'Susan'	EGra EHic WRHF
kiautschovicus	CBrd EPla
latifolius	CMCN CPMA
macropterus	EPla
myrianthus	CBrd EPfP SBid WWat
§ *nanus*	CNic CPle EHol EPla ESis MBal MBlu MBro NHol WOMN WPyg
– var. *turkestanicus*	EHic EPla ESis NPal SRms WWat
obovatus	CHan
oxyphyllus	CBrd CMCN CPMA WMou WWat
§ *pendulus*	CGre CHEx
phellomanus	EBar EHic EPfP GDra LHop LNet MAsh MBar MBlu MBri MUlv SPan WWat
§ *planipes* ♀	CGre CMHG CPle CWit EBar ELan ENot EPla GChr MBlu MBri NHol NSti SPer SSpi WNor WWat
radicans	See *E. fortunei radicans*
'Rokojo'	CLyd MBro NHol WPat
rosmarinifolius	See *E. nanus*
sachalinensis hort.	See *E. planipes*
sanguineus	CPMA
sp. B&L 12543	EHic EPla ESis EWes
tingens	CFil CPle SBid WAbe
verrucosus	CPMA EPla WWes
yedoensis	See *E. hamiltonianus* subsp. *sieboldianus*

EUPATORIUM (Asteraceae)

§ *album*	CHad CSWP CVer EPPr WPer
–'Braunlaub'	EFou EJud EMon LBlm MCli MHlr NSti WCot
altissimum	CBot CGle EPar MSal WCHb WEas
– JLS 88029	EMon
aromaticum	CArn CSev EBee ECro ELan LFis MCLN MLLN MRav MWgw NBro NSti SCro SWat WCHb WPer WWye
cannabinum	CArn CKin CSev EBar ECED ECoo EHon ELan EMFW EOld EWFC GPoy LHol MHew MRav MSal MSta NMir NSti SWat SWyc WCer WGwG WOak WPer WWye
– 'Album'	EMon GBar
– 'Flore Pleno' (d)	CSev ECGP ECha ECro EFou EGar EMon GCal LFis MBel MFir MHlr MLLN MRav MSte NBrk NDov NHol NSti SWat WAlt WCot WPbr WWat
* – 'Not Quite White'	WAlt
– 'Spraypaint'	CNat
capillifolium	CWit MHlr MLLN NSti SAPC SArc SMrm WCot
– 'Elegant Feather'	EWes LFis SMad
coelestinum	LBuc
* *fistulosum* 'Atropurpureum'	WPer
¶ *hyssopifolium*	EBee
§ *ligustrinum* ♀	CB&S CDec CDoC CElw CHan CLan CPle CWit ECha ELan IOrc ISea LGre MAll SAga SDix SMrm SPer WCHb WRus WSHC
maculatum	See *E. purpureum* subsp. *maculatum*
madrense	CLTr
micranthum	See *E. ligustrinum*
occidentale	EBee WCot WLin
perfoliatum	CArn GBar GPoy LHol MNrw MSal WPer WWye
purpureum	CArn EAst ECED ECha ELau GBar GPoy LHol MAus MGra MSal MSte MWat NBro NDea NHol SChu SIde SMrm SPer SWat WEas WHer WOld WOve WPer WRus WSHC WWye
§ – subsp. *maculatum*	CSam EBrP EBre EMon GCal LBre LFis SBre WHil WPer
– – 'Album'	EMon NSti WCot
– – 'Atropurpureum' ♀	Widely available
– – 'Berggarten'	GCal
¶ – – 'Gateway'	CRow
¶ – – 'Glutball'	WCot
– – 'Riesinschirm'	EBee SMad WElm
– 'Purple Bush'	CHad ECha NBrk
rugosum	CBos CGle CHan CSam ECro ELan EOrc EPfP GBar GCra MFir SIde WCHb
– *album*	See *E. album*
¶ – 'Chocolate'	CRow EFou SWas WCot
* 'Snowball'	SMrm
§ *sordidum*	ERav ERea GCal LHil SLMG SMrm
triplinerve	EGar MSte
weinmannianum	See *E. ligustrinum*

EUPHORBIA † (Euphorbiaceae)

acanthothamnos	LGre
¶ *altissima*	MSte
amygdaloides	CKin CRow EWFC SSpi WCer WWye
– 'Brithembottom'	CSam
– 'Craigieburn'	EBee GBri GCal GCra
§ – 'Purpurea'	Widely available
§ – var. *robbiae* ♀	Widely available
– 'Rubra'	See *E. amygdaloides* **'Purpurea'**
– 'Variegata'	CRow ECha ELan GBuc MHar MTho
balsamifera	GBin

biglandulosa	See *E. rigida*
brittingeri	EGar
broteroi	WCot
¶ *canariensis*	SGre
capitata	WPat
capitulata	ELan EWes LHop MBro MTho NMen WWin
ceratocarpa	CB&S CEnd CLTr EGar EMon EPla EWes GBuc GCal MBro SMad SPan WCHb WFar WFox WOve WWeb
characias	CB&S CBot CGle CRow ECha ECtt EMon MBri MBro NHol NNor NOak NPer NPri NSti SPan SPer SRms SSpi WByw WGwG WHen WHoo WPer WWal WWat
* – 'Amber Eye'	IBlr SWas
– Ballyrogan hybrids	IBlr
¶ – 'Black Pearl'	EFou
¶ – 'Blue Wonder'	EFou
– subsp. *characias* ♀	WCru
– – 'Blue Hills'	CLon EFou EGar EMon GBuc GCal IBlr LBlm NLak SMrm WRus
– – 'Burrow Silver' (v)	CBot CRDP EWes MLLN NLak SPar SWat WFar
– – 'Green Mantle'	IBlr
– – 'H.E. Bates'	NBir
– – 'Humpty Dumpty'	COtt EBrP EBre EFou LBre LHop LRHS NPer NWes SBre SChu SMad SMrm WGer
– – 'Percy Picton'	CHan
– dwarf	SMrm
– 'Forescate'	EBrP EBre EMil GCal LBre LRHS MRav SBre SCro WFar WGer WMer WRus WSpi
– 'Goldbrook'	CM&M CSev EBee EMan LFis NCat NHol SChu SHBN SPla SWat
– JCA 475.500	GCal
– 'Jenetta'	NCat WHal
– 'Portuguese Velvet'	CHan CMil EGle EMan LGre MBro MGrG MHar NHaw NHol NPer SMad SMrm SPan SWas WCot WHal WKif WSpi WWoo
* – 'Sombre Melody'	IBlr
¶ – 'Spring Splendour'	NLar
– 'Variegata'	CRow SMad
– subsp. *wulfenii* ♀	Widely available
– – 'Bosahan' (v)	EGar SMad
– – 'Emmer Green' (v)	ECha MGrG SBla SWat WCot WRus
– – JCA 475.603	GCal SAga
§ – – 'John Tomlinson' ♀	CBlo CMil ECha EGar EMon EPPr EPla EWes LHop MBro MSte SChu SUsu WEas
– – Kew form	See *E. characias* subsp. *wulfenii* 'John Tomlinson'
– – 'Lambrook Gold' ♀	CMHG CRow CSam EBar EBrP EBre ECtt EGar EPar EWes LBre LHop MBro MRav MWat NPer NRoo SBre WHoo WPyg WRus WWat
– – 'Lambrook Yellow'	CMil EMon EPla GBuc MWat SMur
– – Margery Fish Group	EFou EHic EMan EPla LRHS MFir MLLN NCat NWes SChu SMrm SPer SWat WMer
– – 'Perry's Tangerine'	NPer SMad
– – 'Perry's Winter Blusher'	ECtt NPer
§ – – 'Purple and Gold'	CMil MGrG SBla SPan WCot WPen WRus
– – 'Purpurea'	See *E. characias* subsp. *wulfenii* **'Purple and Gold'**
– – var. *sibthorpii*	WCot WOld
clava	GBin
¶ *cognata*	ECGN
– CC&McK 607	EWes GCHN
– CC&McK 724	GBin
confinalis	GBin
conifera	CB&S
corallioides	CArn EBee EBrP EBre ECha EGar ELan EMan EPPr IBlr LBre MCLN NFai NLak NPer NPri SBre SMac WBrE WHer WPen WShe WUnu
§ *cornigera*	CFil CHad CLon CRDP EBrP EBre EGar EHic EHoe EMar EMon GAbr GBin GCal GMac IBlr LBre MMil SAxl SBre SWat WPGP WSHC
– CC 720	CPou
¶ *corollata*	SIng
cylindrica	GBin
cyparissias	CArn CHan CRow CSev CWit ECha ELan EPot LFis NHex NHol NMen NNor NRoo NSti NWCA SPer WCru WEas WFoF WHal WOve WPbr WPer WRus WWin
– 'Betten'	See *E. × gayeri* **'Betten'**
– 'Bushman Boy'	EGar GBri IBlr NLak WCot
§ – 'Clarice Howard'	EBee ECha EDAr EGar EGra ELan EMar EPar EPri GCal LGan MAvo MBrN MBri NEgg NFla NOak NRar NSti SCoo SMrm SPan WHal WMer WPbr WPer WRus WWoo
¶ – Clone 2	NCat
– 'Fens Ruby'	Widely available
– 'Orange Man'	EBar EBee ECoo EFou EGar EMar EMon EWes GBin GBri GCal IBlr MBro NBrk NHol NLak NSti SAxl SChu SMad SPan SPla SWat WFox WPbr
– 'Purpurea'	See *E. cyparissias* **'Clarice Howard'**
– red	SPan
– 'Red Devil'	CBre EPla IBlr SChu SUsu WOve
– 'Tall Boy'	EGar EMon EWes GBri IBlr NLak SPan
dendroides	GBin
§ *donii*	ELan EWes GCra IBlr LHop NSti SDix SUsu
dulcis	CGle CRow ECha ECtt EFou ELan LGan NBrk NBro NHex NOak NSti SEas SMac WByw WCot WEas WFox WHen WOld WWat
– 'Chameleon'	Widely available
I – 'Nana'	CBlo EHic EWll GBin NHol
epithymoides	See *E. polychroma*
esula	CGle
Excalibur	See *E.* Excalibur = **'Froeup'**
fasciculata	GBin
fimbriata	GBin
§ Excalibur = 'Froeup'	CMil EHal GBin LRHS LRot MBri MCCP NEgg NHol NSti SHBN SPan SPla SSpi SUsu

fulgens	CHal
'Garblesham Enchanter'	EPPr
§ × *gayeri* 'Betten'	GCal
glauca	CFee ECou IBlr WCot
'Golden Foam'	See *E. stricta*
griffithii	CRow NBrk NBro NCat SSpi SWat WAbb WCru WGer
– 'Dixter' ♀	Widely available
– 'Fern Cottage'	CRDP EWes GAbr SMrm SUsu SWas WHal
– 'Fireglow'	Widely available
– 'King's Caple'	EGar
– 'Robert Poland'	CSWP
– 'Wickstead'	EGar EPla GCal LHop LRHS SMrm
horrida	SLMG
hyberna	GBri IBlr MTho NMen SWat WFox
ingens	GBin SGre
jacquemontii	GCal MRav WCot
× *keysii*	MBri
lathyris	CJew CRow ELan EMar LHol MHew NCat NHex NPer SIde SIng SRms WEas WFox WOak WWye
leucocephala	GBin
longifolia D Don	See *E. donii*
– hort.	See *E. cornigera*
– Lamarck	See *E. mellifera*
mammillaris	GBin SLMG
× *martinii* ♀	Widely available
– 'Red Dwarf'	EOrc SPan
¶ *melanocarpa*	CEnd
§ *mellifera*	Widely available
meloformis	GBin
milii ♀	CHal EBak SRms
– 'Koenigers Aalbäumle'	MBri
monteiroi	GBin
myrsinites ♀	Widely available
nicaeensis	CB&S CFil EMan EOrc GCal LGre LHop MBro MLLN SBla SBod SCro SDix SMrm SPer SSpi SUsu WCot WPGP
oblongata	CB&S EBee ELan EMan EMon EWes GBuc IBlr MUlv NLak NWes SBod WCHb WFox WWeb
obtusifolia	GBin
palustris ♀	CHad CHan CMHG CRDP CRow ECGN EFou ELan GBin GCal LBlm LHop LPBA MAus MNrw MSta MWgw NDea NHol NLar NSti SDix SHel SMad SPer SUsu WEas WWat WWin
– 'Walenburg's Glorie'	EBee EGar GBin NBrk NLak NRoo SAxl SMad
pekinensis	MSal
pilosa	CNat NSti
– 'Major'	See *E. polychroma* 'Major'
pithyusa	CBot CGle CHan CMea ECha EGar EMan EMon LHop MLLN NLak SAxl SHBN WCot WHil WRus WWat WWhi
§ *polychroma* ♀	Widely available
§ – 'Candy'	CBot CMea CRow EBrP EBre ECha ELan EOld EOrc ERav GBin GCHN GCal LBre LFlo LHop MBro MCCP NHar NOak NRoo NSti SBre SMad SPan WHoo
– 'Emerald Jade'	GBri IBlr NLak SPan
– 'Lacy' (v)	CMil ELan ERav EWes GBin MMil NBir NLak SMad SPan WCot WPen
§ – 'Major' ♀	CMHG ECha ELan EPPr GCal NCat SPan WCot WEas
– 'Midas'	CFee EGle EMon NLak SMrm WHoo
– 'Orange Flush'	WHoo
I – 'Purpurea'	See *E. polychroma* 'Candy'
* – 'Senior'	SCro
– 'Sonnengold'	EGar EWes GCal LBlm MBro NRoo WHoo WPyg WSHC
portlandica	CSev EBee EHic ELan EMar GBin MBri NPSI NSti WCHb WHer
§ × *pseudovirgata*	EMon EPla IBlr LHop SAxl SPan
pugniformis	MBri
pulcherrima	EWes MBri
'Purple Preference'	EPPr NPri
reflexa	See *E. seguieriana* subsp. *niciciana*
resinifera	SLMG
§ *rigida*	CBot CFil GCal SBid SBla SIgm SWas WCot
robbiae	See *E. amygdaloides* var. *robbiae*
¶ *sarawschanica*	LGre SMrm WCot
schillingii ♀	CAbb CB&S CFee CHan CMHG CPle CSam EBrP EBre EMar EMon EOrc GCal GCra LBre LFis LHop MBri MCLN NSti SBla SBod SBre SDix SMad WGle WHoo WPGP WWat
schoenlandii	GBin
seguieriana	EBee ECha EMan ERav GBin WLin
§ – subsp. *niciciana*	CBot CGle CHan CMGP CMea CSam ECha ELan ERav IBlr MArl MBro MLLN MRav NBir SBla SDix SMrm SSpi SUsu WEas WHoo WRus WWat
serrulata	See *E. stricta*
sikkimensis	CBot CElw CFee CGre CHan CMHG CRow CStr EBrP EBre ECha ELan EMon LBre MBel MWgw NBrk SBre SMrm SRms WCHb WCru WEas WOld WWat WWin
soongarica	EJud
spinosa	SIgm SMad
§ *stricta*	CChr CRow EBee ECha EGar ELan EMan EWes GBri IBlr MCCP MFir NBro NCat NSti WElm WLRN WRHF WWat
¶ *stygiana*	CFil
* *submammillaris*	MBri
'Variegata'	
susannae	SLMG
transvaalensis	GBin
uralensis	See *E.* × *pseudovirgata*
villosa	GBin MBro SPan
§ *virgata*	EMFP EMon EWes NSti SPan WCHb WCot
* 'Virgile'	EMon
× *waldsteinii*	See *E. virgata*
wallichii Hook.f.	CSam ECha EMan IBlr MBri MUlv NFla NOrc NRoo NSti SMrm SSoC WAbb WRus WWat
– Kohli	See *E. cornigera*
– misapplied	See *E. donii*

zoutpansbergensis   GBin

EUPTELEA (Eupteleaceae)
  franchetii   See *E. pleiosperma*
  § *pleiosperma*   SVen
  polyandra   CBrd CGre WPGP

EURYA (Theaceae)
  japonica   CFil
  – 'Variegata'   See *Cleyera japonica* **'Fortunei'**

EURYOPS (Asteraceae)
  abrotanifolius   LHil SVen WSPU
  § *acraeus* ♀   CBot CHea CPle EHyt ELan
    EPot GCHN GCrs GDra GTou
    LHop MBro MPla MWat NGre
    NLon NNor NRoo NTow
    NWCA SIng WAbe WLin
    WWin
  candollei   WAbe WCot
  § *chrysanthemoides*   CB&S CCan CMHG CPle
    CSam EBar ERav ERea IBlr
    LHil MAll MBEx MMil MSte
    WPer WRHF
  ¶ *decumbens*   NSla
    aff. – JJ&JH 9401309   NWCA
  evansii   See *E. acraeus*
  pectinatus ♀   CB&S CCan CHEx CInt
    CMHG CPle CSam CSev CTrG
    ERea IBlr LHil MAll MBEx
    MBlu MFir MLLN MNrw MRav
    NSty SDry SHBN SMrm SOWG
    SPar SRms WEas WPer WWye
  sericeus   See *Ursinia sericea*
  tysonii   CPle GGar WCot
  virgineus   CB&S CCan CMHG CTrC IBlr
    MAll MBEx

EUSTEPHIA   (Amaryllidaceae) See Plant
Deletions

EUSTOMA (Gentianaceae)
  § *grandiflorum*   MBri
  russellianum   See *E. grandiflorum*

EUSTREPHUS (Philesiaceae)
  latifolius   CPlN ECou

EUTERPE (Arecaceae)
  ¶ *edulis*   LPal

EVOLVULUS (Convolvulaceae)
  convolvuloides   ERea
  glomeratus 'Blue Daze'   See *E. pilosus* **'Blue Daze'**
  § *pilosus* 'Blue Daze'   ERea SSad

EWARTIA (Asteraceae)
  nubigena   NWCA
  ¶ *planchonii*   WAbe

EXACUM (Gentianaceae)
  affine   MBri
  – 'Rococo'   MBri

EXOCHORDA (Rosaceae)
  alberti   See *E. korolkowii*
  giraldii   CBlo CPle

– var. *wilsonii*   CBlo CPMA CSam EBar EBee
  EBrP EBre EHic EPfP GOrc
  LBre MAsh MBlu MBri MPla
  MRav MUlv SBid SBre SSpi
  SSta WWat
§ *korolkowii*   CGre WWat
✕ *macrantha*   GOrc WAbe
– 'The Bride' ♀   Widely available
racemosa   CGre CPMA EHal ISea LHop
  MBal MGos MWhi NNor SHBN
  SPer WHCG WWat
serratifolia 'Snow White'   CPMA

FABIANA (Solanaceae)
  imbricata   CBot CLan CPle EHic EMil
    GQui MBar MBel MBlu SAga
    SBra SPer SSta WAbe
  – 'Prostrata'   CBlo CPle EHic EPfP GCal
    NNrd SBid SDry SSpi WWat
    WWin
  – f. *violacea* ♀   CB&S CFee CGre CPle CTri
    EMil EPla ESis EWes GQui
    MBar SAga SBid SIng SPan
    SPer WKif

FAGOPYRUM (Polygonaceae)
  cymosum   See *F. dibotrys*
  § *dibotrys*   ELan NSti

FAGUS † (Fagaceae)
  crenata   CMCN WNor
  ¶ – 'Mount Fuji'   MBlu
  engleriana   CBlo CMCN
  grandifolia   CMCN
  ¶ – var. *carolinana*   CLyn
  japonica   CMCN
  lucida   CMCN
  orientalis   CMCN WCoo
  sylvatica ♀   CB&S CDoC CDul CKin CLnd
    CPer ELan ENot GChr GRei
    IOrc ISea LBuc LHyr LPan
    MAsh MBar MBri MGos NBee
    NWea SHBN SPer WDin WHar
    WMou WNor WOrn WStI
  § – 'Albomarginata'   CMCN IOrc MBlu
  – 'Albovariegata'   See *F. sylvatica* **'Albomarginata'**
  – 'Ansorgei'   CDul CEnd CMCN CTho
    LRHS MBlu MBri
  N– Atropurpurea Group   Widely available
    – – 'Swat Magret'   SMad
  – 'Aurea Pendula'   CEnd CMCN MBlu SMad
  – 'Birr Zebra'   CEnd
  – 'Black Swan'   CBlo CDul CEnd CMCN MAsh
    MBlu MBri SMad WGer
  – 'Bornyensis'   CMCN
  – 'Cochleata'   CMCN LRHS
  – 'Cockleshell'   CMCN CTho MBri
  – 'Cristata'   CMCN GAri MBlu
  § – 'Dawyck' ♀   CB&S CBlo CDoC CLnd
    CMCN COtt CTho EBrP EBre
    ELan EMil ENot GChr IHos
    IOrc ISea LBre LHyr MAsh
    MBal MBar MWat NWea SBre
    SPer WDin WOrn
  – 'Dawyck Gold' ♀   CAbP CBlo CDoC CDul CEnd
    CMCN COtt CTho EBee GChr
    IOrc LPan MAsh MBar MBlu
    MBri SMad SSpi WOrn
  – 'Dawyck Purple' ♀   CAbP CBlo CDoC CDul CEnd
    CMCN COtt CTho CTri IOrc
    LPan MAsh MBar MBlu MBri
    MGos SMad SPer SSpi WOrn

– 'Fastigiata'	See *F. sylvatica* **'Dawyck'**
– 'Felderbach'	CLyn LRHS MBlu
* – 'Franken'	MBlu SMad
– 'Frisio'	CEnd CMCN
– 'Grandidentata'	CMCN
– 'Greenwood'	LRHS MBlu
¶ – 'Haaren'	LRHS
¶ – 'Haven'	CMCN
– var. *heterophylla*	CBlo CLnd CTho GAri NWea WOrn
– – 'Aspleniifolia' ♀	CBlo CDoC CDul CEnd CMCN COtt EBee ELan EMil ENot EPfP IOrc LPan LRHS MAsh MBal MBar MBri SPer WDin WMou WNor
– – f. *laciniata*	CMCN MBlu
– 'Horizontalis'	CLyn CMCN COtt
¶ – 'Interrupta'	SMad
– 'Luteovariegata'	CEnd CMCN
– 'Mercedes'	CDul CLyn CMCN LRHS MBlu
– 'Miltonensis'	CMCN
N – 'Pendula' ♀	CB&S CBlo CDoC CDul CEnd CLnd CMCN CTho ELan ENot GChr GRei IOrc ISea MAsh MBal MBar NWea SMad SPer WDin WHar WMou WOrn WPyg WStI WWal
– 'Prince George of Crete'	CEnd CMCN CTho
– 'Purple Fountain' ♀	CBlo CDoC CEnd CMCN COtt ELan EMil IOrc LPan MAsh MBar MBlu MBri MGos NBee SMad SPer WPyg WWeb
– Purple-leaved Group	See *F. sylvatica* **Atropurpurea Group**
– 'Purpurea Nana'	CMCN
– 'Purpurea Pendula'	CEnd CMCN CTho ELan ENot GChr GRei IOrc LPan MAsh MBal MBar MBlu MGos MWat NBee NWea SPer WDin WHar WPyg WStI
§ – 'Purpurea Tricolor'	CBlo CDoC CEnd CMCN GChr IOrc LPan MBar MGos NBee SHBN SMer SPer WDin WPyg
– 'Quercifolia'	CMCN
– 'Quercina'	CMCN
– 'Red Obelisk'	CDul CMCN MBlu
– 'Remillyensis'	CMCN
– 'Riversii' ♀	CB&S CBlo CDoC CDul CEnd CLnd CMCN CTho ELan EMil ENot IOrc LPan MAsh MBal MBri MWat NWea SHBN SMer SPer SSta WDin WHar WOrn WStI
– 'Rohan Gold'	CDul CEnd CMCN EBee MAsh MBlu MBri
– 'Rohan Obelisk'	CEnd EBee MBlu
I – 'Rohan Pyramidalis'	CEnd CMCN
– 'Rohan Trompenburg'	CMCN MBlu
– 'Rohanii'	CAbP CB&S CBlo CDoC CDul CEnd CLnd CMCN COtt CTho ELan EMil IHos IOrc LPan MBal MBlu MWat NBee SHBN SPer SSpi WDin
– 'Roseomarginata'	See *F. sylvatica* **'Purpurea Tricolor'**
– 'Rotundifolia'	CDoC CTho NWea SPer
– 'Silver Wood'	CMCN MBlu MBri
– 'Spaethiana'	CMCN MBri
– 'Striata'	CMCN
– 'Tortuosa Purpurea'	CMCN CTho MBlu
– 'Tricolor' (v)	CB&S CDul CLnd COtt EBee ELan MAsh MBal WDin
– 'Tricolor' hort.	See *F. sylvatica* **'Purpurea Tricolor'**
– 'Viridivariegata'	CMCN
– 'Zlatia'	CB&S CBlo CDoC CLnd CMCN COtt CTho ELan ENot IOrc MAsh MBal MBar MBri MGos NBee SHBN SPer WBay WDin WOrn WStI

FALLOPIA (Polygonaceae)

aubertii	See *F. baldschuanica*
§ *baldschuanica* ♀	CChe CMac CRHN EBrP EBre ELan ENot GBur GChr GRei IHos ISea LBre LBuc MBar MGos MPla MRav MWat NBee NEgg NFla NRoo SBra SBre SHBN SPer WFar WHar WWeb
§ *japonica*	CRow ELan
§ – var. *compacta*	CDoC CRow EPfP EPla NPri SAxl SMrm WBea
* – – 'Midas'	IBlr
– – 'Variegata'	CRow EPla IBlr SMad
¶ – 'Crimson Beauty'	CRow
– 'Spectabilis' (v)	CHEx CRow ELan WCot
§ *multiflora*	CArn MSal
– var. *hypoleuca*	WCru
B&SWJ 120	
sachalinensis	CHEx CRow EMon

FALLUGIA (Rosaceae) See Plant Deletions

FARFUGIUM (Asteraceae)

§ *japonicum*	CHEx MTho
– 'Argenteum' (v)	CFir CHEx SMad WCot WFar WSan
– 'Aureomaculatum' (v) ♀	CAbb CB&S CBrP CFir CHEx CHan CSev EGar EHoe LHil MTho SLod SMad SWat WCot WHal WHer WHil WMul WSan
– 'Crispatum'	CFir EHic MTPN SApp SMrm WCot
tussilagineum	See *F. japonicum*

FARGESIA (Poaceae - Bambusoideae)

dracocephala	EPla ISta LJus SDry WJun WPGP
fungosa	ISta WJun WPGP
§ *murieliae* ♀	CHEx EBrP EBre EFul EHoe ELan ENot EPla ISta LBre LJus LNet LPan MBar MBri MCCP MGos MWhi NBee NLon SBre SCob SDry SMer SPer WHow WJun WMul
* – *dana*	WJun
¶ – 'Harewood'	MMoz
¶ – 'Jumbo'	EPla
§ – 'Leda' (v)	EPla SDry
– 'Simba'	CDoC CEnd CFil EBrP EBre EPla ISta LBre LJus MAsh MBrN MGos MTed NDov SBre SCha SCob WCru WJun WLRN
§ *nitida* ♀	CHEx CWSG EBrP EBre EFul EHoe ENot EOas EPla GOrc IOrc ISta LBre LJus LPan MBrN MBri MCCP MGos MUlv MWgw NBee SBre SCha SCob SDry SPer SSoC WHow WJun
– 'Eisenach'	CDoC ISta LRHS MMoz WCru WPGP
– 'Nymphenburg'	CPMA EPla ISta LRHS MMoz MWhi

robusta — EFul EPla ISta SDry WJun
spathacea hort. — See *F. murieliae*
utilis — EPla ISta LJus MMoz SDry WJun
¶ *yulongshanensis* — CFil WPGP

FARSETIA (Commelinaceae)
clypeata — See *Fibigia clypeata*

FASCICULARIA (Bromeliaceae)
andina — See *F. bicolor*
N *bicolor* — CFil CFir CGre CHEx EBak ECre EOas EWes GCal GGar IBlr ICrw LHil LHop MFir MTed MTho SAPC SArc SLMG SSpi SSta WAbe WCot WEas WPGP WPic
§ – subsp. *canaliculata* — WPGP
♦ *kirchhoffiana* — See *F. bicolor* subsp. *canaliculata*
♦ *pitcairniifolia* hort. — See *F. bicolor* subsp. *bicolor*

× **FATSHEDERA** (Araliaceae)
lizei ♀ — CB&S CBot CDoC CHEx EPla GOrc GQui IBlr MAll MBal MBri NRog SArc SBid SBra SDix SDry SMac SPer SPla SSoC WDin WWal WWat
§ – 'Annemieke' (v) ♀ — CBot CDec CHEx CSWP EBee IBlr MBri SMac SMad
§ – 'Aurea' (v) — EPfP LRHS SBra SDry SEND
– 'Aureopicta' — See × *F. lizei* 'Aurea'
– 'Lemon and Lime' — See × *F. lizei* 'Annemieke'
– 'Maculata' — See × *F. lizei* 'Annemieke'
– 'Pia' — CSWP MBri
* – 'Silver Prusca' — EPla
– 'Variegata' ♀ — CB&S CDoC CHEx CMHG IBlr MAll MBal MBri SBid SBra SDry SEND SMer SPer SPla WFar WWat

FATSIA (Araliaceae)
§ *japonica* ♀ — Widely available
– 'Variegata' ♀ — CB&S CBot MBri MGos NPal SAPC SArc SEND SHBN
papyrifera — See *Tetrapanax papyrifer*

FAUCARIA (Aizoaceae)
tigrina — MBri

FAURIA See NEPHROPHYLLIDIUM

FEIJOA See ACCA

FELICIA (Asteraceae)
§ *amelloides* — CHEx CLTr ERea ESis SChu SRms
– 'Astrid Thomas' — CInt CSpe LHil MBEx MRav
– 'Read's Blue' — CCan CSev CSpe LHil LHop LIck
– 'Read's White' — CCan ERea ESis GMac LHil LIck MBEx MSte WEas
§ – 'Santa Anita' ♀ — CCan CSev CSpe CTri ECtt EOrc ERea LHil LHop LIck MBEx NPer SCro WEas
– 'Santa Anita' large flowered — LHil
§ – variegated — CBar CCan CSev EBar ECtt ELan ERea ESis IBlr LHil LHop LIck MBEx MBri MSte NPer SPar WEas WRus

¶ – variegated white flower — LIck
amethystina — See *F.* 'Snowmass'
§ *amoena* — CHEx CHad CInt CTri ELan GBri LHil MBEx MHar SChu SRms
– 'Variegata' — CTri EOrc SChu
bergeriana — WOMN
capensis — See *F. amelloides*
– 'Variegata' — See *F. amelloides* variegated
coelestis — See *F. amelloides*
drakensbergensis — NTow
filifolia — CTrC
natalensis — See *F. rosulata*
pappei — See *F. amoena*
§ *petiolata* — CHan ECha EMan ERea IBlr LHil LIck MBEx NSti WCot WHow WOMN WWin
§ *rosulata* — EHyt ELan EMan EMon GAri LGan LHop MRPP MTho NBro NGre NMen NNrd NRoo NTow SSmi WHil WWin
uliginosa — CFee CHan EWes GGar GTou LBee MDHE MTho NTow WFar

FERRARIA (Iridaceae)
§ *crispa* — CMon LBow
uncinata — CMon
undulata — See *F. crispa*

FERREYRANTHUS (Asteraceae)
excelsus — CB&S CPle

FERULA (Apiaceae)
assa-foetida — CArn EBee MSal
* 'Cedric Morris' — ECha
chiliantha — See *F. communis* subsp. *glauca*
§ *communis* — CArn CHad CRDP CSpe ECGP ECha EOas EPla LGre LHol SDix SMad SMrm WCot WPic WRHF
– 'Gigantea' — See *F. communis*
§ – subsp. *glauca* — SIgm WCot
'Giant Bronze' — See *Foeniculum vulgare* 'Giant Bronze'
tingitana — SIgm

FESTUCA (Poaceae)
amethystina — CCuc CSpe EBee EHoe EMon EPPr EPla EPot ESOG ESis GBin GBri LFlo MBri MBro MCLN MWhi NHol NPla NVic WPer
– 'Aprilgrün' — EHoe EPPr
arundinacea — CKin
curvula subsp. *crassifolia* — EBee EPPr EPla ESOG NHol
elegans — EPPr ESOG
erecta — EHoe EPPr ESOG
eskia — CCuc CSWP EBee EBrP EBre EHoe EPPr EPla ESOG GAri GBin GOrn LBre MWhi NEgg NHol SBre SPer WCot WPer
filiformis — EHoe EMon EPPr LRHS
§ *gautieri* — CSte ECED ELan EMon EPPr ESOG GBin LHil MBar MBrN NOrc WFoF
– 'Pic Carlit' — EMon LRHS
gigantea — CKin EMan GBin LRot WBea
glacialis — EHoe MBal MDHE NHol
glauca — Widely available
I – 'Auslese' — SGre

– 'Azurit' EFou EHoe EMon EPPr EPla ESOG EWes LRHS NHol
§ – 'Blaufuchs' ♀ CDoC CLTr CM&M CSam CWSG EBee EBrP EBre ECot EHoe EPPr EPla EPot EWes GBin GOrn IOrc LBre LHop MBri MSte NHol SBre SHBN WFox WWat
§ – 'Blauglut' EBee EBrP EBre ECED EGar EHoe EOrc EPla ESOG GAri LBre MAvo MWgw NFla NHar NHol NMir NRoo SBre WGer WLRN
– Blue Fox See *F. glauca* 'Blaufuchs'
– Blue Glow See *F. glauca* 'Blauglut'
– 'Elijah Blue' CCuc CElw CEnd CMil CSWP CSte EBee EBrP EBre ECha EFou EPPr EPla ESOG ESis GAbr GBin GBri GOrn LBre LGan LHil MLan NHar NHol NPSI SBre SPer SSoC WLeb
– 'Golden Toupee' CCuc CMea CMil CSte CWSG EBee EBrP EBre ECha EFou EGar EGoo EHoe ELan EMan EPPr EPla ESOG EWes GAbr GOrn IOrc LBre LHop MBel NBir NHar NSti SBre SPla
– 'Harz' CCuc EBee EBrP EBre EGar EHoe EMil EMon EPla ESOG IBlr LBre MBar SBre
§ – 'Meerblau' CCuc
* – *minima* CVer ESOG ESis NGre NHol
– 'Pallens' See *F. longifolia*
– Sea Blue See *F. glauca* 'Meerblau'
– Sea Urchin See *F. glauca* 'Seeigel'
§ – 'Seeigel' CCuc EBee EBrP EBre EGar EGle EHoe EPPr EPla ESOG GOrn LBre LHil MAvo MBel MBri NPro SBre WPbr
– 'Seven Seas' See *F. valesiaca* 'Silbersee'
¶ – 'Silberreiher' EPPr
§ *longifolia* CKin ESOG
mairei CCuc CLTr EHoe EMon EPPr ESOG IBlr
novae-zelandiae GBin MAvo
ovina CSWP EHoe NOrc SIng SPla WFox WPer
– subsp. *coxii* EHoe EPPr
I – 'Kulturform' EBee SGre
– 'Söhrewald' EBee EPPr ESOG
* – 'Tetra Gold' WByw
paniculata EHoe EMon EPla ESOG GOrn LRHS
pulchella EBee
punctoria CCuc CMea EBee ECha EHoe EPPr EPla ESOG EWes NFai NGre NHar SBla SDys SSmi
rubra 'Jughandles' SAsh
¶ – var. *nankotaizanensis* WCru
  B&SWJ 3190
¶ – 'Variegata' WLin
– var. *viridis* NHol SIng
scoparia See *F. gautieri*
  sp. B&SWJ 1555 NGre
tenuifolia CKin
¶ *valesiaca* GOrn
– var. *glaucantha* CSte EPPr ESOG LRHS
§ – 'Silbersee' CCuc CInt EBrP EBre ECha EFou EHoe EPPr EPla ESOG IBlr LBre MBar MBri MSte NCat NHol NOak SBre SIng SRms WFar

– Silver Sea See *F. valesiaca* 'Silbersee'
vivipara CCuc CInt EGoo EHoe EMon EPPr ESOG NHol
* 'Willow Green' CBlo LRot MSte

FIBIGIA (Brassicaceae)
§ *clypeata* WEas WPer

FICUS † (Moraceae)
australis hort. See *F. rubiginosa* 'Australis'
benghalensis MBri
benjamina ♀ CHal EBrP EBre LBre MBri SBre SRms
– 'Exotica' MBri
– 'Golden King' MBri
– var. *nuda* MBri
– 'Starlight' (v) MBri
I *binnendijkii* 'Alii' CHal
carica (F) CHEx GAri LPan MBri
– 'Adam' (F) ERea
– 'Alma' (F) ERea
– 'Angélique' (F) ERea
– 'Beall' (F) ERea
– 'Bellone' (F) ERea
– 'Bifère' (F) ERea
– 'Black Ischia' (F) ERea
– 'Black Mission' (F) ERea
– 'Boule d'Or' (F) ERea
– 'Bourjassotte Grise' (F) ERea
– 'Brown Turkey' (F) ♀ Widely available
– 'Brunswick' (F) CDoC CGre ERea ESim GBon GTwe WCot
– 'Castle Kennedy' (F) ERea
– 'Col de Dame' (F) ERea
– 'Conandria' (F) ERea
– 'Figue d'Or' (F) ERea
– 'Goutte d'Or' (F) ERea
– 'Grise de Saint Jean' (F) ERea
– 'Grise Ronde' (F) ERea
– 'Grosse Grise' (F) ERea
– 'Kaape Bruin' (F) ERea
– 'Kadota' (F) ERea
– 'Lisa' (F) ERea
– 'Longue d'Août' (F) ERea
– 'Malcolm's Giant' (F) ERea
– 'Malta' (F) ERea
– 'Marseillaise' (F) ERea ESim GTwe SDea
– 'Negro Largo' (F) ERea
– 'Noir de Provence' See *F. carica* 'Reculver'
– 'Osborn's Prolific' (F) ERea
¶ – 'Palmata' SMad
– 'Panaché' (F) ERea
– 'Pastilière' (F) ERea
– 'Petite Grise' (F) ERea
– 'Pied de Boeuf' (F) ERea
– 'Pittaluse' (F) ERea
– 'Précoce Ronde de Bordeaux' (F) ERea
§ – 'Reculver' (F) ERea
– 'Rouge de Bordeaux' (F) ERea
– 'Saint Johns' (F) ERea
– 'San Pedro Miro' (F) ERea
– 'Sollies Pont' (F) ERea
– 'Sugar 12' (F) ERea
– 'Sultane' (F) ERea
– 'Tena' (F) ERea
– 'Verte d'Argenteuil' (F) ERea
– 'Violette Dauphine' (F) ERea
– 'Violette de Sollies' (F) ERea
– 'Violette Sepor' (F) ERea
– 'White Genoa' See *F. carica* 'White Marseilles'

– 'White Ischia' (F) ERea
§ – 'White Marseilles' (F) ERea
cyathistipula MBri
deltoidea var. *diversifolia* MBri
elastica 'Robusta' MBri
foveolata Wallich See *F. sarmentosa*
lyrata ♀ MBri
microcarpa STre
– 'Hawaii' (v) CHal MBri
natalensis subsp. MBri
  leprieurii 'Westland'
pumila ♀ CB&S CHEx CHal EBak MBri
SAPC SArc
– 'Minima' CFee
– 'Sonny' (v) CHal MBri
– 'Variegata' CHEx CHal MBri
radicans See *F. sagittata*
§ *rubiginosa* 'Australis' MBri
§ *sagittata* 'Variegata' MBri
§ *sarmentosa* MBri
triangularis See *F. natalensis* subsp.
leprieurii

FILIPENDULA † (Rosaceae)

alnifolia 'Variegata' See *F. ulmaria* 'Variegata'
camtschatica CRow ECoo ELan NDea NLar
NMir WCot
camtschatica rosea IBlr LHop NBrk
digitata 'Nana' See *F. palmata* 'Nana'
hexapetala See *F. vulgaris*
– 'Flore Pleno' See *F. vulgaris* 'Multiplex'
'Kahome' CHan CRow EGol GBuc
GCHN GMaP LFis MBro NHol
NMir NOrc NRoo NSti NTow
SMrm SPer WCot WFar WRus
kiraishiensis B&SWJ 1571 WCru
palmata ECha EFou MCli NFla WByw
– 'Alba' GCal
– 'Digitata Nana' See *F. palmata* 'Nana'
§ – 'Elegantissima' CHea CRow EBee ECha GCal
GGar NCat SAsh
§ – 'Nana' CRow ECha ECro GCal MBal
MBro MCli SAsh WChe WHoo
WPyg
palmata purpurea See *F. purpurea*
palmata 'Rosea' CGle IBlr NBir NCat WCHb
– 'Rubra' CBlo
– *rufinervis* B&SWJ 941 WCru
§ *purpurea* ♀ CDoC CMea CRow ECha EFou
EGar GGar LGan MBel MTis
NFla SSoC WCru WEas
– f. *albiflora* CBre EGol GAbr NCat
– 'Elegans' NFai WHil
♦ 'Queen of the Prairies' See *F. rubra*
§ *rubra* CBlo CHan CRow EAst ECED
LSyl NWoo
§ – 'Venusta' ♀ Widely available
– 'Venusta Magnifica' See *F. rubra* 'Venusta'
§ *ulmaria* CArn CKin ECoo EHon ELau
EPla EWFC GMaP GPoy LHol
MChe MGra MHew MTho
NHol NLan NMir SIde SWat
WCla WOak WPer WShi WWye
– 'Aurea' Widely available
– 'Flore Pleno' (d) CBre CRDP CRow EAst EHon
MBel MCli NFai NHol NSti
SPer SWat WCot WLRN
– 'Rosea' CRDP IBlr SPer

§ – 'Variegata' CFee CRow ECha EGol EHoe
ELan EOrc EPla LHol LHop
MCLN MTho MUlv NFla NHar
NOak NRoo NSti SPer WAbe
WByw WEas WGwG WHal
WLin WPbr WRus WWye
§ *vulgaris* CArn CFee CKin EAst ECtt
EWFC LHol LPBA MChe
MGra MHew MSal NBro NLan
NMir NOrc SIde WByw WChe
WCla WPer WWye
– 'Grandiflora' MUlv NCat WCot
§ – 'Multiplex' (d) CDoC CGle CRow ECha EGol
ELan EOrc GAbr LGan LHop
MBal MCLN MTho MUlv
NDea NHol NSti SEas SPer
SRms WEas WLin WRus WWat
WWye
– 'Plena' See *F. vulgaris* 'Multiplex'

FINGERHUTHIA (Poaceae)
sesleriiformis S&SH 1 CHan

FIRMIANA (Sterculiaceae)
simplex CFil CHEx IDee LPan

FITTONIA (Acanthaceae) See Plant Deletions

FITZROYA (Cupressaceae)
cupressoides CMac GAri IOrc LCon MBal
MBar WCwm

FOENICULUM (Apiaceae)
vulgare CArn CHad EBot ECha EEls
ELan ELau GBar GPoy LHol
MChe MGra MHew MSal NRoo
SIde SRCN WByw WCer WOak
WPer WWye
– 'Bronze' See *F. vulgare* 'Purpureum'
– var. *dulce* CSev SIde WGwG
§ – 'Giant Bronze' CGle ELan SPer WHen
§ – 'Purpureum' Widely available
– 'Smokey' CWit EFou IIve MRav WOve

FOKIENIA (Cupressaceae) See Plant Deletions

FONTANESIA (Oleaceae)
phillyreoides WDin

FONTINALIS (Sphagnaceae; moss)
antipyretica EMFW SAWi

FORESTIERA (Oleaceae)
neomexicana CB&S

FORSYTHIA (Oleaceae)
'Arnold Dwarf' CBlo SEas SRms
N 'Beatrix Farrand' CTri EBee ECtt MGos MPla
MWat NHol NNor SEas SPer
SRms WLRN
§ Boucle d'Or = COtt ENot
'Courtacour'
§ Marée d'Or = 'Courtasol' COtt ENot MBri MGos SPer
WLRN
'Fiesta' (v) CPMA CPle EAst EBrP EBre
ELan ENot IOrc LBre LHop
MBar MBel MBri MHlr MPla
NHol NPro SBre SHBN SLod
SPer SSta WCot WHer WPat
giraldiana CPle SRms WBod WSPU

'Gold Cluster' — See *F.* Melée d'Or
'Gold Splash' — EBee
'Gold Tide' — See *F.* Marée d'Or = **'Courtasol'**
'Golden Curls' — See *F.* Boucle d'Or = **'Courtacour'**
'Golden Nugget' — CBlo EBrP EBre EHic ELan EPfP ESis IOrc LBre SBre SPer WCFE WWeb
'Golden Times' (v) — CBlo CDec EHic EHoe EPla EWes IOrc MBri MGos NPro SApp SCoo SEas SMad SPla SSto WBcn WCot WPat
x *intermedia* 'Arnold Giant' — CBlo MBlu WBod
– 'Densiflora' — NWea
– 'Karl Sax' — CChe NWea SBid SCob WLRN
* – 'Liliane' — EMil
– 'Lynwood' ♀ — CB&S CBlo CChe ELan ENot GRei ISea MBal MBar MBri MGos NBee NFla NHol NNor NRoo NWea SDix SPer SReu SSta WBod WDin WFar WWeb
– 'Lynwood' LA '79 — CDec EHic MLan SPla
– 'Minigold' — ECtt MAsh MGos MWat SEas SRms WPyg WRHF WStI WWeb
– 'Spectabilis' — CBlo ELan IOrc LBuc MBar NBee NFla NWea SPer WDin WRHF WTro WWal
– 'Spectabilis Variegated' — CPle EBar EHic EPla MPla NPro WCot WPyg WWeb
– 'Spring Glory' — EBee ECtt ENot MBri MRav
– 'Variegata' — CBlo MMHG NWea SPer SSta
– Week-End ♀ — CBar CBlo ENot GAri MBri MGos
Maree d'Or — See *F.* Marée d'Or = **'Courtasol'**
§ Melée d'Or — ENot SPer
* 'Melissa' — NWea
'Northern Gold' — CB&S EPfP
ovata — EPla
– 'Tetragold' — CB&S CBlo GOrc MBal MBar NWea
'Paulina' — CBlo ESis GAri
* *pumila* — EWes
* 'Spring Beauty' — MAsh
suspensa ♀ — CB&S CTri ENot EOHP EPfP IOrc MSal MWat NWea SEas SHBN SPer WStI
– f. *atrocaulis* — CPle GAri NWea
– 'Decipiens' — WBod
– var. *fortunei* — WWal
– 'Nymans' — MBri NSti SBid SBra SMad
§ – 'Taff's Arnold' (v) — CBlo CMil CPMA WBcn WSPU
– 'Variegata' — See *F. suspensa* **'Taff's Arnold'**
'Tremonia' — EHal MBal MGos
viridissima — CBlo NNor NWea
– 'Bronxensis' — EHyt ELan EPar EPot ESis MHig MPla NBir NNrd SMad WOMN WPyg
– var. *koreana* — EPla
* – – 'Variegata' — CPMA SBid
– 'Weber's Bronx' — MBar

FORTUNEARIA (Hamamelidaceae) See Plant Deletions

FORTUNELLA (Rutaceae)
x *crassifolia* (F) — SCit
– 'Meiwa' (F) — CAgr ERea
'Fukushu' (F) — ECon ERea SCit
hindsii (F) — SCit
§ *japonica* (F) — LHol LPan SCit

§ *margarita* (F) — CGOG LPan MBri SCit
– 'Nagami' (F) — CAgr ECon ERea

FOTHERGILLA (Hamamelidaceae)
gardenii — CPMA EBrP EBre ELan EPfP IOrc LBre MBlu MBri SBre SPer SSpi WDin WWat
– 'Blue Mist' — CAbP CDoC CPMA CSam EBee ELan GChr IOrc MAsh MBri MGos NHed SMad SPer SPla SReu SSpi SSta WWat
'Huntsman' — CAbP COtt
major ♀ — CB&S CPMA EBrP EBre ECtt ELan GChr LBre MAsh MBal MBri MGos MHlr NBee NFla NHol SBre SHBN SPer SReu SSpi WDin WHar WNor WPat WStI WWat
– Monticola Group — CPMA ELan ENot IHos MBal MBar MBri MPla NHed NPal SChu SHBN SPer SSpi SSta WBod WBrE WHar

FRAGARIA † (Rosaceae)
alpina — See *F. vesca* **'Semperflorens'**
– 'Alba' — See *F. vesca* **'Semperflorens Alba'**
x *ananassa* 'Aromel' (F) ♀ — CWSG GTwe MBri SDea WWeb
¶ – 'Auchincruive Climax' (F) — EMui
– 'Bogota' (F) — GTwe LRHS NBee
* – 'Bolero' — EMui GTwe
– 'Calypso' (F) — CSut EMui GTwe
– 'Cambridge Favourite' (F) ♀ — CMac CTri CWSG EMui GRei GTwe MBri NDal NRog SDea WWeb
– 'Cambridge Late Pine' (F) — CWSG EMui GTwe
¶ – 'Cambridge Sentry' (F) — EMui
– 'Cambridge Vigour' (F) — GTwe NBee NRog SDea
– 'Elsanta' (F) — CTri CWSG EMui GRei GTwe NDal SDea
– 'Elvira' (F) — EMui
* – 'Emily' — CSut EMui GTwe
¶ – 'Eros' (F) — EMui
– 'Evita' (F) — EMui
– 'Fraise des Bois' — See *F. vesca*
– 'Gorella' (F) — NDal WWeb
– 'Hapil' (F) ♀ — EMui GTwe LRHS NDal WLRN
– 'Honeoye' (F) ♀ — EMui GTwe LRHS
– 'Korona' (F) — CSut
– 'Kouril' (F) — LRHS
* – 'Laura' — EMui GTwe
¶ – 'Maraline' (F) — EMui
– 'Marastil' (F) — EMui
– 'Maxim' (F) — EMui
– 'Melody' (F) — GTwe
– 'Ostara' (F) — GTwe
– 'Pandora' (F) — WWeb
– 'Pegasus' (F) ♀ — EMui GTwe LRHS
¶ – pink-flowered — CFee
– 'Rapella' (F) — GTwe NDal
– 'Redgauntlet' (F) — GTwe NRog
– 'Rhapsody' (F) ♀ — EMui GTwe
– 'Royal Sovereign' (F) — CMac EMui GTwe
– 'Serenata' (F) — MHlr
¶ – 'Sophie' — CSut
¶ – 'Symphony' (F) — EMui GRei
– 'Tamella' (F) — EMui GTwe NDal
¶ – 'Tango' (F) — EMui

– 'Totem' (F)	GTwe
§ – 'Variegata' (F)	CGle CHid CLTr CMea CSev EBee ECro ELan EPla MAsh MCCP MHar MRav NEgg NHol NNrd NRoo NSti NTay SIng SPer WBea WOak WRha WRus WWin
¶ – 'Viva Rosa' (F)	EMui
'Baron Solemacher' (F)	EJud WHer
'Bowles' Double'	See *F. vesca* **'Multiplex'**
chiloensis (F)	EMon
– 'Chaval'	CHid ECha EGoo EMon EPPr MRav NChi NWoo
N – 'Variegata'	GCal LBuc MAvo WByw WEas
– x *virginiana*	CArn
daltoniana	NHol SIng
– CC&McK 559	GCHN
Pink Panda = 'Frel' (F)	CM&M CMGP CTri EBee EBrP EBre ECtt EGra LBre MArl MAsh MAus MBri MOne NEgg NHol NRoo SBre SHFr SIng SPer WByw WEas WElm WLRN WMaN WShe
indica	See *Duchesnea indica*
'Red Ruby'	EBrP EBre EMar LBre MAus NLar NRoo SBre SPer
* 'Ruby Surprise'	LRHS
¶ sp. from Taiwan	WHer
'Variegata'	See *F.* x *ananassa* **'Variegata'**
§ *vesca* (F)	CArn CKin ECoo EWFC GPoy LHol LSyl MHew NLon NMir SIde WBea WCla WGwG WJek WOak WPer WShi WWye
– 'Alexandra' (F)	CArn CBod ELau GAbr MChe NRog SIde WCHb
– 'Flore Pleno'	See *F. vesca* **'Multiplex'**
– 'Fructu Albo' (F)	CRow WAlt WPer
– Mara des Bois (F)	EMui GTwe
– 'Monophylla' (F)	CRow EJud EMon NHol SIde WHer
§ – 'Multiplex' (d)	CGle CJew CRow CSev EMon EMou GAbr MInt NChi NHex NHol NSti SSvw WAlt WByw WCHb WHer WOak WWye
§ – 'Muricata'	CFee CHid CLTr CPou CRow EMon GAbr NBrk NChi NSti WAlt WCer WHer WWye
* – 'Pineapple Crush'	WHer
– 'Plymouth Strawberry'	See *F. vesca* **'Muricata'**
– 'Rügen' (F)	CHal WGwy WHoo WPyg
§ – 'Semperflorens' (F)	CLTr EBar ILis MGra NBrk WAlt WOak
N – 'Variegata'	CHid EAst EHoe EPar MCLN MSCN MWgw NMir SMac WPer WSel

FRANCOA (Saxifragaceae)

appendiculata	CGre CSpe EMFP EMar ETen GMac SSca WHer WPic
Ballyrogan strain	IBlr
'Confetti'	SOkh WCot
* dwarf purple	EBee
'Purple Spike'	See *F. sonchifolia* **Rogerson's** **form**
§ *ramosa*	CGle CHan CSpe CTrC CTri GAbr GBuc IBlr LFis MAvo MGed MHlr MNrw NBro NRog NRoo NSti WFar WOve WWeb
– *alba*	See *F. ramosa*
§ *sonchifolia*	Widely available
– 'Alba'	CRDP CSpe SUsu WCot

§ – Rogerson's form	CGle CNic CRDP CSpe EGar EMar GBuc IBlr MAvo SDix SOkh WSan

FRANKENIA (Frankeniaceae)

laevis	CTri GGar SRms WWoo WWye
thymifolia	CHal CInt CMHG ELan EPar EPot ESis GBur GCHN MBar MPla MRav MWat NMen NNrd NRoo SAga SBod SChu SIng SSmi WFar WPer WPyg WWin

FRANKLINIA   (Theaceae) See Plant Deletions

FRASERA   (Gentianaceae) See Plant Deletions

FRAXINUS † (Oleaceae)

americana	CDul CMCN CTho WLRN WPGP
– 'Autumn Purple'	CBlo CEnd CTho MAsh MBlu SSpi
– 'Rose Hill'	CTho
§ *angustifolia*	CMCN CTho
– 'Elegantissima'	CTho
– 'Flame'	See *F. angustifolia* **'Raywood'**
– var. *lentiscifolia*	CTho
§ – 'Monophylla'	CLnd CTho
§ – 'Raywood' ♀	CB&S CBlo CDoC CDul CEnd CLnd CTho ELan ENot GChr IOrc MAsh MBlu MGos NWea SMad SPer WDin WJas WMou WOrn
* – 'Variegata'	CBot CPMA
chinensis	CDul CLnd CMCN CTho
– subsp. *rhyncophylla*	WMou
elonza	CTho
excelsior ♀	CB&S CBlo CDoC CDul CKin CLnd CPer ENot GRei LBuc LHyr LPan MBar MGos NBee NWea SHBN SPer WDin WMou WOrn WStI
– 'Allgold'	CEnd SMad
– 'Crispa'	EMon WMou
– f. *diversifolia*	CDul CLnd CTho EMon WMou
– 'Diversifolia Pendula'	See *F. excelsior* **'Heterophylla** **Pendula'**
– 'Geesink'	ENot IHos
§ – 'Heterophylla Pendula'	GAri WMou
– 'Jaspidea' ♀	CB&S CBlo CDoC CDul CEnd CLnd COtt CTho ENot GChr GRei IOrc MBar MBlu MOrn MGos MRav SHBN SPer SSpi SSta WDin WJas WMou WOrn WStI
– 'Nana'	EMon WPat
– 'Pendula' ♀	CBlo CDoC CDul CEnd CLnd CTho EBrP EBre ELan ENot GChr IOrc LBre LPan MAsh MBlu MBri NBee NWea SBre SHBN SPer WDin WJas WMou WOrn WStI
– 'Pendula Wentworthii'	WMou
– 'R.E. Davey'	CTho
– 'Westhof's Glorie' ♀	CDoC CLnd ECrN ENot SLPl WJas WOrn
holotricha	CTho
mariesii	See *F. sieboldiana*
nigra	CFil CMCN
– 'Fallgold'	CBlo MAsh
oregona	See *F. latifolia*

ornus ♀ — CBlo CBot CLnd CTho ELan ENot EPfP GChr IOrc MBri NWea SPer SSta WDin WFar WMou WTro WWat
– 'Arie Peters' — WStI
¶ – Sch 3177 — WHCr
oxycarpa — See *F. angustifolia*
pennsylvanica — CMCN WWes
– 'Aucubifolia' — CTho WMou
– var. *lanceolata* — See *F. pennsylvanica* var. *subintegerrima*
– 'Patmore' — CBlo
– 'Summit' — CTho
– 'Variegata' — CBlo CLnd CTho EPfP MAsh SSta WMou
quadrangulata — WDin WWoo
§ *sieboldiana* — CFil CLnd CPMA MBlu SSpi WCoo WMou
spaethiana — WMou
'Veltheimii' — See *F. angustifolia* 'Monophylla'
velutina — CBot CDul CMCN CSto CTho SLPl

FREESIA (Iridaceae)

alba Foster — See *F. lactea*
'Diana' — LAma
double mixed (d) — ETub GBur
elimensis — MSto
'Fantasy' (d) — LAma
hybrids — CSut NRog
§ *lactea* — LAma NRog
'Romany' (d) — LAma
'White Swan' — LAma
xanthospila — LBow MSto

FREMONTODENDRON (Sterculiaceae)

'California Glory' ♀ — Widely available
californicum — CAbb CBar CHEx ELan EMil IOrc MBlu MBri MGos MWhi NBee SHBN SOWG WAbe WBod WDin WNor WStI WWat WWin
decumbens — SSpi
mexicanum — CGre SAga
'Pacific Sunset' — CPMA EBee ENot LHop LRHS MBri SBid SMad SMur WWeb

FREYLINIA (Scrophulariaceae)

cestroides — See *F. lanceolata*
§ *lanceolata* — CB&S CPle CTre

FRITILLARIA † (Liliaceae)

acmopetala ♀ — CAvo CBro CMon ELan EPar EPot ERos ETub EWal GBur GCrs ITim LAma MBal MS&S MTho NMen NRog NWCA SSON SUsu SWas WAbe WLin
– subsp. *wendelboi* — EPot LAma
§ *affinis* — EHyt EPot EWal LAma MS&S MSto NHar SBid WLin
§ – var. *gracilis* — CAvo EHyt LAma MSto SBid SPer WLin
– 'Limelight' — EDAr EPot ETub GCrs
– 'Sunray' — GCrs NHar
– 'Vancouver Island' — EDAr EPot
– 'Wayne Roderick' — EPot
alburyana — EPot
arabica — See *F. persica*
armena — EHyt EPot LAma MSto
assyriaca — See *F. uva-vulpis*

atropurpurea — MSto
aurea — CLAP EPot NHar
biflora — CLAP EHyt MSto
– 'Martha Roderick' — CAvo CBro EBee EBrP EBre EDAr EPot ETub EWal LAma LBre MCli NTow SBid SBre
§ *bithynica* — CBro CLAP EPot LAma MSto NMen
brandegeei — EWal LAma
bucharica — CAvo CGra CLAP EHyt EPot MFos
camschatcensis — CAvo CBro CRDP ECha EFEx EHyt EPar EPot ETub GCrs LAma MS&S MSto MTho NDov NHar NMen NRog SSON SSpi WAbe WLin
* – *alpina aurea* — GCrs
– black — MSto
– f. *flavescens* — EFEx
¶ – from Alaska — GCrs
¶ – *multiflora* — WLin
carduchorum — See *F. minuta*
carica — CAvo EHyt EPot GCrs
– subsp. *serpenticola* — EPot
caucasica — CLAP EHyt LAma
'Chatto' — ECha
citrina — See *F. bithynica*
conica — EHyt GCrs NHar
crassifolia — EPot LAma
– subsp. *crassifolia* — CGra
§ – subsp. *kurdica* — EDAr EPot GCrs
davisii — CMea EHyt EPot GBur LAma MSto NHar
delphinensis — See *F. tubiformis*
¶ *drenovskyi* — CLAP
eastwoodiae — EPot ETub GCrs LAma
ehrhartii — EHyt EPot MSto
elwesii — CAvo EHyt MSto
forbesii — EHyt GCrs MSto
glauca — LAma SSON
– 'Goldilocks' — CAvo CMea EPot ETub
graeca — EPot GBur MSto MTho
– subsp. *graeca* — MSto
– subsp. *ionica* — See *F. graeca* subsp. *thessala*
§ – subsp. *thessala* — EHyt MS&S MSto MTho WLin
§ *grayana* — EHyt EPot ERos MSto
– tall form — CLAP
gussichiae — CLAP MS&S MSto
hermonis subsp. *amana* — CAvo EHyt EPot LAma NMen SBid
hispanica — See *F. lusitanica*
¶ *hupehensis* — LAma
imperialis — CAvo CB&S CHEx EBot MBal MBri NRog
– 'Aureomarginata' — LAma LBow MBri NRog
– 'Aurora' — CAvo EBar EBrP EBre EMon EPar ETub GBur LAma LBow LBre LFis MCli MWat NCut NRog SBre
– 'Crown upon Crown' — See *F. imperialis* 'Prolifera'
– 'Lutea' — CMGP EBot EMon GBur
– 'Lutea Maxima' — See *F. imperialis* 'Maxima Lutea'
– 'Maxima' — See *F. imperialis* 'Rubra Maxima'
§ – 'Maxima Lutea' ♀ — CBro CHEx EBee EBrP EBre ELan EPar EPfP ETub LAma LBow LBre LFis MCli MLLN NRog SBre
§ – 'Prolifera' — EBot EPar LAma LBow MLLN
– 'Rubra' — CMGP ELan EPar ETub LAma LBow MCli NBir NCut NRog

§ – 'Rubra Maxima'　CBro EBot EMon EPfP GBur LAma MLLN SMad
– 'Sulpherino'　LRHS
– 'The Premier'　EPar LAma NCat
involucrata　CAvo CBro LAma MS&S MSto SSON
ionica　See *F. graeca* subsp. *thessala*
japonica var. *koidzumiana*　EFEx
karadaghensis　See *F. crassifolia* subsp. *kurdica*
lanceolata　See *F. affinis*
§ *latifolia*　EPot GCrs LAma
– var. *nobilis*　See *F. latifolia*
liliacea　LAma
§ *lusitanica*　CLAP GCrs LAma MS&S MSto WLin
– MS 440　CMon
lutea　See *F. collina*
macrocarpa SB&L 258　CMon
meleagris ♀　CArn CAvo CBro CHar CMea ELan EPot ETub EWFC EWal GBur LAma LBow MBal MBri MBro MRPP MS&S NBir NHar NMen NRog WAbe WCla WHil WHoo WPGP WPat WShi
– 'Aphrodite'　CAvo EPot
– 'Jupiter'　LRHS
– 'Mars'　LRHS
– var. *unicolor* subvar. *alba* ♀　CBro ELan EPot ETub GBur LAma LBow MBri MBro MS&S NHar NRya SUsu WCru
§ *messanensis*　CMon EHyt GCrs LAma MBal MS&S WLin
– subsp. *gracilis*　EHyt MBal MS&S MSto
– subsp. *messanensis*　CBro
michailovskyi ♀　CAvo CBro ELan EPar EPot ETub EWal GBuc GBur GCra GCrs LAma MBri MSto MTho NMen NRog SSoC WAbe WCla WHil WPat WPyg
micrantha　LAma
¶ *minima*　EHyt
– JCA 500.100　MSto
§ *minuta*　EHyt EPot GCrs
montana　GCrs LRHS MS&S
nigra hort.　See *F. pyrenaica*
¶ *obliqua*　EHyt EPot
olivieri　CLAP GCrs MSto
pallidiflora ♀　CAvo CBro CLAP EHyt EMon EPar EPot ERos ETub EWal GBur GMaP LAma MBal MFos MS&S MSto MTho NHar NSla SPer SSpi SUsu WAbe WCru WLin WOMN WPen
§ *persica*　CB&S CBos EBar EBot EPar GBur LAma MBri MCli SBid SMad WFar
– 'Adiyaman' ♀　CAvo CBro EBrP EBre ELan EMon ETub LBow LBre LFis NRog SBre SSON WFar
– S&L 118　CMon
phaeanthera　See *F. affinis* var. *gracilis*
pinardii　EPot
pluriflora　EPot
pontica　CAvo CBro CLAP CMea CMon EHyt EPar EPot ERos ETub EWal GBur GMaP ITim LAma MBal MCli MFos MS&S MTho NSla SBid SBla SSpi WCru WLin
pudica　CMea EHyt GCrs LAma MS&S MSto MTho NHar WLin

* – 'Fragrant'　EDAr EPot GCrs
– 'Richard Britten'　EHyt
¶ *puqiensis*　LAma
purdyi　CAvo CLAP EHyt EPot GCrs NMen SPer
§ *pyrenaica* ♀　CAvo CBro CLAP CMon EHyt GCrs LAma MBal MS&S NHar NMen NSla SChu SSpi WGwy
raddeana　CLAP LAma MSto
recurva　CLAP
¶ – 'Sensational'　LAma
rhodocanakis　EHyt EPot
– JCA 502.600　MSto
roderickii　See *F. grayana*
roylei　MS&S
rubra major　See *F. imperialis* '**Rubra Maxima**'
ruthenica　EHyt ERos MS&S NMen
sewerzowii　EPot LAma MSto
sibthorpiana　CBro EHyt EPot GCrs LAma
spetsiotica　EHyt
sphaciotica　See *F. messanensis*
stenanthera　EHyt EPot LAma MSto
striata　EHyt
tenella　See *F. orientalis*
thunbergii　EHyt NMen SBid
§ *tubiformis*　GCrs
¶ *tuntasia*　GCrs
¶ *usuriensis*　EDAr LAma
§ *uva-vulpis*　CAvo CBro CMea EBee EHyt ELan EPar EPot ETub EWal GBur GMaP ITim LAma MFos MTho NWCA SSpi WAbe WCru
verticillata　CAvo CBro ECha EPar EPot GBur GCrs LAma MTho NHar SSpi WCru
whittallii　EPot MS&S MSto
zagrica　MSto

FUCHSIA † (Onagraceae)

'A.M. Larwick'　CSil EBak
'A.W. Taylor'　EBak SMer
'Aalt Groothuis'　EGou
'Abbé Farges'　CLit CLoc CSil EBak EBly ECtt EKMF LCla LFli MAsk MWhe NArc SKen SLBF
¶ 'Abbigayle Reine'　NArc
'Abigail'　EKMF
'Achievement' ♀　CLoc CSil LCla MAsk MJac NArc SKen
'Ada Perry'　ECtt NArc
'Adagio'　CLoc
'Ada's Love'　EKMF MAld
'Adinda'　EGou
¶ 'Admiration'　CSil
'Adrian Young'　MAsk
'Ailsa Garnett'　EBak
'Aintree'　CLit CSil NArc
'Airedale'　MAsk MJac NArc
'Ajax'　EGou
'Alabama Improved'　MAsk SKen
'Aladna'　CSil
'Aladna's Sanders'　EGou NArc
'Alan Ayckbourn'　CSil MWar NArc
'Alan Stilwell'　SLBF
'Alaska'　CLoc EBak EKMF NArc WGwG
'Albertus Schwab'　EGou
'Alde'　CSil EGou NArc
'Alf Thornley'　CSil EKMF LFli MAsk MWhe NArc

'Alfie' CSil
'Alfred Rambaud' CSil NArc
'Algerine' SLBF
'Alice Ashton' CLit EBak EKMF NArc
'Alice Doran' LCla SLBF
'Alice Hoffman' CLit CLoc CPor CSil EBak
EBly EGou EKMF LCla LFli
LVER MAld MAsk MBar MBri
MGos MJac MWat MWhe NArc
SKen SPer SSea WGwG
'Alice Mary' CLit EBak EBly EKMF EMan
'Alice Rowell' EKMF
'Alice Stringer' ECtt
'Alice Travis' CLit EBak
'Alipatti' EKMF
'Alison Ewart' CLit CLoc CSil EBak EKMF
MAsk MJac MWhe NArc
'Alison June' MBri
'Alison Patricia' CLit CSil EBak EKMF EMan
LCla MAld MWar MWhe SLBF
'Alison Reynolds' MBri NArc
'Alison Ryle' CSil EBak
'Alison Sweetman' CSil EKMF MJac MWhe SKen
'Allure' EGou
'Alma Hulscher' EGou
§ alpestris CLit EBak EGou EKMF LCla
'Alton Water' EGou EKMF
'Alwin' CLit CSil MWhe NArc
'Alyce Larson' CLit CPor CSil EBak LFli
MAsk MJac NArc WGwG
'Amanda Bridgland' EKMF LCla
'Amanda Jones' CLit EKMF MAsk MWhe NArc
'Ambassador' CLit EBak MAsk SKen SMer
'Amelie Aubin' CLoc EBak EKMF NArc
'America' EBak NArc
'American Dream' NArc
'American Flaming Glory' CSil EGou NArc
'Amethyst Fire' CSil
'Amigo' CLit EBak NArc
§ ampliata EGou EKMF LCla
'Amy Lye' CLit CLoc CSil EBak EKMF
MAsk NArc SKen
§ 'Andenken an Heinrich CLoc EBak EKMF LCla LFli
Henkel' MAsk MWhe
'André Le Nostre' EBak NArc
andrei EGou EKMF LCla
'Andrew' EBak EKMF MAsk NArc
'Andrew Carnegie' CLoc
'Andrew George' MJac
'Andrew Hadfield' CSil EKMF MAsk MWar NArc
SLBF
'Andrew Ryle' NArc
'Angela Leslie' CLoc EBak EKMF NArc
'Angela Rippon' CLit MJac MWhe NArc
¶ 'Angelina' EKMF SLBF
'Angel's Dream' CPor CSil MAsk
'Angel's Flight' EBak
'Anita' CLit CSil EGou EKMF MAld
MAsk MWhe NArc SLBF
'Anjo' (v) EGou EKMF NArc SLBF SSea
'Ann Adams' CSil MJac
'Ann Howard Tripp' CLoc CSil LFli MAsk MBri
MJac MWhe NArc
'Ann Lee' CLoc EBak
'Ann Roots' EGou
'Anna of Longleat' CLit CLoc EBak EMan NArc
SKen SLBF
'Annabel' ♀ CGre CLit CLoc CPor CSil
EBak EBly EGou EKMF EMan
LCla LFli LVER MAld MAsk
MBri MJac MWar MWhe NArc
NFai NHaw SLBF SSea WGwG

'Annie Earle' EKMF
'Anthea Day' CLoc
'Antigone' SLBF
'Aphrodite' CLoc EBak NArc
'Applause' CLoc CSil EBak EBly EGou
EKMF EMan LCla LVER
MAld MAsk MJac MWhe NArc
'Apple Blossom' EKMF
aprica hort. See F. × bacillaris
– Lundell See F. microphylla subsp.
aprica
'Aquarius' MWhe
'Arabella Improved' EKMF
arborea See F. arborescens
§ arborescens CLit CLoc CSil EBak EGou
EKMF ERea LCla MAsk NArc
SLBF SMrm WGwG
'Arcadia' MWar
'Arcadia Aubergine' NArc
'Arcadia Gold' ECtt LFli MWhe NArc WGwG
'Arcadia Lady' CLit MAsk MJac NArc
'Arcady' CLoc
'Archie Owen' MAsk
'Arel's Avondzon' NArc
'Ariel' CLit CSil EGou NArc
'Army Nurse' ♀ CLit CLoc CSil EKMF GCHN
LFli LVER MAsk MWhe NArc
SLBF
'Art Deco' CSil EGou NArc
'Ashley Jane' MAld
'Ashmore' CLit NArc
'Athela' EBak
'Atlantic Star' EBly EKMF MBri MJac NArc
WGwG
'Atlantis' CLit MAsk MJac NArc
'Atomic Glow' EBak NArc
'Aubergine' CLoc SLBF SSea
'Audray' CLit LFli MAsk NArc
'Audrey Booth' EGou
'Audrey Hepburn' EKMF NArc
'Aunt Juliana' CLit EBak
'Auntie Jinks' CLit CSil EBak EKMF LCla
LFli MAsk MJac MWar MWhe
NArc NHaw SLBF WGwG
* aureifolia EPfP
'Aurora Superba' CLit CLoc CSil EBak EKMF
SLBF
'Australia Fair' CLoc CSil EBak MAsk NArc
WGwG
§ austromontana EBak LCla
'Autumnale' CLit CLoc CSil EBak EKMF
EMan LCla LFli MAsk MBri
MWhe NArc SKen SLBF SMrm
SSea
'Avalanche' CLit CLoc CSil EBak LFli
MAsk NArc
'Avocet' CLoc EBak NArc
'Avon Celebration' CLoc
'Avon Gem' CLoc CSil
'Avon Gold' CLoc
¶ 'Axel of Denmark' EGou
ayavacensis EGou EKMF LCla
'Azure Sky' EKMF MJac
'Babette' EKMF
'Babs' MAsk
'Baby Blue Eyes' CLit CSil SLBF
'Baby Bright' CLit CSil LCla SLBF
'Baby Chang' CSil EGou MWhe
'Baby Face' NArc
¶ 'Baby Girl' EKMF
'Baby Pink' CLit CSil NArc
'Baby Thumb' CPor CSil

§ × *bacillaris* — CMHG CSam CWit EBak EGoo EHic EWes GAri MBlu MTed SIng SLBF SSoC
§ – 'Cottinghamii' — CDoC CSil WPen WSHC
§ – 'Oosje' — CSil EGou EKMF LCla
§ – 'Reflexa' — CTrC GQui SVen
'Bagworthy Water' — CLoc
'Baker's Tri' — EBak
¶ 'Balcony Queen' — LFli
'Balkonkönigin' — CLit CLoc CSil EBak MAsk SKen SMer
'Ballet Girl' — CLit CLoc CPor CSil EBak ECtt EKMF LCla SLBF
'Bambini' — CSil EBly
'Banks Peninsula' — GQui
'Banzai' — EKMF
'Barbara' — CLit CLoc CSil EBak EKMF LCla LFli MAsk MJac MWar MWhe NArc SKen
¶ 'Barbara Pountain' — LVER
¶ 'Barbara Windsor' — MAld
'Baron de Ketteler' — CSil EKMF NArc
'Baroness van Dedem' — CSil
'Baroque Pearl' — EKMF NArc
'Barry M. Cox' — EGou
'Barry's Queen' — CSil EBak
¶ 'Bart Simpson' — EGou
'Bashful' — CLit CSil EBly LCla LFli MAsk MBri NArc SKen
'Basketfull' — CLit CSil NArc
'Beacon' — CLoc CPor CSil EBak EKMF EMan IHos LCla LFli MAsk MBri MJac MWhe NArc NHaw SKen SSea WStI
'Beacon Rosa' — CLit CLoc CSil EGou EKMF EMan LCla LFli MAld MAsk MBri MJac MWar MWhe NArc SKen SLBF
'Bealings' — CLit CLoc CSil ECtt EGou EMan LCla LFli LVER MAsk MBri MJac MWhe NArc
'Beatrice Burtoft' — EKMF
'Beau Nash' — CLoc
¶ 'Beautiful Bobbie' — SLBF
'Beauty of Bath' — CLoc EBak NArc
'Beauty of Clyffe Hall' — CSil EBak
'Beauty of Exeter' — CLit COtt CSil EBak EKMF MAsk NArc
'Beauty of Prussia' — CLoc CSil ECtt
'Beauty of Swanley' — EBak
'Beauty of Trowbridge' — CDoC LCla NArc SKen
'Becky' — EGou
'Becky Jane' — CSil
'Bella Forbes' — CLoc CPor CSil EBak NArc
'Bella Rozella' — CSil EGou EKMF LFli MAsk SCoo SLBF
'Belsay Beauty' — CLit MJac NArc
'Belvoir Beauty' — CLoc MJac
¶ 'Ben de Jong' — EGou
'Ben Jammin' — CLoc EGou SLBF
N 'Beranger' — CSil EBak
'Berba's Coronation' — EGou EKMF NArc
'Berba's Happiness' — EGou
'Berba's Ingrid' — MAld
'Bergnimf' — EKMF LCla NArc WGwG
'Berliner Kind' — CSil EBak
'Bermuda' — CSil EKMF
'Bernadette' — CLTr
'Bertha Gadsby' — EKMF MAsk
'Beryl Shaffery' — EGou
'Beryl's Choice' — CLit
'Beth Robley' — CLit CSil MAsk

'Betsy Ross' — EBak NArc
'Bette Sibley' — CSil
¶ 'Betty Jean' — EGou
'Beverley' — CSil EBak EBly LFli
'Bewitched' — EBak NArc
'Bianca' — CLit LFli SMur
'Bicentennial' — CLit CLoc CSil EBak EBly EGou EKMF LFli LVER MAsk MJac MWar MWhe NHaw SKen SSea
¶ 'Big Charles' — EGou
'Big Slim' — EGou
'Bill Gilbert' — LCla
'Bill Stevens' — EKMF
'Billy Green' ♀ — CLTr CLit CLoc CSil EBak EBly ECtt EKMF LCla LFli MAld MAsk MJac MWar MWhe NArc SKen SLBF SSoC
'Bishop's Bells' — CSil MAsk MJac NArc
'Bits' — NArc
'Bittersweet' — CLit CSil LFli MAsk NArc
'Black Beauty' — CSil
'Black Prince' — CSil MAsk MBri MWar NArc
I 'Blanche Regina' — MJac MWhe
'Bland's New Striped' — EBak EKMF NArc SLBF
'Blazeaway' — CLit MBri MWar
'Blood Donor' — EKMF MAld MJac
'Blowick' — CLit EMan LFli MAsk MBri NArc SMer
'Blue Beauty' — CSil EBak NArc
'Blue Bush' — CPor CSil EKMF MAsk MJac NArc
'Blue Butterfly' — EBak NArc
¶ 'Blue Eyes' — LFli
'Blue Gown' — CLit CLoc CSil EBak EKMF LCla LVER MAsk MWar MWhe NArc SBid SKen
'Blue Ice' — CSil MWhe
'Blue Lace' — CSil
N 'Blue Lagoon' — MAsk
'Blue Lake' — CLit CSil LVER MAsk
'Blue Mink' — EBak
'Blue Mirage' — CSil LCla MAsk WGwG
'Blue Mist' — EBak
'Blue Pearl' — CLit EBak LFli MAsk NArc
'Blue Petticoat' — CLoc
'Blue Pinwheel' — CSil EBak
'Blue Sails' — NArc
'Blue Satin' — CLit COtt MAld MWhe NArc
'Blue Tit' — CSil SKen
'Blue Veil' — CLit CLoc CSil EKMF LFli LVER MAsk MJac MWar SKen SLBF
'Blue Waves' — CLit CLoc CSil EBak EBly EGou EKMF EMan LFli MAsk MJac MWar MWhe NArc WGwG
'Blush of Dawn' — CLit CLoc CSil EBak EBly EGou EKMF LFli LVER MAld MAsk MWar NArc SLBF WGwG
'Blythe' — EBly EGou
'Bob Pacey' — MJac
'Bob Paisley' — MBri
'Bobby Boy' — EBak
'Bobby Dazzler' — CSil ECtt EKMF NArc
'Bobby Shaftoe' — EBak EKMF MAsk MWhe NArc
'Bobby Wingrove' — EBak NArc
'Bobolink' — EBak NArc
'Bob's Best' — CSil EBly LVER MJac
'Bob's Choice' — MAsk

'Boerhaave' — EBak MAsk
boliviana Britton — See *F. sanctae-rosae*
§ *boliviana* Carrière — CAbb CLit CLoc CSil EBak EKMF GCra LCla MBEx MWhe NArc SBid SMrm
  – 'Alba' — See *F. boliviana* Carrière var. *alba*
§ – var. *alba* ♀ — CLit CLoc CSil EBak EGou EKMF LCla LFli MAsk MBEx MWhe NArc SBid SMrm
  – var. *boliviana* — EGou
  – var. *luxurians* — See *F. boliviana* Carrière var. *alba*
  – f. *puberulenta* — See *F. boliviana* Carrière
'Bon Accorde' — CLoc CSil EBak EBly EKMF LCla MAsk MJac SSea
'Bon Bon' — CLit CSil EBak LFli NArc
'Bonita' — CLit CSil MAsk MJac NArc
'Bonnie Doan' — NArc
'Bonnie Lass' — CLit CSil EBak NArc
'Bonny' — CLoc
'Bora Bora' — CSil EBak EKMF
'Border Princess' — EBak LCla
'Border Queen' ♀ — CLit CLoc CPor CSil EBak EKMF EMan LCla LFli MAld MAsk MJac MWar NArc SLBF
'Border Reiver' — CLit EBak LCla NArc
'Börnemanns Beste' — CLoc CSil EBak EKMF LCla MAsk SKen
'Bouffant' — CLoc CSil EBak MAsk MJac SMer
'Bountiful' — CGre CLit CLoc CSil EKMF MAsk MWhe NArc SKen
'Bouquet' — CSil EKMF LCla SKen
'Bouvigne' — NArc
'Bow Bells' — CLoc CSil MAld MAsk MJac MWhe NArc
'Boy Marc' — CLit EGou LCla
'Brandt's Five Hundred Club' — CLoc EBak
'Breckland' — EBak MJac NArc
'Breeders' Delight' — MBri
'Breeder's Dream' — EBak NArc
'Brenda' — CLit CLoc CSil EBak NArc
'Brenda Pritchard' — CSil ECtt LVER
'Brenda White' — CLit CLoc CSil EKMF MAsk NArc
'Brentwood' — EBak
brevilobis — CSil EGou EKMF
'Brian A McDonald' — EGou
'Brian Breary' — EGou
'Brian C. Morrison' — EGou EKMF LCla MAsk
'Brian Ellis' — NArc
'Brian Soames' — EBak
'Brian Stannard' — EGou LCla
'Bridal Pink' — LFli
'Bridal Veil' — EBak NArc
'Bridesmaid' — CSil EBak EKMF MAsk NArc
'Brigadoon' — CLit CLoc EBak
'Brightling' — CSil
'Brighton Belle' — CLit EGou NArc SSoC WGwG
N 'Brilliant' — CLit CLoc CSil EBak LFli LHil MAsk MGos MPla MWat MWhe SKen
'Briony Caunt' — CSil EKMF
'British Jubilee' — CSil EKMF MAsk NArc
'British Sterling' — NArc
'Brodsworth' — CPor CSil MAsk
¶ 'Bronze Banks Peninsula' — EKMF
'Brookwood Belle' ♀ — CLit EBly LCla MAld MJac SLBF
'Brookwood Dale' — MWhe

'Brookwood Joy' — CLit CSil EGou MAsk MJac NArc SLBF
'Brookwood Lady' — MWhe
'Brutus' ♀ — CLit CLoc CSil EBak EBly EKMF EMan LCla LFli MAsk MWat MWhe NArc NHaw SKen WGwG WStI
'Bryan Breary' — EKMF
'Bubble Hanger' — CSil NArc
'Buddha' — EBak
¶ 'Bugle Boy' — EGou
'Bunny' — CSil EBak LFli NArc
¶ 'Burma Star' — MAsk
'Burton Brew' — MJac
'Buttercup' — CLoc CSil EBak LFli MAsk NArc
'Butterfly' — MAsk
¶ 'Byron Rees' — EGou
'C.J. Howlett' — CSil EBak
'Caballero' — EBak
'Caesar' — CSil EBak EGou MAsk NArc
'Caledonia' — CSil EBak
'Calumet' — EGou
'Cambridge Louie' — CLit CPor CSil EBak LCla LFli MAld MAsk MBri MWar MWhe NArc
'Camel Estuary' — NArc
'Camelot' — EBak NArc
campii — EGou EKMF
* – var. *rubra* — EGou
campos-portoi — CSil EKMF LCla
'Cancun' — MJac
'Candlelight' — CGre CLoc CSil EBak NArc
'Candy Kisses' — CLit
'Candy Stripe' — CLoc
canescens Bentham — EBak
  – Munz — See *F. ampliata*
¶ 'Canny Bob' — NArc
'Capri' — CSil EBak LFli NArc
'Cara Mia' — CLoc CSil SKen
'Caradela' — MAld
'Cardinal' — CLoc NArc
'Cardinal Farges' — CLit CLoc CSil EKMF LCla LFli NArc SKen SLBF SSea
'Carillon van Amsterdam' — CLit MWhe
'Carioca' — EBak
'Carisbrooke Castle' — EKMF
'Carl Drude' — LCla
'Carl Wallace' — EKMF MJac
'Carla Johnston' — CLTr CLit CLoc CSil EBly EKMF LCla MAld MAsk MBri MJac MWar MWhe NArc SSea
'Carlisle Bells' — NArc
'Carmel Blue' — CLTr CLoc CSil EKMF LFli MAsk MWhe NArc WGwG
'Carmen' — CSil
'Carmen Maria' — CLit LCla NArc
'Carmine Bell' — CSil EKMF
'Carnea' — CSil
'Carnival' — LCla NArc
'Carnoustie' — EBak EGou NArc
'Carol Grace' — CLoc NArc
'Carol Nash' — CLoc
'Carol Roe' — EBly EKMF
'Caroline' — CGre CLoc CSil EBak EBly EKMF LFli MAsk MBlu NArc SLBF
'Cascade' — CLit CLoc CSil ECtt EKMF EMan LCla LFli MAsk MBri MJac MWar MWhe NArc NHaw SKen SRms SSea

'Casper Hauser' CLit CSil EGou EKMF MAsk NArc
'Catherina' EGou
'Catherine Bartlett' EKMF NArc
'Catherine Claire' CLit
'Cathie MacDougall' EBak NArc
'Cecile' CSil EBly ECtt EGou EKMF LFli LVER MAsk MJac MWar MWhe NArc SLBF
'Celadore' CLit CSil LFli LVER MAsk MJac NArc SKen
'Celebration' CSil EGou LCla
'Celia Smedley' ♀ CGre CLit CLoc CPor CSil EBak EBly EGou EKMF LCla LFli LVER MAld MAsk MBri MJac MWar MWhe NArc SKen SLBF
'Centerpiece' EBak SMer
'Central Scotland' CLit LCla
'Ceri' CLoc NArc
'Cerrig' NArc
'Chameleon' CSil NArc WGwG
'Champagne Celebration' CLoc
'Chandleri' LCla NArc SLBF
'Chang' CLit CLoc CSil EBak EKMF LBlm LCla LFli MAsk MWar MWhe NArc SLBF
'Chantry Park' EGou LCla SLBF
'Charisma' NArc
'Charles Edward' CSil EKMF
'Charlie Gardiner' EBak EGou MWhe NArc
'Charlie Girl' EBak
'Charlotte Clyne' MJac
'Charming' CLoc CPor CSil EBak GCHN MAsk MJac MWar MWhe NArc
'Chase Delight' CLit EKMF LFli MWar NHaw
'Checkerboard' ♀ CLit CLoc EBak EGou EKMF LCla LFli LVER MAld MAsk MJac MWar MWhe NArc SKen SLBF SSea WEas WGwG
'Cheers' CSil EGou EKMF MAsk MWar MWhe
¶ 'Cherry Pie' SIng
¶ 'Cheryl' MJac
'Chessboard' CLoc CSil
'Chillerton Beauty' ♀ CLTr CLit CLoc CSil CTri ECtt EKMF LCla LFli MAsk MJac MWhe NArc SLBF SPer
'China Doll' CLit EBak LFli MWhe NArc SKen
'China Lantern' CLit CLoc CSil EBak LFli MAsk
'Chiquita Maria' NArc
'Chris' EGou
'Christ Driessen' EGou
'Christina Becker' NArc
'Christine Bamford' EGou
'Christine Shaffery' EGou
'Christmas Ribbons' EGou
cinerea EGou EKMF LCla
'Cinnabarrina' SLBF
'Circe' CLit EBak EKMF MAsk NArc
'Circus' EBak
'Circus Spangles' COtt CSil EGou LFli MAsk SCoo SMur
'Citation' CLoc CSil EBak EKMF LFli MJac SSea
'City of Adelaide' CLoc CSil MWhe
'City of Leicester' CSil LCla MAsk MBri
'Claire Belle' SLBF
'Claire de Lune' EBak LFli MAsk NArc SLBF
'Claire Evans' CLoc SMer

'Claire Oram' CLoc SSea
'Cliantha' MAsk MJac MWhe NArc
'Clifford Gadsby' EBak NArc
'Cliff's Hardy' CPor CSil EKMF LCla MAsk NArc
'Cliff's Own' CSil NArc
'Cliff's Unique' CSil EBly MAsk MWar
'Clifton Beauty' MAsk MJac
'Clifton Charm' CSil EBly MJac
'Clipper' CSil
'Cloth of Gold' CLit CLoc EBak MAsk MJac MWhe SKen SSea
'Cloverdale Jewel' CSil EBak ECtt LCla MWhe NArc
'Cloverdale Joy' EBak MAsk
'Cloverdale Pearl' ♀ CLit CSil EBak EKMF EMan ENot LCla LFli MAsk MJac MWhe NArc WPyg
'Coachman' CLit CLoc CPor CSil EBak EBly EKMF EMan LCla LFli MAld MAsk MWar MWhe NArc NHaw SLBF WGwG
coccinea CGre CSil EGou EKMF LCla
'Coconut Ice' NArc
x *colensoi* ECou EKMF LCla MAsk SHFr
'Colin Chambers' EGou
'Collingwood' CLit CLoc CSil EBak MAsk NArc
'Colne Fantasy' EKMF LFli
'Colne Greybeard' CSil NArc
'Come Dancing' CLit CSil ECtt LCla LFli LVER MAsk NArc SKen
N 'Comet' CLit CLoc CSil EBak NArc
'Conchilla' EBak
'Confection' NArc
'Congreve Road' EGou MAsk
'Connie' CSil EBak
'Conspicua' CSil EBak EGou EKMF NArc
'Constable Country' CLit EGou NArc
'Constance' CLit CLoc CSil EGou EKMF LCla MAsk MJac MWar MWhe NArc SKen SLBF
'Constance Comer' MJac
N 'Constellation' CLoc EBak MAsk MWhe NArc
'Continental' EGou NArc
'Copycat' CSil
'Coquet Bell' EBak MAsk NArc
'Coquet Dale' EBak MAsk MJac MWhe NArc
'Coquet Gold' CSil ECtt NArc
'Coral Baby' EGou
'Coral Seas' EBak
§ 'Coralle' ♀ CLit CLoc CPor CSil EBak EBly EGou EKMF EMan LBlm LCla LFli MAsk MJac MWar MWhe NArc SKen SLBF
'Corallina' ♀ CLit CLoc CMHG CSil EBak EKMF IHos LFli MAsk MWhe NArc SKen SRms SSea WPic WWat
cordifolia Bentham CTre EBak MAsk MBEx
– hort. See *F. splendens*
'Core'ngrato' CLoc EBak
'Cornelia Smith' EGou
'Cornwall Calls' CLit
'Corsage' NArc
'Corsair' CLit CSil EBak EKMF LFli NArc
§ *corymbiflora* EBak EGou EKMF LCla
– *alba* See *F. boliviana* var. *alba* Carrière
'Cosmopolitan' CLit CSil EBak NArc
'Costa Brava' CLoc EBak NArc

'Cotta Bella'   EKMF MJac NArc
'Cotta Bright Star'   CLit EKMF MAsk NArc
'Cotta Fairy'   EKMF
'Cotta Princess'   EKMF
'Cotta Vino'   EKMF MAsk NArc SLBF
'Cottinghamii'   See *F. × bacillaris*
                       'Cottinghamii'
'Cotton Candy'   CLit CLoc CSil EBly EGou
                       LCla LFli MAsk MWhe SLBF
'Countdown Carol'   EBly
'Countess of Aberdeen' CLoc CSil EBak EGou EKMF
                       MAsk NArc SLBF
'Countess of Maritza' CLoc
'County Park'   ECou EWes
'Court Jester'   CLoc EBak NArc
'Cover Girl'   CLit EBak LFli MWhe NArc
                       NHaw
'Coxeen'   EBak
'Crackerjack'   CLit CLoc EBak
crassistipula   EKMF LCla
'Creampuff'   NArc
'Crescendo'   CLoc SKen
'Crinkley Bottom'   EBly EKMF LCla LVER MJac
                       SLBF
'Crinoline'   EBak NArc
'Crosby Serendipidy'   CLoc
'Crosby Soroptimist'   CLit CSil EBly LCla MAsk
                       MWar MWhe
'Cross Check'   CLit EMan MAsk MBri MJac
                       NArc
'Crusader'   CSil
'Crystal Blue'   EBak MAsk NArc
'Crystal Stars'   CSil NArc SKen
'Cupcake'   NArc
'Cupid'   CSil EBak NArc
'Curly Q'   CLit CSil EBak EKMF LFli
                       MAsk NArc
'Curtain Call'   CLit CLoc EBak NArc SKen
cylindracea   EKMF LCla
– (f)   EGou
– (m)   EGou
'Cymon'   CSil MAsk MWhe
'Cymru'   NArc
'Cyril Holmes'   NArc
cyrtandroides   EKMF
'Daffodil Dolly'   NArc
'Dainty'   EBak
'Dainty Lady'   EBak
'Daisy Bell'   CLit CLoc CSil EBak ECtt
                       EGou EKMF LCla LFli MAsk
                       MJac MWhe NArc NHaw SSea
                       WGwG
'Dalton'   EBak NArc
¶ 'Dancing Bloom'   CLit
'Dancing Flame'   CLit CLoc CSil EBly EGou
                       EKMF EMan LCla LFli LVER
                       MAld MAsk MBri MJac MWar
                       MWhe NArc NHaw SKen SLBF
                       WGwG
'Danish Pastry'   LFli NArc
'Danny Boy'   CLoc EBak EGou EKMF EMan
                       MAsk MWhe NArc
'Daphne Arlene'   CSil
'Dark Eyes' ♀   CLit CLoc CPor CSil EBak
                       EGou EKMF EMan LCla LFli
                       LVER MAld MAsk MBri MJac
                       MWar MWhe NArc NFai NHaw
                       SLBF SSea WGwG
¶ 'Dark Lady'   MWhe
'Dark Secret'   EBak NArc
'Dark Treasure'   CDoC CLit CSil LFli

'David'   CSil EGoo EGou EKMF EOHP
                       LCla MAsk MPla MWhe SKen
                       SLBF
'David Alston'   CLoc EBak
'David Lockyer'   CLoc
'David Ward'   EGou EKMF LCla
'Dawn'   EBak LCla SKen SMer
'Dawn Carless'   EGou
'Dawn Sky'   EBak
'Dawn Star'   CSil LVER MJac MWhe NArc
'Dawn Thunder'   LFli NArc SMur
'Dawning'   EGou
'Day by Day'   CPor MAsk
'Day Star'   EBak
'Daytime Live'   EBly EKMF
'De Groot's Pipes'   EGou
'Debby'   EBak NArc
'Deben Petite'   CSil
'Deben Rose'   CSil MAsk NArc WGwG
¶ 'Deborah Mitchell'   WGwG
'Deborah Street'   CLoc
N *decussata*   EBak EGou EKMF LCla
'Dee Copley'   EBak NArc
'Dee Star'   CLit NArc
'Deep Purple'   CLoc CSil EGou EKMF LFli
                       MAsk SCoo SLBF
'Delaval Lady'   CLit CSil
'Delicia'   CSil
'Delilah'   EKMF MJac
'Delta's Bride'   EGou SLBF
'Delta's Delight'   NArc
'Delta's Dream'   NArc WGwG
'Delta's Groom'   EGou
'Delta's K.O.'   NArc
'Delta's Night'   EGou
'Delta's Parade'   EGou NArc
'Delta's Song'   NArc SLBF
'Delta's Sprinkler'   NArc
'Delta's Symphonie'   EGou
'Delta's Trick'   EGou
'Delta's Wonder'   CSil
§ *denticulata*   CLit CLoc CMHG CSil EBak
                       EGou EKMF ERea LCla MAsk
                       NArc SLBF WGwG
dependens   See *F. corymbiflora*
'Derby Imp'   CLit MAsk NArc
'Derby Star'   CSil
'Desperate Daniel'   LCla
'Deutsche Perle'   CLit
'Devonshire Dumpling' CGre CLTr CLit CLoc CSil
                       EBak EBly ECtt EGou EKMF
                       EMan LCla LFli LVER MAld
                       MAsk MBri MJac MWar MWhe
                       NArc NHaw SKen SLBF
'Diablo'   CSil EBak EGou
¶ 'Diamond Celebration' EKMF
'Diana'   EBak MAsk
'Diana Wills'   MWhe SKen
'Diana Wright'   CSil WSPU
'Diane Brown'   CLit EKMF LCla MAsk MWhe
                       SSea
'Dick Swinbank'   EKMF
'Die Fledermaus'   NArc
'Dilly-Dilly'   MAsk
'Dimples'   CSil MAsk MBri
'Diny Hetterscheid'   EGou
'Dipton Dainty'   CLoc CSil EBak LCla NArc
¶ 'Dirk van Delen'   MWhe

'Display' ♀	CLit CLoc CSil EBak ECtt EKMF EMan IHos LCla LFli MAld MAsk MBri MJac MWar MWhe NArc NHaw SLBF SSea WGwG WStI
'Doc'	CLit CSil LCla LFli MAsk
'Docteur Topinard'	CLoc EBak
'Doctor'	See *F.* **'The Doctor'**
'Doctor Brendan Freeman'	MJac NArc
'Doctor Foster'	CLoc CSil CTri EBak ENot NArc SBid WEas
'Doctor Olson'	CLoc EBak
'Doctor Robert'	EBly EKMF MBri MJac MWhe NArc
§ 'Dollar Princess' ♀	CLit CLoc CPor CSil EBak EBly ECtt EGou EKMF EMan IHos LCla LFli MAld MAsk MBri MJac MWar MWhe NArc NFai NHaw SChu SKen SLBF WGwG WStI
'Dolly Daydream'	EKMF NArc
'Domacin'	MWhe
¶ 'Dominique'	EKMF
'Dominyana'	EBak EKMF LCla
'Don Peralta'	EBak
'Dopey'	CHar CSil LCla LFli MAsk
'Doreen Gladwyn'	SLBF
'Doreen Redfern'	CLoc CSil EKMF LFli MAsk MJac MWhe NArc
'Doris Coleman'	CLit EMan LFli
'Doris Hobbs'	EKMF
¶ 'Dorking Delight'	LCla
'Dorothea Flower'	CLoc CSil EBak
'Dorothy'	CSil LCla SLBF
'Dorothy Day'	CLoc
'Dorothy Hanley'	EGou
¶ 'Dorothy M. Goldsmith'	EGou
'Dorothy Shields'	CLit LCla MAld MJac
'Dorrian Brogdale'	EGou LCla
'Dove House'	CSil EKMF
'Drake 400'	CLoc
'Drame'	CLit CPor CSil EBak EKMF LCla LFli MAsk NArc SKen SSea
'Drum Major'	EBak NArc
'Du Barry'	EBak NArc
'Duchess of Albany'	CLit CLoc CSil EBak MAsk NArc
'Duchess of Cornwall'	CSil
'Duet'	CLit CSil SMur
N 'Duke of Wellington'	CLoc
'Dulcie Elizabeth'	CLit CSil EBak LCla LFli MJac MWar MWhe NArc
'Dusky Beauty'	CLit CSil MJac NArc
'Dusky Rose'	CLoc CSil EBak EGou LFli MAsk MJac MWhe NArc SMer WGwG
'Dutch King Size'	EGou
'Dutch Mill'	CLoc EBak
'Duyfken'	CLit CSil NArc
'Earl of Beaconsfield'	See *F.* **'Laing's Hybrid'**
'Earre Barré'	CLit EGou
'East Anglian'	CLoc CSil EBak NArc
'Easter Bonnet'	CLoc
'Easterling'	NArc
'Ebbtide'	CLoc EBak NArc
'Echo'	CLit CLoc
'Ed Largarde'	EBak EKMF MAsk
'Edale'	CSil
'Eden Beauty'	NArc
'Eden Lady'	CLoc CSil MBri MWar NArc

'Eden Princess'	MJac MWhe
'Edith'	CSil EKMF LCla SLBF
'Edith Emery'	LFli
'Edith Hall'	EGou EKMF
¶ 'Edith Jack'	CPor
'Edna W. Smith'	CSil ECtt
'Edwin J. Goulding'	EGou LCla
'Eileen Raffill'	EBak
'Eileen Saunders'	CSil EBak
'Eira Goulding'	EGou
'El Camino'	CLit CSil LFli MAsk MWhe NArc NFai
'El Cid'	CLoc CSil EBak EKMF MAsk NArc
'Elaine Ann'	EBly MJac
'Eleanor Clark'	EKMF LCla NArc
'Eleanor Leytham'	CLit EBak EKMF LCla MAsk NArc
'Eleanor Rawlins'	CSil EBak EKMF NArc SKen
'Elfin Glade'	CLoc CPor CSil EBak
'Elfrida'	CSil EKMF
'Elfriede Ott'	CLit CLoc EBak EKMF MWhe SLBF
'Elisabeth Honorine'	NArc
N 'Elizabeth'	EBak LFli NArc
'Elizabeth Broughton'	EKMF
'Elizabeth Tompkins'	EKMF MJac
'Elizabeth Travis'	EBak
'Ellen Morgan'	EBak
'Elma'	EGou
'Elsa'	CLit ECtt
'Elsie Downey'	NArc
'Elsie Mitchell'	CLit CSil LCla MAsk MWar MWhe NArc
§ 'Emile de Wildeman'	EBak EKMF MWar
'Emily Austen'	EKMF NArc
'Emma Louise'	NArc
'Emma Rowell'	EKMF
'Empress of Prussia' ♀	CLit CLoc CSil EBak EKMF EMan LFli MAsk NArc SKen SLBF SSea
'Enchanted'	CLit EBak MWar
encliandra subsp. *encliandra*	EGou EKMF LCla
§ – subsp. **tetradactyla**	EKMF LCla SLBF
§ 'Enfant Prodigue'	CLTr CLoc CSil EKMF
¶ 'Englander'	EGou
'English Rose'	CSil MAsk
'Enstone'	See *F. magellanica* var. *molinae* **'Enstone'**
'Eppsii'	CSil
'Erica Julie'	NArc SLBF
'Eric's Hardy'	CSil
¶ 'Eric's Majestic'	EKMF MJac
'Erika Frohmann'	SLBF
'Erika Köth'	CSil
'Ernest Rankin'	CSil EKMF NArc
'Ernestine'	EBly EGou MWhe
'Ernie Bromley'	EGou NArc SLBF
'Eroica'	NArc
'Errol'	CLoc
'Estelle Marie'	CLit CLoc CSil EBak EGou EKMF LCla MAsk MBri MJac MWar MWhe SLBF SSea
'Esther Divine'	CSil MAsk
'Eternal Flame'	CLit CSil EBak LFli MBri MWhe NArc SKen
'Eureka Red'	EGou
'Eurydice'	CLoc
'Eusebia'	EGou EKMF MAsk MJac NArc

'Eva Boerg'	CLit CLoc CPor CSil EBak ECtt EKMF EMan IHos LCla LFli MAsk MBri MWar MWhe NArc NFai NHaw SKen WGwG WKif
'Eva Twaites'	EGou
'Evanson's Choice'	SKen
'Eve Hollands'	EGou LCla
'Evelyn Stanley'	EGou
'Evelyn Steele Little'	EBak
'Evening Sky'	EBak NArc
'Evensong'	CLit CLoc CSil EBak LFli MWhe NArc
'Excalibur'	CLit EGou NArc
excorticata	CB&S CDoC CSil CTre CTrw ECou EGou EKMF LCla WPGP WSHC
'Exton Beauty'	NArc
'Fabian Franck'	CLit EGou LCla
¶ 'Fairy Floss'	EGou
'Fairytales'	NArc
'Falklands'	CPor CSil LFli MAsk
'Falling Stars'	CLit CLoc CSil EBak MWhe
'Fan Dancer'	EBak
'Fancy Flute'	CLit CSil NArc
'Fancy Free'	LFli MBri WLRN
'Fancy Pants'	CLoc EBak EGou MAsk MBri
'Fanfare'	CDoC EBak EKMF NArc
'Fascination'	See F. 'Emile de Wildeman'
'Fashion'	EBak
'Fasna 1100'	NArc
'Favourite'	EBak
'Fenman'	EBly MJac NArc
'Fergie'	LCla
'Festival'	MAsk
¶ 'Festival Lights'	EGou
'Festoon'	EBak
'Fey'	CLit EGou EKMF MAsk
'Fiery Spider'	EBak NArc
'Figaro'	EGou
§ 'Filigraan'	CSil NArc
Filigree	See F. 'Filigraan'
'Fine Lady'	CLit
'Finn'	EBly EGou
'Fiona'	CLit CLoc CSil EBak EGou LFli MAsk NArc
'Fiona Jane'	EKMF
'Fiona Lynn'	EGou
'Fiona Pitt'	CLit EGou LCla
'Fire Mountain'	CLit CLoc CSil MWhe NArc SKen SSea
'Firefly'	NArc
'Firefox'	NArc
'Firelite'	EBak NArc
'Firenza'	MWar
'First Lady'	CLit MAsk NArc
'First Success'	EGou EKMF MAsk SLBF
'Flair'	CLoc
'Flame'	EBak
'Flamenco Dancer'	CLoc EGou LFli MAsk SLBF
'Flash' ♀	CLit CLoc CSil CTri EBak EKMF LCla LFli MAld MAsk MJac MWhe NArc SLBF WFar WStI
'Flashlight'	EGou ELan
'Flat Jack o'Lancashire'	ECtt EKMF
'Flavia'	EBak
'Flirtation Waltz'	CGre CLit CLoc CSil EBak EKMF EMan LCla LFli MAld MAsk MBri MJac MWhe NArc SSea
'Flocon de Neige'	EBak NArc
'Floral City'	CLoc EBak NArc
'Florence Mary Abbott'	CSil EGou EMan MWar
'Florence Turner'	CSil EBak EKMF MAsk MWhe SKen
'Florentina'	CLoc CSil EBak EGou EKMF NArc
'Floretta'	NArc
'Fluffy Frills'	CLit CSil
'Flyaway'	EBak NArc
'Fly-by-night'	NArc
'Flying Cloud' ♀	CLoc CSil EBak EKMF LFli MAsk MBri MWhe NArc
'Flying Scotsman'	CLoc CSil EBak EBly EGou EKMF LFli LVER MAsk MJac NArc SLBF
'Folies Bergères'	EBak
'Foline'	NArc
'Foolke'	CSil EBak EBly
'Forest King'	CLit NArc
N 'Forget Me Not'	CLoc EBak EKMF MAsk NArc
'Formosissima'	NArc
'Fort Bragg'	EBak NArc SKen
'Forward Look'	MWhe
'Fountains Abbey'	EMan NArc
'Foxgrove Wood'	CLit EBak EBly LCla MAld NArc SLBF
'Frank Sanford'	NArc
'Frank Saunders'	CSil LCla
'Frank Unsworth'	ECtt EKMF MAsk MJac MWar MWhe NArc
'Frau Hilde Rademacher'	CLit CSil EBak EKMF EMan LFli MAld MPla NArc NHaw SLBF
'Frauke'	NArc
'Fred Swales'	CSil EKMF
¶ 'Fred's First'	CPor CSil
'Freefall'	EBak
'Friendly Fire'	CLit CLoc EKMF LFli NArc
'Friendship'	MAsk
'Frosted Flame'	CLit CLoc CSil EKMF LCla LFli MAsk MJac MWar MWhe NArc SLBF SSea
'Frühling'	CSil EBak
I 'Fuchsia Fan'	EBly
'Fuchsiade '88'	CLoc CSil EBak LCla MAsk MWhe
'Fuchsiarama'	EKMF
'Fuchsiarama '91'	EBly EGou MAsk NArc
'Fuji San'	EGou LCla
'Fuksie Foetsie'	CSil EGou EKMF MAsk SLBF
fulgens ♀	CMHG EKMF LCla LHil MAsk MBal MWhe NArc
– 'Gesneriana'	See F. 'Gesneriana'
– 'Rubra Grandiflora'	See F. 'Rubra Grandiflora'
* – 'Variegata'	CSil EGou LCla
¶ 'Fulpila'	EGou
'Für Elise'	CLit EBak
furfuracea	EKMF
'Gala'	CLit EBak NArc
'Galadriel'	CLit EGou SLBF
'Galahad'	EBak NArc
'Garden News' ♀	CLit CLoc CSil EBly ECtt EGou EKMF LCla LFli LVER MAld MAsk MJac MPla MWar MWhe NArc NHaw SKen SLBF
'Garden Week'	CLit CSil MAsk MWhe
'Gartenmeister Bonstedt' ♀	CLit CLoc CSil EBak EBly EKMF LBlm LCla MAsk MLan NArc SKen SSea WEas WGwG
'Gay Anne'	EKMF LFli NArc
'Gay Fandango'	CLit CLoc CPor CSil EBak LCla MWar NArc SKen

'Gay Future'   EKMF
'Gay Parasol'   CLit CLoc EGou LFli LVER
                        MAsk MWhe
'Gay Paree'   EBak MAsk
'Gay Senorita'   EBak
'Gay Spinner'   CLoc
'Geertien'   See *F.* **'Dutch Geertien'**
gehrigeri   EBak EKMF LCla
'Geisha Girl'   CSil
'Général Charles de   EGou
    Gaulle'
'Général Monk'   CLit CPor CSil EBak ECtt
                        EKMF EMan LVER MBri
                        MPla NArc
'Général Voyron'   CSil MPla
'General Wavell'   CLit LFli NArc WGwG
'Genii' ♀   Widely available
'Geoffrey Smith'   CSil ECtt EKMF
'Georg Börnemann'   NArc
'Georgana'   MWhe NArc
'George Barr'   CSil EKMF NArc SKen
'George Johnson'   CLit CSil NArc WGwG
'George Travis'   EBak NArc
¶ 'Gerald Drewitt'   CSil
'Gerda Manthey'   EKMF
'Gerharda's Aubergine' EGou EKMF
'Gerharda's Kiekeboe'   EKMF
§ 'Gesneriana'   CLoc CSil EBak EGou
'Ghislaine'   EGou
'Giant Pink Enchanted' CLit CLoc EBak LFli NArc
                        SMer
'Gilda'   CSil MAsk NArc
'Gillian Althea'   NArc
'Gilt Edge'   CLoc CSil
'Gina's Gold'   MAsk
'Gingham Girl'   SLBF
'Gipping'   EGou
'Girls Brigade'   EKMF
'Gladiator'   CLit CSil EBak LCla LFli NArc
'Gladys Haddaway'   LCla
'Gladys Miller'   CLoc
glaziouana   CLit CSil EKMF LCla SLBF
'Glenby'   CLit NArc
¶ 'Gleneagles'   EGou
'Glitters'   EBak EKMF NArc
§ 'Globosa'   CAgr EBak EKMF SKen SRms
'Gloria Johnson'   EKMF NArc
'Glow'   CSil EBak
'Glowing Embers'   EBak MAsk NArc
Glowing Lilac   CSil EKMF EMan NArc
'Glyn Jones'   EKMF
'Gold Brocade'   CLit CSil NArc
'Gold Crest'   EBak
'Golden Anniversary'   CLoc EBak EGou EKMF EMan
                        LFli MAld MAsk MJac MWar
                        SSea
'Golden Arrow'   EGou NArc
'Golden Border Queen'   CLoc
'Golden Dawn'   CLoc EBak ECtt LVER NArc
'Golden Eden Lady'   MWhe
'Golden Herald'   SLBF SSea
'Golden Jessimae'   MAsk NArc
'Golden La Campanella' CLit CLoc CSil ECtt MBri SSea
'Golden Lena'   CSil EKMF EMan MAsk
'Golden Marinka' ♀   CLit CLoc EBak ECtt EKMF
                        LFli LHil MAsk MBri MWhe
'Golden Melody'   CSil
'Golden Penny Askew'   MAsk
'Golden Runner'   MAsk
'Golden Swingtime'   CSil EGou LFli MAsk MBri
                        MJac MWhe NArc NHaw SSea
                        WGwG

'Golden Treasure'   CLit CLoc CSil ECtt EKMF
                        LCla MBEx MBri
'Golden Vergeer'   EGou SLBF
'Golden Wedding'   EKMF
'Goldsworth Beauty'   CSil LCla LFli
'Golondrina'   CSil EBak MWhe
'Goody Goody'   EBak
'Gordon Thorley'   EKMF MWhe
'Gordon's China Rose'   LCla SKen
'Gottingen'   EBak
'Göttinger Ruhm'   NArc
'Governor 'Pat' Brown' EBak MAsk
¶ 'Graaf Christian'   EGou
'Grace Darling'   EBak MWhe
'Grace Durham'   EGou
gracilis   See *F. magellanica* var. *gracilis*
'Graf Spee'   EGou
'Graf Witte'   CLTr CLit CSil LFli NArc
                        WGwG
'Grand Duchess'   EGou
'Grand Duke'   EGou
'Grand Prix'   CLit CSil LFli MAsk NArc
                        SKen
'Grand Slam'   LFli SKen
'Grandma Sinton'   CLoc CSil EBly EMan LCla
                        MAld MAsk MBri MJac MWar
                        MWhe NArc
'Grandpa George'   CLit CSil LCla
¶ 'Grandpa Jack'   SLBF
'Grasmere'   MAsk
'Grayrigg'   CSil EKMF EPPr
'Great Ouse'   EBly
'Great Scott'   CLoc CSil SKen
'Green 'n' Gold'   CSil EBak
'Greenpeace'   EKMF LCla MAsk
'Greg Walker'   CLit CSil
'Greta'   CSil EGou
'Gretna Chase'   MBri MWhe NArc
'Grey Lady'   CSil
'Grietje'   EGou
'Groene Kan's Glorie'   CGre CLit EKMF MAsk NArc
'Grumpy'   CLit CSil EBly EHol LCla LFli
                        MAsk MBri MWhe NArc NLak
'Gruss aus dem Bodethal' CLit CLoc EBak EBly EGou
                        EKMF
'Guinevere'   EBak
'Gustave Doré'   CSil EBak NArc
'Guy Dauphine'   EBak
'Gwen Dodge'   EGou LCla WGwG
'Gwen Wakelin'   NArc
'Gwen Wallis'   EGou
'Gwendoline'   EGou
'Gypsy Girl'   CLit CPor MAsk NArc SKen
'Gypsy Prince'   CLoc
'H.G. Brown'   CSil EBak MWhe
'Halsall Beauty'   MBri
'Halsall Belle'   MBri
'Halsall Pride'   LFli MBri
'Hampshire Beauty'   MJac
'Hampshire Blue'   CSil NArc SLBF SSea
¶ 'Hampshire Pride'   WGwG
'Hampshire Prince'   CSil LVER
'Hampshire Treasure'   CSil
'Hanna'   CSil
¶ 'Hannah Gwen'   EKMF
'Hannah Louise'   CInt EBly
'Hannah Williams'   CLTr MAsk NArc
'Hans van Beek'   NArc
'Happiness'   CSil
'Happy'   CLit CSil EBly LCla LFli MAsk
                        MWhe NArc
'Happy Anniversary'   CLoc EKMF MAsk NArc SLBF

'Happy Fellow'	CLoc CSil EBak
'Happy Wedding Day'	CLit CLoc CSil EKMF LCla LFli MAsk MWar MWhe SLBF SSea
'Hapsburgh'	EBak
'Harlow Car'	CLit EKMF LCla LFli MAsk MWar NArc WGwG
'Harlyn'	NArc
N 'Harmony'	EBak
'Harnser's Flight'	CSil EGou LCla
'Harriett'	MAsk
'Harrow Pride'	CSil
'Harry Dunnett'	EBak
'Harry Gray'	CLit CLoc CPor CSil EBak EBly ECtt EMan LCla LFli MAsk MBri MJac MWar MWhe NArc NHaw SKen SLBF SSea WGwG
hartwegii	CSil EGou EKMF LCla MAsk
'Hathersage'	EBak
'Hathor'	EGou
¶ *hatsbachii*	CSil
'Hatschbachii'	EGou EKMF LCla
'Haute Cuisine'	CLoc CSil EGou EKMF EMan LVER MAsk MWhe NArc SLBF
'Hawaiian Night'	NArc
'Hawaiian Princess'	ECtt
'Hawaiian Sunset'	SLBF
'Hawkshead'	CGle CInt CLit CLoc CSil EBly ECha EGou EKMF ELan GCal GOrc GQui LCla LHil MAsk MJac MWhe NArc NRoo SAxl SBid SChu SLBF SMac SMrm SWas WCru
¶ 'Hayley Marie'	SLBF
* 'Hazel'	CLit CSil EKMF LFli MAsk MWhe
'Heart Throb'	EBak
¶ 'Heathfield'	CPor
'Hebe'	EBak MWhe
'Heidi Ann' ♀	CLit CLoc CSil EBak EBly EKMF EMan IHos LCla LFli LVER MAsk MBri MJac MWar MWhe NArc NHaw SLBF SSea WGwG
'Heidi Weiss'	NArc
'Heinrich Henkel'	See *F. 'Andenken an Heinrich Henkel'*
'Heirloom'	ECtt EKMF
'Helen Clare'	CLoc EBak NArc
'Helen Elizabeth'	EKMF MBri
'Helen Spence'	EKMF NArc
'Hellan Devine'	MJac
'Hello Dolly'	CLoc
'Hemsleyana'	See *F. microphylla* subsp. *hemsleyana*
'Henri Poincaré'	EBak EKMF
'Henriette Prins'	EGou
'Herald' ♀	CLit CSil EBak LFli MWhe NArc SLBF WGwG
'Herbe de Jacques'	EKMF SKen
'Heritage'	CLoc CSil EBak NArc
'Herman de Graaff'	EGou
'Hermiena'	CLit CLoc CPor CSil EGou EKMF LCla LFli MAld MWar MWhe NArc SLBF WGwG
'Heron'	CSil EBak EKMF SKen
'Hessett Festival'	CLit CSil EBak EGou LFli LVER MAsk MWhe NArc
'Heston Blue'	EKMF NArc
'Hi Jinks'	EBak MAsk

'Hiawatha'	NArc
hidalgensis	See *F. microphylla* subsp. *hidalgensis*
'Hidcote Beauty'	CLit CLoc CSil EBak EKMF LFli MAsk MWhe NArc SKen SLBF SSea WGwG
'Hidden Beauty'	NArc
'Highland Pipes'	CSil EKMF LCla NArc
'Hilda May Salmon'	NArc
'Hindu Belle'	EBak
'Hinnerike'	CSil EGou EKMF LCla MAsk NArc SLBF
'Hiroshige'	EGou LCla
'His Excellency'	CSil EBak
'Hobo'	EGou
'Hobson's Choice'	LCla MWar SLBF
'Hokusai'	EGou EKMF
'Holly's Beauty'	LFli MAsk SMur WGwG
'Hollywood Park'	EBak
'Horatio'	CSil ECtt MJac
'Hot Coals'	CLit CSil EGou
'Howlett's Hardy'	CLit CLoc CSil EBak ECtt EKMF GCHN LFli MAsk MBal MBri NArc
'Hula Girl'	CLit CSil EBak EKMF LFli MAsk MJac MWar MWhe SLBF
'Humboldt Holiday'	EKMF LFli MAsk NArc
'Hummeltje'	EGou SLBF
'Huntsman'	CLit EKMF LFli MWhe WGwG WLRN
'Ian Brazewell'	CLoc
'Ian Leedham'	CPor CSil EBak EKMF
'Ice Cream Soda'	EBak NArc
'Iceberg'	CSil EBak NArc
'Icecap'	CSil EKMF LFli MBri NArc
'Iced Champagne'	CLit CLoc EBak LCla LFli MAsk MJac MWar NArc
'Ichiban'	CLoc
'Ida'	EBak
'Igloo Maid'	CLit CLoc CSil EBak EGou EKMF LFli MAsk MJac MWhe NArc SSea
'Impala'	EGou
'Imperial Crown'	CSil
'Imperial Fantasy'	EGou NArc
'Impudence'	CLoc CSil EBak MAsk SSea
'Impulse'	CLoc EKMF NArc SKen SLBF
'Ina'	MAsk
'Independence'	CSil
'Indian Maid'	EBak EKMF LVER MAsk MBri NArc SKen WGwG
'Inferno'	CLit CSil
'Ingleore'	NArc
'Ingram Maid'	MAsk
'Insa'	NArc
'Insulinde'	CLit EGou EKMF LCla MAld MWar NArc SLBF
'Intercity'	NArc
'Interlude'	EBak
'Iolanthe'	EGou
'Irene L. Peartree'	EGou LCla
'Irene van Zoeren'	EGou MAld NArc
'Iris Amer'	CLoc CSil EBak
¶ 'Irma'	EGou
'Isis'	CSil EKMF
'Isle of Mull'	CLit NArc
'Isle of Purbeck'	MJac NArc
'Italiano'	MJac
¶ 'Ivy Grace'	CSil
'Ixion'	NArc
¶ 'Jaap Brummel'	EGou

'Jack Acland'	ECtt EGou SKen
¶ 'Jack Rowlands'	EGou
'Jack Shahan' ♀	CLit CLoc CSil EBak EKMF
	EMan IHos LCla LFli MAsk
	MBri MJac MWar MWhe NFai
	SKen SLBF SSea WGwG
'Jack Stanway'	CLit CSil EGou MAsk WEas
'Jackie Bull'	EBak
'Jackpot'	EBak
'Jackqueline'	CSil EGou EKMF LCla MAsk
	NArc
'Jam Roll'	LVER MAsk
'Jamboree'	EBak MAsk NArc
'James Lye'	EBak MAsk SKen
'James Travis'	CSil EBak LCla
'Jan Bremer'	NArc
'Jane Humber'	EGou EKMF LCla NArc
'Jane Lye'	EBak
'Janet Goodwin'	NArc
¶ 'Janet Williams'	CSil
'Janice Ann'	EKMF LCla
'Janie'	CLit CLyn LFli
'Janneke Brinkman-Salentijn'	EGou
'Jap Van't Veer'	EGou
'Jasper's Likkepot'	NArc
'Jayess Wendy'	CLit
'Jayne Louise Mills'	NArc
¶ 'Jean Baker'	CSil
'Jean Campbell'	EBak
'Jean Clark'	MWar SLBF
¶ 'Jean Dawes'	EGou
'Jean Pidcock'	NArc
'Jeane'	EKMF
'Jennie Rachael'	NArc
'Jennifer Hampson'	CSil
'Jennifer Haslam'	EGou LCla
¶ 'Jennifer Lister'	EKMF
'Jenny Sorensen'	CLit CSil EKMF LCla MAld
	MAsk MWar NArc SLBF
'Jess'	LCla NArc SLBF
'Jessimae'	CLit LFli MAsk NArc
N 'Jester'	CLoc CSil
'Jet Fire'	CSil EBak NArc
'Jiddles'	SLBF
'Jill Storey'	EKMF
'Jim Coleman'	CLit MWhe NArc SLBF
'Jim Missin'	EGou MAld MAsk
'Jim Muncaster'	CLit EKMF MAsk NArc
jimenezii	EGou EKMF LCla
'Jimmy Carr'	EKMF
¶ 'Jimmy Cricket'	EKMF
'Joan Barnes'	CSil
'Joan Cooper'	CLoc CSil EBak EKMF MAsk
'Joan Gilbert'	CSil
'Joan Goy'	EBly EKMF LCla MAsk MJac
	MWar MWhe
'Joan Knight'	CLoc
'Joan Margaret'	MJac
'Joan Morris'	SLBF
'Joan Pacey'	CSil EBak LFli MAsk NArc
¶ 'Joan Paxton'	LCla
'Joan Smith'	CLit CSil EBak
'Joan Young'	EGou LCla
'Jo-Anne Fisher'	EBly
'Joe Kusber'	CSil EBak EKMF MAsk MJac
	NArc SKen
'Joe Nicholls'	EKMF
'Joel'	SLBF
'John Boy'	EGou
'John E. Caunt'	CSil EKMF
'John Grooms'	CLit EKMF LFli MJac
'John Lockyer'	CLoc EBak NArc
'John Maynard Scales'	CLit EGou LCla MAsk MJac
	MWhe NArc
'John Oram'	CLit
'John Pitt'	EGou
'John Suckley'	EBak SMer
'Johnny'	CLoc SSea
'Jomam'	CSil LCla MAld MAsk MWar
	MWhe NArc SLBF
'Jon Oram'	CLoc
'Jose's Joan'	CLit MAsk MWhe NArc
'Joy Bielby'	EGou EKMF NArc
'Joy Patmore' ♀	CLit CLoc CSil EBak EBly
	EKMF LCla LFli MAsk MBri
	MWar MWhe NArc SKen SLBF
¶ 'Joyce Maynard'	MJac
'Joyce Sinton'	EKMF EMan MBri MWar
	NArc
'Jubie-Lin'	EGou
'Judith Alison Castle'	GCHN
'Julchen'	EGou
'Jules Daloges'	EBak
'Julia'	CSil EKMF
'Julie'	MAsk
¶ 'Julie Horton'	CPor
'Julie Marie'	CSil LCla MAld MJac NArc
	SLBF
'June Gardner'	EKMF
¶ 'June Spencer'	EGou
N 'Juno'	EBak SMer
juntasensis	EGou EKMF
'Jupiter Seventy'	EBak
'Justin's Pride'	CLit CSil EKMF MAsk
'Kaboutertje'	EKMF
'Kaleidoscope'	CSil EBak LFli NArc
'Karen Bielby'	EKMF
¶ 'Karen Bradley'	NArc
¶ 'Karen Isles'	EGou EKMF
'Karen Louise'	CLoc
'Karin de Groot'	EKMF NArc
'Karin Siegers'	CSil
'Kate Harriet'	CLit LCla WGwG
¶ 'Kath van Hanegem'	EGou
'Kathleen Muncaster'	EKMF
'Kathleen Smith'	ECtt EKMF NArc
'Kathryn Maidment'	EKMF NArc
'Kathy Louise'	EMan SLBF
'Kathy's Prince'	ECtt EKMF NArc
'Kathy's Sparkler'	CSil EGou EKMF NArc
'Katinka'	EGou EKMF LCla
'Katrina'	CLoc EBak NArc
'Katrina Thompsen'	CLoc EKMF LCla MAld MWar
	SLBF SSea
¶ 'Kay Riley'	LVER
'Keele '92'	EKMF
'Keepsake'	CLoc CSil EBak
'Kegworth Beauty'	MAsk
'Kegworth Carnival'	CLit LCla MAsk NArc SKen
'Kegworth Supreme'	MAsk MJac
¶ 'Kelly Jo'	LCla
'Ken Goldsmith'	EBly EGou LCla
'Ken Jennings'	MJac
'Ken Sharp'	CLit NArc
'Kenny Dalglish'	CSil EKMF
'Kernan Robson'	CLoc EBak EGou NArc
'Kerry Anne'	EBly
'Keystone'	EBak
'Khada'	EKMF MWhe
'Kim Wright'	MWhe
'Kimberly'	EBak
'King George V'	MBlu
'King of Bath'	EBak

'King of Hearts'	EBak
'King's Ransom'	CLit CLoc CSil EBak MAsk MWhe NArc
'Kiss 'n' Tell'	EBly MJac MWhe NArc
'Kit Oxtoby'	CLit CSil ECtt EGou EKMF EMan LCla MAsk MJac NArc SKen
'Kiwi'	EBak MAsk SKen
'Klassic'	EGou
¶ 'Kleine Sandra'	EGou
'Knight Errant'	CSil SLBF SSea
'Knockout'	CLit CSil EKMF MAsk
'Kolding Perle'	CLit CSil
'Königin der Frühe'	NArc
'Kon-Tiki'	CLit CLoc CSil EKMF NArc
'Koralle'	See *F.* **'Coralle'**
'Kwintet'	EBak LCla MJac SKen
'Kyoto'	CSil EKMF
'La Apache'	EBak
'La Bianca'	EBak
'La Campanella' ♀	CLoc CPor CSil EBak EBly ECtt EKMF EMan LCla LFli LVER MAld MAsk MBri MJac MWar MWhe NArc NFai NHaw SLBF WGwG
'La Fiesta'	CLit CSil EBak LFli NArc SMer
'La France'	EBak
N 'La Neige'	CLit CSil EBak LCla MAsk
'La Porte'	CLit CLoc
'La Rosita'	CSil EBak MAsk SLBF
N 'La Traviata'	EBak
'Lace Petticoats'	EBak EKMF NArc
'Lady Beth'	CLit NArc
'Lady Boothby'	CHEx CLit CSil EBak EKMF LCla MAsk NArc SBid SKen SLBF SMrm SRms
'Lady in Grey'	EKMF
¶ 'Lady in Pink'	SLBF
'Lady Isobel Barnett'	CLit CLoc CSil EBak EKMF IHos LCla LFli MAsk MBri MJac MWar MWhe NArc NHaw
'Lady Kathleen Spence'	CLit CSil EBak EKMF MAsk MWhe NArc
'Lady Love'	MBri
'Lady Patricia Mountbatten'	CSil EKMF EMan LCla MAsk MBri MWhe NArc WGwG
'Lady Ramsey'	CLit EBak MJac NArc
'Lady Rebecca'	CLoc
'Lady Thumb' ♀	CChe CInt CLit CLoc CMHG CPri CSil EBak EBly EKMF ENot LCla LFli LVER MAld MAsk MBal MBar MBri MJac MPla MWat MWhe NArc SKen SLBF SPar SPer SSea WGwG
'Lady's Smock'	EKMF
'Lakeland Princess'	EBak NArc
'Lakeside'	CLoc EBak
'Lambada'	EKMF SLBF
¶ 'Lancashire Lad'	CLit MWar
'Lancashire Lass'	EMan MBri NArc WLRN
'Lancelot'	CLit EBak EGou LCla
'Land van Beveren'	MWar NArc SLBF
'Lark'	EBly EGou
'L'Arlésienne'	CLit CLoc
'Lassie'	CLoc CPor EBak LFli NArc SMer
N 'Laura'	CLit CLoc CSil EBly EKMF MAsk MWhe SLBF
'Laura Amanda'	EBly
'Lavender Kate'	CLoc EBak MJac
'Lavender Lace'	MWhe

'Lavender Lady'	CSil MAld
'Lazy Lady'	EBak
'Le Berger'	EKMF
'Lechlade Apache'	EGou LCla
'Lechlade Chinaman'	CSil MLan
'Lechlade Debutante'	EGou LCla
'Lechlade Fire-eater'	EGou LCla
'Lechlade Gorgon'	CDoC CSil EKMF LCla NArc
'Lechlade Magician'	CDoC CLit CSil EKMF LCla MAsk NArc
'Lechlade Maiden'	CSil
'Lechlade Martianess'	EGou EKMF
'Lechlade Potentate'	EGou MAsk
'Lechlade Rocket'	EGou EKMF
'Lechlade Tinkerbell'	EGou LCla
'Lechlade Violet'	CLit SSoC
'Lee Anthony'	EGou
'Leica'	EKMF MJac
'Leicestershire Silver'	MJac NArc
'Len Bielby'	CLit EKMF LCla
'Lena' ♀	CLit CLoc CMHG CPor CSil EBak EBly EGou EKMF LFli LVER MAsk MBal MBri MJac MPla MWhe NArc NFai NHaw SKen SPer SRms SSea WEas WGwG
'Lena Dalton'	CLit CLoc EBak EKMF IHos MAsk MBri MJac MWhe NArc SKen
¶ 'Leonhart von Fuchs'	EGou
'Leonora' ♀	CLoc CSil EBak EKMF LCla MAsk MBri MWar MWhe NArc SLBF WGwG
'Lesley'	EGou LCla
'Lett's Delight'	EBly EGou
'Letty Lye'	EBak
'Leverhulme'	See *F.* **'Leverkusen'**
§ 'Leverkusen'	CDoC CLit CLoc CSil EBak EGou EKMF LCla MJac MWhe SLBF SSoC WGwG
'Li Kai Lin'	CSil
N 'Liebesträume'	EBak
'Liebriez'	CLit CPor CSil EBak EBly EKMF NArc
* 'Lilac'	EBak
'Lilac Lady'	MJac
'Lilac Lustre'	CGre CLoc CSil EBak EKMF MBri NArc
'Lilac Princess'	MJac
'Lilac Queen'	EBak
¶ 'Lillian Annetts'	SLBF
'Lillibet'	CLoc CSil EBak LFli NArc SKen WGwG
'Lillydale'	CLit CSil
'Lilo Vogt'	EGou NArc WGwG
'Linda Goulding'	CSil EBak EGou LCla MAld MAsk MWhe NArc SSea
'Linda Grace'	CLit EKMF LCla MJac
'Lindisfarne'	CLit CLoc EBak EKMF LCla LFli MAsk MJac MWar NArc
'Lisa'	CDoC CSil EBly
'Lisa Ashton'	NArc
¶ 'Lisa Jane'	MWhe
'Lisi'	EKMF NArc
'Little Beauty'	EKMF MWhe NArc
'Little Gene'	EBak
'Little Jewel'	SKen
'Little Ouse'	EGou LCla MWhe
'Little Ronnie'	MWhe
'Little Witch'	EGou EKMF SLBF
'Lively Lady'	CLit
'Liver Bird'	NArc

'Liz'	CLit CSil EBak NArc
'Lochinver'	CSil
'Loeky'	CLoc EBak LCla SLBF SSea
'Logan Garden'	See *F. magellanica* **'Logan Woods'**
'Lolita'	CLit EBak MAsk SMer
'Lonely Ballerina'	CLoc
'Long Preston'	EGou
'Long Wings'	CSil EKMF LCla MAld MAsk NArc
¶ 'Look East'	EGou
¶ 'Lora Fairclough'	NArc
'Lord Byron'	CLoc EBak LCla NArc
'Lord Derby'	NArc
'Lord Lonsdale'	CLit CSil EBak EBly LCla MAsk MWhe NArc SKen WEas
'Lord Roberts'	CLoc CSil NArc SKen
'Lorelei'	CLit
'Lorna Swinbank'	CLit CLoc NArc
'Lorraine's Delight'	CLit
'Lottie Hobby'	CDec CInt CLoc CMGP CSil EBly ECtt EGou EKMF LBlm LFli MAld MAsk MHar NArc WFoF WPyg
¶ 'Lou Rinzema'	EGou
'Louise Emershaw'	CSil EBak LFli MAsk MJac
¶ 'Louise Foster'	MWar
'Lovable'	EBak MAsk SMer
¶ 'Love in Bloom'	EGou
'Loveliness'	CLoc CSil EBak EKMF MWhe
¶ 'Lovely Linda'	SLBF
'Love's Reward'	CLit CLoc CSil EBly EKMF LCla MAld MJac MWar MWhe SLBF
I 'Loxensis' ♀	EBak EKMF
N *loxensis*	EGou LCla MAsk
'Loxhore Angelus'	CSil
'Loxhore Calypso'	EKMF
'Loxhore Cancan'	CSil EKMF
'Loxhore Cavalcade'	CSil
¶ 'Loxhore Chorale'	CSil
'Loxhore Cotillon'	CSil
'Loxhore Mazurka'	CSil
'Loxhore Minuet'	CSil
'Loxhore Operetta'	CSil
'Loxhore Posthorn'	CSil
¶ 'Loxhore Tarantella'	CSil
¶ 'Lubbertje Hop'	SLBF
'Lucille'	NArc
'Lucky Strike'	CLit CLoc CSil EBak LFli NArc SMer
'Lucy Harris'	CSil
'Lucy Locket'	MJac
'Lula Bell'	LCla
'Lunter's Trots'	NArc
'Luscious'	CLit LFli
'Lustre'	CLit EBak NArc SLBF
§ 'Lycioides'	CSil LCla
§ *lycioides* Andrews	CSil EBak EGou EKMF
– hort.	See *F.* **'Lycioides'**
'Lye's Elegance'	CSil MAsk
'Lye's Excelsior'	EBak LCla
'Lye's Own'	EBak MAsk
'Lye's Unique'	CLTr CLit CLoc CSil EBak EBly EGou EKMF LCla LFli MAld MAsk MJac MWar MWhe NArc SKen SLBF
'Lylac Sunsa'	EKMF
'Lynette'	CLoc
'Lynn Ellen'	EBak NArc
¶ 'Lynne Marshall'	CSil
'Mabel Greaves'	CSil MAsk
'Machu Picchu'	CLoc CSil EBly EKMF LCla MWar NArc
macrophylla	EKMF
'Madame Butterfly'	CLoc
'Madame Cornélissen' ♀	CLit CLoc CPor CSil EBak EBly EKMF ENot GChr LFli LVER MAsk MBar MBri MJac MWhe NArc NLak SPer SRms WGwG
'Madame Eva Boye'	EBak
'Madelaine Sweeney'	MBri
'Maes-y-Groes'	EKMF
magdalenae	EKMF
magellanica	CMHG EKMF GOrc LHil MWhi NNor NPer SPer WOak WRha WWat
– 'Alba'	See *F. magellanica* var. *molinae*
I – 'Alba Aureovariegata'	EPfP LHop MBri MRav SPer SSea WCru
– 'Alba Variegata'	CLit CMHG CSil EKMF NHaw WEas
– var. *conica*	CSil EKMF
– 'Globosa'	See *F.* **'Globosa'**
§ – var. *gracilis* ♀	CLit CLoc CSil EKMF LBlm MAsk NArc NFla SRms WPic
– – 'Aurea'	CBot CLit CMHG CSil CTre EAst EGou EHoe EKMF ELan ENot GCHN GQui LCla LFli MAsk MWat MWhe SAxl SDix SKen SLBF SMac SPer SPla SSea WGwG WRus
§ – – 'Tricolor' (v)	CDoC CSil EBly EHol EKMF EWes GOrc LCla LFli MAld MAsk SLBF SRms SSea
– – 'Variegata' ♀	CGle CMHG CSil CTre EBak ECha EGou ENot LCla LVER MAsk MAus MBal MGos NArc SChu SDix SKen SPer WAbe WEas
§ – 'Logan Woods'	CSil EKMF GCal SAxl SMrm WAbe
– 'Longipedunculata'	EKMF
– var. *macrostema*	EKMF
– – 'Variegata'	EGou
§ – var. *molinae*	CGle CHad CMHG CSil EBak EGou EKMF ELan GOrc ISea LCla LFli MBlu MNrw MWgw MWhe NChi NFai NNor NPer NRoo SMac SPer WAbe WBod WEas WOak WRus
§ – – 'Enstone'	EGou
– – 'Golden Sharpitor'	WAbe WCot
§ – – 'Sharpitor' (v)	CB&S CDec CSil CTre EBak ECha EGou EKMF ELan LHop MAsk MBar MBri MPla MWat NPer SAxl SMrm SPer SSea WCru WRus WSHC
¶ – var. *prostrata*	CSil
– var. *pumila*	CDoC CSil EAst EGoo EWes GCal SIng
– 'Riccartonii'	See *F.* **'Riccartonii'**
§ – 'Thompsonii' ♀	ECGP EKMF GCal MBel SAxl SKen SRms
§ – 'Versicolor' (v) ♀	Widely available
'Magic Flute'	CLoc CSil MJac
'Maharaja'	CLit EBak NArc
'Maike'	NArc
'Majebo'	NArc
'Major Heaphy'	CSil EBak EKMF MAsk MWar MWhe NArc
'Malibu Mist'	CSil EGou EKMF LCla LVER MAsk NArc

'Mama Bleuss' EBak NArc
'Mancunian' CLit CSil EGou LCla LFli
          MAsk NArc
N 'Mandarin' EBak LFli NArc
'Mandi' EGou EKMF SLBF
'Mandy' CLit
'Mantilla' CLit CLoc CSil EBak EGou
          EKMF LCla LFli MAsk MJac
          MWhe NArc SLBF
'Maori Pipes' CSil EGou
'Marbled Sky' MJac NArc
'Marco Jan' EGou
'Marcus Graham' CLit CLoc EGou EKMF LCla
          LFli MAsk MWar MWhe NArc
          SLBF SMer
'Marcus Hanton' CSil EKMF LCla MAsk NArc
'Mardi Gras' EBak WGwG
'Margaret' ♀ CLit CLoc CPor CSil EBak
          EGou EKMF ENot GCHN ISea
          LCla LFli LVER MAsk MBal
          MWar MWhe NArc NHaw
          SKen SLBF SRms SSea WGwG
          WStI
'Margaret Brown' ♀ CDoC CLTr CLoc CSil CTri
          EBak EKMF LCla LFli MAsk
          MPla MWhe NArc SKen SLBF
          WStI
'Margaret Davidson' CLoc
'Margaret Dawson' MAsk
'Margaret Hazelwood' EKMF
'Margaret Kendrick' MBri
'Margaret Pilkington' CGre EKMF LCla MAsk MBri
          MWar NArc SSea
'Margaret Roe' CDoC CLit CSil EBak EKMF
          MJac MWhe NArc SKen
'Margaret Rose' MJac
'Margaret Susan' EBak
'Margarite Dawson' CLit CPor CSil NArc
'Margery Blake' CSil EBak
'Maria Landy' CLit EKMF EMan LCla MAsk
          MWar NArc SLBF
'Maria Merrills' EKMF EMan LCla NArc
'Marietta' CLit
'Marilyn Olsen' CSil EBly EKMF LCla LFli
          MAld MWar NArc SLBF
'Marin Belle' EBak LCla NArc
'Marin Glow' ♀ CLit CLoc CSil EBak EKMF
          LCla LFli MAsk MWhe NArc
          SLBF
'Marinka' ♀ CLit CLoc CSil EBak ECtt
          EKMF EMan IHos LCla LFli
          LVER MAld MAsk MBri MJac
          MWar MWhe NArc NFai NHaw
          SKen SLBF SSea WGwG
'Marjory Almond' EGou
'Mark Kirby' EKMF
'Marlea's Vuurbol' EGou
'Marlene Gilbee' CLit MAsk MWar
¶ 'Martha Franck' EGou
'Martin Hayward' SKen
¶ 'Martin's Cinderella' EGou
'Martin's Midnight' MAsk
'Martin's Yellow Suprise' EGou EKMF SLBF
'Marton Smith' MWhe
'Marty' EBak
'Mary' ♀ CLit CLoc CSil EBly EGou
          EKMF LCla LFli MAld MAsk
          MLan MWar MWhe NArc SKen
          SLBF SSea WGwG
'Mary Caunt' EKMF
'Mary Ellen Guffey' EGou SLBF
'Mary Fairclo' EGou

'Mary Joan' EKMF MAsk
'Mary Lockyer' CLoc EBak NArc
'Mary Neujean' MBri
'Mary Poppins' LCla NArc
'Mary Reynolds' CLit
'Mary Thorne' CSil EBak
'Mary Wright' MWhe
'Masquerade' EBak EKMF EMan MWhe
          NArc
'Matador' CSil
mathewsii EKMF
'Maureen' NArc
'Maureen Ward' EKMF
'Mauve Beauty' CSil EGou EKMF
'Mauve Lace' CSil LVER
'Mauve Wisp' NArc
'Max Jaffa' CSil MAsk NArc
'May Rogers' EGou
'Mayblossom' ECtt SLBF
'Mayfayre' CLoc
'Mayfield' MWhe NArc SKen
¶ 'Maytime' CLit
'Meadowlark' CLit EBak ECtt EKMF NArc
'Meditation' CLoc CPor CSil
'Melanie' CSil EGou LCla NArc SLBF
'Melody' CSil EBak LFli MAsk MWhe
          NArc
'Melody Ann' EBak
'Melting Moments' EKMF NArc
¶ 'Memo' EGou
'Mendocino Mini' EGou EKMF
'Menna' NArc
'Merlin' CSil LCla
'Merry England' MAsk
'Merry Mary' CSil EBak EKMF NArc
'Mexicali Rose' CLoc
'Michael' CSil EBly MAsk
'Michael Kurtz' NArc
¶ 'Michele Wallace' LCla
michoacanensis EGou
'Micky Goult' CLoc CSil EBly EKMF LCla
          LFli MAld MAsk MJac MWhe
          NArc SSea
'Microchip' EGou SLBF
microphylla CB&S CGle CLit CLoc CMHG
          CSil CTre EBak EBar ERav
          ERea GRei LVER NChi SMad
          SSea STre WCru WEas
§ – subsp. *aprica* EKMF LCla MAsk
§ – subsp. *hemsleyana* CSil EKMF LCla MWhe SKen
§ – subsp. *hidalgensis* CLit CSil EGou EKMF GAri
          LBlm LCla SLBF SRms
– subsp. *microphylla* CSil EGou LCla
– subsp. *quercetorum* EGou EKMF LCla
'Midas' LFli MAsk MBri NArc
'Midnight Sun' CSil EBak EBly LFli NArc
          SKen
'Midwinter' NArc
¶ 'Mieke Alferink' EGou
'Mieke Meursing' CLit CLoc CSil EBak ECtt
          EKMF LCla LFli MBri MJac
          MWar MWhe NArc SLBF
'Miep Aalhuizen' EGou EKMF LCla
N 'Mikado' EGou
'Mike Oxtoby' EKMF MAsk
'Millrace' EGou LCla
'Mimi Kubischta' NArc
'Mina Knudde' NArc
'Ming' CLoc CPor CSil
'Miniature Jewels' SLBF
minimiflora See *F. microphylla* subsp.
          hidalgensis

'Minirose'	CSil EBly EKMF LCla MAsk MWar MWhe SKen
'Minnesota'	EBak
¶ 'Minutifolia'	CLyn
'Mipam'	SLBF
'Mirjana'	NArc
'Mischief'	CSil NArc
'Miss Aubrey'	EGou
'Miss California'	CLit CLoc CSil EBak ECtt EKMF LFli MAsk MBri MWhe NArc
'Miss Debbie'	EGou
'Miss Great Britain'	CLit CSil
'Miss Marilyn'	CLit
¶ 'Miss Muffett'	SIng
'Miss Vallejo'	EBak NArc
'Mission Bells'	CLit CLoc CSil EBak EKMF LCla LFli LVER MAsk MWhe NArc SKen WGwG
'Mistoque'	CSil NArc
'Misty Blue'	CSil NArc
'Misty Haze'	CSil LVER MWar
'Misty Pink'	EKMF NArc
'Moira Ann'	ECtt
'Molesworth'	CLit CSil EBak LFli MJac MWhe NArc SKen SMer
'Mollie Beaulah'	CLit CSil ECtt EKMF NArc
'Molly Chatfield'	NArc
'Money Spinner'	CLoc EBak
'Monsieur Thibaut'	ENot LCla MAld SKen
'Monte Rosa'	CLoc SKen
'Monterey'	MWhe
'Montevideo'	EGou
'Montrose Village'	CSil MWhe
¶ 'Monty Python'	EGou
'Monument'	CSil
'Mood Indigo'	CLit CSil EGou LVER MWar NArc SLBF WGwG
'Moonbeam'	CLoc CPor CSil LCla MAsk MWhe
'Moonlight Sonata'	CLit CLoc CSil EBak MAsk MJac NArc SKen
'Moonraker'	CSil LFli NArc
'Moonshot'	NArc
'Morcott'	NArc
'More Applause'	CLoc EGou EKMF LVER MWhe NArc
'Morning Cloud'	LFli NArc
'Morning Glow'	LFli NArc
'Morning Light'	CLit CLoc CSil EBak NArc SMer
'Morning Mist'	EBak NArc
'Morning Star'	MBri
'Morrells'	EBak
'Moth Blue'	CLit CSil EBak NArc SMer
'Mountain Mist'	CSil EKMF LFli MJac
'Moyra'	EKMF
'Mr A. Huggett'	CLit CLoc CSil EBly EKMF LCla MAsk MWhe NArc
'Mr P.D. Lee'	MWhe
'Mr W. Rundle'	CLit EBak NArc
'Mrs Churchill'	CLoc
'Mrs Janice Morrison'	EGou
'Mrs John D. Fredericks'	CSil
'Mrs Lawrence Lyon'	EBak
'Mrs Lovell Swisher'	CLit CSil EBak EKMF LCla MBri MJac MWhe NArc
'Mrs Marshall'	CSil EBak MAsk NArc SLBF
'Mrs Popple' ♀	Widely available
'Mrs Susan Brookfield'	LCla NArc
'Mrs Victor Reiter'	CSil
'Mrs W. Castle'	CSil NArc WGwG

'Mrs W.P. Wood' ♀	CDoC CLoc EKMF NArc
'Mrs W. Rundle'	CLoc CSil EBak EKMF LFli MAld MWhe NArc SLBF
'Muriel'	CLit CLoc EBak ECtt EKMF MWhe NArc SKen
¶ 'Musi'	EGou
'My Dear'	CLoc
'My Fair Lady'	CLoc CSil EBak NArc
'My Honey'	CSil MAsk NArc
'Mystique'	CLit MAsk
'Nancy Darnley'	EKMF
'Nancy Lou'	CGre CLit CLoc EBly EGou EKMF LCla LFli LVER MAld MAsk MJac MWar MWhe NArc SKen SLBF
'Nancy Scrivener'	NArc SLBF
'Nanny Ed'	LFli MBri
'Natalie Jones'	EGou
'Natasha Sinton'	CLit CLoc CSil ECtt EKMF EMan LCla LFli LVER MAld MAsk MBri MJac MWar MWhe NArc NHaw SLBF WGwG WLRN
'Native Dancer'	EBak
¶ 'Naughty Nicole'	SLBF
'Nautilus'	EBak
¶ 'Navato'	LFli
'Navy Blue'	CSil NArc
'Neapolitan'	EBly MAsk MWhe SKen SLBF
'Neil Clyne'	MWhe
'Nell Gwyn'	CLit CLoc CSil EBak NArc
'Nellie Nuttall' ♀	CLit CLoc CSil EBak EBly EGou EKMF LCla LFli MAld MAsk MWar MWhe NArc NHaw SLBF SSea
'Neopolitan'	CLoc CSil EGou EKMF LCla NArc
'Nettala'	CLit EGou
'Neue Welt'	CSil EBak
'Neville Young'	MAsk
'New Fascination'	EBak NArc SKen
'Nice 'n' Easy'	CLit LVER MBri MJac MWar MWhe NArc
'Nicholas Hughes'	NArc
'Nicis Findling'	CSil EGou EKMF LCla NArc SLBF
'Nicky Veerman'	EGou
'Nicola'	CLoc EBak
N 'Nicola Claire'	EGou NArc
'Nicola Jane'	CSil EBak EBly EKMF LCla LFli MAld MAsk MBri MJac MWhe NArc SLBF
'Nicolette'	MJac
'Nightingale'	CLoc CSil EBak NArc
¶ *nigricans*	EKMF LCla
– × *gehrigeri*	EKMF
'Nimue'	EGou MAsk NArc
'Nina Wills'	EBak
'Niobe'	EBak
'Niula'	EKMF LCla
'No Name'	EBak
'Norah Henderson'	NArc
'Norfolk Belle'	LFli
'Norfolk Ivor'	EGou
'Norma Nield'	LCla
'Norman Mitchinson'	EGou
'Normandy Bell'	CSil EBak
'North Cascades'	MAsk
'Northern Pride'	MAsk
'Northilda'	NArc
'Northumbrian Belle'	EBak MJac NArc WGwG

'Northway'	CLit CLoc CSil LCla LFli MAsk MJac MWhe NArc
'Norvell Gillespie'	EBak
'Novato'	CLit EBak NArc
'Novella'	EBak NArc
'Noyo Star'	CSil LFli
'Nunthorpe Gem'	CSil NArc
'Nuwenspete'	EGou
obconica	EGou EKMF LCla
'Obergärtner Koch'	EKMF LCla NArc SMrm
'Ocean Beach'	EBly MAsk NArc
'Oddfellow'	CSil NArc
'Oetnang'	SCoo
'Old Somerset'	CLit LCla LFli MAsk MWhe
'Ole 7 Up'	MAld
'Olive Moon'	EBly SLBF
'Olive Smith'	CSil EBly MAld MAsk MJac MWhe NArc
¶ 'Olympia'	MWhe
'Olympic Lass'	EBak NArc
'Oosje'	See *F.* × *bacillaris* 'Oosje'
'Opalescent'	CLit CLoc
'Orange Crush'	CLoc CSil EBak LFli MAsk MWar MWhe NArc
'Orange Crystal'	CLit CSil EBak EKMF IHos LFli MAsk MBri MJac MWhe NArc NFai NHaw SKen
'Orange Drops'	CLit CLoc CPor CSil EBak EBly EKMF LFli MAsk MWhe NArc SKen
'Orange Flare'	CLit CLoc CSil EBak EKMF LCla MJac MWhe NArc SLBF SSea
'Orange King'	CLoc CSil EGou EMan SSea
'Orange Mirage'	CLit CLoc CSil EBak LCla LFli LVER MAld MAsk MBri MWar MWhe NArc SKen
'Orangeblossom'	CSil LCla NArc SLBF
'Oranje van Os'	MJac MWhe
'Orient Express'	CLit CSil EGou LCla LFli MAsk MWar MWhe NArc
Oriental Flame	EKMF NArc
'Oriental Sunrise'	MAsk MWhe
'Ornamental Pearl'	CLoc EBak NArc SLBF
'Ortenburger Festival'	NArc
'Orwell'	CLit EGou
'Other Fellow'	CLit CSil EBak EBly EKMF LCla MAsk MJac MWhe NArc SLBF
'Our Darling'	CSil MWhe NArc
'Our Ted'	EGou
'Overbecks'	See *F. magellanica* var. *molinae* 'Sharpitor'
'Overbecks Ruby'	GBuc WCot
'P.J.B.'	LCla LFli NArc
'Pabbe's Teudebel'	EGou
'Pabbe's Tudebekje'	CSil EGou
pachyrrhiza	EKMF
'Pacific Grove'	EBak
'Pacific Queen'	CLoc EBak NArc
'Pacquesa' ♀	CLit CSil EBak EBly EKMF IHos LFli MAsk MJac MWar MWhe NArc
'Padre Pio'	MJac
'Pale Flame'	MWhe NArc
pallescens	EGou EKMF LCla
¶ 'Pam Plack'	LCla
'Pamela Hutchinson'	MAld NArc
'Pamela Knights'	EBak EGou
'Pan'	EGou NArc
'Pan America'	EBak
'Pangea'	EGou

paniculata	CBot CEnd CLTr EBak EGou EKMF LCla LHop MAsk NArc SHFr SLBF SLod SMrm WFoF
'Pantaloons'	EBak NArc
¶ 'Panylla Prince'	EGou
'Papa Bleuss'	CLoc EBak
'Papoose'	CDoC CLit CSil EBak EKMF LCla MAsk MPla NArc
'Paramour'	LFli NArc
'Party Frock'	CLit CLoc CSil EBak LCla LFli NArc SMer
parviflora hort.	See *F.* × *bacillaris*
– Lindley	EBak
'Pastel'	EBak
'Pat Crofts'	NArc
'Pat Meara'	CLoc EBak
'Pathetique'	CLoc
'Patience'	CSil EBak EGou LCla MJac NArc SLBF
'Patio Party'	MBri
'Patio Princess'	CSil LCla LFli MBri MJac MWar MWhe NArc SSea
N 'Patricia'	CSil EBak
'Patricia Ann'	EKMF MWar
¶ 'Patricia Joan Yates'	EGou
'Patty Evans'	EBak MBri NArc
'Patty Sue'	CLit LCla LFli MBri MWar WLRN
'Paul Berry'	EKMF
'Paul Cambon'	EBak EKMF NArc
'Paul Roe'	EKMF MBri MJac
'Paula Jane' ♀	CLit LCla LFli MAsk MBri MJac MWar MWhe SLBF
'Pauline Rawlins'	CLoc EBak
¶ 'Paxos Trail'	MAld
PC&H 247	CFee
'Peace'	EBak SMer
¶ 'Peaches 'n' Cream'	EGou
'Peachy'	EGou
'Peachy Keen'	EBak
'Peacock'	CLoc
'Pee Wee Rose'	CSil EBak EKMF NArc
'Peggy King'	CSil EBak LCla MWhe NArc SRms
'Peloria'	CLoc EBak MAsk NArc
'Pennine'	MBri MWar
¶ 'People's Princess'	MWar
'Peper Harow'	EBak
'Pepi'	CLoc EBak
'Peppermint Candy'	EKMF LFli SCoo WGwG
'Peppermint Stick'	CDoC CLit CLoc CSil EBak EKMF EMan LCla LFli LVER MAsk MBri MJac MWhe NArc NHaw SKen SSea
'Perestroika'	SLBF
'Perky Pink'	CLit EBak EBly LCla MAsk MWhe NArc SKen
'Perry Park'	CLit EBak MAsk MBri MJac NArc
'Perry's Jumbo'	NPer
perscandens	CSil EGou EKMF ISea LCla SLBF SVen
'Personality'	EBak NArc
'Peter Bielby'	EGou EKMF MWar SLBF
'Peter Crooks'	CSil EGou EKMF LCla MAsk MJac NArc
'Peter James'	CSil EKMF
'Peter Pan'	CLit CSil EHol SPer
'Peter Sanderson'	EKMF LCla MJac NArc
petiolaris	EGou EKMF LCla
'Petit Fleur'	CSil
'Petit Four'	CSil

'Petit Point' — LFli
'Petite' — EBak NArc
'Petronella' — MAsk MWar
'Pharaoh' — CLoc
'Phénoménal' — CLit CPor CSil EBak EBly EKMF LFli MAsk SKen
'Phyllis' ♀ — CLit CLoc CPor CSil EBak EBly EKMF LCla LFli LHil MAsk MBal MJac MWhe NArc NFai NHaw SKen SLBF SPla SSoC WGwG
'Phyrne' — CSil EBak EKMF NArc
'Piet G. Vergeer' — NArc
'Piet Heemskerke' — EGou
¶ *pilaloensis* — EKMF
'Pinch Me' — CLit CSil EBak EKMF LFli LVER MAsk SKen
'Pink Aurora' — CLoc CSil
'Pink Ballet Girl' — CLoc CPor EBak ECtt NArc
'Pink Bon Accorde' — CLoc CSil NArc
'Pink Bouquet' — CSil
'Pink Chiffon' — NArc
'Pink Cloud' — CLoc EBak NArc
'Pink Crystal' — LVER
'Pink Darling' — CLit CLoc EBak MWhe SKen
'Pink Dessert' — CSil EBak NArc SKen
'Pink Domino' — EKMF
'Pink Fairy' — CLit CSil EBak NArc
'Pink Fandango' — CLoc
'Pink Fantasia' — CLit CLoc CSil EBak EBly EGou EKMF LCla LFli MAld MAsk MJac MWar MWhe SSea
'Pink Flamingo' — CLit CLoc CSil EBak NArc SMer
'Pink Galore' — CLoc CSil EBak EKMF EMan IHos LCla LFli LVER MAld MAsk MBri MJac MWhe NFai NHaw SSea WGwG
'Pink Goon' — CLit CSil LCla LFli LVER MAsk SLBF
'Pink Jade' — EBak SMer
'Pink la Campanella' — CLit CSil EMan MAld MBri MJac MWhe NArc SLBF SMer WGwG WLRN
'Pink Lace' — CSil
N 'Pink Lady' — MWhe
'Pink Marshmallow' — CLit CLoc CSil EBak EGou EKMF EMan LCla LFli MAld MAsk MJac MWar MWhe NHaw SKen SLBF WGwG
'Pink Panther' — EKMF
N 'Pink Pearl' — CSil EBak EKMF LVER
'Pink Picotee' — LCla MJac
'Pink Profusion' — EBak
'Pink Quartet' — CLoc CSil EBak LCla NArc
'Pink Rain' — CSil EGou EKMF MAsk MJac NArc
'Pink Slipper' — CLoc
'Pink Spangles' — CLit EMan IHos LFli MAsk MBri NHaw SSea WGwG
'Pink Surprise' — MJac NArc
'Pink Temptation' — CLit CLoc CPor CSil EBak
'Pinkmost' — ECtt
'Pinto' — CDoC LFli NArc
¶ 'Pinto de Blue' — EGou
'Pinwheel' — CLoc CSil EBak
'Piper' — CSil MWar
'Piper's Vale' — EGou EKMF SLBF
'Pirbright' — EKMF
'Pixie' — CLoc CSil EBak EKMF MAsk MJac MWhe NArc SKen SLBF
'Pixie Bells' — CInt CMHG

'Playford' — EBak NArc
'Plenty' — CSil EBak
'Ploughman' — EGou
'Plumb-bob' — EGou EKMF
'Poacher' — EGou
'Pop Whitlock' (v) — EKMF LCla NArc SSea
'Popely Pride' — EGou
'Popsie Girl' — EGou LCla SLBF
'Port Arthur' — EBak NArc
'Postiljon' — CLit CSil EBak EKMF MAsk NArc
N 'Powder Puff' — CLit CLoc CSil ECtt EKMF LFli LVER MAsk MBri NArc SKen
N 'Prelude' — CLoc CSil EBak NArc
'President' — CSil EBak LCla SKen
'President B.W. Rawlins' — EBak
§ 'President Elliot' — CSil MWhe
'President George Bartlett' — EKMF MJac SLBF
'President Leo Boullemier' — CLit CSil EBak ECtt EKMF LCla LFli MAsk MJac NArc WGwG
'President Margaret Slater' — CDoC CLit CLoc CPor CSil EBak EMan LFli MAsk MJac MWhe NArc SLBF
'President Moir' — CPor CSil LFli
'President Norman Hobbs' — EKMF MWar NArc
'President Roosevelt' — CDoC CSil ECtt
'President Stanley Wilson' — EBak EBly ECtt MAsk
'President Wilf Sharp' — NArc
'Preston Belle' — EGou
'Preston Field' — CSil SLBF SSea
'Preston Guild' — CLit CLoc CSil EBak EGou EKMF LBlm LFli MAsk MWhe NArc NPer SLBF
'Pride of the West' — CSil EBak
'Prince of Orange' — CLoc CSil EBak NArc
'Prince of Peace' — CSil
'Princess Dollar' — See *F.* **'Dollar Princess'**
'Princess of Bath' — CLoc
'Princess Pamela' — SLBF
'Princess Pat' — EKMF
'Princessita' — CLit CPor CSil EBak ECtt EKMF EMan LFli MAld MAsk MBri MJac MWar MWhe NArc NHaw SKen
¶ 'Priscilla Spek' — EGou
procumbens — CGre CLit CLoc CSil EBak ECou EGou EKMF ELan ERea ESis GCHN LCla LHil MAsk MHar MWhe NArc NWCA SHFr SLBF SSea SSoC WAbe WOMN
I – 'Argentea' — CLit EKMF GCal
'Prodigy' — See *F.* **'Enfant Prodigue'**
'Prosperity' ♀ — CLit CLoc CSil EBak EBee EBly EGou EKMF ENot LCla LVER MAld MAsk MJac MWar MWhe NArc
¶ 'Prove Thyself' — EGou
N 'Pumila' — CTri EKMF ELan MAsk MBal NArc
'Purbeck Mist' — EKMF
'Purperklokje' — CSil EBak EGou EKMF MAld MAsk MWhe NArc
'Purple Emperor' — CLoc
'Purple Graseing' — MAsk
'Purple Heart' — CLoc CSil EBak NArc SKen
'Purple Patch' — CLit LFli MBri SLBF WLRN
'Purple Pride' — MBri
'Purple Rain' — CSil EKMF

'Purple Showers' CSil NArc
'Purple Splendour' CSil
'Pussy Cat' CLoc CSil EBak EKMF LCla
MAsk SKen SSoC
'Putney Pride' EBly
'Put's Folly' EBak MJac SKen SMer
putumayensis CLit CSil EBak
'Quasar' CDoC CLit CLoc CPor CSil
EBly EKMF LFli LVER MAsk
MJac MWhe NHaw SLBF
WGwG
'Queen Mabs' EBak
'Queen Mary' CLoc CSil EBak EKMF
'Queen of Bath' EBak
'Queen of Derby' CSil LCla MAld MAsk
¶ 'Queen of Hearts' CSil
'Queen's Park' EBak
'Query' CSil EBak NArc SKen
'R.A.F.' CLit CLoc CSil EBak EBly ECtt
EKMF LCla LFli MAsk MWar
NArc SKen SLBF SSea
'Rachel Craig' MWar
'Rachel Sinton' EMan LFli MBri WLRN
'Radcliffe Beauty' MWhe
'Radcliffe Bedder' CSil MAsk SKen
'Radings Gerda' EGou
'Radings Inge' EGou EKMF
'Rading's Juma' EGou
'Radings Karin' CDoC EGou EKMF
¶ 'Radings Magma' EGou
'Radings Mapri' EKMF
'Rading's Marjorie' EGou
¶ 'Radings Mia' EGou
'Radings Michelle' CSil EGou
'Raintree Legend' NArc
'Ralph Oliver' EGou
'Ralph's Delight' EGou
'Rambling Rose' CLit CLoc CSil EBak ECtt
EGou LFli MAsk MJac NArc
'Rambo' NArc
'Rams Royal' LCla LVER MAsk MJac NArc
* 'Raspberry' CLit CLoc CSil EBak LCla LFli
MAsk MWar MWhe NArc
'Ratatouille' CSil EKMF LFli MAsk NArc
ravenii EGou EKMF
'Ravensbarrow' NArc
'Ravenslaw' EKMF
'Ray Redfern' MJac
'Raymond Scopes' EGou
'Razzle Dazzle' EBak
'Reading Show' CSil EBly LCla SLBF
'Rebecca Williamson' EGou LCla MJac MWhe NArc
'Rebekah Sinton' CLit EBak LFli MAsk MBri
MWar
'Red Ace' CSil
'Red Imp' CSil
'Red Jacket' EBak NArc
'Red Ribbons' EBak
¶ 'Red Rover' EGou
'Red Rum' CSil
'Red Shadows' CLit CLoc CSil EBak LFli MJac
MWhe NArc WGwG
'Red Spider' CLit CLoc CSil EBak EKMF
EMan LFli LVER MAsk MWar
MWhe NArc NHaw SKen SSea
WGwG
'Red Sunlight' EGou
'Red Wing' CLoc
'Reflexa' See *F. × bacillaris* 'Reflexa'
'Reg Dickenson' MJac MWhe
'Reg Gubler' SLBF
'Regal' CLoc

'Regal Robe' CLit CSil
regia CSil
– var. *alpestris* See *F. alpestris*
¶ – subsp. *regia* CSil EGou EKMF LCla
– subsp. *reitzii* CSil EKMF
– subsp. *serrae* CSil EKMF
'Remembrance' CSil EKMF LCla SSea
'Remus' CSil EKMF LCla MAsk MBri
NArc
'Requiem' CLoc IHos
'Reverend Doctor Brown' EBak NArc
'Reverend Elliott' See *F.* 'President Elliot'
N 'Rhapsody' CLoc
'Riant' NArc
§ 'Riccartonii' ♀ CB&S CChe CLit CLoc CPor
EBak EKMF ELan ENot ISea
LCla MBar MBri NBee NFla
NPer NWea SMrm SPer WPic
WStI WWal
'Riccartonii Variegated' WEas
'Richard John' EGou NArc
'Richard John Carrington' CSil
'Ridestar' CLit CLoc CSil EBak EMan
LCla MAsk MJac MWhe
'Rina Felix' EGou
'Ringwood Market' CLit EBly ECtt EKMF LCla
LFli MJac MWhe NArc
'Robbie' CLit EGou EKMF NArc
'Robert Lutters' NArc
'Robin Hood' CSil
¶ 'Rocket Fire' CLit LFli
'Rodeo' EGou
'Rolla' EBak EGou EKMF NArc
'Rolt's Ruby' EBly EKMF NArc
'Roman City' CLoc
'Romance' EKMF
'Romany Rose' CLoc
'Ron Chambers Love' EGou
'Ron Ewart' EKMF MWhe
'Ronald L. Lockerbie' CLit CLoc EKMF SMur
¶ 'Ron's Ruby' MWhe
'Roos Breytenbach' CDoC EGou EKMF LCla
'Rosamunda' CLoc
'Rose Aylett' EBak NArc
'Rose Bradwardine' EBak NArc SMer
'Rose Churchill' LCla LFli LVER MBri MJac
'Rose Fantasia' CLit CLoc CSil EBly EGou
EKMF LCla MAld MJac MWar
MWhe SLBF SSea
'Rose Lace' CLit
'Rose Marie' CLit CLoc NArc
'Rose of Castile' ♀ CLit CLoc CSil EBak EKMF
LCla LFli MAsk MJac MWhe
NArc SRms
'Rose of Castile CSil EBak EKMF LCla MAsk
Improved' MJac MWar SKen
'Rose of Denmark' CLoc CSil EBak EKMF LFli
MAsk MBri MJac MWar MWhe
NHaw WGwG WLRN
'Rose Reverie' EBak NArc
'Rose Winston' CLit EKMF MWhe
rosea hort. See *F.* 'Globosa'
– Ruiz & Pav. See *F. lycioides* Andrews
'Rosebud' EBak NArc
'Rosecroft Beauty' CSil EBak LFli MAsk MWhe
NArc SKen SSea
'Rosemary Day' CLoc
'Roslyn Lowe' CDoC CLit CSil NArc
'Ross Lea' CSil
'Rosy Frills' CSil EGou LCla LFli MJac
MWhe NArc
'Rosy Morn' CLoc EBak

Rosy Ruffles	EKMF
'Rough Silk'	CLit CLoc CSil EBak LCla LFli SMer
'Roy Walker'	CLit CLoc CSil EGou EKMF MAld MAsk MJac MWar MWhe NArc
'Royal and Ancient'	CLTr EGou
'Royal Orchid'	EBak
'Royal Purple'	CLit CPor CSil EBak EKMF MAsk MBri NArc
'Royal Touch'	EBak
'Royal Velvet' ♀	CLTr CLit CLoc CPor CSil EBak EBly EGou EKMF EMan LCla LFli LVER MAld MAsk MJac MWar MWhe NArc NHaw SKen SLBF WGwG
'Royal Wedding'	CLit CSil LCla LFli NArc
'Rozientje'	NArc
'Rubicon'	NArc
§ 'Rubra Grandiflora'	EBak EKMF LCla SLBF
'Ruby'	CLit
'Ruby Wedding'	CLit CSil EGou LCla SLBF SSea
'Ruddigore'	CSil MAsk NArc
'Ruffles'	CLit CSil EBak NArc
§ 'Rufus'	CLoc CSil CTri EBak EBly EKMF LCla LFli LVER MAsk MJac MWar MWhe NArc SKen SLBF WGwG
'Rufus the Red'	See F. 'Rufus'
'Ruth'	CLit CSil
'Ruth Brazewell'	CLoc
'Ruth King'	CLit EBak ECtt LFli WGwG
'Rutland Water'	LFli MAsk NArc
'Sailor'	MAld MJac
'Sally Ann'	CLit
'Salmon Cascade'	CLit CSil EBak EBly ECtt EKMF EMan LCla LFli MAld MAsk MJac MWar MWhe NArc SLBF SSea
'Salmon Glow'	MAsk MJac MWhe NArc
'Sampson's Delight'	MAsk
'Sam's Song'	MJac
'Samson'	CLit EBak
'San Diego'	CLit CSil NArc
'San Francisco'	EBak
'San Leandro'	EBak NArc
'San Mateo'	EBak NArc
§ sanctae-rosae	EBak EGou EKMF LBlm LCla
'Sandboy'	CSil EBak
'Sanrina'	EKMF
'Santa Cruz'	CLit CSil EBak EGou EKMF LCla LVER MAsk MWhe NArc SMer SSea
'Santa Lucia'	CLoc EBak LFli NArc
'Santa Monica'	CPor EBak
'Sapphire'	CSil EBak NArc
'Sara Helen'	CLoc EBak
'Sarah Eliza'	MJac
'Sarah Greensmith'	EKMF NArc
'Sarah Jayne'	CSil EBak LCla NArc
'Sarong'	CSil EBak NArc
'Saskia'	EKMF NArc
¶ 'Satchmo'	EGou
'Satellite'	CLoc EBak EKMF MAsk NArc
'Saturnus'	EBak
scabriuscula	EKMF LCla
scandens	See F. decussata
'Scarborough Rock'	NArc
'Scarborough Rosette'	EGou
'Scarcity'	CLit CSil EBak MWhe NArc SKen

'Scarlett O'Hara'	EGou
'Schiller'	EKMF
'Schneeball'	CSil EBak EKMF NArc
'Schneewittchen' Hoech	CSil EKMF
'Schneewittchen' Klein	CSil EBak EBly
'Schönbrunner Schuljubiläum'	EBak LCla SLBF
'Schöne Wilhelmine'	NArc
'Scotch Heather'	NArc
'Sea Shell'	EBak MAsk NArc
'Seaforth'	EBak
'Sealand Prince'	CLit CSil ECtt EKMF LCla MAsk NArc
'Sebastopol'	CLoc ECtt EKMF NArc
serratifolia Hooker	See F. austromontana
– Ruiz & Pavón	See F. denticulata
sessilifolia	EKMF LCla
'Seventh Heaven'	CLit CLoc EGou LFli MAsk MWar
'Severn Queen'	CPor CSil
'Shady Lady'	NArc
'Shangri-La'	EBak
'Shanley'	NArc
'Sharon Allsop'	CSil MWhe WGwG
'Sharon Caunt'	CSil EKMF
'Sharpitor'	See F. magellanica var. molinae 'Sharpitor'
'Shawn Rushton'	EKMF MWar
'Shawna Ree'	EKMF LCla
'Sheila Crooks'	EBak EMan LCla MAld MAsk MJac MWhe
'Sheila Kirby'	MJac
'Sheila Mary'	EKMF MJac
'Shell Pink'	CSil
'Shelley Lyn'	NArc SKen
'Shellford' ♀	CLit CLoc CSil EBak EBly EKMF EMan LCla LFli MAld MAsk MJac MWar MWhe NArc SLBF SSea
'Shining Knight'	CSil
'Shirley Halladay'	EKMF
'Shooting Star'	EBak
'Showtime'	CSil
'Shugborough'	EKMF MJac MWar
'Shy Lady'	MWhe
'Sierra Blue'	CLoc EBak EKMF NArc
'Silver Anniversary'	EKMF NArc
'Silver Dawn'	CSil EBly EKMF MAsk MWhe SLBF
'Silver Dollar'	CLit LFli MWhe NArc SKen WGwG
'Silverdale'	CSil EKMF LFli MAsk MWhe NLak
'Simon J. Rowell'	EKMF LCla
simplicicaulis	EBak EGou EKMF LCla MAsk
'Sincerity'	CLit CLoc CSil
'Sinton's Standard'	MBri MWar
'Sir Alfred Ramsey'	EBak MJac MWhe
¶ 'Sir Matt Busby'	MWar
N 'Siren'	EBak NArc
'Sister Ann Haley'	CLit CSil EBly EKMF
'Sleepy'	CLit CSil LCla LFli MAsk MBri NArc
'Sleigh Bells'	CLoc CSil EBak EKMF MAsk MWhe NArc
'Small Pipes'	EGou EKMF NArc
'Smokey Mountain'	EKMF MAsk NArc
'Smoky'	CSil
'Sneezy'	CLit CSil EHol LFli MAsk MWhe NArc
'Snow Burner'	SLBF
'Snow Goose'	EGou

'Snow White'	CLit CSil EGou LFli MAsk NArc SMur WGwG
§ 'Snowcap' ♀	CLit CLoc CSil EBak EBar EBly EKMF EMan IHos LCla LFli LVER MAld MAsk MBri MJac MWar MWhe NArc NFai NHaw NPer SIng SKen SLBF SSea WGwG WStI
'Snowdon'	MWar
N 'Snowdrift'	CLoc EBak EGou
'Snowfire'	CLoc CSil ECtt EGou EKMF LFli MAld MAsk MJac MWhe NArc WGwG
¶ 'Snowflake'	EKMF
'Snowstorm'	CSil ECtt
'Snowy Summit'	CLit CSil SMur WGwG
'So Big'	CLit EKMF NArc
Software	EGou MAsk NArc
'Son of Thumb' ♀	CLit CLoc CSil EAst EBly EKMF ELan EMan GCHN LCla LFli MAld MAsk MBri MJac MWhe NArc SLBF SSea
¶ 'Sonia Ann Bary'	EGou
'Sonota'	CLoc CSil EBak EKMF NArc
'Sophie Claire'	EGou LCla
'Sophie Cochrane'	NArc
'Sophie's Surprise'	EGou EKMF
'Sophisticated Lady'	CLoc CSil EBak EBly ECtt EKMF LFli LVER MAsk MJac MWar NArc
'South Lakeland'	CLit
'South Seas'	EBak NArc
'Southgate'	CLit CLoc CPor CSil EBak EGou EKMF EMan LFli MAsk MBri MJac MWar MWhe NArc NHaw WGwG
'Southlanders'	EBak
'Southwell Minster'	EKMF NArc
'Space Shuttle'	CLoc CSil EKMF LCla LFli MAsk MWhe NArc
'Sparky'	CLit EGou LCla MAsk
'Speciosa'	EBak EKMF LCla MWhe
'Spellbinder'	EGou
'Spion Kop'	CLit CSil EBak EKMF LFli LVER MAsk MJac MWar MWhe NArc NFai NHaw
§ *splendens* ♀	CFee CLoc CSil EBak EGou EKMF LCla NPer SMrm
– 'Karl Hartweg'	LBlm
'Squadron Leader'	CLit EBak EBly EGou LCla LVER
'Square Peg'	LFli NArc
'Stanley Cash'	CLit CLoc CSil EKMF LFli LVER MAsk MWar MWhe NArc SCoo
'Stan's Choice'	CSil
'Star of Pink'	MWhe
'Star Rose'	EKMF
'Stardust'	CSil EBak LCla LFli MJac MWhe NArc
¶ 'Starlight'	EGou
'Steeley'	MWhe
'Steirerblut'	EGou LCla
'Stella Ann'	CLit CSil EBak EBly EGou LCla MAld MWhe NArc
'Stella Marina'	CLoc EBak
'Sterretje'	EGou
¶ 'Stoney Creek'	MWar
'Stormy Sunset'	CLit NArc
¶ 'Straat Napier'	EGou

'Strawberry Delight'	CLit CLoc CSil EBak ECtt EKMF LCla LFli LVER MAsk MJac MWhe NArc SKen
'Strawberry Mousse'	LVER
'Strawberry Sundae'	CLoc CSil EBak NArc
'Strawberry Supreme'	CSil EKMF
'String of Pearls'	CLit CLoc CSil EKMF LCla MAsk MBri MJac NArc SKen SLBF SSea
'Stuart Joe'	EKMF
'Sugar Almond'	MJac
'Sugar Blues'	EBak NArc
Sugarbush	See *F.* 'Suikerbossie'
§ 'Suikerbossie'	MJac NArc
¶ 'Summerwood'	CLit
'Sunkissed'	CLit COtt EBak
'Sunlight Path'	LCla
'Sunningdale'	EGou LCla
'Sunny'	COtt SKen
'Sunny Smiles'	EKMF NArc
'Sunray' (v)	CLTr CLit CLoc CSil EBak EGou EKMF LFli MAld MAsh MAsk MBel MWhe NArc SKen SPla WWeb
'Sunset'	CLit CLoc CSil EBak MAsk MWhe NArc SKen SMer SPer
'Supernova'	NArc
'Superstar'	CLit CSil EBly LCla MAsk MBri SSea
'Surrey Symphony'	LCla
'Susan'	COtt LCla
'Susan Arnold'	MAsk
¶ 'Susan Diana'	EGou
'Susan Ford'	CSil LFli MAsk NArc WGwG
'Susan Green'	CLit CSil EBak EKMF EMan LCla LFli MAld MAsk MJac MWar MWhe NArc WGwG
'Susan McMaster'	CLoc
'Susan Olcese'	EBak NArc
'Susan Travis'	CLTr CLit CLoc CSil EBak EKMF MAsk MWhe NArc SBid SKen
'Susan Young'	MAsk
'Swanley Gem' ♀	CLit CLoc EBak EKMF LCla LFli MAsk MWhe SLBF SSea
'Swanley Pendula'	CLoc
'Swanley Yellow'	EBak NArc SKen
'Sweet Leilani'	CLit CLoc CSil EBak NArc SKen
'Sweet Sixteen'	CLoc
N 'Sweetheart'	EBak NArc
'Swingtime' ♀	CGre CLit CLoc CSil EBak EBly EKMF EMan IHos LCla LFli LVER MAld MAsk MJac MWar MWhe NArc NFai NHaw SKen SLBF WGwG
'S'Wonderful'	CLoc EBak SMer
sylvatica Benth.	EKMF LCla
– Munz	See *F. nigricans*
'Sylvia Barker'	EGou LCla MAld MAsk MWar NArc
'Sylvia Foster'	NArc
'Sylvy'	CLit CSil MWhe NArc
'Symphony'	CLoc EBak MAsk
¶ 'T' Vorske'	EGou
¶ 'Taco'	EGou
'Taddle'	EMan MJac NArc SLBF WGwG
'Taffeta Bow'	CLit CLoc CSil EKMF LFli LVER MAsk SMer
'Taffy'	EBak
'Tam O'Shanter'	CLit CSil LFli
¶ 'Tamino'	SLBF

'Tamworth'   CLit CLoc EBak LCla LFli
                       MAsk MJac NArc SSea
'Tangerine'   CLit CLoc CPor CSil EBak
                       EKMF MWhe NArc SSea
'Tania Leanne'   CLit CSil LVER NArc
'Tanya'   CLoc EKMF
'Tanya Bridger'   EBak NArc
'Tarra Valley'   EGou LCla NArc
'Task Force'   CLit CSil MAsk NArc
'Tausendschön'   CLit CLoc ECtt EKMF NArc
'Tear Fund'   EGou
'Ted Heath'   MAsk NArc
'Ted Perry'   CSil LVER
'Television'   LFli MAsk NArc
'Tempo Doelo'   CLit
N 'Temptation'   CGre CLit CLoc CSil EBak
                       ECtt MBri
'Tennessee Waltz' ♀   CGre CLit CLoc CSil EBak
                       EBly EKMF EMan LCla LFli
                       LVER MAld MAsk MJac
                       MWar MWhe NArc SChu SKen
                       SLBF SPer SPla WGwG
'Terrysue'   EKMF
♦ tetradactyla   See F. enclandra subsp.
                       tetradactyla
'Teupels Erfolg'   NArc
'Texas Longhorn'   CLit CLoc CSil EBak EKMF
                       LFli NArc
'Thalia' ♀   CGre CLit CLoc CSil EBak
                       EBly ECtt EGou EKMF EMan
                       ERea IHos LBlm LCla LFli
                       LHil LVER MAld MAsk MBri
                       MJac MWar MWhe NArc
                       NHaw SKen SLBF SPla WEas
                       WGwG
'Thamar'   CLoc EGou EKMF LCla MWar
                       MWhe
'That's It'   EBak NArc
'The Aristocrat'   CLoc CSil EBak WGwG
§ 'The Doctor'   CLoc CPor CSil EBak EKMF
                       MAsk MWhe NArc
'The Jester'   EBak
'The Madame'   CSil EBak MAsk NArc
'The Patriot'   NArc
'The Rival'   EKMF
'The Tarns'   CLit CSil EBak EKMF MAsk
                       NArc NPla WCru
'Therese Dupois'   CSil
'Théroigne de Méricourt' EBak NArc
'Thilco'   EKMF
¶ 'Think Pink'   EGou WGwG
'This England'   CSil NArc
'Thistle Hill'   EKMF
'Thompsonii'   See F. magellanica
                       'Thompsonii'
'Thornley's Hardy'   CLit CSil EKMF EMan LFli
                       MAsk MBri NArc
'Three Cheers'   CLoc EBak
'Three Counties'   EBak
'Thumbelina'   EGou
'Thunderbird'   CLoc EBak
thymifolia   ELan ESis GCra GMac GQui
                       LHil LHop MBal MPla SBid
                       SHFr SMrm WKif
– subsp. minimiflora   EGou EKMF LCla
– subsp. thymifolia   EGou EKMF LCla
'Tiara'   EBak
N 'Tiffany'   EBak
tillettiana   EGou EKMF
'Tillingbourne'   LCla
'Tillmouth Lass'   EKMF MAsk
'Timlin Brened'   CSil EBak MAsk MWhe NArc

¶ 'Timothy Titus'   EGou
'Ting-a-ling'   CLit CLoc CSil EBak EBly
                       EKMF LFli LHil LVER MAld
                       MAsk MWhe NArc SLBF SSea
N 'Tinker Bell'   CLit CPor CSil EBak EKMF
                       NArc WLRN
'Tintern Abbey'   NArc
'Toby Bridger'   CLoc EBak NArc
'Tolling Bell'   CLit CSil EBak EKMF LCla
                       LFli MAsk MJac MWhe NArc
                       WGwG
'Tom H. Oliver'   EBak
'Tom Knights'   EBak EGou EKMF LCla MAsk
                       MWhe NArc WGwG
'Tom Redfern'   MJac
'Tom Thorne'   EBak
'Tom Thumb' ♀   Widely available
'Tom West' (v)   CGre CInt CLit CLoc CMHG
                       CSil EBak EGou EKMF LBlm
                       LCla LFli LHop MAld MAsk
                       MBEx MJac MWhe NArc
                       NHaw SKen SLBF SMrm SSea
                       WEas
'Tom Woods'   LCla MWhe
¶ 'Tony Galea'   LCla
¶ 'Tony Porter'   MJac
'Toos'   EGou
'Topaz'   CLoc EBak NArc
'Topper'   EMan NArc
'Torch'   CLit CLoc CSil EBak EKMF
                       MJac NArc
'Torchlight'   CSil EBly LCla MAsk
'Torvill and Dean'   CDoC CLit CLoc CSil EBly
                       EGou EKMF LFli LVER MAsk
                       MJac MWar MWhe NArc SLBF
'Towi'   NArc
'Tracid'   CLoc CSil
'Tracie Ann'   EKMF
'Trail Blazer'   CLit CLoc CSil EBak LCla
                       MJac NArc
'Trailing Queen'   CLit CSil EBak EKMF MAsk
                       MJac NArc
'Trase'   CLit CPor CSil EBak EBly
                       EKMF LVER MAsk NArc
'Traudchen Bonstedt'   CDoC CLoc CSil EBak EBly
                       LCla MAsk MWhe NArc SLBF
'Traviata'   LFli NArc
'Treasure'   EBak
'Trés Long'   EGou
'Trewince Twilight'   NArc
'Tricolor'   See F. magellanica var. gracilis
                       'Tricolor'
'Tricolorii'   See F. magellanica var. gracilis
                       'Tricolor'
'Trientje'   EGou
'Trio'   CLoc SSea
triphylla   EBak EGou EKMF LCla
'Tristesse'   CLoc CSil EBak MAsk MJac
                       MWhe NArc
'Troika'   EBak EKMF
'Troon'   MAsk NArc
'Tropic Sunset'   CSil LFli MAsk MBri MWhe
                       NArc
'Tropicana'   CLit CLoc EBak LFli NArc
'Troubadour'   CLoc
'Trudy'   CSil EBak EKMF LCla MAsk
                       NArc
¶ 'Trumpet Voluntary' EGou
N 'Trumpeter'   CDoC CLit CLoc CSil EBak
                       EBly EGou EKMF LCla LFli
                       MAsk MJac MWhe NArc
¶ 'TSJ'   EGou

'Tsjiep'	MAsk
'Tuonela'	CLoc CSil EBak EKMF MAsk MWhe NArc
'Tutone'	MAsk MJac NArc
'Tutti-frutti'	CLoc MWhe SMer
'Tutu'	EKMF NArc
'T'Vosk'	NArc
'Twink'	EGou
'Twinkling Stars'	CSil EKMF LCla MAsk MJac NArc
'Twirling Square Dancer'	EGou
¶ 'Twist of Fate'	EKMF
'Two Tiers'	EKMF NArc WGwG
'UFO'	CSil LFli NArc
'Uillean Pipes'	EGou
'Ullswater'	CLit CSil EBak LVER MAsk NArc
'Ultramar'	EBak NArc
'Uncle Charley'	CDoC CLoc EBak EKMF LFli WEas
'Uncle Steve'	CLit EBak LFli NArc
¶ 'University of Liverpool'	NArc
'Upward Look'	EBak EKMF MAsk SMer SSea
'Vale of Belvoir'	CLit
'Valentine'	EBak
'Valerie Ann'	CLit EBak LCla LFli
'Valiant'	EBak
'Vanessa'	CLoc
'Vanessa Jackson'	CLoc CSil LCla LFli MAsk MJac MWar MWhe NArc SKen WGwG
'Vanity Fair'	CLoc CSil EBak NArc
vargarsiana	EKMF LCla
'Variegated Brenda White'	EKMF MAsk NArc SLBF
'Variegated La Campanella'	MWhe
¶ 'Variegated Lottie Hobby'	CLit MAld
I 'Variegated Procumbens'	See *F. procumbens* **'Argentea'**
'Variegated Snowcap'	MWhe
'Variegated Superstar'	MBri
'Variegated Swingtime'	CSil EBak LFli
'Variegated Vivienne Thompson'	MBri
'Variegated Waveney Sunrise'	MBri
'Variegated White Joy'	EKMF
'Veenlust'	EGou
'Velma'	NArc
'Venus Victrix'	CSil EBak EGou EKMF MWhe SLBF
venusta	EBak EGou EKMF LCla
'Vera Wilding'	NArc
'Versicolor'	See *F. magellanica* **'Versicolor'**
'Vi Whitehouse'	CSil
'Victorian'	CSil
'Victory'	EBak
'Vielliebchen'	CSil
'Vincent van Gogh'	EGou
'Violet Bassett-Burr'	CLoc CSil EBak NArc
'Violet Gem'	CLoc
¶ 'Violet Lace'	CSil
'Violet Rosette'	EBak NArc
'Viva Ireland'	EBak ECtt MAsk NArc SMer
'Vivien Colville'	CLoc SSea
'Vivienne Davis'	EGou
'Vivienne Thompson'	NArc
'Vobeglo'	EKMF
'Vogue'	EBak
'Voltaire'	CSil EBak

'Voodoo'	CGre CLit CLoc CSil EBak EKMF EMan LFli MAsk MWar SCoo SLBF SSea
'Vulcan'	CSil
¶ *vulcanica*	LCla
– André	See *F. ampliata*
– Berry	EKMF
– subsp. *hitchcockii* Berry	EKMF
¶ 'Vuurwerk'	EGou
'Vyvian Miller'	MJac
'W.F.C. Kampionen'	NArc
'W.P. Wood'	CSil MAsk
¶ 'Wagtails White Pixie'	CPor
'Waldfee'	CDoC CSil EGou EKMF LCla MAsk MWhe
¶ 'Wally Yendell'	EGou
'Walsingham'	CSil EBak EGou MAld MAsk MJac MWhe SKen
'Waltraud'	NArc
'Waltzing Matilda'	CLit
'Walz Bella'	CLit LCla SLBF
'Walz Blauwkous'	EGou
'Walz Citer'	NArc
'Walz Doedelzak'	LCla
'Walz Freule'	EKMF MJac
'Walz Gamelan'	NArc
'Walz Gitaar'	NArc
'Walz Harp'	CLit EGou LCla NArc SLBF
'Walz Jubelteen'	CLit CLoc CSil EGou EKMF EMan LCla MAsk MJac MWar MWhe SLBF SSea
'Walz Lucifer'	EGou EKMF SLBF
'Walz Luit'	EGou NArc
'Walz Mandoline'	EGou NArc
'Walz Parasol'	NArc
'Walz Tamtam'	CSil
'Walz Triangel'	CSil EKMF NArc
'Walz Trommel'	NArc
'Walz Waterval'	CSil
'Walz Wipneus'	NArc
'Wapenfeld's 150'	EGou
'Wapenfeld's Bloei'	CLit CSil EGou LCla MAsk NArc SLBF
'War Dance'	MWhe
'War Paint'	CLoc CSil EBak NArc
'Warton Crag'	CSil NArc
'Wassernymph'	CSil
'Water Nymph'	CLit CLoc SLBF
'Waterways'	EGou
'Wave of Life'	CSil EKMF MAld MAsk MWhe SKen
'Waveney Gem'	CLit CSil EBak EGou EKMF EMan LCla MAld MAsk MJac MWar NArc SLBF
'Waveney Queen'	MJac NArc
'Waveney Sunrise'	CPor CSil EKMF LCla MAsk MJac MWar MWhe NArc
'Waveney Valley'	EBak MJac NArc
'Waveney Waltz'	CSil EBak LCla MAsk MJac MWar MWhe NArc
'Wee Lass'	CSil
'Welsh Dragon'	CLoc EBak MAsk NArc
'Wendy'	See *F.* **'Snowcap'**
'Wendy Atkinson'	EKMF
'Wendy Harris'	MJac
'Wendy Leedham'	ECtt EKMF
¶ 'Wendy van Wanten'	SLBF
'Wendy's Beauty'	CLoc EBly
'Wessex Belle'	LCla
'Westgate'	ECtt EKMF
¶ 'Westham'	LCla

'Westminster Chimes' ♀ CLit CLoc CSil EKMF MAsk MWhe NArc
'Wharfedale' CSil MAld MJac NArc
'Whickham Beauty' CSil
'Whickham Blue' MWar
'Whirlaway' CLoc CSil EBak EKMF MAsk NArc SMer
'Whirlybird' NArc
'White Ann' CDoC CLit CLoc LCla MBri
'White Clove' CLit CSil EGou LCla
'White Falls' MAsk NArc
'White Galore' CLit EBak EKMF EMan LVER MAsk NArc SMer
'White Gold' EBak
'White Heidi Ann' CPor LFli MWhe SSea WGwG
'White Joy' CLit CSil EBak EKMF MAsk MWhe NArc
'White King' CLit CLoc CSil EBak EKMF EMan LVER MAld MAsk MWhe SLBF
'White Lady Patricia Mountbatten' EMan
'White Pixie' CDoC CLit CSil EBly EKMF LCla LFli LVER MJac MPla NArc SPer
'White Pixie Wagtail' CSil EBak MWhe
N 'White Queen' CLit CSil EBak MWhe
'White Spider' CLit CLoc CSil EBak EKMF LBlm LFli MAsk MWhe NArc SKen SSea
'Whitehaven' NArc
'Whiteknights Amethyst' CSil SLod
'Whiteknights Blush' CSil GCal GQui SBid SKen SLod SMrm
'Whiteknights Cheeky' CSil EBak EGou NArc
'Whiteknights Goblin' See *F. denticulata* **'Whiteknights Goblin'**
¶ 'Whiteknights Green Glister' CSil
'Whiteknights Pearl' CLit CSil ECtt EKMF LCla MAsk NArc SLBF WGwG
'Whiteknights Ruby' CSil EKMF
'Whitton Pride' MJac
'Wicked Queen' CSil LCla LFli NArc
'Wickham Blue' LCla MJac
'Wiebke Becker' EKMF NArc
'Wild and Beautiful' CLit EKMF LFli MAsk NArc
'Wildfire' CPor NArc
'Wilfred C. Dodson' EGou
'William Caunt' EKMF
'William Jay' EGou
'Wilson's Colours' EBly
'Wilson's Pearls' CLit CSil NArc SLBF WGwG
'Wilson's Sugar Pink' CLit EBly LCla MJac
'Win Oxtoby' EKMF NArc
'Wine and Roses' EBak NArc SMer
'Wingrove's Mammoth' CSil LFli MAsk NArc
'Wings of Song' CSil EBak NArc SMer
'Winifred' NArc
'Winston Churchill' ♀ CLit CLoc CSil EBak EBly EKMF EMan IHos LCla LFli LVER MAsk MBri MJac MWar MWhe NArc NFai NHaw SRms
'Woodnook' CSil MAsk
'Woodside' CSil
* 'Woodside Gem' NArc
wurdackii EKMF ERea MAsk SSea
'Xmas Tree' MAsk
'Y Me' CLit
'Ymkje' EGou
'Yolanda Franck' CSil
'Yorkshire Rally' MJac

'Yuletide' CSil
'Zara' CSil MWhe
¶ 'Zets Bravo' WGwG
'Ziegfield Girl' EBak NArc SMer
'Zulu King' EGou NArc
'Zulu Queen' EGou
'Zwarte Dit' EGou
'Zwarte Snor' EGou NArc

FUMANA (Cistaceae)
thymifolia NWCA

FUMARIA (Papaveraceae)
lutea See *Corydalis lutea*
officinalis MSal

FURCRAEA (Agavaceae)
¶ *bedinghausii* CGre EOas WPGP
§ *foetida* var. *mediopicta* CB&S
 – 'Variegata' See *F. foetida* var. *mediopicta*
 gigantea See *F. foetida*
longaeva CAbb CHEx CTor CTrC EOas LHil SAPC SArc
selloa CHEx LHil
 – var. *marginata* CHEx LHil

GAGEA (Liliaceae)
lutea EPot
pratensis EPot

GAHNIA (Cyperaceae) See Plant Deletions

GAILLARDIA (Asteraceae)
aristata hort. See *G.* × *grandiflora*
'Bremen' CBot CPou EPfP GMaP NPri NTow
'Burgunder' CBot CDoC EAst EBrP EBre ECtt EFou ELan GChr LBlm LBre MBri MNrw MWat MWhi NFai NFla NMir NOak NVic SBre SPer SRms WBea WGor WOve WRus
'Dazzler' ♀ CTri ECtt ELan EMan ENot EOld EPfP MBri NNor SPer WBea WGor WMow WStI
§ 'Fackelschein' CMdw NFai WRHF
 Goblin See *G.* **'Kobold'**
§ 'Goldkobold' ELan EPar MOne
§ × *grandiflora* EMan NOak
¶ – 'Aurea' WLRN
 – 'Aurea Plena' (d) EBee MWhi
§ 'Kobold' CB&S EBrP EBre ECtt EMan ERic GAbr LBre MBri MCLN NBus NRoo SBre SOkh SPer SPla SRms WFar WMow WWin
'Mandarin' COtt EBrP EBre LBre SBre SRms
¶ Monarch Group CMGP
'Nana Nieske' NTow
* New Giant hybrids MRav
¶ *suavis* EBee
'Tokajer' EBee EPfP NVic
 Torchlight See *G.* **'Fackelschein'**
'Wirral Flame' EPar
 Yellow Goblin See *G.* **'Goldkobold'**

GALACTITES (Asteraceae)
tomentosa CInt CPle CRDP ECha ELan EMan EMar GBri MAvo MHlr SUsu WBea WEas WWye

GALANTHUS † (Amaryllidaceae)

allenii	CAvo CBro EMor
alpinus	CLAP LAma
¶ 'Anglesey Abbey'	EMor
¶ 'Anne of Geierstein'	EMor
'Armine'	CAvo EMor LFox
'Atkinsii' ♀	CAvo CBro CLAP EMon EMor EOrc EPot ERav LAma LFox MBri MRav NBir WRus WWat WWye
'Augustus'	CAvo EMor LFox WIvy
¶ 'Barbara's Double' (d)	EMor
'Benhall Beauty'	EMor LFox
¶ 'Benton Magnet'	EMor
'Bertram Anderson'	EMor LFox
'Bitton'	CBro CLAP LFox WRus
'Blewbury Tart'	CMea
bortkewitschianus	CBro LFox
'Brenda Troyle'	CBro CLAP EPar EPot LFox WIvy WRus
byzantinus	See *G. plicatus* subsp. *byzantinus*
cabardensis	See *G. transcaucasicus*
'Cassaba'	EPot
caucasicus ♀	CAvo CBro ECha EMon EMor EPot ERav LAma LFox MTho
¶ – 'Comet'	EMor
– var. *hiemalis*	CBro ECha EMor LAma
¶ – 'John Tomlinson'	EMor
¶ – 'Mrs McNamara'	EMor
¶ 'Charmer Flore Pleno' (d)	EMor
'Clare Blakeway-Phillips'	EMor
¶ 'Colesbourne'	EMor
corcyrensis Spring flowering	See *G. reginae-olgae* subsp. *vernalis*
– Winter flowering	See *G. reginae-olgae* subsp. *reginae-olgae* **Winter-flowering Group**
'Cordelia' (d)	EMon EMor LFox
* 'Curly'	EMor
* 'David Shackleton'	EMor
'Desdemona'	CLAP LFox WIvy
'Dionysus' (d)	CBro CLAP EMor EPot LFox NBir WRus
¶ 'Double Scharlokii' (d)	WRus
¶ 'Edinburgh Ketton'	EMor
§ *elwesii* ♀	CAvo CBro CMon EMon EMor EPot ERav ERos LAma LFox MBri NBir NRog WCot WIvy WShi
– 'Flore Pleno' (d)	LFox
* – 'Grumpy'	EMon
* – 'Magnus'	CLAP
– var. *whitallii*	CLAP
* – 'Zwanenburg'	EMon
¶ 'Falkland House'	EMor
¶ 'Fieldgate Superb'	EMor
fosteri	CAvo CBro EHyt EPot LAma LRHS
– PD 256830	EMor
¶ 'Foxton'	EMor
'Galatea'	CLAP EMon EMor LFox WIvy
§ *gracilis*	CBro CLAP EMor EPar EPot ERav LFox MTho WIvy WOld
¶ – 'Corkscrew'	EMor
– Highdown form	EHyt
graecus Boissier	See *G. elwesii*
– hort.	See *G. gracilis*
¶ 'Grayling'	EMor
Greatorex double (d)	CLAP EMon SSvw
¶ 'Heffalump'	EMor
'Hill Poë' (d)	CBro EMor EPot LFox
'Hippolyta' (d)	CBro CLAP ECha EMor EPot LFox WIvy
¶ 'Icicle'	EMor
ikariae ♀	EHyt EOrc EPar EPot ERav LAma NRar
¶ – subsp. *ikariae* Butt's form	EMor
§ – Latifolius Group	CAvo CBro EMor EOrc EPot LAma LFox WOld
– Woronowii Group	CLAP EMon EPot LAma
¶ 'Imbok'	EMor
'Jacquenetta' (d)	CBro CLAP EMor EPot
'John Gray'	CBro EMon EMor LFox
kemulariae	See *G. transcaucasicus*
ketskovelii	See *G. transcaucasicus*
'Ketton'	CBro EMon EMor ERav LFox WIvy
¶ 'Kingston Double' (d)	CLAP
'Kite'	CBro EMor
'Lady Beatrix Stanley' (d)	CAvo CBro CLAP CMea EMon EMor EPot ERav LAma LFox MTho NHar
lagodechianus	See *G. transcaucasicus*
latifolius	See *G. ikariae* **Latifolius Group**
'Lavinia' (d)	CAvo ERav WRus
'Lime Tree'	CLAP EPot LFox
lutescens	See *G. nivalis* 'Sandersii'
'Magnet' ♀	CAvo CBro CFee CLAP EMor EPot ERav LAma LFox NHar SWas WRus
'Maidwell C'	EMor
'Maidwell L'	CAvo EMor LFox
'Melvillei'	NHar
'Merlin'	EMor EOrc LFox NHar WBon WRus
'Mighty Atom'	CMea EMor ERav LFox
'Moccas'	WOld
'Modern Art'	EMor
'Mrs Backhouse's Spectacles'	EPot
¶ 'Mrs Thompson'	EMor
¶ 'Mrs Wrightson's Double' (d)	EMor
'Neill Fraser'	LFox
'Nerissa' (d)	EPot
nivalis ♀	CBro CKin ELan EMor EPar EPot ERav ETub EWFC LAma LFox MBri MRPP NRog SIng WShi
– var. *angustifolius*	CBro
¶ – 'Appleby'	EPot
– 'April Fool'	LFox
– dwarf form	LFox
– 'Flore Pleno' (d) ♀	CBro CMon EBrP EBre EPar EPla EPot ERav ETub LAma LBre LFox MFos NMGW NRog NRya SBre WHen WShi WWye
¶ – 'Greenish'	EMor
– 'Humberts Orchard'	EMor LFox
– subsp. *imperati* 'Ginns'	CLAP EMor LFox WRus
¶ – JRM 3139	EMor
– 'Lady Elphinstone' (d)	CAvo CBro CRow ECha EMor EPar EPot ERav GCrs LAma LFox MTho NHar WAbe
– 'Lutescens'	See *G. nivalis* 'Sandersii'
– 'Pewsey Vale' (d)	EMor
– (Poculiformis Group) 'Sandhill Gate' (d)	EMor
– 'Pusey Green Tip' (d)	CAvo CBro CLAP EMor EPar EPot ERav ITim LFox MRav
§ – 'Sandersii'	CBro EMor EPot SSpi
§ – Scharlockii Group	CAvo CBro EHyt EMor EOrc LAma LFox NHar SWas

¶ – 'Sibbertoft White'   EMor
 – 'Tiny'   CAvo EMor
¶ – 'Tiny Tim'   EPot
§ – 'Virescens'   CLAP EMor SWas
 – 'Viridapicis'   CAvo CBro ECha EHyt EMor
   EPar EPot ERav LAma LFox
   WIvy WRus
¶ – 'Walrus' (d)   EMor
 – 'Warei'   EMor LFox
 – WM 9615 from E. Slovenia   MPhe
 'Ophelia' (d)   CAvo CBro EMor EPar EPot
   ERav LAma LFox WRus
* 'Paradise Double'   EPar
* 'Paradise Giant'   EPar
 'Peg Sharples'   EMor EPot ERav
¶ peshmenii   EHyt
 platyphyllus   See *G. ikariae* **Latifolius Group**
 plicatus ♀   CAvo CFee CMea EMon EPot
   LFox WOMN
¶ – 'Baxendale's Late'   EMor
§ – subsp. *byzantinus*   CAvo CBro EMor EOrc LFox
   LRHS
¶ – – LB 17   EMor
¶ – – 'Three Ships'   EMor
¶ – – 'Trym'   EMor
¶ – 'Gerard Parker'   EMor
 – large form   EOrc
 – 'Ron Ginns'   LFox
 – 'Warham'   CBro EMor EOrc EPot WOld
 – 'Washfield Warham'   EMon
¶ – 'Wendy's Gold'   EMor
¶ 'Ransom's Dwarf'   EMor
 reginae-olgae   CAvo CBro CMea CMon EHyt
   EMor EPot ERos LAma SSpi
   WCot
 – from Sicily   ERav
¶ – subsp. *reginae-olgae*   EMor
   'Cambridge' ♀
§ – – Winter-flowering   CBro ECha EMor ERav LAma
   Group   LFox
¶ – subsp. *vernalis*   EMor EPot
 – – AJM 75   EMor
 – – CE&H 541   EMor
 rizehensis   CBro EPot
 'Robin Hood'   EMor LFox LRHS
 'S. Arnott' ♀   CAvo CBro CLAP CMea EMon
   EMor EPar EPot ERav LAma
   LFox NBir NHar WOld
 'Sally Ann'   LFox
 'Scharlockii'   See *G. nivalis* **Scharlockii**
   Group
¶ 'Sophie North'   GCrs
 'Straffan'   CAvo CBro EHyt EMor EOrc
   EPot ERav LAma LFox NHar
   WOld WRus
¶ 'Three Leaves'   EMor
 'Titania' (d)   CBro EMor
§ transcaucasicus   CBro EPot ERav LRHS
 'Trotter's Merlin'   EMor
 'Tubby Merlin'   EMor LFox
¶ 'Washfield Colesbourne'   EMor
 'William Thomson'   LFox
 'Winifrede Mathias'   EMor LFox
¶ 'Wonston Double' (d)   EMor

GALAX (Diapensiaceae)
 aphylla   See *G. urceolata*
§ urceolata   CFil CHEx IBlr MBal SSpi
   WCru WThi

GALEGA (Papilionaceae)
 bicolor   CMdw CWit EGar EMFP
   EMon EWes IBlr MSte NBir
   NBrk SIde SMad SRms SWat
   WFar WWhi
 x *hartlandii*   IBlr MRav
 – 'Alba' ♀   EMon EWes GBar GCal IBlr
   MArl MAvo MBel MHlr NBrk
   NBro SOkh SWas WCot WPer
 – 'Candida'   CGle CWit NTow SPer
 'Her Majesty'   See *G.* **'His Majesty'**
§ 'His Majesty'   LFis MArl MAvo MRav NBrk
   NLar WBea WCot
 'Lady Wilson'   CGle CWit EWes MArl MAvo
   MRav NBrk NCat WBea WCot
   WFoF WRus
 officinalis   Widely available
 – 'Alba'   CBot CHad CHan CMdw
   ECED ECGN ECro ELan ELau
   EMan EMar IBlr LFis LHol
   MBrN WBea WByw WCHb
   WEas WHer WHoo WPyg
   WRus
 orientalis   CGle CHan EBee ECGP ECha
   EMon GCal MArl MBel SWat
   WAbb WBea WCot WRus

GALEOBDOLON See LAMIUM

GALEOPSIS (Lamiaceae)
 tetrahit 'Contrast' (v)   WAlt
 – 'Dirbach Variegated'   MInt

GALIUM (Rubiaceae)
 aristatum   MLLN WCot
 aureum   See *G. firmum*
 cruciata   See *Cruciata laevipes*
 mollugo   CArn CKin MHew MSal NLan
   SIde WCHb
§ odoratum   CArn CBre CGle CKin EEls
   EFou ELan ELau EOHP EOrc
   EWFC GPoy LHol LSyl MAus
   MBar MBri MNrw MSal NBro
   NMir NSti SIde SPer SRms
   WBon WCer WHer WMer
   WOak
 palustre   CKin
 perpusillum   See *Asperula perpusilla*
 verum   CArn CKin EJud EWFC MChe
   MGra MHew MSal NLan NMir
   SIde WCHb WGwy WHer
   WOak

GALPHIMIA   (Malpighiaceae) See Plant
Deletions

GALPINIA (Lythraceae)
¶ transvaalica   CTrC

GALTONIA (Hyacinthaceae)
§ candicans   Widely available
 princeps   CAvo CBro CHea EBee EBrP
   EBre ECha ECro EPla GBuc
   GCra LBre NRoo SBre WCot
   WEas
 regalis   CHan GCal
 viridiflora ♀   CBot CBro CEnd CHar CHea
   EAst ECha ECro ELan GCHN
   GCal MHFP MHlr NHol NPSI
   NRoo SAga SDix SIgm WHer
   WOMN WWat

¶ – S&SH 3 | CHan

GAMOCHAETA (Asteraceae) See Plant Deletions

GAMOLEPIS See STEIRODISCUS

GARDENIA (Rubiaceae)
§ augusta | EBak EPfP MBri SLMG
– 'Prostrata Variegata' | See *G. augusta* **'Radicans Variegata'**
florida | See *G. augusta*
globosa | See *Rothmannia globosa*
grandiflora | See *G. augusta*
jasminoides | See *G. augusta*

GARRYA † (Garryaceae)
¶ *elliptica* (m) | EHol WGwG
– | CB&S CPle EBrP EBre ENot GOrc GRei ISea LBre LPan MBri MGos NFla NHol NNor SBre SPer SReu SSoC WBod WHar WPat WWat WWin
– (f) | WPat
– 'James Roof' (m) ♀ | Widely available
fremontii | ELan EPfP ISea NEgg SEas SSta WLRN
x *issaquahensis* 'Glasnevin Wine' | CAbP CFai CPMA EBrP EBre ELan GOrc IOrc LBre MAsh MBlu SBra SBre WWat
– 'Pat Ballard' (m) | ELan EPfP LRHS MAsh SReu SSta

× GAULNETTYA See GAULTHERIA

GAULTHERIA † (Ericaceae)
adenothrix | EPot GDra MBal NGre WAbe
antipoda | MBal SSta
– × *macrostigma* | CMHG
crassa | MHig NHol
cuneata ♀ | ELan EPot GChr GCrs GDra MAsh MBal MBar MGos MHig NGre SSta WAbe
– 'Pinkie' | ELan EPfP MAsh
depressa | MBal
– × *crassa* | MBal
§ *fragrantissima* | NHol
furiens | See *G. insana*
'Glenroy Maureen' | EHic MAll MBal MCCP
¶ *glomerata* var. *petraea* | SSta
griffithiana BM&W 69 | MBal
hispidula | MBal MDun MGos
hookeri | IBlr NHol
– B 547 | MBal
humifusa | MBal
§ *insana* | MBal
itoana | GChr GDra MBal MBar MGos MHig NGre WAbe
¶ – B&SWJ 1576 | WCru
littoralis | MBal
macrostigma | MBal
miqueliana | EHic MBal MGos MMHG NHar SSta WFro WLin WWat
mucronata | CMHG ELan ENot MAsh MBal MBar WWal
– 'Alba' (f) | GRei MAsh MBar MGos MRav
– 'Atrococcinea' (f) | WPat WPyg
– 'Barry Lock' (f) | WPat
– 'Bell's Seedling' (f) ♀ | CChe CDoC CTri EPfP GRei MAsh MBri MGos SHBN SPer SReu SSta WPat WPyg

– C 9510 | GGGa
– 'Cherry Ripe' (f) | IOrc SEas SHBN
– 'Crimsonia' (f) ♀ | CChe CTri ELan EPfP MAsh MBar MGos SEas SHBN SPer SReu SRms WPat WPyg
– 'Indian Lake' | NHol SEas SPan
– 'Lilacina' (f) | CBlo MAsh MBal MGos NCut WGwG
– 'Lilian' (f) | CBlo CTri ENot EPfP GSki MAsh NHol SEas SHBN SPer
– (m) | CTri ELan GRei MBar MBri MGos MRav NHol SEas SPer SReu SRms WPat
– Mother of Pearl | See *G. mucronata* **'Parelmoer'** (f)
– 'Mulberry Wine' (f) ♀ | CBlo CChe EPfP IOrc NHol
– 'October Red' (f) | NHol SEas SPan
§ – 'Parelmoer' (f) | CBlo ELan ENot EPfP SEas SPer WPat WPyg
– 'Pink Pearl' (f) ♀ | MAsh NHol SRms WLRN
– RB 94095 | GTou
– 'Rosalind' (f) | SEas SPer WWeb
– 'Rosea' (f) | MBar
– 'Rosie' (f) | MBri SBod
– 'Sea Shell' (f) ♀ | IOrc
§ – 'Signaal' (f) | CBlo ELan ENot MAsh MBri MGos MPla SPer SReu WLRN WPat
– Signal | See *G. mucronata* **'Signaal'** (f)
§ – 'Sneeuwwitje' (f) | CBlo CChe ENot GSki MAsh MBri NHol SHBN SReu WPat
– Snow White | See *G. mucronata* **'Sneeuwwitje'** (f)
– 'Stag River' (f) | GDra MGos NCut
– 'Thymifolia' (m) | CChe EPfP GAri SHBN SPan SPer SPla
– 'White Pearl' (f) | IOrc WLRN
– 'Wintertime' (f) ♀ | ELan SRms WWeb
§ *myrsinoides* | GAri GDra MBal MHig
nana Colenso | See *G. parvula*
nummularioides | GAri MHig NMen
– B 673 | MBal
§ – var. *elliptica* | SSta
– *minor* | MBal
– 'Minuta' | See *G. nummularioides* var. *elliptica*
ovalifolia | See *G. fragrantissima*
Ɩ *paraguayensis* | MBal
§ *parvula* | ECou
* 'Pearls' | GCrs
phillyreifolia | CMHG SSta
'Pink Champagne' | SSta
poeppigii | CMHG WPyg
– *racemosa* | SSta
procumbens ♀ | Widely available
prostrata | See *G. myrsinoides*
– subsp. *pentlandii* | MBal SRms
* – *purpurea* | See *G. myrsinoides*
pumila | ECou GAri GCrs MBal MBar NHar NHol NMen
§ – C&W 5226 | MBal NHol
– 'E.K. Balls' | EPot NHar NHol
pyroloides | MBal
– BM&W 5 | MBal
rupestris | GDra MBal
schultesii | SSta
shallon | CB&S CDoC ENot GOrc GRei MBar MGos MHlr MPla SHBN SPer SRms SSta WBay WDin WFar WFro WTro
– dwarf form | MBal
sinensis | MBal MDun

tasmanica	ECou GCrs GDra MBal MBar NHol	'Mini Star Yellow'	SRms WHen
– × *pumila*	MBal	'Northbourne' ♀	LHil
– white-berried	GDra	'Orange Beauty'	ELan
– yellow-berried	MBal	'Orange Magic'	WLRN
thymifolia	MBal	'Red Velvet'	CSpe LHop MSte
trichophylla	GCrs GDra MBal MDun MHig NMen WAbe	§ *rigens*	CB&S MBri
		– var. *uniflora* ♀	MBEx MSte WEas
willisiana	See *G. eriophylla*	– – 'Variegata'	CBot
× *wisleyensis*	MAsh MBal SRms SSta WAbe WBod WPat WPyg	– 'Variegata' ♀	CB&S CHal ELan MBEx NPri WLRN WPer
– 'Pink Pixie'	CMHG EHic ELan EPfP EPla MAsh MBar MCCP MGos SIng SPer SSta WAbe	'Silver Beauty'	CBot NTow
		'Silverbrite'	CHal LLWP
		splendens	See *G. rigens*
– 'Wisley Pearl'	EHic GDra IBlr MAll MBar MGos NHar SBid SIng SReu WPat	'Talent' ♀	CHal SRms
		§ 'The Serpent'	CSpe
		'Tiger'	NPla
		§ 'Yellow Buttons' (d)	CHal EHic EMon MBEx WLRN

GAURA (Onagraceae)

lindheimeri ♀	Widely available		
– 'Corrie's Gold' (v)	CChr CKel CMil EBar EBee ECha ECtt EHoe ELan EMan LGre LHop MAus MLLN NHol SAga SChu SUsu WRus		
– 'Jo Adela' (v)	ECha ELan LHop SUsu SWat		
¶ – 'Siskiyou Pink'	CHea CSpe EHic LGre LRHS MBri SHar SMrm SPer WWeb		
– 'The Bride'	EFou MArl MLan MNrw MWgw NFai WOve		
– 'Whirling Butterflies'	CSam EBee EGoo EHic EMil EMon EPfP MAus MCli MLLN MMil NPSI SEas SMrm WCot WMer		

GEISSORHIZA (Iridaceae)

aspera	CMon NRog
inflexa	NRog
monantha	NRog
radians	NRog

GELASINE (Iridaceae)

azurea	See *G. coerulea*
§ *coerulea*	WCot
¶ *uruguaiensis*	WCot

GAUSSIA (Arecaceae)

¶ *maya*	LPal

GELIDOCALAMUS (Poaceae - Bambusoideae)

fangianus	See *Chimonobambusa microphylla*

GAYLUSSACIA (Ericaceae)

brachycera	GGGa

GELSEMIUM (Loganiaceae)

rankinii	CMCN CPlN CPle
sempervirens ♀	CArn CB&S CLTr CMCN CPlN ERea LCns MSal SOWG
– 'Flore Pleno' (d)	CB&S CPlN ERea
– 'Pride of Augusta'	CMCN

GAZANIA (Asteraceae)

'Aztec' ♀	CHal EBar LHil MBEx NHaw NPri
¶ 'Bicton Orange'	NPri
'Blackberry Ripple'	EAst
'Christopher'	CHal CSpe LHil MBEx NHaw NPla NPri WPer
'Circus'	LHil WLRN
'Cookei' ♀	ELan MBEx MSte SMrm WCot WEas
'Cornish Pixie'	CHal
cream	CHal LHop MRav NPla
cream and purple	LHop LLWP NPla SUsu WPer
'Cream Beauty'	MSte NTow SAga
'Cream Dream'	EAst MBEx WLRN
crimson and green	MSte
'Daybreak Bronze'	LIck MLan
¶ 'Daybreak Red Stripe' (Daybreak Series)	LIck
¶ Daybreak Series	LPVe
'Dorothy' ♀	MBEx WPen
double yellow	See *G.* 'Yellow Buttons'
'Dwarf Orange'	LLWP
'Evening Sun'	LHil NHaw
'Flash'	WEas
'Freddie'	SMrm
'Garden Sun'	MLan
hybrids	ELan MRav SDix WPer
'Lemon Beauty'	NPri
'Magenta'	LHop
'Magic'	WLRN

GENISTA (Papilionaceae)

aetnensis ♀	CB&S CMCN CPle CSam ELan ENot IOrc LHop MAll MBri MCCP MWat SArc SDix SHBN SMad SPer SSpi SSta WDin WOMN WWat
§ *canariensis*	CGre ERea LCns MAll WAbe
cinerea	CBlo MAll WCFE
decumbens	See *Cytisus decumbens*
delphinensis	See *G. sagittalis* subsp. *delphinensis*
'Emerald Spreader'	See *G. pilosa* 'Yellow Spreader'
fragrans	See *G. canariensis*
hispanica	CB&S EBrP EBre ELan ENot IOrc LBre MBal MBar MGos MWat NFla NHol SBre SHBN SHel SMer SPer WAbe WDin WGwG WHar WPyg WRHF WStl WWal
– 'Compacta'	EHol EPla ESis SIng SPer
humifusa	See *G. pulchella*
lydia ♀	CB&S EAst EBrP EBre ELan ENot GChr GOrc GRei LBre LBuc LGro LHop MBal MBar MGos MWat NBee NFla NNor SBre SHBN SReu SSta WBod WDin WFar WHar WWat WWeb
monosperma	See *Retama monosperma*
§ *monspessulana*	MAll

pilosa	CTri ENot EPot ISea LNet MBar MBro MGos MHew MPla NHar NMen NRoo SPer SRms WAbe WWin
– 'Goldilocks'	CBlo ECtt EHic MAll MBar MLan NHar WBod WWeb
– 'Lemon Spreader'	See *G. pilosa* **'Yellow Spreader'**
* – *major*	MHig
– var. *minor*	GTou SRms WAbe
– 'Procumbens'	CMea GDra MBal NHol WHoo WPat WPyg
– 'Vancouver Gold'	CB&S EAst EHal ELan ENot GOrc IHos IOrc LBuc MAsh MGos MNrw MRav NHar WGor WHar WStI WWat WWeb
§ – 'Yellow Spreader'	CB&S CLTr CMHG ECtt GOrc MBal WWat WWeb
§ *pulchella*	CTri MBro MHig NHol WLin
sagittalis	CHan EPfP LHop MAll MBal MBro MWhi NNor NWoo SPer
§ – subsp. *delphinensis* ♀	MHig
– *minor*	See *G. sagittalis* subsp. *delphinensis*
§ × *spachiana* ♀	CTri
♦ *striata*	See *Cytisus striatus*
subcapitata dwarf form	NWCA
tenera 'Golden Shower' ♀	SLPl
tinctoria	CArn CJew CKin EWFC GBar GPoy ILis MBar MChe MHew MSal NLon NNor SIde WDin WHer WOak WWye
– 'Flore Pleno' (d) ♀	CLyd CMHG ELan GChr MBal MInt MPla NHar NMen SPer WHar WWeb
– 'Humifusa'	EPot NHar NMen NWCA
– var. *humilior*	MHig
– var. *prostrata*	WOak
– 'Royal Gold' ♀	ECtt ENot GChr MAll MGos MRav NNor SHBN SPer SRms WBod WWeb
tournefortii	MBal
umbellata	MAll
villarsii	See *G. pulchella*

GENNARIA (Orchidaceae) See Plant Deletions

GENTIANA † (Gentianaceae)

§ *acaulis* ♀	Widely available
– f. *alba*	WLin
– 'Belvedere'	GCLN MHig NNrd WAbe WLin
¶ – 'Coelestina'	GCrs
– 'Dinarica'	See *G. dinarica*
– Excisa Group	WLin
– 'Holzmannii'	NNrd
– 'Krumrey'	EHyt EPot GDra NMGW WAbe
♦ – *occidentalis*	See *G. occidentalis*
– 'Rannoch'	EPot MBro NMen NNrd
– 'Undulatifolia'	NHar
– 'Velkokvensis'	EHyt
algida	MSto
– white	MSto
'Alpha'	See *G.* × *hexafarreri* **'Alpha'**
'Amethyst'	NHar WAbe WOld
andrewsii	EBee GAbr
angustifolia	EHyt NTow WAbe
– 'Montagne d'Aurouze'	WAbe
'Ann's Special'	ELan GCrs GMaP MDHE NHar NHol NRoo

asclepiadea ♀	CFil CGle CHea CPla CVer EBrP EBre ELan EPar GCHN GMac LBre LSyl MBri MBro SDix SOkh SPer SSpi WAbe WHoo WPGP WPyg WWat
– var. *alba*	CBot CFil CHea CLyd CPla GMac LHop MBri MBro MTho NRoo SBla SPer SUsu WAbe WHoo WOMN WWat
– 'Knightshayes'	EGle LHop MBri MBro WHoo WOMN
– 'Nymans'	ELan
– pale blue	CFil NRoo WOMN WPGP
– 'Phyllis'	CLyd GBuc MBro MTho WHoo
– 'Pink Cascade'	SBla
– 'Rosea'	GBuc WHoo
'Barbara Lyle'	NHol WAbe
bellidifolia	GTou
× *bernardii*	See *G.* × *stevenagensis* **'Bernardii'**
¶ 'Black Boy'	GCrs
'Blauer Diamant'	GCrs MDHE NHar
¶ 'Blauer Zwerg'	NHar
'Blue Flame'	GDra NHar WAbe
'Blue Heaven'	GCHN GCra GDra NHar WAbe
¶ 'Blue Sea'	NHar
¶ 'Blue Shell'	NHar
'Blue Silk'	NHar WAbe
¶ 'Blue Spot'	NHar
§ *burseri* var. *villarsii*	EBee
N *cachemirica*	GTou MTho NGre
caelestis CLD 1087	EPot
'Cairngorm'	EWes GCrs GMaP MDHE NHar NHed NRoo WHil
Cambrian hybrids	WAbe
× *caroli*	GAri NHar SBla WAbe WPat
'Christine Jean'	GTou MDHE NHar NHed NMen SIng
clusii	CNic GCrs WAbe
¶ – *alba*	GCrs
– subsp. *costei*	WAbe
coelestis CLD 1087	GCrs
'Compact Gem'	EPot NHar WAbe WOld
corymbifera	GCrs MFiF WAbe
crassicaulis	GCra
– SBEL 220	MSte
crinita	See *Gentianopsis crinita*
§ *cruciata*	EBee EMan GTou LHop MLan MTho WLRN WWal
§ *dahurica*	CPea ELan GCal GDra LBee MRav NHar NRoo SMrm
¶ 'Dark Hedgehog'	GCrs
decumbens	GCal LHop MHar MSto NChi
depressa	MTho WAbe
'Devonhall'	GCrs WAbe
§ *dinarica*	CLyd CNic EHyt MTho WAbe
Drake's strain	GDra LRHS MAvo WAbe
'Dumpy'	EPot NHar WAbe WOld WPat
'Dusk'	GDra NHar
'Eleanor'	NHar
'Elizabeth'	EWes MDHE MOne NHar NHed NRoo
× *farorna*	NRoo
farreri	EWes NWCA WAbe
– 'Duguid'	WAbe
¶ 'Fasta Highlands'	NBir
freyniana	GCrs LHop
froelichii	WAbe
gelida	GAbr MBro WLin WOMN
Glamis Strain	GCrs GMaP NHar NHed NRoo

'Glen Isla'	EWes MDHE MOne NHar NHed NRoo
'Glen Moy'	EWes GMaP MDHE MOne NRoo
'Glendevon'	WAbe
§ *gracilipes*	ECho ELan LBee MSte MWat NChi NWCA SRms
– 'Yuatensis'	See *G. wutaiensis*
grossheimii	GAbr MBro WHoo WWin
× *hascombensis*	See *G. septemfida* var. *lagodechiana* **'Hascombensis'**
'Henry'	WAbe
× *hexafarreri*	NHar
§ – 'Alpha'	GCHN NHar WAbe
hexaphylla	NHar
'Indigo'	WAbe
Inshriach hybrids	GDra GMaP MOne NHar NHol
'Inverleith' ♀	ELan EWes MBri MBro MOne NHar NHol NRoo SSpi WGor WOld WPat
ishizuchii	EDAr
¶ 'John Aitken'	GCrs
¶ 'Juwel'	NHar
kesselringii	See *G. walujewii*
'Kirriemuir'	EWes NHed NRoo
¶ 'Kobold'	NHar
kochiana	See *G. acaulis*
kurroo	ELan EOld MHar WPat
– var. *brevidens*	See *G. dahurica*
lagodechiana	See *G. septemfida* var. *lagodechiana*
'Leslie Delaney'	NHar
¶ *loderi*	GCrs
lucerna	MDHE NHar NRoo
lutea	CArn CPla ECha EMan GCra GDra GPoy LFis LHop MHar NHar NSla NSti SDix SMad WGle WLin WSan WWye
× *macaulayi* ♀	CLyd CPla GCrs MBri MHig NHol NRoo NRya SIng WHoo WOld
– 'Blue Bonnets'	MDHE NHar
– 'Edinburgh' ♀	GCrs
– 'Elata'	ELan GCrs MBri MDHE NHar NHed NHol NRoo
– 'Kidbrooke Seedling'	ELan EWes GTou MOne NGre NHar NRoo NRya WAbe WHil
– 'Kingfisher'	CMHG CPla ELan GCra GDra MAvo MHig MOne NBir NHar NMen NNor NRoo SBla SBod SIng SUsu WAbe WOld
§ – 'Praecox'	ELan GCHN GCrs GTou MBri MDHE NHar NHed NNrd NRoo
§ – 'Wells's Variety'	EPot MBri WAbe
macrophylla	See *G. burseri* var. *villarsii*
makinoi	NWCA
'Margaret'	WAbe
melandriifolia	WAbe
– ACE 2515	EPot NHar
¶ 'Merlin'	GCrs
microdonta ACE 1161	EPot NHar
'Multiflora'	EWes GCrs MDHE NRoo
aff. *obconica* ACE 2140	EPot
§ *occidentalis*	EPot
ochroleuca	See *G. villosa*
× *oliviana*	CSam
olivieri	GCrs WAbe
oreodoxa	GTou NRoo WAbe
pannonica	GDra
– hybrids	GDra
paradoxa	EHyt EPot GCHN GCra GCrs LBee MFos NHar NSla SBla WAbe WLin WOMN
parryi	GCrs
phlogifolia	See *G. cruciata*
pneumonanthe	LHop
prolata	NHar WAbe
przewalskii	WWin
pumila	GCrs SIgm WAbe WLin
purdomii	See *G. gracilipes*
purpurea	GMaP
robusta	CRDP ELan EMon NWCA
'Royal Highlander'	ELan MDHE NHar NHol
saxosa	CRDP ECou GCrs GTou ITim LHop MSte MTho NBir NGre NHar NMen NWCA WAbe WOMN
scabra	MHar WWye
§ – var. *buergeri*	GAri
– var. *saxatilis*	See *G. scabra* var. *buergeri*
¶ – 'Toki-rindo'	EDAr
'Sensation'	NHar
septemfida ♀	CPla ELan EMNN EMan EPot GDra LBee LHop MBri MBro MTho MWat SBla SRms WAbe WCla WHoo WPat
§ – var. *lagodechiana* ♀	CSam EHyt GAbr LPVe NGre NRoo NWCA SRms
– – 'Doeringiana'	ECho GCHN NMen NRoo
§ – – 'Hascombensis'	CPla ECho ELan GCHN
¶ – – 'Select'	NLar
'Serenity'	NHar NMen WAbe WOld
'Shot Silk'	NHar NHol NMen WAbe WOld WWin
sikkimensis	WAbe
sino-ornata ♀	CPla EHyt ELan EMan GCHN GCrs GDra LFis MBri NHar NHol NMen NRoo SBla SIng SRms WAbe WOld
¶ – ACE 2190C	EPot MBro
– 'Alba'	CPla GDra NHar NHol NRoo WWin
– 'Angel's Wings'	ELan GTou MBri MDHE NHar NHol NRoo WAbe
– 'Brin Form'	NNrd NRoo SBod SIng SRms WAbe
– 'Downfield'	GCrs MOne NHar NHed NHol
– 'Edith Sarah'	ELan MAvo MBri MHig MOne NHar NHol NRoo SBla WAbe WOld WPat WWin
– 'Lapis'	NHar NHol
– 'Mary Lyle'	CHid MBri MOne MTho NHar NRoo WAbe
– 'Praecox'	See *G.* × *macaulayi* **'Praecox'**
– 'Trogg's Form'	EWes GCrs MOne NHar NHed NHol NRoo
– 'White Wings'	ELan EWes NHar NHed NHol NRoo
– 'Woolgreaves'	WAbe
¶ sp. Olga's pale	GCrs
× *stevenagensis* ♀	CLyd CPla MBri MBro NHar NRoo SIng WHil WHoo WPyg
§ – 'Bernardii'	MBri MDHE SIng WAbe
– dark form	EPot GCrs MBro NRoo WAbe WPat
– 'Frank Barker'	MBri MDHE WAbe
stragulata	WAbe
straminea	GAbr MHar WCot
'Strathmore' ♀	EHyt ELan EWes GCrs MBri MDHE MOne NHar NHol NRoo SIng WAbe WFar WOld
'Susan Jane'	GTou WOld

ternifolia — ELan GCrs GDra MSte NRoo
 – 'Cangshan' ex SBEC 1053 — NHar NHol WAbe
 – 'Dali' ex SBEC 1053 — EWes MBri MOne NHar NHol WAbe
tibetica — CBot CPea CPla EGar GCal GCrs GPoy MNrw NRoo NSti SDys WEas WWye
trichotoma — CNic WAbe
 – ACE 1768 — NHar
 – ACE 2241 — NHar
triflora — GAbr GBuc GCrs
 – 'Alba' — GBuc
 – var. *japonica* — GBuc NGre
 – var. *montana* — GDra
 – 'Royal Blue' — GCal
 Tweeddale Strain — NRoo
veitchiorum — MBri NRoo WAbe
verna — CGle CNic CPBP ELan EWes LHop MBro MOne MTho NNrd NRoo NRya NSla SBla WAbe WLin WOMN WPat
 – 'Alba' — GCLN MBro NHar SBla WAbe WPat WPyg
 – subsp. *angulosa* — See *G. verna* subsp. *balcanica*
§ – subsp. *balcanica* ♀ — CPla ELan GAbr GCrs GDra GTou MBro MHig MTho NGre NHar NHol SBla SIng WAbe WHoo WPat WPyg
 – x *pumila* — WAbe
 – slate blue form — WPat
 'Violette' — MDHE
¶ 'Vip' — NHar
waltonii — ECho ELan EWes
§ *walujewii* — SIng
wellsii — See *G.* x *macaulayi* **'Wells's Variety'**
§ *wutaiensis* — CMea CNic ECho ELan GDra SSca
¶ *yakushimensis* — GCrs

GENTIANELLA (Gentianaceae)
cerastioides JCA 14003 — WAbe
 sp. K&LG 94/63 — EPot

GENTIANOPSIS (Gentianaceae)
¶ sp. ACE 2331 — EPot

GEOGENANTHUS (Commelinaceae)
undatus — See *G. poepigii*

GERANIUM † (Geraniaceae)
aconitifolium L'Héritier — See *G. rivulare*
albanum — CElw CSev EGra EMar EMon EMou EOrc EPPr GCHN MHFP MNFA MNrw NSti SCou SDad SDix WBea WByw WCru
albiflorum — EPPr GCHN MHFP MNFA MWhe NCat NRoo SAxl WMoo
anemonifolium — See *G. palmatum*
'Ann Folkard' ♀ — Widely available
'Anne Thomson' — CBos CElw CMil ECGP ECle EOrc GCHN GCal MCLN MHFP MMil MWhe NDov NRoo NTay SAxl SCro SRGP SSpe SSpi SUsu WBea WCru WHoo
argenteum 'Purpureum' — See *G.* x *lindavicum* **'Alanah'**
'Aria' — WCru

aristatum — CPou EMar EOrc EWes GCHN MHFP NRoo SCou SDad SRGP WCru WIvy WMoo WPGP WPer
 – NS 649 — NWCA
armenum — See *G. psilostemon*
asphodeloides — CElw CGle CLyd EBar ECro EMon EMou EOrc GCHN GMac LFis MNrw NCat NChi NHex NSti SRGP SWat WBea WByw WCru WEas WGwG WHCG WHen WPGP WPbr WRus
§ – subsp. *asphodeloides* white — CElw EBrP EBre ECGP EOrc EPPr LBre SBre SCou SRGP WFar WHen WRus
 – subsp. *crenophilum* — CElw SCou
 – forms — CBre LBlm MHFP NCat SCou WCru WHen
 – 'Prince Regent' — CHid EPPr GCHN MHFP NCat NRoo SAxl SCou
 – 'Starlight' — CElw GCHN LBlm MAvo MBro MHFP NRoo SAxl SCou SHel WCru
 – white — CVer WHil WMoo
atlanticum Hooker f. — See *G. malviflorum*
'Baby Blue' — CElw GBuc GCHN GCal MBro NBrk NBus NCat SAxl SCro SHel SSoC SWas WBea WCru WHen WMoo
'Bertie Crûg' — CElw CHid CSpe EPPr WCru
'Bethany' — CMHG
biflorum — EBee GCal
biuncinatum — EMar SCou WCot WWin
'Black Ice' — GBuc WCru WMoo
'Blue Cloud' — CElw CHil CSpe MHFP NBrk SAxl SCou SHel SMrm SUsu
¶ 'Blue Pearl' — SAxl
bohemicum — GCHN MHFP NSti SCou SHel SRGP SWat WBea WByw WCru WHen WHer
 – DS&T 89077T — EMon
'Brookside' — Widely available
brutium — EJud GCHN WHen
brycei — EBee MNrw
'Buxton's Blue' — See *G. wallichianum* **'Buxton's Variety'**
caffrum — CHan EOrc GBuc GCHN NBus SCou SRGP WBea WCru WEas WMoo
¶ *californicum* — WCru
canariense — CChr CGre CHid CSpe CTbh EWes SCou SDad SRGP WCru
candicans hort. — See *G. lambertii*
§ x *cantabrigiense* — Widely available
¶ – 'Berggarten' — SAxl
 – 'Biokovo' — Widely available
 – 'Cambridge' — Widely available
 – 'Karmina' — CElw CHil EMil EPPr EPla LBlm MAus MBro MCli NBus NRoo NTay SAxl SCou SHel WHoo WMoo
 – 'Show Time' — CMCo SCro WHal
 – 'St Ola' — CBos CElw CHil EBee EFou EPPr GBuc GCHN GCal LLWP MCLN MHFP MNFA MNrw NBro NCat NHaw NRoo SAxl SCou SCro SHel SSpi SUsu SWas WCru WFar WHen WLin WRus
carolinianum — SCou
cataractarum — GCHN SCou WCru

¶ – subsp. *pitardii*	SRGP
'Chantilly'	CElw CMil CSam EGra EPPr
	GAbr GCHN GCal LGan MBro
	MHFP NBir NCat NFai NRoo
	SAxl SCou SCro SUsu WBea
	WCru WMoo WPbr
cinereum	CGle CSev ENot
– 'Apple Blossom'	See *G. × lindavicum* **'Apple**
	Blossom'
– 'Ballerina' ♀	Widely available
– var. *cinereum*	GCHN NRoo SWat WCru
	WViv
– – 'Album'	GCHN MBal NRoo
¶ – hybrids	WCru
– 'Laurence Flatman'	CHil CMea CSam EBrP EBre
	EFou ELan GCHN LBre LGre
	MCLN MHFP MWhe NBrk
	NHar NRoo SAxl SBla SBre
	SCou SHel SIng WByw WCru
	WHCG WHen WPat WRus
	WWin
– subsp. *nanum*	NCat
– var. *subcaulescens* ♀	Widely available
– – 'Giuseppii'	CTri EBrP EBre EFou EMan
	GCHN LBre LGro MCLN
	MGed MHFP MRav MWhe
	NBro NCat NRoo NSti SAxl
	SBre SCou SHel SRGP SUsu
	WBea WCru WHoo WPyg
– subsp. *subcaulescens*	NGre
var. *ponticum*	
– var. *subcaulescens*	CSpe EBar EBrP EBre EFou
'Splendens' ♀	ELan GCHN LBre LFis MBal
	MBri MCLN MHFP MTis
	MWhe NRoo NSla SBre SHBN
	SRGP SRms SWat WCru WHoo
	WIvy WRus
'Claridge Druce'	See *G. × oxonianum* **'Claridge**
	Druce'
♦ *clarkei* 'Kashmir Blue'	See *G.* **'Kashmir Blue'**
– 'Kashmir Pink'	Widely available
§ – 'Kashmir Purple'	Widely available
§ – 'Kashmir White' ♀	Widely available
– Raina 82.83	SCou
¶ 'Coffee Time'	SCro
collinum	CChr CMCo GBuc GCHN
	LLWP MNrw NBus NCat NRoo
	SCou SCro SUsu WByw WCru
	WHen WIvy
columbinum	SCou
'Coombland White'	CElw LGan NPro WBea WCru
	WMoo
'Crûg's Darkest'	WCru
dalmaticum ♀	Widely available
– 'Album'	CHil CMea CVer ELan EPot
	GBur MBal MBro MPla MTho
	MWhe NHol NRoo SCou SIng
	SRGP WAbe WBea WByw
	WCla WEas WHCG WLin
	WOld WWat WWin
¶ – 'Bressingham Pink'	EPPr
– × *macrorrhizum*	See *G. × cantabrigiense*
delavayi Franchet	CBot
– hort.	See *G. sinense*
¶ 'Delight'	CElw
'Dilys'	CElw CFis CMil CRDP CVer
	EPPr GCHN MBro MCLN
	MHFP MNrw NBus NCat NRoo
	SAxl SCou SHel SRGP SUsu
	SWas WBea WCru WHal WHen
	WRus
dissectum	EWFC MSal SCou SIde

'Distant Hills'	CHil GBuc GCHN NRoo
'Diva'	CElw CMCo CMil EPPr MHFP
	NCat SAxl SCou WCot WCru
¶ *donianum* HWJCM 311	WCru
'Dusky Crûg'	WCru
¶ 'Dusky Rose'	LRHS SCoo
'Elizabeth Ross'	CElw EPPr NBus WCru WMoo
	WWeb WWhi
¶ 'Elizabeth Wood'	EBee
endressii ♀	Widely available
– *album*	CElw CMCo MCLN SApp SCro
	SHel
– 'Castle Drogo'	CElw CHil NCat NFai WBea
– dark form	NBus WCru
– 'Prestbury White'	See *G.* **'Prestbury Blush'**
– 'Priestling's Red'	CElw EGra EMar SMrm
– 'Rose'	CHil GBur LBlm WPer
erianthum	GBuc GCHN MSte MUlv
	MWhe NBus NCat NFai NGre
	NLar NSti SCou SRGP WBea
	WCru WElm WPbr
– 'Calm Sea'	CElw GBuc GCHN SHel WCru
	WMoo WPbr
– 'Neptune'	CElw WCru WPbr
eriostemon Fischer	See *G. platyanthum*
§ *farreri* ♀	CBot CLyd GBri GBuc GCHN
	MHFP MNrw NBir NGre NRoo
	NWCA SBla SCou SWat WCru
	WEas WLin WOMN
flanaganii	CElw GCHN WCru
fremontii	GBuc GCHN SCou
'Gillian Perrin'	WWeb
gracile	CChr CElw CHil EMon EMou
	GBuc GCHN GMaP MBro
	MCLN MHFP MNrw NBir
	NChi NRoo SCou SCro WCru
	WHal WMoo WPGP WPrP
– 'Blush'	CMCo EPPr MNFA NCat SAxl
	SHel WBea
– pale form	CElw LBlm SCou
grandiflorum	See *G. himalayense*
– var. *alpinum*	See *G. himalayense* **'Gravetye'**
gymnocaulon	CMCo GCHN LRHS NCat
	NRoo WBea WCru
'Harmony'	NCat
harveyi	CElw CHan CHar CHil CMea
	CPBP CSpe CVer EBee ECre
	EWes GBin LHop MBro MNrw
	SAxl WCot WCru WKif WPat
	WPnn
hayatanum B&SWJ 164	WCru WMoo
§ *himalayense*	CElw CFee CHil EBar ECha
	ELan EMou GCHN LBlm
	MHFP MTho MWat MWhe
	NBir NBrk MBro NChi NHol
	NSti SEas SMrm SRms SWat
	WCru WHCG WHen WMer
	WPer
– *alpinum*	See *G. himalayense* **'Gravetye'**
– 'Birch Double'	See *G. himalayense* **'Plenum'**
– 'Frances Perry'	SMur
§ – 'Gravetye' ♀	Widely available
– 'Irish Blue'	Widely available
– *meeboldii*	See *G. himalayense*
§ – 'Pale Irish Blue'	GCal
§ – 'Plenum' (d)	Widely available
¶ *hispidissimum*	NWCA
ibericum subsp. *jubatum*	CElw CHil EGle EPPr GCHN
	GCal MHFP MNFA MUlv SAxl
	SCou WBea WMoo
¶ – – × *libani*	SAxl
¶ – – × *renardii*	GCal

◆ – misapplied	See *G.* × *magnificum*
– var. *platypetalum* Boissier	See *G. platypetalum* **Fischer & Meyer**
– – hort.	See *G.* × *magnificum*
incanum	CMHG CSev CSpe ECoo EWes GCHN LHop MNrw NBir NTow SCou SDad SMrm SRGP WHal
– var. *incanum*	GCHN WCru
– var. *multifidum*	GCHN LLWP SUsu SWat WCru WFar
– white form	SRGP
'Ivan'	CElw CMil GBuc LGre NCat SCou SHel SWas WPGP
'Janette'	COtt LRHS MAsh MBri MWhe NCat WWeb
'Johnson's Blue' ♀	Widely available
'Joy'	CBos CElw CHad CHil CMCo CStr CVer EGle EPPr GCHN LGan MAvo MHFP NChi NHaw NPro SAxl SHel SMrm SUsu SWat WBea WCru
§ 'Kashmir Blue'	GCHN GMac NCat WRHF
§ 'Kate'	CElw GCHN NBus NChi NRoo SWat WCru WPnn
'Kate Folkard'	See *G.* '**Kate**'
¶ 'Khan'	NCat SWas
kishtvariense	ECGP GCHN GCal MBri MHFP NRoo SBla SCou WCru WMoo
koraiense B&SWJ	WCru
¶ – B&SWJ 878	WCru
koreanum	CFil CMil CSpe EBee GCHN NPSI SPar SSpi SUsu WBea WCru WFar WPGP
¶ – B&SWJ 602	WCru
§ *kotschyi* var. *charlesii*	WCru
krameri B&SWJ 1142	NCat WCru
§ *lambertii*	CVer EWes GBuc NBir WEas
– CC 1077	CPou
¶ – hybrid	EBee NHol
– 'Swansdown'	GCHN WCru
lanuginosum	LLew SCou SRGP
libani	CElw CHan EBrP EBre EMou GBuc GCal LBre MAvo MBel MCLN MHFP MHlr MTho MWhe NBus NRoo NSti SAxl SBre SCou SCro WByw WCot WCru WEas WPGP
'Libretto'	WCru
¶ × *lindavicum*	SIng
§ – 'Alanah'	EMon WLin
§ – 'Apple Blossom'	CFis EPot GBuc MBel MHFP NBus NRoo SAga SAsh SAxl WCru WHCG WWin
– 'Lissadell Purple'	NWCA SBla SIng
¶ *linearilobum* subsp. *transversale*	WCru
'Little Devil'	See *G.* '**Little David**'
'Little Gem'	EBee GCHN MRav NDov SAxl SUsu WCru
lucidum	EJud EPPr EWFC GCHN GCra MHew MSal NCat NSti SCou SDad
× *luganense*	SCou
¶ 'Lydia'	SRGP
§ *macrorrhizum*	CArn CFee CHan EBar GBur GCHN GCal LHol MTho MUlv MWhe NBro NMir SApp SCou SIng SPla WByw WCru WEas WGor WHCG WHal WHen WMow WOak WPbr WWin WWye
¶ – AL & JS 90179YU	EPPr
– 'Album' ♀	Widely available
– 'Bevan's Variety'	Widely available
– 'Bulgaria'	EPPr NBus
– 'Czakor'	Widely available
– 'Ingwersen's Variety' ♀	Widely available
– 'Lohfelden'	CElw CHil EPPr GCHN MBro MHFP SAxl SDys SHel WCru WMoo WRHF
– *macrorrhizum*	CElw SRms
– 'Mount Olympus'	WPbr
– 'Mount Olympus White'	CElw WHal WPGP WSan
– 'Pindus'	CElw CHil EPPr GCHN LGan MBro MHFP MNFA NCat NSti SAxl SDys SHel SRGP SUsu SWas WCru WMoo
– 'Ridsko'	CElw CFee CFis CHil CMCo EBee EOrc EPPr GCHN GCal MHFP NBro NCat NTow SAxl SCou SCro SDys SHel WCru WHen
– *roseum*	See *G. macrorrhizum*
– 'Spessart'	CDoC CRos EPPr MBel MGed MOne MUlv NBee NRoo NTay NTow SCou WCru WPbr WPyg WRHF
– 'Variegatum'	CElw CHan CHil CRDP ECha EFou EGol ELan EPla GBur GCal MBri MCLN MHFP MTho MWhe NBir NRoo NSti NTay SPer WBea WByw WHCG WHen WHil WOld WWin
– 'Velebit'	CElw CHil EPPr GCHN MSte NBus NCat WCru WMoo
– 'White-Ness'	GCHN WCru WMoo
macrostylum	CElw GCHN MBro SSvw WCot WCru WPGP WPer WRus
maculatum	Widely available
– f. *albiflorum*	CElw CGle CHil CRDP CVer EMon EMou GCHN GCal MBel MBro MHFP MNFA NSti SAxl SCou SHel SSpi SUsu WCru
– 'Chatto'	CMil CSpe EBee EFou EGol EMar EMil LBuc MAus MBro MRav NWes WRus WWat
– 'Shameface'	EBee MHFP NBrk SAxl SHel
maderense ♀	CAbb CChr CHEx CInt CPla CPle CSam CTbh CTrC ECro EWes GCHN GCal IBlr MHFP NBrk NFla NPer SArc SAxl SCou SDad SDix SRGP WCru WHal WPer WPic WWin WWye
§ × *magnificum* ♀	Widely available
¶ – Clone C	NCat
magniflorum	CHil GCHN SCou WBea WCru
§ *malviflorum*	Widely available
– pink	CDoC CMil SBla SCro WCru
'Mary Mottram'	MMil NBir WEas
microphyllum	CElw MNrw
molle	EBee EWFC MSal SCou SDad

§ × *monacense* — CBre CElw CHid CHil CMCo CSam EFou ELan EMar EPla GBur GGar MBel MHFP MWat MWhe NFai NRoo NSti SCou SCro SDad SWat WBea WByw WCru WHer WPbr WShe

– var. *anglicum* — CHil ECtt EGle EOrc GAbr GCHN MBel MBro MNFA MWhe NBus NSti SAxl SCou SCro SHel WMoo

¶ – dark form — WMoo

– var. *monacense* — CElw WFar WHen

§ – 'Muldoon' — Widely available

§ – 'Variegatum' — CSev EFou EGol EMar EOld EPla ERic LFis MBro MCLN MSCN MWhe NLar NPro SCou SPer SRGP SWat WAbb WBea WCru WEas WGwG WRha WRus WWal

'Mourning Widow' — See *G. phaeum*

multisectum — WCru

¶ *nakaoanum* HWJCM 504 — WCru

napuligerum Franchet — NSla

– hort. — See *G. farreri*

'Natalie' — NCat

nepalense — CMCo MHFP NBus SCou SRGP SRms WHer WMoo

nervosum — MCCP NBus NLar SCou WGwy WUnu

'Nicola' — CElw NCat SAxl

'Nimbus' — Widely available

nodosum — Widely available

– dark form — See *G. nodosum* 'Swish Purple'

– pale form — See *G. nodosum* 'Svelte Lilac'

§ – 'Svelte Lilac' — CElw ECGP EMon EPPr LRHS MBro MHFP MNFA NBrk NCat NWes SAxl SCou SMrm SWat WBea WCru WPbr

§ – 'Swish Purple' — CBos CElw EMon EPPr MNFA SAxl SWat WCru WHen WMoo WPbr

– 'Whiteleaf' — CElw CLTr EBee EMon MBro NBrk NBus SBla SWas SWat WBea WCru WMoo

ocellatum — LLew SCou

¶ 'Orchid Blue' — LRHS SCoo

oreganum — CElw GCHN NBrk SCou SCro SHel

§ *orientalitibeticum* — Widely available

'Orkney Pink' — CHil CPBP EGra EPPr GBuc GCal MAvo MBro MSte NPro NRoo SAxl WBea WCot WCru WHoo WMoo WWhi WWin

× *oxonianum* — GBur SAga SCou SHel WCru WRHF

– 'A.T. Johnson' ♀ — Widely available

– 'Armitage' — EPPr MBro NCat SAxl SHel

– 'Breckland Sunset' — EPPr

– 'Bregover Pearl' — CBre CElw CHil MBro NCat WMoo

– 'Bressingham Delight' — CElw CMCo EBee EBrP EBre LBre MCLN MUlv MWhe NBus NRoo SBre SCou SHel

– 'Buttercup' — CElw EPPr

I – 'Cally Seedling' — GCal

§ – 'Claridge Druce' — Widely available

– 'Coronet' — EPPr NBrk SAxl SHel WBea WMoo

– 'Crûg Star' — CElw CHil

– 'David McClintock' — CElw CHil EMon EPPr SAxl SHel WMoo

¶ – 'Dawn Time' — SCro

– 'Frank Lawley' — CElw CHil CMCo EPPr GBuc GMac MBro MHFP NCat NChi NHex NRoo NSti SAxl SCou SCro SHel SUsu WBea

– 'Hexham Pink' — NCat NRoo

– 'Hollywood' — Widely available

– 'Julie Brennan' — CElw NCat SAxl WBea WMoo

– 'Kate Moss' — CElw CHil EPPr GBur GCHN GCal NCat NChi NHex NRoo NSti

¶ – 'Kingston' — EBee

– 'Lace Time' — CElw CHil EBee EPPr GMac LFis LGan MBro MWhe NOak SAxl SCro SDys SHel WBea WMoo

– 'Lady Moore' — CElw CHil CMCo EMar EPPr EPla GAbr GBuc GBur GCHN LGan MBro MHFP MNFA MNrw MWhe NBro NBus NChi NRoo SAxl SCou SCro SHFr SHel SRGP WBea WBor WHen

– 'Lambrook Gillian' — CElw CHil EPPr MBro MHFP SAxl SCou SHel SMer WBea

– 'Lasting Impression' — EPPr

– 'Miriam Rundle' — CElw CHil EOrc EPPr MHFP MNFA NBus NRoo SAxl SCou SDys SHel WBea WCru WMoo

– 'Old Rose' — CElw CHil CMCo EMon EPPr GCHN MBri MHFP MNFA NBus NCat NPla SAxl SCou SRGP WBea WCru

– pale form — EOrc

– 'Pat Smallacombe' — CElw CHil LRot NCat WBea WCru WMoo

– 'Phoebe Noble' — CBre CElw CHil CMCo CMil EPPr LGan MBro MNFA NBus NCat NRoo NSti SAxl SCro SHel SRGP SUsu SWas WBea

– 'Phoebe's Blush' — CElw GBur NCat NChi NRoo SAxl SHel WBea

– 'Pink Lace' — WRus

– 'Prestbury White' — See *G.* 'Prestbury Blush'

– 'Rebecca Moss' — Widely available

– 'Red Sputnik' — EPPr

– 'Rose Clair' — CElw CHid CHil CMil ECED EMou EOrc GCHN MCLN MNFA MWhe NFai NRoo SAxl SChu SCou SHel WBea WCru WEas WElm WHen WPer WWeb

– 'Rosenlicht' — CBre CHil CSev EBee EFou EHal EPPr ERic GBur MAus MBro MHFP MNFA NBus NCat NEgg NRoo NTow SAxl SChu SCou SHel SMrm SRGP SSpi WBea WCru WMow WPbr

– × *sessiliflorum* subsp. *novae-zelandiae* 'Nigricans' — CHil

– 'Sherwood' — CElw CHan CHid CHil EBee EOrc EPPr GCHN GCal MBro MCLN MHFP MSCN MTho NBro NCat NFai NMGW NPro NRoo NTay SAxl SCou SCro SHel SRGP WBea WLin WMoo

– 'Southcombe Double' (d) — CElw CHil CM&M CMil CSev EGle EMar EMou GMac MCLN MFir MHFP MNFA MUlv MWhe NCat NFai NRoo SAxl SChu SRGP SUsu WBea WByw WCru WHal WHen WPrP WWin

§ – 'Southcombe Star'	CElw EAst EBee EGar EHal EOrc EPPr GAbr GCal MBel MBro MHFP NBrk NBro NBus NRoo NSti SAxl SHel WBea WCru WHal WHen WPer
– 'Stillingfleet'	GCHN
¶ – 'Summer Surprise'	NCat SAxl
§ – 'Thurstonianum'	Widely available
– 'Wageningen'	CBre CHil EBee EGar GCal GMac LBlm LGan MMil NBus NCat NLak NPro NRoo SAxl SCou SHel SRGP WBea WCru WHal WHen WMoo
– 'Walter's Gift'	Widely available
– 'Wargrave Pink' ♀	Widely available
– 'Waystradi'	CElw EPPr
– 'Winscombe'	Widely available
'Pagoda'	EOrc MNrw
§ *palmatum* ♀	CAbb CBot CDec CElw CGre CHan CPle CSpe EMar EOas LRot MHFP MHlr NBro NChi NFai NPer SAxl SCou SDad SMad SMrm SUsu WCru WEas WHal WHer WKif WOMN WPer
palustre	CElw CHil EBee EMou GCHN LGan LLWP MBel MBro MHFP MNFA MNrw NBro NChi NRoo NSti SCou SRGP WCru WHen
papuanum	GCHN SBla
'Patricia'	CBos CElw CFai CFis CSpe EFou GCHN GCal LGro MAvo MBri MBro MCLN MHFP MMil MNrw MSte NBus NChi NHaw SAxl SCou SCro SWas WBea WCru WHal WMer WRus WSan
¶ *peloponnesiacum*	CStr SAxl WPGP
– NS 660	CElw CPou
§ *phaeum*	Widely available
– 'Album'	Widely available
¶ – 'All Saints'	EMon
– black	See *G. phaeum* **'Mourning Widow'**
– 'Calligrapher'	CElw EPPr MHFP NBrk WBea
– 'Charles Perrin'	CElw
– forms	EMou EPPr SSvw
– 'Golden Spring'	NCat NChi NRoo
– 'Hannah Perry'	CElw CHil CVer EPPr WBea
– var. *hungaricum*	CHil EGar GCal MFir NCat SCou SHel WBea WCru
– 'Joan Baker'	CBre CChr CElw CGle CHil CLTr CMil CSam CVer EBee EPPr GCHN MHFP MNFA MWhe NCat NRoo NSti SAxl SCou SCro SHel SSoC SWat WBea WCru WSan
– 'Langthorn's Blue'	CElw CHil CMCo CMea CSev ELan MHFP MNrw NBus NCat NRoo SCro WHal WHen WPbr
§ – 'Lily Lovell'	Widely available
* – 'Little Boy'	EMon NCat
– var. *lividum*	CBre CElw CFee CGle CHil CMea EMar EMou GCHN LFis LGan MAus NChi SAxl SCou SCro SHel SPer SRGP SWas WBea WByw WCru WElm WHal WHen WHer WPer WPrP WWin
– – 'Majus'	CElw CHil EGle EMil EMon EPPr GCal LBlm LGan MHFP MNFA NRoo NTay SAxl SCou SCro WBea WFar
– 'Mierhausen'	CElw CGle
§ – 'Mourning Widow'	CElw CMil EPPr GBin GCal LBlm MWhe NCat NRoo NTay SAxl SCro SHel SRms WBea WCru WHen WMoo WPbr
– 'Night Time'	MBro SCro SHel WBea
– red form	MRav
– 'Rose Air'	EPPr NBrk SAxl WMoo
– 'Rose Madder'	CBos CElw CFis CHad CHil CMCo CVer GBuc GCal MBro MCLN MHFP MNrw SAxl SCou SHBN SHel WBea
– 'Samobor'	Widely available
– 'Saturn'	WHer
– 'Small Grey'	CHil
– 'Stillingfleet Ghost'	NHex NSti
– 'Taff's Jester' (v)	CElw CHad CMCo LFis NBus NSti SCro SHel WBea WCru WHer WHil
– 'Variegatum'	Widely available
'Phillippe Vapelle'	CBre CElw CHil CMil EFou EMou EPPr GCHN GCal MBro MCLN MHFP NBir NBus NDov NPro NRoo SAxl SCou SCro SHel SMrm SOkh SWat WBea WCot WCru WPGP
¶ 'Pink Spice'	MWhe NHar
§ *platyanthum*	CElw CGle CVer EMou GCHN GCal LBlm MAvo MNrw NChi NRoo NSti SAxl SCou WBea WCru WHCG WHen WMoo WPer
¶ – var. *reinii*	NCat
§ *platypetalum* Fischer & Meyer	CElw CHan EBrP EBre ELan EMou ENot GAri GBur GCHN LBre MBri MHig MNFA MWhe NBir NCat NFla NSti SBre SCou SRms SWat WBea WCru
– 'Georgia Blue'	CFil SSpi WCru WMoo WPGP
platypetalum Franchet	See *G. sinense*
♦ *platypetalum* misapplied	See *G. × magnificum*
§ *pogonanthum*	GBuc GCHN GCal GMac NBir NRoo SCou WCru WMoo WPrP
polyanthes	CElw CRDP EMan GAbr GAri GBuc GBur GCra GDra GTou NGre SCou WCru
potentilloides	CHid GCHN MHFP NBir NBus NCat NHex WBea
pratense	CArn CBre CKin CMCo ECro EFou ELan ELau EMou EOrc EWFC GBur GCHN LHol MHew MWhe NHex NLan NMir NSti SCou SWat WBea WCla WCru WHen WMow WOak WPer WWye
– f. *albiflorum*	CBot CElw CGle CHil ECED GCHN GCal LGan LHop MAus MBri MHew MNrw NFai NOrc NRoo NSti SCou SDad SPer WBea WByw WHCG WHal WHen WPbr WRus WWin
– – 'Galactic'	CHan EMar EMon MBro SHel SRGP WBro WCru WHen WOMN
– – 'Plenum Album' (d)	CElw CHil SCou

– – 'Silver Queen'	CBre CChr CGle CHil ELan EOrc EPPr GCHN MBro MCLN MHFP MNrw MWhe NBrk NRoo SCou SOkh SRGP WBea WCru WHen WHoo WMoo WPyg
– – 'Whimble White'	WElm WWhi
– 'Bittersweet'	CHil EBee EJud EMon NBrk SAxl SHel
– 'Blue Chip'	EMon SHel
– 'Bodenfalle'	CHil
– 'Catforth Carnival'	NCat
– CC&McK 442	CMCo GTou
– 'Cluden Ruby'	GCHN
– 'Cluden Sapphire'	EFou GCHN LRHS NHol NPSI WCru
– 'Flore Pleno'	See *G. pratense* **'Plenum Violaceum'**
– forms	CHil GCHN MHFP SCou WCru
– from Nepal	CHil
¶ – 'Gay Hellyer'	SCro
¶ – Summer Skies = 'Gernic' (d)	CStr SPer
* – 'Himalayanum'	LGro
– 'Mrs Kendall Clark' ♀	Widely available
– 'Nunwood Purple'	CHil SAxl
§ – 'Plenum Caeruleum' (d)	CBos CElw CGle CM&M CMil CSam EOrc EPPr GCHN GCal MAus MBel MBri MCLN MHFP MWat MWhe NHol NNor NRoo NSti SCou SPla SRGP WCru WEas WHCG
– 'Plenum Purpureum'	See *G. pratense* **'Plenum Violaceum'**
§ – 'Plenum Violaceum' (d) ♀	Widely available
– 'Rectum Album'	See *G. clarkei* **'Kashmir White'**
¶ – 'Rosalyn' (d)	EWes
– 'Rose Queen'	EBee NCat NSti SHel WBea WCru WHen WPbr WUnu
– *roseum*	CGle CHil CMea ELan EOrc GBur MBro MNrw NBir NHex SSpi WHoo
¶ – 'Splish-splash'	CChr SCoo WMow
– subsp. *stewartianum*	CElw LLew MRav WCru
– – 'Elizabeth Yeo'	EBee SAxl SCou SCro
– 'Striatum'	Widely available
– 'Striatum' pale form	CBre
– Tibetan Border form	LLew
¶ – Victor Reiter Strain	CHad SMrm
– 'Wisley Blue'	SCou SCro SHel
– 'Yorkshire Queen'	NHex NSti SHel
'Prelude'	CElw NCat WBea
§ 'Prestbury Blush'	CBre CElw EMon EOrc GCHN SAxl SCou WBea WCot WCru WWin
'Prima Donna'	NCat
procurrens	CBre CElw CGle CHil CMHG CSam CSev EBrP EBre ECha GBur GCHN GCal LBre LLWP NFai NSti SAxl SBre SCou SPer WEas WHCG WHen WOld WWat WWin
pseudosibiricum	SCou
§ *psilostemon* ♀	Widely available
– 'Bressingham Flair'	EBrP EBre ECha EGol GCal LBre LHop MCLN MHFP MUlv MWhe NHol NOrc NRoo SBre SChu SCou SMrm WCru WWat
– 'Gold Leaf'	WCot
¶ – hybrid	WCru

pulchrum	CElw CHan CMea CSev CSpe EMon EOrc GCHN MMal MNrw SAxl SCou SRGP SWas SWat WCot WCru
punctatum hort.	See *G.* x *monacense* **'Muldoon'**
– *variegatum*	See *G.* x *monacense* **'Variegatum'**
purpureum	SCou
pusillum	CKin MSal SCou
pylzowianum	CElw CNic GBur GCHN LGan MBro MNFA NGre NMen NNrd NRoo NRya NTay SChu SDys SSmi WBea WCru WHal WHen WHer WMoo
pyrenaicum	CElw CHil CKin CRDP CSev EOrc EPPr EWFC GAbr GCHN MHew NFla NRoo NSti SCou WBea WHen
– f. *albiflorum*	CElw EMou EOrc EPPr ESis GAbr GCHN LLWP MNrw MTho NBir NRoo NSti SCou SCro SHel WBea WCla WHen WWin
– 'Bill Wallis'	Widely available
'Rambling Robin'	EPPr WCru
rectum	NBus SAxl WCru
– 'Album'	See *G. clarkei* **'Kashmir White'**
'Red Dwarf'	GCHN WMoo
reflexum	CBre CElw CHid CSev EGol EPPr GBur GCHN LFis MCLN MHFP MNFA NCat NRoo NVic SAxl SCou SCro WCru WHCG WHal WOve
– dark form	SAxl
regelii	CElw CMCo CMil CSam CVer EBee EOrc EPPr GCHN MHFP NGre NSla SAxl SHel WCru WMoo
– CC 806	CPou
renardii ♀	Widely available
– blue	See *G. renardii* **'Whiteknights'**
– 'Tcschelda'	CFai EFou NBus SPla
§ – 'Whiteknights'	CElw CHil EGol GCHN MAvo MBro NBir NBus NPro SIng SMac WBea WBro WCru WEas WIvy WMoo
– 'Zetterland'	CElw CMCo CMil CSpe EBrP EBre EPPr LBre LFis MAvo MCLN MLLN MUlv NBus SBre SHel SWat WBea WPbr
richardsonii	CHil EPPr GCHN GCal MHFP MNrw NBir NBus NCat NChi NRoo SAxl SChu SCou SCro SRms WBea WCru WMoo
x *riversleaianum*	GBur SCou WCru
– 'Jean Armour'	CHil EPPr GCHN WCru WMoo
– 'Mavis Simpson'	Widely available
¶ – 'Persian Carpet'	NLar
– 'Russell Prichard' ♀	Widely available
§ *rivulare*	CElw GCHN MBro MNFA WBea WHCG
– 'Album'	CHil MBro
robertianum	CKin EEls ELau EPPr EWFC GBur MChe SCou SIde SRCN SRms WHen WJek
§ – 'Album'	MHar NSti SCou SIde SRms
– f. *bernettii*	See *G. robertianum* **'Album'**
– 'Celtic White'	CBre ECoo EMon GCal MHFP NBus NCat NHex NRoo NSti SRGP WHen

robustum	CElw CGle CHan CSpe EFou EMar EMon EPri GAbr GCHN LBlm MNrw NBro NCat NChi SAxl SCou SDad SIgm SRGP SUsu WBea WByw WCru WEas WElm WHal WUnu WWin
– Hannays' form	CSpe
– × **incanum**	CElw WCru
– 'Norman Warrington'	WHer
– S&SH 14	CElw CHan CMea WBea WCru
rotundifolium	SCou
rubescens	EMou GBur GGar MNFA MNrw NBir NBro NCat SCou SRGP WCru WHal WWye
rubifolium	ECGP MCCP MHFP NBrk NBus SCou SSpi WCru WMoo
ruprechtii	CElw CHar CHil CMCo CRDP EMar GCHN MHFP MNrw NBus NCat SCou SRGP WBea WElm WUnu WWin
'Salome'	Widely available
sanguineum	Widely available
– 'Alan Bloom'	EBrP EBre LBre LRHS MCLN MWhe NRoo NWes SBre
– 'Album' ♀	Widely available
¶ – 'Alpenglow'	WCru
– 'Ankum's Pride'	CBlo CChr CGle CRDP EBee EPPr MCLN WCot WWat
– 'Barnsley'	SCou
– 'Belle of Herterton'	GCHN NCat NChi NPro SAxl WCru
– 'Bloody Graham'	MWhe SAxl WMoo
¶ – 'Catforth Carnival'	NCat
– 'Cedric Morris'	CBos CElw CFil CHil ECha EFou EPPr ERav LBlm MHFP MNFA MTho SAxl SCou SHel SUsu WCot WCru WHen
– 'Elsbeth'	CElw CHil CMil CRDP EPPr EWes GBuc GCHN MCLN NBus NCat NHol NRoo SAxl SCou SHel WCru WFar WHal WMoo WSan
– 'Farrer's Form'	EPPr GBuc WCru WMoo
– 'Glenluce'	Widely available
¶ – 'Hampshire Purple'	WCru
– 'Holden'	CElw CMea EPPr NRoo WCru
– 'John Elsley'	CElw CHil CPou CSam EBee EBrP EBre EGol EMou EPPr LBre MMil MSCN MWhe NBus NRoo SBre SWat WPer
– 'Jubilee Pink'	CHil EGar EPPr NRoo SBla SCou SHel SWas WCru
– var. **lancastrense**	See *G. sanguineum* var. *striatum*
* – 'Leeds Variety'	WHal
– 'Max Frei'	Widely available
– 'Minutum'	MHFP NRoo NSla SCou WCru
– 'Nanum'	CMea EPar NHol NMen NNrd WCru
– 'Nyewood'	CFis ECGP EMon EPPr GCHN MHFP MLLN SAxl SEND SRGP WCru
– var. **prostratum** (Cav.) Pers.	See *G. sanguineum* var. *striatum*
¶ – 'Purple Flame'	WCru
– 'Sara'	SDad WHen
– 'Shepherd's Warning' ♀	CHil CMea CSev EBrP EBre ECED ECtt GAbr GCHN LBre LHop MCLN MHFP MLLN MRav MWhe NRoo SBre SCou SIng SRGP SWat WBea WByw WCru WHCG WHoo WIvy WMow WRus
§ – var. **striatum** ♀	Widely available
– – deep pink	SCro
– – 'Splendens'	CElw CSev ECha EGol ELan ENot EPPr GDra LHop MWat NChi NNor NRoo NWes SAga SCou SSmi WCru WEas WOld WWhi
– 'Vision'	LGan NWes
'Sea Fire'	CElw CMCo GCHN MTho NCat SCro WCru WMoo
'Sea Pink'	CElw GCHN MTho NCat NHar SHel WCru WMoo
'Sea Spray'	EWes GBuc GCHN MSte MTho NRoo SWat WMoo
¶ **seemannii**	EBee
sessiliflorum	CHid ECou EPar GBur NHar SAga SCou WElm
– subsp. **novae-zelandiae** green-leaved	GCHN NChi SWat
– – 'Nigricans'	CChr CDec CGle CHan CMea CSev ECED ECha ELan EOrc EPot GBin GCHN MBal MBri NGre NMen NRoo SCou SHFr SIng SRGP WCru WEas WHCG WWin
– – 'Nigricans' × **traversii** var. **elegans**	CBos CHan CRDP ESis GCHN NCat NSti SWat WCot WCru WFar
– – 'Nigricans' × **traversii** var. **elegans** Crûg strain	CMil CSpe MAvo MCCP MHFP MTis NPSI NSti SSpi SVil WCru
§ – – 'Porter's Pass'	CDec CHil CMea EHoe EWes GBri GBuc GCHN MHFP MHar MNrw NBir NChi NHex NRoo SCou SDad SWat WCru WPGP
– – 'Porter's Pass' hybrid	GCal
– – red-leaved	See *G. sessiliflorum* subsp. *novae-zelandiae* 'Porter's Pass'
¶ **shikokianum**	EBee NChi
¶ – var. **quelpartense**	EBee
– var. **yoshiianum**	CElw GBuc GCHN WMoo
sibiricum	GBur GCHN SCou
¶ 'Silver Pink'	CStr LRHS
§ **sinense**	CElw CHil CLTr EMon GCHN GCal GCra LGre MHFP NRoo SCou SSoC WBea WCru WHCG WHal WHer WWhi
'Sirak'	CElw CLAP GCal NCat NChi SAxl SUsu SWas WBea
soboliferum	CFis EBee GCHN GCal NBir SCro WCru
'Sonata'	NRoo
'Southcombe Star'	See *G.* × *oxonianum* 'Southcombe Star'
sp. from Pamirs, Tadzhikistan	EBee EPPr NCat
'Spinners'	Widely available
'Stanhoe'	EMar EPPr MAvo MCLN SCou SCro SHel SOkh SUsu WBea
stapfianum var. **roseum**	See *G. orientalitibeticum*
'Stephanie'	NCat
'Strawberry Frost'	CFai CMil EBee MMil NHol WCot
'Sue Crûg'	CBos CElw GCHN NBus NChi SAxl SUsu WBea WByw WCot WCru WHen WMoo WWin
suzukii B&SWJ 016	WCru
swatense	EMou MNrw NChi NGre SCou SWat WCru
¶ 'Sydney Wharf'	CHan

sylvaticum	CM&M CSev EMou EWFC GMac MBal MNFA MSCN MSal NHex SCou SRGP SSpi WHal WHen WPer WShi
– f. *albiflorum*	CBot CBre CElw CMil EGol ELan EMar EMou GCHN MBro MWhe NRoo NSti SCou SSpi WCru WOld WWin
– 'Album' ♀	Widely available
– 'Amy Doncaster'	Widely available
– 'Angulatum'	EPPr SAxl SCou WMoo
– 'Baker's Pink'	CElw CFil CHil CMea CMil CVer EMou GCHN MBro MCLN MHFP MNFA MWhe NCat SAxl SBla SHel SMrm SSpi SUsu WBea WCru WHCG WLin WMoo WPGP WTin
– 'Birch Lilac'	CHil EGar EMou EPPr GBuc GBur GCal MHFP NBus NCat NRoo SAxl SCou WBea WMoo WPbr
– 'Cyril's Fancy'	NCat SAxl
– 'Mayflower' ♀	Widely available
¶ – 'Meran'	SAxl
– f. *roseum*	ECGP EGle EMou GCHN MHFP NCat NRoo SCro SIng SPer WShe
– 'Silva'	CGle EMan GCHN MRav NBrk SAxl SCou WCru
– subsp. *sylvaticum* var. *wanneri*	CGle CHil CMea EMou EPPr GCHN MBro MRav NCat SCou SCro WCru
§ *thunbergii*	CLTr CVer EAst EMar EMou GCHN LGro MHFP MHew MMal MNrw NBro NFai NHol NOak SCou SDad WBea WByw WHen WPer WUnu
– purple	LBlm
– *roseum*	SRGP WCru
– white	CHil LBlm SRGP
thurstonianum	See *G.* × *oxonianum* 'Thurstonianum'
transbaicalicum	CPou EMan EMon EPPr GCHN MBri MHFP MNrw SCro SRGP WBea WCru WPGP
traversii	CBot CLyd CNic EWes MDHE SIng WSan
– var. *elegans*	CChr CFee CSpe ELan GCHN LGre MHFP MNrw MTho NRoo SCou SRGP SWas WCru WEas WHCG WOMN
– 'Seaspray'	EBrP EBre LBre SBre SCou
¶ *tripartitum*	SRGP
tuberosum	CAvo CBro CChr CElw CHan ECha ELan ETub GCHN GMac LGan MBro MHFP MNFA MTho MWhe NBro NFla NSti SAxl SCou SIng SLMG SPer SRGP SUsu WBea WHoo WPbr WRus
– var. *charlesii*	See *G. kotschyi* var. *charlesii*
– 'Leonidas'	LRHS
¶ – subsp. *linearifolium*	WCru
– M&T 4032	CMon
¶ – pink form	WCru
– S&L 99	CMon
versicolor	Widely available
– album	CElw CHan MHFP NBus NRoo SHel WBea WHer
– 'Snow White'	EOrc EPPr GMac NBrk NMGW SAxl SCou SHel

¶ – 'The Bride'	EBee EGra
– 'White Lady'	WCru
violareum	See *Pelargonium* 'Splendide'
viscosissimum	EMan EPPr GCal GMac LLWP MBri MFir MHFP NRoo NTay SCou SDad SRGP WCot WOMN
wallichianum	CBod CFis CLTr CPou ECGP NBir NChi NSti SBla WBea WHen WPyg WWat
§ – 'Buxton's Variety' ♀	Widely available
– magenta form	GCHN
– pink	GBuc WCru
– purple	WCru
– 'Syabru'	CElw CMea GBuc MHFP SSpi SWas WCru WFar
'Welsh Guinness'	NCat WCru
wilfordii hort.	See *G. thunbergii*
– Maximowicz	WThi
¶ 'Wisley Blue'	WHal
'Wisley Hybrid'	CBos GCHN NBus SAxl WCru WMoo
wlassovianum	Widely available
yesoense	CMea EPPr GBin GCHN MHFP NBir NBus NRoo NSti SCou SWat WCru WFar WHal WPrP
yoshinoi	EPPr EWes GBin GBuc MHar SCou SHel SRGP SWat WMoo
yunnanense Franchet	EBee GGar MNrw SCou
◆ – misapplied	See *G. pogonanthum*

GERANIUM hort. See PELARGONIUM

GERBERA (Asteraceae)
jamesonii	CB&S

GESNERIA (Gesneriaceae)
cardinalis	See *Sinningia cardinalis*
× *cardosa*	See *Sinningia* × *cardosa*

GEUM † (Rosaceae)
aleppicum	CLyd
alpinum	See *G. montanum*
'Beech House Apricot'	CBos CElw CGle CHea CLon CRDP CSev EMan GBri LGre MBel MHFP MNrw SMac SOkh SUsu WLin WPbr WRus
N 'Borisii'	Widely available
'Borisii' × *montanum*	LHop
bulgaricum	CMea LRHS MNrw NBir NPro NRya NTow WByw WMer WPrP
¶ *calthifolium*	CSam EBee MCCP MOne NBro NCut NLak WUnu
canadense	ECro
capense JJ&JH 9401271	EBee
'Carlskaer'	CElw CLon CRDP EBee GCal MNrw SDys
§ *chiloense*	CLyd EBar WBro
– P&W 6513	CHan MSte NWCA
coccineum	WRha
– hort.	See *G. chiloense*
– Sibth. & Sm. NS 653	MRPP
'Coppertone'	Widely available
'Dingle Apricot'	NBir
'Dolly North'	CHea ECED EGar EPPr GAbr GGar MAus MBri NBro NCat NFai WMer WPbr
I 'Farmer John Cross'	CBre WPbr
'Feuermeer'	LHop MBel MSte NLak NPro

'Fire Opal' ♀ — CBlo CSam MAus MNrw NBir SPer WMow

'Georgenburg' — CElw CHad CRDP EBrP EBre ECtt EOrc LBre MAus MCLN MNrw NBir NDov NFai NHol NOak SAxl SBre SChu SPer SRms WByw WHil WMer WMoo WMow WOld WSan

* **hybridum luteum** — MBel NSti
× **intermedium** — CBre CHor CRow EMan EMon MCLN MNrw NChi NLak SChu SCro WLRN WLin

– 'Muriel' (v) — MInt
¶ 'Karlskaer' — EGle
'Lady Stratheden' ♀ — Widely available
'Lemon Drops' — CBre CElw CGle EBee ECha EGol EMan EPPr GCra GMac MNrw MSte NCat SAxl SChu SOkh WMoo WPGP

'Lionel Cox' — CElw CGle CMea CRow CSev EBar ECha EGol EMon EOrc GCHN GMac MBel MCCP MMil MWgw NBir NBrk NBro NCat NFai NSti SAxl SUsu SWas WByw WMow WRus WWin

macrophyllum — EBee GBar MNrw NBus
magellanicum — See *G. parviflorum*
* 'Mandarin' — GCal
'Marika' — CRow MNrw NBrk SChu
§ **montanum** ♀ — CChr CHan CSam ECha EHyt ELan GDra GTou MBro MHig NBir NBro NLak NRoo NRya SIng SRms WCla WHal WPer WWin

¶ – 'Maximum' — NHol
'Mrs J. Bradshaw' ♀ — Widely available
'Mrs W. Moore' — NCat NPro
¶ 'Nordek' — GMac
§ **parviflorum** — EGar MBro MLLN MNrw NBro NBus NCut

pentapetalum — CGle CLyd NRya WAbe
'Prince of Orange' — CElw EGar GAbr NLak SOkh
'Prinses Juliana' — CBos CHan EFou EGar GCal GMac MUlv NCat NLak WCot WMer

pyrenaicum — NBus NLak
quellyon — See *G. chiloense*
'Red Wings' — CM&M EGar GCal WMer WRus

reptans — See *Sieversia reptans*
× **rhaeticum** — MHig NMen
¶ **rhodopeum** — MNrw
'Rijnstroom' — LBuc MBel MTed NFai
rivale — Widely available
– 'Album' — CBre CGle CHad CHan CRow CSam EGol ELan EMar EMon EPla GMac MBal MBel MFir MNrw NBir NFai SChu SHel SSpe WByw WCla WEas WHer WMow WRus

– apricot — LGan LGro WPrP WWin
¶ – lemon seedling — CRDP
* – 'Leonard's Double' — ECtt
– 'Leonard's Variety' — Widely available
'Rubin' — EBar EBee EGar MAus MBel MTis NLak SCro WCot WElm

'Sigiswang' — GAbr MBel MFir MNrw MSte
'Tangerine' — GGar MNrw MRav NRoo
× **tirolense** — EBee

triflorum — EHyt EMan EOld GTou LGre MBri MNrw MRav WHil WLin WMoo
– var. **campanulatum** — EDAr EHyt NTow
urbanum — CArn CKin ELau EWFC GPoy MChe MCli MHew NLan NPri SIde SWat WCla WHer WMoo WMon
– 'Checkmate' (v) — EMon
'Werner Arends' — GCal LRHS MBri MRav WFar

GEVUINA (Proteaceae)
avellana — CB&S CGre CHEx CTrG CTrw GSki

GIBASIS   (Commelinaceae) See Plant Deletions

GIGASPERMUM   (Gigaspermaceae) See Plant Deletions

GILIA (Polemoniaceae)
aggregata — See *Ipomopsis aggregata*
californica — See *Leptodactylon californicum*
stenothyrsa — See *Ipomopsis stenothyrsa*

GILLENIA (Rosaceae)
stipulata — CHea CRDP EMon LGre LHol MSal
trifoliata ♀ — CArn CDoC CFil CRDP CSpe ECha EFou ELan EMon EPar GPoy LGan LGre LHol MBri MSal MUlv NSti SChu SPer SUsu SWas WByw WEas WHoo WMer WOMN WOld WRus WWye

GINKGO (Ginkgoaceae)
biloba ♀ — Widely available
– 'Autumn Gold' (m) — CDul CEnd ETen LNet LRHS MBlu SMad WMou
– 'Fairmount' (m) — MBlu
– 'Fastigiata' (m) — CMCN MGos WMou
– 'Hekt Leiden' — CMCN
– 'Horizontalis' — CMCN MBlu
– 'Icho' — MBlu
– 'King of Dongting' (f) — MBlu WMou
– 'Ohazuki' (f) — WMou
– 'Pendula' (m) — CMCN EPfP LPan WMou
– 'Princeton Sentry' (m) — LRHS MBlu SMad WMou
I – 'Prostrata' — CPMA WWes
– 'Saratoga' (m) — CEnd CMCN CPMA LNet MBlu SMad
– 'Tit' — CMCN EPfP LNet
– 'Tremonia' — LNet LRHS MBlu WMou
– 'Tubifolia' — MBlu WMou
– 'Umbrella' — CMCN
– 'Variegata' (f) — CMCN CPMA EPfP LNet MBlu SMad

GLADIOLUS † (Iridaceae)
alatus — LBow NRog WCot
'Alice' (Min) — LAma
'Aloha' (L) — CSut
'Amanda Mahy' (N) — CBro GCra LAma NRog
'Applause' (L) — LAma NRog
* 'Arabian Night' — CSut
'Atom' (P) — CBro LAma
¶ **atroviolaceus** — WPGP
'Avalanche' (B) — LAma
'Bell Boy' (B) — LAma
'Blackpool' (M) — LAma NRog
blandus var. **carneus** — See *G. carneus*

* 'Bread and Butter' CSut
byzantinus See **G. communis** subsp.
  byzantinus
callianthus ♀ CSWP WFar
§ – 'Murieliae' ♀ CAvo CBro LAma LBow NRog
  SDeJ
'Cambourne' (Min) LAma NRog
cardinalis CFil CHan CMea CRDP GCal
  IBlr WPGP
carinatus NRog
carmineus CMon LBow
§ *carneus* CBro MSto NRog WCot WHal
'Charm' (N) CAvo CBro LAma
'Charming Beauty' (Tub) NRog SCoo
* 'Charming Lady' SCoo
'Chartres' (B) LAma
'Chiquita' (M) CSut
'Christabel' (L) LBow
citrinus LBow
'City Lights' CSut
'Columbine' (P) LAma NRog
x *colvillei* ECha IBlr
'Comet' (N) NRog
communis LAma
§ – subsp. *byzantinus* ♀ CB&S CBro CFee CGle CHEx
  CHad ECha ELan EPar ETub
  GCrs LAma LBow MBri MLLN
  NRog NSti WEas WOMN WShi
¶ *cunonius* LLew
'Don Juan' CSut
'Dyanito' (B) LAma
'Elvira' (N) LAma NRog SCoo
'Eurovision' (L) CSut
'Fair Lady' (Tub) NRog
'Fidelio' (L) LAma
floribundus LBow
'Flower Song' (L) LAma
garnieri CMon SSpi
'Georgette' (B) LAma
'Giallo Antico' CSut
¶ 'Gillian' (L) LBow
'Good Luck' (N) CAvo CBro
grandis See **G. liliaceus**
'Green Woodpecker' (M) LAma NRog
  ♀
'Guernsey Glory' (N) NRog
'Halley' CBro SCoo
'Holland Pearl' (B) LAma NRog
'Hunting Song' (L) LAma NRog
illyricus CFil CMon CSam WPGP
¶ *imbricatus* ERos
'Impressive' (N) NRog
§ *italicus* MSto WPGP
'Jacksonville Gold' (L) LAma
§ *kotschyanus* MSto
'Lady Godiva' (P/Min) LAma NRog
'Leonore' (S) LAma
§ *liliaceus* LBow
'Lowland Queen' (L) CSut
'Madonna' (L) CSut
marlothii MSto
'Mary Housley' (L) CSut LAma
'Mirella' (N) NRog
'Murieliae' See **G. callianthus** 'Murieliae'
'My Love' (L) CSut LAma
§ *natalensis* GCal IBlr WCot
nerineoides CMon
'Nova Lux' (L) LAma NRog
'Nymph' (N) CAvo ETub LAma MNrw
  NRog
'Obelisk' (P) NRog
orchidiflorus CSWP LBow

'Oscar' (G) LAma NRog
papilio Widely available
§ – Purpureoauratus Group CBro CFis CGle CSam EMan
  IBlr MFir MSto SOkh SRms
'Perky' (Min) LAma
'Perseus' (P/Min) LAma
'Peter Pears' (L) LAma NRog
'Picturesque' (P) NRog
'Plum Tart' (L) CSut
'Praha' (L) LAma NRog
primulinus See **G. natalensis**
  Primulinus hybrids SDeJ
'Princess Margaret Rose' LAma
  (Min)
'Prins Claus' (N) CBro LAma NRog
priorii LBow NRog
'Priscilla' (L) LAma
punctulatus LBow
purpureoauratus See **G. papilio** Purpureoauratus
  Group
quadrangularis MSto
'Richmond' (B) NRog
'Robinetta' (*recurvus* hybrid) LAma NRog SCoo
  ♀
'Rougex' NRog
saundersii CFil WPGP
scullyi LBow NRog
segetum See **G. italicus**
'The Bride' (Colv.) ♀ CAvo CBos CBro CGle CMil
  CSpe EBrP EBre LAma LBre
  NCat NRog SBre WPen
'Tout à Toi' CSut
'Trader Horn' (G) LAma NRog
tristis CBro CFee CPou CRow ECha
  ELan LBow LFlo NRog SAga
  SDix SSpi SWas WCot WHal
– var. *concolor* LLew WHer WOMN
undulatus CSWP LBow
'Velvet Joy' (P) LAma
'Vera Lynn' CSut
'Victor Borge' (L) NRog
violaceolineatus MSto
virescens LBow WCot
watsonioides ERos
'White City' (P/B) LAma
'White Friendship' (L) LAma NRog
'Wind Song' (L) LAma

GLANDULARIA (Verbenaceae)

bipinnatifida See *Verbena bipinnatifida*
pulchella See *Verbena tenera*

GLAUCIDIUM (Glaucidiaceae)

palmatum ♀ EFEx EMan EPot GCrs GDra
  MBal NHar NSla WCru WThi
– 'Album' See **G. palmatum** var.
  leucanthum
§ – var. *leucanthum* EFEx GCrs

GLAUCIUM (Papaveraceae)

§ *corniculatum* CBot CGle CLon EBrP EBre
  LBre MHlr SBre SEND SSca
  SSoC SUsu WCot WCru WEas
  WPGP WPyg
flavum CArn CGle CLon CSpe ECha
  EGoo EMFP EWFC SMrm
  SSca WHer WOld WOve WWin
– *aurantiacum* See **G. flavum** f. *fulvum*
§ – f. *fulvum* ECha EMan EPPr LHop MGed
  MSCN SDix
– orange See **G. flavum** f. *fulvum*
– red See **G. corniculatum**

grandiflorum	WCot WWin
phoenicium	See *G. corniculatum*

GLAUX (Primulaceae)

maritima	ELan WPer
– dwarf form	NWCA

GLECHOMA (Lamiaceae)

hederacea	CArn CKin EWFC GBar GPoy IHos MHew NBro NMir SIde SRms WCer WHer WWye
¶ – 'Barry Yinger Variegated' (v)	CRow
¶ – 'Little Crown' (v)	WAlt
– 'Rosea'	EMon LRHS
– 'Spot Check'	EMon
§ – 'Variegata'	CHal CRow ECro ELan EPfP GBar ILis MBri MRav
hirsuta AL&JS 90069YU	EMon

GLEDITSIA (Caesalpiniaceae)

caspica	CB&S
japonica	SMad
koraiensis	CMCN
triacanthos	CAgr CPle ENot IOrc LPan MWhi WFox WNor
– 'Emerald Cascade'	CBlo CEnd CLnd LRHS MAsh
– f. *inermis*	WNor
– 'Rubylace'	CBlo CEnd CLnd COtt ELan EMil EPfP LPan MAsh MBar MBlu MGos SHBN SMad SMer SPer SSpi WDin WOrn
– 'Shademaster'	ENot
– 'Skyline'	LPan
– 'Sunburst' ♀	CB&S CBlo CEnd CLnd ELan EMil ENot GQui GRei IOrc LBuc LHyr LNet LPan MAsh MBar MBlu MBri MGos MWat NBee SHBN SMad SPer SSpi SSta WCFE WDin WJas WOrn

GLOBBA (Zingiberaceae)

winitii	LChe

GLOBULARIA (Globulariaceae)

bellidifolia	See *G. meridionalis*
¶ *bisnagarica*	WLin
– NS 695	NWCA
cordifolia ♀	CHea CMHG CTri EHyt LBee MBro MTho NHar NHol NMen NTow SAga SBla SDys SIng WAbe WHoo WOld
– NS 696	NWCA
– *purpurescens*	CLyd
incanescens	CLyd LBee WCla WWin
§ *meridionalis*	CHea CPBP EPot EWes ITim MBro MHig MWat NHar NNrd NWCA SBla SSmi WFar WHal
– 'Hort's Variety'	CTri GMaP MTho NNrd WAbe
nana	See *G. repens*
nudicaulis	EBot MBro NHar SBla
– 'Alba'	CLyd WIvy
§ *punctata*	LBee LFis MBro NTow NWCA SRms WHoo
pygmaea	See *G. meridionalis*
§ *repens*	CLyd CNic CPBP EHyt MBro MTho
spinosa	WLin
stygia	NSla
trichosantha	GAbr MHig MRPP SMrm WLin
vulgaris	CInt ELan

GLORIOSA (Colchicaceae)

carsonii	See *G. superba* 'Carsonii'
lutea	See *G. superba* 'Lutea'
rothschildiana	See *G. superba* 'Rothschildiana'
§ *superba* ♀	IBlr LAma MBri NRog SDeJ SLMG
§ – 'Lutea'	LAma LBow NRog
§ – 'Rothschildiana'	CB&S CHal CPlN CRHN LAma LBow LCns SLMG SOWG SRms SSoC

GLOXINIA (Gesneriaceae)

'Chic'	NMos
'Medusa'	WDib
perennis	NMos
sylvatica	CHal WDib
– 'Bolivian Sunset'	WDib

GLUMICALYX (Scrophulariaceae)

flanaganii HWEL 0325	NWCA
¶ *goseloides*	MHig
¶ *lesuticus*	WCot
¶ *montanus*	WCot

GLYCERIA (Poaceae)

aquatica variegata	See *G. maxima* var. *variegata*
maxima	WChe
§ – var. *variegata*	CBen CCuc CRow ECha EFou EHoe EHon ELan EMon ESOG GCHN GOrn LPBA MSta NBro NEgg NHol NMir NOrc NSti SCob SDix SPer SWat SWyc WChe WLin WMAq WWye
plicata	See *G. notata*
spectabilis 'Variegata'	See *G. maxima* var. *variegata*

GLYCYRRHIZA (Papilionaceae)

¶ *acanthocarpa*	EOHP
echinata	CAgr CArn MSal
§ *glabra*	CAgr CArn EOHP LHol MHew MSal WHer WJek WWye
– 'Poznan'	GPoy
glandulifera	See *G. glabra*
uralensis	EOHP GPoy MSal

GLYPTOSTROBUS (Taxodiaceae)

lineatus	See *G. pensilis*
§ *pensilis*	IDee

GMELINA (Verbenaceae) See Plant Deletions

GNAPHALIUM (Asteraceae)

'Fairy Gold'	See *Helichrysum thianschanicum* 'Goldkind'
keriense	See *Anaphalis keriensis*
subrigidum	See *Anaphalis subrigida*
trinerve	See *Anaphalis trinervis*

GODETIA See CLARKIA

GOMPHOCARPUS (Asclepiadaceae)

§ *fruticosus*	EBee
§ *physocarpus*	CArn MSte SHFr

GOMPHOLOBIUM (Papilionaceae)

¶ *polymorphum*	MSto

GOMPHOSTIGMA (Buddlejaceae)

¶ *virgatum*	WCot

GONIOLIMON (Plumbaginaceae)
¶ *tataricum*   EMan
§ – var. *angustifolium*   EBee LFis NMir SRms WByw
                                                    WPer

GOODENIA (Goodeniaceae) See Plant Deletions

GOODIA (Papilionaceae)
   lotifolia   CHan

GOODYERA (Orchidaceae)
   biflora   EFEx
   hachijoensis var.   EFEx
      yakushimensis
   pubescens   EFEx WCru WThi
   schlechtendaliana   EFEx

GORDONIA (Theaceae)
   axillaris   CB&S CHEx

GOSSYPIUM (Malvaceae)
   herbaceum   MSal

GRAPTOPETALUM (Crassulaceae)
   bellum   MBri
   – 'Super Star'   SLMG
§ *paraguayense*   CHal EOas SLMG

GRATIOLA (Scrophulariaceae)
   officinalis   CArn EHon EMan LHol MGra
                                                    MHew MSal SIde WHer WSel
                                                    WWye

GREENOVIA (Crassulaceae)
   aizoon   NTow
§ *aurea*   MOne SIng

GREVILLEA † (Proteaceae)
   alpina   CFee CPle GQui MAll SBid
                                                    SMur SOWG WAbe
   – 'Olympic Flame'   CB&S CDoC CTrw MAll
                                                    SOWG
 * – 'Apricot Queen'   CB&S
   banksii   CTrC
 * – 'Canberra Hybrid'   SSto
¶ 'Bonnie Prince Charlie'   SOWG
   'Canberra Gem' ♀   CGre CHan CPle CTrG CWSG
                                                    ECou LCns LHil LHop MAll
                                                    MAsh MBal MBro SAga SDry
                                                    SIgm SMrm SOWG SSpi WCru
                                                    WPat
   'Cranbrook Yellow'   LHil SBid
   crithmifolia   CTrC
   juniperina   CPle
   – 'Aurea'   MAll
   – f. *sulphurea* ♀   CDoC CFil CHEx COtt CTrG
                                                    CTrw EHic EPfP GQui MAll
                                                    SBid SIgm SOWG WAbe WBod
                                                    WPat WPic
   lanigera   MAll
¶ *monticola*   MAll
   prostrata 'Aurea'   CB&S
   robusta ♀   CHal MBri MFiF
   rosmarinifolia ♀   CFil CHEx COtt CTrG CTrw
                                                    EMil EPfP GQui MAll MBal
                                                    SAga SArc SBid SIgm SOWG
                                                    SSto WAbe WBod WCru
                                                    WSHC
   – 'Jenkinsii'   CB&S
 × *semperflorens*   CDoC CGre MAll SOWG

   thelemanniana   CPle ECou MAll
   thyrsoides   CB&S MAll SDry
 * *tolminsis*   MAll
   victoriae   MAll SSpi
¶ – 'Mount Annan'   MAll
¶ *williamsonii*   SOWG

GREWIA (Tiliaceae)
   parviflora   See *G. biloba*

GREYIA (Greyiaceae)
   radlkoferi   CHEx
   sutherlandii   CHEx CTrC

GRINDELIA (Asteraceae)
   chiloensis   CAbb CPle ECha IBlr LLWP
                                                    SAxl SDix SDry SMad WCot
   robusta   EBee EMan SIgm WCot WWye
   squarrosa   SUsu
   stricta   CArn

GRISELINIA (Cornaceae)
 * 'Crinkles'   SDry SMad
   littoralis ♀   Widely available
   – 'Bantry Bay' (v)   CAbP CDoC CHEx CLan CTrC
                                                    CWSG EHoe ELan EPla IOrc
                                                    ISea MAll MBal SAga SEND
                                                    SPer SSto WAbe
   – 'Dixon's Cream' (v)   CB&S CDec CDoC EPfP GQui
                                                    SBid SDry
   – 'Green Jewel' (v)   CB&S CDoC EHic MAll SDry
                                                    SPla
   – 'Variegata'   CB&S CBot CHEx CLan CTre
                                                    CTrw CWSG EHoe ELan ENot
                                                    GOrc GQui GRei IOrc LPan
                                                    MBal MGos MTis NPer SAga
                                                    SHBN SPar SPer SPla SRms
                                                    SSta WAbe WDin WGwG
                                                    WSHC
   lucida   CHEx
¶ *ruscifolia*   CPle MAll
   scandens   CPle WSHC
 * *serrata*   MAll

GUELDENSTAEDTIA (Papilionaceae)
¶ *himalaica* B&SWJ 2631   WCru

GUICHENOTIA (Sterculiaceae)
¶ *ledifolia*   MFiF

GUNDELIA (Asteraceae)
¶ *tournefortii*   EMan

GUNNERA (Gunneraceae)
   arenaria   GAri IBlr
   chilensis   See *G. tinctoria*
   dentata   CFee IBlr
   flavida   CFee CRow GAri GGar IBlr
   fulvida   IBlr
   hamiltonii   CHEx CRow ECha ECou GGar
                                                    IBlr
   magellanica   CB&S CFee CHEx CRow EBrP
                                                    EBre ECha ECoo EPot GAbr
                                                    IBlr LBre MBal NBee NDea
                                                    NHol NMen NNor NWCA SBid
                                                    SBre SMad SPer SWat WCru
                                                    WWat WWye
   manicata ♀   Widely available
   monoica   CRow IBlr
   prorepens   CFee CTre ECha IBlr SSpi
                                                    SWat WWat WWye

scabra	See *G. tinctoria*
§ *tinctoria*	CFil CHEx CRow CWSG ECha EHon ISea MSta NOrc SAWi SBid SDix SSoC SSpi WCru WLRN WPat WWat WWeb
– 'Nana'	IBlr

GUTIERREZIA (Asteraceae)

spathulata F&W 8005	CPBP

GUZMANIA (Bromeliaceae)

'Amaranth'	MBri
'Cherry'	MBri
'Claret'	See *Neoregelia* **Claret Group**
dissitiflora	MBri
'Exodus'	MBri
Festival Group	MBri
'Gran Prix'	MBri
lindenii	MBri
lingulata ♀	MBri
– 'Empire'	MBri
– var. *minor* ♀	MBri
Marlebeca Group	MBri
monostachya ♀	MBri
'Orangeade'	MBri
sanguinea ♀	MBri
* 'Surprise'	MBri
'Vulkan'	MBri
* 'Witten Lila'	MBri

GYMNADENIA (Orchidaceae)

conopsea	EFEx

GYMNOCARPIUM (Thelypteridaceae)

dryopteris ♀	CCuc CM&M EBee EFer EMar EMon EPar EPot LSyl MBri MWgw NMar NWCA SDix SRms WAbe WFib WNor WRic
– 'Plumosum' ♀	CCuc CFil EMon GQui NHar NHed NHol NLak NMar SChu WAbe WFib WHal WPGP
¶ *fedtschenkoanum*	WRic
¶ *oyamense*	NMar
robertianum	EFer NHed NMar SRms WRic

GYMNOCLADUS (Caesalpiniaceae)

dioica	CB&S CFil CSam ELan EPfP ERod GBin MBlu MBri SMad SPer SSpi WDin WPGP

GYMNOGRAMMA See GYMNOPTERIS

GYMNOPTERIS (Adiantaceae)

vestita	EMon

GYMNOSPERMIUM (Berberidaceae)

§ *albertii*	LAma

GYNANDRIRIS (Iridaceae)

setifolia	CMon
sisyrinchium	SSpi
– MS 416	CMon
* – *purpurea* AB&S 4447	CMon

GYNERIUM (Poaceae)

argenteum	See *Cortaderia selloana*

GYNURA (Asteraceae)

§ *aurantiaca* 'Purple Passion' ♀	MBri

sarmentosa hort.	See *G. aurantiaca* 'Purple Passion'

GYPSOPHILA (Caryophyllaceae)

acutifolia	ELan
altissima	CPou
aretioides	MRPP NMen NNrd NWCA
§ – 'Caucasica'	CPBP EBur EHyt EPot MHig NHar NHed SIng
– 'Compacta'	See *G. aretioides* 'Caucasica'
briquetiana	MHig WPat
– Mac&W 5920	EPot
¶ *bungeana*	WLin
cerastioides	CMHG CSpe CTri ELan EMNN EMan ESis GCHN GTou LBee LHop MRPP NBro NMen NTow NWCA WAbe WPbr WPer WWin
* – *farreri*	WEas
dubia	See *G. repens* 'Dubia'
fastigiata	EGar EMan MLLN WPer
'Festival'	CB&S CHan EBrP EBre LBre SBre
¶ 'Festival Happy'	LRHS
¶ 'Festival Pink'	GMac LRHS
¶ *glomerata* HH&K 221	CHan
¶ – HH&K 275	CHan
gracilescens	See *G. tenuifolia*
¶ *muralis* 'Garden Bride'	LIck
* – 'Gypsy'	LIck
nana 'Compacta'	CLyd CPBP
oldhamiana	CBlo EBee LFis MLLN MTed NLak
pacifica	EBee ECtt GBuc NBro NCut NOak WHer
§ *paniculata*	CBlo CTri EHic NMir NNor SRms SWat WEas WWin
– 'Bristol Fairy' (d) ♀	CB&S CHad CSam EBrP EBre ECha EFou ELan EMan ENot ERav LBre MAus MBri NFai NFla NOrc NRoo SBre SMad SPer SPla SRms WHoo
– 'Compacta Plena' (d)	CFis EBee EFou ELan EPfP GCal GMac LHop MMil NHol NRoo SMrm SPer SRms WLRN WPer
– double pink (d)	WRHF
– double white (d)	WRHF
– 'Flamingo' (d)	CB&S CDoC CTrC ECha ECot ECtt EFou MBri NFai SPer SRms WMaN WWal
– 'Perfecta'	WWeb
§ – 'Schneeflocke' (d)	CBlo CTri ECtt LFis MWat NPri NRoo NTow NVic SEas SIde SRms WViv
– 'Snow White'	NOrc
– Snowflake	See *G. paniculata* 'Schneeflocke'
§ *petraea*	SIng WLin
repens ♀	CSpe GTou LBee MHig MOne MPla MWat WPer
– 'Dorothy Teacher' ♀	CLyd EMNN LHop MHig NHol SIng WAbe WEas WGor WPat WPyg
§ – 'Dubia'	CLyd CMHG ECha ELan EMNN EPot ESis LBee MHig MPla SBod SChu SIgm SRms WLin WPer WWin
– 'Fratensis'	ELan EMNN ESis ITim MPla NMen NPro WLin
– 'Letchworth Rose'	EWes
– Pink Beauty	See *G. repens* 'Rosa Schönheit'

§ – 'Rosa Schönheit' EBrP EBre ECha EGar EWes LBre MMil NRoo SBre SMrm SPer
– 'Rose Fountain' NHol WPat WPyg
– 'Rosea' CMHG CPBP EFou EMNN ESis LBuc LFis LPVe MWat NMen NNor NNrd NOak NRoo NWCA SBla SIde SRms WHal WHoo WMaN
– white CHor CM&M CTri EFou ELan ESis GLil MPla NNor SIde WAbe WHoo WPer
§ 'Rosenschleier' (d) ♀ EBrP EBre ECha EFou EGoo ELan LBre LFis LGan MAus NFla NHol NMen NRoo SBre SIgm SMer SMrm SOkh SPer SWat WEas WHoo WMaN WOld WWal
'Rosy Veil' See *G.* 'Rosenschleier'
¶ *stevenii* EBee
§ *tenuifolia* CLyd CMea EHyt EPot ITim LBee MBro MPla MWat NGre NHed NHol NMen NTow WAbe
transylvanica See *G. petraea*
Veil of Roses See *G.* 'Rosenschleier'

HAASTIA   (Asteraceae) See Plant Deletions

HABENARIA (Orchidaceae)
radiata See *Pecteilis radiata*

HABERLEA (Gesneriaceae)
ferdinandi-coburgii CGle CLAP MFos NWCA SIgm SIng WAbe
rhodopensis ♀ EHyt EPar MBal MBro MHig MSte MWat NHar NRya NWCA SBla SIng SRms WAbe WOMN WOld
– 'Virginalis' CLAP GDra NHar SBla SIng WOMN

HABLITZIA (Chenopodiaceae)
tamnoides CPlN

HABRANTHUS (Amaryllidaceae)
andersonii See *H. tubispathus*
brachyandrus CBro SRms
gracilifolius CBro CMon
martinezii CBro
§ *robustus* CBro CMon GCra LAma MBri NRog WOMN
texanus CBro CMon LBee SIng
§ *tubispathus* CBro CMon CPea LBow MFos NWCA SUsu WCot WWin

HACQUETIA (Apiaceae)
§ *epipactis* ♀ Widely available

HAEMANTHUS (Amaryllidaceae)
albiflos CAvo CHEx CHal CMon LAma LHil SLMG SRms
coccineus CMon
humilis subsp. *hirsutus* CHan
  S&SH 72
kalbreyeri See *Scadoxus multiflorus* subsp. *multiflorus*
katherinae See *Scadoxus multiflorus* subsp. *katherinae*
natalensis See *Scadoxus puniceus*
sanguineus NRog

HAKEA (Proteaceae)
dactyloides MAll
epiglottis CTrC
¶ *gibbosa* MAll
laurina CTrC
§ *lissosperma* ECou MAll SAPC SArc
microcarpa CB&S
§ *salicifolia* CB&S MAll MFiF SMad
◆ *saligna* See *H. salicifolia*
sericea hort. See *H. lissosperma*
¶ – pink CTrC
teretifolia CTrC MAll

HAKONECHLOA (Poaceae)
macra CFil EBrP EBre EHoe EMon EPar LBre LRHS NFai SApp SBre
§ – 'Alboaurea' Widely available
* – 'Albolineata' EMon LRHS
– 'Aureola' ♀ CAbb CCuc CElw CFil CHan CHid CInt CRDP ECha ECtt EHoe EPla LHop MBal MBri MWhi NGre NPro NVic SAga SAxl SCob SIng SOkh WCot WEas WPGP WPat WWat
* – 'Mediovariegata' CFil EPPr EPla WPGP
– 'Variegata' See *H. macra* 'Alboaurea'

HALENIA (Gentianaceae)
elliptica GCra GTou

HALESIA (Styracaceae)
§ *carolina* CAgr CBlo CDoC CLnd CMCN CPMA CTho ELan ENot GChr IOrc ISea LPan MAsh MBel MBri MGos NSti SMer SPer SSta WWat
diptera CMCN MBlu
monticola CB&S CMCN COtt EBrP EBre ELan EPfP GGGa LBre MAsh MBal MBri NSti SBre SPer SReu SSpi WFro WNor WWat
– var. *vestita* ♀ CAbP CPMA CSam CTho CWSG CWit GChr GOrc IOrc MBlu SHBN SPer SRms SSpi SSta WPat WWat
– – f. *rosea* CPMA EPfP MAsh MBlu MSta SSpi SSta
tetraptera See *H. carolina*

× HALIMIOCISTUS (Cistaceae)
algarvensis See *Halimium ocymoides*
§ 'Ingwersenii' CB&S CLTr CMHG CVer EGoo EWes MWhi NHol NTow SIng SPer SRms WAbe WBod WPer
revolii hort. See × *H. sahucii*
§ *sahucii* ♀ Widely available
– 'Ice Dancer' (v) LRHS MAsh
'Susan' See *Halimium* 'Susan'
§ *wintonensis* ♀ Widely available
§ – 'Merrist Wood Cream' CB&S CFee EAst EBrP EBre
  ♀ ELan ENot EPla GCal GOrc IHos LBre LHop MAsh MBel MBri MGrG MPla NBir SAxl SBre SChu SPer SSpi SSta WAbe WOve WPat WSHC WWat

HALIMIONE (Chenopodiaceae)
§ *portulacoides* EEls

HALIMIUM † (Cistaceae)

N *alyssoides*	CSam GCHN WAbe
§ *atriplicifolium*	MAll
§ *calycinum*	CHan EGoo ELan GCHN
	MAsh MBel MTis SAga SAxl
	SCoo SPan SSpi WAbe WCFE
	WPyg
commutatum	See *H. calycinum*
formosum	See *H. lasianthum*
N *halimifolium*	WSHC
§ *lasianthum* ♀	CB&S CTri CWit ELan ENot
	GCHN LGre MAll MAsh MBal
	MBel MRav SChu SEas SPer
	WEas WPyg WWat WWin
– f. *concolor*	LHop NTow SAxl SDry SPan
	WAbe WDin WWin
– subsp. *formosum*	CHar CMil GCal MBri SDix
	WSHC
– 'Sandling'	EGoo ELan MAsh SPan
libanotis	See *H. calycinum*
§ *ocymoides* ♀	CB&S ELan LGre MAll MAsh
	MBal MBel MPla MWat SPer
	WBod WHar WSHC WWat
x *pauanum*	MAsh
§ 'Susan' ♀	CDoC CMHG EBrP EBre
	ELan LBre LHop MAsh MBri
	MBro MPla NFai NLon NMen
	NNor SAxl SBre SUsu WAbe
	WPat WPyg WSHC WWat
§ *umbellatum*	LGre MAll MBri SAga WDin
	WKif WTro
wintonense	See x *Halimiocistus wintonensis*

HALIMODENDRON (Papilionaceae)

halodendron	CB&S CPle ELan EMil EPfP
	MBlu SBid

HALLERIA (Scrophulariaceae)

lucida	CGre

HALOCARPUS (Podocarpaceae)

§ *bidwillii*	CDoC ECou

HALORAGIS (Haloragaceae)

colensoi	ECou
erecta	CBos CPle ECou
– 'Rubra'	CElw EBee WCot WFar
* – 'Wellington Bronze'	CVer GBin GSki MCCP NChi
	NCut NSti SDys SMad

HAMAMELIS † (Hamamelidaceae)

§ 'Brevipetala'	CB&S IOrc MAsh MBri NHol
	SBid SSta
x *intermedia* 'Angelly'	SSta
– 'Arnold Promise' ♀	CDoC CEnd COtt CPMA ELan
	IOrc LNet LPan MAsh MBal
	MBri MLan NBee NHol SBid
	SPer SPla SReu SSpi SSta
	WCFE
– 'Aurora'	SSta
– 'Barmstedt Gold'	EPfP MAsh MBri MGos NHol
	SReu SSta
– 'Carmine Red'	SMur SSta WNor
– 'Copper Beauty'	See *H. x intermedia* 'Jelena'
– 'Diane' ♀	CB&S CDoC CEnd EBrP EBre
	ELan IOrc LBre LNet LPan
	MBri MGos MUlv NHol SAga
	SBid SBre SMad SPer SReu
	SSoC SSpi SSta WDin WPGP
	WWat

§ – 'Feuerzauber'	GChr IOrc LBuc NFla SPer
	SSta WPyg
¶ – 'Gimborn's Beauty'	CBlo
– 'Hiltingbury'	LRHS SMur
§ – 'Jelena' ♀	CB&S CDoC CEnd ELan ENot
	IHos IOrc LNet LPan MBal
	MBri MGos NFla SAga SBid
	SHBN SPer SReu SSoC SSpi
	SSta WDin WWat
– 'Luna'	SSta
– Magic Fire	See *H. x intermedia*
	'Feuerzauber'
– 'Moonlight'	CBlo CPMA
– 'Orange Beauty'	CB&S CBlo CPMA MBal
	MGos SReu SSta
– 'Pallida' ♀	Widely available
– 'Primavera'	CBlo CDoC EPfP IOrc MBal
	MBri MUlv SSta
– 'Ruby Glow'	CB&S CBlo MBal SPer SSta
– 'Sunburst'	CBlo EPfP MBri SSta WWeb
¶ – 'Vesna'	CBlo EPfP MBlu MBri SSta
§ – 'Westerstede'	CBlo COtt IOrc LBuc LPan
	MAsh MGos NHol SBid SSta
	WDin
japonica	MBal WWat
– 'Arborea'	SSta WNor
– var. *flavopurpurascens*	SSta
– 'Sulphurea'	SSta
– 'Zuccariniana'	CB&S CBlo MUlv
mollis ♀	CB&S CEnd ELan ENot GRei
	ISea LNet MBal MBar MBri
	MGos NFla NHol NWea SHBN
	SMad SPer SReu SSpi SSta
	WDin WPGP WPat WWat
¶ – 'Boskoop'	SSta
– 'Brevipetala'	See *H.* 'Brevipetala'
– 'Goldcrest'	CAbP CBlo CPMA
– 'Nymans'	CAbP
– 'Select'	See *H. x intermedia*
	'Westerstede'
– 'Superba'	SSta
– Wilson Clone	SSta
vernalis	WDin
– 'Carnea'	SSta
– 'Orange Glow'	SSta
– 'Pendula'	SSta
– 'Red Imp'	SSta
– 'Sandra' ♀	CB&S EPfP LPan MBri MUlv
	SBid SReu SSpi SSta WWat
– f. *tomentella*	SSta
virginiana	CB&S CBlo GPoy LHol MWhi
	WDin WWal WWat

HANABUSAYA (Campanulaceae) See Plant Deletions

HANNONIA (Amaryllidaceae)

hesperidum SF 21	CMon

HAPLOCARPHA (Asteraceae)

rueppellii	MBro NBro SIng SRms WHil
	WPer

HAPLOPAPPUS (Asteraceae)

acaulis	See *Stenotus acaulis*
brandegeei	See *Erigeron aureus*
coronopifolius	See *H. glutinosus*
§ *glutinosus*	CHan CMHG CSev ECha ECtt
	EMan EPot LBee LHop MHig
	MMil MTho NNrd NTow
	NWCA SAga SRms SSmi

* *lanceolatus*	EBee
lyallii	See *Tonestus lyallii*
microcephalus	WPer
prunelloides	LBee MHig NNrd NTow
rehderi	WFar

HARDENBERGIA (Papilionaceae)

comptoniana ♀	CPlN CSpe MSto
* – *rosea* ♀	ERea
violacea ♀	CAbb CPlN CSpe CTrC ELan
	EMil ERea GQui IBlr LBlm
	LCns SBid SBra
– 'Alba'	See *H. violacea* 'White Crystal'
– 'Happy Wanderer'	CB&S EBee EMil ERea SOWG
– 'Rosea'	EBee
§ – 'White Crystal'	EBee ECon ERea

HARPEPHYLLUM (Anacardiaceae)

¶ *caffrum* (F)	LBlo

HARRIMANELLA See CASSIOPE

HAWORTHIA † (Aloeaceae)

× *cuspidata*	SLMG
reinwardtii	CHal

HAYNALDIA See DASYPYRUM

HEBE † (Scrophulariaceae)

albicans ♀	CChe CHan CLan ECou ELan
	ENot ESis MAll MBal MBar
	MBel MBri MGos MWat NMen
	NNor NSti SHBN SPer SSmi
	WBod WEas WHCG WWin
– 'Cobb'	ECou
– 'Cranleigh Gem'	ECou NFai NHed
– 'Pewter Dome'	See *H.* 'Pewter Dome'
* – 'Pink Elephant'	MAsh
– prostrate form	See *H. albicans* 'Snow Cover'
– 'Red Edge'	See *H.* 'Red Edge'
§ – 'Snow Cover'	ECou EWes SPar
– 'Snow Drift'	NHed
– 'Snow Mound'	ECou
§ – 'Sussex Carpet'	ECou ESis
§ 'Alicia Amherst' ♀	CBlo CSam ECou EHol GCHN
	LHop SRms WLRN
allanii	See *H. amplexicaulis* var. *hirta*
'Amanda Cook' (v)	ECou EHoe ESis MPla NHed
	NPer SDry
amplexicaulis	CNic MAll NHed
§ – var. *hirta*	ECou ESis GDra MAll MBro
	NHed NHol NTow
§ 'Amy'	CSam ECou ELan ESis IOrc
	MAll MAsh MBel NFai NPer
	NSti SHBN SPer WAbe WMow
	WRus WSHC
× *andersonii*	See *H.* × *andersonii* 'Variegata'
'Argenteovariegata'	
§ – 'Aurea'	ECou SDry
– 'Aureovariegata'	See *H.* × *andersonii* 'Aurea'
* – 'Compacta'	MAll
§ – 'Variegata'	CB&S CLyn ECou IOrc MAll
	MBri NSti NTow SDry SRCN
	SRms WEas WLRN
'Anne Pimm' (v)	WSHC
anomala hort.	See *H.* 'Imposter'
– (J B Armstr.) Ckn.	See *H. odora*
'Aoira'	See *H. recurva* 'Aoira'

§ *armstrongii*	CBot CInt CMHG ECou EHic
	EHoe ELan EOrn EPla MBar
	NHed NNor SPer WBay WDin
	WPer
¶ 'Arthur'	ECou
astonii	MHig
'Autumn Blush'	MPla
'Autumn Glory'	CB&S CMHG CPri EBrP EBre
	ECou ELan ERav ESis GCHN
	LBre LGro MAll MBar MGos
	NNor NSti SBod SBre SHBN
	SPer WAbe WBod WDin
	WMow WSHC
'Autumn Joy'	MPla
'Autumn Queen'	NNor
♦ 'Azurea'	See *H. venustula*
♦ 'Azurens'	See *H.* 'Maori Gem'
'Baby Marie'	CAbP CLyd COtt ECot ECou
	ELan ESis GBur MAll MAsh
	MBel MGos MWhi NBee NHed
	NPer STre WPer WStI
'Balfouriana'	MAll NHed
barkeri	ECou MAll
¶ 'Barnettii'	EBee
'Beatrice'	ECou NHed
§ × *bishopiana*	ECle ECou ESis LRHS MAsh
– 'Champagne'	See *H.* × *bishopiana*
'Blonde'	NNor
'Blue Clouds' ♀	ECou EHal ELan ESis MAsh
	MLan NHed SAga SIgm SPer
	SSmi SVil WRus
'Blue Diamond'	WEas
'Blue Wand'	MBal
'Bluebell'	ECou
'Blush Wand'	MAll NCut WAbe
bollonsii	ECou MAll MSte
'Boscawenii'	CTrG MAll MGos
♦ 'Bowles' Variety'	See *H.* 'Bowles's Hybrid'
§ 'Bowles's Hybrid'	CNic CPri ECou LHil MGos
	MPla MRav NBee NFai NGre
	NNor SRms WAbe WEas
brachysiphon	ECou ENot GOrc MGos MWhi
	SPer WDin WHCG WMow
– 'White Gem'	See *H.* 'White Gem'
	(*brachysiphon* hybrid)
breviracemosa	ECou
'Brill Blue'	CLyd NMen WWin
'Brockiei'	ECou
buchananii	ECou ESis GAbr GDra GTou
	MAll MDHE MGos MTho NFai
	NHed NNor NPer WPer
– 'Christchurch'	ECou
§ – 'Minor'	CLyd ECou EPot ESis GAbr
	GCHN GCrs LBee MBar MBri
	MHig NBir NHar NHed NHol
	NMen NNrd NWCA
– 'Nana'	See *H. buchananii* 'Minor'
– 'Ohau'	ECou
– 'Otago'	ECou
§ – 'Sir George Fenwick'	ECou MBro WHoo
– 'Wanaka'	ECou
buxifolia	CMHG EBrP EBre ELan ENot
(Benth.) Ckn.& Allan	GAbr GCHN IHos LBre MAll
	MBal NFai NSti NWea SBre
	SPer WDin WStI
– 'Nana'	CLyd CSam EPot ESis MAsh
	MBri MHig NCut NPer SRms
	WWin
buxifolia hort.	See *H. odora*
– 'Champagne'	See *H.* × *bishopiana*
* – 'Nana'	EHoe NFla
N 'C.P. Raffill'	ECou

§ 'Caledonia' — CDec CNic ECou ESis GAbr MAll MAsh MBri MGos MHig MSte NFai NHed NHol NLon NPer NTow SPer WEas WHoo WOMN WOld WPat WPer WPyg WSHC

'Candy' — ECou

§ *canterburiensis* — ECou EHal MAll

N 'Carl Teschner' — See *H.* '**Youngii**'

'Carnea Variegata' — CLyn ECou EHoe ESis LHop MAll SBod SPer

carnosula — CMHG ECou EHoe ESis MAll MBrN MGos NNor SDys SPer WMow WPer

'Cassinioides' — ESis MAll

catarractae — See *Parahebe catarractae*

I 'Chalk's Buchananii' — CNic

* 'Charming White' — LRHS

chathamica — ECou ESis MAll MBal MMHG MPla NMen SDry WSHC

cheesemanii — ECou EHyt ESis GDra MHig

'Christabel' — CLyn ECou ESis MAll

§ 'Christensenii' — ECou MAll NFai NHed NMen

ciliolata — ECou

coarctata — CMHG ECou MAll

cockayneana — ECou MAll

colensoi — ECou ESis

– 'Glauca' — See *H.* '**Leonard Cockayne**'

'Colwall' — CBlo CLyd ECho EHic ESis SSto WAbe WHen

'Cookiana' — See *H. stricta macroura* '**Cookiana**'

'Coral Blue' — LHop

'Coral Pink' — LHop WWeb

corriganii — ECou

'County Park' — CLyd CNic ECou ECtt EMNN ESis EWes MAll MBal MGos MHig MMil NHed NHol NMen SBod SSmi WMow

'Craig Park' — MAll

'Cranleighensis' — ECou MAll SBod SMac SSto

¶ 'Crawii' — ECou

'Cupins' — ESis SIng

cupressoides — CMHG ECou GOrc MAll MAsh MBal MBar MGos NHed NNor SEND WDin WGwG WWal

– 'Boughton Dome' ♀ — ECha ECou EHoe EMNN ESis GCHN GTou LHil MAsh MBri MBro MGos MHig MPla MTho NCat NMen NNrd SAga SMac WAbe WEas WHoo WOld WPer WSHC

– 'Golden Dome' — CB&S EAst ESis MAll WAbe

– 'Nana' — ECou NNrd

darwiniana — See *H. glaucophylla*

'David Hughes' — NFai

* 'Deans Fya' — ESis

'Debbie' — ECou

decumbens — CLyd CNic ECou EHic ESis EWes GDra MAll NHol

* 'Denise' — ELan ENot NFai WWeb

¶ 'Diana' — ECou

* 'Dianne' — CLyn

dieffenbachii — ECou

diosmifolia — CBot CDoC CHon CLan ECou ESis WSHC

– 'Marie' — ECou ESis MAll

divaricata — ECou

– 'Marlborough' — ECou

– 'Nelson' — ECou

× *divergens* — CLan NHed

'Dorothy Peach' — See *H.* '**Watson's Pink**'

'Douglasii' — NHed

'E.A. Bowles' — CBlo ECou

'E.B. Anderson' — See *H.* '**Caledonia**'

'Early Blue' — CSpe NBir

'Edinensis' — CMHG CNic ECou NMen NNor WPer WSHC

'Edington' — CHal CLyn ECou SCoo WCFE

'Ellen' — WRus

elliptica — ECou IBlr SPer

– 'Anatoki' — CLTr ECou

– 'Bleaker' — ECou

– 'Charleston' — ECou MAll

– 'Kapiti' — ECou

– 'Variegata' — See *H.* × *franciscana* '**Variegata**'

'Emerald Dome' — NGre NMen WPer

'Emerald Gem' — See *H.* '**Emerald Green**'

§ 'Emerald Green' ♀ — CChe CSam ECou EPot ESis MAll MBar MBri MBro MGos MPla MTis MWat NHed NHol NMen NWCA SEas WAbe WPat WPer WPyg

epacridea — ECou ESis EWes GDra GTou MAll MHig NHed NHol NMen WAbe

§ 'Eveline' — CChe CPri MBal NBir SPer

evenosa — ECou MAll NMen

'Eversley Seedling' — See *H.* '**Bowles's Hybrid**'

'Fairfieldii' — EHol ESis IBlr NMen WAbe WSHC

'Fairlane' — CNic ECou NHed

¶ *formosa* — WSPU

'Fragrant Jewel' — ELan SEND SEas SMrm

× *franciscana* — CHEx ECou

§ – 'Blue Gem' ♀ — CLan CPri EHal ENot ESis LPVe MAll MAsh MGos NBir NFai NFla NPer NWea SPer SRms WBod WHar WMow

– 'Jura' — ECou

– 'Purple Tips' — See *H. speciosa* '**Variegata**'

– 'Tresco Magenta' — ECou

§ – 'Variegata' ♀ — CB&S CChe CHEx EBrP EBre ECou ELan EMil ENot ESis GRei LBre MAll MBal MBar MGos NFai NPer NSti SBre SHBN SPer SSoC WBod WHar WStI

– 'White Gem' — SRms

'Franjo' — ECou SSmi

* 'Garths Glory' — SSto

'Gauntlettii' — See *H.* '**Eveline**'

gibbsii — ECou

'Gibby' — ECou

§ *glaucophylla* — ECou NMen SBod

– 'Clarence' — ECou NHed

'Glaucophylla Variegata' — CB&S CNic ECou ESis MAll MBel MHig NFai NHed NSti SBod SPer WHer WKif WRus WSHC

'Glengarriff' — MAll NHol

§ 'Gloriosa' — CSam IOrc MAll NPla

'Gnome' — CBlo ECou

◆ 'Godefroyana' — See *H. pinguifolia* '**Godefroyana**'

gracillima — CBlo CMHG ECou

'Gran's Favourite' — CLyn ECou

'Great Orme' ♀ — Widely available

'Green Globe' — See *H.* '**Emerald Green**'

'Greensleeves' — CBlo CMHG CSam EBee ECou EPfP ESis MGos NHed

haastii — CBlo ECou EPot ESis GDra MHig NHed NNor

¶ 'Hadspen Pink'   CLyn
'Hagley Park'   CSam ECou ESis LFlo LHil LRHS MAsh MMil MPla SAga SUsu WEas WHCG WKif WSHC
§ 'Hartii'   MAll MRav SPer
'Havering Green'   ECou MHig
'Headfortii'   CLyn
hectorii   CBlo ESis GTou MAll MBal MHig NFla NHed
– var. *demissa*   ECou NHed
'Heidi'   ESis MBri
'Hidcote'   WMow
'Hielan Lassie'   CLyn
'Highdownensis'   ECou SEas SSto
'Hinderwell'   NPer
'Hinerua'   ECou
hookeriana   See *Parahebe hookeriana*
hulkeana ♀   CBot CHan ECou ELan LHil MAsh MBel MHig MPla NBir NFai NLon SAga WAbe WEas WHCG WHoo WKif WMaN WOMN WPat WWat
– 'Averil'   ECou
– 'Lilac Hint'   ECou
– 'Sally Blunt'   ECou
§ 'Imposter'   ECou ESis NFai SRms
'Inspiration'   CDoC ECou
insularis   CBlo ECou
'Jack's Surprise'   ECou
'James Platt'   ECou ESis MAll NHed
'James Stirling'   See *H. ochracea* 'James Stirling'
'Jane Holden'   NLak SBla WSHC
'Jasper'   CNic ECou ESis MAll
'Jewel'   SDix
'Joan Lewis'   ECou ESis NHed
¶ 'Joanna'   ECou
§ 'Johny Day'   CLyn ECou
'Joyce Parker'   ECou NHed
'Judy'   ECou
'June Small'   CNic
¶ 'Karo Golden Esk'   ECou
'Killiney Variety'   ECou MBal
'Kirkii'   CBlo ECou EMil LWak MWhi SPer
'Knightshayes'   See *H.* 'Caledonia'
♦ 'La Séduisante'   See *H. speciosa* 'La Seduisante'
'Lady Ardilaun'   See *H.* 'Amy'
laevis   See *H. venustula*
laingii   ECou
lapidosa   See *H. rupicola*
latifolia   See *H.* × *franciscana* 'Blue Gem'
lavaudiana   ECou ESis MRPP WAbe WWat
'Lavender Spray'   See *H.* 'Hartii'
§ 'Leonard Cockayne'   CBlo MOne NFai NSti WSHC
ligustrifolia   ECou
'Lilac Haze'   MAll
'Lindleyana'   CLyd
'Lindsayi'   CNic ECou MAll NHed
§ 'Loganioides'   CTri ECou EMNN ESis GAbr MAll MBal NMen NNor SBod SSmi WPer
'Longacre Variety'   ECou
'Lopen' (v)   ECou EWes
lyallii   See *Parahebe lyallii*
lycopodioides   ECou ESis EWes NHed
– 'Aurea'   See *H. armstrongii*
– var. *patula*   ECou
– 'Peter Pan'   ECou MBro WAbe
§ 'Macewanii'   CMHG ECou ESis MAll NFai NHed WHCG

mackenii   See *H.* 'Emerald Green'
macrantha ♀   ECou EPla ESis GAbr GCHN GCrs ITim LGre MAll MAsh MBal MHig MPla NHed NMen NNor SIng SPer SRms WAbe WOMN WSHC WWin
– var. *brachyphylla*   ECou
macrocarpa   ECou
– var. *brevifolia*   ECou EWes
– var. *latisepala*   ECou
§ 'Maori Gem'   CHEx EWes SCoo SEND SMrm WLRN
'Margery Fish'   See *H.* 'Primley Gem'
'Margret'   CHid COtt EBar EBrP EBre EMil GRei LBre MAsh MBel MGos NMen NRoo SBre SCoo SHBN SMrm SPer WStI WWhi
'Marjorie'   ECou ENot GOrc MAll MBal MGos MRav NFai NHed NNor NPer NRoo NWea SBod SPer WDin WMow
matthewsii   ECou
'Mauve Queen'   EHol
'McEwanii'   See *H.* 'Macewanii'
'McKean'   ECou NHed
'Megan'   ECou
'Melanie'   WRus
'Menzies Bay'   MAll
♦ 'Mercury'   See *H. pimeleoides* 'Mercury'
'Midsummer Beauty' ♀   CB&S EBrP EBre ECou ELan ENot GOrc IOrc LBre MAll MGos MLan MRav NFai NFla NNor SBod SBre SDix SHBN SPar SPer WAbe WDin WGwG WStI WWal
'Milmont Emerald'   See *H.* 'Emerald Green'
'Mini'   ECou
* *minima* 'Calvin'   ESis
'Miss E. Fittall'   ECou
'Mist Maiden'   ESis NHed
Purple Pixie = 'Mohawk'   COtt MAsh MGos WGor WLRN
'Monica'   ECou GCHN NHed NHol
* 'Moppets Hardy'   SPer
'Morning Clouds'   ECou
§ 'Mrs Winder' ♀   Widely available
× *myrtifolia*   MRav
'Mystery'   ECou
'Nantyderry'   CHal MBel MSCN MWgw NMen WEas WLRN WWat
'Neil's Choice'   ECou EWes MSte
'Netta Dick'   ECou
'Nicola's Blush'   CLTr CSam CSpe EBar EBrP EBre ECou ERav ESis GCHN LBre LHop LLWP MAsh MBel MPla MRav MWat NBee NFai SBre SCoo SHBN SMrm SPer SSta SUsu SVil WRus WWhi
'Northumbria Beauty'   NNor
'Northumbria Gem'   NLon NNor
obtusata   ECou
ochracea   ECou MAll MGos MMal NFla STre
§ – 'James Stirling' ♀   Widely available
'Oddity'   ECou
§ *odora*   CBlo CChe EBee ECou EPfP ESis MWhi SMac SPer WIvy WWal
– 'New Zealand Gold'   CNic CSam EBee ECou ESis MAll MAsh NFai NHed SAga WPyg WStI
* – *patens*   MGos WHCG

– prostrate form	ECou
– 'Stewart'	ECou
– 'Wintergreen'	EBee
'Oratia Beauty'	CLyn MAsh NCut NFai
'Orientale'	NHed
'Otari Delight'	CMHG
'Pageboy'	ECou NHed
§ *parviflora*	ECou EPla EWes LBlm MAll
(Vahl) Ckn. & Allan var.	MTed SAPC SArc SDix SHFr
angustifolia♀	SMac
parviflora hort.	See *H.* 'Bowles's Hybrid'
¶ – 'Holdsworth'	SDys
– 'Palmerston'	ECou
* 'Patti Dussett'	CLTr
pauciflora hort.	See *H.* 'Christensenii'
– Simpson & Thomson	ESis NMen
pauciramosa	ECou MAll NTow SRms SSto
'Penny Day'	ECou
perfoliata	See *Parahebe perfoliata*
'Perryhill Lilac'	SPer
* 'Perry's Cerise'	NFai
'Perry's Rubyleaf'	NPer
* 'Peter Chapple'	EPot
'Petra's Pink'	ECou ESis MAll WEas
¶ *petriei*	WLin
§ 'Pewter Dome' ♀	CSam EBrP EBre ECou ECtt
	EHoe EPla ESis IOrc LBre
	LHop MBal MBri MGos NBee
	NHed NNor SBod SBre SDix
	SEas SIng SPer SRms WAbe
	WHen WWat
'Pimeba'	NHol
pimeleoides	ECou MAll MHig MWhi NHed
	NMen NTow
– 'Glauca'	NPer SHBN
– 'Glaucocaerulea'	CMHG ECou ESis NHed SDys
	SPer WKif
§ – 'Mercury'	ECou
– var. *minor*	ECou EHyt ESis WPat
– – 'Elf'	ECou
– – 'Imp'	ECou
– 'Quicksilver' ♀	EBrP EBre ECou EHoe ELan
	ENot ESis GOrc LBre LHop
	MAsh MBar MBri MGos NFai
	NPer SBre SHBN SPer SSmi
	WAbe WEas WGwG WHCG
	WSHC WWal
– var. *rupestris*	ECou ESis
pinguifolia	ECou NHed SPer WFar
– 'Forma'	MAll
§ – 'Godefroyana'	CNic ECou
– 'Hutt'	ECou
– 'Mount Dobson'	ECou NHol
– 'Pagei' ♀	CB&S ECou EHoe ELan ENot
	ESis GAbr ISea LGro LHop
	MBal MBar MBri MPla MWat
	MWgw NFai NGre NHed NNor
	NRoo NWCA SHBN SReu
	WAbe WBod WDin WEas
	WHCG WWin
– 'Sutherlandii'	CDoC CNic ECou ESis GCHN
	GDra MBar NBee NFai NHed
	NLon NSti SMac
§ – 'Wardiensis'	CMHG ECou SIng
¶ 'Pink Fantasy'	MAsh WWeb
'Pink Payne'	See *H.* 'Eveline'
'Pink Pearl'	See *H.* 'Gloriosa'
'Pink Wand'	CB&S CLTr LHop WGer
'Polly Moore'	MBal NTow
poppelwellii	ITim NHed
'Porlock Purple'	See *Parahebe catarractae*
	'Delight'

¶ 'Port e Vullen'	MAll
§ 'Primley Gem'	CLyn EBar ESis WSHC
'Princess'	ECou
propinqua	ECou ESis NMen
§ – 'Aurea'	MBal
– 'Minor'	NHed
'Prostrata'	ECou MAll NHed
* 'Purple Elf'	EHic SPer
'Purple Emperor'	MAsh MBri SPla
'Purple Picture'	ECou ECtt MAsh NCut NFai
	SDry
'Purple Princess'	CLyn MAll
'Purple Queen'	See *H.* 'Amy'
'Purple Tips' hort.	See *H. speciosa* 'Tricolor'
rakaiensis ♀	CMHG ECou EHoe ELan ENot
	GAbr ISea LHop MAsh MBar
	MBri MGos MWat NBir NNor
	SPer STre WAbe WBod WDin
	WHCG WMow WPer WWin
ramosissima	ESis GTou NHed
raoulii	ECou GAbr WAbe WHCG
	WHoo WSHC
– var. *maccaskillii*	ECou ESis
– 'Mount Hutt'	GTou
– var. *pentasepala*	ESis
§ *recurva*	CMHG CNic CPle CSam ECou
	EPla ESis LHop MAll MAsh
	MBri NBee NFai NHol NNor
	SHFr SRms WAbe WBod WDin
	WPer WRus
§ – 'Aoira'	ECou NHed SPer
– 'Boughton Silver' ♀	EBar SDry SMac
– green-leaved	NHed
– 'White Torrent'	ECou
§ 'Red Edge' ♀	Widely available
'Red Ruth'	See *H.* 'Eveline'
rigidula	ECou ESis MAll NHed NMen
¶ 'Ritt'	ESis
'Ronda'	ECou
'Rosie'	CNic MAsh NBee SCoo SRms
	WEas WGor WLRN
* 'Royal Blue'	CLyn
'Royal Purple'	See *H.* 'Alicia Amherst'
salicifolia	CChe CLTr CPri ECou ELan
	ENot GCHN LGro MLan NFai
	NNor SHBN SPer SRms WFar
	WHCG WTro
◆ – 'Snow Wreath'	See *H.* 'Snow Wreath'
salicornioides	
– 'Aurea'	See *H. propinqua* 'Aurea'
'Sapphire'	CDoC CLyn ECle ECou ESis
	MAll MAsh MBar MGos NPla
	NTow WGer WMow
'Sarana'	ECou
selaginoides hort.	See *H.* 'Loganioides'
'Silver Gilt'	CBot
'Silver Wings' (v)	ECou NFai
'Simon Delaux' ♀	CB&S CSam ECou GAbr MAll
	MBal NPla NTow SHBN SPer
	WEas WRus
§ 'Snow Wreath' (v)	ECou IBlr
speciosa	MLan
– 'Dial Rocks'	ECou
◆ – 'Johny Day'	See *H.* 'Johny Day'
§ – 'La Seduisante' ♀	CB&S CLTr CLyn EBee ECou
	ENot IOrc MAll MGed MLan
	SEND SHBN SPer WSHC
◆ – 'Purple Queen'	See *H.* 'Amy'
– 'Rangatira'	ECou EWes
– 'Ruddigore'	See *H.* 'La Séduisante'
§ – 'Variegata' (v)	CHal ECou EMil IBlr NPer
	SDry WEas

'Spender's Seedling'	CLan CLyn ECou GOrc MAll MWgw NBee SEND SPer SRms STre
'Spender's Seedling' hort.	See *H. parviflora* var. *angustifolia* (Vahl) Ckn. & Allan
¶ 'Spring Glory'	EBrP EBre LBre LRHS SBre
stricta	CLyn ECou
– var. *egmontiana*	ECou
– var. *macroura*	ECou EPla SDry
subalpina	CLan EBee EBrP EBre ECou ESis LBre MOne MTis NCut NHed SBre
subsimilis var. *astonii*	ESis MHig NHed
¶ 'Susan'	ECou
'Sussex Carpet'	See *H. albicans* 'Sussex Carpet'
tetrasticha	ESis
* – AGS 74	MRPP
'Tiny Tot'	CLyd ECou EHyt ESis MTho
'Tom Marshall'	See *H. canterburiensis*
topiaria	Widely available
* – 'Doctor Favier'	CLyn
'Torlesse'	ECou
townsonii	ECou MAll
traversii	CBlo ECou MSte SPla SRms SSto
– 'Mason'	ECou
– 'Woodside'	ECou
'Trenchant Rose'	CBlo
'Tricolor'	See *H. speciosa* 'Tricolor'
'Trixie'	CNic ECou
tumida	ECou
'Underway'	WWat
urvilleana	ECou
'Veitchii'	See *H.* 'Alicia Amherst'
§ *venustula*	CMHG ECou ELan ESis MAll MAsh MBri MRav NHed NMen SMrm WPer
– 'Blue Skies'	ECou NFai
– 'Patricia Davies'	CLTr ECou NHed
vernicosa	CMHG CNic ECou EPla ESis GDra GRei LHop MAll MBar MBrN MBri MGos MHig NBee NHed NHol NNor NPer NTow SIgm SPer WAbe WHCG
'Waikiki'	See *H.* 'Mrs Winder'
'Walter Buccleugh'	ECou WOMN
♦ 'Wardiensis'	See *H. pinguifolia* 'Wardiensis'
'Warleyensis'	See *H.* 'Mrs Winder'
§ 'Watson's Pink'	CLTr ECou MAll SPer SUsu WAbe WKif
§ 'White Gem'	COtt ECou ECtt ESis GRei MAll MBal MGos NBee NFla NHed NNor NPer WEas WStI
(*brachysiphon* hybrid)	
* 'White Grape'	CM&M
'White Heather'	ESis MTPN
'White Wand'	CB&S NFai
* 'White Wings'	WWhi
'Willcoxii'	See *H. buchananii* 'Sir George Fenwick'
'Wingletye'	CAbP CLyd CMHG ECou EGoo ESis MBal MBri MGos NHed WAbe WPat WPer WPyg
'Winter Glow'	CLyd CMHG COtt ECou EHic NFai
¶ 'Wiri Blush'	CLyn
'Wiri Charm'	CAbP CDoC COtt EBee ECle ELan EMil ENot ESis IOrc MAll MAsh MLan MTis SPla SSto SVil WGer WWeb
'Wiri Cloud'	ECle ELan ESis IOrc MAsh MGed MTis SSto SVil WWeb
'Wiri Dawn'	CAbP CLyn COtt ECle ELan ESis EWes IOrc MAsh MTis NFai SPla SVil WLRN WWeb
'Wiri Gem'	EMil LRHS
'Wiri Image'	COtt EMil IOrc LRHS MAll SVil
'Wiri Joy'	CLyn LRHS SVil
'Wiri Mist'	COtt EMil ESis IOrc LRHS MAsh NFai
'Wiri Splash'	CDoC COtt ECle ELan EMil MAsh SPan WWeb
'Wiri Vision'	COtt LRHS SSto
§ 'Youngii'	CChe CMea CPri ECha ECou ELan EMNN ENot ESis GDra GRei MBal MBar MGos MPla NBee NMen NNrd NWCA SPer SRCN SSmi WEas WMow WSHC WWat WWin

HEBENSTRETIA (Scrophulariaceae) See Plant Deletions

HECHTIA (Bromeliaceae)

tillandsioides	LHil

HECTORELLA (Hectorellaceae) See Plant Deletions

HEDEOMA (Lamiaceae)

pulegioides	CArn

HEDERA † (Araliaceae)

algeriensis	See *H. canariensis* hort.
§ *azorica*	CWhi WCot WFib WWat
– 'Aurea'	EMon
– 'Pico'	CWhi WFib
– typica	See *H. azorica* 'Sao Miguel'
– 'Variegata'	WCot
§ *canariensis* hort.	CDoC CHEx SAPC SArc WFib
– 'Algeriensis'	See *H. canariensis* hort.
– 'Argyle Street'	WFib
– var. *azorica*	See *H. azorica*
– 'Cantabrian'	See *H. maroccana* 'Spanish Canary'
* – 'Casablanca'	CWhi
* – 'Etna'	CWhi
– 'Gloire de Marengo' hort. (v) ♀	Widely available
– 'Marginomaculata' ♀	EPfP EPla LRHS NEgg WFib WLeb WWeb
* – 'Mirandela'	CWhi
– 'Montgomery'	LRHS WFib
* – 'Nevada'	CWhi
– 'Ravensholst' ♀	CMac EHic NSti WFib WWat
– 'Stauss'	WFib
– 'Variegata' hort.	See *H. canariensis* 'Gloire de Marengo' hort.
caucasigena	See *H. helix* f. *caucasigena*
chinensis	See *H. nepalensis* var. *sinensis*
– typica	See *H. nepalensis* var. *sinensis*
§ *colchica* ♀	CBlo CHEx ENot EPfP SPer WDin WFib
– 'Arborescens'	See *H. colchica* 'Dendroides' Arborescent
* – 'Arborescens Variegata'	SPer
– 'Dentata' ♀	CBlo CHEx CWhi EPla LBuc LPri MBal MHlr SEas WFib
– 'Dentata Aurea'	See *H. colchica* 'Dentata Variegata'
§ – 'Dentata Variegata' ♀	Widely available
– 'My Heart'	See *H. colchica*

– 'Paddy's Pride'	See *H. colchica* 'Sulphur Heart'
§ – 'Sulphur Heart' (v) ♀	Widely available
– 'Variegata'	See *H. colchica* 'Dentata Variegata'
cristata	See *H. helix* 'Parsley Crested'
§ *cypria*	EPla WFib
helix	CKin CTri CWhi EWFC GChr MBar MGos NWea WFib WHer
– 'Abundance'	See *H. helix* 'California'
– 'Adam' (v)	CBlo CWhi EAst EPPr MAsh MBri MGos MTho NPla SEND SHFr STre WByw WFib WLeb WWat WWeb
I – 'Ahorn'	CWhi WFib
– 'Albany'	See *H. hibernica* 'Albany'
– 'Alpha'	CWhi
– 'Alte Brücke'	CWhi WFib
– 'Alte Heidelberg'	CWhi WFib
– 'Amberwaves'	WFib
I – 'Ambrosia' (v)	CWhi WFib
– 'Anchor'	CWhi
§ – 'Angularis'	CWhi ECot
– 'Angularis Aurea' ♀	CWhi EHoe EPfP EPla MPla NBir NPla SHBN SMad WFib
– 'Anne Borch'	See *H. hibernica* 'Anne Marie'
– 'Anne Marie'	See *H. hibernica* 'Anne Marie'
– 'Annette'	See *H. helix* 'California'
– 'Appaloosa'	WFib
– 'Aran'	See *H. hibernica* 'Aran'
– 'Aran' misapplied	See *H. helix* 'Rutherford's Arran'
– 'Arapahoe'	WFib
– 'Arborescens'	CNat WFib
– 'Ardingly' (v)	CWhi MWhi NBea SPer WFib
– 'Arran'	See *H. helix* 'Rutherford's Arran'
– 'Asterisk'	CWhi EPla NBrk WBro WFib WLeb
– 'Astin'	CWhi WFib
– 'Atropurpurea' ♀	CBlo CNat CWhi EPPr EPla ETen MBar MHlr NHol SLPl WBay WFib
– 'Aurea Densa'	See *H. helix* 'Aureovariegata'
§ – 'Aureovariegata'	CMac CNic CWhi WFib
– 'Avon' (v)	WFib
– 'Baby Face'	CWhi
– 'Baccifera'	CWhi WFib
– 'Baden-Baden'	CWhi WFib
– var. *baltica*	CWhi WFib
¶ – 'Barabits' Silver'	EPla
– 'Big Deal'	CWhi
– 'Bill Archer'	CWhi EPPr EPla WFib
– 'Bird's Foot'	See *H. helix* 'Pedata'
– 'Blodwen' (v)	WFib
– 'Bodil' (v)	CWhi SHFr WFib
– 'Boskoop'	CWhi WFib
– 'Bowles Ox Heart'	WFib
– 'Bredon'	WFib WSPU
– 'Brigette'	See *H. helix* 'California'
– 'Brightstone'	WFib
§ – 'Brokamp'	CWhi EPPr NFai SLPl WFib
– 'Bruder Ingobert' (v)	CWhi WFib
– 'Buttercup' ♀	CMac CNat CWhi ECha EHoe ELan EPla GDra GOrc LHop MAsh MBal MBar MBri MGos MPla MTho NBea NBrk NFai NNor SBra SDix SHBN SMad SPer WEas WFib WLeb WWat
– 'Butterflies'	WFib
§ – 'Caecilia' (v)	CBlo CMac ELan EPPr EPla LHop MBrN NFai NSti SMad WCot WCru WDin WFib WLRN WLeb WStI
– 'Caenwoodiana'	See *H. helix* 'Pedata'
– 'Caenwoodiana Aurea'	CWhi WFib
– 'Calico' (v)	See *H. helix* 'Schäfer Three'
§ – 'California'	CWhi MBri NSti WFib
– 'California Fan'	CWhi
– 'California Gold' (v)	CWhi NPro WFib
– 'Caristian'	WFib
– 'Carolina Crinkle'	CNat CWhi MWhi NBrk WBro WFib
– 'Cascade'	WFib
– 'Cathedral Wall'	WFib
§ – 'Cavendishii' (v) ♀	CWhi MPla NBrk WCru WFib WLRN
§ – 'Ceridwen' (v)	CRHN CWhi EPPr MBri WFib
¶ – 'Chedglow' fasciated	CNat
– 'Chester' (v)	CWhi MBri WFib WWat
– 'Chicago'	CBlo WFib
– 'Chicago Variegated'	See *H. helix* 'Harald'
– 'Christian'	See *H. helix* 'Direktor Badke'
– 'Chrysanna'	WFib
– 'Chrysophylla'	CWhi EPla
– 'Cleeve'	WFib
– 'Clotted Cream'	See *H. helix* 'Caecilia'
– 'Cockle Shell'	CWhi WFib
– 'Congesta' ♀	CWhi EPPr EPla EPot GDra MBal MTho SMac SRms SSmi STre WEas WFib WLeb
– 'Conglomerata'	CWhi ELan EPPr EPla MAsh MBal MBar MBri MBro NBir NNor NRya SMad SPer SRms SSmi WAbe WDin WEas WFib WPat WPyg
– 'Conglomerata Erecta'	CSWP MAsh WFib
– 'Corrugata'	WFib
– 'Crenata'	CWhi WFib
– 'Crispa'	MRav NNor
– 'Cristata'	See *H. helix* 'Parsley Crested'
– 'Cristata Melanie'	See *H. helix* 'Melanie'
– 'Curleylocks'	See *H. helix* 'Manda's Crested'
– 'Curley-Q'	See *H. helix* 'Dragon Claw'
– 'Curvaceous' (v)	WCot WFib
– 'Cuspidata Major'	See *H. hibernica* 'Cuspidata Major'
– 'Cuspidata Minor'	See *H. hibernica* 'Cuspidata Minor'
– 'Cyprus'	See *H. cypria*
* – 'Dead Again'	WCot
– 'Dean' (v)	WFib
– 'Deltoidea'	See *H. hibernica* 'Deltoidea'
– 'Denmark' (v)	WFib
– 'Denticulata'	CWhi WFib
– 'Diana'	CWhi
– 'Dicke von Stauss'	CWhi
§ – 'Direktor Badke'	CWhi WFib
– 'Discolor'	See *H. helix* 'Minor Marmorata'
– 'Domino' (v)	CWhi EPla EWes WFib WLeb
§ – 'Donerailensis'	CWhi GAri NFai WFib WPer
– 'Dovers'	WFib
§ – 'Dragon Claw'	CNat CWhi EHic EPPr EPla ETen NBrk NPla SMad WCot WCru WFib WLeb
– 'Duckfoot'	CLTr CSWP CWhi EPPr MTho MWhi NFai NPla NSti WBro WFib WLeb WWat
– 'Dunloe Gap'	EPla
– 'Edison'	CWhi
– 'Elegance'	CWhi WFib
– 'Elfenbein' (v)	CWhi WFib

– 'Emerald Gem'	See *H. helix* **'Angularis'**
– 'Emerald Globe'	CWhi WFib
– 'Emerald Jewel'	See *H. helix* **'Pittsburgh'**
– 'Erecta' ♀	CMac CNat CTri CWhi EHic
	EMFP EPPr EPla GAri MBar
	MBri MTho MWhi NRya WFib
	WPat
– 'Erin'	See *H. helix* **'Pin Oak'**
– 'Ester'	See *H. helix* **'Harald'**
– 'Eugen Hahn' (v)	CWhi EPla WCot WFib WHer
§ – 'Eva' (v) ♀	CMac CWhi MBal MBri MGos
	NBir WFib
– 'Evesham'	WFib
– 'Fallen Angel'	CWhi EPPr WFib
– 'Fan'	CWhi
– 'Fantasia' (v)	CMac CWhi WFib
– 'Ferney'	WFib
– 'Filigran'	CNat CWhi SMad WFib WHer
	WLeb
– 'Flamenco'	CWhi EPla WFib
– 'Flava' (v)	CWhi
– 'Fleur de Lis'	CNat CWhi WFib
– 'Florida'	WFib
– 'Fluffy Ruffles'	CWhi EPla WLeb
* – 'Francis'	MBri
– 'Fringette'	See *H. helix* **'Manda's Fringette'**
– 'Gavotte'	CWhi EPPr MTho WFib
– 'Gertrud Stauss' (v)	CWhi MBri WFib
– 'Glache' (v)	SHFr WFib
¶ – 'Glacier' (v) ♀	Widely available
¶ – 'Glacier Improved' (v)	NBea
– 'Glymii'	CWhi EPPr EPla SLPl WFib
– 'Gold Harald'	See *H. helix* **'Goldchild'**
– 'Gold Nugget'	CWhi
§ – 'Goldchild' (v) ♀	CB&S CSam CWhi EBrP EBre
	ELan EPla GBur GOrc LBre
	MAsh MBar MBri MGos MTho
	MWhi NBir NFla NHol SBre
	SEas SHFr SPer WBay WByw
	WFib WLeb
– 'Goldcraft' (v)	CWhi WFib
– 'Golden Ann'	See *H. helix* **'Ceridwen'**
* – 'Golden Arrow'	EPPr MAsh
– 'Golden Curl' (v)	EPPr
– 'Golden Ester'	See *H. helix* **'Ceridwen'**
– 'Golden Gate' (v)	MBri
– 'Golden Ingot'	CWhi ELan EPPr MAsh MBar
	MGos MWhi NFai WFib WLeb
– 'Golden Kolibri'	See *H. helix* **'Midas Touch'**
– 'Golden Mathilde'	CHal
– 'Golden Medal'	EPPr WFib
– 'Golden Shamrock'	See *H. helix* **'Golden Envoy'**
– 'Golden Snow' (v)	MBri
– 'Goldfinger'	See *H. helix* **'Goldstern'**
– 'Goldheart'	See *H. helix* **'Oro di Bogliasco'**
§ – 'Goldstern' (v)	CNat CWhi MWhi WFib WLeb
	WWat
– 'Goldwolke' (v)	SLPl
– 'Gracilis'	See *H. hibernica* **'Gracilis'**
§ – 'Green Feather'	CWhi ESis WFib WHer WOak
– 'Green Finger'	See *H. helix* **'Très Coupé'**
§ – 'Green Ripple'	CB&S CMac CNat CSam CTri
	CWhi ENot IOrc MAsh MBar
	MHlr NBro NCat NNor NPla
	SEND SEas SPer WFib WHen
	WLeb
– 'Green Spear'	See *H. helix* **'Spear Point'**
– 'Hahn's Green Ripple'	See *H. helix* **'Green Ripple'**
– 'Hamilton'	See *H. hibernica* **'Hamilton'**
§ – 'Harald' (v)	CBlo CDoC CWhi EBar MAsh
	MBal MBri NSti WFib WLeb
– 'Harlequin' (v)	WFib
– 'Harrison'	CWhi
– 'Harry Wood'	See *H. helix* **'Modern Times'**
* – 'Hazel' (v)	EPPr WFib
– 'Heise' (v)	CWhi WFib
– 'Heise Denmark' (v)	WFib
– 'Helvetica'	CWhi
– 'Helvig'	See *H. helix* **'White Knight'**
– 'Heron'	EMon SMad
– subsp. *hibernica*	See *H. hibernica*
– 'Hispanica'	See *H. maderensis* subsp. *iberica*
– 'Hite's Miniature'	See *H. helix* **'Merion Beauty'**
– 'Holly'	See *H. helix* **'Parsley Crested'**
– 'Humpty Dumpty'	CDoC MBar
– 'Ideal'	See *H. helix* **'California'**
– 'Imp'	See *H. helix* **'Brokamp'**
– 'Ingelise'	See *H. helix* **'Sagittifolia Variegata'**
– 'Ingrid'	See *H. helix* **'Harald'**
– 'Innuendo'	WFib
♦ – 'Itsy Bitsy'	See *H. helix* **'Pin Oak'**
– 'Ivalace' ♀	CB&S CNat CWhi ECha EPla
	ESis GOrc MAsh MBal MBrN
	MGos MHlr MNrw MRav
	MWhi NChi NFai NSti NWoo
	SEas SRms WFib WLeb
– 'Jack Frost' (v)	EHic ETen
– 'Jane's Findling' (v)	CNat
– 'Jasper'	WFib
– 'Jerusalem'	See *H. helix* **'Schäfer Three'**
¶ – 'Jester's Gold'	MBri NEgg WWeb
– 'Jubilee' (v)	CWhi ELan EPPr WCFE WFib
	WLeb
– 'Knülch'	EHic EPla WFib
– 'Kolibri' (v) ♀	CBlo CDoC CWhi EAst EBrP
	EBre EMil EPfP LBre MAsh
	MBar MBri NPla SBre WFar
	WFib WWeb
– 'Königers Auslese'	CRHN CWhi EPla MBrN NBea
	SLPl WFib
– 'Kurios'	CNat CWhi
– 'La Plata'	CWhi
§ – 'Lady Kay'	WFib
– 'Lalla Rookh'	CWhi EPPr NBrk WFib WLeb
– 'Lemon Swirl' (v)	CWhi WFib
– 'Leo Swicegood'	CSWP CWhi EPla MWhi WFib
– 'Light Fingers'	CNat SPer WFib
* – 'Lime Regis'	CWhi
– 'Limey'	CWhi
– 'Little Diamond' (v) ♀	CLTr CSam CTri CWhi EBee
	EHoe EMil EPPr EPla GChr
	MAsh MBar MBri MGos MHar
	NPla SHBN WAbe WBay WFib
	WWat
– 'Little Gem'	CWhi WFib
– 'Little Luzii' (v)	WFib
– 'Little Picture'	WFib
– 'Little Witch'	EPla
– 'Liz' (v)	See *H. helix* **'Eva'**
– 'Liziz' (v)	WFib
– 'Lopsided'	CNat
– 'Lucy Kay'	See *H. helix* **'Lady Kay'**
§ – 'Luzii' (v)	CBlo EBee EHic EHoe EPla
	MBar MGos NFai NNor NSti
	SHBN SPer SRms WByw WFib
– 'Maculata'	See *H. helix* **'Minor Marmorata'**
– 'Malvern'	WFib
§ – 'Manda Fringette'	CWhi MTho NFai WFib WLeb
§ – 'Manda's Crested' ♀	CBlo CDec CSWP CWhi ELan
	MBal NPla WFib WLeb
– 'Manda's Fan'	WFib
– 'Maple Leaf'	CNat CWhi EPla WCot WFib
– 'Maple Queen'	MBri

– 'Marginata' (v)	CBlo SRms
– 'Marginata Elegantissima'	See *H. helix* 'Tricolor'
– 'Marginata Major' (v)	CWhi WFib WLeb
– 'Marginata Minor'	See *H. helix* 'Cavendishii'
– 'Marie-Luise'	WFib
– 'Marmorata'	See *H. helix* 'Luzii'
– 'Masquerade' (v)	CBlo WGor WLeb
– 'Mathilde' (v)	CSpe CWhi WFib WWeb
– 'Meagheri'	See *H. helix* 'Green Feather'
§ – 'Melanie'	ECha ELan EPla NBrk NPla SAxl SOkh WCot WCru WFib WLeb WRHF
– 'Meon'	WFib
§ – 'Merion Beauty'	CWhi EHic GAri NPro WFib
§ – 'Midas Touch' (v) ♀	CBlo COtt CWhi EBee EPfP EPla LHop MBri SHFr SPer WFib
– 'Midget'	CRow WEas WFib
– 'Mini Ester' (v)	CWhi MBri
– 'Mini Heron'	MBri
– 'Miniature Knight'	CNat
– 'Minima'	See *H. helix* 'Donerailensis'
§ – 'Minor Marmorata' (v)	CWhi EPla MBal MTho WEas WFib
– 'Mint Kolibri'	EHoe EPla MBri
– 'Minty' (v)	EPPr WLeb
* – 'Minutissima'	EPPr EPla
– 'Miss Maroc'	See *H. helix* 'Manda Fringette'
– 'Misty' (v)	CWhi WFib
§ – 'Modern Times'	CWhi
– 'Mrs Pollock' (v)	CWhi WFib
– 'Mrs Ulin'	CWhi
– 'Needlepoint'	CBlo IOrc
– 'Neilson'	CLTr CWhi SPer WFib
– 'Neptune'	CWhi
– 'New Ripples'	CWhi EHal NBrk WFib
– 'Nigra'	CWhi
– 'Nigra Aurea' (v)	CWhi WFib
– 'Norfolk Lace'	EWes
– 'Northington Gold'	WFib
– 'Obovata'	CWhi
– 'Olive Rose'	CWhi EPla MTho WCot WFib
§ – 'Oro di Bogliasco' (v)	CChe CMac CSam CWhi EAst EBee ELan ENot GOrc MBal MBar MBri NBea NBee NFai NFla NSti NWea SBra SPer SRCN SRms WEas WMow WPat WWat
– 'Pallida'	See *H. hibernica* '**Hibernica Variegata**'
– 'Paper Doll' (v)	CWhi
– 'Parasol' (v)	EPla
§ – 'Parsley Crested' AM	CBlo CHEx CNat EBee ELan GOrc MAsh MBal MBar MHlr NChi NSti SPer SRms WAlt WCru WLeb WMow WOak WRHF WWat
§ – 'Pedata' ♀	CSWP CWhi EPfP WFib WLeb
– 'Pencil Point'	CWhi
– 'Pennsylvanian'	CWhi
– 'Perkeo'	CWhi EPPr EPla ESis NPla SPan WFib
– 'Perle' (v)	CWhi EPPr NBir WFib
– 'Persian Carpet'	CWhi WFib
– 'Peter' (v)	NBrk WFib
* – 'Pin Oak'	CBlo NPla WCru
I – 'Pink 'n' Very Curly'	WCot
– 'Pirouette'	WFib
§ – 'Pittsburgh'	WFib WWal
– 'Pixie'	CWhi WFib
– 'Plume d'Or'	CHal CSam MTho WFib
§ – f. *poetarum*	EPla IOrc WFib
– – 'Poetica Arborea'	ECha SDix
– 'Poetica'	See *H. helix* subsp. *poetarum*
– 'Preston Tiny'	NBir
– 'Professor Friedrich Tobler'	CNat CWhi EPla NPro WFib WLeb
– 'Quatermas'	WFib
¶ – 'Raleigh Delight'	WCot
– 'Ralf'	CWhi EPla WFib
– 'Rambler'	NBir
– 'Ramsgate'	EMon
– 'Rauschgold' (v)	CWhi
– 'Ray's Supreme'	See *H. helix* 'Pittsburgh'
– 'Reef Shell' (v)	WFib
– 'Regency' (v)	CWhi
– subsp. *rhizomatifera*	EPla WFib
– 'Ritterkreuz'	CWhi WFib
– 'Romanze' (v)	CWhi WFib
◆ – 'Rottingdean'	See *H. hibernica* '**Rottingdean**'
– 'Rüsche'	CNat CWhi WFib
– 'Russell's Gold'	WFib
§ – 'Rutherford's Arran'	CWhi WFib
– 'Sagittifolia'	CLTr CMac CNic CTri CWhi ELan ENot GOrc MAsh MBal NChi NNor SHFr SRms WCot WEas WFib WWat
§ – 'Sagittifolia Variegata'	CBlo CMac CWhi EBee EHal EMil EPla GOrc MAsh MBri NBea SBra SPer SRms WAbe WFib WLeb WRHF
– 'Sally' (v)	CWhi EPla WFib
– 'Salt and Pepper'	See *H. helix* '**Minor Marmorata**'
§ – 'Schäfer Three' (v)	EPPr WFib
– 'Serenade' (v)	WFib
– 'Shamrock' ♀	CWhi EPPr EPfP EPla MBri SPer WCot WFib
– 'Shannon'	CWhi
– 'Silver Emblem' (v)	WFib
– 'Silver King' (v)	EPla NBir SHFr WFib
– 'Silver Queen' (v)	See *H. helix* '**Tricolor**'
– 'Sinclair Silverleaf'	WFib
– 'Small Deal'	CWhi WFib
§ – 'Spear Point'	CWhi WFib
– 'Spectabilis Aurea'	WLeb
– 'Spectre' (v)	CNat CWhi EPPr MTho WFib WHer WLeb
– 'Spetchley' ♀	CNic CSWP CWhi EPPr EPla ESis EWes MAsh MBar MRav MTho NPer SHel SMad WAlt WBay WBcn WCFE WFib WLeb WPat
– 'Spinosa'	CWhi EPla
– 'Spiriusa'	EPPr WFib
– 'Staghorn'	CWhi
– 'Stevenage' (v)	WFib
– 'Stift Neuberg' (v)	WFib
– 'Stuttgart'	CWhi WFib
– 'Succinata'	EPPr WFib
– 'Sunrise'	WFib
– 'Suzanne'	See *H. nepalensis* var. *nepalensis* '**Suzanne**'
– 'Sylvanian'	WFib
– 'Symmetry'	CWhi
– 'Tango'	EPPr WFib
– 'Teardrop'	EPPr WBro
– 'Telecurl'	CWhi EPPr EPla WFib
– 'Tenerife'	ELan WFib WLeb
– 'Thorndale'	CWhi WFib
– 'Tiger Eyes'	CWhi
* – 'Touch of Class'	CWhi

§ – 'Très Coupé'	CB&S CSWP EBee EPPr MBal MTho NPla SAPC SArc SPer WDin WFib WLeb
§ – 'Tricolor' (v)	CB&S CBlo CMac CTri CWhi ELan EPfP EPla MAsh SBra SHBN SPer
– 'Trinity' (v)	CRHN WByw WFib
– 'Tristram' (v)	CWhi MAsh WFib
– 'Triton'	CWhi EPla MBal MBar MTho WFib WHer
– 'Troll'	CWhi WLeb
– 'Trustee'	CWhi
– 'Tussie Mussie' (v)	CWhi WFib
– 'Ursula' (v)	CSWP EPPr NChi WFib
– 'Ustler'	CWhi
* – 'Variegata'	WLeb
* – 'Verity'	CWhi
I – 'Victoria'	MAsh WWeb
– 'Walthamensis'	CWhi WFib
§ – 'White Knight' (v)	CWhi MBri WFib
– 'White Kolibri'	MBri
– 'Whitehall'	WFib
– 'Wichtel'	CWhi
– 'William Kennedy' (v)	CWhi WFib WLeb
– 'Williamsiana' (v)	CWhi
– 'Woeneri'	CWhi SLPl WFib
– 'Woodsii'	See *H. helix* **'Modern Times'**
– 'Zebra' (v)	CWhi WFib
§ *hibernica* ♀	CB&S CBlo CNat CWhi GCHN GChr LBuc MBar MBri MHlr MRav NBea NNor SBra SPer SRms WFib WLeb WStI WWat
§ – 'Albany'	WFib
§ – 'Anna Marie' (v)	CMac CPri CWhi GOrc MBri WEas WFib WLeb
– 'Aracena'	EMon EPla
§ – 'Cuspidata Major'	CWhi WFib
§ – 'Cuspidata Minor'	CWhi WFib
– 'Dealbata' (v)	CMac CWhi GOrc WFib
– 'Deltoidea'	CWhi EPPr EPla MBal MBri WCot WFib
– 'Digitata'	WFib
I – 'Digitata Crûg Gold'	WCru
§ – 'Gracilis'	CWhi WFib
– 'Hamilton'	WFib
– 'Helena' (v)	WFib
* – 'Lactimaculata'	CWhi
– 'Lobata Major'	SRms
– 'Maculata' (v)	EPla
– 'Palmata'	WFib
– 'Rona'	CWhi WFib
– 'Sulphurea' (v)	CWhi WFib
– 'Tess'	CNat EPla WFib
– 'Variegata'	CPri CWhi MBar WWat
maderensis	WFib
§ – subsp. *iberica*	WFib
maroccana 'Morocco'	WFib
§ – 'Spanish Canary'	WFib
nepalensis	MBal WFib
§ – var. *nepalensis* 'Suzanne'	WFib
§ – var. *sinensis*	CWhi WFib
pastuchovii	CWhi WFib
– from Troödos, Cyprus	See *H. cypria*
* – 'Volga'	CWhi
§ *rhombea*	CWhi WCot WFib
– var. *formosana*	WFib
– 'Japonica'	See *H. rhombea*
– var. *rhombea* 'Variegata'	WFib

HEDYCHIUM † (Zingiberaceae)

aurantiacum	CMon NRog SLMG WCru WMul
chrysoleucum	CGle LAma LBow NRog
coccineum ♀	CB&S CMon LAma LBlm LBow LChe NRog SLMG WCru
¶ – var. *angustifolium*	WMul
– var. *aurantiacum*	LAma LBow
– 'Tara' ♀	CFil CGle EOas MSte SAPC SArc SLMG WMul
coronarium	CAvo CGle CHEx LBlm LBow LChe MBEx MSte NFai SLMG WMul
– var. *flavescens*	See *H. flavescens*
densiflorum	CFil CHEx CMon CTre EOas MBEx SDix SSpi WPGP
– 'Assam Orange'	CB&S CFil CGle CHEx CInt EOas GCal LChe MBEx MSte SAPC SArc WMul WPGP
– 'Stephen'	CFil
ellipticum	LAma LBlm LBow NRog
§ *flavescens*	LAma LHil NRog WCru WPGP
forrestii	CFil CGle CHEx CTre EOas MSte SArc WPGP
gardnerianum ♀	CFil CFir CGre CHEx CHan CLTr CTrC EOas ERea LAma LBlm LBow LChe MSte NRog SArc SDix SLMG SMad SSoC WCru WFar WMul WPGP
¶ 'Goldflame'	CFir
greenei	CFil CFir CGle CGre CHEx LBow MSte NRog SDix SLMG
longicornutum	MSte
¶ *muluense*	WMul
¶ *pradhanii*	CFir WMul
× *raffillii*	WCot
* 'Shamshiri'	LBlm
spicatum	CFil CFir CHEx CHan CMdw CMon MSte NRog SLMG
¶ *thyrsiforme*	WMul
villosum	LAma LBow NRog WMul
yunnanense	CFil EOas WCot WPGP

HEDYSARUM (Papilionaceae)

coronarium	CArn CGle CHan CPle CSev CSpe ECGN ELan EMan GCra LFis MAvo MHlr MNrw MSte NPSI SAga SHFr SRCN SUsu WCot WFar WOMN WOve WWin
hedysaroides	EMan
multijugum	CB&S CDoC MBlu NFla SPer WSHC
– var. *apiculatum*	ELan
occidentale	SIgm

HEDYSCEPE (Arecaceae) See Plant Deletions

HEIMERLIODENDRON See PISONIA

HEIMIA (Lythraceae)

salicifolia	CArn CPle ELan MBlu MSal MWhi SOWG WOMN WWin WWye

HELENIUM † (Asteraceae)

autumnale	CBlo CMea CTri EBar EHal MBel MSal NBus NMir SEas SSvw WBea
– 'All Gold'	WPer

– JLS 88007WI	EMon
¶ – 'Praecox'	ECGN
'Baudirektor Linne'	CSam CWit ECED SCro
* 'Biedermeier'	EFou
bigelovii	WByw
'Blütentisch'	SUsu
'Bruno'	CRDP EBrP EBre ECGN ELan LBre MArl MMil MRav SBre SMrm SOkh
'Butterpat'	CB&S CWit ECED EFou EHic EMan EPPr GMaP MAvo MBel MCLN MMil NFai NFla NPri NTow NVic SChu SPer WHoo WOld
'Chipperfield Orange'	CBlo CHad CMGP EBee EFou EGar EMan EPPr EPfP LRHS MArl MHlr MMil NCat NLak NVic SUsu WLRN
'Coppelia'	CKel CSam EBrP EBre ECED LBre MBro NFla SBre WHoo
Copper Spray	See *H.* 'Kupfersprudel'
'Crimson Beauty'	EBrP EBre ELan LBre MBri MLLN MRav NFai NRoo SBre WMer
'Croftway Variety'	SCro
Dark Beauty	See *H.* 'Dunkelpracht'
¶ 'Die Blonde'	LGre
§ 'Dunkelpracht'	LRHS WCot
'Feuersiegel'	EFou LGre WOld
'Flammendes Käthchen'	EFou SAga
'Gold Fox'	CKel CSam CWit WMer
Golden Youth	See *H.* 'Goldene Jugend'
§ 'Goldene Jugend'	ELan MRav NRoo SSpe WEas
'Goldrausch'	EFou
hoopesii	CKel CPea EBar EBrP EBre EOld GChr GMaP LBre MFir MRav NBro NFai NOak NPri NSti NVic SBre SCro SMrm SRms WBea WOve WPer WWal WWye
'July Sun'	SSpe
'Kanaria'	EFou EPPr SPla WOld
§ 'Kupfersprudel'	MRav
'Kupferzwerg'	EFou LGre
'Mahogany'	See *H.* 'Goldlackzwerg'
'Moerheim Beauty'	Widely available
'Pumilum Magnificum'	CDoC CSam EPar EPfP MBri MWat NRoo SCro SPer WByw WMer
Red and Gold	See *H.* 'Rotgold'
'Riverton Beauty'	CBre
'Riverton Gem'	ECtt
§ 'Rotgold'	CBlo CM&M CMGP ECGN ECtt MSCN NOak SIde SRms WHil WLRN WPer
¶ 'Rubinkuppel'	SUsu
¶ 'Rubinzwerg'	SUsu
¶ 'Sahin's Early Flowerer'	WCot
'Septemberfuchs'	EBee EFou EPPr
'Sonnenwunder'	CWit ECha EFou EGar
'Sunshine'	WSan
'The Bishop'	CBlo CHea CSam EFou EGar EMan LFis MAus MBri MLLN MRav MTis NBro NCut NFai NLak NSti SChu SSpe WMer WOld
'Waldtraut'	CBlo CKel CM&M CMGP CMil CSam EBee ECot EFou EGar ELan MRav NFai NOak SCro SPer WHoo WMer
'Wonadonga'	EFou
'Wyndley'	CB&S CBos CSam EBrP EBre ECED ECGN EFou EGar LBre MAus MBel MRav NFai NRoo SBre SChu SEas WCot WMer
'Zimbelstern'	CMil ECha EFou EGar SAga SOkh WFar

HELIAMPHORA (Sarraceniaceae)

heterodoxa	WMEx
heterodoxa × *ionasii*	WMEx
– × *minor*	WMEx
– × *nutans*	WMEx
minor	MHel WMEx
nutans	WMEx
tatei	WMEx

HELIANTHELLA (Asteraceae)

§ *quinquenervis*	EBrP EBre EMan GCal LBre MBel MSte NTow SBre WFar

HELIANTHEMUM † (Cistaceae)

'Alice Howarth'	CMea ESis EWes MBro MDHE SRms WHCG WHoo WPnn WPyg
alpestre serpyllifolium	See *H. nummularium* subsp. *glabrum*
'Amabile Plenum' (d)	EBar EPfP GAbr GCal GDra NCut SIgm
* 'Amber'	GAbr
'Amy Baring' ♀	EBrP EBre EGle EGoo EMNN GAbr GDra LBee LBre LHop NMen SBod SBre SMer WPer WSHC
'Annabel'	CPri EPfP GAbr GCHN MPla NMGW NSla SChu SIde SMer WHCG WLin WPer
apenninum	MDHE WCla WPer
– var. *roseum*	WCla
'Apricot'	SBod
'Apricot Blush'	WAbe
'Baby Buttercup'	CLyd CMea CPBP GAbr MBro MPla NPro WPat
'Barbara'	MHig
'Beech Park Red'	CMea CPBP ESis GAbr LBee LBuc MBro MDHE MMil MWat SChu SIgm WCer WHoo WKif WPyg
'Ben Afflick'	GAbr LBee MHig NHol NSty SAga SBod SIgm SRms WCer WPnn
'Ben Alder'	GAbr LFis MDHE NHol NMen NSty SSca
'Ben Dearg'	CMea ECtt EGle EMNN ESis GAbr NSty SBod SRms
'Ben Fhada'	CMHG CMea CPBP CPri EGle ELan EMNN ESis GAbr GBur GDra LBee MBal MHig NSty SAga SBod WAbe WEas WPer WPnn WWin
'Ben Heckla'	CMHG CPri CSam GAbr GCHN MSte NMen NRoo WEas WPer
'Ben Hope'	CPri EMNN EPfP GAbr GDra LIck MBal MOne NMen NRoo NSty SAga SRms WPer WWin
'Ben Lawers'	NHol
'Ben Ledi'	CInt CMea CPri ELan EMNN ESis GAbr GBur GCHN GDra LHop MBal MHig MTis NSla NSty NVic SBod WAbe WCer WHoo WLin WPer WPnn WWin

'Ben Lomond'	GAbr MBal	§ 'Golden Queen'	CPri ECtt ENot EPfP GAbr
'Ben Macdui'	GAbr		LIck MOne NHol NMen NSty
'Ben More'	CB&S CPri EGle ELan EMNN		SChu WCla WHil WPer WPyg
	ESis GAbr GDra GTou IHos	'Henfield Brilliant' ♀	Widely available
	LBuc MBal MWat NLak NLon	'Hidcote Apricot'	GAbr MMHG MTis NHol
	NMen SBod SIng SSmi WPat	'Highdown'	CLTr GAbr SRms WAbe
	WWin	'Honeymoon'	MDHE SIde WLRN
'Ben Nevis'	CLon CTri ECha ELan GAbr	'John Lanyon'	LRHS MDHE
	GDra MDHE SRms WHoo	'Jubilee' (d) ♀	CMHG CPri EGle ELan EMNN
	WPyg WWin		GAbr GOrc LBuc LFis LHop
'Ben Vane'	EGle EMNN MDHE NHol SIng		NChi NNor NRoo NSty SChu
'Birch White'	GAbr MDHE SIng		SDix SRms WAbe WCla WEas
'Boughton Double	CGle ELan EMan EWes GAbr		WHCG WHoo WWin
Primrose' (d)	GCal GMac GOrc LFlo LHop	I 'Jubilee Variegatum'	GAbr NRoo
	MGed SChu SIgm SMer WEas	'Kathleen Druce' (d)	EWes GAbr LHop MWat
	WHoo WPen WSHC		WHoo
'Broughty Beacon'	GAbr GDra MDHE WGor	*ledifolium*	WPer
'Broughty Sunset'	CLTr CSam GAbr MBro	'Lucy Elizabeth'	GAbr
	MDHE NBir SIgm WHoo WPyg	*lunulatum*	CInt CLyd EGoo ESis LBee
'Bunbury'	CMea GAbr MDHE MWhi		MBro MPla MSto NHol NMen
	NCat NPri NRoo		NTow SIgm WAbe WPat WWin
* 'Butter and Eggs'	CInt SRms	'Magnificum'	MDHE MWat
'Butterball' (d)	MDHE	'Moonbeam'	WWin
canum	WPer	§ 'Mrs C.W. Earle' (d) ♀	CHar CInt CLTr CMHG CPri
– subsp. *balcanicum*	NTow		CTri ELan ESis GAbr LFis
'Captivation'	EGoo GAbr NHol		LHop NHol NRoo NSty SBod
'Cerise Queen' (d)	EBrP EBre ECha GAbr GMac		SDix SRms WAbe WPer WWin
	LBre LHop MBro MPla NCut	'Mrs C.W. Earle	ELan
	SBre SDix SIgm SRms SSoC	Variegated' (d)	
	WCla WHoo WPer WPnn WPyg	'Mrs Clay'	See *H.* **'Fire Dragon'**
chamaecistus	See *H. nummularium*	'Mrs Croft'	WPer
'Cheviot'	CMea MBro MDHE WEas	'Mrs Hays'	GMac
	WHoo WPer WPyg WSHC	'Mrs Jenkinson'	CMHG
	WWat	'Mrs Lake'	EMNN GAbr NSty
'Chocolate Blotch'	CLTr ECtt GAbr LBuc LFis	'Mrs Moules'	SRms
	MGed MHar NPri NSty SChu	'Mrs Mountstewart	LHop MBro
	SEND SIng WBea WPer WRHF	Jenkinson'	
'Coppernob'	SRms	*mutabile*	WPer
'Cornish Cream'	CLTr EWes GAbr	§ *nummularium*	CKin EHic EWFC GOrc GPoy
croceum	NTow		MDHE MHew NMir NWCA
cupreum	CInt EFou NHol		SIde WCla WHil WPat
'David'	EGoo	§ – subsp. *glabrum*	CMHG GAbr MBro NHol
'Doctor Phillips'	WHCG		NMGW NMen WHoo WPat
double apricot (d)	EGle GAbr		WPer WPyg
double cream (d)	CMea ECha ECtt EGar ESis	– subsp. *grandiflorum*	MWat
	MDHE NHol WFar	'Variegatum'	
'Double Orange' (d)	EBar LHop MWat NCut	* – 'Lemon Queen'	WBcn
¶ double pale yellow	NWoo	§ – subsp. *tomentosum*	MWat
double pink (d)	CMGP ECha GAbr MWat	¶ *oelandicum*	NWCA
	NWoo WFar	– subsp. *alpestre*	CLyd MBro NNrd NTow SRms
'Double Primrose' (d)	SIng		SSmi WPer
double red (d)	ECha NChi	– subsp. *piloselloides*	MHig WAbe WWin
double yellow (d)	ECha MPla	(Lapeyr) Greater &	
'Elaine'	ELan	Burdett	
'Elisabeth'	EGoo	'Old Gold'	CLTr EBrP EBre GAbr LBee
'Fairy'	EDAr EGle ESis MDHE		LBre MHar MHig NRoo SBre
§ 'Fire Dragon' ♀	CPea CPri CSam CTri EGle		SIgm SRms WAbe WPer WPnn
	ELan EMar GAbr GCHN LBee	*ovatum*	See *H. nummularium* subsp.
	LBuc MTis MWgw NRoo		*obscurum*
	NWCA SChu SIgm SRms	*pilosum*	LRHS SIgm
	WAbe WPyg WRHF	'Pink Beauty'	WBcn
'Fireball'	See *H.* **'Mrs C.W. Earle'**	'Pink Glow'	WPer
¶ 'Firefly'	SGre	'Pink Perfection'	CMHG CSam
'Firegold'	WAbe	'Praecox'	CMea CTri EHic LBee MBal
'Georgeham'	CLTr CMHG CSam ELan		MPla NSty SMer WHoo WPer
	EMan GAbr LBee LHop		WPyg
	MDHE NCat SMer SRms WEas	'Prostrate Orange'	SRms
	WGor WHCG WHoo WLin		
	WPer		
georgicum	NSla		
globulariifolium	See *Tuberaria globulariifolia*		

'Raspberry Ripple'	CInt CPBP EBrP EBre EGle ELan ENot GAbr GCHN GMac LBre LBuc LFis LHop MPla NEgg NHol NRoo SBre SChu SRms WAbe WHoo WPat WRus WWin
'Red Dragon'	WAbe
'Red Orient'	See H. 'Supreme'
¶ 'Regenbogen'	SWas
§ 'Rhodanthe Carneum' ♀	CMHG CMea EFou ELan ENot GAbr GCHN GDra GTou LBee LGro LHop MBal MWat NHol NMir NRoo NSty SSmi WAbe WEas WHil WHoo WLin WSHC WWin
§ 'Rosa Königin'	EMNN GAbr GBur LBee MDHE MOne NMen NSty SEND WAbe
'Rose of Leeswood' (d)	CInt CMea ELan GAbr GMac LFis LHop MBro MHar NChi NEgg SAga SIgm SIng SMrm SRms WEas WHCG WHoo WKif WPyg WSHC WWin
Rose Queen	See H. 'Rosa Königin'
'Roxburgh Gold'	SRms
'Rushfield's White'	WHCG WRus
'Saint John's College Yellow'	CLTr CMea CSam EBar GAbr SSmi WFar WHCG WPer
'Salmon Queen'	CMHG CPri EMNN ESis GAbr LBee MHar MSCN NPri NRoo SAga SIng WPer WWin
serpyllifolium	See H. nummularium subsp. glabrum
'Shot Silk'	EWes MDHE NRoo
'Silvery Salmon' (v)	WAbe
'Snow Queen'	See H. 'The Bride'
'Southmead'	GAbr
'Sterntaler'	GAbr GDra SIng SRms
'Sudbury Gem'	CPri CTri EBrP EBre ECha GAbr LBre LHop NRoo NSla SBre SMer WPer WPnn
¶ × sulphureum	SDys
'Sulphureum Plenum' (d)	EPfP
'Sunbeam'	CSam EMNN GAbr MDHE NHol NMen NSty SRms
'Sunburst'	GAbr
§ 'Supreme'	CLTr ELan EPfP EWes GAbr LBee LHop MWat SDix SIgm WHCG WPer
'Tangerine'	GAbr
§ 'The Bride' ♀	Widely available
'Tigrinum Plenum' (d)	CPBP ESis EWes LBee MDHE NPro NRoo WWin
'Tomato Red'	ECha NSla SMrm
◆ tomentosum	See H. nummularium
umbellatum	See Halimium umbellatum
'Venustum Plenum' (d)	CInt MBro WEas
'Voltaire'	EMNN GAbr MDHE MOne NHol NPri WRHF WWin
'Watergate Rose'	MWat NBir
'Welsh Flame'	WAbe
'Windermere'	SIgm
'Wisley Pink'	See H. 'Rhodanthe Carneum'
'Wisley Primrose' ♀	Widely available
'Wisley White'	CLon CPri CSam CTri ECha EGoo GAbr LHop MBal MBro NRoo WHCG WHoo WPyg
'Yellow Queen'	See H. 'Golden Queen'

HELIANTHUS † (Asteraceae)

angustifolius	ECGN WCot
atrorubens	CDoC LFis MBel MBri MRav
'Capenoch Star' ♀	EBee ECha EFou GBuc LFis MArl MBel MFir MHlr MLLN MRav NDov SDix SMad WByw WCot WLRN
decapetalus	NFla WCot WWye
– 'Maximus'	SRms
– 'Morning Sun'	CBlo CTri MLLN WCot
– 'Soleil d'Or'	CTri ECtt EHic WCot
– 'Triomphe de Gand'	EMon GBri LGre MRav MTed MWat SAga SSvw WCot WFar WOld
doronicoides	CFee
giganteus 'Sheila's Sunshine'	WCot
grosseserratus	WCot
'Gullick's Variety'	CBre EFou EPfP IBlr LLWP NBro NSti WCot WOld
× kellermanii	EMon MTed SMad
§ × laetiflorus	ECGN ELan EMan EMon MTis NChi NOrc WCot
* – 'Superbus'	IBlr
§ 'Lemon Queen'	Widely available
§ 'Loddon Gold' ♀	CBlo EBrP EBre ECED ECtt EFou ELan EMan EPfP IBlr LBre LFis MHlr MTis NVic SBre WCot WMow WRHF WWye
§ maximilianii	MSte MTed
mollis	EMon
'Monarch' ♀	ECED MFir WCot WOld WOve
nuttallii	EMon MTed
¶ occidentalis	EMon IBlr WPer
orgyalis	See H. salicifolius
quinquenervis	See Helianthella quinquenervis
rigidus	See H. × laetiflorus
§ salicifolius	CRDP CStr EBrP EBre ECED ECGN ECha EGar EMon LBre LFis MBri MLLN MSte NSti SBre SDix SMad SSoC SSpe WCot WOld
scaberrimus	See H. × laetiflorus
strumosus	WCot
tuberosus	GPoy NRog

HELICHRYSUM † (Asteraceae)

acuminatum	See Bracteantha subundulata
alveolatum	See H. splendidum
ambiguum	CHan EFou LHop MPla NNor NOak
angustifolium	See H. italicum
– Cretan form	See H. italicum subsp. microphyllum
arenarium	SSmi
§ arwae	EHyt SBla WAbe
asperum	See Ozothamnus purpurascens
basalticum	NWCA
bellidioides	ECha ECou ELan MBal NGre NMen SMer WCru WOMN WPer
bellum	LHop NHol
bracteatum	See Bracteantha bracteata
chionophilum	NWCA
'Coco'	See Bracteantha 'Coco'
confertum	MHig
coralloides	See Ozothamnus coralloides
◆ 'County Park Silver'	See Ozothamnus 'County Park Silver'
diosmifolium	See Ozothamnus diosmifolius
'Elmstead'	See H. stoechas 'White Barn'
ericifolium	See Ozothamnus purpurascens
ericoides	See Dolichothrix ericoides

fontanesii	LHil SPer WHer	§ *sessilioides*	CLyd EHyt EPot ITim NHar
frigidum	CPBP EPot ITim LBee MHig		NNrd NSla NTow NWCA SBla
	NNrd NTow NWCA SBla	§ *sibthorpii*	CPBP CSev ITim LBee LHil
	WOMN		MDHE NMen NTow SIng
glomeratum	See *H. aggregatum*		WAbe
gmelinii	CHan	*siculum*	See *H. stoechas* subsp. *barrelieri*
heldreichii	CGra EPot NHol SIng SMrm	'Silver Bush'	LHil
– NS 127	NWCA	* 'Skynet'	GCal WCot
hookeri	See *Ozothamnus hookeri*	sp. from Drakensburg	GAbr NHol NWCA
§ *italicum* ♀	CArn CHan ECha ELau GCHN	Mountains, South Africa	
	GPoy LHol MBar MBri	sp. H&W 336	EHyt
	MGra MPla NChi NRoo SMac	sp. JJ&JH 9401733	NWCA
	SPar SRCN SRms WCer WDin	§ *splendidum* ♀	CFee CHan ECha EHoe GAbr
	WEas WHCG WOak WOve		GCHN LFis LHil NBro NNor
	WWat WWye		SDix SPer SRms WBrE WDin
– 'Dartington'	CBod WJek WSel		WHer WPer WWat
§ – subsp. *microphyllum*	CSam ECha ELan ELau ESis	*stoechas*	CArn
	GBar LHol NPri NWoo SIde	§ – subsp. *barrelieri*	CNic WHer
	SIgm WEas WOak WSel WTro	§ – 'White Barn'	EBee ECha WEas WSPU
– 'Nanum'	See *H. italicum* subsp.	Sulphur Light	See *H.* 'Schwefellicht'
	microphyllum	'Sussex Silver'	NPro
§ – subsp. *serotinum*	CChe CTri EGoo EPfP GChr	§ *thianschanicum*	EBee EMan ENot MRav
	GPoy LHop MAsh NFla SPer		NWCA SRms
	SPla SRms SSoC STre WAbe	– Golden Baby	See *H. thianschanicum*
	WPer WSel WWeb		'Goldkind'
lanatum	See *H. thianschanicum*	§ – 'Goldkind'	GAbr LFis NBir NPri
ledifolium	See *Ozothamnus ledifolius*	*thyrsoideum*	See *Ozothamnus thyrsoideus*
lingulatum JJ&JH 9401733	NWCA	*trilineatum*	See *H. splendidum*
lobbii	NGre	aff. – JJ&JH 9401783	NWCA
marginatum	See *H. milfordiae*	*tumidum*	See *Ozothamnus selago* var.
microphyllum	See *Ozothamnus microphyllus*		*tumidus*
Bentham & Hooker		*virgineum*	See *H. sibthorpii*
– Cambessedes	See *H. italicum*	*woodii*	See *H. arwae*
– hort.	See *Plecostachys serpyllifolia*		
§ *milfordiae* ♀	CMHG EPot ITim MBal NGre	**HELICODICEROS** (Araceae)	
	NHar NNrd NSla NWCA SBla	*muscivorus*	CAvo
	SIng SRms WPat		
'Mo's Gold'	See *H. argyrophyllum*	**HELICONIA** (Musaceae)	
orientale	CHan EPot NHol SGre SMer	*bihai*	LChe WMul
pagophilum	CLyd CPBP GCrs ITim	§ 'Bucky'	WMul
¶ – JJ&JH 9401304	NWCA	◆ 'Guyana Red'	See *H.* 'Bucky'
– JJH from Lesotho	EHyt	*psittacorum*	LChe WMul
¶ 'Pale Skynet'	GCal	*rostrata*	LChe
§ *petiolare* ♀	CHad EBak EBar ECtt IHos	¶ – dwarf	WMul
	LBlm LPVe MRav SRms WEas	*stricta* 'Dwarf Jamaican'	LChe WMul
– 'Aureum'	See *H. petiolare* 'Limelight'		
– 'Goring Silver'	CHal LHil MBEx NPri	**HELICTOTRICHON** (Poaceae)	
§ – 'Limelight' ♀	EBar ECtt IHos LBlm MBEx	*pratense*	EHoe EMon EPPr ESOG
	MRav SLod	§ *sempervirens* ♀	Widely available
– 'Roundabout' (v)	LBlm LHil MBEx NPri	¶ – 'Berlin Oxblood'	SApp
– 'Variegatum' ♀	CHal EBar ECtt IHos LBlm	– var. *pendulum*	CSte EMon MUlv SPer SPla
	MRav		WWat
petiolatum	See *H. petiolare*	* *splendens*	SSoC
plicatum	EBar MBEx MWhi		
plumeum	EHyt GCLN ITim MHig	**HELIOPHILA** (Brassicaceae)	
	NWCA	¶ *carnosa*	WCot
populifolium	MBEx WHer		
praecurrens	CPBP EHyt ITim NHol NWCA	**HELIOPSIS** † (Asteraceae)	
purpurascens	See *Ozothamnus purpurascens*	Golden Plume	See *H. helianthoides* var. *scabra*
rosmarinifolium	See *Ozothamnus rosmarinifolius*		'Goldgefieder'
§ 'Schwefellicht'	CSam ECED ECha EFou MBri	*helianthoides*	EMon
	MCLN MRav MWgw NFla	– 'Benzinggold'	MRav SMrm
	NRoo NSti SChu SMer SPer	– 'Hohlspiegel'	ECha EMan WFar WLRN
	SWat WBea WEas WSHC	– 'Limelight'	See *Helianthus* 'Lemon Queen'
	WWal	– var. *scabra*	CBlo EPfP WCot
scorpioides	MAll	– – Golden Plume	See *H. helianthoides* var. *scabra*
selaginoides	See *Ozothamnus selaginoides*		'Goldgefieder'
selago	See *Ozothamnus selago*	§ – – 'Goldgefieder' ♀	EPfP MAus MBel WBea
serotinum	See *H. italicum* subsp.	– – 'Goldgrünherz'	ECED LRHS MBri
	serotinum	– – 'Incomparabilis'	EBee ECED
serpyllifolium	See *Plecostachys serpyllifolia*	– – 'Light of Loddon'	MWat
sessile	See *H. sessilioides*		

¶ – – New hybrids	NLar
§ – – 'Sommersonne'	CM&M EBrP EBre ECGN ECtt EFou GMaP LBre LHop MRav NFai NMir NPer NTow SBre SPer SRCN SRms WHoo WPer WWin
– – Summer Sun	See *H. helianthoides* var. *scabra* **'Sommersonne'**
– – 'Sunburst'	WPyg
– 'Sonnenglut'	LRHS MBri
– 'Spitzentänzerin'	LRHS MBri

HELIOTROPIUM (Boraginaceae)

§ *amplexicaule*	SIgm SSad
anchusifolium	See *H. amplexicaule*
§ *arborescens*	CArn EPfP
'Chatsworth' ♀	CHad CPle CSev EHol ERea LBlm LHil MBEx MSte SAxl SIde SMer SSad SSoC WEas WPen
'Dame Alicia de Hales'	ERea MBEx WEas
'Gatton Park'	ERea MBEx MRav SMrm SSad
'Lord Roberts'	ERea EWoo MBEx
¶ 'Marine'	LIck
'Netherhall White'	ERea
'P.K. Lowther'	ERea MBEx WEas
peruvianum	See *H. arborescens*
'President Garfield'	LHil MBEx
'Princess Marina' ♀	CSev ERea MBEx MSte SSad WEas
'The Speaker'	MBEx
'W.H. Lowther'	LChe
'White Lady'	CSev EHol ERea LBlm LHil MBEx SSad WEas
'White Queen'	LHil

HELIPTERUM (Asteraceae)

albicans	See *Leucochrysum albicans*
anthemoides	See *Rhodanthe anthemoides*

HELLEBORUS † (Ranunculaceae)

§ *argutifolius* ♀	Widely available
– mottled-leaved	See *H. argutifolius* **'Pacific Mist'**
¶ – 'Pacific Frost' (v)	CAvo ECha EMon WHal
¶ – silver-leaved form	CRDP
atrorubens hort.	See *H. orientalis* subsp. ***abchasicus* Early Purple Group Lamarck**
atrorubens Waldst. & Kit.	CLCN ECha WStI
– WM 9216 from Slovenia	MPhe WCru
–WM 9317	MPhe
–WM 9319 from Slovenia	MPhe
¶ – WM 9407	WLin
¶ – WM 9617 from Slovenia	MPhe
x *ballardiae*	LRHS MAsh MBri NRar WAbe
♦ *bocconei* subsp. *bocconei*	See *H. multifidus* subsp. *bocconei*
colchicus	See *H. orientalis* subsp. *abchasicus* **Lamarck**
corsicus	See *H. argutifolius*
¶ *croaticus*	MAsh
– WM 9313	MPhe
– WM 9416	MPhe
cyclophyllus	CFil EBee EPfP GBuc MAsh MPhe NHol SPer WFar WPGP
– JCA 560.625	CLCN
* – WM 9412	WLin
dumetorum	CAvo CFil CLCN MAsh WPGP
– from Hungary WM 9209	MPhe
– from Slovenia WM 9301	MPhe
¶ – WM 13.1	WLin
¶ – WM 13.3	WLin
– WM 9025 from Croatia	MPhe
– WM 9413	WCru
– WM 9627 from Croatia	MPhe
§ x *ericsmithii*	CRDP LRHS MAsh MBri SBla WAbe
foetidus ♀	Widely available
– Bowles' form	CBro EWes
– 'Chedglow'	CNat LHop
* – 'Curio' (v)	CNat
¶ – 'Geddington Mist'	MGed
– 'Green Giant'	MTho WCru
– Italian form	GBin MAsh NHol NTow WRus
– Kurt's Strain	WCot
¶ – 'Miss Jekyll's Scented'	WLin
– 'Ruth'	MPhe
– 'Sopron'	GBin MPhe WCru WLin
– Wester Flisk Group	Widely available
lividus ♀	CAvo CBot CBro CGle CHan CLCN CLon EBrP EBre ELan EWes GCra LBlm LBre MAsh NHar NLar SBla SBre SWas SWat WAbe WCru
– subsp. *corsicus*	See *H. argutifolius*
multifidus	EBee EPfP NBir NHol SPer
§ – subsp. *bocconei*	MAsh NDov WFar WPGP
¶ – – WM 9713 from Italy	MPhe
¶ – – WM 9719 from Italy	MPhe
¶ – – WM 9720 from Italy	MPhe
¶ – subsp. *hercegovinus*	MDun WFar
– – WM 9105	MPhe
– subsp. *istriacus*	CBro MAsh WCot WFar
– – WM 9322	WLin
– – WM 9324	MPhe
¶ – – WM 9421	WLin
– subsp. *multifidus*	MAsh
– – WM 9104	MPhe
– – WM 9529	MPhe
¶ – – WM 9748 from Croatia	MPhe
– WM 9225	WCru
niger ♀	Widely available
¶ – Ashwood strain	MAsh
– Blackthorn Group	SBla
– 'Crûg Hybrid'	WCru
¶ – Farmyard strain	WFar
– Harvington hybrids	COtt LRHS
– 'Louis Cobbett'	EHyt
– subsp. *macranthus* WM 9030	WCru
– 'Madame Fourcade'	MBri
– *major*	See *H. niger* subsp. *macranthus*
– pink strain	NRar
– 'Potter's Wheel'	CPMA CRDP EBrP EBre ECot GBuc LBre NRar SBla SBre SSpi WCru WPyg
– 'Saint Brigid'	NRar
– Sunrise Group WM 9519	CLCN MPhe
– Sunset Group WM 9113	GBuc MPhe NRar SPla
– 'White Magic'	CB&S CBlo CPMA SSON WWeb
x *nigercors* ♀	CHan CRDP LHop MAsh MBri WAbe WCru
– 'Alabaster'	NBir
x *nigristern*	See *H.* x *ericsmithii*
odorus	CFil CLCN EFou MAsh NRoo SBla SSpi
– WM 9103	MPhe
– WM 9202	MPhe WCru
¶ – WM 9310	GBuc
– WM 9415	MPhe
¶ – WM 9728 from Hungary	MPhe
N *orientalis* hort.	Widely available
– 'Agnes Brook'	WFib

– Anderson's Red hybrids	CLCN NHol
– 'Angela Tandy'	WFib
– 'Apricot'	LCTD WFar
– Aquarius	CLCN
– 'Ariel'	LCTD
¶ – Ashwood Garden hybrids	EBee MAsh MUlv
¶ – Ashwood Garden hybrids, anemone-centred	MAsh
¶ – Ashwood Garden hybrids, double	MAsh
– 'Baby Black'	ECot
– Ballard's Group	EBrP EBre ECha LBlm LBre MBri NRar SBre WAbe WCru WFar WRus
– black seedlings	CGle CLCN CRDP GDra NRar WCru
¶ – 'Button'	LCTD
– 'Carlton Hall'	WFib
– 'Cheerful'	LCTD NBir
– 'Citron'	LCTD
¶ – cream	MCCP NHol
– 'Cygnus'	ECha
– 'Dawn'	LCTD
¶ – deep red	ERav
¶ – 'Dick Crandon'	WPnz
– Draco strain	CLCN
– 'Dusk'	LCTD
§ – Early Purple Group	CLCN CTri MAsh NBee NFla NRoo SPer WCru
– 'Elizabeth Coburn'	WFib
– 'Eric's Best'	ECha
– 'Fred Whitsey'	WFib
– 'Gertrude Raithby'	WFib
– 'Gladys Burrow'	WFib
– green spotted	CRDP EBrP EBre LBre SBre WFar
– 'Greencups'	LCTD WFar
– subsp. *guttatus* hort.	CAvo CLCN EBrP EBre LBlm LBre SBla SBre WAbe WCot WCru
– – cream	ECha
– – pink	NHol WCru
¶ – 'Hades' seedling	NHol WCru
– Hadspen hybrids	CHad
¶ – 'Harvington Pink'	LRHS
¶ – 'Harvington Red'	LRHS
¶ – 'Harvington Speckled'	LRHS
¶ – 'Harvington White'	LRHS
¶ – 'Harvington Yellow'	LRHS
– 'Helen Ballard'	LCTD
– 'Ian Raithby'	WFib
– 'Ingot'	LCTD
– ivory	CLCN CRDP
– 'Joan Bridges'	LCTD
– 'John Raithby'	WFib
– Kochii Group	CAvo ECha NBrk NRar WCru
– 'Lady Charlotte Bonham-Carter'	WFib
– 'Leo'	MTed
– 'Limelight'	ECha
– 'Little Black'	ECho
– maroon	CRDP EBrP EBre ERav LBre MTis NRar SBre
– 'Mary Petit'	WFib
– 'Maureen Key'	WFib
– Midnight Sky Group	WPyg WWat
¶ – nearly black	ERav
– 'Orion'	LCTD
– 'Pebworth White'	WFib
– 'Philip Ballard'	LCTD
– 'Philip Wilson'.	LCTD
– 'Picotee'	CRDP
– pink	CLCN CPMA CRDP EBee ERav LFis MBro MCCP NRar WAbe WCru WFar
– pink spotted	CRDP EBrP EBre LBre NDov NRar SBre WFar
¶ – plum	WFar
– 'Plum Stippled'	ECha
– primrose	CRDP EBrP EBre LBre NRar SBre SPer WAbe WFar
¶ – Primrose Spotted Strain	WFar
– purple	CLCN CPMA CRDP ECha MBro NRar SApp WAbe WCru
– 'Queen of the Night'	CRDP
¶ – 'Rosa' hort.	LCTD
– 'Rubens' hort.	LCTD
¶ – 'Shades of Night'	LRHS
¶ – Slaty Blue Strain	CRDP EBrP EBre LBre SBre WCot WFar
¶ – smokey purple	WFar
– 'Sunny'	LCTD
– 'Sylvia'	LCTD
¶ – 'Tommie'	LCTD
– 'Trotter's Spotted'	GDra
– 'Ushba'	EBee LCTD
– 'Ushba' seedlings	GCal
– 'Victoria Raithby'	WFib
– white	CGle CRDP EBrP EBre ECha ERav LBre MBal MBro NRar SBre WCru WFar
– white spotted	CRDP EBrP EBre LBre NDov SBre WFar
¶ – white veined	WFar
¶ – yellow	ERav
– Zodiac Group	CLCN EOrc GBuc
orientalis Lamarck	MBro MPhe
¶ – IBT 9401-7	WLin
– JCA 562.402	CLCN
§ – subsp. *abchasicus*	CDec GCra WCru
– subsp. *guttatus*	SSpi
– *olympicus*	See *H. orientalis* subsp. *orientalis* Lamarck
§ – subsp. *orientalis*	WPyg WWat
purpurascens	CAvo CRos EBar MAsh NBir NHol NRoo SBla SPer SWas WFar WPyg
– Hungary WM 9211	MPhe
¶ – WM 18/1	WLin
¶ – WM 18/3	WLin
– WM 9303	MPhe
– WM 9412	MPhe
¶ – WM 9644	GBuc
× *sternii*	Widely available
¶ – Ashwood strain	MAsh
– Blackthorn Group ♀	CDec CFil CPMA CRos EBrP EBre GBuc LBre MBri MBro NRoo SBla SBre SPer SPla SSpi WAbe WByw WCru WHoo WPGP WWat
¶ – Blackthorn dwarf strain	CLCN
– Boughton Group	LBlm MAsh
– 'Boughton Beauty'	CAvo CMGP CMea ECha ELan GBuc MTho WByw WCot
¶ – Bulmer's Blush Strain	MAsh
– Cally Strain	GCal
¶ – dwarf strain	WFar
– Pewter Strain	WHal
¶ *thibetanus*	EFEx GBuc LAma MPhe WCru WViv
torquatus	CAvo CBro CFil CLCN MTho NHol WMer
¶ – 'Dido' (d)	WFar
¶ – double-flowered hybrids (d)	SAxl

– hybrids	ECGP SBla WCru
¶ – Montenegran Doubles (d)	WFar
– Party Dress Group (d)	CRDP SBla
¶ – semi-double (d)	CRDP
– WM 9106 from Montenegro	GBuc MPhe
¶ – WM 9743 from Bosnia	MPhe
¶ – WM 9745 from Bosnia	MPhe
– Wolverton hybrids	SBla WFar
¶ *vesicarius*	MPhe
viridis	EBrP EBre ECha EPfP LBre
	MSal SBre SRms WAbe WCru
	WTin WUnd
– subsp. *occidentalis*	CAvo CBro MAsh
– – WM 9401	MPhe
¶ – – WM 9502 from Germany	MPhe
¶ – subsp. *viridis*	MAsh
¶ – – WM 9723 from Italy	MPhe

HELONIOPSIS (Melanthiaceae)

acutifolia B&SWJ 218	WCru
japonica	See *H. orientalis*
§ *orientalis*	CBro CPou EPot WCru
* – var. *albiflora*	WCru
¶ – B&SWJ 956 from Korea	WCru
§ – var. *breviscapa*	CFil WCru WPGP WThi
§ – var. *kawanoi*	SWas WCru
– var. *yakusimensis*	See *H. orientalis* var. *kawanoi*
¶ *umbellata* B&SWJ 1839	WCru

HELWINGIA (Helwingiaceae)

chinensis	CPle
japonica	CBot CPle EFEx WWat

HELXINE See SOLEIROLIA

HEMEROCALLIS † (Hemerocallidaceae)

¶ 'Absolute Zero'	SDay
¶ 'Adah'	SDay
'Addie Branch Smith'	EGol SDay
'Adoration'	SPer
'Aglow'	NCut
'Alan'	EBrP EBre ENot LBre SBre
	SCro WFar
'Albany'	SApp
'Alec Allen'	SDay SRos
¶ 'Alpine Mist'	SDay
altissima	EMon
'Amazon'	LRHS
¶ 'Amazon Amethyst'	MAus
'Ambassador'	CKel
'Amber Star'	LPBA
'Amen'	WGle
'American Revolution'	LBuc WCot WRus
'Amersham'	EBee ECGP GSki MNFA SAxl
	SMrm WLRN
'Angel Curls'	EGol
'Angel's Delight'	WGle
'Anne Welch'	EPla
¶ 'Annie Go Lightly'	SDay
'Anzac'	EBrP EBre ECha ECro ECtt
	EPla ERou GAri LBre MBri
	NHol NMGW NWes SBre
	WCot WFar WSan
'Apricot Beauty'	CBlo EBee LBuc NPri
'Apricot Surprise'	WGle
'Apricotta'	CKel WCot
'Arctic Snow'	SRos
'Arriba'	NBro WCot WFox WLRN
¶ 'Arthur Moore'	SDay
'Artistic Gold'	EGol
'Artist's Brush'	LBuc
'Atalanta Bouquet'	SRos

'Aten'	CBlo MNFA
'Attention Please'	WGle
'Aurora Raspberry'	WGle
'Autumn Red'	CBlo ERou NBir NCat NFai
	NHaw NOak NWes
'Ava Michelle'	SDay
'Baby Betsy'	SDay
'Baby Darling'	SDay
'Baby Julia'	WGle
* 'Bailey Hay'	EBar LRHS
'Bald Eagle'	EFou MSCN NWes WMer
'Ballerina Girl'	SRos
'Ballet Dancer'	ERou
'Baroni'	ECha
'Beauty Bright'	MAus
'Beauty to Behold'	SRos
'Bed of Roses'	MNFA
'Beijing'	SDay
'Bejewelled'	CBlo EBee EGol
'Beloved Country'	EHal
¶ 'Benchmark'	SRos
'Berlin Red' ♀	ECGN EMar LBuc LRHS
	MNFA SChu
'Berliner Premiere'	MNFA
'Bernard Thompson'	SApp
'Bertie Ferris'	EBee LBuc SDay
'Bess Ross'	MAus
'Bess Vestale'	ENot ERou MWat NHol
'Bette Davis Eyes'	SRos
'Betty Woods' (d)	CRDP SRos
'Bibury'	SCro
'Big World'	LRHS MNFA
'Bitsy'	EGol MSte SDay WRHF
'Black Knight'	SRms
'Black Magic'	CBlo CBro CHad CMGP CSev
	ECED EGol ELan EMan EPla
	ERou GMaP MAus MBro
	MNFA MRav NHol NWes
	SChu SDay SMad SPer WHer
¶ 'Black Prince'	EWll SPer
'Blonde Is Beautiful'	SRos
¶ 'Blue Sheen'	CFir EBee EFou MSCN NWes
	WWeb
'Blushing Belle'	CMil EBee EMar LRHS MNFA
	SAxl WWin
'Bold Courtier'	CKel
'Bold One'	SRos
'Bonanza'	CBro CHea CKel CM&M
	CMGP CTri EBar EBrP EBre
	ECha ECtt EHon ELan EPla
	ERou LBlm LBre LPBA LRot
	MBri MRav NBro NFai SBre
	SHBN SPer WFox WPer WWin
¶ 'Booger'	SRos
'Border Honey'	WGle
'Bourbon Kings'	EBee EGar EGol ERou MBel
	SDay
'Bowl of Roses'	WGle
'Bright Spangles'	SApp SDay SRos
¶ 'Brilliant Circle'	EFou
'Brocaded Gown'	SDay SRos
'Brunette'	SApp
¶ 'Bubbly'	SDay
'Buffy's Doll'	SDay SRos
'Bugs Ears'	SDay
'Bumble Bee'	SDay
'Buried Treasure'	LRHS MNFA
'Burning Daylight' ♀	CMGP CMil EBee EBrP EBre
	EGar EPla ERou GSki LBre
	LHop MBel MHlr MNFA
	MNrw NHol NVic SBre SMrm
	SPer SRms WOld WViv

¶ 'Buttercurls' MNFA
¶ 'Butterfly Ballet' SDay
'Buzz Bomb' CRDP EBrP EBre GSki LBre
MAus MNFA SBre SPer SRos
WLRN WWal
'California Sunshine' SRos
'Camden Gold Dollar' SDay
'Canary Glow' CTri EBrP EBre ECro ERav
LBre NWes SAsh SBre SRos
SSpe WWat
'Caramea' EAst EBee NFai WWal
¶ 'Carolpiecrust' SApp
'Cartwheels' ♀ EBrP EBre ECha EPfP EPla
LBre MAus MBel MCli MMil
MNFA NFai SBre SPer SUsu
'Casino Gold' SRos
'Catherine Woodbery' CHea COtt CSev EAst EBrP
EBre ECro ECtt EFou EGol
ELan EMar EPla ERav GMac
LBre MAus MNFA MRav NFla
NHol NRoo SAga SApp SBre
SPer SSpe WCot WPyg
'Cedar Waxwing' CBlo EBee EGol WMer
'Chantilly Lace' CMHG
'Charles Johnston' SRos
¶ 'Charlie Brown' SDay
'Charlie Pierce Memorial' MBel SRos
'Chartreuse Magic' ECro EGol NHol SChu SPer
'Cherry Cheeks' EBar EBrP EBre ECro EGol
ELan EPfP EPla ERav ERou
LBre MAus MBri MRav SAxl
SBre SRos WCot WMow
'Cherry Kiss' SRos
'Chic Bonnet' SPer
'Chicago Apache' LRHS MBel MBri MUlv SRos
'Chicago Arnie's Choice' WGle
'Chicago Cattleya' CFir EGol MRav NWes
'Chicago Coral' WGle
'Chicago Fire' EGol
'Chicago Heirloom' COtt EGol MAus
¶ 'Chicago Jewel' CFir EBee NWes SCro
'Chicago Knobby' WGle
'Chicago Petite Lace' WGle
'Chicago Petticoats' EGol SApp SDay WGle
'Chicago Picotee WGle
Memories'
'Chicago Picotee Pride' WGle
'Chicago Picotee Queen' EBrP EBre LBre LRHS MBri
MNFA MUlv SBre WGle
'Chicago Plum Pudding' WGle
'Chicago Princess' WGle
¶ 'Chicago Royal' SDay
'Chicago Royal Crown' MBri SApp
'Chicago Royal Robe' EBar EBrP EBre EFou EGol
LBre MBel MRav MSte MUlv
NCat SBre SCro SDay WCot
WWin
'Chicago Silver' COtt MAus
'Chicago Sunrise' CHad EBar EGol ENot EPla
IBlr MNFA MSta NHaw NHol
NOrc NWes SApp SRos WMer
WPer
¶ 'Chicago Violet' MAus
'Chief Sarcoxie' ♀ MAus
'Children's Festival' CHad CMGP CSev EBar EBrP
EBre ECtt EGol EMar EMil
GMaP GSki LBre MBel MGed
MRav NHol SBre SCro SRos
SSpe WFar WPer WRus
'Childcraft' CLTr
'Chinese Autumn' SApp SRos
'Chinese Coral' CKel WBcn

'Chloe's Child' SCro
'Choral Angel' WGle
'Chorus Line' MBel SRos
¶ 'Chosen Love' SApp
'Christmas Is' EBar EFou
'Cinnamon Glow' WGle
citrina CAvo ECED ELan EMon NPla
SEas SPla
'Civil Rights' SRos
'Classic Simplicity' LRHS MAus
'Classy Lassie' WGle
'Colonial Dame' CKel
¶ 'Colour Me Mellow' SApp
'Coming up Roses' SDay SRos
'Contessa' CBro ECro ELan SCro
¶ 'Cookie Monster' SApp
'Cool Jazz' SRos
'Coral Mist' EFou
'Corky' ♀ CHad EBrP EBre ECGP ECha
EMar GCal GMaP GMac LBre
MAus MBel MNFA SApp SBre
SChu SDay SDix SPer SRos
SSpi
'Cosmic Hummingbird' SDay
'Countess Zora' CMHG
¶ 'Country Club' CBlo EBee EFou WWeb
'Court Magician' SRos
'Cranberry Baby' SDay SRos
'Cream Cloud' WGle
'Cream Drop' EBrP EBre ECtt EGol EMar
GMaP LBlm LBre LGan MBel
MRPP MRav MWat NHol NOrc
NPla NSti NWes SBre SChu
SPer SSpe WHow WMer WRus
'Crimson Icon' MSte SDay
'Crimson Pirate' EMil ERou LRot NHol WRHF
'Croesus' NHol SCro SRms
'Croftway' SCro
'Cupid's Bow' EGol
'Cupid's Gold' SDay SRos
'Dad's Best White' EGol SCro
'Daily Bread' SDay
'Daily Dollar' LRHS MBri
'Dainty Pink' EGol
'Dance Ballerina Dance' MAus SDay SRos
¶ 'Dancing Dwarf' SApp
'Dawn Play' CKel
'Decatur Imp' EGol
'Decatur Piecrust' MBel
'Demetrius' MNFA
¶ 'Designer Gown' SDay
'Devon Cream' SChu
'Devonshire' SRos
'Diamond Dust' LRHS MTed NCat SChu SPer
WLRN
'Dido' CTri ERou GBuc MSte
'Display' CKel
'Dominic' SRos
'Dorethe Louise' CRDP SDay SRos
'Dorothy McDade' EGol
¶ 'Double Coffee' (d) SDay
'Double Cutie' (d) EFou SApp
¶ 'Double Firecracker' (d) NLar
'Double Gardenia' (d) WGle
'Double Honey' (d) WGle
'Double Oh' (d) WGle
'Double Oh Seven' (d) SDay
'Double Pleasure' (d) MBel
'Double Pompom' (d) MAus WGle
'Double River Wye' CBlo CFir EGol LBuc MAus
SHBN WWat
'Dresden Doll' SPer

§ 'Dubloon' — CKel CMGP ERou GAbr GBuc NHol

dumortieri — CAvo CBot CBro CDec CHea EBrP EBre ECGN ECha ECro EFou EGol ELan EMar EMon EOrc LBre MWat NBir NHaw NHol NSti NVic SBre SPer SSpe WWin

'Dutch Beauty' — EBrP EBre LBre SBre
'Dutch Gold' — NBro
'Ed Murray' — MAus SRos
'Edelweiss' — SDay
'Edna Spalding' — EBrP EBre LBre SBre SRos
'Eenie Allegro' — CBro EFou NWes SPer SPla
'Eenie Fanfare' — CSpe EFou LRHS MBri NWes
¶ 'Eenie Gold' — LRHS
'Eenie Weenie' — CBro CFee CKel EBrP EBre ECtt EGol EMil LBre MBel MBri NHol SApp SBre SDay WMer WPer WRus
'Eenie Weenie Non-stop' — ECha SAxl SWas WHal
'Elaine Strutt' — SApp SDay WCot
'Elegant Greeting' — EBee LBuc
¶ 'Emerald Dew' — SDay
'Esther Walker' — CKel WBcn
'Evelyn Claar' — CKel SCro
'Evening Gown' — WGle
'Fairy Charm' — WGle
'Fairy Tale Pink' — MBel SApp SRos
'Faith Nabor' — SRos
'Fan Dancer' — EGol
'Fandango' — SPer
'Fashion Model' — CKel SApp WPer
'Felicity' — CKel
'Femme Osage' — SRos
'Fire Dance' — SCro
'First Formal' — SPer
'Flames of Fantasy' — CKel NCut SRos
'Flaming Sword' — GBuc NHol
flava — See *H. lilioasphodelus*
'Florissant Charm' — WGle
¶ 'Floyd Cove' — SDay
forrestii 'Perry's Variety' — EMon
'Fragrant Pastel Cheer' — WGle
'Frances Fay' — SRos
'Francis Russell' — CKel
'Frans Hals' — EBrP EBre ECGN EFou EMar EPla ERou LBre LLWP LSpr MBri MBro MNFA MNrw MRav NFai SBre SPer SPla SRos WHoo WPer WPyg
¶ 'Frosted Encore' — SDay
fulva — CRow ECED ECro IBlr MHar NLon SHBN SRms WWin
N– 'Flore Pleno' (d) — CAvo CFee CHan CKel CRow ECGN EFou EGol EHon ELan EMon EPla IBlr LFis LHop MAus MFir NBro NFai NSti SAxl SHBN SPer SSvw SWat WEas WFox WWin
N– 'Green Kwanso' (d) — CHar CRow CSWP EMon IBlr MMHG NTow SPla WRha
§ – 'Kwanzo Variegata' — CBot CGle CRow ELan EMon IBlr LHop MTho WBcn WCot WFar WSan
¶ 'Gala Gown' — SApp
'Garnet Garland' — CKel
'Gay Nineties' — CKel
'Gay Rapture' — SPer
'Gay Troubadour' — CKel
'Gemini' — SRos
'Gentle Country Breeze' — SRos

'Gentle Shepherd' — CBro CKel CMil CSpe EAst EBar EBrP EBre EFou EGol EMar EMil LBre LFis MAus MBro MNFA MUlv NCut NHaw NSti NWes SApp SBre SHBN SRos WRus WWat
'George Cunningham' — CMGP CSev ECro ECtt EGol ELan EPla ERou MAus MBri MCli MRav SChu
'Georgette Belden' — WGle
'Giant Moon' — EBrP EBre ECro EGol ELan EPla EPri ERou LBre MBri MUlv SBre SChu SDay WRus
'Gingerbread Man' — CRDP
'Gold Crest' — LRHS MNFA
'Gold Imperial' — EWll NFla
'Golden Bell' — EGar LWak NHol
'Golden Chimes' ♀ — Widely available
'Golden Ginko' — LRHS MBri MNFA
'Golden Orchid' — See *H. 'Dubloon'*
'Golden Peace' — SRos
'Golden Prize' — EBrP EBre EFou EPla LBre MBri SBre SRos
'Golden Scroll' — SRos
¶ 'Grand Palais' — SDay
'Grape Magic' — EGol
¶ 'Grape Velvet' — CBlo CSpe MNFA MSCN NWes WMer
'Green Chartreuse' — ECha
'Green Drop' — WFar WMow
¶ 'Green Eyed Giant' — MNFA
'Green Flutter' ♀ — CSev NBir SAsh SRos WCot
'Green Glitter' — LRHS
'Green Gold' — CMHG LRHS MNFA
'Grumbly' — EBee ELan
'Guardian Angel' — WGle
'Halo Light' — CKel
'Happy Returns' — ECha EGol SRos
¶ 'Harvest Hue' — SDay
'Hawaian Punch' — EGol
'Hazel Monette' — EGol WGle
'Heavenly Treasure' — SRos WGle
'Heaven's Trophy' — WGle
'Heirloom Lace' — MAus MUlv WFar
¶ 'Hemlock' — SApp
'Her Majesty' — CKel
'Hercules' — NFla
¶ 'Hermitage Newton' — SDay
'Heron' — WGle
'Hey There' — SRos
'High Tor' — GCal GQui
'Holiday Mood' — ELan ERou NWes
'Honey Redhead' — CKel
'Hope Diamond' — CRDP
'Hornby Castle' — CBro NHol NVic WPer
¶ 'Hortensia' — CBlo
'Hot Ticket' — SRos
'Humdinger' — SRos
'Hyperion' — CSev EBrP EBre ECED ECGP ECha ECtt EGol EMan GAri LBre MAus MNFA MRav NHol SApp SBre SChu SHBN SPer WOld
'Ice Cap' — MCli
'Ice Carnival' — EBar LRHS
¶ 'Ice Castles' — SApp SDay
'Icy Lemon' — SRos
'Imperator' — CBen EPla LPBA MWgw NHol
'Imperial Blush' — CKel
'Inspired Word' — SRos
'Invictus' — SRos
¶ 'Iridescent Jewel' — SDay

'Irish Elf'	LRot SApp
¶ 'Iron Gate Iceberg'	SApp
'Jade Bowl'	WGle
¶ 'Jake Russell'	MNFA
'James Marsh'	MAus SRos
¶ 'Janice Brown'	SRos
'Jedi Dot Pearce'	SRos
'Jenny Wren'	GSki LRHS MNFA SAxl
'Jo Jo'	WWin
'Joan Senior'	EBee EGol LBlm MAus MBel
	NWes SApp SDay SRos WCot
	WRus
'John Bierman'	SRos
'Joylene Nichole'	SRos
'Judah'	SDay SRos
'Kate Carpenter'	SDay SRos
'Katie'	NPri
'Katie Elizabeth Miller'	SRos
¶ 'Kazuq'	SApp
¶ 'Kecia'	SApp
'Kindly Light'	SRos
¶ 'King Haiglar'	SApp
N 'Kwanso Flore Pleno'	See *H. fulva* 'Green Kwanso'
N 'Kwanso Flore Pleno	See *H. fulva* 'Kwanzo Variegata'
Variegata'	
'La Mer'	EFou
¶ 'La Peche'	SDay
'Lady Cynthia'	CKel
¶ 'Lady Mischief'	SApp
¶ 'Lady Neva'	SApp
'Lady of Leisure'	MBel
'Ladykin'	SDay
'Lark Song'	CKel EBrP EBre EGol LBre
	SBre WBcn
'Late Cream'	WGle
'Lavender Aristocrat'	WGle
'Lavender Bonanza'	MAus NWes
'Lemon Bells' ♀	EMan EMar EPfP EPla EWll
	GSki MAus MNFA NCat SChu
'Lemon Mint'	EGol
'Lenox'	SRos
'Lilac Wine'	ECha EPla WMer
§ *lilioasphodelus* ♀	Widely available
'Lillian Frye'	EGol
'Linda'	CBlo CMGP ERou EWll
	MNFA MRav NHol
'Lion Cub'	WGle
¶ 'Little Audrey'	NWes
'Little Bee'	EFou
'Little Beige Magic'	EGol
'Little Bumble Bee'	EGol NWes
'Little Business'	SApp SDay
'Little Cameo'	EGol
¶ 'Little Carnation'	SCro
'Little Cranberry Cove'	EGol
'Little Dandy'	EGol
'Little Dart'	ECha
'Little Deeke'	SRos
¶ 'Little Dream Red'	SDay
'Little Fantastic'	EGol
'Little Fat Dazzler'	SDay
'Little Grapette'	CHad EGol MAus MNFA
	SApp SCro SRos
'Little Gypsy Vagabond'	SDay SRos
'Little Lavender Princess'	EGol
'Little Maggie'	MSte SDay
¶ 'Little Men'	CBlo WMer
'Little Missy'	EFou
'Little Prince'	SDay
'Little Pumpkin Face'	EGol
'Little Rainbow'	EGol MNFA
'Little Red Hen'	LRHS MNFA SDay

¶ 'Little Tawny'	MAus
'Little Violet Lace'	GSki SDay
'Little Wart'	EGol
'Little Wine Cup'	CHad CLTr EAst EBrP EBre
	ECGN ECtt EGol EMar GMaP
	LBre LFis LHop MBel MBro
	NHaw NHol NOrc NPla SApp
	SBre SPer SPla SRms SSvw
	WHoo WPer WRus WTin
	WWal
'Little Woman'	SDay
'Little Zinger'	SDay
¶ 'Littlest Angel'	SDay
'Lochinvar'	EBee ENot
longituba B&SWJ 625	GCra
'Lotus Land'	CKel
'Lullaby Baby'	EGol SDay SRos
luna	LWak NOak WFox
'Lupine'	WGle
¶ 'Lusty Leland'	CBlo NWes SCro
x *luteola*	SDay
'Luxury Lace'	CDec CMGP EAst EBrP EBre
	EFou EGol ELan EOrc LBre
	MAus MBel MNFA MOne
	MUlv NBir NHaw NMGW
	NWes SBre SPer SRos WFox
	WWhi
'Lynn Hall'	EGol
'Mabel Fuller'	SCro SPer
'Malaysian Monarch'	MBel
'Mallard'	EBrP EBre ECro ECtt EGol
	LBre MBri MRav SBre SRos
	WBcn WCot WGle WMer WPer
'Manchurian Apricot'	SRos
'Marion Moss'	CKel
'Marion Vaughn' ♀	CM&M CMil CSev EBrP EBre
	ECGP ECot EFou EGol ELan
	EMan GSki LBre MAus MMil
	MNFA MWat NRoo NSti NWes
	SBre SDix SSpi WCot WPbr
'Mariska'	SRos
'Mary Todd'	EGol MAus MNFA
'Mary's Gold'	SRos
'Matt'	SRos
'Mavoureen Nesmith'	SCro
'May Colven'	EBrP EBre EGol LBre SBre
'Meadow Gold'	CKel
'Meadow Mist'	EGol
'Meadow Sprite'	SRos
¶ 'Mega Stella'	SApp
'Melody Lane'	EGol
'Meno'	EGol
¶ 'Mexican Way'	NWes
'Michele Coe'	EMan LBuc LRHS MAus
	MNFA SChu WLRN
middendorffii	CAvo EPPr GCal MCli
– var. *esculenta*	EMon
¶ – 'Major'	CFee
'Mikado'	MWgw
'Millie Schlumpf'	SApp SRos
'Ming Lo'	SDay
'Ming Porcelain'	SRos
'Ming Snow'	WGle
'Mini Pearl'	EGol SDay SRos WPer
'Mini Stella'	CBro EMil EPla LRHS MBri
	SDay
Miniature hybrids	SRms WPer
minor	CBro EBrP EBre EGol GCal
	LBre SBre SPla SRms
'Missenden' ♀	MNFA NHaw
'Mission Moonlight'	COtt
'Missouri Beauty'	CRos EBar

'Monica Marie'	SRos
'Moonlight Mist'	SDay SRos
¶ 'Morning Dawn'	CBlo EFou WMer
'Morocco Red'	CBro CTri ELan GSki WWat
'Mountain Laurel'	LRHS MBri MUlv
'Mrs David Hall'	CKel SCro SMrm
'Mrs Hugh Johnson'	CHad CMGP CSev ECGN
	ECot EHon EOld LGan LWak
	NHol SHBN
'Mrs John J. Tigert'	ERou
'Mrs Lester'	CKel SDay
multiflora	NHol
'My Belle'	SApp SDay
'My Hope'	WCot WGle
'Naomi Ruth'	EGol
'Nashville'	CBro EBrP EBre ELan ERou
	IBlr LBre SBre
'Neal Berrey'	SRos
'Neyron Rose' ♀	CHea EGar EGol ERou GSki
	MAus MNFA SAxl SChu
¶ 'Night Beacon'	EFou
'Night Raider'	SRos
'Nigrette'	CBen LPBA MWat NHol
'Nob Hill'	CLTr ECGP EGol MNFA
	SApp SRos
'North Star'	GCal
'Norton Beauté'	MBel
'Numinous Moments'	WGle
¶ 'Ocean Rain'	SDay
¶ 'Ochroleuca'	SSpi
'Olive Bailey Langdon'	EGol SRos
'Oom-pa-pa'	ECha
'Optic Elegance'	SAsh
'Orangeman' hort.	CDoC GSki
'Orchid Beauty'	ECha
'Orford'	WWin
'Oriental Ruby'	SDay
'Paige Parker'	EGol
'Painted Lady'	CKel
'Painted Trillium'	WGle
'Pandora's Box'	EFou EGol
'Paper Butterfly'	SDay SRos
¶ 'Paradise Pink'	EFou
'Paradise Prince'	EGol
'Pardon Me'	CMHG EGol LRHS SRos
'Parian China'	WGle
'Pastel Ballerina'	SRos
'Pastel Classic'	SRos
¶ 'Patchwork Puzzle'	SRos
¶ 'Patricia Fay'	SApp
'Penelope Vestey'	LRHS MNFA SDay SRos
'Penny's Worth'	EGol EMil MBri SApp
'Persian Princess'	CKel WBcn
'Persian Shrine'	EGol
¶ 'Petite Ballerina'	SDay
'Phoebe'	WGle
'Piccadilly Princess'	MBel SRos
'Pink Charm'	CHan CM&M CMGP EMan
	ENot LPBA MAus MBal
	MNFA MWat NHol NOrc SChu
	SEas SHBN WMow WViv
'Pink Damask' ♀	Widely available
'Pink Dream'	EGar GChr LRHS MNFA
	NHol
'Pink Heaven'	EGol
'Pink Interlude'	CKel
'Pink Lady'	ERou MNrw MRav SHBN
	SRms
'Pink Lavender Appeal'	EGol
'Pink Opal'	CKel
'Pink Prelude'	CBlo EBee ENot EWll LRHS
	SChu

'Pink Salute'	SRos
'Pink Sundae'	ECha
'Pink Super Spider'	SRos
'Piquante'	EBee
'Pixie Pipestone'	SApp
'Pojo'	SDay
'Pompeian Purple'	EGol WGle
'Poneytail Pink'	EGol
'Pony'	EGol WGle
'Pookie Bear'	SApp
'Potter's Clay'	WGle
'Prairie Bells'	CSWP EHal MAus MBro NFai
	NPla WHoo WLRN
'Prairie Blue Eyes'	EGol MNFA NWes SApp SCro
	WBcn
¶ 'Prairie Sunset'	MAus
'Pretty Mist'	WGle
'Pretty Peggy'	MNFA
'Prima Donna'	CKel SCro
'Primrose Mascotte'	NBir WWin
'Prize Picotee Deluxe'	WGle
'Prize Picotee Elite'	WGle
¶ 'Protocol'	SDay
'Puddin'	See *H.* **'Brass Buckles'**
'Pumpkin Kid'	SRos
'Puppet Show'	SDay
'Purple Rain'	EFou
'Purple Waters'	EMar EPfP EWll SDay
'Pursuit of Excellence'	SRos
'Pyewacket'	SDay
'Queen of May'	WCot
'Quick Results'	SDay SRos
'Quietness'	SRos
¶ 'Quinn Buck'	SDay
'Raindrop'	EGol
'Rajah'	EGra LWak MBel MGed NBro
	NBus NPla WFox WRHF
'Raspberry Wine'	ECha
'Real Wind'	SApp SDay
'Red Precious' ♀	EGol LRHS MBel MNFA SAsh
'Red Rum'	EFou EWll LBuc MCli
'Red Torch'	CKel
¶ 'Roger Grounds'	SApp
'Romany'	LPBA
'Root Beer'	MAus WGle
'Rose Emily'	SRos
'Rose Festival'	WGle
¶ 'Royal Charm'	SRos
'Royal Corduroy'	MBel
¶ 'Royal Crown'	MBri
'Royal Palace Prince'	WGle
'Royal Prestige'	SApp
'Royal Robe'	EFou EGar
'Royalty'	CKel
'Ruffled Apricot'	LRHS SDay SRos
'Russell Prichard'	ERou
¶ 'Rutilans'	CFee
¶ 'Sabie'	SApp
¶ 'Sabra Salina'	SRos
'Salmon Sheen'	CKel
'Sammy Russell'	CHan CMGP EAst EBar
	ECGN ECro EFou EGol EMar
	EOrc EPla ERic GBuc GMac
	LHop MBal MBro MCli MNFA
	MWat NBro NFai NHol NSti
	SBod SEas SRms WFox WPer
	WWhi
'Sandra Walker'	EGol
'Satin Clouds'	EGol WGle
'Satin Glow'	ECha
'Satin Silk'	EBrP EBre LBre SBre
'Scarlet Flame'	ECha

* 'Scarlet Oak'	MBri SApp
'Scarlet Orbit'	SDay SRos
'Scarlet Romance'	WGle
'Scarlet Royalty'	WGle
'Scarlet Tanager'	LRHS
'Schoolgirl'	EBrP EBre LBre SBre
'Screech Owl'	LRHS
'Searcy Marsh'	EGol
'Sebastian'	SRos
'Serena Sunburst'	MBel SRos
'Shaman'	SRos
'Shooting Star'	EGol SPla
¶ 'Show Amber'	SApp
'Silent Stars'	WGle
'Silken Fairy'	EGol SDay
'Siloam Angel Blush'	SDay
'Siloam Baby Talk'	CRDP EFou EGol NBir SRos
	WGle
¶ 'Siloam Bertie Ferris'	EFou
'Siloam Bo Peep'	CRDP EGol SDay
'Siloam Brian Henke'	SRos
'Siloam Button Box'	EGol
'Siloam Byelo'	EGol SDay
'Siloam Cinderella'	EGol SDay SRos
'Siloam David Kirchhoff'	SRos
'Siloam Doodlebug'	EGol WGle
'Siloam Double Classic'	MBel SRos
(d)	
'Siloam Edith Scholar'	EGol WGle
'Siloam Ethel Smith'	EGol SDay
'Siloam Fairy Tale'	CRDP EGol SDay
¶ 'Siloam Gold Coin'	SDay
'Siloam Grace Stamile'	SRos
'Siloam Gumdrop'	WGle
'Siloam Joan Senior'	EGol
'Siloam June Bug'	EGol NWes WCot
'Siloam Kewpie Doll'	EGol WGle
'Siloam Little Girl'	EGol SDay SRos WGle
'Siloam Merle Kent'	SRos
'Siloam Orchid Jewel'	EGol SDay
'Siloam Pee Wee'	EGol
'Siloam Pink Glow'	EGol WGle
'Siloam Pink Petite'	EGol
'Siloam Plum Tree'	EGol
'Siloam Pocket Size'	EGol
'Siloam Prissy'	EGol
'Siloam Purple Plum'	EGol
'Siloam Red Ruby'	EGol
'Siloam Red Toy'	EGol
'Siloam Red Velvet'	EGol
'Siloam Ribbon Candy'	EGol
'Siloam Rose Dawn'	SDay SRos
¶ 'Siloam Royal Prince'	SCro
'Siloam Shocker'	EGol
'Siloam Show Girl'	EGol
'Siloam Sugar Time'	EGol
'Siloam Tee Tiny'	EGol
'Siloam Tinker Toy'	EGol WGle
'Siloam Tiny Mite'	EGol SDay
'Siloam Toddler'	EGol WGle
'Siloam Tom Thumb'	EGol
'Siloam Ury Winniford'	CRDP EGol SDay
'Siloam Virginia Henson'	EGol MAus SRos
'Silver Ice'	SRos
¶ 'Silver Trumpet'	EFou MSCN NWes SCro
'Sirius'	NHol
¶ 'Sirocco'	CBlo EBee EFou NWes
'Snowfall'	EGol
¶ 'Snowy Apparition'	MNFA
¶ 'Sombrero Way'	NWes
'Someone Special'	SRos
'Song Sparrow'	CBro WPer

'Sparkling Dawn'	MBel
'Sparkling Stars'	WGle
'Spiderman'	SRos
'Stafford'	CMGP EBrP EBre ECED
	ECGN ECtt EFou ELan EPla
	ERou LBre LGro LHop MBel
	MBri MNFA MNrw MTis NBrk
	NHol NOrc NVic NWes SBre
	SChu SDay SMac SRos WHoo
	WPer
'Starling'	EGol
'Stars and Stripes'	MNFA
'Stella de Oro' ♀	Widely available
'Stineette'	WCot
'Stoke Poges' ♀	CSev EBee ECGP EMar EPfP
	ERic LRHS MMil MNFA SAxl
	SChu SRos
'Strawberry Candy'	SRos
'Streaker' hort. (v)	WCot
'Sugar Cookie'	CRDP SApp
'Summer Air'	LRHS MBri
¶ 'Summer Interlude'	WMoo
¶ 'Summer Jubilee'	SApp
'Summer Wine'	CMGP CRos EBar EFou EGol
	EMar EPla LBlm LRHS MAus
	MBro MNFA MUlv NFai NPri
	NSti NWes SAxl SChu SDay
	SMrm SUsu WCot WHoo
	WMer WPyg WWat
'Sunday Gloves'	EGol
'Superlative'	SRos
'Suzie Wong'	MArl MNFA
'Sweet Pea'	EGol
'Swirling Water'	SDay
¶ 'Tang'	MNFA
'Tasmania'	SPer
'Techny Peach Lace'	WGle
'Techny Spider'	SRos
'Teenager'	EGol
'Tejas'	EMil
'Tender Sheperd'	EGol WGle
'Tetraploid Stella de Oro'	SDay
'Thousand Voices'	WGle
'Thumbelina'	ECha MNFA
§ thunbergii	ECha SMac SSpi
'Timeless Fire'	SRos
'Tinker Bell'	SRos
'Todd Munroe'	WGle
'Tom Wise'	SRos
'Tonia Gay'	CRDP SRos
'Tootsie Rose'	SDay SRos
'Torpoint'	LRHS MNFA
'Towhead'	EGol ENot LRHS MRav SDay
	WCot
'Toyland'	CMGP CSev EBee EGar EGol
	GSki LRHS MNFA NRoo SAxl
	SSpe WLRN
'Triple Threat'	SDay
'Tropical Toy'	SDay
'Upper Class Peach'	WGle
'Varsity'	EBee EBrP EBre EGol LBre
	MAus NBir SBre SRos
¶ 'Vera Biaglow'	SDay
vespertina	See H. thunbergii
'Vicountess Byng'	LFis
'Victoria Aden'	CBro
* 'Vohann'	SApp SDay
'Walk Humbly'	WGle
'Wally Nance'	LRHS
'Water Witch'	EGol
'Waxwing'	CKel WPer

'Wayside Green Imp'   EBee EFou EGol NWes SCro
                        WGle
'Wayside Princess'   WGle
'Wee Chalice'   EGol
'Whichford' ♀   CBro CLTr CMea EBrP EBre
                        ECro ECtt EGol ELan LBre
                        MNFA NRoo SBre SChu SUsu
                        WWal WWat WWin
'White Coral'   LRHS MNFA
'White Dish'   EGol
'White Temptation'   EGol MBel
'Whooperie'   MBel
¶ 'Wind Song'   SDay
'Window Dressing'   EGol
'Wine Bubbles'   EGol LRHS SApp
¶ 'Wine Delight'   SDay
¶ 'Winnetka'   MAus
¶ 'Winnie the Pooh'   SDay
'Winsome Lady'   ECha
'Wishing Well'   SChu
* 'Witch Hazel'   WGle
'Woodbury'   WRus
'Wren'   WGle
'Wynn'   MBel
'Yellow Lollipop'   SDay SRos
'Yellow Mantle'   MNFA
'Yellow Petticoats'   MUlv
'Yellow Rain'   SAsh WCot
'Yesterday Memories'   SRos
'Zampa'   SDay
'Zara'   SPer

HEMIGRAPHIS (Acanthaceae)
§ *alternata*   LChe
colorata   See *H. alternata*

HEMIONITIS   (Adiantaceae) See Plant Deletions

HEMIPHRAGMA   (Scrophulariaceae) See Plant Deletions

HEMIZYGIA   (Lamiaceae) See Plant Deletions

HEPATICA † (Ranunculaceae)
acutiloba   CBro CLAP EPar GCrs GMaP
                        LAma MAvo WCot WCru
americana   CArn GBuc GCrs WCot WCru
angulosa   See *H. transsilvanica*
¶ *henryi*   NRya WCru
× *media* 'Ballardii' ♀ IBlr
§ *nobilis* ♀   CAvo CBro CSpe EBrP EBre
                        EHyt EPot GTou IBlr LBre
                        LHop MBri MHig MTho MWat
                        NHar NHed NHol NMen NNrd
                        NTow NWoo SBre SIgm SPer
                        SWas WAbe WCru WIvy
                        WSHC
– blue   CRDP GAbr MS&S NHar
                        NRar NSla SBla SWas
¶ – 'Cobalt'   WHil
– double pink   See *H. nobilis* **'Rubra Plena'**
¶ – grey/lilac semi-double (d) CRDP
– var. *japonica*   CBro CRDP EPar LAma WCru
– lilac   MTho SWas
– mottled leaf   EHyt MTho
– pink   CRDP ELan EPot MS&S SBla
                        SWas WIvy
* – 'Pyrenean Marbles' CLAP
– red   MBro NNrd
– var. *rubra*   CLAP CRDP MHig NMen NSla
– white   CNic CRDP ELan GAbr MHig
                        MS&S NSla SBla SIng WIvy

§ *transsilvanica* ♀   CBro CLAP ECha EHyt ELan
                        EPar EPla EPot GCrs GDra
                        LAma LHop MBro MHig
                        MS&S MWat NHar NMen
                        NRya SBla SMad SPer WAbe
                        WCru
– 'De Buis'   CAvo MDun
– 'Elison Spence' (d) IBlr
– 'Lilacina'   CBro
triloba   See *H. nobilis*

× HEPPIMENES (Gesneriaceae)
I 'Purple Queen'   NMos

HEPTACODIUM (Caprifoliaceae)
¶ *miconioides*   CBar CBot CFil CPMA CPle
                        CWSG ELan EPfP ERav GBin
                        GQui LBuc MBlu MTis SAga
                        SMac SMad SPan WCot WCwm
                        WPGP WWat

HEPTAPLEURUM See SCHEFFLERA

HERACLEUM (Apiaceae)
antasiaticum   See *H. stevenii*
lehmannianum   ECGN WCot
mantegazzianum   CRow EOas MFir NSti WOak
minimum 'Roseum'   CInt ELan WFar WOMN WPat
sphondylium roseum   CNat

HERBERTIA (Iridaceae)
§ *lahue*   LRHS

HERMANNIA (Sterculiaceae)
candicans   See *H. incana*
erodioides   See *H. depressa*
§ *incana*   CHal MBEx
* *stricta*   MFos
verticillata   See *H. pinnata*

HERMODACTYLUS (Iridaceae)
§ *tuberosus*   CAvo CBos CBro CMea CMil
                        CMon CTri ECha EGoo ELan
                        LAma MAvo MNrw MRav
                        MSto NFai NRog WHil
– MS 976/762   CMon

HERNIARIA (Caryophyllaceae)
glabra   EOHP EWFC GBar GPoy LHol
                        MHew MSal NHol SIde WHer
                        WWye

HERPOLIRION   (Anthericaceae) See Plant Deletions

HERTIA See OTHONNA

HESPERALOE (Agavaceae)
funifera   CTbh
parviflora   CTbh EOas SIgm

HESPERANTHA (Iridaceae)
§ *baurii*   GBuc MDun NMen SSpi WAbe
                        WCot
buhrii   See *H. cucullata* **'Rubra'**
§ *cucullata* 'Rubra' NWCA
* *geminata*   WCot
huttonii   GBuc MFir WCot
mossii   See *H. baurii*
¶ *pauciflora*   WCot

¶ *vaginata*　　　WCot

HESPERIS † (Brassicaceae)
　lutea　　　See *Sisymbrium luteum*
　matronalis　　　CArn CBre CGle CRow CSev
　　　　EBar EBot ECoo EEls EFou
　　　　ELan EWFC LFis LHol MHew
　　　　NBrk NBro NFla SIde SPer
　　　　SSvw SWat WBea WBon WCla
　　　　WHer WMaN WOak WPer
　　　　WWye
　– *alba*　　　See *H. matronalis* var. *albiflora*
　§ – var. *albiflora*　　　EFou EMar MCLN SMrm SPer
　　　　SSvw WCot WHil WOve WPer
　　　　WWat
　– – 'Alba Plena' (d)　　　CGle CMea CRDP LHol MNrw
　　　　MTis SIde SWat WCot WRus
　– double form (d)　　　CHad CRow CSev MBri WCru
　– double pink (d)　　　SWat
　¶ – 'Lilacina'　　　MBel
　– 'Lilacina Flore Pleno'　　　CBos CGle CHan CMil EBar
　　(d)　　　GMaP GMac LFis MCLN
　　　　MRav NBrk NChi NHaw NHol
　　　　NSti SUsu SWat
　¶ – violet　　　LRHS
　* *silviniana*　　　SAxl
　steveniana　　　CGen CHan EBar ECoo MTis
　　　　NSti SWat WEas

HESPEROCHIRON (Hydrophyllaceae) See
Plant Deletions

HETEROCENTRON (Melastomataceae)
　§ *elegans*　　　CLTr CTre

HETEROMELES See PHOTINIA

HETEROMORPHA (Apiaceae)
　arborescens　　　CTrC

HETEROPAPPUS (Asteraceae)
　altaicus　　　WPer

HETEROTHECA (Asteraceae)
　¶ *horrida*　　　EBee
　mucronata　　　EBee
　§ *villosa*　　　CChr CRDP EMon LBuc MAvo
　　　　WCot

HEUCHERA † (Saxifragaceae)
　§ *americana*　　　CRDP CRow ECha EOrc EPar
　　　　GBar MHar MUlv NBir NFai
　　　　NSti SCro SLod WCot WLin
　　　　WTin WWat
　¶ – Dale's Strain　　　EBee EMan GMaP MNrw
　　　　MTed NCat NLar WWoo
　– 'Picta'　　　EBrP EBre EPPr LBre SBre
　¶ 'Amethyst Mist'　　　SApp WCot
　¶ 'Autumn Leaves'　　　NLar
　　Bressingham hybrids　　　EAst EBrP EBre GDra LBre
　　　　MBri MBir NFla NMir NOak
　　　　NRoo SBre SPer SRms SSca
　　　　WPer WWin WWoo
　× *brizoides* 'Gracillima'　　　CGle EPPr
　¶ 'Can-can'　　　EBee NHol WCot
　'Canyon Delight'　　　WCot
　'Cascade Dawn'　　　CBos CDec CHEx CHid CMHG
　　　　EMan EMar EPPr LFis LHop
　　　　LRot MBel MBri MCLN MHlr
　　　　NCut NHol NLak NPro SBid
　　　　SWat WFox

'Cathedral Windows'　　　WCot
§ Charles Bloom = 'Chablo'　　　EBrP EBre LBre SBre
　Charles Bloom　　　See *H.* Charles Bloom =
　　　　'Chablo'
¶ 'Chiqui'　　　SWas
chlorantha　　　CPea GBin
'Chocolate Ruffles'　　　Widely available
　Coral Bells　　　See *H. sanguinea*
'Coral Cloud'　　　CB&S EBrP EBre ENot GCHN
　　　　LBre SBre
cylindrica　　　CHid EBar GCHN GCra MBel
　　　　MRav MSte NChi SSca WPer
　　　　WWin
– var. *alpina*　　　NGre WLin
¶ – – NNS 96-116　　　MRPP
– 'Chartreuse'　　　CGle
– 'Greenfinch'　　　Widely available
– 'Hyperion'　　　EBrP EBre EPPr LBre MBal
　　　　SBre
'Dennis Davidson'　　　See *H.* 'Huntsman'
I 'Eco Magnifiolia'　　　CLAP NWes WCot WGle
'Edge Hill'　　　SRms WRHF
¶ 'Emperor's Cloak'　　　NLar NPri
'Firebird'　　　CBlo ELan EPPr MBal NVic
　Firefly　　　See *H.* **'Leuchtkäfer'**
glabra　　　EMon
glauca　　　See *H. americana*
'Green Ivory'　　　CGle CHar EBrP EBre EHal
　　　　ELan EMan EOrc EPPr GCHN
　　　　GMaP LBre LWak MAus MBal
　　　　MBel MBri MRav MUlv NBus
　　　　NCat NSti SBre SPer SRCN
　　　　WRHF
¶ 'Greenfinch'　　　WGwG
grossulariifolia　　　EBee MTho WCot WPer
¶ *hallii*　　　NTow WCot
'Helen Dillon' (v)　　　CElw CFai CHid CLAP CMHG
　　　　CMil MCLN MGed MLLN
　　　　MMal NHol NSti NWes SApp
　　　　SPla WBea WCot WFox WKif
　　　　WSan
§ Rosemary Bloom =　　　EBrP EBre LBre SBre SPer
　'Heuros'　　　SWat
hispida　　　EMan MSte SAga
§ 'Huntsman'　　　CGle EBee ECha EGar ELan
　　　　EWes EBri GBuc MRav SUsu
　　　　WBcn WPbr
'Jack Frost'　　　NWes WGle
'Lady Romney'　　　GCal SHel
§ 'Leuchtkäfer'　　　CFee EGoo ESis GChr LFis
　　　　MBro MCli MFir MRav NBrk
　　　　NFai NMir NOrc NRoo SCro
　　　　SMac SPer SWat WAbe WBro
　　　　WGor WHoo WPer
mexicana　　　WCot
* *micans*　　　EHyt NHar NMen
micrantha　　　ELan GGar SRms WCot
– var. *diversifolia*　　　LGan LRHS MOne NHol SPer
　　Bressingham Bronze =　　　SPla
　'Absi'
N – – 'Palace Purple' ♀　　　Widely available
　– JLS 86275CLOR　　　EMon
　– 'Martha Roderick'　　　WCot
¶ 'Mint Frost'　　　EHic NHol WCot
¶ 'Northern Fire'　　　CLAP
¶ 'Oakington Jewel'　　　MBri WCot
'Orphei'　　　NChi
'Painted Lady'　　　CDec GBuc LFis WPbr
¶ *parishii*　　　NWCA WLin
¶ *parvifolia*　　　EBee
¶ – var. *nivalis*　　　EBee
'Pearl Drops'　　　EBrP EBre EPPr LBre SBre

'Persian Carpet' — CBos CDec CHid CMil EHal EHic GCal LFis LHop LRot MBri MCLN MHlr MLLN NBir NCut NHaw NHol NLak NSti SBid SMad SMrm SSpi SMac WFox WGle WRus WWeb

'Pewter Moon' — CBro CDec CHEx EFou EHal EHoe ELan EMil EPla GBri LFis LHop LRHS MBel MHlr MSta NBir NCat NHol NLak NSti SChu SMac SMad SPer SPla WAbe WCot WGle WWat

'Pewter Veil' — CBos EMar WCot WEas WGle

pilosissima — EPla GBin GBuc WCot

¶ 'Pink Spray' — EPPr

§ Rain of Fire = 'Pluie de Feu' — CFir EPfP GBri GCal MCli SSte WGle WMow

'Plum Puddin' — CBlo CDec CHid CMHG EHic EWes LRHS MBri MBro MCLN MTPN MTed NChi NDov NHol NPro WCot WHoo WWeb

'Pretty Polly' — EBrP EBre LBre MHFP SBre

pringlei — NBro WPer

pubescens — GBri GCHN MHlr

– 'Alba' — WCot WHoo

pulchella — CPBP EBee ESis NFla NGre NTow SSca

– JCA 9508 — NMen NWoo

¶ 'Purple Petticoats' — EFou WCot

'Rachel' — Widely available

◆ Rain of Fire — See *H.* Rain of Fire = **'Pluie de Feu'**

'Raspberry Regal' — MCLN MLLN NHol NSti NWes WCot WFox

'Red Spangles' ♀ — CGle CKel EBrP EBre GCHN LBre NBir SBre

'Regal Robe' — WCot

richardsonii — ECED GBin

'Ring of Fire' — EFou EHic NHol WCot

Rosemary Bloom — See *H.* Rosemary Bloom = **'Heuros'**

rubescens — EDAr ELan MTho WWin

rubra 'Redstart' — SUsu

'Ruby Ruffles' — WCot WGle

'Ruby Veil' — EFou EHic NHol NWes WCot WGle

'Ruffles' — CRow

§ *sanguinea* — CGle GCHN MBal NBro NCat NNor NRoo SHFr SHel WByw WLin WPer

– 'Alba' — EMon WPbr

– 'Sioux Falls' — EPPr

– 'Splendens' — GLil

– 'Taff's Joy' (v) — CRow EGra EPPr EWes LHop MBel MCLN MNrw NPro SMac WCot

– 'White Cloud' (v) — WPbr

'Santa Anna Cardinal' — WCot

'Schneewittchen' (v) — EPPr LBuc NCat WMer

'Scintillation' ♀ — CB&S CKel EBrP EBre ECED ECtt GCHN LBre NCat SBre SRms

¶ 'Shere Variety' — EBee

'Silver Veil' — CRow

¶ 'Sioux Falls' — EWes

'Snow Storm' (v) — CB&S CDec EBrP EBre EFou ELan GBur GCHN LBre LHop MBar MBel MBri SBre SMad SPer WAbe WGle WPbr WWhi

'Souvenir de Wolley-Dod' — WCot

'Splish Splash' — WGle

'Stormy Seas' — Widely available

'Strawberry Swirl' — CDec CFai CMHG EFou EHal EHic GMac LFis LHop LRot MBel MLLN MMil NHol NSti NWes SSpi WCot WFox WHil

¶ Super hybrids — WHil

villosa — EBrP EBre ECGN ECha EGar GCHN LBre MRav SBre WCot

– 'Royal Red' — ECha EGar GMac

'Wendy Hardy' — WCot

'Widar' — EPPr WCot

¶ 'Winter Red' — EFou

¶ 'Yeti' — EFou

'Zabelliana' — GCal NPro NRoo

× HEUCHERELLA (Saxifragaceae)

alba 'Bridget Bloom' — CB&S CDoC CGle CSam ECha ELan EMar EOld GCHN GMaP LGro LHop MBri MBro MRav MUlv NFai NHol NOrc NRoo NVic SPer SRms WBea WHil WHoo WHow WRus

– 'Rosalie' — CDec CElw CFee CGle CMHG CMea EBrP EBre ECha EMon EPri LBre MBri MMal MSte MUlv NLak SAxl SBre SLod SOkh SSpe SUsu SWas WAbe WFar WHal WHoo WRus WWhi

'Pink Frost' — WThi

¶ 'Quicksilver' — EBee EHic WCot

¶ 'Silver Streak' — CMil CSpe EBee EHic NHol WCot

tiarelloides ♀ — CMGP CSev EBee EMan EPfP MWgw NCat NFai NNor NRoo SOkh SPer WRus

* 'White Blus' — WThi

HEXAGLOTTIS (Iridaceae) See Plant Deletions

× HIBANOBAMBUSA (Poaceae - Bambusoideae)

I *tranquillans* — EFul EPla NDov SCha SDry WJun

I – 'Shiroshima' (v) — CPMA EBee EOas EPla ERod ESOG ISta MBrN MWhi NDov SCha SDry WCot WJun WPGP

HIBBERTIA (Dilleniaceae)

aspera — CGre CPle LHil SAga WWat

§ *cuneiformis* — CPle ERea LHil

dentata — SLMG

procumbens — ESis ITim WAbe

§ *scandens* ♀ — CB&S CGre CHEx CPIN CPle ECou ELan ERea GQui LBlm LCns LHil SAga SOWG WMul

tetrandra — See *H. cuneiformis*

volubilis — See *H. scandens*

HIBISCUS † (Malvaceae)

¶ *acetosella* — WMul

biseptus — MSto

¶ *cannabinus* — SIde

cardiophyllus — MSto

coccineus — MSte MSto SOWG

hamabo — MSto SSta

huegelii — See *Alyogyne huegelii*

leopoldii — IOrc SPer SRms

manihot — See *Abelmoschus manihot*

* *moesiana* — MBri

moscheutos	CArn CFir CHan MSte MSto SMad
mutabilis	SOWG
paramutabilis	SMad
¶ *pedunculatus*	WMul
rosa-sinensis	EBak MBri SLMG SOWG
– 'Casablanca'	MBri
– 'Cooperi' (v)	CHal LChe SOWG
– 'Dainty Pink'	See *H. rosa-sinensis* 'Fantasia'
§ – 'Dainty White'	LChe
– 'El Capitolio'	SOWG
– 'El Capitolio' sport	LChe
§ – 'Fantasia'	LChe
– 'Full Moon'	LChe
– 'Helene'	ELan MBri
– 'Herm Geller'	LChe
– 'Holiday'	MBri
– 'Kardinal'	MBri
– 'Koeniger'	MBri
– 'La France'	See *H. rosa-sinensis* 'Fantasia'
– 'Lemon Chiffon'	LChe
– 'Meteor'	LChe
– 'Pink la France'	See *H. rosa-sinensis* 'Fantasia'
– 'Rose of China'	MBri
– 'Swan Lake'	See *H. rosa-sinensis* 'Dainty White'
– 'Thelma Bennell'	SOWG
– 'Tivoli'	MBri
– 'Weekend'	LChe MBri
– 'White la France'	See *H. rosa-sinensis* 'Dainty White'
rubis	ELan
sabdariffa	MSal MSto
schizopetalus ♀	LChe
sinosyriacus 'Lilac Queen'	WBcn
– 'Ruby Glow'	MGos
syriacus	CHEx WNor WOMN
– 'Admiral Dewey'	IOrc SPla
– 'Ardens' (d)	CBlo CEnd ELan IOrc MGos MRav SPer WSel
– Blue Bird	See *H. syriacus* 'Oiseau Bleu'
– 'Coelestis'	IOrc MGos SPer WSel
– 'Diana' ♀	EPfP EPla SBid WBcn
– 'Dorothy Crane'	CBlo CEnd EBee ENot WWes
– 'Duc de Brabant' (d)	IOrc SCoo SEas SHBN SPer SRms
– 'Elegantissimus'	See *H. syriacus* 'Lady Stanley'
– 'Hamabo' ♀	CDoC EBee ECle ELan EMil ENot IHos IOrc MBri MGos MRav MWat SBid SHBN SPar SPer SPla WSel WStI
– 'Jeanne d'Arc' (d)	IOrc
§ – 'Lady Stanley' (d)	CMil IOrc SEas SPer SPla
¶ – 'Lenny'	ENot
§ – 'Meehanii' (v)	CBot CEnd EBee ELan ENot EPfP MAsh MBri MGos SBid SCoo SPla SSta
– 'Monstrosus'	CBlo IOrc
§ – 'Oiseau Bleu' ♀	CB&S CDoC CTri ELan EMil ENot EPla IHos IOrc MBri MGos MWat NBee NFla SEas SHBN SPer SPla SReu SSpi SSta WDin WGwG WSHC WStI
– Pink Giant™ ♀	CB&S CEnd EBrP EBre ELan EPfP IOrc LBre MGos SBid SBre SPer WDin
– 'Red Heart' ♀	CDoC EBee ECle ELan EPfP GChr IOrc MWat SBid SPer SRms WDin WStI WWeb
– Russian Violet	CDoC CEnd COtt ELan IOrc MRav
– 'Speciosus'	IOrc SPer
– 'Totus Albus'	EMil IOrc
– 'Variegatus'	See *H. syriacus* 'Meehanii'
– 'William R. Smith'	CBlo EBee ECle ELan ENot IOrc SHBN SPer SSta WWeb WWes
– 'Woodbridge' ♀	CB&S CEnd CTri ELan EMil ENot EPfP GChr IHos IOrc MBri MGos MRav MWgw NFla SEas SHBN SPer SPla SReu SSpi SSta WDin WSel WStI
¶ *tiliaceus*	LLew
trionum	CArn CHad CInt MSto SLMG SOWG
– 'Sunny Day'	ELan

HIERACIUM (Asteraceae)

argenteum	WGwy
aurantiacum	See *Pilosella aurantiaca*
bombycinum	See *H. mixtum*
brunneocroceum	See *Pilosella aurantiaca* subsp. *carpathicola*
§ *glaucum*	LWak NHol WByw WEas WWin
§ *lanatum*	CGle GBin NBir NBro NNrd SSvw WEas WPer WWin
maculatum	CInt CRow ECoo EHoe ELan EMar EPar EPla GGar MFir MPEx MUlv NCat NPer NSti WBea WOak WPer
murorum	CPea
pilosella	See *Pilosella officinarum*
praecox	See *H. glaucum*
scotostictum	EMon LRHS
× *stoloniflorum*	See *Pilosella stoloniflora*
variegatum	See *Hypochaeris variegata*
villosum	CBot CInt CNic CSam EHoe MDun NBro NNor SIng WHer WLin WPer WWin
waldsteinii	MAvo MBro NNor WCru
welwitschii	See *H. lanatum*

HIEROCHLOE (Poaceae)

odorata	ELau GPoy
redolens	GAbr GAri GOrn

HIMALAYACALAMUS (Poaceae - Bambusoideae)

§ *falconeri*	CFil EFul EPla SDys WPGP
§ – 'Damarapa'	EPla ISta LJus SCha SCob SDix WJun
§ *hookerianus*	ISta LJus WJun

HIPPEASPREKELIA (Amaryllidaceae) See Plant Deletions

HIPPEASTRUM (Amaryllidaceae)

× *acramannii*	CMon GCal
advenum BCW 4764	MSto
'Ambiance'	ETub
'Apple Blossom'	ETub LAma NRog
'Baby Star'	ETub
'Beautiful Lady'	LAma
'Bestseller' ♀	LAma
bifidum	See *Rhodophiala bifida*
'Byjou'	NRog
'Christmas Gift'	ETub
'Double Record' (d)	ETub
'Dutch Belle'	LAma
elwesii	MSto SBla
– BCW 4999	MSto

'Fantastica'   LAma
'Germa'   ETub
'Green Goddess'   ETub
'Jewel'   ETub
'Lady Jane'   ETub
'Ludwig's Goliath'   LAma
'Oskar'   NRog
papilio   LAma NRog
* – 'Butterfly'   ETub
'Papillon'   ETub LAma
'Pasadena'   ETub
'Picotee'   LAma
'President Johnson'   ETub
'Red Lion'   ETub
roseum   See *Rhodophiala rosea*
  sp. BCW 5038   MSto
  sp. BCW 5154   MSto
'Star of Holland' ♀   ETub
stylosum   CMon
'United Nations'   LAma
'White Dazzler'   LAma
'Yellow Pioneer'   LAma

HIPPOBROMA See LAURENTIA

HIPPOCREPIS (Papilionaceae)
§ *comosa*   CKin EWFC
 – 'E.R. Janes'   MPla
§ *emerus*   CHan CMHG CPle CTri EHic
                            ELan ERea GOrc LHop MBal
                            SUsu WCot WHCG WSHC
                            WTro

HIPPOLYTIA (Asteraceae)
§ *herderi*   CHan EHoe LHop LLWP
                            WCot

HIPPOPHAE (Elaeagnaceae)
rhamnoides ♀   Widely available
 – 'Leikora' (f)   MGos NFla SPer WMou WPat
 – 'Pollmix' (m)   MGos NFla SPer
salicifolia   CLnd WPGP

HIPPURIS (Hippuridaceae)
vulgaris   CBen CRDP EHon EMFW
                            MHew WMAq WWye

HIRPICIUM (Asteraceae)
¶ *armerioides*   NWCA

HISTIOPTERIS (Dennstaedtiaceae)
incisa   CFil

HOHERIA † (Malvaceae)
§ *angustifolia*   CBot CHan ECou WPGP WPic
'Borde Hill'   SBid SPer SSpi SSta WHCG
glabrata ♀   CB&S CBot CFil CPle ECou
                            MBal WPGP WSpi
'Glory of Amlwch' ♀   CFil CGre CMHG CSam CWit
                            GCal SBid SSpi SSta WCru
                            WSHC
§ *lyallii* ♀   CB&S CDoC CPle CSam ECou
                            ELan EPfP IOrc SHBN SSta
                            WDin
microphylla   See *H. angustifolia*
populnea   CB&S CBot
sexstylosa ♀   CAbb CBot CDoC CFee CHEx
                            CHid ELan EPfP IOrc ISea
                            MBel MBlu SPer SSta WOMN
 – 'Pendula'   CB&S

 – 'Stardust' ♀   CAbP CFil CMCN CPMA
                            LRHS SMad SPer SReu SSpi
                            WPGP WWat

HOLBOELLIA (Lardizabalaceae)
coriacea   CBot CGre CHEx CPlN CSam
                            EPfP SAPC SArc SBra SOWG
                            WCru
¶ *fargesii* DJHC 506   WCru
latifolia   COtt CPlN CSam CTrG CTri
                            EHic SAPC SArc SOWG WCot
                            WCru WSHC WWat
 – SF 95134   ISea

HOLCUS (Poaceae)
lanatus   CKin
mollis 'Albovariegatus'   CBen CCuc ECha EHoe ELan
                            EMon EPla ESOG GCHN
                            GMaP LGan MBar MFir NBro
                            NHol NNrd NPer NRya NSti
                            NVic SCob SPer SSoC WEas
                            WLin WPer WWat

HOLODISCUS (Rosaceae)
discolor   CFil CGre CPle ELan EPla
                            EWes GCal GOrc MBlu MTis
                            MWhi NFla SBid SDys SHBN
                            SSpi SSta WHCG WSHC
¶ – var. *ariifolius*   EPfP
¶ – NJM 94044   WPGP
dumosus   CPle

HOMALOCLADIUM (Polygonaceae)
§ *platycladum*   CHal

HOMALOTHECA (Asteraceae) See Plant Deletions

HOMERIA (Iridaceae)
breyniana   See *H. collina*
 – var. *aurantiaca*   See *H. flaccida*
§ *collina*   ETub SLMG SMrm
§ *flaccida*   LAma LBow NRog
marlothii   CMon
ochroleuca   LAma LBow NRog

HOMOGLOSSUM See GLADIOLUS

HOMOGYNE (Asteraceae) See Plant Deletions

HOOKERIA (Hookeriaceae) See Plant Deletions

HORDEUM (Poaceae)
jubatum   CCuc CInt EHoe EPla ESOG
                            EWes GAri LHil LIck NChi
                            NSti SIng SLod WWhi WWye

HORKELIA (Rosaceae)
¶ *rydbergii*   NHol

HORMINUM (Lamiaceae)
pyrenaicum   CNic ELan GCrs GDra MBro
                            MHig NGre NMen SBla SHFr
                            SRms SSmi WCla WLin WPer
                            WPyg WWin WWye
pyrenaicum pale blue   GBur MSte

HOSTA † (Hostaceae)
'Abba Dabba Do' (v)   CBdn EGol

'Abby'   CBdn EGol EPGN LHos
'Abiqua Ariel'   SApp
'Abiqua Blue Krinkles'   CWin SApp
'Abiqua Drinking Gourd'   EGol GSki
'Abiqua Moonbeam' (v)   CBdn EPGN
'Abiqua Recluse'   EGol
'Abiqua Trumpet'   EGol
  (*tokudama*)
aequinoctiiantha   EGol LHos
'Aksarben'   EMic
'Alba' (*sieboldiana*)   See **H. 'Elegans Alba'**
                                    (*sieboldiana*)
albomarginata   See **H. 'Paxton's Original'**
                                    (*sieboldii*)
§ 'Albomarginata' (*fortunei*)   CB&S CBdn EBee EGol EMic
                                    EPGN LFis MBar MOne NBir
                                    NFai SPer WHoo WViv
'Allan P. McConnell' (v)   CBdn EGol EMic EPGN LHos
                                    NHar SApp
'Alpine Aire'   EMic
'Amanuma'   EGol EMic NWes
'Amber Maiden' (v)   EGol LHos
'Antioch' (*fortunei*) (v)   CBdn CWin EGol EMic MBel
                                    MMiN MMoz MRav MSte
'Aoki' (*fortunei*)   EMic EPGN NHol NWes
'Aphrodite' (*plantaginea*)   CFir EGol EPGN LHos LRHS
  (d)   NWes WRus
'Apple Green'   EMic
'Aqua Velva'   EGol LHos
'Argentea Variegata'   See **H. undulata** var. **undulata**
  (*undulata*)
'Aspen Gold'   EMic
  (*tokudama* hybrid)
¶ 'August Beauty'   CBdn
'August Moon'   Widely available
I 'Aurea' (*nakaiana*)   NWoo
'Aurea' (*sieboldii*)   See **H. sieboldii f. subcrocea**
aureafolia   See **H. 'Starker Yellow Leaf'**
'Aureoalba' (*fortunei*)   See **H. 'Spinners'**
'Aureomaculata' (*fortunei*)   See **H. fortunei** var. **albopicta**
§ 'Aureomarginata'   CBdn EBrP EBre EGol EHoe
  (*montana*)   EMic EPGN GCal LBre LSyl
                                    MMiN NHol NWes SApp SBre
                                    SCro SPla SSpi WRus WWoo
§ 'Aureomarginata'   CBdn CBro CHad EBrP EBre
  (*ventricosa*) ♀   ECha EGol EMic EPGN LBre
                                    MBro SAxl SBre SPer SRms
                                    WHil WRus
'Aureostriata' (*tardiva*)   See **H. 'Inaho'**
'Aurora Borealis'   EGol EPGN LHos
  (*sieboldiana*) (v)
'Azure Snow'   EGol LHos
'Banyai's Dancing Girl'   EMic
'Barbara White'   EGol
¶ 'Beauty Substance'   CBdn EGol
bella   See **H.** var. **obscura (fortunei)**
'Bennie McRae'   EGol
'Betcher's Blue'   EGol
'Betsy King'   EBee EHic EMic EPGN LBuc
                                    LHos MRav NHol WMer
                                    WWoo
'Bette Davis Eyes'   EGol
'Betty'   EGol
'Big Boy' (*montana*)   EGol
'Big Daddy'   CBdn CBro CHad COtt EBrP
  (*sieboldiana* hybrid)   EBre ECtt EGol ELan EMic
                                    EOrc EPGN GMaP LBre LGre
                                    LHos MMiN NBir NFla NSti
                                    NTay SApp SBre SMad SPla
                                    SSoC WAbe WCru WRus
'Big Mama'   EGol EMic LHos LRHS
  (*sieboldiana* hybrid)

'Bill Brincka' (v)   EGol
§ 'Birchwood Parky's Gold'   CBdn CHan EBar EGol EMic
                                    EPGN LHos MMiN MTed
                                    NHar NHol SApp SAxl SRms
                                    SSpi SWas
'Birchwood Ruffled   EGol EMic
  Queen'
'Black Beauty'   EPGN
¶ 'Black Hills'   CBdn EGol LHos LRHS
§ 'Blonde Elf'   EGol EMic EPGN LHos SApp
'Blue Angel' (*sieboldiana*) ♀   CB&S CBdn EGol EHoe ELan
                                    EMic EOrc EPGN LFis LHos
                                    MAvo MBal MBel MBro MMiN
                                    MWat NOrc NTay
'Blue Arrow'   CBdn EGol LHos
(Tardiana Group) 'Blue   CBdn ECha EGol EMic LHos
  Belle'   MBro MMiN MSte WHoo
¶ 'Blue Blazes'   LHos
(Tardiana Group) 'Blue   CBdn CWin EGol
  Blush'
'Blue Boy'   CBdn CHad EGol EMic EPGN
                                    LHos MMiN NHol
'Blue Cadet'   CBdn CHad EAst EGol EMic
                                    GSki LHos MBar MBel MMiN
                                    NCat NCut NFai NHol WWoo
(Tardiana Group) 'Blue   EGol EMic MMiN
  Danube'
(Tardiana Group) 'Blue   CHad EGol EMic MMiN
  Diamond'
(Tardiana Group) 'Blue   CWin EGol EMic LRHS MMiN
  Dimples'
'Blue Edger'   CBdn ECha
'Blue Heart'   ECha EMic
  (*sieboldiana* var. *elegans*)
'Blue Jay'   EGol
'Blue Mammoth'   CBdn EGol EMic EPGN
  (*sieboldiana*)
(Tardiana Group) 'Blue   CBro CMHG EBar EBrP EBre
  Moon'   EFou EGol ELan EMic EOrc
                                    EPGN ERos LBre LGre LHop
                                    LHos MLov MRPP NHol SBre
                                    SMad WEas WWat
'Blue Seer' (*sieboldiana*)   CBdn EGol
'Blue Shadows' (*tokudama*)   CBdn LHos
  (v)
(Tardiana Group) 'Blue   CBlo EGol EMic EPGN LHos
  Skies'
'Blue Umbrellas'   CBdn EFou EGol ELan EMic
  (*sieboldiana* hybrid)   EOrc EPGN GSki LHos MMiN
                                    NHol NWes
'Blue Velvet'   CBdn
'Blue Vision'   EMic EPGN LHos
(Tardiana Group) 'Blue   CBro CMHG CRow EGol ELan
  Wedgwood'   EMic EOrc EPGN LHos MWat
                                    NHol NTay SChu SPla WRus
                                    WWat
¶ 'Bold Edger' (v)   CBdn LHos
'Bold Ribbons' (v)   CBdn EGol EMic LHos NWes
'Bold Ruffles' (*sieboldiana*)   EGol LRHS
'Bonanza' (*fortunei*)   EMic
'Border Bandit' (v)   EGol
'Borsch 1'   CBdn
'Borwick Beauty'   CBdn MMiN
  (*sieboldiana*) (v)
'Bountiful'   EGol EMic
'Bouquet'   EGol
'Bressingham Blue'   CBdn EBrP EBre ECtt EGol
                                    EMic LBre LHos NDea NMir
                                    SAxl SBre SPer WFar
(Tardiana Group) 'Bright   EGol EMic
  Glow'
¶ 'Bright Gold'   LHos

'Bright Lights' (*tokudama*) CBdn EGol EMic EPGN LHos
(v)
'Brim Cup' (v) CBdn CWin EGol EMic EPGN
LHos MMiN NWes WRus
'Brooke' EGol EMic
(Tardiana Group) EGol LRHS
'Brother Ronald'
'Bruce's Blue' EGol GSki
'Buckshaw Blue' CBos EGol EMic EPGN GBin
MBal MMiN MMoz NBir NTay
SAxl SSpi
'Butter Rim' (*sieboldii*) (v) EGol
* 'Caerula' (*ventricosa*) CWin
(Tardiana Group) EGol EMic LRHS
'Camelot'
'Camouflage' ECha
'Candy Hearts' CBdn CHan EGol EMic EPGN
MMiN WMer
capitata MSF 850 CFil WPGP
caput-avis See *H. kikutii* var. *caput-avis*
'Carnival' (v) CBdn
'Carol' (*fortunei*) (v) CBdn CLAP CWin EGol EMic
EPGN LHos MMiN WHal
'Carrie' (*sieboldii*) (v) EGol EMic
'Celebration' (v) EGol ELan EMic EPGN LBuc
LHos MRPP
'Challenger' EMic
'Change of Tradition' (v) CBdn EMic
'Chantilly Lace' (v) EGol
'Chartreuse Wiggles' CBdn EGol EPGN LHos
(*sieboldii*)
'Cheatin Heart' (v) EGol
'Chelsea Babe' (v) EGol LHos
¶ 'Cherry Berry' CBdn EGol
'Chinese Sunrise' CBdn EGol EMic EOrc EPGN
(*cathayana*) (v) MBel MMiN NHol SCro WHil
WMer
'Chiquita' EGol LHos
'Chôkô Nishiki' (*montana*) CBdn EGol EPGN MMiN
(v) NWes
'Christmas Tree' (v) CBdn EGol EMic EPGN GBri
LHos LRHS NWes WRus
'Citation' (v) EGol
'Clarence' CBdn
¶ 'Claudia' MMiN
clausa EMic
– var. *normalis* CBdn EBrP EBre EGol EMic
GCal GQui LBre LHos MCli
MGed SBre
'Collectors Choice' EGol
'Color Glory' (*sieboldiana*) EGol EPGN LHos MMiN
(v)
'Colossal' CWin EGol EMic LRHS
'County Park' EGol
'Cream Delight' (*undulata*) See *H. undulata* var. *undulata*
'Cream Edge' See *H. 'Fisher Cream Edge'*
(*fortunei*)
'Crepe Suzette' (v) EGol LHos LRHS
'Crested Reef' EBee EGol EMic NHol
§ *crispula* ♀ CB&S CBdn CHad CRow EGol
EHon EMic EPGN EPar GGar
LGro LHos MBal MBar NChi
NFai SChu SRms SSpi
'Crown Jewel' (v) EMic EPGN LHos
'Crown Prince' CBdn EGol EMic
§ 'Crowned Imperial' CBdn EMic EPGN NHol
(*fortunei*) (v)
¶ 'Crumples' (*sieboldiana*) CWin
'Crusader' (v) CBdn EGol LHos
'Cupid's Dart' (v) EGol
(Tardiana Group) CBdn EGol EMic
'Curlew'

'Dawn' CBdn EGol LHos
'Daybreak' CBdn EGol EPGN LHos LRHS
decorata CBdn EGol EMic LHos MBar
MCli MMiN
'Delia' EPGN
(Tardiana Group) 'Devon EGol EMic MMiN NWes
Blue'
'Devon Gold' CBdn
'Devon Green' CBdn EPGN LHos SApp WIvy
WRus
'Devon Mist' CBdn NWes
'Devon Tor' CBdn EPGN NWes
'Dew Drop' (v) CBdn EGol
'Diamond Tiara' (v) CBdn EGol EPGN LHos LRHS
'Dimple' ECha
¶ 'Domaine de Courson' CWin
'Don Stevens' (v) EGol
'Dorothy' EMic
'Dorset Blue' EGol EMic EPGN GSki MMoz
(Tardiana Group) 'Dorset CBdn EGol EMic MBal MMiN
Charm'
(Tardiana Group) 'Dorset EGol EMic
Flair'
'Doubloons' EGol LHos LRHS
'Drummer Boy' EGol EMic MGan
'Duchess' LHos
'DuPage Delight' CBdn EGol LHos
(*sieboldiana*) (v)
'El Capitan' (v) CBdn EGol EPGN LRHS
§ *elata* EBrP EBre EGol EMic LBre
MCli MMiN MUlv NWes SBre
WWat
'Elatior' (*nigrescens*) CBdn EMic LHos
'Eldorado' See *H. 'Frances Williams'*
(*sieboldiana*)
'Elegans' See *H. sieboldiana* var. *elegans*
'Elfin Power' (*sieboldii*) (v) EGol
'Elisabeth' CBdn CWin EAst LBuc
'Elizabeth Campbell' CLAP EMic EPGN LHos
(*fortunei*) (v) MMiN MSte SSpi
'Ellen' EMic
'Ellerbroek' (*fortunei*) (v) EGol EMic GSki MMiN
'Elsley Runner' EGol
¶ 'Elvis Lives' CBdn
'Emerald Carpet' EMic
'Emerald Skies' EGol
'Emerald Tiara' (v) CBdn EGol EPGN LHos LRHS
'Emily Dickinson' (v) CBdn EGol LRHS
(Tardiana Group) 'Eric CWin EGol EMic EPGN SChu
Smith' WFar
'Eric Smith Gold' ECha
'Evelyn McCafferty' EGol
(*tokudama* hybrid)
'Evening Magic' (v) EGol EMic EPGN LHos
'Excitation' EGol EMic
'Fair Maiden' (v) EGol EPGN
'Fall Bouquet' EGol
(*longipes hypoglauca*)
'Fall Emerald' CBdn EMic
'Fantastic' EGol
(*sieboldiana* hybrid)
'Feather Boa' EMic EPGN NHar SApp
* 'Fenman's Fascination' EMic
§ 'Fisher Cream Edge' CBdn WMer
(*fortunei*)
'Floradora' CBdn EGol EMic EPGN NDov
'Flower Power' EGol LHos LRHS
fluctuans EMic
'Fond Hope' (*sieboldiana*) MMiN
'Fool's Gold' (*fortunei*) CBdn CWin EMic WMer
'Formal Attire' EGol LHos
(*sieboldiana* hybrid) (v)

'Forncett Frances' (v) — EGol LHos

'Fortis' — See *H. undulata* var. *erromena*
(*fortunei*) — CBdn CHad CMHG CRow EGol EMic MBal NDea NHol SChu SPer WEas WWal

§ *fortunei* var. *albopicta* ♀ — Widely available

§ – – f. *aurea* ♀ — CBdn CHad CMGP CMHG CRow ECha EGol EHoe ELan EPGN EPla GMaP LHyd MBal MLov SChu SCro SPer SPla WRus

– f. *aurea* — See *H. fortunei* var. *albopicta* f. *aurea*

§ – var. *aureomarginata* ♀ — Widely available

– var. *gigantea* — See *H. montana*

§ – var. *hyacinthina* ♀ — CBdn CGle CHad EGol EMic EOld EOrc EPGN GCal LHos MBal MBar MMiN NBus NCut NDea NOrc SSpi WFox WWin

– – variegated — See *H. 'Crowned Imperial'* (*fortunei*) , *H.* 'Hyacinthina Variegata'

§ – var. *obscura* — CBdn ECho EGol EMic LHos LHyd NWes

– var. *rugosa* — EMic

'Fountain' — NHol

'Fragrant Blue' — CBdn EGol

'Fragrant Bouquet' (v) — CBdn EGol EMic EPGN LHos SChu

'Fragrant Gold' — EGol EMic EPGN LHos MMiN

'Francee' (*fortunei*) (v) ♀ — Widely available

'Frances Williams Improved' (*sieboldiana*) (v) — EGol MMiN

¶ 'Frances Williams' seedlings — NSti

§ 'Frances Williams' (*sieboldiana*) (v) ♀ — Widely available

¶ 'Freising' (*fortunei*) — EBee

'Fresh' (v) — EGol EPGN LHos

'Fringe Benefit' (v) — CBdn EBrP EBre EGol EMic EPGN LBre LHos MMiN NWes SApp SBre WLin WMer

'Frosted Jade' (v) — CBdn EGol EMic EPGN LHos LRHS NDov NWes

'Gaiety' (v) — EGol EMic

'Gala' (v) — EMic EPGN

'Gay Blade' (v) — EGol

'Geisha' (v) — CBdn EGol EPGN LHos

'Gene's Joy' — EPGN LHos

'Gigantea' (*sieboldiana*) — See *H. elata*

'Gilt Edge' (*sieboldiana*) (v) — EMic

'Ginko Craig' (v) — Widely available

glauca — See *H. sieboldiana* var. *elegans*

I 'Gloriosa' (*fortunei*) (v) — EGol EMic EPGN MMiN

'Gold Drop' — CBdn ECho EGol EMic EOrc EPGN LHos MMiN NHol WMer

'Gold Edger' — Widely available

'Gold Flush' (*ventricosa*) — EMic

§ 'Gold Haze' (*fortunei*) — CBdn CHad EGol EMic EOrc EPGN MBel NHol NTay

'Gold Leaf' (*fortunei*) — EGol

'Gold Regal' — CBdn EGol EMic MMiN

¶ 'Gold Splash' — MBro WHoo

'Gold Standard' (*fortunei*) (v) — CBdn EBrP EBre ECha EGol ELan EMic EPGN EPla GMaP LBre LGre LHos MBri MLov MMiN MWat NDov NFai NRoo NTay SApp SBre SChu SSpe SSpi SUsu WLin WRus

'Goldbrook' (*fortunei*) (v) — EGol WBcn

'Goldbrook Genie' — EGol

'Goldbrook Glamour' (v) — EGol
(Tardiana Group) — EGol

'Goldbrook Glimmer' (v)

'Goldbrook Gold' — EGol

'Goldbrook Grace' — EGol

'Goldbrook Gratis' (v) — EGol

'Goldbrook Grayling' — EGol

'Goldbrook Grebe' — EGol

'Golden Age' — See *H. 'Gold Haze'* (*fortunei*)

'Golden Anniversary' — CBdn EMic LHos MBri NHol WRHF

'Golden Bullion' (*tokudama*) — CBdn EGol EMic GBri

'Golden Circles' — See *H. 'Frances Williams'* (*sieboldiana*)

'Golden Decade' — EGol

'Golden Isle' — EGol EMic

'Golden Medallion' (*tokudama*) — CBdn CBro CTri EBar EBrP EBre EGol ELan EMic EOrc EPGN LBre LHos MBel MMiN NFai NHol SApp SBre WFar WWat

'Golden' (*nakaiana*) — See *H. 'Birchwood Parky's Gold'*

'Golden Nakaiana' — See *H. 'Birchwood Parky's Gold'*

¶ 'Golden Oriole' — CBdn LHos

'Golden Prayers' (*tokudama*) — CBdn CBro CHad EGol ELan EMic ENot EOrc EPGN ERos GSki LGre LHos MMiN MRPP MRav NBro NFai NHol NOrc NTay SApp SChu SPer SSpi WAbe WHow WRus

'Golden Scepter' (*nakaiana*) — CBdn EGol EMic EPGN LHos MMiN NHol

'Golden Sculpture' (*sieboldiana*) — CBdn EGol

'Golden Spider' — EGol EMic

'Golden Sunburst' (*sieboldiana*) — CBdn CHad EGol ELan EMic EPGN GSki LHos MBal MMiN MOne NHol WFar

'Golden Tiara' (v) ♀ — Widely available

'Goldsmith' — EGol EMic

'Good as Gold' — EMic EPGN LHos

gracillima — CRow EPGN EPar LHyd NGre

'Granary Gold' (*fortunei*) — EGol EPGN LHos LRHS

'Grand Master' — CBdn EGol EMic EPGN LHos

'Grand Tiara' (v) — CBdn EPGN

'Great Expectations' (*sieboldiana*) (v) — CBdn CLAP CWin EBar EGol EMic EPGN GBri LHos LRHS NWes WRus

'Green Acres' (*montana*) — EMic MMiN

'Green Angel' — EGol

'Green Fountain' (*kikutii*) — CBdn EFou EGol EMic EPGN LHos MMiN MSte NWes WMer

'Green Gold' (*fortunei*) (v) — CBdn EMic MMiN WMer

'Green Piecrust' — CBdn CWin EGol EMic EPGN LHos

'Green Sheen' — CWin EGol EMic EPGN LHos SApp

¶ 'Green Summer Fragrance' — CBdn

'Green Velveteen' — EGol

'Green with Envy' (v) — EGol

'Greenwood' — EMic

¶ 'Grey Beauty' — EHic

'Ground Master' (v) — Widely available

'Ground Sulphur' — EGol EMic

'Guacamole' (v) — CBdn EGol EPGN

'Gum Drop' — EMic EPGN

(Tardiana Group)	CMHG EAst EBar EBrP EBre
'Hadspen Blue'	EGol EMic EPGN LBre MBel
	MBro MRav NBir NBro NHol
	NRoo SBre SChu SMrm SUsu
	WHow WRus WWat
(Tardiana Group)	CBro CHad
'Hadspen Blue Jay'	
(Tardiana Group)	EMic
'Hadspen Dolphin'	
(Tardiana Group)	CBdn EGol LGre LRHS
'Hadspen Hawk'	
(Tardiana Group)	CBdn CHad EGol EMic EPGN
'Hadspen Heron'	LHos MBal SChu
'Hadspen Samphire'	CBos CHad CHan EGol EMic
	EPGN
'Hadspen Seersucker'	CHad SLod
'Hadspen White' (*fortunei*)	EMic LHos
'Haku-chu-han' (*sieboldii*)	CBdn
(v)	
'Hakujima' (*sieboldii*)	EGol LGre
§ (Tardiana Group)	Widely available
'Halcyon' ♀	
(Tardiana Group)	CWin EGol EHoe EMic LHos
'Happiness'	
'Happy Hearts'	EGol EMic MMiN
(Tardiana Group)	EGol EMic LRHS
'Harmony'	
'Harrison'	EMic
'Harvest Glow'	EGol EMic
* 'Hazel'	EMic
¶ 'Heart Ache'	EGol
'Heartleaf'	EMic MMiN
'Heartsong' (v)	EGol LHos
'Heide Eurm'	LHos
'Helen Doriot' (*sieboldiana*)	EGol EMic SApp
'Helen Field Fischer'	CBdn EMic
(*fortunei*)	
helonioides f. *albopicta*	See *H. rohdeifolia*
hort.	
'Herifu' (v)	CBdn EGol EMic
'Hirao Majesty'	CBdn EGol
¶ 'Hirao Splendor'	LHos
'Hirao Supreme'	EGol
¶ 'Hirao Tetra'	CBdn
'Hoarfrost'	EMic
'Holstein'	See *H.* (**Tardiana Group**)
	'Halcyon'
§ 'Honeybells' ♀	Widely available
'Honeysong' (v)	CBdn EPGN
'Hoosier Harmony' (v)	CBdn EGol
'Hyacintha Variegata'	CMHG GBri MMiN
(*fortunei*)	
'Hydon Gleam'	EMic EPGN LHos MMiN
'Hydon Sunset' (*nakaiana*)	CBdn CHan CMHG EBrP EBre
	EGol EMic EOrc EPGN LBre
	LHos LHyd MBal MBro MHig
	MMiN NFai NHol NOak NSti
	NTay SAxl SBre SUsu WAbe
	WHoo WWat
hypoleuca	EGol NGre WLin
§ 'Inaho'	EGol EMic EPGN LHos MMiN
	NWes
'Inniswood' (*montana*) (v)	CLAP CWin EGol EPGN
	MMiN NWes
'Invincible'	CBdn CLAP EFou EGol EMic
	EPGN LHos MMiN NWes
	WMer
'Iona' (*fortunei*)	CBdn EGol EMic EPGN LHos
	SApp SSpi
'Irish Breeze'	EPGN
'Iron Gate Glamor'	EGol EPGN LHos
'Iron Gate Supreme' (v)	EMic

'Iwa Soules'	EGol
'Jade Beauty'	CBdn
'Jade Cascade'	CLAP CMil EBee EGol EHic
	NHol NWes SApp WCot
'Jade Scepter' (*nakaiana*)	EGol EMic LRHS
'Jadette' (v)	EGol
'Janet' (*fortunei*) (v)	CBdn EGol EMic EOrc MMiN
	WMer WSan
'Japan Boy'	See *H.* **'Montreal'**
'Japan Girl'	See *H.* **'Mount Royal'**
	(*sieboldii*)
'Joker' (*fortunei*) (v)	CBdn EBee NHol
'Jolly Green Giant'	EMic
(*sieboldiana* hybrid)	
'Journeyman'	EGol LHos
'Julie Morss'	CBdn EGol EMic EPGN LHos
	MMiN MMoz
'Jumbo' (*sieboldiana*)	EMic LHos
(Tardiana Group) 'June'	CBdn EBrP EBre EGol EMic
(v)	ENot EPGN GSki LBre LHos
	MLov NHar SApp SBre SMrm
	SPer WWeb
'June Beauty' (*sieboldiana*)	MMiN
'Just So' (v)	CBdn EGol LHos
'Kabitan'	See *H. sieboldii* f. *kabitan*
¶ 'Kath's Gold'	SIng
'Kelsey'	EMic
'Kifukurin' (*kikutii*) (v)	CBdn
I 'Kifukurin' (*pulchella*) (v)	EGol
'Kifukurin Ubatake'	EPGN
(*pulchella*)	
kikutii	EGol EMic EOrc MMiN NGre
§ – var. *caput-avis*	EBrP EBre EGol EMic LBre
	SBre
– var. *polyneuron*	CLAP EGol
– var. *tosana*	EGol
§ – var. *yakusimensis*	CRDP EGol EMic GCrs GDra
	NTow SMad
§ 'Kirishima'	CBdn CSev EMic EPGN MBel
	NHar SIng
kiyosumiensis	CRow CWin NHol
'Klopping Variegated'	EGol EMic
(*fortunei*)	
'Knave's Green'	EPGN
'Knockout' (v)	CBdn EGol EPGN LHos
'Krinkled Joy'	EMic NWes
¶ 'Krossa Cream Edge'	EBee NHol
(*sieboldii*) (v)	
'Krossa Regal' ♀	Widely available
'Lacy Belle' (v)	EGol
'Lady Helen'	EMic MMiN
'Lakeside Symphony' (v)	EGol LHos
§ *lancifolia* ♀	Widely available
'Leather Sheen'	EGol EMic EPGN
'Lee Armiger'	EGol
(*tokudama* hybrid)	
'Lemon Delight'	CBdn EPGN LHos
'Lemon Lime'	CBdn EGol EMic EPGN EPPr
	LHos MMiN SIng WMer
'Leola Fraim' (v)	CBdn EGol EPGN LHos
'Leviathan'	EMic
* *lilacina*	SCro
'Little Aurora'	EGol EMic EPGN MBal SIng
(*tokudama* hybrid)	
'Little Blue' (*ventricosa*)	EGol EMic SLod
'Little Fatty'	MMiN
'Little Razor'	EGol
'Little White Lines' (v)	EGol EMic EPGN LHos LRHS
'Little Wonder' (v)	EGol LHos
longipes	EGol
longissima	EGol LHyd WCru
– var. *longissima*	LHyd

'Pooh Bear' (v) — EGol
'Popo' — EGol
'Potomac Pride' — CBdn EPGN
'Puck' — EGol
'Purple Dwarf' — CWin EGol LBuc NHol WFox
¶ 'Purple Lady Finger' — SApp
'Purple Profusion' — EGol EMic
pycnophylla — EGol SWas
'Queen Josephine' (v) — CBdn EGol
'Radiant Edger' (v) — CBdn EGol EPGN LHos LRHS
'Raleigh Remembrance' — EGol LHos LRHS
'Rascal' (v) — CBdn EGol
'Raspberry Sorbet' — CBdn EGol
¶ *rectifolia* — CMHG EMic LHos NHol
'Regal Splendor' (v) — CBdn EGol EMic EPGN GSki LHos NWes
'Resonance' (v) — EBrP EBre EMic EPGN LBre LHos LRHS MMiN NTay SBre
'Reversed' (v) — CBdn CBlo EGol ELan EMic EPGN LHos NWes WRus
'Rhapsody' (*fortunei*) (v) — EGol
'Richland Gold' (*fortunei*) — EGol EMic LRHS
* 'Rippling Waters' — EGol
'Rippling Waves' — EMic
¶ 'Robert Frost' (v) — EGol
'Robusta' (*fortunei*) — See *H. sieboldiana* var. *elegans*
§ *rohdeifolia* (v) — CLAP EGol EMic LBuc WHal
§ – f. *albopicta* — CBdn EGol ELan EPGN EPar NDov NHol SChu
'Rosemoor' — EGol
¶ 'Royal Sovereign' — CHEx
§ 'Royal Standard' ♀ — Widely available
'Royalty' — EGol LHos
rupifraga — EGol EMic
'Russell's Form' — EMic
  (*ventricosa*)
'Ryan's Big One' — EMic
§ 'Sagae' ♀ — CBdn CLAP EBrP EBre EGol EMic EPGN LBre NWes SApp SBre WFar
§ 'Saishu Jima' — EGol EMic NHol WCru
  (*sieboldii spathulata*)
'Samual Blue' — EMic
'Samurai' (*sieboldiana*) (v) — CBdn EGol EMic LHos MRav
¶ 'Savannah' — EGol LHos
'Sazanami' (*crispula*) — See *H. crispula*
¶ 'Scooter' — CBdn
'Sea Bunny' — EGol
'Sea Dream' (v) — CWin EGol EMic EPGN LHos SApp
'Sea Drift' — EGol EPGN
'Sea Fire' — EGol
'Sea Gold Star' — EGol EPGN LRHS
'Sea Lotus Leaf' — CBdn EGol EMic EPGN LRHS
'Sea Monster' — EGol LRHS
'Sea Octopus' — EGol EMic
'Sea Sapphire' — EGol LHos LRHS
'Sea Sprite' (v) — EPGN LBuc LHos MRPP
'Sea Thunder' (v) — CBdn EGol
'Sea Yellow Sunrise' — CBdn EGol EMic SApp
¶ 'Second Wind' (*fortunei*) (v) — LHos
'See Saw' (*undulata*) — CBdn EGol EMic MMiN
¶ 'Semperaurea' (*sieboldiana*) — GSki
'Sentinels' — MMiN
'September Sun' (v) — CBdn EGol EMic EPGN LHos LRHS
'Serendipity' — CBdn EGol EMic EPGN LHos

'Shade Fanfare' (v) ♀ — CBdn CBro CHid EBar EBrP EBre EGol ELan EMic EOrc EPGN EPar LBre LHos MBal MBri MMiN MRav MWat NBir NFai NSti NTay SBre SCro WHil WHoo
'Shade Master' — CBlo EBrP EBre EGol EMic GBin GMac LBre MMil MOne NHol SBre
§ 'Sharmon' (*fortunei*) (v) — CBdn EGol EMic EPGN MBel MMiN NHol NTay NWes SChu SPer
¶ 'Sheila West' — CBdn
'Shelleys' (v) — EGol
(Tardiana Group) — EMic
  'Sherborne Profusion'
(Tardiana Group) — EMic
  'Sherborne Songbird'
(Tardiana Group) — EMic
  'Sherborne Swan'
'Sherborne Swift' — CBdn EGol EMic MMiN MMoz
'Shining Tot' — EGol EPGN LHos
'Shogun' (v) — EGol LHos
* 'Showboat' — CBdn EPGN
sieboldiana — CHad CHan CMHG CRow EBar EFou EGol ELan EMic EPar LFis LHos LHyd MBal MMiN NChi NHol NNor SPer WAbe WWat
§ – var. *elegans* ♀ — CB&S CBdn CBot CBro CGle CHad ECha EGol ENot EOrc EPGN GDra LBuc LGro LHop LHyd LPBA MBal MBar MBri MMiN NHol NNor NRoo SApp SMad SPer WEas WWat
§ *sieboldii* var. *alba* — CHad CHan CMGP EGol ELan SSpi
§ – f. *kabitan* (v) — CBdn CLAP CWin EGol EPGN LHos MHig NHar
– f. *shiro-kabitan* (v) — EGol EPGN
– var. *thunbergiana* — See *H. sieboldii* f. *spathulata*
¶ 'Silver and Gold' — MMiN
* 'Silver Chimes' — WHil
♦ 'Silver Crown' — See *H.* 'Albomarginata'
'Silver Lance' (v) — EGol EMic EPGN
(Tardiana Group) 'Silvery — CBdn SApp
  Slugproof'
'Sitting Pretty' (v) — EGol EPGN
'Snow Cap' (v) — CBdn EGol EPGN LHos NWes
'Snow Crust' (*elata*) (v) — CBdn EGol EMic LRHS
'Snow Flakes' (*sieboldii*) — CBdn CHEx EGol EMic EMil EPGN GCal LHos MBar MBri MCli NBro NFla NHol NPro SLod SPer WFar WMer
'Snowden' — CBdn CHad EBrP EBre ECha EGol EMic EOrc EPGN GMaP LBre LHos MBal MBro MMiN NBir NHol NTay SBre SCro SSpi WHoo WRus WTin WViv WWat
¶ 'Snowstorm' (*sieboldii*) — CBdn NHol
'So Sweet' — CBdn CBlo CLAP EGol EMic EPGN GSki LHos MBro WRus WWat
'Something Blue' — CBdn LHos
sp. from Japan — EPPr
'Sparkling Burgundy' — CBdn EGol
'Special Gift' — EGol EMic LBuc LHos
§ 'Spinners' (*fortunei*) (v) — CBdn CHad ECha EGol EMic MMiN SChu SSpi
'Sprengeri' — MMiN
'Spritzer' (v) — CBdn EGol EMic EPGN LHos

'Squash Edge' (*sieboldiana*) EPGN
(v)
'Squiggles' (v) — EGol LHos
§ 'Starker Yellow Leaf' — EMic
¶ 'Stenantha' (*fortunei*) — EMic
¶ 'Stenantha Variegated' — NHol
(*fortunei*) (v)
'Stiletto' (v) — CBdn EGol EPGN LHos NHar
¶ 'Striptease' (*fortunei*) (v) — EGol
'Sugar and Cream' (v) — CBdn EGol EMic EOrc EPGN
LHos MMiN NWes SApp
'Sugar Plum Fairy' — EGol
(*gracillima*)
¶ 'Sultana' (v) — CBdn
'Sum and Substance' ♥ — CB&S CBdn CBlo CDec CHad
EAst EBar EBrP EBre EGol
ELan EMic EPGN GBin GMaP
LBre LRot MCLN MLov MMiN
MRav NBro NEgg NTay NWes
SApp SBre SSpi WCot WMer
'Summer Fragrance' — CBdn CWin EGol EMic EPGN
LHos LRHS SApp
'Summer Music' (v) — CBdn EGol EPGN LHos
'Summer Snow' — EPGN
(*sieboldiana*) (v)
'Sun Glow' — EMic
'Sun Power' — CBdn CBro CSpe EBrP EBre
EGol EMic EOrc EPGN EPar
LBre LHos MMiN MMoz MWat
NTay SBre WRus
'Sundance' (*fortunei*) (v) — EGol EMic
* 'Sunflower' — NOak
'Super Bowl' — EGol LRHS
'Super Nova' (v) — EGol
'Suzuki Thumbnail' — EMic
'Sweet Susan' — CBlo EGol EMic EOrc MMiN
SPer WMer
'Sweet Tater Pie' — CBdn EPGN
'Sweetheart' — EMic
¶ 'Swirling Hearts' — EGol
'Tall Boy' — CBdn CSev ECha EGol EMic
EPGN GCal LHos MWgw NHol
SApp SPer SSpi WWat
'Tall Twister' — EMic
'Tamborine' (v) — EGol EPGN LHos
Tardiana Group — CBdn CBro CMGP EGol ELan
EMon MBal NHol SPer WKif
Tardiana Group — MMiN
pink-flowered
tardiflora — CBdn CFil EGol EMic ERos
MBal MHig SApp WCot WPGP
tardiva — CMHG LHos NGre
¶ 'Temple Bells' — EGol LHos
'Tenryu' — EGol LHos
'The Twister' — EGol EMic MMiN
'Thomas Hogg' — See *H. undulata* var.
albomarginata
'Thumb Nail' — CBdn ECha EGol GAri GSki
tibae — EMic
'Tiny Tears' (*venusta*) — EGol
tokudama — CHad CHan EFou EGol EPGN
IHos LWak MBri MBro NBir
NFai NHol NSti SChu SPla
WKif
§ – f. *aureonebulosa* — EGol EPGN LGre LHos
– f. *flavocircinalis* (v) — CBdn EBee EBrP EBre ECha
EGol EMic EPGN LBre LHos
MMiN MApp SBre
'Tot Tot' — EMic GAri
'Trail's End' — EMic
'True Blue' — CBdn EBee EGol EMic EPGN
LHos MMiN NWes

'Tutu' — EGol
'Twinkle Toes' — EMic
undulata — EMic LFis NDea SRms WFar
§ – var. *albomarginata* — CBdn CBro CHEx CHan CKel
CMHG ECha EFou EGol ELan
EMic ENot EPGN GDra LHos
LHyd MBar MMiN MTho
MWat NDea NFai NHol NNor
NRoo NSti SPer WEas WWat
§ – var. *erromena* ♥ — CBdn CHan CMGP EHon EMic
LFis LHos LPBA MBro NFla
NHol SChu SPer SSpi WLin
§ – var. *undulata* (v) ♥ — CBdn CBot CBro CRow EAst
EHoe EHon ELan ENot EPGN
GChr LGro LHyd LPBA MBri
MMiN SChu SPer WEas WKif
WRus WWin
– var. *univittata* (v) ♥ — CBro CRow ECha EGol EMic
EPGN EPfP LHos LHyd MMiN
MMoz NDov NFai NPro NTay
SPla WKif
'Urajiro Hachijo' — EGol
'Urajiro' (*hypoleuca*) — EGol
'Valentine Lace' — CBdn EGol EMic EPGN NWes
WMer
'Vanilla Cream' (*cathayana*) — EGol EMic EPGN LHos
'Variegata' (*gracillima*) — See *H.* 'Vera Verde'
'Variegata' (*tokudama*) — See *H. tokudama* f.
aureonebulosa
'Variegata' (*undulata*) — See *H. undulata* var. *undulata*
'Variegata' (*ventricosa*) — See *H.* 'Aureomarginata'
(*ventricosa*)
'Variegated' (*fluctuans*) — See *H.* 'Sagae'
ventricosa ♥ — CBro CHad CHid CKel EAst
EBot EBrP EBre EGol EGoo
EMic EPGN GDra GMaP LBre
LHyd LPBA MNrw NHar NHol
NVic SBre SMrm SSpi WFox
WWat
– var. *aureomaculata* — CHad EBee EGol EMic ENot
EPGN LHos MMiN NCut NTay
SPer
I 'Venucosa' — EGol EMic
'Venus Star' — EPGN GSki
venusta ♥ — CBro CMHG CRow CSWP
EBrP EBre EGol ELan EMic
EOrc EPGN EPar ERos LBre
LGre LHil MBal MHig NHar
NMen NNrd SBre SHFr WEas
WHil WOMN WWat
– dwarf form — CSWP LGre
– × *sieboldiana* — CHan
– *yakusimensis* — See *H. kikutii* var. *yakusimensis*
§ 'Vera Verde' (v) — CBdn CHid CWin EPGN GCra
GQui
¶ 'Verna Jean' (v) — EGol
¶ 'Veronica Lake' (v) — EGol
'Verte' (*sieboldii*) — See *H. sieboldii* f. *spathulata*
'Viette's Yellow Edge' — MMiN
(*fortunei*) (v)
'Vilmoriniana' — EGol EMic MMiN
'Viridis Marginata' — See *H. sieboldii* f. *kabitan*
(Tardiana Group)
'Wagtail' — EMic
'Wahoo' (*tokudama*) (v) — EGol
'Waving Winds' (v) — EGol LHos
'Wayside Blue' — EMic
'Wayside Perfection' — See *H.* 'Royal Standard'
'Weihenstephan' (*sieboldii*) — EGol
'Wheaton Blue' — CBdn LHos
'Whirlwind' (*fortunei*) (v) — CBdn EGol EPGN
'White Fairy' (*plantaginea*) — CBdn EPGN

'White Gold' — CBdn EGol EPGN LHos
'White Tacchi' — EMon
'Wide Brim' (v) ♀ — Widely available
'Wind River Gold' — EGol SApp
'Windsor Gold' — See *H.* **'Nancy Lindsay'** (*fortunei*)
* 'Winfield Gold' — CBdn EGol
'Winning Edge' (*tokudama*) — EGol
'Wogon Giboshi' — See *H.* **'Wogon'** (*sieboldii*)
§ 'Wogon' (*sieboldii*) — CBdn CM&M CRDP CRow EFou EGol EMic EPGN EPla GMaP NHar NHol
'Wogon's Boy' — EGol EPGN
'Wrinkles and Crinkles' — EMic LRHS
'Yakushima-mizu' (*gracillima*) — CBdn EGol EMic
* *yakushimana* — NHar
'Yellow Boa' — EMic
'Yellow Edge' (*fortunei*) — See *H. fortunei* var. *aureomarginata*
'Yellow Edge' (*sieboldiana*) — See *H.* **'Frances Williams'** (*sieboldiana*)
'Yellow River' (*montana*) — CBdn ECha EGol EMic EPGN LHos LRHS (v)
'Yellow Splash' (v) — CBdn CWin ECha EPGN LHos MBel MMiN NTay
'Yellow Splash Rim' (v) — EGol LHos MBel MMiN WBcn
yingeri — EGol
– B&SWJ 546 — WCru
'Zager Blue' — EMic
'Zager Green' — EMic
'Zager White Edge' (*fortunei*) (v) — CLAP EMic EPGN LHos
'Zounds' — Widely available

HOTTONIA (Primulaceae)

palustris — CBen ECoo EHon ELan EMFW LPBA MSta NDea NVic SWat SWyc

HOUSTONIA (Rubiaceae)

caerulea hort. — See *H. michauxii*
caerulea Linnaeus — CSam ECho ELan NGre WWin
– var. *alba* — CInt ELan EWes NGre WPer
§ *michauxii* — GAri SGre
– 'Fred Mullard' — EHyt EPot EWes NPri

HOUTTUYNIA (Saururaceae)

cordata — GBar IBlr MWgw NLak NSti SWat
§ *cordata* 'Chameleon' (v) — Widely available
¶ – 'Flame' — LRHS
– 'Flore Pleno' (d) — CBen CGle CRow ECha EHon ELan EPla LGan LPBA MBal MRav MSta NBir NBro NWes SIde SIng SPer SRms SWat SWyc WChe WMAq WOld WRus WWin
– 'Tricolor' — See *H. cordata* **'Chameleon'**
– Variegata Group — EPot GBar IBlr LPBA MAsh NBro NDea WChe
* 'Pied Piper' — CDoC SCoo

HOVEA (Papilionaceae)

celsii — See *H. elliptica*

HOVENIA (Rhamnaceae)

¶ *acerba* — WPGP
dulcis — CB&S CGre CMCN CPle ELan EPfP SCob

HOWEA (Arecaceae)

§ *belmoreana* — LPal NPal
forsteriana ♀ — LPal MBri

HOYA (Asclepiadaceae)

acuta — LChe
angustifolia — LChe
¶ *archboldiana* — LChe
arnottiana — SLMG
§ *australis* — ECon LCns SLMG SOWG
bandaensis — SLMG
bilobata — LChe
carnosa ♀ — CB&S EBak ELan GQui LCns NRog SLMG SRms
– 'Compacta' — CHal SLMG
* – *compacta* 'Hindu Rope' — NPer
– 'Exotica' ♀ — SLMG
* – 'Jungle Garden' — SLMG
* – 'Krinkle' — NPer
– 'Krinkle Eight' — SLMG
¶ – 'Latifolia' — ECon
– 'Red Princess' — MBri
– 'Rubra' — SLMG
¶ – 'Tricolor' — NPer
– 'Variegata' — LCns MBri SLMG SRms
cinnamomifolia — LCns SOWG
* *compacta* 'Tricolor' — NPer
cumingiana — LChe
darwinii hort. — See *H. australis*
¶ *densifolia* — LChe
¶ *eitapensis* — LChe
engleriana — SLMG
fuscomarginata — See *H. pottsii*
globulosa — LChe
imperialis — LChe SLMG
¶ *inconspicua* — LChe
kerrii — LChe
lacunosa — LChe
lanceolata subsp. *bella* ♀ — CB&S CHal GQui MBri NRog SRms
linearis — LChe
longifolia — LChe
macgillivrayi — ECon LChe
¶ *magnifica* — LChe
motoskei — LChe
multiflora — LChe LCns MBri SOWG
¶ – 'Variegata' (v) — LChe
neocaledonica — SLMG
nicholsoniae — LChe
¶ *nummularioides* — LChe
¶ *odorata* — LChe
¶ *parviflora* — LChe
pauciflora — LChe
polyneura — SLMG
pubicalyx 'Red Buttons' — LChe SLMG
* – 'Silver Pink' — LChe
purpureofusca — LChe
shepherdii — LChe
'Shibata' — LChe

HUGUENINIA (Brassicaceae)

alpina — See *H. tanacetifolia*

HUMATA (Davalliaceae)

◆ *pyxidata* — See *Davallia solida* var. *pyxidata* (Hook.) Noot.

HUMEA (Asteraceae)

elegans — See *Calomeria amaranthoides*

HUMULUS (Cannabaceae)
japonicus	ECoo MSal
lupulus	CAgr CArn CB&S CPlN ECoo
	ELau GAri GBar GPoy ILis
	LHol MHew MSal NBee SIde
	WBea WHer WSel WStI WWye
– 'Aureus' ♀	Widely available
– 'Aureus' (f)	WWat
– 'Aureus' (m)	WWat
¶ – 'Cobbs'	GPoy
– 'Fuggle'	GPoy
– 'Hip-hop'	EMon
– 'Taff's Variegated'	EMon EWes
– 'Wye Challenger'	GPoy

HUNNEMANNIA (Papaveraceae)
fumariifolia 'Sunlite'	CPle

HUTCHINSIA See THLASPI

HYACINTHELLA (Hyacinthaceae)
lineata M&T 5048	CMon
millingenii	EHyt

HYACINTHOIDES (Hyacinthaceae)
§ *hispanica*	CAvo CBro CHid EWFC GBur
	IBlr MBri NBir NHol WWye
– 'Alba'	GBur
– *algeriensis* AB&S 4337	CMon
– Donau	See *H. hispanica* 'Danube'
– 'Excelsior'	ETub
– 'La Grandesse'	CBro
– 'Rosabella'	CBro
§ *italica*	CMon
§ – *vicentina*	CMon
§ *non-scripta*	CArn CAvo CBro CKin EOld
	EPar EPot ETub EWFC GBur
	GDra IBlr LAma LFox MBri
	MMal NMir NRog WCla WShi
– pink bell	MSto

HYACINTHUS † (Hyacinthaceae)
amethystinus	See *Brimeura amethystina*
azureus	See *Muscari azureum*
comosus 'Plumosus'	See *Muscari comosum*
	'Plumosum'
fastigiatus	See *Brimeura fastigiata*
orientalis 'Amethyst'	EWal LAma NRog
– 'Amsterdam'	ETub EWal LAma NRog
– 'Anna Liza'	NRog
– 'Anna Marie' ♀	CAvo CBro ETub EWal LAma
	MBri NRog
– 'Ben Nevis' (d)	LAma MBri NRog
– 'Bismarck'	LAma NRog
– 'Blue Giant'	LAma NRog
– 'Blue Jacket' ♀	CBro ETub LAma NRog
– 'Blue Magic'	EWal LAma NRog
– 'Blue Orchid' (d)	LAma
– 'Blue Star'	LAma
– 'Borah' ♀	EWal LAma NRog
– 'Carnegie'	CBro ETub EWal LAma NRog
– 'City of Haarlem' ♀	CBro ETub EWal LAma NRog
– 'Colosseum'	LAma
– 'Concorde'	LAma
– 'Delft Blue' ♀	CAvo CBro EWal LAma MBri
	NRog
– 'Distinction'	LAma
– 'Edelweiss'	LAma
– 'Fondant'	LAma
– 'Gipsy Queen' ♀	CBro ETub EWal LAma MBri
	NRog

– 'Hollyhock' (d)	ETub EWal LAma MBri NRog
– 'Jan Bos'	CAvo EWal LAma NRog
– 'King Codro' (d)	LAma MBri NRog
– 'King of the Blues'	LAma NRog
– 'La Victoire'	LAma NRog
– 'Lady Derby'	EWal LAma
– 'L'Innocence' ♀	CBro LAma NRog
– 'Lord Balfour'	LAma
– 'Madame Krüger'	LAma
– 'Marconi' (d)	LAma NRog
– 'Marie'	LAma NRog
– 'Mont Blanc'	EWal
– 'Mulberry Rose'	EWal LAma NRog
– 'Myosotis'	LAma
§ – 'Oranje Boven'	LAma
– 'Ostara' ♀	CBro EWal LAma MBri NRog
– 'Peter Stuyvesant'	EWal LAma NRog
– 'Pink Pearl' ♀	CBro LAma NRog
– 'Pink Royal' (d)	LAma NRog
– 'Princess Margaret'	LAma
– 'Prins Hendrik'	LAma
– 'Queen of the Pinks'	LAma NRog
– 'Queen of the Violets'	NRog
– 'Rosalie'	EWal
– 'Rosette' (d)	LAma
– 'Salmonetta'	See *H. orientalis* 'Oranje
	Boven'
§ – 'Sneeuwwitje'	LAma NRog
– Snow White	See *H. orientalis* 'Sneewwitje'
– 'Violet Pearl'	CBro LAma NRog
– 'Vuurbaak'	LAma
– 'White Pearl'	CAvo LAma NRog
* 'Woodstock'	ETub

HYBANTHUS (Violaceae)
¶ *floribundus*	MFiF

HYDRANGEA † (Hydrangeaceae)
¶ *angustipetala*	CFil
¶ *angustipetala* B&SWJ 3454	WCru
¶ *anomala* subsp. *anomala*	SSpi
¶ – – B&SWJ 2411	WCru
¶ – from Taiwan B&SWJ 3117	WCru
§ – subsp. *petiolaris* ♀	Widely available
§ – – var. *cordifolia*	CFil CHan EBar EPla MTho
	SBra SReu SSta WPGP WWeb
– – dwarf form	See *H. anomala* subsp.
	petiolaris cordifolia
– subsp. *petiolaris*	EPfP MBlu SNut
tiliifolia	
– subsp. *petiolaris*	CFil WPGP
'Yakushima'	
§ *arborescens*	CArn CFil MRav NNor WPGP
	WWeb
– 'Annabelle' ♀	Widely available
§ – subsp. *discolor*	WCru
– – 'Sterilis'	CFil EHic EPla SPla SSpi WCru
	WPGP
– 'Grandiflora' ♀	CB&S CBot CFil ELan GOrc
	SBod SPer WDin WHCG
	WPGP WSHC WWin
– subsp. *radiata*	CFil CHan ELan SNut SSpi
	WCru WPGP WWat
aspera	CBlo CFil CGre GOrc IOrc
	SAga SMac SSpi SSta WCru
– Kawakamii Group	CFil EPla WPGP
§ – 'Macrophylla' ♀	CBlo CFil EPfP EPla MBri NPal
	SSpi WCru WGer WPGP WWat
– 'Mauvette'	CFil MBlu NPal SSpi SSta
	WCru WPGP
– 'Peter Chappell'	SSpi

§ – subsp. *robusta*	CMil GAri SMac SNut WPGP WShe
¶ – 'Rocklon'	CFil WPGP
– 'Rosthornii'	See *H. aspera* subsp. *robusta*
¶ – 'Sam Macdonald'	CFil SSpi WPGP
§ – subsp. *sargentiana* ♀	CB&S CBot CFil CHEx CHad COtt ELan LNet MBal MBlu MBri NPal SArc SHBN SMad SPer SSpi SSta WAbe WCru WDin WPGP WWat
– subsp. *strigosa*	CFil ELan EPfP SBid SVen WPGP
– 'Taiwan'	SSpi
§ – Villosa Group ♀	Widely available
¶ – – 'Kawakami'	WCru
§ 'Blue Deckle' (L)	CFil CMHG EBar SBid SNut SSpi WPGP
'Blue Tit'	See *H. macrophylla* '**Blaumeise**'
cinerea	See *H. arborescens* subsp. *discolor*
¶ 'Diabolo'	MRav
§ 'Grant's Choice' (L)	EHic NHol
heteromalla	CFai CFil CMHG WCru WPGP
¶ – B&SWJ 2142	WCru
– Bretschneideri Group ♀	GAri GQui WCru WWat
¶ – HWJCM 148	WCru
¶ – HWJCM 493	WCru
– 'Morrey's Form'	WCru
– SF 338	ISea
– 'Snowcap'	GQui WBcn WCru
– f. *xanthoneura*	CFil GAri WPGP
¶ – – 'Wilsonii'	WCru
integerrima	See *H. serratifolia*
integrifolia	CPlN
– B&SWJ 022	WCru
involucrata	CFil EPfP MBal MPla SBid SMrm SSpi SSta WCru
¶ – dwarf form	WCru
– 'Hortensis' (d) ♀	CFil CPle IOrc SSpi WCru WKif WSHC
¶ 'Korale Red'	WBcn
¶ 'Lady Fujiyo'	CB&S
¶ 'Lady Katsuko'	CB&S
¶ 'Lady Mariko'	CB&S
¶ 'Lady Nobuko'	CB&S
¶ 'Lady Taiko Blue'	CB&S
¶ 'Lady Taiko Pink'	CB&S
longipes	CFil WPGP
luteovenosa	WCru
macrophylla Alpen Glow	See *H. macrophylla* '**Alpenglühen**'
§ – 'Alpenglühen' (H)	CB&S CFil ELan ESis IOrc NPro SBid SBod SHBN SPla SRms WPGP
– 'Altona' (H) ♀	CB&S CFil GAri IOrc ISea MAll MBal MGos MRav SAxl SBid SBod SPer WPGP WStI
– 'Amethyst' (H/d)	CFil WPGP
– 'Ami Pasquier' (H) ♀	CB&S CBlo CDoC CFil EBee EPfP IOrc SBid SSpi WGer WPGP
– 'Aureovariegata'	CEnd CFil ELan SNut WPGP
– 'Ayesha' (H) ♀	Widely available
¶ – 'Ayesha Blue'	MAsh
– 'Beauté Vendômoise' (L)	CFil SBid SSpi WPGP
– 'Benelux' (H)	CB&S CWSG EHic MAll SBid WGwG WLRN WTro
* – 'Bicolour'	MAsh
§ – 'Blauer Prinz' (H)	CB&S GCHN IOrc MAll SAxl SHBN WLRN

§ – 'Blaumeise' (L)	CFil MAsh SBid SSpi WGer WPGP
– 'Blue Bird'	CWSG
– 'Blue Bonnet' (H)	COtt EPfP MAsh SPer WHen WLRN WPGP
– Blue Prince	See *H. macrophylla* '**Blauer Prinz**'
– 'Blue Sky'	See *H. macrophylla* '**Blaumeise**'
– 'Blue Wave'	See *H. macrophylla* '**Mariesii Perfecta**'
– 'Bodensee' (H)	CB&S COtt NFla SBod SPla WStI
– 'Bouquet Rose' (H)	CBlo COtt ECtt EHal EHic MAll MGos NBee NFla WGwG
– 'Brunette' (H)	CFil
– 'Buchfink'	CFil WPGP
– 'Cordata'	See *H. arborescens*
– 'Covent Garden'	MAll
– 'Deutschland' (H)	CTri IOrc
– 'Domotoi' (H/d)	CFil SPan WPGP
* – 'Dwaag Pink'	MRav
¶ – 'Eldorado' (H)	EHol
§ – 'Enziandom' (H)	CB&S CFil SMrm SSpi WAbe WPGP
– 'Europa' (H) ♀	CB&S CTrw IOrc MAll MAsh MGos NCut SBod SEND WGwG WStI WWal
§ – Fasan℗	CFil WPGP WSPU
◆ – 'Firelight'	See *H. macrophylla* '**Leuchtfeuer**'
– 'Fischers Silberblau' (H)	CFil
– 'Forever Pink'	EBrP EBre LBre MAsh SBre
– 'Frillibet' (H)	CFil LRHS SBid WCru WPGP
– 'Gartenbaudirektor Kuhnert' (H)	SMer
§ – 'Générale Vicomtesse de Vibraye' (H) ♀	CB&S CEnd CFil CMHG CTri EPfP GCHN ISea MBal MBar MBri NFla SAxl SBid SHBN SNut SPer SReu SSpi WBod WLRN WPGP WWin
– Gentian Dome	See *H. macrophylla* '**Enziandom**'
– 'Geoffrey Chadbund' (L) ♀	CB&S CEnd CFil ECtt ENot EPla IHos MBri SAxl SBod SChu SDix SMad SNut SPer SRms SSpi SSta WPGP WWeb
– 'Gerda Steiniger'	CB&S CBlo
– 'Gertrud Glahn' (H)	CB&S CBlo NCut
– 'Glowing Embers'	CFil SEND WPGP
¶ – 'Gold Dust'	WPGP
– 'Goliath' (H)	CBlo CFil EPfP MBri SBid WPGP
– 'Hamburg' (H)	CB&S CEnd CFil CTri EBee ECtt ENot EPfP IOrc LPVe MGos NBee NCut SAxl SBid SDix WAbe WPGP WStI WWeb
– 'Harlequin'	CFil WPGP
– 'Harry's Pink Topper' (H)	MAsh
– 'Hatfield Rose' (H)	CB&S
– 'Heinrich Seidel' (H)	CB&S CFil MAll WPGP
– 'Holstein' (H)	CFil MAsh NBee SBid WPGP
§ – 'Hörnli'	CFil WPGP
– 'Intermezzo'	MAll WLRN
¶ – 'Izu-no-hana' (L/d)	SWas
– 'James Grant'	See *H.* '**Grant's Choice**'
§ – 'Joseph Banks' (H)	EHic
– 'Kardinal'	CFil WPGP

– 'King George' (H)   CB&S CFil CWSG EBee EBrP EBre EHic IOrc LBre MBar MGos MRav SBid SBre SPer WPGP WStI WWal

– 'Kluis Superba' (H)   CB&S CBlo CFil CTri IOrc MRav WPGP

§ – 'Koningin Wilhelmina' (H)   CFil WPGP

– 'La France' (H)   CB&S CBlo COtt CTri CWSG EHic GChr MBar MRav SBid

– 'Lanarth White' (L) ♀   CB&S CFil CTri EBee EHic ELan MPla SBid SHBN SPer SReu SRms SSpi WBod WPGP WWat WWeb

§ – 'Leuchtfeuer' (H)   WGer

§ – 'Libelle' (L)   CB&S CBlo CFil CWSG EBee EHic MAsh MBri SLPl SMrm SNut SPer WKif WPGP WWat WWeb

– 'Lilacina' (L)   CFil EHic EPfP MAll MWhi SAxl SBid SLPl SPer SSpi WKif WPGP

§ – 'Maculata' (L)   EHol ELan GQui IOrc MAll SEas WWat

– 'Madame A. Riverain' (H)   COtt CWSG EHic MAll SBod WLRN WTro

§ – 'Madame Emile Mouillère' (H) ♀   CB&S CBot CEnd CFil ENot IOrc MAll MBri NFla SAga SAxl SBod SDix SHBN SMad SMer SNut SPer SPla SRms SSoC SSpi SSta WGwG WPGP WTro

– 'Maréchal Foch' (H)   CFil CTri IOrc WPGP

– 'Mariesii' (L)   CMHG CTri EBee ELan ENot EPla ISea MAll MBal NBee SAxl SBid SDix SPer WKif WLRN WStI WWat

§ – 'Mariesii Perfecta' (L) ♀   CChe CMHG CPri CTri ELan ENot ISea MBar MGos MRav NFla SAxl SDix SNut SPer SSta WFar WGwG WHen WStI WWal WWat

– 'Mariesii Variegata' (L)   WCot

– 'Masja' (H)   CB&S COtt CWSG EBee EGra EHic IHos IOrc MBri MGos NBee NFla SHBN SVil WAbe

– 'Mathilda Gutges' (H)   CFil CWSG EHic SSpi WPGP WStI

– 'Mini Hörnli'   See *H. macrophylla* **'Hörnli'**

– 'Miss Belgium' (H)   CTri IOrc MBal MBri SBod SEas

– 'Miss Hepburn'   COtt SPer

– Morning Red   See *H. macrophylla* **'Morgenrot'**

– 'Mousmée'   CFil WPGP

– 'Niedersachsen' (H)   CFil EPla MRav SBid SMer WPGP

– 'Nigra' (H) ♀   CChe CFil CGre CHan CTre ELan EPla IOrc MAll MBal MGos SBid SDix SHBN SNut SPer WAbe WCru WGwG WPGP WStI WWal

– 'Nikko Blue'   CB&S CBlo CFil EGra EPfP SBid SEND WPGP

§ – 'Nymphe' (H)   SNut

– 'Otaksa' (H)   MAll

– 'Parzifal' (H) ♀   CB&S CFil CTrw EHic EPfP MBri WPGP WWal

◆ – 'Pax'   See *H. macrophylla* **'Nymphe'**

◆ – Pheasant   See *H. macrophylla* **'Fasan'**

– 'Pia' (H)   CB&S CDec CFil EHyt ELan ESis IOrc MAsh MBal MHig MPla MTho NHol SApp SBod SIng SMad SMrm SPer SPla SRms WOMN WPGP WPat WWat

– 'Pink Wave' (L)   CB&S

– 'Prinses Beatrix'   CChe CFil WBcn WPGP

– 'Quadricolor' (L/v)   CAbb CDec CFil CHan CMil EHoe EPla MBri MRav NRoo NSti SDix SHBN SNut SPer SPla SRms WCru WHCG WPGP WSHC

– Queen Wilhelmina   See *H. macrophylla* **'Koningin Wilhelmina'**

– 'R.F. Felton'   CB&S

– Redbreast   See *H. macrophylla* **'Rotkehlchen'**

– 'Regula' (H)   CTrw

– 'Rosita' (H)   LPan MAsh

§ – 'Rotkehlchen'   CFil SBid WCru WPGP

– 'Rotschwanz' (L)   CFil SSpi WPGP

– 'Saint Claire'   CB&S

– 'Sea Foam' (L)   EPla IOrc WSPU

– 'Sibylla' (H)   CB&S CFil MAll WPGP WWeb

– Sister Therese   See *H. macrophylla* **'Soeur Thérèse'**

§ – 'Soeur Thérèse' (H)   CB&S CBlo CFil GAri IOrc MAll MAsh MGos WPGP WStI WWeb

– 'Souvenir du Président Paul Doumer' (H)   CB&S CBlo

– 'Taube'   CB&S CFil GQui WPGP

– Teller Blau (L)   CBlo COtt MBri SCoo SSta WDin WWeb

– Teller Rosa (L)   EBrP EBre LBre MAsh SBre SCoo SSta

– Teller Rot (L)   CBlo EHic IHos MAsh MBri NHol SCoo WDin

– 'Teller Variegated'   See *H. macrophylla* **'Tricolor'**

– Teller Weiss   See *H. macrophylla* **'Libelle'**

– 'Tokyo Delight'   CB&S CBlo CBrd CChe CEnd CFil EBee EHic IOrc SBid SSpi WPGP

– 'Tovelit'   GAri MBri WWeb

§ – 'Tricolor' (L/v) ♀   CB&S CBot CFil CGre EAst EOrn EPla ERav GOrc MAll MAsh MBri MGos NBee SAga SBod SPer SReu WCru WKif WPGP WPyg WWal

– 'Val de Loire'   CBlo CWSG

– 'Variegata'   See *H. macrophylla* **'Maculata'**

– 'Veitchii' (L) ♀   CB&S CBot CFil CMHG ENot EPfP MBri SAxl SBid SBod SDix SPer SSpi WPGP WWat

– 'Vicomte de Vibraye'   See *H. macrophylla* **'Générale Vicomtesse de Vibraye'**

– Vulcan   See *H. macrophylla* **'Vulcain'**

– 'Westfalen' (H) ♀   NCat SMrm SPla WWal

– 'White Lace' (L)   ELan

– White Swan   See *H. macrophylla* **'Le Cygne'**

– 'White Wave' (L) ♀   CBlo CFil CHad EBee ENot MBar NFla SBid SBod SEND SHBN SNut SPer SRms SSpi WDin WLRN WPGP WStI CFil CMCN CTrw

paniculata

– 'Brussels Lace'   CAbP CFil CPMA LRHS MAsh SNut SPla SSpi WPGP

– 'Burgundy Lace'   CPMA MBlu

– 'Everest'   LRHS SNut

– 'Floribunda' ♀   CFil LRHS SNut SPer SSpi WPGP WRHF

¶ – from Taiwan B&SWJ 3804 — WCru
- 'Grandiflora' ♀ — Widely available
- 'Greenspire' — CPMA LRHS SPla WBcn
- 'Kyushu' ♀ — Widely available
- 'Pink Diamond' — CAbP CBlo CLAP CMCN CPMA EBee EBrP EBre ENot LBre LHop MAsh NRoo SBre SMad SSpi SSta WCru WHCG
- 'Praecox' ♀ — SPer WPat WWin
- 'Tardiva' — CB&S CBot EMil EPla LPan MAsh MRav SDix SPer SPla SRms WFar WHCG WLRN WPat WPyg
- 'Unique' ♀ — CB&S CDoC CFil CPMA EHic GOrc LHop MAsh MBri SNut SPer SPla SSpi WCru WPGP WWat
- 'White Moth' — CFil CPMA SNut WPGP
§ 'Preziosa' ♀ — Widely available
quelpartensis — CB&S CHan CPlN CRHN CTre GQui SBid SSpi WCru
quercifolia ♀ — Widely available
- 'Flore Pleno' — See *H. quercifolia* Snow Flake
- 'Harmony' — CEnd CFil CHad SSta WPGP
- 'Sike's Dwarf' — CEnd CFil LRHS SSpi SSta WPGP
* – 'Snow' — CWSG
§ – Snow Flake® (d) — CAbP CB&S CEnd CFil COtt CPMA CSPN ELan EMil IOrc MBri SMad SPer SSpi SSta WHCG WPGP WWat
- 'Snow Queen' — CB&S CDoC CMil CPMA GOrc IOrc MAsh MBal MBri MGos SCob SPer SPla SSta WHCG
- 'Stardust' — CRos
- 'Tennessee Clone' — CFil WPGP
sargentiana — See *H. aspera* subsp. *sargentiana*
scandens — CPle
¶ – subsp. *chinensis* B&SWJ 3420 — WCru
- subsp. *liukiuensis* — WCru
seemannii — CAbP CB&S CBot CFil CGre CHEx CMac CPlN CRHN CSam CTrw ECre ELan GQui ISea LHop SArc SBra SSpi WCru WPGP WSHC WWal WWat
serrata — CTrw WCru
- 'Acuminata' — See *H. serrata* 'Bluebird'
¶ – 'Aigaku' — WPGP
¶ – 'Amacha' — WPGP
- 'Belle Deckle' — See *H.* 'Blue Deckle'
- 'Beni-gaku' — CB&S CFil NFla SBid WLRN WPGP
¶ – 'Blue Deckle' (L) — WPGP
§ – 'Bluebird' ♀ — Widely available
- 'Diadem' — CBlo CBrd CFai CFil CHan NPro SBid SBod SDix SNut SSpi WCru WLRN WPGP
- 'Grayswood' ♀ — CEnd CFil CHig CPle ENot GQui LHop MBal SBid SDix SPer WAbe WKif WLRN WPGP WWat
- 'Intermedia' — CFil WPGP
¶ – *koreana* — WLRN
- 'Macrosepala' — EHic
- 'Miranda' (L) — CBrd CEnd CFil COtt EHic SBid WLRN WPGP
- 'Preziosa' — See *H.* 'Preziosa'
* – 'Pulchella' — SPla

* – 'Pulchra' — CEnd SSpi
- 'Rosalba' ♀ — CBrd CFil EPfP MRav SPer SPla WPGP WSHC
- var. *thunbergii* — CB&S CFil CMHG GQui WPGP
- 'Tiara' — SSpi WPGP
- subsp. *yezoensis* — CFil WPGP
'Wryneck' (H)
§ *serratifolia* — CBot CFil CGre CHEx CPlN EPfP EPla SAPC SArc SBra SSpi SSta WCru WPGP WSHC
¶ 'Silver Slipper' — WWeb
sinensis — See *H. scandens* subsp. *chinensis*
tiliifolia — See *H. anomala* subsp. *petiolaris*
umbellata — See *H. scandens* subsp. *chinensis*
villosa — See *H. aspera* Villosa Group

HYDRASTIS (Ranunculaceae)
canadensis — CArn GBuc GPoy MSal WCru WThi

HYDROCHARIS (Hydrocharitaceae)
morsus-ranae — CBen CRDP CRow CWat EHon EMFW LPBA MSta NDea NVic SWat WChe

HYDROCLEYS (Limnocharitaceae) See Plant Deletions

HYDROCOTYLE (Apiaceae)
§ *americana* — NHol
asiatica — See *Centella asiatica*
moschata — GAri WPer WWin
* *palustris* — SBla
ranunculoides — See *H. americana*
* *sibthorpioides* 'Variegata' — EMon EPPr
vulgaris — CRDP EMFW EWFC MSta WChe WWeb

HYDROPHYLLUM (Hydrophyllaceae)
canadense — EMar WCot WCru
virginianum — MSal
¶ – purple form — EBee

HYLOMECON (Papaveraceae)
§ *japonica* — CRDP EPar ERos GCrs MSte MTho NBir NHol NMGW NRya NTow WAbe WCru WElm WFar WOMN WPer

HYLOTELEPHIUM See SEDUM

HYMENANTHERA See MELICYTUS

HYMENOCALLIS (Amaryllidaceae)
'Advance' — LAma LBow
§ *caroliniana* — LAma WCot
× *festalis* — CMon ERea LAma LBow MBri NRog SDeJ SLMG
- 'Zwanenburg' — ETub
harrisiana — LBow
littoralis — NRog
§ *longipetala* — LBow
occidentalis — See *H. caroliniana*
'Sulphur Queen' — LBow NRog SDeJ SLMG

HYMENOSPORUM (Pittosporaceae) See Plant Deletions

HYMENOXYS (Asteraceae)
grandiflora   See *Tetraneuris grandiflora*
subintegra   WLin

HYOPHORBE (Arecaceae)
§ *lagenicaulis*   LPal
¶ *verschaffeltii*   LPal

HYOSCYAMUS (Solanaceae)
albus   GBar MChe MSal WWye
niger   CArn CJew EMFP EWFC GPoy
   MChe MSal WHer WWye

HYPERICUM † (Clusiaceae)
¶ *acmosepalum*   WPGP
§ *addingtonii*   EPla
adenotrichum   CNic GCHN SIng
aegypticum   CInt CLyd CTri EDAr EHyt
   ELan EPot GCHN LBee NMen
   NWCA NWoo WAbe WFar
   WPat WPer WPyg
amblycalyx   SIgm
androsaemum   CArn CKin CPle ECha EGoo
   ENot ISea MHew MSal NMir
   NPer NRoo WDin
§ – 'Albury Purple'   CBlo CDec CHad CHan CPle
   GBuc GCHN MCCP MHlr
   MTed MWhi NLak WCot
* – 'Autumn Blaze'   MBal SSte SSto
§ – 'Dart's Golden Penny'   SLPl SPer WBcn
 – 'Mrs Gladis Brabazon'   CBlo MHar WCot WWeb
   (v)
 – 'Orange Flair'   See *H.* × *inodorum* 'Orange
   Flair'
 – 'Variegatum'   See *H. androsaemum* 'Gladys
   Brabazon'
§ *annulatum*   ELan EMon
ascyron   EBee EWes
athoum   CLyd EHyt ESis GCHN LHop
   MBro MHig MPla NBir NTow
   WPat WPer
¶ *atomarium*   WPGP
augustinii   CPle
balearicum   CFil CHan CLyd CMea CPle
   EPot MAll MAsh MHar MPla
   MTho SDry SIgm WAbe
§ *beanii*   LRHS MBlu WAbe
bellum   CPle EPfP GCal SBid
buckleyi   GCHN MDHE MHig NGre
   SIng WPat
calycinum   CB&S CLan ELan ENot GChr
   LBuc LGro MBal MBar MGos
   MWat NLon NNor NWea
   SHBN SPer SRms WDin
   WGwG
§ *cerastioides*   CMHG ECGP ESis GCHN
   LBee MBro MHar MHig MPla
   NGre NTow SIgm SIng SRms
   WAbe WDin WWin
coris   CLyd ECED ECha EHyt EWes
   LBee MBro MHar MTho MWat
   NFla NMen NTow SRms SUsu
   WCla WHoo
* *coum*   SGre
¶ *crux-andreae*   EBee
cuneatum   See *H. pallens*
× *cyathiflorum* 'Gold Cup'   MBal SBid SPan SVil
× *dummeri* 'Peter   CBlo EMil MBri NHol SMac
   Dummer'   WWat
elatum   See *H.* × *inodorum*
elodeoides   CLyd MSta SRms

elongatum   EMon ESis
empetrifolium   EWes MHig
§ – subsp. *oliganthum*   ECha ESis GCHN
 – 'Prostatum'   See *H. empetrifolium* subsp.
   tortuosum
§ – subsp. *tortuosum*   CLyd EWes MDHE
* 'Excellent Flare'   NPro
§ *forrestii* ♀   CBot CLan CPle EBee EPfP
   MBal MGos SBid WPGP WWat
N*fragile* hort.   See *H. olympicum* f. *minus*
frondosum   CLTr SPer
 – 'Buttercup'   CBlo
 – Sunburst⏣   CBlo EPfP MBri MGos SBid
   SPan
 'Gold Penny'   See *H. androsaemum* 'Dart's
   Golden Penny'
grandiflorum   See *H. kouytchense*
henryi L 753   SRms
'Hidcote' ♀   Widely available
* 'Hidcote Gold'   WRHF
'Hidcote Variegated'   COtt EBee ELan EMon GCHN
   GOrc MBal MCCP SHFr SPer
   SRms WFar WWeb
hircinum   CPle SIde
 – subsp. *albimontanum*   SPan
 – subsp. *cambessedesii*   EMon LRHS
 – subsp. *majus*   EMon
hirsutum   CKin
hookerianum   CPle
humifusum   EHyt GAri WCla
hyssopifolium   CPle SHFr
× *inodorum* 'Albury   See *H. androsaemum* 'Albury
   Purple'   Purple'
 – 'Elstead'   ECtt ELan MBal MBar MGos
   MWat NFla NRoo SHBN SRms
   WDin WHCG WWin
§ – 'Orange Flair'   CBlo MGos
 – 'Summergold'   CBlo CBos MCCP
 – 'Ysella'   ECha ECtt ELan EPla EWes
   MRav SDry
japonicum   ECou EWes
kalmianum   CBot CChe EWes SBid
kamtschaticum   EDAr MHar
kelleri   GCHN ITim
§ *kiusianum* var.   CInt CLyd GCHN MBar MTho
   yakusimense   NGre NWCA
§ *kouytchense* ♀   CPle CSam EPfP EWes GOrc
   GQui MBri SDry SPan WKif
   WPat WPyg
lagarocladum   ELan MBlu
lancasteri   CBlo CPle ELan EMon EPfP
   LRHS SMac SPan WWat
leschenaultii hort.   See *H.* 'Rowallane'
linarioides   EHyt GTou
maclarenii L 863   CPle
montanum   MSal
× *moserianum* ♀   CB&S CLan EBrP EBre ENot
   LBre MBal MBar MBri NNor
   NPer SBre SHBN SPer SRms
   WStI
§ – 'Tricolor' (v)   CB&S CBot EAst EBrP EBre
   EHoe ELan ENot GCHN GOrc
   IOrc LBre LHop MBal MBar
   MBri MGos MWat NNor SBre
   SHBN SMad SPer SReu WAbe
   WDin WEas WPyg WSHC
   WWin
 – 'Variegatum'   See *H.* × *moserianum* 'Tricolor'
 'Mrs Brabazon'   See *H. androsaemum* 'Gladys
   Brabazon'
nummularium   NBir
oblongifolium   CPle WLRN

¶ – CC 1706 | MRPP
olympicum ♀ | CArn CInt CNic ECha EFer
 | ELan EPot GBur GCHN GDra
 | GLil LGro MFir MPla MWat
 | NMen NNor SBla SEas SHel
 | SIng SPer SPla SRms SSmi
 | WHen
I – 'Calypso' | CBlo NPro
* – 'Eden Star' | NPro
 – 'Edith' | SAsh WPyg
 – 'Grandiflorum' | See *H. olympicum* f. *uniflorum*
§ – f. *minus* | ECtt EGoo ELan EMNN
 | GCHN GCal GDra MOne
 | MRav NRoo SMer SRms WPer
 | WStI WWin
§ – – 'Sulphureum' | CBot ESis EWes LFlo MHar
 | MLLN MRav SPer SRms
 | WSHC WWin
§ – – 'Variegatum' | ELan EWes LBee LHop MHar
 | MHig NRoo SIng WPat WPyg
§ – f. *uniflorum* | CM&M GAri LIck MBal MBar
 | MBro NBro NPri NRoo NVic
 | SEND WAbe WCla WHoo
 – – 'Citrinum' ♀ | CLyd CMea CNic ECha ECtt
 | EPot GCHN LBee LHop MBal
 | MBro MWat NBro NRoo SBid
 | SBla SIgm WAbe WCla WEas
 | WHoo WKif WLin WOMN
 | WPat WWat
orientale | CMHG EWes GCHN MBro
 | MPla NMen NRoo WCla WPer
 – JCA 3302 | NHol
§ *pallens* | ECho MDHE
patulum var. *forrestii* | See *H. forrestii*
 – var. *henryi* Rehder et hort. | See *H. pseudohenryi*
 – – Veitch ex Bean | See *H. beanii*
* – 'Variegatum' | LHop SEas
perforatum | CArn CJew CKin ELau EWFC
 | GPoy LHol MChe MHew NHex
 | NMir SIde WCla WHer WJek
 | WOak WSel WWye
polyphyllum | See *H. olympicum* f. *minus*
 – 'Citrinum' | See *H. olympicum* f. *minus* 'Sulphureum'
 – 'Grandiflorum' | See *H. olympicum* f. *uniflorum*
 – 'Sulphureum' | See *H. olympicum* f. *minus* 'Sulphureum'
 – 'Variegatum' | See *H. olympicum* f. *minus* 'Variegatum'
prolificum | CMHG CPle ECtt ELan ENot
 | EPla GCHN MAsh MMHG
 | SChu SPan SSpi
pseudohenryi L 1029 | GBuc
pseudopetiolatum | GTou
* – *orientale* | WUnu
 – var. *yakusimense* | See *H. kiusianum* var. *yakusimense*
pulchrum | CKin IIve
quadrangulum Linnaeus | See *H. tetrapterum*
reptans Dyer | ECha ESis EWes
 – hort. | See *H. olympicum* f. *minus*
rhodoppeum | See *H. cerastioides* subsp. *meuselianum*
roeperianum | SBid
§ 'Rowallane' ♀ | CB&S CBot CLTr CLan CPle
 | CTrw EPfP EPla ISea SDix
 | SHBN
stellatum | CGre EPla WWat
subsessile B&L 12486 | EMon
'Sungold' | See *H. kouytchense*
tenuicaule KR 743 | ISea
§ *tetrapterum* | CArn CKin EWFC MHew MSal

tomentosum | GCHN
trichocaulon | CLyd ELan EWes GCHN MBro
 | NMen NRoo WPat WPyg WWin
yakusimense | See *H. kiusianum* var. *yakusimense*
¶ *yezoense* | WLRN

HYPOCALYMMA (Myrtaceae)
robustum | MAll

HYPOCHAERIS (Asteraceae)
radicata | CKin NMir
uniflora | NGre
§ *variegata* | CLTr EPfP

HYPOCYRTA See NEMATANTHUS

HYPOESTES (Acanthaceae)
aristata | ERea
§ *phyllostachya* (v) ♀ | MBri SRms
 – 'Bettina' (v) | MBri
 – 'Carmina' (v) | MBri
 – 'Purpuriana' (v) | MBri
 – 'Wit' (v) | MBri
sanguinolenta misapplied | See *H. phyllostachya*

HYPOLEPIS (Hypolepidaceae)
millefolium | CFil GAri NMar

HYPOXIS (Hypoxidaceae)
hirsuta | EWes WThi WWye
hygrometrica | CRDP ECou EPot WAbe
parvula | SBla
 – var. *albiflora* | EPot
 – pink-flowered | EPot

HYPOXIS × RHODOHYPOXIS (Hypoxidaceae)
H. *parvula* × R. *baurii* | CRDP SBla SIng SWas
¶ H. *parvula* × R. *baurii* 'Biscuit' | EHyt

HYPSELA (Campanulaceae)
longiflora | See *H. reniformis*
§ *reniformis* | CNic EBrP EBre ELan EMNN
 | ESis LBee LBre MHig MRav
 | NGre NHar NMen NNrd NOak
 | NVic NWCA SBre SDys SRms
 | SSmi WAbe WFar WWin
 – 'Greencourt White' | CLyd ESis GBuc GGar
 sp. RB 94066 | ELan MNrw

HYPSEOCHARIS (Oxalidaceae)
¶ *bilobata* | CGen

HYSSOPUS (Lamiaceae)
♦ *aristatus* | See *H. officinalis* subsp. *aristatus*
officinalis | CArn CChr CHan CSev EBar
 | ECha ELan ELau GPoy LBuc
 | LHol MBar MBri MChe NChi
 | NFai NRoo SChu SIde WCHb
 | WGwG WHer WOak WOve
 | WPer WWye
 – f. *albus* | ECED ECha ELau GPoy MChe
 | SChu SIde SPil WCHb WCer
 | WHer WJek WPer WSel WWye
 – subsp. *angustifolius* | See *H. officinalis officinalis*

§ – subsp. *aristatus* — EBrP EBre ELau ESis GPoy LBre LHol LLWP MChe NRoo SBre SIde SPil WCHb WEas WHoo WJek WSel WWin WWye

– *roseus* — CHar CM&M EBar ECha ELau GPoy MChe MLLN NChi NFai NNor SChu SIde SSca WCHb WCer WHer WJek WKif WPer WWye

§ – f. *ruber* — LLWP

* *schugnanicus* — EBee

tianschanicus — MFos

HYSTRIX (Poaceae)

patula — CCuc CInt EBee EHoe EMan EMon EPPr EPla ESOG GBin GCal LGan MAvo MCCP MNrw MWhi NBro NChi NFai NSti WHal WLRN WPbr WPer

IBERIS (Brassicaceae)

amara — EWFC MSal

candolleana — See *I. pruitii* **Candolleana Group**

commutata — See *I. sempervirens*

'Correvoniana' — WEas

'Dick Self' — EBrP EBre LBre NRoo SBre

gibraltarica — CFir EMan NNor NPri SRms WGor

jordanii — See *I. pruitii*

§ *pruitii* — CPBP EBur MBal SBla

§ – Candolleana Group — EHyt

saxatilis — WPer

– *candolleana* — See *I. pruitii* **Candolleana Group**

semperflorens — MAvo MHlr WCot WSPU

§ *sempervirens* ♀ — CB&S CMHG CTri EAst ELan EMan ERic LGro MBal MWat NBro NFai NFla NNor NOrc NRoo NVic SRms WCot WPer WWal

– 'Little Gem' — See *I. sempervirens* **'Weisser Zwerg'**

– 'Pinky Perpetual' — NPer

– 'Pygmaea' — CLyd EWes MHig MWat NHar NMen

§ – 'Schneeflocke' ♀ — ENot GAri MBro MCLN MOne SIng SPer SRCN WBea WHoo WPyg

I – Snowdrift — See *I. sempervirens* **'Zwergschneeflocke'**

– Snowflake — See *I. sempervirens* **'Schneeflocke'**

§ – 'Weisser Zwerg' — CMea CNic EBrP EBre ECha EFou ELan EMNN GLil LBee LBre MBro MHig MPla MTho NGre NHar NMen NRya NTow SBla SBre SIng WHoo WWin

spathulata — MHig

IDESIA (Flacourtiaceae)

polycarpa — CB&S CFil CMCN CPle LRHS MBel SSpi SSta WWat WWoo

¶ – Sich 848 — WPGP

ILEX † (Aquifoliaceae)

N x *altaclerensis* — SHHo

– 'Atkinsonii' (m) — CRos

¶ – 'Balearica' — WWat

¶ – 'Barterberry' (f) — CBar

– 'Belgica' (f) — SHHo

– 'Belgica Aurea' (f/v) ♀ — CB&S CMHG CRos ELan EPfP LNet MAsh MBal MBar MBri MWat SEND SHBN SHHo

– 'Camelliifolia' (f) ♀ — CMCN CMHG CRos EBee LPan MBlu MBri MRav MWat NWea SBid SBod SHHo SPer WWat

– 'Golden King' (f/v) ♀ — Widely available

– 'Hendersonii' (f) — CBlo SBod WBcn

– 'Hodginsii' (m) ♀ — CBlo CMCN CRos ECot IOrc MBar SBid SEND SHHo

– 'Howick' (f/v) — SHHo WBcn

– 'Lady Valerie' (f/v) — SHHo

– 'Lawsoniana' (f/v) ♀ — CB&S CDec CMHG CPle CRos CSam ELan ENot LNet MBal MBar MBri MGos MWat NHol NWea SBod SHBN SHHo SPer SRms SSta WDin WGwG WPat WTro

– 'Maderensis Variegata' — See *I. aquifolium* **'Maderensis Variegata'**

– 'Marnockii' (f) — NHed SHHo

– 'Purple Shaft' (f) — CMCN SHHo

– 'Ripley Gold' (f/v) — CBlo CMHG MAsh NHol SAga SBid SHHo

– 'Silver Sentinel' — See *I. x altaclerensis* **'Belgica Aurea'**

– 'W.J. Bean' (f) — SHHo

– 'Wilsonii' (f) ♀ — CMHG IOrc LPan MWat SBid SBod SHHo

aquifolium ♀ — CB&S CChe CKin CPer CSam CTri ELau ENot GChr GRei IOrc LHyr LNet MBar MBri MGos MWat NLon SHBN SHFr SHHo WDin WMou WOrn WStI

– 'Alaska' (f) — CBlo CDoC CEnd CMCN EBee EBrP EBre EMil ENot IHos LBre LBuc MAsh MBal NHol SBre SHHo

– 'Alcicornis' (m) — CMCN

– 'Amber' (f) ♀ — CTri MWat SHHo WLRN

– 'Angustifolia' (m or f) — CB&S EPla GAri IOrc MBar MWat SHHo WPat

– 'Angustimarginata Aurea' (m) — WPyg

§ – 'Argentea Marginata' (f) ♀ — CB&S CBlo CSam CTri EAst EBrP EBre ECtt ENot LBre LHyr LPan MAsh MBri MGos MLan MRav NBee NWea SBre SHHo SPer SReu SRms WAbe WDin WPat WStI WWal WWeb

§ – 'Argentea Marginata Pendula' (f) — CBlo CTri ELan ENot EPfP LPan MAsh MBal MBri NHol NWea SBod SHHo SPer SRms WPat WPyg WShe WWat

– 'Argentea Pendula' — See *I. aquifolium* **'Argentea Marginata Pendula'**

– 'Argentea Variegata' — See *I. aquifolium* **'Argentea Marginata'**

– 'Atlas' (m) — CB&S CDoC LBuc SHHo

– 'Aurea Marginata' (f) — CBlo CMHG EBee ECtt EHic EHoe ELan LPan MGos SBod SHBN SHHo WAbe WCFE WPat WRHF

– 'Aurea Marginata Pendula' (f) — CBlo CDoC CRos NHol WPat WPyg

– 'Aurea Marginata Stricta' (f) — WCru

– 'Aurea Ovata' — See *I. aquifolium* **'Ovata Aurea'**

– 'Aurea Regina'	See *I. aquifolium* **'Golden Queen'**
– 'Aureovariegata Pendula'	See *I. aquifolium* **'Weeping Golden Milkmaid'**
– 'Aurifodina' (f)	EHic WLRN
§ – 'Bacciflava' (f)	CEnd CPle CSam CTri ECtt ELan GCHN IOrc MAsh MBal MBlu MGos MMea MRav MWat NBee SHHo SPer SRms WDin WWal WWat WWeb
¶ – 'Bowland' (f/v)	NHol
– 'Crassifolia' (f)	SHHo SMad
– 'Crispa' (m)	CPle EHic MBal MBlu NHol SHHo
– 'Crispa Aureomaculata'	See *I. aquifolium* **'Crispa Aureopicta'**
§ – 'Crispa Aureopicta' (m)	WPat
– 'Ferox' (m)	CBlo CLan EHal ELan LPan MBal SHHo
– 'Ferox Argentea' (m/v) ♀	Widely available
* – 'Ferox Argentea Picta' (m)	LRHS SPla
– 'Ferox Aurea' (m/v)	CBlo CMHG CPle EAst EBee ELan MCCP MWat NHol SHHo SPer WPat WPyg WRHF
§ – 'Flavescens' (f)	CBot EBee EPfP EPla NHed NHol SHHo WLRN
* – 'Forest Weeping'	LRHS
– 'Foxii' (m)	SHHo
¶ – 'Fructo Aurantiaco' (f)	EBee
– 'Fructu Luteo'	See *I. aquifolium* **'Bacciflava'**
– 'Gold Flash' (f/v)	ECtt ELan EMil MAsh MBri NBee NHol SHHo
– 'Golden Milkboy' (m/v) ♀	CB&S CLan CRos EBee ECtt ELan EMil ENot IHos LNet MBal MBlu NHol SBid SHHo SPla WPat WPyg
– 'Golden Milkmaid' (f/v)	CBlo CRos EHol IOrc SBid
§ – 'Golden Queen' (m/v) ♀	CB&S CRos ELan ENot LHyr LNet MBal MGos MWat SPer SReu SRms WPat
¶ – 'Golden Showers'	SPer
* – 'Golden Tears'	SHHo WBcn
– 'Golden van Tol' (f/v)	CB&S CRos CTri EAst EBrP EBre ECtt ELan ENot IOrc LBre LNet LPan MAsh MBal MBar MBri MGos NBee SBre SHBN SHHo SRms WGwG WStI WWal
– 'Green Pillar' (f) ♀	CMCN SHHo
– 'Handsworth New Silver' (f/v) ♀	CB&S CDec CPle CRos CSam EBrP EBre EHoe ELan IOrc LBre LNet MAsh MBal MBar MBri MMea MWat NHol NTow NWea SBod SBre SHHo SPer SPla WMou WPat WStI WWat
– 'Harpune' (f)	CPle SHHo
§ – 'Hascombensis'	CRos EHol EPot GDra LGre LHop MBal MGos MPla NHar NHol SAxl SMac WFar WPyg WWat
– 'Hastata' (m)	CMHG EPla MWat SHHo
– 'Ingramii' (m/v)	EHic SHHo WBcn
– 'J.C. van Tol' (f) ♀	Widely available
– 'Latispina' (f)	SHHo
– 'Laurifolia Aurea' (m)	WGwG WWal
– 'Lichtenthalii' (f)	SHHo
– 'Madame Briot' (f/v) ♀	CDoC CMHG CTri ELan ENot IOrc LHyr MAsh MBal MBar MBri NHol NWea SBod SHHo SPer SPla SReu SRms WDin WWal WWeb
§ – 'Maderensis Variegata' (m)	SHHo
– 'Monstrosa' (m)	SHHo
– Moonlight holly	See *I. aquifolium* **'Flavescens'**
– 'Myrtifolia' (m)	CDoC ELan EPfP LRHS MBar MBlu MBri MGos
¶ – 'Myrtifolia Aurea' (m/v)	SHHo
– 'Myrtifolia Aurea Maculata' (m/v) ♀	CBlo CDoC CMHG CPle CRos EHoe ELan LNet MAsh MBal MBri MWat NHol NWea SMad SPer WPat
– 'Myrtifolia Aureovariegata'	See *I. aquifolium* **'Myrtifolia Aurea Maculata'**
§ – 'Ovata Aurea' (m/v)	CRos SHHo
– 'Pendula' (f)	CBlo CRos EPfP MAsh MBri MWat SBod SHHo
– 'Pendula Mediopicta'	See *I. aquifolium* **'Weeping Golden Milkmaid'**
§ – 'Pyramidalis' (f) ♀	CBlo CEnd CTri ELan ENot GCHN GChr GRei IHos LHyr MAsh MBar MBri MGos MLan NBee NHol NWea SHHo SPer SPla SRms WDin WOrn
– 'Pyramidalis Aureomarginata' (f)	MGos MLan SHHo WBcn WGwG WWal
– 'Pyramidalis Fructu Luteo' (f) ♀	CBlo MBar SHHo WBcn
– 'Rubricaulis Aurea' (f/v)	MBal NHol SHHo WBcn
– 'Silver King'	See *I. aquifolium* **'Silver Queen'**
– 'Silver Milkboy' (f/v)	CB&S ELan EMil MBal MBlu SEas
– 'Silver Milkmaid' (f/v) ♀	CMHG EAst EPfP MBar MRav MWat NHol SHBN SHHo SPla SSta WWal
§ – 'Silver Queen' (m/v) ♀	CB&S CEnd CLan EBrP EBre ELan GRei LBre MBal MBar MBri MGos MWat NBee NWea SBre SHHo SPer SPla WDin WHen WOrn WStI WWeb
– 'Silver Sentinel'	See *I.* × *altaclerensis* **'Belgica Aurea'**
– 'Silver van Tol' (f/v)	EAst ELan ENot IOrc MBri NHol SHHo WAbe WLRN WStI WWeb
§ – 'Watereriana' (m/v)	EHol MAsh MBal SBod SMur
– 'Waterer's Gold'	See *I. aquifolium* **'Watereriana'**
§ – 'Weeping Golden Milkmaid' (f/v)	NHol SHHo WPat
× *aquipernyi*	SHHo
– Dragon Lady®	See *I.* × *aquipernyi* Dragon Lady = **'Meschick'** (f)
§ – Dragon Lady® = 'Meschick' (f)	COtt SHHo
– 'San Jose' (f)	CMCN SHHo
× *attenuata*	CMCN CRos
– 'Sunny Foster' (f/v) ♀	CMCN EBee ENot MBlu MGos SHHo WBcn
§ *bioritsensis*	CMCN CTri NWea
¶ *buergeri*	CMCN
¶ *cassine*	CMCN
chinensis misapplied	See *I. purpurea*
ciliospinosa	CMCN CPle
colchica	CMCN
corallina	CMCN
cornuta	CLan CMCN CRos ERom LPan SHHo
* – 'Aurea'	EAst SHHo

§ – 'Dazzler' (f)	SHHo
– 'O. Spring' (f/v)	CMHG SBid SHHo
crenata	CBlo CMCN EHic ERom GAri MBar SRms WHCr WNor WWat
– 'Aureovariegata'	See *I. crenata* **'Variegata'**
– 'Compacta'	See *I. crenata* **'Bennett's Compact'**
– 'Convexa' (f) ♀	CB&S EHic ENot GDra MBal MBar MBri MWhi NHol NWea SHHo WPat WPyg WWat
– 'Fastigiata'	CBlo CRos EBar EBee EBrP EBre ECle EPla LBre LHol LHop MAsh MBri MGos MLan SBre SCoo SHHo SPer WGwG WTro WWal WWes
– 'Fukarin'	See *I. crenata* **'Shiro-fukurin'**
– 'Golden Gem' (f) ♀	Widely available
¶ – 'Green Hedge'	LBuc
– 'Green Island' (m)	CRos LRHS SHHo
– 'Helleri' (f)	CMCN MAsh MBar MBro NHol SSta WPat WPyg
– 'Luteovariegata'	See *I. crenata* **'Variegata'**
– 'Mariesii' (f)	CMCN MBlu MBro MPla NGre NHed NHol SBla SHHo SIng WPat WPyg
– 'Mount Halla' (f)	CMCN
I – 'Pyramidalis' (f)	CMil EHic LPan MPla NHar NHol SPan WPat WShe
§ – 'Shiro-fukurin' (f/v)	CBlo CMCN CMHG EAst EHic ELan EPfP NHar NHol SBid SHHo WCru WPat WPyg
¶ – 'Sky Pencil' (f)	CMCN
– 'Snowflake'	See *I. crenata* **'Shiro-fukurin'**
– 'Stokes' (m)	GAri LRHS MBri SHHo WPat WPyg
– upright form	CMCN
§ – 'Variegata'	CMCN CMHG ELan EPla MBar MBlu NHol SHHo SRms WPat
◆ 'Dazzler'	See *I. cornuta* **'Dazzler'**
decidua	CMCN
¶ – 'Warren Red' (f)	CMCN
¶ – 'Warren's Red' (f)	CMCN
dimorphophylla	CDoC CMCN EPla SHHo
– 'Somerset Pixie'	SHHo
'Doctor Kassab' (f)	CMCN SHHo
'Drace' (f)	ELan SHHo
fargesii	CMCN
ficoidea	CMCN
glabra 'Snow-White' (f)	MBal
hascombensis	See *I. aquifolium* **'Hascombensis'**
'Indian Chief' (f)	CSam MBlu SMad WWat
insignis	See *I. kingiana*
¶ *integra*	CMCN
'John T. Morris' (m)	MBal
§ *kingiana*	CB&S CMCN WWat
× *koehneana*	CBot
– 'Chestnut Leaf' (f) ♀	CMCN CMHG MRav MWat SHHo SMad WBcn WCru WWat
§ *kusanoi*	CMCN
latifolia	CHEx CMCN SHHo SMad
longipes	CMCN
* *loropetalum* 'Zuhou'	CMCN
'Lydia Morris' (f)	CMHG CSam SBid SHHo WWat
macropoda	CMCN
'Mary Nell' (f)	SHHo
◆× *meservae* Golden Girl®	See *I.* × *meservae* Golden Girl = **'Mesgolg'**

× *meserveae*	SHHo
– Blue Angel® (f) ♀	COtt CPle CRos CSam ECtt EMil ENot IOrc LHol LHyr LPan MAsh MBal MBar MBri MMea MWat NHed NHol NNor SHHo SPer SRms SSta WDin WPat WStI WWal WWat WWeb
– Blue Maid® (f)	See *I.* × *meserveae* Blue Maid = **'Mesid'**
– Blue Prince® (m)	CB&S CMHG COtt CRos EHoe IOrc LBuc LHol MAsh MBal MBar MBlu MMea NHed NHol SHBN SHHo SPer WDin WStI WWeb
– Blue Princess® (f) ♀	CB&S CDec CMHG COtt EAst ENot LBuc LPan MAsh MBal MBar MBlu MMal MMea NHol SHBN SHHo SPer WDin WStI
* – 'Glenroy Purple'	MBal
§ – Golden Girl® = 'Mesgolg' (f)	COtt EMil
§ – Blue Maid® = 'Mesid' (f)	EMil
muchagara	CB&S CMCN
myrtifolia	CBlo CMCN ECot NHar SBid SPar WCFE WLRN
'Nellie R. Stevens' (f)	CBlo EBee ENot IHos WBcn
opaca	CGre CMCN
pedunculosa	CMCN SHHo
perado latifolia	See *I. perado* subsp. *platyphylla*
§ – subsp. *platyphylla*	CB&S CHEx CMCN CMHG EPla MBlu SAPC SArc SHHo
pernyi	CMCN CTrG EPla IOrc MBal SHHo WWat
◆– var. *veitchii*	See *I. bioritsensis*
poneantha	See *I. kusanoi*
pringlei	CMCN
'Pyramidalis'	See *I. aquifolium* **'Pyramidalis'**
rotunda	CMCN
rugosa	CMCN
'September Gem' (f)	CMCN
serrata	CMCN WWes
'Sparkleberry' (f)	LPan
suaveolens	CMCN
verticillata	CGre CMCN LPan NWea
– 'Afterglow' (f)	MBlu
– f. *aurantiaca* (f)	CBlo MBlu SMur
– f. *chrysocarpa*	CMCN
– 'Compacta'	See *I. verticillata* **'Nana'**
– (f)	CPle CRos EPfP GAri SBid SMur
* – 'Fructu Albo' (f)	CMCN
* – 'Golden Male' (m)	CMCN
* – 'Golden Rain'	CMCN
¶ – 'Jim Dandy' (m)	MBlu
– (m)	CDoC EPfP GAri SBid SMur WWat
§ – 'Nana' (f)	CMCN MBlu
– 'Red Sprite'	See *I. verticillata* **'Nana'**
¶ – 'Southern Gentleman' (m)	MBlu
– 'Stop Light' (f)	MBlu
– 'Sunset' (f)	MBlu
– 'Winter Red' (f)	CDoC CMCN CWSG MBlu MMHG WRHF WWat
vomitoria	CMCN
× *wandoensis*	CMCN SHHo
'Washington' (f)	CPle NHol
yunnanensis	CMCN CMHG GAri

ILIAMNA See SPHAERALCEA

ILLICIUM (Illiciaceae)
anisatum — CArn CB&S CFil CHan CPle SSpi WPat WPyg WSHC WWat
floridanum — CPle EPfP GOrc MBal SBid SSpi SSta WBod WPGP WSHC WWat
henryi — CFil CMCN CPle WPGP WSHC

ILYSANTHES (Scrophulariaceae) See Plant Deletions

IMPATIENS (Balsaminaceae)
auricoma — EBak
balfourii — MSto
'Ballerina' — CInt
'Blackberry Ice' — CHal
capensis — MSto
'Cardinal Red' — CHal CInt
¶ 'Diamond Orange' — CInt
'Diamond Rose' — CHal
'Diamond Scarlet' — CHal
double flowered (d) — EBak
'Evening Blush' — CInt
glandulifera — WHer
– 'Candida' — CBre EMon
hawkeri — EBak
'Madame Pompadour' — CHal
New Guinea Group — CHal EBak MBri WLRN
niamniamensis — EBak ERea GCra LCns LHil
– 'Congo Cockatoo' — CHal CInt ECon EOHP LIck SHFr SRms
I – 'Variegata' — ECon
omeiana — WCot
'Orange Surprise' — CHal
'Peach Ice' — CHal
pseudoviola — LHil LIck SHFr
– 'Woodcote' — CSpe LHil
'Purple Chico' — CInt
'Raspberry Ripple' — CHal
'Salmon Princess' — CInt
sodenii — GCal LHil
¶ sp. from Uganda — GCal
sulcata — SHFr
sultani — See *I. walleriana*
tinctoria — CDoC CFil CFir CGre CHEx CTre CWit GCal LHil SIgm SVen WCot WCru WPGP
– subsp. *elegantissima* — CFee
– subsp. *tinctoria* — GCra
ugandensis — GCal
§ *walleriana* — EBak MBri
* – 'Variegata' — CHal

IMPERATA (Poaceae)
cylindrica — EPar MHlr MSal NSti WCot
– 'Red Baron' — See *I. cylindrica* 'Rubra'
§ – 'Rubra' — Widely available

INCARVILLEA (Bignoniaceae)
§ *arguta* — CBot CHan GCal GCra LGre MHar MSto SAxl WAbe WOMN WPer WWin
brevipes — See *I. mairei*
compacta — GMac MSto NHar SIng
– ACE 1455 — EBee
delavayi — CBot EAst EBrP EBre ECha EFou EHyt ELan ENot LBow LBre LHop MBri MDun MFir NFla NLar NRoo NVic SBre SDeJ SPer SRms WCla WHil WHoo WMow WOld WWin

– 'Bees' Pink' — EBee GBuc GCra
¶ *diffusa* — EHyt MSto
¶ *forrestii* — NSla
– KGB 43 — MSto
lutea L 1986 — SBla
§ *mairei* — EAst GDra LHop MHar MLLN MTho NLar SAxl SLod SMrm WPer
– B&L 12602 — SWas
– 'Frank Ludlow' — GBuc GCrs GDra NGre NHar NSla SBla SIgm
– var. *grandiflora* — CLAP CRDP ELan MSto MTho NWoo SBla
– var. *mairei* ACE 2233 — NHar
– – ACE 2420 — NHar
¶ – – CLD 101 — GCrs
◆ – – f. *multifoliata* — See *I. zhongdianensis*
– – – ACE 64 — See *I. zhongdianensis* ACE 2201
– 'Nyoto Sama' — GBuc GDra SBla
§ *olgae* — CSam EBee ELan EMan MHar MSto NPSI SMac WCot
¶ *przewalskii* — MSto
sinensis 'Alba' — MSte MSto SMac WCru
– 'Cheron' — WCot WSan
'Snowtop' — Widely available
younghusbandii — MSto
¶ *zhongdianensis* — EBee GBuc NSla
§ – ACE 2201 — NHar
– ACE 2278 — NHar
¶ – CLD 233 — EHyt MSto

INDIGOFERA (Papilionaceae)
amblyantha ♀ — CPle EHic EMil EPfP GCal MBlu NSti SBid SDry SSpi WCru WKif WOMN WSHC WSpi
australis — CTrC SOWG
¶ *decora* f. *alba* — EPfP
dielsiana — CB&S
* *frigida* HWJCM 107 — WCru
gerardiana — See *I. heterantha*
hebepetala — WAbe WCru WDin WSHC
§ *heterantha* ♀ — CArn CB&S CBar CBot CMCN CPle ELan EMil ENot IOrc LHop MBlu MPla NFla NPro SCob SHBN SPer SReu SSpi SSta WAbe WFar WOve WPer WSHC WWat
¶ – CC 1708 — MRPP
kirilowii — CGre EPfP SOWG WSHC
¶ *pendula* — WPGP
potaninii — SHBN WCru WHer
pseudotinctoria — CHad EPfP SPan SRms
tinctoria — CArn MSal

INDOCALAMUS (Poaceae - Bambusoideae)
hamadae — EPla ERod SDry
latifolius — EOas EPla ISta LJus SDry WJun
longiauritus — EPla SDry
solidus — EPla ISta LJus MMoz SDry WJun WMul
§ *tessellatus* — CFil EBee EFul EOas EPfP EPla ISta LJus SCha WJun

INULA † (Asteraceae)
acaulis — NNrd SSca WCot
conyzae — CKin MHew MSal
crithmoides — WHer
dysenterica — See *Pulicaria dysenterica*

ensifolia	CHan CSam ECro ELan IBlr LFis MHar MLLN MRav MSte MTho NBro NDea NFai NVic WBea WEas WHoo WMer WPyg
– 'Gold Star'	CBlo CMGP ECtt MWgw NBir NNor NOak WLRN WMow WPer
glandulosa	See *I. orientalis*
'Golden Beauty'	See *Buphthalmum salicifolium* 'Golden Wonder'
helenium	CArn CKin CSev ECGN ECro ELau EWFC GPoy ILis LHol MChe MFir MHew MLLN MSal NMir SRCN SRms WBea WByw WCer WGwy WHer WOak WPer WWye
hookeri	Widely available
magnifica	Widely available
* 'Mediterranean Sun'	MCLN
oculus-christi	ECro EWes
§ *orientalis*	CKel CPea ECro EFou GCra MBri MBro NFai NFla NLak NMir NSti SMad WBea WByw WHoo WOld WPer WPyg
racemosa	ECha ECro EMon EPPr EPla GBin GCal IBlr MNrw MSte NChi NSti SMad SMrm SRms WFar
– CC&McK 620	GCHN
¶ – 'Sonnenspeer'	NLar SGre
rhizocephala	CSam
royleana	CHan ECED GCal GCra GMac MNrw MRav MSte SMad SSca
verbascifolia	EMan SSca

IOCHROMA (Solanaceae)

coccinea	ECon WMul
cyanea	CGre CPle ECon ERea LHil SLMG SOWG WMul
– dark form	LHil
¶ – large form	LHil
grandiflora	CHEx CSev LHil SLMG SOWG SVen
¶ *macrocalyx*	CGen
violacea	See *Cestrum violaceum*
warscewiczii	ECon WMul

IPHEION (Alliaceae)

'Alberto Castillo'	CAvo CBro CMea CMon EHyt ELan EWes MTho WCot
dialystemon	CMon
§ 'Rolf Fiedler' ♀	CAvo CBro CMea CMon CSpe EBrP EBre EBur ECho EHyt ELan EPar EPot EWes LAma LBre LHil MHig MRPP MTho SBla SBre WAbe WCot WOMN
sellowianum	LBow
§ *uniflorum*	CBro CHal EBrP EBre ECha ETub LAma LBre MBri MBro MNrw MRav NMen NRog NWCA NWoo SBre SIng SRms WAbb WCla WHil WHoo WPer
– 'Album'	CBro CMea ECha EHyt ELan EPar EPot ERos ETub EWes GDra MTho NMGW SBla SIng WFar
¶ – 'Charlotte Bishop'	SWas

– 'Froyle Mill' ♀	CAvo CBro CHal CMea EBur EHyt ELan EPar EPot ERos EWes GDra LGan MBro MHig MTho NMGW SAga SBla SIng WHoo
– 'Wisley Blue' ♀	CAvo CBro CMea ECha ELan EPar EPot ERos ETub LAma LHil MBro MFos MHig MS&S MTho NMen NNrd SBla SIng SRms WHoo WPyg

IPOMOEA (Convolvulaceae)

acuminata	See *I. indica*
alba	CPlN
* *andersonii*	CPlN MSto
batatas 'Blackie'	CPlN
bonariensis	SVen
¶ *brasiliensis*	LLew
carnea	LChe
– subsp. *fistulosa*	NGno
coccinea	MSto
◆ – var. *hederifolia* (L.) A. Gray	See *I. hederifolia*
§ *hederifolia*	MSto
horsfalliae ♀	CPlN
§ *indica* ♀	CB&S CHEx CHal CLTr CPlN ERea LCns SLMG SOWG WMul
learii	See *I. indica*
¶ *leptophylla*	EBee
§ *lobata*	LIck MSto SUsu
palmata	See *I. cairica*
pennata 'Relli Valley'	MSto
purpurea	SRCN WHer
– 'Kniola's Purple-black'	MSto
quamoclit	CPlN
¶ 'Quebra Plata'	NGno
tuberosa	See *Merremia tuberosa*
versicolor	See *I. lobata*
violacea hort.	See *I. tricolor*

IPOMOPSIS (Polemoniaceae)

§ *aggregata*	CPBP

IRESINE (Amaranthaceae)

herbstii	CHal EBak ERea IBlr LHil SLMG
– 'Aureoreticulata'	CHal LHil
– 'Brilliantissima'	CHal LHil MBEx
lindenii ♀	LHil MBEx SLMG

IRIS † (Iridaceae)

'A.W. Tait' (Spuria)	GCal
'Abracadabra' (SDB)	LBro LGre MS&S
'Abridged Version' (MTB)	NZep
'Acapulco Gold' (TB)	SCro
'Ace of Clubs' (SDB)	NZep
'Action Front' (TB)	CHad CMil COtt EHic ERou NCat WLRN
'Actress' (TB)	EFou
'Adobe Sunset' (Spuria)	LBro
'Adrienne Taylor' (MDB)	LBro MAus
	♀
afghanica	MSto
¶ 'Agnes James' (CH) ♀	CBro LBro
'Ain't She Sweet' (IB)	SCro
'Alastor' (TB)	MS&S
'Albatross' (TB)	CKel
albicans ♀	CMon MAus SCro
'Alcazar' (TB)	EPfP GLil

'Alenette' (TB) — MAus
'Alien' (IB) — LBro
'All Right' (IB) — NZep SCro
'Allegiance' (TB) — MAus WEas
'Alpine Lake' (MDB) — NZep
'Already' (MDB) — EHyt
'Altruist' (TB) — SCro
'Amadora' (TB) — LBro
'Amaranth Gem' (SDB) — LBro
'Ambassadeur' (TB) — ERou GLil
'Amber Blaze' (SDB) — NZep
'Amber Queen' (DB) — CBlo CGle COtt ECtt ELan EMan ERos MCCP NMen SCro SPer WGwG WLRN WWal WWeb
¶ 'Amber Tambour' (TB) — LIri
¶ 'American Sweetheart' (TB) — LIri
'Amethyst Crystal' (CH) — LBro
'Amethyst Flame' (TB) — EBrP EBre ERou LBre MAus MS&S NMGW SBre
'Amethyst Sunset' (MTB) — LBro
'Amigo' (TB) ♀ — SCro
'Amphora' (SDB) — CBro NNrd
'Anastasia' (TB) — CKel
'Ancilla' (Aril) — CLAP
'Angel Unawares' (TB) — MAus
'Angelic' (SDB) — LBro
'Angel's Tears' — See *I. histrioides* 'Angel's Eye'
anglica — See *I. latifolia*
'Anna Belle Babson' (TB) — MAus SCro
'Annabel Jane' (TB) — LBro MAus SCro
'Anne Elizabeth' (SDB) — CBro ERos
'Apache Warrior' (IB) — LBro
aphylla — NOrc
¶ 'Aplomb' (TB) — LIri
'Apollodorus' (TB) — LIri
¶ 'Apollo's Touch' (IB) — NZep
* 'Apple Court' — SApp
'Appledore' (SDB) — CBro EHyt ERos MBro NNrd
'Apricot Skies' (BB) — NZep
'April Ballet' (MDB) — NZep
'Arab Chief' (TB) — CKel
'Arabi Pasha' (TB) — MAus SCro SPer WLRN
'Arabi Treasure' (IB) — LBro
'Archie Owen' (Spuria) — LBro
'Arctic Fancy' (IB) ♀ — LBro MMil
¶ 'Arctic Snow' — MAus
'Arctic Star' (TB) — CKel MFir
'Arctic Tern' (TB) — LBro
'Arden' (BB) ♀ — LBro
arenaria — See *I. humilis*
'Argus Pheasant' (SDB) — MAus
'Arnold Sunrise' (CH) ♀ — LBro
'Arnold Velvet' (SDB) — LBro
¶ 'Around Midnight' (TB) — LIri SCro
¶ 'Arpège' (TB) — EBee
'Ask Alma' (IB) — NZep SCro
* 'Atlantique' (TB) — CKel
atrofusca MS&CL 56 — CMon
¶ – S&L 38 — CMon
'Attention Please' (TB) — CKel
§ *attica* — CBro CFai CHan CMea CMon CPBP ERos GCrs LBee MBro MFos MSto NNrd SIng WAbe WLin
– S&L 486 — CMon
§ *aucheri* ♀ — CBro EPot LAma
'Audacious' (BB) — NZep
'Aunt Martha' (BB) — MBri NMGW

'Austrian Sky' (SDB) — CMea CSam EBrP EBre EHyt ELan ENot LBre MBro MMil SBre SIng WCot
'Autumn Leaves' (TB) — MAus MMil
'Avanelle' (IB) — EFou ERou LBro WBcn
'Az Ap' (IB) — LIri MAus NZep SCro
'Aztec Star' (SDB) — LBro
¶ 'Azure Excho' (IB) — MMil
'Azurea' (MDB) — NFla
¶ 'Baboon Bottom' (BB) — LIri
'Babushka' (SDB) — LBro
¶ 'Baby Bengal' (BB) — LIri
'Baby Bibs' (MTB) — NZep
'Baby Blessed' (SDB) — CBro NZep
'Baby Face' (TB) — MMil
'Baccarat' (TB) — CKel MAus
'Baked Alaska' (TB) — MMil
bakeriana — LAma LRHS
'Ballerina Blue' (TB) — ERou
'Ballyhoo' (TB) — LRHS MAus MBri
'Banbury Beauty' (CH) ♀ — CLAP NSti
'Banbury Fair' (CH) — LBro
'Banbury Gem' (CH) ♀ — LBro
'Banbury Melody' (CH) ♀ — CFee WBcn
'Banbury Ruffles' (SDB) — MAus MMil NMGW NMen NSti SCro
'Banbury Welcome' (CH) — IBlr
'Bang' (TB) — CKel
'Baria' (SDB) — LBro
¶ 'Barletta' (TB) — MAus
¶ 'Barnett Anley' — MBri
barnumae — EHyt
– *polakii* — See *I. polakii*
'Baroque Prelude' (TB) — CKel MMil
¶ 'Barrymore Charmer' (TB) — CKel
'Basso' (IB) — SCro
'Batik' (BB) — LIri SCro
'Batsford' (SDB) — CBro NNrd
'Battle Shout' (IB) — LBro
'Bayberry Candle' (TB) — LIri
'Be Dazzled' (SDB) — EFou
'Be Happy' (SDB) — NZep
'Beauty Mark' (SDB) — NZep
'Beckon' (TB) — CKel
¶ 'Bedford Lilac' (SDB) — NZep
'Bee Wings' (MDB) — NZep WEas
'Before the Storm' (TB) — LIri SCro
'Belise' (Spuria) ♀ — LBro
'Belissinado' (Spuria) — LBro
¶ 'Bellboy' (MTB) — NZep
'Belvi Queen' (TB) — MNrw
* 'Ben Hasel' — ECha
N 'Benton Arundel' (TB) — SCro
'Benton Dierdre' (TB) — SCro SRms
'Benton Evora' (TB) — ENot EOld
N 'Benton Lorna' (TB) — SCro
'Benton Nigel' (TB) — MAus
'Benton Sheila' (TB) — SCro
'Berkeley Gold' (TB) — CBlo COtt EBrP EBre ECtt EPfP ERav EWes LBre LBro LWak MAus NMGW NOrc SBre SPer SWat WLRN
'Betsey Boo' (SDB) — CKel NZep
'Betty Chatten' (TB) — MHig NMen NNrd WLRN
'Betty Cooper' (Spuria) — LBro
¶ 'Betty Simon' (TB) — CKel
'Betty Wood' (SDB) — LBro
'Beverly Sills' (TB) — CKel LBro LIri MAus SCro
'Bewdley' (IB) — LBro
¶ 'Bewilderbeast' (TB) — LIri
'Beyond' (TB) — SCro

'Bibury' (SDB) ♀ — EGle LBro MAus MMil SCro
N'Big Day' (TB) — CKel WBcn
biglumis — See *I. lactea*
biliottii — CBro
'Black as Night' (TB) — LIri
'Black Dragon' (TB) — SCro
¶ 'Black Gamecock' (La) — SAWi
'Black Hills' (TB) — CKel MAus
¶ 'Black Knight' (TB) — CKel
'Black Swan' (TB) — CHad COtt EBee EBrP EBre
ECtt ELan EMan ERav LBre
MMil MRav SBre WCot WWal
'Black Watch' (IB) — CKel
¶ 'Blackbeard' (BB) — CKel
'Blazing Saddles' (TB) — NZep
'Blenheim Royal' (TB) — MAus SCro
'Blitz' (SDB) — NZep
¶ 'Blood Covenant' (SDB) — NZep
bloudowii — CLAP CPBP
¶ 'Blue Admiral' (TB) — CKel
'Blue Ballerina' (CH) ♀ — LBro
'Blue Denim' (SDB) — CBro CKel CM&M EBar EBrP
EBre ECtt EGle EHyt ENot
GMaP LBre LBro MRav NBir
NNrd SBre WHoo WMer
WWeb
'Blue Doll' (MDB) — NZep
'Blue Duchess' (TB) — CKel
'Blue Eyed Blond' (IB) — SCro
¶ 'Blue Eyed Brunette' (TB) ♀ — MAus MBri
'Blue Hendred' (SDB) — LBro MAus NBir
'Blue Horizon' — ERos NMen
'Blue Lassie' (Spuria) — LBro
'Blue Line' (SDB) — NZep
'Blue Luster' (TB) ♀ — CKel LBro SCro
'Blue Magic' (Dutch) — NRog
'Blue Moss' (SDB) — LBro
'Blue Pigmy' (SDB) — CBlo CGle CMil MCCP NCat
NMen NNrd SCro SPer WGwG
WLRN WWal
'Blue Pools' (SDB) — EFou EGle EHyt LBro MBri
MHFP NZep SCro
'Blue Reflection' (TB) — MMil
'Blue Rhythm' (TB) — CBlo CKel CM&M CMil EMan
ERou LBro MAus NFai SCro
SMrm SPer WLRN
'Blue Shimmer' (TB) — CBlo COtt ECGN ECro ELan
EMan ENot MAus MRav NFai
SChu SCro SPer SWat WGwG
WWal
'Blue Smoke' (TB) — CKel
'Blue Staccato' (TB) — SCro
'Blue Zephyr' (Spuria) — LBro
¶ 'Bluebeard' (TB) — EHyt
¶ 'Bluebird Wine' (TB) — MAus
'Blushes' (IB) — SCro
'Blushing Pink' (TB) — SCro
'Bodderlecker' (SDB) — EFou
'Bold Lassie' (SDB) — WHer
'Bold Print' (IB) — MAus SCro
'Bonny' (MDB) — CBro
'Boo' (SDB) — CKel MAus NZep
'Bourne Graceful' — EBee GCal MAus MRav NSti
SSpi WElm WGwG WHow
WLRN WWal
bracteata — CFil CNic EWoo MHig SIng
WPGP WPer
– JCA 13427 — CLAP

'Braithwaite' (TB) — CBlo CKel CMGP COtt EBrP
EBre EHic ELan ENot ERou
LBre LBro NLak SBre SChu
SCro SMrm SRms SSpe SWat
WElm WLRN
brandzae — See *I. sintenisii* subsp. *brandzae*
'Brannigan' (SDB) — CBro EHyt LBro MBri MMil
NBir
'Brass Tacks' (SDB) — LBro NZep
'Brassie' (SDB) — CBro CKel EBar ERos LBro
NNrd
'Bridal Crown' (TB) — SCro
§ 'Bride' (DB) — CM&M MBro NNrd
'Bride's Halo' (TB) — SCro
'Bright Button' (DB) — CKel
'Bright Moment' (SDB) — LBro
'Bright Vision' (SDB) — NZep
'Bright White' (MDB) — CBlo CBro CKel EHyt ERos
LBro NMen NNrd
'Bright Yellow' (DB) — MRav
'Brighteyes' (IB) — ESis LBro MBro MHig MTho
NNrd SChu SCro SRms WLin
WPer
'Brilliant Excuse' (TB) — NZep
'Brindisi' (TB) — CKel SCro SSte
'Bristo Magic' (TB) — SCro
'Bristol Gem' (TB) — SCro
'Broad Grin' (SDB) — LBro
'Broadleigh Ann' (CH) — CBro
'Broadleigh Carolyn' (CH) ♀ — CBro
'Broadleigh Charlotte' — CBro
'Broadleigh Clare' (CH) — CBro
'Broadleigh Dorothy' (CH) — CBro
'Broadleigh Elizabeth' (CH) — CBro
N 'Broadleigh Emily' (CH) — CBro
N 'Broadleigh Florence' (CH) — CBro
'Broadleigh Jean' — CBro
'Broadleigh Joan' (CH) — CBro
'Broadleigh Joyce' (CH) — CBro
'Broadleigh Lavinia' (CH) — CBro
'Broadleigh Mitre' (CH) — CBro MBri
'Broadleigh Nancy' (CH) — CBro
'Broadleigh Peacock' (CH) — CBro CHad IBlr MMil
N 'Broadleigh Rose' (CH) — CBro CElw CHad GBuc IBlr
MBri NSti SMrm SWas WLin
'Broadleigh Sybil' (CH) — CBro
'Broadleigh Victoria' (CH) — CBro GBuc
'Broadway' (TB) — NZep SCro
¶ 'Broadway Baby' (IB) — LIri
'Bromyard' (SDB) ♀ — CBro MMil
'Bronzaire' (IB) ♀ — MAus
'Bronze Beauty' (*hoogiana* hybrid) — CMon EPot
'Bronze Bird' (TB) — CKel MS&S
N 'Bronze Charm' (TB) — CKel
'Bronze Cloud' (TB) — CKel
¶ 'Bronze Queen' (Dutch) — SHel
'Broseley' (TB) — LBro
'Brown Lasso' (BB) ♀ — LBro LIri MAus SCro SSte
'Brummit's Mauve' — MAus
'Bryngwyn' (TB) — LBro
'Bubbling Over' (TB) — SCro
bucharica Foster ♀ — CBro CMon EBee EHyt EPar
EPot GCra LAma MFos NRog
SCro
– hort. — See *I. orchioides*

bulleyana	EWoo GCrs MBro NWoo SIgm SIng SRms SSpi SWas WCot
– ACE 1665	EBee
– ACE 2296	EHyt GBuc
'Bumblebee Deelite' (MTB)	NZep
'Burford' (BB)	LBro
'Burgundy Brown' (TB)	NZep
'Butter Pecan' (IB)	SCro
'Buttercup Bower' (TB)	MAus MBri NMGW
'Buttercup Charm' (MDB)	NZep
'Buttermere' (TB)	SRms
'Butterpat' (IB)	NZep
'Butterscotch Kiss' (TB)	CHad EBrP EBre ECGP ELan EMan ERou LBre MMil MRav MS&S SBre SCro SMrm
'Button Box' (SDB)	NZep
¶ 'Bygone Era' (TB)	LIri
'Byword' (SDB)	LBro
¶ 'Cable Car' (TB)	CKel
caerulea	See *I. albomarginata*
'Caliente' (TB)	EPfP MAus
'California Style' (IB)	NZep
§ Californian hybrids	CElw CGle CLTr ELan GCra MBal SSpi WBon WLin WWhi
'Calypso Mood' (TB)	SCro
'Cambridge Blue'	See *I. 'Monspur Cambridge Blue'*
¶ 'Camelot Rose' (TB)	MAus
'Campbellii'	See *I. lutescens 'Campbellii'*
♦ *canadensis*	See *I. hookeri*
'Canary Bird' (TB)	CKel
'Cannington Bluebird' (TB)	LBro
'Cannington Skies' (IB) ♀	LBro MMil
'Cannington Sweet Puff' (TB)	LBro
¶ 'Cannonball' (TB)	LIri
'Cantab' (Reticulata)	CAvo CBro EBrP EBre EHyt ELan EPar EPot ETub LAma LBre NRog SBre
'Capricious' (TB)	SCro
'Caramba' (TB)	SCro
'Caramel' (TB)	EWoo
'Cardew' (TB) ♀	LBro
N 'Carey' (TB)	CKel
'Carilla' (SDB)	LBro LGre
'Carnaby' (TB)	LBro MAus MBri WBcn
'Carnival Time' (TB)	EFou
'Carnton' (TB)	WEas
'Carolina Gold' (TB)	SCro
'Carolyn Rose' (MTB)	LBro NZep
'Carved Pink' (TB)	SCro
'Casbah' (TB)	SCro
¶ 'Cascade Sprite' (SDB)	SRms
'Cascadian Skies' (TB)	ERou
'Catalyst' (TB)	SCro
¶ *caucasica*	MHar
'Cayenne Capers' (TB)	MMil MWat
* 'Cedric Morris'	EWes
'Centering Point' (Spuria)	LBro
'Centerpiece' (SDB)	LBro
'Centre Court' (TB)	SCro
'Chain White'	See *I. 'Chian Wine'*
chamaeiris	See *I. lutescens*
'Champagne Elegance' (TB)	LBro LIri MAus MMil NBir
¶ 'Champagne Waltz' (TB)	LIri
'Change of Pace' (TB)	SCro
¶ 'Chanted' (SDB)	NZep
'Chanteuse' (TB)	SCro

'Chantilly' (TB)	CBlo CM&M COtt EBrP EBre ELan EMan ERav LBre MRav NOrc SBre SCro
'Chapeau' (TB)	MAus
'Chapel Hill' (SDB)	LBro
'Charger' (TB)	MMil
'Charm Song' (IB)	LBro
'Charmaine' (TB)	CKel
I 'Charming' (TB)	CKel
'Chartreuse Ruffles' (TB)	SCro
'Cheers' (TB)	LBro NZep
'Cherry Falls' (TB)	LBro
'Cherry Garden' (SDB)	CBlo CBro CKel EBar ECro ECtt EGoo ELan EWes LGre MBro MMil MRav MS&S MTis NBir NNrd NRoo SCro SIng WWeb
'Cherry Orchard' (TB)	NNor
'Cherry Smoke' (TB)	SCro
'Cherub Tears' (SDB)	NZep
'Cherub's Smile' (TB)	SCro
§ 'Chian Wine' (MTB)	LBro
¶ 'Chickee' (MTB)	NZep
'Chicken Little' (MDB)	CBro
'Chief Chickasaw' (TB)	LBro
'Chief Moses' (TB)	MBri
'Chief Quinaby' (TB)	SCro
'Chief Waukesha' (TB)	SCro
I 'Chieftain' (SDB)	MRav NSti
¶ 'Chiltern Gold' (IB) ♀	CKel
'China Dragon' (TB)	SCro
'Chivalry' (TB)	LBro
¶ 'Chocolate Vanilla' (TB)	LIri
'Chorus Girl' (TB)	CKel
'Christening Party' (TB)	CKel
'Christmas Angel' (TB)	EBrP EBre ERou LBre MAus SBre WWeb
'Christmas Time' (TB)	NMGW NZep
Chrysofor Group	WPGP WRHF
chrysographes ♀	CGle CVer EBar EBrP EBre GCra GMac LBre LBro MBal MRav MSCN MTho NRya SBre SHel SMac SRms SUsu SWas WRHF WWin
– *alba*	NBir
chrysographes B&L 12617	EMon
– black	CBos CHad CHan CHar CMil CRow CSam ECGN GAbr GCal GDra IBlr MBal MBro MFir NBrk NHar NMen NWoo SChu SSpi SWyc WCru WHoo WLin WPyg
I – 'Black Beauty'	CFir SPer
I – 'Black Knight'	CBot EPfP GBuc GCHN GCal NChi NNor NOrc NSti SPer WPen WWin
I – 'Black Velvet'	SMad
– crimson	IBlr NCat NWoo
– x *forrestii*	GDra NBir
N – 'Inshriach'	CFai CHan EHyt GBuc GDra IBlr WLin
– 'Mandarin Purple'	EBee GBuc GCal GMac NCat NSti SPer SWyc
– purple	MBro MS&S
– red	MBal
¶ – 'Rob'	GMac
§ – var. *rubella*	CRow GDra GMac LGre MMil MSte SCro SWyc WPGP
* – – 'Wine'	CHad
– 'Rubra'	See *I. chrysographes* var. *rubella*
chrysophylla	MSto
– JCA 13233	CLAP CPou SSpi

'Church Stoke' (SDB)	SCro
N 'Cider Haze' (TB)	CKel
¶ 'Cimarron Rose' (SDB)	NZep
¶ 'City Lights' (TB)	LIri
'City of David' (TB)	SCro
'Clairette' (Reticulata)	CBro LAma
'Clap Hands' (SDB)	LBro
¶ 'Clara Garland' (IB) ♀	CKel
'Clarke Cosgrove' (Spuria)	LBro
clarkei	CHan ELan LGan NNrd
'Clay's Caper' (SDB)	EFou LBro
'Cleeton Buff' (Sino-Sib)	CMil MAus
N 'Cleo' (TB)	LBro NBir
'Cliffs of Dover' (TB) ♀	CKel MS&S WBcn
N 'Climbing Gold'	NPri
N 'Clotted Cream' (CH)	ECha MRav
'Cloudcap' (TB)	SRms
'Cloudless Sunrise' (TB)	ERou
¶ 'Clyde Redmond' (La)	SAWi
¶ 'Codicil' (TB)	LIri
'Color Brite' (BB)	SCro
'Color Focus' (Spuria)	LBro
'Color Splash' (TB)	SCro
'Columbia Blue' (TB)	SCro
'Colwall' (TB)	LBro WBcn
'Combo' (SDB)	CKel
¶ 'Competitive Edge' (TB)	LIri
'Condottiere' (TB)	SCro
'Confetti' (TB)	LRHS MBri
confusa ♀	CGle CHEx CHad CHan CKel CSev ECha ECre EPla MTho SAPC SArc SEND SSpi WFar WMul WPic
§ – 'Martyn Rix'	CHad CHid CLAP CPou CSev LHil MHlr NPla WCot
'Conjuration' (TB)	LIri MMil
'Connoisseur' (Spuria)	LBro
'Constant Wattez' (IB)	CKel LBuc
'Consummation' (MTB)	NZep
'Copper Classic' (TB)	NZep SCro
¶ 'Cops' (SDB)	NZep
'Coral Chalice' (TB)	ERou LIri
'Coral Joy' (TB)	LBro
'Coral Strand' (TB)	MAus
'Coral Wings' (SDB)	NZep
'Corn Harvest' (TB)	MMil NZep
'Corrida' (TB)	LBuc
'Côte d'Or' (TB)	SCro
'Cotton Blossom' (SDB)	LBro
'Cotton Plantation' (La)	LBro
'Cozy Calico' (TB)	SCro
'Cracklin Burgundy' (TB)	LIri SCro
'Cranberry Ice' (TB)	CKel SCro
'Cream Cake' (SDB)	NZep
'Creative Stitchery' (TB)	LIri SCro
'Cregrina' (TB)	LBro
cretensis	See *I. unguicularis* subsp. *cretensis*
'Cricket Lane' (SDB)	NZep
'Crimson Fire' (TB)	SCro
¶ 'Crinoline' (TB)	SCro
N 'Crispen Rouge' (TB)	CKel
¶ 'Crispette' (TB)	MAus
cristata ♀	CAvo CHea CPBP EPot GBuc ITim LAma MDHE MOne SRms
¶ – 'Abbey's Violet'	SWas
– 'Alba'	EPot LBee MBal MDHE NHar SChu SIng SWas WAbe
– × *gracilipes*	EPot
– × *lacustris*	CHan EPot NMen NTow
crocea ♀	GCra MSto
'Croftway Lemon' (TB)	SCro
'Cross Stitch' (TB)	MMil NZep
'Crown Sterling' (TB)	SCro
¶ 'Crushed Velvet' (TB)	MAus
'Cruzin' (TB)	LIri
'Cum Laude' (IB)	SCro
cuniculiformis ACE 2224	EHyt
'Cup Race' (TB)	NZep
¶ 'Curlew' (IB)	MAus
'Cutie' (IB)	NZep
¶ 'Cyanea' (DB)	SIng
cycloglossa	SWas
– HW&E 7727	CLAP
'Daisy Fresh' (MDB)	LBro
'Dale Dennis' (DB)	LBro
'Dancer's Veil' (TB) ♀	CKel EBrP EBre ECtt EFou EHic ELan ERou LBre LBro NRar NVic SBre SCoo SCro SMer
'Dancin'' (IB)	NZep
'Dancing Eyes' (SDB)	LBro
'Dancing Gold' (MTB)	NZep
danfordiae	CAvo CB&S CBro EBar EBrP EBre ELan EPar EPot ETub GCrs LAma LBre MBri NRog SBre WCot
'Dante' (TB)	CKel
'Dark Blizzard' (IB)	NZep
'Dark Bury' (TB)	LBro
'Dark Rosaleen' (TB) ♀	LBro
'Dark Spark' (SDB)	NSti
'Dark Vader' (SDB)	NZep
'Darkover' (SDB)	LBro
'Darkside' (TB)	SCro
'David Chapman' (TB)	LBro
'Dawn Candle' (Spuria)	LBro
'Dawn Favour' (SDB)	LBro
'Dawn Glory' (TB)	SCro
¶ 'Dawning' (TB)	LIri
'Dazzling Gold' (TB)	SCro
§ *decora*	CBro WLin
¶ – B&SWJ 2122	WCru
'Deep Black' (TB)	CBlo CMGP CMil COtt EMan EPfP ERav NOrc SCro SPer SWat
'Deep Fire' (TB)	SCro
'Deep Pacific' (TB)	LRHS MAus MBri
'Deft Touch' (TB)	MAus
delavayi ♀	GMaP GMac IBlr LSyl MRPP WCot WViv
'Delicate Air' (SDB)	LBro
'Delphi' (TB)	SCro
'Demelza' (TB)	LBro
'Demon' (SDB)	CKel EFou EHyt LBro LRHS MBri MS&S
'Denys Humphries' (TB)	CKel LBro
'Depth of Field' (TB)	LRHS
'Derring Do' (SDB)	LBro MS&S
'Derwentwater' (TB)	CBlo CKel MAus MMil SRms
¶ 'Desert Dream' (Sino-sib)	GDra
'Desert Dream' (AB)	SWyc
'Desert Echo' (TB)	EFou LIri
'Desert Quail' (MTB)	LBro
'Desert Song' (TB)	CKel MAus
'Designer Gown' (TB)	ERou
'Designer's Choice' (TB)	LBro
'Dew Point' (IB)	SCro
'Die Braut'	See *I.* 'Bride'
'Discretion' (TB)	SCro
¶ 'Dixie Pixie' (SDB)	EGle MAus

'Doctor Behenna' (TB)	LBro
'Doll Dear' (SDB)	LBro
'Doll House' (MDB)	CBlo CMea
'Doll Ribbons' (MTB)	NZep
'Doll Type' (IB)	LBro
* 'Don Brownsay'	MMil
¶ 'Dorothy Marquart' (TB)	LIri
'DoSiDo' (SDB)	SCro
¶ 'Dot and Dash' (TB)	MBri WWeb
'Dotted Doll' (MTB)	NZep
'Double Lament' (SDB)	CBro LBro MMil NNrd SCro
♀	SSte
douglasiana ♀	CBre CHad CMil EPar EPla
	EPot GDra IBlr LGan NNrd
	NSti SMac SSpi
* – 'Bandon Strain'	SSpi
'Dovedale' (TB) ♀	LBro MAus
'Doxa' (IB)	SCro
¶ 'Dream Builder' (TB)	NMGW
'Dreamcastle' (TB)	CKel
'Dreamsicle' (TB)	SCro
'Dresden Candleglow'	CKel MAus
(IB)	
'Driftwood' (Spuria)	LBro
'Drive You Wild' (CH)	LBro
'Dualtone' (TB)	CKel
'Dundee' (TB)	SCro
'Dunlin' (MDB)	CBro ERos NMen NNrd NRar
'Dusky Challenger' (TB)	LBro LIri MAus SCro SSte
¶ 'Dutch Chocolate' (TB)	MAus MMil
dykesii	CRow
'Eagle's Flight' (TB)	LBro NMGW NZep
'Eardisland' (IB) ♀	LBro MMil
'Earl' (TB)	MMil
'Earl of Essex' (TB)	MMil SCro
'Early Edition' (IB)	LBro
¶ 'Early Frost' (IB)	SCro
'Early Light' (TB) ♀	LBro
'East Indies' (TB)	MS&S
'Eastertime' (TB)	LIri
'Easy Strolling' (SDB)	LBro
'Edge of Winter' (TB)	CKel
'Edith Wolford' (TB)	LBro LIri MAus SCro
'Edward' (Reticulata)	EPot LAma
'Edward of Windsor' (TB)	CHad CMil EHic ELan ERou
	GLil NOrc WLRN
'Eirian' (TB)	LBro
'Eleanor's Pride' (TB)	CKel LBro MAus MMil
elegantissima	See *I. iberica* subsp.
	elegantissima
'Elixir' (Spuria)	LBro
'Elizabeth Arden' (TB)	CKel
'Elizabeth Poldark' (TB)	LBro LIri
¶ 'Ellen Manor' (TB)	MAus
'Elvinhall'	CBro
'Ember Days' (TB)	MMil
'Enchanted Gold' (SDB)	NZep
'English Cottage' (TB)	EGar GCal MAus MMil MWat
	SCro WIvy
'Ennerdale' (TB)	SRms
§ *ensata* ♀	CBen CBlo CMHG ECGP
	ELan ERic LBro LPBA LSyl
	MSta NBro NRoo SAWi SWat
	WHil WPer WPyg WWin
– 'Activity'	CBlo LRHS
– 'Alba'	CGle ECha
– 'Apollo'	CBen CRow ETub
– 'Bellender Blue'	LBro
I – 'Blue Peter'	CBen CRow
– 'Blue Skies'	SIng
– 'Butterflies in Flight'	LBro
– 'Caprician Butterfly'	SWyc

* – 'Carnival Prince'	NPri
– 'Center of Attention'	LBro
– 'Chico Geisho'	SWyc
– 'Chitose-no-tomo'	CRow
* – 'Cry of Rejoice'	MAus
– 'Crystal Halo'	LBro NBrk
– 'Dancing Waves'	CRow NBrk
– 'Darling' (I)	IBlr LRHS NBrk
– 'Dresden China' (TB)	CRow NBrk
– 'Enchanting Melody'	CRow
– 'Fairy Carillon'	LBro
– 'Flashing Koi'	NBrk
– 'Freckled Geisha'	CRow
– 'Fringed Cloud' ♀	SWyc
– 'Frosted Pyramid'	NBrk
– 'Galatea Marx'	CRow
* – 'Galathea'	GCal
– 'Geisha Parasol'	SWyc
N – 'Ghost' (v)	CGle
– 'Gipsy'	CSpe LRHS
– 'Glitter and Gayety'	CRow NBrk
– 'Hakug-yokuro'	CRow
– 'Hana-aoi'	CRow IBlr
– 'Happy Awakening'	SWyc
– 'Hatsu-shimo'	CRow IBlr
– 'Hercule'	CDoC NBrk
– Higo hybrids	CRow IBlr LPBA MSta
N – 'Hokkaido'	See *I. ensata* 'Perry's Hokkaido'
– 'Imperial Magic' ♀	SWyc
* – 'Innocence'	CBlo MBri NCat
N – 'Iso-no-ob'	MBri WMer
– 'Komo-no-ibo'	EBee SWat
– 'Kuma-funjin'	IBlr
– 'Labby White'	SWyc
– 'Laced'	SPer
– 'Landscape at Dawn'	CMHG CRow
* – 'Laughing Lion'	CDoC COtt LRHS MBri
– 'Light at Dawn'	LBro
– 'Lilac Blotch'	SPer
– 'Magic Opal' ♀	CRow
– 'Manadzuru'	IBlr
I – 'Mandarin'	CGle CRow NBrk
– 'Midnight Stars'	LBro
– 'Midsummer Reverie'	CRow
§ – 'Moonlight Waves'	CMGP CRDP CRow ELan
	EOld LHop MFir MSte NBrk
	NRoo SChu SSpi SWat WElm
	WHow WRus WWal WWat
– 'Narihira'	CRow IBlr
– 'Oku-banri'	IBlr
– 'Oriental Eyes'	LBro
– pale mauve	SPer
– 'Peacock'	SMrm SUsu
§ – 'Perry's Hokkaido'	CGle CRow IBlr NBrk NCat
¶ – 'Pin Stripe'	CBlo
– 'Pink Frost'	CHad CRDP CRow EBrP EBre
	EGle GAri LBre LRHS MBri
	NCat SBre
¶ – 'Pleasant Journey'	NPri
– 'Prairie Twilight'	LBro NBrk
– purple	SPer
I – 'Purple East'	CRow NBrk
– 'Ranpo'	CRow
I – 'Red Dawn'	CRow
§ – 'Rose Queen' ♀	CRDP CRow EBrP EBre
	ECGN ECha EGle ELan
	EMFW EPar ERou GCal LBre
	LPBA MSta NBrk NBro NRoo
	SBre SChu SPer SSpi WChe
	WRus
– 'Rowden'	CRow
– 'Royal Crown'	CRow NBrk SWyc

– 'Royal Purple'	CGle CMHG
I – 'Ruby King'	CBlo LRHS MBri
* – 'Sensation'	EOld
N – 'Shihainami'	IBlr
– 'Silverband'	NBrk
– 'Summer Storm' ♀	SPer SWyc
– 'Taga-sode'	CRow NBrk SWyc
– 'The Great Mogul' ♀	SWyc
– 'Time and Tide'	SWyc
– 'Umi-botaro'	CRow
– 'Valiant Prince'	CRow
– 'Variegata' ♀	CBen CMil CRDP CRow EBee
	ECha EHoe EHon IBlr LPBA
	MBri MSta MUlv SCro SWat
	WCot WFar WRus
– 'Vintage Festival' ♀	SWyc
– 'Waka-murasaki'	MBri WMer WRus
I – 'White Pearl'	CRow NBrk
– 'Worley Pink'	CRow
– 'Yako-no-tama'	CRow
– 'Yezo-nishiki'	LBro LRHS
– 'Yusho'	CRow
'Erleen Richeson' (TB)	SCro
'Escalona' (CH)	LBro
'Essay' (Spuria)	LBro
'Evening Gown' (TB)	LBro
'Evening Magic' (TB)	SCro
'Everything Plus' (TB)	ERou
ewbankiana	See *I. acutiloba* subsp. *lineolata*
¶ 'Exotic Gem' (TB)	MAus
'Exotic Isle' (TB)	NZep
'Exotic Shadow' (SDB)	LBro
'Extravagant' (TB)	SCro
'Eyebright' (SDB) ♀	CBro LBro MAus MBri WWeb
'Fairy Footsteps' (SDB)	LBro
'Fairy Time' (IB)	LBro
¶ 'Fakir's Fire' (MTB)	NZep
¶ 'Fall Fiesta' (TB)	LIri
¶ 'Fancy Woman' (TB)	LIri
'Fanfaron' (TB)	SCro
'Fantaisie' (TB)	CKel
'Farolito' (Spuria)	LBro WBcn
'Fashion Lady' (MDB)	CBro NNrd
'Favorite Angel' (SDB)	NMGW NZep
¶ 'Feature Attraction' (TB)	LIri
'Feminine Charm' (TB)	MAus
'Feminist' (TB)	SCro
fernaldii	MSto
– J&JA 12807	SSpi
'Festival Crown' (TB)	LBro
'Festive Skirt' (TB)	CKel MAus
'Fierce Fire' (IB) ♀	CKel
'Fiery Song' (TB)	CKel
filifolia	CBro
– var. *latifolia* SF 332	CMon
– MS 437	CMon
N 'Fire and Flame' (TB)	NBir
'Fire One' (SDB)	LBro
'Fire Siren' (TB)	MMil
'Firecracker' (TB)	ERou MBri MRav
'First Interstate' (TB)	SCro
¶ 'First Step' (SDB)	NZep
'First Violet' (TB)	LBro MAus
'Five Star Admiral' (TB)	SCro
'Flaming Dragon'	CKel EBee NPri
I 'Flamingo' (TB)	CKel
'Flapjack' (SDB)	NZep
¶ 'Flareup' (TB)	MBri WWeb
¶ 'Flash'	WHil
'Flashing Beacon' (MTB)	NZep
flavescens	MAus NSti
'Flea Circus' (MDB)	NZep

'Flirty Mary' (SDB)	EGle
'Florentina' (IB) ♀	CArn CBro CRow ECha EFou
	ELau EMFP ERav GPoy IBlr
	LBro LHol MAus MChe MHew
	MRav NFai SCro SIde WPic
	WWye
¶ *florentina alba*	ELau
¶ – blue	WOak
'Focal Point'	LBuc
'Focus' (TB)	SCro
§ *foetidissima* ♀	Widely available
– 'Aurea'	CMon
– *aurea* MS 902	CMon
– *chinensis*	See *I. foetidissima* var. *citrina*
§ – var. *citrina*	CFil CKel CRow ECha EFou
	EGle ELan EPla GAbr GCal
	IBlr LBro MBal MBro SSpi
	SUsu WAbe WHoo WOMN
	WPGP WPyg WRus WWin
	WWye
– 'Fructu Albo'	CRow SUsu
– var. *lutescens*	EMon
– 'Moonshy Seedling'	CSWP EGol
– 'Variegata' ♀	CBro CFil CGle CHan CRow
	CSam EGle ELan EOrc EPla
	LHil MBrN MBri NDea NHol
	NPer NRoo SSpi WAbe WEas
	WHil WRus WWat WWhi
– yellow seeded	EFou
'Foggy Dew' (TB)	MBri
¶ 'Fondation Van Gogh' (TB)	LIri
'Forest Hills' (TB)	CKel MS&S
'Forest Light' (SDB)	CBro LBro MBro NNrd
formosana	CHEx
forrestii ♀	CHad CHan CHea CLon CRow
	GBin GCal GDra GMac IBlr
	LGan LPBA LSyl MBri MNrw
	NBro NChi NHol NNrd NRya
	NSla NSti SSpi WAbe WCla
	WHer WWat
– hybrids	IBlr NHol
I – 'Sibirica'	MPEx
'Fort Apache' (TB)	SCro
'Fort Regent' (TB)	LBro
'Frank Elder' (Reticulata)	CBro EHyt EPot LAma MTho
	WIvy
'French Gown' (TB)	EFou
'Fresno Flash' (TB)	NZep SCro
¶ 'Fringe of Gold' (TB)	SCro
'Frontier Marshall' (TB)	CKel
'Frost and Flame' (TB)	CM&M EBrP EBre ECtt ELan
	ENot ERav ERou EWll LBre
	MBri MRav NOrc SBre SCro
	SPer
'Full Tide' (TB)	SCro
fulva	EBee GCal IBlr LBro NBro
	NSti SMrm SWyc WChe WCot
	WEas
× *fulvala* ♀	EMon IBlr LBlm MAus NBir
	NSti SWyc WChe WRus WWat
¶ 'Funtime' (SDB)	WViv
'Furnaceman' (SDB)	CBro ERos MBro MMil NNrd
'Fuzzy' (MDB)	LBro
'Fuzzy Face' (SDB)	NZep
¶ 'Gala Gown' (TB)	MAus
◆ 'Galathea'	See *I. ensata* 'Galathea'
§ *galatica*	EPot
¶ 'Galleon Gold' (SDB)	NZep
gatesii	EPot LAma
'Gay Parasol' (TB) ♀	LBro
N 'Gay Prince' (TB)	CKel MS&S

N'Gay Trip' (TB)   CKel WBcn
§ 'Gelbe Mantel' (Sino-sib)   CBot EHic GCra NBir NSti
'George' (Reticulata)   CAvo CBro EBrP EBre EPar
   EPot ERos LBre MHlr SBre
'Gerald Darby'   See *I.* × *robusta* **'Gerald Darby'**
germanica ♀   LBro NNor WPyg
– 'Kharput'   LBro
¶ – 'Nepalensis'   EGoo
* – 'The King'   MAus
'Gibson Girl' (TB)   MMil
¶ 'Gift of Dreams' (TB)   LIri
'Gigglepot' (SDB)   LGre MMil
'Ginger Swirl' (TB)   SCro
¶ 'Gingerbread Castle' (TB)   MAus
'Gingerbread Man' (SDB)   CBro CLon CMea EFou EGle
   ERos LBro LGre MAus MBro
   MMil MS&S NMen WHoo
¶ 'Giraffe Kneehiz' (TB)   LIri
¶ 'Glacier' (TB)   CKel
¶ 'Glacier Gold' (TB)   CKel
'Glad Rags' (TB)   NZep
¶ 'Glenwillow' (MDB)   NZep
¶ 'Gnu Again' (TB)   LIri
'Godfrey Owen' (TB)   MAus WBcn
¶ 'Godsend' (TB)   LIri
'Going My Way' (TB)   LRHS MAus MBri SCro
'Gold Burst' (TB)   SCro
'Gold Canary' (MDB)   NZep
I 'Gold Flake' (TB)   CKel
'Gold Galore' (TB)   SCro
'Gold of Autumn' (TB)   CKel
¶ 'Goldberry' (IB)   MAus
'Golden Alps' (TB)   ENot LBro
I 'Golden Bow' (TB)   CKel
'Golden Dewdrops'   LBro
   (SDB)
'Golden Encore' (TB)   CKel MAus MWat
'Golden Fair' (SDB)   NBir SIng
¶ 'Golden Forest' (TB)   MAus MBri
'Golden Harvest' (Dutch)   CB&S LAma SHel
'Golden Lady' (Spuria)   LBro
'Golden Muffin' (IB)   LBro NZep
'Golden Oldie' (La)   LBro
'Golden Planet' (TB)   CKel WBcn
'Golden Ruby' (SDB)   LBro
'Golden Spice' (TB)   LBro
'Golden Starlet' (SDB)   LBro
N 'Golden Surprise' (TB)   CKel
'Golden Veil' (TB)   CKel
'Golden Waves' (Cal-Sib)   CBro CMHG LBro
   ♀
N 'Goldfinder' (TB)   CKel
I 'Goldilocks' (TB)   CKel
'Good and True' (IB)   SCro
'Good Nature' (Spuria)   LBro
'Good Show' (TB)   SCro
'Gordon' (Reticulata)   EPot LAma
gormanii   See *I. tenax*
gracilipes   MBal
– 'Alba'   SSpi SWas
graeberiana   CLAP EPot
– white fall   LRHS
– yellow fall   LRHS
graminea ♀   CAvo CBro CHad CHan CMon
   CRow ECha EFou ELan EPla
   ERos IBlr LBee LBlm LBro
   MBel MBro MRPP NMen NNrd
   NSti SAxl SCro SMrm SOkh
   WOMN WPyg WRus WWat
– 'Hort's Variety'   EGar GCal
– var. *pseudocyperus*   CMon CRow NSti SDys
graminifolia   See *I. kerneriana*

¶ 'Granada Gold' (TB)   ENot
'Grand Baroque' (TB)   MMil
'Grand Waltz' (TB)   SCro
'Grandpa's Girl' (MTB)   LBro
'Grapelet' (MDB)   NZep
'Grapesicle' (SDB)   NZep
'Graphic Arts' (TB)   NZep
'Grecian Skies' (TB)   SCro
'Green Halo' (DB)   EGle LBro
'Green Ice' (TB)   CKel EFou MRav
'Green Jungle' (TB)   LBro
'Green Spot' (IB) ♀   CBot CBro CHad CHan ECtt
   EHyt ELan EPla ESis LGre
   MHig MMil MRav MWat NBir
   NHol NMGW NMen NNrd
   NRoo SChu SPer WEas WElm
   WHoo
'Greenstuff' (SDB)   LBro MMil
¶ 'Gudrun' (TB)   LBlm
'Gypsy Boy' (SDB)   MMil NMGW NZep
'Gypsy Caravan' (TB)   CKel SCro
¶ 'Gypsy Jewels' (TB)   CKel
¶ 'Gypsy Romance' (TB)   LIri
¶ 'Gyro' (TB)   LIri
'H.C. van Vliet' (Dutch)   LAma NRog SHel
'Hagar's Helmet' (IB)   LBro
'Hallowed Thought' (TB)   MMil MWat
halophila   See *I. spuria* subsp. *halophila*
¶ 'Handshake' (TB)   LIri
'Happening' (SDB)   NZep
* 'Happy Border'   MAus
'Happy Choice' (Spuria)   EFou LBro
'Happy Song' (BB)   NZep
'Harbor Blue' (TB)   CKel EWes MAus MWat SCro
'Harleqinade' (BB)   LBro
'Harlow Gold' (IB)   NZep
'Harmony' (Reticulata)   CAvo CBro EBrP EBre EPot
   ETub LAma LBre MBri MHlr
   NRog SBre
'Harriette Halloway' (TB)   CBlo ECGP SMrm WElm
hartwegii subsp.   WLin
   pinetorum
'Hazy Skies' (MTB)   LBro
'Headlines' (TB)   CKel MAus
¶ 'Heather Hawk' (TB)   MAus
'Helen Boehm' (TB)   SCro
'Helen McGregor' (TB)   CKel
'Helen Proctor' (IB)   NZep SCro
¶ 'Helen Traubel' (TB)   MBri
'Helge' (IB)   EPfP NFai
'Hellcat' (IB)   NZep
¶ 'Hello Darkness' (TB)   LIri
'Hell's Fire' (TB)   SCro
'Hercules' (Reticulata)   GCal LAma SIng
'Hers' (IB)   SCro
¶ 'High Barbaree' (TB)   MBri
'High Command' (TB)   CKel SCro
'High Life' (TB)   SCro
'Highline Halo' (Spuria)   EFou
'Hills of Lafayette' (IB)   NZep
'Hindu Magic' (TB)   LBro
'His' (IB)   SCro
histrio   LAma
– subsp. *aintabensis*   EHyt EPot LAma
– subsp. *histrio*   EPot
§ *histrioides* 'Angel's Eye'   CLAP
– 'Angel's Tears'   See *I. histrioides* **'Angel's Eye'**
– 'Lady Beatrix Stanley'   CLAP
N – 'Major' ♀   CBro CLAP LAma MBal MBri
– 'Reine Immaculée'   GCLN
¶ – var. *sophenensis*   CLAP
'Hocus Pocus' (SDB)   EFou EPPr LBro

'Holden Clough' ♀ — CBot CBre CGle CHad CHar EFou ELan EMFW EPri GMaP LBro MAus MFir MHFP MMil MRav MUlv NChi NSti SSvw SUsu SWat SWyc WChe WEas WLin WMaN WOld WSan WWin

¶ 'Honey Behold' (SDB) — CKel
'Honey Glazed' (IB) — LBro MAus MS&S NZep WBcn
'Honey Mocha' (TB) — SCro
'Honey Pot' (MDB) — CKel
'Honington' (SDB) ♀ — LBro MAus MMil
'Honky Tonk Blues' (TB) — LIri
'Honorabile' (MTB) — CKel MAus
hoogiana ♀ — EPot LAma MTho
– 'Alba' — EPot
– 'Purpurea' — EPot LRHS
§ *hookeri* — CMea CNic EDAr EHyt ELan GCHN GDra MBal MHar NTow NWoo SPer WAbe WOMN
hookeriana — WRHF
'Hopscotch' (BB) — SCro
¶ 'Hot Chocolate' (TB) — LIri
'Hot Fudge' (IB) — NZep
'Hot Spice' (IB) — NZep
'Hubbub' (IB) — SCro
'Hula Doll' (MDB) — CBlo CMea EGle MBri NMen
§ *humilis* — NNrd
hyrcana — CBro LAma
'I Do' (TB) — MMil NZep
§ *iberica* — EPot
§ – subsp. *elegantissima* — EPot
'Ice Chip' (SDB) — LBro
'Ida' (Reticulata) — LAma
'Ideal' (Dutch) — LAma SHel
'Ila Remembered' (Spuria) — LBro
illyrica — See *I. pallida*
¶ *imbricata* — MAus
'Immortality' (TB) — MAus SCro
'Imperator' (Dutch) — CB&S SHel
'Imperial Bronze' (Spuria) — EFou LBro
'Impetuous' (BB) — LBro
'Indeed' (IB) — LBro MS&S
'Indian Chief' (TB) — LBro LRHS MBri
'Indian Jewel' (SDB) — EGle
'Indian Pow Wow' (SDB) — CRDP LBro
N 'Indian Sunset' (TB) — CKel
'Indigo Flight' (IB) — EFou LBro
'Infinite Grace' (TB) — SCro
'Ingenuity' (SDB) — LBro
'Innocent Heart' (IB) ♀ — LBro SCro
innominata — CFil CGle CLon CRow CSam ECha EPot GMac IBlr LBee MNrw MRPP MSto MTho NBro NGre NHar NMen NSti NTow SIng SRms SUsu WCla WEas WGwG WOMN WPGP WWal WWat
– 'Alba' — NGre
– apricot — IBlr NWoo
– Ballyrogan hybrids — IBlr
– copper — IBlr
N – 'Doctor Riddle's Form' — CGle GDra MBal
– J&JA 12897 — SSpi
– JCA 13225 — CLAP SSpi
– JCA 13227 — SSpi
– JCA 1460800 — CPBP
– rose — CNic EROs
N – 'Spinners' — SSpi SWas
– yellow — NNrd

'Inscription' (SDB) — EGle LBro NZep
¶ 'Interpol' (TB) — MAus
'Irish Doll' (MDB) — CMea EGle LBro
* 'Irish Temper' (SDB) — MMil
'Irish Tune' (TB) — SCro
'Ishmael' (SDB) — EGle LBro
¶ J 437 — NSti
'J.S. Dijt' (Reticulata) — CAvo CBro EBar EBrP EBre EPar EPot LAma LBre MBri NRog SBre
'Jack o' Hearts' (SDB) — CMea LBro
'Jade Mist' (SDB) — EGle LBro LRHS MBri
'Jaime Lynn' (TB) — LIri
'Jan Reagan' (SDB) — NZep
'Jane Phillips' (TB) ♀ — CKel EBrP EBre ECha ECtt EGle ELan ENot ERav ERou LBre LBro MAus MCLN MHFP MMil MRav MS&S NCat NOrc SBre SChu SCro SMrm SPer SWat
'Jane Taylor' (SDB) — CBro EGle
'Janice Chesnik' (Spuria) — LBro
japonica ♀ — NPer WHil
– 'Aphrodite' (v) — WCot
– L 638 — SCro
N – 'Ledger's Variety' — CAvo CBro CGre CHan CMon CRow ECha ELan EPar EPri LGan LHil MRav WAbe WEas WRus WWat
– 'Variegata' ♀ — CAvo CBot CHad CHan CKel CLon CMon CRow ECha EPar EPla MBal NFai NOrc NPer SArc SSpi WEas WHer WPic WRus WViv WWeb
'Jasper Gem' (MDB) — EGle MMil NBir
'Java Charm' (TB) — MMil
'Jay Kenneth' (IB) — LBro
'Jazzamatazz' (SDB) — LBro
'Jazzebel' (TB) — SCro
'Jean Guymer' (TB) — MMil NBir WBcn
'Jeannine' (Reticulata) — LAma
'Jeremy Brian' (SDB) ♀ — LBro MAus MMil NZep SUsu
'Jersey Lilli' (SDB) — NSti
'Jesse's Song' (TB) — LBro MAus NZep SCro
'Jewel Baby' (SDB) — CBro NMGW NZep
'Jewel Bright' (SDB) — EFou MAus
'Joanna Taylor' (MDB) — CBro EROs NMen NNrd NZep
N 'Joe Elliott' (CH) — EGle EWes
'Joette' (MTB) — LBro
'John' (IB) — SCro
¶ 'John Taylor' (SDB) — CKel
'Jolly Fellow' (SDB) — LBro SUsu WHal
¶ 'Jolt' (TB) — LIri
♦ *jordana* — See *I. atrofusca*
'Joyce' (Reticulata) — CAvo CBro ELan EPar EPot LAma MBri NRog
'Joyce Terry' (TB) — LRHS MBri
'Joyful' (SDB) — LBro SCro
'Jubilee Gem' (TB) — CKel
juncea — CArn CMon
'June Prom' (IB) — SCro
'Juneau' (TB) — CKel WCot
'Jungle Shadows' (BB) — LGre MRav
'Just Jennifer' (BB) — LBro MAus
'Just Magic' (TB) — LBro
kaempferi — See *I. ensata*
'Karen Christine' (TB) — SCro
'Karen Maddock' (TB) — LBro
'Katharine Hodgkin' (Reticulata) ♀ — CAvo CBro CLAP EBrP EBre EHyt EPot EROs GAbr GCrs LAma LBre MRPP MTho NHar NRog SBre SMrm WAbe WIvy

¶ 'Katie-Koo' (IB) ♀	CKel	I – 'Elegante'	CRow SWat SWyc
'Katinka' (CH)	LBro	– 'Goshobeni'	CRow
'Katy Petts' (SDB)	EFou MRPP NZep	I – 'Midnight'	See *I. laevigata* 'Weymouth Midnight'
'Kayo' (SDB)	EFou EGle LBro MMil MS&S NZep	N– 'Monstrosa'	SWyc
¶ 'Kelway Renaissance' (TB)	CKel	– 'Mottled Beauty'	CBen CRow CWat MSta SWyc
		– 'Murasama'	CRow
¶ *kemaonensis*	GDra NHar WOMN	– 'Odiham'	SWyc
'Kent Pride' (TB)	CMGP CMil EBee EBrP EBre	– 'Plena' (d)	SWyc
	EFou EHic EPPr ERou LBre	N– 'Plum Purple'	EGle
	LBro MMil MRav MS&S MWat	– 'Purity'	See *I. laevigata* 'Weymouth Purity'
	NLak SBre SChu SCro SMrm		
	SPer SWat	– 'Regal'	SWyc
'Kentucky Bluegrass' (SDB)	EFou LBro MMil SUsu WWin	I – 'Reveille'	EGle
		– 'Richard Greany'	CRow
'Kentucky Derby' (TB)	SCro	– 'Rose Queen'	See *I. ensata* 'Rose Queen'
'Kermit' (IB)	SCro	– 'Shirasagi'	CRow
§ *kerneriana* ♀	CBro ELan EMon ERos GBuc	I – 'Snowdrift'	CBen CRow CWat EGol EHon
	MNrw SIgm WEas		EMFW LPBA MAus MBri
'Keyhaven' (SDB)	LBro		MSta NDea SAWi SCro SWat
'Kilt Lilt' (TB)	MAus SCro		SWyc WChe WMAq
¶ 'Kinetic' (SDB)	CKel	– 'Surprise'	See *I. laevigata* 'Weymouth Surprise'
kirkwoodii MS&CL 555	CMon		
'Kissing Circle' (TB)	LBro	– 'Tamagawa'	CRow
'Kista' (SDB)	MS&S	– 'Variegata' ♀	CBen CBos CRDP CRow CWat
'Kiwi Capers' (SDB)	NZep		ECha EGol EHon EMFW
¶ 'Kiwi Slices' (SDB)	NMGW		LPBA MHar MSta NDea NOrc
klattii	See *I. spuria* subsp.		NRoo SPer SSpi SWat SWyc
	musulmanica		WChe WMAq WRus WShe
'Knick Knack' (MDB)	CBro CGle CM&M CPBP EGle		WWat
	EHyt ELan EMan ERos GMaP	– 'Violet Garth'	CRow
	LGre MBrN MHig MRav	I – 'Weymouth'	See *I. laevigata* 'Weymouth Blue'
	NMGW NMen NNrd SChu		
	SCro SIng WGwG WWal WWin	§ – 'Weymouth Blue'	CRDP CRow EGol SAWi SWyc
kochii	LBro	§ – 'Weymouth Midnight'	CRow CWat ECGP EGol EHon
korolkowii 'Violacea'	LRHS		SAWi SWat SWyc
kuschakewiczii	MSto	¶ – 'Weymouth Surprise'	CWat
* 'Kuvatuib' (SDB)	MBri	'Lake Placid' (TB)	SCro
'La Nina Rosa' (BB)	MAus	'Land o' Lakes' (TB)	SCro
'Lace Artistry' (TB)	SCro	N 'Langport Chapter' (IB)	CKel
'Laced Cotton' (TB)	SCro	N 'Langport Chief' (IB)	CKel
'Laced Lemonade' (SDB)	EFou LBro LRHS MBri	N 'Langport Chimes' (IB)	CKel
§ *lactea* ♀	GBin NSla SCro	N 'Langport Claret' (IB)	CKel
– CC 220	MRPP	N 'Langport Curlew' (IB)	CKel
lacustris ♀	CBro ELan EPot ERos GCrs	N 'Langport Duchess' (IB)	CKel
	MBro MSto NBro NCat NGre	N 'Langport Fairy' (IB)	CKel
	NHar NMen NTow NWCA	N 'Langport Flame' (IB)	CKel MMil
	WAbe	N 'Langport Flush' (IB)	SCro SSte
– x *gracilipes*	CRDP EPot GDra SIng SWas	N 'Langport Haze' (IB)	CKel
	WAbe	N 'Langport Honey' (IB)	CKel
'Lady Belle' (MTB)	LBro	N 'Langport Hope' (IB)	CKel
'Lady Friend' (TB)	ERou LIri SCro	N 'Langport Jane' (IB)	CKel
'Lady Madonna' (TB)	SCro	N 'Langport Lord' (IB)	CKel
'Lady Mohr' (AB)	CKel	N 'Langport Magic' (IB)	MMil
'Lady of Nepal' (IB)	LBro	N 'Langport Minstrel' (IB)	CKel
§ *laevigata* ♀	CBen CRow CWat EBrP EBre	N 'Langport Myth' (IB)	CKel
	ECha EGle EGol EHon ELan	N 'Langport Pagan' (IB)	CKel
	LBre LPBA MRav MSta NBrk	N 'Langport Pearl' (IB)	CKel
	NBro NDea SBre SPer SWat	N 'Langport Phoebe' (IB)	CKel
	SWyc WAbe WChe WMAq	¶ 'Langport Phoenix' (IB)	CRow
	WShi	N 'Langport Pinnacle' (IB)	CKel
– 'Alba'	CBen CRDP CRow ECha EGol	N 'Langport Pleasure' (IB)	CKel
	EHon LPBA SAWi SSpi SWat	N 'Langport Prince' (IB)	MMil
	SWyc WChe	N 'Langport Robe' (IB)	CKel
– 'Albopurpurea'	EMFW	N 'Langport Robin' (IB)	CKel
– 'Atropurpurea'	CRow EGol IBlr LPBA MSta	N 'Langport Romance' (IB)	CKel
– 'Colchesterensis'	CBen CRDP CRow CWat	N 'Langport Smoke' (IB)	CKel
	ECGP EGol EHon EMFW	N 'Langport Song' (IB)	CKel MMil
	LPBA MSta SWat SWyc WChe	N 'Langport Star' (IB)	CKel
I – 'Dorothy'	LPBA MSta SAWi WChe	N 'Langport Storm' (IB)	CKel EFou MMil WBcn
– 'Elegant'	See *I. laevigata* 'Weymouth Elegant'	N 'Langport Sultan' (IB)	CKel
		N 'Langport Sun' (IB)	CKel

N 'Langport Sunbeam' (IB)   CKel
N 'Langport Swift' (IB)   CKel
¶ 'Langport Sylvia' (IB)   CKel
N 'Langport Tempest' (IB)   CKel
N 'Langport Vale' (IB)   CKel
N 'Langport Violet' (IB)   CKel
N 'Langport Vista' (IB)   CKel
N 'Langport Warrior' (IB)   CKel MS&S
N 'Langport Wren' (IB)   CBro CKel CMil LBro LGre
     MBel MMil MTPN
§ *latifolia* ♀   WCot WLin WMaN
 – *alba*   ELan
'Latin Rock' (TB)   SCro
¶ 'Lavanesque' (TB)   CKel MAus
§ *lazica* ♀   CAvo CBro CMea CMon ECre
     EHyt EPot GMac IBlr MBel
     NChi NSti SChu SCro SIng
     SUsu WCot WEas WRus WWat
'Leda's Lover' (TB)   SCro
I 'Lemon Drop' (TB)   CKel
'Lemon Flare' (SDB)   EBrP EBre ECtt LBre LBro
     MAus MRav SBre
'Lemon Flurry' (IB)   LBro
'Lemon Glitter' (TB)   EFou EPri
'Lemon Ice' (TB)   MMil
'Lemon Mist' (TB)   MAus MMil
'Lemon Puff' (MDB)   CBro LBro NNrd
'Lemon Reflection' (TB)   MMil
'Lemon Tree' (TB)   MAus
¶ 'Lemon Wine' (IB)   CKel
N 'Lena' (SDB)   CBro WGwG
¶ 'Lenna M' (SDB)   CKel
'Lent A Williamson' (TB)   CBlo MAus SCro
'Libation' (MDB)   LBro
'Light Cavalry' (IB)   NZep
¶ 'Light Laughter' (IB)   MAus
'Lighted Signal' (Spuria)   LBro
'Lighted Within' (TB)   SCro
¶ 'Lighten Up' (SDB)   NZep
'Lilac and Lavender'   MMil NZep
 (SDB)
'Lilli-white' (SDB)   CKel EBrP EBre EGle ENot
     LBre LBro MAus MMil MRav
     NNrd SBre SPer
'Lime Grove' (SDB) ♀   SIng
¶ 'Limelight' (TB)   SRms
'Limpid Pools' (SDB)   SCro
¶ 'Linesman' (SDB)   NZep
¶ 'Lions Share' (TB)   LIri
¶ 'Liquid Smoke' (TB)   MMil
'Listowel' (IB)   LBro
'Little Amigo' (SDB)   NZep
N 'Little Amoena'   ERos NMen
'Little Annie' (SDB)   NZep
'Little Bill' (SDB)   EFou EGle
'Little Black Belt' (SDB)   EFou LBro NZep
'Little Blackfoot' (SDB)   CHad MAus MMil WHoo
     WWin
'Little Chestnut' (SDB)   LBro WWin
'Little Cottage' (SDB)   SCro
'Little Dandy' (SDB)   EGle
'Little Dogie' (SDB)   EGle LBro
'Little Dream' (SDB)   EGle NZep
'Little Episode' (SDB)   NZep
'Little Paul' (MTB)   LBro
'Little Pearl' (MDB)   NZep
'Little Rosy Wings' (SDB)   CBro ERos LBro LGre MBri
     MMil
'Little Shadow' (IB)   ECtt ENot GMaP LBro MRav
     SRms
'Little Sheba' (AB)   LBlm
'Little Snow Lemon' (IB)   NZep

'Live Jazz' (SDB)   MAus MMil NZep
'Lively Rose' (MTB)   LBro
'Llanthony' (SDB)   MAus
loczyi   MSto
'Lodestar' (TB)   LBro
'Lodore' (TB)   CKel MBri SRms
¶ 'Lofty Dreams' (TB)   LIri
longipetala   NBir NSti
'Look Again' (Spuria)   LBro
'Lookin' Good' (IB)   NZep
'Loop the Loop' (TB)   CKel EBee EGle SMer
'Lord Baltimore' (TB)   SCro
'Lord Warden' (TB)   EFou
'Lord Wolseley' (Spuria)   LBro
'Lorilee' (TB)   SCro
'Los Angeles'   LRHS MBri
'Lothario' (TB)   CKel MAus MS&S
'Loud Music' (TB)   MAus MBri WWeb
'Loudmouth' (AB)   LBro
Louisiana hybrids   MSta
'Louisiana Lace' (TB)   SCro
'Louvois' (TB)   MAus
'Loveday' (TB)   LBro
'Lovely Again' (TB)   MAus MWat
'Lovely Kay' (TB)   SCro
'Lovely Letty' (TB)   MBri
'Lovely Light' (TB)   MBri
'Love's Tune' (TB)   SCro
'Loveshine' (SDB)   MMil NZep
'Low Snow' (SDB)   NZep
'Lucky Charm' (MTB)   LBro
'Lucky Duck' (SDB)   NZep
'Lugano' (TB)   MMil
'Lullaby of Spring' (TB)   LIri
'Luscious One' (SDB)   LBro
§ *lutescens* ♀   CPBP ERos LGan MAus
§ – 'Campbellii'   CBro EHyt ERos LGre MBri
     MBro MHig MSto NMen NNrd
 – *cyanea*   NNrd
* – 'Goldcrest'   MBro
¶ – L 22   WPGP
 – subsp. *lutescens*   CMon WLin
'Lydia Jane' (Spuria) ♀   LBro WBcn
'Madeira Belle' (TB)   MAus
I 'Maestro' (TB)   CKel
'Magic Carpet' (TB)   CKel
'Magic Flute' (MDB)   EGle LBro MBri
'Magic Hills' (TB)   CKel
'Magic Man' (TB)   LBro
magnifica ♀   CBro CLAP EHyt EPot GCrs
     NWCA
 – f. *alba*   LRHS
* – 'Samarkhand Gem'   GCrs
'Mahogany Snow' (SDB)   MMil NZep
¶ 'Malaguena' (TB)   LIri
I 'Mandarin' (TB)   GDra
'Mandarin Purple'   IBlr NHol
 (Sino-sib)
maracandica   MSto
¶ 'Margarita' (TB)   MAus
'Margot Holmes' (Cal-Sib)   EBee GCal GDra GMac IBlr
     NCat NHol SChu
¶ 'Margrave' (TB)   MAus
'Marhaba' (MDB)   CBro ERos NNrd
'Maria Tormena' (TB)   SCro
'Marilyn Holloway'   ECha
 (Spuria)
'Marmalade Skies' (BB)   LBro MS&S NZep
'Marshlander' (TB)   EFou SCro
'Marty' (IB)   MS&S
'Martyn Rix'   See *I. confusa* **'Martyn Rix'**
'Mary Frances' (TB) ♀   LBro LIri MAus SCro

'Mary McIlroy' (SDB) ♀ CBro LBro MMil
'Master Touch' (TB) LIri SCro
'Matchpoint' (TB) LBro
'Matinata' (TB) CKel
'Maui Moonlight' (IB) ♀ LIri MMil NZep
'May Melody' (TB) CKel MBri
'Meadow Court' (SDB) CBro CKel ERos MAus NNrd
              NZep WMer WSan
'Media Luz' (Spuria) LBro
'Meg's Mantle' (TB) ♀ CKel LBro
'Melissa Sue' (TB) SCro
mellita See *I. suaveolens*
– var. *rubromarginata* See *I. suaveolens*
'Melon Honey' (SDB) ♀ CKel EGle LBro MAus MMil
              MS&S NZep WWin
'Merseyside' (SDB) CNic EGle LBro
¶ 'Mesmerizer' (TB) LIri
'Metaphor' (TB) MMil
'Michele Taylor' (TB) SCro
¶ 'Midday Blues' (IB) NZep
'Midnight Fire' (TB) ERou
'Midnight Madness' NZep
   (SDB)
milesii ♀ CPou NBir SCro WPer
– CC&McK 741 GCHN
– CR 346 WPer
¶ 'Mini Agnes' (DB) CBro
'Minnesota Glitters' (TB) SCro
'Minnie Colquitt' (TB) CKel SCro
'Miss Carla' (IB) ♀ LBro MMil SCro
'Mission Ridge' (TB) CKel
'Mission Sunset' (TB) EBrP EBre LBre MAus SBre
'Missouri Gal' (Spuria) LBro
missouriensis ♀ CRow EWoo IBlr LBro MSto
              NMen SSpi
– var. *arizonica* EBee
'Mister Roberts' (SDB) LBro NZep
'Moment' (SDB) NZep
'Monaco' (TB) EFou
'Money' (TB) SCro
monnieri CMon EFou IBlr SDix
Monspur Group GCal SSpi WCot
§ 'Monspur Cambridge MAus
   Blue' (Spuria)
¶ 'Moon Shadows' (SDB) WViv
'Moon Sparkle' (IB) CKel WSan
'Moonlight' (TB) LBro MRav NNor NNrd
'Moonlight Waves' See *I. ensata* 'Moonlight Waves'
'Morning Hymn' (TB) SCro
'Morning Show' (IB) SCro
'Morocco' (TB) SCro
'Morwenna' (TB) ♀ LBro
* 'Mount Stewart Black' EBee GCal
'Mrs Horace Darwin' CFir
   (TB)
'Mrs Kate Rudolph' EFou EGle EHyt LBro MBri
   (SDB)
* 'Mrs Richmond' SAWi
¶ 'Mulberry Rose' (TB) CKel
munzii EWoo
'Muriel Neville' (TB) MAus
'Music Box' (SDB) NZep
'My Honeycomb' (TB) MAus MBri MS&S
'My Mary' (TB) CKel
N 'My Seedling' (MDB) CBro ERos NCat NMen NNrd
              WIvy
'My Smoky' (TB) CKel MS&S
'Mystique' (TB) SCro
¶ 'Naivasha' (TB) CKel
'Nambe' (MTB) LBro
'Nampara' (TB) LBro
'Nancy Hardy' (MDB) CBro ERos NNrd

'Nancy Lindsay' See *I. lutescens* 'Nancy Lindsay'
'Nashborough' (TB) CKel
'Natascha' (Reticulata) EHyt ELan LAma
'Navajo Blanket' (TB) SCro
'Nectar' (TB) CKel
¶ *nectarifera* EHyt
'Needlecraft' (TB) CKel MMil
'Needlepoint' (TB) SCro
* 'Nel Jupe' (TB) EOld
'Neon Pixie' (SDB) NZep
'Neophyte' (Spuria) LBro
nepalensis See *I. decora*
nertschinskia See *I. sanguinea*
'New Idea' (MTB) LBro MS&S
'New Snow' (TB) CKel LBlm MAus WCot
'Nibelungen' (TB) CKel EPfP NFai
'Nice 'n' Nifty' (IB) NZep WTin
¶ 'Niebelungen' (TB) EOld
'Night Owl' (TB) CKel MMil SCro
nigricans S&L 148 CMon
'Nimble Toes' (SDB) LBro
¶ 'Nineveh' (AB) MAus
'Nylon Ruffles' (SDB) LBro SUsu
'Ochraurea' (Spuria) EBee GCal
ochroleuca See *I. orientalis*
'Offenham' (TB) LBro
'Oklahoma Bandit' (IB) LBro
'Ola Kala' (TB) CMGP EBrP EBre ECle ECro
              EHic ERou LBre LBro MAus
              SBre SCro SPer WLRN
'Oliver' (SDB) LBro
'Olympiad' (TB) LIri
'Olympic Challenger' MAus
   (TB)
'Olympic Torch' (TB) ♀ CKel
'One Accord' (SDB) SCro
'One Desire' (TB) MAus NZep
'Open Sky' (SDB) MMil NZep
'Orange Blaze' (SDB) CBro
'Orange Caper' (SDB) EBrP EBre LBre MRav NZep
              SBre
§ 'Orange Chariot' (TB) MAus
'Orange Dawn' (TB) ♀ LBro MMil
¶ 'Orange Grove' (TB) MBri
¶ 'Orange Jewelius' (TB) LIri
'Orange Maid' (Spuria) WBcn
N 'Orange Plaza' NMen NPri WLin
'Orange Tiger' (SDB) MMil NZep
'Orchardist' (TB) CKel
'Orchidarium' (TB) CKel
§ *orchioides* ELan EPot ERos
– yellow LRHS
'Oregold' (SDB) NZep
'Oregon Skies' (TB) SCro
¶ 'Oriental Baby' (IB) CKel
'Oriental Blush' (SDB) LBro WBcn
'Oriental Glory' (TB) MAus
'Oriental Touch' CRow
   (SpecHybrid)
§ *orientalis* ♀ CAvo CBot CHan CMil CRow
              ECGP ELan LBlm LBro LPBA
              MAus MBal MWgw SChu WPic
              WWat WWin
– 'Alba' See *I. sanguinea* 'Alba'
'Orinoco Flow' (BB) ♀ CKel LIri
'Oritam' (TB) SCro
'Ornament' (SDB) LBro
'Out Yonder' (TB) MAus
'Ovation' (TB) SCro
'Overnight Sensation' SCro
   (TB)
'Pacer' (IB) NZep

'Pacific Coast Hyb'	See *I.* **Californian Hybrids**
'Pacific Gambler' (TB)	EFou
'Pacific Mist' (TB)	SCro
¶ 'Pagan Pink' (TB)	LIri
¶ 'Pagan Princess' (TB)	MAus
¶ 'Paint It Black' (TB)	LIri
'Pajaro Dunes' (CH) ♀	LBro
'Pale Primrose' (TB)	WEas
'Pale Shades' (IB) ♀	CBro CKel LBro
'Pale Suede' (SDB)	LBro
¶ pale yellow (Sino-sib)	NWoo
§ *pallida*	CSWP ECGN EFou ELau LHol
	MAus MCCP
– 'Argentea Variegata'	CGle CHad EAst EBee ECro
	EHoe ERav ERic LHop MAus
	MBrN MBro MLLN MTis MUlv
	NCat NMGW NMir NPla NRoo
	NSti NTay SCro SSpi WGwG
	WHoo WHow WRus WWat
	WWeb
– 'Aurea'	See *I. pallida* **'Variegata'**
– 'Aurea Variegata'	See *I. pallida* **'Variegata'**
– subsp. *cengialtii* ♀	CMon
– var. *dalmatica*	See *I. pallida* subsp. *pallida*
§ – subsp. *pallida* ♀	CBot CKel EBrP EBre ECha
	ELan LBre LBro LHil MBri
	MUlv NSti SBre SCro SDix
	SMrm SPer WWal
N– 'Variegata' ♀	Widely available
'Paltec'	CHad CPou LGre SWas
'Pandora's Purple' (TB)	SCro
'Paradise' (TB) ♀	EPfP LBro SCro
'Paradise Bird' (TB) ♀	LBro
paradoxa f. *choschab*	EHyt EPot
'Paricutin' (SDB)	CBro EGle
'Paris Lights' (TB)	SCro
'Party Dress' (TB)	CMGP EBee EBrP EBre ECro
	ECtt EHic ELan ENot EPla
	ERav ERou LBre LBro MRav
	NOrc SBre SChu SCoo SMrm
	SPer WWal
'Pascoe' (TB) ♀	LBro
'Pastel Charm' (SDB)	CKel MSCN WSan
'Pastel Delight' (SDB)	NZep
'Path of Gold' (DB)	CBro LBro MBri NNrd SIng
	WWeb
'Patterdale' (TB)	NBir NMGW NVic
'Pauline' (Reticulata)	CAvo CBro EPot LAma NRog
¶ 'Peace and Harmony'	LIri
(TB)	
'Peach Band' (TB)	ERou
'Peach Eyes' (SDB)	LBro NZep
'Peach Petals' (BB)	LBro NZep
'Peach Picotee' (TB)	SCro
'Peach Spot' (TB)	MAus MMil
¶ 'Peaches ala Mode' (BB)	MAus
'Peaches 'n' Topping'	LBro
(BB)	
'Peachy Face' (IB)	LBro
'Pearly Dawn' (TB)	CHad EBrP EBre ECtt LBre
	MTis MWat SBre SCro SPer
	WLRN
'Pegasus' (TB)	SCro
'Peggy Chambers' (IB) ♀	EFou LBro MMil
'Peking Summer' (TB)	SCro
'Pennies' (MDB)	NZep
'Pennyworth' (IB)	SCro
'Penrhyn' (TB)	LBro
'People Pleaser' (SDB)	NZep SCro
'Peppermint Twist' (SDB)	NZep
'Persian Berry' (TB)	SCro
'Persian Doll' (MDB)	NZep

'Persian Romance' (TB)	MS&S
persica	LAma
'Pet' (SDB)	NSti NZep
¶ 'Phil Keen' (TB) ♀	CKel
'Pied Pretty' (SDB)	SCro
'Pigeon' (SDB)	NZep
'Pigmy Gold' (IB)	ECro ENot LBro
'Pinewood Amethyst'	LBro
(CH)	
'Pinewood Charmer' (CH)	LBro
'Pinewood Poppet' (CH)	LBro
'Pinewood Sunshine' (CH)	LBro
'Pink Angel' (TB)	SCro
'Pink Bubbles' (BB)	NZep
'Pink Clover' (TB)	LBro
'Pink Confetti' (TB)	SCro
'Pink Divinity' (TB)	MMil
'Pink Horizon' (TB)	SCro
'Pink Kitten' (IB)	NZep
'Pink Lamb' (BB)	LBro
N 'Pink Lavender' (TB)	SCro
'Pink 'n' Mint' (TB)	SCro
'Pink Pussycat'	MBri
N 'Pink Randall' (TB)	SCro
'Pink Ruffles' (IB)	CKel WBcn
'Pink Taffeta' (TB)	CKel SCro
'Pinnacle' (TB)	CKel
'Pipes of Pan' (TB)	MRav
'Piquant Lass' (MTB)	NZep
'Pixie Flirt' (MDB)	LBro
planifolia AB&S 4609	CMon
* – 'Alba'	CMea
– S&L 301	CMon
¶ 'Planned Treasure' (TB)	LIri
'Playgirl' (TB)	SCro
'Pledge Allegiance' (TB)	LIri MMil SCro
'Plickadee' (SDB)	EPot NNrd
'Plum Perfect' (SDB)	SCro
* 'Plums 'n' Cream'	EHyt
'Pogo' (SDB)	CMil ECtt EGle EHyt ELan
	ENot GMaP MMil MRav NNrd
	NRoo SCro SRms
'Pogo Doll' (AB)	LBro
'Pony' (IB)	LBro MS&S
'Port of Call' (Spuria)	LBro
'Post Time' (TB)	SCro
'Powder Pink' (TB)	CKel MS&S
'Praise the Lord' (TB)	LBro
'Prancing Pony' (TB)	CKel SCro
'Pretender' (TB)	LRHS MAus MBri
'Prettie Print' (TB)	SCro
¶ 'Priceless Pearl' (TB)	SCro
'Pride of Ireland' (TB)	SCro
'Prince' (SDB)	EFou EGle LBro
¶ 'Prince Indigo' (TB)	ENot
'Princess Beatrice'	See *I. pallida* subsp. *pallida*
prismatica	CMon EPla NNrd
– *alba*	CLAP GAbr
'Professor Blaauw'	ETub LAma SHel
(Dutch) ♀	
'Prosper Laugier' (IB)	SCro
'Protégé' (Spuria)	LBro
'Proud Tradition' (TB)	LIri SCro
'Provencal' (TB)	CKel MAus
pseudacorus ♀	Widely available
– 'Alba'	CRow SSpi SWyc WChe
– var. *bastardii*	CRDP CRow CWat ECGP
	ECha EGol EMFP EMFW
	LPBA SWyc WChe
– 'Beuron'	CRow
– cream	EGol MUlv NBir NBrk
– dwarf form	SWyc

'Rosy Wings' (TB)	NNrd
'Roustabout' (SDB)	EFou EGle LBro
N 'Roy Elliott'	CHad MBro NMen WPer
'Royal Ascot' (TB)	LBro
'Royal Contrast' (SDB) ♀	LBro MMil NZep
'Royal Fairy' (SDB)	LBro
'Royal Intrigue' (TB)	SCro
'Royal Magician' (SDB)	WHoo
'Royal Midget' (SDB)	LBro
'Royal Regency' (TB)	SCro
N 'Royal Toss' (MDB)	CKel
'Royal Touch' (TB)	EFou
'Royal Yellow' (Dutch)	NRog
'Ruby Chimes' (TB)	LGre MS&S SCro
'Ruby Contrast' (TB)	CHad MS&S
'Ruby Gem' (TB)	CKel
'Ruby Locket' (SDB)	LBro
'Ruby Mine' (TB)	MAus
rudskyi	See *I. variegata*
'Ruffled Ballet' (TB)	SCro
¶ 'Ruffled Revel' (TB)	CKel
'Ruffled Surprise' (TB)	SCro
'Ruffles and Lace' (TB)	SCro
'Russian White' (Spuria)	LBro
'Rustam' (TB)	CKel
'Rustic Cedar' (TB)	EPfP
N 'Rustic Jewel' (TB)	CKel
'Rustler' (TB)	LIri SCro
'Rusty Dusty' (SDB)	NZep
'Ruth Couffer' (BB)	LBro MS&S
'Ruth Knowles' (SDB)	LBro
'Ruth Margaret' (TB)	CKel
ruthenica	CMon ERos NMen NNrd SIng SSpi WOMN WPer
– var. *nana* L 1280	EPot SBla
'Sable' (TB)	EHic MWat NOrc SCro SMrm SPer WLRN
'Sable Night' (TB)	CKel ERou
'Sager Cedric' (TB)	MAus
'Sahara Sands' (Spuria)	ECha
'Saint Crispin' (TB)	CM&M EBrP EBre ERou LBre LBro MRav MWat NLak SBre SChu SCro SMrm SPer WGwG WLRN WWal ♀
'Sally Jane' (TB)	MAus
'Salonique' (TB)	MAus NFai
* 'Saltbox' (SDB)	WIvy
'Saltwood' (SDB) ♀	CBro LBro
'Sam' (SDB)	NZep
¶ 'Sam Carne'	MAus
'Samurai Warrior' (TB)	SCro
¶ 'San Leandro' (TB)	MBri
'Sand and Sea' (TB)	LBro
'Sand Princess' (MTB)	EFou
¶ 'Sandy Caper' (IB)	MAus
'Sangreal' (IB)	GLil
§ *sanguinea* ♀	CAvo EMon MSto WCot
– AGSJ 625	NGre
§ – 'Alba'	CRow GCHN
– × *laevigata*	SCro
¶ – 'Nana Alba'	SWas
§ – 'Snow Queen'	CHad CKel EBar ECED EGle EHon ELan EMan ERou LGan LPBA MBro NSti SCro SOkh SPer SSpe SSpi WPer
'Santana' (TB)	SCro
'Sapphire Beauty' (Dutch)	NRog
'Sapphire Gem' (SDB)	CKel MAus
'Sapphire Hills' (TB)	MAus SCro
'Sapphire Jewel' (SDB)	NZep
'Sarah Taylor' (SDB) ♀	CBro EFou LBro MAus SCro
sari	EHyt EPot LAma
¶ 'Sass with Class' (SDB)	WTin
'Satin Gown' (TB)	EPri MAus MBri
'Saturnalia' (TB)	SCro
'Saucy Peach' (BB)	LBro
'Saxon Princess' (TB)	LBro
schachtii MS&CL 510	CMon
'Schortman's Garnet Ruffles' (TB)	LIri SCro
'Scintilla' (IB) ♀	MMil SCro SSte
'Scintillation' (TB)	SCro
'Scribe' (MDB)	CBro EGle LRHS MBri
'Scrimmage' (SDB)	NZep
'Sea Double' (TB)	MMil
'Sea Fret' (SDB)	CBro
'Sea of Joy' (TB)	SCro
'Second Opinion' (MTB)	NZep
'Senlac' (TB)	GLil
serbica	See *I. reichenbachii*
'Serenity Prayer' (SDB)	NZep
setosa ♀	CBro CHea CRow ECha EGle EMNN ERos GCra GMaP ITim LGan MHig MHlr MNrw MOne MSta NHed SCro
– *alba*	CMea CRow EBee LGan MBro SIng WLin
– var. *arctica*	CRDP CRow EMon EPot GCHN LBee MBro NHol NMen NWCA SBla SCro SIng SUsu SWas WHoo WPer WPyg
♦ – subsp. *canadensis*	See *I. hookeri*
♦ – dwarf form	See *I. hookeri*
§ – 'Hondoensis'	EMon SApp
♦ – 'Hookeri'	See *I. hookeri*
♦ – 'Kirigamini'	See *I. setosa* **'Hondoensis'**
♦ – var. *nana*	See *I. hookeri*
– *tricuspis*	NNrd
'Shampoo' (IB)	EFou MAus
'Sheila Ann Germaney' (Reticulata)	EHyt EPot
'Shelford Giant' (Spuria) ♀	CRow LBro
'Shepherd's Delight' (TB)	MBri
'Sherbet Lemon' (IB) ♀	MAus
'Short Order' (CH) ♀	LBro
'Show Me Yellow' (SDB)	NZep SCro
'Showcase' (TB)	NMGW
'Showman' (TB)	ERou
shrevei	See *I. virginica* var. *shrevei*
'Shrinking Violet' (MTB)	LBro
'Shy Violet' (SDB)	NZep
sibirica ♀	CChr CMHG CMea CVer EGle EHon LAma LLWP LSyl MBro MCLN MFir MPEx MWat NChi NDea NNor NVic SEas SHel SMad WEas WHer WHoo WShi WWeb WWhi WWin
§ 'Sibirica Alba'	CRow ECGP ECha EHic GDra LLWP SBla
sibirica 'Alba'	See *I.* **'Sibirica Alba'**
– 'Anglesey'	LBro
– 'Ann Dasch'	EFou EGar LBro WLin
– 'Annemarie Troeger' ♀	EFou LBro NCat
– 'Anniversary' ♀	CBos LBro LRHS MAus MBri MUlv SCro
¶ – 'Baby Sister'	EFou
§ 'Sibirica Baxteri'	CFee CRow WLin
sibirica 'Baxteri'	See *I.* **'Sibirica Baxteri'**
– 'Beaumaris'	LBro
– 'Berliner Runde'	LBro
– 'Blue Brilliant'	WLin
– 'Blue Burgee'	ECha SCro

– 'Sea Shadows' ♀ LBro MBel NBir
– 'Shirley Pope' ♀ EGar LBro MBri NPri
– 'Showdown' CB&S EBrP EBre ECtt EGar LBre LBro MUlv NFai NHol SAxl SBre SCro WHal WWat
N – 'Shrawley' EGar
– 'Silver Edge' ♀ CRos EFou EGar GMac LBlm LBro MAus MBri MBro MUlv NFai SCro SWat WEas WFar WHoo WLin WPen
– 'Sky Wings' CB&S CRow EBee ECha EGle EMou MArl
– 'Snow Queen' See *I. sanguinea* 'Snow Queen'
– 'Snowcrest' CBre NBrk NPla WLin
– 'Soft Blue' ♀ LBro SCro
N – 'Southcombe White' CRow CVer EGar GBuc GCal MBel SWas WRHF
– 'Sparkling Rosé' CBot EBrP EBre ECtt EFou EGol LBlm LBre LBro MBel MBri MBro MNrw NHar NHol NRoo SBre SChu SCro SMrm SSvw WHoo WPer WRus WWal WWhi
– 'Summer Sky' WCot WLin WTin WViv
¶ – 'Super Ego' WCot WTin
¶ – 'Superba' WLin
– 'Swank' LBro
– 'Teal Velvet' LBro
– 'The Gower' CLAP
– 'Thelma Perry' WCot
– 'Towanda Redflare' EGle EHon ELan LBro SOkh WHer
– 'Tropic Night' CHad CHea CVer ECGP EFou ERou GMac LHop MBri MRav MSta NBrk NHol NRoo NRya SMad SPer SSoC WFar WHal WRus WWat
– 'Tycoon' MAus NChi NHol SPer WLRN WLin
– 'Vi Luihn' CB&S ECha EGle LBro
– 'Violetmere' LBro WLin
¶ – 'Weisse Etagen' ♀ SCro
– white EGle
¶ – 'White Magnificence' WLin
I – 'White Queen' LBro SSvw
– 'White Swirl' ♀ Widely available
– 'Wisley White' ♀ EGle LBro NFai WLin
♦ *sieboldii* See *I. sanguinea*
¶ 'Sierra Grande' (TB) LIri
'Sierra Nevada' (Spuria) EFou LBro WBcn
'Silent Strings' (IB) LBro MBri
¶ 'Silicon Prairie' (TB) LIri
'Silkirim' (TB) LBro
¶ 'Silver Down' (SDB) MAus
'Silver Tide' (TB) WEas
'Silverado' (TB) LIri MAus MMil SCro
'Silvery Moon' (TB) SCro
sindjarensis See *I. aucheri*
'Sing Again' (IB) CBlo
sintenisii ♀ CBro CHan EHyt LBlm NGre SIng
'Sister Helen' (TB) MMil
'Siva Siva' (TB) EBrP EBre ENot ERou LBre SBre WHer
'Skating Party' (TB) LIri
'Skiers' Delight' (TB) LIri SCro
'Skip Stitch' (SDB) LBro
'Sky Hooks' (TB) LIri SCro
¶ 'Sky Search' (TB) LIri
'Slap Bang' (SDB) NZep
'Sleepy Time' (MDB) NZep
'Slim Jim' (MTB) LBro

'Small Sky' (SDB) CBro LBro NNrd
'Small Wonder' (SDB) LBro
N 'Smart Girl' (TB) CKel
'Smarty Pants' (MTB) LBro
'Smell the Roses' (SDB) NZep
'Smoke Rings' (TB) SCro
'Smokey Dream' (TB) CKel
♦ 'Smooth Orange' (TB) See *I.* 'Orange Chariot' (TB)
'Sneak Preview' (TB) NZep
'Sno Jo' (SDB) SCro
'Snow Elf' (SDB) LBro
¶ 'Snow Festival' (IB) MMil
'Snow Fiddler' (MTB) NZep
'Snow Tracery' (TB) ENot MBri
'Snow Tree' (SDB) NZep
¶ 'Snow Troll' (SDB) MMil WWin
'Snowbrook' (TB) SCro
¶ 'Snowcone' (IB) SCro
'Snowdrift' See *I. laevigata* 'Snowdrift'
'Snowmound' (TB) SCro
'Snowshill' (TB) LBro
'Snowy Owl' (TB) ♀ LBro MAus
¶ 'Snowy River' (MDB) NZep
'Snowy Wonderland' (TB) NZep
'Soaring Kite' (TB) ♀ LBro
¶ 'Social Event' (TB) LIri
¶ 'Social Register' (TB) MAus
'Soft Breeze' (SDB) NZep
'Solid Mahogany' (TB) MAus MMil MRav
¶ 'Somerset Blue' (TB) CKel
¶ 'Somerset Girl' (TB) CKel
N 'Somerset Vale' (TB) CKel
* 'Somerton Brocade' (SDB) CKel
* 'Somerton Gold' (SDB) CKel
'Song of Norway' (TB) ♀ MAus MMil NZep SCro WBcn
¶ 'Sonja's Selah' (BB) LIri
'Sonoran Senorita' (Spuria) LBro
'Soul Power' (TB) ERou
'Southern Clipper' (SDB) LRHS MBri
¶ 'Souvenir de Madame Gaudichau' (TB) CKel
sp. AGSJ 431 EWoo NGre
¶ 'Space Mist' (TB) CKel
'Spanish Coins' (MTB) LBro NZep
'Spanish Lime' (Spuria) LBro
'Sparkling Cloud' (SDB) EGle WWin
¶ 'Spartan' CKel
N 'Specify' (TB) CKel
'Spiced Custard' (TB) SCro
'Spin-off' (TB) SCro
'Spirit of Memphis' (TB) MMil
'Splash of Red' (SDB) LBro MMil NZep
'Split Decision' (SDB) NZep
'Spring Bells' (SDB) EFou
'Spring Dancer' (IB) SCro
'Spring Festival' (TB) CKel
'Spring Signal' (TB) SCro
'Springtime' (Reticulata) LAma NRog WSan
spuria ECGP ELan MSto SWyc
N 'Spuria Alba' SWyc
spuria subsp. *carthaliniae* EHic WPer
§ – subsp. *halophila* CMon EHic LBro MSto
– subsp. *maritima* NNrd SIng
§ – subsp. *musulmanica* EHic LBro
¶ – subsp. *notha* CC 1550 SGre
– subsp. *ochroleuca* See *I. orientalis*
x *squalens* LBro
'Stapleford' (SDB) CBro EGle NNrd
'Star Sailor' (TB) SCro
'Star Shine' (TB) CKel MAus

¶ 'Twice Thrilling' (TB) — LIri
'Twist of Fate' (TB) — SCro
'Two Rubies' (SDB) — NZep
'Tyke' (MTB) — NZep
¶ 'Ultimatum' (TB) — LIri
'Ultra Pretty' (TB) — SCoo
§ *unguicularis* ♀ — Widely available
– 'Abington Purple' — CAvo CBro EBee
– 'Alba' — CBro ECha
N– 'Bob Thompson' — CAvo ECha
– broken form — MHlr
– subsp. *carica* var. *angustifolia* — IBlr SWas
§ – subsp. *cretensis* — EHyt
– – MS 720 — CMon
– – S&L 478 — CMon
– – S&L 550 — CMon
N– 'Francis Wormsley' — ECha MRav
– L&R 65 — CMon
– var. *lazica* — See *I. lazica*
– 'Mary Barnard' — CAvo CBro CFee CGle CMon CPou CSam CSev ECGP ECha GCHN LBro MBro MRav NMen SApp SBla SMad SOkh SUsu SWas WGwG WLin WRus
N– 'Oxford Dwarf' — CBro ECho
– 'Palette' — ELan
– 'Unguicularis Marginata' — LBro
§ – 'Walter Butt' — CAvo CGle ECGP ECha MRav NBir SBla SWas WCot WLin WRus
uniflora var. *caricina* — WCot
urmiensis — See *I. barnumae* f. *urmiensis*
uromovii — MArl MBro WHoo WPyg
¶ 'Vamp' (IB) — CKel
'Vanity' (TB) ♀ — LBro NZep SCro
'Vanity's Child' (TB) — ERou
§ *variegata* ♀ — CMea CRDP EHic EPar GCal SIng SUsu
– var. *pontica* — SCro
'Vegas Showgirl' (SDB) — NZep
'Velvet Bouquet' (MTB) — LBro
'Vera' (Aril) — CLAP EPot ETub
verna — CGle CNic EPot NHol
versicolor ♀ — CArn CBen CRow EGol EHon EMFW EPar IBlr LBro LPBA MHew MNrw MSal MSta NDea SDix SRms SWyc
– 'Between the Lines' — CRow
N– 'Blue Light' — CBlo WChe
– 'Dottie's Double' — CRow
N– 'Goldbrook' — EGol
– 'Kermesina' — CRDP CRow ECha EGol EHon ELan EMFW EPar GCal GGar IBlr MSta NDea NRoo NSti SRms SWat WChe WRus
– 'Mysterious Monique' — CRDP CRow
– 'Party Line' — CRow
– purple — CRow
– var. *rosea* — CRow
* – 'Signagoniga Ridska' — NCat
– 'Silvington' — CRow
– 'Version' — CRow LBlm
vicaria — CLAP LRHS
'Victor Herbert' (TB) — SCro
'Victoria Falls' (TB) — MAus SCro
'Vigilante' (TB) — LIri
'Vintage Year' (Spuria) — EFou LBro
violacea — See *I. spuria* subsp. *musulmanica*

'Violet Beauty' (Reticulata) — EPot LAma
'Violet Classic' (TB) — EFou MMil
'Violet Icing' (TB) ♀ — CKel LBro
'Violet Lass' (TB) — NZep
'Violet Miracle' (TB) — MMil
I *virginica* 'Crown Point' — CRow
– 'De Luxe' — See *I.* × *robusta* 'Dark Aura'
I – 'Lilac Dream' — CRow
N– 'Purple Fan' — CRow
§ – var. *shrevei* — CRow MAus MSto
'Visual Arts' (TB) — SCro
'Vitality' (IB) — SCro
'Vivien' (TB) — SCro
'Voila' (IB) — EFou LBro NZep
¶ 'Voltage' (TB) — LIri
'Volts' (SDB) — LBro
'Wabash' (TB) — CBlo EBrP EBre ERou LBre LBro MAus MMil MS&S SBre
'Walter Butt' — See *I. unguicularis* 'Walter Butt'
'Warleggan' (TB) ♀ — LBro
¶ 'Waterboy' (SDB) — NZep
'Watercolor' (SDB) — NZep
wattii — CHEx
'Webelos' (SDB) — CLon EGle LBro LGre MBri MBro
'Wedding Candles' (TB) — SCro
'Wedgwood' (Dutch) — GLil
* 'Wedgwood Blue' (Sino-sib) — NWoo
'Wenlock' (IB) — MAus
'West Vale' (IB) — LBro
'Westar' (SDB) — NZep
'Westwell' (SDB) — MAus
'What Again' (SDB) — SCro
'White Bridge' (Dutch) — NRog
'White Canary' (MTB) — LBro
'White City' (TB) — CHad CMGP EGle EMan EOrc EPfP ERav LBro MMil MWat NPer SChu SWat
'White Excelsior' (Dutch) — CB&S LAma SHel
'White Gem' (SDB) — WWin
'White Heron' (Spuria) — LBro
'White Knight' (TB) — ELan EPfP SMer WCot WLin
'White van Vliet' (Dutch) — NRog
¶ 'White Wedgwood' (Dutch) — SHel
'Whiteladies' (IB) ♀ — LBro
'Whoop 'em Up' (BB) — LBro NZep
'Why Not' (IB) — NMGW NZep WBcn
'Widecombe Fair' (SDB) — WWin
'Widget' (MTB) — LBro
'Wild Dancer' (TB) — SCoo
N 'Wild Echo' (TB) — CKel
¶ 'Wild Ginger' (TB) — MBri WWeb
'Wild Thing' (TB) — SCro
willmottiana 'Alba' — EPot
'Willow Ware' (IB) — SCro
'Willowmist' (SDB) — NZep
wilsonii ♀ — CVer GBuc MMil
– 'Gelbe Mantel' — See *I.* 'Gelbe Mantel'
¶ 'Windrose' (SDB) — NZep
'Windsor Rose' (TB) — CKel SCro
'Winged Melody' (TB) — MBri
winogradowii ♀ — CBro ECha ERos GCrs LAma MTho NHar SDix
'Winter Olympics' (TB) — EFou MRav
'Wisteria Sachet' (IB) — MAus
'Witch of Endor' (TB) — MMil
¶ 'Witch's Wand' (TB) — LIri
'Wizard of Id' (SDB) — EGle NZep WTin
'World News' (TB) — SCro

'Wow' (SDB) — EGle LBro
N 'Wright's Pink' (SDB) — MAus
'Wyckhill' (SDB) — LBro
'Wyevale' (TB) — LBro
xanthospuria LT 10 — CMon
xiphioides — See *I. latifolia*
xiphium — SSpi
'Yellow Girl' (SDB) — NMGW NZep
¶ 'Yellow Queen' (Dutch) — SHel
'Yo-yo' (SDB) — NZep
¶ 'Yvonne Pelletier' (TB) — MAus
'Zantha' (TB) — CKel
'Zeeland' (BB) — LBro
'Zink Pink' (BB) — SCro
'Zowie' (SDB) — NZep
'Zua' (IB) — MTed SCro

ISATIS (Brassicaceae)
tinctoria — CArn CSev EOHP EWFC GPoy
ILis LHol MChe MHew MSal
SIde WCHb WHer WJek WOak
WPer WSel WWye

ISCHYROLEPIS (Restionaceae)
¶ *acreata* — WNor
§ *subverticillata* — CHEx

ISMENE See **HEMEROCALLIS**

ISOLEPIS (Cyperaceae)
§ *cernua* — CHal EMFW MBri MCCP

ISOLOMA See **KOHLERIA**

ISOMERIS See **CLEOME**

ISOPLEXIS (Scrophulariaceae)
canariensis — CAbb CBot CFil CHEx CSpe
EOas GCra SSoC SUsu WEas
sceptrum — CBot CFil CFir CHan GSki
SAPC SArc SIgm SSoC WCot

ISOPOGON (Proteaceae)
anethifolius — MSto

ISOPYRUM (Ranunculaceae)
ohwianum — See *I. nipponicum* var.
sarmentosum
thalictroides — CGle EPot

ISOTOMA (Campanulaceae)
♦ *axillaris* — See *Laurentia axillaris*
* 'Fairy Carpet' — CLTr

ITEA (Escalloniaceae)
ilicifolia ♀ — Widely available
japonica 'Beppu' — MGos SLPl
virginica — CB&S CDoC CLTr CMCN
CPle CWit ECro ELan MBal
MBlu MGos SBid SPer SSta
WBod WDin WHCG WPGP
WSHC WTro WWat
§ – 'Henry's Garnet' — CFai CMCN CPMA CWSG
MBlu WCwm WWes
¶ – 'Sarah Eve' — CMCN
– Swarthmore form — See *I. virginica* 'Henry's Garnet'
yunnanensis — IOrc MAll

ITOA (Flacourtiaceae)
orientalis SF 92300 — ISea

IVESIA (Rosaceae)
gordonii — NWCA
¶ *pygmaea* — WLin

IXIA (Iridaceae)
Bird of Paradise — See *I.* 'Paradijsvogel'
'Blue Bird' — LAma
'Castor' — ETub
flexuosa — NRog
'Hogarth' — LAma
hybrids — SDeJ
'Mabel' — NRog
maculata — NRog
'Marquette' — NRog
monadelpha — LBow
paniculata — LBow NRog
§ 'Paradijsvogel' — LAma
polystachya — LBow NRog
'Rose Emperor' — LAma NRog
'Venus' — LAma
viridiflora — CAvo NRog WCot

IXIOLIRION (Amaryllidaceae)
pallasii — See *I. tataricum*
§ *tataricum* — LAma MBri NRog
– Ledebourii Group — CAvo LAma

IXORA (Rubiaceae)
¶ *chinensis* 'Apricot Queen' — SOWG
coccinea — MCCP
¶ 'Golden Ball' — SOWG
¶ 'Pink Malay' — SOWG

JABOROSA (Solanaceae)
integrifolia — CFee CFir EBee ELan GCal
MNrw WCot WCru WPGP
squarrosa F&W 7836 — EWes

JACARANDA (Bignoniaceae)
acutifolia hort. — See *J. mimosifolia*
acutifolia Kunth — MBri
§ *mimosifolia* — CB&S ECon ERea GQui LCns
SOWG

JACOBINIA (Acanthaceae)
♦ 'Carnea' — See *Justicia carnea*

JAMESIA (Hydrangeaceae)
americana — CPle WWin

JASIONE (Campanulaceae)
§ *crispa* — ECro
§ *heldreichii* — GAbr MBro NNrd NRoo SBla
SChu SIng SRms WElm WPyg
WWin
humilis — See *J. crispa* subsp. *amethystina*
jankae — See *J. heldreichii*
§ *laevis* — CNic ECot ELan LRot NBro
SAga SRms SSca WCot
§ – 'Blaulicht' — CMCo EAst EBar ECha EMan
EPfP ESis MBri NBrk SLod
WMow WOve WPer WWal
– Blue Light — See *J. laevis* 'Blaulicht'
montana — CKin CMea EWFC MChe SSca
WCla WHer
perennis — See *J. laevis*

JASMINUM † (Oleaceae)
angulare — CGre CPIN CRHN EHol ERea
SOWG

azoricum ♀	CB&S CGre CPlN ECon ELan EPfP ERea GQui LCns LRHS NPal WMul
beesianum	Widely available
bignoniaceum	CPlN
floridum	CPlN
fruticans	CDoC CMac CPle ECro ELan EPla MAll WCru
¶ – HH&K 126	CHan
grandiflorum 'De Grasse'	CPlN ERea LCns SOWG
humile	CBlo CPle GOrc GSki IBlr MAsh SHFr WBod WKif WPic
– f. *farreri*	WCru
§ – 'Revolutum' ♀	CArn CB&S CBot CHan CMHG CMac CPle EAst EBrP EBre ELan EPla IOrc LBre LHop MBal MGos NBrk NHol SBre SCob SHBN SPer SUsu WAbe WEas WGwG WHCG WSHC WWat
– f. *wallichianum*	CPle
¶ – – B&SWJ 2987	WCru
§ *laurifolium* f. *nitidum*	CPlN ERea LChe
§ *mesnyi* ♀	CBot CDoC CGre CMac CPlN CPle EBak ECtt ELan ERea ERom IOrc LBlm LPan NBea SBra SLMG SOWG SSta WSHC
multipartitum	CSpe
nitidum	See *J. laurifolium* f. *nitidum*
§ *nobile* subsp. *rex*	CPlN LChe
nudiflorum ♀	Widely available
– 'Argenteum'	See *J. nudiflorum* 'Mystique'
– 'Aureum'	CBos CDec CDoC ELan EPla GQui MAsh MRav NHol NSti SPer SPla WHCG WPat WRus
* – 'Compactum'	MAsh
§ – 'Mystique' (v)	CPMA ELan EPfP LRHS MAsh SMur SPla WCot WPat
– 'Nanum'	ELan MBro WPat
odoratissimum	ERea LCns SOWG
officinale ♀	Widely available
§ – f. *affine*	CB&S CRHN CTri EBrP EBre ELan ENot EOrc EPla ERea IOrc LBre LPri MAsh NHol SBre SDix SEas SMad SRms WCru WWeb
§ – 'Argenteovariegatum' ♀	CArn CB&S CBot CDec EAst ECha EHoe ELan EPla GQui LHop MAsh MBri MGos MSta NHol SBra SHBN SHFr SMad SPar SPer SPla SSta WPat WSHC WWat WWeb
– 'Aureovariegatum'	See *J. officinale* 'Aureum'
§ – 'Aureum'	CB&S CBot CMac ECtt ELan EPla GOrc LHol LPri MAsh MBri MWat NBir NHol SApp SHBN SIde SMad SPer SSta WFar WGwG WHCG WPat WSHC WWat
¶ – 'Devon Cream'	SPar
– Fiona Sunrise = 'Frojas'	CB&S EBrP EBre ECle LBre LHop LPan MAsh MBri MCCP MGos MMil NBea NCut NEgg NHol SBre SCob SCoo SHBN SVil WCru WSHC WWat WWeb
– 'Grandiflorum'	See *J. officinale* f. *affine*
– 'Inverleith'	EBar EHic ELan GCal GOrc LHop MBri MCCP SCoo SMad SPan SPla SSoC SVil WWal

– 'Variegatum'	See *J. officinale* 'Argenteovariegatum'
parkeri	CB&S CBot CFee EBar EHyt EMil EPla EPot ESis GOrc LBee LHop MAsh MBlu MBro MPla MUlv NHol NNrd SHBN SIde SIgm SIng WAbe WCru WOMN WPat WPyg WWat
polyanthum ♀	CArn CB&S CPlN CRHN CSpe CTri CTrw EBak ELan ERea ERom GQui ISea LBlm LHop MBri NBea NRog SRms
primulinum	See *J. mesnyi*
reevesii	See *J. humile* 'Revolutum'
rex	See *J. nobile* subsp. *rex*
sambac	CPlN ECon ELan EPfP LChe LCns LPri LRHS NPal SOWG WMul
– 'Grand Duke of Tuscany'	ERea LChe SOWG
– 'Maid of Orleans'	ERea LChe SOWG
§ *simplicifolium* subsp. *australiense*	CPlN
§ – subsp. *suavissimum*	SVen
× *stephanense* ♀	Widely available
♦ *suavissimum*	See *J. simplicifolium* subsp. *suavissimum*
tortuosum	CPlN
♦ *volubile*	See *J. simplicifolium* subsp. *australiense*

JATROPHA (Euphorbiaceae)

podagrica	LChe

JEFFERSONIA (Berberidaceae)

diphylla	CArn CBro CElw CGle EPar LAma MDun MSal MTho NBir NHar NHol NRog NRya SBla SWas WAbe WCru WFar WWat
dubia	EWes NBir NRog NRya NTow SAxl SBla SIgm SWas WCru
¶ – 'Alba'	SBla

JOHANNESTEIJSMANNIA (Arecaceae)

¶ *lanceolata*	LPal
¶ *magnifica*	LPal

JOVELLANA (Scrophulariaceae)

punctata	CDec CGre CHan CPle LHil MBlu
repens	CFir ECou IDac LFis WCot
sinclairii	CGle CPle ECou EHyt EMan SBla SSpi SUsu WCru
violacea ♀	CAbP CAbb CB&S CDec CGle CHEx CMHG CPle CSpe CWit EMil ERea GCal ISea ITim LHil LHop MAll MBal MTho SArc SBid SDry SMad WBod WKif WSHC

JOVIBARBA (Crassulaceae)

§ *allionii*	CMea CTri CWil EPot GBur LBee MBro MOne NNrd SIng SSmi WAbe WPer WWin
– × *hirta*	CWil GAbr MBro NHol NNrd SDys SSmi
– × – 'Oki'	CWil MOne NHed
– × *sobolifera*	SSmi
§ *arenaria*	CWil ESis GAbr GCHN MBro MDHE MOne MRPP NMen SIng SSmi

– from Murtal	CWil MDHE SSmi
'Emerald Spring'	CWil MOne
§ *heuffelii*	CWil NMen NPri WPer
– 'Aga'	SSmi
– 'Alemene'	SSmi
– 'Almkroon'	SSmi
– 'Angel Wings'	CWil SSmi
– 'Apache'	SSmi
– 'Aquarius'	CWil SSmi
– 'Artemis'	SSmi
– 'Beacon Hill'	CWil MBro SSmi
– 'Belcore'	CWil SSmi
– 'Bermuda'	CWil SSmi
– 'Bermuda Sunset'	SSmi
– 'Brandaris'	SSmi
– 'Bronze Ingot'	CWil
– 'Bros'	SSmi
– 'Chocoleto'	CWil
– 'Cleopatra'	SSmi
– 'Copper King'	SSmi
– 'Cythera'	SSmi
– 'Fandango'	CWil SSmi
– 'Gento'	CWil SSmi
– 'Giuseppi Spiny'	CWil NHol SSmi
– var. *glabra*	NGre
– – from Anabakanak	CWil
– – from Anthoborio	CWil NMen SSmi
– – from Backovo	SSmi
– – from Bansko Vihren	SSmi
– – from Galicica	SSmi
– – from Haila	CWil
– – from Jakupica, Macedonia	CWil
– – from Kapaenianum	SSmi
– – from Koprovnik	CWil
– – from Kosovo, Yugoslavia	SSmi
– – from Ljuboten	CWil NGre SSmi
– – from Osljak	SSmi
– – from Pasina Glava	CWil
– – from Pelister	SSmi
– – from Rhodope	CWil NGre SSmi
– – from Stogovo	SSmi
– – from Treska Gorge, Macedonia	CWil MBro
– – from Vitse	CWil
– 'Goya'	SSmi
– 'Grand Slam'	SSmi
* – 'Green Land'	CWil
– 'Greenstone'	CWil MBro NMen SSmi
– 'Harmony'	SSmi
– 'Helena'	SSmi
– 'Henry Correvon'	CWil SSmi
– 'Iason'	SSmi
– 'Ikaros'	SSmi
– 'Inferno'	CWil
– 'Iole'	SSmi
– 'Iuno'	CWil SSmi
– 'Jade'	CWil SSmi
– 'Kapo'	SSmi
– var. *kopaonikensis*	CWil
– 'Mary Ann'	SSmi
– 'Miller's Violet'	CWil
– 'Minuta'	CWil SSmi
– 'Mont Rose'	SSmi
– 'Mystique'	CWil MBro
– 'Nannette'	SSmi
– 'Nobel'	SSmi
– 'Orion'	CWil NMen SSmi
– 'Pampero'	SSmi
– 'Passat'	SSmi
¶ – var. *patens*	MOne
– 'Pink Skies'	MBro SSmi
– 'Prisma'	CWil SSmi

– 'Purple Haze'	MBro SSmi
– 'Pyrope'	SSmi
– 'Red Rose'	SSmi
¶ – 'Rhodope'	MOne
– 'Springael's Choice'	SSmi
– 'Suntan'	CWil SSmi
– 'Sylvan Memory'	CWil
– 'Tan'	CWil MBro SSmi
– 'Tancredi'	SSmi
– 'Torrid Zone'	CWil SSmi
– 'Tuxedo'	CWil SSmi
– 'Vesta'	SSmi
– 'Violet'	CWil SSmi
– 'Vulcan'	SSmi
§ *hirta*	CHal CWil GAbr GCrs MDHE MOne NHol NMen STre WPer
– subsp. *borealis*	CWil MBro NHed NHol
* – 'Dunbar Red'	NHol
– subsp. *glabrescens*	ESis
– – from Belansky Tatra	CWil GCHN MDHE MOne NGre NHed SSmi
– – from High Tatra	MDHE
– – from Smeryouka	CWil MBro SIng SSmi
– – var. *neilreichii*	SIng
¶ – 'Lowe's 66'	MOne
– 'Preissiana'	CWil MBro MOne NHed NHol NMen NNrd
x *mitchellii* 'Sandy'	SSmi
– 'Suzan'	SSmi
x *nixonii* 'Jowan'	SSmi
§ *sobolifera*	CHEx CNic CWil ESis GCHN MBro MOne NGre NHol SIng SSmi WPer
– 'Green Globe'	CWil MDHE NGre NNrd SDys
* – 'Miss Lorainne'	CWil

JUANIA (Arecaceae) See Plant Deletions

JUANULLOA (Solanaceae)

aurantiaca	See *J. mexicana*

JUBAEA (Arecaceae)

§ *chilensis*	CBrP CHEx LPJP LPal NPal SAPC SArc
spectabilis	See *J. chilensis*

JUGLANS † (Juglandaceae)

§ *ailanthifolia*	CHEx CMCN ESim SSta
– var. *cordiformis*	CAgr
¶ – – 'Fodermaier' seedling	CAgr
§ x *bixbyi*	ESim WGWT
californica (F)	WGWT
cathayensis (F)	WGWT
cinerea (F)	CMCN ESim WGWT
– x *ailanthifolia*	See *J.* x *bixbyi*
– 'Craxezy' (F)	CAgr
¶ – 'Kenworthy' seedling	CAgr
§ *elaeopyren*	CTho
x *intermedia* (F)	WGWT WMou
mandschaurica	CMCN WGWT
microcarpa	WGWT
♦ – subsp. *major*	See *J. elaeopyren*
nigra (F) ⚥	CB&S CLnd CMCN ESim GChr GTwe IOrc LHol LHyr LNet MGos NRog NWea SDea SHBN SKee SPer WBay WDin WMou WStI WWal
– 'Emma Kay' (F)	CAgr
– 'Laciniata'	CMCN CTho MBlu SMad WGWT
¶ – 'Purpurea'	MBlu
regia (F) ⚥	Widely available

– 'Axel' (F)	WGWT
– 'Broadview' (F)	CBlo CEnd CTho EMui ERea ESim GTwe MAsh MBlu MBri MCoo MGos SCoo SDea SPer WGWT WMou
– 'Buccaneer' (F)	CTho ERea ESim GTwe SDea WGWT WMou
– 'China B' (F)	WGWT
– 'Coenen' (F)	WGWT WMou
– 'Franquette'	CTho EBee ENot GTwe MAsh MCoo SKee WMou
– 'Hansen' (F)	WGWT
– 'Hartley' (F)	SKee
– 'Laciniata'	IDee MBlu WGWT WMou
– 'Lara'	GTwe
– 'Mayette' (F)	SKee
¶ – 'Northdown Clawnut'	WMou
– Number 139	ESim
– Number 16 (F)	WGWT
– Number 26	ESim
– 'Parisienne' (F)	SKee
– 'Plovdivski' (F)	WGWT WMou
– 'Proslavsk' (F)	WGWT WMou
– 'Purpurea'	CDul CMCN WGWT
– 'Rita'	WGWT WMou
– 'Soleze' (F)	SKee WGWT
sieboldiana	See *J. ailanthifolia*

JUNCUS (Juncaceae)

acutus	WWye
articulatus	CKin
* *balticus* 'Spiralis'	WCot
bulbosus	CKin
'Carmen's Grey'	EPla SApp WCot
compressus	CKin
conglomeratus	CKin EHoe
§ *decipiens* 'Curly-wurly'	CCuc CFee CMea CMil CSpe EBrP EBre EHoe EMan EMon ESOG EWes GCal LBre MFir NWCA SAxl SBre SUsu SWat WHal WHil
– 'Spiralis'	See *J. decipiens* 'Curly-wurly'
effusus	CKin EMFW LPBA SWat SWyc WMAq
– 'Cuckoo' (v)	CNat WAlt
§ – 'Spiralis'	CCuc CFee CFil CRow CWat EHoe ELan EMFW EMon ESOG GCal GDra IBlr LPBA MBal MSta NCat NDea SAxl SUsu WChe WHal WPGP WPbr
* – 'Spiralis' dwarf	LPBA
ensifolius	CAgr CCuc CRow CWat EHoe ESOG MSta WChe
inflexus	CAgr CKin EHon SWat SWyc
– 'Afro'	CMea EMon LRHS WAlt
pallidus	GCal
squarrosus	CKin
tenuis	ESOG
xiphioides	EHoe ESOG
– JLS 86161LACA	EPPr

JUNELLIA (Verbenaceae)

wilczekii	WFar

JUNIPERUS † (Cupressaceae)

chinensis	SEND
– 'Aurea' ♀	CKen CMac CTri EHul EPla LCon LNet MAsh MBal MBar MGos
§ – 'Blaauw' ♀	CDoC CMac EHul ENot GAri LCon LLin MAsh MBar MGos SHBN SLim STre WStI
– 'Blue Alps'	CDoC CMHG EBrP EBre EHul EOrn EPla LBre LCon LLin LNet LPan MAsh MBal MBar MBri MGos SBre SEND SLim WGwG
– 'Blue Point'	CBlo EHul MBar
– 'Densa Spartan'	See *J. chinensis* 'Spartan'
– 'Echiniformis'	CKen CMac
– 'Expansa Aureospicata'	CBlo CDoC CKen CMac EBrP EBre EHul EPfP LBre LCon LLin MBar SBod SBre SLim SRms SSmi
§ – 'Expansa Variegata'	CMac EBrP EBre EGra EHul GAri LBre LCon LLin MBal MBar MGos MPla NHol SBod SBre SLim SRms SSmi WDin WGwG WStI WWal
– 'Globosa Cinerea'	MBar
* – 'Golden Rod'	CBlo
– 'Japonica'	MBar SMer
– 'Japonica Variegata'	EBrP EBre LBre SBre SLim
– 'Kaizuka' ♀	CBlo CDoC EBrP EBre EHul GAri LBre LCon MAsh MBal MBar SBre SLim SMer WLRN
– 'Kaizuka Variegata'	See *J. chinensis* 'Variegated Kaizuka'
– 'Kuriwao Gold'	CBlo CMac EBrP EBre EHul GRei LBee LBre LLin LNet MBar MGos NHol SBod SBre SLim SPla WStI
– 'Kuriwao Mist'	CBlo
– 'Kuriwao Sunbeam'	NHol
– 'Obelisk' ♀	CBlo CDoC EHul LBee LCon MBar MGos SBod WLRN WShe
– 'Oblonga'	EHul LLin MAsh MBar SMer STre
§ – 'Parsonsii'	CMac EHul MBar SHBN STre WCFE
– 'Plumosa'	MBar
– 'Plumosa Albovariegata'	LCon MBar
– 'Plumosa Aurea' ♀	CBlo CDoC EHul ENot LCon MBar WDin
– 'Plumosa Aureovariegata'	CKen LCon MBar SLim
– 'Pyramidalis' ♀	CDoC CMac EBrP EBre EHul ENot GAri LBre LCon LLin MGos MWat NRoo SBod SBre SRms WAbe WWeb
– 'Pyramidalis Variegata'	See *J. chinensis* 'Variegata'
I – 'Robusta Green'	CBlo LCon MBar SLim
– 'San José'	CDoC EHul LCon LLin MAsh MBar MPla SLim WLRN
– 'Shimpaku'	CKen EGra EPla LCon LLin MBar
§ – 'Spartan'	EHul
– 'Stricta'	CKen EHul IHos LBee MAsh MBal MBar MGos MPla NBee NEgg SLim SPla STre WDin WStI
– 'Stricta Variegata'	See *J. chinensis* 'Variegata'
– 'Sulphur Spray'	See *J. virginiana* 'Sulphur Spray'
§ – 'Variegata'	EHul MBar MPla
§ – 'Variegated Kaizuka'	EHul EPla LCon MBar NHol WWeb
¶ *communis* (f)	SIde
–	CArn CKin CSev CTrG EHul GAri GChr GPoy GRei ITim LHol MSal NHex NWea SIde
– 'Arnold'	CBlo LCon MBar MGos
– 'Arnold Sentinel'	CKen

– 'Atholl'	CKen GAbr
I – 'Aureopicta'	MBar
– 'Barton'	CBlo LLin MBar NHol
– 'Berkshire'	CKen
– 'Brien'	CDoC CKen
– 'Compressa' ♀	Widely available
§ – 'Constance Franklin' (v)	ECho EHul MBar WBcn
– 'Corrielagen'	CKen MBar MGos MPla MWat
– 'Cracovia'	CKen EHul
– var. *depressa*	GPoy MBal MBar
– 'Depressa Aurea'	CDoC CKen CMac EHul ENot LBee LLin LPan MBal MBar MBri MGos MPla NHed NHol NRoo SBod SHBN WStI
– 'Depressed Star'	MBar
– 'Derrynane'	EHul
¶ – 'Effusa'	CKen
– 'Gelb'	See *J. communis* 'Schneverdingen Goldmachandel'
§ – 'Gold Cone'	CDoC CKen EBrP EBre EHul EPla ESis LBee LBre LCon LLin MAsh MBar MBri MPla NHed NHol SBre SLim WAbe
– 'Golden Showers'	See *J. communis* 'Schneverdingen Goldmachandel'
– 'Green Carpet' ♀	CDoC CKen EBrP EBre EPla LBre LCon LLin MAsh MBar MBri SBre SLim SMer SSmi WCFE WFar WStI WWeb
– 'Greenmantle'	SPla
¶ – 'Haverbeck'	CKen
– var. *hemispherica*	ECho MBar NHed SRms
– 'Hibernica' ♀	CDoC CKen CMac CSam EHul GRei LBee LCon LLin MBal MBar MGos MPla MWat NWea SBod SHBN SLim SPer SPla WDin WStI
– 'Hibernica Variegata'	See *J. communis* 'Constance Franklin'
– 'Hornibrookii' ♀	CDoC CMac EHul ENot GDra LLin MBal MBar MGos MWat NWea SBod SHBN SPla STre WDin WWin
– 'Horstmann'	EPla GAri LPan MBar
I – 'Horstmann's Pendula'	CBlo LCon
¶ – 'Kemerton Priory'	WCFE
§ – 'Minima'	SBod
§ – var. *montana*	EHul
¶ – 'Prostrata'	ISea
– 'Pyramidalis'	WGor
– 'Repanda' ♀	CB&S CDoC CMac EHul ENot EPfP EPot GChr GRei IHos LCon LLin MBar MGos NHed NRoo NWea SBod SLPl SLim SPer SSta WCFE WGwG
§ – 'Schneverdingen Goldmachandel'	CBlo EOrn LCon SLim SMer WAbe WWeb
– 'Sentinel'	CDoC EBrP EBre EHul EPfP IHos IOrc LBee LBre LCon LPan MBar MBri MPla NBee SBre SLim
– 'Sieben Steinhauser'	CKen
– 'Silver Mist'	CKen
– 'Spotty Spreader' (v)	SCoo SLim
– f. *suecica*	EHul ENot IHos MBar NWea SBod SRms
– 'Suecica Aurea'	CBlo EHul
– 'Zeal'	CKen

conferta	CDoC EHul LBee LCon LLin MBar MWat SAga SBod SLim SPer SRms WWal
* – 'Blue Ice'	CKen LCon LLin WGwG
– 'Blue Pacific'	CBlo CMac COtt EHul GAri LCon MBar MBri SLim
– 'Emerald Sea'	EHul
– var. *maritima*	See *J. taxifolia* var. *lutchuensis*
davurica	EHul
– 'Expansa'	See *J. chinensis* 'Parsonsii'
– 'Expansa Albopicta'	See *J. chinensis* 'Expansa Variegata'
deppeana var. *pachyphlaea*	GAri WCwm
– 'Silver Spire'	EGra MBar MGos
x *gracilis* 'Blaauw'	See *J. chinensis* 'Blaauw'
horizontalis	NWea
– 'Alpina'	CKen
§ – 'Andorra Compact'	CKen CMac ESis MBar
– 'Banff'	CKen MBar
– 'Bar Harbor'	CB&S CKen CMac EHul LLin MBar MGos NWea SBod WGor
§ – 'Blue Chip'	CKen CMac EBrP EBre EHul ENot EPfP LBee LBre LCon LLin MAsh MBar MBri MGos NRoo SBod SBre SLim SPer SPla SSmi
– 'Blue Moon'	See *J. horizontalis* 'Blue Chip'
– 'Blue Pygmy'	CKen EPot
– 'Blue Rug'	See *J. horizontalis* 'Wiltonii'
– 'Douglasii'	CKen CMac EHol EHul MBal MBar WGor
– 'Emerald Spreader'	CKen EHul ENot MBar MGos SLim
– 'Glacier'	CKen
– 'Glauca Group'	CMac EHul ENot GDra GOrc LLin MBal MBar MGos MOne WWin
– 'Glomerata'	CKen MBar
¶ – 'Golden Carpet'	LCon SLim
– 'Golden Spreader'	CDoC
– 'Grey Pearl'	CKen EBrP EBre EHul ESis LBre LCon MAsh MBri NHed NHol SBod SBre SLim SMer SPer
– 'Hughes'	CKen CMac EBrP EBre EGra EHul ENot IHos LBee LBre LCon LLin MAsh MBar MBri MGos MPla NHed SBod SBre SLim
– 'Jade River'	CKen LRHS MGos NEgg SLim WLRN
– 'Montana'	See *J. communis* var. *montana*
– 'Mother Lode'	CKen
– 'Neumänn'	CKen
– 'Petraea'	CBlo
– 'Plumosa' ♀	NHed
– 'Plumosa Compacta'	See *J. horizontalis* 'Andorra Compact'
– 'Prince of Wales'	CDoC CKen EBrP EBre EHul GRei LBee LBre LCon LLin MAsh MGos NHol SBre SLim WGor WLRN WStI
– var. *saxatalis*	See *J. communis* var. *montana*
– 'Turquoise Spreader'	CBlo CKen EHul MBar MPla WWeb
– 'Variegata'	MBar
– 'Venusta'	CBlo CKen
– 'Villa Marie'	CKen
– 'Webberi'	MAsh MBar SLim
– 'Wilms'	CBlo

§ – 'Wiltonii' ♀	CKen EHul ENot IHos LLin MAsh MBal MGos
– 'Winter Blue'	LBee LRHS SLim SPla
– 'Youngstown'	CBlo CMac CSWP EBrP EBre LBre LCon MBar NHol SBod SBre SPla SSta WFar WGor
– 'Yukon Belle'	CKen
macropoda	See *J. excelsa* var. *polycarpos*
N× *media*	See *J.* × *pfitzeriana*
oxycedrus	GAri
× *pfitzeriana* 'Armstrongii'	EHul
– 'Blaauw'	See *J. chinensis* **'Blaauw'**
§ – Gold Sovereign = 'Blound'	EBrP EBre LBre LCon MAsh MGos NHol SBre SMer
– 'Blue and Gold'	CKen EHul MBar SHBN SLim SPer
♦ – 'Blue Cloud'	See *J. virginiana* **'Blue Cloud'**
§ – 'Carbery Gold'	CDoC CMac CSam EHul LBee LCon MAsh MBar MGos NHol SAga SLim SSmi WLRN WWeb
– 'Gold Coast'	CDoC CKen CMac EBrP EBre EHul ENot IHos LBee LBre LCon MBar MBri MGos MWat SBre SLim
♦ – Gold Sovereign	See *J.* × *pfitzeriana* Gold Sovereign = **'Blound'**
– 'Gold Star'	NEgg
– 'Golden Saucer'	MAsh MBar MBri SBod SCoo
– 'Goldkissen'	MBri
§ – 'Mint Julep'	CDoC CMac EBrP EBre EHul ENot EGra GRei LBee LBre LCon LLin LPan MBar MGos MPla SBre SLim SPer
– 'Mordigan Gold'	EGra
– 'Old Gold' ♀	CChe CDoC CKen CMac EHul ENot EPfP GOrc GRei LBee LBuc LCon LLin MAsh MBal MBar MGos MPla MWat NHed NHol NRoo NWea SBod SLim SPer WAbe WDin
– 'Old Gold Carbery'	See *J.* × *pfitzeriana* **'Carbery Gold'**
§ – 'Pfitzeriana' ♀	CMac EHul ENot LLin MBal MBar MGos NWea SBod SLim SPer SRms WStI WWin
– 'Pfitzeriana Aurea'	CB&S CDoC CMac EHul ENot EPfP EPot GChr GDra IHos LCon LLin MBal MBar MBri MGos MPla MWat NFla NWea SBod SHBN SLim SPer SRms WDin WGwG WWal
– 'Pfitzeriana Compacta' ♀	CMac ECho EHul MBar SLim
– 'Pfitzeriana Glauca'	EHul GChr LCon LPan MWat SLim WGor
– 'Richeson'	MBar
– 'Sea Green'	See *J.* × *pfitzeriana* **'Mint Julep'**
– 'Silver Cascade'	EHul
– 'Winter Surprise'	CBlo LCon MGos
§ *pingii* 'Glassell'	ECho LCon MBar
§ – 'Loderi'	CKen EHul LCon MBar
§ – 'Pygmaea'	CBlo CDoC LCon MBar MPla
§ – 'Wilsonii'	CBlo CKen ECho MBar
procumbens	WBod
– 'Bonin Isles'	CSam LLin MBal MBar MGos SLim SPla SRms
– 'Nana' ♀	CDoC CKen CMac EBrP EBre EHul LBee LBre LCon LLin MAsh MBal MBar MBri MGos MPla MWat NHol SBre SHBN SLim SPla SSmi SSta WPyg WWal
recurva 'Castlewellan'	EPla LCon MGos SMad WCwm
– var. *coxii*	CMac EHul EPla GGGa ISea LCon MBar MBri MGos SLim SRms WCFE WCwm
§ – 'Densa'	CKen EHul GAri LLin MBar NHol SHBN SPla
– 'Embley Park'	EHul MAsh MBar SLim
– 'Nana'	See *J. recurva* **'Densa'**
rigida	MBar SIng STre
sabina	GPoy NWea
– 'Arcadia'	CMac SRms
§ – 'Blaue Donau'	CBlo CMac EHul MBar MGos SRms WGor
– Blue Danube	See *J. sabina* **'Blaue Donau'**
– 'Broadmoor'	EHul
– 'Buffalo'	EHul
– 'Cupressifolia'	MBar
– 'Hicksii'	CMac MBar MGos NWea
– 'Knap Hill'	See *J.* × *pfitzeriana* **'Pfitzeriana'**
– 'Mountaineer'	EHul
– 'Rockery Gem'	CBlo EHul EOrn MGos MOne SLim SPla WGor
– 'Skandia'	CKen
– 'Tamariscifolia'	Widely available
– 'Tripartita'	MBar
– 'Variegata'	CMac EHul LBee MAsh MBar SLim WPyg
sargentii	CBlo GAri MBal STre
– 'Glauca'	GAri
– 'Viridis'	GAri
scopulorum 'Blue Arrow'	CBlo CKen COtt EOrn LBee LCon LLin MAsh MBri MGos MWat NEgg SCoo SLim
– 'Blue Banff'	CKen
– 'Blue Heaven' ♀	EHul GAri LCon MBal MBar SLim SPla
– 'Blue Pyramid'	EHul
– 'Boothman'	EHul
– 'Gray Gleam'	EHul
– 'Moonglow'	EBrP EBre EHul LBre MBar MBri SBre
– 'Mrs Marriage'	CKen
– 'Repens'	MBar MGos
– 'Silver Star'	CBlo CKen EHul MBar MGos
– 'Skyrocket'	CB&S CDoC CKen CMHG CMac EBrP EBre EHul ENot EPfP GRei LBee LBre LCon LLin LPan MAsh MBal MBar MGos MPla NWea SBod SBre SLim SPer WDin
– 'Springbank'	EHul LBee LCon MAsh MBar
– 'Table Top'	MBar WBcn
– 'Wichita Blue'	CBlo EHul EOrn LCon SEND WGor
seravshanica	See *J. excelsa* var. *polycarpos*
squamata	NWea
– 'Blue Carpet' ♀	Widely available
– 'Blue Spider'	CKen LLin LRHS MBar MBri SLim WLRN
– 'Blue Star' ♀	Widely available
– 'Blue Star Variegated'	See *J. squamata* **'Golden Flame'**
– 'Blue Swede'	See *J. squamata* **'Hunnetorp'**
– 'Chinese Silver'	EHul LCon MBar WLRN
– var. *fargesii*	ISea
– 'Filborna'	CBlo CDoC CKen EOrn LBee MBar MWat NHol SLim SMer

– 'Forrestii'	See *J. pingii* 'Forrestii'
– 'Glassell'	See *J. pingii* 'Glassell'
§ – 'Golden Flame'	CKen
– 'Holger' ♀	CDoC CKen CMac EBrP EBre
	EHul EOrn EPla GAri LBee
	LBre LCon LLin MAsh MBar
	MBri MGos MPla MWat SBod
	SBre SLim WStI WWeb
§ – 'Hunnetorp'	CBlo EOrn LCon MAsh MBar
	MBri MGos
– 'Loderi'	See *J. pingii* 'Loderi'
– 'Meyeri'	EHul ENot EOrn GDra GOrc
	MAsh MBal MBar MWat NWea
	SBod SLim SPer SRms STre
	WStI WWin
– 'Pygmaea'	See *J. pingii* 'Pygmaea'
– 'Wilsonii'	See *J. pingii* 'Wilsonii'
§ *taxifolia* var. *lutchuensis*	LBee LCon MBal MPla MWat
	WWeb
virginiana	CAgr
§ – 'Blue Cloud'	CDoC EHul LCon MBar SLim
	WLRN
– 'Burkii'	EHul LCon MBal
– 'Frosty Morn'	CKen ECho EHul LCon MBar
– 'Glauca'	CSWP EHul NWea
– 'Golden Spring'	CKen
– 'Grey Owl' ♀	CMHG CMac EHul ENot GRei
	LCon LLin MBal MBar MGos
	MPla SLim SPla SRms STre
	WDin WGor WGwG WPyg
	WWal
– 'Helle'	See *J. chinensis* 'Spartan'
– 'Hetz'	CB&S CBlo CKen CMac ECho
	EHul LCon MBal MBar NWea
	SBod WLRN
– 'Hillii'	MBar
– 'Hillspire'	EHul
– 'Nana Compacta'	MBar
– 'Silver Spreader'	CBlo EHul LCon MGos WGwG
– 'Staver Blue'	EHul
§ – 'Sulphur Spray' ♀	CBlo CDoC CKen CMac EAst
	EBrP EBre EHul EOrn EPla
	GRei LBee LBre LCon MBar
	MBri MGos MPla NHol SBre
	SLim SPer SPla SSmi

JURINEA (Asteraceae)

ceratocarpa	See *Saussurea ceratocarpa*
mollis	EMan GBuc

JURINELLA See JURINEA

JUSSIAEA See LUDWIGIA

JUSTICIA (Acanthaceae)

¶ *aurea*	ERea
§ *brandegeeana* ♀	CHal MBri SLMG
– 'Lutea'	See *J. brandegeeana* 'Yellow Queen'
§ – 'Yellow Queen'	CHal SLMG
§ *carnea*	CHEx CHal CSev EBak EHol
	ERea GCal LCns MBri SMad
	SOWG WMul
floribunda	See *J. rizzinii*
guttata	See *J. brandegeeana*
* 'Norgard's Favourite'	MBri
¶ *pectoralis*	NGno
– Puerto Rican cultivar	NGno
* – var. *stenophylla*	NGno
peruviana	GCra
pohliana	See *J. carnea*

§ *rizzinii* ♀	CHal CInt CSev ERea IBlr
	LBlm LCns LHil SOWG
spicigera	ERea LHil
suberecta	See *Dicliptera suberecta*

KADSURA (Schisandraceae)

japonica	CGre CPlN CPle EMil EPfP
	SBid
¶ – B&SWJ 1027	WCru
– 'Shiromi'	CPlN EMil SMur
– 'Variegata'	CPle EAst EMil EPfP GOrc
	SAga SBid SBra SPer WSHC
¶ sp.	CMac

KAEMPFERIA (Zingiberaceae)

ovalifolia	See *K. parishii*
rotunda	LAma LChe

KALANCHOE (Crassulaceae)

beharensis	CHal MBri SLMG
blossfeldiana	EOHP
daigremontiana	CHal SRms
§ *delagoensis*	CHal STre
fedtschenkoi	CHal
§ *lateritia*	LHil
manginii	CHal EOHP
pumila ♀	CHal EWoo IBlr WEas
'Tessa' ♀	MBri MLan SLMG
tomentosa ♀	CHal WEas
tubiflora	See *K. delagoensis*
'Wendy' ♀	MBri
◆ *zimbabwensis*	See *K. lateritia*

KALIMERIS (Asteraceae)

§ *incisa*	EGar EMon EWll
– 'Alba'	EFou EMon SHel
– 'Blue Star'	EFou
integrifolia	ECha WCot WTin
§ *mongolica*	EBee WPer
§ *yomena* 'Shogun' (v)	Widely available
– 'Variegata'	See *K. yomena* 'Shogun'

KALMIA † (Ericaceae)

angustifolia ♀	MBar NHol SPar SRms WDin
– var. *angustifolia* f. candida	GGGa
– var. *pumila*	WAbe
– f. *rubra*	CB&S CDoC CMHG EBrP
	EBre ELan GChr ISea LBre
	MBal MGos NHed NHol NRoo
	SBre SHBN SPer SReu SSta
	WBay WHar WPat WPyg WWat
latifolia ♀	CB&S CTrG ELan EMil ENot
	GGGa GRei ISea LNet MBal
	MBar MGos NBee NWea SBrw
	SPer SReu SSpi SSta WBrE
	WDin WGer WHar WNor
	WPyg WStI WWat WWeb
– 'Alpine Pink'	WAbe
– 'Brilliant'	NHol
– 'Bullseye'	GGGa
– 'Carol'	SBid
– 'Carousel'	CAbP ELan EPfP GGGa SVil
– 'Clementine Churchill'	CBlo ECot MRav
– 'Elf'	MGos
– 'Freckles'	ELan GGGa GOrc ISea MDun
	MLan NHed
– 'Fresca'	CBlo SVil
– 'Goodrich'	CBlo
– 'Heart of Fire'	CAbP GGGa ISea MBri NHed
– 'Heart's Desire'	SBid

– 'Little Linda'	CBlo CTrh GGGa GOrc NHed SBid
– 'Minuet'	CAbP CBlo CDoC EPfP GGGa MMHG NHed SSpi
– 'Olympic Fire'	ELan GGGa MBal MGos NHed SBrw SPer SSpi
– 'Ostbo Red' ♀	CB&S CBlo EMil GGGa GOrc IOrc ISea LNet MBal MBri MDun MGos MLan NHed SHBN SPer SReu SSpi SSta WBod WLRN
– 'Pink Charm'	EHic ELan GGGa ISea MBal MGos NHed WLRN
– 'Pink Frost'	CB&S GGGa MGos SBid SBrw WWat
¶ – 'Richard Jaynes'	SVil
– 'Sarah'	SBid SSpi
– 'Silver Dollar'	GGGa NHol WFar
– 'Snowdrift'	LRHS SPer
§ *microphylla*	GGGa MBal WAbe
* – 'Mount Shasta'	GGGa
– var. *occidentalis*	GGGa
polifolia	CB&S GGGa MBar MBro MRav NHol WPat WPyg
– *compacta*	WSHC
– 'Glauca'	See *K. microphylla*
– f. *leucantha*	GGGa

KALMIOPSIS (Ericaceae)

leachiana ♀	EPot MBal NHar SSta WAbe
¶ – 'Curry County'	WAbe
– 'Glendoick'	GGGa MAsh MDun NHar NHol WPat WPyg
– 'Marcel le Piniec'	GGGa
* – 'Shooting Star'	WAbe WPat

× KALMIOTHAMNUS (Ericaceae)

ornithomma	GGGa WAbe
¶ – 'Cosdon'	WAbe
¶ – 'Haytor'	WAbe

KALOPANAX (Araliaceae)

pictus	See *K. septemlobus*
§ *septemlobus*	CB&S CHEx ELan NPal SCob SMad
– var. *maximowiczii*	CHEx EPfP MBlu NBee SMad

KECKIELLA (Scrophulariaceae)

§ *cordifolia*	CPle EMan LHop
corymbosa	CGra NTow
– JCA 11618	NWCA
¶ *rothrockii*	NWCA

KELSEYA (Rosaceae)

uniflora	CGra

KENNEDIA (Papilionaceae)

beckxiana	LChe SOWG
coccinea	CB&S CPlN GQui LPan SOWG
macrophylla	CPlN SHFr
nigricans	CPlN LChe SOWG
¶ *prostrata*	SVen
rubicunda	CPlN CRHN MAll

KENTIA (Arecaceae)

belmoreana	See *Howea belmoreana*
canterburyana	See *Hedyscepe canterburyana*

KENTRANTHUS See CENTRANTHUS

KERNERA (Brassicaceae) See Plant Deletions

KERRIA (Rosaceae)

♦ *japonica* (single)	See *K. japonica* '**Simplex**'
– 'Albescens'	CBot CPMA NPro WWat
– 'Golden Guinea' ♀	EBrP EBre ECtt ELan EPfP LBre MAsh MGos MNrw NPro SBre SCoo SMac SPer SPla WTro WWat WWeb
§ – 'Picta' (v)	CB&S CHan CPle EAst EBrP EBre EHoe ELan GOrc IOrc LBre LFis MBar MBri MGos MHar NFla SBre SHel SPer SRms WDin WSHC WWal WWat
– 'Pleniflora' (d) ♀	widely available
§ – 'Simplex'	CB&S CPle ELan IOrc NFla NWea WDin
– 'Variegata'	See *K. japonica* '**Picta**'

KHADIA (Aizoaceae)

¶ sp.	CTrC

KICKXIA (Scrophulariaceae)

elatine	EWFC
spuria	EWFC MHew

KIRENGESHOMA (Hydrangeaceae)

palmata ♀	Widely available
§ – Koreana Group	CRDP EBee ECha ELan EPar LHop MBel MBri MCli MRav SCro SLod WFar WMer

KITAIBELA (Malvaceae)

vitifolia	CFee CGen CGle CHan CPea CSpe ECoo ECro ELan EMar EMon EOrc GCal LFis LGan MHlr MNrw NBro NSti WBea WCer WCot WFar WHer WPer WPic WWin WWye

KITCHINGIA See KALANCHOE

KLEINIA (Asteraceae)

articulata	See *Senecio articulatus*
senecioides	WEas

KNAUTIA (Dipsacaceae)

arvensis	CArn CKin ECoo EMan EWFC MChe MLLN NLan NMir WCla WGwy WHer WJek WOak LFis WCot
dipsacifolia	LFis WCot
* *jankiae*	WHer
§ *macedonica*	Widely available
– Melton Pastels	EBee MCLN SCoo SWat
– pink	CBos CMil SSpi SWas WPbr
– 'Red Dress'	EMon

KNIGHTIA (Proteaceae)

excelsa	CHEx MAll

KNIPHOFIA † (Asphodelaceae)

'Ada'	EBrP EBre ECGP EGar ERou EWes GCHN LBre MLLN MRav MUlv SBre
'Alcazar'	CKel EBee ECot EFou EPar EPfP MAus MHlr MNrw NPri WCot WFar WMer WViv
* 'Amber'	IBlr
'Apple Court'	NBir
'Apricot'	CHad CMdw EPla
'Apricot Souffle'	ECha MHlr MLLN WCot

'Atlanta' — EBrP EBre GCal IBlr LBlm LBre MUlv SBre SHel WCot
¶ *baurii* — LLew WCot
'Bees' Flame' — SMad
'Bees' Lemon' — CCuc IBlr WCot
'Bees' Sunset' ♀ — ECED IBlr MAus MRav MWgw SHBN SMrm WCot WLRN
* *bicolor* — MHlr WCot
'Border Ballet' — CMHG ECtt EMan MFir MOne NBir NBro NFai NMir SMrm SPla WByw
¶ *brachystachya* — CTrC LLew
'Bressingham Comet' — CGle CLon CPea EBrP EBre ECGN EGle LBre MRav SBre WRus
'Bressingham Gleam' — WCot
Bressingham hybrids — EBrP EBre IBlr LBre NBir SBre
'Bressingham Sunbeam' — EGar
¶ *breviflora* — EBee
¶ Bridgemere hybrids — LRHS
'Brimstone' ♀ — EPla IBlr WAbb WCot
¶ *buchananii* — EBee
'Buttercup' ♀ — CGle CMHG CMdw
'C.M. Prichard' hort. — See *K. rooperi*
'C.M. Prichard' Prichard — WCot
'Candlelight' — SApp SAxl SWas WCot WWin
* 'Candlemass' — EGar
'Catherine's Orange' — WCot
caulescens ♀ — CBot CHEx CHan CMil CPou CSam EBrP EBre EMan EMon GCra LBlm LBre LLew MUlv MWat SAPC SArc SBla SBre SCro WCot WPGP
citrina — CB&S CBot CFir EBee EMan EPfP MBal NBus SIgm WWat
'Cobra' — CPou CRDP EBee EFou ERou GCHN MRav MTed WCot
'Corallina' — EHal EWll MNrw NPri WCot
'Dawn Sunkiss' — WCot
'Dorset Sentry' — GBuc WCot
* 'Drummore Apricot' — WCot
'Earliest of All' — COtt EBar EBee NHol SPer
'Early Buttercup' — ECot GBri MMil NCat NHaw WCot
elegans — See *K. schimperi*
§ *ensifolia* — CMdw CPou EGar LLew MBal WBcn
'Erecta' — IBlr WCot
'Ernest Mitchell' — MRav WCot
Express hybrids — EBee WCot
'Fairyland' — NBus NCut WCot
* 'Fat Yellow' — MWgw
¶ *fibrosa* — CTrC WCot
'Fiery Fred' — CBlo CMHG EFou EGar EGle ELan EOld WCot
foliosa — EBee LLew
galpinii Baker ♀ — CBot CGle CHan CMGP CMdw EBee ECGN ENot LHil MBal NBir NFla SAga SPer SRms WCot WWat
– hort. — See *K. triangularis* subsp. *triangularis*
'Goldelse' — CLon ECha EGle IBlr NBir SAxl SBla
'Goldfinch' — CMdw SAxl SMrm
¶ *gracilis* — SApp WCot
'Green Jade' — CMdw COtt CRow ECha EGar EPar GBri IBlr LGre MTed NBir NCat SChu SEND SIgm WCot

'H.E. Beale' — GCal SAxl WCot
hirsuta — EBrP EBre LBre MUlv SBre
– H&B 16444 — EMon
¶ – JCA 346 900 — SSpi
'Hollard's Gold' — WCot
'Ice Queen' — EFou EGle EOrc MAus MRav SApp WCot
ichopensis — CHan EBee GBuc IBlr LLew WCot WPGP
'Innocence' — WCot
isoetifolia — IBlr
'Jenny Bloom' — Widely available
'John Benary' — IBlr WCot
'Kingston Flame' — WCot
late orange — WCot
laxiflora — CFil CPou CTrC ECGN LLew
'Lemon Ice' — WCot
'Light of the World' — CBos CFai CMil EBee MMil MTPN NHol
linearifolia — GBin GBur IBlr SMrm
'Little Elf' — CLon EMan SBla SWas WCot
'Little Maid' ♀ — Widely available
littoralis — EBee
'Lord Roberts' — WCot
'Lye End' — WCot
macowanii — See *K. triangularis* subsp. *triangularis*
'Maid of Orleans' — IBlr WCot
'Mellow Yellow' — IBlr
'Mermaiden' — CMHG EGar MTed WCot
¶ 'Minister Verschuur' — WCot WViv
'Modesta' — GBri IBlr SUsu WCot
'Mount Etna' — CGle WCot
multiflora — EBee
'Nancy's Red' — CMil COtt ECha GBri MSte SSvw SWas WCot WPGP
natalensis — EBee GBuc LLew WCot
nelsonii — See *K. triangularis* subsp. *triangularis*
'Nobilis' — See *K. uvaria* 'Nobilis'
northiae — CBot CFil CFir CHEx CPou EOas GCal IBlr SAPC SArc SAxl SIgm SSpi WCot
'Notung' — IBlr
* 'Old Court Seedling' — WCot
'Painted Lady' — CTri GCal MBro MHlr MRav WCot WHoo
¶ *parviflora* — WCot
pauciflora — WCot
'Percy's Pride' — Widely available
'Pfitzeri' — SRms
¶ *porphyrantha* — EBee WCot
praecox — CTrC EBee LLew WCot
'Primrose Beauty' — WCot WMer
'Prince Igor' — ECha EFou LBlm MBal MRav MTed SIgm
pumila — EGar LLew MTis WCot
ritualis — GCal WCot WPGP
§ *rooperi* — CBlo CBot EBee GCal IBlr LGre LLew MBal WCot WViv
'Royal Caste' — EBee MMil MRav NCut NOrc WWeb
'Royal Standard' ♀ — CB&S CHEx CMHG COtt EBee EBrP EBre ELan EMan ENot EPfP IBlr LBre LHil MNrw MRav SAga SBre SMad WCot
rufa — CPou EBee WCot
'Safranvogel' — ECGN EFou EGar IBlr MMHG
'Samuel's Sensation' ♀ — EBrP EBre EGar IBlr LBre MTed SBre SHBN WCot

sarmentosa	EBee LLew WCot WPGP WWoo
'September Sunshine'	MRav
'Shining Sceptre'	CMHG CSam EBee EBrP EBre ECha ECtt EFou EGar LBre LIck MLLN MUlv NCut SBre SMad WCot WMer
'Sir C.K. Butler'	EGar IBlr
splendida	GCal
'Springtime'	WCot
'Star of Baden-Baden'	NBir WCot
'Strawberries and Cream'	EMan MGrG MRav MSte SAga SUsu WCot
stricta	EBee LLew WCot
'Sunbeam'	NBir
'Sunningdale Yellow' ♀	CMdw CPou ECha EGar MFir SChu SLod SRms WCot WEas
'Tawny King'	WCot
thomsonii var. *thomsonii*	CBot CFir CMon EBee ECha EOrc GBri IBlr LHil MNrw MSte NTow SAxl WCot WHal
'Timothy'	EFou EGle SAga SAxl SChu WCot
'Toffee Nosed' ♀	EFou EGar ERou GBri GCal IBlr LBlm MRav NBir SAxl WCot
'Torchbearer'	EGar IBlr WCot
triangularis ♀	CBot CHad CInt CMon EBee ECGN EPfP NChi SMrm SPla
§ – subsp. *triangularis*	CBot CGle EBee GBuc IBlr LLew NBro SIgm WCot
I 'Tuckii'	CHan EBee EWll LHil MBal MNrw SIgm
tuckii Baker	See *K. ensifolia*
¶ *typhoides*	LLew WCot
uvaria	CHEx CTrC EBee EOas LRHS MAus MHFP NBir NVic SIgm SPer SRms SSpi WByw WHoo WPyg
* – Fairyland hybrids	LIck
§ – 'Nobilis' ♀	CHEx IBlr LBlm MHlr MLLN SDix WCot
'Vanilla'	MAus MRav WCot
'Vesta'	EGar
'Wrexham Buttercup'	EBee EGar EMan IBlr MLLN WCot
'Yellow Hammer'	CBot GBri IBlr NCat
'Zululandiae'	WCot

KNOWLTONIA (Ranunculaceae) See Plant Deletions

KOBRESIA (Cyperaceae) See Plant Deletions

KOCHIA See BASSIA

KOELERIA (Poaceae)

cristata	See *K. macrantha*
glauca	CCuc CInt CPea EBar ECha ECoo EHoe EMon EPla ESOG ESis GCHN GOrn LHil LHop LRot MBrN MBri MSCN NBro NFai NSti NVic SLod WHoo WPer WWat
§ *macrantha*	EPPr
vallesiana	CCuc EHoe EJud EMon EPPr EPla ESOG ESis LRHS

KOELLIKERIA (Gesneriaceae)

'Red Satin'	NMos

KOELREUTERIA (Sapindaceae)

bipinnata	CGre WCoo
¶ – var. *integrifoliola*	CFil WPGP
paniculata ♀	Widely available
– var. *apiculata*	CMHG
– 'Fastigiata'	MBlu SSpi

KOHLERIA (Gesneriaceae)

'Clytie'	MBri
'Dark Velvet'	CHal WDib
digitaliflora	See *K. warscewiezii*
eriantha ♀	CHal CPle MBri SLMG WDib
'Hanna Roberts'	WDib
hirsuta	CPle
* × *hybrida*	NMos
'Jester'	WDib
'Strawberry Fields' ♀	MBri NMos
§ *warscewiczii* ♀	CHal WDib

KOLKWITZIA (Caprifoliaceae)

amabilis	CB&S CGre CTrw ELan EMil GOrc GRei ISea LPan MGos MHar MPla MWat NBee NNor NWea SEas SRms WDin WFar WFro WGwG WHCG WHar WNor WStI WWin
– 'Pink Cloud' ♀	CB&S CTrw EAst EBrP EBre ENot IOrc LBre LHop MAsh MBal MBar MBri MGos NHol SBre SHBN SPer SPla SReu SSpi SSta WBod WDin WSHC WWal WWat WWeb

KOSTELETZKYA (Malvaceae)

¶ *virginica*	EMan

KUMMEROWIA (Papilionaceae) See Plant Deletions

KUNZEA (Myrtaceae)

ambigua	CDoC CGre ECou MAll SOWG
baxteri	CTrC SOWG
capitata	SOWG
§ *ericoides*	CHon ECou GAbr MAll SOWG SUsu
muelleri	MAll
parvifolia	CB&S CTrC MAll SOWG
pomifera	CHon
recurva	MAll

LABICHEA (Caesalpiniaceae) See Plant Deletions

LABLAB (Caesalpiniaceae) See Plant Deletions

+ LABURNOCYTISUS (Papilionaceae)

'Adamii'	CBlo CDoC COtt CPMA ELan EPfP GAri IOrc LBuc MBlu MBri SHBN SPer SSpi WHer

LABURNUM † (Papilionaceae)

alpinum 'Pendulum'	CBlo CDoC EBrP EBre ELan EPfP IOrc LBre LNet MAsh MBar MBri MGos MRav MWat NBee SBre SHBN SPer WDin WStI
§ *anagyroides*	CBlo ENot GAri GRei ISea NWea SEND SRms WDin
– 'Aureum'	SPer

– 'Pendulum'	CLnd
vulgare	See *L. anagyroides*
x *watereri* 'Vossii' ♀	Widely available
* – 'Vossii Pendulum'	CBlo

LACCOSPADIX (Arecaceae) See Plant Deletions

LACHENALIA (Hyacinthaceae)

§ *aloides*	LBow LHil MBri WOMN
– var. *aurea* ♀	LBow MSte
– var. *luteola*	LBow
– var. *quadricolor* ♀	LBow WCot
– var. *vanzyliae*	LBow
§ *bulbifera*	LBow MBri NRog
– 'George'	LBow
contaminata	LBow
liliiflora	CMon
pallida	NRog
pendula	See *L. bulbifera*
purpureocoerulea	CMon
pustulata	NRog
rubida	NRog
tricolor	See *L. aloides*

LACHNANTHES (Haemodoraceae)

§ *caroliana*	MSal
tinctoria	See *L. caroliana*

LACTUCA (Asteraceae)

alpina	See *Cicerbita alpina*
perennis	MAvo MTho NChi
virosa	CArn MSal

LAGAROSIPHON (Hydrocharitaceae)

§ *major* (m)	CBen CRow EHon ELan EMFW NDea SRms SWyc WChe

LAGAROSTROBOS (Podocarpaceae)

§ *franklinii*	CTrG IOrc LLin WPic

LAGENOPHORA (Asteraceae) See Plant Deletions

LAGERSTROEMIA (Lythraceae)

indica ♀	CPle LPan SEND SLMG
indica 'Rosea'	CB&S LPan SEND
subcostata	CB&S

LAGUNARIA (Malvaceae)

patersonii	CFil LHil WPGP
– 'Royal Purple'	ERea

LALLEMANTIA (Lamiaceae) See Plant Deletions

LAMARCKIA (Poaceae) See Plant Deletions

LAMBERTIA (Proteaceae)

formosa	CTrC

LAMIASTRUM See LAMIUM

LAMIUM † (Lamiaceae)

album	CKin EWFC SMrm
– 'Aureovariegatum'	See *L. album* 'Goldflake'
– 'Brightstone Gem'	EMon NBrk
– 'Friday' (v)	EGar EHoe EMon EPPr LHop MBel MCLN MSCN MTho NPla WCHb WCot WHer WHil WPbr
– 'Golden Halo'	EMon
§ – 'Goldflake' (v)	EMon MBel WCHb
– 'Pale Peril'	EMon NBrk
armenum	EHyt
eriocephalum subsp. *eriocephalum*	EHyt
flexuosum	EMon
§ *galeobdolon*	CArn CTri EMon EWFC LGro MHar MSal MWat NFai SRms WOak
– subsp. *galeobdolon*	EMon
– 'Hermann's Pride'	Widely available
– 'Kirkcudbright Dwarf'	EBee EMon EWes
– subsp. *montanum* 'Canford Wood'	EMon
§ – – 'Florentinum'	CRow ECha ECro EHoe ELan EMar ENot EPPr EPar MAus NVic SEas SHel SIng WFar WPer
– 'Purple Heart'	EMon
§ – 'Silberteppich'	CRow ECha EFou ELan EMar EMon EOrc EPla GGar MTho NNor NSti NVic SBla SMad WPer WWat
– 'Silver Angel'	EMon MBel NSti
– Silver Carpet	See *L. galeobdolon* '**Silberteppich**'
– 'Silver Spangled'	EGar EMon
– 'Variegatum'	See *L. galeobdolon* '**Florentinum**'
garganicum subsp. *garganicum*	CFis CGle CHan EBee EGar EMon EPPr EWes NChi WCot WPer WWye
– – LM&S 94023B	EMon
– 'Laevigatum'	EMon MBel
– subsp. *laevigatum* HH&K 315	CHan
– – HH&K 332	CHan
– subsp. *pictum*	See *L. garganicum* subsp. *striatum*
– subsp. *reniforme*	See *L. garganicum* subsp. *striatum*
§ – subsp. *striatum*	ELan LFlo SBla SMrm
– – DS&T 89011T	EPPr
luteum	See *L. galeobdolon*
maculatum	CArn CRow EGoo EMon MMal SEND SHFr SMac SRms WByw WWye
– – AL&JS 90226JU	EMon
– 'Album'	CGle CRow EFou ELan EMon ENot LGro MWat NChi SHel SPer SRms WByw WCru WWat
¶ – 'Anne Greenaway'	MGrG SMrm WCot
– 'Annecy'	MInt
§ – 'Aureum'	CArn CB&S CGle CInt EBrP EBre EHoe ELan EMon EPla LBre LGro LHop MBel MBro MCLN MTho NFai NVic SBre SMad WEas WHil WOak WPer
– 'Beacon Silver'	Widely available
– 'Beedham's White'	MRav NBir NSti SCro WRus
– 'Brightstone Pearl'	EGoo EMon WCer
– 'Cannon's Gold'	EBee ECha ECtt EGar EHoe ELan EMon EWes GBuc MCLN NSti WCru
N – 'Chequers'	CDoC CJew EBee EMon SPer SPla
– 'Dingle Candy'	CElw EMon MCLN

– 'Edinburgh Broadstripes'	EPla
– 'Elaine Franks'	CHid NCat
– 'Elizabeth de Haas' (v)	CLTr EBee EGar EGoo EMan EMon EPla EWes LHil LHop MMal WCHb WCer WHer WPer
– 'Gold Leaf'	See *L. maculatum* **'Aureum'**
¶ – 'Golden Anniversary' (v)	EBee WWeb
– 'Golden Nuggets'	CMGP EAst LFis LHop MLLN NCut NPla NPro NTay SMrm WEas
– 'Hatfield'	EMon GAbr GBuc
– 'Ickwell Beauty' (v)	EMon EWes GBri LFis MBrN MLLN NCat NLak WCot WRHF
– 'Immaculate'	CBre EMon EPla
– 'James Boyd Parselle'	CLTr EGoo EMon EPPr MAus MHlr MLLN SCro WCHb WCot WRHF WWat
– 'Margery Fish'	SRms WEas
– 'Pink Nancy'	CBot CMea EGoo GAbr MTho WCer WFar
– 'Pink Pearls'	CBre EGar EMan EPPr NHaw NPla
– 'Pink Pewter'	CElw CGle CLTr EBrP EBre ECGP ECha ECtt EFou EMon EPla LBre LGro MBel MGed NBrk NSti SBre SCro SPer SUsu WBea WByw WCHb WCru WPer WRus WWhi
– 'Purple Winter'	EPla
– 'Red Nancy'	CBlo EGar EMar EMon EPPr EPla GCal MCLN NChi WCer CGle CHan CRow EBee EFer EFou ELan EMar EPar EPla LGro LHop MRav MWat NChi NFai NFla NLon NNor SPer WBon WMow WPer WWat WWhi
§ – 'Roseum'	
– 'Shell Pink'	See *L. maculatum* **'Roseum'**
– 'Sterling Silver'	EWes WPer
– 'White Nancy' ♀	Widely available
– 'Wild White'	EPla
– 'Wootton Pink'	CBos CLTr EGar GBuc GCal GMac LFis MBri MBro NBir NChi NLak SSvw WEas WHoo WPer
¶ *microphyllum*	EHyt
orvala	CBot CGle CHan CLyd CPle EBrP EBre ECha EGar EMon EPla LBre LFis MAus MFir NChi SBre SIgm SSpi WBon WCot WCru WHer WPer WWat WWye
– 'Album'	CBot CHan CPle ECro EGar ELan EMon EOrc EPPr MFir SAga SEas SMrm WCot WHer
sandrasicum	EHyt

LAMPRANTHUS (Aizoaceae)

aberdeenensis	See *Delosperma aberdeenense*
aurantiacus	CB&S CHEx NBrk
aureus	CTrC EOas
¶ 'Bagdad'	CHEx
blandus	CB&S CHEx
§ *brownii*	CB&S CHEx CHal ECho ELan EOas NBir WPat
'Carn Brea'	CB&S CHal
coccineus	SLMG
coralliflorus	CTrC

§ *deltoides*	CHEx CTrC MRav
edulis	See *Carpobrotus edulis*
glaucus	CB&S CHEx SEND
haworthii	CHal SLMG SVen
lehmannii	See *Delosperma lehmannii*
multiradiatus	CTrC SEND
oscularis	See *L. deltoides*
pallidus	See *Delosperma pallidum*
roseus	EOas SSoC WEas
¶ *scaber*	CTrC
spectabilis	CB&S EOas SAPC SArc SLMG WBrE
– 'Tresco Apricot'	CB&S
– 'Tresco Brilliant'	CB&S CHEx
– 'Tresco Fire'	CHal
– 'Tresco Peach'	CHEx
– 'Tresco Red'	CB&S
¶ 'Tresco Pearl'	CHEx

LANTANA (Verbenaceae)

'Aloha'	LHil NPri
camara	ELan EPfP ERea MBri SRms WMul
– 'Brasier'	ERea
– Cloth of Gold	See *L. camara* **'Drap d'Or'**
– 'Cocktail'	NPri
– 'Feston Rose'	ERea
– 'Firebrand'	SLMG
– forms	ERea IBlr
– 'Mine d'Or'	ERea
– 'Mr Bessieres'	ERea
– 'Snow White'	ERea SLMG
* 'Cocktail'	CLTr LIck
'Gold Dust'	SLMG
'Gold Mound'	MBEx
§ *montevidensis*	ERea LHil MBEx SLMG WIvy
* – *alba*	ERea LHil
§ – 'Boston Gold'	CHal MBEx
– 'Malans Gold'	ERea
– 'White Lightning'	LHop
– 'Whiteknights'	MBEx
'Radiation'	ERea
sellowiana	See *L. montevidensis*
'Spreading Sunset'	SOWG

LAPAGERIA (Philesiaceae)

rosea ♀	CB&S CGre CHEx CMac CPlN CSam CWSG ERea GQui MBal MDun NPal SHBN SOWG SPer SReu SSpi WNor WWat
– var. *albiflora*	CPlN
– – 'White Cloud'	CGre
– 'Flesh Pink' ♀	CB&S CGre CPlN ISea
– 'Nash Court' ♀	CB&S CPlN CSam ECot ELan EMil ERea ISea WStI

LAPEIROUSIA (Iridaceae)

cruenta	See *Anomatheca laxa*
laxa	See *Anomatheca laxa*

LAPIEDRA (Amaryllidaceae)

martinezii MS 423	CMon

LAPSANA (Asteraceae)

communis 'Inky'	CNat
– 'Patchy' (v)	CNat

LARDIZABALA (Lardizabalaceae)

biternata	CGre CPlN CTrG

LARIX (Pinaceae)

decidua ♀	CB&S CDoC CPer ENot GChr GRei IHos LCon LPan MBal MBar NWea SHBN SPar SPer WDin WFar WHar WMou WStI WWal
– 'Corley'	CKen LCon LLin MBlu
¶ – 'Croxby Broom'	CKen
– 'Little Bogle'	CKen NHol
– 'Oberförster Karsten'	CKen
– 'Pendula'	CB&S
– 'Poulii'	CEnd COtt MBlu NHol SPer
x *eurolepis*	See *L.* x *marschlinsii*
gmelinii	ETen GAri ISea
– var. *olgensis*	GAri
– 'Tharandt'	CKen
§ *kaempferi* ♀	CDoC CLnd CPer ENot GChr GRei LBuc LCon LNet MBar MGos NWea SLim SPer STre WFro WMou WNor WStI
– 'Bambino'	CKen
– 'Blue Ball'	CKen LLin
– 'Blue Dwarf'	CEnd CKen COtt LCon LNet MAsh SLim
– 'Blue Rabbit Weeping'	CBlo COtt LCon LLin LPan MGos NHol SLim WDin
– 'Cruwys Morchard'	CKen
– 'Diane'	CBlo CEnd CKen GAri LCon LLin MAsh MBlu MBri NHol SLim
– 'Elizabeth Rehder'	CKen
– 'Grant Haddow'	CKen LLin
– 'Green Pearl'	CKen LLin
– 'Grey Pearl'	CKen
– 'Hobbit'	CKen
* – 'Jacobsen's Pyramid'	LLin NHol
I – 'Nana'	CKen GAri LLin WWes
– 'Nana Prostrata'	CKen
– 'Pendula'	CBlo CDoC CEnd IOrc MBar MBlu MGos NHol SLim SPer
– 'Varley'	CKen
– 'Wehlen'	CKen
– 'Wolterdingen'	CKen LLin MBlu
– 'Yanus Olieslagers'	CKen
laricina	GAri
– 'Arethusa Bog'	CKen
* – 'Bear Swamp'	CKen
¶ – 'Newport Beauty'	CKen
leptolepis	See *L. kaempferi*
§ x *marschlinsii*	ENot GChr GRei NWea WMou
– 'Domino'	CKen LLin
– 'Gail'	CKen
– 'Julie'	CKen
occidentalis	GAri
x *pendula* 'Pendulina'	GAri
russica	See *L. sibirica*
§ *sibirica*	GAri ISea MBar
sukaczevii	See *L. sibirica*

LARREA (Zygophyllaceae)

tridentata	MSal

LASER (Apiaceae) See Plant Deletions

LASERPITIUM (Apiaceae)

siler	SIgm

LASIAGROSTIS See STIPA

LATANIA (Arecaceae)

¶ *loddigesii*	LPal

¶ *verschaffeltii*	LPal

LATHYRUS † (Papilionaceae)

albus	CEnd
amphicarpos	MSto
angulatus	MSto
angustifolius	MSto
annuus	MSto
¶ – red	MSto
aphaca	MSto
§ *articulatus*	MSto
aurantius	MSto WLRN WLin
§ *aureus*	CHEx CHan CLTr ECha ECoo EMon GCal GCra MAvo MHar MSto MTho NChi SUsu WCru WEas WHal WOMN WViv
azureus hort.	See *L. sativus*
¶ *belinensis*	MSto
chilensis	EBee MSto
chloranthus	EWll MSto WPbr WWye
cicera	MSto
cirrhosus	EMon
¶ *clymenum*	MSto
– *articulatus*	See *L. articulatus*
* *cyaneus* 'Alboroseus'	CGle MTho
– hort.	See *L. vernus*
– (Steven)K.Koch	MSto
davidii	MSto WCot
¶ *filiformis*	NChi
fremontii hort.	See *L. laxiflorus*
¶ *gloeospermus*	MSto
¶ *gmelinii*	MSto
– 'Aureus'	See *L. aureus*
gorgonii	MSto
grandiflorus	CGle CSev ECha EMon LGre MSto NChi SAxl SMad SMrm SSad SUsu SWat WCot WPbr
heterophyllus	EMon MNrw WHal
hierosolymitanus	MSto
hirsutus	MLLN MSto
¶ *hirticarpus*	MSto
¶ *inconspicuus*	MSto
inermis	See *L. laxiflorus*
japonicus	WViv
– subsp. *maritimus*	LFis MHlr MSto
laetiflorus var. *vestitus*	See *L. vestitus*
lanzwertii	MSto
latifolius ♀	CArn CGle CRHN EAst EBrP EBre ECGP ELan EOld GCHN LBre LHop MFir NChi NFla NPer NSti SBre SHFr SIng SRCN SUsu WCot WEas WHer WOak WPer WStI WWin WWye
– 'Albus'	CBot ELan EMan EMon GDra LGre MNrw SHFr SRms SSpi SUsu SWas WCot WEas WHoo
– 'Blushing Bride'	WCot
– deep pink	NSti
– pale pink	CSam NSti
– Pink Pearl	See *L. latifolius* 'Rosa Perle'
– 'Red Pearl'	CBlo CPlN EBrP EBre ECtt EFou LBre MBri NCut SBre SMrm SPer SSvw WPer WRus
§ – 'Rosa Perle' ♀	CBlo CDoC CHid CTri ECtt EFou EMan GAbr MAus MAvo MBri MSte NCut NLar NPer SMrm SPer SSvw WRus WViv
– 'Rose Queen'	CB&S
I – 'Rubra'	EPfP
– 'Splendens'	CB&S
– Weisse Perle	See *L. latifolius* 'White Pearl'

§ – 'White Pearl' ♀   CB&S CGle CHad CHea CMea EBar EBrP EBre ECha EFou EOrc GAbr LBre LPVe MAus MBri MSte NChi NLar NPer NSti SBre SMad SPer SSoC SSvw WOve WPer WRus WWat

§ *laxiflorus*   CSpe EMon GMac MNrw MSto MTho NTow SAxl SOkh SSca WCot WWin

linifolius   EMon MSto

– var. *montanus*   CKin EBee WGwy

luteus 'Aureus'   See *L. aureus*

¶ *marmoratus*   MSto

¶ *montanus*   WViv

§ *nervosus*   CBot CPlN CPla CPou CSpe MAvo MTho SBla SMad SRms WOMN

neurolobus   CNic EHyt MOne MSto

niger   CHan EMar EMon LFis MSto SHFr SOkh WGwy

nissolia   ELan MSto

ochrus   MSto

odoratus ♀   CGle CHan SAga SUsu WEas

– 'Bicolor'   ELan

– 'Matucana'   CSpe EJud WOMN

– 'Painted Lady'   CGle EJud

¶ – 'The Busby Pea'   WOMN

palustris   LFis MSto

pannonicus   MFir MSto

¶ *paranensis*   MSto

polyphyllus   WCot

pratensis   CKin EWFC MSto SSca

pubescens   CRHN EMon GBuc GCra SUsu

rotundifolius   CPlN ECoo GCal GDra LGre MHlr MNrw MTho NSti SUsu SWas WCot WEas WHoo WPyg

– hybrids   LGre MSto

– 'Tillyperone'   EMon

§ *sativus*   CHad CSpe LHop MSto SHFr SSad WEas WWye

– var. *azureus*   See *L. sativus*

¶ *setifolius*   MSto

sphaericus   MSto

sylvestris   CKin ELan EMon MLLN MNrw MSCN MSte MSto WGwy

¶ – 'Wagneri'   CSpe

tingitanus   CRHN SHFr

– 'Flame'   MSto

¶ – *roseus*   MSto

¶ – 'Roseus'   MSto

– salmon pink   MSto

tuberosus   EBee EMon MNrw MSto WCot WOMN

¶ 'Tubro'   EMon

* *uniflorus*   MSCN MSto

venetus   EMon MNrw

§ *vernus* ♀   Widely available

– 'Alboroseus' ♀   Widely available

– var. *albus*   EWes GAri SRms

– *aurantiacus*   See *L. aureus*

– 'Caeruleus'   CRDP LGre SMrm WPGP

* – *cyaneus*   NTow SOkh SWas SWat WRus WSan

–'Flaccidus'   EMon WKif

– 'Rosenelfe'   CBot EMan WHil WSan

– f. *roseus*   ECha

– 'Spring Melody'   LFis SMrm WPat WRHF

§ *vestitus*   MSto

– var. *alefeldii*   MSto

¶ *vinealis*   MSto

LAURELIA (Monimiaceae)

§ *sempervirens*   CB&S CGre CHEx CTrw SAPC SArc

serrata   See *L. sempervirens*

LAURENTIA (Campanulaceae)

§ *axillaris*   CBar CLTr CSpe GBur LHil LHop LIck SCoo SHFr WWin

LAURUS (Lauraceae)

§ *azorica*   CB&S CGre WWat

canariensis   See *L. azorica*

nobilis ♀   Widely available

– f. *angustifolia*   CPle CSWP GQui LHol MAll MBlu SAPC SArc SDry WCHb WSel

– 'Aurea' ♀   CB&S CDec CGre CMHG CPle ELan ELau EMil ERav ERea GQui IOrc LHol LNet MBlu MChe SMad SPer WCHb WPat WPyg WWat

– 'Crispa'   MRav

LAVANDULA † (Lamiaceae)

N 'Alba'   CArn CB&S CBot CSev EFou ELan ERav GCHN LHol NYoL SIde SPer SWat WEas WOak WPer

x *allardii*   CArn ENor EOHP GBar MChe NHHG SPan WJek WPen WSel

– 'African Pride'   SDow

– Clone B   SDow

– forms   WTus

§ *angustifolia*   CArn CLan ELau ENot GOrc GPoy LBuc MBar MBri MChe MGos MPla MWat NChi NFla NNor NPer NYoL SEas SHBN SMac WAbe WPyg WTus WWye

– 'Alba'   CChe EBar EHic EHoe ELau GChr GPoy LBuc LHop MChe NFai NMen WAbe WPbr WSel WWat

– 'Alba Nana'   See *L. angustifolia* 'Nana Alba'

– 'Ashdown Forest'   CSev ECle MChe SDow WJek WLRN WTus

– 'Beechwood Blue'   NYoL SDow WTus

§ – 'Bowles' Early'   CSam GBar MChe SDow WJek WTus

– 'Bowles' Grey'   See *L. angustifolia* 'Bowles' Early'

– 'Bowles' Variety'   See *L. angustifolia* 'Bowles' Early'

– 'Cedar Blue'   CSev ELau NYoL SDow SHDw SIde SPla WTus

– 'Compacta'   WTus

– 'Dwarf Blue'   EMil SAxl

I – 'Eastgrove Nana'   WEas

– 'Folgate'   CArn CB&S EAst EFou LHol MChe MPla MWat NHHG NYoL SDow SIde WGwG WSel WTus

– 'Fring Favourite'   WTus

§ – 'Hidcote' ♀   Widely available

– 'Hidcote Pink'   CArn CGle EFou ELan ESis LHol MWat NBee NFai NFla NNor NRoo NSti SDow SMad SPer SSoC WPbr WPer WSel WStI WTus WWat

– 'Imperial Gem'	CRos EBee EHic ENor ESis GBar MAsh MBri MChe NHHG NPer SDow SEas SIde WHoo WSel WTus WWeb
§ – 'Jean Davis'	EBee GBar LHop NBee NHHG SDow SIde WSel WTus
– 'Lady'	CM&M CPri EOHP GBar LFis MChe MWat NOrc NRoo SDow SHDw WLRN WTus
N– 'Lavender Lady'	EAst NYoL WPer WWeb
– 'Loddon Blue'	CWSG GBar LHol NFla NHHG NYoL SDow SIde WJek WSel WTus
§ – 'Loddon Pink'	CWSG ECle ELan ENor ENot EOHP ERea GBar GCHN GCra MAsh MChe MPla MUlv NYoL SDow WAbe WEas WGwG WHoo WJek WSHC WSel WStl WTus WWal WWeb
– 'Miss Katherine'	ENor
– 'Munstead'	Widely available
§ – 'Nana Alba'	CB&S CSev ECha EFou ELan ELau ENor ENot GPoy LHol LHop MBar MBri MPla MUlv NHHG SDow SHBN SMad SPer WEas WGwG WHoo WHow WKif WPat WSel WTus WWin
– 'Nana Atropurpurea'	SDow WTus
– 'Princess Blue'	EBar ELan ENor ESis GBar LFis MAsh NYoL SDow SIde SSca WPer WSel WTus WWeb WWoo
§ – 'Rosea'	CArn CB&S CMea CPri ECha EHoe GChr GPoy LHop MBar MBri NBee NChi NHHG SDow SIde SPer WHer WOMN WOak WTus WWat WWeb
– 'Royal Purple'	CArn EBar ENor EOld EWes GBar LHol MUlv NHHG NYoL SDow SIde WSel WTus WWye
N– 'Twickel Purple' ♀	EBar EBee LHop MChe MPla NHHG NYoL SAga SAxl SCoo SDow SIde SSoC WGwG WSel WTus
'Blue Cushion'	EBrP EBre LBre MAsh SBre
* 'Bowers Beauty'	WTus
buchii var. *gracilis*	SDow WTus
N 'Cambridge Lady'	WHer
canariensis	CSev CStr ENor ERea NHHG SDow SHDw SSad WCHb WJek WTus
¶ × *christiana*	SDow SHDw
'Cornard Blue'	See *L.* 'Sawyers'
dentata	CArn CInt CSev ELan ENor EPri ERea LBlm LFis LHol MChe NBrk NHHG SDow SDry SPil WAbe WHer WOak WTus WWye
§ – var. *candicans*	CGle ENor LHil LHol LHop MAll MChe NHHG SAga SDow SMrm SPil SSad WCHb WEas WPer WTus WWye
¶ – 'Linda Ligon'	SDow WTus
¶ – 'Ploughman's Blue'	SDow
¶ – 'Royal Crown'	SDow WTus
– silver	See *L. dentata* var. *candicans*
¶ – 'Silver Queen'	SHDw
¶ 'Devantville Cuche'	NSti WJek
'Dilly Dilly'	SAxl WTus
'Fragrant Memories'	EBrP EBre ELau ERea GAbr LBre MAsh SBre SDow SSoC WTus
'Goodwin Creek Grey'	MChe SDow WTus
'Hidcote Blue'	See *L. angustifolia* 'Hidcote'
× *intermedia* 'Abrialii'	SDow WTus
– 'Alba'	ECle ENor NHHG SDow SSca WLRN WTus
N– 'Arabian Night'	LRHS SDow WTus
§ – Dutch Group ♀	CArn EFou ELan ENot EOld EPfP MBar MBri NYoL SChu SCoo SDow SPer SWat WHen WJek WPer WSel WShe WTus
– 'Grappenhall'	CArn CEnd EBar ELau EMil ENor LHol LHop MAsh MChe MPla NFai NFla NHHG NLon NVic NYoL SChu SDow SPer WGwG WOak WPer WSel WTus WWat WWye
– 'Grey Hedge'	LHol NHHG SDow WTus
– 'Grosso'	COtt CPri ENor LHol NSti NYoL SDow WAbe WJek WLRN WTus
– 'Hidcote Giant'	EHal MAsh NPer SAga SDow WSel WTus WWat
* – 'Hidcote White'	WTus
– 'Lullingstone Castle'	CBod NYoL SDow SIde WJek WTus
– Old English Group	CArn CBod ELan ELau MGra NBrk NYoL SDow SIde WHoo WJek WOak WSel WTus WWat
– 'Seal'	CArn CEnd ECle EFou ELau GBar LHol MChe NHHG NSti NWoo NYoL SDow SIde WGwG WPer WSel WTus WWal WWat
– 'Super'	SDow
N– 'Twickel Purple'	CArn CMHG CSev ECGP ELau ENot EWes LFis LHol NFai NHHG SChu SWat WJek WOak WWat WWye
'Jean Davis'	See *L. angustifolia* 'Jean Davis'
lanata ♀	CArn CBot CChr CGle CHan CLon ECha ELan ENor GPoy MBro MChe MPla MWat NHHG NSti SDow SDry WEas WOMN WSHC WTus WWye
– × *angustifolia*	NHHG SDow WTus
§ *latifolia*	CArn GBar SDow WSel WTus
'Loddon Pink'	See *L. angustifolia* 'Loddon Pink'
mairei × *intermedia*	WTus
minutolii	SDow
multifida	CArn CSev EEls ENor ERea MChe NHHG SDow SSad WCHb WGwG WHer WTus WWal WWye
officinalis	See *L. angustifolia*
§ *pinnata*	CArn ENor ERea GBar MChe NHHG SDow SDry SSad WCHb WEas WTus
pterostoechas pinnata	See *L. pinnata*
'Richard Gray'	EBee EMon GBar LHop NBrk SAxl WAbe WBcn WTus
'Rosea'	See *L. angustifolia* 'Rosea'
¶ *rotundifolia*	SDow
¶ 'Saint Brelade'	SDow

§ 'Sawyers' — CEnd CLon EBrP EBre ELan ELau ENor ESis EWes LBre LGre MAsh MBri MLan NPer NSti NYoL SBod SBre SChu SDow SHBN SIde WSHC WSel WTus WWoo

spica 'Hidcote Purple' — See *L. angustifolia* **'Hidcote'**
N – nom. rejic. — See *L. angustifolia* , *L. latifolia* , *L. x intermedia*

stoechas ♀ — Widely available
– var. *albiflora* — See *L. stoechas* f. *leucantha*
¶ – subsp. *atlantica* — SDow
¶ – subsp. *cariensis* — SDow
– dark form — NHol WTus
– 'Fathead' — LRHS SDow WTus
– 'Helmsdale' — CBos CJew CRos CSam CStr EBrP EBre ELan ENor IOrc LBre LHop MAsh MBri MLan MUlv MWgw NYoL SAga SBre SCoo SDow SPer SPla SVil WTus WWat WWeb
¶ – 'Kew Red' — SDow
§ – f. *leucantha* — CArn CBot CMHG CMea CSev CTre EBar ECha ELan LHol MBri MChe MPla MRav NChi NSti NWoo SChu SDow SPer WAbe WCHb WPer WTus
– subsp. *luisieri* — SDow WHer
¶ – subsp. *lusitanica* — SDow WTus
– 'Marshwood' — CRos EBrP EBre ELan ENor EPfP IOrc LBre LBuc MAsh MBri MUlv NYoL SAga SBre SCoo SDow SMad SPer SPla WTus WWeb
* – 'Nana' — CArn
– 'Papillon' — See *L. stoechas* subsp. *pedunculata*
§ – subsp. *pedunculata* ♀ — Widely available
– – 'Avonview' — CB&S SDow
– subsp. *pendunculata* — CHid EHic EMon EREa LHop 'James Compton' — MAsh NPSI SDow SSoC WKif WTus
¶ – 'Pippa' — WTus
¶ – 'Pukehou' — WTus
¶ – subsp. *sampaioana* — SDow WTus
– 'Snowman' — ENor IOrc LRHS MAsh MWat NYoL SDow WFar WTus WWal
¶ – 'Sugar Plum' — WTus
¶ – 'Summerset Mist' — WTus
– 'Willow Vale' — CMHG LGre SDow SPan WSPU WTus
subnuda — WTus
vera De Candolle — See *L. angustifolia*
– hort. — See *L. x intermedia* **Dutch Group**
viridis — CArn CSev EEls ELan ENor ERav GOrc LGre LHol MAsh MChe MRav NHHG NPer SDow SPer SSad WCHb WEas WHer WPer WTus WUnu WWat WWye

LAVATERA (Malvaceae)
arborea — CArn GBar WHer
– 'Rosea' — See *L.* **'Rosea'**
– 'Variegata' — CB&S CHan CInt ECro ELan GBar LHop MHlr NPer NSti SBod SEND WCru WEas WHer WPbr WWal
assurgentiflora — EMon GBri LHil
'Barnsley' ♀ — Widely available
bicolor — See *L. maritima*

'Blushing Bride' — CBlo EBee EBrP EBre EHic ELan EPfP GMac LBre MAsh MLLN MSCN SBod SBre SHBN SMad SMrm WHar
'Bredon Springs' — CB&S EBrP EBre ECha EMil EMon GBri LBre LFis LHop MAsh MBri MGos NBrk SBid SBod SBre SMad SMrm SPan SPar SSoC WPyg WStI WWal WWeb
* 'Bressingham Pink' — SMad
'Burgundy Wine' — CB&S CChe EAst EBrP EBre ECtt ELan GRei LBre MBar MBri MGos MRav NBee NPer NRoo SBod SBre SHBN SMad SPer WCFE WDin WHar WHen WOld WStI WWeb
cachemiriana — EBee ELan GBuc GCal MFir NLak NPer NSti WLin WRus WWat
'Candy Floss' — CB&S EBar ELan ENot ERic GChr MAsh MBar MGos MRav NPer SHBN SMrm SPer WDin WOld WStI WWal WWeb
'Chedglow' (v) — CNat
'Eye Catcher' — LRHS MAsh MAvo SUsu
'Kew Rose' — CB&S CBlo EBee EMil EPfP LHop MAll MAsh NPer SBid SMad SPla SSoC
¶ 'Lara Rose' — MGos
'Lavender Lady' — SMrm
'Lilac Lady' — LRHS MAsh MAvo SLod SMad SPer WPbr
¶ 'Linda' — WBcn
'Lisanne' — EHic EOrc MCCP MNrw NChi NHol NPro SUsu
§ *maritima* ♀ — CBot CDoC CGle CGre CHan CMHG ELan GBur GMac LHil LHop MAll MAsh SDry SHBN SMrm SPer SUsu WEas WHCG WKif WOMN WOld
– *bicolor* — See *L. maritima*
'Mary Hope' — CHan LHop NPro WWeb
¶ 'Memories' — LRHS
'Moonstone' — SMrm
oblongifolia — CBlo CBot MAll SMad
N *olbia* — CGle MPla MSCN MWat NFai SDix SIde
'Pavlova' — EBee EBrP EBre LBre LRHS MAsh MCCP MTis NHol SBre SPla SSto
'Peppermint Ice' — See *L. thuringiaca* **'Ice Cool'**
'Pink Frills' — CBot CFee EBrP EBre EMil LBre LHop MAll MAvo MBar MHlr MNrw NBrk SAxl SBid SBre SDry SHBN SMad SSoC SUsu WHar WPyg WRus WStI WWeb
plebeia — MSto
¶ 'Poynton Lady' — NEgg
§ 'Rosea' ♀ — CB&S CChe CMHG EBrP EBre ECha ELan ENot GBur GRei LBre LHop MBar MBri MGos NNor SBod SBre SHBN SMad SPer WAbe WBod WDin WHCG WOld WPbr WWin
'Shorty' — ELan NBrk WFar
'Snowcap' — CBlo CDoC
N *thuringiaca* — EBot MWhi NBro NPri
– AL&JS 90100YU — EMon

§ – 'Ice Cool' CBot CElw CMil ECha ECtt
 ELan EOrc ERav GCal LHop
 MAll MAsh MBar NBee NBrk
 NPer NRoo SBid SHBN SMad
 SMrm SPer SSoC WHen
'Variegata' See *L.* **'Wembdon Variegated'**
§ 'Wembdon Variegated' ELan MCCP MLLN NPer SMad

LAWSONIA (Lythraceae)
inermis MSal

LEDEBOURIA (Hyacinthaceae)
adlamii See *L. cooperi*
§ *cooperi* CHal CMea CMon CRDP EHyt
 ELan ERos ESis GCal IBlr LHil
§ *socialis* CHEx CHal CMon CSWP CSev
 CSpe EOHP ERav ERos IBlr
 LCns LHil MBro NChi NRog
violacea See *L. socialis*

× LEDODENDRON (Ericaceae)
§ 'Arctic Tern' ♀ CDoC CSam EHic EPot GChr
 GGGa ITim LHyd LMil MAsh
 MBal MBar MDun MGos MLea
 NHar NHol SPer SReu WAbe
 WPic

LEDUM (Ericaceae)
glandulosum var. MBal
 columbianum
groenlandicum MBar WAbe WGer WSHC
 – 'Compactum' LRHS MAsh MBal
hypoleucum See *L. palustre* f. *dilatatum*
¶ *macrophyllum* CFir
palustre EPot GGGa GPoy MBal MGos
¶ – subsp. *decumbens* GCrs GGGa
'Teshio' SSta

LEEA (Leeaceae)
coccinea See *L. guineensis*
¶ *guineensis* MBri

LEGOUSIA (Campanulaceae)
hybrida EWFC

LEIBNITZIA (Asteraceae)
anandria NWCA

LEIOPHYLLUM (Ericaceae)
buxifolium ♀ CB&S EPfP GCrs LRHS MBal
 MBro MHig NHol SBrw SSpi
 WPat WPyg
– var. *hugeri* NHar WAbe

LEMBOTROPIS See CYTISUS

LEMNA (Lemnaceae)
gibba CBen CWat LPBA MSta SAWi
minor CBen CWat EHon EMFW
 LPBA MSta SAWi SWat
polyrhiza See *Spirodela polyrhiza*
trisulca CWat EHon EMFW LPBA
 MSta SAWi SWat

LEONOTIS (Lamiaceae)
dysophylla WCot
¶ – 'Pussytoes' WHer
– 'Toastytoes' WCot
leonurus See *L. ocymifolia*
nepetifolia EMan WCot

§ *ocymifolia* CFee EPPr LBlm SAxl SLMG
 WCot WHer WWye
¶ – var. *ocymifolia* NGno
'Staircase' WSan

LEONTICE (Berberidaceae)
albertii See *Gymnospermium albertii*

LEONTODON (Asteraceae)
autumnalis CKin
hispidus CKin NMir

LEONTOPODIUM (Asteraceae)
alpinum EBot EBrP EBre ESis GAbr
 GCHN GLil GTou LBre MBal
 MBro NFla NMen NNor NNrd
 SBre SIng SRms WPer WWin
– 'Mignon' CMea ELan EMNN EWes
 GBur GCrs GDra GTou MBro
 NMen NNrd NRoo NVic SIng
 SSmi WHoo
¶ – subsp. *nivale* WLin
hayachinense CLyd
 miyabeanum
himalayanum EWes
kamtschaticum EWes
§ *ochroleucum* var. WPer
 campestre
palibinianum See *L. ochroleucum* var.
 campestre
sibiricum See *L. leontopodioides*
tataricum See *L. discolor*
wilsonii ECha

LEONURUS (Lamiaceae)
artemisia MSal
cardiaca CArn CPle EMan EMar EMon
 EWFC GBar GPoy MChe
 MHew MSal NHex SIde WHer
 WOak WSel WWye
¶ – 'Crispus' EMon
¶ *macranthus* EFEx
¶ – var. *alba* EFEx
sibiricus EBee GBar IIve MSal

LEOPOLDIA (Hyacinthaceae)
comosa See *Muscari comosum*
spreitzenhoferi See *Muscari spreitzenhoferi*
tenuiflora See *Muscari tenuiflorum*

LEPECHINIA (Lamiaceae)
¶ *calycina* CPle
§ *chamaedryoides* CGre
floribunda CPle

LEPIDIUM (Brassicaceae)
barnebyanum NNS 93-420 MFos
nanum EHyt MFos MRPP

LEPIDOTHAMNUS (Podocarpaceae)
§ *laxifolius* CMHG SIng

LEPIDOZAMIA (Zamiaceae)
hopei LPal
peroffskyana LPal

LEPTARRHENA (Saxifragaceae) See Plant
Deletions

LEPTINELLA (Asteraceae)

§ *albida*	GCrs LGro
§ *atrata*	MDHE NMen
– subsp. *luteola*	EWes GAri GGar MDHE NGre
	NMen NWCA SChu SDys SSmi
	WAbe
§ *dendyi*	EHyt EWes MHig NMen
filicula	ECou
* *hispida*	NGre
maniototo	ECou
§ *minor*	ECou MOne SSmi
§ *pectinata*	ECou NGre
– var. *sericea*	See *L. albida*
§ *potentillina*	CTri EBar ECha EHoe ELan
	ESis MRav NHol NNrd SChu
	SIng SRms WCru WPer WRHF
	WWin
§ *pusilla*	SDys SSmi
§ *pyrethrifolia*	CInt SSmi
– var. *linearifolia*	ELan SIng
¶ – var. *pyrethrifolia*	NTow
reptans	See *L. scariosa*
§ *rotundata*	ECou WPer
§ *scariosa*	ECou
serrulata	GCHN GCLN MBar NHol
	WCru
* aff. *socialis* JJ&JH 9401641	NGre
§ *squalida*	CNic ECha ECou ESis IBlr
	MBar MLLN NRya NSti NVic
	SIng SSmi WByw WPer
¶ – 'Platt's Black'	NSti SSmi

LEPTODACTYLON (Polemoniaceae)

§ *californicum*	CPBP LGre
– subsp. *glandulosum*	NHol
¶ *pungens pulchriflorum*	NHol

LEPTOPTERIS (Osmundaceae) See Plant Deletions

LEPTOSPERMUM † (Myrtaceae)

arachnoides	MAll
argenteum	CB&S
¶ *brachyandrum*	CHon
weeping, silver-leaved form	
citratum	See *L. petersonii*
cunninghamii	See *L. myrtifolium*
epacridoideum	MAll
ericoides	See *Kunzea ericoides*
◆ *flavescens* misapplied	See *L. glaucescens*
◆ – Sm.	See *L. polygalifolium*
§ *glaucescens*	CHon MAll
§ *grandiflorum*	CFil CHan CPle CTrG ELan
	EPfP ISea MAll SOWG WSHC
	WWeb
grandifolium	CHon ECou MAll SSpi
'Green Eyes' (*minutifolium* X *scoparium*)	ECou MAll
humifusum	See *L. rupestre*
juniperinum	CB&S CPle MAll
laevigatum 'Yarrum'	ECou
§ *lanigerum* ♀	CB&S CMHG CPle CTri ECou
	GCHN IOrc MAll SOWG
	WBod WWin
* – 'Citratum'	ECou
– 'Cunninghamii'	See *L. myrtifolium*
– 'King William'	ECou
– 'Silver Sheen'	See *L. myrtifolium* 'Silver Sheen'
– 'Wellington'	ECou
liversidgei	CPle ECou MAll

minutifolium	ECou MAll
§ *myrtifolium*	CPMA CTri ECou ELan EPfP
	EPla EWes MAll SDry SOWG
	SPer SSta WPat WPic WPyg
– 'Newnes Forest'	ECou
– X *scoparium*	ECou
nitidum	CTrC ECou
obovatum	CMHG MAll
§ *petersonii*	CArn CPle ECou EOHP MFiF
phylicoides	See *Kunzea ericoides*
'Pink Surprise'	ECou MAll SOWG
(*minutifolium* X *scoparium*)	
polyanthum	MAll
§ *polygalifolium*	CTrC MAll SRms
prostratum	See *L. rupestre*
pubescens	See *L. lanigerum*
¶ *riparium*	MAll
rodwayanum	See *L. grandiflorum*
rotundifolium	CTrC ECou EOHP
– from Jervis Bay	MAll
§ *rupestre* ♀	CPle CTri ECou EPot GTou
	LHop MAll MBal MBar MGos
	MHig NHar NHol SDry SIng
	SRms WLin WSHC WWat
– X *scoparium*	ECou
scoparium	CArn ECou GAri IOrc WDin
– 'Autumn Glory'	EHoe GOrc MAll SMrm WStI
– 'Avocet'	ECou EWes
– 'Black Robin'	SOWG
– 'Blossom'	CB&S ECou MAll SOWG
– 'Burgundy Queen'	CB&S ECou
– 'Chapmanii'	CB&S CMHG CTrG CTri
– 'Charmer'	CB&S
– 'Cherry Brandy'	CB&S
– 'Coral Candy'	CB&S CTrC
– 'Elizabeth Jane'	CB&S EWes GCHN GQui
– 'Fascination'	CB&S CGre
– 'Fred's Red'	EWes
– 'Grandiflorum'	CTrw GCHN WGer
– var. *incanum* 'Keatleyi' ♀	CMHG ECou EPfP MAll SOWG WFar WPyg
– – 'Wairere'	ECou
– 'Jubilee' (d)	CB&S ISea
– 'Leonard Wilson' (d)	CTri ECou EWes LBlm MAll
– 'Lyndon'	ECou
– 'Martini'	CB&S CDoC CTrC CTrG IOrc SOWG WWeb
– 'McLean'	ECou
– (Nanum Group) 'Huia'	CB&S ECou ENot IOrc
– – 'Kea'	ECou ESis GQui WPyg
– – 'Kiwi' ♀	CB&S ELan ENot EWes GOrc
	GQui IOrc ISea ITim MAll
	MAsh MDun NHol WLRN
	WPat WPyg
– – 'Kotuku'	EPot
– – 'Nanum'	SBod SHBN SIng
– – 'Pipit'	EPot EWes
– – 'Tui'	CTrC MAll
– 'Nichollsii' ♀	CB&S CGre CHan CMHG CTri
	ENot GQui ITim SOWG WHar
	WSHC
– 'Nichollsii Nanum' ♀	CMea EPot ITim NHol NSla
	SIng WAbe WPat WPyg
– 'Pink Cascade'	CB&S CBlo CTri IOrc MAll
	MBal SAga
– var. *prostratum* hort.	See *L. rupestre*
– 'Red Damask' (d) ♀	CB&S CChe CGre CLan CTrC
	CTre ELan GQui IOrc LHop
	MAll MAsh SBod SHBN
	SOWG SRms WDin WSHC
	WStI WWeb
– 'Red Ensign'	MAll SBod

– 'Red Falls'	CDoC ECou MAll SOWG
– 'Redpoll'	ECou
– 'Robin'	ECou
– 'Rosy Morn'	ISea
– 'Ruby Glow' (d)	LRHS WBod
* – 'Silver Spire'	SOWG
– 'Snow Flurry'	CB&S CTrC ENot GOrc ISea
	MAll SSte WDin WWeb
– 'Sunraysia'	CDoC CTrw LBlm MAll
– 'Winter Cheer'	CB&S
sphaerocarpum	MAll
squarrosum	CTrC MAll
trinervium	MAll

LESCHENAULTIA (Goodeniaceae) See Plant Deletions

LESPEDEZA (Papilionaceae)

bicolor	CAgr CB&S CTrC CWit EHal
	GOrc WFar
buergeri	ELan LRHS MAsh SMur SSta
floribunda	CPle WSHC
hedysaroides	See *L. juncea*
sp. from Yakushima	MPla
thunbergii ♀	CB&S ELan EMil LHop LPan
	MAsh MBlu MGos MWhi NFla
	SBid SMad SOWG SPer SSpi
	SSta WDin WFar WSHC
– 'Albiflora'	WThi
* – 'Variegata'	LRHS
tiliifolia	See *Desmodium elegans*

LESQUERELLA (Brassicaceae)

alpina	NWCA
arctica var. *purshii*	WPat

LEUCADENDRON (Proteaceae)

argenteum	CBrP CHEx SIgm
comosum	CTrC
¶ *galpinii*	CTrC
¶ *laureolum*	CTrC
salicifolium	CTrC
¶ *salignum*	CTrC
tinctum	CTrC

LEUCAENA (Mimosaceae)

leucocephala	See *L. latisiliqua*

LEUCANTHEMELLA (Asteraceae)

§ *serotina* ♀	CBre CGle CHan CHea CSev
	ECGP ECha EJud ELan EMFP
	EMan GAbr GMaP LCot LFis
	LGan MBrN MHlr MLLN MSte
	NSti SHel SPer WEas WHoo
	WOve WWin

LEUCANTHEMOPSIS (Asteraceae)

§ *alpina*	GCrs LBee MDHE SSpi
hosmariensis	See *Rhodanthemum*
	hosmariense
§ *pectinata*	LBee NSla WLin
– JCA 627.801	CPBP
radicans	See *L. pectinata*

LEUCANTHEMUM † (Asteraceae)

atlanticum	See *Pyrethropsis atlantica*
catananche	See *Pyrethropsis catananche*
'Fringe Benefit'	EMon NPer
hosmariense	See *Rhodanthemum*
	hosmariense
mawii	See *Rhodanthemum gayanum*

¶ *maximum*	MWgw
§ – (Ramond) DC	CBlo GAbr GCHN NBro NPer
	NVic WBea WByw WCer
	WOak WWin
– *uliginosum*	See *Leucanthemella serotina*
nipponicum	See *Nipponanthemum*
	nipponicum
* 'Schneehurka'	SAsh
§ × *superbum*	MNrw
– 'Aglaia' (d) ♀	CBos CMil CRDP EMon EWes
	GBri LFis LRHS MAus MBel
	MCLN MHlr MLLN MTed
	MTis NPer NVic SChu SUsu
	WCot WHoo WLin WRHF
– 'Alaska'	CDoC EMan MAus NFai NOak
	SPer SRCN WPer WViv WWal
¶ – 'Amelia'	NCut
– 'Anita Allen'	CMil MAvo WCot
– 'Antwerp Star'	MFir NCat
– 'Beauté Nivelloise'	CHea CMil ECha LFis MAvo
	MBel WCot WPer WRHF
	WRha
– 'Bishopstone'	CBre CDec CMGP CMil ELan
	MRav NCat SCou WEas
– 'Christine Hagemann'	LRHS MBri MRav NHaw
– 'Cobham Gold' (d)	CBre CElw CMil ECha EREa
	GBuc NFla NOrc SHel WMaN
– 'Coconut Ice'	EWll GAbr WPer
¶ – 'Droitwich Beauty'	WSPU
– 'Esther Read' (d)	CBlo CGle CM&M CMCo
	CMdw EAst ECED ELan
	EMan EREa EWes LFis MFir
	NFla NRoo SRms SWat WByw
– 'Everest'	EMan NOak SRms
– 'Fiona Coghill'	CElw EBee GBri IBlr LFis MFir
	MLLN NBrk WCot WLin
– 'H. Seibert'	CMil CSam ECED MArl
– 'Horace Read' (d)	CHea CMGP CMil CSev ECED
	ECha ELan EMan EMon EREa
	LFis NPer WEas WPer
– 'Jennifer Read'	EREa
– 'John Murray'	WAbb
– 'Little Miss Muffet'	LRHS
– 'Little Princess'	See *L.* × *superbum*
	'Silberprinzesschen'
– 'Manhattan'	CMGP EMon GBuc NCat
– 'Mayfield Giant'	WPer
– 'Mount Everest'	CBlo EGar SRms WCot
– 'Phyllis Smith'	CGle CHea CMdw CVer ECha
	EGar EJud EMan GAbr LFis
	MAvo MBel MBri MTis NFai
	NPla SHel SSvw WAbb WBea
	WFar WLin
– 'Polaris'	NFai NOak WHer
¶ – 'Rheinblick'	NCut WLRN
¶ – 'Rijnsburg Glory'	SGre
¶ – 'Schwabengruss'	CStr
– 'Shaggy'	CBos CVer GMaP LFis MLLN
	NFla NRoo SWat WRHF
§ – 'Silberprinzesschen'	CDoC CMea GAbr GBur MFir
	NHol NMir NOak NPri NRoo
	SRms SSea WBea WCot WHen
	WPer
– 'Snow Lady'	GCHN NMir NPer NRoo SHel
	WFar WHen
– 'Snowcap'	CBlo EBrP EBre ECha EGar
	EHic EMan ENot EPla GAri
	LBre MBri MOne NFla NLon
	SBre SMrm SPer SUsu WLRN
	WMow

§ – 'Sonnenschein'   CElw CHea CPou CSam EBee
ECha EFou EGar EMan EMon
GBuc LRHS MArl MAus
MAvo MBel MBri MBro MHlr
NBrk NFai SChu SMrm SUsu
WBea WCot WHoo
– 'Starburst' (d)   EFou EMan MBri NRoo SHel
SRms WHen
– 'Summer Snowball'   CElw EBrP EBre EWes LBre
MBri NCat SBre SHel WCot
WFar
– Sunshine   See **L.** × **superbum**
'Sonnenschein'
¶ – 'Supra'   SGre
– 'T.E. Killin' (d) ♀   CGle ECha EJud EMon MAus
MAvo
– 'White Iceberg'   MAvo WPer
§ – 'Wirral Supreme' (d) ♀   Widely available
'Tizi-n-Test'   See **Rhodanthemum gayanum**
'Tizi-n-Test'
§ **vulgare**   CArn CKin ECoo EPar EWFC
MHew MMal NLan NMir WCla
WHen WHer WJek WOak
WWye
– 'Avondale'   MAvo MCCP
– 'Hullavington' (v)   CNat
§ – 'Maikönigin'   GCal NCut NSti WRHF
¶ – 'Maistern'   MBro
– May Queen   See **L. vulgare 'Maikönigin'**
* – 'Sunny'   CBre
– 'Woodpecker's'   WCot

LEUCOCHRYSUM (Asteraceae)
¶ **albicans**   EBee

LEUCOCORYNE (Alliaceae)
coquimbensis   CMon
ixioides   LBow
– **alba**   CMon

LEUCOGENES (Asteraceae)
acklandii   GCLN NHar NSla
grandiceps   GCLN GCrs GTou ITim NHar
NSla SBla WAbe WLin
leontopodium   EPot GCLN GGar GTou ITim
NHar NMen NRoo NSla WAbe
¶ **tarahaoa**   EPot

LEUCOJUM † (Amaryllidaceae)
aestivum   CB&S CBlo CFee GBur LAma
MBri NEgg MGW NMen
NRog SRms WAbe WCla WEas
WGwy WHil WHoo WShi
– 'Gravetye Giant' ♀   CAvo CBro CHad ECha ELan
EMar EPar EPot ERav ETub
LAma LFox LHop MAus MBro
MRav NFla NRog SIng WAbb
WPGP
autumnale ♀   CAvo CBro CFee CLyd CRDP
EBrP EBre EHyt ELan ERos
ESis EWes ITim LAma LBee
LBow LBre MFos MHig MTho
NMen SBre SRms SSpi SWas
WHoo WOMN
– 'Cobb's Variety'   GCal LHop WCot
– var. **oporanthum**   CMon EPot NRog
– var. **pulchellum**   CBro CMon EPot
nicaeense ♀   CBro CGra CLyd CRDP EBur
EHyt EPot GCrs LHop MFos
MHig MTho NMen SSpi WAbe
WOMN

roseum   CLyd EBur EHyt EPot LAma
SWas
tingitanum   CMon
trichophyllum   CBro CMon ERos
– **purpurascens**   EPot
valentinum   CAvo CBro CMon
vernum ♀   CBro ELan EMon EPar ETub
GCrs GDra LAma MBri MNrw
MRav NMGW NMen SRms
WAbe WBod WFar WHil
WPGP WShi
– var. **carpathicum**   ECha EMon EPot LAma MRav
– var. **vagneri**   CMea ECha LFox

LEUCOPHYTA (Asteraceae)
§ **brownii**   CInt ECou LHil MBEx MRav
SVen

LEUCOPOGON (Epacridaceae)
ericoides   MBar WPat
§ **fasciculatus**   ECou
§ **fraseri**   ECou WAbe
parviflorus   See **Cyathodes parviflora**

× LEUCORAOULIA (Asteraceae)
§ **loganii**   EPot GDra ITim MHig NHar
NWCA WAbe

LEUCOSCEPTRUM (Lamiaceae)
stellipilum formosanum   WCru
B&SWJ 1804

LEUCOSIDEA (Rosaceae)
¶ **sericea**   CTrC

LEUCOSPERMUM (Proteaceae) See Plant
Deletions

LEUCOTHOE (Ericaceae)
¶ **axillaris** 'Royal Red'   WLRN
◆ – 'Scarletta'   See **L.** Scarletta = **'Zeblid'**
carinella   LRHS MBri MGos
catesbyi   GCHN
davisiae   GGGa MBal
fontanesiana   See **L. walteri**
grayana   MBal
keiskei   EPfP MAsh WAbe
– 'Royal Ruby'   MAsh SEas WDin WWeb
populifolia   See **Agarista populifolia**
◆ Scarletta   See **L.** Scarletta = **'Zeblid'**
§ **walteri** ♀   EHic MBal MGos STre WStI
WWat
– Lovita®   GCal MBri MRav NHol SBid
SSta
– 'Nana'   MAsh
– 'Rainbow'   CB&S CLan ELan EMil ENot
GRei IOrc LHop LNet MAsh
MBal MBar MGos NBee NHol
SHBN SPer SReu SSta WDin
WWal WWeb
– 'Rollissonii' ♀   MBal MBar SPla SReu SRms
SSta WBod
§ Scarletta® = 'Zeblid'   CB&S CHig CMHG COtt CSam
EBrP EBre ELan EMil IOrc
LBre LBuc LHop MAsh MBal
MBar MBri MGos NHol SBre
SPer SPla SReu SSta SSto SVil
WDin WFar WHar WWeb

LEUZEA (Asteraceae)

§ *centauroides*	CGle EBrP EBre ECED ECha EGle ELan EMan GCal LBre LGre MBro MFir NWoo SBre WByw WOMN
¶ *conifera*	NWCA
– *macrocephala*	WAbe
§ *rhapontica*	EMan

LEVISTICUM (Apiaceae)

officinale	CAgr CArn CSev ECha EJud ELan ELau GPoy LHol MBar MChe MHew SDix SIde SWat WHer WMow WOak WPer WWye

LEWISIA † (Portulacaceae)

'Archangel'	NRya
¶ 'Ashwood Carousel Hybrids'	MAsh
'Ashwood Pearl'	MAsh
'Ben Chace'	MAsh
Birch strain	CB&S ECho ELan SIng
brachycalyx ♀	CGra EWes GTou ITim MAsh MBal MTho NGre NHar NNrd NWCA SIng WLRN
cantelovii	CPBP MAsh NGre
columbiana	EHyt GTou MAsh MDHE NGre NHar NTow SIng
– 'Alba'	CLAP EHyt GCHN GDra MAsh
– 'Edithiae'	MFos
– 'Rosea'	CMea GCrs MAsh NGre SIng WAbe WGor
– subsp. *rupicola*	GCHN MAsh MFos NGre NNrd NWCA WGor
– subsp. *wallowensis*	CGra EHyt EPot MAsh NMen WGor
congdonii	MAsh NGre WAbe
cotyledon ♀	CPla ESis MAsh MNrw MOne NNrd NWCA WBrE WPat
– f. *alba*	CLyd CPla EHyt EPot ESis GDra GTou LHop MAsh MBro NGre NWCA SBla WAbe WCla WHoo WPyg
– Ashwood Ruby Group	CLAP MAsh NHar
– Ashwood strain	CNic EBrP EBre EHyt ESis EWes LBee LBre MAsh MBri MOne NRoo NRya NSla SBre SIng SRms WAbe WGor WHoo WPyg
– Crags hybrids	NCLN
– var. *heckneri* ♀	GDra MAsh WGor
– – JCA 11031	CLAP
– var. *howellii*	CPla ELan SRms WGor
– hybrids	CFee CGra CMHG CNic EMMN EPot GDra GTou ITim LHop MBro MFos NGre NHar NMen WAbe WGor WLin WWin
– J&JA 12959	NWCA
– 'John's Special'	CLAP GCHN GCrs GDra
– magenta strain	MAsh WGor WPyg
– 'Rose Splendour'	ELan EPar MAsh WGor
– 'Sundance'	GDra
– Sunset Group ♀	ELan GAbr GCHN GDra MBal MBri NGre NHar WCla WPer
– 'White Splendour'	MAsh SIng WGor
'George Henley'	CLAP EBrP EBre EHyt EPot EWes LBre LHop MAsh NHed NMen NNrd NRya SBre SIng SRms WAbe

* 'Holly'	MDHE
¶ 'Joyce Halley'	GCrs
leana	EHyt MAsh SIng WGor
'Little Plum'	GCHN
longifolia	See *L. cotyledon* var. *cotyledon*
§ *longipetala*	GCHN GCrs GDra GTou MAsh MOne NGre NRya NTow NWCA WAbe
– × *cotyledon*	GTou
* *longiscapa*	MAsh NGre
§ *nevadensis*	CMea CNic CPla EHyt ELan EPot ERos ESis GCHN GDra GTou ITim MAsh MBri MBro MNrw MTho NGre NMen NNrd NWCA WAbe WCla WLin WPer WPyg
– *bernardina*	See *L. nevadensis*
– 'Rosea'	WAbe
oppositifolia	EHyt MAsh NNrd WGor
– J&JA 13450	NWCA
'Phyllellia'	MAsh
'Pinkie'	CLAP CPBP EPot GCrs MAsh MBro MDHE NMen NNrd
pygmaea	CGra CNic EHyt EPot ESis EWes GCHN GTou ITim MAsh MBri NBir NGre NHar NNrd NWCA WAbe WPer
– subsp. *longipetala*	See *L. longipetala*
¶ – 'Whiskey Peak'	NNrd
rediviva	CGra CLAP EWes GCHN GCrs GTou ITim MAsh MFos NGre NHar NRya NSla NWCA WAbe WLin
– Jolon strain	MAsh WGor
– subsp. *minor*	CGra EPot NMen WAbe
– white	MAsh NGre NWCA
'Regensbergen'	WPer
serrata	CGra MAsh NGre
sierrae	GCLN MAsh MBro NGre NMen NNrd SIng WGor
'Trevosia'	EHyt MAsh MDHE MHig SIng
triphylla	MAsh NGre NNrd NWCA
tweedyi ♀	CLAP CPBP EBrP EBre EHyt EWes GCrs GDra GTou LBre LHop MAsh MOne NGre NHar NWCA SBre SIng SRms WAbe WGor
– 'Alba'	CLAP EHyt GDra MAsh NGre NWCA WGor
– 'Elliott's Variety'	MAsh WGor
– 'Rosea'	GDra MAsh NGre WAbe WGor WLin

LEYCESTERIA (Caprifoliaceae)

crocothyrsos	CAbb CGre CHEx CInt CPle GQui WLRN WRHF WWat
formosa	Widely available

LEYMUS (Poaceae)

§ *arenarius*	CCuc CElw CHan CInt ECha EHoe ELan EOrc EPla ESOG GCHN GCal MAvo MBar MLLN MUlv MWhi NBro NFai NSti SDix SMad SPar SSoC WRus WWat
hispidus	See *Elymus hispidus*
mollis	EBee
§ *racemosus*	MMHG

LHOTZKYA See CALYTRIX

LIATRIS (Asteraceae)

aspera	EBee EMan SIgm
¶ *elegans*	WHil
ligulistylis	EMan SIgm WCot
pycnostachya	CMil CPea EBar ECro EMon
	GMac MLLN SRCN SRms
	WPer WRHF
scariosa 'Magnifica'	CB&S
¶ – 'September Glory'	WViv
§ *spicata*	Widely available
– 'Alba'	CHor ECha ECro EFou ELan
	GGar LAma LBow LHol MBel
	NFai SDeJ SPer WFox WHoo
	WPer
– *callilepis*	See *L. spicata*
– 'Floristan Violett'	CBlo CSam EAst EPfP GAbr
	GCHN GMac NPri NRoo SCoo
	SMer SUsu WFar WLRN WPer
– 'Floristan Weiss'	CArn CBlo CMGP CSam EAst
	EBrP EBre ELau EMan GAbr
	GBuc GCHN LBre MRav MTis
	NOak NRoo SBre SCro SMrm
	WLRN WPer WWin
– Goblin	See *L. spicata* **'Kobold'**
§ – 'Kobold'	CB&S CBlo CHan CSam ECED
	ECtt EMan ENot EPfP GMac
	MBri MRav NLak NRoo SPla
	SSea WHil WHoo WMer WPer

LIBERTIA (Iridaceae)

'Amazing Grace'	IBlr SAxl SLod SMrm
'Ballyrogan Blue'	IBlr
Ballyrogan hybrid	IBlr
* *breunioides*	IBlr
caerulescens	CAbb CHan CLTr CPou ECro
	GBin IBlr MHar NBir NChi
	WOMN WPic WSan WWhi
chilensis	See *L. formosa*
elegans	GBuc IBlr
§ *formosa*	Widely available
– brown-stemmed form	IBlr
– form	IBlr LBlm
grandiflora	CAbb CB&S CDoC CElw
	CHEx CHan ECha ECro ELan
	EPla GAbr GCHN GCal GMac
	IBlr LRot MBel MFir MNrw
	NCat NFai SLPl SMad SPer
	WAbe WBod WCru WPer
ixioides	CAvo CGle CSam ECou EGoo
	GGar IBlr MFir WPyg WRHF
– 'Tricolor'	IBlr
'Nelson Dwarf'	ECou IBlr
paniculata	CHan IBlr
peregrinans	CAbb CElw CFee CHan EBrP
	EBre ECha EMan EPla ESis
	GCal IBlr LBre MFir SBre
	SChu SUsu WAbe WHal WThi
– East Cape form	IBlr
– 'Gold Leaf'	CB&S IBlr SOkh
* *procera*	CHan IBlr
pulchella	CGle GBin IBlr
sessiliflora	CFee IBlr NBir
– RB 94073	CNic MNrw SMad
Shackleton hybrid	IBlr
¶ *tricolor*	GBuc
* *umbellata*	IBlr

LIBOCEDRUS (Cupressaceae)

chilensis	See *Austrocedrus chilensis*
decurrens	See *Calocedrus decurrens*

LIBONIA See JUSTICIA

LICUALA (Arecaceae)

grandis	MBri
¶ *spinosa*	LPal

LIGULARIA † (Asteraceae)

alatipes	GBin
¶ *altaica*	EBee
amplexicaulis	GCra IBlr
calthifolia	CRow EBee GCal
clivorum	See *L. dentata*
§ *dentata*	CHEx CHan CRow EGar NBro
	SPla SRms SWat WCru WOld
	GSki
– 'Dark Beauty'	GSki
– 'Desdemona' ♀	Widely available
– 'Orange Princess'	EBee NPer WPer
– 'Othello'	CBlo CRow EAst EBee EGar
	EMan GBur IBlr MBal MBri
	NCut SCro SMad SSpe SWat
	WCot WHil WMer
¶ – 'Ox-eye'	WGer
– 'Rubrifolia'	GDra
– 'Sommergold'	ECha EGar IBlr
fischeri	EGar GCal GCra WCot
– B&SWJ 2570	WCru
– B&SWJ 606a	WCru
glabrescens	CRow
§ 'Gregynog Gold' ♀	CBlo CHad CRow EAst EBrP
	EBre ECha EGol EOld GMaP
	IBlr LBlm LBre MBri MRav
	NBro NDea NOrc SBre SChu
	SCro SMrm SPer WCru WHoo
	WMer WMow WOld WPyg
× *hessei*	CRow ECha EGar GAri GMaP
	SWat WCot WFar
hodgsonii	EBrP EBre EGar IBlr LBre
	MBri MNrw NMGW SBre
	WCru WMer WOld WPer
japonica	CRow ECha EGar
macrophylla	CHan CRow WFar
oblongata	See *Cremanthodium*
	oblongatum
× *palmatiloba*	CFir EBrP EBre ECha EGar
	EGol EPar GCal IBlr LBre
	MCli NDea NOak NSti NWes
	SBre SCro SWat WCot
§ *przewalskii*	Widely available
reniformis	See *Cremanthodium reniforme*
sachalinensis	GBin GCal WCot
sibirica	WCot
smithii	See *Senecio smithii*
¶ sp. B&SWJ 2977	WCru
¶ sp. from Nepal HWJCM 211	WCru
* *speciosa*	ECha EGar
stenocephala	CBlo CHEx EGar EGol EMil
	IBlr LFis MSCN NBro NDea
	WCot
– B&SWJ 283	WCru
tangutica	See *Sinacalia tangutica*
'The Rocket' ♀	Widely available
¶ *tsangchanensis*	EBee
tussilaginea	See *Farfugium japonicum*
veitchiana	CHan CRow EGar EOas GCal
	GDra IBlr MSte NDea SWat
	WCot WCru
'Weihenstephan'	IBlr LRHS MBri WGer WMer
wilsoniana	CHan CRow EBee EBrP EBre
	ECtt EGar EGos LBre MAus
	MCli MLLN MRav NCut SBre
	WFar
'Zepter'	EGar GBuc

LIGUSTICUM (Apiaceae)

lucidum	EHol IIve MSal SIgm WCwm
porteri	MSal
scoticum	EOHP GBar GPoy ILis LHol
	MHew MSal NLak

LIGUSTRUM † (Oleaceae)

◆ *chenaultii*	See *L. compactum*
§ *compactum*	CDoC CFai WWat
delavayanum	CB&S ERom GAri LPan SAPC
	SArc WWat
japonicum	ENot SMur WCwm WDin
	WWat
– 'Coriaceum'	See *L. japonicum*
	'Rotundifolium'
§ – 'Rotundifolium'	CDec CDoC CHEx CPle CTrC
	EMil EPfP LNet MTed SBid
	SMad SPer
* – 'Silver Star'	CPMA
§ – 'Texanum'	CDec LPan
* – 'Texanum Argenteum'	LPan
lucidum ♀	CDoC CHEx CPle ELan ELau
	ENot IOrc MGos SAPC SArc
	SMad SPer SSpi WDin WWat
– 'Excelsum Superbum'	CAbP CEnd CPMA ELan EPfP
(v) ♀	LPan MAsh MBar MGos MMea
	SPer SPla SSpi WWat
– 'Golden Wax'	MRav WBcn
– 'Tricolor' (v)	CPMA ELan EPfP IOrc MAsh
	MBal SHBN SPer SPla SSpi
	WWat
obtusifolium 'Dart's Elite'	SLPl
ovalifolium	CB&S CChe CDoC CLnd CPer
	CTri EBrP EBre GChr GRei
	ISea LBre LBuc LPan MBar
	MBri MGos NBee NNor NWea
	SBre SPer WDin WGwG WMou
	WWal
§ – 'Argenteum' (v)	CB&S CDoC CGle EHoe ISea
	LBuc MBar MBri NBee NFla
	NHol SPer SPla WFar WWin
– 'Aureomarginatum'	See *L. ovalifolium* **'Aureum'**
§ – 'Aureum' (v) ♀	Widely available
* – 'Lemon and Lime' (v)	SPla
– 'Taff's Indecision' (v)	CPMA
– 'Variegatum'	See *L. ovalifolium* **'Argenteum'**
quihoui ♀	CFai CHan CMHG EHol ELan
	EPfP MGos SDix SPer SSpi
	WHCG WPat WWat
sempervirens B&L 12033	EPla
sinense	CHan CMCN MRav WWat
– 'Midsummer Lady'	LRHS
– 'Multiflorum'	WWat
– 'Pendulum'	EPla NHol
– 'Variegatum'	CMHG CPMA CPle EBar EHic
	SBid SPla WWat
– 'Wimbei'	CPMA CPle EPla ESis NPro
	SSpi WWat
texanum	See *L. japonicum* **'Texanum'**
tschonoskii	CBlo SLPl SMad
'Vicaryi'	CBlo CPMA EAst EBrP EBre
	ELan EPla LBre MAsh MBar
	NHol NPro SBre SPer WBay
	WPyg WWat
vulgare	CCVT CKin CPer CTri EBrP
	EBre ENot EWFC GRei LBre
	LBuc NWea SBre WDin WHer
	WMou
– 'Lodense'	SLPl
– variegated	WWat

LILAEOPSIS (Apiaceae) See Plant Deletions

LILIUM (Liliaceae)

'Acapulco' (VIId)	CB&S LAma
African Queen Group	CB&S EBrP EBre ECot LAma
(VIa)	LBre NRog SBre SDeJ SMad
	SRms
◆ *albanicum*	See *L. pyrenaicum* subsp.
	carniolicum var. *albanicum*
'Alliance' (VII)	CB&S
amabile	CLAP
'Angela North' (Ic)	WFar
'Anton Geesink'	CB&S
'Apeldoorn' (Ie)	LAma SCoo
¶ 'Aphrodite' (Ia)	NBir
'Apollo' (Ia)	CB&S CHar ETub LAma MBri
	SDeJ
'Aristo'	See *L.* **'Orange Aristo'**
* Asiatic hybrids (VI/VII)	LAma SDeJ
'Attila' (Ib)	SDeJ
auratum	CB&S EFEx LAma SDeJ
– 'Crimson Beauty' (IX)	LAma
– 'Gold Band'	See *L. auratum* var.
	platyphyllum
§ – var. *platyphyllum* (IX)	CB&S GCra
♀	
– var. *virginale*	ETub
'Avignon' (Ia)	LAma
'Barcelona' (Ia)	ETub MNrw
¶ 'Batist' (Ia)	LAma
'Bel Ami'	CB&S
Bellingham Group (IV) ♀	SSpi
'Bellona' (Ia)	NRog
'Berlin' (VIId)	CB&S
'Black Beauty' (VIId)	CB&S CLAP LAma
'Black Dragon' (VIa) ♀	LAma
Black Magic Group (VIa)	SDeJ
bolanderi (IX)	MSto
'Bonfire' (VIIb)	SDeJ
'Brandywine' (Ib)	WRHF
'Bright Star' (VIb)	EBrP EBre ETub LAma LBre
	SBre SDeJ
brownii	EFEx
'Buff Pixie' (Ia)	CB&S ETub LAma
bulbiferum	CLAP ETub GCrs MSto SIng
'Bums' (Ia)	EMon
'Butter Pixie' (Ia)	CB&S LAma
§ *canadense*	GGGa LAma MBal NRog SDeJ
	SSpi
– var. *editorum*	CLAP LAma
– var. *flavum*	See *L. canadense*
candidum ♀	CArn CAvo CB&S CBro CGle
	CHEx CSWP EBrP EBre ECha
	ELan ETub GAbr GCra LAma
	LBre MBri NRog SBre SDeJ
	SIgm
– 'Plenum' (d)	EMon
'Capitol' (VII)	CB&S
'Carmen' (VIIc)	CB&S
◆ *carniolicum*	See *L. pyrenaicum* subsp.
	carniolicum
'Casa Blanca' (VIIb) ♀	CB&S CBro EBrP EBre ETub
	LAma LBre NRog SBre SDeJ
	SMad
'Casa Rosa'	CB&S CSWP NBir SWat
§ Golden Pixie = 'Ceb	CB&S
Golden' (Ia)	
cernuum	SDeJ
chalcedonicum ♀	CLAP
'Charisma' (Ia)	MBri
'Chinook' (Ia)	NRog
Citronella Group (Ic)	CAvo LAma NRog
columbianum (IX)	MSto
'Concorde' (Ia)	SDeJ

'Connecticut King' (Ia) — CB&S CBro EBrP EBre ETub LAma LBre MHlr NBrk NRog SAga SBre SDeJ

'Corina' (Ia) — CB&S CHar MBri NCat SDeJ

'Corsage' (Ib) — NRog

'Côte d'Azur' (Ia) — CB&S CBro EBrP EBre ETub LAma LBre NCat SBre SDeJ

'Crimson Pixie' (Ia) — CB&S

× **dalhansonii** — CLAP

§ – 'Marhan' (II) ♀ — LAma

¶ 'Dame Blanche' (VII) — LAma

¶ 'Dandy' (Ia) — WWeb

'Darling' (VII) — CB&S

§ **dauricum** — CPou

§ **davidii** var. **willmottiae** (IX) — EPot SRms

'Delta' — See *L. leichtlinii* 'Delta'

'Denia' (Ib) — CB&S LRHS

'Destiny' (Ia) — NRog

¶ 'Devon Early Gems' — CLAP

'Dominique' (VII) — NRog

duchartrei — CBro GCrs LAma SMac WAbe

§ 'Ed' (VII) — LAma

'Electric' (Ia) — CB&S LAma

'Elfin Sun' — CB&S LAma LRHS

'Elite' — See *L.* 'Gibraltar'

'Elvin's Son' — CB&S

'Elysee' — CB&S

'Enchantment' (Ia) ♀ — CB&S LAma MBri MHlr NRog SDeJ WLRN

'Esperanto' — CB&S

'Exception' (Ib) — LAma

'Festival' (Ia) — CB&S LAma

'Fire King' (Ib) — CB&S LAma NRog SDeJ SRms

formosanum — NBro NGre WCot WSan

– B&SWJ 1589 — WCru

– var. **formosanum** — NBro

– var. **pricei** (IX) ♀ — CGle CGra CInt CMea CSWP ELan ITim LBee LGre LHop LSyl MBal MBri MFir MHlr MNrw MSto MTho NChi NMen NNrd NWCA NWoo SAga SBla WAbe WHer WPer WPyg

¶ – 'White Swan' — GCrs

'Fresco' (VII) — CB&S

'Friendship' (VII) — CB&S

'Furore' (VIIc) — CB&S

'Geisha' (VII) — CB&S

'Golden Melody' (Ia) — CB&S LSyl

♦ Golden Pixie — See *L.* Golden Pixie = 'Ceb Golden' (Ia)

Golden Splendor Group (VIa) — ETub LAma NRog SWat

'Gran Cru' (Ia) — CB&S

'Gran Paradiso' (Ia) — CB&S LAma

'Grand Cru' — CSut LAma SDeJ

hansonii ♀ — IBlr LAma NRog

Harlequin Group (Ic) — SDeJ

henryi ♀ — CAvo CB&S CSWP LAma LBow MAvo MLLN NRog SDeJ SSoC WCot

¶ 'Hit Parade' (VII) — LAma

Imperial Silver Group (VIIc) — CB&S LAma

japonicum — EFEx

'Jetfire' (Ia) — CB&S SDeJ

'John Dix' (Ib) — ETub

'Journey's End' (VIId) — CB&S CHar ETub GBur LAma MAvo MLLN NRog SDeJ

§ 'Joy' (VIIb) — LAma

§ **kelleyanum** — CLAP GGGa

kelloggii — MSto

'King Pete' (Ib) — NOak SCoo SDeJ

'Kiss Proof' (VIIb) — CB&S

¶ 'Kyoto' (VIId) — LAma

¶ 'Lady Alice' (VI) — CLAP

'Lady Ann' (VIb) — SDeJ

'Ladykiller' (Ia) — NRog

§ **lancifolium** — CLTr EMFP LAma LBow MHar MHlr SDeJ WRHF

¶ – B&SWJ 539 — WCru

– 'Flore Pleno' (IX) (d) — CMil CSWP EMFP EMar EMon EPot GCal GSki IBlr MHar NSti WCot WFar WHal

– Forrest's form — IBlr

§ – var. **splendens** (IX) — CBro EBot EMon LAma LBow MLLN SDeJ

lankongense — GCrs NPro

– ACE 2210 — EPot

'Le Rêve' — See *L.* 'Joy'

'Lemon Pixie' (Ia) — LAma LRHS

¶ **leucanthum** — LAma

'Liberation' (I) — CB&S NBir

'Limelight' (VIa) ♀ — LAma

¶ 'Little Kiss' (Ia) — SCoo

'Little Snow White' (V) — WHer

longiflorum (IX) ♀ — CAvo CB&S LAma MAvo MHlr NRog WCot

– 'Gelria' (IX) — SDeJ

– 'White American' (IX) — CB&S CBro CSWP MBri

lophophorum ACE 1767 — EHyt EPot GCLN

'Lovely Girl' (VIIb) — ETub

'Luxor' (Ib) — CSut NBir NCat

mackliniae ♀ — CBos ECha EHyt GBuc GCra GGGa GTou IBlr MBal MSto NHar SBla SSpi WAbe

maculatum var. **davuricum** — See *L. dauricum*

– **monticola** — EHyt

¶ 'Marco Polo' (Ia) — LAma

'Marhan' — See *L.* × **dalhansonii** 'Marhan'

× **marhan** 'J.S. Dijt' — See *L.* 'Jacques S. Dijt'

martagon — CArn CAvo CB&S CBro CMea EBot ECha EFou EMon ETub LAma LBow MBal NBir NPSI NRog SDeJ WAbe WGwy WShi WWat

– var. **album** (IX) ♀ — CAvo CB&S CBro CMea CPou EBot ECGP EFou ETub LAma MFir MHlr MRav MTho SDeJ WAbe

– var. **cattaniae** (IX) ♀ — EMon

– 'Netherhall Pink' (IX/d) — EMon

– 'Netherhall White' (IX/d) — EMon

– 'Plenum' (IX) (d) — EMon

'Mecca' — CB&S

'Medaillon' (Ia) — LAma NRog

medeoloides — EFEx

michiganense — GCrs

'Milano' (Ia) — CB&S

'Miss America' — LRHS

¶ 'Miss Burma' (VII) — LRHS

¶ 'Miss Rio' (VII) — SCoo

'Mona Lisa' (VIIb/d) — CB&S ETub LAma LRHS MBri SCoo

§ **monadelphum** ♀ — CBro LAma MHar NRog SIgm

'Mont Blanc' (Ia) — CB&S CBro ETub LAma MLLN NBir SDeJ

'Monte Rosa' (Ic) — SDeJ

'Montreux' (Ia) — CB&S LAma LSyl NCat

'Moonflower' (Ia) — CB&S

'Moulin Rouge' (Ib) — NRog

◆ 'Mr Ed' See *L.* **'Ed'**
'Mr Ruud' See *L.* **'Ruud'**
'Muscadet' (VII) CSut
§ *nanum* EHyt GCLN GCrs GGGa MSto
  NRog NSla WAbe
– var. *flavidum* (IX) EHyt EPot
¶ – from Bhutan WCru
¶ – Kirkpatrick 242 GCrs
– 'Len's Lilac' (IX) EHyt
nepalense CBro CFir CLAP CSWP GCrs
  LAma NRog SBla SDeJ SSpi
  WCru
¶ – B&SWJ 2985 WCru
'New Yellow' MBri
¶ 'Nippon' (VIId) CSut
nobilissimum EFEx
'Olivia' (Ia) CHar ETub LAma MLLN SDeJ
Olympic Group (VIa) LAma SDeJ
'Omega' (VII) CB&S LAma SDeJ
§ 'Orange Aristo' (Ia) MBri
¶ 'Orange Delight' WWeb
'Orange Pixie' (Ia) EBrP EBre LAma LBre LRHS
  MBri SBre
'Orange Triumph' (Ia) LAma
'Orchid Beauty' (Ia) MBri
oxypetalum GGGa
– var. *insigne* (IX) EHyt EPot GCLN GDra GGGa
  LAma NHar NSla NTow SSpi
  WAbe WCru
'Pandora' (Ia) CB&S
pardalinum CAvo CGle CMea ELan MSto
  NSla
– var. *giganteum* (IX) ♀ CLAP GBur
parryi WAbe
¶ 'Peach Pixie' (Ia) LAma NBir
'Peachblush' (Ia) CB&S
¶ 'Perugia' (VIId) LAma
philadelphicum CGra MSto
philippinense EGar NTow
¶ – B&SWJ 4000 WCru
Pink Perfection Group CAvo CB&S CBro EBrP EBre
  (VIa) ♀ LAma LBre NRog SBre SWat
¶ 'Pink Pixie' (Ia) NCat
I 'Pink Regale' CSut
'Pink Sunburst' (VId) SDeJ
'Pink Tiger' (Ib) CB&S CBro
'Pirate' (Ia) LAma
pitkinense EMon
¶ 'Polka' WWeb
pomponium CLAP MSto SIng
'Prominence' See *L.* **'Firebrand'**
§ *pumilum* ♀ CAvo CBro CLAP EBrP EBre
  EHyt ETub LAma LBre MLLN
  MSto MTho NBir SBre SDeJ
pyrenaicum ♀ CBro CMea ELan GDra MSto
  WByw WCot WOMN WRha
  WShi
– var. *aureum* See *L. pyrenaicum* var.
  pyrenaicum
¶ – var. *rubrum* (IX) MAvo
– yellow See *L. pyrenaicum* var.
  pyrenaicum
'Red Carpet' (Ia) CB&S CBro ETub MBri NBir
  NCat
Red Jewels Group (Ic) LAma
Red Knight See *L.* **'Roter Cardinal'**
'Red Lion' (Ia) SDeJ
'Red Night' (I) EGoo NRog

regale ♀ CArn CAvo CB&S CBro CSam
  CSut EBrP EBre EFou ETub
  LAma LBow LBre MBal MCLN
  MLLN NEgg NRog SBre SDeJ
  SRms WCru WEas WPyg WWat
– 'Album' (IX) CAvo CHad CSWP EBrP EBre
  EFou LAma LBow LBre
  MWgw NRog SBre SDeJ
§ – 'Royal Gold' (IX) CB&S CMil LAma NEgg SAga
  SDeJ SRms
'Roma' (Ia) LAma NBir
'Rosita' (Ia) MBri NRog
'Royal Gold' See *L. regale* **'Royal Gold'**
rubellum EFEx
§ 'Ruud' (VII) CBro LAma SCoo
¶ 'Sam' (VII) LAma SCoo
'Sancerre' (Ia) CB&S
'Sans Pareil' (Ia) ETub SDeJ
'Sans Souci' (VIId) MBri
sargentiae CPou NGre
'Sensation' CB&S
shastense See *L. kelleyanum*
¶ 'Showbiz' (VIII) LAma
'Silly Girl' (Ia) CB&S
'Simoen' (Ia) SDeJ
'Snow Princess' LAma
'Snow Trumpet' (V) CSam WLRN
¶ sp. from Hong Kong B&SWJ WCru
  4082
speciosum var. *album* CB&S CBro EBot LAma NBir
  (IX) SDeJ
– 'Grand Commander' SDeJ
  (IX)
– var. *roseum* (IX) SDeJ
– var. *rubrum* (IX) CAvo CB&S CBro CHar CLAP
  EBot ETub LAma LBow
  MLLN NBir NRog SAga SDeJ
§ – 'Uchida' (IX) GBur LAma SDeJ
¶ 'Sphinx' (Ia) SCoo
'Star Gazer' (VIIc) CB&S CBro CSut EBrP EBre
  ECot LAma LBre MHlr NRog
  SBre SDeJ SSoC
* 'Sterling Silver' LAma
'Sterling Star' (Ia) CB&S CLAP CSut ETub LAma
  NRog SDeJ
¶ *stewartianum* (IX) LAma
'Sun Ray' (Ia) NRog
superbum ♀ LAma NRog
¶ 'Sweet Kiss' (Ia) SCoo
szovitsianum See *L. monadelphum*
'Tamara' (Ib) CB&S MBri NRog
tenuifolium See *L. pumilum*
× *testaceum* (IX) ♀ LAma NRog SDeJ
tigrinum See *L. lancifolium*
'Trance' (VIIb) CB&S MBri
'Uchida Kanoka' See *L. speciosum* **'Uchida'**
vollmeri GCLN WAbe
wallichianum CPou LAma NRog SDeJ WCru
'Walter Bentley' (Ic) SRms
washingtonianum (IX) MSto
– var. *purpurascens* MSto
'White America' CB&S CBro ETub LRHS
'White Happiness' (Ia) LAma
'White Henryi' (VId) EFEx
'White Journey's End' CB&S
  (VIId)
¶ 'White Kiss' (Ia) LAma SCoo
'White Mountain' (VIIc) SDeJ
wigginsii GCrs GGGa
willmottiae See *L. davidii* var. *willmottiae*
Yellow Blaze Group (Ia) LAma NRog
'Yellow Giant' See *L.* **'Joanna'**

'Zephyr' (Ia)   CSut

LIMNANTHES (Limnanthaceae)
  douglasii ♀   CFee CMGP CTrG CTri ELan
                           IBlr NBus SIng WEas WElm
                           WFox WHer

LIMNOPHILA (Scrophulariaceae)
  ¶ *aromatica*   EOHP MSal

LIMONIUM (Plumbaginaceae)
  bellidifolium   ECha ELan ESis MBro MGed
                           MHig SBla WCla WEas WHoo
                           WPer
  cosyrense   CInt CMea ESis NMen SIng
                           SRms WAbe WPer WWin
  dumosum   See *Goniolimon tataricum* var.
                           angustifolium
  globulariifolium   See *L. ramosissimum*
  gmelinii   WPer
  – 'Perestrojka'   EBee SIgm
  gougetianum   CLyd NTow
  latifolium   See *L. platyphyllum*
* *maritimum*   CSpe
  minutum   ELan MHig MTPN
  otolepis   CLTr CM&M
  paradoxum   ELan
  peregrinum   CSpe EBee
  § *platyphyllum*   CGle EFou LFis MAus MWat
                           MWgw NFla NMir SPer SRCN
                           SRms SUsu WBrE WEas
                           WGwG WHoo WOld WPer
                           WWal WWin
  – 'Robert Butler'   GCal MMil MRav
  – 'Violetta'   CTri EBrP EBre ECED ECGN
                           ECGP ECha ELan EMan LBre
                           MBri MRav MUlv SBre SPer
                           WHoo
  purpuratum   CSpe
  § *ramosissimum*   EBee
  tataricum   See *Goniolimon tataricum*
  tetragonum   See *L. dregeanum*
  tomentellum   EBee
  vulgare   EEls

LINANTHASTRUM See LINANTHUS

LINANTHUS (Polemoniaceae) See Plant
Deletions

LINARIA (Scrophulariaceae)
  aeruginea   MSto
  – subsp. *nevadensis*   WCla
  alpina   CMea EBee ELan EPfP EWes
                           GTou LFis LPVe MSto MTho
                           NWCA SRms WCla WPer
  – 'Purpurea'   NMGW
  – 'Rosea'   NMGW WCla
  'Anstey'   CElw EMan
  anticaria   MSto
  – 'Antique Silver'   CSpe ECha EFou EMan EPPr
                           GBuc MBro MRav NLak WCot
                           WHoo WPbr
  cymbalaria   See *Cymbalaria muralis*
  dalmatica   CChr CGle CHad CHan ECha
                           ECro ELan LBay MFir MInt
                           NBro NCat NChi SChu SIgm
                           SOkh WBor WGwy WKif WOld
                           WPer

x *dominii* 'Carnforth'   CGle CHan CVer ECGP EJud
                           EMar EPPr LHop MBrN NBro
                           NLak NSti WMaN WWhi
  – 'Yuppie Surprise'   CMGP EMan EMon LBay NBir
                           SMad WLRN
  genistifolia   CBlo LFis MGed
  'Globosa Alba'   See *Cymbalaria muralis*
                           'Globosa Alba'
  glutinosa   See *L. bipunctata*
  hepaticifolia   See *Cymbalaria hepaticifolia*
  'Natalie'   LGre SAga
  nevadensis   MSto
  origanifolia   See *Chaenorhinum*
                           origanifolium
  pallida   See *Cymbalaria pallida*
  pilosa   See *Cymbalaria pilosa*
  purpurea   CGle CKin ECro EFou ELan
                           ERav EWFC LHol MAus
                           MCLN MChe MFir NBro NCat
                           NChi NFai NFla NNor NPer
                           SIde SRms WCla WHen WOve
                           WPer WWin
  – 'Alba'   See *L. purpurea* **'Springside
                           White'**
  – 'Canon Went'   CBre CGle CHan ECha ECro
                           EFou ELan EOrc LGan LGre
                           LHop MFir MNrw NBro NFai
                           NNor NRoo SAga SPer SSvw
  – 'Radcliffe Innocence' See *L. purpurea* **'Springside
                           White'**
  § – 'Springside White'   CElw CGle CHea ECha EFou
                           EMan EMon EOHP GBuc
                           LGre LHop MAvo MCLN MSte
                           SSvw SUsu SWat WCot WLRN
                           WMaN WRha
  – 'Thurgarton Beauty'   WCot
  – 'Winifrid's Delight'   CBlo CMil CSpe EBee EBrP
                           EBre EMan EWll GCal LBre
                           LHop MAus MCLN MTis
                           MWgw NBrk NLak NSti SBre
                           SChu SCoo SSpe SUsu SWat
                           WCot WGle WHow WLRN
                           WPbr
  repens   CKin EWFC MHlr SSvw WCot
                           WHer
  'Sue'   EMan LHop
  supina   MSto WCla WHer
  'Tony Aldis'   CSpe SSvw WKif
  triornithophora   CBrd CChr CFir CGle CPea
                           CSpe ECha ECro EMar GBin
                           GBuc GCra MBel MFir MHlr
                           MSCN NLak WBea WBor
                           WByw WCot WFar WHoo
                           WOld WOve WRha WWin
                           WWye
  – pink   CBot CGle CHan CSpe EMan
                           WEas WPer
  – purple   CHan ELan WBea
  tristis var. *lurida* SBla WOMN
     'Toubkal'
  vulgaris   CArn CKin EJud ELau EOHP
                           EWFC LHol MChe MHew
                           NMir SIde WHer WJek WPer
  – peloric form   CNat CPBP EMon WAlt

LINDELOFIA (Boraginaceae)
  anchusoides hort.   See *L. longiflora*
  § *anchusoides* Lehmann CHan GMac

§ *longiflora* — CFir CMdw CWit ECGN GBin GBuc GCal LLew MLLN MRav MTed NVic WPer
– 'Alba' — ECha

LINDERA (Lauraceae)
aggregata — CMCN
¶ *angustifolia* — CFil WPGP
benzoin — CB&S CFil CMCN SBid WPGP WWoo
erythrocarpa — CFil CMCN WPGP
obtusiloba ♀ — CFil CMCN MBlu SSpi WNor WPGP WWoo
praecox — CFil WPGP
¶ *praetermissa* — CFil WPGP
triloba — CFil WPGP
umbellata — CFil

LINNAEA (Caprifoliaceae)
borealis — GAri GDra ILis MBal MHar MHig NGre WOMN
borealis var. *americana* — MHig NHar NMen NWCA

LINUM † (Linaceae)
¶ *alpinum* subsp. *julicum* — WLin
altaicum — MSto NChi
arboreum ♀ — CLon MBro MPla MSto NHol NMen SBla SIgm SMrm WAbe WKif WOMN WPat WWat
austriacum — EBee MSto
bienne — CKin
bulgaricum — See *L. tauricum*
campanulatum — MSto
capitatum — CPBP EBee WAbe WLin WPat
* *columbianum* — MSto
dolomiticum — WAbe
flavum — CGle CTri EPfP GTou NLak WHoo
– 'Compactum' — ECha ELan LHop MBro MHar NMen NRoo NWCA SBla SMer SMrm SRCN SRms WCot WMer WWin
'Gemmell's Hybrid' ♀ — CLyd CMGP CMea CStr EPot LBee MBro NBir NGre NHar NHol NMen NRya NWCA SBla WAbe WLin WPat
¶ *kingii* var. *sedoides* — WLin
leonii — WKif WRus
marginale — MSto
monogynum — ECou LFlo MTho NTow NWCA SBla WPGP
§ – var. *diffusum* — ECou
– dwarf form — CLyd EHyt GTou NWCA
– 'Nelson' — See *L. monogynum* var. *diffusum*
narbonense — CLon CLyd CSam LGre LGro MBri MBro NFai NOak SIgm SMrm SRms WHoo WKif WMer WOMN WOld WPyg
– 'Heavenly Blue' ♀ — ECGN SUsu WEas WHen
§ *perenne* — CArn CMea ECha EFer ELan EWFC GCal GMaP LHol MAus MBri MCLN MChe NChi NMir NNor NVic NWoo SIde SPer SRCN WHer WPer WWin
– *album* — CGle ECha EFou ELan EMan LHol MAus NChi SPer SRms WHen WPer WRus
– subsp. *alpinum* — WPer
– – 'Alice Blue' — CPBP NHar NMen SBla SMrm WLin WWin

§ – 'Blau Saphir' — CChr CSam EGar ESis GAbr NOrc NRoo SMrm SRms WAbe WHen WLRN
– Blue Sapphire — See *L. perenne* 'Blau Saphir'
– 'Diamant' — CBod EBar LPVe NPri NRoo WLRN
– subsp. *extra-axillare* — CLyd
– subsp. *lewisii* — CHad EBee EHyt LHop MSto NBir NTow SMrm
– 'White Diamond' — WHen
rubrum — MChe
sibiricum — See *L. perenne*
suffruticosum — CPBP
– subsp. *salsoloides* — CLyd MBro NHar NWCA SBla
'Nanum' — WPat
– – 'Prostratum' — GBuc SIgm
§ *tauricum* — EBee MSto
tenuifolium — MSto
* *tweedyi* — NBir
viscosum — MSto

LIPARIS (Orchidaceae)
cordifolia — EFEx
fujisanensis — EFEx
krameri var. *krameri* — EFEx
kumokiri — EFEx
makinoana — EFEx
nigra — EFEx
sootenzanensis — EFEx

LIPPIA (Verbenaceae)
¶ *alba* — MSal
canescens — See *Phyla canescens*
chamaedrifolia — See *Verbena peruviana*
citriodora — See *Aloysia triphylla*
dulcis — CArn EOHP MSal
nodiflora — See *Phyla nodiflora*
repens — See *Phyla nodiflora*

LIQUIDAMBAR † (Hamamelidaceae)
acalycina — SSta WPat
formosana — CGre CLnd CMCN CPle CTho ELan GAri LPan MBlu SSta WCoo WNor
– Monticola Group — SSta
orientalis — CBar CMCN CPMA LPan SSta
styraciflua — Widely available
– 'Andrew Hewson' — CLnd CPMA SMad SSta
– 'Anja' — SSta
– 'Anneke' — SSta
– 'Aurea' — CBlo CLnd COtt IOrc LNet SSta WPat
– 'Aurea Variegata' — CDoC CPMA
– 'Burgundy' — CBlo CLnd CPMA SSta WPat WWes
* – *festeri* — CEnd SSta
¶ – 'Festival' — SSta
– 'Golden Treasure' (v) — CPMA ELan LNet WPat
– 'Gumball' — CLnd CPMA SSta WPat
– 'Kia' — CEnd CPMA LPan
– 'Lane Roberts' ♀ — CDoC CLnd CMCN CTho EPfP IOrc LNet LPan MAsh MBri SMad SReu SSta WDin WPat WPyg WShe
– 'Manon' (v) — CEnd CPMA SPla
– 'Moonbeam' (v) — CBlo CEnd CPMA MAsh SSta WPat
– 'Palo Alto' — SSta WPat
– 'Parasol' — CPMA SMad SSta
– 'Pendula' — CPMA SSta WWes
¶ – 'Rotundiloba' — SSta
– 'Silver King' (v) — CPMA EBee EPfP SPer SSta

– 'Stared' CLnd CPMA
– 'Thea' SSta
– 'Variegata' CBot CPMA ELan EPfP LNet
LPan NHol NPal SPer SSpi SSta
WDin WPat
– 'Worplesdon' ♀ CB&S CDoC CEnd CMCN
COtt CTho EBrP EBre ELan
ENot IHos IOrc LBre LNet
LPan MAsh MBri MGos SBre
SMad SPer SReu SSpi SSta
WAbe WDin WPat WWat

LIRIODENDRON † (Magnoliaceae)
chinense CAbP CMCN EPfP MBlu SSpi
WPGP WWat
tulipifera ♀ CB&S CBot CLnd CMCN ELan
ENot GRei IHos ISea LHyr
LPan MAsh MBal MBar MBri
MDun MGos NHol SHBN
SMad SPer SReu SSpi SSta
WDin WMou WOrn WPat
WWat
– 'Ardis' CMCN
– 'Arnold' CMCN
– 'Aureomarginatum' ♀ Widely available
– 'Aureum' CMCN
– 'Crispum' CMCN
– 'Fastigiatum' ♀ CB&S CMCN COtt CTho EBee
ELan ENot LPan MAsh MBlu
MBri SPer WOrn
– 'Glen Gold' SMad
– 'Mediopictum' CMCN CTho LNet MBlu

LIRIOPE (Convallariaceae)
¶ 'Big Blue' ENot
§ exiliflora CRDP EMan LHop MCLN
'Ariaka-janshige' (v) SWat WGle
– Silvery Sunproof See L. exiliflora
'Ariaka-janshige'
gigantea SWat
graminifolia See L. muscari
hort. non (L.) Bak.
hyacinthifolia See Reineckea carnea
koreana GCal
¶ 'Majestic' ENot
§ muscari ♀ Widely available
– 'Alba' See L. muscari 'Monroe White'
– 'Aztec Gold' WWal
¶ – B&SWJ 561 WCru
– 'Big Blue' EBee EMan EWll LRHS MRav
NFla SApp
– 'Christmas Tree' WGle WWal
– 'Evergreen Giant' WWal
– 'Gold-banded' CHea GCal IOrc SWat WFar
WGle WGwG WWal
– 'John Burch' (v) SUsu WPer WWeb
– 'Lilac Beauty' WGle
– 'Majestic' EBee EBrP EBre EMan EPPr
EPar GCal LBre NLar SApp
SBre SMad WBea WCot
– 'Mini Mondo' WGwG WWal
§ – 'Monroe White' CBro CHad EBee EMan EMar
EPar EPla GCal MBri NFai
NLar NOrc SLMG SMad SPla
SWat WGle WWye
– 'Royal Purple' ENot NOrc WCot WGwG WPer
WWal
¶ – 'Silver Ribbon' SPer
– 'Silvery Midget' (v) MCLN WWal

– 'Variegata' CAbb CFir CRow CWSG ECot
ELan EMan EPPr EPar EPla
ERav EWes IOrc MCLN MTho
NBir NSti SBid SMad SPla
WCot WPGP WRus
– variegated white bloom SAga
– 'Webster Wideleaf' WPer
'New Wonder' SApp
♦ platyphylla See L. muscari
'Samantha' LRHS SPla
§ spicata CHor NFai NOrc SSpi SWat
WEas WHoo
– 'Alba' CRow EPPr GCal MRav MTho
SAxl SUsu WTin WWin
– 'Silver Dragon' (v) CAvo CFir EBee EWes LHop
MBel MCLN MSte SCob WCot
WWal

LISTERA (Orchidaceae)
ovata WHer

LITHOCARPUS † (Fagaceae)
densiflorus CMCN
edulis CHEx SAPC SArc
§ glaber CHEx

LITHODORA (Boraginaceae)
§ diffusa MWat SBla
– 'Alba' CFee CMHG ELan EMil EPot
GAri IOrc LBee LHop MAsh
MBri MGos MPla NEgg NHar
NMen NRoo SIng SPer WAbe
WPat
– 'Cambridge Blue' EPfP MPla NHol SAga SMer
– 'Compacta' EGle ELan EPot EWes LHop
– 'Grace Ward' ♀ CGle EWes MBro MGos MPla
NHar NHol NRoo SBod SEas
SIng WAbe WHen WPat
– 'Heavenly Blue' ♀ Widely available
– 'Inverleith' CMHG ELan EWes LHop
LRHS WFar
– 'Picos' CLyd EDAr EGle EHyt EPot
GTou MHig NHol NMen SIgm
WAbe WPat
– 'Star' MAsh MHig SCoo WWeb
graminifolia See Moltkia suffruticosa
hispidula NMen SIng WAbe
× intermedia See Moltkia × intermedia
§ oleifolia ♀ CLyd CMea EPot MBro MWat
NBir NHol NMen NSla NTow
WCot WCru WOMN WPat
rosmarinifolia CSpe
zahnii CMHG NTow SIgm WPat

LITHOPHRAGMA (Saxifragaceae)
bulbiferum See L. glabrum
parviflorum CMea EHyt EPot GCrs GDra
MHig MNrw MSte MTho NBir
NHol NMen NRya NWCA SIng
WCru WGle WOMN

LITHOSPERMUM (Boraginaceae)
diffusum See Lithodora diffusa
doerfleri See Moltkia doerfleri
erythrorhizon MSal
officinale ELau EWFC GBar GPoy MSal
WCla WCot WHer
oleifolium See Lithodora oleifolia
purpureocaeruleum See Buglossoides
purpurocaerulea

LITSEA (Lauraceae)
  japonica   CHEx

LITTONIA (Colchicaceae)
  modesta   CGre CHal CMon CRHN

LITTORELLA (Plantaginaceae)
  § *uniflora*   WCot

LIVISTONA (Arecaceae)
  australis   CHEx CTrC LPal NPal
  chinensis ♀   LPJP LPal NPal
  decipiens   LPal
  ¶ *mariae*   LPal

LLOYDIA (Liliaceae)
  ¶ *serotina*   EPot

LOASA (Loasaceae)
  lateritia   See *Caiophora lateritia*
  triphylla var. *volcanica* GCal MSto

LOBELIA † (Campanulaceae)
  'Alice'   WCot
  anatina   CFai CFir EBee EWll WLRN
                             WRha
  angulata   See *Pratia angulata*
  'Bees' Flame'   CFir CRos CRow SWat WLRN
  bridgesii   CSpe CTbh
  'Brightness'   CRos CRow ELan SPer
  'Butterfly Blue'   CB&S EBrP EBre EGle GBuc
                             LBre MTis NChi NPla SBre
                             WAbe WWat
  'Butterfly Rose'   EBrP EBre EGle GBuc GMac
                             LBre LFis SAga SBre WAbe
                             WCHb
  cardinalis ♀   CArn CRDP CRow CWat EAst
                             EFou EHon GCHN GCal GCra
                             LHol LPBA MSal MSta NDea
                             SChu SPer SRms SUsu SWyc
                             WChe WMAq WMer WOld
                             WWin WWye
  – 'Alba'   WCot WPyg
  – *multiflora*   CFir WCot
  – 'Rose Beacon'   WCot
  * 'Cherry Pie'   EMan EPfP
  'Cherry Ripe'   CElw CRos CSev ELan SChu
                             SMrm WCHb WEas WLRN
  'Cinnabar Deep Red'   See *L.* 'Fan Tiefrot'
  'Cinnabar Rose'   See *L.* 'Fan Zinnoberrosa'
  'Complexion'   CHad GCHN SWat
  Compliment Blue   See *L.* 'Kompliment Blau'
  Compliment Deep Red   See *L.* 'Kompliment Tiefrot'
  Compliment Purple   See *L.* 'Kompliment Purpur'
  Compliment Scarlet   See *L.* 'Kompliment Scharlach'
  'Dark Crusader'   CBos CElw CMHG CRos
                             CRow EFou ELan LFis LHop
                             MBri MCLN MLLN NDea
                             NPro NSti SChu SMrm WCHb
                             WEas WMow WRus WSan
  ¶ *deckenii* subsp. *elgonensis* CFir
  dortmanna   EMFW
  erinus 'Kathleen Mallard' CSpe ELan LHop LIck MBEx
                             (d)   NPri WEas
  – 'Richardii'   See *L. richardsonii*
  'Eulalia Berridge'   CDoC CGle CKel CMGP CMil
                             CRos CSam EFou GBuc LBlm
                             LHop MMil SAga SMrm SWas
  excelsa   CHEx CSpe CTbh EWes GCal
                             WPic
  Fan Deep Red   See *L.* 'Fan Tiefrot'

  * Fan Orchid Rose ♀   EMan LIck WHil WLRN
  'Fan Scharlach' ♀   LIck WHil WWeb
  'Fan Tiefrot'   EAst GBuc GCHN GMac SMad
                             SRms SSpi SWat WCHb WChe
                             WLRN WPer
  'Fan Zinnoberrosa' ♀   CB&S CFir CGle EAst EMan
                             LGan MHlr NCut NVic NWes
                             SAga SMad SRms WCHb WHil
                             WPer WWin WWye
  'Flamingo'   See *L.* 'Pink Flamingo'
  'Frances'   WCot
  fulgens   IBlr MHlr WByw WEas
  – 'Elmfeuer'   CSpe EHic SMrm WElm
  – 'Illumination'   GBuc
  'Galen'   CRow
  x *gerardii*   EWll NLak SSca WBor
  – 'Eastgrove Pink'   WEas
  – 'Rosencavalier'   CFai LRHS SMrm WRus
  § – 'Vedrariensis'   CB&S CGle CMHG CRow
                             ECha EFou ELan EMFW
                             GCHN GCal GMac LPBA
                             MCCP NCut NDea NSti SLMG
                             SMad SPer SSpi WEas WOld
                             WRus WWin
  gibberoa   CHEx
  inflata   CArn GPoy MSal SIde WCHb
                             WWye
  'Kompliment Blau'   CBlo CFir CHor CSpe EMan
                             LIck NCut NVic WHil WPer
  'Kompliment Purpur'   CSpe
  'Kompliment Scharlach' ♀ CBlo CHor CRos CRow CSWP
                             EBar EBrP EBre EPfP GCHN
                             LBre LGan NCut NPer SBre
                             SSpi WCHb WHil WPer
  § 'Kompliment Tiefrot'   CHor WPer
  laxiflora   CBot CInt EGra MTho SIgm
                             WHer
  – var. *angustifolia*   CGre CHEx CPle CSpe CTbh
                             ELan ERea GCal IBlr LBlm
                             LHil LHop MSte NWes SHFr
                             SMac SMrm SUsu WAbe WPer
                             WWye
  'Lena'   SWat
  lindblomii   CLTr EHic EWes
  linnaeoides   EWes GCHN MTho NGre
                             WEas
  lutea   CGen CInt
  pedunculata   See *Pratia pedunculata*
  perpusilla   See *Pratia perpusilla*
  physaloides   See *Pratia physaloides*
  'Pink Elephant' ♀   CGle CMHG CMil CRos CSWP
                             CSev EFou EPri GMac NBrk
                             WCot WFar
  § 'Pink Flamingo'   CRow EAst EBrP EBre ECha
                             EFou EMFW EPar GCHN
                             LBre MCLN NFai NLon NNor
                             NSti SAga SBre SChu SCro
                             SMrm SPer SWat WBor WCHb
                             WPyg WWye
  puberula   CFir
  'Purple Towers'   GBuc WCot
  'Queen Victoria' ♀   Widely available
  repens   See *Pratia repens*
  § *richardsonii* ♀   CInt LHil LIck MBEx WEas
                             WLRN
  'Rowden Magenta'   CRow
  'Royal Robe'   CRow
  'Ruby Slippers'   WCot

N 'Russian Princess'	CGle CRDP CRos CRow CSam EMFW LHil MBEx MBri MCLN NBrk SChu SHFr SMad SUsu WCHb WFar WLRN WMer WWeb
'Sandy's Pink'	SWat
sessilifolia	GBuc GCal GMac NGre SMrm SRms SUsu WChe WCot WLRN WMow WPer WViv WWye
¶ – B&L 12396	EMon
– B&SWJ 520	GCra
siphilitica	CArn CB&S CFee CGle CHad CHan CRow EFou ELan EMil EOrc EPri GCHN GCal LHol MBro MSCN MSta NSti SMrm SPer SSpe WCHb WChe WHil WOld WPbr WRus WWat WWin
– 'Alba'	CB&S CBlo CNic CPea CPou CRow CSam ECro EPfP EPri LBlm LGan LHil MCLN MLLN NChi NSti SSca SSvw WByw WCHb WChe WHoo WMow WPer WPyg WRHF WWye
¶ – Blue selection	NLar
¶ – 'Rosea'	MNrw
'Sonia'	CGle
'Spark'	GBuc WCot
'Sparkle Divine'	WCot
× *speciosa*	CBrd CRow MNrw WLRN
– dark form	CRos CRow SHFr SMrm
'Tania'	CFir CGle CHEx CRDP CRow EFou EMan GBri GMac IBlr LHil MHlr MLLN MUlv SChu SCro SMad SMrm WByw WRus
treadwellii	See *Pratia angulata* 'Treadwellii'
tupa	CBot CDoC CGen CGre CHEx CHan CInt CSam CSpe ECha ELan GCal GGar IBlr LHop WCHb WCru WHer WPer WSan WWat WWin WWye
– dark orange form	SAPC SArc SMrm
– JCA 12527	WCot
urens	SSpi
valida	CFir CInt GBuc GQui SCoo WCot WLRN
¶ – 'South Seas'	EBee
vedrariensis	See *L.* × *gerardii* 'Vedrariensis'
'Will Scarlet'	CCuc CRos EBrP EBre LBre SBre SHFr
'Zinnoberrosa'	See *L.* 'Fan Zinnoberrosa'

LOBELIA × PRATIA (Campanulaceae)

L. sp. × P. sp.	NGre

LOBOSTEMON   (Boraginaceae) See Plant Deletions

LOESELIA (Polemoniaceae)

mexicana	ERea LHop

LOISELEURIA (Ericaceae)

procumbens	NHar WAbe
¶ – from Japan	GCrs

LOMANDRA (Xanthorrhoeaceae)

longifolia	ECou

LOMARIA See BLECHNUM

LOMATIA (Proteaceae)

dentata	CB&S CHEx
ferruginea	CAbb CFil CHEx CLan CTrG ISea MAll MBal SAPC SArc WCru WPGP WWat
longifolia	See *L. myricoides*
§ *myricoides*	CAbb CDoC CFil CHEx CTrG CTrw ELan EPfP MAll SAPC SArc SPer SSpi WBod WWat
§ *silaifolia*	EPfP
§ *tinctoria*	CB&S CDoC CHEx CTrw ELan EPfP ISea MAll SAPC SArc SPer SSpi

LOMATIUM (Apiaceae)

brandegeei	SIgm
columbianum	SIgm
grayi	SIgm
utriculatum	MSal SIgm

LOMATOGONIUM (Gentianaceae)

¶ sp. ACE 2331*	WAbe

LONICERA † (Caprifoliaceae)

§ *acuminata*	EHal EHic ETen LRHS WCru WSHC
¶ – B&SWJ 2150	WCru
¶ – B&SWJ 3480	WCru
albertii	EBar EHic MRav SPan WHCG
albiflora	CPlN CPle
– var. *albiflora*	SBra
alpigena	MSto
alseuosmoides	CPlN ETen SBra WWeb
altmannii	CPle
N × *americana* hort.	See *L.* × *italica*
§ – (Miller) K. Koch	CBlo CHad CRHN CSPN EPfP LHop MAsh MBri MGos NBea SAxl SBra SEas SReu SSta WCru WWeb
¶ 'Anna Landers'	WCFE
× *brownii*	CMac CRHN
§ – 'Dropmore Scarlet'	Widely available
N – 'Fuchsioides'	EPfP MBro NBrk NSti SPer WSHC WWat
caerulea	CPle MRav WHCG
– var. *altaica*	CPle
– var. *edulis*	ESim MSto
– f. *emphyllocalyx*	CPle
§ *caprifolium* ♀	CDoC CPlN CRHN ELan EOrc EPla LBuc LHol LPri MBar MBri NBea NFai NMGW NSti SBra SHBN SPan SPer WCru WWat
– 'Anna Fletcher'	CRHN EBar ELan MTed MUlv NHol SBra SPan WCru WEas WWat WWeb
– 'Cornish Cream'	NTay
– f. *pauciflora*	See *L.* × *italica*
chaetocarpa	CMHG CPle WBod WPat
chrysantha	CMCN CPle GBin
ciliosa	CPlN MSto NBea SBra
'Clavey's Dwarf'	IOrc MPla NBrk NHol
cyanocarpa KGB 438	MSto
deflexicalyx KGB 165	MSto
dioica	SBra
'Early Cream'	See *L. caprifolium*
etrusca	EHal EPla LPri WWeb
– 'Donald Waterer'	CBlo CSam EHic LHop MUlv SBra WFar WGor WWat
– 'Michael Rosse'	EBar EBrP EBre EHic ETen LBre LRHS SBra SBre SRms

– 'Superba'	CBlo CPlN CRHN EBee ECtt ELan EPfP NBrk NSti SBra SEND WCru WPen WSHC WWat
ferdinandii	MSto
flexuosa	See *L. japonica* var. *repens*
fragrantissima	Widely available
giraldii hort.	See *L. acuminata*
– Rehder	CB&S CBot CHan CPlN EBee ETen LPri NHol SBra
glabrata	EHic SBra WCru
glaucohirta	See *L. periclymenum* var. *glaucohirta*
¶ *gracilis*	MBlu
grata	See *L.* × *americana* (Miller) K. Koch
× *heckrottii*	CBlo CDoC CMac CRHN CTri ECtt GOrc LPri MAsh MBar NBea SPer WCru WDin WLRN WStI WWeb
N– 'Gold Flame'	Widely available
§ *henryi*	Widely available
– var. *subcoriacea*	See *L. henryi*
hildebrandiana	CGre CHEx CPlN SOWG
hirsuta	NBea SBra
¶ 'Honey Baby'	MGos
implexa	CHan CPlN EBar EHol EPla GCal LGre MBlu NPro SBra SEas WPat WSHC
insularis	CMCN CPle MBlu
involucrata	CB&S CHan CMCN CMHG CPle EBar GBin GOrc LHil LHop MBar MBlu MRav NChi SMac SPer WDin WHCG WPyg
– var. *ledebourii*	CHan CPle ELan EPfP EPla GChr GRei MBel MSto MWat NHol SBid SDys WOve WWin
§ × *italica* ♀	CMac CRHN EBrP EBre ELan ENot EPla LBre LHol LPri MWat NSti SBra SBre SPer SPla SSpi WCru WPyg WSHC WWat
♦ – Harlequin	See *L.* × *italica* Harlequin = 'Sherlite' (v)
§ – Harlequin = 'Sherlite' (v)	CBlo CBot EAst EBee EMil ENot MAsh MBel MGos NBea NEgg NHol NRoo NSti SBra SMad SPer SPla WCot WCru WLRN WWat WWeb
§ *japonica* 'Aureoreticulata'	Widely available
– 'Dart's Acumen'	SLPl
– 'Dart's World'	MBel NHol SBra SLPl SVil WLRN
– 'Halliana' ♀	Widely available
– 'Hall's Prolific'	CBlo CSam EBee EBrP EBre ECtt EHic ELan ENot EWll GChr LBre LBuc MAsh MBar MBlu MBri MGos MRav MUlv NBea NHol SBra SBre SCoo SPla WPyg WWat WWeb
§ – 'Horwood Gem' (v)	ECtt EHic NHol WWeb
– 'Peter Adams'	See *L. japonica* 'Horwood Gem'
§ – var. *repens*	CDoC CMac EBrP EBre ECtt ELan ENot EPla GOrc IHos LBre LPri MPla MRav NBea NEgg NFla SBra SBre SHBN SLPl SPer SRms WCru WWat WWeb
– 'Variegata'	See *L. japonica* 'Aureoreticulata'
korolkowii	CBot CHan CPle CSam EBar EBee EHic LFis MUlv MWat NBir SBid SPan SPla WHCG WSHC WWat WWin
– var. *zabelii*	ELan SEas
lanceolata KGB 488	MSto
maackii	CMCN CMil CPMA MRav WHCG WWat
– f. *podocarpa*	CPle
microphylla	CPle MSto
morrowii	MSto
× *muscaviensis*	CPle
myrtillus KGB 298	MSto
nigra	CPle EPla
nitida	CB&S CKin CTri EBee ELan GBur GOrc LHyr MRav NWea SHBN SPer STre WDin WGwG WHar WHen WStI
– 'Baggesen's Gold' ♀	Widely available
¶ – 'Eden Spring'	NPro
– 'Elegant'	ELan IOrc LBuc
– 'Ernest Wilson'	MBar SRms
– 'Fertilis'	SPer SRms
– 'Hohenheimer Findling'	SLPl
¶ – 'Lemon Beauty'	EBee EHoe EPla MBri
¶ – 'Lemon Queen'	EHal WLRN
§ – 'Maigrün'	CChe EMil MBri NFla NPro SPer WTro
– Maygreen	See *L. nitida* 'Maigrün'
– 'Red Tips'	CWSG EHic LBuc LRHS MBel MBri MGos MLLN NHol
– 'Silver Beauty'	Widely available
* – 'Silver Cloud'	CWSG EHic WCot
– 'Silver Lining'	See *L. pileata* 'Silver Lining'
¶ – 'Silver Queen'	WEas
¶ – 'Twiggy'	NPro SVil WGer WLRN
nummulariifolia	CPle
periclymenum	CArn CKin CPer CTri EPla EWFC GChr GPoy MHew NBea NMir NNor NWea SHFr WDin WHCG WMou WOak
§ – 'Belgica' ♀	Widely available
♦ – 'Belgica' misapplied	See *L.* × *italica*
– 'Florida'	See *L. periclymenum* 'Serotina'
– 'Graham Thomas' ♀	Widely available
– 'Harlequin'	See *L.* × *italica* Harlequin = 'Sherlite'
– 'Heaven Scent'	EMil
– 'La Gasnaérie'	EPla GAri NHol SPan
– 'Liden'	SBra
– 'Munster'	EBee MBri NBrk SBra WBcn
¶ – 'Purple Queen'	CBlo
– 'Red Gables'	CBlo EBar EHic MBri MHlr NHol SPan SPla SVil WGor WPat WWat
N– 'Serotina' ♀	Widely available
– 'Serotina' EM '85	MBri
– 'Serpentine'	SBra
– *sulphurea*	EPla EWll NFai
– 'Sweet Sue'	ELan EPfP LRHS MAsh SBla SBra WBcn WFar WWeb
pileata	Widely available
– 'Moss Green'	CBlo CDoC MGos SBid SLPl WHCG WRHF
§ – 'Silver Lining' (v)	CBlo EPla GBuc MLLN WCot
– 'Stockholm'	SLPl
pilosa Maxim.	See *L. strophiophora*
– Willd. CD&R 1216	CHan
prolifera	SBra
prostrata	MSto SIgm

× *purpusii* — CChe CPle CSam EBar ECle EMil GChr LHol MBar MBel MPla NBea SRms WBea WBod WCru WEas WHCG WHar WPyg WSHC WWeb WWin

– 'Winter Beauty' ♀ — Widely available

pyrenaica — CPle

quinquelocularis — CPle EHal EPla

– f. *translucens* — MBlu

ramosissima — CMCN MSto

§ *rupicola* var. *syringantha* — CHan CHar CMHG CPle CSam EAst ELan LHol LHop MBlu MGos MHlr MTis MWat MWhi NBea NLon SHBN SPan SPer SPla WFar WHCG WSHC WWat WWin

– – 'Grandiflora' — GQui WPyg

ruprechtiana — CPle

segreziensis — CPle

sempervirens ♀ — CBot CPlN CRHN EPar EPfP GAri LBlm LPri NBea SBra WLRN WSHC WWeb

– 'Dropmore Scarlet' — See *L.* × *brownii* 'Dropmore Scarlet'

N– f. *sulphurea* — CBlo CPlN EBee EHic EPfP LRHS NBea SBra SPan SPer WSHC WWat WWeb

serotina 'Honeybush' — CPle MAsh MBlu

setifera — CBot CPle EHol

similis var. *delavayi* — CBot CDoC CHan CLTr CPlN CSPN CSam EPla LBuc MAsh NBea SBra SDix SPan SPla SWas WCru WEas WPGP WPen WSHC WWat

'Simonet' — SBra WGwG

sp. ACE 1413 — MSto

sp. KBE 062 — NHol

sp. LS&H 17465 — WWat

splendida — CBot SBra WCru WSHC

standishii — CB&S ECle LHol MBel MGos MRav SPer WDin WHCG WRha WWat WWin WWye NLak NPro SPla

'Stone Green' — NLak NPro SPla

§ *strophiophora* — WWat

syringantha — See *L.* *rupicola* var. *syringantha*

tangutica KGB 535 — MSto

tatarica — CFai CHan CMHG CPle MHlr MWhi WHCG WWin

– 'Alba' — CHan CPMA MTed

– 'Arnold's Red' — CB&S CBot CDoC CPle EBee EHal ELan EPfP EPla MBal MBlu MPla

– 'Hack's Red' — CB&S CFai EPfP MPla SPan SPer WHCG WPyg

– 'Zabelii' — MGos

× *tellmanniana* ♀ — Widely available

– 'Joan Sayer' — EBar EBrP EBre EHic EPla LBre LHop NBrk SBra SBre SPan WBcn WWat

thibetica — CPle MBlu SPer

tragophylla ♀ — CB&S CHad CPlN EBar ELan EPla GCal ICrw IOrc LHop LPri MAsh MBri NHol SBra SPar SPer SSpi SSta WCru WDin WSHC WWat

trichosantha KGB 404 — MSto

× *xylosteoides* — MRav

– 'Clavey's Dwarf' — MBel MBlu MGos SLPl

– 'Miniglobe' — ESis NPro

* *yunnanensis* 'Variegata' — ESis

LOPEZIA (Onagraceae)

¶ *racemosa* — CPla LLew

LOPHOMYRTUS (Myrtaceae)

§ *bullata* — CGre CPle CTre ECou GQui MAll WCHb

'Gloriosa' — CB&S CPle WCHb

§ *obcordata* — CGre CPle MAll WWat

§ × *ralphii* — MAll WCHb WPic WWat

– 'Andrea' — MAll

§ – 'Kathryn' — CB&S CDoC CHan CPle CTre EREa MAll WCHb WFar WSHC WWat

– 'Pixie' — SBid

§ – 'Traversii' — MAsh SMur

– 'Variegata' — EBrP EBre EREa LBre MAll SBre

'Sundae' — CPle MAll

'Tricolor' — CPle CTre MAll

'Versicolor' — CB&S

LOPHOSORIA (Lophosoriaceae)

quadripinnata — CFil

LOPHOSPERMUM (Scrophulariaceae)

§ *erubescens* ♀ — CBot CHEx CHal CPlN CRHN LFis LHop MSte MTis SLMG WOMN

¶ 'Red Dragon' — CSpe

§ *scandens* — CPlN

LOPHOSTEMON (Myrtaceae)

§ *confertus* — CHon CPle

LOROPETALUM (Hamamelidaceae)

chinense — CFil CMCN SBid

¶ – 'Blush' — CFil WPGP

♦ – 'Burgundy' — See *L. chinense* f. *rubrum*

§ – f. *rubrum* — CFil WPGP

LOTUS (Papilionaceae)

berthelotii ♀ — CFee CGle CHEx CHad CHal CSev CSpe ECon ELan EREa LBlm LHil MBEx SChu SHFr SLMG SRms SSoC WEas WKif

– deep red — LIck

– × *maculatus* — CBar CLTr CSpe LHil MBEx SAxl WIvy

corniculatus — CArn CKin CLTr CTri EWFC MCoo MHew NLak NLan SIde WGwy

– 'Plenus' (d) — CInt ELan EMon EPot IBlr LFis MTho NHol WAlt WCot WPer

'Gold Flash' — LIck

§ *hirsutus* — CBot CGle CHan CLTr CMea CSam CSev ELan EMil ENot EPri GCal LHil LHop MHar MPla MRav NMen NSti SDix SHFr SIng SMac SPer WEas WPyg WWat WWin

¶ – 'Brimstone' — GBin GCal SPer SPla SVil

– dwarf form — CHan

¶ – 'Lois' — WSPU

– 'Silver Mist' — SCro

jacobaeus — CInt

maculatus ♀ — CGle CSpe ECon LBlm MBEx SHFr SOWG SSoC SVen WIvy

maritimus — CMea SHFr WHal

mascaensis hort. — See *L. sessilifolius*

pedunculatus — See *L. uliginosus*

pentaphyllus subsp. *herbaceus*	GCal
§ – subsp. *pentaphyllus*	NBrk
§ *sessilifolius*	ERea LHil MBEx
suffruticosus	See *L. pentaphyllus* subsp. *pentaphyllus*
§ *uliginosus*	EWFC NMir

LOXOSTYLIS (Anacardiaceae) See Plant Deletions

LUCULIA (Rubiaceae)

¶ *grandifolia*	SOWG
gratissima ♀	CB&S CHEx
¶ – 'Rosea'	SOWG
¶ *pinceana* 'Fragrant Cloud'	CB&S

LUDWIGIA (Onagraceae)

grandiflora	CRow SWyc WChe
¶ *uruguayensis*	LPBA

LUETKEA (Rosaceae)

pectinata	GCHN GDra NHol WAbe

LUMA (Myrtaceae)

§ *apiculata* ♀	CAbb CArn CEnd CHEx CMHG CPle CTrG CTre CTri CTrw EBrP EBre ISea LBre MBal MBlu SArc SBre SDix SEND SPer STre WBod WCHb WHCr WPic WSHC WTro WWat WWye
§ – 'Glanleam Gold' (v)	Widely available
– 'Variegata'	CMHG CTri ISea NHol WWat WWeb WWye
§ *chequen*	CFee CGre GAri LHol MAll NHex WCHb WJek WWat

LUNARIA (Brassicaceae)

§ *annua*	EBot EPfP GAbr MMal MWgw NCat SIde SWat WByw WHer WOak WRha
I –'Alba Variegata'	CSpe EMan EMar EMon EPla MAvo MFir WBon WByw
– var. *albiflora* ♀	CSev EBot NBir NCat SIde SWat WCer WCot WOak
* – 'Stella'	GCal WHen
– *variegata*	CJew EBot IBlr MTho NBir SWat WEas WHer WOMN WRha WSan
– violet	NBir
biennis	See *L. annua*
rediviva	EBrP EBre ECGP ECha EJud EMon GAri GCHN GCra GGar GLil IBlr LBre NBro NSti SAxl SBre SSpi WCot WEas WFar WHen WHer

LUPINUS † (Papilionaceae)

'Alan Titchmarsh'	MWoo
albifrons	CGen CSpe ECGN LHil SIgm
* – *flumineus*	MSto
alopecuroides	MSto
angustifolius	MSto
'Ann Gregg' ♀	MWoo
arboreus ♀	Widely available
– 'Barton on Sea'	CNat
¶ – blue	CMea MCCP NCut NLar
¶ – ex blue form	WOMN
– 'Golden Spire'	SMad
– 'Mauve Queen'	CB&S SEND

– mixed	NFla
– 'Snow Queen'	CB&S MAll
arcticus	MSto
argenteus	MSto
– var. *depressus*	MSto
¶ – var. *wyethii*	MSto
Band of Nobles Series ♀	ECtt GAbr
'Barnsdale'	MWoo
¶ *benthamii*	CChr
¶ 'Beryl, Viscountess Cowdray'	GBuc
bicolor	MSto
breweri	MSto
caespitosus	MSto
chamissonis	CHEx CHan CSpe EBrP EBre EMan EWes LBre LGre LHop MTho SBre SDry SDys SMad SMrm SSpi SUsu WPGP WRus
'Chandelier'	CHad CTri EBrP EBre ECtt EFou ELan EMan GAbr GAri GCHN LBre MAus MBri MCLN MWgw NBrk NFai NMir NRoo NVic SBre SPer SPla WHen WPer WRHF
'Chelsea Pensioner'	MWoo
'Deborah Woodfield' ♀	MWoo
densiflorus var. *aureus*	MSto
Dwarf Gallery hybrids	LIck
'Dwarf Lulu'	See *L.* 'Lulu'
'Esmerelder' ♀	MWoo
¶ 'Gallery Blue' (Gallery Series)	NLar WHil
¶ 'Gallery Pink' (Gallery Series)	NLar WHil
¶ 'Gallery Red' (Gallery Series)	NLar WHil
Gallery Series	EBrP EBre EFou LBre NCut NFai NPri NRoo SBre SCoo WHil WLRN
¶ 'Gallery White' (Gallery Series)	LPVe NLar WHil
¶ 'Gallery Yellow' (Gallery Series)	NLar WHil
'Garden Gnome'	WPer
'Helen Sharman' ♀	MWoo
'Household Brigade'	MWoo
'Judith Chalmers'	MWoo
'Kayleigh Ann Savage' ♀	MWoo
latifolius	WAbe
¶ – subsp. *parishii*	MNrw
¶ – var. *subalpinus*	WLin
lepidus	EMan MSto
– var. *lobbii*	SIgm WAbe
– var. *sellulus*	SIgm
– var. *utahensis*	MSto
'Little Eugenie'	MWoo
littoralis	EMan GDra MHar MSto SIgm WPer
§ 'Lulu'	COtt EBrP EBre ECtt ELan LBre MRav NCat NMir SBre SPer
luteus	MSto
micranthus	MSto
microphyllus	MSto
Minarette Group	CBlo ECtt MAvo MBri NCut SRms WGor
Mirakel hybrids	CBlo
'Misty'	MWoo
montanus	MSto
'Mrs Perkins'	SMrm
mutabilis var. *cruckshanksii*	MSto

'My Castle'	EBrP EBre ECtt EFou ELan EOld GAbr GAri GCHN GLil LBre MAus MBri MCLN MRav NBrk NFai NMir NOak NRoo NVic SBre SPer SPla WFar WHen WPer
nanus	MSto
'Noble Maiden'	CHad EBrP EBre ECtt EFou ELan EMan GAbr GAri GCHN GLil LBre LRot MAus MBri MCLN NBrk NFai NMir NOak NRoo NVic SBre SPer SPla WHen WPer WRHF WShe
nootkatensis	CPea EDAr MSto WPat
'Olive Tolley' ♀	MWoo
'Party Dress'	MWoo
perennis	CGle EBee ECGN SCou
pilosus	See *L. varius* subsp. *orientalis*
'Poached Salmon'	SMrm
'Polar Princess'	EBar EBee EWes LRHS MGrG SUsu SWat WLRN WMow
polyphyllus	MSto
¶ – var. *burkei*	WLin
'Pope John Paul' ♀	MWoo
propinquus	MSto
¶ 'Rising Sun'	CChr
¶ 'Rote Flamme'	ECGN LPVe
'Royal Wedding'	MWoo
Russell hybrids	CB&S ELan GChr NFla SSea
sericeus	EMan MSto
¶ *sparsiflorus*	MSto
succulentus	MSto
'Sunset'	MWoo
'Sunshine'	CGle
texensis	MSto
'The Chatelaine'	CHad EBrP EBre ECtt EFou ELan EOld GAbr GAri GCHN GLil LBre LWak MAus MBri MRav MWgw NBrk NFai NLon NMir NRoo SBre SPer SPla WHen WPer
'The Governor'	CTri EBrP EBre ECtt EFou ELan EMan GAbr GAri GCHN GLil LBre LPVe MAus MBri MCLN MRav NBrk NFai NMir NRoo NVic SBre SPer SPla WGwG WPer
'The Page'	CDoC EBrP EBre EFou ELan EMan EOld GAbr GAri LBre LWak MBri MRav NBrk NFai NMir NRoo SBre SPer SPla WGwG WPer
'Thundercloud'	CHad SMrm
variicolor	CGen CHid CSpe NChi SIgm
– JJA 11167	MSto NChi
versicolor	CPea EDAr EMan LGro MCCP MLLN MSCN MSto SMad
'Yellow Boy'	CB&S

LUZULA (Juncaceae)

¶ *alpinopilosa*	GBin
× *borreri* 'Botany Bay' (v)	CCuc EMon EPPr EPla MCCP
campestris	CKin
canariensis	CPle WWye
forsteri	EPPr
lactea	EMon EPPr EPla LRHS
leptophylla	NHar
luzuloides	WPer
– 'Schneehäschen'	CInt EGar EMon EPla ESOG GBin GCal MWgw WCot
maxima	See *L. sylvatica*
multiflora	EHoe

nivea	CCuc CHan CInt CRow ECha EFer EFou EHoe EPar EPla ESOG GCal MBri MFir NCat NHar NOrc NSti SApp SChu SHel SLPl SMac SSpi WBea WOMN WPer WPic WWat WWye
pilosa	EGar EPla GCal IBlr
pumila	ECou
rufa	ECou
¶ sp. from New Guinea	GCal
§ *sylvatica*	CCuc CKin CRow CSWP EFou EPPr EPla GBur GOrn LWak MFir MLLN NBro NOrc WHer WPGP WShi
– 'A. Rutherford'	See *L. sylvatica* 'Taggart's Cream'
– 'Aurea'	CDoC CHan CLTr CRDP CSWP CSte EBee ECha EFou EPPr EPla ESOG GAbr GCal MBri NSti SHel SMac SMad SPla WBea WCot WPat WRus WWat
– 'Aureomarginata'	See *L. sylvatica* 'Marginata'
I – 'Auslese'	EBee GBin LRHS
– 'Hohe Tatra'	CCuc CElw CMil CSte EBar EBee EHoe EMan EMon EPPr EWes GBin GChr LFis MAvo MCCP MWhi NBro NHar NHol SPla WFox WLeb
§ – 'Marginata'	CB&S CCuc CElw CHEx CRow CSte EBar ECha ECro EGol EHoe EPla ESOG GAbr LGan MBal NBro NHol NSti NVic SApp SArc SUsu WBea WPat WRus WWat WWin
¶ – f. *nova*	MMoz
– 'Select'	SLPl
§ – 'Taggart's Cream' (v)	CRow EHoe EMon LRHS SApp
– 'Tauernpass'	EHoe EMon EPPr EPla GCal WRus
– 'Wäldler'	CCuc CSte EHoe EMon EPPr LRHS
ulophylla	CInt ECou EPPr GBin GBuc NHol WPat

LUZURIAGA (Philesiaceae)

radicans	CFee WCot WCru WSHC

× **LYCENE** (Caryophyllaceae) See Plant Deletions

LYCHNIS † (Caryophyllaceae)

alpina	CMHG CTri ECro ELan EWFC GDra GTou NFla NMen NNor NPri NRoo NVic WBea WCla WPer WWal WWin
– 'Alba'	CLyd GTou NBir
– compact form	GTou
– 'Rosea'	SRms
§ × *arkwrightii*	CGle EBrP EBre ECha EFou ELan LBee LBre SAga SBre WBea WCla WOMN WWin
– 'Vesuvius'	CB&S CBos CDoC CGle CRDP EBrP EBre ENot EOld LBre MCLN MNrw MTis NBir NFai SBre SPer SPla SRms WCot WMer WOve WPer
* 'Blushing Bride'	SCoo
chalcedonica ♀	Widely available

– var. *albiflora*	CSam ECha ECro EFou ELan EMon IBlr LFis LGan MAus MBri MCLN NBro NChi NFai NOak NSti SPer WCer WHen WMow WPer WUnu WWhi
– – 'Snow White'	EWll
– apricot	MBro WPyg
– Beverley seedling	CHan
– 'Carnea'	CVer ECro EJud EMon GCal NCat WCot
– 'Flore Pleno' (d)	CMil CSpe ECha ECle ELan GBuc GCal MCLN MLLN MMil MOne MUlv NChi NHaw NHol NLar NPri NSti NWes SPer WCot WFar WOld WSan
¶ – 'Morgenrot'	NLar SGre
¶ – 'Rauhreif'	SGre
– 'Rosea'	CGle CHad EAst ECro EFou EHal EMan LIck MCLN NFai WByw WCer WGwG WHen WPer WUnu
– 'Rosea Plena' (d)	CBot
* – 'Salmonea'	EAst EBar ECle LBuc MBri MHlr MTis NBir NPla SPer SRms WCot WLRN
– salmon-pink	WWhi
cognata	CBos CGle MAvo MSto SHel SWas
§ *coronaria*	Widely available
– 'Abbotswood Rose'	See *L.* × *walkeri* 'Abbotswood Rose'
– 'Alba' ♀	CGle CStr EBar ECha EFou EHoe ELan GCHN MAus MBri MBro MCLN MHew MWgw NFai NOak NOrc NSti SPer SSvw WCla WEas WHer WMer WOMN WPer WWin
– 'Angel's Blush'	CSev EBar ECro EMan GCHN MTis NBus SPer WMow WPer WRHF WRha WRus WWal
– Atrosanguinea Group	CBre EBee ECro EFou EPPr GCHN IBlr MCLN NFai SPer WPer
– Gardeners' World = 'Blych' (d)	MCLN MUlv
– 'Cerise'	MArl NBus
– 'Dancing Ladies'	WRHF
– 'Eastgrove Pink'	WEas
¶ – 'Flottbek'	MOne NCut NLar
– 'Hutchinson's Cream' (v)	EBee MAvo WCot
– Oculata Group	CGle CHan CMHG ECro EGoo ELan EMar GCHN IBlr LGan MCLN MFir MTho NFai NOak NSti SSvw WCer WHen WHer WLin
§ *coronata* var. *sieboldii*	EBee
dioica	See *Silene dioica*
flos-cuculi	CArn CKin CNic CSam EBrP EBre EHon EMFW EWFC GAbr GCHN LBre LPBA MHew MHig MMal MSal MSta NDea NLan NMir SBre SIng WBon WCla WGwy WHen WHer WWhi
– var. *albiflora*	CInt CSam EBee ECoo EJud EPar NBro NBus NDea SIde WAlt WCla WGwy WHer WWhi
* – 'Little Robin'	GBur

– 'Nana'	CInt CNic ELan GAbr GGar LHop MBro NGre NHol NRya WBea WCla WOMN WPat WPer WPyg WWin
flos-jovis	CElw CGle CTri ECha EEls ELan EMan EPfP MCLN MFir NOak SRCN SRms WEas WLRN WPer
– 'Hort's Variety'	CDec CKel CLTr EFou EJud MAvo MHig MHlr NFla NSti NTow SBla SCro SUsu WCla WCot
– 'Minor'	See *L. flos-jovis* 'Nana'
§ – 'Nana'	CInt GCHN MSCN NFai NPla NPro NWCA SSca WOMN WPyg
– 'Peggy'	EMan GCal MCCP SRCN
× *haageana*	EBee NWCA SIng SRms SSca WOve
– 'Burning Desire'	SRCN WRHF
kubotae	See × *Lycene kubotae*
lagascae	See *Petrocoptis pyrenaica* subsp. *glaucifolia*
miqueliana	EBar EGar LFis MTis
'Molten Lava'	CBlo CInt CM&M GMaP MCli MLan NLak NOrc NPro SRms WPer
nutans	MHew MSal
¶ 'Terry's Pink'	NLar
§ *viscaria*	CGle CKin ECha EGar EGra MHew MSal NNor NPla SCro SUsu WBea WCla WGwy WHer WWhi
– *alba*	CNic EBee ECha EMan GCal NBro NPri WWeb
– *alpina*	See *L. viscaria*
– subsp. *atropurpurea*	NLon SGre WBea WWhi
¶ – 'Feuer'	NLar WLRN
– 'Firebird'	EFou
– 'Plena' (d)	CDoC EFou EMFW LFis NSti WHil WOld
¶ – 'Schnee'	SGre WBea
– 'Snowbird'	EFou GMac
– 'Splendens'	CBlo EPfP NChi NFla SGre WBro
* – 'Splendens Alba'	EPPr SSvw
– 'Splendens Plena' (d) ♀	CGle EBee ECha EGar ELan GMac MArl MBal MBri MWgw NBro WBea WEas WOve EMan EMon GBuc
§ × *walkeri* 'Abbotswood Rose' ♀	
wilfordii	CPou CRDP EBee EHic EJud WBea
§ *yunnanensis*	CPea CSam EBee ECro EGar GBin GBuc GCHN GCra LLWP MFir MSte NHol WBea WPer WWhi
– *alba*	See *L. yunnanensis*

LYCIANTHES (Solanaceae)

rantonnetii	See *Solanum rantonnetii*

LYCIUM (Solanaceae)

barbarum	ELan SMad WSHC WWye
chinense	CArn CPlN

LYCOPODIUM (Lycopodiaceae)

clavatum	GPoy

LYCOPSIS See ANCHUSA

LYCOPUS (Lamiaceae)

¶ *americanus*   MSal
europaeus   CArn CJew ELau EWFC GBar
   GPoy MChe MHew MSal WChe
   WGwG WHer WJek WWye
exaltatus   WChe
virginicus   MSal

LYCORIS (Amaryllidaceae)

albiflora   SDeJ
¶ *radiata*   EBot

LYGEUM (Poaceae)

¶ *spartum*   EPPr

LYGODIUM (Schizaeaceae)

¶ *japonicum*   WRic

LYONIA (Ericaceae)

ligustrina   EHic SMur SSta
ovalifolia var. *elliptica*   SSta
¶ *villosa* B&SWJ 2161   WCru

LYONOTHAMNUS (Rosaceae)

floribundus subsp.   CAbb CHEx SAPC SArc SIgm
aspleniifolius   WCru WWat

LYSICHITON (Araceae)

americanus ♀   CB&S CBen CHEx CHad
   CRow CTrw CWat ECha EHon
   ELan EMFW EPar GAbr GDra
   LPBA LSyl MRav MSta NChi
   NDea NHol SPer SRms SSoC
   SSpi SWat WChe WNor WWat
camtschatcensis ♀   CB&S CBen CHEx CRow
   CWat ECha EHon ELan
   EMFW EPar LPBA MSta Ndea
   NOrc SPer SSpi SWat WChe
– × *americanus*   SSpi

LYSIMACHIA † (Primulaceae)

atropurpurea   CHal CLTr CMil CPle EAst
   ECGN EGar ELan EMar GBin
   GBri MCCP MCli MNrw MTis
   NFai NSti WCot WFar WMaN
   WPer
– 'Geronimo'   CBlo NPri
barystachys   CHea CRow GCHN GMaP
   MRav WCot WOve
ciliata   CGle CMHG CRow ECha EFer
   EGol EHoe ELan EMar EPar
   GMac LFis LWak MAus MBri
   MCLN MFir MNrw NChi NDea
   SChu WEas WHal WLin WOld
   WOve WPbr WPer WWin
§ – 'Firecracker' ♀   Widely available
– 'Purpurea'   See *L. ciliata* 'Firecracker'
clethroides ♀   CFee CGle CHal CHan CKel
   CMHG CPle CRDP CRow
   ECha EEls ELan EMil LGan
   LHop MBri MHlr MWat NDea
   NSti SAxl SHel SPer WBea
   WEas WLin WMow WOld
   WRus
– from Guizhou, China   EWes
– 'Lady Jane'   CBlo
§ *congestiflora*   CLTr LHil LHop LPVe MBEx
   NCut NPer SHFr WLRN
– 'Outback Sunset'   CHal EMan LHop MLLN NBir
   NPri WLRN WWeb
– 'Sunbeam'   WCot

ephemerum   Widely available
fortunei   EMon SHel WCot
henryi   CHal CLTr EHic EWes GBuc
   MHlr WBrE
japonica 'Minutissima'   CInt CRow EPPr GBuc GCHN
   MTho WAbe WCru WPer
lanceolata   WCot
lichiangensis   CFir EMFP GSki MCCP MHar
   MLLN SHFr SMac SOkh WBor
   WLin WMaN WPer
– B&L 12317   CGle NChi
– B&L 12464   CRow WCot WThi
lyssii   See *L. congestiflora*
minoricensis   CBot CPle CRow EBrP EBre
   ECro EEls ELan EPri GBri
   LBre NChi SBre SMad SSca
   SWat WByw WCot WLRN
   WOve WPer WWin
nemorum   EFer EWFC WCot WPer
   WRHF
nummularia   CBen CHal CWat EBrP EBre
   ECtt EHon ELau EWFC GPoy
   LBre LHol LPBA MBar MBri
   MHew MWgw NBro NDea
   NNor SBre SHFr SWat SWyc
   WBea WByw WChe WMow
   WOak WWye
– 'Aurea' ♀   Widely available
punctata   CHal CKel CRow ECha EEls
   EHon ELan EWFC LHol
   MCLN MWat NBro NHol NMir
   NNor NPer NSti SPer SWat
   SWyc WBea WByw WEas
   WOld WOve WPer WWin
– 'Alexander' (v)   CDec CHea CRDP CRow EAst
   EBee EHic EMar EMon GAri
   MAus MAvo MLLN MWat
   NCat NDov NHol NPer NPro
   NSti WBea WCot WGer WHil
   WOve WPbr WSan
– dwarf form   EHic
* – 'Snow Lady'   SHel
– *verticillata*   See *L. verticillaris*
* 'Purpurea'   MGrG
* *serpyllifolia*   SHFr
sertulata   WCot
thyrsiflora   CRow EHon MSta NDea SWat
   WChe WCot WHer WMAq
§ *verticillaris*   MHlr WCot
vulgaris   CArn EHon EWFC LPBA
   MHew SIde WChe WGwy WPer
   WWye
– var. *davurica*   WCot

LYSIONOTUS (Gesneriaceae)

pauciflora   MHig NTow WCru
– B&SWJ 1679   WCru
– B&SWJ 189   WCru
– B&SWJ 303   WCru
– B&SWJ 335   WCru

LYTHRUM (Lythraceae)

'Red Wings'   NBro
salicaria   CArn CBen CKin CRow CWat
   ECoo EHon EMFW EWFC
   GCHN LHol LPBA MFir
   MHew MSCN MSal NBro NLan
   NMir NNor SWat WByw WChe
   WCla WGwG WHer WMAq
   WPbr WShi WWye
– 'Blush'   Widely available
– 'Brightness'   NCat NFla NHol WMow

§ – 'Feuerkerze' ♀ — CRDP CRow EBrP EBre EFou EHal ELan GCal LBre LFis MBel MCLN MRav MUlv NCat NFai NHol NSti SBre SChu SPer WFar WPer
– Firecandle — See *L. salicaria* **'Feuerkerze'**
– 'Florarose' — EFou
– 'Happy' — SMrm
– 'Lady Sackville' — CBos EBar EFou GBuc GCal GGar GMaP LFis NCat WAbe
– 'Morden Pink' — CDoC EFou LBuc LRHS MBri
– 'Robert' — CMGP CRow CTri EBrP EBre ECha ELan ENot EPar EPfP LBre MCLN MHlr MTis MWat NCut NHol NOak SBre SChu SPer WChe WEas WMow WOld WUnu
– 'Rose' — ELan MWgw
– 'Stichflamme' — EFou
– 'The Beacon' — CDoC CRow EMan GCal MAvo SRms WCot
– Ulverscroft form — MTed
– 'Zigeunerblut' — CRDP LBuc LGre MRav
virgatum 'Dropmore Purple' — CLTr CRDP EFou LRHS MAus MBri NCut
– 'Rose Queen' — ECha MRav SUsu WPer
– 'Rosy Gem' — CM&M CRow EBar ECtt EGar EMar GMac LSyl MFir MOne MWat NBro NOak NTow SRms SSvw WBea WHoo WPer
– 'The Rocket' — CRow CTri NCat NHol NLak NSti SPer WChe WWin

LYTOCARYUM (Arecaceae)
§ *weddellianum* ♀ — MBri

MAACKIA (Papilionaceae)
amurensis — CAgr CB&S ELan EPfP SRCN WFro WNor
¶ – var. *buergeri* — MBlu
chinensis — MBlu
¶ *fauriei* — CPle

MACFADYENA (Bignoniaceae)
§ *unguis-cati* — CPlN CRHN GCra

MACHAERANTHERA (Asteraceae)
pattersonii — See *M. bigelovii*

MACHILUS See PERSEA

MACKAYA (Acanthaceae)
§ *bella* ♀ — ERea LBlm LCns WMul

MACLEANIA (Ericaceae)
insignis — CPlN

MACLEAYA (Papaveraceae)
N *cordata* ♀ — CArn CHEx CMCo ECoo ELan EMar EPar MRav MSCN MTis MWat NOrc NTow SPar SPer SRCN SRms WEas WFar WHal WHoo WPer WWhi WWin
– 'Flamingo' — EAst EBee ECha GCHN GCal GMaP MCLN MRav MUlv NSti SMrm WWye
x *kewensis* — MBro WHoo WPyg
§ *microcarpa* — CBlo EGar EHal EPPr LBlm SRCN SWat WGwy WHer WSel

– 'Kelway's Coral Plume' ♀ — CB&S CGle CHEx CHad ECha ELan EOrc EPar GMaP MAus MBri MCLN MRav NBro NFla SChu SPer SSoC WEas WOld WOve WWal WWat
¶ 'Spetchley Ruby' — WCot

MACLURA (Moraceae)
pomifera — CB&S CLnd CMCN CPle WDin WPGP WPic

MACRODIERVILLA See WEIGELA

MACROPIPER (Piperaceae)
crocatum — See *Piper ornatum*
§ *excelsum* — CHEx ECou
– 'Aureopictum' — CHEx

MACROZAMIA (Zamiaceae)
communis — CBrP LPal MAll WNor
diplomera — CBrP
dyeri — See *M. riedlei*
¶ *lucida* — CBrP
miquelii — CBrP LPal
moorei — CBrP LPal
mountperiensis — CBrP
§ *riedlei* — CBrP LPal
¶ *spiralis* — MFiF

MAGNOLIA † (Magnoliaceae)
acuminata — CB&S CBlo CFil CMCN MBal SSpi WPGP
* – 'Kinju' — CFil WPGP
¶ – 'Koban Dori' — CFil CPMA WPGP
¶ – large yellow — CFil WPGP
§ – var. *subcordata* — WPGP
♦ – – 'Miss Honeybee' — See *M. cordata* **'Miss Honeybee'**
¶ 'Albatross' — CMHG CTho
'Ann' ♀ — COtt SSpi WPGP
'Anne Rosse' — CFil WPGP
'Apollo' — CB&S CFil CPMA WPGP
¶ *ashei* — CFil SSpi WNor WPGP
'Athene' — CB&S CMHG CPMA WPGP
'Atlas' — CB&S CEnd CFil CMHG CPMA SSpi WPGP
'Betty' ♀ — CB&S CBlo CDoC EMil IOrc LNet MGos SSta WLRN WPyg
'Big Dude' — CFil WPGP
biondii — CFil
x *brooklynensis* — CB&S CPMA SSta
  'Woodsman'
¶ 'Butterflies' — CFil SSpi WPGP
'Caerhays Belle' — CB&S CFil CPMA WPGP
campbellii — CB&S CFil CMCN CPMA CRos CSam CTho ELan EPfP ICrw IOrc ISea MAsh SSpi WPGP
– var. *alba* — CB&S CTho
– 'Betty Jessel' — CTho
– subsp. *mollicomata* — CB&S CEnd CPMA CTrw EPfP ISea SPer WPGP
– – 'Lanarth' — CB&S CEnd SSta
– (Raffillii Group) 'Charles Raffill' ♀ — CB&S CBlo CDoC CPMA EBee ELan GGGa MDun MLan SHBN SMad WCwm WPGP
– – 'Kew's Surprise' — CB&S
– 'Strybing White' — CPMA
¶ 'Cecil Nice' — CFil WPGP
'Columbus' — CFil WPGP

cordata	See *M. acuminata* var. *subcordata*
§ – 'Miss Honeybee'	CFil
cylindrica hort. ♀	CB&S GGGa IOrc ISea SSta
¶ – Wilson	SSpi
* 'David Clulow'	CFil SSpi WPGP
dawsoniana	CB&S CMCN CPMA
delavayi	CB&S CFil CHEx EPfP GGGa SAPC SArc SSpi WPGP
– SF 432	ISea
§ *denudata* ♀	CB&S CMCN CTho CTrw EPfP IOrc LPan MBal SPer SReu SSpi SSta WNor WWat
– 'Forrest's Pink'	CFil COtt CPMA
– var. *purpurascens*	See *M. sprengeri* var. *diva*
¶ 'Elisa Odenwald'	CFil WPGP
'Elizabeth' ♀	CFil CMCN CPMA ELan EPfP GGGa LHyd LRHS MAsh NHol SSpi SSta WPGP
'Full Eclipse'	CFil WPGP
'Galaxy' ♀	CB&S CEnd CFil CPMA CTho IOrc MBar MBlu MGos SSpi SSta SSto WGwG WPGP
'George Henry Kern'	CBlo CDoC COtt CPMA IOrc LPan MAsh MGos SSpi SSta
globosa	CB&S CFil GGGa WPGP
'Goldstar'	CFil LRHS SSpi WPGP
grandiflora	CBlo CHEx CMCN EAst EBrP EBre EMil LBre MRav SAPC SArc SBre WDin WNor WWat
¶ – 'Angustifolia'	WPGP
– 'Edith Bogue'	ENot SBid
– 'Exmouth' ♀	CB&S CBlo CBot CGre CLan CMCN EBrP EBre ELan ENot IOrc LBre LHyd LNet MAsh MBal MBri SBid SBre SFam SHBN SMad SPer SReu SSpi SSta WGwG WWat
– 'Ferruginea'	CLan
– 'Galissonière'	CBlo COtt GOrc IOrc LPan SBid SSpi
I – 'Galissonière Nana'	LPan
– 'Goliath' ♀	CB&S CBlo CEnd CFil CHEx CTrC ELan IOrc LHyd LNet MBal SBid SPer SSpi SSta WPGP
– 'Little Gem'	CBlo CPMA CTrC LRHS MAsh SSpi WPGP WStI
* – 'Nana Flore Pleno'	CPMA
– 'Russet'	CPMA LNet
– 'Saint Mary'	CPMA
– 'Samuel Sommer'	CHEx CMCN CPMA SAPC SArc SSpi WGer
¶ – 'Silver Tip'	WPGP
– 'Undulata'	IOrc
– 'Victoria'	CFil ELan MAsh MBlu MBri SReu SSta WCwm WPGP
¶ 'Hawk'	CFil WPGP
'Heaven Scent' ♀	CAbP CB&S CBlo CMCN COtt CSam CTho CTrw ELan IOrc LHyd LPan MAsh MBal MBar MBlu MGos SPer SSpi SSta WDin WPGP WPyg
¶ 'Helen Fogg'	CFil WPGP
heptapeta	See *M. denudata*
¶ 'Hot Lips'	CFil WPGP
§ *hypoleuca* ♀	CDoC CFil CHEx CMCN CTho EPfP GGGa ISea MBlu MLan SHBN SSpi WCwm WWat
'Iolanthe' ♀	CB&S CDoC CEnd CFil CMCN CMHG CPMA CTho MAsh NHol SPer SSta WPGP
'Jane' ♀	CBlo CDoC COtt ELan IOrc ISea MAsh MBri MGos NHol SSta
'Joe McDaniel'	CDoC SSta
'Jon Jon'	CFil
¶ 'Judy' ♀	COtt
§ × *kewensis* 'Kew Clone'	CB&S
♦ – 'Kewensis'	See *M.* × *kewensis* 'Kew Clone'
– 'Wada's Memory' ♀	CB&S CFil CMCN CMHG CTho EBee EPfP GGGa MAsh MBri SPer SSpi SSta
kobus	CB&S CBlo CGre CMCN CPMA CTho ENot IOrc LHyd LPan SHBN SPer SSpi SSta WDin WNor WSpi WWat
– var. *borealis*	CTho
♦ – 'Norman Gould'	See *M. stellata* 'Norman Gould'
* – 'Laura'	CFil WPGP
– 'Lilenny'	SSta
§ *liliiflora*	CBlo CTrw MAsh MBar
§ – 'Nigra' ♀	CB&S CBlo CGre EBrP EBre ELan EMil ENot GChr IOrc LBre LPan MGos NFla SBre SHBN SPer SPla SReu SSpi SSta WBay WDin WFar WStI
* 'Limelight'	CFil WPGP
× *loebneri*	CB&S WNor
– 'Ballerina'	CDoC CMCN COtt SSta
– 'Leonard Messel' ♀	Widely available
– 'Merrill' ♀	CB&S CBlo CFil CMCN CMHG CPMA CSam CTho CTrh EBrP EBre ELan IOrc ISea LBre LPan MAsh MBal MBri NHol SBre SPer SReu SSpi SSta WDin WGwG WPGP WPyg WWat
– 'Neil McEacharn'	IOrc
¶ – 'Powder Puff'	CFil WPGP
¶ – 'Raspberry Fun'	CFil WPGP
¶ – 'Snowdrift'	CMCN SSta
¶ – 'Spring Joy'	CFil WPGP
¶ – 'Spring Snow'	CMCN
– 'Star Bright'	CMCN
macrophylla	CBrP CFil CHEx CMCN EOas EPfP SAPC SArc SSpi WCoo WPGP
– 'Sara Gladney'	CHEx
'Manchu Fan'	CPMA IOrc SSta
'Mark Jury'	CB&S CPMA
'Marwood Spring'	CTho
'Maryland' ♀	CBlo CFil CPMA SSpi WPGP
'Milky Way'	CB&S CFil CMHG COtt CPMA CTho WPGP
♦ *obovata* Diels	See *M. officinalis*
♦ – Thunb.	See *M. hypoleuca*
§ *officinalis*	CFil WPGP
'Peppermint Stick' ♀	CPMA MGos SSta
'Peter Smithers'	CFil IOrc WPGP
¶ 'Phelan Bright'	CFil WPGP
'Pickard's Coral'	MBal
'Pickard's Opal'	LHyd
'Pickard's Ruby'	CDoC COtt CPMA
§ 'Pickard's Schmetterling'	CDoC SSta
♦ 'Pickard's Sundew'	See *M.* 'Sundew'
'Pinkie'	COtt IOrc MAsh MBri SSta
× *proctoriana* ♀	CAbP CFil ELan EPfP IOrc ISea MAsh SSta
– 'Proctoriana'	LHyd
* 'Purple Glow'	CFil WPGP
'Purple Prince'	CFil
quinquepeta	See *M. liliiflora*
¶ 'Randy' ♀	COtt

'Raspberry Ice' — CDoC CMHG COtt CRos CTho CTrw IOrc MBal SSta

'Ricki' ♀ — COtt CPMA IOrc MBri MGos SSta WWat

'Royal Crown' — SSta

salicifolia ♀ — CFil ISea MAsh SBid SPer SSpi SSta WPGP WPic

¶ – var. *concolor* — CFil SSpi WPGP

* – 'Rosea' — CFil WPGP

◆ – 'W.B. Clarke' — See M. 'W.B. Clarke'

sargentiana — CFil IOrc WPGP

– var. *robusta* — CB&S CEnd CTrw ELan EPfP IOrc MAsh SSpi SSta WCwm WPGP

– var. *robusta alba* — CTrw

'Sayonara' ♀ — CB&S COtt CPMA EPfP IOrc MBlu SSpi SSta WDin

◆ 'Schmetterling' — See M. 'Pickard's Schmetterling'

'Serene' — CB&S CFil CPMA SSpi

* 'Seyu' — SSpi

sieboldii — CB&S CBlo CGre CMCN CPMA ELan EMil IOrc LPan MAsh MBal MBar MBri MDun MGos SHBN SSpi SSta WBod WCoo WCwm WNor WSpi

– subsp. *sinensis* ♀ — CB&S CBlo CMCN CSam ELan EPfP GGGa MDun SPer SSpi WDin WWat

× *soulangeana* — CB&S CBlo CLan CTrh CTrw EBrP EBre ELan EMil ENot GOrc IOrc ISea LBre MAsh MBal MBar MBri MGos MWat NBee SBre SHBN SPer WDin WNor

§ – 'Alba' — CB&S CBlo CEnd ENot IOrc LPan MAsh MGos SPer SSpi WWat

◆ – 'Alba Superba' — See M. × *soulangeana* 'Alba'

– 'Alexandrina' ♀ — CBlo CDoC COtt ELan IOrc MBri SPer

– 'Alexandrina Alba' — CTho

– 'Amabilis' — CDoC COtt IOrc

– 'Brozzonii' ♀ — CB&S CMCN CMHG CSam IOrc ISea LPan MAsh SSpi

– 'Burgundy' Clarke — CB&S CBot CDoC SSta

– 'Lennei' ♀ — CB&S CBlo CEnd CMCN CMHG IOrc LPan MAsh MGos NHol SHBN SPer SRms WNor WPyg WStI WWat

– 'Lennei Alba' ♀ — CMCN ELan IOrc

– 'Nigra' — See M. *liliiflora* 'Nigra'

◆ – 'Pickard's Sundew' — See M. 'Sundew'

– 'Picture' — CBlo CDoC CMCN IOrc WDin

– 'Rubra' misapplied — See M. × *soulangeana* 'Rustica Rubra'

§ – 'Rustica Rubra' ♀ — CB&S CEnd CMCN CPMA CSam EBrP EBre ELan ENot IOrc LBre LNet LPan MAsh MBri SBre SHBN SPer SReu SSpi SSta WBay WGwG WPGP WWat WWeb

– 'San José' — CRos IOrc MAsh SPer SSta

– 'Verbanica' — LRHS MAsh

– 'White Giant' — CDoC

'Spectrum' — CB&S CFil CPMA SSpi WPGP

sprengeri — CTrw WNor WShe WWes

§ – var. *diva* — CB&S CFil CMCN SSpi WPGP

– – 'Burncoose' — CB&S

¶ – – 'Claret Cup' — CFil SSpi WPGP

– var. *elongata* — COtt IOrc ISea

¶ – 'Eric Savill' — CFil WPGP

– 'Lanhydrock' — CFil SSpi

'Star Wars' — CB&S CDoC CFil CPMA CTho SSpi SSta

§ *stellata* ♀ — Widely available

– 'Centennial' — CDoC SSta

– 'Chrysanthemiflora' — LHyd LRHS SPer SSpi

¶ – 'Jane Platt' — SSpi

– f. *keiskei* — CEnd COtt

– 'King Rose' — CB&S CBlo CDoC COtt MAsh MBlu MBri NHed SPer

§ – 'Norman Gould' — CMCN COtt EPfP SSta

– 'Rosea' — COtt ELan IOrc MGos SHBN WPyg WStI

– 'Royal Star' — CB&S CBlo CBot CEnd CLan CMCN ECtt EMil ENot IOrc LPan MAsh MBri MGos SPer SSpi SSta WHCG WHar WStI

– 'Waterlily' ♀ — CB&S CBlo CBot CEnd CMCN CRos CSam ELan GOrc IOrc MAsh SPer SSpi SSta WPyg

'Sundance' — CFil WPGP

§ 'Sundew' — CB&S CDoC CMCN CPMA EPfP IOrc MBri MGos SHBN

'Susan' ♀ — Widely available

× *thompsoniana* — CMCN

¶ 'Tiffany' — CFil WPGP

¶ 'Tina Durio' — WPGP

¶ 'Todd Gresham' — CPMA WPGP

tripetala — CB&S CHEx CMCN EPfP LPan MDun MLan SHBN SSpi SSta WCoo WCwm WDin WWat

× *veitchii* — CDoC SSpi

¶ – 'Isca' — CTho WPGP

– 'Peter Veitch' — CFil CGre CTho

virginiana — CGre CMCN SSpi WPGP

¶ – 'Havener' — WPGP

– 'Vulcan' — CB&S CFil COtt CPMA CTho

× *watsonii* — See M. × *wiesneri*

§ × *wiesneri* — CFil CPMA ELan EPfP MBlu SPer SSpi SSta WPGP

wilsonii ♀ — CB&S CFil CMCN CSam CTho CTrw ELan GGGa ICrw IOrc MBal SHBN SMad SPer SReu SSpi SSta WCwm WDin WNor WPGP WPic WSHC WTro WWat

¶ 'Winelight' — CFil WPGP

'Yellow Bird' — CFil COtt EPfP SSpi WPGP

'Yellow Fever' — CFil CPMA WPGP

¶ 'Yellow Lantern' — CFil WPGP

× MAHOBERBERIS (Berberidaceae)

aquisargentii — CAbP CPle ENot EPla GBin LHop MAll MPla MRav NHol SBid SPer WGwG WPat WPyg WWat

'Dart's Treasure' — EPla WFar

'Magic' — MRav

miethkeana — CMHG MAll MBar

MAHONIA † (Berberidaceae)

acanthifolia — See M. *napaulensis*

§ *aquifolium* — CAgr CB&S CPer EAst ENot GCHN GChr GOrc GRei ISea MAsh MBal MBar MBri MGos MWat NFla NNor NRoo NWea SHBN SPer SReu SSoC WCFE WDin WHCG WStI

– 'Apollo' ♀ — ECtt ELan EMil ENot EPla IOrc MAsh MBar MBri MGos NBee NHol SHBN SPer SReu SSta WPyg WWat

– 'Atropurpurea'	CDoC ELan ENot EPla MHlr NBee SHBN SPer SPla WWat
* – 'Cosmo Crawl'	MGos
– 'Fascicularis'	See *M.* × *wagneri* **'Pinnacle'**
– 'Green Ripple'	COtt EPfP EPla MBri SPla WFar
– 'Mirena'	MGos
– 'Orange Flame'	MBlu
– 'Smaragd'	CBlo CDoC ELan ENot EPfP EPla IOrc MBlu MGos NHol WBay WHCG WPyg
– 'Versicolor'	MBlu
bealei	See *M. japonica* **Bealei Group**
confusa	CFil CHEx WPGP
eutriphylla	EPla
fortunei	EPla MBal WBcn WSHC
fremontii	GCal LGre WSHC
– × *haematocarpa*	GCal
haematocarpa	GCal
japonica ♀	CBot CChe CEnd CHEx CTre CTrw ELan ENot MAsh MBal MBar MBri MWat NHol SHBN SPer SReu SRms SSpi SSta WDin WHCG WPat WSHC WWal WWat
§ – Bealei Group	CB&S CHar CLan EAst EBee EBrP EBre ELan EPfP GRei IOrc LBre MAsh MBar MGos SBre SEas SSoC WDin WWeb
– 'Hiemalis'	See *M. japonica* **'Hivernant'**
§ – 'Hivernant'	EPla NFla WBay WPyg
lomariifolia ♀	CB&S CBot CHEx CPle ENot IHos IOrc ISea MBal SAPC SArc SDry SPer SPla SSpi WSHC
¶ × *media* 'Arthur Menzies'	EPla
– 'Buckland' ♀	CAbP CB&S CEnd CSam CTrw ECtt ISea MAsh MBal MBri SBid SPer SRms WPat WPyg WRHF WWat WWeb
– 'Charity' ♀	CB&S CLan EBrP EBre ELan ENot EPla GOrc GRei LBre LHop MAsh MBal MBar MBri MGos NFla NHol SBre SHBN SMad SPer SReu SSoC SSta WDin WHCG WHar WPat WWat
– 'Charity's Sister'	EPla MBri
– 'Faith'	EPla
– 'Lionel Fortescue' ♀	CB&S CBlo CEnd CSam CTre CTrw EBrP EBre ELan ENot EPla GCHN ISea LBre LHop MAsh MBal MBri MPla SBid SBre SEas SMad SPer SReu SSpi SSta WHCG WWat
– 'Underway' ♀	CSam EPfP EPla MAsh MBri SMur SPla WWat WWes
– 'Winter Sun' ♀	CB&S CEnd COtt EBar EBrP EBre ELan EMil EPla IOrc ISea LBre MAsh MBal MBlu MBri MGos MWat NHol SBid SBre SHBN SPla SSta WDin WHar WPyg WWat WWin
nervosa	COtt EPfP EPla LPan MBlu NBee NHol SBid SPer SSta
pallida	CFil EPla WPGP WWat
N*pinnata*	EBee ELan ENot EPfP EPla IOrc MBal MBar MBro SPer
pumila	EPla
repens	CPle EPla ERav MAll
– 'Rotundifolia'	EPla
¶ *russellii*	CGre
* × *savillii*	EPla
siamensis	CGre
trifoliolata var. *glauca*	CEnd
× *wagneri* 'Moseri'	EMil SSpi WPat
§ – 'Pinnacle' ♀	EPfP EPla MGos SMur SPer
¶ – 'Sunset'	EPla MBlu
– 'Undulata' ♀	ECtt ENot EPfP EPla IHos NHol SDix SRms WHCG

MAIHUENIA (Cactaceae) See Plant Deletions

MAIANTHEMUM (Convallariaceae)

bifolium	CAvo CRDP CRow CVer ELan EMon EPot EWFC GBuc MBal MDun MNrw MTho NBro NMen SRms WAbe WCru WGwy WLin WTin WWat WWye
– subsp. *kamtschaticum*	CAvo CRDP CRow ECro EMon EPar LSyl SDys WCot
¶ – – 'Variegatum'	WCru
canadense	GCal MSal
dilatatum	See *M. bifolium* var. *kamtschaticum*
¶ *oleraceum*	WCru

MALEPHORA (Aizoaceae)

lutea	CNic MHig

MALLOTUS (Euphorbiaceae) See Plant Deletions

MALPIGHIA (Malpighiaceae) See Plant Deletions

MALUS † (Rosaceae)

× *adstringens* 'Hopa'	CBlo CLnd
– 'Simcoe'	CDoC CLnd EBee MGos
'Aldenhamensis'	See *M.* × *purpurea* **'Aldenhamensis'**
* *arborescens*	CTho
× *atrosanguinea*	NWea
§ – 'Gorgeous'	CBlo COtt GChr GTwe MAsh MBri SIgm WDin WJas
baccata	CLnd CMCN CTho GTwe WNor
– 'Lady Northcliffe'	CLnd SFam
¶ *brevipes*	CTho
'Butterball'	MBri WJas
* 'Cheal's Weeping'	SPer WStI
coronaria var. *dasycalyx*	CBlo CDoC CEnd CLnd COtt
'Charlottae' (d)	CSam CTho ENot MAsh SPer
'Crittenden'	EBee ENot
* 'Directeur Moerlands'	CBlo EPfP MAsh MGos WJas
domestica (F)	MGos
– 'Acme' (D)	SDea SKee
– 'Adam's Pearmain' (D)	CCAT CTho GTwe SDea SFam SIgm SKee WHow WJas
– 'Advance' (D)	SKee
– 'Akane' (D)	SDea
§ – 'Alexander' (C)	SKee
– 'Alfriston' (C)	SKee
– 'Alkmene' (D)	GTwe SKee
– 'Allen's Everlasting' (D)	GTwe SDea SKee
– 'Allington Pippin' (D)	CCAT CCVT CSam CTho CTri NRog SDea SKee WHow WJas
– 'American Mother'	See *M. domestica* **'Mother'**
– 'Anna Boelens' (D)	SDea
– 'Annie Elizabeth' (C)	CCAT CCVT CTho GTwe SDea SFam SKee WJas
¶ – 'Anniversary'	SDea

– 'Api Noir' (D)   SKee
– 'Api Rose' (D)   CCVT SKee WJas
– 'Ard Cairn Russet' (D)   GTwe SDea SKee
– 'Aromatic Russet' (D)   SKee
– 'Arthur Turner' (C) ♀   CCVT CDoC EMui GTwe LBuc MGos NRog SDea SFam SKee WJas
– 'Ashmead's Kernel' (D) ♀   CCAT CCVT CSam CTho EBrP EBre EMui ERea GTwe LBre LBuc MWat NRog SBre SDea SFam SIgm SKee WHow WJas
– 'Ashton Bitter' (Cider)   CCAT CCVT CEnd CSam CTho GTwe
– 'Ashton Brown Jersey' (Cider)   CCAT CTho
– 'Autumn Pearmain' (D)   CTho SDea WJas
– 'Baker's Delicious' (D)   SDea SIgm SKee
– 'Balsam'   See *M. domestica* **'Green Balsam'**
– 'Banns' (D)   SKee
– 'Barnack Beauty' (D)   CTho SKee
– 'Barnack Orange' (D)   SKee
– 'Bascombe Mystery' (D)   SKee
– 'Baumann's Reinette' (D)   SKee
– 'Baxter's Pearmain' (C/D)   SKee
– 'Beauty of Bath' (D)   CCVT CDoC CTho CTri GTwe IOrc LBuc NRog SFam SKee WJas
– 'Beauty of Hants' (D)   SKee
– 'Beauty of Kent' (C)   SDea SKee
– 'Beauty of Moray' (C)   SKee
– 'Bedwyn Beauty' (C)   CTho
– 'Beeley Pippin' (D)   GTwe SDea SKee
– 'Bell Apple' (Cider/C)   CTho
– 'Belle de Boskoop' (C/D) ♀   CCAT CSam CTho GTwe SDea SKee
– 'Bembridge Beauty' (F)   SDea
– 'Ben's Red' (D)   CEnd CTho SKee
– 'Bess Pool' (D)   SDea SFam SKee
◆ – 'Bewley Down Pippin'   See *M. domestica* **'Crimson King'**
– 'Billy Down Pippin' (F)   CTho
– 'Bismarck' (C)   CTho SKee
– 'Black Dabinett' (Cider)   CCAT CTho
– 'Black Tom Putt' (C/D)   CTho
– 'Blaze' (D)   GTwe
– 'Blenheim Orange' (C/D) ♀   CCAT CCVT CDoC CTho EMui GBon GTwe LBuc MBri MWat NRog SDea SFam SIgm SKee SPer WHow WJas WWeb
– 'Blenheim Red'   See *M. domestica* **'Red Blenheim'**
– 'Bloody Ploughman' (F)   SKee
– 'Blue Pearmain' (D)   SDea SKee
– 'Blue Sweet' (Cider)   CTho
– Bolero   See *M. domestica* Bolero = **'Tuscan'**
– 'Boston Russet'   See *M. domestica* **'Roxbury Russet'**
– 'Bountiful' (C)   CCAT COtt EMui GTwe MGos SDea SIgm WStI
– 'Bow Hill Pippin' (D)   SKee
– 'Box Apple' (D)   SKee
– 'Braddick Nonpareil' (D)   SKee
– 'Braeburn' (D)   SDea SKee

– 'Bramley's Seedling' (C) ♀   CB&S CCAT CCVT CMac CSam EBrP EBre EMui ERea GBon GChr GRei GTwe IOrc LBre LBuc MBri MWat NBee NDal NRog SBre SDea SFam SIgm SKee SPer WJas WWeb
– 'Bread Fruit' (C/D)   CEnd
– 'Breakwell Seedling' (Cider)   CCAT CTho
– 'Bridgwater Pippin' (C)   CTho WJas
– 'Bringewood Pippin' (D)   WJas
– 'Broad-eyed Pippin' (C)   SKee
– 'Brown Snout' (Cider)   CCAT CTho
– 'Brown Thorn' (Cider)   CCAT
– 'Brownlees Russet' (D)   CTho EMui GTwe NRog SDea SFam SKee
– 'Brown's Apple' (Cider)   CCAT GTwe
– 'Broxwood Foxwhelp' (Cider)   CTho
¶ – 'Bulmer's Norman' (Cider)   CCAT
– 'Burn's Seedling' (D)   CTho
– 'Burr Knot' (C)   SKee
– 'Burrow Hill Early' (Cider)   CTho
– 'Bushey Grove' (C)   SDea SKee
– 'Calville Blanc d'Hiver' (D)   SKee
– 'Cambusnethan Pippin' (D)   SKee
– 'Camelot' (Cider/C)   CCAT CTho
– 'Cap of Liberty' (Cider)   CCAT
– 'Captain Broad' (Cider)   CCAT CEnd CTho
– 'Captain Smith' (F)   CEnd
– 'Carlisle Codlin' (C)   GTwe
– 'Carswell's Orange' (D)   SKee
– 'Catshead' (C)   CCAT CCVT GQui SDea SKee WJas
– 'Cellini' (C/D)   SDea
– 'Charles Ross' (C/D) ♀   CCAT CCVT CMac CSam CTho EBrP EBre EMui GBon GRei GTwe LBre MWat NDal NRog SBre SDea SFam SIgm SKee WHow WJas
– 'Charlotte' (C/Ball)   LBuc MGos
– 'Chaxhill Red' (Cider/D)   CTho
– 'Cheddar Cross' (D)   CTri SKee
– 'Chelmsford Wonder' (C)   SKee
– 'Chisel Jersey' (Cider)   CCAT CTho
– 'Chiver's Delight' (D)   CCAT EMui GTwe SDea SIgm SKee WJas
– 'Chorister Boy' (D)   CTho
– 'Christmas Pearmain' (D)   CTho GTwe SDea SFam SKee WHow
– 'Cider Lady's Finger' (Cider)   CCAT
– 'Claygate Pearmain' (D)   CCAT CTho GTwe LBuc SDea SFam SIgm SKee WJas
¶ – 'Coat Jersey' (Cider)   CCAT
– 'Cockle Pippin' (D)   CTho GTwe SDea SKee
– 'Coeur de Boeuf' (C/D)   SKee
– 'Coleman's Seedling' (Cider)   CTho
– 'Collogett Pippin' (C/Cider)   CEnd CTho
– 'Colonel Vaughan' (C/D)   CTho SKee
– 'Cornish Aromatic' (D)   CSam CTho EMui GTwe SDea SFam SIgm SKee WJas

- 'Cornish Crimson Queen' (F) — GTwe
- 'Cornish Gilliflower' (D) — CCAT SDea SFam SIgm SKee WJas
- 'Cornish Honeypin' (D) — CTho
- 'Cornish Longstem' (D) — CEnd CTho
- 'Cornish Mother' (D) — CEnd
- 'Cornish Pine' (D) — CEnd CTho SDea SKee
- 'Coronation' (D) — SDea SKee
- 'Costard' (C) — GTwe SKee
- 'Cottenham Seedling' (C) — SKee
- 'Coul Blush' (D) — SKee
- 'Court of Wick' (D) — CCAT CTho SKee
- 'Court Pendu Plat' (D) — CCAT CCVT CTho LBuc MWat NRog SDea SFam SIgm SKee WJas
- 'Court Royal' (Cider) — CCAT CTho
- 'Cox's Orange Pippin' (D) — CB&S CCAT CCVT CMac EBrP EBre GTwe LBre LBuc MBri MWat NRog SBre SDea SFam SKee SPer WJas WWeb
- 'Cox's Pomona' (C/D) — CTho SDea SKee WJas
- 'Cox's Rouge de Flandres' (D) — SKee
- 'Cox's Selfing' (D) — CBlo CWSG ERea GTwe LBuc MGos SKee WJas WWeb
- 'Crawley Beauty' (C) — GTwe SDea SFam SKee WHow WJas
- 'Crimson Cox' (D) — SDea
§ – 'Crimson King' (Cider/C) — CCAT CTho
- 'Crimson Queening' (D) — SKee WJas
- 'Crimson Victoria' (Cider) — CTho
- Crispin — See *M. domestica* 'Mutsu'
§ – 'Crowngold' (D) — CEnd EMui GBon GTwe
- 'Cummy Norman' (Cider) — CCAT
- 'Curl Tail' (D) — SKee
- 'Dabinett' (Cider) — CCAT CCVT CEnd CTho CTri EMui GTwe LBuc SDea SKee
- 'D'Arcy Spice' (D) — CCAT SDea SFam SIgm SKee
- 'Dawn' (D) — SKee
- 'Deacon's Blushing Beauty' (C/D) — SDea
¶ – 'Deacons Millenium' — SDea
- 'Decio' (D) — SKee
- 'Delbards' — See *M. domestica* Jubilee (Delbards)
- 'Delkid' (F) — GTwe
- 'Devon Crimson Queen' (D) — CTho
- 'Devonshire Buckland' (C) — CEnd CTho WJas
¶ – 'Devonshire Crimson Queen' (D) — SDea
- 'Devonshire Quarrenden' (D) — CCAT CEnd CSam CTho EMui SDea SFam SKee WJas
- 'Dewdney's Seedling' (C) — GTwe
- 'Diamond Jubilee' (D) — SKee
- 'Discovery' (D) ♀ — CB&S CSam EBrP EBre EMui GBon GRei GTwe IOrc LBre LBuc MBri MWat NBee NDal NRog SBre SDea SFam SIgm SKee SPer WJas WWeb
- 'Doctor Hare's' (C) — WJas
- 'Doctor Harvey' (C) — SFam
- 'Doctor Kidd's Orange Red' (D) — SDea
- 'Domino' (C) — SKee

- 'Don's Delight' (C) — CTho
- 'Doux Normandie' (Cider) — CCAT
- 'Dove' (F) — CTho
- 'Downton Pippin' (D) — SKee WJas
- 'Dredge's Fame' (D) — CTho
- 'Duchess of Oldenburg' (C/D) — SKee
- 'Duchess's Favourite' (D) — SKee
- 'Dufflin' (Cider) — CCAT CTho
- 'Duke of Devonshire' (D) — CSam CTho SDea SFam SKee
- 'Duke of Gloucester' (C) — WJas
N – 'Dumeller's Seedling' (C) ♀ — CCAT CTho SDea SKee
- 'Dunkerton Late Sweet' (Cider) — CCAT CTho
- 'Dunn's Seedling' (D) — SDea
- 'Dutch Codlin' (C) — CTho
§ – 'Dutch Mignonne' (D) — SKee
- 'Early Blenheim' (D/C) — CEnd CTho
- 'Early Bower' (D) — CEnd
- 'Early Julyan' (C) — SKee WJas
- 'Early Victoria' (D) — See *M. domestica* 'Emneth Early'
- 'Early Worcester' — See *M. domestica* 'Tydeman's Early Worcester'
- 'Easter Orange' (D) — GTwe SFam SKee
- 'Ecklinville' (C) — SDea SKee WJas
- 'Edward VII' (C) ♀ — CDoC GTwe SDea SFam SKee WJas
- 'Egremont Russet' (D) ♀ — CCAT CCVT CSam CTho EBrP EBre EMui GBon GTwe IOrc LBre LBuc MBri MWat NBee NRog SBre SDea SFam SIgm SKee SPer WJas WWeb
- 'Ellis' Bitter' (Cider) — CCAT CEnd CTho GTwe
- 'Ellison's Orange' (D) ♀ — CCAT CSam CTri GBon GTwe MBri NRog SDea SFam SIgm SKee WJas WStI
- 'Elstar' (D) ♀ — CCAT EMui GTwe IOrc SDea SIgm SKee
- 'Elton Beauty' (D) — SDea SKee
§ – 'Emneth Early' (C) ♀ — CSam CTho GTwe NRog SDea SFam SKee WHow WJas
- 'Emperor Alexander' — See *M. domestica* 'Alexander'
- 'Empire' (D) — SKee
- 'Encore' (C) — SDea SKee
- 'English Codling' (C) — CTho
§ – 'Epicure' (D) ♀ — CDoC CSam CTho GBon GTwe IOrc NRog SDea SFam SIgm SKee WJas
- 'Ernie's Russet' (D) — SDea
- 'Evening Gold' (C) — SDea
- 'Eve's Delight' (D) — SDea
- 'Exeter Cross' (D) — CCAT SDea SFam SKee
¶ – 'Fair Maid of Devon' (Cider) — CCAT
- 'Fair Maid of Taunton' (D) — CCAT WJas
- 'Fairfield' (D) — CTho
- 'Fall Russet' (D) — GTwe
- 'Falstaff' (D) ♀ — CCAT CDoC EMui GTwe MGos SDea SIgm SKee WJas
- 'Fameuse' (D) — SKee
- 'Fearn's Pippin' (D) — SKee
- 'Fiesta' (D) ♀ — CDoC CSam EBrP EBre EMui GBon GChr GTwe LBre LBuc MBri MGos NDal SBre SDea SFam SIgm SKee WJas WWeb

– 'Fillbarrel' (Cider)	CCAT CTho
– 'Fireside' (D)	SIgm
– 'Firmgold' (D)	SDea
– 'Five Crowns' (D)	SKee
– Flamenco® (D/Ball)	MGos
§ – 'Flower of Kent' (C)	CCAT SDea SIgm SKee
– 'Flower of the Town' (D)	SKee WJas
– 'Forfar'	See *M. domestica* **'Dutch Mignonne'**
– 'Forge' (D)	SDea SKee
– 'Formosa Nonpareil' (C)	WJas
§ – 'Fortune' (D) ♀	CCAT CDoC CMac CSam CTri EMui GTwe MGos NRog SDea SFam SIgm SKee WHow WJas
– 'Foster's Seedling' (D)	SKee
¶ – 'Frederick' (Cider)	CCAT
– 'French Crab' (C)	CTho SDea
– 'Freyberg' (D)	SKee
– 'Fuji' (D)	SDea SKee
– 'Gala' (D)	GBon GTwe MBri SDea SFam SIgm SKee
– 'Gala Mondial' (F)	SKee WJas
I – 'Gala Royal'	See *M. domestica* **'Royal Gala'**
– 'Galloway Pippin' (C)	GTwe SKee
– 'Gascoyne's Scarlet' (D)	SDea SFam SKee
– 'Gavin' (D)	SDea SKee
– 'Genesis II' (D/C)	SDea
– 'Genet Moyle' (C)	CTho WJas
– 'George Carpenter' (D)	SDea SKee
– 'George Cave' (D)	CCVT GTwe NBee NRog SDea SFam SIgm SKee WJas
– 'George Neal' (C) ♀	SDea SFam SIgm
– 'Gilliflower of Gloucester' (D)	CTho
– 'Gladstone' (D)	CTho SIgm SKee WJas
§ – 'Glass Apple' (C/D)	CEnd
– 'Gloria Mundi' (C)	SDea
– 'Glory of England' (C)	WJas
– 'Gloster '69' (D)	GTwe SDea SIgm SKee
– 'Gloucester Cross' (D)	SKee
– 'Golden Bittersweet' (D)	CCAT CTho
– 'Golden Delicious' (D) ♀	CB&S CMac EBrP EBre GBon LBre MBri NRog SBre SDea SKee SPer WStI WWeb
– 'Golden Harvey' (D)	CCAT CTho
– 'Golden Knob' (D)	CCAT CTho SKee
– 'Golden Noble' (C) ♀	CCAT CDoC CSam CTho EMui GTwe SDea SFam SIgm SKee
– 'Golden Nugget' (D)	SIgm
– 'Golden Pearmain' (D)	SIgm
– 'Golden Pippin' (C)	CTho SKee
– 'Golden Reinette' (D)	GTwe SKee
– 'Golden Russet' (D)	GTwe SDea SKee WJas
– 'Golden Spire' (C)	CTho NRog SDea SKee
– 'Golden Wonder' (C)	CEnd
– 'Goldilocks' (D)	GTwe
– 'Gooseberry' (C)	SKee
– 'Goring' (Cider)	CCAT CTho
– 'Grand Sultan' (D)	CTho
– 'Granny Smith' (D)	GTwe SDea SIgm SKee SPer
– 'Gravenstein' (D)	CCAT SDea SFam SKee
§ – 'Green Balsam' (C)	NRog
– 'Green Roland'	See *M. domestica* **'Greenup's Pippin'**
– 'Greensleeves' (D) ♀	CCAT CDoC CSam EBrP EBre EMui GTwe LBre MBri MGos NBee NDal NRog SBre SDea SIgm SKee WJas WWeb
§ – 'Greenup's Pippin' (D)	SKee
– 'Grenadier' (C) ♀	CCAT CDoC GRei GTwe IOrc MBri MGos NBee NDal NRog SDea SIgm SKee SPer WJas WStI
– 'Halstow Natural' (Cider)	CCAT CTho
– 'Hambledon Deux Ans' (C)	SDea SKee WJas
– 'Hambling's Seedling' (C)	SKee
– 'Hangy Down' (Cider)	CTho
– 'Haralson' (D)	SIgm
§ – 'Harry Master's Jersey' (Cider)	CCAT CTho CTri SDea
– 'Harvey' (C)	SDea SKee
– 'Hawthornden' (C)	CTho SKee
– 'Herefordshire Beefing' (C)	CEnd SKee WJas
– 'Herring's Pippin' (D)	CTri GTwe SDea SKee
– 'Heusgen's Golden Reinette' (D)	CCAT SKee
– 'High View Pippin' (D)	SKee
– 'Hill's Seedling' (C)	SKee
– 'Histon Favourite' (D)	SKee
– 'Hoary Morning' (C)	CCAT CTho SDea SKee
– 'Hocking's Green' (C/D)	CEnd CTho
– 'Holland Pippin' (C)	SKee
– 'Hollow Core' (C)	CTho
– 'Holstein' (D)	COtt CSam CTho GTwe SDea SIgm SKee
§ – 'Honeygold'	CEnd
– 'Horneburger Pfannkuchen' (C)	SKee
– 'Howgate Wonder' (C)	CCAT CDoC CSam EMui GBon GChr GTwe IOrc LBuc MBri MGos NBee NRog SDea SFam SIgm SKee SPer WJas
– 'Hubbard's Pearmain' (D)	SKee
– 'Idared' (D) ♀	GBon GTwe MGos SDea SKee
– 'Improved Cockpit' (D)	NRog
¶ – 'Improved Dove' (Cider)	CCAT
– 'Improved Keswick' (C/D)	CEnd
– 'Improved Lambrook Pippin' (Cider)	CCAT CTho
¶ – 'Improved Pound' (Cider)	CCAT
– 'Improved Redstreak' (Cider)	CTho
– 'Improved Woodbine' (Cider)	CCAT
– 'Ingrid Marie' (D)	SDea SKee WJas
– 'Irish Peach' (D)	GTwe SDea SFam SIgm SKee WJas
– 'Isaac Newton's Tree'	See *M. domestica* **'Flower of Kent'**
– 'Isle of Wight Pippin' (D)	SDea
– 'Isle of Wight Russet' (D)	SDea
¶ – 'Jackson's' (Cider)	CCAT
– 'James Grieve' (D) ♀	CB&S CCAT CCVT CMac EMui GBon GChr GRei GTwe IOrc LBuc MBri MWat NBee NDal NRog SDea SFam SIgm SKee SPer WJas WWeb
– 'Jerseymac' (D)	SDea
– 'Jester' (D)	GTwe SDea SIgm SKee
– 'John Apple' (C)	SKee
– 'John Standish' (D)	GTwe SDea

◆ – 'John Toucher's'   See *M. domestica* **'Crimson King'**
 – 'Johnny Andrews' (Cider)   CCAT CTho
 – 'Johnny Voun' (D)   CEnd CTho
 – 'Jonagold' (D) ♀   GTwe LBuc MBri SDea SFam SIgm SKee SPer WJas
◆ – 'Jonagold Crowngold'   See *M. domestica* **'Crowngold'**
 – 'Jonagored' (D)   EBee
 – 'Jonared' (D)   GTwe
 – 'Jonathan' (D)   SDea SKee
 – 'Jordan's Weeping' (C)   GTwe SDea WJas
 – 'Josephine' (D)   SDea
 – 'Joybells' (D)   SKee
 – 'Jubilee'   See *M. domestica* **'Royal Jubilee'**
 – 'Jupiter' (D) ♀   CCAT CDoC CSam CTri GBon GTwe IOrc MGos NDal NRog SDea SFam SIgm SKee WJas
 – 'Kandil Sinap' (D)   SKee
 – 'Kapai Red Jonathan' (D)   SDea
 – 'Karmijn de Sonnaville' (D) SDea SKee
§ – 'Katja' (D)   CDoC CSam EMui GBon GChr GTwe IOrc LBuc MBri NBee SDea SIgm SKee SPer WJas
 – Katy   See *M. domestica* **'Katja'**
 – 'Kendall' (D)   SKee
 – 'Kent' (D)   GTwe SDea SKee
 – 'Kentish Fillbasket' (C) SKee
 – 'Kentish Pippin' (C/Cider/D) SKee
 – 'Kentish Quarrenden' (D) SKee
 – 'Kerry Pippin' (D)   SKee
 – 'Keswick Codling' (C)   CSam GTwe NRog SDea SKee WJas
 – 'Kidd's Orange Red' (D) ♀ CCAT COtt EBrP EBre EMui GTwe LBre LBuc SBre SDea SFam SIgm SKee WJas
 – 'Kilkenny Pippin' (F)   GTwe
 – 'Killerton Sharp' (Cider) CTho
 – 'Killerton Sweet' (Cider) CTho
 – 'King Byerd' (C/D)   CEnd CTho
 – 'King Charles' Pearmain' (D) CTho SKee
 – 'King Coffee' (D)   SKee
 – 'King George V' (D)   SKee
 – 'King Luscious' (D)   SDea
§ – 'King of the Pippins' (D) ♀ CCAT CSam CTho CTri GTwe SDea SFam SKee
 – 'King of Tompkins County' (D) SKee
 – 'King Russet' (D) ♀   SDea
 – 'King's Acre Bountiful' (C) SKee WJas
 – 'King's Acre Pippin' (D)   CTho SDea SFam SKee WHow WJas
 – 'Kingston Bitter' (Cider) CTho
 – 'Kingston Black' (Cider)   CCAT CSam CTho SDea SKee
 – 'Knobby Russet' (F)   GTwe
 – 'Knobby Russet' (D)   SKee
 – 'Lady Henniker' (D)   CCAT CTho GTwe SDea SKee WJas
 – 'Lady of the Wemyss' (C)   SKee
 – 'Lady Sudeley' (D)   CTho SDea SKee WJas
 – 'Lady's Finger' (C/D)   CEnd
 – 'Lady's Finger of Hereford' (D) CTho WJas

 – 'Lady's Finger of Lancashire' (C/D) CSam SKee
 – 'Lady's Finger of Offaly' (D) SDea
 – 'Lamb Abbey Pearmain' (D) SKee
 – 'Landsberger Reinette' (D) SKee
 – 'Lane's Prince Albert' (C) ♀ CCAT CCVT CSam EMui GBon GTwe MGos MWat NRog SDea SIgm SKee WJas
 – 'Langley Pippin' (D)   SDea SKee
§ – 'Langworthy' (Cider)   CCAT CTho
 – 'Lass o' Gowrie' (C)   SKee
 – 'Laxton's Epicure'   See *M. domestica* **'Epicure'**
 – 'Laxton's Fortune'   See *M. domestica* **'Fortune'**
 – 'Laxton's Rearguard' (D)   SKee WJas
 – 'Laxton's Royalty' (D)   SDea SFam
§ – 'Laxton's Superb' (D)   CB&S CCAT CCVT CSam CTri GBon GTwe IOrc LBuc MBri NRog SDea SIgm SKee SPer WJas
 – 'Leathercoat Russet' (D)   CTho SKee
 – 'Lemon Pippin' (C)   CTho SDea SKee WJas
 – 'Lewis's Incomparable' (C) SKee
 – 'Liberty' (D)   SDea
 – 'Limberland' (C)   CTho
 – 'Linda' (D)   SKee
 – 'Listener' (Cider/D)   CCAT CTho
§ – 'Loddington' (C)   SKee
 – 'Lodi' (D)   SDea
 – 'London Pearmain' (D)   WJas
 – 'London Pippin' (C)   CTho
 – 'Longkeeper' (D)   CEnd CTho
 – 'Longstem' (Cider)   CTho
 – 'Lord Burghley' (D)   GTwe SDea SKee
 – 'Lord Derby' (C)   CCAT CMac CSam CTho EMui GTwe MBri MWat NRog SDea SKee WJas
 – 'Lord Grosvenor' (C)   GTwe SKee
 – 'Lord Hindlip' (D)   GTwe LBuc SDea SFam SKee WJas
 – 'Lord Lambourne' (D) ♀   CCAT CCVT CDoC CSam EBrP EBre EMui GChr GTwe IOrc LBre MWat NDal NRog SBre SFam SIgm SKee WJas
 – 'Lord Stradbroke' (C)   SKee
 – 'Lord Suffield' (C)   SKee
¶ – 'Loyal Drain' (Cider)   CCAT
 – 'Lucombe's Pine' (D)   CEnd CTho
 – 'Lucombe's Seedling' (D)   CTho SKee
¶ – 'Mabbott's Pearmain'   SDea
 – 'Madresfield Court' (D)   SDea SKee WJas
 – 'Major' (D)   CCAT CTho
 – 'Malling Kent' (D)   CSam EMui SDea SFam
 – 'Maltster' (D)   GTwe SKee WJas
 – 'Manaccan Primrose' (C/D) CEnd
 – 'Manks Codlin' (C)   CTho SKee
 – 'Margil' (D)   CCAT CTho GTwe SDea SFam SIgm SKee
 – 'May Queen' (D)   SDea SFam SKee WJas
 – 'Maypole' (D/Ball)   MGos SDea
 – 'McCutcheon' (F)   SIgm
 – 'McIntosh Red' (D)   SKee WJas
¶ – 'Medaille d'Or' (Cider) CCAT
 – 'Medina' (D)   GTwe

– 'Melba' (D)   CSam SKee
– Melcombe Russet' (D)   CTho
– 'Melon' (D)   SDea
– 'Melrose' (D)   GTwe SKee
¶ – 'Merchant Apple' (D)   CCAT
– 'Merchant Apple of   CTho
    Illminster' (D)
– 'Merton Knave' (D)   GTwe MGos SDea
– 'Merton Russet' (D)   SDea
– 'Merton Worcester' (D)   SDea SKee
– 'Michaelmas Red' (D)   GTwe SKee WJas
– 'Michelin' (Cider)   CCAT CCVT CEnd CTho
     EMui GTwe SDea
◆ – Miel d'Or   See *M. domestica* 'Honeygold'
– 'Miller's Seedling' (D)   GTwe SIgm SKee WHow WJas
– 'Millicent Barnes' (D)   SDea
– 'Mollie's Delicious' (D)   GTwe SKee
– 'Monarch' (C)   CCAT CTri GTwe NRog SDea
     SFam SKee WHow WJas
I – 'Mondial Gala'   See *M. domestica* **'Gala**
     Mondial'
– 'Morgan's Sweet'   CCAT CTho CTri SDea SKee
    (C/Cider)
– 'Moss's Seedling' (D)   GTwe SDea
§ – 'Mother' (D) ♀   GTwe LBuc SDea SFam SKee
     WJas
– 'Mrs Phillimore' (D)   SKee
– 'Muscadet de Dieppe'   CCAT CSam
    (Cider)
§ – 'Mutsu' (D)   CCAT GTwe NRog SDea SIgm
     SKee
– 'Neasdale Favorite' (F)   SKee
– 'Nettlestone Pippin' (D)   SDea
– 'Newton Wonder' (D/C)   CCAT CDoC CMac CSam CTri
   ♀   GTwe NDal NRog SDea SFam
     SIgm SKee WJas
– 'Newtown Pippin' (D)   SDea
– 'Nittany Red' (D)   SDea
¶ – 'No Pip' (C)   CTho
– 'Nonpareil' (D)   CTho SKee
– 'Norfolk Beauty' (C)   SKee
– 'Norfolk Beefing' (C)   SDea SFam SKee
– 'Norfolk Royal' (D)   CDoC GTwe SDea SIgm SKee
– 'Norfolk Summer   SKee
    Broadend' (C)
– 'Norfolk Winter   SKee
    Coleman' (C)
– 'Northcott Superb' (D)   CTho
– 'Northern Greening' (C)   GTwe SKee
– 'Northwood' (Cider)   CCAT CTho
¶ – 'Nutmeg Pippin' (D)   SDea
– 'Oaken Pin' (C)   CTho
– 'Old Pearmain' (D)   CTho SDea SKee
– 'Old Somerset Russet'   CTho
    (D)
– 'Opalescent' (D)   SKee
– 'Orange Goff' (D)   SKee
– 'Orin' (D)   SKee
– 'Orkney Apple' (F)   SKee
– 'Orleans Reinette' (D)   CCAT CCVT CTho EMui
     GTwe LBuc MWat SDea SFam
     SIgm SKee WHow WJas
¶ – 'Osier' (Cider)   CCAT
– 'Oslin' (D)   SKee
– 'Owen Thomas' (D)   CTri
– 'Paignton Marigold'   CTho
    (Cider)
– 'Paulared' (D)   SKee
– 'Payhembury' (C/Cider)   CTho
– 'Peacemaker' (D)   SKee
– 'Pear Apple' (D)   CEnd
– 'Pearl' (D)   CTho SDea

– 'Peasgood's Nonsuch'   CCAT GTwe LBuc SDea SFam
    (C) ♀   SKee WJas
– 'Peck's Pleasant' (D)   SKee
– 'Pendragon' (D)   CTho
– 'Penhallow Pippin' (D)   CTho
¶ – 'Pennard Bitter' (Cider)   CCAT
– 'Peter Lock' (C/D)   CCAT CEnd CTho
¶ – 'Peter's Pippin' (D)   SDea
¶ – 'Peter's Seedling' (D)   SDea
– 'Pickering's Seedling'   SKee
    (D)
– 'Pig's Nose Pippin' (D)   CEnd CTho SKee
– 'Pig's Nose Pippin'   CTho
    Type III (D)
– 'Pig's Snout'   CCAT CEnd CTho
    (Cider/C/D)
– 'Pine Golden Pippin'   SKee
    (D)
– 'Pitmaston Pine Apple'   CCAT CSam CTho SDea SFam
    (D)   SKee WJas
– 'Pitmaston Pippin   SKee
    Nonpareil' (F)
– 'Pixie' (D) ♀   CCVT CSam GTwe SDea SFam
     SIgm SKee WJas
– 'Plum Vite' (D)   CTho CTri
– 'Plympton Pippin' (C)   CEnd CTho
– Polka   See *M. domestica* Polka =
     'Trajan'
– 'Polly' (C/D)   CEnd
– 'Polly Whitehair' (C/D)   CTho SDea SKee
¶ – 'Pomeroy' (D)   CCAT
– 'Pomeroy of Somerset'   CTho
    (D)
– 'Ponsford' (C)   CCAT CTho
◆ – 'Port Wine'   See *M. domestica* **'Harry**
     Master's Jersey'
– 'Porter's Pefection'   CCAT CTho
    (Cider)
– 'Pott's Seedling' (C)   SKee
– 'Priscilla' (D)   GTwe
– 'Queen' (C)   CEnd CTho SKee
– 'Queen Cox' (D)   EMui GBon MRav SDea SIgm
     SKee
– 'Queens' (D)   CTho
– 'Racky Down' (F)   SKee
– 'Red Astrachan' (D)   SKee
§ – 'Red Blenheim' (C/D)   SKee
– 'Red Charles Ross'   SDea
    (C/D)
– 'Red Devil' (D)   COtt CWSG EMui GTwe LBuc
     MBri NBee NDal SDea SIgm
     SKee WJas
– 'Red Ellison' (D)   CTho CTri GTwe NRog SDea
– 'Red Fuji' (D)   SDea
– 'Red James Grieve' (D)   SDea
– 'Red Jersey' (Cider)   CCAT
– 'Red Joaneting' (D)   SKee
¶ – 'Red Jonagold' (F)   SDea
– 'Red Miller's Seedling'   COtt SDea
    (D)
– 'Red Robin' (F)   CEnd
– 'Red Ruby' (F)   CTho
– 'Red Victoria' (C)   GTwe WJas
– 'Redfree' (D)   GTwe
– 'Redsleeves' (C)   GTwe SDea SIgm
– 'Redstrake' (Cider)   CCAT
– 'Reine de Pommes'   CCAT
    (Cider)
– 'Reine des Reinettes'   See *M. domestica* **'King of the**
     Pippins'
¶ – 'Reinette d'Obry'   CCAT
    (Cider)

– 'Reinette Doreé de Boediker' (D)	GTwe
– 'Reinette du Canada' (D)	CTho SKee
– 'Reinette Rouge Etoilée' (D)	CCAT SDea
– 'Reverend Greeves' (C)	SDea
– 'Reverend W. Wilks' (C)	CCAT CCVT CDoC COtt EMui LBuc MWat NDal NRog SFam SIgm SKee WJas
– 'Ribston Pippin' (D) ♀	CCAT CTho CTri EMui GTwe LBuc MWat SDea SFam SIgm SKee WJas
– 'Rival' (D)	SDea SKee WJas
– 'Rivers' Nonsuch' (D)	WJas
– 'Robin Pippin' (D)	GTwe
– 'Rome Beauty' (D)	SDea
– 'Rosemary Russet' (D) ♀	CCAT COtt CSam CTho GTwe LBuc SDea SFam SIgm SKee WHow WJas
– 'Ross Nonpareil' (D)	GTwe SDea SKee
– 'Rough Pippin' (D)	CEnd CTho
– 'Roundway Magnum Bonum' (D)	CCAT CTho SDea SFam SKee
§ – 'Roxbury Russet' (D)	SKee
§ – 'Royal Gala' (D) ♀	EMui SDea SKee
§ – 'Royal Jubilee' (C)	SKee
– 'Royal Russet' (C)	SDea
– 'Royal Snow' (D)	SKee
– 'Royal Somerset' (C/Cider)	CCAT CTho
– 'Rubens' (D)	SKee
– 'Rubinette' (D)	CDoC COtt CTho GTwe MBri MGos NDal WHow WJas
– 'Saint Albans Pippin' (D)	SKee
– 'Saint Augustine's Orange' (D)	SKee
– 'Saint Cecilia' (D)	SDea SKee WJas
§ – 'Saint Edmund's Pippin' (D) ♀	CSam CTho ERea GTwe SDea SFam SIgm SKee
– 'Saint Edmund's Russet'	See *M. domestica* 'Saint Edmund's Pippin'
– 'Saint Everard' (D)	SKee
– 'Saint Magdalen' (D)	SKee
– 'Saltcote Pippin' (D)	SKee
– 'Sam Young' (D)	SKee
¶ – 'Sandlands'	SDea
– 'Sandringham' (C)	SKee
– 'Sanspareil' (D)	CTho SKee
– 'Saw Pits' (F)	CEnd SKee
– 'Scarlet Nonpareil' (D)	SKee
– 'Scilly Pearl' (C)	WJas
– 'Scotch Bridget' (C)	SKee WHow WJas
– 'Scotch Dumpling' (C)	EBee GTwe
– 'Seaton House' (C)	SKee
– 'Sercombe's Natural' (Cider)	CTho
– 'Shakespeare' (D)	WJas
– 'Sheep's Nose' (C)	CCAT SDea SKee
– 'Shenandoah' (C)	SKee
– 'Shoesmith' (C)	SIgm
– 'Sidney Strake' (C)	CEnd
– 'Sir Isaac Newton's'	See *M. domestica* 'Flower of Kent'
– 'Sir John Thornycroft' (D)	SDea
– 'Sisson's Worksop Newtown' (D)	SKee
– 'Slack Ma Girdle' (Cider)	CCAT CTho
– 'Smart's Prince Arthur' (C)	SDea
– 'Snell's Glass Apple'	See *M. domestica* 'Glass Apple'
– 'Somerset Lasting' (C)	CTho
– 'Somerset Red Streak' (Cider)	CCAT CTho
– 'Sops in Wine' (C/Cider)	CCAT CTho SKee
– 'Sour Bay' (Cider)	CTho
♦ – 'Sour Natural'	See *M. domestica* 'Langworthy'
– 'Spartan' (D)	CDoC CSam EBrP EBre EMui GBon GTwe LBre MBri MGos NRog SBre SDea SFam SIgm SKee WJas WStI
– 'Spencer' (D)	CTri SKee
– 'Spotted Dick' (Cider)	CTho
– 'Spur Mac' (D)	SDea
¶ – 'Stamford Pippin' (D)	SDea
– 'Star of Devon' (D)	CCAT CTho SDea
– 'Stark' (D)	SDea
– 'Starking' (D)	SKee
– 'Starkrimson' (D)	SKee
– 'Starkspur Golden Delicious' (D)	SKee
– 'Stembridge Clusters' (Cider)	CCAT
– 'Stembridge Jersey' (Cider)	CCAT
– 'Steyne Seedling' (D)	SDea
– 'Stirling Castle' (C)	GTwe SKee
– 'Stobo Castle' (C)	SKee
– 'Stockbearer' (C)	CTho
– 'Stoke Edith Pippin' (D)	WJas
– 'Stoke Red' (Cider)	CCAT CTho
– 'Stone's'	See *M. domestica* 'Loddington'
– 'Stoup Leadington' (C)	SKee
– 'Strawberry Pippin' (F)	WJas
– 'Striped Beefing' (C)	SKee
– 'Stub Nose' (F)	SKee
– 'Sturmer Pippin' (D)	GTwe MWat SDea SFam SIgm SKee WJas
– 'Sugar Bush' (C/D)	CTho
– 'Summer Golden Pippin' (D)	SKee
– 'Summer Stubbard' (D)	CTho
– 'Summerred' (D)	CWSG WStI
– 'Sunburn' (D)	SIgm
– 'Sunset' (D) ♀	CCAT CDoC CMac CSam EMui GTwe LBuc MBri NBee NRog SDea SFam SIgm SKee SPer WJas
– 'Suntan' (D) ♀	CCAT CSam CTho GBon GTwe MWat NBee SDea SKee
– 'Superb'	See *M. domestica* 'Laxton's Superb'
– 'Surprise' (D)	GTwe
– 'Sweet Alford' (Cider)	CCAT CTho
– 'Sweet Bay' (Cider)	CTho
– 'Sweet Blenheim' (Cider)	CCAT
– 'Sweet Cleave' (Cider)	CTho
– 'Sweet Coppin' (Cider)	CCAT CTho
– Swiss Orange	See *M. domestica* 'Schweizer Orange'
– 'Tale Sweet' (Cider)	CCAT CTho
– 'Tamar Beauty' (F)	CEnd
– 'Tan Harvey' (Cider)	CCAT CEnd
– 'Taunton Fair Maid' (Cider)	CCAT CTho
– 'Taylor's' (Cider)	CCAT SDea
– 'Taylor's Sweet' (Cider)	CCAT
– 'Telamon'	See *M. domestica* Waltz = 'Telamon'

§ – Waltz = 'Telamon' (D/Ball)	MGos SDea
– 'Ten Commandments' (D)	CCAT SDea SKee WJas
– 'The Rattler' (F)	CEnd
– 'Thomas Rivers' (C)	CTho SDea SKee
– 'Thorle Pippin' (D)	SKee
¶ – 'Tidicombe Seedling'	CTho
– 'Tillington Court' (C)	WJas
– 'Tom Putt' (C)	CCAT CCVT COtt CSam CTho CTri GTwe LBuc SDea SKee WHow WJas
– 'Tommy Knight' (D)	CEnd
– 'Tower of Glamis' (C)	GTwe SKee
– Town Farm Number 59 (Cider)	CTho
– 'Trajan'	See M. domestica Polka = 'Trajan'
§ – Polka = 'Trajan' (D/Ball)	MGos SDea
– 'Transparente de Croncels' (C)	CTho
– 'Tregoana King' (C/D)	CEnd CTho
– 'Tremlett's Bitter' (Cider)	CCAT CTho SDea
– 'Tuscan'	See M. domestica Bolero = 'Tuscan'
§ – Bolero = 'Tuscan' (D/Ball)	MGos SDea
– 'Twenty Ounce' (C)	CCAT GTwe SKee WJas
– 'Twinings Pippin' (D)	SKee
§ – 'Tydeman's Early Worcester' (D)	GTwe NBee NRog SDea SKee WJas
– 'Tydeman's Late Orange' (D)	GTwe NRog SDea SFam SKee
– 'Underleaf' (D)	CCAT
– 'Upton Pyne' (D)	CCAT CSam CTho SDea SKee
– 'Veitch's Perfection' (C/D)	CTho
– 'Venus Pippin' (C/D)	CEnd
– 'Vickey's Delight' (D)	SDea
¶ – 'Vilberie' (Cider)	CCAT
– 'Vista-bella' (D)	GTwe NBee SDea SKee WJas
– 'Wagener' (D)	SDea SKee
– Waltz	See M. domestica Waltz = 'Telamon'
– 'Wanstall Pippin' (D)	SKee
– 'Warner's King' (C) ♀	CCAT SDea SKee WJas
– 'Wealthy' (D)	SDea SKee
– 'Wellington'	See M. domestica 'Dumeller's Seedling'
– 'Wellspur Red Delicious' (D)	GTwe
– 'Welsh Russet' (D)	SDea
– 'White Alphington' (Cider)	CTho
– 'White Close Pippin' (Cider)	CTho
¶ – 'White Jersey' (Cider)	CCAT
– 'White Joaneting' (D)	CTho
– 'White Melrose' (C)	GTwe SDea SKee
– 'White Paradise' (C)	SKee
– 'White Transparent' (C/D)	GTwe SDea SKee
– 'William Crump' (C)	CCAT SDea SFam SKee WHow WJas
– 'Winston' (D) ♀	CCAT CCVT CTri GTwe NRog SDea SFam SIgm SKee WJas
– 'Winter Banana' (D)	SDea SKee
* – 'Winter Gem'	COtt EBee EMui MGos
– 'Winter Peach' (D/C)	CEnd CTho
– 'Winter Pearmain' (D)	SKee
– 'Winter Quarrenden' (D)	SDea SKee
– 'Winter Queening' (D/C)	CTho SDea
– 'Winter Stubbard' (C)	CTho
– 'Woodbine' (Cider)	CCAT
– 'Woolbrook Pippin' (D)	CTho
– 'Woolbrook Russet' (C)	CTho SKee
– 'Worcester Pearmain' (D) ♀	CB&S CCAT CCVT CTho EMui GBon GRei GTwe LBuc MBri MWat NRog SDea SFam SIgm SKee SPer WJas WStI WWeb
– 'Wormsley Pippin' (D)	SKee WJas
♦ – 'Wyatt's Seedling'	See M. domestica 'Langworthy'
– 'Wyken Pippin' (D)	GTwe SDea SFam SKee WJas
– 'Yarlington Mill' (Cider)	CCAT CTho CTri SDea SKee
– 'Yellow Ingestrie' (D)	SFam SKee WJas
– 'Young America' (F)	SIgm
– 'Zabergäu Renette' (D)	SKee
¶ 'Donald Wyman'	CBlo
'Echtermeyer'	See M. × gloriosa 'Oekonomierat Echtermeyer'
§ 'Evereste' ♀	CBar CBlo CDoC CLnd EMui EPfP GChr GTwe LPan MAsh MBlu MBri SIgm WDin WJas CTho WMou
florentina	
floribunda ♀	CBlo CDoC CLnd CSam CTho ELan ENot GChr GTwe IHos IOrc LBuc LHyr LPan MBri MGos MHlr MRav NBee SHBN SIgm SPer SSta WDin WJas WNor WOrn
¶ 'Gardener's Gold'	CEnd
§ × gloriosa 'Oekonomierat Echtermeyer'	CBlo GQui SSta WDin WJas
'Golden Gem'	CBlo CEnd EPfP GTwe SIgm WJas
'Golden Hornet'	See M. × zumi 'Golden Hornet'
'Goldsworth Purple'	CTho
× heterophylla 'Redflesh'	CTho
'Hillieri'	See M. × schiedeckeri 'Hillieri'
hupehensis ♀	CB&S CBlo CLnd CMCN CTho ENot GTwe IHos MBri SFam SHBN SIgm SLPl SPer WMou WWat
'John Downie' (C) ♀	Widely available
'Kaido'	See M. × micromalus
kansuensis	CLnd WMou
* 'Laura'	CBlo
× magdeburgensis	CLnd MRav NWea SIgm
§ × micromalus	CLnd GAri
× moerlandsii	CLnd
– 'Liset'	CBlo CLnd COtt EBee EBrP EBre ECtt ENot GChr LBre MAsh SBre SFam SIgm SPer WFar WJas WStI
§ – 'Profusion'	CBlo CLnd EBrP EBre ELan ENot IOrc LBre LHyr LPan MAsh MBri MGos NBee NWea SBre SHBN SIgm SPer SSta WDin WJas WStI
orthocarpa	CLnd
Perpetu	See M. 'Evereste'
'Pink Perfection'	CLnd EBee ENot MAsh SHBN SPer
prattii	CTho
'Profusion'	See M. × moerlandsii 'Profusion'
prunifolia 'Cheal's Crimson'	NRog
– 'Pendula'	GAri

pumila 'Cowichan'	CBlo LRHS MBri
– 'Dartmouth'	CBlo CLnd CTho CTri NRog SFam SPer
– 'Montreal Beauty'	MAsh MBri WJas
– 'Niedzwetzkyana'	CLnd
§ × *purpurea* 'Aldenhamensis'	CBlo CLnd CTho SDea WDin
– 'Eleyi'	CBlo CLnd ENot EPfP MAsh MGos NWea WDin
– 'Lemoinei'	IOrc
– 'Neville Copeman' ♀	CDoC CLnd EPfP MAsh WJas
– 'Pendula'	See *M.* × *gloriosa* **'Oekonomierat Echtermeyer'**
'Red Glow'	CBlo CDoC CLnd COtt EBee GQui LHyr WJas WLRN
◆ 'Red Jade'	See *M.* × *schiedeckeri* **'Red Jade'**
× *robusta*	CBlo CDoC CLnd CTri EBee GTwe MBal NWea
– 'Red Sentinel' ♀	CBlo CLnd COtt CSam CTho EBrP EBre ELan EMui ENot LBre MAsh MBar MBri NBee SBre SFam SIgm SPer WCFE WJas
– 'Red Siberian' ♀	SDea SHBN SPer
– 'Yellow Siberian' ♀	CLnd
'Royal Beauty' ♀	CBlo CLnd COtt EBee EBrP EBre GTwe LBre LBuc MAsh MBri SBre WDin
'Royalty'	CB&S CBlo CLnd CTho EBrP EBre ELan ENot GChr GRei GTwe IHos LBre LBuc LPan MAsh MBri MGos MHlr MRav NBee SBre SFam SHBN SIgm SPer SSta WJas WStI
'Rudolph'	EBee ENot LPan
sargentii	See *M. toringo* subsp. *sargentii*
× *schiedeckeri* 'Exzellenz Thiel'	SIgm
§ – 'Hillieri'	CLnd CTho ECrN SFam
§ – 'Red Jade'	CBlo CLnd EBrP EBre ECtt ELan ENot GChr GTwe IOrc LBre LBuc MAsh MBar MBri MGos MRav MWat NBee SBre SHBN SIgm SPer WDin WJas WOrn WStI
sieboldii	See *M. toringo*
– 'Professor Sprenger'	CLnd
sikkimensis	WHCr
¶ – B&SWJ 2431	WCru
'Snowcloud'	CBlo CLnd ENot MBri SHBN
spectabilis	CLnd
'Sun Rival'	CBlo CEnd GTwe MAsh MGos SCoo SFam WWeb
sylvestris	CKin CLnd CPer GAri GChr LBuc LHyr NBee NRog NRoo NWea WDin WLRN
§ *toringo*	CSto
§ – subsp. *sargentii*	CBlo ECtt ENot MBri MGos NWea SFam SIgm WNor WWat
¶ – – 'Tina'	MAsh
toringoides	CLnd CTho MBri SHBN SIgm WHCr WNor
transitoria ♀	CBlo CEnd CLnd CTho EPfP MBri SSpi WWat
– 'R.J. Fulcher'	CTho
– 'Thornhayes Tansy'	CTho
trilobata	CBlo CLnd WMou

tschonoskii ♀	CBlo CDoC CLnd CSam CTho EBrP EBre ELan ENot GTwe IOrc LBre LBuc LHyr LPan MAsh MBal MBri MGos MRav MWat NWea SBre SHBN SIgm SPer WDin WJas WStI WWat
* – 'White Star'	ECrN
'Van Eseltine'	CBlo CLnd CSam EBrP EBre GTwe LBre MBri SBre SIgm SPer WJas
'Veitch's Scarlet'	CLnd CTho GQui GTwe NRog SFam SIgm
¶ 'White Candle' (d)	CBlo
'White Star'	CBlo CEnd MAsh WDin
'Winter Gold'	CBlo CDoC CLnd CSam EBee ECtt MAsh SIgm WStI
'Wisley Crab'	CLnd GTwe SDea SFam SKee
× *zumi* var. *calocarpa*	CLnd
§ – 'Golden Hornet' ♀	Widely available

MALVA (Malvaceae)

alcea	EPfP
¶ – 'Alba'	NPro
– var. *fastigiata*	CArn CGle CMGP EBrP EBre ECED ELan EMan EPPr LBre LGan NBro NCat NRoo NSti NVic SAga SBre SPer SRCN SRms WEas
'Bibor Fehlo'	CSpe WRha
bicolor	See *Lavatera maritima*
crispa	See *M. verticillata*
'Gibbortello'	MCLN NBro
hispida	CNat
moschata	Widely available
– f. *alba* ♀	Widely available
– f. *alba* 'Pirouette'	CM&M WHen WOve WRHF
– 'Romney Marsh'	See *Althaea officinalis* **'Romney Marsh'**
– *rosea*	ECha LFis MHFP NCut NNor NPer WByw
neglecta	EWFC WPer
sylvestris	CGle CKin EOld EWFC GCHN MChe NBro SMad SSoC SWat WHer WJek WPer WWin WWye
– 'Brave Heart'	GBri MCLN NBro NPer SLod SWat WHer WRha
– 'Highnam'	WAlt
– 'Inky Stripe'	WHil
– 'Marina'	LRHS MArl MAsh MAvo MBri WCot
– subsp. *mauritanica*	CHan CSpe ECoo ECro ELan EMar EPfP GBri LHop NBro NChi NFai NHol NNor NPer WHil WRus
– 'Perry's Blue'	NPer
– 'Primley Blue'	CB&S CBot CElw CGle CHan ECha ELan ERav GBri LFis LGre LHop LRot MAvo MCLN MTho NBrk NPer NSti SAxl SMad WBea WHal WOld WWin
¶ – 'Richard Perry'	NPer
– 'Zebrina'	CM&M EAst ECro GBri NBrk NFai NPer SLod SMad SSoC WOve WRha
§ *verticillata*	ELan
– 'Crispa'	MChe WRha

MALVASTRUM (Malvaceae)

× *hypomadarum*	See *Anisodontea* × *hypomadara* **(Sprague) Bates**

lateritium — Widely available
* – 'Variegatum' — SMrm
peruvianum — See *Modiolastrum peruvianum*

MALVAVISCUS (Malvaceae)
arboreus var. *mexicanus* — ERea WMul

MANDEVILLA (Apocynaceae)
x *amabilis* — LRHS
x *amoena* 'Alice du Pont' — CB&S CHEx CPlN CSpe ECon
  ♀ — ELan EMil EPfP ERea GQui
  IHos LCns SOWG WMul
boliviensis — CPlN CSpe ECon ELan EPfP
  LChe SOWG WMul
§ *laxa* — CAbb CBot CHEx CHan CPlN
  CPle CSPN ELan ERea IHos
  LBlm LHil LLew SOWG WCru
  WOMN WPic WSHC
sanderi — MBri
– 'Rosea' — ERea
splendens — EBak SLMG SOWG
suaveolens — See *M. laxa*
yellow form — SOWG

MANDRAGORA (Solanaceae)
autumnalis — EEls GCal MSal WThi
§ *officinarum* — EEls GCal GPoy MSal SMad
  WWye

MANETTIA (Rubiaceae)
inflata — See *M. luteorubra*
§ *luteorubra* — CPlN ELan LHop SLMG

MANGIFERA (Anacardiaceae) See Plant
Deletions

MANGLIETIA (Magnoliaceae) See Plant
Deletions

MANIHOT (Euphorbiaceae) See Plant Deletions

MANSOA (Bignoniaceae)
hymenaea — CPlN

MARANTA (Marantaceae)
leuconeura var. — MBri
  erythroneura
leuconeura var. — CHal LBlo MBri
  kerchoveana ♀

MARCHANTIA (Marchantiaceae) See Plant
Deletions

MARGYRICARPUS (Rosaceae)
§ *pinnatus* — CFee ESis MAll NWCA
  WOMN WPer
setosus — See *M. pinnatus*

MARISCUS See CYPERUS

MARKHAMIA (Bignoniaceae)
platycalyx — See *M. lutea*

MARRUBIUM (Lamiaceae)
candidissimum — See *M. incanum*
catariifolium — EMon
cylleneum — ECha EGar EMFP EMar WPer
  WWin
* – 'Velvetissimum' — CMGP EGle EOrc LHop SBla
  SCro WCHb

'Gold Leaf' — EBar ECha
§ *incanum* — CGle CMHG EHal IIve MBri
  NTow WEas
libanoticum — ECha EGar EMon MSte WPer
supinum — CArn EBee ECGP EMon
  NWoo WLin
velutinum — CGle EGar
vulgare — CArn CSev EEls EJud ELau
  GBar GPoy MChe MHew NOrc
  SIde WCHb WCer WHer WOak
  WPer WSel WWye
¶ – 'Green Pompon' — IIve NLar

MARSDENIA (Asclepiadaceae)
erecta — See *Cionura erecta*

MARSHALLIA (Asteraceae)
caespitosa — WCot
grandiflora — EBee
trinerva — WCot

MARSILEA (Marsileaceae)
mutica — SWyc
quadrifolia — SWyc
* *schelpiana* — SWyc

MASCAGNIA (Malpighiaceae)
macroptera — CPlN

MASCARENA See HYOPHORBE

MASSONIA (Hyacinthaceae) See Plant
Deletions

MATELEA (Asclepiadaceae)
¶ *obliqua* — MNrw

MATRICARIA (Asteraceae)
chamomilla — See *M. recutita*
maritima — See *Tripleurospermum
  maritimum*
parthenium — See *Tanacetum parthenium*
§ *recutita* — EJud GPoy MChe MGra MHew

MATTEUCCIA (Aspidiaceae)
orientalis — MBri NHar NMar NOrc WRic
pensylvanica — CCuc EMon NHar WRic
struthiopteris ♀ — Widely available

MATTHIOLA (Brassicaceae)
arborescens — WGwy WPer
§ *fruticulosa* — CArn NMen
– subsp. *perennis* — MAvo NSti NWCA
incana — MArl MHlr WCot WRHF
  WRha WRus
– *alba* — LGan NBir
¶ – hybrid — NCut
  pink perennial — CHan
scapifera — CPBP MFos NTow
sinuata — CNat EWFC
thessala — See *M. fruticulosa*
  white perennial — CArn CGle CHad CHan CMil
  CSev CSpe LCot MCLN NBrk
  NFai NPer NTow SEND WEas
  WHoo WPyg

MAURANDELLA (Scrophulariaceae) See Plant
Deletions

MAURANDYA (Scrophulariaceae)
§ *barclayana*   CBot CPlN CRHN GCra MBri
       MNrw SAxl SLMG
– *alba*   CBot
erubescens   See *Lophospermum erubescens*
lophantha   See *Lophospermum scandens*
lophospermum   See *Lophospermum scandens*
* 'Pink Ice'   CLTr SLMG SOWG
purpusii   CPlN
'Red Dragon'   CPla
§ *scandens*   CPlN CRHN ELan EWes
* 'Victoria Falls'   SLMG SOWG

MAYTENUS (Celastraceae)
boaria   CGre CMCN CPle MAll SAPC
       SArc WWat

MAZUS (Scrophulariaceae)
alpinus B&SWJ 119   WCru
pumilio   ECou
radicans   ECou WCru
reptans   CNic ELan EPar NNrd NPri
       NWCA WPer WPyg
– 'Albus'   ECha ELan NNrd WCru WPer

MECONOPSIS † (Papaveraceae)
aculeata   GCra GGGa GPoy GTou
baileyi   See *M. betonicifolia*
× *beamishii*   GBuc GGar WAbe WCru
§ *betonicifolia* ♀   Widely available
– var. *alba*   CB&S GAbr GBuc GCan GChr
       GCra GGGa GMac IBlr LSyl
       MBal MBri NChi NHar NHol
       NLak NLar NRoo SPer SRms
       WAbe WCru
* – 'Hensol Lilac'   GCal
– var. *pratensis*   GGGa
– purple   IBlr
– violet   GCra
cambrica   CGle CKin CMea CNic EBrP
       EBre ELan EMar EWFC GTou
       LBre NCat NFla NHol NMir
       NVic SBre SChu SIng WAbe
       WBon WHen WHer
       WMow WOve WPer WWye
– var. *aurantiaca*   CTri EBee ELan NBir NLak
       WAbe WBon WHen
– *flore-pleno*   CGle EPar GBuc MTho NCat
       WAbe WFar
– orange (d)   WCru
– yellow (d)   WCru
§ – 'Frances Perry'   CCuc GBuc GCal IBlr NTow
       WAbe WCot WCru WOMN
– 'Muriel Brown' (d)   CMil WAbe WCot WPGP
       WWhi
– 'Rubra'   See *M. cambrica* 'Frances Perry'
chelidoniifolia   CFil EBrP EBre GCal GCra
       IBlr LBre SBre SSpi WCru
       WPGP
delavayi   GGGa
dhwojii   GCan GCra MNes WAbe
¶ *gracilipes*   WAbe
grandis ♀   CBrd CGle CPBP CSam GAbr
       GCan GCra GGGa GMac NBrk
       NHar NLak NRoo NSla SBla
       SRms WAbe WBor WEas WViv
– Balruddry form   GGGa
¶ – 'Betty Sheriff's Dream   GBuc
       Poppy'
– GS 600   CLAP GAbr GBuc GCra IBlr
       NBir SRms

– PS&W 5423   GDra
horridula   CNic CSam EHyt GCan GCra
       GGGa MTho SMrm
¶ – var. *racemosa*   EHyt
– Rudis Group   GCra WCru
integrifolia   GCra GCrs GDra GGGa LSyl
       WAbe
– ACE 1798   GTou
– subsp. *integrifolia*   GCrs
    'Wolong'
◆ 'James Cobb'   See *M. integrifolia* subsp.
       integrifolia 'Wolong'
¶ Kingsbarns hybrids   GGGa
lancifolia   GGGa
¶ aff. – KGB 737   EHyt
§ *napaulensis*   CB&S CSam ELan GCan GCra
       GCrs GDra GGGa IBlr LHop
       MBal MBri MNes NChi NRoo
       NWCA WBor WEas WWin
– ex CMC 127   GCra
– forms   GAbr
¶ – HWJCM 301   WCru
– red   GBuc NBir
– scarlet   GCra
nudicaulis   See *Papaver nudicaule*
paniculata   GCra GGGa IBlr NBir WAbe
– BC 9314   GCra
– CC&McK 296   GTou
– compact form   GCra
¶ – Ghopte Group   WAbe
¶ – Ghunsa Group   WAbe
– ginger foliage   WAbe
¶ *pseudointegrifolia*   GGGa
¶ – subsp. *robusta*   GCra
punicea   GCan GCra GCrs GGGa NHar
       WAbe WViv
* *quintuplinerva* 'Kay's   GBuc IBlr
    Compact'
quintuplinervia ♀   CLAP CPBP GCra GDra
       GGGa GTou IBlr NBir NHar
       NRoo NRya NSla SBla
regia   CSam GCra NLak NRoo SMrm
       WFar
– × *grandis*   GBuc GCra
– hybrids   CAbP GTou
robusta   GCra
× *sarsonsii*   GCan GCra
× *sheldonii* ♀   CBrd CSam GAbr GBuc GCrs
       GGGa GMaP MBri MFir NBir
       NHar NLon NRoo SSpi WViv
– Ballyrogan form   IBlr
– 'Blue Ice'   GTou
– 'Branklyn'   GCrs IBlr
– Crewdson hybrids   CLAP GBuc GCra GDra MNes
       MOne NBrk WAbe
– 'Jimmy Bayne'   GCra GMaP
– 'Lingholm'   CLAP GCal GCan GCra GCrs
       GGar WCru
* – 'Mrs McMurtrie'   IBlr
– 'Ormswell'   GBuc IBlr NRoo SRms
– 'Silver'   GCra
– 'Slieve Donard' ♀   CLAP GBuc GCra GDra GGar
       IBlr MNes NHar NRoo
– 'Springhill'   IBlr
simplicifolia   GCra
sp. CH&M 1013   GCra
superba   GBuc GCan GCra GGGa MBal
       MNes WAbe
villosa   GBuc GCra GGGa GTou IBlr
       NBir WAbe
wallichii   See *M. napaulensis*
– *alba* BC 9370   GCra

– BC 9361 GCra

MEDEMIA (Arecaceae)
 argun LPal

MEDEOLA (Convallariaceae)
 virginica LAma WCru

MEDICAGO (Papilionaceae)
 arborea CPle ELan IBlr WHer
 echinus See *M. intertexta*
 sativa CKin EWFC MPEx WHer
  WPbr
 – subsp. *sativa* IBlr

MEDINILLA (Melastomataceae)
 magnifica LCns LRHS MBri

MEEHANIA (Lamiaceae)
* *garganica garganica* WCru
 B&SWJ 1210
 urticifolia EMon MHar MSte WOMN

MEGACARPAEA (Brassicaceae)
 polyandra GDra

MELALEUCA (Myrtaceae)
 acerosa SOWG
¶ *acuminata* CHon
 alternifolia CArn CHon ECou ELau EOHP
  MAll MSal SOWG
 armillaris CHon MAll SOWG
 bracteata CHon CTrC MAll
¶ *brevifolia* CHon
¶ *calycina* subsp. *dempta* CHon
¶ *capitata* CTrC MAll
 coccinea SOWG
 cuticularis CHon MAll
 decora CHon SOWG
 decussata CHon CTrC ECou MAll SOWG
§ *densa* CHon
§ *diosmatifolia* CHon MAll
¶ *elliptica* CHon CTrC
 ericifolia CTri MAll SOWG
¶ *– nana* CHon
 erubescens See *M. diosmatifolia*
 filifolia SOWG
 fulgens CTrC MFiF
 gibbosa CHon CPle MAll SBid WTro
 halmaturorum CHon MAll
 holosericea SOWG
 huegelii SOWG
 hypericifolia CHon CPle ECou MAll SBid
  SOWG
 incana CHon CTrC MAll SOWG
¶ *lanceolata* CHon MAll
 lateritia CHon MAll
 leucadendra MSal
 linariifolia CHon CTrC ECou
 nesophila CHon ECou MAll SOWG
 pauciflora See *M. biconvexa*
 platycalyx SOWG
 pustulata ECou MAll SOWG
 quinquenervia See *M. viridiflora* var.
  rubriflora
¶ *radula* CHon
¶ *rhaphiophylla* CHon
* *rosmarinifolia* SOWG
¶ *sieberi* CHon
 spathulata SOWG
¶ *spicigera* CHon

 squamea CHon ECou LHil MAll
 squarrosa CGre CHon CLTr CTrC ECou
  MAll SOWG
¶ *striata* CHon
 styphelioides MAll
§ *suberosa* CHon
¶ *tenella* CHon
¶ *teretifolia* CHon
 thymifolia CHon ECou MAll
¶ *thymoides* CHon
¶ *uncinata* MAll
¶ *undulata* CHon
¶ *viminea* CHon
 viridiflora CB&S GQui IDee
§ – var. *rubriflora* CHon MAll
 wilsonii CHon CTrC MAll SOWG

MELANDRIUM See VACCARIA

MELANOSELINUM (Apiaceae)
§ *decipiens* CHEx EOHP SIgm

MELANTHIUM (Melanthiaceae) See Plant Deletions

MELASPHAERULA (Iridaceae)
 graminea See *M. ramosa*
§ *ramosa* CAvo CBre CLTr CMon NRog

MELASTOMA (Melastomataceae) See Plant Deletions

MELIA (Meliaceae)
§ *azedarach* CArn CB&S CHEx CPle LPan
  MWhi
 – var. *japonica* See *M. azedarach*

MELIANTHUS (Melianthaceae)
 comosus CTrC LFlo LLew MAvo WCot
 major ♀ Widely available
 minor CFir CHEx CSpe LLew
 pectinatus WCot
¶ sp. from Richtersveld, North LLew
 Cape, South Africa
 villosus LFlo LLew

MELICA (Poaceae)
 altissima EMon MWhi
 – 'Atropurpurea' CCuc CDec CHan CHea CWSG
  ECGN ECha EGar EHoe
  EMon EPPr EPla ESOG LBlm
  LGan LGre LLWP MNrw MSte
  NHol NSti NVic WBro WCot
  WFoF WPer WWye
 ciliata CCuc CPea CSam EBee ECGN
  EHoe EMon EPPr EPla GBin
  GCHN WPer
* – 'Pearl Eyelash' CInt
 macra EHoe ESOG
 nutans CCuc EHoe GBin NHol WHal
 penicillaris WPer
 transsilvanica EBee ECGN EMan GBin
 – 'Atropurpurea' EBee NHol
 uniflora CKin
 – f. *albida* CCuc CFil EHoe EMon EPPr
  MAvo SUsu WCot WRHF
 – 'Variegata' CCuc CFil CVer EHoe EMan
  EMon EPPr EPla GCal MAvo
  MBri MHlr WCot WWye

MELICOPE (Rutaceae)
   ternata   ECou

MELICYTUS (Violaceae)
   alpinus   ECou MAll
   angustifolius   CPle ECou MAll MHig
   crassifolius   CPle ECou EMon EPfP MAll
                 WHCG
   obovatus   CPle ECou MAll
   ramiflorus   ECou MAll

MELILOTUS (Papilionaceae)
   officinalis   CArn CJew CKin GBar GPoy
                 MChe SIde WHer WSel
   – subsp. *albus*   SIde WHer

MELINIS (Poaceae)
   ¶ *nerviglumis*   EBee

MELIOSMA (Meliosmaceae)
   myriantha   WCoo
   pendens   See *M. dilleniifolia* subsp.
                 flexuosa
   simplicifolia subsp. CB&S
    pungens
   veitchiorum   CHEx

MELISSA (Lamiaceae)
   officinalis   CArn CChe CHal EBar EFer
                 ELau GPoy LHol MBal MBar
                 MBri MChe MHew SIde SSoC
                 WBea WEas WGwG WOak
                 WPer WWye
   – 'All Gold'   CBre CHal CMGP CSev ECha
                 EGoo EHoe EJud ELan ELau
                 EPla LHol MBri MChe MMal
                 NFai NSti NVic SPer WWye
   § – 'Aurea' (v)   CArn CFee CHal CMHG CSev
                 ECha EHoe ELan ELau ENot
                 GPoy LGro LHol MBar MBri
                 MCLN MFir MHew MWgw
                 NBro NFai NSti SIde SPer
                 WBea WMow WOak WShe
                 WWin
   * – 'Compacta'   ELau GPoy
   – 'Small-Ness'   MNes
   N– 'Variegata' hort. See *M. officinalis* **'Aurea'**

MELITTIS (Lamiaceae)
   melissophyllum CFir CHan CRDP ECha EMan
                 MRav SIgm SIng SRms SSpi
                 WAbb WWye
   – subsp. *albida*   SSpi
   – pink   EMon MInt SOkh

MENISPERMUM (Menispermaceae)
   canadense   CPlN GPoy MSal SHBN
   davuricum   CPlN

MENTHA † (Lamiaceae)
   aquatica   CAgr CArn CBen CKin CRow
                 CWat ECoo EHon EJud ELau
                 EWFC GAbr GBin GPoy
                 LPBA MChe MHew MSta SWat
                 SWyc WChe WHer WMAq
                 WOak
   arvensis   CArn ELau EOHP IIve MHew
                 MSal SIde WHer
   ¶ – var. *piperascens* EOHP MSal
   asiatica   ELau EOHP SIde SPil WHer

   * *brevifolia*   EOHP SPil WHer
   § *cervina*   CBen CWat EMFW EOHP
                 LPBA MSta SPil SWat WChe
   – *alba*   WChe
   citrata   See *M.* × *piperita* f. *citrata*
   cordifolia   See *M.* × *villosa*
   corsica   See *M. requienii*
   ¶ *crispa* × *piperita* EOHP
   diemenica   EOHP
   'Eau de Cologne' See *M.* × *piperita* f. *citrata*
   ¶ Eucalyptus Mint EOHP
   gattefossei   CArn EOHP
   × *gentilis*   See *M.* × *gracilis*
   § × *gracilis*   CArn ELau EOHP GBar LHol
                 MChe NDea NPri SIde WBea
                 WJek WOak WRHF WWye
   – 'Aurea'   See *M.* × *gracilis* **'Variegata'**
   § – 'Variegata'   CDec CSev ECha ECoo EHoe
                 EMar GPoy ILis MBal MBar
                 NRoo NSti SHel WGwG WHer
                 WOak WOve WPer
   ¶ *haplocalyx*   ELau EOHP MSal
   * 'Hillary's Sweet Lemon' ELau EOHP
   * *lacerata*   SPil
   Lavender Mint   CBod GBar GPoy MRav NPri
                 WJek WRha
   § *longifolia*   CAgr CRDP ECha ECoo ELau
                 EMar GBar LHop NSti WEas
                 WGwG WHer WJek WOak
                 WPer WSel WWye
   – Buddleia Mint Group ELau EWes GAbr MRav NBus
                 SIde SPil WBea WRha WSel
   ¶ – silver form   SPil
   * – 'Variegata'   CBod ELau NCat NSti WJek
   × *piperita*   CAgr CArn CSev EBar ECha
                 EHoe EJud ELau GBar GBur
                 GPoy ILis LHop MBri MChe
                 MHew NNor NRoo WBea
                 WGwG WOak WPer WWye
   § – f. *citrata*   CAgr CArn ECha ECoo ELau
                 GAbr GBar GPoy LHol MBar
                 MBri MChe MHew NFai NSti
                 NVic SHDw SIde SRms WBea
                 WCer WGwG WOak WOve
                 WPer WSel WWye
   * – – 'Basil'   CBod EJud ELau EOHP LLWP
                 SHDw SIde WGwG WJek
   – – 'Chocolate'   CBod ELau EOHP SDys SHDw
                 SIde SPil WBea WJek WPer
   – – 'Lemon'   ELau EOHP GAbr MBri SHDw
                 SIde SPil WBea WJek WPer
                 WRha WSel
   – – 'Lime'   EOHP MTed SHDw SIde SPil
                 WBea WGwG
   – 'Logee' (v)   EGoo EOHP EWes WAlt
                 WCHb WHer WJek
   – f. *officinalis*   ELau SIde
   ¶ – 'Reverchonii'   SPil
   pulegium   CArn CSev EBar EBot ECha
                 ELau EPar EWFC GPoy LHol
                 MChe SIde WGwG WHer WJek
                 WOak WPer WWye
   – 'Upright'   CArn CBod EOHP GPoy MGra
                 SHDw SIde WJek WPer WSel
   § *requienii*   CArn CRow EBar ELan ELau
                 EPot ESis GBar GPoy ILis
                 LHol MBal MBar MBri MChe
                 MMal NRoo SDix SIde SIng
                 SRms WCla WEas WGwG
                 WOMN WOak WPat WPer
                 WWhi WWye

rotundifolia 'Bowles' — See *M.* × *villosa* f. *alopecuroides* **Bowles' Mint**
– hort. — See *M. suaveolens*
rubra var. *raripila* — See *M.* × *smithiana*
¶ 'Sayakarze' — EOHP
§ × *smithiana* — CArn EJud ELau EOHP GAbr GBar GPoy ILis MChe NPri SIde WBea WHer WPer WRha WSel WWye
– 'Capel Ulo' — EOHP WHer
sp. Nile Valley Mint — CArn ELau EOHP SHDw
§ *spicata* — CAgr CArn CSev EBar GPoy ILis LHol MBal MBar MBri MChe MHew NFai NNor NRoo WBea WGwG WHer WJek WOak WPer WWye
* – 'Brundall' — EOHP MTed
– 'Crispa' — CArn CBre EJud ELau EOHP GAbr GAri GBar MGra NFai NPri NRoo NSti SIde SMac WCer WCot WGwG WPer WRha WSel WWye
– 'Moroccan' — CArn CInt CJew CSev EJud ELau EOHP GAbr GPoy NPri SHDw SIde WBea WCer WHer WJek WOak WSel WWye
– 'Newbourne' — ELau
¶ – 'Spanish Furry' — EOHP
¶ – 'Spanish Pointed' — EOHP
– 'Tashkent' — ELau MTed SHDw WJek
¶ – subsp. *tomentosa* — SPil
§ *suaveolens* — CAgr CArn EJud ELau GBar GPoy ILis LHol MBal MBri MHew NRoo SIde WBea WGwG WHer WOak WPer
* – 'Mobillei' — SPil
– subsp. *timija* — ELau WJek
§ – 'Variegata' — CArn CDec CRow EBar ECha EHoe ELau GAbr GPoy MBal MBar MBri MCLN MChe NChi NFai NHol NNor NSti SRms WBea WGwG WHer WMow WOak WOve WPer
sylvestris — See *M. longifolia*
¶ × *villosa* f. *alopecuroides* — IIve
Bowles' Mint
¶ – f. *alopecuroides* — CBre EGoo ELau GBar GPoy ILis LHol MChe NFai NSti SIde SWat WHer WJek WOak WWye
Bowles' Mint
viridis — See *M. spicata*

MENYANTHES (Menyanthaceae)
trifoliata — CBen CNic CRow CWat EBrP EBre ECha ECoo EHon ELau EMFW EWFC GBin GPoy LBre LPBA MHew MSta NDea NVic SBre SRms SWyc WChe WMAq WShi WWye

MENZIESIA (Ericaceae)
alba — See *Daboecia cantabrica* f. *alba*
ciliicalyx dwarf form — SSta
– *lasiophylla* — See *M. ciliicalyx* var. *purpurea*
– var. *multiflora* — GDra GGGa MBal MDun
§ – var. *purpurea* — GGGa SSta
– 'Spring Morning' — SSta
ferruginea — MBal
polifolia — See *Daboecia cantabrica*

MERCURIALIS (Euphorbiaceae)
perennis — GPoy WHer WShi

– 'Cae Rhos Llingwy' — WHer

MERENDERA (Colchicaceae)
attica — EPot
eichleri — See *M. trigyna*
filifolia AB&S 4665 — CMon
kurdica — EHyt EPot LAma
§ *montana* — EHyt ERos WIvy
– MS 900/913 — CMon
– SF 221 — CMon
pyrenaica — See *M. montana*
raddeana — See *M. trigyna*
sobolifera — EDAr EHyt EPot GCrs
§ *trigyna* — EPot LAma

MERREMIA (Convolvulaceae)
§ *tuberosa* — CPIN

MERTENSIA (Boraginaceae)
ciliata — CHan CMdw EBee EBrP EBre LBre MArl MBri MRav SBre SPer SWat WPbr WRus
echioides — NTow
franciscana — EBee GCal NChi NPSI WCru
maritima — GPoy MHlr MSal SMer WCru WFar WOMN WWin
– subsp. *asiatica* — See *M. simplicissima*
primuloides — GCal
pterocarpa — See *M. sibirica*
§ *pulmonarioides* ♀ — CBot CBro CGle CLAP CRDP EAst EBot EBrP EBre EHoe ELan EOrc EPot GDra GGar LAma LBre LHop MHlr NLar NRoo SBre SMac SPer SRms WCru WHoo WShi WWat
§ *sibirica* — CHan CLAP CSpe GCrs LGre MDun MHar NChi NTow
§ *simplicissima* — CBos CBot CHad CSpe EBrP EBre ECho EHyt ELan EMan LBre LHop MHar MNrw MTho NBir NGre NWCA SBla SBre SMad SWas WCru WHoo WWhi
virginica — See *M. pulmonarioides*
viridis — NGre

MERXMUELLERA See RYTIDOSPERMA

MERYTA (Araliaceae)
sinclairii — CHEx
– 'Variegata' — See *M. sinclairii* 'Moonlight'

MESEMBRYANTHEMUM (Aizoaceae)
'Basutoland' — See *Delosperma nubigenum*
brownii — See *Lampranthus brownii*
ornatulum — See *Delosperma ornatulum*
putterillii — See *Ruschia putterillii*

MESPILUS (Rosaceae)
germanica (F) — CB&S CBlo CLnd ECrN ELan IOrc LHol LPan MWat NDal SHBN WBay WDin WMou
– 'Breda Giant' (F) — GTwe
– 'Dutch' (F) — SDea SFam SKee
– 'Large Russian' (F) — ERea ESim GTwe SKee
– 'Monstrous' (F) — CBar GTwe SDea
– 'Nottingham' (F) — CSam CTho EMui ENot ERea GTwe LBuc MBlu NBee SDea SFam SIgm SKee SPer WJas WMou
– 'Royal' (F) — ESim

METAPANAX See PSEUDOPANAX

METASEQUOIA (Taxodiaceae)
  glyptostroboides ♀   CB&S CGre CMCN CMac
    EHul ELan ENot GChr GRei
    ISea LCon LHyr LNet MBal
    MBar MBri MGos NWea SHBN
    SMad SPer SReu SSta STre
    WBod WDin WMou WNor
    WWal WWat
  – 'Fastigiata'   See *M. glyptostroboides*
    'National'
* – 'Green Mantle'   EHul
§ – 'National'   CSam
  – 'Sheridan Spire'   CEnd LNet

METROSIDEROS (Myrtaceae)
  carmineus   CHEx
  – 'Carousel'   ERea
  – 'Ferris Wheel'   ERea
  diffusus   CPlN
§ *excelsus*   CAbb CHEx CTrC CTrG ECou
  – 'Aureus'   ECou
  – 'Parnell'   CTrC
  – 'Scarlet Pimpernel'   ERea SOWG
  – 'Spring Fire'   CAbb CB&S GQui
  fulgens   ECou
  'Goldfinger'   ERea
  kermadecensis   ECou LHil
  – 'Variegatus'   CAbb CB&S ECou ERea GQui
    LHil SBid
  lucidus   See *M. umbellatus*
  'Moon Maiden'   ERea
  'Pink Lady'   ERea
  robustus   CB&S CHEx GQui
  'Thomasii'   ECon LCns SOWG
  tomentosus   See *M. excelsus*
§ *umbellatus*   CGre CHEx ECou MAll
  villosus   SOWG
  – 'Tahiti'   CB&S GQui

MEUM (Apiaceae)
  athamanticum   CGle CRDP CSev EFou EGol
    EMan EPla GCal GPoy LHop
    MHew MRav MSal MTho MUlv
    NBrk NHol NRoo SIgm SMrm
    WFar WPbr WPer

MIBORA (Poaceae) See Plant Deletions

MICHAUXIA (Campanulaceae)
  campanuloides   NChi SMrm WBor
  tchihatchewii   CBot CGen CSpe EWll MNrw

MICHELIA (Magnoliaceae)
  compressa   CGre WPGP
  doltsopa   CFil CGre CHEx CPle GQui
    IDee SBid SSpi
  figo   CAbb CFil CGre EMil ERea
    GQui SBid
§ *sinensis*   SSta
  wilsonii   See *M. sinensis*

MICRANTHUS (Iridaceae)
  alopecuroides   NRog
¶ *plantagineus*   LBow

MICROBIOTA (Cupressaceae)
  decussata ♀   CDoC CKen CMHG CMac
    EBrP EBre EHul EOrn EPla
    ESis GRei LBee LBre LCon
    LLin MAsh MBar MBri MGos
    MWat NHol SBre SSmi WPyg
    WWat
  – 'Jakobsen'   CKen
  – 'Trompenburg'   CKen

MICROCACHRYS (Podocarpaceae)
  tetragona   CDoC ECho ECou EPla LCon
    SIng

MICROCOELUM See LYTOCARYUM

MICROGLOSSA (Asteraceae)
  albescens   See *Aster albescens*

MICROLEPIA (Dennstaedtiaceae)
  speluncae   MBri

MICROLOMA (Asclepiadaceae)
  hereroense   MSto
  sagittatum   MSto

MICROMERIA (Lamiaceae)
  chamissonis   ELau EOHP
  corsica   See *Acinos corsicus*
  croatica   EHyt NTow
¶ *dalmatica*   EBee
  rupestris   See *M. thymifolia*
§ *thymifolia*   EMan MPla NMen

MICROSERIS (Asteraceae)
  ringens   ECha EMan GAri GBri GBuc
    LFis NSti NTow SMrm WCot
  – 'Girandole'   CInt EBee LBuc LIck MNrw
    NHol SUsu WPer WWal

MICROSORUM (Polypodiaceae)
  diversifolium   CFil CHEx
¶ *punctatum* 'Grandiceps'   WRic

MICROSTROBOS (Podocarpaceae)
  fitzgeraldii   CKen

MIKANIA (Asteraceae)
§ *dentata*   CPlN MBri
  scandens   CPlN
  ternata   See *M. dentata*

MILIUM (Poaceae)
  effusum   CKin
  – 'Aureum'   CCuc CTrC EFou EHoe ELan
    EPot ESOG LGro MBal MBar
    MBrN MFir MRPP NBro NGre
    NHol NMir NRoo NSti SApp
    SIng SMad SPer SUsu WEas
    WHoo WOMN WRus WWat
    WWin
  – var. *esthonicum*   EBee EMon EPPr ESOG

MILLIGANIA (Asteliaceae) See Plant Deletions

MIMOSA (Mimosaceae)
  hostilis   NGno
  pudica   EAnd LPVe MLan
  scabrella   NGno

MIMULUS (Scrophulariaceae)

'A.T. Johnson'	GCHN MSCN NVic
¶ *alatus*	EBee
* 'Andean Nymph'	CPBP
F & W 8384	
'Andean Nymph' forms	CGle MNrw WLin
§ 'Andean Nymph'	CLTr CMea EBrP EBre ELan
Mac&W 5257 ♀	GCHN LBre MBal MSCN
	NMGW NNrd SBre SWat WCla
	WOMN
§ *aurantiacus* ♀	CBot CFee CInt CPle CSpe
	EBak EBrP EBre ELan EOrc
	EPot ERea IBlr LBre LHil
	LHop MPla NPer SBre SDry
	SHFr SIng SMrm SUsu WEas
	WLin WOMN WPer
– orange	See *M. aurantiacus* var.
	puniceus
§ – var. *puniceus*	CBot CLTr CSpe ELan LHil
	LHop MBEx SDry SMrm SUsu
	WLin
x *bartonianus*	EBee EWes WFar
bifidus	CSpe EBee EOrc LHop SMac
– 'Verity Buff'	CSpe LHil LIck
– 'Verity Purple'	CSpe
– 'Verity Rose'	CLTr LHil
– 'Wine'	LIck
x *burnetii*	LPBA MRav NVic SRms
californicus	CHan
Calypso Series	SRms SWat
cardinalis ♀	CGen EHon ELan GMac LHop
	LPBA MFir MHar MNrw MTho
	NDea NMGW NNor SHFr SPer
	WHer WOve WPer WWeb
	WWin
cupreus	MBal SIng
– 'Minor'	ECho
– 'Whitecroft Scarlet' ♀	EBrP EBre ECha ELan GDra
	LBre LPBA MOne NGre NHar
	NNrd SBod SBre SIng WLin
	WPer WWin
¶ *cusickii*	EBee
'Eleanor'	SMrm SUsu
glutinosus	See *M. aurantiacus*
– *atrosanguineus*	See *M. aurantiacus* var.
	puniceus
– *luteus*	See *M. aurantiacus*
§ *guttatus*	CBen CKin CRow EMan
	EWFC GAbr GAri GBar NDea
	SRms WChe WPer
– 'Richard Bish' (v)	CMea CRDP CSpe EPot LHop
	MAvo NCat SAga WByw WCot
	WHal
– variegated	See *M. guttatus* **'Richard Bish'**
'Highland Orange'	GAri GCHN MOne NHar
	WGor WPer
'Highland Pink'	ECtt EMan GMac MOne NHar
	NRoo SBod WGor WPer
'Highland Red' ♀	ECtt GCHN GDra LPBA
	MOne NNrd WHen WPer
	WWin
'Highland Yellow'	ECtt GAri GCHN NLak NRoo
	NVic SBod WHen WPer
hose-in-hose	CDec CLTr CRow EBee ECha
	NDea WCot WHer
hose-in-hose yellow	EBee GCal
'Inca Sunset'	EWes WOMN
'Inshriach Crimson'	GAri GCHN
langsdorffii	See *M. guttatus*
lewisii ♀	CGen CMea ELan EMan GCra
	GDra GTou MFir MTho
	NWCA SRms WOMN WPer

longiflorus	CBot CLTr LHop MBEx
– 'Santa Barbara'	CLTr LHil MBEx SMrm SUsu
¶ 'Lothian Fire'	WWeb
luteus	CBen CRow CWat ECha EHon
	LPBA MBal MSta NDea NFai
	SHFr WByw WChe WMAq
	WWin
* – 'Variegatus'	CRow EAst GBar GMac NNrd
	NPer
* 'Major Bees'	CDoC EPfP GCal
¶ 'Malibu Scarlet'	GMac
(Malibu Series)	
Malibu Series	NNor
'Mandarin'	EBrP EBre LBre SBre
moschatus	CRow CSam NCat NMen WCla
	WEas
nanus	MSto
'Old Rose'	EBee ECha
'Orange Glow'	EPfP WHal
'Orkney Gold'	NCat
'Popacatapetl'	CHal CSpe LHil LHop LIck
	MBEx SChu SMrm
primuloides	ELan EPot GCHN GCrs MBro
	NGre NHar NMen NNrd
	NWCA SBod WFar WPnn
'Puck'	GAri GMac NCat NPro
'Quetzalcoatl'	MBEx SMrm
Red Emperor	See *M.* **'Roter Kaiser'**
ringens	CBen CDoC CRow CWat EBrP
	EBre EHon EMFW GBri GMac
	LBre LPBA MSCN MSta NDea
	SBre SPer SRms WBon WChe
	WHil WMAq WOMN WPer
	WWeb
§ 'Roter Kaiser'	MNrw MTPN SRms
sp. Mac&W 5257	See *M.* **'Andean Nymph'**
	Mac&W 5257
Threave variegated	EBee GBri GBuc GCal NBir
	NRoo
¶ 'Tigrinus Queen's Prize'	LIck
tilingii	CFee CHal ECho ELan GTou
	NLak NNrd
Verity hybrids	ERea MBEx
'Wisley Red'	ECha ECot ELan

MINA See IPOMOEA

MINUARTIA (Caryophyllaceae)

capillacea	MSto
♦ *caucasica*	See *M. circassica*
§ *circassica*	CLyd ESis MDHE MHig
	NWCA WAbe WLin WPer
¶ *dianthifolia*	WLin
¶ *inamoena*	WLin
juniperina NS 270	NWCA
laricifolia	LBee
¶ *obtusiloba*	NWCA
parnassica	See *M. stellata*
§ *stellata*	EPot LBee NHed NMen NNrd
	NTow SIng
– NS 758	NWCA
§ *verna*	CLyd NHar NMen
– subsp. *caespitosa*	See *Sagina subulata* **'Aurea'**
'Aurea'	
– subsp. *gerardii*	See *M. verna* subsp. *verna*

MIRABILIS (Nyctaginaceae)

jalapa	CArn CSWP EBot ELan LAma
	LIck MBri MHlr MLLN NRog
	SEND SLMG SRms

MISCANTHUS (Poaceae)

§ *floridulus* ♀ — CSev CSte EFou EHoe GCal MTed MUlv SDix SMad SSoC WCot

nepalensis — EHoe EWes LRHS

¶ × *oligonensis* — CSte MMoz
  'Zwergelefant'

oligostachyus — EPPr GCal

§ – 'Nanus Variegatus' — CRow EHoe EMon EPPr EPla EWes

sacchariflorus — CB&S CHEx CRow CSte EBrP EBre ECED ECGN ECha EFul ELan EOas EPPr EPla ESOG GOrn LBre LPBA MBrN MLLN MUlv MWgw NHol NVic SBre SCob SPer SPla WWat WWye

§ 'Silberfeder' — Widely available

sinensis ♀ — CArn CHEx CHan EPla GBin

– 'Adagio' — CSte SApp

¶ – 'Arabesque' — CSte MMoz

– 'Augustfeder' — CSte

– 'Autumn Light' — CSte

– C&L 143a — EPla

– 'China' — EHoe EPPr EPla

– var. *condensatus* — EFou

– – 'Cabaret' — SRos WCot WHal

– – 'Cosmopolitan' (v) — WCot

¶ – 'Dixieland' — CSte MMoz SApp

¶ – 'Emerald Giant' — SApp

– 'Ferne Osten' — CCuc CSte CWit EBrP EBre ECGN ECha EFou EGar EPPr EPla LBre MBri SBre WFar

– 'Flamingo' — CSte EBrP EBre EHoe EPPr EPla LBre LGre LRHS MBri MMHG NHol SBre

¶ – 'Gearmella' — EPPr

– 'Giganteus' — See *M. floridulus*

– 'Goldfeder' (v) — EBrP EBre EPla LBre SBre WBcn

– 'Goliath' — CSte EFou

– 'Gracillimus' — CB&S CDoC CFil CHEx CHid CRow CSte EBrP EBre ECha EFou EFul ELan ENot EPla ESOG EWes GOrn LBre LHil MBal MBrN MLLN NBro SAxl SBre SCob SDix SPer

– 'Graziella' — CSte EBrP EBre EPla LBre MBri NHol SAxl SBre WLRN WPGP

– 'Grosse Fontäne' — CSte ECha EFou EHoe EPla SMad WCot

– 'Hercules' — CSte

¶ – 'Juli' — CSte

– 'Kaskade' — CSte EBrP EBre EPla LBre LRHS MBri SBre

– 'Kleine Fontäne' — CFee CMil CSte EBee EBrP EBre ECGN EGar EHoe EMan EPPr EPla GBri LBre MAus MBri NHol SAxl SBla SBre SChu SMad SWas

– 'Kleine Silberspinne' — CCuc CHad CHea CLon CSte EBrP EBre ECGN EFou EGle EHoe EMan EPPr EPla ESOG GCal LBre NHol SBre WRus

– 'Malepartus' — CHad CLon CMil CRow CSte EBrP EBre ECha EFul EGar EHoe EOld EPPr EPla GCal LBre LGre NHol SAxl SBre SChu SWas WCot

– 'Morning Light' (v) — CCuc CSte CVer CWit EBrP EBre ECha EFou EMan EPPr EPla LBre MCCP MLLN MNrw SAxl SBre WCot

– 'Nippon' — EHoe EPPr EPla LHil MAus MBri NHol SAxl SChu SMad WRus

¶ – 'November Sunset' — CSte MMoz

– 'Poseidon' — EPPr SAxl

¶ – 'Positano' — CSte MMoz

– 'Pünktchen' (v) — CSte ECha EFou EPPr EPla SMad SWas

– var. *purpurascens* — CInt CSte CWit EBrP EBre ECGN ECha EGar EGol EHoe EMan EOas EPPr EPla ESOG GAri LBre MAus MBrN MBro MLLN MWhi SBre SCob SSoC WWat

¶ – 'Roland' — LGre

– 'Roterpfeil' — EPla

– 'Rotfuchs' — CLon LGre

– 'Rotsilber' (v) — EBrP EBre ECha EFou EGle EHoe EOld EPPr EPla LBre SApp SBre SHBN

– 'Sarabande' — CSte ECGN EHoe

– SF 92302 — ISea

– 'Silberpfeil' (v) — EPla LRHS SMad

– 'Silberspinne' — EFou EPla ESOG LHil

¶ – 'Silberturm' — CSte

– Silver Feather — See *M.* 'Silberfeder'

– 'Sioux' — CSte EBee EPla WBcn

– 'Sirene' — CSte EBee EBrP EBre EPla LBre SApp SBre SMad

– 'Slavopour' — EPla

– 'Spatgrun' — EPPr EPla

– 'Strictus' (v) — ECha EFul EGar EHoe EPPr EPla MBri MHlr NBee SDix WCot WViv

– 'Undine' — CCuc CSte CWit ECha EGle EHoe EMan EPPr EPla LHil MAus MAvo MBri NHol SAxl SChu SDix SMad SOkh SPla SUsu WLRN

– 'Variegatus' — Widely available

– 'Vorläufer' — EHoe EPla

¶ – 'Wetterfahne' — EPPr

– 'Yakushima Dwarf' — CCuc CMil CSte CVer CWit EBrP EBre EGle EHoe EMil EPPr EPla GBin GCal GOrn LBre LHil MGed NFai NHol NPSI NSti SBre SSoC SWas WCot

– 'Zebrinus' (v) — Widely available

sp. from Yakushima — EPla

tinctorius 'Nanus Variegatus' — See *M. oligostachyus* 'Nanus Variegatus'

¶ – 'Variegatus' — CSte

transmorrisonensis — EBee EHoe EMan EPPr EPla ESOG GBin SLPl WWoo

* *yakushimensis* — EBee ECha EGle EPPr EPla WPGP

MISOPATES (Scrophulariaceae)

orontium — EWFC WCla

MITCHELLA (Rubiaceae)

repens — MHig WCru WWat

MITELLA (Saxifragaceae)

breweri	CGle CHal CHan CLyd CNic ECha ECro EEls ELan GBin LSyl MLLN MSte MWgw NHol NRoo NSti SHFr SRms SSpi WByw WEas WFar WOMN WPbr WPer WWat
caulescens	ECha ECro GAbr LFis MLLN MRav NBro NHol WPer
formosana B&SWJ 125	WCru
stauropetala	NCat NWoo

MITRARIA (Gesneriaceae)

coccinea	CAbb CB&S CHEx CMac CNic CPlN CPle CRHN CTrG CTrw CWit ELan EPot ERea GGGa IOrc MAll MBal MBlu MHig MPla SArc SPer SSoC SSpi WAbe WBod WGwG WSHC WWat
¶ *coccinea* Clark's form	MDun
– 'Lake Caburgua'	GCal
– Lake Puye form	CFee CGre ERea GQui LHop LRHS SAga SBra SSta WAbe WCru WWal

MITRASACME (Loganiaceae) See Plant Deletions

MITRIOSTIGMA (Rubiaceae) See Plant Deletions

MNIUM See PLAGIOMNIUM

MODIOLA (Malvaceae) See Plant Deletions

MODIOLASTRUM (Malvaceae) See Plant Deletions

MOEHRINGIA (Caryophyllaceae) See Plant Deletions

MOLINIA (Poaceae)

altissima	See *M. caerulea* subsp. *arundinacea*
caerulea	CInt COtt
§ – subsp. *arundinacea*	CCuc ECGN ECha EFou EPla GBin LHil WPer
– – 'Bergfreund'	ECGN EHoe EMon EPPr EPla ESOG GBin GCal SAxl SUsu
– – 'Fontäne'	EFou EPla MSte
– – 'Karl Foerster'	EBee ECGN EFou EHoe EPPr EPfP EPla GBin GCal MMil SApp WCot WLRN
– – 'Skyracer'	CSte MMoz WCot
– – 'Transparent'	CLon EFou EGle EHoe EPla GCal SAxl WChe WCot WRHF
– – 'Windspiel'	CInt CLTr CRow CSte EBee ECGN ECha EHoe EMil EPPr EPla ESOG GCal NHol NSti WChe WCot
– *arundinacea* 'Zuneigung'	EHoe SApp
– subsp. *caerulea* 'Edith Dudszus'	CCuc CSte EBee ECGN ECha EHoe EMon EPPr EPla MBrN
– – 'Heidebraut' (v)	CCuc CSte ECGN ECha EGle EHoe EMon EPPr EPla NHol
– – 'Moorflamme'	EPPr
– – 'Moorhexe'	CInt EBee ECGN ECha EHoe EMan EMon EPPr EPla ESOG GBri GCal MAvo NSti SSoC WChe
– – 'Variegata' ♀	Widely available
– 'Carmarthen' (v)	CElw CNat EMon EPPr LRHS WCot
– 'Claerwen'	EMan EPPr EPla GBuc GCal SApp
¶ – 'Dauerstrahl'	NHol
– 'Strahlenquelle'	CElw EMan EMon EPPr EPla GCal LRHS WChe
litoralis	See *M. caerulea* subsp. *arundinacea*

MOLOPOSPERMUM (Apiaceae)

peloponnesiacum	LGre NLar SIgm SMrm

MOLTKIA (Boraginaceae)

§ *doerfleri*	CPle MBro MHar NChi WWat
graminifolia	See *M. suffruticosa*
§ × *intermedia* ♀	CMea ELan LHil WWin
petraea	CHea ECha EMan MWat SIgm SIng
§ *suffruticosa*	LBee

MOMORDICA (Cucurbitaceae)

balsamina	CPlN MSal
charantia	CPlN MSal MSto

MONADENIUM (Euphorbiaceae)

lugardae	MBri
'Variegatum'	MBri

MONARDA † (Lamiaceae)

'Adam'	ECED GAbr GCal MBri MLLN MSte SMad
'Aquarius'	CBlo CGle CHea CLTr ECha EFou EGle EMan EMon MSte NHol NLak NPro NRoo SChu SCro SHel SMrm SOkh WCHb WMer WOve WRha WRus WWat WWeb WWhi
austromontana	CArn CBlo ECoo EWes EWll SIde SMac WFar WHer WMaN LRHS SCoo
¶ 'Baby Spice'	
§ 'Balance'	CGle CSev EGar EGle EMon ERic GCal LHol MSte MTis NHol NRoo NSti SChu SCro SMrm SOkh WCHb WHoo WOve WPyg WRha WRus WWat
'Beauty of Cobham' ♀	CBlo CGle CHad CHan ECha EFou EHal GAbr GMaP GMac MBri MCLN MRav MSte MUlv NChi NRoo NSti SChu SLod SMad SMrm SPer WMer WOve WRus WSan
'Blaukranz'	EFou SChu
§ 'Blaustrumpf'	CElw EFou GBri LFis MArl MSte NOrc NPla SPer WMer WRus
Blue Stocking	See *M.* 'Blaustrumpf'
Bowman	See *M.* 'Sagittarius'
bradburyana	CBot EMon WHil WViv
'Cambridge Scarlet' ♀	CB&S CGle CHad CSev ECha ELan EMil EMon GMaP GPoy LHop LSyl MBal MCLN MGrG MSCN MWgw NBir NRoo SPer WEas WMer WMow WOld WRus

'Capricorn' CBlo CGle CLTr CMGP CSev EBee EFou EGar EGle GBuc GMac LHol LRHS MCLN MSte NCat NSti SChu SCro SHel SOkh WCHb WHoo WPyg WRus WWal

'Cherokee' EGar MAvo MRav WCHb

citriodora CArn EBrP EBre GPoy LBre MChe MSal SBre SIde SRms SWat WCot WGwG WJek WPer WSel WWye

– PC&H 215 CPle

'Comanche' CSpe EFou LGre SAga SMrm WCHb

'Croftway Pink' ♀ Widely available

'Dark Ponticum' EGar EMon LRHS MCLN MGrG

didyma CAgr CArn CBlo CJew CTri EAst LHol LLWP LSyl MChe MFir MHew MSal NBro SWat WJek WOak WOld

– 'Alba' CBot GAbr MGra MSCN WBea

– 'Duddiscombe' CSam

¶ – 'Goldmelisse' WBea

'Donnerwolke' SChu

'Elsie's Lavender' CHal CLTr EFou EGar EGle EMon GBri GBuc GCal NBro NChi WCHb WViv

§ 'Feuerschopf' EBrP EBre EFou LBre MSte SAga SBre WRHF

Firecrown See *M.* 'Feuerschopf'

§ 'Fishes' CBlo CHea CHid ECha EFou EGle EHal EMon ERic EWes GCal MAus MCLN MSte NCat NHol NLak SChu SHel SIde SMrm SOkh WCHb WHoo WMow WRus

fistulosa CAgr CArn CMea EBee EMon GPoy LHol LRot MChe MHew MMal MSal NLak NTay SIde WBea WGwG WHer WJek WPer WWye

'Forncett Bishop' EFou

'Gardenview' EWes GCal NBrk SMrm WRHF

'Gardenview Scarlet' EFou EOrc NChi

'Hartswood Wine' LBlm MRav SMad

'Kardinal' CGle EFou LIck MSte NTay SIde

* 'Keureschol' NCat

'Kruisbekje' SMrm

'Lambada' EOHP

'Libra' See *M.* 'Balance'

'Loddon Crown' CBos CLTr EFou EMon MBri

* 'Mahogany' CDoC CSam EFou EGle EHic EMon GAbr GMaP LHop MCLN MHlr MMil MRav NHaw NHol NPla NRoo NSti SHel SPer WCHb WMow WSan WWye

'Marshall's Delight' SMrm WMer WRus

* 'Melissa' CGle EFou EGle EHal

menthifolia CArn CHan EBee EGar EOHP EWll LBlm LGre NLak SAga WCot WHer

'Mohawk' EFou EGle LFis MAus MAvo NCat NHol SAga SIde SMrm WCHb WMow WRus

'Mrs Perry' EBee EFou EHic EWes LBuc WMer WRHF

'Osage' EFou

'Ou Charm' CBos EBee EFou EMon EWes MLLN NPla SAga SCro SMac SMad SMrm WCHb WSan

'Pale Ponticum' EMon

'Panorama' CBlo CBot ECtt EOld GCra MBal MSal NRoo WFar WPer

'Pawnee' EFou SChu SMrm WCHb

'Pink Tourmaline' EWes LGre LRHS MBri MCli SAga SMad

'Pisces' See *M.* 'Fishes'

'Poyntzfield Pink' GPoy

Prairie Night See *M.* 'Prärienacht'

'Präriebrand' MBri SUsu

Prairie Glow = 'Prärieglut' MBri

§ 'Prärienacht' Widely available

punctata CArn CBot CGle CInt ELan EMan GCal LGan MLLN MSal SIde SMad SMrm SUsu SWat WCHb WCot WHil WWye

purple MGra

'Ruby Glow' MArl MAus MBri MTis NCat NHol NPla SMrm SUsu WLRN

§ 'Sagittarius' CGle CHea CSev EGar EGle EMan EMon LBlm LRHS MBel MCLN MWgw NCat NHol NRoo SChu SMrm SOkh WCHb WHoo WLRN WRus WWal WWat

§ 'Schneewittchen' CBlo CKel EAst EBrP EBre ECED ECha ECtt EGar ELan EMon GAbr LBre MLLN MSCN MTis NBro NOrc NRoo NSti SBre SChu SIde SPer WHil WMer WRus WWin

'Scorpio' See *M.* 'Scorpion'

§ 'Scorpion' CGle CM&M EFou EMon LBlm MBel MBro MSte MTis NCat NChi SAga SChu SHel SMad SMrm SOkh WCHb WHoo WOve WPyg WRHF WRus

'Sioux' EFou EWes GBuc GMac MAvo NCut SAga SMrm WCHb WCot WElm

'Snow Maiden' See *M.* 'Schneewittchen'

'Snow Queen' CMGP EFou EGle EPfP NHol SCoo SMrm SPla WSan WWat

Snow White See *M.* 'Schneewittchen'

'Squaw' Widely available

'Talud' EGar EMon SMrm

'Twins' CBod CMil EBee EFou MLLN NHaw SWat WHil WHoo WMer WRus WViv

'Vintage Wine' CLTr ECtt EGar EGle ELan EMon NFla WCHb WHal WRus WWye

* *violacea* CStr WRha

¶ 'Violet Queen' MBel NCat NPro

MONARDELLA (Lamiaceae)

cinerea CPBP NHol NWCA

¶ *linioides* subsp. *stricta* NHol

¶ *macrantha* CPBP

* *nana arida* CPBP

* – subsp. *tenuiflora* NWCA

odoratissima CGle EMan

¶ *palmeri* NNS 95354 IDac

villosa subsp. *neglecta* SBla

¶ – 'Sheltonii' EBee

MONOPSIS (Campanulaceae)

¶ *debilis* CSpe

¶ 'Goldfinch' — EMan
lutea — See *Lobelia lutea*
¶ 'Midnight' — CSpe

MONOTOCA (Epacridaceae) See Plant Deletions

MONSONIA † (Geraniaceae)
emarginata — GCHN
speciosa — CSpe MHul

MONSTERA (Araceae)
deliciosa ♀ — LBlo MBri SRms
– 'Variegata' ♀ — MBri SRms

MONTBRETIA See CROCOSMIA

MONTIA (Portulacaceae)
australasica — See *Neopaxia australasica*
californica — See *Claytonia nevadensis*
parvifolia — See *Naiocrene parvifolia*
perfoliata — See *Claytonia perfoliata*
sibirica — See *Claytonia sibirica*

MORAEA (Iridaceae)
alpina — SBla
alticola — SBla
– CDR 180 — CHan
§ *aristata* — LBow NRog
§ *bellendenii* — LBow MSto
§ *fugax* — CMon IBlr
gawleri — CMon
glaucopsis — See *M. aristata*
huttonii — CGre CHan
iridioides — See *Dietes iridioides*
longifolia — See *Hexaglottis longifolia*
– Sweet — See *M. fugax*
loubseri — CMon NRog
pavonia var. *lutea* — See *M. bellendenii*
polystachya — NRog
sp. S&SH 4 — CHan
sp. S&SH 47 — CHan
sp. S&SH 78 — CHan
spathacea — See *M. spathulata*
§ *spathulata* — CBro CHan CMon ERos GCal MAvo MFir MHig MSto SBla WCot WSHC
villosa — LBow NRog

MORICANDIA (Brassicaceae)
¶ *arvensis* — EBee

MORINA (Morinaceae)
longifolia — CBot CGle CHan CSpe ECGN ECha ELan EMon GBin GMac LFis MAus MBri MFir MNrw MTis MWat NChi NSti NTow NWoo SMrm SRCN WEas WHoo WPer WWye
¶ *nepalensis* — WPGP
persica — ECGN EGar GBuc NLak

MORISIA (Brassicaceae)
hypogaea — See *M. monanthos*
§ *monanthos* — CInt MBar MHig NTow WAbe WPat
– 'Fred Hemingway' — EBrP EBre EHyt EPot GCrs ITim LBre NHar NMen SBla SBre WAbe WPat

MORUS (Moraceae)
§ *alba* — CB&S CHEx CLnd CMCN CPle CTho ELan ERea GTwe IOrc LBuc SHBN SPer WDin WMou WPGP WSpi WWal WWat
¶ – 'Black Tabor' — WShe
– 'Globosa' — See *M. alba* 'Nana'
– var. *multicaulis* — ERea
– 'Pendula' — CDoC CEnd ELan ERea GTwe LHol LNet LPan MAsh MBlu MBri MLan MWat SHBN WDin
¶ – var. *tatarica* — CAgr
bombycis — See *M. alba*
'Illinois Everbearing' (F) — ESim
nigra (F) ♀ — Widely available
§ – 'Chelsea' (F) — COtt ERea GTwe SPer
◆ – 'King James' — See *M. nigra* 'Chelsea'
¶ – 'Large Black' (F) — EMui
– 'Wellington' (F) — WDin
platanifolia — MBlu

MUCUNA (Papilionaceae)
bennettii — CPlN LBlo
macrocarpa — CPlN
pruriens var. *utilis* — CPlN

MUEHLENBECKIA (Polygonaceae)
astonii — ECou ELan
australis — MAll
axillaris hort. — See *M. complexa*
§ – Walpers — CPle CTri ECou EPla ESis GAri GCal MAll MHar NCat NTow SDry
§ *complexa* — CB&S CDoC CHEx CHal CPlN CPle ECou EPla ESis GQui IBlr ISea LBlm MAll NFai NRar SArc SBra SDry WCru WSHC WWat WWye
– 'Nana' — See *M. axillaris* Walpers
– var. *trilobata* — CPlN CPle EGar EPla IBlr WCru
ephedroides — ECou MAll
– 'Clarence Pass' — ECou
– var. *muriculata* — ECou
gunnii — CPlN ECou MAll
platyclados — See *Homalocladium platycladum*

MUHLENBERGIA (Poaceae)
japonica 'Cream Delight' (v) — CCuc EBee EHoe EMan EMon EPPr ESOG MCCP WCot
lindheimeri — WCot
rigens — WCot

MUKDENIA (Saxifragaceae)
§ *rossii* — CLTr CRDP ECro EPla GCal NCat SSpi WCot WOld

MUNDULEA (Papilionaceae) See Plant Deletions

MURBECKIELLA (Brassicaceae) See Plant Deletions

MURRAYA (Rutaceae)
* *elliptica* — SOWG
exotica — See *M. paniculata*
koenigii — LChe
§ *paniculata* — ERea LChe

MUSA (Musaceae)
§ *acuminata* (F) — LPal MBri
§ – 'Dwarf Cavendish' ♀ — ERea LBlo LCns WMul
¶ – 'Zebrina' — WMul
basjoo — CAbb CB&S CBrP CFil CHEx CTrC ECon EOas EPfP ERea LPJP LPal NPal SAPC SArc SPar SSoC WJun WMul WPGP
cavendishii — See *M. acuminata* '**Dwarf Cavendish**'
coccinea — See *M. uranoscopus*
ensete — See *Ensete ventricosum*
§ *lasiocarpa* — LPal
nana — See *M. acuminata*
¶ *ornata* ♀ — WMul
¶ 'Rajapuri' — WMul
§ *uranoscopus* ♀ — LBlo
velutina — WMul

MUSCARI † (Hyacinthaceae)
ambrosiacum — See *M. muscarimi*
armeniacum ♀ — CBro EPar ETub MBri NMGW NRog WPer WShi
– 'Argaei Album' — LAma NEgg
* – 'Babies Breath' — CMil SWas
– 'Blue Spike' — CBro EPar ETub LAma MBri MHlr NEgg NRog WCot WPer
– 'Early Giant' — LAma
– 'Fantasy Creation' — ETub LRHS WCot
– 'Heavenly Blue' — LAma
– 'Saffier' — LAma LRHS
§ *aucheri* ♀ — EHyt EPar LAma MFos NRog
§ *azureum* ♀ — CAvo CBro CNic ELan EPfP ERos LAma MHlr NMen NRog
– 'Album' — CBro EPar ERos ETub LAma MHlr NRog WCot
botryoides — LAma NRog
– 'Album' — CAvo CBro ELan EPfP LAma MBri NRog WShi
chalusicum — See *M. pseudomuscari*
§ *comosum* — CBro EPar WPer
– 'Monstrosum' — See *M. comosum* '**Plumosum**'
§ – 'Plumosum' — CAvo CBro CRDP ELan EMan EMon EPar ETub GBur LAma MBri MHlr WCFE
grandifolium JCA 689.450 — CMil
– var. *populeum* AB&S 5357 — CMon
inconstrictum S&L 19/20 — CMon
latifolium — CAvo CBro CMon EHyt EPar ETub LAma NMGW NRog WHil WPen WPer
* – 'Blue Angels' — NBir
§ *macrocarpum* — CAvo CBro EHyt EPot LAma MHig
mirum — EHyt
moschatum — See *M. muscarimi*
§ *muscarimi* — CAvo CBro EPar LAma
– var. *flavum* — See *M. macrocarpum*
§ *neglectum* — CSWP EHyt ELan LAma SEND WShi
– B&S 349 — CMon
pallens — CMon
paradoxum — See *Bellevalia paradoxa*
§ *pseudomuscari* ♀ — CMon
– BSBE 842 — EHyt
racemosum — See *M. neglectum*
spreitzenhoferi MS 712 — CMon
§ *tenuiflorum* — EHyt
– S&L 91 — CMon
tubergenianum — See *M. aucheri*

MUSCARIMIA (Hyacinthaceae)
ambrosiacum — See *Muscari muscarimi*
macrocarpum — See *Muscari macrocarpum*

MUSSCHIA (Campanulaceae)
wollastonii — CHEx

MUTISIA (Asteraceae)
brachyantha × *oligodon* — MSto
clematis — CRHN
coccinea — CPlN
decurrens — CB&S CPlN IBlr MSto
ilicifolia — CPlN IBlr ISea MSto SBra SIgm SMur WSHC
latifolia — MSto
oligodon — CGre CPlN IBlr SBra
retrorsa — CPlN
– JCA 14345 — MSto
retusa — See *M. spinosa* var. *pulchella*
sinuata JCA 14351 — MSto
spinosa — CGre CPlN MSto
§ – var. *pulchella* — MSto SSpi
subulata — CPlN MSto

MYOPORUM (Myoporaceae)
acuminatum — See *M. tenuifolium*
debile — CPle ECou MAll SIgm
insulare — CPle
laetum — CHEx CPle ECou LHil MAll SMad

MYOSOTIDIUM (Boraginaceae)
§ *hortensia* — CFil CHEx CPla ECre EWes GBin GBuc GCal IBlr LHop NPla SBid SSpi WCot WCru WSan
– white — LHop
nobile — See *M. hortensia*

MYOSOTIS (Boraginaceae)
§ *alpestris* — WPat
§ – — WLin
– 'Ruth Fischer' — NBir NMen NNrd NTow
arvensis — EWFC
australis — GCal GGar NChi NMen NWCA
'Bill Baker' — CHan
colensoi — ECou EHic ELan MRPP MTho NNrd NWCA
explanata — MAvo NMen NNrd WEas
palustris — See *M. scorpioides*
'Popsy' — ECou
¶ *pulvinaris* — CPBP
rakiura — GTou WCla
rehsteineri — LBee
rupicola — See *M. alpestris*
§ *scorpioides* — CBen CRow ECoo EHon ELan EWFC LPBA MHew MSta NDea SRms SWat SWyc WChe WEas WFar WMAq
§ – Maytime = 'Blaqua' (v) — EBrP EBre EMFW LBre LPBA MSta NRoo SBre
– 'John Beaty' — LBlm
♦ – Maytime — See *M. scorpioides* Maytime = '**Blaqua**'
– 'Mermaid' — CBen CLyd CMGP CRow CWat ECha EPPr GBin GMac LHop LPBA MAvo MFir MSta NBrk NCat NNrd SDix SWat WChe WPer WRus

– 'Pinkie' CRDP CRow CWat EMFW
LHop MAvo MSta SWat WChe
WMAq
¶ – 'Snowflakes' CRow
secunda CKin
sylvatica EWFC
– alba See *M. sylvatica* f. *lactea*
§ – f. *lactea* CRow

MYOSURUS (Ranunculaceae) See Plant Deletions

MYRCEUGENIA (Myrtaceae)
chrysocarpa CGre

MYRICA (Myricaceae)
californica CAgr CFil CPle GAri MAll
SSta WPGP
cerifera CArn MAll
gale GAri GPoy LHol MGos MUlv
SWat WDin WGwG WGwy
WSel WWye
pensylvanica CBlo LHol MAll MBal

MYRICARIA (Tamaricaceae) See Plant Deletions

MYRIOPHYLLUM (Haloragaceae)
§ *aquaticum* CBen CHEx CRow CWat EHon
ELan EMFW LPBA MSta
NDea SWat SWyc WChe WFar
WMAq WWeb
brasiliense See *M. aquaticum*
proserpinacoides See *M. aquaticum*
* 'Red Stem' LPBA
spicatum CBen EHon EMFW SWyc
WChe
verticillatum CBen EHon

MYRRHIS (Apiaceae)
odorata CArn CKin CSev ECha EEls
EFer EJud ELan ELau EWFC
GPoy ILis LBay LHol MCLN
MChe MHew MMal MSal SIde
SPer WByw WCer WEas WHer
WOak WPer WWye
– 'Forncett Chevron' EFou

MYRSINE (Myrsinaceae)
africana CPle EPfP SAPC SArc SBid
WHCr WWat
australis MAll
nummularia ECou MAll

MYRTEOLA (Myrtaceae)
§ – CMHG GAri GDra MAll MBal
MHig SIng

MYRTUS (Myrtaceae)
apiculata See *Luma apiculata*
bullata See *Lophomyrtus bullata*
chequen See *Luma chequen*
communis ♀ Widely available
– 'Flore Pleno' (d) GQui LHol MPla
– 'Jenny Reitenbach' See *M. communis* subsp. *tarentina*
– 'Microphylla' See *M. communis* subsp. *tarentina*
– 'Nana' See *M. communis* subsp. *tarentina*

§ – subsp. *tarentina* ♀ Widely available
– – 'Compacta' WWye
§ – – 'Microphylla Variegata' CBlo CInt CMHG CPle EPla
ERav LHol MBal MPla SAPC
SAga SArc SLMG SPer WHal
WJek WOak WSHC WWat
– 'Tricolor' See *M. communis* 'Variegata'
§ – 'Variegata' CArn CBot CEnd CMCN COtt
CPle ECtt EMil ERav LHop
SDry SHBN SLMG SPer SPla
STre WFar WHar WSel WStI
WWat WWye
'Glanleam Gold' See *Luma apiculata* 'Glanleam Gold'
lechleriana See *Amomyrtus luma*
luma See *Luma apiculata*
nummularia See *Myrteola nummularia*
obcordata See *Lophomyrtus obcordata*
× ralphii See *Lophomyrtus* × *ralphii*
'Traversii' See *Lophomyrtus* × *ralphii* 'Traversii'
ugni See *Ugni molinae*
* variegata 'Penlee' CTrG

NAIOCRENE (Portulacaceae)
§ parvifolia CNic

NANDINA (Berberidaceae)
domestica ♀ CB&S CBot CDoC CHad CSam
ELan GOrc IOrc ISea LHop
LPan MUlv NFla NPal NRog
SPla SReu SRms SSpi SSta
WCru WDin WGwG WStI
WWat
– 'Fire Power' Widely available
– 'Harbor Dwarf' WWat
¶ – var. *leucocarpa* CPle
– 'Nana' See *N. domestica* 'Pygmaea'
– 'Nana Purpurea' EPla
§ – 'Pygmaea' GAri MAll WDin
– 'Richmond' CB&S CBlo EBee ELan EMil
EPfP EPla MAsh MBlu MGos
MMea MUlv SHBN SPer SPla
WFar

NANNORRHOPS (Arecaceae)
ritchieana CBrP LPal

NARCISSUS † (Amaryllidaceae)
'Abalone' (2) EWal
'Accent' (2) ♀ CQua ICar
'Accord' (2) ICar
'Achduart' (3) CQua EHof ICar
'Achentoul' (4) ICar
'Achnasheen' (3) CQua ICar
'Acropolis' (4) CQua ETub EWal ICar LAma
'Actaea' (9) ♀ ETub MBri NRog
'Admiration' (8) CQua
'Advocat' (3) CQua
'Affable' (4) ICar
'Aflame' (3) LAma MBri
'Ahwahnee' (2) IDun
'Aintree' (3) CQua
'Aircastle' (3) CQua EHof EWal ICar
'Akepa' (5) CQua
* albidus occidentalis (13) ERos
'Albus Plenus Odoratus' See *N. poeticus* 'Plenus'
'Alley Inn' (4) IDun
'Alliance' (1) EWal
alpestris See *N. pseudonarcissus* subsp. *moschatus*

'Alpine Glow' (1)	CQua
'Altruist' (3)	CQua EWal
'Altun Ha' (2)	CQua EHof
'Amber Castle' (2)	CQua ICar
¶ 'Amber Light' (2)	EWal
'Ambergate' (2)	EWal LAma
'Amberglow' (2)	EWal
'Amboseli' (3)	IDun
'Amor' (3)	EWal
'Amstel' (4)	CQua
'Andalusia' (6)	CQua ICar
'Androcles' (4)	ICar IDun
'Angel' (3)	ICar
¶ 'Angel Face' (3)	EHof
Angel's Tears	See *N. triandrus* var. *triandrus*
'Angkor' (4)	ICar
'Ann Abbott' (2)	EWal
'Annalong' (3)	IBal
'Anniversary' (2)	EWal
'Anthea' (2)	EWal
'Apostle' (1)	ICar
'Apotheose' (4)	EWal
'Apricot' (1)	CBro
'Apricot Sundae' (4)	ICar
'April Charm' (2)	ICar
'April Love' (1)	CQua EHof IBal ICar
'April Snow' (2)	CBro CQua EWal
'April Tears' (5) ♀	EWal LAma NRog
'Apropos' (2)	CQua
'Aranjuez' (2)	LAma
'Arbar' (2)	EWal
'Arcady' (2)	EWal
'Arctic Char' (2)	ICar
¶ 'Arctic Gem' (3)	EHof
'Arctic Gold' (1) ♀	CQua EHof ICar
'Ardglass' (3)	IBal ICar
'Ardour' (3)	ICar
'Ardress' (2)	CQua IDun
'Argosy' (1)	CQua
'Arish Mell' (5)	CQua EWal ICar IDun
'Arizona Sunset' (3)	IDun
'Arkle' (1)	ICar
'Armley Wood' (2)	ICar
'Arpege' (2)	CQua
'Arran Isle' (2)	IDun
'Arthurian' (1)	IDun
'Artillery' (3)	EWal
'Asante' (1)	IDun
'Ashmore' (2)	CQua EHof IDun
¶ 'Ashton Wold' (2)	EHof
'Asila' (2)	IDun
'Aslan' (4)	ICar
'Aspasia' (8)	CBro
§ *assoanus* (13)	CBro CLAP EBrP EBre EPar
	EPot LAma LBre SBre
− MS 582/581/511 (13)	CMon
§ − var. *praelongus* MS 656	CMon
(13)	
§ *asturiensis* (13) ♀	CBro CSam ELan EPar IBlr
	LAma
'Atholl Palace' (4)	IDun
atlanticus (13)	CLAP
− SB&L 78 (13)	CMon
'Attrus' (2)	EWal
'Audubon' (3)	CQua ETub EWal
'Auntie Eileen' (2)	CQua
§ *aureus* (13)	CQua
'Avalanche' (8) ♀	CQua EWal
'Avalon' (2)	CQua
'Ave' (2)	ICar
'Avenger' (2)	ICar
'Baby Doll' (6)	EWal ICar

'Baby Moon' (7)	CQua EBar ELan EPar EPot
	ETub LAma MBri NRog WBro
'Baccarat' (11)	ICar LAma MBri
'Badbury Rings' (3)	IDun
baeticus	See *N. assoanus* var. *praelongus*
	MS 656
'Bailey' (2)	ICar
'Balalaika' (2)	CQua EHof
'Baldock' (4)	IDun
'Ballyarnett' (1)	ICar
'Ballycastle' (3)	ICar
'Ballyfrema' (1)	ICar
'Ballygarvey' (1)	CQua EWal
'Ballygowan' (4)	IBal
'Ballykinler' (3)	IBal
'Ballylig' (1)	ICar
'Ballylough' (1)	ICar
'Ballymorran' (1)	IBal
'Ballynahinch' (3)	IBal
'Ballynichol' (3)	IBal
'Ballyrobert' (1)	EHof
'Ballyvoy' (1)	ICar
'Baltic Shore' (3)	IBal
'Balvenie' (2)	CQua
'Bambi' (1)	CBro ERos NRog
'Banbridge' (1)	IBal ICar
'Bandesara' (3)	IDun
'Bandleader' (2)	EWal
'Bantam' (2) ♀	CBro CQua ERos EWal
'Barley Sugar' (3)	ICar
'Barleygold' (2)	IBal
'Barleythorpe' (1)	EWal
'Barleywine' (4)	IBal
'Barlow' (6)	CQua
'Barnesgold' (1)	IDun
'Barnum' (1)	IDun
'Baronscourt' (1)	ICar
'Barrett Browning' (3)	MBri NRog
'Bartley' (6)	EWal
'Beach Party' (2)	IDun
'Beauvallon' (1)	IDun
'Bebop' (7)	CBro
'Bedgebury' (3)	ICar
'Beefeater' (2)	EWal
'Beige Beauty' (3)	EWal ICar
'Belcanto' (11)	CQua
'Belisana' (2)	LAma
'Bell Song' (7)	CAvo CBro CQua ERos EWal
	WShi
'Beltrim' (2)	ICar
'Ben Aligin' (1)	CQua
'Ben Hee' (2)	CQua
'Ben Vorlich' (2)	ICar
'Bere Ferrers' (4)	CQua
'Bergerac' (11)	CQua
'Berkeley Court' (4)	IDun
'Berlin' (2)	EWal
bertolonii (13)	CMon
'Beryl' (6)	CBro CQua ERos EWal ICar
	LAma
'Best of Luck' (3)	IBal
'Bethany' (2)	EWal
'Betsy Macdonald' (6)	CQua
'Bilbo' (6)	CQua IDun
'Binkie' (2)	CBro EWal LAma MBri
'Birdsong' (3)	CQua
'Birma' (3)	ETub EWal LAma
'Birthright' (1)	EWal
'Bishopstone' (1)	ICar
'Bittern' (2)	ICar
'Blarney' (3)	EWal
'Blessing' (2)	EWal

'Blue Bird' (2) — EWal
'Blushing Maiden' (4) — CQua
'Bob Minor' (1) — CQua
'Bobbysoxer' (7) — CBro CQua ERos EWal ICar LAma MTho
'Bobolink' (2) — CQua
'Bodilly' (2) — EWal
'Bodwannick' (2) — CQua
'Bolton' (7) — CBro
'Bonamargy' (2) — ICar
'Border Beauty' (2) — IDun
'Border Chief' (2) — ICar
'Borrobol' (2) — EHof
'Bosbigal' (11) — CQua
'Boslowick' (11) — CQua
'Bosmeor' (2) — CQua
'Bossa Nova' (3) — CQua IDun
'Boudoir' (1) — ICar
'Bouzouki' (2) — IDun
'Bowles' Early Sulphur' (1) — CRow
'Bracken Hill' (2) — ICar
'Brandaris' (11) — CQua
'Brave Journey' (2) — ICar
'Bravoure' (1) ♀ — CQua EWal
'Breakthrough' (2) — EWal
'Brentswood' (8) — CQua
'Bridal Crown' (4) — ETub EWal LAma
'Bridesmaid' (2) — IBal
'Bright Flame' (2) — CQua
'Brighton' (1) — LAma
'Brindle Pink' (2) — IDun
'Broadland' (2) — CQua
'Broadway Star' (11) — EWal LAma
'Brodick' (2) — IDun
'Brookdale' (1) — IDun
'Broomhill' (2) ♀ — CQua
broussonetii (13) — CFil WPGP
– SF 269 (13) — CMon
'Brunswick' (2) — LAma
'Bryanston' (2) — IDun
'Bryher' (3) — ICar
'Buffawn' (7) — EWal
¶ 'Bugle Major' (2) — EHof
'Bulbarrow' (2) — IDun
bulbocodium (13) ♀ — CBro CFil CMea ESis ETub LBee LBow MFos MHig NMGW NWCA WCla
– subsp. *bulbocodium* (13) — CBro
– – var. *citrinus* (13) — EHyt EPot MS&S SSpi
– – var. *conspicuus* (13) — CAvo CBro CQua CSam CVer EHyt EPar EPot ERos GCrs LAma MBal MBri MS&S NMen NNrd NRog NRya WPyg WShi
§ – – var. *graellsii* (13) — EHyt
– – – MS 567/ 408 (13) — CMon
§ – – var. *tenuifolius* (13) — CAvo CMon CQua EHyt EPot
– – – S&B 189 (13) — CMon
– – – × *triandrus* (13) — EHyt
* – *filifolius* (13) — CBro EHyt
– subsp. *genuinus* S&F 177/180 (13) — CMon
– subsp. *mairei* S&F 181 (13) — CMon
– var. *mesatlanticus* — See *N. romieuxii* subsp. *romieuxii* var. *mesatlanticus*
* – 'Monserrat' — EHyt
– subsp. *praecox* var. *paucinervis* (13) — EHyt
– *tananicus* — See *N. tananicus*
– subsp. *viriditubus* MS 453 (13) — CMon EHyt

'Bullseye' (3) — EWal
'Bunclody' (2) — CQua ICar
'Bunting' (7) — CQua ICar IDun
'Burma Star' (2) — ICar
'Burning Bush' (3) — IDun
'Burntollet' (1) — CQua IDun
'Bushmills' (3) — ICar
'Buster' (2) — EWal
'Buttercup' (7) — CBro
'Butterscotch' (2) — CQua ICar
'By Jove' (1) — EWal
'Cabra' (1) — ICar
'Cadence' (3) — ICar
'Caedmon' (9) — CQua
'Cairn Toul' (3) — CQua EHof
'Cairndhu' (2) — CQua ICar
'Cairngorm' (2) — ICar
'Calabar' (2) — EWal
calcicola B&S 413 (13) — CMon
– MS 450 (13) — CMon
'California Rose' (4) — IDun
'Callaway' (3) — ICar
'Camelford' (2) — CQua
'Camelot' (2) ♀ — EWal
'Campernelli Plenus' — See *N.* × *odorus* 'Double Campernelle'
'Campion' (9) — CQua IDun
'Canaliculatus' (8) — CBro CMon CQua EHyt EPar LAma LBow MBri
canaliculatus Gussone — See *N. tazetta* subsp. *lacticolor*
'Canarybird' (8) — CBro
'Canasta' (11) — CQua
'Candida' (4) — EWal
'Canisp' (2) — CQua ICar
'Cantabile' (9) — CBro CQua IBal
cantabricus (13) — CFil CQua WPGP
– subsp. *cantabricus* (13) — CLAP EHyt ERos SWas
– – var. *foliosus* (13) ♀ — CAvo CQua EPot LRHS
– – – S&F 284/2 (13) — CMon
– – var. *petunioides* (13) — LAma
– – – S&F 365/2 (13) — CMon
– – S&F 396 (13) — CMon
– var. *eualbidus* S&F 362 (13) — CMon
– – S&F 385 (13) — CMon
– subsp. *monophyllus* var. *laciniatus* (13) — CMon EHyt
– × *romieuxii* (13) — NHar
'Canticle' (9) — IBal
'Capax Plenus' — See *N.* 'Eystettensis'
'Cape Cool' (2) — ICar
'Capisco' (3) — CQua IBal
'Caracas' (2) — CQua
'Caramba' (2) — CQua
'Carbineer' (2) — LAma
'Carclew' (6) — CQua
'Cardinham' (3) — CQua
'Cargreen' (9) — CQua
'Cariad' (5) — CQua
¶ 'Carib Gipsy' (2) — EHof
'Carlingford' (2) — IBal
'Carlton' (2) — ETub LAma MBri NRog
'Carnearny' (3) — ICar
'Carnkief' (2) — CQua
'Caro Nome' (2) — EWal
¶ 'Carrara' (3) — EWal
'Carrickbeg' (1) — CQua
'Carson Pass' (2) — IDun
'Cassata' (11) — CQua EWal LAma NBir NRog
'Casterbridge' (2) — IDun
'Castle Dobbs' (4) — ICar
'Castlehill' (3) — IBal

'Catistock' (2)	CQua
'Cauldron' (2)	CQua IDun
'Cavendish' (4)	IDun
'Cavoda' (1) or (2)	ICar
¶ 'Caye Chapel' (3)	EHof
'Cazique' (6)	CQua
'Ceasefire' (2)	IDun
'Cedric Morris' (1)	CBro ECha IBlr SWas
¶ 'Celestial Fire' (2)	EHof
¶ 'Celtic Gold' (2)	EHof
'Ceylon' (2) ♀	EWal LAma
'Changing Colors' (11)	ETub
'Chania' (1)	ICar
'Chanterelle' (11)	EWal ICar LAma NRog
'Charity May' (6) ♀	CBro CQua EWal IBal ICar
	LAma MBri NRog
'Charleston' (2)	IDun
'Charter' (2) ♀	EWal
'Chat' (7)	CQua ICar
'Cheer Leader' (3)	CQua
'Cheerfulness' (4) ♀	EWal LAma MBri NRog
'Cheetah' (1)	IDun
'Chemeketa' (2)	IDun
'Chenoweth' (2)	CQua
'Chérie' (7)	CBro CQua
'Cherrygardens' (2)	CQua EHof
'Chesterton' (9)	CQua IDun
'Chickadee' (6)	CBro CQua
'Chickerell' (3)	IDun
'Chief Inspector' (1)	CQua IDun
'Chig' (2)	EWal
'Chilmark' (3)	IDun
'Chiloquin' (1)	CQua
¶ 'China Doll' (2)	EHof
'Chinchilla' (2)	IDun
'Chinese White' (3)	ICar
'Chinita' (8)	CBro CQua EWal
'Chit Chat' ♀	CBro
'Chivalry' (1)	EWal
'Chobe River' (1)	IDun
'Churchfield' (2)	ICar
'Churchman' (2)	IBal ICar
'Churston Ferrers' (4)	CQua
'Citronita' (3)	CQua EHof
'Clady Cottage' (2)	ICar
'Clare' (7)	CBro CQua
'Claridges' (4)	IDun
'Clockface' (3)	EWal
'Cloneytrace' (1)	ICar
'Close Encounter' (2)	ICar
'Cloud Nine' (2)	CBro EWal
¶ 'Clouded Yellow' (2)	EHof
'Clouds Rest' (2)	IDun
'Colblanc' (11)	ICar
'Collector's Choice' (3)	ICar
'Colorama' (11)	CQua
'Colour Sergeant' (2)	IBal
'Columbus' (2)	ICar
'Colville' (9)	CQua
compressus	See *N.* × *intermedius*
§ *concolor* (13)	CBro MS&S
'Conestoga' (2)	IBal
'Congress' (11)	CQua EWal
* 'Connie Number 2'	EHyt
'Connor' (2)	ICar
'Conval' (2)	CQua
'Cool Autumn' (2)	CQua
'Cool Crystal' (3)	CQua EHof ICar IDun
¶ 'Cool Shades' (2)	EHof
'Coolattin' (2)	ICar
'Cophetua' (1)	ICar
'Copper Nob' (2)	IBal
¶ 'Coquille' (2)	EWal
'Cora Ann' (7)	CBro
'Coral Light' (2)	ICar
'Corbiere' (1)	CQua EHof
'Corbridge' (2)	EWal
cordubensis (13)	EHyt
− MS 434 (13)	CMon
− MS 91-71 (13)	EHyt
'Cornerstone' (2)	EWal
'Cornet' (6)	CQua
'Corofin' (3)	CQua
'Coromandel' (2)	IDun
¶ 'Corozal' (3)	EHof
'Cosmic Dance' (3)	IDun
'Cotehele' (1)	CQua
'Country Morning' (3)	ICar
'Crackington' (4)	CQua IDun
'Cragford' (8)	EWal LAma
'Craig Stiel' (2)	CQua
'Craigarusky' (2)	IBal
'Craigdun' (2)	ICar
'Craigywarren' (2)	EWal
'Creag Dubh' (2)	CQua ICar IDun
'Crenelet' (2)	IDun
'Crimson Chalice' (3)	IDun
'Crinoline' (2)	EWal
'Cristobal' (1)	CQua
'Crock of Gold' (2)	EWal
'Croila' (2)	CQua
'Crown Royalist' (2)	IBal
'Cryptic' (2)	IDun
'Crystal River' (3)	EWal
'Cuan Gold' (4)	IBal
cuatrecasasii (13)	CMon
− MS 429 (13)	CMon
− var. *segimonensis* MS 559	CMon
(13)	
'Cuesta' (2)	IDun
'Cul Beag' (3)	CQua
'Cupid's Eye' (2)	IDun
cyclamineus (13) ♀	CBro CFil LAma NRog SBla
	SRms SSpi SWas WAbe WCru
	WPGP
'Cyclataz' (8)	CQua
cypri (8)	CBro CQua
'Cyros' (1)	CQua
'Dailmanach' (2)	CQua EHof IDun
'Daiquiri' (3)	ICar
'Dallas' (3)	CQua
'Dalliance' (2)	ICar
'Dancing Partner' (2)	EWal
'Danes Balk' (2)	ICar
'Dateline' (3)	CQua IDun
'Daviot' (2)	ICar
'Dawn' (5)	CBro
'Dawn Chorus' (1)	CQua
'Dawn Mist' (2)	EWal
'Dawn Run' (2)	IDun
'Daydream' (2) ♀	CQua EHof ETub EWal ICar
	LAma
'Debutante' (2)	CQua
'Decoy' (2)	ICar
'Del Rey' (1)	CQua
'Delabole' (2)	CQua
'Delia' (6)	IDun
'Delibes' (2)	LAma
'Dell Chapel' (3)	EHof ICar
'Delnashaugh' (4)	CQua ICar
'Delos' (3)	CQua
'Delphin Hill' (4)	IBal
'Delta Flight' (6)	IDun
'Delta Wings' (6)	IDun

'Demand' (2)	ICar
'Derryboy' (3)	IBal
¶ 'Dervock' (4)	ICar
'Desdemona' (2)	EWal NRog
'Desert Bells' (7)	CQua
'Desert Rose' (2)	ICar
'Diane' (6)	EWal
'Diatone' (4)	IDun
'Dick Wilden' (4)	EWal LAma
'Dickcissel' (7)	CBro CQua ICar
'Dimity' (3)	CQua
'Dimple' (9)	IDun
'Dinkie' (3)	CBro
'Discovery' (4)	ICar
'Dispatch Box' (1)	IDun
'Diversion' (3)	ICar
'Divertimento' (7)	ICar
'Doctor Alexander Fleming' (2)	EWal
'Doctor Hugh' (3)	CQua EHof EWal IDun
'Dolly Mollinger' (11)	EWal ICar LAma
'Don Carlos' (2)	ICar
'Dorchester' (4)	IDun
'Double Blush' (4)	ICar
'Double Campernella'	See *N.* × *odorus* 'Double Campernelle'
'Double Diamond' (4)	CQua
'Double Fashion' (4)	EWal
Double Roman (4)	CQua
'Doubleday' (4)	IDun
'Doubtful' (3)	CQua ICar
'Dove of Peace' (6)	IBal
'Dove Wings' (6) ♀	CBro CQua EWal IBal ICar LAma
'Dovekie' (12)	ICar
'Dover Cliffs' (2)	CQua
'Downpatrick' (1)	CQua ICar
'Dream Castle' (3)	EWal
'Drenagh' (2)	ICar
'Drumadarragh' (1)	ICar
'Drumawillan' (2)	ICar
'Drumbeg' (2)	IBal
'Drumboe' (2)	CQua
'Drumlin' (3)	IBal
'Drumnabreeze' (2)	ICar
'Drumrunie' (2)	ICar
dubius var. *dubius* MS 512 (13)	CMon
'Duet' (4)	EWal
'Dulcimer' (9)	CQua
'Dunadry Inn' (4)	IDun
'Dunkery' (4)	IDun
'Dunmurry' (1)	CQua
'Dunskey' (3)	CQua
'Dutch Master' (1) ♀	ETub EWal LAma MBri NRog
'Dynamite' (2)	EWal
'Earendil' (2)	IDun
'Early Blossom' (1)	ICar
'Early Splendour' (8)	CQua LAma
'Earthlight' (3)	EHof
'East Wind' (1)	ICar
'Easter Bonnet' (2)	ETub LAma
'Easter Moon' (2)	ICar
'Eastern Dawn' (2)	EWal
'Eastertide' (4)	CQua
'Eaton Park' (3)	IDun
'Eaton Song' (12)	CBro CQua
'Eclat' (2)	ICar
¶ 'Edgbaston' (2)	EHof
'Edge Grove' (2)	ICar
'Edward Buxton' (3)	LAma MBri
'Egard' (11)	CQua EWal

'Egg Nog' (4)	ICar
'Eland' (7)	CQua IDun
'Elburton' (2)	CQua
elegans var. *elegans* S&F 316 (13)	CMon
'Elf' (2)	CBro CQua
'Elfin Gold' (6)	IDun
'Elizabeth Ann' (6)	CQua IDun
'Elka' (1)	CQua IBal ICar
'Elmley Castle' (1)	EHof
'Elphin' (4)	CQua ICar
'Elrond' (6)	CQua IDun
'Elven Lady' (2)	IDun
'Elvira' (8)	CBro CQua
'Elwing' (5)	IDun
'Elysian Fields' (2)	EWal
'Emily' (2)	CQua IBal ICar
'Eminent' (3)	CQua EWal
'Emperor's Waltz' (6)	CQua
'Empress of Ireland' (1) ♀	CQua EHof EWal IBal IDun
'Englander' (6)	EPot
'Ensemble' (4)	CQua
'Entrancement' (1)	EWal
'Erlicheer' (4)	CQua
'Eskylane' (2)	ICar
'Estrella' (3)	CQua
'Estremadura' (2)	ICar
'Ethereal Beauty' (2)	IDun
'Ethos' (1)	IDun
'Euphony' (2)	EHof
'Euryalus' (1)	CQua
'Evendine' (2)	EWal
'Everglades' (4)	IDun
'Everpink' (2)	CQua
'Exalted' (2)	ICar
'Exemplar' (1)	EWal
'Eye Level' (9)	IBal
'Eyecatcher' (3)	ICar
§ 'Eystettensis' (4)	CBro CQua EBot ECha IBlr
'Fair Prospect' (2)	CQua EHof ICar
'Fairgreen' (3)	ICar
'Fairhead' (9)	CQua IBal
'Fairsel' (3)	IBal
'Fairy Chimes' (5)	CBro CQua
'Fairy Footsteps' (3)	IBal ICar
'Fairy Island' (3)	ICar
'Fairy Spell' (3)	IBal
'Falconet' (8)	CBro CQua ERos EWal
'Falstaff' (2)	CQua ICar
'Fanad Head' (9)	IBal
'Far Country' (2)	CQua ICar
'Faro' (1)	IBal
'Farranfad' (2)	IBal
'Fastidious' (2)	CQua
'Favor Royal' (3)	IBal
'Favourite' (2)	EWal
'February Gold' (6) ♀	CAvo CBro CNic EBar EPar ETub EWal IBal LAma LBow MBri NBir NMGW NRog SRms WShi
'February Silver' (6)	CBro EPar ETub EWal LAma NMGW NRog WShi
'Feeling Lucky' (2) ♀	EWal
'Felindre' (9)	CQua EWal IBal
'Feock' (3)	CQua
fernandesii (13)	CBro CMon EHic
'Ferndown' (3)	CQua EHof IDun
'Festivity' (2)	CQua EWal
'ffitch's Ffolly' (2)	CQua
'Fieldfare' (3)	ICar
'Fiji' (4)	ICar
'Filly' (2)	EWal

'Fine Gold' (1) CQua
¶ 'Fine Romance' (2) EHof
'Fionn' (2) ICar
'Fire Raiser' (2) ICar
'Firestorm' (2) IBal
'First Hope' (6) CQua
'Flaming Meteor' (2) ICar
'Flirt' (6) CQua ICar
'Flomay' (7) CBro
'Florida Manor' (3) IBal
'Flower Carpet' (1) LAma
'Flower Drift' (4) LAma
'Flower Record' (2) LAma
'Fly Half' (2) CQua
'Flycatcher' (7) CQua
'Flying Saucer' (2) EWal
'Focal Point' (2) ICar
'Fool's Gold' (4) ICar
'Foray' (2) EWal
'Foresight' (1) ICar LAma
'Forge Mill' (2) CQua ICar
'Fort Knox' (1) EWal
'Fortissimo' (2) ETub
'Fortune' (2) EWal LAma NRog
'Foundling' (6) ♀ CBro CQua EHof EWal IBal
ICar IDun
'Foxfire' (2) ICar
'Fragrant Breeze' EWal
'Fragrant Rose' (2) CQua EHof EWal ICar IDun
'Francolin' (1) IDun
'Frank's Fancy' (9) IBal
¶ 'Fresh Lime' (1) EHof
'Fresh Season' (10) CQua
'Fresno' (3) IDun
'Frigid' (3) IBal ICar
'Frolic' (2) EWal
'Front Royal' (2) CQua ICar
'Frostbite' (4) IBal
'Frostkist' (6) CBro CQua
'Frou-frou' (4) ICar
'Fruit Cup' (7) CQua
'Fuego' (2) ICar
¶ 'Full House' EWal
'Fulwell' (4) IDun
'Furnace Creek' (2) IDun
'Fynbos' (3) IDun
'Gabriël Kleiberg' (11) ICar
gaditanus (13) CBro CMon
− MS 526/633 (13) CMon
'Galway' (2) EWal
'Garden News' (3) IDun
'Garden Princess' (6) CBro LAma
'Gay Cavalier' (4) CQua
'Gay Kybo' (4) ♀ CQua IDun
'Gay Mood' (2) EWal
'Gay Song' (4) CQua ICar
'Gay Time' (4) EWal
gayi (13) CQua
'Geevor' (4) CQua
genuinus × 'Jessamy' EHyt
'George's Pink' (2) ICar
'Georgie Girl' (6) CQua IDun
'Geranium' (8) ♀ CBro CQua ETub EWal LAma
MBri NRog
'Gettysburg' (2) CQua EHof
'Gigantic Star' (2) EWal LAma MBri
'Gilda' (2) IBal
'Gin and Lime' (1) CQua EHof ICar IDun
'Gipsy Queen' (1) CQua
'Gironde' (11) CQua
'Glasnevin' (2) ICar
'Glaston' (2) ICar

'Glen Clova' (2) CQua EHof
'Glenamoy' (1) ICar
'Glendermott' (2) ICar
'Glendun' (3) ICar
'Glenfarclas' (1/2) EHof ICar
'Glenganagh' (4) ICar
'Glenside' (2) CQua EHof
'Gloriosus' (8) CQua
'Glowing Red' (4) CQua
¶ 'Goff's Caye' (2) EHof
'Gold Bond' (2) IDun
'Gold Bullion' (1) ICar
'Gold Convention' (2) ♀ CQua IDun
'Gold Medal' (1) EWal LAma
'Gold Mine' (2) IBal
'Gold Phantom' (1) ICar
'Gold Strike' (1) ICar
'Golden Amber' (2) CQua IBal ICar
'Golden Aura' (2) ♀ CQua EHof EWal IBal ICar
IDun
'Golden Bear' (4) IDun
'Golden Bells' (12) CBro EWal
'Golden Cycle' (6) CQua
'Golden Dawn' (8) ♀ CQua EWal
'Golden Ducat' (4) EWal ICar LAma MBri NBir
NRog
'Golden Girl' (1) ICar
'Golden Halo' (2) IBal ICar
'Golden Harvest' (1) LAma MBri NRog
'Golden Jewel' (2) ♀ EHof ICar IDun
'Golden Joy' (2) CQua ICar IDun
'Golden Perfection' (7) LAma
'Golden Radiance' (1) IBal
'Golden Rapture' (1) ♀ CQua
'Golden Riot' (1) EWal
'Golden Sceptre' (7) CBro
'Golden Sheen' (2) IDun
'Golden Sovereign' (1) IBal
'Golden Strand' (2) IBal
'Golden Topaz' (2) IBal
'Golden Vale' (1) ♀ CQua
'Golden Wings' (6) IBal
'Goldfinger' (1) IDun
¶ 'Goldhanger' (2) EHof
'Goldsithney' (2) CBro
'Golly' (4) EWal
'Good Measure' (2) EWal
'Goose Green' (3) IBal
'Gossamer' (3) EWal
'Gouache' EWal
'Grace Note' (3) CQua ICar
gracilis See *N.* × *tenuior*
'Gracious Lady' (2) IDun
¶ 'Graduation' (2) EHof
graellsii See *N. bulbocodium* subsp.
bulbocodium var. *graellsii*
'Grand Monarque' (8) CQua
'Grand Primo Citronière' CQua
(8)
'Grand Prospect' (2) CQua
'Grand Soleil d'Or' (8) CQua LAma NRog
'Gransha' (3) IBal
* 'Green Bridge' (3) ICar
'Green Glens' (2) ICar
'Green Gold' (2) EWal
¶ 'Green Island' (2) EWal
'Green Lodge' (9) IBal
'Greenfinch' (3) ICar
'Greenlet' (6) CQua
'Greenodd' (3) CQua
'Greenpark' (9) IBal
'Greenstar' (4) EWal

'Gresham' (4)	CQua IDun
'Grey Lady' (3)	ICar
'Gribben Head' (4)	CQua
'Grosvenor' (4)	IDun
'Gwennap' (1)	CQua
'Gwinear' (2)	CQua
'Halley's Comet' (3)	CQua EHof IDun
'Hallworthy' (2)	CQua
'Halolight' (2)	EWal
'Halstock' (2)	IDun
'Halvose' (8)	CBro
'Hambledon' (2)	CQua EHof IDun
'Hammoon' (3)	EWal
'Happy Face' (2)	ICar
¶ 'Happy Fellow' (2)	EHof
'Harmony Bells' (5)	CQua ICar
'Hartington' (2)	CQua
'Hartlebury' (3)	CQua
* 'Hat' (10)	EHyt SWas
'Hawaii' (4)	IBal
'Hawangi' (3)	IDun
'Hawera' (5) ♀	CAvo CBro CMea CQua EPar
	EPot ETub EWal LAma MBri
	MBro MRPP NMGW NRog
	WElm WHil
'Haye'	CQua
'Heart's Desire' (4)	EWal
'Heat Haze' (2)	ICar
hedraeanthus (13)	EPot
− MS 543/419 (13)	CMon
'Helen's Tower' (2)	IBal
hellenicus (13)	CQua
¶ 'Hembleton' (2)	EHof
henriquesii	See *N. jonquilla* var. *henriquesii*
'Hero' (1)	CQua EWal IDun
'Hesla' (7)	CBro ICar
¶ 'Heslington' (3)	EHof
'Hessenford' (2)	CQua
'Hexameter' (9)	CQua
'Hexworthy' (3)	CQua
'High Note' (7)	EWal
'High Society' (2)	CQua EHof EWal IDun
'Highfield Beauty' (8)	CQua EWal IDun
'Highland Wedding' (2)	ICar
'Highlite' (2)	ICar
'Highway Song' (2)	ICar
'Hilford' (2)	IBal
'Hill Head' (9)	IBal
'Hillstar' (7)	CQua
'Hilltown' (2)	IBal
'Holiday Fashion' (2)	EWal
'Holland Sensation' (1)	LAma
'Hollypark' (3)	IBal
¶ 'Holme Fen' (2)	EHof
'Homage' (2)	EWal
'Honey Guide' (5)	CQua
'Honeybird' (1)	CQua EWal ICar
'Honolulu' (4)	EWal
'Hoopoe' (8)	CBro CQua ICar
'Hope' (4)	EWal
'Horace' (9)	ICar
'Horn of Plenty' (5)	CQua
'Hors d'Oeuvre' (8)	CBro
'Hot Gossip' (2)	CQua EHof
'Hot Toddy' (4)	ICar
'Hotspur' (2)	CQua
* *humilis humilis* AB&S 4301	CMon
(13)	
− *mauretanicus* S&F 260	CMon
(13)	
¶ 'Hunting Caye' (2)	EHof
'Ice Dancer' (2)	IDun

'Ice Follies' (2) ♀	ETub EWal LAma MBri NBir
	NRog
'Ice King' (4)	EWal NBir
'Ice Wings' (5)	CAvo CBro CQua EWal IDun
'Idless' (1)	CQua
'Immaculate' (2)	CQua ICar
¶ 'Impresario' (2)	EHof
'Inara' (4)	CQua
'Inca' (6)	CQua
'Indian Maid' (7)	CQua
'Indora' (4)	CQua
'Inglescombe' (4)	LAma
'Ingrid Evensen' (2)	CQua
'Initiation' (1)	ICar
'Innis Beg' (2)	ICar
'Inniswood' (1)	ICar
'Interloper' (6)	IDun
§ × *intermedius* (13)	CBro
'Interval' (2)	IBal
'Intrigue' (7)	EWal ICar IDun
'Inverpolly' (2)	EHof ICar
'Ireland's Eye' (9)	IBal
'Irene Copeland' (4)	EWal
¶ 'Irish Coffee' (3)	EHof
'Irish Light' (2)	CQua ICar
'Irish Linen' (3)	EHof ICar
'Irish Luck' (1)	EWal LAma
'Irish Mist' (2)	CQua ICar
'Irish Nymph' (3)	ICar
'Irish Ranger' (3)	ICar
'Irish Rover' (2)	EHof
'Irish Splendour' (3)	ICar
'Islander' (4)	ICar
'Islandhill' (3)	IBal
'It's True' (1)	EWal
'Itzim' (6) ♀	CAvo CBro CQua ERos
jacetanus MS 580 (13)	CMon
'Jack Snipe' (6) ♀	CAvo CBro CNic CQua EBar
	ERos ETub EWal LAma LBow
	MBri NRog WShi
'Jackadee' (2)	IDun
'Jacobin' (1)	IDun
'Jamage' (8)	CQua
'Jamaica Inn' (4)	CQua
'Jambo' (2)	IDun
'Jamboree' (2)	CQua
'Jamestown' (3)	IBal
'Jana' (6)	CQua ICar
'Janis Babson' (2)	ICar
'Jennie Tait' (2)	ICar
'Jenny' (6) ♀	CAvo CBro CQua EPar EPot
	ETub EWal IBal ICar LAma
	NBir NRog WBro
'Jetfire' (6) ♀	CBro CQua EWal ICar IDun
	LAma
'Jewel Song' (2)	ICar
'Jezebel' (3)	CBro
'Johanna' (5)	CBro
'John Ballance' (1)	IBal
'John Daniel' (4)	CQua
'John of Salisbury' (2)	EWal
§ 'Jolity' (2)	EWal
jonquilla (13) ♀	CAvo CBro CQua EPar EPot
	LAma LBow MHig MSto NRog
	WPGP WShi
§ − var. *henriquesii* (13)	CBro CFil
− − MS 455 (13)	CMon
− var. *jonquilla* B&S 420	CMon
(13)	
− var. *stellaris* MS 466 (13)	CMon
'Joppa' (7)	CQua
'Joseph Macleod' (1)	EWal

'Joy'	See *N.* 'Jolity'	'Latchley' (2)	CQua
'Joy Bishop'	See *N. romieuxii* 'Joy Bishop'	'Late Call' (3)	IBal
'Joybell' (6)	CQua	'Lavender Lass' (6)	CQua
'Jubilation' (2)	EWal	'Lee Moor' (1)	CQua
'Jules Verne'	LAma	'Lemon Beauty' (11)	EWal
'Julia Jane'	See *N. romieuxii* 'Julia Jane'	'Lemon Cloud' (1)	EWal
'Jumblie' (12) ♀	CBro CMea CQua EHyt EPot	'Lemon Heart' (5)	CBro
	EWal LAma MBri NRog WShi	'Lemon Silk' (6)	CQua
'Jumbo Gold' (1)	IDun	¶ 'Lemon Snow' (2)	EHof
juncifolius	See *N. assoanus*	'Lemonade' (3)	CQua
'June Lake' (2)	IDun	'Lennymore' (2)	IDun
'Kamau' (9)	IDun	'Leonaine' (2)	EWal
'Karachi' (2)	CQua	'Leslie Hill' (1)	ICar
'Karamudli' (1)	CQua	'Lewannick' (2)	CQua
'Kaydee'	CQua IDun	'Liberty Bells' (5)	CBro CQua EWal LAma MBri
¶ 'Kazuko' (3)	EWal		NRog
'Kea' (6)	CQua	'Lichfield' (3)	EWal
'Keats' (9)	CBro CQua ICar	'Lighthouse' (3)	IDun
'Kebaya' (2)	IDun	¶ 'Lighthouse Reef' (1)	EHof
'Kehelland' (4)	CBro	'Lilac Charm' (6)	CQua IDun
'Kelanne' (2)	IDun	'Lilac Hue' (6)	CBro IDun
'Kenbane Head' (9)	IBal	'Lillande' (1)	ICar
'Kenellis' (10)	CBro	'Limbo' (2)	CQua EWal IDun
'Ken's Favourite' (2)	CQua	'Limegrove' (3)	EHof
'Kernow' (2)	CQua	'Limehurst' (2)	CQua
'Kidling' (7)	CQua	'Limelight' (1)	EWal
'Kildrum' (3)	EWal ICar	'Limerick' (3)	EWal
'Killara' (8)	CQua	¶ 'Lingerie' (4)	NZep
'Killearnan' (9)	CQua EHof	'Lintie' (7)	CBro CQua EWal LAma MBri
'Killeen' (2)	IBal		NRog
'Killyleagh' (3)	IBal	'Lionheart' (4)	EWal
'Kilmood' (2)	IBal	'Lisanore' (2)	ICar
'Kiltonga' (2)	IBal	'Lisbarnett' (3)	IBal
'Kilworth' (2)	EWal LAma	'Lisnamulligan' (3)	IBal
'Kimmeridge' (3)	CQua	'Lisnamurrican' (2)	ICar
'Kindled' (2)	ICar	'Lisrenny' (1)	ICar
'King Alfred' (1)	EWal LAma	'Little Beauty' (1)	CAvo CBro CQua EPot LAma
'King Size' (11)	CQua	'Little Dancer' (1)	CBro
'Kinglet' (7)	ICar	'Little Gem' (1) ♀	CAvo CBro CQua EPot LAma
'King's Bridge' (1)	IDun		NRog
'King's Grove' (1)	CQua IDun	'Little Princess' (6)	ICar
'King's Pipe' (2)	CQua	'Little Rusky' (7)	CQua
'King's Stag' (1)	ICar IDun	'Little Sentry' (7)	CBro CQua
'Kingscourt' (1) ♀	CQua ICar	'Little Soldier' (10)	CQua
'Kirkcubbin' (3)	IBal	'Little Spell' (1)	CBro CQua
'Kirkinriola' (3)	ICar	'Little Witch' (6)	CAvo CBro CQua EPot ERos
'Kirklington' (2)	CQua		ETub EWal LAma MBri NRog
'Kissproof' (2)	EWal	'Lizard Light' (2)	EWal
'Kitty' (6)	CBro	*lobularis*	See *N. pseudonarcissus*
'Klamath' (2)	EWal		'Lobularis'
'Knockanure' (2)	ICar	'Loch Assynt' (3)	CQua ICar
'Knocklayde' (3)	ICar	'Loch Brora' (2)	CQua ICar
'Krakatoa' (2)	EWal	'Loch Carron' (2)	ICar
'La Vella' (2)	IDun	'Loch Fada' (2)	CQua
'Ladies' Choice' (7)	IDun	'Loch Hope' (2)	CQua EHof ICar
'Lady Ann' (1)	IDun	'Loch Lundie' (2)	CQua EHof ICar IDun
'Lady Emily' (2)	IBal	'Loch Maberry' (2)	CQua
'Lady Serena' (9)	CQua	'Loch Naver' (2)	CQua IDun
'Lake Tahoe' (2)	IDun	'Loch Stac' (2)	CQua ICar
'Lamanva' (2)	CQua	'Logan Rock' (7)	CQua
'Lamerton' (2)	CQua	*longispathus* MS 546 (13)	CMon SSpi
'L'Amour'	See *N.* 'Madelaine'	'Lorikeet' (1)	CQua NZep
'Lanarth' (7)	CBro	'Lostwithiel' (2)	CQua
'Lancaster' (3)	CQua IBal	'Lothario' (2)	LAma NRog
'Landmark' (2)	EWal	'Lough Bawn' (2)	ICar
'Lapwing' (5)	CBro CQua EWal	'Lough Cuan' (1)	IBal
'Larkelly' (6)	CBro CQua	'Lough Ryan' (1)	IBal
'Larkfield' (2)	ICar	'Loughanisland' (1)	IBal
'Larkhill' (2)	CQua	'Loughanmore' (1)	ICar
'Larkwhistle' (6) ♀	CBro	'Lovable' (3)	EWal
'Last Promise' (1)	ICar	'Loveny' (2)	CQua
'Last Word' (3)	EWal	'Ludgvan' (4)	CQua

'Lunar Sea' (1)	EWal
'Lurgain' (1)	EWal
'Lurig' (2)	ICar
'Lyrebird' (3)	CQua
'Lyric' (9)	CQua
'Lysander' (2)	CQua
§ 'Madelaine' (2)	EWal
* 'Madison'	EWal
'Magic Flute' (2)	ICar
¶ 'Magician' (2)	NZep
'Magna Carta' (2)	IDun
'Magnet' (1)	LAma MBri
'Magnificence' (1)	LAma
'Majestic Star' (1)	CQua
'Makasa Sun' (2)	IDun
'Malin Head' (5)	IBal
'Manchu' (2)	EWal
'Manly' (4)	CQua EWal
'Manon Lescaut' (2)	EWal
'Marabou' (4)	CQua IDun
'Maraval' (1)	EWal
'March Sunshine' (6)	CBro EWal LAma
'Marie-José' (11)	LAma
'Marjorie Treveal' (4)	CQua
'Marlborough' (2)	CQua
'Martha Washington' (8)	CBro CQua
'Martinette' (7)	CQua
marvieri	See *N. rupicola* subsp. *marvieri*
'Mary Bohannon' (2)	EWal
'Mary Copeland' (4)	EWal LAma
'Mary Kate' (6)	CQua IDun
'Mary Lou' (6)	IDun
¶ 'Mary Robinson' (2)	ECou ICar
'Mary Sumner' (1)	ICar
¶ 'Mary Veronica' (3)	EHof
'Mary's Pink' (2)	ICar
'Marzo' (7)	IDun
'Masai Mara' (2)	IDun
'Matador' (8)	CQua
'Max' (11)	CQua
'Mayan Gold' (1)	IBal
x *medioluteus* (13)	CBro CMon
'Medusa' (8)	CBro
'Megalith' (2)	IDun
'Melbury' (2)	CQua
'Meldrum' (1)	EHof
'Mellon Park' (3)	IDun
'Melodious' (6)	CQua
'Menabilly' (4)	CQua
'Men-an-Tol' (2)	CQua
'Menehay' (11)	CQua
'Mentor' (2)	IDun
'Menucha' (2)	ICar
'Mercato' (2)	LAma
'Meredith' (3)	ICar
'Merida' (2)	IBal
'Merlin' (3) ♀	CQua EHof IBal
'Merlin's Castle'	ICar
'Merry Bells' (5)	CQua ICar
'Merrymeet' (4)	CQua
'Mexico City' (2)	IBal
¶ 'Michaels Gold' (2)	EHof
'Midas Touch' (1)	CQua IDun
'Midget'	CAvo CBro EPot
'Milan' (9)	CQua
'Millennium' (1)	CBro
'Millgreen' (1)	EWal
'Minicycla' (6)	CBro LRHS
minimus	See *N. asturiensis*
'Minnow' (8) ♀	CAvo CBro CQua EPot ERos ETub EWal LAma MBri NRog WShi

§ *minor* (13) ♀	CBro CQua EBot LAma NRya WShi
§ – var. *pumilus* (13)	ERos
– – 'Plenus'	See *N.* **'Rip van Winkle'**
– Ulster form	IBlr
'Mint Cup' (3)	ICar
minutiflorus B&S 412 (13)	CMon
'Miss Kitty' (2)	ICar
'Mission Bells' (5)	CQua ICar
'Missouri' (2)	EWal
'Mistral' (11)	ICar
'Misty Dawn' (3)	IBal
'Misty Glen' (2) ♀	CQua ICar
'Misty Moon' (3)	ICar
'Mite' (6)	CBro
'Mockingbird' (7)	IDun
'Modern Art' (2)	ETub EWal
'Mol's Hobby' (11)	EWal LAma
'Mona Lisa' (2)	EWal
'Mondragon' (11)	CQua EWal
'Mongleath' (2)	CQua
'Montego' (3)	CQua
'Monza' (4)	IDun
'Moon Ranger' (3)	IBal
'Moon Rhythm' (4)	IBal
'Moon Tide' (3)	IBal
'Moon Valley' (2)	IDun
'Moonshine' (5)	CBro
'Moonshot' (1)	EWal
'Moonspell' (2)	IBal ICar
'Moralee' (4)	IDun
'Mother Catherine Grullemans'	LAma
'Mount Angel' (3)	IDun
'Mount Fuji' (2)	CQua IDun
'Mount Hood' (1) ♀	ETub EWal LAma MBri NBir
'Mount Oriel' (2)	IBal
'Mountjoy' (7)	EWal
'Mourneview' (1)	IBal
'Movie Star' (2)	IDun
'Mowana' (2)	IDun
'Moyarget' (3)	ICar
'Moyle' (9)	IBal
'Moyola' (2)	ICar
'Mrs R.O. Backhouse' (2)	LAma MBri WShi
'Mrs William Copeland' (4)	EWal
'Mulatto' (1)	EWal
'Mulroy Bay' (1)	IDun
'Murlough' (9)	CQua IBal
'Murrayfield' (3)	IDun
'Muscadet' (2)	CQua
'My Lady' (2)	EWal
'My My' (2)	EWal
'My Word' (2)	ICar
'Naivasha' (2)	IDun
'Nampa' (1)	CQua
'Namraj' (2)	CQua EHof
'Nancegollan' (7)	CBro CQua
'Nansidwell' (2)	CQua
nanus	See *N. minor*
'Narok' (4)	IDun
'Neahkahnie' (1)	IDun
'Nether Barr' (2)	IDun
nevadensis (13)	SSpi
'New Penny' (3)	ICar
'New Song' (2)	EWal
'New Star' (1)	EWal
'New World' (2)	EWal
'New-baby' (7)	EWal
'Newcastle' (1)	CQua EHof EWal ICar IDun
'Newton Ferrers' (4)	CQua

'Night Music' (4)	CQua
'Nightcap' (1)	CQua
'Nirvana' (7)	CBro
'Niveth' (5)	CQua ICar
nobilis var. *nobilis* MS 486 (13)	CMon
– var. *primigenius* MS 593 (13)	CMon
'Nor-nor' (2)	CBro
'North Rim' (2)	IDun
'Northern Sceptre' (2)	IBal ICar
'Noss Mayo' (6)	CBro CQua
'Notre Dame' (2)	IDun
'Nouvelle' (3)	IBal
'Nuage' (2)	EWal
'Numen Rose' (2)	IDun
Nylon Group (10)	CBro CLAP CQua EHyt EPot SSpi
'Oadby' (1)	CQua
'Oakwood' (3)	EWal
'Obdam' (4)	EWal
'Obelisk' (11)	CQua
obesus (13)	CLAP EHyt EPot ERos ESis MMil
– MS 451 (13)	CMon
'Obsession' (2)	IDun
obvallaris (13) ♀	CAvo CBro EPot LBow NRog WCla WShi
'Ocarino' (4)	CQua
§ × *odorus* 'Double Campernelle' (4)	CQua ETub LAma
– 'Rugulosus' (7) ♀	CAvo CBro EBot EPar ERos LAma NRog
'Odyssey' (4)	ICar
'Oecumene' (11)	CQua
'Ohio' (2)	EHof
Old Pheasant's Eye	See *N. poeticus* var. *recurvus*
'Olympic Gold' (1)	IDun
'Omaha' (3)	IBal
'Orange Beacon' (2)	ICar
¶ 'Orange Walk' (3)	EHof
'Orangery' (11)	LAma MBri NRog
'Oratorio' (2)	EWal
'Ormeau' (2) ♀	CQua
'Oryx' (7)	CQua IDun
'Osmington' (3)	CQua EHof IDun
'Ottoman Gold' (2)	IBal
'Ouma' (1)	CQua
'Ouzel' (6)	CQua
'Owston Wood' (1)	EHof
'Oykel' (3)	CQua ICar
'Oz' (6)	CQua
'Painted Desert' (3)	CQua ICar
'Pale Sunlight' (2)	CQua ICar
'Palmares' (11)	EWal
'Palmyra' (3)	ICar
'Panache' (1)	CQua EHof EWal ICar
panizzianus (13)	CMon
'Pankot' (2)	ICar
'Paolo Veronese' (2)	EWal
'Paper White'	See *N. papyraceus*
'Papillon Blanc' (11)	EWal LAma
'Papua' (4) ♀	CQua
§ *papyraceus* (8)	CMea CQua ETub EWal LAma LBow MBri NRog
– subsp. *papyraceus* AB&S 4399 (13)	CMon
'Parcpat' (7)	CBro
'Parfait' (4)	ICar
'Paricutin' (2)	EWal
'Parisienne' (11)	EWal LAma NRog
'Park Avenue' (4)	IDun
'Park Gate' (2)	ICar
'Park Springs' (3)	CQua EHof ICar
'Parterre' (2)	IDun
'Parthenon' (4)	ICar
'Passionale' (2) ♀	CQua EWal IBal LAma NBir WShi
'Pastiche' (2)	CQua
'Pastorale' (2)	EWal
'Patabundy' (2)	CQua IDun
'Patois' (9)	IDun
patulus (13)	CMon
'Paula Cottell' (3)	CBro
'Pawley's Island' (2)	IDun
'Pay Day' (1)	EHof ICar
'Peach Prince' (4)	CQua
'Peacock' (2)	ICar
'Pearl Shell' (11)	CQua
'Pearlax' (11)	EWal
'Peeping Tom' (6) ♀	CBro EPar ETub EWal LAma MBri NRog SRms
'Pelynt' (3)	CQua
'Pencrebar' (7)	CAvo CBro CQua LAma MBri WShi
* 'Pengarth' (2)	CQua
'Penkivel' (2)	CQua
'Pennine Way' (1)	CQua
'Penpol' (7)	CBro CQua
'Penril' (6)	CQua
'Pentille' (1)	CQua
'Penvose' (2)	EWal
'Pepper' (2)	CBro
'Pequenita' (7)	CBro
'Percuil' (6)	CQua
perez-chiscanoi MS 560 (13)	CMon SSpi
'Perimeter' (3)	CQua EWal IBal ICar
'Peripheral Pink' (2)	CQua
'Perseus' (1)	ICar
'Pet Finch' (7)	EWal
'Petit Four' (4)	ETub EWal LAma NRog
'Petrel' (5)	CAvo CBro CMea CQua ETub ICar NMGW
'Phantom' (11)	CQua
'Picasso' (3)	ICar
'Pick Up' (11)	ICar
'Picoblanco' (2)	CBro
'Pinafore' (2)	EWal
'Pink Angel' (7)	CQua ICar
'Pink Champagne' (4)	CQua
'Pink Charm' (2)	EWal
'Pink Gin' (4)	EWal
'Pink Monarch' (2)	EWal
'Pink Pageant' (4)	CQua EWal IDun
'Pink Paradise' (4)	CQua ICar IDun
'Pink Silk' (1)	CQua EHof NZep
'Pink Wing' (2)	CQua
'Pinza' (2) ♀	CQua
'Pipe Major' (2)	CQua EWal
'Piper's Barn' (7)	CBro CQua
'Pipit' (7)	CAvo CBro CMea CQua EWal ICar IDun LAma NBir WShi
'Piraeus' (4)	IDun
'Pismo Beach' (2)	CQua EHof ICar
'Pitchroy' (2)	CQua
'Playschool' (3)	ICar
poeticus (13)	CAvo LAma
– var. *hellenicus* (13)	EWal
– Old Pheasant's Eye	See *N. poeticus* var. *recurvus*
* – *physaloides* (13)	ICar
N– 'Plenus' (4)	CAvo CBro CQua ETub GQui
– 'Praecox' (9)	CBro CQua MFos

§ – var. *recurvus* (13) ♀	CBro CGle CQua EBot ETub EWal LAma LBow NBir WShi
'Poet's Way' (9)	CQua
¶ 'Pol Dornie' (2)	EHof
¶ 'Pol Voulin' (2)	EHof
'Polar Circle' (2)	ICar
'Polar Imp' (3)	ICar
'Polbathic' (2)	CQua
'Polglase' (8)	CBro
'Polindra' (2)	EWal
'Polly's Pearl' (8)	CQua
'Polnesk' (7)	CBro
'Pomona' (3)	LAma
'Pops Legacy' (1)	EHof IBal
'Port Patrick' (3)	IBal
'Port William' (3)	IBal
'Porthchapel' (7)	CQua
'Portnagolan' (2)	ICar
'Portrait' (2)	CQua
'Portrush' (3)	EWal
'Portstewart' (3)	IBal
'Post House' (4)	IDun
'Powder Room' (2)	ICar
'Prairie Fire'	CQua IDun
'Preamble' (1)	CQua IBal ICar
'Premiere' (2)	CQua
'President Carter' (1)	LAma
'Pride of Cornwall' (8)	CBro
'Primrose Path' (2)	ICar
'Prince of Brunswick' (2)	IBal
'Princess Zaide' (3)	CQua
'Professor Einstein' (2)	LAma NRog
'Prologue' (1)	EWal
'Prophet' (1)	EWal
'Prosperity' (1)	ICar
'Prototype' (6)	IDun
'Pryda' (2)	ICar
pseudonarcissus (13)	CBro CGle CQua CRow EMon ETub EWFC LAma LBow SSpi WJek WShi
– subsp. *gayi* (13)	CBro
§ – 'Lobularis'	CAvo CBro NRog
§ – subsp. *moschatus* (13)	CBro
– – 'Cernuus Plenus' (4)	ICar
– subsp. *nevadensis* (13)	MFos WOMN
– subsp. *pallidiflorus*	See *N. pallidiflorus*
'Pueblo' (7)	ICar
'Pukawa' (7)	ICar
pumilus	See *N. minor* var. *pumilus*
'Puppet' (5)	CQua ICar
'Puppy' (6)	EWal
'Purbeck' (3)	CQua EHof EWal ICar IDun
'Quail' (7)	CBro CQua EWal ICar LAma NRog
'Quasar' (2)	ICar IDun NZep
'Queen Anne's Double'	See *N. 'Eystettensis'*
'Queenscourt' (1)	ICar
'Quetzal' (9)	CQua
'Quick Step' (7)	CQua
'Quiet Day' (2)	CQua ICar
¶ 'Quiet Waters' (1)	EHof
'Quince' (12)	CAvo CBro CQua EWal
'Quirinus' (2)	LAma
'Raceview' (2)	ICar
'Radiation' (2)	EWal
'Radjel' (4)	CQua
'Rainbow' (2)	CQua EWal ICar
'Ramada' (2)	ICar
'Rame Head' (1)	CQua
'Rameses' (2)	CQua EHof
'Rapture' (6)	CQua
'Rarkmoyle' (2)	ICar

'Rashee' (1)	ICar
'Raspberry Ring' (2)	CQua EHof
'Ravenhill' (3)	CQua EHof IDun
readinganorum B&S 434 (13)	CMon
'Recital' (2)	CQua
'Reckless' (3)	ICar
'Red Cameo' (2)	IDun
'Red Cottage' (2)	ICar
'Red Devil' (2)	ICar
'Red Ember' (3/2)	IDun
'Red Goblet' (2)	LAma
'Red Haze' (2)	IDun
'Red Hot' (2)	CQua
'Red Hugh' (9)	IBal
'Red Mission' (2)	IDun
'Red Spartan' (2)	IDun
'Redhill' (2)	EWal
'Redman' (2)	IBal
'Redstart' (3)	EWal
¶ 'Refrain' (2)	EHof
'Regal Bliss' (2)	CQua IDun
'Reggae' (6)	ICar IDun
'Rembrandt' (1)	LAma MBri
'Replete' (4)	CQua ICar
requienii	See *N. assoanus*
'Resplendent' (2)	ICar
'Revival' (4)	EWal
'Ridgecrest' (3)	IDun
'Riding Mill' (3)	EWal
'Riesling' (11)	CQua
rifanus	See *N. romieuxii* subsp. *romieuxii* var. *rifanus*
'Rijnveld's Early Sensation' (1) ♀	CBro CQua EWal MBri
'Rikki' (7)	CBro CQua ERos
'Rim Ride' (3)	ICar
'Rima' (1)	CQua
'Rimmon' (3)	CQua EHof IDun
'Rimski' (2)	IDun
'Ringhaddy' (3)	IBal
'Ringleader' (2)	CQua EHof EWal IDun
'Ringmaster' (2)	CQua ICar
'Ringwood' (3)	IDun
'Rio Bravo' (2)	IBal
'Rio Gusto' (2)	IBal
'Rio Lobo' (2)	IBal
'Rio Rondo' (2)	IBal
'Rio Rouge' (2)	IBal ICar
§ 'Rip van Winkle' (4)	CAvo CBos CBro EPar EPot ERos ETub LAma LBow MBri NMGW NRog WShi
'Rippling Waters' (5) ♀	CBro CQua ICar LAma
'Riptide' (1)	ICar
'Ristin' (1)	CQua
'Rivendell' (3)	ICar IDun
'River Dance' (2)	IDun
'Rob Roy' (3)	EWal
'Rock Creek' (3)	IDun
'Rockall' (3)	CQua ICar
'Rockport' (2)	ICar
'Rococo' (2)	EWal
'Roger' (6)	CBro
'Romance' (2) ♀	CQua EWal LAma
'Romany Red' (3)	IDun
romieuxii (13) ♀	CAvo CBro CFil CGra CNic CQua EHyt EPot ERos MFos MHig NMen SSpi WAbe WPGP NHar
– AB&S 4384 (13)	
– subsp. *albidus* (13)	CQua
– – S&F 110 (13)	CMon
– – S&F 256 (13)	EHyt

– – var. *zaianicus* (13)	CQua MMil
§ – – f. *albus* MS 168 (13)	CMon
§ – – – f. *lutescens* (13)	EHyt
§ – – – – S&F 374 (13)	CMon NHar
– 'Atlas Gold'	EPot
¶ – 'Atlas Gold' JCA 805Y	GCrs
– JCA 805 (13)	EHyt EPot NHar
§ – 'Joy Bishop'	EHyt EPot
§ – 'Julia Jane'	ERos GCrs NHar
§ – subsp. *romieuxii* var.	CMon EHyt SWas
mesatlanticus (13)	
§ – – var. *rifanus* SB&L 207	CMon
(13)	
– – var. *romieuxii*	NHar
JCA 805Y (13)	
– S&F 370 (13)	CMon
– 'Treble Chance'	EPot
¶ 'Rosado' (11)	EWal
'Roscarrick' (6)	CQua
'Rose Gold' (1)	IDun
'Rose of May' (4)	ICar
'Rose Royale' (2)	CQua IBal ICar
'Roseate Tern' (2)	CQua IDun
'Rosedown' (5)	CBro
'Roseworthy' (2)	LAma
'Rossferry' (2)	IBal
'Rosy Sunrise' (2)	LAma
'Rosy Trumpet' (1)	CBro
'Rosy Wonder' (2)	EWal
'Round Robin' (2)	ICar
'Royal Coachman'	ICar
'Royal Command'	See *N.* 'Royal Decree'
§ 'Royal Decree' (2)	EWal
'Royal Orange' (2)	EWal
'Royal Princess' (3)	CQua EHof IDun
'Royal Regiment' (2)	CQua ICar
'Royal Wedding' (2)	ICar
'Rubh Mor' (2)	CQua EHof
'Ruby Rose' (4)	IDun
'Ruby Tail' (2)	EWal
'Rubyat' (6)	IBal
rupicola (13)	CAvo CLAP CMon EPot ERos LAma MRPP MS&S
– subsp. *marvieri*	CMon NHar
AB&S 4414 (13)	
– – S&F 126 (13)	CMon
– MS 567/455 (13)	CMon
'Rushmore' (2)	IDun
'Ruth Haller' (5)	ICar
'Rytha' (2)	CQua
'Saberwing' (5)	CQua ICar
'Sabine Hay' (3)	CQua ETub EWal ICar IDun
'Sacajawea' (2)	EWal
'Saint Dilpe' (2)	CQua
'Saint Keverne' (2) ♀	CQua EWal IBal LAma NRog
'Saint Keyne' (8)	CQua
'Saint Mawes' (2)	CQua
'Saint Patrick's Day' (2)	ETub EWal LAma
'Saint Piran' (7)	CQua
'Salmon Trout' (2)	CQua EWal LAma
'Salomé' (2)	EWal LAma MBri NBir NRog
'Samantha' (4)	CQua
'Samaria' (3)	CBro
'Samba' (5)	ERos
'Samite' (1)	EWal
'Sancerre' (11)	CQua
'Sandy Cove' (2)	IDun
'Sandymount' (2)	IBal
'Sarah' (2)	EWal
'Sarah Dear' (2)	CQua
'Sateen' (2)	EWal
'Satellite' (6)	EWal ICar

'Satin Pink' (2)	EWal MBri
'Saturn' (3)	CQua ICar
'Savoir Faire' (2)	IDun
scaberulus (13)	CBro ERos
¶ 'Scamp' (3)	ICar
'Scarlet Elegance' (2)	LAma
'Scarlet Gem' (8)	ETub EWal LAma
'Scarlett O'Hara' (2)	LAma
'Sea Dream' (3)	CQua EWal
'Sea Gift' (7)	CBro CQua
'Sea Green' (9)	CQua
'Sealing Wax' (2)	CQua EWal
'Segovia' (3) ♀	CBro CQua ERos
'Sempre Avanti' (2)	LAma MBri NRog
'Sennocke' (5)	CBro
'Serena Beach' (4)	IDun
'Serena Lodge' (4)	IDun
serotinus (13)	CMon EHyt
– S&F 285 (13)	CMon
– S&F 298 (13)	CMon
'Sextant' (6)	CQua EWal
'Shanes Castle' (1)	ICar
'She' (2)	EWal
¶ 'Sheelagh Rowan' (2)	EHof
'Sheer Joy' (6)	IDun
'Sheerline' (2)	IDun
'Sherborne' (4)	IDun
'Sherpa' (1)	IDun
'Sheviock' (2)	CQua
'Shimna' (1)	IBal
'Shining Light' (2)	CQua ICar
'Shorecliffe' (2)	IDun
'Shot Silk' (5)	LAma
'Show Band' (2)	IDun
'Sidley' (3)	CQua IDun
'Sidney' (9)	CQua
'Signorina' (2)	IDun
'Silent Valley' (1)	CQua EHof IDun
'Silk Cut' (2)	CQua IDun
'Silken Sails' (3)	ICar
'Silver Bells' (5)	IDun
'Silver Blaze' (2)	IDun
'Silver Chimes' (8)	CBro CQua ETub EWal LAma NBir NRog
'Silver Crystal' (3)	IDun
'Silver Plate' (11)	CQua
'Silver Standard' (2)	EWal
'Silver Surf' (2)	CQua IDun
'Silverwood' (3)	IDun
'Simply Bloomfield' (2)	ICar
'Sir Winston Churchill' (4)	CQua EWal LAma NRog
'Skerry' (2)	ICar
'Slaney' (3)	ICar
'Small Talk' (1)	CQua
'Smokey Bear' (4)	CQua IDun
'Snoopie' (6)	CQua
'Snow Bunting' (7)	CBro
'Snowcrest' (3)	CQua IDun
'Snowfire' (4)	ICar
'Snowshill' (2)	CQua
'Society Belle' (2)	IDun
'Solar Tan' (3)	IDun
'Soldier Brave' (2)	EWal
'Soledad' (2)	ICar
'Soleil d'Or' (8)	EWal MBri
'Sonata' (9)	CQua
'Songket' (2)	IDun
'Sophia' (2)	CQua
'Soprano' (2)	IDun
'Sorbet' (11)	EWal
'Sorcerer' (3)	CQua
'South Street' (2)	CQua EHof

'Sovereign' (11)	ETub
'Spaniards Inn' (4)	CQua
'Spanish Moon' (1)	EWal
'Sparkling Eye' (8)	IBal
'Spellbinder' (1) ♀	EWal LAma MBri
'Sperrin Gold' (1)	IDun
'Spirit of Rame' (3)	CQua
'Split Image' (2)	IDun
'Sportsman' (2)	CQua EHof IDun
'Spring Dawn' (2)	EWal
'Stadium' (2)	EWal
'Standard Value' (1)	LAma
'Stanway' (3)	CQua
'Star Glow' (2)	IDun
'Star War' (2)	CQua
'Starfire' (7)	CQua ICar
'State Express' (2)	CQua EHof IDun
'Statue' (2)	EWal
'Steenbok' (3)	IDun
'Stilton' (9)	CQua
'Stint' (6)	CBro CQua IDun
¶ 'Stocken' (7)	CBro
'Stoke Charity' (2)	EHof ICar
¶ 'Stoke Doyle' (2)	EHof
'Stormy Weather' (1)	ICar
'Stourbridge' (2)	ICar
¶ 'Stranocum' (3)	ICar
'Strathkanaird' (1)	ICar
'Stratosphere' (7)	CQua ICar IDun
'Stray' (6)	ICar
'Strines' (2)	CQua EHof EWal
'Stromboli' (2)	EWal
'Suave' (3)	EHof
'Suda Bay' (2)	ICar
¶ 'Sugar and Spice' (3)	EHof
'Sugar Loaf' (4)	CQua
'Sugarbush' (7)	CBro LAma MBri NRog
'Sumo Jewel' (6)	CQua
'Sun Disc' (7) ♀	CAvo CBro CQua ERos EWal
	IDun LAma MBri WShi
'Sunapee' (3)	EHof
'Sundial' (7)	CAvo CBro CMea CQua EPot
	ERos EWal ICar LAma
'Suntory' (3)	CQua IDun
'Surfside' (6)	CQua
'Surrey' (2)	IDun
'Susan Pearson' (7)	ICar
'Suzie Dee' (6)	IDun
'Suzy' (7) ♀	CBro EWal ICar LAma MBri
	NRog WShi
'Swaledale' (2)	CQua
'Swansdown' (4)	EWal ICar
'Sweet Charity' (2)	EWal
'Sweet Pepper' (7)	CBro
¶ 'Sweet Sue' (3)	EHof
'Sweetness' (7) ♀	CAvo CBro CQua EWal IBal
	LAma NRog WShi
'Swing Wing' (6)	CQua IDun
'Sydling' (5)	CQua
'Sylvan Hill' (1)	IBal
'Taffeta' (10)	CAvo CBro CQua EHyt LRHS
'Tahiti' (4) ♀	CQua EWal LAma MBri NRog
'Tain' (1)	ICar
'Takoradi' (4)	ICar
'Talwyn' (1)	CQua
'Tamar Fire' (4)	CQua
'Tamar Snow' (2)	CQua
'Tamara' (2)	CQua
tananicus SF 44 (13)	CMon
'Tangent' (2)	CQua EWal ICar
'Tardree' (1)	ICar
'Tarlatan' (10)	CBro

'Taslass' (4)	CQua
'Tater-Du' (5)	CQua
tazetta aureus	See *N. aureus*
– 'Compressus' (13)	CQua
¶ – subsp. *lacticolor* (13)	CQua
– – MS 517 (13)	CMon
– – MS 519 (13)	CMon
– *papyraceus*	See *N. papyraceus*
¶ 'Teal' (1)	EHof
'Tedstone' (1)	EWal
§ 'Telamonius Plenus' (4)	CBro LAma WShi
tenuifolius	See *N. bulbocodium* subsp.
	bulbocodium var. *tenuifolius*
§ × *tenuior* (13)	CAvo CQua
'Terracotta' (2)	IDun
'Testament' (2)	EWal
'Tête-à-tête' (12) ♀	CAvo CBro CQua EBar EPar
	EPot ERos ETub EWal IBal
	LAma LBow MBri WHil
'Texas' (4)	LAma MBri
'Thalia' (5)	CAvo CBro ETub EWal ICar
	LAma LBow MBri NBir NRog
	WShi
'The Alliance' (6)	CQua
'The Knave' (6)	CQua
'The Little Gentleman' (6)	CBro
'Thoughtful' (5)	CBro CQua EWal
'Three Trees' (1)	ICar
'Thunderbolt' (1)	EWal
'Tibet' (2)	EWal
'Tiercel'	CQua
'Tiffany' (10)	EHyt
'Tiger Moth' (6)	IDun
'Timolin' (3)	CQua ICar
'Tiri Tomba' (11)	CQua EWal
'Titania' (6)	CQua
'Tittle Tattle' (7)	CBro CQua EWal IBal LAma
'Toby' (2)	EWal
'Toby the First' (6)	CQua
'Tonga' (4)	ICar
'Top Hit' (11)	CQua
'Top of the Hill' (3)	IBal ICar
'Topkapi' (2)	IBal
'Topolino' (1)	CAvo CBro CQua EPot LAma
	NRog
'Torcross' (3)	IDun
'Torr Head' (9)	IBal
'Torridon' (2)	CQua EHof ICar IDun
'Tracey' (6)	CQua
'Tranquil Morn' (3)	EWal
'Trebah' (2)	CQua
'Trefusis' (1)	CQua
'Tregarrick' (2)	CQua
'Trehane' (6)	CQua
'Trena' (6)	CQua EWal IDun
'Tresamble' (5)	CBro CQua EWal LAma
'Trevelmond' (2)	CQua
'Treverva' (6)	CQua
'Treviddo' (2)	CQua
'Trevithian' (7) ♀	CBro CQua EWal IBal LAma
	NRog
'Trewidland' (2)	CQua
'Trewirgie' (6)	CBro CQua
triandrus (13) ♀	CQua NSla WPGP
– var. *albus*	See *N. triandrus* var. *triandrus*
– var. *concolor*	See *N. concolor*
– var. *pulchellus* (13)	LAma
§ – var. *triandrus* (13)	EBot MSto
'Tricollet' (11)	EWal
'Triller' (7)	ICar
'Tripartite' (11)	CQua EWal ICar NZep
'Triple Crown' (3)	IDun

'Tristram' (2)   CQua EHof
'Tropic Isle' (4)   ICar
'Trousseau' (1)   CQua EWal
'Troutbeck' (3)   CQua
'Tudor Grove' (2)   IDun
'Tudor Minstrel' (2)   CQua EWal
'Tuesday's Child' (5) ♀   CQua EBar EWal ICar IDun
'Tullygirvan' (2)   ICar
'Tullynog' (4)   ICar
'Tullyroyal' (2)   IBal
'Turncoat' (6)   CQua
'Tutankhamun' (2)   CQua
'Tweeny' (2)   CQua
'Twicer' (2)   IDun
'Tyee' (2)   CQua
¶ 'Tykky-dew'   EHof
'Tynan' (2)   ICar
'Tyneham' (3)   IDun
'Tyrian Rose' (2)   IDun
'Tyrone Gold' (2)   IDun
'Ufo' (3)   EWal
'Ulster Bank' (3)   IDun
'Ulster Bullion' (2)   IBal
'Ultimus' (2)   EWal
'Uncle Duncan' (1)   CQua EHof
'Uncle Remus' (1)   EWal
'Unique' (4)   CQua EWal ICar IDun LAma
'Unsurpassable' (1)   LAma
'Urchin'   See *N.* **'Pzaz'**
'Vahu' (2)   IDun
'Val d'Incles' (3)   IDun
'Valdrome' (11)   CQua ICar MBri
'Valediction' (3)   IDun
'Valinor' (2)   IDun
'Value' (2)   IDun
'Van Dyke' (2)   IDun
'Van Sion'   See *N.* **'Telamonius Plenus'**
'Verdin' (7)   CQua ICar
'Verger' (3)   LAma MBri
'Vernal Prince' (3)   CQua IDun
'Verona' (3) ♀   CQua IDun
'Vers Libre' (9)   CQua IDun
'Verwood' (3)   IDun
'Victory' (2)   EWal
'Vigil' (1) ♀   CQua EWal
'Vigilante' (1)   IDun
'Viking' (1) ♀   CQua EHof
'Vilna' (2)   EWal
'Violetta' (2)   CQua EWal ICar
'Vireo' (7)   ICar
viridiflorus MS 500 (13)   CMon
 – S&F 323 (13)   CMon
'Vivarino' (11)   EWal
'Volare' (2)   CQua
'Voltage' (2)   IDun
'Vulcan' (2) ♀   CQua EHof EWal
'W.P. Milner' (1)   CAvo CBro CMea LAma MBri
                                   NRog
'Waldorf Astoria' (4)   CQua IDun
'Walesby' (2)   CQua
'Warleigh' (2)   CQua
'Warm Day' (2)   ICar
'Waterperry' (7)   CBro ETub LAma NRog
watieri (13)   CBro CGra CMon EHyt GCrs
                                   MTho WOMN WPGP
 – AB&S 4518 (13)   CMon
'Waxwing' (5)   CQua
'Wee Bee' (1)   CQua
'Wendy Walsh' (2)   ICar
'Westbury' (4)   IDun
'Westward' (4)   CQua EWal
'Wetherby' (3)   IDun

'Whang-hi' (6)   CQua
'Wheal Kitty' (7)   CQua
'Whetstone' (1)   CQua
'Whipcord' (7)   IDun
'Whisper' (5)   EWal
'Whitbourne' (3)   EWal
'White Butterfly' (2)   EWal
'White Cross' (2)   IBal
'White Hill' (2)   IBal
'White Lady' (3)   CQua
'White Lion' (4) ♀   EWal LAma NRog
'White Marvel' (4)   CQua EWal LAma NRog
'White Mist' (2)   ICar
'White Phantom' (1)   ICar
'White Plume' (2)   EWal
'White Star' (1)   CQua EHof ICar IDun
'Whiteabbey' (2)   IBal
'Widgeon' (2)   EWal
willkommii (13)   CBro
'Winchester' (2)   EWal
¶ 'Wind Song' (2)   EHof
'Windjammer' (1)   EWal
'Winfrith' (2)   EWal
'Winged Victory' (6)   CQua
'Witch Doctor' (3)   IBal
'Witch Hunt' (4)   IBal
'Woodcock' (6)   CBro CQua
'Woodgreen' (2)   EWal
'Woodland Prince' (3)   CQua
'Woodland Star' (3)   CQua
'Woodvale' (2)   CQua
'Worcester' (2)   EWal
'Xit' (3)   CBro CQua SWas
¶ 'Xunantunich' (2)   EHof
'Yeats' (9)   ICar
'Yellow Cheerfulness' (4)   ETub EWal LAma MBri NRog
 ♀
'Yellow Standard' (2)   LAma
'Yellow Sun' (3)   LAma
'Yes Please' (2)   EWal
¶ 'York Minster' (1)   EHof
'Yoshiko' (2)   IDun
'Young Blood' (2)   IDun
'Young Idea' (7)   EWal
¶ 'Your Grace' (2)   EHof
zaianicus var. *albus*   See *N. romieuxii* subsp. *albidus*
  MS 168   var. *zaianicus* f. *albus* MS 168
 – *lutescens* S&F 374   See *N. romieuxii* subsp. *albidus*
                                   var. *zaianicus* f. *lutescens* SF 374
'Zelah' (1)   CQua
'Zion Canyon' (2)   IDun

NARDOPHYLLUM (Asteraceae)
bryoides   GTou

NARDOSTACHYS (Valerianaceae)
grandiflora   GPoy

NARTHECIUM (Melanthiaceae)
ossifragum   WShi

NASSAUVIA (Asteraceae)
gaudichaudii   EHyt

NASSELLA (Poaceae)
trichotoma   CSte EGar EHoe EMon EPPr
                                   EPla ESOG GBin LHil SApp
                                   SPla

NASTURTIUM (Brassicaceae)
officinale   CBen SWat WHer

NAUTILOCALYX (Gesneriaceae)
¶ *pemphidius*　　　　　　　WDib

NECTAROSCORDUM (Alliaceae)
§ *siculum*　　　　　　　　Widely available
§ – subsp. *bulgaricum*　　CBro CHad CRDP ECha EFou
　　　　　　　　　　　　EPar EPot ERos ETub GBur
　　　　　　　　　　　　IBlr LBow LFis MNrw NOrc
　　　　　　　　　　　　SIng SOkh SSpi WAbb WBrE
　　　　　　　　　　　　WBro
¶ *tripedale*　　　　　　　CLAP

NEILLIA (Rosaceae)
affinis　　　　　　　　CDec CPle ECro EHal EHic
　　　　　　　　　　　　MBal NPro WHCG
longiracemosa　　　　See *N. thibetica*
sinensis　　　　　　　CMCN CPle EPla MRav
¶ – var. *ribesioides*　　MBel
§ *thibetica*　　　　　　CB&S CGre CHan CPle EAst
　　　　　　　　　　　　ELan EMil ENot GOrc IOrc
　　　　　　　　　　　　ISea MBri MBro MRav MTis
　　　　　　　　　　　　MUlv SMac SPer SPla SSpi SSta
　　　　　　　　　　　　WAbe WHar WWat WWin

NELUMBO (Nymphaeaceae)
'Kermesina'　　　　　　MSta
lutea 'Flavescens'　　　MSta
nucifera　　　　　　　MSta
– 'Alba Grandiflora'　　MSta
– 'Alba Striata'　　　　MSta
– 'Pekinensis Rubra'　　MSta
– 'Rosea'　　　　　　　MSta
– 'Rosea Plena' (d)　　MSta
'Osiris'　　　　　　　　MSta
'Pulchra'　　　　　　　MSta

NEMASTYLIS　(Iridaceae) See Plant Deletions

NEMATANTHUS (Gesneriaceae)
'Black Magic'　　　　　CHal MBri WDib
'Christmas Holly'　　　WDib
'Freckles'　　　　　　　WDib
§ *glaber*　　　　　　　MBri
§ *gregarius*　　　　　　CHal EBak LCns MBri WDib
§ – 'Golden West' (v)　　CHal MBri WDib
– 'Variegatus'　　　　　See *N. gregarius* **'Golden West'**
radicans　　　　　　　See *N. gregarius*
strigillosus　　　　　MBri
'Tropicana' ♀　　　　　CHal CSpe MBri WDib

NEMESIA (Scrophulariaceae)
¶ 'Ainstable Charm'　　NPro
'Blue Bird'　　　　　　EHic LIck WPeH
¶ 'Blue Cloud'　　　　　NPri WPeH
§ *caerulea*　　　　　　CBot CDoC ECtt LHil MArl
　　　　　　　　　　　　MBEx MTho NFai NPri NTow
　　　　　　　　　　　　SLMG SUsu WPer WWin
– 'Elliott's Variety'　　CBar LHil
– 'Joan Wilder' (clonal)　EMan WEas WOMN WPeH
N– 'Joan Wilder'　　　　See *N. caerulea* **lilac/blue**
　　(seed raised)
§ – lilac/blue　　　　　CSam CSpe EBar EOrc LHil
　　　　　　　　　　　　LHop MBEx WPer WPyg
　　　　　　　　　　　　WWin
– 'Woodcote'　　　　　LHil MArl MBEx NPri WPeH
§ *denticulata*　　　　　CBar CDec CHad CSpe EBar
　　　　　　　　　　　　ECtt EMar EOrc GMac LHil
　　　　　　　　　　　　LHop MArl MAsh MBEx NPri
　　　　　　　　　　　　SAxl SCoo SUsu WFar WFoF
　　　　　　　　　　　　WPeH WRus WWeb WWhi
– 'Confetti'　　　　　　See *N. denticulata*

¶ 'Evening Wine'　　　　WPeH
foetens　　　　　　　See *N. caerulea*
'Fragrant Cloud'　　　CB&S CMil EOrc MAsh MBEx
　　　　　　　　　　　　MCCP MLLN MNrw NLak
　　　　　　　　　　　　NPri NTow SPer WPeH
¶ *fruticans* Benth.　　　WPeH
◆ – misapplied　　　　See *N. caerulea*
¶ 'Georgina'　　　　　　MBEx
'Innocence'　　　　　　CSpe EHic EMan LFis LHil
　　　　　　　　　　　　LHop LIck MArl MBEx NLak
　　　　　　　　　　　　SMrm WLRN WPeH
¶ 'Melanie'　　　　　　NPri WPeH
¶ 'Orchard Blue'　　　　WPeH
¶ 'Penhow Pride'　　　　NPri WPeH
¶ 'Snow Storm'　　　　　WPeH
umbonata hort.　　　See *N. caerulea* **lilac/blue**

NEMOPANTHUS　(Aquifoliaceae) See Plant Deletions

NEMOPHILA　(Hydrophyllaceae) See Plant Deletions

NEODYPSIS (Arecaceae)
◆ *decaryi*　　　　　　See *Dypsis decaryi*
◆ *leptocheilos*　　　　See *Dypsis leptocheilos*

NEOLITSEA (Lauraceae)
glauca　　　　　　　See *N. sericea*
§ *sericea*　　　　　　CHEx WCoo

NEOMARICA (Iridaceae)
northiana　　　　　　SLMG

NEOPANAX See PSEUDOPANAX

NEOPAXIA (Portulacaceae)
§ *australasica*　　　　CMHG ECou ESis NGre WWin
– blue-leaved　　　　See *N. australasica* **'Kosciusko'**
– bronze-leaved　　　See *N. australasica* **'Ohau'**
– green-leaved　　　　See *N. australasica* **'Great Lake'**
– grey　　　　　　　　See *N. australasica* **'Kosciusko'**
§ – 'Kosciusko'　　　　GDra NBir
– 'Lyndon'　　　　　　ECou
§ – 'Ohau'　　　　　　ECou GGar

NEOREGELIA (Bromeliaceae)
carolinae　　　　　　MBri SRms
§ – (Meyendorffii Group)　MBri
　　'Flandria'
– – 'Meyendorffii'　　MBri
– f. *tricolor* (v) ♀　　CHal MBri
§ Claret Group　　　　MBri

NEOTTIANTHE (Orchidaceae)
cucullata　　　　　　EFEx

NEPENTHES (Nepenthaceae)
alata　　　　　　　　WMEx
bongso × *hamata*　　WMEx
× *coccinea*　　　　　MBri WMEx
gracilis　　　　　　WMEx
gymnamphora　　　　WMEx
　hybrids　　　　　　MHel
khasiana　　　　　　WMEx
lowii　　　　　　　WMEx
madagascariensis　　WMEx
maxima　　　　　　WMEx
¶ – × *mixta*　　　　　WMEx
mirabilis　　　　　　WMEx

muluensis	WMEx
rafflesiana	WMEx
– × *ampullaria*	See *N.* × *hookeriana*
rajah	WMEx
reinwardtiana	WMEx
sanguinea	WMEx
tentaculata	WMEx
tobaica	WMEx
tomoriana	WMEx
truncata	WMEx
ventricosa	WMEx
– slim × *spectabilis*	WMEx
vieillardii	WMEx

NEPETA † (Lamiaceae)

argolica	See *N. sibthorpii*
'Blue Beauty'	See *N. sibirica* 'Souvenir d'André Chaudron'
bucharica	GBuc
* *buddlejifolium*	NLar
camphorata	CSam EMFP GAbr GTou LHol MLLN MSte SCro SIde WOve WRha WWye
cataria	CArn CSev EJud ELau GBar GPoy LHol MChe MHew MMal MSal NBro SIde WHer WOak WPer WSel WWye
– 'Citriodora'	CArn CBot CLTr CSam EFou EHal ELau GBar GPoy LHol MSal NFai SChu SIde SSpe WCHb WHer WRha WSel WWye
* *citriodora*	EMon
clarkei	CHan CLon CMGP CMHG CMea CSam EBee EFou MSte NCat NLak SBla SCro SWat WPer
¶ *dinphya*	EBee
× *faassenii*	CGle CHad EAst EBrP EBre ECGN EMon GLil LBre MAus MBel MRav MWat MWhi NPer NVic SAga SBre SChu SCro SEas SIng SPla SRms
¶ – 'Alba'	CStr NLar
glechoma 'Variegata'	See *Glechoma hederacea* 'Variegata'
govaniana	CHad CHan CPle CSam ECGN ECha EFou ELan GCal LGre LHol MAus MMil MUlv NBro NChi NSti NTow SIgm SPer SUsu WCHb WHoo WHow WOld WPer WWin WWye
grandiflora	CLTr EFou LFis LHol MGrG MRav NFai SIde SMrm WHer WWhi
– 'Bramdean'	CRDP CSam SHel SWas
– 'Dawn to Dusk'	Widely available
– 'Pool Bank'	CRDP CStr ECoo EFou EGoo EMon MBel NCat NFai SAga SChu SDys SMrm
hederacea 'Variegata'	See *Glechoma hederacea* 'Variegata'
¶ *laevigata*	EBee
lanceolata	See *N. nepetella*
latifolia	MLLN
* *longipes*	CHan CSam EMan EMon MLLN MSte SAga SBla SChu SCro SHel SMrm SUsu SWas WCot WHal WPbr WPer WRus WViv
macrantha	See *N. sibirica*
melissifolia	EBee WCHb WPer WWye
mussinii	See *N. racemosa*
§ *nepetella*	CSam GBar GBri LHol NBir NChi SIde WPer WWhi
nervosa	Widely available
– 'Forncett'	CSam
– 'Forncett Select'	EFou LFlo SWas
§ *nuda*	CPle CSam EBee ECha EHal EMan EMon LHol MLLN WCot WPbr WPer WRus
– subsp. *albiflora*	CHan EGar EMon
* – 'Anne's Choice'	LBuc LFis WCot
– 'Nacre'	EMon
– subsp. *nuda*	CHan EGar EMou
pannonica	See *N. nuda*
parnassica	CMil EBee LLew LRHS MAvo NChi NSti SAga SMad SMrm SWat WElm WWhi
– CDB 13073	SCro
§ *phyllochlamys*	CBot CLTr CPBP MSte NTow SAga SBla WOMN
'Porzellan'	CLTr EFou EMon MSte
§ *prattii*	EHal EPPr
¶ 'Purple Blotch'	CStr
§ *racemosa*	CArn CBot CPle CSev EBrP EBre ECGN ELan ELau ERic GBar LBre LHol MChe MFir NFai NRoo NWes SBre SHFr SIde SMac SPla WWin WWye
¶ – *alba*	SSvw
– 'Blue Ice'	GBuc SMer WHoo
– 'Grog'	EFou
¶ – 'Karen's Blue'	EFou
– 'Little Titch'	EBee EFou GCal SChu SCro SMrm SSpe
– 'Snowflake'	CBlo CBot CGle CMea EAst EBee EFou EHal ELan EMil ERav GCal GCra LHop MAus MSte MWat NBir NBrk NCat NChi NLon NSti SChu SEas SHel SPer SSpe WHow WPbr
§ – 'Superba'	CBlo CLTr EFou ELan ELau EMon GBuc MBro SEas WHoo WPbr
– 'Walker's Low'	CBlo CEnd CSev EBee ECGP EFou EGar GBar GCal MAus MBel MLLN NCat NChi NRoo SChu SHel SMrm SSpe SWas SWat WLRN WPen WRus WWoo
reichenbachiana	See *N. racemosa*
§ *sibirica*	Widely available
§ – 'Souvenir d'André Chaudron'	Widely available
§ *sibthorpii*	NChi WPer
sintenisii	EGar EMon LBlm
'Six Hills Giant'	Widely available
sp. DS&T 89048T	EMon
sp. DS&T 89054T	EMon
stewartiana	CHar CStr GBuc MFir MLLN WElm WSan
– ACE 1611	CMil EPot GBuc SMrm
– CLD 551	EBee
subsessilis	Widely available
¶ – AGSJ 251	SDys
– forms	MNrw WBon WCot
– pink form	CStr EMon GBuc SOkh WPbr
* – *sensibilis*	SWat
– var. *yesoensis*	CHan
tenuifolia	MSal
teydea	MNrw
transcaucasica	SDix

tuberosa	CFir CHan CPle CSam ECha EMan GBar LGan SChu SCro SSca WPen WWhi WWye
ucranica	NHex

NEPHROLEPIS (Oleandraceae)

cordifolia	GQui MBri NMar
exaltata ♀	ERea
– 'Bostoniensis'	LBlm MBri SRms
– 'Rooseveltii'	MBri
– 'Smithii'	MBri
– 'Smithii Linda'	MBri
– 'Teddy Junior'	MBri
– 'Todeoides'	NMar

NEPHROPHYLLIDIUM (Menyanthaceae)

cristagalli	IBlr

NERINE † (Amaryllidaceae)

¶ 'Afterglow'	LAma
¶ 'Angelico'	SSpr
angustifolia	LLew
'Baghdad'	CMon SSpr
¶ 'Berlioz'	SSpr
'Betty Hudson'	CRDP
'Blanchefleur'	SSpr
* 'Borde Hill White'	SSpr
bowdenii ♀	Widely available
¶ – 'Alba'	SCoo
¶ – Logan strain	GCal
– 'Manina'	WCot
– 'Mark Fenwick'	CAvo CB&S ECha ECro EPot GCal LHop SAxl WCot
* – 'Mollie Cowie'	EMon EMul WCru
– 'Pink Triumph'	CB&S CBlo CLyd GBuc IBlr LAma LWak NRog SDeJ SPer
– 'Wellsii'	CMon CRDP WCot
'Brocade'	CMon
'Canasta'	SSpr
¶ 'Caroline'	SSpr
'Catherine'	SSpr
¶ 'Clarabel'	SSpr
¶ 'Clarissa'	SSpr
'Clent Charm'	SSpr
corusca 'Major'	See *N. sarniensis* var. *corusca*
crispa	See *N. undulata*
¶ 'Dame Alice Godman'	SSpr
¶ 'Darius'	SSpr
¶ 'Dorellia'	SSpr
'Dunkirk'	SSpr
¶ 'Elspeth'	SSpr
'Eve'	SSpr
'Ffiske'	SSpr
filamentosa	CMon SWas
filifolia	CAvo CRDP EHyt EPot GCal MNrw WCot
flexuosa	CMon MRav SLMG SSpr
– 'Alba'	CAvo CBro LAma LGre SDeJ SLMG SSpr
– pink	CMon
¶ 'Fortune'	SSpr
'Gaby Deslys'	CMon
¶ 'Glensavage Gem'	SSpr
¶ 'Glensavage Spider'	SSpr
'Gloaming'	SSpr
¶ 'Goya'	SSpr
'Grilse'	CMon
'Hamlet'	SSpr
'Harlequin'	SSpr
'Harry Dalton'	SSpr
¶ 'Hawaii'	SSpr
'Helen Smith'	SSpr
humilis	CMon WCot
– Breachiae Group	CMon
– Tulbaghensis Group	CMon
'Inchmery Kate'	SSpr
innominata	SSpr
'Janet'	SSpr
¶ 'Jenny Wren'	SSpr
'Jill'	SSpr
¶ 'Joan'	CAvo
¶ 'Judith'	SSpr
¶ 'Kasmir'	SSpr
* 'Killi'	CRDP
¶ 'Kilwa'	SSpr
'King of the Belgians'	LAma SSpr
¶ 'Kingship'	SSpr
¶ 'Kola'	SSpr
¶ 'Konak'	SSpr
¶ 'Koriba'	SSpr
krigei	LLew
¶ 'Kymina'	SSpr
¶ 'Kyoto'	SSpr
'Lady Cynthia Colville'	SSpr
¶ 'Lady Eleanor Keane'	CAvo SSpr
¶ 'Lady Llewellyn'	CAvo
¶ 'Lambourne'	SSpr
laticoma	LLew
¶ 'Lawlord'	SSpr
¶ 'Leila Hughes'	SSpr
¶ 'Locharber'	SSpr
'Lord Grenfell'	IBlr
¶ 'Lucinda'	SSpr
¶ 'Lyndhurst Salmon'	SSpr
'Mansellii'	CMon SSpr
¶ 'Maria'	SSpr WCot
'Marnie Rogerson'	CBro CGle LGre
masoniorum	CBro CLyd EHyt LGre MTho WCot WOMN
¶ 'Meadowbankii'	SSpr
¶ 'Miss Edith Godman'	SSpr
¶ 'Nena'	CAvo
¶ 'Oberon'	SSpr
¶ *peersii*	WCot
¶ 'Pink Galore'	SSpr
pudica	CMon
* 'Red Pimpernel'	EBar LAma
¶ 'Rembrandt'	SSpr
'Rose Camellia'	CMon
'Rushmere Star'	SSpr
sarniensis	CBro EBot ECha NRog SLMG
* – 'Alba'	WCot
§ – var. *corusca*	LAma
– – 'Major'	LBow SSpr
– var. *curvifolia* f. *fothergillii*	SSpr WCot
– – – 'Queen Mary'	CMon
Smee No. 11	CMon
'Smokey Special'	SSpr
'Snowflake'	SSpr
'Stephanie'	LAma SSpr
'Stephanie' x 'Moscow'	SSpr
§ *undulata*	CAvo CBlo CBro CMon EBot ECha ERos LAma LBow MBri NRog SPer WCot
* – 'Alba'	WCot
'Vestal'	SSpr
'Vicky'	CRDP
'White Swan'	EBar LAma SSpr
'Wolsey'	SSpr
'Zeal Giant'	CAvo

NERIUM † (Apocynaceae)

oleander	CBrP CHEx CMdw EBak LPan SRms
– 'Album'	EEls
– 'Album Plenum' (d)	EEls
– 'Alsace'	EEls ERea
– 'Altini'	EEls
– 'Angiolo Pucci'	EEls
* – 'Avalanche'	CB&S
– 'Belle Hélène'	EFlo
¶ – 'Bouquet d'Or'	EEls
¶ – 'Carneum Plenum' (d)	EEls
¶ – 'Cavalaire' (d)	EEls
* – 'Clare'	EEls ERea SOWG
¶ – 'Cornouailles'	EEls
¶ – 'Docteur Golfin'	EEls
¶ – 'Emile Sahut'	EEls
– 'Emilie'	EEls ERea
¶ – 'Flavescens Plenum' (d)	CFee EEls EFlo ERea
– forms	EEls SLMG
– 'Géant des Batailles'	EEls EFlo ERea SOWG
– 'Hardy Pink'	EFlo ERea
– 'Hardy Red'	EEls ERea
– 'Hawaii'	EEls
* – 'Isabelle'	EEls
– 'Isle of Capri'	EEls EFlo ERea SOWG
– 'Italia'	ERea
¶ – 'J.R.'	EEls
– 'Jannoch'	EEls EFlo ERea
¶ – 'Louis Pouget' (d)	EEls
– 'Madame Allen' (d)	EEls EFlo
– 'Madame Léon Blum'	EFlo
– 'Madame Planchon' (d)	ERea
– 'Magaly'	ERea
– 'Maresciallo Graziani'	EEls
– 'Margaritha'	EEls ERea
¶ – 'Marie Gambetta'	EEls
¶ – subsp. *mascatense*	EEls
¶ – 'Mont Blanc'	EEls
◆ – 'Mrs Roeding'	See *N. oleander* 'Carneum Plenum'
¶ – 'Nana Rosso'	EEls
¶ – 'Oasis'	EEls
¶ – subsp. *oleander*	EEls
– 'Papa Gambetta'	EEls EFlo
* – 'Peach Blossom'	ERea
¶ – 'Petite Pink'	EEls
¶ – 'Petite Red'	EEls
– 'Petite Salmon'	EEls
– 'Professeur Granel' (d)	EEls ERea
– 'Provence' (d)	EEls ERea SOWG
– 'Rosario' (d)	ERea
¶ – 'Rose des Borrels'	EEls
– 'Rosée du Ventoux' (d)	EEls ERea SOWG
– 'Roseum'	EEls SLMG
– 'Roseum Plenum' (d)	CB&S EEls
– 'Rosita'	EEls ERea
– 'Sealy Pink'	CB&S EEls
* – 'Snowflake'	EEls ERea SOWG
– 'Soeur Agnès'	EEls ERea
– 'Soleil Levant'	EEls ERea
– 'Souvenir d'Emma Schneider'	EEls
– 'Souvenir des Iles Canaries'	EEls EFlo
– 'Splendens' (d)	ERea SOWG
– 'Splendens Giganteum' (d)	EEls
¶ – 'Splendens Giganteum Variegatum' (d/v)	EEls
– 'Tito Poggi'	EEls ERea
– 'Variegatum'	CBot CGre EEls ERea LHop LPan SLMG
– 'Variegatum Plenum' (d)	WCot
¶ – 'Villa Romaine'	EEls
– 'Ville de Carpentras' (d)	EEls EFlo ERea
* – 'Yellow Queen'	CB&S

NERTERA (Rubiaceae)

balfouriana	ECou
depressa	ECou
granadensis	MBri WOMN

NEVIUSIA (Rosaceae)

alabamensis	CHan

NICANDRA (Solanaceae)

physalodes	CArn EMan NBir NHex SIde SSoC
– *alba*	LCot NBir WHer
* – 'Blacky'	SMrm WCot
– 'Violacea'	SLod SRms

NICOTIANA (Solanaceae)

acuminata	MSto
alata	MSto
¶ *colossea*	CTrG
glauca	CGle CMdw EMar EOas ERea LFlo MAll MSte SLMG
knightiana	MSto
langsdorffii ♀	CB&S CHad CHan ECro ELan EMon GBri MBEx NBro SLMG SMrm SUsu WEas WHal WHer WMaN WOve WPer WRus WWye
– 'Cream Splash' (v)	CPla EBee WHer
noctiflora	EBar
rustica	ECro MSto
suaveolens	WRus
sylvestris ♀	CHEx CHad CHan CJew CSpe EBar EMan GBri LPVe MBEx MGed SEND SMrm WEas WHer WRus WWye
tabacum	CArn CHEx WWye

NIDULARIUM (Bromeliaceae)

flandria	See *Neoregelia carolinae* (Meyendorffii Group) 'Flandria'

NIEREMBERGIA (Solanaceae)

§ *caerulea* ♀	ECha EMan LFlo WThi
frutescens	See *N. scoparia*
hippomanica	See *N. caerulea*
§ *repens*	CMHG CTri ELan EPot MBro NBus NNrd WHil WOMN WWin
rivularis	See *N. repens*
§ *scoparia*	CGle CHad CHan LHop MTho SSpe WRus
– 'Mont Blanc'	WRus
– 'Purple Robe'	WRus

NIPHAEA (Gesneriaceae)

oblonga	NMos

× NIPHIMENES (Gesneriaceae)

'Lemonade'	NMos

NIPPONANTHEMUM (Asteraceae)
§ *nipponicum*   CHan CMGP CNic CSam EAst
ECha EMon ERic GCal NFai
NRoo NSti WCot WEas WPGP
– *roseum*   CSam

NIVENIA (Iridaceae) See Plant Deletions

NOCCAEA See THLASPI

NOLANA (Nolanaceae) See Plant Deletions

NOLINA (Dracaenaceae)
beldingii   SIgm
brevifolia   SIgm
durangensis   CTbh
greenii   SIgm
palmeri   SIgm
¶ *parryi*   WCot
§ *recurvata* ♀   LCns LPal MBri
texana   SIgm

NOMOCHARIS (Liliaceae)
aperta   EPot GBuc GDra LAma MDun
SSpi WAbe WCru
¶ – ACE 2271   GCrs
farreri   EHyt
¶ × *finlayorum*   GCrs
mairei   See *N. pardanthina*
¶ *meleagrina*   LAma
nana   See *Lilium nanum*
§ *pardanthina*   GBuc NHar NSla WAbe
– f. *punctulata*   GBuc GDra GGGa MDun
WAbe
saluenensis   GTou

NONEA (Boraginaceae)
lutea   CMea EAst MFir MLLN NChi
NOrc NRoo WAbb WByw
WHal WPen

NOTELAEA (Oleaceae) See Plant Deletions

NOTHOFAGUS † (Fagaceae)
alessandrii   ISea
§ *alpina*   CDoC CLnd CMCN CMHG
CPer GAri GRei IOrc MBal
SMad WMou WNor
antarctica   CB&S CDoC CLnd CMHG
ELan EMil ENot IOrc ISea
LPan MBal MBar MBri MGos
NBee NHol NPal SPer WDin
WNor WSHC
– 'Prostrata'   See *N. antarctica* **'Benmore'**
cunninghamii   GAri GGGa ISea STre WNor
dombeyi   GAri IOrc ISea SAPC SArc
WBod WNor
menziesii   CLnd
moorei   CFil
obliqua   CDoC CGre CLnd CMCN CPer
CSam EPfP GAri IOrc ISea
MBal NWea WDin WFro
WMou WNor
procera   See *N. alpina*
pumilio   GAri
solandri   CMHG
– var. *cliffortioides*   CFai CLnd MBal STre

NOTHOLAENA See CHEILANTHES

NOTHOLIRION (Liliaceae)
bulbuliferum   GCra
– C 5074   GGGa
campanulatum   SWat
macrophyllum   EBee GCrs WCru
thomsonianum   GCrs

NOTHOPANAX See POLYSCIAS

NOTHOSCORDUM (Alliaceae)
inodorum   GBuc
– *macrostemon* CL 7/76   CMon
neriniflorum   See *Caloscordum neriniflorum*

NOTOBUXUS (Buxaceae)
natalensis   SLan

NOTOSPARTIUM (Papilionaceae)
carmichaeliae   ECou MAll
glabrescens   ECou MAll
torulosum   ECou MAll
– × *glabrescens*   ECou MAll

NOTOTRICHE (Malvaceae)
compacta   MTho

NUPHAR (Nymphaeaceae)
advena   MSta
japonica var. *variegata*   CRow
lutea   CBen CRow EHon EMFW
LPBA MSta NDea SWat WChe
– subsp. *variegata*   See *N. variegata*
pumila   MSta
– *variegata*   MSta
'Shirley Bryne'   MSta

NUXIA (Buddlejaceae)
¶ *congesta*   CTrC

NYMPHAEA † (Nymphaeaceae)
'Afterglow' (T/D)   MSta
alba   CBen CRow EHon EMFW
LPBA MSta SAWi SWat SWyc
WChe WMAq WStI WWeb
§ – subsp. *occidentalis* (H)   MSta SWyc
– 'Plenissima' (H)   MSta SWyc
– var. *rubra* (H)   MSta
'Albatros' (H)   EHon LPBA MSta SWat SWyc
WBcn
'Albatros' hort.   See *N.* **'Hermine'**
'Albert Greenberg' (T/D)   MSta
'Amabilis' (H)   CBen CRow EMFW LPBA
MSta SWat SWyc WBcn WMAq
'American Star'   CWat MSta SWat SWyc WMAq
'Andreana' (H)   CWat EMFW LPBA MSta
SWat SWyc
'Anna Epple'   SWyc
'Apple Blossom Pink'   See *N.* **'Marliacea Carnea'**
'Apricot Pink' (T)   MSta
'Arc-en-ciel' (H)   MSta SWat SWyc WMAq
'Arethusa' (H)   MSta SWyc
'Atropurpurea' (H)   CBen EMFW LPBA MSta SWat
SWyc WMAq
'Attraction' (H)   CBen CRow EHon EMFW
LPBA MSta SWat SWyc WChe
WMAq WStI
'Aurora' (H)   EMFW LPBA MSta SWat SWyc
WMAq
'Ballerina'   SWyc
'Barbara Davies'   MSta

'Barbara Dobbins'	MSta SWyc
'Baroness Orczy' (H)	MSta SWyc
'Bateau' (H)	MSta SWyc
'Berit Strawn'	SWyc
'Berthold'	MSta SWyc
'Betsy Sakata'	SWyc
¶ 'Black Princess'	SWyc
'Bleeding Heart'	SWyc
'Blue Beauty' (T/D)	CBen
'Bory de Saint-Vincent' (H)	MSta SWyc
'Brakeleyi Rosea' (H)	EMFW LPBA MSta SWyc
'Burgundy Princess'	SWyc
caerulea (T/D)	MSta
candida	CBen EHon EMFW LPBA MSta SWyc
– var. *biradiata* (H)	SWyc
– var. *neglecta* (H)	SWyc
– var. *rubra* (H)	MSta
'Candidissima' (H)	MSta SWyc
'Candidissima Rosea' (H)	MSta SWyc
'Cardinal' (H)	SWyc
'Caroliniana' (H)	CWat MSta SWyc
'Caroliniana Nivea' (H)	CBen CWat EMFW MSta SWyc
'Caroliniana Perfecta' (H)	CBen LPBA MSta SWat SWyc
'Caroliniana Rosea' (H)	MSta
'Celebration'	MSta SWyc
§ 'Charlene Strawn'	EMFW MSta SWat SWyc WBcn WMAq
'Charles de Meurville' (H)	CBen CRow EMFW LPBA MSta SWyc WMAq
'Charles's Choice'	SWyc
'Château le Rouge'	MSta SWyc
'Cherokee'	SWyc
'Chromelia'	SWyc
'Chrysantha' (H)	EMFW MSta SWyc
'Chubby'	MSta SWyc
'Citrus Star'	SWyc
¶ 'Clyde Itkins'	SWyc
'Colonel A.J. Welch' (H)	CBen CRow EHon EMFW LPBA MSta SAWi SWat SWyc WChe WMAq
'Colonel Lindbergh' (T/D)	MSta
'Colorado'	SWyc
colorata	CBen MSta
'Colossea' (H)	CBen EHon EMFW LPBA MSta SWyc WMAq
'Comanche' (H)	CBen EMFW MSta SWat SWyc WMAq
'Comte de Bouchaud'	MSta
'Conqueror' (H)	EMFW LPBA MSta SAWi SWat SWyc WMAq WWeb
'Dallas'	SWyc
'Danieda'	SWat
§ 'Darwin' (H)	CBen MSta SWat SWyc WMAq
× *daubenyana* (T/D)	MSta
'David'	MSta
'Denver'	SWyc
'Deva'	MSta
'Director George T. Moore' (T/D)	MSta
'Doll House'	SWyc
¶ 'Dorothy Lamour' (H)	SWyc
'Ellisiana' (H)	CBen EMFW LPBA MSta SWat SWyc
'Elysée' (H)	MSta
'Ernst Epple Senior'	SWyc
'Escarboucle' (H) ♀	CBen CRow CWat EHon EMFW LPBA MSta SAWi SWat SWyc WBcn WMAq
'Esmeralda' (H)	MSta SWat

'Eucharis' (H)	MSta
'Evelyn Randig' (T/D)	CBen MSta
'Evelyn Stetston'	SWyc
'Exquisita'	See *N.* **'Odorata Exquisita'**
§ 'Fabiola' (H)	CBen CRow EHon EMFW LPBA MSta SWat SWyc WBcn WMAq
'Fantastic Pink'	SWyc
¶ 'Fenna Harder'	SWyc
'Fiesta'	SWyc
'Firecrest' (H)	CBen CWat EHon EMFW LPBA MSta SWat SWyc WBcn WMAq
¶ 'Fishers Pink'	SWyc
'Florida Sunset'	SWyc
'Formosa' (H)	MSta SWyc
'France'	MSta
'Fritz Junge' (H)	MSta SWyc
'Froebelii' (H)	CBen CRow CWat EHon EMFW LPBA MSta SWat SWyc WBcn WChe WMAq
'Fulva' (H)	MSta SWyc
'Galatée' (H)	MSta SWyc
'General Pershing' (T/D)	MSta
gigantea	MSta
'Gladstoneana' (H) ♀	CBen CRow EHon EMFW LPBA MSta SAWi SWat SWyc WMAq
'Gloire du Temple-sur-Lot' (H)	CBen EMFW MSta SWat SWyc WMAq
'Gloriosa' (H)	CBen EMFW LPBA MSta SWat SWyc WWeb
'Gold Medal' (H)	SWyc
'Golden West' (T/D)	MSta
'Goliath' (H)	MSta SWyc
'Gonnère' (H) ♀	CBen CRow CWat EHon EMFW LPBA MSta SWat SWyc WBcn WMAq
'Gracillima Alba' (H)	SWyc
'Granat'	SWyc
'Graziella' (H)	EMFW LPBA MSta SWat SWyc WBcn WMAq
'Green Smoke' (T/D)	MSta
'Grésilias' (h)	MSta
¶ 'Gypsy'	SWyc
'H.C. Haarstick' (T/D)	MSta
'Hal Miller' (H)	EMFW MSta SWyc
'Helen Fowler' (H)	EMFW MSta SWat SWyc WMAq
× *helvola*	See *N.* **'Pygmaea Helvola'**
§ 'Hermine' (H)	CBen EMFW MSta SWat SWyc WMAq
'Hever White' (H)	MSta SWyc
¶ 'High Life'	SWyc
'Hollandia' hort.	See *N.* **'Darwin'**
'Hollandia' Koster (H)	SWyc
'Improved Firecrest'	SWyc
'Indiana' (H)	CBen CWat EMFW LPBA MSta SWat SWyc WMAq
'Irene' (H)	SWyc
'Irene Heritage'	SWyc
'J.C.N. Forestier' (H)	MSta
'Jack Wood' (T)	MSta
'James Brydon' (H) ♀	CBen CRow CWat EHon EMFW LPBA MSta SAWi SRms SWat SWyc WBcn WMAq
'James Hudson' (H)	MSta SWyc
¶ 'Jean de Lamarsalle'	MSta
'Jean Laydeker'	MSta
'Jean Marie'	SWyc
'Jim Saunders'	SWyc

'Joanne Pring'	MSta SWat SWyc
'Joey Tomocick'	SWyc WMAq
'Julian Decelle'	MSta
'Juliana' (h)	CWat EMFW MSta
'Kiss of Fire' (H)	SWyc
¶ 'Labeaugere'	SWyc
'Lactea' (H)	MSta
¶ 'Laura Strawn'	SWyc
'Laydekeri Fulgens' (H)	CBen EMFW LPBA MSta SWat SWyc WMAq
'Laydekeri Lilacea' (H)	CBen CRow EMFW LPBA MSta SWat SWyc WMAq
'Laydekeri Purpurata' (H)	EMFW LPBA MSta SWat SWyc WBcn WMAq
'Laydekeri Rosea' hort.	See *N.* **'Laydekeri Rosea Prolifera'**
§ 'Laydekeri Rosea Prolifera' (H)	CBen EMFW LPBA MSta SWyc
'Lemon Chiffon'	SWyc
'Leviathan' (H)	MSta
'Lily Pons'	SWyc
'Limelight'	SWat
'Liou'	SWyc
'Little Sue'	SWyc
'Livingstone' (H)	MSta SWyc
¶ 'Loose' (H)	SWyc
'Louise' (H)	SWyc
'Louise Villemarette'	SWyc
'Luciana'	See *N.* **'Odorata Luciana'**
'Lucida' (H)	CBen CWat EMFW LPBA MSta SWat SWyc
'Lusitania' (H)	MSta SWyc
'Lustrous' (H)	SWyc
'Madame Bory Latour-Marliac' (H)	MSta
'Madame de Bonseigneur' (H)	MSta
'Madame Julien Chifflot' (H)	MSta
'Madame Maurice Laydeker' (H)	MSta SWyc
'Madame Wilfon Gonnère' (H)	CBen CWat EHon EMFW LPBA MSta SWat SWyc WBcn WMAq WWeb
'Margaret Randig' (T/D)	MSta
'Marguerite Laplace' (H)	MSta SWyc
'Marliacea Albida'	CBen CWat EHon LPBA MSta SWat SWyc WChe
§ 'Marliacea Carnea' (H)	CBen CRow EHon EMFW LPBA MSta SWat SWyc WBcn WMAq
§ 'Marliacea Chromatella' (H) ♀	CBen CRow EHon EMFW LPBA MSta SAWi SWat SWyc WBcn WChe WMAq
'Marliacea Flammea' (H)	MSta SWyc
'Marliacea Ignea' (H)	MSta SWyc
'Marliacea Rosea' (H)	EMFW MSta SWyc WMAq
'Marliacea Rubra Punctata' (H)	MSta SWyc
'Maroon Beauty' (T/N)	MSta
'Martha'	SWyc
'Mary'	SWyc
'Mary Exquisita' (H)	MSta
'Mary Patricia' (H)	MSta SWyc
'Masaniello' (H)	CBen CRow EHon EMFW LPBA MSta SWat SWyc WBcn WMAq
'Maurice Laydeker' (H)	EMFW MSta SWyc
¶ 'Maxima' (H)	WMAq
'Mayla'	SWyc
§ 'Météor' (H)	CWat EMFW MSta SWyc WBcn
mexicana	MSta SWyc
'Moorei' (H)	CBen EHon EMFW LPBA MSta SWat SWyc WMAq
'Mount Shasta'	SWyc
'Mrs C.W. Thomas' (H)	MSta SWyc
'Mrs C.W. Ward' (T/D)	MSta
'Mrs Richmond'	See *N.* **'Fabiola'**
'Murillo' (H)	MSta SWyc
'Neptune' (H)	MSta SWyc
'Newton' (H)	EMFW MSta SWat SWyc WMAq
'Nigel' (H)	MSta SWat SWyc
'Nobilissima' (H)	MSta
'Norma Gedye' (H)	CBen CWat MSta SWat SWyc WMAq
'Occidentalis'	See *N. alba* subsp. *occidentalis*
'Odalisque' (H)	CWat EMFW MSta SWyc WBcn
§ *odorata* (H)	CBen CRow EHon LPBA MSta SWyc WBcn WMAq
'Odorata Alba'	See *N. odorata*
¶ 'Odorata Eugénia de Land'	MSta
§ 'Odorata Exquisita' (H)	MSta SWyc
odorata var. *gigantea* (H)	MSta
* – 'Jasmine'	SWyc
'Odorata Juliana'	SWyc
§ 'Odorata Luciana'	EMFW MSta SWyc
odorata 'Maxima' (H)	SWyc
§ – var. *minor* (H)	CBen CRow EMFW LPBA MSta SWat SWyc WMAq
– 'Pumila'	See *N. odorata* var. *minor*
– var. *rosea* (H)	EMFW MSta SWyc
– 'Roswitha' (H)	SWyc
– f. *rubra* (H)	MSta
'Odorata Sulphurea' (H)	MSta SWat SWyc WBcn
§ 'Odorata Sulphurea Grandiflora' (H)	CRow EHon EMFW LPBA MSta SWat SWyc WMAq
'Odorata Turicensis' (H)	EMFW LPBA MSta SWyc
'Odorata William B. Shaw'	See *N.* **'W.B. Shaw'**
¶ 'Osceola'	SWyc
'Pam Bennett' (H)	MSta
'Pamela' (T/D)	CBen MSta
¶ 'Patio Joe'	SWyc
'Paul Hariot'	CWat EHon EMFW LPBA MSta SWat SWyc WBcn WMAq
'Peach Blossom'	SWyc
'Peaches and Cream'	SWyc
Pearl of the Pool (H)	MSta SWat SWyc
'Pennsylvania' (T/D)	MSta
'Perry's Almost Black'	SWyc
'Perry's Baby Red'	SWyc
'Perry's Black Opal'	SWyc
'Perry's Cactus Pink'	SWyc
'Perry's Crinkled Pink'	SWyc
'Perry's Darkest Red'	SWyc
'Perry's Double White' (d)	SWyc
'Perry's Dwarf Red'	SWyc
'Perry's Fire Opal'	SWyc
'Perry's Magnificent'	SWyc
'Perry's Pink'	MSta SWat SWyc WMAq
'Perry's Pink Beauty'	SWyc
'Perry's Pink Bicolor'	SWyc
'Perry's Pink Delight'	SWyc
'Perry's Pink Heaven'	SWyc
'Perry's Red Beauty'	SWyc
'Perry's Red Bicolor'	SWyc
'Perry's Red Blaze'	SWyc
'Perry's Red Glow'	SWyc
'Perry's Red Star'	SWyc

'Perry's Red Wonder'   SWyc
'Perry's Rich Rose'   SWyc
'Perry's Stellar Red'   SWyc
'Perry's Strawberry Pink'   SWyc
'Perry's Super Red'   SWyc
'Perry's Super Rose'   SWyc
'Perry's Vivid Rose'   SWyc
'Perry's Viviparous Pink'   SWyc
'Perry's White Star'   SWyc
'Perry's White Wonder'   SWyc
'Perry's Wildfire'   SWyc
'Peter Slocum'   MSta SWat SWyc
'Philippe Laydeker'   MSta
'Phoebus' (H)   MSta SWat SWyc WBcn
'Phoenix' (H)   MSta
'Picciola' (H)   MSta SWyc
'Pink Beauty'   SWyc
'Pink Cameo'   SWyc
'Pink Glory' (H)   SWyc
¶ 'Pink Grapefruit'   SWyc
'Pink Opal' (H)   CBen CWat EMFW LPBA
    MSta SWyc
'Pink Peony'   SWyc
'Pink Platter' (T/D)   CBen
'Pink Pumpkin'   SWyc
'Pink Sensation' (H)   CBen CWat EMFW MSta SWat
    SWyc WMAq
'Pink Shadow'   SWyc
¶ 'Pink Sparkle'   SWyc
'Pink Starlet'   SWyc
'Pink Sunrise'   MSta SWyc
'Pöstlingberg' (H)   MSta SWyc WMAq
'Président Viger'   MSta
¶ 'Pride of Palm Beach'   SWyc
'Princess Elizabeth' (H)   EMFW LPBA MSta SWyc
'Pygmaea Alba'   See *N. tetragona*
§ 'Pygmaea Helvola' (H) ♀   CBen CRow EHon EMFW
    LPBA MSta SWat SWyc
    WMAq WWeb
'Pygmaea Rubis' (H)   CRow EHon LPBA MSta SWat
    SWyc WMAq
'Pygmaea Rubra' (H)   CBen CWat EMFW MSta SWyc
    WMAq
'Radiant Red' (T/D)   SWyc
'Ray Davies'   MSta SWyc
'Red Beauty'   MSta
'Red Cup' (T)   MSta
'Red Flare' (T/N)   MSta
'Red Sensation'   SWyc
'Red Spider'   SWyc
¶ 'Reflected Flame'   SWyc
'Regann'   SWyc
'Rembrandt' hort.   See *N.* '**Météor**'
'Rembrandt' Koster (H)   SWyc
'René Gérard' (H)   CBen CWat EHon EMFW
    LPBA MSta SWat SWyc WBcn
    WMAq
'Robinsoniana' (H)   EMFW MSta SWyc
'Rosa Mundi'   SWyc
'Rosanna'   SWyc
'Rosanna Supreme' (H)   MSta SWat SWyc
'Rose Arey' (H)   CBen CRow EHon EMFW
    LPBA MSta SWat SWyc WBcn
    WMAq
'Rose Magnolia' (H)   EMFW MSta SWat SWyc
§ 'Rosea' (H)   CBen EMFW LPBA MSta
    SWyc
¶ 'Rosea Minima'   SWyc
'Rosennymphe' (H)   CBen LPBA MSta SWat SWyc
    WMAq
'Rosita' (H)   MSta
'Rosy Morn' (H)   EMFW MSta SWyc

'Saint Louis' (T/D)   MSta
'Saint Louis Gold' (T/D)   MSta
'Sanguinea' (H)   EMFW MSta SWyc
'Seignouretti' (H)   EMFW MSta SWyc WBcn
'Senegal' (H)   MSta SWyc
'Sioux' (H)   CBen CWat EHon EMFW
    LPBA MSta SAWi SWat SWyc
    WMAq
'Sir Galahad' (T/N)   MSta
'Sirius' (H)   CWat EMFW MSta SWat SWyc
'Solfatare' (H)   EMFW MSta SWyc
'Somptuosa' (H)   EMFW MSta SWyc
'Souvenir de Jules   MSta SWyc
    Jacquier' (H)
'Speciosa' (H)   MSta
'Spectabilis'   MSta
'Splendida' (H)   MSta SWyc WMAq
'Stardust'   SWyc
'Steven Strawn'   SWyc
'Sturtevantii' (T/N)   MSta
'Suavissima' (H)   MSta
'Sultan' (H)   EMFW MSta SWyc
'Sunburst'   SWyc
¶ 'Sunny Pink'   SWyc
'Sunrise'   See *N.* '**Odorata Sulphurea
    Grandiflora**'
'Superba' (H)   MSta
'Sylphida' (H)   MSta
'Temple Fire' (H)   MSta
§ *tetragona* (H)   CBen CRow EHon EMFW
    LPBA MSta SWyc
– 'Alba'   See *N. tetragona*
– 'Johann Pring' (H)   EMFW
§ – var. *rubra* (H)   MSta
'Texas Dawn'   EMFW MSta SWyc
¶ 'Thomas O'Brian'   SWyc
tuberosa (H)   CBen LPBA MSta SWyc
♦ 'Tuberosa Flavescens'   See *N.* '**Marliacea Chromatella**'
tuberosa 'Maxima' (H)   MSta
– 'Richardsonii' (H)   EHon EMFW MSta SWyc
    WWeb
– 'Rosea'   See *N.* '**Rosea**'
'Tulipiformis' (H)   MSta
'Venus'   SWyc
'Venusta' (H)   MSta SWyc
'Vera Louise' (H)   MSta SWyc
'Vésuve' (H)   CWat EMFW MSta SWat SWyc
'Victoria Longwood' (T)   MSta
'Virginalis' (H)   EMFW MSta SWat SWyc
'Virginia' (H)   EMFW MSta SWyc
§ 'W.B. Shaw' (H)   CBen EHon EMFW LPBA
    MSta SWat SWyc WMAq
'Walter Pagels'   MSta SWyc
'White Cup'   SWyc
'White Sultan'   SWyc
'William Doogue' (H)   EMFW MSta SWyc WBcn
    WMAq
'William Falconer' (H)   CBen CWat EMFW LPBA
    MSta SWat SWyc
'Wood's White Knight'   MSta
    (T/N)
'Wow'   SWyc
'Wucai'   SWyc
'Yellow Dazzler' (T/D)   MSta
'Yellow Princess'   SWyc
'Yellow Queen'   SWyc
'Yellow Sensation'   SWyc
'Yogi-gi'   SWyc
'Yul Ling'   EMFW SWat SWyc
'Ziyu'   SWyc

NYMPHOIDES (Menyanthaceae)

peltata	CRDP CWat ECoo EMFW
	MHew NDea SWat SWyc WChe
§ – 'Bennettii'	CBen EHon IBlr LPBA MSta

NYSSA (Nyssaceae)

aquatica	CFil CMCN SSpi SSta WPGP
sinensis ♀	CAbP CB&S CDoC CEnd
	CGre CMCN CPMA CSam
	CTho ELan MBri SReu SSpi
	SSta WCwm WPGP WPat
	WWat
sylvatica ♀	CB&S CLnd CMCN CPMA
	CPle CTho ELan EMil GChr
	LPan MBal MBar MBri MMea
	SHBN SPer SReu SSpi SSta
	WBod WDin WFro WNor
	WWat
– 'Sheffield Park'	LRHS
– 'Windsor'	LRHS SSpi
– 'Wisley Bonfire'	LRHS SSpi

OAKESIELLA See UVULARIA

OCHAGAVIA (Bromeliaceae)

rosea	CFil CHEx

OCHNA (Ochnaceae)

serrulata	CSpe

OCIMUM (Lamiaceae)

'African Blue'	EOHP GPoy
§ americanum	WHer WPer
– 'Meng Luk'	See O. americanum
basilicum	CArn CSev EEls GPoy LHol
	MBri MChe SIde SWat WGwG
	WHer WPer WSel WWye
– 'Anise'	See O. basilicum 'Horapha'
* – 'Cinnamon'	CSev MChe MGra MSal SHDw
	SWat WGwG WHer WJek
	WPer WSel
– 'Dark Opal'	CBod MGra SHDw SWat WJek
	WSel
– 'Genovese'	ELau EOHP
– 'Glycyrrhiza'	See O. basilicum 'Horapha'
– 'Green Globe'	MChe
– 'Green Ruffles'	MChe MGra SWat WJek WSel
– 'Holy'	See O. tenuiflorum
§ – 'Horapha'	CArn CSev GPoy MChe MLan
	MSal SIde WJek WPer
* – 'Horapha Nanum'	WJek
– 'Napolitano'	CBod MChe MGra SIde SWat
	WJek WPer
– 'Purple Ruffles'	EOHP MChe MGra MMal SIde
	SWat WJek WPer WSel
– var. purpurascens	CArn CSev GPoy LHol MBri
	MChe SIde WHer WPer
– 'Red Rubin'	MChe
* – 'Rubin'	EOHP
– 'Thai'	See O. basilicum 'Horapha'
canum	See O. americanum
x citriodorum	CArn MChe MSal SHDw SIde
	SWat WGwG WJek WPer WSel
kilimandscharicum x	GPoy
basilicum var.	
purpurascens	
minimum	CArn CBod CJew CSev ELau
	EOHP GPoy LHol MBri MChe
	SIde WHer WJek WPer WSel
	WWye
sanctum	See O. tenuiflorum

'Spice'	MChe WPer
§ tenuiflorum	CArn CSev GPoy MChe MSal
	SHDw SIde SWat WHer WJek
	WPer

ODONTONEMA (Acanthaceae)

strictum	LHil WMul

OEMLERIA (Rosaceae)

§ cerasiformis	CB&S CFil CHan CPle EPla
	SSpi WCot WEas WHCG
	WPGP WSHC WWat WWin

OENANTHE (Apiaceae)

aquatica 'Variegata'	EMFW
crocata	WChe
japonica	See O. javanica
* javanica 'Atropurpurea'	EHoe
– 'Flamingo'	CBen CBre CHid CRow CSpe
	EBar EHal ELan EMar EMon
	EPla EPri LFis LHop MBel
	MCLN MNrw MRav MSCN
	NBro NRoo NWes SLod WBea
	WFar WHer WOve WPer

OENOTHERA † (Onagraceae)

§ acaulis	CBot CHan CSpe GCal GMac
	LHop MNrw SAxl SChu SOkh
– alba	WCot
§ – 'Aurea'	LHop NTow NWCA WCla
	WPer
– 'Lutea' hort.	See O. acaulis 'Aurea'
¶ 'African Sun'	SBod
* alpina	CPle
'Apricot Delight'	MCCP NCut
argillicola	MSto WPer
'Beach'	SUsu
berlandieri	See O. speciosa 'Rosea'
§ biennis	CKin CRow CSev EBrP EBre
	ECha EHoe ELau EWFC GPoy
	LBre LHol MChe MHew NBro
	SBre SIde SIng WHer WJek
	WOak WPer WSel
caespitosa	CPBP EMan MGed MLLN
	MTho SPil WHer
* campylocalyx	LHop
cheiranthifolia	WPer
childsii	See O. speciosa 'Rosea'
cinaeus	See O. fruticosa subsp. glauca
'Colin Porter'	CInt EBur EFou LFis MNrw
	NWCA SOkh
coryi	EBee
deltoides var. howellii	CSpe
§ elata subsp. hookeri	EMan SPil WPer
erythrosepala	See O. glaziouana
flava	CNic MTho
§ fruticosa	EBrP EBre LBre NBro SBre
* – 'Camel' (v)	CBos CVer EMan SUsu WCot
– Fireworks	See O. fruticosa 'Fyrverkeri'
– subsp. fruticosa	CHan
§ – 'Fyrverkeri' ♀	CBlo CDoC CSam EBrP EBre
	ECED ECro EFou ELan ENot
	EPla LBre LHop MAus MCLN
	MRav NVic SBre SOkh SPar
	SPer WEas WHil WHoo WMow
	WPyg WRus WWal WWin
§ – subsp. glauca ♀	CBlo CElw CHan EBrP EBre
	ECGN EPfP LBre MNrw MTho
	NBro SBre SRms WEas WPer

– – 'Erica Robin' (v)	CMGP CMea CMil EBee EFou EGra EMan EMon GBuc LHop MArl SOkh SUsu WCot WSan
– – 'Frühlingsgold' (v)	EMon WCot
– – Solstice	See *O. fruticosa* subsp. *glauca* 'Sonnenwende'
§ – – 'Sonnenwende'	EBee EBrP EBre EMon LBre MLLN NPro SBre SOkh WCot
¶ – – 'Sundrops'	CLTr
¶ – – 'Sunspot'	GBuc
– Highlight	See *O. fruticosa* 'Hoheslicht'
¶ – 'Hoheslicht'	LBuc
– 'Lady Brookborough'	LHop MRav
– 'Michelle Ploeger'	EBee MUlv
– var. *riparia*	ELan SAga SOkh WRus
– 'Silberblatt'	LBuc
– 'Yellow River'	CB&S ECED WWeb
– 'Youngii'	CM&M CMGP EPfP LFis LIck MCCP MLLN SSte WPer
glabra hort.	CLyd NSti SIng SUsu
– Miller	See *O. biennis*
§ *glaziouana*	ECoo IBlr NBir SIde WPer WWye
* 'Hollow Meadows'	MTho
hookeri	See *O. elata* subsp. *hookeri*
kunthiana	CElw CStr EDAr EGoo EMan NLak NWCA WPer
lamarckiana	See *O. glaziouana*
lavandulifolia	EBee MSto
'Lemon Sunset'	EAst ECoo MCCP SWat
linearis	See *O. fruticosa*
'Longest Day'	EPfP MArl NFai WHil
§ *macrocarpa* ♀	CSev EBrP EBre ECha ELan ENot EOld GCHN LBre LHop MAus MBro MCLN MTho MWat NFai NRoo SBre SDix SMad SPer SPil SRCN WBea WFar WHoo WOld WWin
– 'Greencourt Lemon'	NSti
¶ *macrosceles*	CChr ECGN
mexicana	See *O. laciniata*
missouriensis	See *O. macrocarpa*
* *mollis*	EBee
* 'Moonlight'	SAsh
muricata	EBee
¶ *odorata* cream form	WHal
– Hook. & Arn.	See *O. biennis*
– hort.	See *O. glaziouana*
– Jacquin	CArn CSam CSpe GBar GCal IBlr LGan LHil NOrc SSvw
– 'Sulphurea'	See *O. stricta* 'Sulphurea'
organensis	EBee MLLN
pallida	EAst IBlr NFai SWat
– 'Innocence'	CBot CM&M LRHS SPil WHer WPer
– 'Wedding Bells'	NPer
'Penelope Hobhouse'	GBuc SUsu
§ *perennis*	CNic EBrP EBre EMFP EMan LBre LFis MTho NFai NNrd NPri SBre SMac SOkh SRms SWat WCla WEas WHil WPer WWin
pumila	See *O. perennis*
rosea	CHan CMea NPer WOMN WWye
sp. South America	CLyd MTho
speciosa	CBlo CMea CSev EFou MBel SEND SPer SWat WCot WPer WSan
– 'Ballerina'	CSpe EMan LHop
– var. *childsii*	See *O. speciosa* 'Rosea'

– 'Pink Petticoats'	CChr CM&M CSpe EAst EBee ECoo EHal MArl MCCP MWgw NFai NPer SIde SOkh SWat WBea WBro WElm WHil WSan
§ – 'Rosea'	CBot CFir CGle CNic CRDP ECGP ELan LIck MCCP MCLN MCli MNrw WCot WHer WPer WWin
– 'Siskiyou'	CHea CLTr COtt CRDP CSpe EMan GMac LRHS MArl MAvo MTis NLak SAxl SCoo SHar SIng SMrm SUsu WCru WMaN WRus WWeb
§ *stricta*	CHad CHan CKin CSpe ECGP EWFC MAus WPer WWye
§ – 'Sulphurea'	CHad CHan CM&M CMil CSam ECoo ELan EMan GCal IBlr LBlm LGre MBel NPer SAga SAxl SChu SMrm SUsu WAbb WBea WBro WCot WPer
taraxacifolia	See *O. acaulis*
tetragona	See *O. fruticosa* subsp. *glauca*
– var. *fraseri*	See *O. fruticosa* subsp. *glauca*
– 'Sonnenwende'	See *O. fruticosa* subsp. *glauca* 'Sonnenwende'
tetraptera	NWCA
texensis	SWat
– 'Early Rise'	CSev ELan EMan LHop SAga
¶ *versicolor*	CHan
– 'Sunset Boulevard'	CMil CPou CRDP EAst EBee ECoo NBus SMrm WBea WElm WHer WSan WWin
'Woodside White'	LRHS

OLEA (Oleaceae)

europaea ♀	CArn CFil CHan CSWP CTrC EEls EPfP ERea ERom GAri LBlm LCns LHol LPan SAPC SArc STre WMul WNor
¶ – 'Cailletier' (F)	ERea
¶ – 'Chelsea Physic Garden'	WPGP
§ – var. *europaea*	ERea LPan
'Cipressino'	
– – 'El Greco'	CB&S ERea GAri
– – 'Picholine'	ERea
– – 'Pyramidalis'	See *O. europaea* var. *europaea* 'Cipressino'

OLEARIA † (Asteraceae)

albida var. *angulata*	CPle MAll
albida Hooker f.	CB&S
– x *paniculata*	CPle
albida hort.	See *O.* 'Talbot de Malahide'
algida	CPle ECou MAll
arborescens	GSki MAll
argophylla	ECou MAll
avicenniifolia	CPle ECou EPla MAll SDys WGer WLRN WSHC
– 'White Confusion'	MAll WPen WWat
canescens	MAll SBid
capillaris	CChe CPle ECou GGar IDee ISea MAll SDry SIgm WCot WPen WTro WWat
chathamica	ICrw IDee
§ *cheesemanii*	CMHG CPle MAll WSHC
coriacea	MAll
erubescens	CPle MAll
floribunda	CPle MAll
fragrantissima	MAll
frostii	CPle WFar WKif

furfuracea   CB&S CDoC CHEx CPle
glandulosa   CPle ECou MAll
gunniana   See *O. phlogopappa*
x *haastii*   Widely available
– 'McKenzie'   ECou
§ 'Henry Travers' ♀   CDoC CPle GQui IBlr ISea MAll MBal WGwG
¶ *hookeri*   EPot
§ *ilicifolia*   CFil CPle GSki MAll MDun SDry SSpi WCru WSHC
insignis   MAll WCru
– var. *minor*   WCru
lacunosa   ICrw IDee ISea MDun
lepidophylla   ECou
– silver   ECou MAll
lineata 'Dartonii'   ECou MAll
lirata   CPle ECou
macrodonta ♀   Widely available
– 'Intermedia'   MAll
– 'Major'   EPfP SHBN SSoC
– 'Minor'   ELan EPfP GQui WPat WWat
microphylla   CPle
x *mollis* hort.   See *O. ilicifolia*
x *mollis* (Kirk) Ckn.   CB&S CPle GQui MAll NNor SBid SPer SSpi WCru WSHC
– 'Zennorensis' ♀   CDoC CGre CLan CMHG CPle ISea MAll MDun SDry SOWG SSpi WCru
moschata   CPle GSki MAll SBid SSpi WStI
myrsinoides   CMHG CPle MAll
§ *nummulariifolia*   CHEx CMHG COtt CPle CTri ECou EPla MAll MBal NNor SAPC SArc SDry SEND SSto WBod WPic WSHC WWal
– var. *cymbifolia*   ECou MAll
– hybrids   ECou MAll
obcordata   MAll
odorata   CPle ECou MAll WBod WHCG
oleifolia   See *O.* 'Waikariensis'
paniculata   CGre CHEx CMHG CPle CTri GSki ISea MAll SDry WCru
§ *phlogopappa*   CMHG CPle ECou ISea MAll MTis SVen WBrE WCot
– 'Comber's Blue'   CB&S CPle IBlr ISea MLLN SAga SPer SSta
§ – 'Comber's Pink'   CB&S CDoC CPle ELan EMil EPfP IBlr SAga SPan SPer
– pink   MAll SReu SSta
– 'Rosea'   See *O. phlogopappa* 'Comber's Pink'
– Splendens Group   CAbb
– var. *subrepanda*   CGre CPle MAll SEND WBod
§ *ramulosa*   CDoC CInt CPle LHil SBid WCot WGwG WWal WWat
– 'Blue Stars'   ECou
– *ramulosa*   ECou
rani hort.   See *O. cheesemanii*
¶ x *scilloniensis*   CTrG
Dorrien-Smith ♀
– 'Master Michael'   CBlo CBot CDoC CTrw EMil MRav NFai SOWG SPan SPer SPla WSHC
x *scilloniensis* hort.   See *O. stellulata* De Candolle
semidentata   See *O.* 'Henry Travers'
solandri   CHan CMHG COtt CPle CSam CTrC CWSG ECou EMil EPla GBin GOrc ISea MAll NFai SDix SDry SHFr SPer SSto
– 'Aurea'   CB&S GQui

§ *stellulata* De Candolle   CBot CGre CMHG CTrG CTrw CWit EAst ECou ELan ENot ISea MWat SDix SOWG SPer SPla SSta WAbe WBea WEas WHCG WHCr WStI WWeb
– hort.   See *O. phlogopappa*
traversii   CAbb CDoC CMHG CPle CTre EHic IOrc MAll SEND WCru WLRN
§ – 'Tweedledum' (v)   CLyn CPle ECou EHoe
– 'Variegata'   See *O. traversii* 'Tweedledum'
virgata   CMHG COtt CPle ECou ELan GSki ISea
– 'Laxifolia'   CTrC CTre
– var. *lineata*   CPle MAll SEND WCru WDin WPic WSHC
– – 'Dartonii'   SLPl
– var. *ramuliflora*   MAll
viscosa   CPle MAll
§ 'Waikariensis'   CBlo CBot CPle CSam CTrC ECou EHic EPla LHop MAll SChu SEND WBod WCFE WWat

OLIGOSTACHYUM (Poaceae)

♦ *lubricum*   See *Semiarundinaria lubrica*

OLSYNIUM (Iridaceae)

§ *douglasii* ♀   CBro EBur EHyt ELan EPar EPot GCrs GDra NHar NHol NMen NRya NTow SIng WLin
– *album*   EBur EHyt EPot GAbr GDra NHar NHol NRya
– var. *inflatum*   EWes
– JCA 11132   SBla
§ *filifolium*   CLyd EMar MHar MNrw
§ *junceum*   EBee
– JCA 12289   MTho
¶ – JCA 14211   CFir

OMPHALODES (Boraginaceae)

cappadocica ♀   CElw CGle CRow EBrP EBre ECGN ECha ELan EOrc EPar EPot LBre MBro NBrk NBro NFla NNor NPer NRya SBre SDix SMac SSpi WEas WHoo WLin WOMN WPbr WWat
– 'Alba'   LLWP SRms WEas
– 'Anthea Bloom'   IBlr NTow WPbr
– 'Cherry Ingram' ♀   CFil CLyd CRow CSam ECha EHyt GBuc MBel MBri MCLN NBir NCat SAxl SBid SBla SDix SLod SMrm SSpe SSpi SWas WCer WCot WCru WFar WLin WPrP WWhi
– 'Starry Eyes'   Widely available
§ *linifolia* ♀   CLyd CMea CRDP CSpe ECoo MHlr NTow NWes WEas
– *alba*   See *O. linifolia*
¶ *lojkae*   GCLN
luciliae   NTow WHoo
nitida   MAvo WCot
verna   Widely available
– 'Alba'   CBot CBre CGle EAst ECha EFou ELan GAbr GCal LFis LHop MCLN MTho NChi NHol NLar SIng SPer SSvw WBea WHoo WLin WMer WOve WPbr WPrP WRus WWat
¶ – 'Elfenauge'   CMil EMon SWas

OMPHALOGRAMMA (Primulaceae) See Plant Deletions

ONCOBA (Flacourtiaceae) See Plant Deletions

ONIXOTIS (Colchicaceae) See Plant Deletions

ONOBRYCHIS (Papilionaceae)
¶ *gracilis* HH&K 185 — CHan
¶ *montana* HH&K 325 — CHan
viciifolia — CKin ELan ESis EWFC MHew MSal SOkh WCot

ONOCLEA (Aspidiaceae)
sensibilis ♀ — CCuc CFil CGre CHan CRow ECha EFer EGol EHon ELan IOrc LPBA MBri NBir NDea NHar NHed NHol NMar NOrc NVic SChu SCob SPer SRms SWat WEas WFib WRic
– copper — CFil CRow CVer SRms WPGP

ONONIS (Papilionaceae)
cenisia — See *O. cristata*
repens — CArn CInt CKin EWFC MSal NMir WGwy
rotundifolia — CHan CLyd CPle MSal WOMN WPat
spinosa — CKin CLyd EWFC LFis MSal WFar WPer

ONOPORDUM (Asteraceae)
acanthium — CArn CBos CKin CLTr ECGP ECha ECoo ELan EMan EMil GAbr GBar GCra LHol MAus MHar MWat NSti SIde SRCN SSoC WCHb WCot WCru WElm WHer WHil WShe WWye
arabicum — See *O. nervosum*
bracteatum — WPer
§ *nervosum* ♀ — CArn EBee EBot ERav LFis NBro NVic SMad WFar WWhi

ONOSERIS (Asteraceae)
¶ *salicifolia* — IDac

ONOSMA (Boraginaceae)
alborosea — CLyd CMea CSev ECha EGoo ELan EOrc GBri GCal GCra LFlo MFir NChi SBla SChu WEas WKif WOMN WPGP WPer WWye
helvetica — MBro MSto WPat
nana — EPot LFlo MSto
stellulata — CLyd NChi SSpi
taurica ♀ — NBir WWin

ONYCHIUM (Adiantaceae)
contiguum — CFil WAbe
japonicum — CFil CRDP ECha GQui NMar SBla SChu SWas WAbe
– 'Dali' L 1649 — SBla

OPHIOPOGON (Convallariaceae)
'Black Dragon' — See *O. planiscapus* '**Nigrescens**'
bodinieri — EWes SApp SIng SMac
– B&L 12505 — CHid EBee EMon EPPr EPla SAxl
chingii — EMon GCal

¶ *formosanus* B&SWJ 3659 — WCru
¶ 'Fuku-ho-ryu' — EMon
graminifolius — See *Liriope muscari*
intermedius — CHid EPPr EPla MSte WCot WPGP
§ – 'Argenteomarginatus' — ERos EWes LHop WPGP
– *parviflorus* — NSti
– 'Variegatus' — See *O. intermedius* '**Argenteomarginatus**'
§ *jaburan* — CHan CHid CMGP ERos LAma MHFP MSte WWat
– 'Variegatus' — See *O. jaburan* '**Vittatus**'
§ – 'Vittatus' (v) — EBee EHoe EWes LRHS NFla SMad WCot WFar WRus
japonicus — CBro CRow EPPr EPla NSti
– 'Albus' — NHol
– 'Compactus' — CFil CHid SMac SPla WCot WPGP
– 'Kigimafukiduma' — CDec CElw CSte CWSG WCot WGwG
– 'Minor' — CInt EGar EPla WPGP
¶ – 'Nanus Variegatus' — EMon SBla
– 'Nippon' — EPPr
* – Tamaryu Number Two — ECho EHic EHyt ESis EWes NHar
planiscapus — CFee CPea CSWP CSev EPar EPla GCal GOrn LHil MBel MSte MTho NBro NHar NHol NLon NPSI WHil WWal
– *leucanthus* — WCot
– 'Little Tabby' — SBla WCot
* – *minimus* — ERos
§ – 'Nigrescens' ♀ — Widely available
– 'Silver Ribbon' — SWat
¶ 'Rhyuko' — EMon
¶ 'Spring Gold' — EMon
¶ 'Tama-hime-nishiki' — EMon
* *tamaryu* — WThi
wallichianus — WCot WOMN WPGP WWat

OPHRYS (Orchidaceae)
apifera — WHer

OPITHANDRA (Gesneriaceae) See Plant Deletions

OPLISMENUS (Poaceae)
§ *africanus* 'Variegatus' ♀ — CHal
hirtellus — See *O. africanus*

OPUNTIA † (Cactaceae)
humifusa — EOas SMad WCot
§ *lindheimeri* — CHEx EOas SAPC SArc
linguiformis — See *O. lindheimeri*
phaeacantha — CHEx SAPC SArc

ORCHIS (Orchidaceae)
elata — See *Dactylorhiza elata*
foliosa — See *Dactylorhiza foliosa*
fuchsii — See *Dactylorhiza fuchsii*
laxiflora — SWes
maculata — See *Dactylorhiza maculata*
maderensis — See *Dactylorhiza foliosa*
majalis — See *Dactylorhiza majalis*
§ *mascula* — SWes WChe WHer
§ – — WShi
morio — LAma SWes
spectabilis — EFEx

OREOBOLUS (Cyperaceae) See Plant Deletions

OREOPANAX (Araliaceae)
epremesnilianus   CHEx

OREOPTERIS (Thelypteridaceae)
§ *limbosperma*   CCuc CFil NHar SRms

ORIGANUM † (Lamiaceae)
acutidens   WCHb
amanum ♀   CLyd CPBP CRDP ECha EDAr
                  ELan EWes LBee LHop MBro
                  MFos MHig MTho NBir NTow
                  SAga SBla SChu SIng WFar
                  WOMN WWye
– *album*   CPBP CRDP ECho WPat
'Barbara Tingey'   CElw CLon CLyd CRDP CSpe
                  ECha ECou EHyt ELan EPot
                  EWes LBee LHop MBro MHig
                  MTho SBla SChu SUsu WAbe
                  WCru WHil WHoo WPat
                  WWye
I 'Bristol Cross'   CElw CLyd ECha GBri NHex
                  WPat
'Buckland'   CGle CLon CLyd CRDP EPot
                  ESis LBee LGre MSte NWCA
                  SBla SWat WPat WPyg
caespitosum   See *O. vulgare* 'Nanum'
§ *calcaratum*   CLyd ELan LBee MTho SBla
                  SSad WAbe WPat WPyg
♦ *creticum*   See *O. vulgare* subsp. *hirtum*
dictamnus   CMea EEls EHyt ELan EPot
                  GPoy LBee SSad WAbe
                  WOMN WRus WWye
'Dingle Fairy'   EBee EMan EWes MLLN
                  MMHG MNrw NHex WWye
'Erntedank'   EFou
'Frank Tingey'   CElw CPBP ECho EHyt ELan
                  SUsu
'Gold Splash'   GBar
¶ 'Goudgeel'   WCot WLin
heracleoticum hort.   See *O.* × *applei*
– Linnaeus   See *O. vulgare* subsp. *hirtum*
§ × *hybridinum*   CLyd LBee LHop MBro SBla
                  SChu WLin WPat WPyg WWat
                  WWin WWye
¶ 'Ingolstadt'   EBee
'Kent Beauty'   CDec CLTr CLon CMHG
                  CMea CRDP CSpe ECha ELan
                  EPot LGre LLWP MAus MBro
                  MSte NLak SAga SBla SChu
                  SUsu SWas WAbe WHoo
                  WOMN WPat WWye
kopatdaghense   See *O. vulgare* subsp. *gracile*
laevigatum ♀   CArn CElw CGle CLyd CMHG
                  CMea CStr ECGN ELan EPot
                  MBro MHig NBro NHol NMir
                  NPer SAga SBla SMer SUsu
                  WAbe WByw WEas WHoo
                  WLin WPer WWat WWin
                  WWye
– *album*   EOHP
* – *aureum*   WJek
– 'Herrenhausen' ♀   Widely available
– 'Hopleys'   Widely available
– 'Springwood'   WCot WWye
libanoticum   EPot NTow
majorana   CArn CJew CSev ELan ELau
                  GPoy LHol MChe MMal MSal
                  NHex SIde SWat WGwG WJek
                  WMow WOak WPer WSel
                  WWye

microphyllum   CArn CBot CFee CGle CLon
                  CLyd CMHG EDAr EHyt ESis
                  GBar ITim LBee LGre MTho
                  SBla SChu SIng WCru WHoo
                  WPat WPyg WWye
minutiflorum   ECho ELan EPot
'Norton Gold'   CElw CJew CLTr EBee ECha
                  EHal EPot GBar GBuc LHop
                  MBro NHex NPer SIde WCHb
                  WHoo WPyg
'Nymphenburg'   CFee ECha EHic MBro MSte
                  SDys SUsu SWas WCru WLin
onites   CArn EEls ELau GBar GPoy
                  ILis LHol MChe MSal MWat
                  NRoo SBla SIde WGwG WHer
                  WJek WOak WPer WSel WWye
                  SIde
* *prismaticum*
pulchellum   See *O.* × *hybridinum*
'Rosenkuppel'   CGle CLon CRDP EBee ECha
                  ELan EMan EPot GBar GCal
                  MRav MSte NFai NHex NHol
                  SChu SHel SIde SMrm SOkh
                  SPla SSpe SUsu SWas WOve
                  WRus WWye
* 'Rotkugel'   CElw CRDP LGre SAga
rotundifolium ♀   CArn CElw CGle CLyd CRDP
                  CSev ECha ELan ESis LGre
                  LHop NBir NHex SBla SChu
                  SMer SUsu SWas WAbe WMer
                  WOve WRus WSan
scabrum   CArn NHex WWye
– subsp. *pulchrum*   CElw CLyd
sipyleum   EHyt SBla WLin
sp. from Santa Cruz   CArn
sp. from Yunnan,china   NWoo
sp. Mac&W 5882   See *Nepeta phyllochlamys*
tournefortii   See *O. calcaratum*
villosum   See *Thymus villosus*
vulgare   CArn CKin CSev ECoo EWFC
                  GBar GPoy LHol MBar MChe
                  MHew MMal NBro NFai NHex
                  NMir NRoo SIde WByw WHer
                  WOak WPer WWye
¶ – 'Acorn Bank'   CBod SIde WJek
– var. *album*   CElw LGre WHer WJek
– 'Aureum' ♀   CArn CGle CHan CMea CSev
                  ECha EEls EHoe ELan EPot
                  GPoy LGro LHol LHop MBar
                  MBro MFir MHig NFai NRoo
                  NSti SIde SPer SWat WByw
                  WCla WEas WOak WSel WWin
– 'Aureum Album'   EMar MCLN WHer WHil WLin
                  WWhi
– 'Aureum Crispum'   EGoo ELau EOrc ESis GAbr
                  GBar ILis NFai NHex NLak
                  NSti SIde SWat WCer WJek
                  WRha WSel WWye
– 'Compactum'   CArn CJew CLyd CRDP CSev
                  ECha EGoo ELau EOHP GAbr
                  GCal GPoy ILis LHol MHig
                  NHex NLak SAga SBla SIde
                  SWat WCHb WPer WWye
– 'Compactum Album'   MHig
– 'Corinne Tremaine' (v)   WHer
– 'Country Cream' (v)   CArn CBar EAst EBar EGoo
                  EHic EHoe EMan EMar EWes
                  GAbr MCLN MLLN MMil
                  NFai NLak NPri NRoo SChu
                  SHDw SPer SWat
¶ – *formosanum* B&SWJ 3180   WCru

§ – 'Gold Tip' (v) | CLTr CMea CSev CStr EBrP
EBre EHoe EJud ELau EMar
EOrc GAbr ILis LBre NFai
NHex NHol NRoo NSti SBre
SIde SWat WCHb WHer WPat
WWye
– 'Golden Shine' | CBod CM&M EGra EJud EWes
MWat NRoo SIde WRha
§ – subsp. *hirtum* | EOHP GPoy MSal NWoo SIde
WJek WPer
– – 'Greek' | CBod IIve MGra MMal WGwG
– × *majorana* | ELau
§ – 'Nanum' | ESis GBar LHop NCat WCla
WCot WJek
– 'Polyphant' (v) | CBre CElw CFis CHan CInt
CLTr CMil CSev EMan EOHP
ESis LHop MHig MLLN NHex
NPro NWoo WBea WCHb
WCot WJek WOve WSel WWye
¶ – s.s.o.p Israeli | ELau
– 'Thumble's Variety' | CBod CTri EBrP EBre ECGP
ECha ECoo EHic EHoe GBar
LBre MRav NHex NHol SBre
SWat
– 'Variegatum' | See *O. vulgare* **'Gold Tip'**
¶ – 'Webb's White' | SPil
'Webb's White' | SIde

ORIXA (Rutaceae)
japonica | CBot CMCN EPla SSpi WDin
WPGP

ORLAYA (Apiaceae)
grandiflora | CRDP WCot WHal

ORNITHOGALUM (Hyacinthaceae)
arabicum | CBro CGle CMil EBot LAma
LBow MBri NRog WCot
arcuatum | CMon
balansae | See *O. oligophyllum*
caudatum | See *O. longibracteatum*
¶ *chionophilum* | CMon
comosum | CNic
concinnum MS 452 | CMon
dubium | ETub
exscapum | CMon
fimbriatum | EPot
lanceolatum | CAvo EHyt LRHS
§ *longibracteatum* | CGre CHEx ELan LHil SLMG
WHer
magnum | CAvo ETub
montanum BSBE 2360 | CMon LSyl
nanum | See *O. sigmoideum*
narbonense | CBro GBuc WCot
nutans ♀ | CAvo CBro CMea CMon
CRDP EMan EPar EPot ETub
EWFC GBur LAma LBow
MLLN MNrw MTho NMen
NRog WCot WPer WShi
§ *oligophyllum* | CBro EPot MNrw
¶ *orthophyllum* subsp. | EPot
kotchii
ponticum | ERos
pyramidale | CLyd EBot MNrw
pyrenaicum | CArn CAvo ECha ERos WShi
– AB&S 4600 | CMon
– Flavescens Group | CMon
reverchonii | CAvo CMea CMon
saundersiae | LBow
sessiliflorum AB&S 4619 | CMon
sibthorpii | See *O. sigmoideum*
§ *sigmoideum* | EPot

spicatum MS 585 | CMon
tenuifolium | CMon WOMN
thyrsoides | EBot LAma LSyl MBri SRms
umbellatum | CAvo CBro CMea ELan EPar
ETub EWFC GPoy LAma MBri
MNrw NChi NHol NRog WCot
WFar WPer WShi WWye
unifolium MS 435 | CMon

ORONTIUM (Araceae)
aquaticum | CBen CHEx CWat EBrP EBre
EHon EMFW LBre LPBA
MSta NDea SBre SWat WChe
WWeb

OROSTACHYS (Crassulaceae)
§ *aggregata* | NGre
iwarenge | ESis
malacophylla | See *O. aggregata*
§ *spinosa* | MOne NGre NMen NTow

ORPHIUM   (Gentianaceae) See Plant Deletions

ORTHOSIPHON   (Lamiaceae) See Plant Deletions

ORTHROSANTHUS (Iridaceae)
chimboracensis | CFir EBee WAbe WPer WPic
– JCA 13743 | CPou
laxus | CPBP ERos GBuc SMad WWin
multiflorus | CHan NTow
polystachyus | CHan

ORYZOPSIS (Poaceae)
miliacea | CLTr EMon LRHS
¶ *paradoxa* | EBee

OSBECKIA   (Melastomataceae) See Plant Deletions

OSCULARIA (Aizoaceae)
deltoides | See *Lampranthus deltoides*

OSMANTHUS (Oleaceae)
armatus | CFil CTri EPfP NHol WWat
§ × *burkwoodii* ♀ | Widely available
§ *decorus* | CB&S CTri ELan ENot GOrc
MGos MRav NWea SPer SSta
WDin WWat
delavayi ♀ | Widely available
– 'Latifolius' | WWat
forrestii | See *O. yunnanensis*
× *fortunei* | CGre CPle EPfP LRHS
– 'Variegatus' | See *O. heterophyllus* **'Latifolius Variegatus'**
fragrans | SAPC SArc
§ *heterophyllus* | CB&S CGre CLan EMil ENot
ERav GCHN GOrc LPan MBar
NFla NNor SCob SPer SReu
SRms SSpi SSta WBay WDin
WStI WWat
§ – all gold | CBlo EAst MBlu
– 'Argenteomarginatus' | See *O. heterophyllus* **'Variegatus'**
§ – 'Aureomarginatus' | CB&S CDoC CFil CMHG
CPMA CPle EHoe ELan EMil
IOrc ISea LHop MBal MPla
SAga SHBN SPer WStI
– 'Aureus' misapplied | See *O. heterophyllus* all gold
– 'Aureus' Rehder | See *O. heterophyllus* **'Aureomarginatus'**

§ – 'Goshiki' (v)   CAbP CB&S CDoC CEnd EAst
ELan EMil EPla IOrc ISea
LHop MAll MAsh MBal MBar
MBlu MBri MGos MPla MWat
NHed NHol SCob SDry SHBN
SPer SReu SSta WPyg WStI

N – 'Gulftide' ♀   CBlo EHic ELan EMil EPfP
MGos NHol SCob WFar WRHF
WStI WWat

– 'Purple Shaft'   CAbP ELan EPfP LRHS WWat

– 'Purpureus'   CAbP CB&S CBot CMHG CPle
EAst EHoe ELan MAll MBal
MBri MGos MRav NHed SDry
SSpi SSta WStI

– 'Rotundifolius'   CB&S CFil MBri

– Tricolor   See *O. heterophyllus* 'Goshiki'

§ – 'Variegatus' ♀   Widely available

ilicifolius   See *O. heterophyllus*

serrulatus   CBot EPla

¶ *suavis*   WWat

§ *yunnanensis*   CHEx CMHG EPfP MBlu
SAPC SArc WWat

× OSMAREA (Oleaceae)

burkwoodii   See *Osmanthus* × *burkwoodii*

OSMARONIA See OEMLERIA

OSMORHIZA (Apiaceae)

¶ *aristata* B&SWJ 1607   WCru

¶ *longistylis*   GPoy

OSMUNDA † (Osmundaceae)

cinnamomea ♀   CFil CLAP GBin GCal NHar
NMar WFib WPGP WRic

claytoniana ♀   CFil LSyl NMar WRic

regalis ♀   Widely available

– 'Crispa'   NMar

– 'Cristata' ♀   CFil CRDP ELan EMon LPBA
MBri NHol SAxl WFib WPGP
WRic

– 'Purpurascens'   CCuc CFil CLAP CRDP CRow
CVer EBrP EBre ELan EMan
EMon GBuc GQui IOrc LBre
MBri MWgw NHar NHol NOrc
SAxl SBid SBre SSpi SWat
WCru WFib WRic WWat

§ – 'Undulata'   ELan EMon GBin NHol SAxl
WFib WHol WWoo

– Undulata Group   See *O. regalis* Cristata Group

¶ *schroderi* 'Contorta'   WRic

OSTEOMELES (Rosaceae)

schweriniae B&L 12360   SAga

subrotunda   CPle

OSTEOSPERMUM † (Asteraceae)

'African Queen'   See *O.* 'Nairobi Purple'

'Anglia Yellow'   MBEx

barberae hort.   See *O. jucundum*

'Blackthorn Seedling'   See *O. jucundum* 'Blackthorn
Seedling'

'Bloemhoff Belle'   See *O.* 'Nairobi Purple'

'Blue Streak'   CB&S CCan CMHG EBar
EBee ECtt ELan ERav MBEx
SMrm

'Bodegas Pink' (v)   ELan MBEx

'Brickell's Hybrid'   See *O.* 'Chris Brickell'

'Buttermilk' ♀   CB&S CBar CCan CGle CHEx
CLTr CSpe CTbh CTrw EBrP
EBre ELan EOrc GCal GMac
LBre LHop MBEx MBri MLan
NFai NHaw SBre SLod SSoC
SUsu WEas WOMN WPer
WRus

'Cannington John'   CCan CMHG EBee LBlm
LHop MArl

'Cannington Joyce'   CCan

'Cannington Katrina'   CCan MBEx

¶ 'Cannington Kira'   CCan

'Cannington Roy'   CBar CCan CGle CLTr CMHG
CSam CTrw EBar EBrP EBre
ECtt ELan LBre LFis LHop
LLWP MBri NFai NHaw NPer
SBre SMrm SRms WAbe WHer

¶ 'Cannington Vernon'   CCan

'Catriona'   GAbr

caulescens hort.   See *O.* 'Prostratum'

§ 'Chris Brickell'   CCan CLTr CMHG CSev EBar
GCal MBEx MSte NHaw WHen
WPer

'Coconut Ice'   See *O.* 'Croftway Coconut-ice'

'Dennis Weston'   ECtt

'Durban'   LHil WRus

ecklonis   CGle CHEx CMHG CTbh EPla
GMaP ISea MCLN MTho NBro
NFla SCro SMrm WFar WPer
WWin

– var. *prostratum*   See *O.* 'Prostratum'

§ – 'Starshine'   EBar

'Edna Bond'   WEas

'Giant'   CCan CSpe

'Giles Gilbey' (v)   CLTr CTbh EBar EBee LHil
LHop NHaw NPri SVen WEas
WLRN WWeb

'Glistener'   CB&S

'Gold Sparkler' (v)   LHop NHaw SAga SMrm

'Gweek Variegated' (v)   CLTr EBar MBEx NPer WWin

'Hopleys' ♀   EBar LHop

'James Elliman'   CCan EBee ECtt LHop LLWP
MBEx MSte NHaw SAga SRms
COtt

'Jewel'   EOtt

§ *jucundum* ♀   CCan CChr CMHG CMea
ECha ENot MBEx MCLN
MNrw MRav MTis MWat NBrk
NChi NFai NHol NPer SDix
SIng SRms WHen WPat

– 'Ballyrogan Pink'   IBlr

§ – 'Blackthorn Seedling' ♀   CSWP ECha GMac MBri NPla
SAga SBla

– var. *compactum*   CB&S CLyd CMea CPBP ECha
ELan LBlm LHop MHig MSte
NMGW WAbe WHen WLin

¶ – 'Elliott's Form'   WLin

§ – 'Killerton Pink'   CCan CMHG WPer

§ – 'Langtrees' ♀   CCan ECtt EOrc GAbr LHop
NPla SMrm

§ – 'Merriments Joy' ♀   SMrm

'Killerton Pink'   See *O. jucundum* 'Killerton
Pink'

¶ 'Kirsty Louise'   CCan

¶ 'La Mortola'   CCan CHad CLTr MAll MBEx

§ 'Lady Leitrim' ♀   CHEx CHea CLTr CTbh EBar
ECha EOld EOrc GBri LHop
MArl MCLN MMal NBrk NBus
SAxl SChu SSvw SUsu WAbe
WRus

'Langtrees'   See *O. jucundum* 'Langtrees'

'Merriments Joy'   See *O. jucundum* 'Merriments
Joy'

'Molly's Choice'	SMrm
§ 'Nairobi Purple'	CCan CFee CHEx EBar EBee
	EBrP EBre ELan GBuc GMac
	LBre MBEx MLan SBre WLRN
	WOMN WPer
¶ 'Painted Lady'	SCro
'Pale Face'	See O. **'Lady Leitrim'**
'Peggyi'	See O. **'Nairobi Purple'**
'Penny Pink'	CCan ECtt NFai WHer
'Pink Whirls' ♀	CB&S CBot CCan CHEx
	CMHG CTrw ELan ERav
	GMac LHop MBEx MBri NFai
	NHaw SRms SSoC SUsu
	WOMN WPer WRus
'Port Wine'	See O. **'Nairobi Purple'**
I 'Prostratum'	See O. **'White Pim'**
'Royal Purple'	WCot
'Seaspray'	COtt
'Silver Sparkler' (v) ♀	CBar CCan CMHG CSpe CTbh
	EBar EBrP EBre ELan ERav
	IHos LBre LHop MBEx MLan
	NFai NHaw SAxl SBre SChu
	WEas
'Silver Spoons'	See O. **'Croftway Silverspoons'**
'Snow White'	SMrm
¶ 'Soler'	EBar
* 'Sophie'	CSpe
'Sparkler'	CHEx EBrP EBre LBre LHil
	MSte SBre SVen
'Stardust' ♀	COtt NPer SCoo WWeb
'Starshine'	See O. **ecklonis 'Starshine'**
¶ 'Sunny Alex'	LHil LIck
'Sunny Boy'	EBar EBee LIck
¶ 'Sunny Caroline'	LIck
'Sunny Girl'	EBee ECtt LIck SSte
'Sunny Gustav'	LIck
¶ 'Sunny Ingrid'	LIck
'Sunny Lady'	CTbh LHil LIck MLLN
¶ 'Sunny Martha'	LIck
* 'Superbum'	CHEx
'Tauranga'	See O. **'Whirligig'**
'Tiberias'	EBar
'Tresco Peggy'	See O. **'Nairobi Purple'**
'Tresco Pink'	IBlr
'Tresco Purple'	See O. **'Nairobi Purple'**
'Tresco Sally'	SMrm
'Weetwood' ♀	EBar ECtt EOld GAbr GCal
	GMaP LHop MBEx MBri
	MHar MHig MSte NBrk SAga
	SMrm SWas WAbe
'Whirlygig' ♀	CB&S CCan CMHG CTrw
	EBrP EBre ELan ERav LBre
	LHop MBEx MBri MLan NHaw
	SBre SRms SUsu WEas WOMN
	WPer WRus
'White Pim' ♀	CHan CLTr CLyd ELan IBlr
	MBEx NPer SAxl SChu SCro
	SDix SLMG SMad SPla SUsu
	SWas
'Wine Purple'	See O. **'Nairobi Purple'**
Wisley hybrids	WEas WElm WRus
'Zambesi'	CSpe
'Zimbar'	ELan
'Zulu'	CSpe EBar EBee MLan SSoC

OSTROWSKIA (Campanulaceae) See Plant
Deletions

OSTRYA (Corylaceae)

carpinifolia	CB&S CDoC CLnd CMCN
	GChr IOrc MBar MBlu WMou
	WNor

¶ *japonica*	CMCN
virginiana	CDoC CMCN WFro WNor

OTACANTHUS (Scrophulariaceae)

caeruleus	CSpe

OTANTHUS   (Asteraceae) See Plant Deletions

OTHONNA (Asteraceae)

capensis	CHal
§ *cheirifolia*	CBot CHan CPle CSam CSev
	EBar ECha ELan MAll MHar
	NBir NNor NTow SDry SIgm
	SMac SPer SRms WEas WPer

OTHONNOPSIS See OTHONNA

OURISIA † (Scrophulariaceae)

caespitosa	ELan GCrs GGar NMen
	NWCA
– var. *gracilis*	GGar GTou IBlr NGre
§ *coccinea*	CGle GBuc GCra GDra GGar
	NBir NTow SMac SRms SSpi
	WAbe WGle WWat
crosbyi	IBlr
elegans	See O. **coccinea**
fragrans	NGre
'Loch Ewe'	GAbr GCal GDra GGar IBlr
	MDun NHar NHol NRoo
	WAbe WCru WOMN WPGP
macrophylla	GAbr GAri GBuc GDra GGar
	IBlr NGre NHar NHol NRoo
	WAbe WCru
¶ *microphylla*	EHyt GCrs
* – *alba*	CGra EHyt
polyantha F & W 8487	CPBP WAbe
'Snowflake' ♀	CFir EMan EPot GAbr GCrs
	GDra GGar IBlr MDun MOne
	NBir NHar NMen NWCA SBla
	WAbe WGle WLin WWin

OXALIS † (Oxalidaceae)

acetosella	CKin EWFC IIve LWak MSal
	NGre NMir WBon WGwy
	WHer WShi
– deep pink	WCot
adenophylla ♀	CBro CElw CMea ELan EPot
	ESis ETub GAbr GDra LAma
	LHop MBal MBar MHig NEgg
	NGre NHar NMen NNrd NRog
	SIng SRms WAbe WEas WHil
	WPat WPer
– dark form	GDra MHig MTho
§ *articulata*	EMan MTho NPer WCot WWin
– 'Aureoreticulata'	MTho
'Beatrice Anderson'	CPBP EHyt GCrs GDra MBro
	MDHE MTho NHar NHol
	NNrd SBla WAbe
bowiei	EPot NGre WOMN
'Bowles' White'	MTho
brasiliensis	EPot GCrs MTho NNrd
chrysantha	EHyt WAbe
compacta F&W 8011	CPBP
corniculata var.	MTho
atropurpurea	
corymbosa	WCot
'Aureoreticulata'	
deppei	See O. **tetraphylla**
§ *depressa*	CNic EPot EWes MTho NBir
	NGre NHol NMen NNrd NRya
	NSla SRms WFar WOMN

§ *drummondii* — GCal SMrm
enneaphylla ♀ — ECou EPot GCrs MTho NMen NRya SIng
  – × *adenophylla* — See *O.* **'Matthew Forrest'**
  – 'Alba' — CGra EHyt EPot MBro MDHE MFos MHig NHol NNrd NTow WAbe WIvy
I – 'Hythe Seedling' — EHyt
  – 'Minutifolia' — EHyt EPot GCrs MBro MHig MTho NGre NHol NMen NRya SSmi WAbe WIvy
* – 'Minutifolia Alba' — MTPN
* – 'Minutifolia Rosea' — CGra
* – 'Patagonia' — EPot
  – 'Rosea' — CBro EPot GDra MBal MTho NGre NHar NHol NMGW NRya SBla
  – 'Rubra' — GDra NHar NHol WAbe
¶ – 'Ruth Tweedie' — EHyt
  – 'Sheffield Swan' — EHyt
flava — LAma NNrd
floribunda — See *O. articulata*
¶ *geminata* — NBir
glabra — CMon
¶ 'Gwen McBride' — GCrs
hedysaroides — GCra
'Hemswell Knight' — CPBP EHyt NMen
hirta — CBro CMon LBow LHil MTho NGre NNrd
  – 'Gothenburg' — ERos LBow MHig MTho
¶ *imbricata* — EPot
inops — See *O. depressa*
'Ione Hecker' ♀ — CAvo CBro CLyd CSpe EHyt EPot ERos GMaP GTou LBee LHop MHig MRPP MTho NHar NHol NMen NNrd NRya NSla NTow NWoo SMrm WAbe WIvy
§ *laciniata* — EHyt EPot MFos MTho NHar NHol NMen NSla SBla
  – dark form — EHyt
  – × *enneaphylla* — NGre
  – hybrid seedlings — NHar
lactea double form — See *O. magellanica* **'Nelson'**
lobata — CBro EHyt EPot ERos EWes LBow LHop MTho NTow SWas WOMN
magellanica — CFee CHal CHid CMHG CSam CSpe CVer ESis GCHN LBee MTho NHol SIng WCru WPer
  – 'Flore Pleno' — See *O. magellanica* **'Nelson'**
§ – 'Nelson' (d) — CElw CFee CHal CHan CHid CLyd CRDP CRow CSpe CVer EPot ESis EWes GCHN GCal LBee MTho NBir NBro NHar NHol NPer NRya NWoo WCru WLin WPer
  – 'Old Man Range' — ECou
§ 'Matthew Forrest' — NNrd WAbe
melanosticta — LBow
obtusa — CLyd CMon ECha EPot ESis MTho NCat NTow SSad SWas WFar WOMN
oregana — CAvo CNic CPBP CRDP CRow ECha GBuc NChi WCru WPbr
  – f. *smalliana* — WCru
palmifrons — CMon MTho
patagonica — GCrs MHig NHar NHol
§ *purpurea* — LHop NGre NHol WAbe

  – 'Ken Aslet' — CBro CFee CLyd CMon CNic EDAr EHyt EPot MFos MTho NGre NHol NNrd NTow WAbe WOMN
regnellii — See *O. triangularis* subsp. *papilionacea*
rosea hort. — See *O. rubra*
  – Jacquin — See *O. articulata*
§ *rubra* — WCot
speciosa — See *O. purpurea*
squamata — CPBP
squamosoradicosa — See *O. laciniata*
stipularis — CMea CMon
succulenta Barnèoud — CFee LHil
¶ 'Superstar' — WAbe
§ *tetraphylla* — CM&M CSam EBot EPot LAma MBri MTho NCat NOrc NPer NRog SLMG SSoC WByw
  – 'Iron Cross' — CAvo CMea EBee EMan LAma MAvo NBir NHol SAga SAxl SBid SUsu WBro WHal
triangularis — CMea EMan ETub GBur LAma NBir NHol NPer NTay SBid SPar WPyg
  – 'Cupido' — CB&S CRDP EBee WPer WWin
§ – subsp. *papilionacea* — CMon LAma LHop MMHG NRog WHal WWin
  – – 'Atropurpurea' — WCot
  – subsp. *papilionacea rosea* — CMon
  – subsp. *triangularis* — MDun
tuberosa — GPoy WHer
¶ *valdiviensis* — NTow WElm
versicolor — EHyt EPot EWes MTho SBla SIng SSad WAbe WCot
vespertilionis Torrey & A Gray — See *O. drummondii*
  – Zuccarini — See *O. latifolia*
vulcanicola — CFee SBid SDix WLRN

OXERA (Verbenaceae)
pulchella — CPlN

OXYCOCCUS See VACCINIUM

OXYDENDRUM (Ericaceae)
arboreum — CAbP CAgr CB&S EHic EMil EPfP MBal MBri MGos SBrw SSpi SSta WCru WDin WNor WWat
  – 'Chameleon' — EPfP LRHS MAsh SPer SSpi SSta

OXYLOBIUM (Papilionaceae) See Plant Deletions

OXYPETALUM (Asclepiadaceae)
caeruleum — See *Tweedia caerulea*

OXYRIA (Polygonaceae)
digyna — CAgr GCHN GGar NBro WGwy WHer

OXYTROPIS (Papilionaceae)
¶ *campestris* — CGra
oreophila JCA 13585 — CPBP
  – var. *jonesii* NNS 93-517 — MFos
podocarpa — NWCA
¶ *shokanbetsuensis* — EPot

OZOTHAMNUS (Asteraceae)
antennaria	MAll WSHC
§ *coralloides* ♀	EPot MHig NWCA SIng
§ 'County Park Silver'	CMHG CSam ECou EHyt EPot
	ESis EWes MSto NHar NSla
	NTow NWCA SBla SSmi WAbe
	WPat
§ *hookeri*	CAbb CDoC ECou NWCA
	SChu SPan SPer WPat
§ *ledifolius* ♀	CMHG CPle CSam ECha ELan
	EMil GTou LHop MAll MBri
	MPla NNor SChu SIgm SPer
	SSpi WHCG WHar WPat
	WSHC WWat
lycopodioides	ECou
§ *microphyllus*	ITim
'Rose Dazzler'	MAll
§ *rosmarinifolius*	CB&S CDoC CMHG CPle
	CTrG CWit ELan EPla ERea
	IOrc MAll MBlu MNrw NLon
	NNor SChu SPer WAbe WBod
	WBrE WHCG WSHC WWat
– 'Purpureus'	CMHG
– 'Silver Jubilee' ♀	CB&S CBlo CDoC CEnd CHEx
	CHan CMHG CSam CTrC
	ELan GOrc LHop MAll MAsh
	NNor NSti SAga SHBN SPer
	SSpi WHCG WSHC WTro
scutellifolius	ECou
¶ *secundiflorus*	CPle
§ *selago*	ESis EWes ITim MAll MHig
	SBla
– 'Minor'	EWes GCrs NWCA
'Sussex Silver'	CFis CPle MAll SBid SVen
	WPyg WTro
'Threave Seedling'	SMrm SPer
§ *thyrsoideus*	CB&S CPle MAll WWat

PACHYLAENA (Asteraceae) See Plant Deletions

PACHYPHRAGMA (Brassicaceae)
§ *macrophyllum*	CSev ECha ELan EMon IBlr
	MRav NChi NPla NSti SSpi
	WCru WEas WWin

PACHYPODIUM (Apocynaceae)
lamerei	MBri

PACHYSANDRA (Buxaceae)
procumbens	EPla WCot WCru WThi
stylosa	EPla MRav SMad
terminalis ♀	Widely available
– 'Green Carpet'	CBlo CDoC EBrP EBre ECot
	EFou EGol ENot EPfP EPla
	GAri LBre MAsh MBar MBri
	MGos MUlv NPro SBre SCoo
	SPla WRHF WRus WWat
– 'Variegata' ♀	Widely available

PACHYSTACHYS (Acanthaceae)
lutea ♀	CHal ERea MBri

PACHYSTEGIA See OLEARIA

PACHYSTEMA See PAXISTIMA

PACKERA (Asteraceae)
§ *aurea*	MRav MSal WCot
¶ *fendleri* RMRP 96515	IDac

PAEDERIA (Rubiaceae)
scandens	CPlN WCru WSHC
– var. *velutina*	WCru

PAEDEROTA (Scrophulariaceae)
§ *bonarota*	CLyd
lutea	WLin

PAEONIA † (Paeoniaceae)
albiflora	See *P. lactiflora*
¶ 'America'	MAus
'Angel Cobb Freeborn'	MAus
anomala	CFil EPot WPGP
arietina	See *P. mascula* subsp. *arietina*
'Avant Garde'	WKif
¶ 'B.G. Fahr'	MBri
'Ballerina'	CKel
banatica	See *P. officinalis* subsp.
	banatica
beresovskii	CFil
broteroi	CLAP CMon LGre SBla WPGP
brownii	MFos
'Buckeye Belle'	EBee MAus MBri WGle
californica	CLAP MFos
cambessedesii ♀	CBrd CBro CFil CKel CLAP
	CLyd CMon EPot LGre MTho
	NBir SBla SIgm SSpi WAbe
	WOMN WPGP
* 'Carl G.Klehm'	WGle
'Carol'	MAus
caucasica	See *P. mascula* subsp. *mascula*
chamaeleon	WPGP
¶ 'Chinese Dragon'	CKel
'Claire de Lune'	MAus WGle
¶ 'Claudia'	MAus
clusii	CBro CMon
'Coral Fay'	MAus WGle
corallina	See *P. mascula* subsp. *mascula*
coriacea var. *maroccana*	SSpi
¶ 'Cytherea'	MAus
daurica	See *P. mascula* subsp. *triternata*
'Daystar'	CKel
decora	See *P. peregrina*
'Defender' ♀	MAus
delavayi ♀	Widely available
– dark red	GGGa
¶ – x *delavayi* var. *lutea*	SPla
¶ – hybrid	ENot
§ – var. *ludlowii* (S) ♀	CB&S CBlo CGle CGre CKel
	CSam ELan GGGa ISea MBal
	NBrk NPer NRoo SBla SMad
	SPer SSpi WEas WHoo WSHC
	WWat WWoo
§ – var. *lutea* (S)	CBlo CKel ELan MAsh MBro
	SHBN SRms STre WEas WHar
	WPyg WWat
– 'Mrs Sarson'	CBlo SLPl SWat
¶ 'Early Bird'	EBee
'Eastgrove Ruby Lace'	WEas
¶ 'Ellen Cowley'	MAus
emodi	CKel MAvo
¶ Feng-dan-bai	MPhe
¶ 'Flame'	WCot
¶ Gansu Mudan Group	MPhe
'Heritage'	WGle
'High Noon'	CKel MAus
'Horizon'	WGle
humilis	See *P. officinalis* subsp.
	microcarpa
'Illini Belle'	MAus
'Illini Warrior'	MAus
◆ 'Isani Gidui'	See *P. lactiflora* 'Isami-jishi'

japonica hort. — See *P. lactiflora*

¶ 'Jean E. Bockstoce' — MAus

kevachensis — See *P. mascula* subsp. *mascula*

'Kinkaku' — See *P.* × *lemoinei* **'Souvenir de Maxime Cornu'**

'Kinko' — See *P.* × *lemoinei* **'Alice Harding'**

'Kinshi' — See *P.* × *lemoinei* **'Chromatella'**

'Kintei' — See *P.* × *lemoinei* **'L'Espérance'**

Kohlein's hybrid — CLAP

§ *lactiflora* — ECha SSpi

– 'A.F.W. Hayward' — CKel

– 'Adolphe Rousseau' — CB&S CKel LRHS MBri

* – 'Afterglow' — CKel

– 'Agida' — EBrP EBre GCHN LBre MRav SBre

– 'Albâtre' — CKel

– 'Albert Crousse' — CB&S CKel MAus

– 'Alexander Fleming' — CKel EBrP EBre ECot LBre MAus NBir SBre SMrm

– 'Alice Harding' — MAus WCGr

– 'Anna Pavlova' — CKel

– 'Antwerpen' — CKel

– 'Arabian Prince' — CKel

– 'Argentine' — CB&S CKel

– 'Armance Dessert' — CKel

– 'Artist' — CKel

– 'Asa Gray' — CKel

– 'Auguste Dessert' — CB&S CBlo CKel MAus MPhe

– 'Aureole' — CKel

– 'Avant Garde' — MAus

– 'Ballerina' — CKel

– 'Banner of Purity' — CKel

– 'Baroness Schröder' — ELan

– 'Barrington Belle' — MBri

– 'Barrymore' — CKel

– 'Beacon' — CKel

– 'Beatrice Kelway' — CKel

– 'Beau Geste' — CKel

– 'Beauty Spot' — CKel

– 'Beersheba' — CKel

– 'Belle Center' — MAus

– 'Belle of Somerset' — CKel

– 'Bertha Gorst' — CKel

– 'Bethcar' — CKel

– 'Blaze of Beauty' — CKel

– 'Blaze of Glory' — CKel

– 'Blenheim' — CKel

– 'Blithe Spirit' — CKel

– 'Bloodshot' — CKel

– 'Bloodstone' — CKel

– 'Blush Queen' — CKel ELan MAus MBel

– 'Blush White' — CKel

– 'Border Gem' — EBrP EBre GCHN LBre MRav SBre

– 'Bouchela' — CKel

– 'Boulanger' — CKel

– 'Bower of Roses' — CKel

– 'Bowl of Beauty' ♀ — CB&S CBlo CKel EBrP EBre ELan EMAus MBel MBri MPhe MTis NVic SBre SMad SMrm SPer SSpe SSpi WEas WKif WPyg WViv WWeb

– 'Bowl of Cream' — EBrP EBre LBre MAus MBri SBre WCGr

– 'Boy Kelway' — CKel

– 'Break o' Day' — MAus

– 'Bridal Veil' — CKel

– 'Bridesmaid' — CKel

– 'British Beauty' — CKel

– 'British Empire' — CKel

– 'Bunker Hill' — CB&S CBlo CDoC CKel SMur

– 'Butch' — MAus

¶ – 'Butter Bowl' — MAus

– 'Calypso' — CKel

– 'Candeur' — CKel

– 'Captain Alcock' — CKel

– 'Captivation' — CKel

– 'Carmen' — CKel

– 'Carnival' — CKel

– 'Cascade' — CKel

– 'Catherine Fontijn' — CKel WCGr

– 'Charles' White' — EFou MAus SPer WCGr

– 'Charm' — MAus

– 'Cheddar Cheese' — MAus WGle

– 'Cheddar Gold' — MBri

– 'Cherry Hill' — CKel

– 'Chestine Gowdy' — CKel

– 'Christine Kelway' — CKel

– 'Cincinnati' — WGle

– 'Claire Dubois' — MAus WCGr

– 'Colonel Heneage' — SPer

– 'Cornelia Shaylor' — CKel EBrP EBre ELan LBre MAus SBre

– 'Coronation' — CKel

– 'Countess of Altamont' — CKel

– 'Country Girl' — CKel

– 'Couronne d'Or' — MAus

– 'Crimson Banner' — CKel

– 'Crimson Glory' — CKel MPhe

– 'Crimson Velvet' — CKel

¶ – 'Dandy Dan' — MAus

– 'Dark Lantern' — CKel

– 'Dark Song' — CKel

– 'Dark Vintage' — CKel

– 'David Kelway' — CKel

– 'Dawn Crest' — CKel

– 'Dayspring' — CKel

– 'Daystar' — CKel

– 'Denise' — CKel

– 'Desire' — CKel

– Diana Drinkwater — CKel

– 'Dinner Plate' — MAus MBri WCGr

– 'Display' — CKel

– 'Docteur H. Barnsby' — CKel

– 'Dominion' — CKel

– 'Doreen' — MAus MRav

– 'Dorothy Welsh' — CKel

– 'Dresden' — CKel

– 'Duchess of Bedford' — CKel

– 'Duchess of Somerset' — CKel

– 'Duchesse de Nemours' ♀ — CBlo CKel COtt EBar EBrP EBre EFou ENot EPfP GChr GMaP LBre MAus MBri MMil MTis NBir NBro NLar NVic SBre SPer SSpe WWeb

– 'Duke of Devonshire' — CKel

– 'Edith Cavell' — CKel

– 'Edmund Spencer' — CKel

– 'Edouard Doriat' — CKel

– 'Edulis Superba' — CBlo CKel EBar EBrP EBre ELan ENot LBre MAus MBri SBre SPer WWeb

– 'Ella Christine Kelway' — CKel

– 'Elsa Sass' — MAus WCGr

¶ – 'Emma Klehm' — MAus

– 'Emperor of India' — CKel

– 'Empire State' — EBee

– 'Enchantment' — CKel

– 'English Princess' — CKel

– 'Ethelreda' — CKel

– 'Evening Glow' — CKel

– 'Evening World' — CKel

– 'Fantin-Latour' — CKel

– 'Félix Crousse' ♀	CBlo CKel CTri EBrP EBre ELan EPfP GChr GMaP LBre MAus MBri NRoo SBre SMrm SPer SWat WWeb
– 'Festiva Maxima' ♀	CBlo CKel CTri EBee EBrP EBre ECot ELan EPfP LBre MAus MBri MBro NLar SBre SMrm SPer WHoo WPyg WWal
– 'Flag of War'	CKel
– 'Flamboyant'	CKel
– 'Flamingo'	CKel
– 'France'	CKel
– 'Gainsborough'	CKel
– 'Garden Beauty'	CKel
– 'Gay Ladye'	CKel
– 'Gay Paree'	MAus MBri
– 'Gay Sister'	CKel
– 'Gayborder June'	CKel MAus
– 'Gazelle'	CKel
– 'Général Joffre'	CKel
– 'Général MacMahon'	See *P. lactiflora* 'Augustin d'Hour'
– 'General Wolfe'	CKel
– 'Germaine Bigot'	CKel
– 'Gertrude'	CKel
– 'Gilbert Barthelot'	MAus WCGr
– 'Gleam of Light'	CKel
¶ – 'Gloriana'	MAus
¶ – 'Glory Hallelujah'	MAus
– 'Glory of June'	CKel
– 'Glory of Somerset'	CKel
– 'Gold Mine'	CKel
– 'Golly'	WGle
– 'Grace Loomis'	CKel MAus
– 'Great Lady'	CKel
– 'Great Sport'	CKel
– 'Grover Cleveland'	CKel
– 'Gypsy Girl'	CKel
– 'Heartbeat'	CKel
– 'Heirloom'	CKel MPhe
– 'Helen Hayes'	MAus
– 'Henri Potin'	CKel
– 'Her Grace'	CKel
– 'Her Majesty'	CKel
– 'Herbert Oliver'	CKel
¶ – 'Hit Parade'	MAus
– 'Honey Gold'	MAus WGle
– 'Huge Delight'	CKel
– 'Hyperion'	CKel
– 'Immaculée'	CKel
– 'Indian Pink'	CKel
– 'Ingenieur Doriat'	CKel
– 'Inspecteur Lavergne'	CKel EFou MAus MBel MBri MRav SPer WWeb
– 'Instituteur Doriat'	CKel MPhe
§ – 'Isami-jishi'	MAus
– 'Jacques Doriat'	CKel
– 'James Kelway'	CKel
– 'James Pillow'	MAus
– 'James R. Mann'	CKel
– 'Jan van Leeuwen'	CKel
– 'Jeanne d'Arc'	CKel
– 'Joan Kelway'	CKel
– 'Joseph Plagne'	CKel
– 'Joy of Life'	CKel
– 'June Morning'	CKel
– 'June Rose'	MAus
– 'Kansas'	CKel ELan MAus WCGr
¶ – 'Karen Gray'	MAus
– 'Karl Rosenfield'	CBlo CKel EBrP EBre ECot ENot EPfP LBre MBri MBro MTis NBee NVic SBre SMrm SPer SPla SSpe WHoo WViv
– 'Katherine Havermeyer'	CKel
– 'Kathleen Mavoureen'	CKel
– 'Kelway's Brilliant'	CKel
– 'Kelway's Fairy Queen'	CKel
– 'Kelway's Glorious'	CBlo CKel EBar MAus MBri WCGr
– 'Kelway's Lovely'	CKel
– 'Kelway's Majestic'	CKel
– 'Kelway's Malmaison'	CKel
– 'Kelway's Queen'	CKel
– 'Kelway's Scented Rose'	CKel
– 'Kelway's Supreme'	CKel SWat
– 'Kelway's Unique'	CKel
– 'Kestrel'	CKel
– 'King Arthur'	CKel
– 'King George VI'	CKel
– 'King of England'	CKel
– 'Knight of the Thistle'	CKel
– 'Knighthood'	CKel
– 'Krinkled White'	MAus MRav WCGr WGle
– 'La France'	CKel
¶ – 'La Lorraine'	MAus
– 'Lady Alexandra Duff' ♀	CB&S CBlo CKel COtt EBee EBrP EBre EPfP LBre MAus MBri MRav SBre WCGr
– 'Lady Ley'	CKel
– 'Lady Mayoress'	CKel
– 'Lady Orchid'	MAus
– 'Langport Triumph'	CKel
¶ – 'Largo'	MAus
– 'Laura Dessert' ♀	CKel EBrP EBre LBre LRHS SBre SPer WCGr
– 'L'Eclatante'	CKel MMil WWal
– 'Legion of Honor'	CKel
– 'Lemon Ice'	CKel
– 'Letitia'	CKel
¶ – 'Lillian Wild'	MAus
– 'Lois Kelsey'	MAus
– 'Lora Dexheimer'	MAus
– 'Lord Avebury'	CKel
– 'Lord Cavan'	CKel MAus WGle
– 'Lord Kitchener'	CKel MPhe
– 'Lord Rosebery'	CKel
– 'Lorna Doone'	CKel
– 'Lottie Dawson Rea'	CKel
– 'Lotus Queen'	MAus
– 'Louis Barthelot'	CKel MAus
– 'Louis van Houtte'	CKel MBri
– 'Lyric'	CKel
– 'Madame Calot'	CKel MAus WCGr
– 'Madame Claude Tain'	LRHS MHlr WCot
– 'Madame Ducel'	CKel MAus
– 'Madame Emile Debatène'	CKel EBar
– 'Madame Jules Dessert'	CKel
– 'Madelon'	CKel
– 'Magic Melody'	CKel
– 'Magic Orb'	CKel
– 'Major Loder'	CKel
– 'Margaret Truman'	CKel
– 'Marguérite Gerard'	CKel
¶ – 'Marie Crousse'	MAus
– 'Marie Lemoine'	CKel MAus SMur
¶ – 'Marietta Sisson'	MAus
– 'Marquisite'	CKel
– 'Mary Brand'	CKel
¶ – 'Matilda Lewis'	MAus
– 'Meteor Flight'	CKel

¶ – 'Mikado'	NLar
¶ – 'Minnie Shaylor'	MAus
– 'Mischief'	MAus
– 'Miss America'	MAus
– 'Miss Eckhart'	CKel MAus WCGr
– 'Mister Ed'	MAus
– 'Monsieur Jules Elie' ♀	CBot CKel EBrP EBre EFou EPfP LBre MAus MBri MMil MPhe SBre SPer SPla WCGr
– 'Monsieur Martin Cahuzac'	MAus
– 'Mother's Choice'	MAus WGle
– 'Mr G.F. Hemerik'	CKel LRHS MAus
¶ – 'Mrs Edward Harding'	WCGr
– 'Mrs F.J. Hemerik'	MAus
– 'Mrs Franklin D. Roosevelt'	ELan MAus
– 'Mrs J.V. Edlund'	MAus
– 'My Pal Rudy'	MAus
– 'Myrtle Gentry'	CKel
– 'Nancy Nicholls'	MAus
– 'Nectar'	CKel
– 'Newfoundland'	CKel
– 'Nice Gal'	MAus
– 'Nick Shaylor'	MAus WGle
– 'Nobility'	CKel
– 'Noonday'	CKel
– 'Ornament'	CKel
– 'Orpen'	CKel
– 'Othello'	CKel
– 'Pageant'	CKel
– 'Paper White'	CKel
– 'Paul M. Wild'	MAus
– 'Pauline Maunder'	CKel
¶ – 'Peche'	EBee
– 'Peregrine'	CKel
– 'Peter Brand'	LRHS
– 'Peter Pan'	CKel
– 'Petticoat Flounce'	WGle
– 'Phedar White'	MPhe
¶ – 'Philippe Rivoire'	MAus
– 'Philomèle'	MAus
– 'Pillow Talk'	MAus WCGr
– 'Pink Dawn'	CKel
– 'Pink Delight'	CKel
¶ – 'Pink Giant'	MBri
– 'Pink Lemonade'	WGle
– 'Pink Parfait'	MAus
– 'Pink Princess'	MAus
– 'President Franklin D. Roosevelt'	CBlo EBrP EBre ELan GCHN LBre SBre SPer SWat
– 'Président Poincaré'	CBlo CKel EBrP EBre LBre MRav SBre SMur SPer SWat
– 'President Taft'	See *P. lactiflora* 'Reine Hortense'
– 'President Wilson'	CKel
– 'Pride of Huish'	CKel
– 'Pride of Somerset'	CKel
– 'Primevere'	EFou LBuc LRHS MAus
– 'Princess Beatrice'	CKel
– 'Pure Delight'	CKel
– 'Queen Elizabeth'	CKel
– 'Queen of the Belgians'	CKel
– 'Queen's Grace'	CKel
– 'Raspberry Sundae'	MAus MRav
– 'Red Dwarf'	CKel
– 'Red King'	CKel
– 'Red Warrior'	CKel
§ – 'Reine Hortense'	CKel MAus MRav WGle
– 'Rembrandt'	CKel
– 'Rose of Delight'	CKel
– 'Ruby Light'	CKel

¶ – 'Ruth Cobb'	MAus
– 'Sainfoin'	CKel
– 'Sarah Bernhardt' ♀	Widely available
¶ – 'Shawnee Chief'	MAus
– 'Shimmering Velvet'	CKel
– 'Shirley Temple'	CBlo CKel EBar EFou ELan MAus MBri MMil WCGr WCot WFar WPyg
– 'Silver Flare'	CKel
– 'Sir Edward Elgar'	CKel
– 'Smiling Morn'	CKel
– 'Solange'	CKel MAus SPer
– 'Souvenir de Louis Bigot'	CKel
– 'Spearmint'	CKel
– 'Strephon'	CKel
– 'Surugu'	ELan
– 'Sweet Sixteen'	MAus
¶ – 'Tamate-boko'	MAus
– 'Thérèse'	CKel MAus
– 'Top Brass'	CBot MAus MRav
– 'Torpilleur'	CKel
– 'Tourangelle'	CKel
– 'Translucient'	CKel
– var. *trichocarpa*	WPGP
– 'Utopia'	CKel
– 'Victoire de la Marne'	CKel SMur
– 'Vogue'	CBlo CKel LRHS MAus SMur
– 'Westerner'	MAus
– 'White Wings'	CB&S CBlo CKel COtt EBrP EBre EFou ELan LBre MAus MBri SBre SPer SSpe WGle
– 'Whitleyi Major' ♀	CKel LRHS MBri
– 'Wiesbaden'	CKel MAus
– 'Wilbur Wright'	CKel
– 'Windsor Lad'	CKel
– 'Wings of Love'	CKel
– 'Winston Churchill'	CKel
– 'Wladyslawa'	SPla
– 'Zus Braun'	CKel
– 'Zuzu'	MAus
'Late Windflower'	ECha
¶ × *lemoinei*	WHal
§ – 'Alice Harding' (S)	SPer
§ – 'Chromatella' (S)	CKel LAma
§ – 'L'Espérance' (S)	LAma
§ – 'Souvenir de Maxime Cornu' (S)	CKel LAma LRHS MAus SPer
♦ *lithophila*	See *P. tenuifolia* subsp. *lithophila*
lobata 'Fire King'	See *P. peregrina*
¶ 'Lois Arleen'	MAus
lutea	See *P. delavayi* var. *lutea*
– var. *ludlowii*	See *P. delavayi* var. *ludlowii*
¶ *macrophylla*	WPGP
from W Georgia	
'Mai Fleuri'	LRHS MAus MBri
§ *mascula*	CAvo CBro NBir WPGP
§ – subsp. *arietina*	WKif WPGP
– – 'Northern Glory'	LSpr
§ – subsp. *mascula*	EPot SBla WWoo
¶ – – from SE Georgia	WPGP
§ – subsp. *triternata*	CLAP MPhe SBla SSpi WHoo
¶ – – from Crimea	WPGP
mlokosewitschii ♀	CAvo CBlo CBro CFil CKel CLAP EBrP EBre ECha EOrc EPot LBre LGre LHop MAvo MBro NPSI NTow SAxl SBre WAbe WEas WHoo WPGP WPyg
¶ – from E Georgia	WPGP
mollis	See *P. officinalis* subsp. *villosa*

'Montezuma'	MAus MBri
¶ 'Moonrise'	MAus
'Nymphe'	CKel MAus MRav WCGr
obovata ♀	CLAP SSpi WPGP WThi
– var. *alba* ♀	CAvo WAbe WEas
– 'Grandiflora'	EBrP EBre LBre MRav MWgw SBre
officinalis	CBlo CFil NBrk WPGP
– 'Alba Plena'	CBlo CKel CPou MAus MBri MRav SPer WCot
– 'Anemoniflora Rosea' ♀	LRHS MAus MBri
§ – subsp. *banatica*	CAvo WPGP
¶ – – WM 9727	MPhe
– 'China Rose'	ELan LRHS MAus MBri
– subsp. *humilis*	See *P. officinalis* subsp. *microcarpa*
– 'Lize van Veen'	EBrP EBre ELan LBre SBre
§ – subsp. *microcarpa*	SSpi WPGP
– 'Mutabilis Plena'	IBlr
– 'Rosea Plena' ♀	CBlo CDoC CKel EBee EPfP GAbr LRHS MAus MRav NMGW SPer SWat WLRN
– 'Rosea Superba Plena'	CKel EFou NRoo
– 'Rubra Plena' ♀	CBlo CDoC CKel CPou EBee EBrP EBre EFou ENot EPfP LBre MAus MBri NRoo SBre SPer SWat WWeb
§ – subsp. *villosa*	EBee ELan
¶ *ostii*	MPhe
paradoxa	See *P. officinalis* subsp. *microcarpa*
'Paula Fay'	MAus MRav
'Peppermint Stick'	WGle
§ *peregrina*	CFil CLAP ECho MAus MPhe SSpi
¶ – from Macedonia	WPGP
§ – 'Otto Froebel' ♀	CBlo EBrP EBre ELan LBre MBri SBre SMad SPer
– 'Sunshine'	See *P. peregrina* 'Otto Froebel'
potaninii	See *P. delavayi* Potaninii Group
* 'Raspberry Ice'	WGle
'Reine Supreme'	WGle
'Requiem'	MAus WGle
¶ *rhodia*	MPhe
rockii	See *P. suffruticosa* subsp. *rockii*
romanica	See *P. peregrina*
¶ 'Rose Garland'	MAus
'Roselette'	MAus
russoi	See *P. mascula* subsp. *russoi*
'Scarlett O'Hara'	MAus
sinensis	See *P. lactiflora*
'Smouthii'	EBrP EBre LBre SBre
'Sorbet'	COtt WCGr
steveniana	CLAP
¶ – from SE Georgia	WPGP
suffruticosa	CBlo CPMA ELan GOrc MGos SSpi WStI
–	EPla
* – 'Alice Palmer'	CKel
– 'Bai Yu' (S)	MPhe
– 'Bang Ning Zi' (S)	MPhe
– Bird of Rimpo	See *P. suffruticosa* 'Rimpo'
– Black Dragon Brocade	See *P. suffruticosa* 'Kokuryu-nishiki'
– Brocade of the Naniwa	See *P. suffruticosa* 'Naniwa-nishiki'
– 'Cai Die' (S)	MPhe
* – 'Cai Jing Qui' (S)	MPhe
¶ – 'Cang-zhi-hong'	WViv
– 'Cardinal Vaughan' (S)	CKel
– Charming Age	See *P. suffruticosa* 'Howki'
– Cherries of Imperial Palace	See *P. suffruticosa* 'Gosho-zakura'
¶ – Chinese hybrids (S)	SSON
– 'Da Zong Zi' (S)	MPhe
– 'Dou Lu' (S)	MPhe
– Double Cherry	See *P. suffruticosa* 'Yae-zakura'
– 'Duchess of Kent' (S)	CKel
– Eternal Camellias	See *P. suffruticosa* 'Yachiyo-tsubaki'
– 'Fen Lan Zhu' (S)	MPhe
– 'Fen Qiao' (S)	MPhe
¶ – 'Fen-dang-bai'	WViv
– Flight of Cranes	See *P. suffruticosa* 'Renkaku'
– Floral Rivalry	See *P. suffruticosa* 'Hana-kisoi'
– 'Ge Jin Zi' (S)	MPhe
* – 'Glory of Huish'	CKel
– 'Godaishu' (S)	LAma SPer
§ – 'Hakuojisi' (S)	EBee LRHS MAus
§ – 'Hana-daijin' (S)	LAma MAus SPer
§ – 'Hana-kisoi' (S)	LAma LRHS MAus SPer
– Lotus Green = 'He Hua Lu' (S)	MPhe
* – 'Hei Hue Kui' (S)	MPhe
§ – 'Higurashi' (S)	EBee LAma
– 'Hou Lian Jin Dan' (S)	MPhe
§ – 'Howki' (S)	LRHS MAus
– Hu Die Qun Wu' (S)	MPhe
◆ – Jewel in the Lotus	See *P. suffruticosa* Jewel in the Lotus = 'Tama-Fuyo'
◆ – Jewelled Screen	See *P. suffruticosa* Jewelled Screen = 'Tama-sudare'
¶ – 'Jia-ge-jin-zi' (S)	WViv
– 'Jiao Rong San Bian' (S)	MPhe
– 'Jin Pao Hong' (S)	MPhe
– Kamada Brocade	See *P. suffruticosa* 'Kamada-nishiki'
§ – 'Kamada-fuji' (S)	LAma
§ – 'Kaow' (S)	LRHS MAus
– King of Flowers	See *P. suffruticosa* 'Kaow'
– King of White Lions	See *P. suffruticosa* 'Hakuojisi'
* – 'Kingdom of the Moon'	LRHS MAus
– 'Kinkaku'	See *P.* × *lemoinei* 'Souvenir de Maxime Cornu'
– 'Kinshi'	See *P.* × *lemoinei* 'Alice Harding'
– Knight's Dance	See *P. suffruticosa* 'No-kagura'
§ – 'Kokuryû-nishiki' (S)	CKel LAma
– 'Lan Tian Yu' (S)	MPhe
– 'Li Hua Xue' (S)	MPhe
– 'Liu Li Guan Zhu' (S)	MPhe
– 'Lord Selbourne' (S)	CKel
¶ – 'Lu-he-hong (Lu's Red Lotus)'	MAus
¶ – 'Luo-han-hong'	WViv
– Magnificent Flower	See *P. suffruticosa* 'Hana-daijin'
– 'Montrose' (S)	CKel
– Moon World	See *P. suffruticosa* 'Gessekai'
* – 'Mrs Shirley Fry'	CKel
– 'Mrs William Kelway' (S)	CKel
§ – 'Naniwa-nishiki' (S)	MAus
– Palace of Gems	See *P. suffruticosa* 'Shugyo-kuden'
– Pride of Taisho	See *P. suffruticosa* 'Taisho-no-hokori'
– 'Qing Long Wo Mo Chi' (S)	MAus MPhe
¶ – 'Qing-shan-guan-xue' (S)	WViv
– 'Raphael' (S)	CKel
§ – 'Renkaku' (S)	MAus NBir
§ – 'Rimpo' (S)	EBee LAma NBir SPer

¶ – subsp. *rockii* (S) — MPhe SSpi
¶ – 'Ruan-zhi-lan' — WViv
¶ – 'San-bian-sai-yu' (S) — WViv
– Seven Gods of Fortune — See *P. suffruticosa* 'Sitifukujin'
§ – 'Shugyo-kuden' (S) — MAus
– 'Si He Lian' (S) — MPhe
§ – 'Sitifukujin' (S) — MAus
– 'Superb' (S) — CKel
§ – 'Taisho-no-hokori' (S) — LRHS MAus
§ – 'Taiyo' (S) — LAma SPer
§ – Jewel in the Lotus = 'Tama-Fuyo' (S) — LAma
§ – Jewelled Screen = 'Tama-sudare' (S) — LRHS MAus
– 'Tao Hong Xian Mei' (S) — MPhe
– The Sun — See *P. suffruticosa* 'Taiyo'
– Twilight — See *P. suffruticosa* 'Higurashi'
– Wisteria at Kamada — See *P. suffruticosa* 'Kamada-fuji'
– 'Xue Gui' (S) — MPhe
§ – 'Yachiyo-tsubaki' (S) — CKel LAma LRHS MAus NBir
§ – 'Yae-zakura' (S) — LAma NBir
– 'Yin Fen Jin Lin' (S) — MAus
¶ – 'Ying-luo-bao-zhu' (S) — WViv
¶ – 'Yomo-zakura' (S) — LRHS
– 'Yoshinogawa' (S) — EBee
– 'Yu Hu Die' (S) — MPhe
– 'Yu Pan Zheng Yan' (S) — MPhe
¶ – 'Yu-lu-dian-cui' (S) — WViv
¶ – 'Zhu-sha-lei (Cinnabar Rampart)' (S) — MAus
– 'Zi Ban Bai' (S) — MPhe
¶ – 'Zi-jin-pan' (S) — WViv
'Sunshine' — See *P. peregrina* 'Otto Froebel'
tenuifolia — CBot CLAP EPot GCal MAus NRoo
– subsp. *biebersteiniana* — GCal MPhe
¶ – subsp. *carthalinica* — MPhe
¶ – from E Georgia — WPGP
– subsp. *lithophila* — GCal MPhe
– 'Plena' — CLAP LRHS MBri
– 'Rosea' — MAus
¶ *turcica* — MPhe
veitchii — CKel CLAP LGre MBal MTho SIgm SSpi WAbe
– var. *woodwardii* — CAvo CBro CLyd EBee ERos GDra LGre MAus MBel MTho NHar NSla NWCA SSpi WCot WHoo
'Windchimes' — WGle
wittmanniana — CBot CLAP MAus NTow WSPU
'Yao Huang' (S) — MAus MPhe
¶ 'Yellow Crown' (S) — MAus
¶ 'Yellow Dream' (S) — MAus

PAESIA (Hypolepidaceae)
scaberula — CBos CFil GCal SSpi WAbe WRic

PALISOTA (Commelinaceae) See Plant Deletions

PALIURUS (Rhamnaceae)
spina-christi — CPle EWes MWhi SMad WSPU

PALLENIS (Asteraceae)
spinosus — See *Asteriscus spinosus*

PANAX (Araliaceae)
ginseng — GPoy
japonicus — GPoy
¶ *pseudoginseng* — GPoy
quinquefolius — GPoy

PANCRATIUM (Amaryllidaceae)
foetidum S&L 354 — CMon
maritimum — CMon CSpe EBee EBot GBur

PANDANUS (Pandanaceae) See Plant Deletions

PANDOREA (Bignoniaceae)
jasminoides — CPIN CSpe EBak ECon ECot ELan IBlr SBid SLMG SOWG
– 'Alba' — See *P. jasminoides* 'Lady Di'
§ – 'Charisma' (v) — CAbb CPIN CSpe EBee EHol ELan EMil EPfP LCns SHFr SOWG
§ – 'Lady Di' — CB&S CPIN CSpe ELan EMil ERea LCns SOWG
¶ – 'Rosea' — MCCP
– 'Rosea Superba' ♀ — CB&S CRHN EBee ECon EHic EHol ELan EMil ERea SPer
– 'Variegata' — See *P. jasminoides* 'Charisma'
lindleyana — See *Clytostoma callistegioides*
pandorana — CB&S CPIN CSpe EHic ERea WCot
* – 'Alba' — CPIN
– 'Golden Rain' — CPIN ECon ERea LCns SOWG
– 'Ruby Heart' — CPIN

PANICUM (Poaceae)
bulbosum — CHan EHoe EPla ESOG
clandestinum — EHoe EPPr EPla ESOG EWes MCCP NPro WCot
miliaceum — EFou EGle
virgatum — CTri ECha MSte MWhi NHol WBro WHil WPer WWat
– 'Hänse Herms' — CInt EHoe EPla MBri
– 'Heavy Metal' — CSte EMon SApp WCot
– 'Rehbraun' — CDec ECGN EFou EHoe MHlr SApp WCot WRus
– 'Rotstrahlbusch' — EFou EPPr LBuc SPla
– 'Rubrum' — Widely available
– 'Squaw' — CSte LGre SApp WCot
– 'Strictum' — EHoe EMil EWes
– 'Warrior' — CInt CSte EFou LGre MMoz SApp SAsh

PAPAVER † (Papaveraceae)
aculeatum — MSto
alboroseum — CInt EHyt GCHN GTou WPat
alpinum — MPla
– cut petal form — CInt
– subsp. *ernesti-mayeri* — MSto
§ *alpinum* Linnaeus — CSpe EMNN ESis GCHN GDra GTou LHol MBal MOne MRPP SIng SPla SRms WWin
¶ – *album* — CMea
– 'Flore Pleno' (d) — NBir
anomalum — EMan MSto
– *album* — CSpe ECGP EMon EWll GAbr GMac LFlo LGan MLLN NFai NLak WElm WSan
argemone — EWFC
§ *atlanticum* — CLTr CNic EBee ECoo EMan EMar GBuc GCHN NBro
– 'Flore Pleno' (d) — CM&M LFis MCCP NBro NFai WCot WOld
bracteatum — See *P. orientale* var. *bracteatum*

burseri	GCrs MSto
§ *commutatum* ♈	CInt ELan LHol MAvo SMrm WCot WEas
– 'Ladybird'	See *P. commutatum*
corona-sancti-stephani	MSto
degenii	GCHN
¶ *fauriei*	CChr
§ 'Fireball'	CBre CMHG CRow CSpe ECha ELan GCal LHop MTis MWat NCat NTow SIng WCot WMaN WRHF
heldreichii	See *P. spicatum*
× *hybridum* 'Flore Pleno' (d)	EMon MCLN NBrk SWat WWal
kluanense	MSto NLak
lapponicum	MSto
– *occidentale*	MSto
lateritium	CPou MLLN MMal MSto SRms
– 'Flore Pleno' (d)	EBee WSan
¶ *micocarpum*	WLin
§ *miyabeanum*	CGle CHea CMea CSpe ELan GCHN GCra GDra GTou LHop MPla NWCA WOMN WPer WWin
– *album*	ECho ELan
– 'Pacino'	ESis
– *tatewakii*	See *P. miyabeanum*
nanum 'Flore Pleno'	See *P.* '**Fireball**'
§ *nudicaule*	CBlo ELan MHlr WOMN WPer
– Champagne Bubbles Group	EBrP EBre LBre SBre SRms WFar WLRN
– Constance Finnis Group	EMon GBuc LHop
– var. *croceum*	MSto NWCA
– Garden Gnome Group	See *P. nudicaule* **Gartenzwerg Group**
¶ – Gartenzwerg Group	CBlo
¶ – Gartenzwerg Group	CSpe EMil GAbr MBri MPla NFla NPri NTay
§ – Oregon Rainbow Group	NFla
– 'Pacino'	SRms WFar WLRN WWeb
– 'Wonderland Mixed'	LPVe
oreophilum	MSto
orientale	CB&S EPfP MBro NCut SCou SWat WHil WPer
– 'Aglaja' ♈	WCot
– 'Allegro'	CBlo CSam EBar EBrP EBre ECtt EGar LBre MAus MBri MCLN MRav NBrk NFai NRoo NVic SBre SPer SSvw SWat SWyw WOve WWal
– 'Avebury Crimson'	MWat
– 'Beauty Queen'	CBlo EBrP EBre ECot GMac LBre MBri MRav NBrk NCat NRoo SBre SCoo SDix WElm WLRN WPbr
– 'Black and White' ♈	CElw CGle CHad CLon CRDP CSpe EBrP EBre ECha EFou ELan EMan GCHN LBre MAus MAvo MCLN MRav NBrk NRoo SBre SChu SSoC SWat WCot WPbr WWin
– 'Blue Moon'	CMil EFou GGar MRav NBir SWat WHal WLRN
– 'Bonfire Red'	ELan NLak
§ – var. *bracteatum* ♈	EBot ECha EMon GCHN GDra NBir
¶ – – JCA 751202	WPGP
– 'Brilliant'	CM&M NFai
– *carneum*	CM&M EBee
– 'Cedar Hill'	EFou LBuc WMer
– 'Cedric Morris' ♈	CBos CGle CHad CMil EBee ECha EFou EGle EMan EOld EPri GCal GCra MAus MRav NFai NRoo SChu SMrm SWas SWat WCot WEas WElm WKif WLRN WMaN
– 'Charming'	CHad CLon LGre MHlr SWat WCot
– 'China Boy'	EFou
* – 'Choir Boy'	NBrk SPla
– 'Curlilocks'	CLon CMGP EBrP EBre ELan EMan GAbr LBre MArl MAus MAvo MCLN MRav NBrk NRoo SBre SChu SPer SPla SRms SWat WCot WPbr WWin WWoo
* – 'Diana'	CBos CHad SMrm
– 'Doubloon'	CDoC EBrP EBre LBre MBri NBrk NRoo SBre
– 'Dwarf Allegro'	GBuc MFir MOne NNor NOak
– 'Elam Pink'	CLon ECha LGre MTis WCot
– 'Erste Zuneigung'	ECha
– 'Fatima'	CHad EFou LFis SMrm
N – 'Flore Pleno' (d)	EFou GLil SSvw
– 'Garden Glory'	EFou MArl MAus WLRN
– 'Glowing Embers'	EBrP EBre LBre SBre
* – 'Goldie'	ELan
– Goliath Group	CGle CHan CMil CSev EBee EFou MCLN NBrk NBro NOak NVic SDix SPer SWat WCot WEas WHoo WPyg
– – 'Beauty of Livermere' ♈	CDoC CHad CLon CM&M EMan MAus MBro MMal NBro NCat NLar NSti SAga SChu SLod SRms SWat WCot WElm WLRN WPyg WWhi
– 'Graue Witwe'	CHad CLon EFou GBuc LFlo NBrk SApp SWas SWat WRha
– 'Harvest Moon'	CFir EBrP EBre EHol GLil LBre MAus MBri MRav NCut SBre WCot WWeb
– 'Helen Elisabeth'	CBlo CSpe ECtt EFou EHal GCra MAus MBel MHlr MLLN MRav NBrk NFai NRoo SChu SWat WCot WMer WMow WCot
– 'Hewitt's Old Rose'	WCot
– 'Indian Chief'	CRDP EGle MAus WMer
¶ – 'Joanne'	NLar
– 'John Metcalf'	CRDP EBee EFou MAus SUsu WCot
– 'Juliane'	CLon ECha EGle EPri LGre WCot WPbr
– 'Karine' ♈	CHea CLon CMil ECha LGre MAus MAvo MBri NBrk NRoo SPla SWas SWat WBro WCot WLRN WPen WWoo
– 'King George'	GBuc MWat
– 'Kleine Tänzerin'	CLon CMil CPou EFou LGre MAus MCLN MTis MWgw SWat WCot WLRN
– 'Lady Frederick Moore'	LBuc MTed SWat WCot WMer WPbr
– 'Ladybird'	ELan MRav NBrk NRoo SPla WCot
– 'Lilac Girl'	CLon ECha EGle MAus NSti WCot
– 'Marcus Perry'	CBlo CDoC EBee ENot EPfP GChr GGar GMaP NFla NPri SPer SWat WCot WMer WMow
– 'May Queen' (d)	CMGP EBee EWes GBuc IBlr MArl NLak SUsu WCot WPen

– 'May Sadler'	ENot EOld LBuc MAus MTed SApp SCoo
¶ – 'Mrs H.G. Stobart'	CRDP
– 'Mrs Marrow's Plum'	See *P. orientale* **'Patty's Plum'**
– 'Mrs Perry' ♀	CM&M CMGP CSam CSev EBrP EBre EFou ELan GAbr LBre LHop MAus MAvo MBri MCLN MFir MNrw MWat NBrk NFai NPer NRoo NSti SBre SChu SPer WHoo WMow
– 'Nanum Flore Pleno'	See *P.* **'Fireball'**
– 'Orange Glow'	WMer
¶ – 'Orangeade Maison'	NLak
– 'Oriana'	EHol LBuc MBri MMil WLRN
– pale pink form	WWhi
§ – 'Patty's Plum'	Widely available
– 'Perry's White'	Widely available
– 'Picotée'	CBlo CHea CMGP EBrP EBre EFou ELan EMan LBre MAus MCLN MGrG MRav MWat NBro NRoo SBre SChu SPer WBro WByw WCot WHoo WPbr WWal
– 'Pinnacle'	CSWP GLil MAvo MSCN NFai NPri WCot WWoo
– 'Pizzicato'	CBlo CHor CKel CM&M LGre MCli MGed NPer NRoo SSvw SWat WLRN WOve
– Princess Victoria Louise	See *P. orientale* **'Prinzessin Victoria Louise'**
§ – 'Prinzessin Victoria Louise'	CBlo CMGP CSWP EFou EHal EMan GLil GMaP LFis MArl MAus MBel MLLN MMil NBro SSoC SSvw SWat WCer WCot WMer WPer
¶ – 'Queen Alexandra'	NLar
– 'Raspberry Queen'	CMil EFou ELan GBin MArl MHlr MTis NCut SWat WBro WCot WHal WMer WPbr WWoo
– 'Rembrandt'	CBlo ECot MMil NCut NFla NPri WMer WPer WViv
– 'Rose Queen'	WCot
¶ – 'Rosenpokal'	NLak
– 'Royal Wedding'	CMil CSev LBuc MMil NPri NRoo SChu SMrm WHow WLRN
* – 'Saffron'	CMil
– 'Salmon Glow'	EBee GLil SCoo WMer WPbr WPer
¶ – scarlet	MWgw
– 'Scarlet King'	CBlo EWll MMil WLRN WMow
– 'Showgirl'	CRDP
– 'Sindbad'	CMil EBee EFou WCot
– 'Snow Queen'	NCut
¶ – *splendidissima*	SIng
– 'Springtime'	EBee MAus MRav MSCN NCut WWoo
– Stormtorch	See *P. orientale* **'Sturmfackel'**
§ – 'Sturmfackel'	MAus SCoo
– 'Suleika'	EFou
– 'Sultana'	ECha GMac LGre SSoC WPbr
– 'Türkenlouis'	EFou MAus MSCN SPar WCot
– 'Turkish Delight' ♀	CBlo EFou ELan GCHN GMaP GMac MAus MCLN MMil MRav MTis NBir NBro NCat SChu SLod SPer SSoC SWat WMow
– 'Watermelon'	CKel COtt LBuc MAus MRav WBro WMer WPbr WWoo
¶ – 'Wunderkind'	EBee

paucifoliatum	CHan
¶ – JCA 752300	WPGP
pilosum	EMan GBuc MSto NCat SRms SWat
radicatum	MSto
rhaeticum	ELan EMan
rhoeas	CArn CJew EWFC GPoy MHew MMal WElm WJek
– angels choir	SWat WHer
– 'Mother of Pearl'	SWat
– Shirley	MMal WSel
– 'Valerie Finnis'	ELan
rupifragum	CFir CGle CSpe ECha ESis GAbr GCHN GCra LGan LHil MFir MLLN MRPP MSto NHex SUsu WEas WOve WPer WRha WWin
– 'Flore Pleno' (d)	CSWP MRPP NChi WCot WCru WHen WHer WWhi
sendtneri	GCLN MSto
§ *spicatum*	CBos CHea CSWP CSam CSpe ECGP ECha EMan GAbr GCal LHil LHop MHar MHlr NBir NFai SMrm SUsu WBro WCot WEas WPbr
triniifolium	CSpe
* 'Witchery'	WWeb

PARABENZOIN See LINDERA

PARADISEA (Asphodelaceae)

liliastrum ♀	EBee EMan ERos LGan NCat NChi NWoo SSpi WOMN WWhi
– 'Major'	CAvo
lusitanica	CAvo CGle CMHG CMil CRDP ERos SSpi

PARAHEBE † (Scrophulariaceae)

× *bidwillii*	CMHG ECou EMNN GAri GGar LFis MHig MRav NHed NMen SBod SRms WLin WWat
– 'Kea'	CFee ECou ECtt ELan EMNN ESis GCHN MAll MHig NHar NMen SBla SHel WFar WPer WRHF
canescens	ECou
§ *catarractae* ♀	CLyd CMHG ECou ELan EMNN EMar MFir MNrw MPla MWat NBee NBro NMen NNor NTow SBod SMer SOkh SUsu WBrE WHen WLin WOve WPer WWhi
– blue	EHic GMac NBee SPan SPer SPla WWat
§ – 'Delight' ♀	CChe CLTr ECou ELan ESis EWes GCHN GGar LFis LHop MAsh MBro NBrk NPer SDix SHFr WEas WHen WHoo WPyg
– subsp. *diffusa*	CMHG ECou EMNN IOrc MAsh MMil NHar NMen NPer NVic
– – 'Annie'	ECou
– – 'Pinkie'	CLTr ECou
– garden form	ECha LLWP SBla WAbe
– subsp. *martinii*	ECou EWes MAll NCut
– 'Miss Willmott'	LFlo LGan MAll MSCN NMen NPri NVic SPer WPer
– 'Porlock Purple'	See *P. catarractae* **'Delight'**
– 'Rosea'	CPri ESis MAll NVic SBla SIng WWat

– 'Tinycat'　　　　MAll
– white　　　　CBot ECha ELan EMNN ESis
　　　　　　　GCHN IBlr LHop MBro MFir
　　　　　　　NCat NFla NMen SHel SOkh
　　　　　　　SUsu WEas WPer WWat WWhi
decora　　　　CLyd ECou GAri GCHN NSla
　　　　　　　WLin
derwentiana　　　ECou EMon
§ *formosa*　　　CPle ECou MAll
– erect form　　　ECou
– lax form　　　ECou
– white　　　　ECou
'Gillian'　　　　ECou ECtt EHyt GAri GGar
　　　　　　　LFis MMil MBro WFar WPer
'Greencourt'　　　See *P. catarractae* **'Delight'**
§ *hookeriana*　　　GGar MAll NMen SAga SMrm
　　　　　　　WHoo WPyg WRHF WStI
　　　　　　　WWat
'Joy'　　　　　ECou EWes
linifolia　　　CTri EMNN NMen
– 'Blue Skies'　　　ECou EHyt LHop MHig
§ *lyallii*　　　CBot CPri EAst ECou ELan
　　　　　　　ESis LHop MAll MAsh MBar
　　　　　　　MPla MRav MWat NBee NHed
　　　　　　　NHol NMen NNor NWCA
　　　　　　　SAga SIng SRms WAbe WTro
　　　　　　　WWin
– 'Clarence'　　　CLyd ECou MAll
– 'Engel's Blue'　　LFlo LGan
– 'Glacier'　　　CLTr ECou
– 'Julie-Anne'　　　CMHG ECou ELan EPfP ESis
　　　　　　　GCal LRHS MAsh SPan
– 'Rosea'　　　CTri GGar LFis MBal WHoo
　　　　　　　WPer WPyg
* *martinii*　　　LRHS MAsh
'Mervyn'　　　CLyd CPBP ECou ECtt GCHN
　　　　　　　GGar LFis LHop MAll NHed
　　　　　　　NHol NLon NMen SUsu WHen
　　　　　　　WPer
olsenii　　　　ECou GGar MAll NTow
§ *perfoliata* ♀　　CAbb CBot CHan CMHG
　　　　　　　CMea CRDP ECha ELan ESis
　　　　　　　GCHN GCal LGre LHop MBal
　　　　　　　MBro MFir MRav NNor SBla
　　　　　　　SPer SSpi SUsu WAbe WLin
　　　　　　　WPat WPer WSHC WWat
– dark blue　　　GBuc GCal MBro SMad
¶ – 'Pringle'　　　CAbP EPfP LRHS MAsh
'Snowcap'　　　ELan EPfP LRHS MAsh

PARAJUBAEA (Arecaceae)
cocoides　　　CBrP LPJP LPal

PARAQUILEGIA (Ranunculaceae)
adoxoides　　　See *Semiaquilegia adoxoides*
§ *anemonoides*　　GCrs GGGa GTou NHar WAbe
　　　　　　　WLin
¶ – ACE 1370　　　EHyt
grandiflora　　　See *P. anemonoides*

PARASERIANTHES (Mimosaceae)
distachya　　　See *P. lophantha*
§ *lophantha* ♀　　CAbb CHEx CPle EREa ISea
　　　　　　　LCns LHil SAPC SArc SOWG
　　　　　　　WMul

PARASYRINGA See LIGUSTRUM

× PARDANCANDA (Iridaceae)
norrisii　　　CArn CFir EAst EBee EMan
　　　　　　　EWes GSki LIck NPri WFoF

PARDANTHOPSIS (Iridaceae) See Plant
Deletions

PARDOGLOSSUM (Boraginaceae)
¶ *cheirifolium*　　EBee

PARIETARIA (Urticaceae)
§ *judaica*　　　ELau EWFC GPoy MHew MSal
　　　　　　　WHer
officinalis　　　See *P. judaica*

PARIS (Trilliaceae)
¶ *birmanica*　　　WCru
¶ *bockiana*　　　WCru
¶ *fargesii*　　　WCru
* *hepatica henryi*　LAma
japonica　　　WCru
¶ *lancifolia*　　　WCru
§ *polyphylla*　　　EMar WCru
¶ – var. *stenophylla*　LAma
¶ *pubescens*　　　WCru
quadrifolia　　CAvo CFil CFir CLAP CRDP
　　　　　　　GPoy LGre MSal SSpi WCru
　　　　　　　WHer
– JMH 79　　　MDun
¶ *thibetica*　　　WCru
¶ *verticillata*　　LAma WCru

PARKINSONIA (Caesalpiniaceae) See Plant
Deletions

PARNASSIA (Parnassiaceae)
cabulica　　　GDra
nubicola　　　GDra MBal NHar
palustris　　　WAbe WHer

PAROCHETUS (Papilionaceae)
africanus ♀　　CHan CHid EWes GBuc
communis　　　CB&S CFee CGle CNic GCra
　　　　　　　GDra GMac NBro NPer SIng
　　　　　　　SVen WAbe WOMN WWhi
– dark form　　　GCal
– Himalayan form　IBlr
¶ – Himalayan form HWJCM　WCru
　　526
¶ – summer-flowering　CRDP

PARONYCHIA (Illecebraceae)
argentea　　　MBro WPat WPer
§ *capitata*　　　CHal CLyd CMHG CTri ELan
　　　　　　　NMen NNrd SRms WPat WPer
　　　　　　　WRHF WWin
§ *kapela*　　　EMan MHig NPri NTow SSmi
　　　　　　　WPer
– 'Binsted Gold' (v)　CMGP EMon MBro SSmi
– subsp. *serpyllifolia*　CPea
nivea　　　　See *P. capitata*
serpyllifolia　　See *P. kapela*

PARROTIA (Hamamelidaceae)
persica ♀　　　Widely available
¶ – 'Burgundy'　　CPMA
– 'Pendula'　　　CPMA ELan IOrc MBal
– 'Vanessa'　　　CMCN CPMA LPan LRHS
　　　　　　　MBri SMad SSpi SSta
– 'Variegata'　　CPMA

PARROTIOPSIS (Hamamelidaceae)
jacquemontiana　CB&S CEnd CPMA LBuc SMur
　　　　　　　SSpi

PARRYA (Brassicaceae)
¶ *eriocalyx* — EFou
menziesii — See *Phoenicaulis cheiranthoides*

PARSONSIA (Apocynaceae)
capsularis — CPlN ECou MAll
heterophylla — ERea

PARTHENIUM (Asteraceae)
integrifolium — CArn GPoy MSal SPil

PARTHENOCISSUS † (Vitaceae)
§ *henryana* ♀ — Widely available
himalayana — ECtt
– 'Purpurea' — See *P. himalayana* var. *rubrifolia*
§ – var. *rubrifolia* — CBlo EHic EPfP ETen LHol MAsh WCru WWat
§ *quinquefolia* ♀ — Widely available
– var. *engelmannii* — LBuc MGos NFla SPer WAbe
striata — See *Cissus striata*
thomsonii — See *Cayratia thomsonii*
§ *tricuspidata* ♀ — CHEx EBee ECtt GOrc MAsh MBal MGos NNor SBid SPer SReu SSoC WDin
– B&SWJ 1162 — WCru
– 'Beverley Brook' — CBlo CMac EBrP EBre ETen LBre MBri SBid SBra SBre SPla SRms WAbe
– 'Green Spring' — CBlo IHos MBlu MBri MGos NBrk
– 'Lowii' — CBlo CDoC CMac EBrP EBre ECot EHic EPfP EPla LBre MBlu MGos MRav SBre
¶ – 'Minutifolia' — SMad
– 'Robusta' — CSam LPan
§ – 'Veitchii' — Widely available

PASITHEA (Asphodelaceae) See Plant Deletions

PASPALUM (Poaceae) See Plant Deletions

PASSIFLORA † (Passifloraceae)
actinia — CPas CPlN CRHN LChe LPri
acuminata — CPas
adenopoda — CPas
'Adularia' — CPas LChe LPri WHer
alata (F) ♀ — CAbb CPas CPlN ELan ERea LChe LCns LPri
– 'Shannon' (F) — CPas
× *alatocaerulea* — See *P.* × *belotii*
allantophylla — CPas
'Allardii' — CPas SMad
ambigua — CPas
'Amethyst' ♀ — CAbb CPas CPlN CSPN ELan EMil EOrc LBlm LCns LHop LPri SAga SBid SBra WMul
§ *amethystina* — CB&S CDoC CPas CPlN CRHN ECre EHol ERea LCns NPal SLMG
ampullacea (F) — CPas LPri
anfracta — CPas
N *antioquiensis* Karst ♀ — CB&S CBot CGre CHEx CPlN CSPN CTbh EHol ELan ERea GQui IBlr LChe LPri LRHS MBlu MTis SLMG
apetala — CPas
§ *aurantia* — CPas ERea WHer
auriculata — CPas
banksii — See *P. aurantia*

§ × *belotii* — CPas ECre ELan ERea LChe LCns LPri LRHS WDin
– 'Impératrice Eugénie' — See *P.* × *belotii*
biflora Lamarck — CPas
boenderi — CPas WMul
brevipes — CPas
'Byron Beauty' — LPri
§ *caerulea* ♀ — Widely available
– 'Constance Elliot' ♀ — CB&S CBot CMac CPas CPlN CRHN CSPN ELan EMil EOrc LBlm LChe LHop LPri NBea SBra SLMG SOWG SPer SPla SReu SSta SSto WCru WHen
× *caerulea racemosa* — See *P.* × *violacea*
caerulea rubra — CBlo ECtt SBid
* *caerulea* 'Star of Kingston Seymour' — CPlN
× *caeruleoracemosa* — See *P.* × *violacea*
× *caponii* — ERea
capsularis — CPas MSto SLMG
chinensis — See *P. caerulea*
cincinnata — CPas
cinnabarina — CPas
citrina — CPas CPlN ECon ELan ERea LChe LCns LPri SOWG WMul
coccinea (F) — CB&S CPas CPlN LPri LRHS
colinvauxii — CPas
× *colvillii* — CPas CPlN LPri
conzattiana — CPas
§ *coriacea* — CPas CPlN LChe LPri LRHS
costaricensis — CPas
¶ *crenata* — CPas
cumbalensis — CPas
– var. *cumbalensis* JCA 13988 — MSto
cuneata — CPas LPri
cuprea — CPas
cuspidifolia — CPas
§ *cyanea* — CPas
× *decaisneana* (F) — CPas LPri WMul
§ – 'Innesii' — CPas
discophora — CPas
edulis (F) — CAgr CPas CPlN EBak LPri WHer
– 'Crackerjack' (F) — CB&S COtt ERea
¶ – f. *edulis* (F) — NBea
– f. *flavicarpa* (F) — CPas ECon ELan LChe LPri
* – 'Golden Nuggett' (F) — CPas
– 'Norfolk' (F) — CPas
– 'Supreme' — CB&S
'Elizabeth' (F) — CPas LChe
'Empress Eugenie' — See *P.* × *belotii*
* *escorbariana* — CPas
× *exoniensis* ♀ — CBot CGre CPas CPlN CRHN ECre LPri WHer WPic
filipes — CPas
foetida — CPas MSto SOWG
¶ – *hibiscifolia* — WHer
– var. *hirsuta* (F) — CPas
– var. *hirsutissima* — CPas
– var. *orinocensis* — CPas
* *garayaglia* — CPas
garckei — CPas
gibertii — CPas
gigantifolia — CPas
gilbertiana — CPas
glandulosa — CPas
gracilis — CPas MSto
gracillima — CPas
guatemalensis — CPas
hahnii — CPas
helleri — CPas CPlN WMul

herbertiana (F)	CPas CPlN LPri WMul
holosericea	CPas
incana	See *P. seemannii*
incarnata (F)	CAgr CArn CBlo CPas CPlN LChe LPri MSal NBrk NGno
'Incense' (F) ♀	CBlo CPas CPlN ECre LChe LPri NBea
× *innesii*	See *P.* × *decaisneana* 'Innesii'
* *jalunsachensis*	CPas
jilekii	CPas
jorullensis	CPas
juliana	CPas
kalbreyeri	CPas
karwinskii	CPas
× *kewensis*	CPas LChe LPri
* *kirkii*	CPlN
lancearia	CPas
laurifolia (F)	CPas
§ *ligularis* (F)	CPas LBlo LPri LRHS
'Lilac Lady'	See *P.* × *violacea* 'Tresederi'
lindeniana	CPas
* *lourdesae*	CPas
lowei	See *P. ligularis*
lutea	CPas
maliformis (F)	CPas CPlN
manicata (F)	CPas CPlN CRHN NBrk WHer
'Mavis Mastics'	See *P.* × *violacea* 'Tresederi'
mayana	See *P. caerulea*
menispermifolia	See *P. pilosa*
* *microstipula*	CPas
¶ *miersii*	CPas
misera	CPas
mixta (F)	CPlN ERea LPri
– × *antioquiensis*	CPas SAga
mollissima (F) ♀	CAbb CB&S CBot CGre CPas CPlN CRHN CSPN EBak ELan ERea LBlm LChe LPri SLMG SOWG SVen WHer WMul
morifolia	CPas CPlN LPri MSto WHer
mucronata	CPas
multiflora	CPas
murucuja	CPas
naviculata	CPas
nelsonii	CPas
nitida (F)	CPas
oblongata	CPas
obtusifolia	See *P. coriacea*
oerstedii	CPas
– var. *choconhiana*	CPas
onychina	See *P. amethystina*
organensis	CPas
pallens	CPas
¶ *palmeri*	CPas
¶ *penduliflora*	CPas
perfoliata	CPas
* 'Perfume'	CPas
phoenicea	CPas LPri
– 'Ruby Glow' (F)	CPas
pinnatistipula (F)	CGre CPas
× *piresii*	CPas
¶ *pittieri*	CPas
platyloba	CPas CPlN
punctata	CPas
'Pura Vida'	CPas LPri
'Purple Haze'	CPas CRHN LPri
'Purple Passion'	See *P. edulis* f. *edulis*
quadrangularis L. (F) ♀	CB&S CPas CPlN CTbh ERea LChe LPan LPri NBea WHer WMul
* – *macrocarpa* (F)	CPas
quadrifaria	CPas
quadriflora	CPas

quinquangularis	CPas
racemosa ♀	CBlo CPas CPlN CSPN ELan ERea ERom IBlr LChe LPri NBea SOWG WGor
'Red Inca'	CPas
retipetala	See *P. cyanea*
rovirosae	CPas LRHS
rubra	CBlo CPas ELan EWes LPri WStI
* *rufa*	CPas
'Saint Rule'	CPas LPri
sanguinolenta	CPas ELan ERea LChe LPri LRHS
'Sapphire'	CPas LPri
§ *seemannii*	CPas LPri WMul
serrata	See *P. serratodigitata*
serratifolia	CPas LPri
§ *serratodigitata*	CPas
serrulata	CPas
sexflora	CPas
'Smythiana'	CPas
standleyi	CPas
'Star of Bristol' ♀	CHEx CPas LPri
'Star of Clevedon'	CPas CPlN
'Star of Kingston'	CPas
stipulata	CPas
suberosa	CPas LPri
subpeltata	CPas LPri
'Sunburst'	CPas CPlN LPri SOWG WMul
talamancensis	CPas
tatei	CPas
tenuifila	CPas
§ *tetrandra*	CGre CPas ECou
tica	CPas
× *tresederi*	See *P.* × *violacea* 'Tresederi'
tricuspis	CPas
tridactylites	CPas
trifasciata	CPas CPlN
tripartita	CPas
– JCA 13982	MSto
* *triphostemmatoides*	CPas
trisecta	CPas
tuberosa	CPas
tulae	CPas
umbilicata	CBot CPas CPlN LPri WCru
urbaniana	CPas
vespertilio	CPas
§ × *violacea* ♀	CAbb CB&S CBlo CPas CPlN CRHN ECon ERea LCns MBri SSto
– 'Dedorina'	CPas
– 'Eynsford Gem'	CPas
– 'Lilac Lady'	See *P.* × *violacea* 'Tresederi'
§ – 'Tresederi'	CPas
– 'Victoria'	CPas LPri
viridiflora	CPas
vitifolia (F)	CHEx CPas CPlN ECon ELan ERea LChe LCns LPri LRHS SOWG WHer WMul
– 'Scarlet Flame' (F)	CPas LPri
xiikzodz	CPas
yucatanensis	CPas
zamorana	CPas

PASTINACA (Apiaceae)
sativa	CKin

PATERSONIA (Iridaceae)
¶ *occidentalis*	MFiF

PATRINIA (Valerianaceae)
gibbosa	CLyd CRDP ECha ECro GCHN LGan MHig SMrm SSca WCru WRHF
¶ *rupestris*	IIve
* *sambucifolia*	EBee
¶ *saniculifolia*	WCru
scabiosifolia	CBlo CMil ECha EJud EMan GBuc SMrm WWin
¶ – 'Nagoya'	MNrw
triloba	CLyd CRDP ECha LGan NGre NMen NRya NWoo SSpi SUsu
* – 'Minor'	ECho
– var. *palmata*	GCHN NBro NBus WFar
– var. *triloba*	CGle GCal MHig NTow WWin
villosa	WCot

PAULOWNIA (Scrophulariaceae)
coreana	CGre
fargesii Franchet	CEnd CHEx CLnd ERod ICrw SLPl SMad
– Osborn	See *P. tomentosa* **'Lilacina'**
fortunei	CMCN CWSG ERod GAri WLRN WNor
tomentosa ♀	CB&S CBot CHEx CLnd CPle ELan EMil ENot ERod EWes ICrw IOrc LPan NPal SBid SHBN SMad SPer SRms SSta WHCG WMou WNor WPat

PAVONIA (Malvaceae)
§ × *gledhillii*	LHil
× *intermedia*	See *P.* × *gledhillii*
multiflora hort.	See *P.* × *gledhillii*
– Jussieu	ERea
praemorsa	CBot LHil

PAXISTIMA (Celastraceae)
canbyi	MAll NPro WPat WWin
myrsinites	See *P. myrtifolia*
§ *myrtifolia*	CPle

PECTEILIS (Orchidaceae)
* *dentata*	EFEx
§ *radiata*	EFEx
* – 'Albomarginata'	EFEx
– 'Aureomarginata'	EFEx

PEDICULARIS (Scrophulariaceae) See Plant Deletions

PEDILANTHUS (Euphorbiaceae)
tithymaloides 'Variegatus'	LChe

PEGANUM (Zygophyllaceae)
harmala	CArn MSal NGno

PELARGONIUM † (Geraniaceae)
'A Happy Thought'	See *P.* **'Happy Thought'**
'A.M. Mayne' (Z/d)	CWDa SDen
'Abba' (Z/d)	CWDa
'Abel Carrière' (I/d)	SKen WFib
abrotanifolium (Sc)	CNat CSev ERav MHul SKen WEas WFib
– broad-leaved	SDen
'Acapulco'	NPri WLRN
acerifolium hort.	See *P. vitifolium*
– L'Héritier	See *P. cucullatum* subsp. *strigifolium*

acetosum	GCal MHul MSte SAga SHFr SMrm
* – 'Variegatum'	CSpe MSte
acraeum	MHul WFib
Action (Z/d)	WFib
¶ 'Acushla by Brian' (Sc)	MWhe
'Ada Sutterby' (Dw/d)	SKen WFib
'Adagio' (Dw)	ESul
'Adam's Quilt' (Z/C)	SKen WEas
'Adele' (Min/d)	ESul WFib
'Aerosol' (Min)	ESul WFib
¶ 'African Belle' (R)	CLit
'Afterglow' (Z)	WFib
'Ailsa' (Min/d)	ESul MBri SKen
'Ainsdale Angel' (A)	ESul LDea
* 'Ainsdale Beauty' (Z)	LVER
'Ainsdale Claret' (Z)	LVER
'Ainsdale Eyeful' (Z)	LVER
'Akela' (Min)	ESul
'Alan West' (Z/St)	LHil LVER SDen
'Alberta' (Z)	SKen WFib
'Albert's Choice' (R)	WFib
album	CWDa MHul
alchemilloides	CNat MHul WFib
'Alcyone' (Dw/d)	ESul IHos SKen WFib
'Alde' (Min)	ESul LHil LVER MWhe SKen WEas
'Aldenham' (Z)	WFib
'Aldham' (Min)	ESul LVER WFib
'Aldwyck' (R)	EBSP LDea WFib
'Alex' (Z)	CWDa SKen
'Alex Mary' (R)	SDen SSea WFib
'Algenon' (Min/d)	ESul WFib
'Alice Crousse' (I/d) ♀	SDen SKen WFib
'Alison' (Dw)	ESul
'Alison Jill' (Z/d)	CWDa
'Alison Wheeler' (Min/d)	MWhe
'All My Love' (R)	LDea WFib
'Alma' (Min/C)	ESul
'Almost Heaven' (Dw/Z/v)	MWhe
'Alpine Glow' (Z/d)	MWhe
'Alpine Orange' (Z/d)	CWDa SDen
'Alta Bell' (R)	WFib
'Altair' (Min/d)	ESul LVER WFib
alternans	CSev MHul WEas
'Always' (Z/d)	SDen WFib
'Alys Collins' (Z/d)	WFib
'Amarantha' (Z)	WFib
'Amari' (R)	LDea
'Ambrose' (Dw/d)	ESul WFib
§ 'Amethyst' (I/d) ♀	ECtt GHCN IHos LDea LVER MWhe NPri WFib WLRN
'Amethyst' (R)	EBSP LDea MBri SDen SKen WFib
'Ami' (R)	WFib
'Anabell Stephenson' (Dw/d)	WFib
'Andersonii' (Sc)	EWoo WFib
'Andrew Salvidge' (R)	LDea WFib
I 'Andromeda' (Min)	WFib
'Ange Davey' (Z/d)	WFib
'Angela Brook'	CWDa
'Angela Read' (Dw)	ESul
'Angela Woodberry' (I/d)	CWDa
'Angelique' (Dw/d)	ESul LVER WFib
'Anglia' (Dw)	ESul
¶ 'Ann Hoystead' (R) ♀	WFib
'Ann Redington' (R)	LDea WFib
'Ann Sothern' (Z)	WFib
'Anna' (Dw)	ESul SDen WFib
¶ 'Anna Scheen' (Dw)	ESul

'Anne Wilkie-Millar'   WFib
  (Z/d)
¶ 'Annsbrook Jupitor' (St)   ESul
  antidysentericum   MHul
'Antigua' (R)   LDea WFib
'Antoine Crozy' (ZxI/d)   WFib
'Antoinette' (Min)   ESul
'Apache' (Z/d) ♀   CHal CWDa WFib
'Aphrodite' (Z)   CWDa ECtt WFib
'Apollo' (R)   CWDa
'Apple Betty' (Sc)   LDea WFib
'Apple Blossom Rosebud'   CLit ECtt ERic LVER MBri
  (Z/d) ♀   MWhe SDen SKen SMrm SUsu
    WEas WFib
¶ 'Appledram' (R)   EBSP LDea WFib
¶ 'Apri Parmer' (Min)   ESul
'Apricot' (Z/St/d)   ESul SDen SKen
'Apricot Queen' (I/d)   LDea SDen
'Apricot Star'   CSpe MWhe
'April Hamilton' (I)   WFib
'Arctic Frost'   SDen
§ 'Arctic Star' (Z/St/d)   CLit CSpe ESul LHil LVER
    SKen WEas
'Arcturus' (Min)   WFib
'Ardens'   CSpe LHil MHul SSad SUsu
    WCot WEas
'Ardwick Cinnamon'   ESul GHCN LDea
  aridum   MHul
'Aries' (Min/C)   ESul MBri MWhe
'Arizona' (Min/d)   ESul SDen SKen WFib
'Arnside Fringed Aztec'   LDea
  (R)
'Aroma' (Sc)   LIck WFib
'Arthington Slam' (R)   LDea
'Arthur Biggin' (Z)   MWhe SKen
  articulatum   MHul
* 'Ashey'   SDen
'Ashfield Blaze' (Z/d)   SDen WFib
'Ashfield Jubilee' (Z/C)   SKen
'Ashfield Monarch' (Z/d)   LVER MWhe WFib
  ♀
'Ashfield Serenade' (Z) ♀ SKen WFib
'Ashley Stephenson' (R)   WFib
'Askham Fringed Aztec'   EBSP LDea LVER
  (R) ♀
'Askham Slam' (R)   LDea
  asperum Ehr. ex Willd.   See *P.* 'Graveolens'
'Astrakan' (Z/d)   SDen
'Athabasca' (Min)   ESul
'Atomic Snowflake' (Sc/v)   CArn CHal CInt EBar ERav
    ESul GBar GHCN LDea LHil
    LVER MSte MWhe SDen SIde
    SKen SSea WCHb WEas WFib
    WJek WPer WWye
'Attar of Roses' (Sc) ♀   CArn CHal CInt CLTr CLit
    CNat EOHP ERav ESul GBar
    IHos LBlm LDea LHil LVER
    MWhe NHHG NSty SDen SIde
    SKen WCHb WEas WFib
    WWye
'Attraction' (Z/St/d)   WFib
'Aubusson' (R)   WFib
'Audrey' (Z/d)   WFib
'Audrey Baghurst' (I)   CWDa
'Audrey Clifton' (I/d)   ECtt SDen SKen WFib
'Augusta'   LHil LHop SMrm
Auralia (Z/d)   WFib
  auritum   CMon
'Aurora' (Z/d)   MWhe SKen
'Aurore'   See *P.* 'Unique Aurore'
  australe   CFir CNat EWes MHul MSte
    SMrm SSpi WFib

'Australian Mystery'   LHil
'Autumn' (Z/d)   IHos LVER MWhe WFib
'Autumn Colours' (Min)   ESul
'Autumn Festival' (R)   WFib
'Autumn Haze' (R)   EBSP WFib
'Autumn Mist' (R)   WFib
'Avril'   ESul
'Aztec' (R) ♀   EBSP LDea LVER MSte WEas
    WFib
'Aztec Fimbriant'   SMrm
'Baby Birds Egg' (Min)   CSpe ESul WFib
'Baby Brocade' (Min/d)   ESul LVER WFib
'Baby Helen' (Min)   ESul
'Baby James' (Min)   ESul
'Baby Snooks' (A)   WEas
'Babylon' (R)   EBSP WFib
'Badley' (Dw)   ESul
Balcon Imperial   See *P.* 'Roi des Balcons
    Impérial'
'Balcon Lilas'   See *P.* 'Roi des Balcons Lilas'
'Balcon Rose'   See *P.* 'Hederinum'
'Balcon Rouge'   See *P.* 'Roi des Balcons
    Impérial'
'Balcon Royale'   See *P.* 'Roi des Balcons
    Impérial'
'Bali Surprise' (Z/St)   ESul
'Ballerina' (Dw/d)   ERav MWhe
♦ 'Ballerina' (R)   See *P.* 'Carisbrooke'
'Bandit' (Min)   ESul
'Bantam' (Min/d)   ESul WFib
§ 'Barbe Bleu' (I/d)   ECtt LDea LVER MWhe SDen
    SKen WFib
'Barking' (Min)   ESul
  barklyi   MHul
'Barnston Dale' (Dw)   ESul
¶ 'Barock '96'   NPri
'Baron de Layres' (Z/d)   WFib
'Baronne A. de   WFib
  Rothschild' (Z/d)
'Bath Beauty' (Dw)   SDen SKen WEas
'Baylham' (Min)   ESul
'Beacon Hill' (Min)   ESul
'Beatrice Cottington' (I/d)   SKen WFib
'Beatrix' (Z/d)   LVER SKen WFib
'Beau Geste' (R)   EBSP
'Beauty' (Z)   WFib
'Beauty of Bath' (R)   WFib
'Beauty of Calderdale'   WFib
  (Z/C)
N 'Beauty of Eastbourne'   See *P.* 'Lachskönigin'
'Beauty of El Segundo'   SKen WFib
  (Z/d)
'Beauty of Jersey' (I/d)   WFib
'Beckwith's Pink' (Z)   SDen SKen
'Belinda Adams' (Min/d)   MWhe WFib
  ♀
§ 'Belladonna' (I/d)   ECtt IHos
¶ 'Belvedere' (R)   EBSP
'Bembridge'   SDen SSea
'Ben Franklin' (Z/v) ♀   CLit IHos LVER MWhe SDen
'Ben Matt' (R)   WFib
'Ben Nevis' (Dw/d)   ESul LVER SDen
'Bentley' (Dw)   ESul
'Bergpalais' (Z/d)   WFib
'Berliner Balkon' (I)   SDen SKen
'Bern'   CLit
'Bernado'   WLRN
'Beromünster' (Dec)   ERav ESul EWoo LDea LHil
    LIck MSte SKen WEas WFib
'Bert Pearce' (R)   EBSP LDea WFib
'Beryl Bodey'   See *P.* 'Mrs L.R. Bodey'

'Beryl Gibbons' (Z/d) LVER MWhe
'Beryl Read' (Dw) ERea ESul
'Beryl Reid' (R) LDea WFib
'Berylette' (Min/d) ESul SKen WFib
'Bess' (Z/d) ESul SDen SKen
'Beta' (Min/C) ESul
'Bette Shellard' (Z/d) MWhe
'Betty Dollery' (Z/d) SDen
'Betty Hulsman' (A) ESul LDea
'Betty Read' (Dw) ESul
'Betty West' (Min/d) SDen
betulinum MHul WFib
'Betwixt' (Z/v) SDen SKen SSea WFib
¶ 'Bev Foster' (d) SDen
'Bewerley Park' (Z/C/d) LVER WFib
'Bianca' (Min/d) ESul
'Bicester Gem' SDen
'Bi-coloured Startel' MWhe
  (Z/St/d)
'Biedermeier' (R) LVER
'Bildeston' (Z/C) ESul
'Bill West' (I) SDen
'Billie Read' (Dw/d) ERea ESul
'Bingo' (Min) ESul
'Bird Dancer' (Dw/St) ♀ CInt CSpe ERav ESul LHil
  LVER MSte MWhe SDen SKen
  WEas WFib
'Birthday Girl' (R) WFib
'Bitter Lemon' (Sc) ESul
'Black Butterfly' See *P.* **'Brown's Butterfly'**
'Black Country Bugle' CWDa
  (Z/d)
'Black Knight' (R) CMdw CSpe ESul LVER MSte
  WFib
'Black Magic' (R) WFib
'Black Night' (A) CLit ESul
'Black Pearl' (Z/d) LVER SDen WFib
'Black Prince' (R) WEas WPen
'Black Velvet' (R) LDea
'Black Vesuvius' See *P.* **'Red Black Vesuvius'**
'Blackcurrant Sundae' LVER
'Blakesdorf' (Dw) ESul MWhe
'Blanche Roche' NPri SCoo WLRN
§ 'Blandfordianum' (Sc) EWoo LVER SSad
§ 'Blauer Frühling' (I/d) IHos LVER SKen
'Blaze Away' SDen SSea
'Blazonry' (Z/v) MBEx MWhe SKen WFib
'Bloomfield Abundance' LBlm
'Blooming Gem' (Min/I/d) LDea
'Blue Beard' See *P.* **'Barbe Bleu'**
'Blue Blizzard' NPri WLRN
'Blue Fox' (Z) CWDa
'Blue Orchid' (R) LDea WFib
'Blue Peter' (I/d) SKen
'Blue Spring' See *P.* **'Blauer Frühling'**
'Bluebeard' ERav
§ 'Blues' (Z/d) CWDa IHos
'Blush Kleine Liebling' WFib
  (Min)
'Blush Mariquita' (R) WEas WFib
'Blush Petit Pierre' (Min) ESul
'Blushing Bride' (I/d) IHos LDea SKen
'Blushing Emma' (Z) ESul WFib
'Bob Legge' (Z/d) WFib
'Bode's Trina' (I) CWDa
'Bodey's Picotee' (R) ♀ WFib
'Bold Flame' (Z/d) WFib
'Bold Sunrise' (Z) LVER
'Bold Sunset' (Z/d) LVER WFib
'Bolero' (U) ♀ EWoo IHos LVER SSea WFib
'Boogy' WLRN
'Bosham' (R) EBSP LDea WFib

¶ 'Botham's Surprise' (Z/d) CLit
'Botley Beauty' (R) EBSP LDea WFib
'Boudoir' (Z/C/d) ESul
'Bouldner' SDen
bowkeri MHul
'Brackenwood' (Min/d) ♀ ESul LVER WFib
'Bramford' (Dw) ESul
'Braque' (R) LDea WFib
'Brasil' WLRN
'Bravo' (Z/d) MWhe WFib
'Break o' Day' (R) LDea LVER SDen WEas
'Bredon' (R) ♀ WFib
'Brenda' (Min/d) ESul LVER
'Brenda Hyatt' (Dw/d) ESul WFib
'Brenda Kitson' (Z/d) LVER MWhe WFib
'Brialyn Beauty' (A) LDea
'Brialyn Moonlight' (A) ESul LDea SSea
'Bridesmaid' (Dw/C/d) ESul WFib
'Brightstone' SDen
'Brightwell' (Min/d) ESul WFib
'Brilliant' (Dec) CNat EWoo WFib
'Bristol' (Z/v) SKen SSea WFib
'Britannia' (R) LDea
'Brixworth Boquet' MWhe
  (Min/C/d)
'Brixworth Charmer' (Z/v) MWhe
'Brixworth Melody' (Z/v) MWhe
'Brixworth Pearl' (Z) MWhe
'Brixworth Rhapsody' MWhe
  (Z/v)
'Brixworth Starlight' (I/v) MWhe
'Broadway' (Min) WFib
'Brocade' (Z/d) IHos LVER WFib
'Brockbury Scarlet' (Ca) WFib
'Bronze Corinne' (Z/C/d) SDen SKen
'Bronze Nuhulumby' (R) EBSP WFib
'Bronze Queen' (Z/C) LIck MWhe
'Bronze Velvet' (R) WFib
'Brook' SDen SSea
'Brook's Purple' See *P.* **'Royal Purple'**
¶ 'Brookside Abigail' LVER
'Brookside Astra' LVER
'Brookside Betty' ESul
  (Dw/C/d)
'Brookside Bolero' (Z) ESul
'Brookside Candy' (Dw/d) ESul WFib
'Brookside Champagne' ESul
  (Min/d)
'Brookside Cinderella' ESul
  (Z/C/d)
'Brookside Flamenco' ESul LVER MWhe WFib
  (Min/d)
'Brookside Primrose' ESul MWhe WFib
  (Min/C/d)
'Brookside Rosita' (Min) ESul
'Brookside Serenade' (Z) ESul WFib
'Brookside Spitfire' ESul
  (Dw/d)
§ 'Brown's Butterfly' (R) EBSP ERav LDea LHop SAga
  WFib
§ 'Bruni' (Z/d) CHal MWhe WFib
'Brunswick' (Sc) ESul EWoo LVER MSte SDen
  WFib
'Brutus' (Z) CWDa
¶ *bubonifolium* CMon MHul
'Bucklesham' (Dw) ESul
'Bumblebee' (Dw) ESul
'Burgenlandmädel' (Z/d) LVER SKen WFib
'Burgundy' (R) LDea LVER WFib
'Burnaby' (Min) WFib
'Burstall' (Min/d) SDen
'Bushfire' ♀ EBSP LDea WFib

'Butley' (Min)	ESul
§ Butterfly (I)	IHos WFib
'Butterfly' (Min/v)	ECtt NPri
§ Cabaret (Z/d)	MBri
caffrum	MHul
'Cal'	See *P.* 'Salmon Irene'
'Caledonia' (Z)	LVER SKen
'Caledonian Maiden' (Z)	WFib
'Caligula' (Min/d)	WFib
'Calypso' (Z)	WFib
'Cameo' (Dw/d)	LVER MWhe WFib
'Camilla' (Dw)	SDen
'Camphor Rose' (Sc)	CLTr ESul GBar
* 'Canadian Centennial'	CBar
'Can-can' (I/d)	WFib
candicans	MHul WFib
'Candy' (Min/d)	ESul
'Candy Kisses' (D)	ESul
canescens	See *P.* 'Blandfordianum'
'Capel' (Dw/d)	ESul
'Capella' (Min)	WFib
Capen (Z/d)	WFib
capitatum	CInt CNat MHul SDen WCHb WEas WFib
'Capri' (Sc)	WFib
'Caprice' (R)	EWoo WFib
'Capricorn' (Min/d)	ESul
'Captain Starlight' (A)	CLit ESul EWoo LDea LHil LVER SSea WEas WFib
'Cardinal'	See *P.* 'Kardinal'
'Cardinal Pink' (Z/d)	CWDa
'Carefree' (U)	EWoo WFib
'Cariboo Gold' (Min/C) ♀	ESul SKen
§ 'Carisbrooke' (R) ♀	ERav LDea SDen SKen SSea WEas WFib
'Carmel' (Z)	WFib
'Carnival' (R)	See *P.* 'Marie Vogel'
'Carnival' (Z)	WFib
carnosum	MHul
'Carol Gibbons' (Z/d)	MWhe
'Carol Munroe' (Z/d)	LVER
'Carole' (R)	EBSP
'Caroline Plumridge' (Dw)	ESul WFib
'Caroline Schmidt' (Z/d/v)	CHal CLit LDea LVER MBEx MBri MSte MWhe NWoo SDen SKen SSea WFib
'Carousel' (Z/d)	CWDa LVER
'Casanova' (Z/d)	WLRN
* 'Cascade Lilac'	WFib
* 'Cascade Pink'	WFib
* 'Cascade Red'	WFib
§ Casino (Z/d)	IHos
'Cassata' (R)	WFib
'Catford Belle' (A) ♀	CLit CSpe ESul GHCN LDea LHil LVER MWhe SDen SKen SSea WEas WFib
'Cathay' (Z/St)	ESul
caucalifolium subsp. *caucalifolium*	MHul
– subsp. *convolvulifolium*	MHul WFib
caylae	MHul
'Cayucas' (I/d)	SKen
'Celebration' (Z/d)	ESul LVER
'Celia' (Min)	WFib
ceratophyllum	MHul
'Cerise Carnation'	See *P.* 'Mrs H.J. Jones'
'Cézanne' (R)	LDea LVER SAga SMrm WFib
§ Champagne (Z)	CWDa
'Chantilly Claret' (R)	EBSP LDea
'Chantilly Lace' (R)	EBSP LDea
'Charity' (Sc) ♀	ERav LDea LIck LVER MWhe WFib

§ 'Charles Gounod' (Z/d)	SKen
§ Charleston (Z)	IHos
'Charlie Boy' (R)	LDea WFib
'Charlotte Bidwell'	ESul
'Charlotte Read' (Dw)	ERea
'Charm' (Min)	ESul
'Charmant'	CWDa
'Charmer' (R)	LDea
'Charmy Snowflake'	WFib WHer
'Chelmondiston' (Min/d)	ESul MWhe
§ 'Chelsea Gem' (Z/d/v) ♀	LVER MBEx SDen SKen SSea WFib
'Chelsea Morning' (Z/d)	WFib
'Chelsworth' (Min/d)	ESul LVER WFib
'Chelvey' (R)	WFib
'Cherie' (Min)	WFib
'Cherie' (R)	LDea WFib
'Cherie Bidwell'	ESul SDen
'Cherie Maid' (Z/v)	LHil WFib
'Cherry' (Min)	LVER WFib
'Cherry' (Z/d)	WFib
'Cherry Cocktail' (Z/v)	MWhe SDen
¶ 'Cherry Galilee' (I/d)	SKen
'Cherry Hazel Ruffled' (R)	LDea
'Cherry Orchard' (R)	LDea LVER SDen SKen SSea WFib
'Cherry Sundae' (Z/d/v)	ESul LVER SDen WFib
'Cherryade' (Dw)	SDen
¶ 'Cheryldene' (R)	LDea
¶ 'Chessington' (Z/C)	SSea
'Chew Magna' (R)	WFib
¶ 'Chic'	NPri
'Chi-Chi' (Min)	ESul LVER
'Chieko' (Min/d)	ESul MWhe SDen WFib
'Chime' (Min/d)	ESul
'China Doll' (Dw/d)	WFib
'Chintz' (R)	LDea
'Chiquita' (R)	LDea WFib
'Chocolate Blotch' (Z/C)	CNat
§ 'Chocolate Peppermint' (Sc) ♀	CHal CInt CLTr CSev ERav ESul IHos LDea LHil MWhe NHHG SDen SKen WCHb WEas WFib WHer WJek WPer
'Chocolate Tomentosum'	See *P.* 'Chocolate Peppermint'
'Choice Cerise' (R)	LDea
'Chorus Girl' (R)	LVER
'Chrissie' (R)	EBSP
'Christie' (Z/d)	WFib
'Christopher Ley' (Z)	LVER SDen SKen
'Cindy' (Dw/d)	ESul
'Circus Day' (R)	LDea WFib
'Citriodorum' (Sc) ♀	CArn CInt LDea NHHG SIde WCHb WEas WFib WPer
'Citronella' (Sc)	LDea MSte NHHG WCHb WFib
citronellum (Sc)	CInt MHul NSty SDen WFib WHer WPer
'Clair' (Min)	WFib
'Clara Read' (Dw)	ESul
'Claret Cruz' (I)	CWDa
'Claret Rock Unique' (U)	CLTr CLit EWoo MSte SDen SKen SMrm WFib
'Clarissa' (Min)	ESul
'Clatterbridge' (Dw)	ESul LVER WFib
'Claude Read' (Dw)	ERea ESul
'Claudette' (Min)	ESul
'Claudius' (Min)	ESul
'Claydon' (Dw/d)	ESul LVER
'Claydon Firebird' (R)	EBSP
'Cleopatra' (Z)	WFib

'Clorinda' (U/Sc) CHal CSev EBar ERea ESul EWoo GBar LHil LVER MSte SDen SKen WCHb WFib WHer WJek

'Clorinda Variegated' See *P.* **'Variegated Clorinda'**
'Clown' (R) WFib
'Coddenham' (Dw/d) ESul LVER WFib
'Colette' (Min) WFib
§ 'Colonel Baden-Powell' LDea
  (I/d)
'Colonel Drabbe' (Z/d) WFib
§ 'Columbia' (Z/Sc) IHos
columbinum MHul
'Comedy' NPri WLRN
'Concolor Lace' (Sc) CLTr CLit ESul
'Conspicuous' (R) WFib
'Contrast' (Z/d/C/v) MBri MWhe SDen SKen SSea WEas WFib
'Cook's Red Spider' (Ca) WFib
'Copdock' (Min/d) ESul
'Copthorne' (Sc) ♀ CLTr CMdw CNat CSpe ESul LVER WFib
'Coral Frills' (Dw) ESul
'Coral Sunset' (d) CWDa
'Coralglow' (Z/d) IHos
cordifolium EWoo LHil MHul WFib WHer
'Coriand' (Z/d) WFib
coriandrifolium See *P. myrrhifolium*
'Cornell' (I/d) ECtt IHos MBri WFib
'Coronia' (Z/Ca) CWDa
coronopifolium MHul
'Corsair' (Z/d) ♀ MWhe WFib
cortusifolium MHul
'Cotswold Queen' (Z/d) WFib
¶ 'Cotta Lilac Queen' (I) LVER
¶ 'Cottenham Beauty' (A) LDea
'Cottenham Surprise' (A) LDea
'Cotton Candy' (Dw/d) ESul
'Cottontail' (Min/d) ESul LVER
cotyledonis MHul WHel
'Countess Mariza' See *P.* **'Gräfin Mariza'**
'Countess of Birkenhead' WFib
  (Z)
'Countess of Scarborough' See *P.* **'Lady Scarborough'**
'Country Girl' (R) IHos WFib
'Cover Girl' (Z/d) WFib
'Cramdon Red' (Dw) SKen WFib
'Crampel's Master' (Z) LVER SKen
'Cranbrook Black' EWoo
'Cransley Blends' (R) EBSP LDea WFib
'Cransley Star' (A) ESul LDea WEas WFib
crassicaule MHul
'Cream and Green' CSpe
'Creamery' (Z/d) CSpe WFib
§ 'Creamy Nutmeg' (Sc/v) CArn CHal CLTr ESul GBar LDea LVER MWhe NSty SSea
'Creed's Seedling' (Z/C) ERav
'Creeting St Mary' (Min) ESul
'Creeting St Peter' (Min) ESul
'Crescendo' (I/d) ECtt
'Crimson Crampel' (Z) CWDa
'Crimson Fire' (Z/d) MBri MWhe SKen WFib
'Crimson Unique' (U) ♀ CLit EWoo LHil SKen SSea WFib
crispum (Sc) CJew CNat GBar GPoy LDea NHHG SDen WCHb WEas WFib WJek WRha
– 'Major' (Sc) ESul NSty SDen SKen WFib WHer WPer
– 'Minor' MGra
– 'Peach Cream' (Sc/v) CHal CInt CSev MGra MWhe SDen WFib WJek

– 'Variegatum' (Sc/v) ♀ CHal CSev ERav GBar GHCN GPoy IHos LDea LHil LVER MBEx MWhe NSty SDen SKen SSea WCHb WEas WFib WHer WWye
'Crocketta' (I/d) LVER
'Crocodile' See *P.* **'The Crocodile'**
'Crowfield' (Min/d) ESul LVER
'Crystal Palace Gem' LVER MWhe SDen SKen
  (Z/v) SMrm SSea WFib
cucullatum EWoo MHul SVen WFib
§ 'Culm' (A) LDea
'Culpho' (Min/C/d) ESul
'Cupid' (Min/Dw/d) ESul WFib
'Cyril Read' (Dw) ERea ESul
§ 'Czar' (Z/C) WFib
'Dainty Lassie' (Dw/v) ESul
'Dainty Maid' ESul
'Dale Queen' (Z) WFib
'Dame Anna Neagle' ESul LVER WFib
  (Dw/d) ♀
'Dancer' (Dw) ESul
'Dandee' (Z/d) WFib
'Danny West' SDen
'Dark Lady' (Sc) WFib
'Dark Presidio' See *P.* **'Dark Mabel'**
'Dark Red Irene' (Z/d) LVER MWhe WFib
'Dark Secret' (R) CSpe EBSP LDea SDen SKen WFib
'Dark Venus' (R) LDea SDen WFib
'Darmsden' (A) ♀ ESul LDea
§ 'Dart' (A) LDea
dasyphyllum MHul
'David John' (Dw/d) ESul LVER SDen
'Davina' (Min/d) ESul WFib
'Dawn' (Z/d) WFib
'Dawn Star' (Z/St) CSpe ESul WFib
'Deacon Arlon' (Dw/d) ESul LVER MWhe SKen
'Deacon Avalon' (Dw/d) WFib
'Deacon Barbecue' (Z/d) ESul MWhe SDen SKen
'Deacon Birthday' (Z/d) CLit ESul LVER MWhe WFib
'Deacon Bonanza' (Z/d) CLit ESul LVER MWhe SDen SKen WFib
'Deacon Clarion' (Z/d) ESul LVER SKen
'Deacon Constancy' (Z/d) CLit ESul LVER MWhe SDen
'Deacon Coral Reef' (Z/d) CLit ESul LVER MWhe SKen WFib
'Deacon Finale' (Z/d) ESul LVER SDen
'Deacon Finito' See *P.* **'Finito'**
'Deacon Fireball' (Z/d) ESul LVER MWhe SDen SKen WFib
'Deacon Flamingo' (Z/d) ESul MWhe SDen
'Deacon Gala' (Z/d) ESul LVER MWhe SDen
'Deacon Golden Bonanza' ESul WFib
  (Z/C/d)
'Deacon Golden Gala' ESul SKen
  (Z/C/d)
I 'Deacon Golden Lilac ESul SKen WFib
  Mist' (Z/C/d)
'Deacon Golden Mist' See *P.* **'Golden Mist'**
'Deacon Jubilant' (Z/d) ESul MWhe SDen SKen
'Deacon Lilac Mist' (Z/d) CLit ESul LVER MWhe SDen SKen WFib
'Deacon Mandarin' (Z/d) ESul MWhe SKen
'Deacon Minuet' (Z/C/d) CLit ESul LVER MWhe SDen SKen
'Deacon Moonlight' (Z/d) ESul LVER MWhe
'Deacon Peacock' (Z/C/d) ESul MWhe SDen SKen
'Deacon Picotee' (Z/d) ESul IHos LVER MBri MWhe SDen SKen
'Deacon Regalia' (Z/d) CLit ESul MWhe SDen SKen WFib

'Deacon Romance' (Z/d) ESul LVER MWhe SDen SKen WFib
'Deacon Summertime' (Z/d) CLit ESul LVER MWhe
'Deacon Sunburst' (Z/d) ESul LVER MWhe SDen SKen
'Deacon Suntan' (Z/d) ESul LVER MWhe SKen WFib
'Deacon Trousseau' (Z/d) ESul LVER MWhe SDen WFib
¶ 'Debbie Parmer' (Dw/d) ESul
¶ 'Deborah Miliken' (Z/d) LVER
'Decora Impérial' (I) LDea LVER SKen
* 'Decora Lavender' (I) LVER
§ 'Decora Lilas' (I) ECtt LDea SKen
'Decora Mauve' See *P.* 'Decora Lilas'
§ 'Decora Rose' (I) ECtt IHos LDea SKen
'Decora Rouge' (I) ECtt LDea NPri
'Deerwood Lavender Lad' (Sc) ESul WFib
'Degas' (R) WFib
'Delhi' (R) WFib
'Delightful' (R) WFib
'Delilah' (R) LDea
'Delta' (Min/d) ESul
'Denebola' (Min/d) ESul LVER WFib
denticulatum NHHG SDen SKen WCHb WFib WJek
– 'Filicifolium' (Sc) CHal CInt CLTr CLit EWoo GBar IHos NHHG SDen WFib WHer WJek WWye
desertorum MHul
'Destiny' (R) WFib
¶ 'Devon Cream' LHil
'Diabolo' WLRN
'Diadem' (R) WFib
'Diana Palmer' (Z/d) SKen WFib
'Diane' (Min/d) ESul SDen WFib
¶ 'Diane Louise' (d) SDen
'Dibbinsdale' (Z) ESul
dichondrifolium EWoo MHul NSty SSad WFib
'Diddi-Di' (Min/d) ESul
'Didi' (Min) ESul SKen WFib
'Dinky' (Min/d) ESul
§ Disco (Z/d) CWDa
'Distinction' (Z) CSpe IHos LHil MBEx MWhe SDen SKen WFib
'Doctor A. Chipault' (I/d) LDea WFib
* 'Doctor A. Vialetts' CWDa
'Doctor Margaret Sturgis' (Z/d) WFib
'Dodd's Super Double' (Z/d) CHal LVER WFib
'Dolce Vita' WLRN
'Dollar Bute' (R) LDea
'Dollar Princess' (Z/C) SKen
'Dolly Read' (Dw) ERea ESul WFib
'Dolly Varden' (Z/v) ♀ CLit IHos LDea LHil LVER MBri MWhe SKen SLMG WFib
dolomiticum MHul WFib
'Dolphin' (Min) WFib
'Don Quixote' (A) LDea
'Don's Carosel' (Z/v) WFib
¶ 'Don's Judith Ann' (Z/C) LVER
'Don's Mona Noble' (Z/C/v) SDen SKen
'Don's Silva Perle' (Dw/v) SDen SKen
¶ 'Doreen' (Z/d) LVER
'Doreen Featherby' (R) WFib
* 'Doreen Maddison' LDea
'Doris Brook' (Z/d) WFib
'Doris Frith' (R) LDea SDen WFib
'Doris Hancock' (R) WFib
'Doris Moore' (Z) LVER
'Doris Shaw' (R) WFib

'Double Bird's Egg' (Z/d) CWDa
'Double Grace Wells' (Min/d) ESul
'Double Henry Jacoby' See *P.* 'Double Jacoby'
§ 'Double Jacoby' (Z/d) SDen WFib
'Double Lilac White' (I/d) IHos
'Double New Life' (Z/d) CHal CWDa
'Double Orange' (Z/d) SKen
'Double Pink Bird's Egg' (Z/d) SKen
'Double White Lilac Eye' (I/d) SDen
'Dove' (Z) WFib
'Dovedale' (Dw/C) ESul
'Downlands' (Z/d) LVER SDen
'Dream' (Z) CWDa WFib
'Dresden China' (R) LDea
'Dresden Pink' (Dw) CLit LVER WFib
¶ 'Dresden Pippa Rosa' (Z/S) WFib
'Dresden White' (Dw) LHil LVER
'Drummer Boy' (Z) CWDa SKen
'Dryden' (Z) LVER SDen SKen WFib
'Dubonnet' (R) LDea WFib
'Duchess of Devonshire' (Z) SKen
'Duke of Buckingham' (Z/d) LVER SDen
'Duke of Devonshire' (Z/d) LVER
'Duke of Edinburgh' See *P.* 'Hederinum Variegatum'
'Dulcie' (Min) ESul
'Dunkery Beacon' (R) LDea WFib
'Dusty Rose' (Min) ESul WFib
§ 'Dwarf Miriam Baisey' (Min) LVER WFib
'Dwarf Miriam Read' See *P.* 'Dwarf Miriam Baisey'
'E. Dabner' (Z/d) CWDa SKen WFib
'Earl of Chester' (Min/d) ♀ WFib
'Earliana' (Dec) ESul LDea SKen
'Earls Four' (R) LDea
'Eastbourne Beauty' (I/d) SLMG WFib
'Easter Greeting' See *P.* 'Ostergruss'
'Easter Morn' (Z/St) WFib
echinatum LVER MHul
– 'Album' SDen SSad
– 'Miss Stapleton' See *P.* 'Miss Stapleton'
'Eclipse' (I) ESul MWhe SDen SKen WFib
'Eden Gem' (Min/d) ESul SDen WFib
'Edith Steane' (Dw/d) ESul LVER
'Edmond Lachenal' (Z/d) WFib
'Edna' (Z/d) WFib
'Edward Hockey' (Z) WFib
'Edward Humphris' (Z) SDen SKen
'Edwin Clarke' (Dw/Min) ESul
'Eileen' (I) LVER WFib
'Eileen Postle' (R) ♀ WFib
'Eileen Stanley' (R) LDea
'Elaine' (R) LDea
'Eldorado' WLRN
'Eleanor' (Z/d) SDen
'Electra' (Z/d) CWDa LVER SDen SKen WFib
elegans MHul
'Elfin Rapture' (R) WFib
'Elgar' (R) WFib
'Elizabeth Angus' (Z) SDen SKen WFib
'Elizabeth Cartwright' (Z) WFib
'Elizabeth Read' (Dw) ERea ESul WFib
'Elmsett' (Z/C/d) ESul LVER
'Elna' (Min) ESul
elongatum MHul

'Els' (Min/St) ESul LHil LVER SKen
'Els Variegated' SMrm
'Elsi' (I/d/v) LVER WFib
'Elsie Hickman' (R) LDea SDen WFib
'Elsie Portas' (Z/C/d) ESul SKen
'Embassy' (Dw) ESul WFib
'Emerald' (I) SDen SKen
'Emma Hössle' See *P.* **'Frau Emma Hössle'**
'Emma Jane Read' CLit ERea ESul MWhe WFib
  (Dw/d)
'Emma Louise' (Z) LVER SKen
¶ 'Emmy Sensation' (R) LDea
'Emperor Nicholas' (Z/d) MWhe SKen
'Empress' (Z) SKen
'Ena' (Min) ESul
'Enchantress' (I) MBri SDen SKen
'Encore' LVER MWhe
endlicherianum CGen CMon EPot MHul NGre
  NWCA SIgm
'Endora' (Min) ESul SDen
'Endsleigh' (Sc) SDen
englerianum MHul
'Enid Blackaby' (R) WFib
'Enid Read' (Dw) ERea WFib
'Eric Ellis' (Dw/d) WFib
'Eric Hoskins' (Z/d) WFib
* 'Eric Lee' CWDa
'Erwarton' (Min/d) ESul LVER SDen
'Escapade' (Dw/d) ESul WFib
'Esteem' (Z/d) WFib
'Etna' (Min) WFib
'Evelyn' ESul
'Evesham Wonder' (Z/d) SDen WFib
exhibens MHul
'Explosive' WLRN
exstipulatum MHul WEas WFib
'Fair Dinkum' (Z/v) MWhe
§ 'Fair Ellen' (Sc) CLTr ERav EWoo SKen WFib
  WPer
'Fairlee' (DwI) SDen
'Fairy Orchid' (A) CLit ESul LDea LVER
'Fairy Princess' (R) LDea
'Fairy Queen' CLit EWoo LDea WEas
'Fairy Tales' (Dw) ESul WFib
'Falkland Brother' (Z/C/v) WFib
'Falkland Hero' (Z/v) MWhe WFib
'Fandango' (Z/St/d) ESul LHil WFib
* 'Fanfare' CWDa
'Fanny Eden' (R) WFib
'Fantasia' white (Dw/d) ♀ ESul MWhe WFib
'Fareham' (R) ♀ EBSP LDea MSte WFib
'Fascination' (Z/Ca) WFib
'Feneela' (Dw/d) ESul
'Fenton Farm' (Z/C) ESul SDen
'Festal' (Min/d) ESul
'Feuerriese' (Z) LVER SKen
'Fiat' (Z/d) CWDa SKen
'Fiat Queen' (Z/d) SKen WFib
'Fiat Supreme' (Z/d) SKen WFib
§ 'Fidelio' (Z/d) IHos
'Fiery Sunrise' (R) EBSP LDea LVER
'Fiesta' (I/d) LDea
'Fiesta' (R) WFib
'Fifth Avenue' (R) CSpe MSte SDen WFib
'Filicifolium' See *P.* **(Denticulatum Group)**
  'Filicifolium'
§ 'Finito' (Dw/d) CLit ERea
'Fire Cascade' (I) NPri
'Fire Dragon' (Z/St/d) SKen
'Fire Light' (Min/d) WFib
'Firebrand' (Z/d) LVER
'Firefly' (Min/d) ESul WFib

'Firestone' (Dw) ESul
'First Blush' (R) WFib
'First Love' (Z) LVER
fissifolium MHul
'Flair' (R) WFib
¶ 'Flair Greetings' (Z/C) LVER
'Flakey' (I/d/v) ♀ CSpe ESul LDea MWhe WFib
'Flame' (Z) WFib
'Flesh Pink' (Z/d) CWDa
'Fleur d'Amour' (R) WFib
'Fleurette' (Dw/d) CHal ESul MWhe SDen SKen
  WFib
§ Flirt (Min) ESul MBri WFib
'Floral Cascade' (Fr/d) WFib
'Florence Storey' (Z/C/d) WFib
'Flower Basket' (R) LDea
'Flower of Spring' (Z/v) ♀ CHal LVER MWhe SDen SKen
  SSea WFib
'Flowerfield' (Z) SDen WFib
'Flowton' (Dw/d) ESul
* 'Forever' (d) CWDa
'Fox' (Z/d) CHal WFib
'Foxhall' (Dw) ESul
Fragrans Group (Sc) CHal CLTr CLit CMil CSev
  ERav ESul EWoo GCra GHCN
  GPoy LVER MGra MWhe
  NHHG NSty SDen SKen WFib
  WHer WPer WWye
– 'Creamy Nutmeg' See *P.* **'Creamy Nutmeg'**
§ – 'Fragrans Variegatum' CInt CMil CSev CSpe EBar
  (Sc/v) ERav LIck MWhe NSty SDen
  SKen WCHb WFib WJek WPer
– 'Snowy Nutmeg' See *P.* **(Fragrans Group)**
  'Fragrans Variegatum'
'Fraiche Beauté' (Z/d) CWDa WFib
'Francis James' (Z) SDen WFib
'Francis Parrett' (Min/d) ESul LVER MWhe WFib
  ♀
'Francis Read' (Dw/d) ERea ESul
'Frank Headley' (Z/v) ♀ CHal CLit CSpe ERav ESul
  IHos LDea LHil LVER MBEx
  MMil MSte MWhe SDen SKen
  SMrm SSea WEas WFib
'Frank Parrett' (Min/d) ESul
§ 'Frau Emma Hössle' WFib
  (Dw/d)
'Frau Käthe Neubronner' CWDa SDen
  (Z/d)
'Freak of Nature' (Z/v) IHos LHil MWhe SDen SKen
  SSea WEas WFib
'Freckles' (Z/d) WFib
'Frensham' (Sc) ESul IHos WFib
'Freston' (Dw) ESul
'Friary Wood' (Z/C/d) ESul SSea WFib
'Friesdorf' (Dw) ERav ESul LHil LVER MWhe
  SDen SKen WEas WFib
'Frills' (Min/d) ESul SKen WFib
¶ 'Fringed Angel' (A) LDea
§ 'Fringed Aztec' (R) ♀ EBSP LDea LVER SAga SDen
  SKen WFib
'Fringed Rouletta' (I) LDea
'Frosty' See *P.* **'Variegated Kleine**
  Liebling'
'Frosty Petit Pierre' See *P.* **'Variegated Kleine**
  Liebling'
'Frühlingszauber Lilac' EBSP
  (R)
frutetorum MHul
fruticosum MHul WFib
fulgidum MHul WFib
'Funny Girl' (R) WFib
'Fynn' (Dw) ESul

¶ 'Gabriel' (A)   LDea
'Galilee' (I/d) ♀   IHos LDea LVER SDen SKen
                                 WFib
'Galway Star' (Sc/v) ♀   CNat CSpe LVER SDen WFib
'Garda' (I/d)   ECtt
'Garibaldi' (Z/d)   CWDa WFib
'Garland' (R)   ESul
'Garnet' (Z/d)   ESul LVER WFib
'Garnet Rosebud' (Min/d)   ESul LVER
'Garnet Wings' (R)   WFib
'Gartendirektor Herman'   ERav EWoo SMrm WFib
  (Dec)
'Gary Salvidge' (R)   LDea
'Gay Baby' (DwI)   ESul LDea MWhe SDen
'Gay Baby Supreme'   ESul SDen
  (DwI)
'Gazelle' (Z)   SDen SKen
§ 'Gemini' (Z/St/d)   ESul WFib
'Gemma' (Min/C)   LVER WFib
'Gemma' (R)   LDea LVER
'Gemma Jewel' (R) ♀   EBSP
'Gemstone' (Sc) ♀   ESul LDea WFib
'Genetrix' (Z/d)   WFib
'Genie' (Z/d)   LVER MWhe SDen SKen WFib
'Gentle Georgia' (R)   WFib
'Geoff May' (Dw)   ESul SDen WFib
'Geoffrey Harvey' (Z/d)   WFib
'Geoffrey Horsman' (R)   WFib
'Georgia' (R)   WFib
'Georgia Peach' (R)   EBSP SDen WFib
'Georgina Blythe' ♀   WFib
'Geo's Pink' (Z/v)   MWhe
¶ 'Gerald Caws' (d)   SDen
'Gerald Portas' (Dw/C)   ESul LIck
'Gerald Wells' (Min)   ESul
'Geraldine' (Min)   ESul LVER
'Geronimo' (R)   WFib
'Gess Portas' (Z/v)   ESul SKen
'Giant Butterfly' (R)   LDea SDen
'Giant Oak' (Sc)   MSte WFib
gibbosum   CNat LBlm MHul SDen WFib
'Gilbert West' (Z)   SDen SKen
'Gilda' (R)   EBSP LDea
'Gill' (Min/Ca)   ESul
'Gillian Clifford' (Z/d)   SDen
* 'Giro Fly'   CLit
¶ 'Glacier Crimson' (Z)   SKen
'Glacis' (Z/d)   WFib
'Gladys Evelyn' (Z/d)   WFib
'Gladys Stevens' (Min/d)   ESul
× *glaucifolium*   MHul
glaucum   See *P. lanceolatum*
'Gleam' (Z/d)   LVER
'Glenn Barker' (Z/d)   WFib
'Glenshree' (R)   LDea LVER WFib
'Gloria Pearce' (R)   LDea SDen WFib
'Glory' (Z/d)   WFib
'Glowing Embers' (R)   LDea WFib
'Goblin' (Min/d)   ESul IHos SDen SKen WFib
* 'Godshill'   LDea
* 'Gold Medallion'   CLit
'Gold Star' (Z/St/C)   ESul
'Golden Baby' (DwI/C)   LDea MWhe
'Golden Brilliantissimum'   LVER MWhe SKen WFib
  (Z/C)
'Golden Butterfly' (Z/C)   ESul
'Golden Chalice' (Min/v)   ESul LVER MWhe
'Golden Clorinda'   CLit EWoo SDen WEas
  (U/Sc/C)
'Golden Crest' (Z/C)   SKen SMrm SSea

'Golden Ears' (Dw/St/C)   ESul MBri MWhe NPer SDen
                                 WFib
'Golden Everaarts'   ESul
  (Dw/C)
'Golden Fleece' (Min/C/d)   ESul SDen
'Golden Gates' (Z/C)   ESul SDen SKen
'Golden Harry Hieover'   ESul LVER MBEx MBri SDen
  (Z/C)   SKen WEas
'Golden Mirage' (Z/v)   SSea WFib
§ 'Golden Mist' (Dw/C/d)   CLit LVER
'Golden Orange' (Dw/C)   ESul
'Golden Orfe' (Dw/C)   WFib
'Golden Petit Pierre'   CLit ESul
  (Min/C)
'Golden Princess' (Min/C)   ESul WFib
'Golden Princess' (R)   LDea
'Golden Roc' (Min/C)   ESul
'Golden Ruth' (Z)   WFib
'Golden Staphs' (St/C)   ESul LIck LVER SDen WFib
¶ 'Golden Stardust' (Z/St)   LVER
'Golden Tears' (MinI/C/d)   ESul
'Golden Wedding' (Z/d/v)   LVER MWhe
'Golden Well Sweet' (Sc)   ERav WFib
'Goldie' (R)   WFib
'Goldilocks' (A)   ESul LDea WFib
'Gooseberry Leaf'   See *P. grossularioides*
'Gordano Midnight' (R)   WFib
'Gordino Pixie' (R)   LDea
'Gosbeck' (A)   ESul LDea SDen SSea
'Gosport Girl' (R)   EBSP LDea
¶ 'Gothenburg'   EBSP
'Grace Thomas' (Sc) ♀   WFib
'Grace Wells' (Min)   ESul SDen WFib
'Gracious Lady' (Z/d)   WFib
§ 'Gräfin Mariza' (Z/d)   IHos SDen SKen WFib
'Grand Slam' (R)   EBSP LDea LVER SDen SKen
                                 WFib
grandiflorum   MHul WFib
'Grandma Fischer'   See *P. 'Grossmutter Fischer'*
'Grandma Ross' (R)   EBSP LDea
'Granny Hewitt' (Min/d)   ESul
§ 'Graveolens' (Sc)   CHal CLTr CNat CSev ESul
                                 GHCN GPoy LVER MWhe
                                 NSty SDen SKen SSea WFib
                                 WJek
'Great Blakenham' (Min)   ESul
'Great Bricett' (Min/d)   ESul LVER
'Green Ears' (Z/St)   ESul WFib
'Green Eyes' (I/d)   LDea SDen
'Green Goddess' (I/d)   LDea SKen
'Green Gold Petit Pierre'   ESul SDen
  (MiN)
'Green Lady' (Sc)   WFib
'Green Woodpecker' (R)   LDea LVER SDen SSea
§ 'Greengold Kleine   ESul SDen SKen
  Liebling' (Min/C/v)
'Greengold Petit Pierre'   See *P. 'Greengold Kleine
                                 Liebling'*
'Greetings' (Min/v)   ESul MBri SDen WFib
§ 'Grenadier' (Z)   CWDa
§ 'Grenadier' (Z/St/d) ♀   SDen
'Grey Lady Plymouth'   ESul EWoo GBar LBlm LDea
  (Sc/v)   SIde WFib
'Grey Sprite' (Min/v)   ESul WFib
greytonense   MHul
griseum   MHul WFib
* 'Groombridge Success' (d)   CWDa
§ 'Grossmutter Fischer' (R)   LDea WEas WFib
§ *grossularioides*   CInt CNat ESul MHul
'Grozser Garten' (Dw)   ESul
'Grozser Garten Weiss'   ESul
  (Dw)

Wico = 'Guimongol' — NPri WLRN
Vinco = 'Guivin' — CWDa
'Gurnard' — SDen
'Gustav Emich' (Z/d) — SDen SKen WFib
'H. Guinier' — See *P.* 'Charles Gounod'
'H. Rigler' (Z) — SDen SKen
'Hadleigh' (Dw) — ESul
'Hamble Lass' (R) — EBSP LDea
'Hanchen Anders' (Z) — WFib
§ 'Hannaford Star' (Z/St/d) — ESul WFib
'Hannah' (A) — ESul
'Hans Rigler' (Z/d) — WFib
§ 'Happy Thought' (Z/v) ♀ — CHal CLTr CLit IHos LDea
    MBri MWhe SDen SKen SSea
'Happy Valley' (R) — EBSP LVER WFib
'Harbour Lights' (R) — EBSP LDea WFib
'Harewood Slam' (R) — LDea LVER MSte SDen SMrm
    WEas WFib
'Harkstead' (Min) — ESul
¶ 'Harlequin' (Dw) — ESul
'Harlequin Alpine Glow' — LDea LVER MWhe WFib
    (I)
'Harlequin Candy Floss' — CWDa
    (I/d)
'Harlequin Liverbird' (I) — WFib
'Harlequin Mahogany' — LDea LVER MBri MWhe SDen
    (I/d) — SKen WFib
§ 'Harlequin Miss Liver — LDea SDen SKen
    Bird' (I)
'Harlequin Picotee' (I/d) — LDea LVER SDen SKen
'Harlequin Pretty Girl' (I) — MWhe SDen WFib
'Harlequin Rosie O'Day' — LDea MWhe SDen SKen WFib
    (I)
'Harlequin Ted Day' (I) — LDea LVER
'Harold Bowie' (Z/d) — WFib
'Harold Headley' (Z/v) — WFib
'Harriet Le Hair' (Z) — SKen
'Harvard' (I) — LVER SDen WFib
'Harvey' (Z) — MWhe
¶ *havlasae* — MHul
'Hayley Charlotte' (Z/v) — MWhe
'Hay's Radiant' (Z/d) — WFib
* 'Hazel' (R) — LVER SDen WFib
* 'Hazel Adair' — LDea
'Hazel Anson' (R) — LDea
'Hazel Barolo' (R) — LDea
'Hazel Beauty' (R) — LVER
'Hazel Birkby' (R) — EBSP LDea SDen WFib
'Hazel Blake' (R) — WFib
'Hazel Burgundy' (R) — EBSP
'Hazel Burtoff' (R) — EBSP LDea WFib
'Hazel Carey' (R) — LDea
'Hazel Cherry' (R) — LDea WFib
'Hazel Chick' (R) — LDea
'Hazel Choice' (R) — EBSP LDea SDen WFib
'Hazel Gipsy' (R) — LDea SDen WFib
'Hazel Glory' (R) — LDea WFib
'Hazel Gowland' (R) — LDea
'Hazel Harmony' (R) — LDea
'Hazel Heather' (R) — LDea
'Hazel Henderson' (R) — LDea LHil
'Hazel Herald' (R) — EBSP LDea SDen
'Hazel Mistique' (R) — LDea
'Hazel Peach' (R) — LDea
'Hazel Perfection' (R) — LDea
'Hazel Rose' (R) — LDea
'Hazel Saga' (R) — EBSP WFib
'Hazel Satin' (R) — LDea
'Hazel Shiraz' (R) — LDea
'Hazel Star' (R) — EBSP LDea
'Hazel Stardust' (R) — EBSP LDea
* 'Hazel Whitaker' — LDea

'Hazel Wright' (R) — LDea
§ 'Hederinum' (I) — IHos LDea NPri SKen WEas
§ 'Hederinum Variegatum' — CHal CSpe LDea WFib
    (I/v)
'Heidi' (Min/d) — ESul
* 'Helen Bowie' — CWDa
'Helen Christine' (Z/St) — WFib
'Helena' (I/d) — LDea MWhe SDen SKen WFib
'Helter Skelter' (Z/v) — SDen
'Hemingstone' (A) — ESul LDea
'Henhurst Gleam' — ESul WFib
    (Dw/C/d)
'Hermione' (Z/d) — CHal MWhe WFib
'High Tor' (Dw/C/d) — CLit ESul SKen WFib
'Highfields Always' (Z/d) — IHos LVER
'Highfields Appleblossom' — IHos LVER SKen
    (Z/d)
'Highfields Attracta' (Z/d) — LVER SDen SKen
'Highfields Ballerina' — LVER WFib
    (Z/d)
'Highfields Candy Floss' — LVER SDen
    (Z/d)
'Highfields Charisma' — LVER
    (Z/d)
'Highfields Choice' (Z) — LVER SDen SKen
'Highfields Comet' (Z) — SKen
'Highfields Contessa' — LVER SDen SKen WFib
    (Z/d)
'Highfields Dazzler' (Z) — LVER
'Highfields Delight' (Z) — LVER
'Highfields Fancy' (Z/d) — IHos LVER SDen SKen
'Highfields Festival' (Z/d) — LVER MWhe SDen SKen
¶ 'Highfields Flair' (Z/d) — LVER
'Highfields Joy' (Z/d) — SDen SKen
'Highfields Melody' (Z/d) — SDen
'Highfields Orange' (Z) — LVER MWhe
'Highfields Paramount' — SDen SKen
    (Z)
'Highfields Pearl' (Z) — LVER
'Highfields Perfecta' (Z) — CWDa
'Highfields Pink' (Z) — LVER
'Highfields Pride' (Z) — LVER SDen SKen
'Highfields Prima Donna' — LVER MWhe SKen WFib
    (Z/d)
'Highfields Promise' (Z) — SDen SKen
'Highfields Serenade' (Z) — LVER
'Highfields Snowdrift' (Z) — LVER SKen
'Highfields Sonata' (Z/d) — LVER
'Highfields Sugar Candy' — ECtt IHos LVER SDen SKen
    (Z/d) — WFib
'Highfields Supreme' (Z) — LVER
'Highfields Symphony' (Z) — LVER WFib
'Highfields Vogue' (Z) — LVER
'Highscore' (Z/d) — WFib
'Hi-jinks' (Z/v) — MWhe
'Hildegard' (Z/d) — CHal SKen WFib
'Hills of Snow' (Z/v) — CHal LVER MBri SDen SKen
    WFib
'Hillscheider Amethyst' — See *P.* 'Amethyst'
'Hindoo' (R) — CNat SSea WFib
'Hintlesham' (Min) — ESul
hirtum — MHul
hispidum — MHul
'Hitcham' (Min/d) — ESul WFib
'Holbrook' (Min/C/d) — ESul SDen
'Holly West' — SDen
'Holmes Miller' (Z/d) — ESul
'Honeywood Hannah' (R) — WFib
'Honeywood Jonathan' — EBSP WFib
    (R)
'Honeywood Lindy' (R) — EBSP LDea SDen

'Honeywood Matthew' (Dw)   ESul
'Honeywood Suzanne' (Min/Fr)   ESul LVER SKen WFib
'Honne Früling' (Z)   SKen WFib
'Honneas' (Min)   ESul
'Honnestolz' (Min)   ESul SKen
'Hope' (Z)   WFib
'Hope Valley' (Dw/C/d) ♀   ESul MWhe SKen SSea
'Horace Parsons' (R)   LDea WFib
'Horace Read' (Dw)   ERea ESul
'Horning Ferry' (Dw)   ESul
'House and Garden' (R)   SDen WFib
'Howard Stanton' (R)   SDen WFib
'Howard's Orange' (R)   LDea
'Hugo de Vries' (Dw/d)   CWDa WFib
'Hula' (U)   EWoo LVER WFib
'Hulda Conn' (Ca/d)   WFib
'Hunter's Moon' (Z/C)   ESul SDen
'Hurdy-gurdy' (Z/d/v)   ESul MWhe SDen WFib
HWD Corelli   IHos
HWD Gabrieli   IHos
HWD Monteverdi   IHos
HWD Onyx   IHos
HWD Romanze   IHos
HWD Vivaldi   IHos
hypoleucum   MHul
'Ian Read' (Min/d)   ERea ESul WFib
'Icecrystal'   CWDa WLRN
'Icing Sugar' (I/d)   ESul LDea SSea WFib
* 'Ilse Fisher'   CWDa
'Immaculatum' (Z)   WFib
'Imperial Butterfly' (Sc)   CLit ESul LDea LVER WFib
'Improved Petit Pierre' (Min)   ESul
'Improved Ricard' (Z/d)   WFib
'Ina' (Z/d)   WFib
'Inca' (R)   LDea SDen WFib
incrassatum   MHul
'Ingres' (I/d) ♀   ECtt IHos
inquinans   MHul WFib
iocastum   MHul
ionidiflorum   CSpe MHul
'Ipswich Town' (Dw/d)   ESul
'Irene' (Z/d) ♀   LVER SKen SLMG WFib
'Irene Cal' (Z/d) ♀   SKen
* 'Iris Monroe'   CWDa
§ 'Isabell' (Z/d)   WFib
'Isidel' (I/d) ♀   SKen WFib
'Italian Gem' (I)   SKen
'Ivalo' (Z/d)   IHos MWhe SDen SKen WFib
'Ivory Snow' (Z/d/v)   LVER MWhe SKen
'Jacey' (Z/d)   LVER SDen SKen
'Jack Read' (Dw)   ERea
'Jack Wood' (Z/d)   ESul
'Jackie' (I)   WFib
'Jackie's Gem' (I/d)   MWhe
'Jacky Gall' (I/d)   IHos MBri SKen
'Jacqueline' (Z/d)   SKen
'Jana' (Z/d)   WFib
'Jane Biggin' (Dw/C/d)   ESul MWhe SKen
'Janet Hofman' (Z/d)   WFib
¶ 'Janet James'   LVER
'Janet Kerrigan' (Min/d)   ESul MWhe WEas WFib
'Janet Scott' (Z)   CWDa
'Janna Whelan' (Dw/d)   SDen
'Jasmin' (R)   EBSP LDea
'Jaunty' (Min/d)   ESul SDen WFib
'Jayne Eyre' (Min/d)   CHal CLit ESul MWhe SDen SKen WFib
§ 'Jazz'   CWDa IHos
'Jean Bart' (I)   CWDa SDen

'Jean Beatty' (Dw/d)   LVER
'Jean Oberle' (Z/d)   SDen SKen WFib
§ 'Jeanne d'Arc' (I/d)   SKen WFib
'Jenifer Read' (Dw)   ERea ESul
'Jennifer' (Min)   ESul
¶ 'Jer-Rey' (A)   CLit LDea
'Jessel's Unique' (U)   LBlm LHil SDen
'Jessika' (Z/d)   WFib
* 'Jetfire' (d)   CWDa
'Jewel' (R)   EBSP
'Jeweltone' (Z/d)   WFib
'Jill Portas' (Z/C)   ESul
'Jim Field' (R)   WFib
'Jimmy Read' (Min)   ERea
'Jinny Reeves' (R)   EBSP LDea WFib
'Joan Cashmore' (Z/d)   ESul WFib
'Joan Fairman' (R)   WFib
'Joan Fontaine' (Z)   WFib
'Joan Hayward' (Min)   ESul
'Joan Morf' (R)   EBSP LDea SDen SKen SSea WFib
'Joan of Arc'   See *P.* 'Jeanne d'Arc'
'Joanna Pearce' (R)   EBSP LDea SKen
'John Thorp' (R)   LDea
'John's Angela'   LVER
'John's Chameleon'   LVER
'John's Pride'   MBri
'Joseph Haydn' (R)   EBSP
'Joseph Haydon' (R)   LDea
'Joseph Paul' (R)   SDen
'Joseph Warren' (I/d)   LDea SKen
'Joseph Wheeler' (A)   MWhe
'Joy' (R) ♀   EBSP LDea LVER SSea WFib
¶ 'Joy' (Z/d)   SKen
'Joy' (I)   SDen
'Joy Lucille' (Sc)   CNat CSev ESul LDea SDen WCHb WFib
'Joyce Delamere' (Z/C/d)   WFib
'Joyden'   CWDa
'Jubel Parr' (Z/d)   CWDa SDen
'Judith Thorp' (R)   EBSP
'Judy Read' (Dw)   ESul
'Julia' (R) ♀   EBSP LDea
¶ 'Juliana' (R)   LDea
'Julie' (A)   CLit ESul
'Julie Smith' (R)   LDea WFib
¶ 'June Patricia' (d)   SDen
'Jungle Night' (R)   EBSP WFib
'Juniper' (Sc)   WFib
'Jupiter' (Min/d)   SKen WFib
'Jupiter' (R)   EBSP LDea
'Just William' (Min/C/d)   ESul
'Kamahl' (R)   WFib
¶ 'Kandy Waterman' (d)   SDen
§ 'Kardinal' (Z/d)   IHos
'Kardino'   WLRN
'Karl Hagele' (Z/d)   LVER SKen SLMG WFib
'Karmin Ball'   CWDa WFib
karooicum   MHul
karrooense 'Graham Rice'   See *P.* 'Grollie's Cream'
'Kath Peat' (Z/d)   WFib
'Kathleen Gamble' (Z)   SKen
'Kathryn' (Min)   ESul
'Kathryn Portas' (Z/v)   ESul SKen
'Kayleigh West' (Min)   ESul
'Keepsake' (Z/d)   ESul LVER WFib
'Keith Vernon' (Fr/d)   LVER
'Kelvedon Beauty' (Min)   WEas
'Ken Salmon' (Dw/d)   ESul
'Kennard Castle' (Z)   CWDa
'Kenny's Double' (Z/d)   WFib
'Kerensa' (Min/d)   ESul SKen

'Kershy' (Min) ESul
'Kesgrave' (Min/d) ESul LVER
'Kettle Baston' (A) ♀ ESul LDea LHil LVER MWhe WFib
'Kimono' (R) EBSP LDea LHil LVER
'King Edmund' (R) LDea SDen WFib
'King of Balcon' See *P.* **'Hederinum'**
'King of Denmark' (Z/d) LVER SKen WFib
'Kingsmill' (R) LDea SDen
'Kingswood' (Z) SDen
'Kirton' (Min/d) ESul
'Kiwi' MBri
§ 'Kleine Liebling' (Min) EWoo LHop MWhe SKen WFib
¶ 'Kosset' (Min/d) LVER
'Krista' (Min/d) ESul SDen WFib
* 'Kristy' CLit
'Kyra' (Min/d) ESul WFib
'L.E. Wharton' (Z) SDen SKen
'La France' (I/d) ♀ LDea LVER MBri MWhe SDen SKen WEas WFib
'La Jolla' (Z/d) SDen
'La Paloma' (R) LDea WEas WFib
'Laced Mini Cascade' ESul
Lachsball (Z/d) SKen WFib
§ 'Lachskönigin' (I/d) IHos LDea LVER SDen SKen WEas WFib
'Lady Alice of Valencia' See *P.* **'Grenadier' (Z)**
'Lady Churchill' (Z/v) WFib
'Lady Cullum' (Z/C/v) MWhe
'Lady Ilchester' (Z/d) SDen SKen WFib
'Lady Love Song' (R) EBSP
'Lady Mary' (Sc) ESul EWoo GBar LVER SDen WFib
'Lady Plymouth' (Sc/v) ♀ CHal CInt CLTr CMil CSpe ESul IHos LBlm LDea LHil LVER MSte MWhe NHHG NSty SDen SKen SSea WEas WFib WHer WWye
§ 'Lady Scarborough' (Sc) CArn LDea WFib WWye
laevigatum MHul WEas
¶ 'Lakeland' (I) CLit SKen
'Lakis' (R) LDea
¶ 'Lambada' NPri
'Lamorna' (R) LDea SDen SKen WFib
'Lancastrian' (Z/d) WFib
§ *lanceolatum* MHul
'Langley' (R) LDea SDen
'Lanham Lane' (I) LDea MWhe
'Lanham Royal' (Min/d) ESul
'Lara Aladin' (A) WFib
'Lara Candy Dancer' (Sc) CLit EOHP ESul LDea WFib ♀
'Lara Jester' (Sc) EWoo WFib
'Lara Maid' (A) ♀ ESul WEas WFib
'Lara Nomad' (Sc) EWoo
'Lara Starshine' (Sc) ♀ ESul EWoo SSea WFib
'Lark' (Min/d) ESul
¶ 'Larkfield' SSea
N 'Lass o'Gowrie' (Z/v) LVER MBEx MWhe SKen WFib
'Lass o'Gowrie' (American) WFib (Z/v)
'Laura' (Z/d) WFib
'Laura Wheeler' (A) MWhe
* 'Laurel Heywood' (R) WFib
'Lauripen' (Z/d) WFib
'Lavender Feathers' (R) WFib
'Lavender Grand Slam' EBSP IHos LDea LVER SDen (R) ♀ WFib
'Lavender Harewood EBSP LDea Slam' (R)
'Lavender Mini Cascade' See *P.* **'Lila Mini Cascade'**

'Lavender Sensation' (R) WFib
'Lavender Wings' (I) LDea
laxum MHul
'Layham' (Dw/d) ESul
'Layton's White' (Z/d) CWDa SKen
'Le Lutin' (Z/d) CWDa WFib
'L'Elégante' (I/v) ♀ CHal CLit CSpe EAst IHos LDea LVER MBri MWhe SDen SKen SSea WEas WFib WLRN
'Lemon Air' (Sc) ESul
'Lemon Fancy' (Sc) CInt ESul IHos LVER MWhe SDen WFib WJek
'Len Chandler' (Min) ESul
'L'Enfer' See *P.* **'Mephistopheles'**
'Lenore' (Min) ESul
'Leo' (Min) ESul
'Leonie Holbrow' (Min) ESul
'Leopard' (I/d) CWDa
¶ 'Lerchenmuller' (Z/d) LVER
'Leslie Judd' (R) WFib
'Leslie Salmon' (Min/C) ESul MWhe
'Lethas' (R) LDea
'Letitia' (A) ESul LHil
§ Leucht-Cascade WFib
'Levington' (Min/d) WFib
Lila Compakt-Cascade See *P.* **'Decora Lilas'**
§ 'Lila Mini Cascade' (I) ESul MWhe
'Lilac Cascade' See *P.* **'Roi des Balcons Lilas'**
'Lilac Domino' See *P.* **'Telston's Prima'**
'Lilac Elaine' (R) LDea
'Lilac Gem' (Min/I/d) IHos LDea LVER MWhe SDen SKen WFib
'Lilac Jewel' (R) EBSP
'Lilac Mini Cascade' (I) LDea LVER
'Lili Marlene' (I) LVER SKen
'Lilian' (Dw) ESul
'Lilian Pottinger' (Sc) CArn CHal CInt ESul GHCN LDea LVER MWhe NSty SDen SIde SKen WEas WFib WHer
¶ 'Limelight' SSea
'Limoneum' (Sc) CSev SDen WEas WFib
'Lin Davis' (Z/C) WFib
'Linda' (R) EBSP LDea WFib
'Linda' (Z/d) WFib
'Lindsey' (Min) ESul
'Lindy Portas' (I/d) SKen
'Lisa' (Min/C) CLit ESul WFib
'Little Alice' (Dw/d) ♀ ESul LVER MWhe SDen WFib
'Little Blakenham' (A) ESul LDea
'Little Fi-fine' (Dw) ESul WFib
'Little Gem' (Sc) EWoo LDea LVER NSty SDen WFib
'Little John' (Min/d) WFib
'Little Margaret' (Min/v) ESul LVER
'Little Primular' (Min) ESul
'Little Trot' (Z/v) WFib
'Little Vectis' (D) SDen
'Lively Lady' (Dw/C) ESul SDen
'Liverbird' See *P.* **'Harlequin Miss Liver Bird'**
lobatum MHul
'Lolette' (Min) ESul
'Lollipop' (Z/d) SDen WFib
'Longshot' (R) WFib
* 'Loraine Howarth' ERav
'Lord Baden-Powell' See *P.* **'Colonel Baden-Powell'**
'Lord Bute' (R) ♀ CLit CNat CSpe EBSP ERav EWoo LDea LHil LHop LIck LVER MSCN MSte NPla SBid SIde SKen SMer SMrm SUsu WEas WFib
* 'Lord Constantine' LDea

'Lord de Ramsey'	See *P.* **'Tip Top Duet'**
'Lord Roberts' (Z)	WFib
'Lorelei' (Z/d)	CWDa WFib
'Loretta' (Dw)	ESul
'Loripen' (Z/d)	WFib
'Lorna' (Dw/d)	ESul
* 'Lotus'	WLRN
'Louise' (Min)	EBSP ESul
'Love Song' (R)	EBSP EWoo LDea SSea
'Love Story' (Z/v)	ESul
* 'Loverly' (Min/d)	ESul
Lovesong (Z/d)	WFib
'Lowood' (R)	WFib
'Lucilla' (Min)	ESul SDen
'Lucinda' (Min)	ESul
'Lucy' (Min)	ESul
'Lucy Gunnett' (Z/d/v)	ERav MWhe SDen WFib
'Lucy Jane' (R)	LDea
'Luna'	NPri
luridum	MHul
'Lustre' (R)	EBSP WFib
'Luz del Dio' (R)	WFib
'Lyewood Bonanza' (R)	EBSP LDea
'Lynne Valerie' (A)	LDea LVER
'Lyric' (Min/d)	ESul LVER WFib
'M.J. Cole' (I/d)	LDea
'Mabel Grey' (Sc) ♀	CSev CSpe ERav ESul EWoo
	IHos LBlm LIck LVER MWhe
	NHHG SDen SKen WEas WFib
	WHer WJek WWye
§ 'Madame Auguste Nonin'	CHal LHil LVER NWoo SAga
(Sc)	SDen SKen WFib
'Madame Butterfly'	ESul MWhe SKen
(Z/C/d)	
'Madame Crousse' (I/d) ♀	SDen WEas WFib
'Madame Dubarry' (Z)	WFib
'Madame Fournier'	ESul
(Min/C)	
'Madame Guinier'	See *P.* **'Charles Gounod'**
'Madame Hibbault' (Z)	SKen
'Madame Kingsbury' (U)	SSea
'Madame Layal' (A)	CSpe ESul EWoo LDea LIck
	SDen SKen WFib
'Madame Margot'	See *P.* **'Hederinum Variegatum'**
'Madame Recamier' (Z/d)	WFib
'Madame Salleron'	CLit LDea LVER MBEx MSte
(Min/v) ♀	SDen SKen
'Madame Thibaut' (R)	LDea WFib
'Madge Hill' (Min)	WFib
'Magaluf' (I/C/d)	SDen SSea WFib
'Magda' (Z/d)	ESul LVER WFib
magenteum	MHul
'Magic'	WLRN
'Magic Lantern' (Z/C)	IHos SKen
'Magic Moments' (R)	WFib
'Magnum' (R)	WFib
* 'Mahogany' (I/d)	ECtt
'Maid of Honour' (Min)	ESul SDen
'Mairi' (A)	ESul LDea WEas WFib
'Maja' (R)	WFib
'Maloja' (Z)	SKen WFib
'Mamie' (Z/d)	SDen SKen
'Mangles' Variegated'	SKen SSea
(Z/v)	
'Manx Maid' (A)	ESul LDea SDen SKen WFib
'Marble Sunset'	See *P.* **'Wood's Surprise'**
'Marchioness of Bute' (R)	CLit LDea MSte WFib
'Maréchal MacMahon'	MBEx SDen SKen WFib
(Z/C)	
'Margaret Pearce' (R)	LDea
'Margaret Salvidge' (R)	LDea WFib
'Margaret Soley' (R) ♀	LDea

'Margaret Stimpson' (R)	LDea
'Margaret Thorp'	LVER
'Margaret Waite' (R)	WFib
'Margery Stimpson'	ESul LVER SDen WFib
(Min)	
'Maria Wilkes' (Z/d)	WFib
'Marie Rober' (R)	SKen WFib
§ 'Marie Vogel' (R)	WFib
¶ 'Marilyn' (Dw)	ESul
'Marion' (Min)	ESul
'Mariquita' (R)	WFib
* 'Marja'	LDea
'Marktbeherrscher' (Z/d)	WFib
'Marmalade' (Dw/d)	ESul MWhe SDen SKen WFib
§ 'Mars' (Z/d)	ESul WLRN
'Martin Parrett' (Min/d)	WFib
'Martin's Splendour'	ESul
(Min)	
'Martlesham'	ESul
'Mary Read' (Min)	ERea ESul
¶ 'Mary Spink' (Z/C)	LVER
'Mary Webster' (Min)	ESul
'Masquerade' (R)	ESul
'Masterpiece' (Z/C/d)	ESul SKen
'Mataranka' (Min/d/C/v)	MWhe
'Matthew Salvidge' (R)	EBSP LDea WFib
'Maureen' (Min)	ESul
'Maureen Mew'	SDen
'Mauve Beauty' (I/d)	IHos SKen WFib
'Mauve Duet' (A)	ESul
'Maxime Kovalevski' (Z)	WFib
¶ 'Maxine Colley' (Z/C)	LVER
'May Day' (R)	LDea
'May Magic' (R)	WFib
'May Rushbrook' (Z)	LVER
* 'Maya'	NPri SCoo.
'Mayor of Seville' (Z/d)	WFib
'Maytime' (Z/d)	WFib
I 'Meadowside Dark and	LHil
Dainty'	
'Meadowside Midnight'	LHil
'Meadowside Orange'	LVER
'Medallion' (Z/C)	SKen WFib
'Meditation' (Dw)	ESul
'Medley' (Min/d)	ESul LVER MWhe WFib
'Melanie' (R)	ESul LDea WFib
* 'Melissa' (Min)	ESul
Melody (Z/d)	WFib
'Melva Bird' (Z/d)	WFib
'Memento' (Min/d)	ESul LVER SKen WFib
'Memories' (Z/d)	LVER WFib
'Mendip' (R)	WFib
'Meon Maid' (R)	EBSP LDea WFib
Mercutio (Z/d)	WFib
'Mere Casino' (Z)	LVER
* 'Mere Champagne'	LDea
'Mere Cocktail' (R)	WFib
'Mere Flamenco' (R)	WFib
'Mere Greeting' (Z/d)	MWhe
'Mere Iced Cocktail' (R)	WFib
'Mere Meteor' (R)	WFib
'Mere Sunglow' (R)	LDea WFib
'Merry-go-round' (Z/C/v)	ESul LVER MWhe WFib
'Meshed Pink Gay Baby'	See *P.* **'Laced Sugar Baby'**
'Mexically Rose' (R)	WFib
'Mexican Beauty' (I)	CHal MWhe SDen SKen WEas
	WFib
'Mexicanerin'	See *P.* **'Rouletta'**
'Michelle' (Min/C)	LDea WFib
'Michelle West' (Min)	ESul SDen
¶ 'Midas Touch' (Dw)	ESul
'Milden' (Z/C)	ESul LHil

'Milkmaid' (Min)   WFib
'Millbern Choice' (Z)   MWhe
'Millbern Clover' (Min/d) MWhe
'Millbern Engagement'   MWhe
  (Min/d)
'Millbern Peach' (Z)   MWhe
¶ 'Millbern Serenade'   MWhe
'Millbern Sharna' (Min/d) MWhe
'Miller's Valentine'   ESul WFib
'Millfield Gem' (I/d)   LBlm LDea LVER SDen SKen
                          WFib
'Millfield Rival' (Z)   WFib
'Millfield Rose' (I/d)   CLit IHos LVER MWhe SDen
                          SKen WEas
'Millie' (Z/d)   CWDa WFib
'Mimi' (Min/C/d)   ESul SSea
'Mini-Czech' (Min/St)   ESul
minimum   MHul
'Minstrel'   ESul
'Minstrel Boy' (R)   EBSP LDea SDen WFib
'Minuet' (Z/d)   WFib
'Minx' (Min/d)   ESul WFib
* 'Mirage'   CWDa
'Miranda' (Dw)   ESul
'Miriam Basey'   See *P.* **'Dwarf Miriam Baisey'**
'Miss Australia' (R/v)   LDea SKen WFib
'Miss Burdett Coutts'   ESul IHos LVER MWhe SKen
  (Z/v)   WFib
'Miss Farren' (Z/v)   SDen SSea
'Miss Flora' (I)   CLit CWDa MWhe
'Miss Liverbird' (I/d)   ECtt
'Miss Muffett' (Min/d)   ESul
§ 'Miss Stapleton'   SDen
'Miss Wackles' (Min/d)   ESul SDen WFib
'Misty' (Z)   ESul
'Modesty' (Z/d)   SDen SKen WFib
'Mohawk' (R)   EBSP LVER WFib
'Mole' (A)   LDea LVER SKen
'Molina'   SCoo
mollicomum   MHul
'Mollie' (R)   LDea WFib
* 'Molly'   LDea
¶ 'Mona Lisa'   EBSP
'Monarch' (Dw/v)   ESul SKen
'Monica Bennett' (Dw)   ESul SDen SKen WEas
'Monks Eleigh'   ESul
'Monkwood Charm' (R)   LDea
'Monkwood Delight' (R)   SDen
'Monkwood Dream' (R)   LDea
'Monkwood Rhapsody'   SDen
  (R)
'Monkwood Sprite' (R)   LDea
'Monsal Dale' (Dw/C/d)   ESul SKen
'Monsieur Ninon' (U)   CLTr EWoo MSte WFib
'Monsieur Ninon' hort.   See *P.* **'Madame Auguste Nonin'**
'Mont Blanc' (Z/v)   EWoo MWhe SKen WFib
'Moon Maiden' (A)   CLit ESul LDea WFib
'Moonflight' (R)   WFib
'Moonlight'   SDen
'Moor' (Min/d)   ESul
'Moppet' (Min/d)   ESul
'Morello' (R)   SDen WFib
'Morning Cloud' (Min/d)   ESul
'Morning Star' (Z/St/d)   WFib
'Morph Red' (R)   WFib
'Morval' (Dw/C) ♀   ESul MWhe SKen WFib
'Morwenna' (R)   CMdw LDea LVER MSte SKen
                          WFib
¶ 'Mosaic Silky' (Z/v)   LVER
¶ 'Mosaic Sugar Baby'   CLit
  (Dwl)
'Mountie' (Dw)   ESul

'Mr Everaarts' (Dw/d)   ESul MWhe WFib
'Mr Henry Apps'   MWhe
  (Dw/C/d)
'Mr Henry Cox' (Z/v) ♀   CLit IHos LDea LVER MBEx
                          MWhe SKen SLMG WFib
'Mr Pickwick' (Dw)   ESul
'Mr Ritson' (Min)   ESul
'Mr Wren' (Z)   CHal LVER MWhe SDen SKen
                          WFib
'Mrs Cannell' (Z)   SKen
'Mrs Dumbrill' (A)   ESul LDea LIck LVER SDen
                          SKen
'Mrs E G Hill' (Z)   CWDa
'Mrs Farren' (Z/v)   SKen WFib
'Mrs G.H. Smith' (A)   CLit ESul EWoo LDea LHil
                          LVER MSte MWhe SDen SSea
                          WFib
'Mrs G. More' (R)   SSea WFib
'Mrs J.C. Mappin' (Z/v) ♀ EBSP EWoo SKen SSea
'Mrs Kingsbury' (U)   EWoo SKen WEas WFib
'Mrs Langtry' (R)   LDea
'Mrs Lawrence' (Z/d)   SDen SKen WFib
'Mrs Margaret Thorp' (R) WFib
'Mrs Martin' (I)   WFib
'Mrs Mary Bard' (R)   WFib
'Mrs McKenzie' (Z/St)   WFib
'Mrs Morf' (R)   EBSP LDea
'Mrs Parker' (Z/v)   CLit IHos LVER MWhe WFib
'Mrs Pat' (Min/St/C)   ESul MWhe
'Mrs Pollock' (Z/v)   LDea LVER MBEx MWhe
                          SKen SSea WFib
'Mrs Quilter' (Z/C)   LDea LIck LVER MBri MWhe
                          SDen SKen SMrm SSea WFib
'Mrs Reid's Pink'   EWoo
'Mrs Salter Bevis'   ESul LVER SDen WFib
  (Z/Ca/d)
'Mrs Strang' (Z/d/v)   LVER SKen SSea WEas
'Mrs Tarrant' (Z/d)   WFib
'Mrs W.A.R. Clifton' (I/d) LDea SKen WFib
multibracteatum   MHul
multicaule   MHul
'Music Man' (R)   WFib
mutans   MHul
'Müttertag' (R)   EBSP
'Mutzel' (I/v)   LDea
'My Choice' (R)   LDea
'My Love' (I/d)   LDea
§ *myrrhifolium*   CNat SDen
– var. *coriandrifolium* CSpe MHul
'Mystery' (U) ♀   CLit ESul
'Nacton' (Min)   CLit ESul
'Nadine' (Dw/C/d)   ESul WFib
Nadja (Z/d)   WFib
'Nancy Grey' (Min)   ESul
'Nancy Hiden' (R)   WFib
nanum   MHul
'Naomi' (R)   LDea
'Natalie' (Dw)   ESul
'Naughton' (Min)   ESul
'Naunton Velvet' (R)   WFib
'Naunton Windmill' (R)   WFib
'Navajo' (R)   WFib
'Nedging Tye' (A)   ESul
'Needham Market' (A)   CLit CSpe ESul LDea LHil
'Neene' (Dw)   ESul
'Neil Clemenson' (Sc)   ESul WFib
'Neil Jameson' (Z/v)   LVER SKen
'Nell Smith' (Z/d)   WFib
'Nellie' (R)   LDea
'Nellie Nuttall' (Z)   WFib
'Nels Pierson' (I)   WFib
'Neon Fiat' (Z/d)   WFib

'Nervosum' (Sc)   ESul
'Nervous Mabel' ♀   ESul LDea SDen WFib
'Nettlestead' (I)   ESul
'Nettlestead' (Dw)   LVER WFib
'Neville West' (Z)   SSea
'New Life' (Z)   ESul LHil MWhe
'New Phlox' (Z)   WFib
'Nicholas Purple' (R)   LDea
* 'Nicky'   LDea
¶ 'Nicola Buck' (R)   LDea
'Nicor Star' (Min)   ESul WFib
'Nimrod' (R)   LDea
'Noche' (R)   LDea SAga SKen SMrm WFib
nodosum   WEas
'Noel' (Z/Ca/d)   LVER SDen WFib
'Noele Gordon' (Z/d)   LVER WFib
'Noir' (R)   LDea
'Nono' (I)   LDea WFib
'North Star' (Dw)   ESul
'Northern Lights' (R)   LDea
* 'Norvic' (d)   CWDa
'Notting Hill Beauty' (Z)   SKen
'Nouvelle Aurore' (Z)   WFib
'Nuhulumby' (R)   EBSP
'Oakfield'   SDen
'Obergarten' (Z/d)   WFib
'Occold Embers'   ESul LVER SDen WFib
  (Dw/C/d)
'Occold Lagoon' (Dw/d)   ESul SKen WFib
'Occold Orange Tip'   ESul
  (Min/d)
'Occold Profusion'   ESul
  (Min/d)
'Occold Ruby' (Dw/C)   CWDa
'Occold Shield' (Dw/C/d)   ESul WFib
'Occold Surprise' (Min/d)   ESul
¶ 'Occold Tangerine' (Dw)   ESul LVER
'Occold Volcano' (Dw/d)   ESul
* 'Odessy' (Min)   WFib
odoratissimum (Sc)   CHal ESul GPoy IHos LDea
                            LVER MHul NHHG NSty
                            SDen SIde SKen WCHb WEas
                            WFib WJek WWye
 – 'Variegatum' (Sc)   WEas
oenothera   MHul
'Offton' (Dw)   ESul
¶ 'Old Orchard' (A)   LDea
'Old Rose' (Z/d)   WFib
'Old Spice' (Sc/v)   ESul GBar LVER WFib
'Olga' (R)   IHos LDea
'Olivia' (R)   EBSP
'Olympia' (Z/d)   CWDa WFib
'Onnalee' (Dw)   ESul
'Opera House' (R)   WFib
'Orange Imp' (Dw/d)   ESul
'Orange Parfait' (R)   WFib
'Orange Puff' (Min)   WFib
'Orange Ricard' (Z/d)   SKen WFib
'Orange River' (Dw/d)   ESul SKen WFib
'Orange Sal' (R)   LDea
'Orange Splash' (Z)   SKen
'Orangeade' (Dw/d)   ESul LVER SKen WFib
'Orangesonne' (Z/d)   LVER WFib
'Orchid Paloma' (Dw/d)   ESul LVER SKen
'Oregon Hostess' (Dw)   ESul
oreophilum   MHul
'Orion' (Min/d)   CLit ESul MWhe SDen SKen
                            WFib
'Orsett' (Sc) ♀   LVER
* 'Oscar'   CWDa
'Osna' (Z)   SKen
otaviense   MHul

ovale subsp. *hyalinum*   MHul
 – subsp. *ovale*   MHul WFib
 – subsp. *veronicifolium* MHul
'Oyster' (Dw)   ESul
PAC cultivars   See under cultivar name
'Paddie' (Min)   ESul
'Pagoda' (Z/St/d)   CSpe ESul LVER MSte SDen
                            SKen WFib
'Paisley Red' (Z/d)   WFib
'Palais' (Z/d)   SKen WFib
'Pamela Underwood' (R)   WFib
panduriforme   MHul WFib
papilionaceum   CHEx EWoo LHil MHul WEas
                            WHer
'Parasol' (R)   WFib
'Parisienne' (R)   EBSP LDea SDen
'Parmenter Pink' (Min)   ESul
'Party Dress' (Z/d)   MWhe SDen SKen WFib
'Pascal' (Z)   SKen
'Pat Thorpe' (R)   WFib
'Patience' (Z/d)   IHos WFib
'Paton's Unique' (U/Sc) ♀   CHal ERav EWoo IHos LBlm
                            LHil LIck LVER MSte SDen
                            WEas WFib
* 'Patricia' (I)   CWDa
'Patricia Andrea' (T)   LVER NPer SDen
'Patricia Read' (Min)   ERea ESul
'Patsy "Q"' (Z/C)   SKen
patulum   MHul
'Paul Crampel' (Z)   CHal LVER MBEx WFib
'Paul Gotz' (Z)   SKen
'Paul Gunnett' (Min)   MWhe
'Paul Humphries' (Z/d)   WFib
'Paul Sloan' (Z)   WFib
'Paul West' (Min/d)   ESul
'Paula Scott' (R)   LDea
'Pauline' (Min/d)   ESul MWhe WFib
'Pavilion' (Min) ♀   ESul
'Pax' (R)   LDea WFib
'Peace' (Min/C)   ESul WFib
'Peace Palace' (Dw)   ESul
'Peach' (Z)   LDea
'Peach Princess' (R)   EBSP
'Pearl Brocade' (R)   WFib
'Pearl Eclipse' (I)   SDen SKen
Pearl Necklace   See *P.* **'Perlenkette'**
'Pearly Queen' (Min/d)   ESul
'Pegasus' (Min)   CLit LVER
'Peggy Sue' (R)   EBSP LDea LVER
'Peggy West' (Min/C/d)   SDen
PELFI cultivars   See under cultivar name
peltatum   MHul SDen WFib
 – 'Lateripes'   MHul SKen
Meloblue = 'Penblue'   WLRN
'Penny' (Z/d)   LVER MWhe SDen SKen WFib
'Penny Lane' (Z)   LVER
'Penny Serenade' (Dw/C)   ESul SKen
'Pensby' (Dw)   ESul
'Penve' (Z/d)   WFib
¶ 'Peppermint Star' (Z/St) LVER
'Perfect' (Z)   SDen SKen
* 'Perle Blanche' (I)   CWDa
§ Perlenkette Orange (Z/d) WFib
'Persian King' (R)   LDea
'Persimmon' (Z/St)   WFib
'Petals' (Z/v)   SKen
'Peter Godwin' (R)   EBSP LDea WFib
'Peter Grieve' (Z/v)   WFib
'Peter Read' (Dw/d)   ERea ESul
'Peter's Choice' (R)   EBSP LDea LVER
¶ 'Peter's Luck' (Sc) ♀   LDea
'Petit Pierre'   See *P.* **'Kleine Liebling'**

'Petite Blanche' (Dw/d)   LVER WFib
'Petronella' (Z/d)   ESul
'Phil Rose' (I)   CWDa MWhe
'Philomel' (I/d)   SDen WFib
'Philomel Rose' (I/d)   LDea
'Phlox New Life' (Z)   ESul
'Phyllis' (U/v)   LHil LVER SSea
'Phyllis Mary' (R)   WFib
'Phyllis Read' (Min)   ERea ESul WFib
'Phyllis Richardson' (R/d)   LDea LVER SDen WFib
'Phyllis Variegated'   LHop
¶ 'Picardy' (Z/d)   SKen
'Pickaninny' (Min)   ESul
'Pin Mill' (Min/d)   ESul
'Pink Aura'   ESul
'Pink Aurore' (U)   LVER MSte
'Pink Black Vesuvius'   WFib
  (Min/C)
'Pink Blizzard'   ERav NPri WLRN
'Pink Bonanza' (R)   EBSP LDea WFib
'Pink Bouquet' (Z/d)   IHos
'Pink Bouquet' (R)   EBSP WFib
'Pink Capitatum'   See P. 'Pink Capricorn'
§ 'Pink Capricorn' (Sc)   LHil WFib
'Pink Carnation' (I/d)   IHos LDea SDen
'Pink Cascade'   See P. 'Hederinum'
'Pink Champagne' (Sc)   ESul SDen WFib
'Pink Cloud' (Z/d)   WFib
'Pink Countess Mariza'   SKen
  (Z)
'Pink Crampel' (Z)   CWDa
'Pink Flamingo' (R)   LDea
'Pink Fondant' (Min/d)   ESul
'Pink Gay Baby' (DwI)   See P. 'Sugar Baby'
¶ 'Pink Golden Ears'   SKen
  (Dw/St/C)
'Pink Golden Harry   ESul
  Hieover' (Z/C)
'Pink Grace Wells' (Min)   ESul
'Pink Grozser Garten'   SDen
  (Dw)
'Pink Happy Thought'   WFib
  (Z/v)
'Pink Ice' (Min/d)   ESul LVER
'Pink Kewense' (Min)   ESul
'Pink Margaret Pearce'   SDen WFib
  (R)
'Pink Mini Cascade'   See P. 'Rose Mini Cascade'
'Pink Pearl' (Z/d)   WFib
'Pink Rambler' (Z/d)   MWhe SKen WFib
'Pink Raspail' (Z/d)   WFib
'Pink Rosebud' (Z/d)   IHos SDen WFib
'Pink Ruffles' (R)   EBSP
'Pink Satisfaction' (Z)   IHos
'Pink Snow' (Min/d)   ESul
'Pink Splash' (Min/d)   ESul SDen
'Pink Star' (Z/St)   WFib
'Pink Tiny Tim' (Min)   ESul WFib
'Pinnochio' (R)   WFib
'Pixie' (Dw)   ESul
'Pixie Rose' (Z/St)   WFib
'Platinum' (Z/v)   SDen
'Playmate' (Min/St)   ESul LVER SKen WFib
'Plenty' (Z/d)   CWDa WFib
'Plum Rambler' (Z/d)   EWoo SKen WFib
'Poetesse' (A)   LDea
'Polka' (U)   EWoo WFib
'Pom Pom' (Z/d)   WFib
'Pompeii' (R)   LDea SAga WFib
'Potpourri' (Min)   SKen
'Potter Heigham' (Dw)   ESul
'Powder Puff' (Dw/d)   ESul

praemorsum   MHul
'Prairie Dawn' (Z/d)   WFib
'Presto' (Min)   ESul MWhe
'Preston Park' (Z/C)   LBlm MBEx SKen SMrm WFib
'Pretty Girl' (I)   LDea
'Pretty Polly' (Sc)   WFib
'Pride of the West' (Z)   SKen
'Prim' (Min/d)   ESul
'Primavera' (R)   EBSP LDea
'Prince Consort' (R)   LVER
'Prince of Orange' (Sc)   CArn CInt CLTr CNat CSev
   ESul EWoo GBar GPoy IHos
   LDea LIck LVER MSte MWhe
   NHHG NSty SDen SSea WCHb
   WFib WHer WPer WWye
'Prince of Wales' (Z)   WFib
'Prince Regent' (R)   CChr
'Princeanum' (Sc) ♀   CSpe EWoo WFib
'Princess Alexandra' (R)   LVER SSea
'Princess Alexandra'   MWhe WFib
  (Z/d/v)
'Princess Anne' (Z)   CSpe LHil MSte
'Princess Josephine' (R)   WFib
'Princess of Balcon'   See P. 'Roi des Balcons Lilas'
'Princess of Wales' (R)   EBSP LDea WFib
'Princess Virginia' (R/v)   EBSP LDea LIck LVER WFib
'Professor Eckman' (R)   WFib
'Promenade' (Z/d)   WFib
'Prospect' (Z/d)   MWhe
pseudofumarioides   MHul
pseudoglutinosum   WFib
pulchellum   MHul
pulverulentum   MHul
'Purple Ball'   See P. Purpurball
'Purple Emperor' (R)   LDea WFib
'Purple Heart' (Dw/St)   ESul
'Purple Light'   See P. 'Purple Gem'
'Purple Orchard' (R)   LDea
'Purple Pride' (I/d)   CWDa
'Purple Rambler' (Z/d)   MWhe SDen
'Purple Unique' (U/Sc)   CLit EWoo IHos MSte SDen
   SKen WCHb WFib
Purple Wonder (Z/d)   WFib
§ Purpurball (Z/d)   SKen WFib
'Pygmalion' (Z/d/v)   SDen SSea WFib
'Quakeress' (R)   LDea WFib
'Quakermaid' (Min)   ESul
'Quantock' (R)   WFib
¶ 'Quantock Rory' (A)   LDea
¶ 'Quantock Rose' (A)   LDea
'Queen Ingrid' (Z)   IHos
'Queen of Denmark'   LVER SDen SKen WFib
  (Z/d)
'Queen of Hearts' (I/d)   LVER WFib
I 'Queen of the Lemons'   EWoo
¶ *quercetorum*   CGen
N *quercifolium* (Sc)   CLit CNat CSev EWoo GHCN
   GPoy MHul NHHG NSty SKen
   SSea WCHb WEas WFib WJek
   WWye
– 'Fair Ellen'   See P. 'Fair Ellen'
quinquelobatum   CSpe MHul
'R.A. Turner' (Z/d)   WFib
'Rachel' (Min)   ESul
'Rachel Fisher' (Z)   WFib
radens (Sc)   MHul SIde WFib
'Radiance' (Z/d)   WFib
'Radiant' (Z/d)   WFib
'Radio' (Z/d)   WFib
'Radior' (Min)   WFib
'Rads Star' (Z/St)   ESul WFib

'Radula' (Sc) ♀	CLTr CSev ERav ESul GBar LIck LVER MWhe SDen SKen WCHb WFib WPer
'Radula Roseum'	LHil SSea
radulifolium	MHul
'Ragamuffin' (Min/d)	ESul MWhe WFib
'Rager's Pink' (Dw/d)	ESul
'Rager's Star' (Min)	ESul
'Rakastani' (Z)	SKen
ranunculophyllum	MHul
rapaceum	MHul
'Rapture' (R)	LDea WFib
'Raspberry Parfait' (R)	LDea SDen
'Raspberry Ripple' (A)	CLit ESul LDea WEas WPen
'Raspberry Sundae' (R)	CLTr LDea
'Raspberry Sweet' (Z/St)	LHil WFib
'Raviro' (I)	WFib
'Ray Bidwell'	CLit ESul SDen
'Ray Coughlin' (Z/C/d)	WFib
'Raydon' (Min)	ESul
'Rebecca' (Min/d)	ESul WFib
'Red Admiral' (Min/d/v)	ESul
§ 'Red Black Vesuvius' (Min/C)	CHal CLit CSpe ESul LHil LVER MWhe SKen WEas WFib
¶ 'Red Blizzard'	NPri
'Red Cascade' (I) ♀	MWhe SKen
'Red Fox' (Min)	SDen
¶ 'Red Gables'	WCFE
'Red Galilee' (I/d)	MWhe SKen
'Red Gem' (Min)	ESul
'Red Glow' (Min)	ESul
'Red Ice' (Min/d)	ESul LVER
* 'Red Irene' (Z/d)	CWDa SKen
* 'Red Kewense'	ESul
'Red Light' (Z/d)	WFib
'Red Magic Lantern' (Z/C)	SKen
'Red Mini Cascade' (T)	See *P.* **'Rote Mini-cascade'**
'Red Pandora' (T)	LVER
'Red Rambler' (Z/d)	CHal CLit LVER MWhe SDen SKen WFib
'Red Satisfaction' (Z)	IHos
'Red Silver Cascade'	LVER
'Red Spangles' (R)	WFib
'Red Spider' (Min/Ca/d)	ESul WFib
'Red Startel' (Z/St/d)	MWhe SKen WFib
'Red Susan Pearce' (R)	EBSP LDea
'Red Tiny Tim' (Min)	WFib
'Red Velvet' (R)	WFib
'Red Witch' (Dw/St)	ESul LHil LVER SDen WFib
'Redondo' (Min/d)	ESul LHil LVER MWhe SDen WEas WFib
'Reflections' (Z/d)	WFib
'Regal Perchance'	SDen
'Regina' (Z/d)	LVER SKen WEas WFib
'Reifi Vanderlea'	EWoo
'Rembrandt' (R)	LDea LVER SDen SKen SSea WEas WFib
'Remo' (Z/d)	WFib
¶ 'Renate Parsley'	WFib
'Rene Roué' (Dw)	ESul
'Renee Ross' (I/d) ♀	CWDa LVER WFib
reniforme	CNat CSpe GBar LVER MHul WEas WFib
'Retah's Crystal' (Z/v)	LVER MWhe
'Rhineland' (I)	SKen
'Rhodamant' (I/d)	MWhe WFib
'Rhodamine' (R)	EBSP LDea
'Rhodo' (R)	WFib
ribifolium	MHul
Rica (Z/d)	WFib
'Richard Gibbs'	EWoo
'Richard Key' (Z/d/v)	WFib
'Richard West' (I/d)	CWDa
'Rietje van der Lee' (A)	ESul WFib
'Rigel' (Min/d)	ESul MWhe SKen WFib
'Rigi' (I)	ECtt IHos LDea MBri SDen SKen WFib
'Rigoletto' (I)	LDea MWhe SKen
'Rimfire' (R)	CLit EBSP LDea WFib
'Rio' (Z)	WLRN
'Rio Grande' (I/d)	LDea LVER MWhe NWoo SKen WEas WFib
'Rising Sun'	LDea
'Rita Brook' (Z/d)	WFib
'Rita Coughlin' (R)	WFib
'Rita Scheen' (A)	ESul LDea LVER MWhe SKen SSea WFib
'Rita Thomas' (Z)	WFib
¶ 'Ritchie'	EBSP
'Robbie Hare' (R)	WFib
'Robe' (Z/d)	WFib
'Rober's Lavender' (Dw)	ESul
'Rober's Lemon Rose' (Sc)	CInt CJew CNat ERav ESul EWoo GBar LBlm LHil SDen SIde SKen WCHb WEas WFib WHer WJek WWye
'Rober's Salmon Coral' (Dw/d)	ESul
'Robert Fish' (Z/C)	CLit ESul SDen SSea
'Robert McElwain'	WFib
'Robin' (R)	EWoo LDea LVER WEas
rodneyanum	MHul
'Roger's Delight' (R)	WFib
rogersianum	See *P. worcesterae*
'Rogue' (R)	EBSP LDea WFib
'Roi des Balcons'	See *P.* **'Hederinum'**
§ 'Roi des Balcons Impérial' (I) ♀	IHos LDea MWhe
§ 'Roi des Balcons Lilas' (I) ♀	IHos LDea MWhe SKen
'Roi des Balcons Rose'	See *P.* **'Hederinum'**
§ Rokoko (Z)	CWDa IHos
'Roller's David' (I)	CWDa LVER SDen
'Roller's Echo' (A)	ESul LDea LIck
'Roller's Pathfinder' (I/v)	LDea LVER
'Roller's Pioneer' (I/v)	CLit LDea SKen
'Roller's Satinique' (U) ♀	LIck WFib
'Rollisson's Unique' (U)	LVER MGra MSte SDen WFib
§ Romy (I)	LDea
'Rosaleen' (Min)	ESul
'Rosalie' (Min)	ESul
'Rosamunda' (Z/d)	WFib
'Roscobie' (Z/d)	SDen SKen
'Rose Bengal' (A)	CLit CMil ESul LDea LVER NSty SDen WEas WFib
'Rose Irene' (Z/d)	MWhe SDen WFib
¶ 'Rose Jewel'	EBSP
§ 'Rose Mini Cascade' (I)	ESul LVER MWhe SDen WLRN
'Rose of Amsterdam' (Min/d)	ESul
'Rose Silver Cascade' (I)	LDea LVER
'Rose Slam' (R)	LDea WFib
'Rose Unique' (Z)	CLit LHil
¶ 'Rosecrystal' (Z/d)	LVER
'Rosee Normande' (Z/d)	WFib
* 'Roselo'	CWDa
'Rosemarie' (Z/d)	MWhe
'Rosemie' (Z/d)	WFib
'Rose's Orange'	EWoo
'Rosette' (Dw)	SKen WFib
'Rosina Read' (Dw)	ERea ESul WFib

'Rosmaroy' (R) — EBSP LDea LVER
§ 'Rospen' (Z/d) — LVER SKen WFib
* 'Rosseau' (Min) — WFib
'Rosy Dawn' (Min/d) — WFib
§ 'Rote Mini-cascade' (I) — IHos LDea LVER MWhe SDen
 — SKen WFib
'Rotherfield' (I/d) — LDea
'Rotlieb' (Z/d) — WFib
§ 'Rouletta' (I) — ECtt GHCN IHos LDea LVER
 — MWhe NPri SDen SKen WFib
 — WLRN
'Rousillon' (R) — LDea WFib
'Roussseau' (Dw/C) — ESul
'Royal Ascot' (R) — ERav EWoo LDea LHil MBEx
 — MSte SMrm
'Royal Carpet' (Min/d) — ESul
'Royal Fiat' (Z/d) — WFib
'Royal Norfolk' (Min/d) — ESul LVER MWhe SDen SKen
'Royal Oak' (Sc) ♀ — CInt CJew CSev GBar LDea
 — LHil LVER MWhe WFib WHer
 — WPer WRha
* 'Royal Princess' ♀ — LVER
§ 'Royal Purple' (Z/d) — CHal WFib
* 'Royal Salmon' — CWDa
'Royal Sovereign' (Z/d/v) — LHil
'Royal Star' (R) — LVER
'Royal Surprise' (R) — LDea
'Royal Wedding' (R) — LDea
'Rubella' (Z/d) — WFib
* 'Rubican' — CWDa
'Rubin Improved' (Z/d) — SKen WFib
'Ruby' (Min/d) — ESul WFib
'Ruby Orchid' (A) — LDea
'Ruffled Velvet' (R) — EWoo SDen SSea
'Rushmere' (Dw/d) — ESul WFib
'Russet Wings' (R) — WFib
'Rustler' (Min) — WFib
'Rusty' (Dw/C/d) — ESul SDen
'Ruth Karmen' (I/d) — LDea
'Ryecroft Pride' (Z/d) — WFib
'Ryecroft White' (Z/d) — WFib
'Sally Anne' (R) — LDea WEas
'Sally Munro' (R) — LDea
'Sally Read' (Dw/d) — ERea ESul
'Salmon Beauty' (Min/d) — WFib
'Salmon Black Vesuvius' — ESul
 (Min/C)
§ 'Salmon Irene' (Z/d) — WFib
'Salmon Queen' — See *P.* 'Lachskönigin'
'Salmon Slam' (R) — LVER SDen WFib
'Salmon Startel' (Z/St/d) — MWhe
salmoneum — SDen
'Saltford' (R) — WFib
'Samantha' (R) — EBSP LDea WFib
'Samantha Stamp' (Dw) — WFib
'Samba' (R) — WFib
'Sancho Panza' (Dec) ♀ — CLit CSpe ESul LDea LVER
 — MSte SDen SKen SSea WEas
 — WFib
'Sandra Haynes' (R) — WFib
¶ 'Sanguineum' — CSpe MHul
'Santa Maria' (Z/d) — LVER SKen WFib
'Santa Marie' (R) — LDea
'Santa Paula' (I/d) — ECtt LDea LVER MWhe SDen
 — SKen
'Sasha' (Min) — WFib
Sassa (Z/d) — CWDa WFib
§ Satellite (Z/St) — IHos WFib
'Satsuki' (R) — EBSP LDea
'Saxifragoides' — SDen SSea
§ *scabrum* — MHul WFib
¶ 'Scandens' — MHul

* 'Scarlet Kewense' — ESul
'Scarlet Nosegay' — CHal
'Scarlet Pet' (U) — CLTr ESul
'Scarlet Pimpernel' — ESul WFib
 (Z/C/d)
'Scarlet Queen' (Z) — LHil
'Scarlet Rambler' (Z/d) — LVER SKen SMrm WEas WFib
'Scarlet Unique' (U) — CLit EWoo LHil LVER MSte
 — SDen SKen SSea WCHb WFib
'Scatterbrain' (Z) — CWDa
schizopetalum — MHul
§ 'Schneekönigin' (I/d) — ECtt IHos LDea LVER MSte
 — WEas
§ 'Schöne Helena' (Z/d) — CWDa
* 'Schone von Grenchen' (I) — NPri
× *schottii* — See *P.* × *sanguineum*
'Secret Love' (Sc) — WFib
'Seeley's Pansy' (A) — CLit CSpe ESul LDea WFib
'Sefton' (R) ♀ — EBSP LDea WFib
'Selby' (Z/C/d) — WFib
'Selina' — ESul
'Semer' (Min) — ESul LVER SKen
senecioides — MHul
'Senorita' (R) — LDea
¶ 'Sensation' (Z) — SKen
'Serena' (Min) — ESul
sericifolium — MHul
* 'Serre de la Madone' (Sc) — WEas
'Shalimar' (St) — CSpe LHil MSte WFib
'Sharon' (Min/d) — ESul WFib
'Sharon Louise' (Min) — SDen
'Sharon West' (Dw) — CNat SDen
'Shaun Jacobs' (Min/d) — SDen
'Sheila' (Dw) — ESul
'Shelley' (Dw) — ESul SKen
'Shenandoah' (Min) — WFib
'Sheraton' (Min/d) — ESul
'Shimmer' (Z/d) — IHos LVER MWhe SKen WFib
'Shirley Anne' (Dw/d) — SDen
'Shirley Ash' (A) — ESul LDea SKen WEas WFib
'Shirley Maureen' (R) — LDea WFib
'Shiva' — NPri WLRN
'Shotley' (Min) — ESul
'Shottesham Pet' (Sc) — EWoo SKen
'Shrubland Pet' (U/Sc) — LHil SDen SKen
'Shrubland Rose' (Sc) — WFib
sidoides — MHul
'Sienna' (R) — LDea
'Silberlachs' (Z/d) — SDen WFib
'Silky' — ESul
'Silpen' (Z/d) — WFib
* 'Sils' — CWDa
'Silver Anne' (R) — WFib
* 'Silver Cascade' — ERav NPri
'Silver Kewense' (Dw/v) — ESul SDen SKen WFib
* 'Silver Lights' — CWDa
'Silver Monarch' — ESul
'Silver Wings' (Z/v) — CSpe ESul LVER MWhe SSea
 — WFib
¶ 'Silvia' (R) — EBSP
'Simon Portas' (I/d) — SKen
'Simon Read' (Dw) — ERea ESul
'Simplicity' (Z) — LVER
'Sir Arthur Hort' (I) — WFib
'Sister Henry' (Z/d) — WFib
'Sister Teresa' (Z/d) — IHos
'Skelly's Pride' (Z) — LVER SDen SKen WEas
'Skies of Italy' (Z/C/d) — MBri SKen SSea WFib
'Sleuring's Robin' (Min/d) — SDen WFib
'Small Fortune' (Dw) — ESul LVER SKen
'Smuggler' (R) — LDea
'Snape' — ESul

'Sneezy' (Min)   ESul
Snow Queen   See *P.* **'Schneekönigen'**
'Snow White' (Min)   ESul
'Snowbaby' (Min/d)   ESul
'Snowball' (Z/d)   SDen
'Snowberry' (R)   EBSP
'Snowdon' (Min)   WFib
'Snowdrift' (I/d)   LVER WFib
'Snowmass' (Z/d)   CHal MWhe SDen SKen
'Snowstorm' (Z)   SKen WFib
'Snowy Baby' (Min/d)   SDen WFib
'Sofie'   See *P.* **'Decora Rose'**
'Solano' (R)   WFib
'Solent Waves' (R)   EBSP LDea WFib
'Solferino' (A)   ESul LDea SKen
§ Solidor (I/d) ♀   LDea WFib
¶ 'Solo' (Z/I)   LVER
'Sombrero' (R)   WFib
'Somersham' (Min)   ESul
'Something Special' (Z/d) LVER MWhe WFib
'Sonata' (Dw/d)   ESul
'Sonnesport' (Z)   WFib
'Sophie Cascade'   CWDa
'Sophie Dumaresque'   LVER MBri MWhe SDen SKen
  (Z/v)   SSea WFib
'Sophie Koniger' (Z/d)   WFib
'Sorcery' (Dw/C)   ESul IHos MWhe SKen
'South American Bronze'   LDea SDen SKen SMrm WFib
  (R) ♀
'Southern Belle' (A)   LDea
'Southern Belle' (Z/d)   WFib
'Southern Charm'   LVER
'Souvenir' (R)   CHal LDea LVER SDen SSea
'Spanish Angel' (A) ♀   ESul LDea SSea
¶ 'Sparkler' (Z)   LVER
'Special Moment' (R)   WFib
'Speckles' (Z)   MWhe
'Spellbound' (R)   WFib
'Spital Dam'   ESul
'Spitfire' (Z/Ca/v)   ESul WFib
'Spithead Cherry' (R)   EBSP LDea WFib
'Splash Down'   SDen
§ 'Splendide'   CMdw CRDP CSpe LHil LHop
                          LVER MHul SAga SIgm SSad
                          WEas WOMN
* 'Spotlight Winner'   LDea
'Spot-on-Bonanza' (R)   EBSP LDea WFib
'Spring Bride' (R)   LDea SDen
'Spring Park' (A)   CLit ESul SDen WFib
'Springfield Ann' (R)   EBSP
'Springfield Betty' (R)   EBSP
'Springfield Black' (R)   EBSP LDea LVER
'Springfield Charm' (R)   EBSP
'Springfield Kate' (R)   EBSP
'Springfield Mary Parfitt' EBSP
  (R)
'Springfield Pearl' (R)   LDea
'Springfield Purple' (R) EBSP
'Springfield Stripey' (R) EBSP
'Springfield Unique' (R) EBSP LDea
'Springtime' (Z/d)   LVER MWhe SDen SKen WFib
'Sproughton' (Dw)   ESul
'St Helen's Favourite'   ESul
  (Min)
'Stacey' (R)   LDea
'Stadt Bern' (Z/C)   LVER MBri MWhe SKen WEas
                          WFib
'Stanton Drew' (Z/d)   WFib
'Staplegrove Fancy' (Z)   SKen
x *stapletoniae*   See *P.* **'Miss Stapleton'**
'Star Flecks'   SDen
'Star Glitter'   SDen

'Star of Persia' (Z/Ca)   WFib
'Starlet' (Ca)   WFib
'Starlight' (R)   WFib
'Starlight Magic' (A) ♀   ESul LDea WEas
'Starry Eyed' (Dw)   ESul
'Startel Salmon' (Z/St)   WFib
'Stella Ballerina'   ERav
'Stella Read' (Dw/d)   ERea ESul WFib
'Stellar Apricot' (Z/St) CLit ERav LHil LVER
'Stellar Arctic Star'   See *P.* **'Arctic Star'**
'Stellar Cathay' (Z/St/d) CLit CSpe WFib
'Stellar Dawn Star' (Z/St) WEas WFib
'Stellar Grenadier'   See *P.* **'Grenadier'**
'Stellar Hannaford Star' See *P.* **'Hannaford Star'**
* 'Stellar Orange Pixie' (d) CWDa
'Stellar Ragtime' (Z/St/d) LVER SDen
stenopetalum   MHul
'Stephen Read' (Min)   ERea ESul
'Stewart Read' (Dw)   ERea
stipulaceum   MHul
'Stirling Stent' (Z)   CWDa LVER
'Strawberry Sundae' (R)   EBSP LDea LVER SDen WFib
'Stringer's Delight'   ESul
'Stringer's Souvenir'   ESul LVER
¶ 'Stuart Mark' (R)   LDea
'Stutton' (Min)   ESul
sublignosum   MHul
suburbanum subsp.   MHul
  bipinnatifidum
'Suffolk Gold' (Min/C)   SDen SSea
§ 'Sugar Baby' (DwI)   CLit ECtt ESul GHCN IHos
                          LDea MBri MWhe SDen SKen
                          WEas WFib
'Summer Cloud' (Z/d)   SAxl SKen WFib
'Summertime' (R)   SDen
'Sun Kissed' (Min)   ESul
'Sun Rocket' (Dw)   ESul LIck LVER MWhe WFib
¶ 'Sunbeam' (Dw/d)   ESul
'Sundridge Moonlight'   WFib
  (Z/C)
'Sunraysia' (Z/St)   WFib
'Sunrise' (R)   EBSP LDea SDen SKen WEas
                          WFib
'Sunset' (Z)   WFib
'Sunset Snow' (R)   LDea LVER WFib
'Sunspot Petit Pierre'   ESul SDen
  (Min/v)
'Sunstar' (Min/d)   ESul LVER WFib
'Super Rose' (I)   MBri MWhe SDen SKen
'Supernova' (Z/St/d)   CWDa ESul SKen WFib
'Surcouf' (I)   WFib
'Susan Baldwin'   See *P.* **'Salmon Kovalevski'**
'Susan Payne' (Dw/d)   ESul LVER
'Susan Pearce' (R)   LDea SKen WFib
'Susan Read' (Dw)   ERea ESul
* 'Susan Screen'   CWDa
'Susie 'Q' (Z/C)   ESul LHil LVER MWhe SDen
                          SKen
'Sussex Beauty' (Dw/C/d) CWDa ESul
'Sussex Delight' (Min)   CWDa ESul
'Sussex Gem' (Min)   LVER SKen
'Sussex Jewel' (Min)   SKen
'Sussex Lace'   See *P.* **'White Mesh'**
'Swanland Lace' (I)   LVER WFib
'Swedish Angel' (A)   ESul LDea LVER SSea
* 'Sweet Lady Mary' (Sc) WFib
'Sweet Mimosa' (Sc) ♀   CInt CLTr CLit CSpe EWoo
                          LDea LHil LIck LVER MSte
                          SDen SKen SSea WEas WFib
'Sweet Sue' (Min)   ESul LVER WFib
'Swilland' (A)   ESul LDea LVER MWhe SDen
'Sybil Bradshaw' (R)   LDea WFib

'Sybil Holmes' (I/d)	ECtt IHos LVER MBri MWhe SKen WFib
'Sylvia Gale' (R)	SDen WFib
'Sylvia Marie' (Dw/d)	LVER MWhe SKen
'Sylvia Mariza'	IHos
* 'Tamara'	CWDa
'Tamie' (Dw/d)	ESul LVER MWhe
'Tammy' (Dw/d)	ESul LVER MWhe WFib
'Tangerine' (Min/Ca/d)	ESul SDen WFib
§ 'Tango' (Z/d)	IHos
'Tanzy' (Min)	ESul
'Tapestry' (R)	LDea
'Tapestry' (Min/v)	WEas
'Tashmal' (R)	EBSP
'Tattingstone' (Min)	ESul
'Tavira' (I/d)	LDea LVER SDen WFib
'Ted Brooke' (Z/d)	WFib
'Ted Dutton' (R)	SDen WFib
'Teddy Roosevelt' (Z/d)	WFib
'Telstar' (Min/d)	ESul SKen WFib
§ 'Telston's Prima' (R)	LDea
'Tenderly' (Dw/d)	ESul
'Tenerife Magic' (MinI/d)	ESul
tenuicaule	MHul WFib
'Terence Read' (Min)	ERea
ternatum	MHul
tetragonum	CInt MHul SSea WFib
'The Barle' (A) ♀	LDea
'The Boar' (Fr) ♀	CLit CSpe EWoo LVER MBEx MSte SRms WEas WPer
'The Creedy' (A)	LDea
§ 'The Crocodile' (I/C/d)	CSpe ECtt IHos LDea MWhe SDen SKen SSea WEas WFib
I 'The Culm'	See P. 'Culm'
'The Czar'	See P. 'Czar'
I 'The Dart'	See P. 'Dart'
'The Duchess' (I/d)	WFib
'The Joker' (I)	WFib
¶ 'The Kenn-Lad' (A)	LDea
'The Lowman' (A)	LDea
'The Lynn' (A)	LDea
¶ 'The Otter' (A)	LDea
'The Speaker' (Z/d)	SDen SKen WFib
'The Tamar' (A)	LDea
'The Tone' (A) ♀	LDea
'Thomas Earle' (Z)	WFib
'Thomas Gerald' (Min/C)	ESul SKen
'Tiberias' (I/d)	WFib
'Tiffany' (Min/d)	WLRN
'Tilly' (Min)	CHal
'Tim' (Min)	ESul
'Timothy Clifford' (Min/d)	ESul MWhe WFib
§ 'Tip Top Duet' (A) ♀	CLit ESul EWoo LDea LHil LIck LVER MWhe NWoo SAga SDen SLod SSea WEas WFib
'Token' (Z)	IHos
'Tom Portas' (Dw/d)	ESul
¶ 'Tomboy'	LVER
'Tomcat' (Z/d)	WFib
tomentosum (Sc) ♀	CArn CHEx CHal CSev CSpe EWoo GPoy LDea LVER MHul MSCN MWhe NHHG NSty SAga SDen SKen WEas WFib WWye
– 'Chocolate'	See P. 'Chocolate Peppermint'
'Tommay's Delight' (R)	EBSP LDea WFib
tongaense	CSpe MHul WEas WFib
'Tony' (Min)	ESul
'Topscore' (Z/d)	SKen WFib
'Toreador' (Z/d)	WFib
'Torento' (Sc)	CNat ESul SDen SKen WFib
'Tornado' (R)	EBSP LDea WFib
'Tortoise Shell' (R)	WFib
'Toyon' (Z/d)	SDen SKen WFib
'Tracy' (Min/d)	ESul LVER
tragacanthoides	MHul
transvaalense	MHul WFib
¶ 'Traute Hausler' (A)	LDea
'Trautlieb' (Z/d)	CWDa WFib
'Treasure' (Z/d)	LVER
'Treasure Chest' (Z)	SDen
'Trésor' (Dw/d)	CWDa
tricolor Curt.	CSpe MHul SSad
– hort.	See P. 'Splendide'
trifidum	MHul SSad SSea WEas WFib
'Trimley' (Dw/d)	ESul
'Trinket' (Min/d)	IHos SKen
'Triomphe de Nancy' (Z/d)	WFib
triste	CSpe MHul SDen SSad WFib
'Trudie' (Dw)	ESul LVER SKen WFib
'Trulls Hatch' (Z/d)	LVER MWhe SKen
'Tu Tone' (Dw/d)	ESul
'Tuddenham' (Min/d)	WFib
'Tuesday's Child' (Dw/C)	SKen
'Tunias Perfecta' (R)	WFib
'Turkish Coffee' (R)	EBSP WFib
'Turkish Delight' (Dw/v)	ESul LVER MWhe WFib
'Turtle's Surprise' (Z/d/v)	SDen SKen
'Turtle's White' (R)	LDea SKen
'Tuyo' (R)	WFib
'Tweedle-Dum' (Dw)	MWhe
'Twinkle' (Min/d)	ESul WFib
'Tyabb Princess' (R)	WFib
'Ullswater' (Dw/C)	ESul
§ 'Unique Aurore' (U)	LVER MSte SKen WEas WFib
'Unique Mons Ninon'	EWoo
'Unity'	LVER
'Urchin' (Min)	CSpe ESul MWhe SDen WFib
'Ursula Key' (Z/v)	SKen WFib
'Valanza' (A)	ESul LDea
'Valencia' (R)	EBSP LDea
'Valenciana' (R)	WFib
'Valentin' (R)	LDea
'Valentina' (Min/d)	ESul WFib
¶ 'Valentine'	EBSP
'Vancouver Centennial' (Dw/St/C) ♀	CInt CLit CSpe ERav ESul LDea LVER MBri MWhe SKen WFib
§ 'Variegated Clorinda' (Sc/v)	EWoo WCHb WFib WHer
'Variegated Fragrans'	See P. (Fragrans Group) 'Fragrans Variegatum'
§ 'Variegated Kleine Liebling' (Min/v)	ESul SDen SKen WFib
'Variegated La France' (I)	WFib
'Variegated Madame Layal' (A/v) ♀	ESul LDea WFib
* 'Variegated Peppermint'	MGra
'Variegated Petit Pierre'	See P. 'Variegated Kleine Liebling'
'Vasco da Gama' (Dw/d)	ESul WFib
'Vectis Cascade'	SDen
'Vectis Glitter'	LVER
'Vectis Gold' (Z/St/C)	SDen
'Velvet' (Z)	CWDa IHos LVER
'Velvet Duet' (A) ♀	ESul EWoo LDea LIck LVER SDen SSea
'Venus' (Dw/d)	ESul
'Vera Dillon' (Z)	SKen WFib
'Verdale' (A)	LDea WFib
'Verity Palace' (R)	WFib
'Verona' (Z/C)	CHal MBri SDen SKen
'Verona Contreras' (A)	CLit LDea WFib

* 'Veronica' (Z)	MWhe SKen
'Vicki Town' (R)	LDea WFib
'Vicky Claire' (R)	EBSP LDea SBid SKen SMrm WFib
'Victoria' (Z/d)	SKen
'Victoria Regina' (R)	LDea WFib
'Video Blush' (Min)	CLit
'Viking' (Min/d)	SKen
'Viking Red' (Z)	MWhe
'Village Hill Oak' (Sc)	ESul LVER
* 'Ville de Dresden' (I)	CSpe SDen
'Ville de Paris'	See *P.* **'Hederinum'**
'Vina' (Dw/C/d)	ESul LVER MWhe SKen WFib
violareum hort.	See *P.* **'Splendide'**
'Violet Lambton' (Z/v)	WFib
'Violetta' (R)	LDea WFib
'Virginia' (R)	IHos LDea WEas WFib
'Virginia Ley' (Z)	LVER SKen
'Viscossisimum'	ERav WCHb
viscosum	See *P. glutinosum*
'Vivat Regina' (Z/d)	WFib
'Voodoo' (U) ♀	CMdw CSpe EWoo LHil MSte NPla WFib
§ Vulcan (Z/d)	IHos WLRN
'W.H. Heytman' (R)	WFib
'Wallace Fairman' (R)	LDea
'Wallis Friesdorf' (Dw/C/d)	ESul LHil MWhe
'Wantirna' (Z/v)	ECtt LVER SDen
'Warrior' (Z/c)	LVER WFib
'Washbrook' (Min/d)	ESul
'Watersmeet' (R)	LDea
'Wattisham' (Dec)	ESul LDea WEas
'Waveney' (Min)	ESul
'Wayward Angel' (A) ♀	CLit ESul EWoo LDea LVER SKen WFib
'Wedding Gown' (R)	LDea
'Wedding Royale' (Dw/d)	ESul LVER
Weisse Perle (Z/d)	WFib
'Welcome' (Z/d)	WFib
'Welling' (Sc)	LVER
'Wellington' (R)	LDea WFib
'Wendy Anne'	SKen
'Wendy Hawley' (R)	LDea
'Wendy Read' (Dw/d)	ERea ESul LVER MWhe WFib
'Wensum' (Min/d)	ESul LVER WFib
¶ 'Westdale Appleblossom' (Z/C)	LVER
* 'Westdale Beauty' (d)	CWDa
'Western Zoyland' (R)	WFib
'Whisper' (R)	CSpe WFib
'White Birds Egg' (Z)	WFib
'White Blizzard'	NPri WLRN
'White Boar' (Fr)	CLit EWoo LBlm MBEx MSte SDen
'White Bonanza' (R)	EBSP LDea WFib
'White Charm' (R)	EBSP LDea
'White Chiffon' (R)	CSpe EBSP LDea LVER
'White Eggshell' (Min)	ESul LVER
'White Feather' (Z/St)	WFib
'White Frills' (Z/d)	WFib
'White Gem' (Min)	ESul
'White Glory' (R) ♀	EBSP LDea SDen WFib
'White Lively Lady' (Dw/C)	ESul
§ 'White Mesh' (I/v)	ECtt MBri MWhe SDen SKen WEas WFib
White Pearl Necklace	See *P.* Perlenkette Weiss = **'Perlpenei'**
'White Queen' (Z/d)	CWDa

'White Unique' (U)	CLit EWoo LHil MSte NSty SDen WFib
whytei	MHul
* 'Wickham Lad'	LDea
* 'Wild Spice'	LDea
¶ 'Wilf Vernon' (Min/d)	ESul
'Wilhelm Kolle' (Z)	WFib
'William Sutton' (R)	WFib
¶ 'Winford Festival'	LVER
¶ 'Winford Winnie'	LVER
'Winnie Read' (Dw/d)	ERea ESul
'Winston Churchill' (R)	LDea
'Wirral Target' (Z/d)	ESul MWhe
'Wishing Star'	ESul
'Witnesham' (Min/d)	ESul
§ 'Wood's Surprise' (MinI/d)	ESul LDea LVER MWhe SDen WFib
'Wookey' (R)	WFib
§ *worcesterae*	MHul
'Wrington' (R)	WFib
'Wroxham' (Dw)	ESul
* 'Wychwood'	LDea
'Wyck Beacon' (I/d)	SKen
'Wycombe Maid' (Min/d)	WFib
¶ 'Wydcombe' (d)	SDen
'Xenia Field' (Z)	SDen
xerophyton	MHul
'Yale' (I/d) ♀	CHal GHCN IHos LBlm LDea LVER MBri MSte MWhe SDen SKen SLMG WFib
'Yarrabee Jane' (R)	WFib
'Yhu' (R)	EBSP LDea WFib
'Yolanda' (Min/C)	ESul
'York Florist'	LVER
'York Minster' (Dw/v)	SKen
'Yvonne' (Z)	WFib
¶ 'Zena' (Dw)	ESul
'Zinc' (Z/d)	WFib
'Zoe' (D)	SDen
zonale	MHul WFib
'Zulu King' (R)	WFib
'Zulu Warrior' (R)	WFib

PELLAEA (Sinopteridaceae)

¶ *atropupurea*	EFer
boivinii var. *viridis*	NMar
§ *calomelanos*	NMar
¶ *cordifolia*	WRic
falcata	MBri
hastata	See *P. calomelanos*
¶ *ovata*	WRic
rotundifolia ♀	CHal MBri NMar
sagittata	NMar

PELLIONIA See ELATOSTEMA

PELTANDRA (Araceae)

alba	See *P. saggitifolia*
§ *saggitifolia*	SWyc
§ *undulata*	CRow EHon LPBA MSta SRms SWat SWyc
¶ *virginica*	EMFW
– Rafinesque	SWyc
– Schott	See *P. undulata*

PELTARIA (Brassicaceae) See Plant Deletions

PELTIPHYLLUM See DARMERA

PELTOBOYKINIA (Saxifragaceae)

§ *tellimoides*	EMan NHol SMac WCru WFar

watanabei — CHan GTou LFis SMac WFar

PENNANTIA (Icacinaceae)
corymbosa — ECou MAll

PENNISETUM (Poaceae)
§ *alopecuroides* — CHEx CLTr CSte EBrP EBre
ECGN EGar GBin GCal LBre
MBrN MHar MHlr MLLN
NHol NOrc NVic SApp SBre
SCob SOkh SPer WHil WPGP
WPic WWat WWye

– 'Hameln' — CDoC CInt CMea CSpe EBee
EBrP EBre ECGN ECha EFou
EHoe EMan EMar EMon EPPr
EPla ESOG LBre LHop MBri
MSte MWhi NFai SApp SBre
SLod SMad SPla WPer WRus

¶ – 'Herbstzauber' — CSte
¶ – 'Little Bunny' — CSte GCal
¶ – 'Moudry' — EFou
– f. *viridescens* — CCuc EBee ECha EFou EHoe
ELan EMan MLLN MTis NPSI
NSti SLPl SPla SSoC WBea
WHil WWat

¶ – 'Weserbergland' — CElw EPPr
– 'Woodside' — CCuc EBrP EBre EHoe EMan
EPPr EPla LBre SApp SBre

* 'Burgundy Blaze' — CSte
'Cassian's Choice' — EFou
compressum — See *P. alopecuroides*
flaccidum — EMon EPPr LRHS MLLN
incomptum — EBee EBrP EBre EHoe LBre
SBre

– purple — EPPr
longistylum — See *P. villosum*
macrourum — CCuc CHan CHea CInt CRDP
EHoe EPPr EPla ESOG
orientale ♀ — CBos CInt CPea EBee EBrP
EBre ECha EGar EMan EMar
LBre LFis LHop MHlr MLLN
MMil MNrw NBir SAxl SBre
SMrm SUsu SWas WBro WCot
WHoo WKif WOMN WPGP
WPyg

¶ *purpureum* — MMoz
rueppellii — See *P. setaceum*
§ *setaceum* ♀ — CInt MNrw WLRN WLin
¶ sp. B&SWJ 3854 — WCru
§ *villosum* — CCuc CInt CKel CRDP EBar
EBrP EBre ECha EHoe LBre
LHop MLLN NBro NSti SApp
SAxl SBre SLod SMad SPla
SUsu WCot

PENSTEMON † (Scrophulariaceae)
* 'Abberley' — WPer
¶ 'Abbotsmerry' — EFou WSPU
§ *albidus* — EBee
§ 'Alice Hindley' ♀ — Widely available
alpinus — CLyd EWes GAbr GTou MLLN
MSto NOak WRHF WThi

– subsp. *brandegeei* — See *P. brandegeei*
§ 'Andenken an Friedrich Hahn' ♀ — CHan CMCo CMHG CMea
CSev CStr EBee ECha ELan
GCHN GMac ISea LHop NFai
NHar NHol NMir NRoo SAga
SChu SIgm SMad SUsu WAbe
WHCG WHil WMaN WMer
WRus WSPU

§ *angustifolius* — MHew MNrw MWgw SRms
WPer

antirrhinoides — See *Keckiella antirrhinoides*
'Apple Blossom' ♀ — Widely available
'Apple Blossom' hort. — See *P.* 'Thorn'
aridus — CPBP EBee WLin
arizonicus — See *P. whippleanus*
arkansanus — CGen MNrw
'Astley' — CAxe WPer
attenuatus — MSto WPer
azureus — WCot WPer WRha
'Barbara Barker' — See *P.* 'Beech Park'
§ *barbatus* — CBot CGle CKel CLon EBrP
EBre ECha ELan EMar GCHN
LBlm LBre LGre LPen MBel
MBro MWat SBre SChu SMac
SPer SSea SUsu WCFE WEas
WHCG WHer

¶ – subsp. *coccineus* — NLar WMow
– 'Jingle Bells' — EHic
– K 92.319 — CMdw NHar
– Limoges form — GCal
¶ – orange form — SHFr
– var. *praecox* — WPer
– – f. *nanus* — CBot EMil GCHN GSki LRHS
MSte SRms

¶ – – – 'Rondo' — NBro NLar
barrettiae — CMea GCHN
¶ 'Beckford' — WSPU
§ 'Beech Park' ♀ — CInt EBar ELan EWes LHil
LHop LPen MBel MCLN
MLLN NHaw SAga WHCG
WHil WPen WRus WSPU

§ *berryi* — NLak
'Bisham Seedling' — See *P.* 'White Bedder'
'Blackbird' — Widely available
I 'Blue Spring' — See *P. heterophyllus* 'Blue Springs'
'Bodnant' — EBee SSte WPer
§ *brandegeei* — EBee
'Breitenbush Blue' — CAxe LHop LPen SAga
bridgesii — See *P. rostriflorus*
'Burford Purple' — See *P.* 'Burgundy'
'Burford Seedling' — See *P.* 'Burgundy'
'Burford White' — See *P.* 'White Bedder'
§ 'Burgundy' — CAxe CDec CDoC CElw CLTr
CMHG CSam EAst EOrc
GCHN GMac IHos LLWP LPen
NFai NPer NSti SChu SPer
WHCG WLin WMaN WPer
WRus

caeruleus — See *P. angustifolius*
caespitosus — EBrP EBre LBre SBre
– 'Cloud Barr' — CGra CPBP
§ – subsp. *suffruticosus* — CPBP MFos
¶ – white — CGra
calcyosus — NLak
♦ *californicus* — See *P. linarioides* subsp. *californicus*
§ *campanulatus* — CMHG CSam EHyt EWes GCal
LFis LHop LPen MBro MLLN
MTho NHar NHol NMen NNrd
NTow SAga WAbe WHCG
WLin WPer WRus WSPU
WWal

– CD&R 1355 — CHan
– var. *chihuahuensis* — SAga
– *pulchellus* — See *P. campanulatus*
– *roseus* — CAxe WEas WSPU
'Candy Pink' — WEas
¶ *cardinalis regilis* — WLin
cardwellii — CMea ECha EPot EWes GTou
LGre NHar SAga SRms
¶ – × *davidsonii* — CGra WAbe

¶ 'Caroline Orr' WCot
'Castle Forbes' GMac WEas WHCG WPer
 WWoo
'Catherine de la Mare' ♀ CGle CHad CLTr CLyd EBrP
 EBre ECtt EFou ELan ERav
 GCHN LBre LFis LGre LHop
 LPen MHFP MRav MSCN
 MWat NBir NBro SAga SBre
 SChu SMrm SOkh WHoo WPer
 WSPU
* 'Centra' GCHN
 centranthifolius JJA 13106 SIgm
'Charles Rudd' CBlo CBod CGle LPen MLLN
 NFai NLak SAga SChu WHCG
 WMaN WOMN WOve
'Cherry' GMac
'Cherry Ripe' ♀ CBlo CMea EBar EBee EOrc
 LHil LPen LRHS MLLN NLak
 NPla SCro SMrm SPla SSte
 WHCG WHal WLin WPer
 WPyg WRus WSPU WWoo
§ 'Chester Scarlet' ♀ CMCo EBrP EBre EOrc GBri
 GCHN GGar GMac LBre LHop
 LPen MBel MBri MCLN MNrw
 MRav NBrk NFai SAga SBre
 SSte WEas WHCG WMaN
 WPer WRus WSPU WWhi
¶ *comarrhenus cyaneus* WLin
 confertus CGra CMHG CNic CTri EBar
 EHyt ELan EMNN GAbr LPen
 MHig MSto NChi NGre NLak
 NMen NRoo NWCA SHFr
 SRms WAbe WHCG WLin
 WPer WSPU
'Connie's Pink' ♀ CAxe ENot LPen MLLN MSte
 WHCG WLin WSPU
* 'Coral Pink' GAbr GMac
 cordifolius See *Keckiella cordifolia*
'Cottage Garden Red' See *P.* 'Windsor Red'
§ 'Countess of Dalkeith' CBlo CHea CLTr EBee EOrc
 EWes GBri LHil LHop LLWP
 LPen MLLN MNes NHaw NLak
 SOkh SSte WHCG WSPU
 WWhi
'Craigieburn Chenille' GCra
'Craigieburn Taffeta' GCra
 crandallii CPBP
 – subsp. *glabrescens* LGre SAga SUsu WHCG WLin
 cristatus See *P. eriantherus*
 davidsonii CLyd EWes LGre MHig WAbe
 – subsp. *davidsonii* CGra WLin
§ – var. *menziesii* ♀ EBee GTou MFir NBus NHar
 NLak NWCA SBla WAbe
 WEas WIvy WSPU
 – – 'Microphyllus' CLyd CMea GCLN MAsh MSto
 NBus NHar NMen NSla WAbe
 WLin
* – – 'Tolmiei Peak' CGra
 – var. *praeteritus* EHyt GCLN LGre NHar WLin
'Dazzler' CBlo CBod CM&M CMdw
 NRoo WPer WSPU
 deustus CPBP MBel SRms
'Devonshire Cream' CAxe CElw LPen WHCG
'Diane' WMer
 diffusus See *P. serrulatus*
 digitalis CHan CLyd CNic CSpe EBar
 ECha EGar EMan GCra LGan
 LGre LPen NChi WAbb WEas
 WHCG WMow WPer
§ – 'Husker's Red' Widely available
 – 'Purpureus' See *P. digitalis* 'Husker's Red'

 discolor CMea CNic LGre SAga SMrm
§ 'Drinkstone' CGle EGoo EHol LGre LHop
 LPen MLLN NChi SAga SDix
 SMrm WHCG WPer WSPU
'Drinkwater Red' See *P.* 'Drinkstone'
 eatonii SRms WCot
¶ – subsp. *undosus* NWCA
'Edithiae' EOrc LFlo MBal MBro NLak
 NRoo SChu WEas WHCG
 WHoo WIvy WKif
§ *eriantherus* CElw WHCG
 euglaucus CAxe WLin
§ 'Evelyn' ♀ Widely available
'Firebird' See *P.* 'Schoenholzeri'
'Flame' CGle EBee EMan LHop LPen
 WHCG WPer WSPU
'Flamingo' EBar EWes LPen MBro MCLN
 NHaw NLak SAga SMrm SSte
 SUsu WHoo WLRN WMaN
 WSPU WWoo
 frutescens GTou WSPU
 fruticosus LFis MLLN MNrw NHar
 NWCA SRms WAbe WLin
§ – var. *scouleri* ♀ EHic MAsh MBro MHar MOne
 SRms WIvy WSPU
 – – f. *albus* ♀ CBot CMea CNic EHyt ELan
 LGre LHop LPen NWCA SAga
 SBla SChu WAbe WEas WIvy
 WKif WSPU WSan
 – – 'Amethyst' WAbe WLin
 – – 'Hopleys' LHop
 – var. *serratus* WLin
 – – 'Holly' CHan CMea LFis LGre SAga
 SBla SMrm
* 'Gaff's Pink' SChu
¶ 'Gaiety' CAxe
'Garden Red' See *P.* 'Windsor Red'
'Garnet' See *P.* 'Andenken an Friedrich
 Hahn'
'Garnet Variegated' CAxe CLyd NLak
 gentianoides CMdw MNrw MWhi NBro
 NLak WRus WSPU
¶ 'Geoff Hamilton' EBar
'George Elrick' EBar LPen
§ 'George Home' ♀ CGle CLTr EBar EBee ECGP
 ECtt EHic EWes GAbr LHil
 LPen MLLN NHaw WByw
 WHCG WMaN WRus WWoo
 glaber CElw CHan CMHG CSev EBar
 EBee GMac LGre LHop LLWP
 LPen MBro MLLN MRav NBro
 NSti SAga SHFr SHel SMrm
 WEas WHCG WHoo WKif
 WPer WRus WSPU WWhi
¶ × *gloxinioides* 'Stapleford MBro
 Gem'
 gormanii CNic EPot MLLN
 gracilis CNic GCHN WPer WSPU
 grandiflorus NLak
 hallii CGra CLyd EWes GTou LPen
 NSla WSPU
 hartwegii ♀ GMac LHil LHop LPen SAga
 SChu SSea WAbe WHCG WPer
 WRus WSPU
 – *albus* CAxe EBee LGre LHop LPen
 LRHS MCLN MMil MSte NNor
 SAga SPer WHCG WRus
 WSPU WWhi
 harvardii EBee WAbe
 heterodoxus WLin
§ *heterophyllus* Widely available
 – subsp. *australis* See *P. australis*

Name	Sources
– 'Blue Eye'	CAxe WMaN WSPU
– 'Blue Fountain'	LPen WSPU
– 'Blue Gem'	CBod CElw CTri CVer EBrP EBre EOrc LBre MBro NRoo SBre SIng SMrm SPla SSte WHoo WSPU
– 'Blue Springs'	CBlo CBot CGle CLon CM&M CMea EBrP EBre LBre LFis LPen MBri MLLN MSte NBir NFla SAga SBla SBre SMrm SPla WAbe WRus
– 'Heavenly Blue'	CBlo EBar EBrP EBre ECtt LBre LFis LHop MAvo MCLN MTis NHaw NPla SBre SWat WLRN WOve WRus WWal WWhi
– subsp. *purdyi*	NLak SMrm WHCG
– 'True Blue'	See *P. heterophyllus*
– 'Züriblau'	MBro SMrm WWat
'Hewell Pink Bedder' ♀	CBlo CGle CLTr EBar EBee EBrP EBre EFou ENot GBri GCHN LBre LPen MBel MCLN NChi NRoo SBre SChu SPar SSte WHCG WPer WSPU
§ 'Hidcote Pink' ♀	Widely available
'Hidcote Purple'	CElw LFis LHil NBrk NPla SChu
* 'Hidcote White'	CBot CM&M EOrc SUsu WAbe WRus
¶ 'Hillview Pink'	WHil
'Hillview Red'	WHil
§ *hirsutus*	CGle EBee EPPr NHol SOkh WOMN WPer WSan WThi
¶ – f. *albiflorus*	CMea WThi
– bronze-leaved	WThi
– var. *minimus*	MLLN WThi
– var. *pygmaeus*	CHan CLyd CNic CRDP ELan GCLN GTou LFis MBro MHar MHig MPla NHar NMen NWCA SBla SRms WByw WHoo WOMN WPer WRus WThi WWin
– – f. *albus*	CMea EHyt WPer
¶ – – 'Purpureus'	WLin
'Hopleys Variegated'	EGar EOrc EWes LFis LHop LPen MBel MNrw MSCN NBir NLak SLod SSte WCot WHer WSPU WSan WWeb
humilis	CM&M EAst EBee MLLN NWCA WShe
– Mckay's form	WLin
– 'Pulchellus'	LGre NWCA
* 'Hyacinth'	ELan
isophyllus ♀	CLyd EBee EPfP LPen MBEx MMil MNes SChu WEas WFar WHCG WPer WSPU
jamesii	CGra CHan EBee EOrc NChi WLin
janishiae	CBlo
¶ 'Jill Lucas'	SCro
'John Booth'	WEas
'John Nash'	CAxe CSWP CSam NLak SHFr SIgm SMrm SSte
'John Nash' hort.	See *P.* 'Alice Hindley'
'Joy'	CBlo EBrP EBre LBre MBro MGed MLLN MSte NPla SBre SSte WHal WOve WPer WPyg WWoo
'June'	See *P.* 'Hidcote Pink'
'King George V'	Widely available
* 'Knight's Purple'	WHCG
'Knightwick'	CAxe WPer WSPU
'Kummel'	ELan
kunthii	See *P. campanulatus*
laetus var. *laetus*	GCLN
§ – var. *roezlii*	EDAr GChr GDra MLLN MLan MPla MSto NHar NLak NMen NWCA SIng SRms WAbe WEas WWin
laricifolius	CPBP
leiophyllus	MBro
¶ *leonensis*	CGen
linarioides	CPBP EWes LPen MBro WAbe WPat
§ – subsp. *californicus*	WLin
– subsp. *coloradensis*	WLin
– JCA 9694	WLin
'Little Witley'	CAxe LPen WHCG WPer
* 'Logan Pink'	GMac
'Lord Home'	See *P.* 'George Home'
lyallii	CAxe CKel CMCo EBee ELan EMar ESis ITim LFis LPen MCCP MLLN MNrw MSCN NLak NLon SMac SSca WSPU WSan WWeb
* 'Lynette'	CAxe CLyd EHic LFis LPen WHCG WHil WPer
'Macpenny's Pink'	WWoo
'Madame Golding'	CGle CSWP EBar EBee LGre LHil MLLN MMil SAga SMrm SSte SUsu WHCG WPer WSPU
'Margery Fish' ♀	CElw CLyd CM&M CPou CSev EHic ESis LFlo LGan MMil MNrw MSte NFai SMac SSte WPer WRha WSPU WSel
'Maurice Gibbs' ♀	CAxe CBlo LPen SIgm WHCG WSPU
¶ *mensarum*	EBee
menziesii	See *P. davidsonii* var. *menziesii*
'Merlin'	EHic
'Midnight'	CElw CGle CHan CLTr GBri LFis LPen MAvo MBEx MBel MBro MMil NBrk SAga SChu SDys SIgm SMrm WCFE WCot WHCG WMer WPer WRus WSPU WWin
'Modesty'	CBlo EBar LPen LRHS NPla SMac WHCG WSPU
¶ 'Molly Margaret'	GCHN
montanus	GCHN
'Mother of Pearl'	CElw EBar ECtt EFou EOrc GMac LHop LPen MBel MCLN MNrw NChi NFai NHaw NRoo SAga SChu SIgm SPer WHCG WHal WMaN WOve WPer WSPU
* 'Mountain Wine'	WThi
* 'Mrs Miller'	EBar LPen
'Mrs Morse'	See *P.* 'Chester Scarlet'
¶ *multiflorus*	LPen
'Myddelton Gem'	CGle CLTr ECGP LPen MWat NPla WFoF WHCG WSPU
'Myddelton Red'	CRos
¶ *nemorosus*	EBee
¶ *neomexicanus*	EBee
newberryi ♀	CMHG CMea ELan EPot LGre MAsh MFos NBir NMen NRoo WAbe WKif WSPU WWin
– subsp. *berryi*	See *P. berryi*
– f. *humilior*	MSto
§ – var. *sonomensis*	EPot GCLN NHar NWCA WAbe WLin
§ *nitidus*	CGra MNrw
'Oaklea Red'	ECtt LHil MLLN SSoC SWat

* old candy pink	LLWP LPen MBel MBri WPer WRus WSPU WWhi
¶ *oliganthus*	WLin
¶ *ophianthus*	EBee
'Osprey' ♀	Widely available
ovatus	CLyd CMCo ELan GCHN GCal GCra LFis LGan LPen MBro MLLN NChi NLak SAga SIgm SRms SSca WHCG WKif WLin WSan
palmeri	CFir CGen EWll GCra NLak
'Papal Purple'	CKel CLyd CM&M CMHG EBar GMac LLWP LPen MBro MLLN MMil MSte NBrk NLak SAga SChu SMac SMrm SRms WElm WHCG WHal WHil WHoo WRus WSPU WWhi WWye
¶ 'Papal Purple' x 'Evelyn'	CAxe
parvulus	CPBP NWCA
'Patio Coral'	EHic MBri MLLN
'Patio Pink'	MBri MLLN
'Patio Shell'	EHic MBri
'Patio Swirl'	MBri
'Patio Wine'	EHic MBri MLLN
'Peace'	CLTr CRos EBar EBee LHop LPen LRHS NLak NPla SSca SSte WHCG WMaN WRus WSPU WWhi
peckii	MSto
'Pennington Gem' ♀	Widely available
'Pershore Pink Necklace'	EBrP EBre LBre LPen MCLN MLLN SBre WEas WHCG WMaN WSPU WSan
'Phare'	CBod EBar WHCG WPer WSPU
'Phyllis'	See *P.* 'Evelyn'
pinifolius ♀	Widely available
– 'Mersea Yellow'	Widely available
– 'Wisley Flame' ♀	ESis SIgm SWas
'Pink Dragon'	CLyd GCHN GDra LGre MPla NHar SAga SChu SMrm WHCG WSPU
§ 'Pink Endurance'	CMea CStr EBrP EBre ELan LBre LGan LLWP LPen MBro MCLN MLLN MMil NHaw NRoo SAga SBre WEas WHCG WHal WHoo WMaN WPer WSPU
'Pink Ice'	NPla WHil
'Pink Profusion'	SIgm SMrm
'Port Wine' ♀	CAxe CBlo CGle CLTr CRDP CSam GCHN LHil LPen MBel MLLN NPla SMac SPer SSte WHCG WMaN WOve WPer WSPU WSel
'Powis Castle'	EWes WPer WWye
'Prairie Dusk'	LPen
'Prairie Fire'	LPen WSPU
* 'Prairie Pride'	LPen
'Primrose Thomas'	CAxe MBel NHaw
'Priory Purple'	NLak WHCG WPer
procerus	CM&M GBri GCra LPen MDHE SRms SSte WPer
¶ – subsp. *procerus*	EHyt
– var. *tolmiei*	EPot GCHN GCal LGre LPen NChi NHol NRoo NTow NWCA WCla
¶ – subsp. *tolmiei* white	CGra
pruinosus	CGra EBee EPot GCLN WLin
pubescens	See *P. hirsutus*
¶ *pulchellus*	WLin

– Lindley	See *P. campanulatus*
pulcherrimus	NBro
pumilus	MSto
'Purple and White'	See *P.* 'Countess of Dalkeith'
'Purple Bedder'	CGle CHea EHic EMar GAbr LPen MCLN MLLN MWat NHaw NHol NPla SSoC SWat WGor WHCG WSPU WSel WWal
'Purple Dragon'	MPla
'Purple Gem'	GDra
'Purple Passion'	EBrP EBre EPfP EWes LBre MAus NRoo SBre WLRN
'Purpureus Albus'	See *P.* 'Countess of Dalkeith'
purpusii	CPBP EPot SIgm WAbe
'Rajah'	CVer EBee LHop WLin
'Raven' ♀	CLon EOrc GBri LBlm LPen MAus MBel MBro MCLN NBrk NBro NHaw SChu WCot WEas WHCG WHal WHoo WMaN WMer WPer WPyg WRus WSPU WWin
'Razzle Dazzle'	LRHS WPer
'Red Ace'	MLLN MNrw
'Red Emperor'	CMHG EBar ECtt MLLN NFai NHaw WEas WHCG WMer WPer WSPU
'Red Knight'	EBar LPen
'Rich Purple'	EBar NDov SPer WMaN
'Rich Ruby'	CGle CMGP EBrP EBre ELan EWes LBre LGre LHil LHop LLWP LPen MBEx MGrG MNrw SAga SBre SChu SMrm SOkh SUsu WEas WHCG WMaN WPer WRus WSPU WWhi
richardsonii	CVer ECro MNrw MSCN NChi NLak SIgm SRms WOMN
'Ridgeway Red'	WSPU
roezlii Regel	See *P. laetus* var. *roezlii*
* 'Rose Blush'	CAxe LPen NLak WHCG
* *roseocampanulatus*	SPan WSPU
§ *rostriflorus*	SAga SBla
– JJA 9548	SBla
'Roundhay'	CFee
* 'Roy Davidson' ♀	CMea CNic CPBP LBee SBla WFar WLin
'Royal White'	See *P.* 'White Bedder'
'Rubicundus' ♀	CBot CGle CLyd EBar EBee ECtt ELan GMac LHil LHop LPen MCLN SAga SMrm WAbe WCot WHCG WHoo WMer WRus WSPU WWal WWeb
'Ruby'	See *P.* 'Schoenholzeri'
'Ruby Field'	GAbr NPla WHCG WWoo
rupicola ♀	CMea GDra GTou LHop MBro MPla NSla NWCA SBla SIgm WAbe WOMN WWin
– 'Albus'	LGre WAbe
– 'Diamond Lake'	CPBP MBro NHar WIvy WLin WPat
– mauve hybrid	GDra LGre
'Russian River'	CLTr CSWP EAst EBee EFou EHic EWes LLWP LPen MBel MBro NHaw NLak SMrm SOkh SSte WHCG WPer WPyg WSPU
* Saskatoon hybrids	NChi
¶ *scariosus* var. *garrettii*	WLin
'Scarlet Queen'	CSWP

§ 'Schoenholzeri' ♀ — CElw CLTr EBee EOrc LFis LGre LHop LLWP LPen MBri MNes MNrw NFai NRoo NSti SAga SChu SIgm SPer SUsu WAbe WEas WHCG WHil WHoo WPer WRus WSPU WWat

scouleri — See *P. fruticosus* var. *scouleri*

secundiflorus — CNic WCot

§ *serrulatus* — CGen CVer EBee ECha EWes GTou LPen MBel MSte NWCA SHFr SMad SRms WEas WLin WSPU

– 'Albus' — LPen MSte SIgm SMac WSPU WWin

'Shell Pink' — WPer

* 'Sherbourne Blue' — WPer

* 'Shrawley' — WPer

'Sissinghurst Pink' — See *P. 'Evelyn'*

'Six Hills' — CPBP MPla NHar NHol NRoo SAga SDys WHCG WLin WPer WSPU

* 'Skyline' — EPfP WWeb

smallii — LPen NLak SIgm

'Snow Storm' — See *P. 'White Bedder'*

'Snowflake' — See *P. 'White Bedder'*

'Snowstorm' — EBar WEas WHCG

sonomensis — See *P. newberryi* var. *sonomensis*

'Sour Grapes' hort. — See *P. 'Stapleford Gem'*

§ 'Sour Grapes' M. Fish — CBot CElw CHan CMil CRos CSWP EAst EBee ECot EHic ELan GBuc GCal GMac LHil MBel MBri MRav MTis MWgw NHaw NPla NRoo SMrm SPla SUsu WEas WPer WSPU WWat

'Southcombe Pink' — MLLN WHCG WPen

'Southgate Gem' — LPen MNrw MWat SCro WHCG

'Souvenir d'Adrian Regnier' — CStr GCHN

'Souvenir d'André Torres' — CBod LLWP

'Souvenir d'André Torres' misapplied — See *P. 'Chester Scarlet'*

sp. P&C 150 — CFee

¶ sp. tall pink — LPen

¶ *speciosus* — EHyt

– subsp. *kennedyi* — EHyt

§ 'Stapleford Gem' ♀ — CElw CGle CKel CMHG CMil CSam EBrP EBre ELan GCHN LBre LHil LPen MAus MBro MCLN NBro SAga SBre SIgm SMad SRms WEas WHCG WSPU WSel WWal WWat WWhi

strictus — CBlo CVer EBar ECro GCHN LGre MLLN NBro NChi NLak SIgm SMac WPer WRHF WSPU

– 'Bandera' — MHlr NLak WCot

'Sutton's Pink Bedder' — EBar LRHS WSPU

¶ 'Sylvia Buss' — LPen

N 'Taoensis' — CLTr EWes SMac SSea WAbe WRus

taosensis — See *P. crandallii* subsp. *taosensis*

ternatus — See *Keckiella ternata*

teucrioides — CMea EPot NWCA SMrm WThi

¶ – JCA 1717050 — CPBP

§ 'Thorn' — CBod CGle CLTr CLon CSWP CSam CSpe EAst EFou ELan EOrc LHop LPen LRHS MBel MLLN MNrw NBrk NFai NRoo SAga SCro SMrm SOkh WHCG WHoo WRus WSPU WWal

I 'Thorn Cross' — GMac

'Threave Pink' — See *P. 'Pink Endurance'*

* 'Threave White' — WPen

'Torquay Gem' — GBuc LHop LPen NLak WHCG WPer WRus

traceyi — NLak

'True Sour Grapes' — See *P. 'Sour Grapes' M. Fish*

tusharensis — See *P. caespitosus* subsp. *suffruticosus*

* *uintahensis* — CGra

unilateralis — MSto

utahensis — CBot EBrP EBre EWes GBri LBre MHlr SBre WMow WPer

¶ – white — WHil

venustus — CFir CSam GBuc GBur MHar MNrw NChi SRms WHCG WWye

virens AM — EHyt MHig NRoo NTow NWCA WPat WWhi

– *albus* — GCHN LFis NPri WWin

– R/Mr 7890 — WPer

virgatus subsp. *arizonicus* — CPBP MGed NLak WSPU

¶ – subsp. *putus* — WLin

¶ *washingtonensis* — CGra

watsonii — EBee EHic EMan LHop MLLN SAga SWat WCot WHCG WMow WPer

¶ 'Welsh Dawn' — WSPU

§ *whippleanus* — CBot CGle CHan CLon CLyd CRDP ECGN ECro EWes GCra LFlo LGre LPen MBel MSte NChi NLak SAga WAbb WLin WPer

– dark form — MBro

§ 'White Bedder' ♀ — CGle CMea EBrP EBre EFou GMac LBre LHop LLWP LPen MCLN MNes MSte NFai SAga SBre SChu SIgm SOkh SPer SRms WHCG WHil WMaN WPbr WPer WRus WSPU WWat WWin

'Whitethroat' — EBar LPen MHlr MLLN SOkh SRCN WCot WHCG WMaN WMer WPer WSPU WWin

wilcoxii — MFos

§ 'Windsor Red' — CBlo CBod EBar EFou EHic LPen MHFP MSte NPla WGor WHCG WSPU WSel WWoo

§ *wislizenii* — CBos EBrP EBre EHic EPfP LBre LGre MLLN MLan MNrw MOne MTis NOak SBid SBre SRms WFar WMaN WWal

¶ *wrightii* — EBee

PENTAGLOTTIS (Boraginaceae)

§ *sempervirens* — CArn CKin EJud EPfP GPoy MHew MSal WBea WGwy WHen WOak WWye

PENTALINON (Apocynaceae) See Plant Deletions

PENTAPTERYGIUM See AGAPETES

PENTAS (Rubiaceae)

lanceolata — CHal ELan MBri WMul

¶ – 'Candy Stripe'   WMul
¶ – 'New Look Pink'   LPVe
¶ – 'New Look Red'   LPVe
¶ – 'Red Star'   WMul

PENTASCHISTIS (Poaceae) See Plant Deletions

PEPEROMIA (Piperaceae)
§ *argyreia* ♀   CHal MBri
  arifolia   CHal
  caperata   MBri
  – 'Little Fantasy' ♀   CHal
  clusiifolia   CHal
  – 'Variegata'   CHal
  glabella   CHal
  griseoargentea   CHal
  magnoliifolia   See *P. obtusifolia* Magnoliifolia
                           Group
  obtusifolia 'Jamaica' MBri
§ – Magnoliifolia Group   SRms
  – – 'Golden Gate'   MBri
  – – 'Greengold'   CHal MBri
  – – 'USA'   MBri
  – 'Tricolor'   MBri
  orba 'Pixie'   MBri
I – 'Pixie Variegata'   MBri
  pulchella   See *P. verticillata*
  resediflora   See *P. fraseri*
  sandersii   See *P. argyreia*
  scandens ♀   MBri
  – 'Variegata'   CHal MBri
§ *verticillata*   CHal

PERESKIA (Cactaceae)
  aculeata f. *rubescens*   WCot

PERESKIOPSIS (Cactaceae)
§ *diguetii*   CHal
  spathulata   See *P. diguetii*

PEREZIA (Asteraceae)
  linearis   GBuc
  recurvata   EPot GCrs GTou NNrd NWCA
                           WFar

PERICALLIS (Asteraceae)
  lanata Kew form   CSpe SMrm
§ – (L'Herit.) B.Nord.   CHan CSev ELan LHil LHop
                           MBEx MBlu SMrm SRms WEas

PERILLA (Lamiaceae)
§ *frutescens* var. *crispa* ♀   CArn MChe WJek
  – var. *nankinensis*   See *P. frutescens* var. *crispa*
  – *rubra*   CArn MChe WJek

PERIPLOCA (Asclepiadaceae)
  graeca   CArn CB&S CMac CPlN CPle
                           CRHN GQui NBea NFla SBra
                           SPer WCru WSHC
  sepium   CPlN CPle

PERISTROPHE (Acanthaceae)
  speciosa   ERea SLMG

PERNETTYA See GAULTHERIA

PEROVSKIA (Lamiaceae)
  atriplicifolia   CArn CBot CPle GPoy LGre
                           LHol MBri SIde SLod WHCG
                           WOld WViv

'Blue Haze'   GCal
'Blue Spire' ♀   Widely available
'Filigran'   ECGP EFou GCal NLak
¶ 'Hybrida'   WWeb
  scrophulariifolia   CPle

PERROTTETIA (Celastraceae) See Plant Deletions

PERSEA (Lauraceae)
  thunbergii   CGre

PERSICARIA (Polygonaceae)
§ *affinis*   CB&S CBen CBlo CHan CTri
                           ECha MBar MTho NBro NVic
                           SWat WEas WHil WOld WOve
                           WWat
  – 'Darjeeling Red' ♀   CB&S CBlo CRow CSev ECED
                           ELan ENot EPla GCal GChr
                           LGro LHil MBal MBri NBir
                           NChi NFla NHol SMrm WAbe
                           WBea WHen
  – 'Dimity'   See *P. affinis* 'Superba'
  – 'Donald Lowndes' ♀   CBlo CRow ECha ELan EMar
                           ENot GMac LHop LLWP
                           LPBA MBal MSta MWat NChi
                           NDea NFla NGre NHol NRoo
                           SPer SRms WAbe WBea WLin
                           WOld WPer
  – 'Ron McBeath'   ECha
§ – 'Superba' ♀   CBlo CRow EBrP EBre EFou
                           EPla LBre LFis MBri MFir
                           MHlr MRav MWgw NBro NFai
                           NHol NRoo SBre SIng SMrm
                           SSpi WHoo WPer WPyg WRus
  alata   CRow NHol SMad
  alpina   CRow
  amphibia   CRow
§ *amplexicaulis*   CBre CRow ELan EMar GMaP
                           LGro MBal MBro MSCN MWat
                           NChi NDea NNor NOrc SChu
                           SEND SUsu WFar WHoo WPyg
                           WRHF
  – 'Alba'   CRow ECha EGar EPla LGre
                           WBea
  – 'Arun Gem'   See *P. amplexicaulis* var.
                           pendula
  – 'Atrosanguinea'   CBlo CNic CRow ECED ECha
                           EMan EPla LFis MAus MFir
                           NBir NDea NFai NFla NHol
                           NTow NVic SPer SRms WOld
                           WWin
§ – Taurus = 'Blotau'   EGar MLLN WFar
  – 'Cottesbrooke Gold'   CRow
  – 'Firetail' ♀   CDec CHan CRow EBrP EBre
                           ECED ECha ECtt EFou EPla
                           LBre LHop LLWP NHol NRoo
                           NSti SBre SUsu WBea WFar
                           WHil WOld WRus WWhi
                           WCot
  – 'Gold Leaf'   CBre CRow ECha ECtt EGar
  – 'Inverleith'   EPla NCat NLak NRoo SDys
                           WOld WPGP WRHF WWye
§ – var. *pendula*   CRow ECha GAri NBir NRoo
                           WBea
¶ – 'Rosea'   CRow ECha ELan EMon EPla
                           MRav NSti SUsu WBea
  – 'Rowden Gem'   CRow
¶ – 'Rowden Jewel'   CRow
¶ – 'Rowden Rose Quartz'   CRow
♦ – Taurus   See *P. amplexicaulis* Taurus =
                           'Blotau'

¶ *amplexicaullis* 'Firedance' SMrm
§ *bistorta* — CArn CBlo CJew CKin CRow ELau GPoy LHol MChe MHew MSal SWat WSel WWye
 – subsp. *carnea* — CRow EBee ECha EGar ELan EMon EPPr NBir
 – 'Hohe Tatra' — CRow SMrm
 – 'Superba' ♀ — Widely available
bistortoides — MSal
* 'Blush Clent' — WSPU
campanulata — CElw CHan COtt CRow ECED ECha ECro ELan EMar EPar LBlm LHop MHar MSCN MWat NBro NFai NNor NRoo SPer WBea WOve WWat WWin WWye
 – Alba Group — CRow ELan EMar GCal NBro NSti SChu WHer WWat
 – pale pink — GBuc GCal WBcn
 – 'Rosenrot' — CBlo CBre CJew CRow GBuc GCal IBlr LFis NHol SSpi SWat WBea WOld
 – 'Southcombe White' — CRow EBar EPla GAri LBlm WBea
capitata — CInt CLTr CRow ELan MMil SCro SIng SMac SRms WBea WEas
 – from Afghanistan — WBea
* *coriacea* — CRow
elata — CHor EGoo EMar EMon GAri GBuc GGar SLod
emodi — CRow WCot WWat
filiformis — See *P. virginiana*
§ *macrophylla* — CRow NFla WOld
microcephala — CRow EWes SAga SCro SMac WCot
milletii — CRDP CRow EPPr EWes GAri GBuc GDra MTho NLak NOak WCot WCru WMer WOMN
§ *mollis* — CHan CRow EHal
odorata — CArn EOHP MSal WJek
orientalis — MSal SMrm
polymorpha — CRow EFou EMon LGre SMrm WPbr
polystachya — ECha SDix
§ *runcinata* — CLTr CRow ECED EHal EMar GCHN NLar SAxl WCot WCru WFar WFox WOld WPer WWin
* *rupestris* — WMoo
scoparia — See *Polygonum scoparium*
sphaerostachya Meissner — See *P. macrophylla*
tenuicaulis — CBlo CBre CLyd CRow EMon EPar EPla GGar MBal MUlv NChi NDea NHol SIng WCru WOMN
vacciniifolia ♀ — CB&S CNic CPle CRow ECha ESis GCHN GMac MBal MBar MHig MPla MTho MWat NGre NHar NHol NRoo NSla SBla SDix SIng SSmi WAbe WRus WWat WWin
 – 'Ron McBeath' — CRow
§ *virginiana* — CMHG EPla MFir
 – Compton's form — WCot
§ – 'Painter's Palette' (v) — CArn CB&S CBot CGle CHad CRow ECha ECtt EFou ELan EMar EPla GCal LHop NSti NVic SAga SMad SPer SVil WCru WEas WMer WOld WPer

§ – Variegata Group — CBot CHan CRow EBee ECha EMar EPla GCal LHop WCot WOld
vivipara — CRow WCot
§ *wallichii* — CRow IBlr NSti
weyrichii — EMan GCal MTed NBir NBro NChi WBea WCot WOld

PETALOSTEMON See DALEA

PETAMENES See GLADIOLUS

PETASITES (Asteraceae)
albus — CRow EMon GPoy MCli MSal NSti
fragrans — CHEx CNat ELan EMon EPar MSta SWat WOak
hybridus — CKin EMFW MCli WHer
japonicus var. *giganteus* — CHEx CRow ECha EGol ELan EMan EMon EOld EPar EPfP MSCN NVic SBid WCru
 – – 'Variegatus' — CHEx CRow ECoo EEls EGar EMon EPla IBlr MSCN NTow SBid WCHb WCru WHer WHil
palmatus — GCal MHlr NSti WCru
 – JLS 86317CLOR — EMon SMad WCot
paradoxus — CRDP EMon WCot

PETREA (Verbenaceae)
volubilis — CPlN ECon LChe SOWG WMul

PETROCALLIS (Brassicaceae)
lagascae — See *P. pyrenaica*
§ *pyrenaica* — GCrs NWCA WLin WPer
¶ – *alba* — GCrs

PETROCOPTIS (Caryophyllaceae)
pyrenaica — EBur GBin MDHE NMen SRms SSca
§ – subsp. *glauciofolia* — ESis GTou MNrw MPla NBir WHil WPer WWin
 – – 'Alba' — SSca

PETROCOSMEA (Gesneriaceae) See Plant Deletions

PETROMARULA (Campanulaceae)
¶ *pinnata* — GBin WCot

PETROPHYTUM (Rosaceae)
caespitosum — CGra GTou NHar NWCA
cinerascens — MFos NWCA SIng
§ *hendersonii* — GCLN NHol WAbe

PETRORHAGIA (Caryophyllaceae)
nanteuilii — CNat EWFC
§ *saxifraga* ♀ — CSpe EBur MNrw NMen NPri SAxl SIng SRms WPer WWhi
§ – 'Rosette' — ECha MTho WAbe WWin

PETROSELINUM (Apiaceae)
§ *crispum* — CArn CJew CSev EJud GPoy ILis LHol MBar MChe NPri SIde WPer WSel WWye
¶ – 'Bravour' ♀ — ELau MMal
 – 'Darki' — CSev
 – French — CArn CBod ELau IIve MMal WJek
 – 'Greek' — ELau

– 'Italian'   See *P. crispum* var.
                               neapolitanum
§ – var. *neapolitanum*   CBod EBar ELau IIve MGra
§ – var. *tuberosum*   CBod SIde WHer
hortense   See *P. crispum*
tuberosum   See *P. crispum* var. *tuberosum*

PETTERIA (Papilionaceae)
ramentacea   CB&S CFil SLPl SMad

PEUCEDANUM (Apiaceae)
¶ *formosanum* B&SWJ 3647   WCru
ostruthium   GPoy LHol
¶ – 'Daphnis'   EMon
verticillare   EMan MUlv SDix SMrm

PEUMUS (Monimiaceae)
boldus   CGre

PHACELIA (Hydrophyllaceae)
bolanderi   CHan CPBP
sericea subsp. *ciliosa*   MFos SIgm
– subsp. *sericea*   MFos

PHAEDRANASSA (Amaryllidaceae)
dubia   CMon
viridiflora   CMon

PHAEDRANTHUS See DISTICTIS

PHAENOCOMA   (Asteraceae) See Plant Deletions

PHAENOSPERMA (Poaceae)
globosa   EBee EGar EHoe EPPr EPla
                               ESOG EWes LHil

PHAGNALON   (Asteraceae) See Plant Deletions

PHAIOPHLEPS (Iridaceae)
biflora   See *Olsynium biflorum*
nigricans   See *Sisyrinchium striatum*

PHAIUS (Orchidaceae)
minor   EFEx

PHALARIS (Poaceae)
¶ *aquatica* 'Austalia'   NGno
¶ – 'Uneta'   NGno
arundinacea   CKin EBar EPla MLan SWat
– 'Elegantissima'   See *P. arundinacea* var. *picta*
                               'Picta'
– 'Luteovariegata'   EMon
¶ – var. *picta*   LSyl
– 'Picta'   CSte ENot LPBA LRHS NLon
                               NOak WFar
– var. *picta*   CB&S CRow CSWP MRav
  'Aureovariegata'   NPer SAga SWat
– – 'Feesey' (v)   Widely available
– – 'Luteopicta'   EBee EHoe EPPr EPla ESOG
                               LRHS WChe
§ – – 'Picta' (v) ♀   CRow EBrP EBre ECED EHoe
                               EHon ELan EPPr EPla EPot
                               ESOG GCHN IBlr LBre LGro
                               MBal MBar NFai NHol NNor
                               NSti SBre SCob SPer SWat
                               SWyc WChe WEas WWin
                               WWye
– – 'Tricolor' (v)   EBee EHoe EMon EPla GAri
                               GOrn SSoC WBea

– 'Streamlined' (v)   EMon EPla LRHS WLeb
¶ – 'Turkey Red'   NGno
¶ – 'Yugoslavian'   NGno
tuberosa stenoptera   See *P. aquatica*

PHALOCALLIS (Iridaceae)
¶ *coelestis*   EBee

PHANEROPHLEBIA (Dryopteridaceae)
caryotidea   See *Cyrtomium caryotideum*
falcata   See *Cyrtomium falcatum*
fortunei   See *Cyrtomium fortunei*

PHARBITIS See IPOMOEA

PHASEOLUS (Papilionaceae)
caracalla   See *Vigna caracalla*

PHEGOPTERIS (Thelypteridaceae)
§ *connectilis*   CCuc CFil EFer LSyl MBal
                               NHed NMar SRms
decursive-pinnata   CCuc EMon NHol NMar WRic

PHELLODENDRON (Rutaceae)
amurense   CB&S CGre CMCN ELan EPfP
                               NPSI SSpi WDin WNor
¶ – var. *sachalinense*   WPGP
¶ *chinense*   EMon
lavalleei   WPGP

PHILADELPHUS † (Hydrangeaceae)
¶ ACE 1907   WHCr
¶ 'Atlas'   CBlo
'Avalanche'   CMHG EBrP EBre LBre NFla
                               NPro SBre SEas SPer SRms
                               WDin WHCG WWat
'Beauclerk' ♀   CB&S CDoC CMHG EBrP
                               EBre ENot GChr LBre MAsh
                               MBri MGos MRav NBee NHol
                               SBre SEas SPer SPla SReu
                               SRms SSpi WHCG WWat
                               WWin
'Belle Etoile' ♀   Widely available
'Boule d'Argent' (d)   CMHG
'Bouquet Blanc'   CB&S GQui SEas SPer SRms
                               WKif
brachybotrys   CFil EPfP NHol WPGP
'Buckley's Quill'   SVen WBcn
'Burfordensis'   MAsh SBid SPer WWat WWeb
'Burkwoodii'   SBid
coronarius   CTri LBuc MWat NNor SHBN
                               SPer
– 'Aureus' ♀   Widely available
– 'Bowles' Variety'   See *P. coronarius* **'Variegatus'**
– 'Gold Mound'   MGos
§ – 'Variegatus' (v) ♀   CPMA ECtt ELan ENot IOrc
                               LHop MAsh MBri MGos MPla
                               MRav MWat NBir NSti SDix
                               SEas SHBN SMad SPer SPla
                               SSpi WAbe WHCG WPat
                               WSHC WWat WWin
¶ *coulteri*   CPle
'Coupe d'Argent'   MRav
'Dame Blanche' (d)   NPro
delavayi   CFil CPle EPfP WCru WHCG
                               WPGP
¶ – ACE   WHCr
– var. *calvescens*   See *P. purpurascens*
'Enchantment' (d)   MRav MTis SBid SDix WLRN

§ 'Erectus' CBlo EBee EHol ENot EPfP MBal MRav NWea WHCG WWat
¶ *fragrans* CFil WPGP
'Frosty Morn' CB&S EHal EHic MGos MUlv NHol NTow SPer SPla
¶ 'Glacier' WPGP
§ 'Innocence' (v) CBot CDec CEnd CHar CPMA CPle ECtt EHoe ELan EMil EPla LHop MBri MGos MPla MRav SEas SHBN SMac SPer SReu SSta WHCG WRus
'Innocence Variegatus' See *P.* **'Innocence'**
¶ *inodorus* var. *grandiflorus* CPle
§ *insignis* MRav
¶ *intectus* ISea
x *lemoinei* CBlo CTri EBee EMil MGos NNor SEas SHBN WFar WGwG WStI WWal
◆ – 'Erectus' See *P.* **'Erectus'**
¶ 'Lemon Hill' WBcn
¶ *lewisii* CAgr WUnu
¶ – L 1896 CFil WPGP
madrensis LHop
– CD&R 1226 CHan
'Manteau d'Hermine' (d) ♀ Widely available
'Marjorie' CHan CHar
mexicanus WPGP
microphyllus CBlo CBot CHan CMHG ESis LGre MAsh MBro MPla NHol SPer SReu SSpi WCot WHCG WPat WSHC WWat
'Minnesota Snowflake' (d) EBee ECtt EHic EWes IOrc NCut NPro SBid WBcn
x *monstrosus* 'Monster' SSte
¶ 'Mont Blanc' WRHF
'Mrs E.L. Robinson' CBlo ECtt EPla SBid WWoo
'Natchez' EBar ECtt MMHG MPla
'Perryhill' SPer
¶ *pubescens* CPle
purpurascens MRav SSta
¶ x *purpureomaculatus* WIvy
¶ *schrenkii* CFil WPGP
§ 'Silberregen' CBlo CPle ECtt IOrc MBal MBar MGos NBee SBid SEas SHBN SRms WAbe WDin WPat WWat
Silver Showers See *P.* **'Silberregen'**
'Snowflake' EMil MBal WAbe WLRN
'Souvenir de Billiard' See *P. insignis*
subcanus GOrc MRav
'Sybille' ♀ CBlo CMHG ENot GOrc ISea MAsh MBri MRav NFla SBid SPer SRms SSpi SSta WHCG WKif WSHC WWat
tomentosus CFil WHCG WPGP
¶ 'Velléda' CFil WPGP
'Virginal' (d) ♀ Widely available
'Virginal' LA '82 MBal
'Voie Lactée' MRav
White Rock COtt EBee LRHS MBal MBri SPer WLRN

PHILESIA (Philesiaceae)
buxifolia See *P. magellanica*
§ *magellanica* EMil GGGa GSki MBal SAPC SArc SBid SPer SSpi WCru

PHILLYREA (Oleaceae)
angustifolia CFil CHan COtt CPle EPfP ERom MAll SHFr WPGP WWat
– f. *rosmarinifolia* CFil EPfP WPGP
decora See *Osmanthus decorus*
§ *latifolia* CFil CPle LRHS SAPC SArc SHBN SSpi WPGP WWat
media See *P. latifolia*

PHILODENDRON (Araceae)
§ *angustisectum* ♀ MBri
elegans See *P. angustisectum*
'Emerald Queen' MBri
epipremnum See *Epipremnum pinnatum*
erubescens ♀ MBri
– 'Burgundy' ♀ MBri
– 'Imperial Red' MBri
– 'Red Emerald' CHal EBak MBri
melanochrysum MBri
'New Red' MBri
panduriforme See *P. bipennifolium*
pedatum MBri
'Purple Queen' MBri
radiatum MBri
scandens ♀ CHal
¶ *selloum* WMul
sodiroi See *P. ornatum*
tuxtlanum 'Royal Queen' MBri
– 'Tuxtla' MBri

PHLEBODIUM See POLYPODIUM

PHLEUM (Poaceae)
pratense EHoe EPla
– subsp. *bertolonii* CKin

PHLOMIS † (Lamiaceae)
* *anatolica* CHan EFou ELan LRHS
* – 'Lloyd's Variety' CAbP EHic ELan EPla GCal LHop MSte MUlv SBid SPan WEas WPen WWat
angustifolia SBid
aff. *anisodonta* WPhl
atropurpurea WPhl
betonicoides WPhl
– B&L 12600 EMon
bourgaei JMT 260 WPhl
– 'Whirling Dervish' JMT 271 WPhl
bovei subsp. *maroccana* CBot CHan CPle EPla GCal LFis NLak NTow SAxl WCot WPbr WPhl WWat
breviflora WPhl
cancellata CHan WPbr
cashmeriana CArn CBot CGle CHan CPle ECha NLar WPhl WPic
chrysophylla ♀ CAbP CB&S CBot CHan CMil CPle CSam EAst ELan MDun NTow SBid SDix SDry SPan SPer SRms WPhl WWat
crinita WPhl
cypria WPhl
§ 'Edward Bowles' SDry SPan WCot WPhl
fruticosa ♀ Widely available
– SCH 3149 WHCr
grandiflora CBot ELan SEND
– JMT 256 WPhl
italica Widely available

lanata	CAbP CFee CHan CMil ELan EPPr IDee LHop SBid SBla SDry SPan SPer WEas WPhl WWat WWye
leucophracta	EFou LRHS
– 'Golden Janissary' JMT 255	WPhl
¶ – 'White Janissary'	WPhl
¶ *linearis* var. *plumosa* JMT 416	WPhl
longifolia	CBot CHad CHan SPer WCru
– var. *bailanica*	CPle LRHS WWat
– var. *longifolia*	WPhl
lunariifolia JMT 258	WPhl
lychnitis	WPhl
lycia	CAbP CHan EFou LRHS SIgm WPhl
monocephala	WPhl
nissolii JMT 268	WPhl
platystegia	WPhl
purpurea	CHan CPle CSam EFou ELan EPfP NBir NPSI SBid SPan WCot WPhl WSHC
– *alba*	CBot CHan EPfP LHop SBid WPhl
– subsp. *almeriensis*	CHan NLak WPhl
¶ – 'Green Leaf' JMT 499	WPhl
rigida	EBee WCru
§ *russeliana* ♀	Widely available
samia Boissier	See *P. russeliana*
¶ *samia* Linnaeus 'Green Cap'JMT 285	WPhl
¶ – 'Green Glory'	WPhl
– JMT 285	WPhl
tuberosa	CBot CFir CHan CPou EGar EMan EPPr GCal MAus NChi SIgm SOkh WCot WCru WPGP WPhl
– 'Amazone'	CWit EAst EBee ECha EFou LFis LGre NPSI WHil
viscosa hort.	See *P. russeliana*
– Poiret	WPhl

PHLOX † (Polemoniaceae)

adsurgens ♀	ITim SBla WAbe
– 'Alba'	CMea SBla WAbe
– 'Red Buttes'	CGle CLyd ELan EPot GCrs LHop SAga SBla SCro
– 'Wagon Wheel'	CHea CLyd EBrP EBre EHyt ELan EPot EWes LBee LBre LHop MBro MHig NGre NHar NMen SBre SIng SMrm SUsu WAbe WFar WPat WRus WWin
albomarginata	CGra
amoena hort.	See *P.* × *procumbens*
× *arendsii* 'Anja'	WCot
– 'Hilda'	WCot
– 'Lisbeth'	WCot
§ – 'Luc's Lilac'	EFou MHlr WCot
– 'Suzanne'	NLar WCot
austromontana	EPot NWCA
bifida	CMea CPBP ITim MBro NHol WLin
– 'Alba'	EHyt WAbe WLin
– blue	CMea CStr ELan LBee SUsu
– 'Colvin's White'	CLyd CPBP LBee SBla
– 'Minima Colvin'	ECtt EPot
– 'Petticoat'	CLyd CMea CPBP LBee MDHE NCat NGre SBla WLin
– 'Ralph Haywood'	CLyd MHig NGre

– 'Starbrite'	CLyd CMea CPBP ITim LBee MDHE MHig MOne NGre NMen SBla
– 'Sunset'	SBla
* – 'The Fi'	EWes NCat WIvy
'Black Buttes'	CLyd CPBP NNrd NTow WAbe WIvy
'Bleeklila'	WCot
borealis	CGra ELan EWes GDra ITim
* – *arctica*	EPot
¶ *bryoides*	EWes
caespitosa	CLyd CMea EWes GCHN ITim NHed NMen
– subsp. *condensata*	NWCA
canadensis	See *P. divaricata*
carolina 'Bill Baker'	CBot CGle CHan CSam ECha ECoo EMar EMon GCra GMac LBlm LHop MBel MMil MNrw MSte NBrk NCat NHol SCro SMrm SUsu SWas WAbe WHer WLin WMaN WOld WWin
– 'Magnificence'	EMon GBuc MAvo MSte SMrm SOkh SWas
– 'Miss Lingard' ♀	CBos CGle CMGP CSam EBee EFou EMan EMon GBuc GCal LRHS MBel MBro MMil MSte NTow SChu SCro SDix SHel SMrm SOkh WCot WMaN
* 'Casablanca'	EFou
* 'Chanel'	MLan
'Charles Ricardo'	CBos CMil GBuc GMac LFlo MBro NCat NTow SHel SMrm SPla SSca SUsu SWas SWat WAbe WElm WHoo WPbr WPyg WRus
'Chattahoochee'	See *P. divaricata* subsp. *laphamii*
covillei	GCrs ITim
'Daniel's Cushion'	See *P. subulata* **'McDaniel's Cushion'**
depressa	See *P. multiflora* subsp. *depressa*
diffusa	LHop
¶ – NNS 95-46	MRPP
§ *divaricata* ♀	EHol MSte SHBN SHel WPer WRus WWin
– f. *albiflora*	ELan
– 'Blue Dreams'	CBos CDec CFir CRDP EBee ECha GBuc LFlo MAvo MNrw MSte SAga SAxl SCro SHel SLod SMrm SUsu SWas SWat WFar WHal WLin WOve WPGP WPbr WRHF WSan
– 'Blue Perfume'	EFou NBrk
– 'Clouds of Perfume'	EBee EFou GBri MRav NCat NSti SBla SCro SHBN SMrm SWat WRus WSan
– 'Dirigo Ice'	CLyd CMil EMan ERav LFis LFlo LGre MBel NBrk NHol SBla WIvy WRHF WRus
¶ – 'Eco Regal'	CGra
– 'Eco Texas Purple'	CBos CLAP CRDP MAvo NBrk NHar NMen WRus WThi
– 'Fuller's White'	CLyd MAvo SHBN
§ – subsp. *laphamii*	CLyd EBrP EBre EWes LBre LFlo NVic SBla SBre WCru WFoF WHer WRus WThi

– – 'Chattahoochee' ♀ CBot CHea CSpe EBrP EBre
ELan EMNN EPot EWes GCrs
GMac LBee LBre LHop MBro
NGre NHol NWes SBla SBod
SBre SIng SLod SMrm SUsu
WAbe WMaN WPat WSHC
WWin

– – 'Chattahoochee EWes LHop LRHS SUsu WCot
Variegated'

¶ – 'Louisiana Purple' SWas WThi
– 'May Breeze' Widely available
* – 'White Perfume' MRav
douglasii NHol NWCA SOkh SRms
– 'Apollo' CLyd CPBP ELan EMNN EPot
GDra MHig NGre NHol NMen
SAga WAbe WWin

– 'Boothman's Variety' ♀ CGle CLyd CNic ECha ELan
EPar EPot MHig MPla MWat
NMen SBod SRms WEas WHoo
WShe WWin

– 'Concorde' GDra
– 'Crackerjack' ♀ CLyd ELan EMNN EPot ESis
GAbr GDra ITim LBee MHig
MPla MWat NGre NHar NMen
NRoo SAga SBod WAbe WLin

– 'Eva' CLyd CM&M EBrP EBre ELan
EMNN ETou LBee LBre MHig
MOne MRav NBir NFla NGre
NHar NHol NRoo SBod SBre
SMrm WPer WWin

– 'Galaxy' CLyd ESis EWes GDra NHar
– 'Holden Variety' NHol
– 'Ice Mountain' ECho ELan IHos NPri SMrm
– 'Iceberg' ♀ CLyd EPot GDra ITim NHar
NHol NMen SIng WAbe WWin

– 'J.A. Hibberson' CLyd ESis MHig
– Lilac Queen See _P. douglasii_ 'Lilakönigin'
§ – 'Lilakönigin' CLyd
– 'Red Admiral' ♀ CMHG EBrP EBre EMNN
EPot EWes GCHN GCrs GDra
IHos LBre MHig MOne NHar
NHol NLon NMen NRoo SBod
SBre SMrm WFar

– 'Rose Cushion' EWes GDra LRHS MDHE
MPla NHol

– 'Rose Queen' CLyd CMHG ESis GDra
– 'Rosea' EBrP EBre ELan EMNN EPar
GBur LBee LBre MBal MRav
NGre NRoo SBod SBre SMer
SMrm SSmi

– 'Silver Rose' GCrs GTou
– 'Sprite' SRms
– 'Tycoon' See _P. subulata_ 'Tamaongalei'
– 'Violet Queen' ELan EMNN EWes GDra NHar
NHol WFar

– 'Waterloo' CLyd CPBP CTri EBrP EBre
EPfP EPot GAri GBur LBre
LHop MRav NHar NHol NMen
SBre SChu WWin

¶ **drummondii** SAga
¶ 'Geddington Cross' MGed MWgw
* 'Herfstsering' EFou
* 'Hesperis' EFou
hirsuta NWCA
hoodii CLyd CPBP ECho
* 'Hortensia' EFou
'Kelly's Eye' ♀ CLyd CM&M CMHG CPBP
CSam ECha ECtt ELan EMNN
EPot GAbr LBee LHop MHig
MMil NMen NRoo SBod SIng
SWas WFar WPer

kelseyi NWCA WLin

¶ – 'Lemhi Purple' CGra
– 'Rosette' CLyd ESis LBee MHig NGre
NMen WOMN WPer

longifolia WLin
maculata NOrc WPer
– 'Alpha' ♀ CGle CHea CMHG EBrP EBre
ECha EFou ENot GCHN
GMaP GMac LBre MAus MBri
MRav NHol NOrc NRoo SBla
SBre SChu SCro SMrm SPer
SSpe WMaN WRus

– Avalanche See _P. maculata_ 'Schneelawine'
– 'Delta' CBos CHea EBee EFou LRot
MLLN NCut NHol NPri NSti
SCro SPla WHil WMaN WRus

– 'Good White' SMrm
* – 'Natascha' CHea CSev EBee EBrP EBre
EFou ENot EPfP EWes GBri
GBuc GMaP GMac LBre MAus
MBri MLLN NFai NHol SBre
SPer SPla SSpe SVil WCot WHil
WPGP WPbr WSan

– 'Omega' ♀ CDec CHad CHan CHea
CMHG EBar EFou GCHN
GMaP LRot MAus MBri MRav
MUlv NBrk NRoo NSti SChu
SMrm SPer SSpi WByw WMaN
WRus WSHC

¶ – 'Princess Sturdza' SDix
– 'Rosalinde' EFou MBel MRav MSte SChu
SCro WMaN

§ – 'Schneelawine' EBee EBrP EBre EFou LBre
MRav NCat SBre WRus

mesoleuca See _P. nana_ subsp. _ensifolia_
  Mexican hybrids See _P. nana_
'Millstream' See _P._ × _procumbens_
'Millstream'

'Millstream Jupiter' NHol
¶ – 'Miss Jill' CSpe EFou MSCN WCot WRus
  (Springpearl hybrid)
¶ 'Miss Jo Ellen' EFou GBri MSCN
  (Springpearl hybrid)
¶ 'Miss Karen' MSCN
  (Springpearl hybrid)
¶ 'Miss Margie' EFou GBri MSCN WHil
  (Springpearl hybrid)
¶ 'Miss Mary' EFou GBri WRus
  (Springpearl hybrid)
'Mrs Campbell' See _P. paniculata_ 'Elizabeth
Campbell'

¶ **muscoides** EWes
¶ **nana** 'Vanilla Cream' SBla
nivalis MHig NMen
– 'Camla' CLyd ELan EPot ITim LHop
WPat

– 'Nivea' LBee NGre WLRN
paniculata CHad NNor SChu SDix SHel
WCot WOld

– 'A.E. Amos' CTri EFou ERou
– 'Aida' CB&S EFou EGar ERou MWat
– var. **alba** CBos GCal MAus SDix WCot
– 'Alba Grandiflora' ♀ WEas
– 'Albert Leo Schlageter' ERou LBuc SRms
  ♀
¶ – 'Alexander' NCat
– 'Amethyst' CFir CKel CSam EBar EFou
EGar EPfP ERou GHCN GMac
LFis MAus MBel NBir WHil
WWoo

– 'Balmoral'	CGle CM&M ECtt EOld MLLN MRav MSte NCat NSti SChu SMrm SWat WHil WLRN WWal WWoo
– 'Barnwell'	EFou ELan WMer
– 'Betty Symons-Jeune'	ERou
– 'Bill Green'	ECGP LRHS SMrm
– 'Blue Boy'	CM&M EFou ERou GMac MAvo NCut WBay WHoo WMer WSan
– 'Blue Ice' ♀	CHea CSev EBee EFou ELan EMan EPfP MWat NRoo SMrm SUsu WCot WLRN WWoo
– 'Blue Moon'	GHCN
– 'Blue Paradise'	EBar EFou LGre MSte SAga SMrm
– 'Blushing Bride'	SRms
– 'Bonny Maid'	CBla
– 'Border Gem'	CB&S EBrP EBre ECED EFou EMan EMon LBre MHlr MSte NCut NRoo SBre SHel SMrm SWat WCot
– 'Branklyn'	EBrP EBre LBre MArl MGrG MMil MRav SBre WFar
¶ – 'Bressingham White'	NBrk
– 'Brigadier' ♀	CBla CSam CTri ELan EMan EPfP GHCN GMaP MFir MLLN MWat NPri NRoo SMrm SPer SRms SSoC
– 'Bright Eyes' ♀	CBla CBlo CKel COtt EBrP EBre EFou ENot EPfP GBur LBre LRHS MArl MBel NRoo SBre
– 'Caroline van den Berg'	CTri EGar ERou SMer SRms WCot
– 'Cecil Hanbury'	CBlo ERou SRms WHoo WWoo
– 'Charmaine'	CBla
– 'Chintz'	MRav SRms
– 'Cinderella'	ERou MBel NPri WMer WRHF
– 'Cool of the Evening'	CBla CDec MRav WCot
– 'Count Zeppelin'	See *P. paniculata* 'Graf Zeppelin'
– 'Darwin's Joyce'	EBee EFou EMan MSCN NCut SMad WSan
¶ – 'David'	CStr NLak
– 'Dodo Hanbury Forbes' ♀	CBla CKel EGar EHol
– 'Dresden China'	ERou GCra
– 'Düsterlohe'	CSam GBuc SMrm
– 'Eclaireur'	EBee
– 'Elie'	LFis MSCN NFai
– 'Elizabeth Arden'	EFou ERou MSte WMaN WMer
– 'Endurance'	ERou
– 'Etoile de Paris'	SUsu SWas
– 'Europe'	CB&S CGle EBee EFou ELan EMan ERou MFir MWat NFai SMrm SPer WMer WWal
– 'Eva Cullum'	CM&M CTri EBrP EBre EFou LBre LHop MArl MLLN MRav NFai NRoo SBre SHel SPer WCot
– 'Eventide' ♀	EBrP EBre ECED ECtt EFou EGar EHal ERou GChr LBre MArl MAus NRoo SBre SMrm SOkh SPer WCot WViv
– 'Excelsior'	CBlo EBrP EBre LBre MRav SBre
– 'Fairy's Petticoat'	MWat WCot
– 'Flamingo'	EBar EBrP EBre EFou LBre SBre
– 'Franz Schubert'	CTri EBee EBrP EBre EFou EGar EMan GMac LBre MHlr MTis NRoo NSti SBre SHFr WCot WMaN WSan WWoo
§ – 'Frau A. von Mauthner'	CBlo LBuc
§ – 'Fujiyama' ♀	CKel CSam CStr EBee EBrP EBre ECha EFou EMon EOrc GCra LBre LHop LLWP MSte MWat NBir NRoo NSti NWes SBre SHel SMad SMrm WAbb WCot WEas WHil WMaN WWoo
– 'Glamis'	CBla MWat
§ – 'Graf Zeppelin'	CBla ELan MAvo MWat NCat SRms WMer
– 'Hampton Court'	NBrk WCot
– 'Harewood'	ERou
– 'Harlequin' (v)	CMil EBrP EBre ECha GBuc LBre MRav SBre SPla WCot
– 'Iceberg'	MFir
– 'Iris'	GBuc SMrm SRms SWas
§ – 'Juliglut'	ELan MWat NCat WCot
– July Glow	See *P. paniculata* 'Juliglut'
– 'Kirmesländler'	CB&S EBee ERou LBuc MLLN
– 'Lady Clare'	SRms
– 'Latest Red'	See *P. paniculata* 'Spätrot'
* – 'Laura'	COtt LFis MSCN NCut WHoo
§ – 'Lavendelwolke'	ELan LBuc
– Lavender Cloud	See *P. paniculata* 'Lavendelwolke'
– 'Le Mahdi' ♀	ELan MRav MWat SRms WCot
– 'Lilac Time'	CBla EBee NCat NPla
¶ – 'Little Boy'	EBee MSCN WHil
¶ – 'Little Lovely'	WSan
– 'Look Again'	ERou
– 'Mary Fox'	CSam ERou MRav NRoo
– 'Mia Ruys'	EFou EHal ERou MArl MLLN WMer
– 'Mies Copijn'	GMaP WMer
* – 'Miss Elie'	EFou WHil WHoo
¶ – 'Miss Holland'	EFou WHoo
– 'Miss Kelly'	EFou MSCN NCut WSan
* – 'Miss Pepper'	CM&M EFou LFis NFai SSte
¶ – 'Miss Universe'	EBee EFou NCut WHoo
* – 'Monica Lynden-Bell'	WCot
– 'Mother of Pearl' ♀	CBla CGle CHad CKel CMil EBrP EBre EFou ELan LBre MHlr MWat NCat NVic SBre SChu SPer WCot
– 'Mount Fujiyama'	See *P. paniculata* 'Fujiyama'
– 'Mrs A.E. Jeans'	SRms
– 'Mrs Fincham'	LFis
– 'Newbird'	ERou SRms
* – 'Nicky'	EFou LFis MRav SSte WHil WSan
– 'Norah Leigh' (v)	Widely available
– 'Orange Perfection'	CB&S CBlo CM&M EBar EPfP NCut NPri WBay
– 'Othello'	CBla
– 'Otley Choice'	CBlo CM&M CMil EMan LFis MSte MWat NLak NPla NRoo NSti SCoo SMrm WLRN
– 'Pastorale'	MWat WCot
– 'Pax'	EMon WBay WViv
– 'Pike'	MHlr WCot
– 'Pink Posy' (v)	MBri SCoo SPer WWeb
¶ – 'Prime Minister'	CStr NLak
– 'Prince of Orange' ♀	CBla CBlo CElw CGle CMGP CSam EBrP EBre EFou ELan EMan ERou LBre MRav MWat NCat NRoo SAga SBre SMrm SPer SSoC WCot WWal

– 'Prospero' ♀	CBla CMil EBee EBrP EBre EMan EOrc LBre LFis MBel MRav NRoo SBre SChu SMrm SPer WCot WOld
– 'Rapture'	MWat
– 'Red Indian'	ERou MWat
– 'Rembrandt'	ERou WCot
– 'Rijnstroom'	CB&S ECot EFou ERou LFis MBel NCat NFai SMrm WCot WViv WWal WWoo
¶ – 'Rosa Pastell'	SAga
– 'Rosa Spier'	WMer
– 'Rougham Supreme'	ERou
– 'Russian Violet'	MRav MWat
– 'San Antonio'	MBel MRav SMrm WCot
– 'Sandringham'	CBlo CDec CSam CTri EBrP EBre ELan EMan LBre MArl MNrw MRav MSte NBir NLak NRoo NVic SBre SMrm SPer
– 'Schneerausch'	WCot
– 'Septemberglut'	EBee SSte WHil
– 'Silver Salmon'	WCot
– 'Sir Malcolm Campbell'	ERou
– 'Skylight'	MWat NVic SMrm SPer SSte WCot WLRN WLin WWal WWoo
– 'Snowdrift'	ERou
§ – 'Spätrot'	EFou WMer
– 'Spitfire'	See *P. paniculata* 'Frau A. von Mauthner'
– 'Starfire'	Widely available
* – 'Steeple Bumpstead'	WCot
– 'Sternhimmel'	ERou LGre
¶ – 'Sweetheart'	CStr
– 'Tenor'	CBlo CFir CKel CM&M EBee ECGP EFou LRot MSte NCut NFai NPri SMrm WFar WHil WWoo
– 'The King'	LRHS WBay
– 'Toits de Paris'	MWat
* – 'Úspech'	EFou
– 'Vintage Wine'	CTri LBuc WMer
– 'Violetta Gloriosa'	EFou
– 'White Admiral' ♀	CB&S CBla CGle CHad CM&M EBar EBrP EBre ELan ENot GChr GMaP LBre MBel MRav MUlv MWat NFai NRoo NVic SBre SChu SMrm SPer WMer WMow WWal
– 'William Ramsay'	CTri ELan EOld
– 'Windsor' ♀	CBla CBlo EFou EPfP ERou GChr LFis MAus MBel MLLN MTis SCoo SMrm
pilosa	CMGP EBrP EBre ECha EFou LBre NHol NPro SBre SMrm SUsu WRus
§ × *procumbens* 'Millstream' ♀	CGra ELan LHop NTow SAga SBla WOMN WThi WWin
– 'Variegata'	CBot CGra CPBP ECha EHyt ELan EMNN ESis MHig MPla MTho NGre NHol NNor NRoo NWCA SBla WAbe WLin WPat WWin
¶ *pulchra* 'Eco Pale Moon'	CStr WThi
¶ – 'Eco Place'	CRDP
× *rugellii*	NHol SRms WWin
¶ 'Scented Pillow'	WWeb
stolonifera	EPar GMaP MHar MNrw MTho SAga WCot WMer WPbr

– 'Ariane'	ECha ELan EPar LHop MAvo MBro NHar SAga SBla SMrm SWas SWat WAbe WFar WHal WHer WLin WPbr WViv WWin
– 'Blue Ridge' ♀	CFir CHan CPea CSpe ECha ECle EGle ELan EMan EPar GBuc LFis LHop NGre NHar NPSI NRoo SAga SBla SIng SMrm SRms SSca SWat WSan WWin
* – 'Bob's Motley' (v)	WCot
¶ – compact form	EPot
– 'Compact Pink'	LHop NCat SAga SWas
– 'Fran's Purple'	CLAP CLyd EHyt NCat NHar SCro SWas WAbe WFar WLin
¶ – 'Home Fires'	NHar
– 'Mary Belle Frey'	ECha EMan EOrc LHop MSte NSti SAga SBla SCro SMrm SWas WWin
– 'Pink Ridge'	CGra CLAP CMGP GBuc NCut NHar NRoo SIng WLin
¶ – 'Purpurea'	NHar
– variegated	MHlr MRav NCat WAbe WCot WPen
– 'Violet Vere'	CLAP CLyd CMil CPBP CSpe EGle GBuc LHop MAvo MBro MHlr MNrw NHar SAga SBla SIng SLod SMrm SUsu WHal WLin WPyg
subulata	EPar NWCA
– 'Alexander's Surprise'	CGle CMea ECtt EPot GAbr GCHN LHop MBal NBir NFla NGre NHol NMen SChu
– 'Amazing Grace'	CTri ELan EWes LHop MOne MPla NMen NPri NRoo NSla SChu WAbe WPer WWin
– 'Apple Blossom'	GAbr GDra NPri SAga WLRN
– 'Atropurpurea'	EBrP EBre GCHN LBre NNor SBre WWin
– 'Beauty of Ronsdorf'	See *P. subulata* 'Ronsdorfer Schöne'
– 'Betty'	CTri ECtt EMNN MDHE NMen NRoo WPer
– 'Blue Eyes'	See *P. subulata* 'Oakington Blue Eyes'
– 'Blue Saucer'	MDHE NHol
– 'Bonita'	CStr EMNN GAri LBee MRav NPri NRoo SMer SMrm WWin
– 'Bressingham Blue Eyes'	See *P. subulata* 'Oakington Blue Eyes'
– 'Brightness'	CTri GCHN GTou SIng
– subsp. *brittonii* 'Rosea'	EPot NHol WPer WRHF
– 'Candy Stripe'	EPfP LRHS
¶ – 'Christine Bishop'	SAga
– 'Coral Eye'	EPfP
– 'Daisy Hill'	NHol
– 'Drumm'	See *P. subulata* 'Tamaongalei'
¶ – 'Eco Pale Moon'	CGra
– 'Emerald Cushion'	CSam EMan NLon SAga
– 'Emerald Cushion Blue'	CLyd EBrP EBre ELan GBur GTou LBee LBre LGan MBal NHol NRoo SBod SBre SMrm SSmi WAbe WPer
– 'Fairy'	SAga WPer
– 'G.F. Wilson'	CLyd CMea ECha ECtt ELan GTou LBee LGro MBal MHig MWat NGre NMen NNor NRoo NVic SChu SSca SSmi WAbe WPer WWin
– 'Greencourt Purple'	NCat
* – 'Holly'	EPot MDHE
– 'Jupiter'	SChu

– 'Kimono'	See *P. subulata* 'Tamaongalei'
§ – 'Maischnee'	CLyd EBrP EBre ECtt ELan EMNN EPot GAbr LBee LBre LGro LHop MBal MHig MOne MPla MWat NGre NNor NNrd NRoo SBre SMrm WEas WWin
– May Snow = 'Maischnee'	See *P. subulata* 'Maischnee'
– 'Marjorie'	CLyd ECtt ELan EMNN MBal MHar MOne NMen NPri SSca WEas WLRN
¶ – 'Mauve Queen'	MWat
§ – 'McDaniel's Cushion' ♀	CHea CLyd CMHG EBrP EBre ECha ELan EMNN EPot ESis GTou ITim LBee LBre MHig MMil NGre NMen NNor NRoo SBre WHil WHoo WPer WWin
– 'Mikado'	See *P. subulata* 'Tamaongalei'
– 'Model'	LGro NSla
– 'Moonlight'	CLyd ECtt MBro SAga SLod WPer WRHF
* – 'Nettleton Variation'	CGra CMea CPBP EDAr ELan EPot EWes LHop NPri SAga WAbe WCot WPat
§ – 'Oakington Blue Eyes'	CMHG EBrP EBre EPar GCHN GDra LBee LBre NGre NRoo SBre SMrm SRms WPer
– 'Pink Pearl'	EWes
– 'Red Wings' ♀	CGra CPBP EBrP EBre ECtt GCHN LBre MBal MRav NMen NNor NPri NRoo SAga SBre SIng SRms
§ – 'Ronsdorfer Schöne'	EPot LBee NNrd
– 'Samson'	CNic ELan GAbr GTou LBee MHar SBod SMer WPer WWin
– 'Scarlet Flame'	CMea CSam EBrP EBre ECha ECtt ELan EMNN GDra LBre LGro MBal MRav MWat NHol SAga SBod SBre SMrm WPer WWin
– 'Schneewittchen'	CLyd NHol
– 'Sensation'	GTou SRms
– 'Snow Queen'	See *P. subulata* 'Maischnee'
– 'Starglow'	GTou SIng WPer
§ – 'Tamaongalei'	CGra CLyd CMea CMil CPBP EDAr EHyt EMan EWes GDra GMac LHop MDHE MNrw NCat NHar NHol NRoo SAga SBla SChu SCoo SLod SMrm SRms SUsu WAbe WHoo WLin WWin
– 'Temiskaming'	CMHG ECha ELan EMNN ENot EWes GCHN GDra LGro MHar NGre NMen NRoo SAga SChu SRms WAbe WEas
– violet seedling	CLyd NHol
– 'White Delight'	CLyd EBrP EBre ECha ECtt ELan EMNN GCHN GTou LBre MHig NHol NMen NRoo SBod SBre SRms WPer
* 'Sweet William'	EFou
¶ 'Uspech'	NLak
'Vivid'	EDAr MDHE

PHOEBE (Lauraceae) See Plant Deletions

PHOENICAULIS (Brassicaceae)
§ *cheiranthoides*	NWCA WOMN

PHOENIX (Arecaceae)
canariensis ♀	CBrP CGre CHEx CTbh CTrC LPJP LPal MBri NPal SEND WMul
dactylifera (F)	CHEx LPal
paludosa	LPal
reclinata	NPal
roebelenii ♀	CBrP LPal MBri NPal WMul
rupicola	LPal
sylvestris	LPal
theophrasti	LPJP LPal NPal

PHORMIUM † (Phormiaceae)
'Apricot Queen' (v)	CAbb CB&S EBee ECre GQui IBlr IOrc MBal
Ballyrogan variegated	IBlr
* 'Black Edge'	IBlr MRav
'Bronze Baby'	CAbb CB&S CEnd CLTr CSam ECtt EHoe ELan EMil GQui IBlr IOrc LPan MAsh MBal MNrw MSte MWat SHBN SPar SPer SPla WPat WWat
colensoi	See *P. cookianum*
§ *cookianum* ♀	CAgr CB&S CHEx CHan CTrC ECre EMil IBlr LPal MAll MBal MGos SAPC SArc WWat
– 'Alpinum Purpureum'	See *P. tenax* 'Nanum Purpureum'
* – 'Flamingo'	ECre SPla
– subsp. *hookeri* 'Cream Delight' (v) ♀	CAbb CB&S CEnd EBee EBrP EBre EHoe ELan ENot IOrc LBre MBal MBlu NFla SAga SBre SHBN SPer WLRN
– – 'Tricolor' ♀	CB&S CFil CHEx CMGP CTrC EBrP EBre ELan ENot EPla IBlr IOrc LBre MBal SApp SArc SBre SHBN SHFr SRms SSpi WDin WPGP WWye
* 'Copper Beauty'	CBlo CDoC COtt CTrC EHic WLRN
'Dark Delight'	CB&S IBlr MAsh
'Dazzler' (v)	CSpe IBlr IOrc MBal
'Duet' (v) ♀	CB&S CDoC COtt CTrC EBee EHoe IBlr IOrc WBcn
* 'Emerald Pink'	COtt
'Evening Glow'	IBlr LRHS MAsh
'Gold Sword' (v)	COtt EBee IBlr
'Guardsman' (v)	CHEx IBlr
'Jack Spratt' (v)	COtt ECou EHoe IBlr IOrc
'Jester'	CB&S CFir CHEx COtt EHoe ENot EWll GQui IBlr MAsh MCCP SPla WBcn
§ 'Maori Chief' (v)	CB&S CFil GQui IBlr IOrc SHBN WLRN WPGP
'Maori Eclipse'	CBlo
§ 'Maori Maiden' (v)	CB&S CSam ECre EHoe GQui IOrc MBal SPla
§ 'Maori Queen' (v)	CB&S EHic GQui IBlr IOrc WLRN
§ 'Maori Sunrise' (v)	CB&S CBlo CDoC EBee IBlr IOrc MCCP MSte SAga SSoC WLRN
'Pink Panther' (v)	CAbb CB&S CBlo CDoC ELan EPfP EWll GQui IBlr IOrc WDin
* 'Pink Stripe'	EBee IBlr
'Rainbow Chief'	See *P.* 'Maori Chief'
Rainbow hybrids	CSpe MBal SEas
'Rainbow Maiden'	See *P.* 'Maori Maiden'
'Rainbow Queen'	See *P.* 'Maori Queen'
'Rainbow Sunrise'	See *P.* 'Maori Sunrise'
'Sea Jade'	IBlr

'Sundowner' (v) ♀	CB&S CSpe CTrC EBrP EBre ECre ELan EMil ENot GQui IBlr IOrc LBre MBal MGos SBre SHBN SPer SSoC WFar WStI
'Sunset' (v)	IBlr IOrc
'Surfer' (v)	COtt EHoe IBlr IOrc WLeb
tenax ♀	CAgr CB&S CHEx EAst ELan EMil ENot EOas ISea LPan MAsh MBal MNrw MWat NNor SArc SMad SPer SSoC WBod WCot WOld WPic WWat
– 'Co-ordination'	CAbb IBlr WBcn
* – 'Dwarf'	EMil IBlr
* – *lineatum*	CTrC SEND
§ – 'Nanum Purpureum' ♀	CHad CRDP IBlr MSte SAxl SEND SWas
– Purpureum Group ♀	CB&S CBot CElw CGre CHEx CHad CSpe CTrC EBrP EBre EHoe ELan EMil ENot EOas GOrc IOrc LBre MAsh MAus MBal MSte SBre SEND SEas SMad SPer SSoC WDin WPGP
– 'Radiance' (v)	IBlr MBal
– 'Rainbow Queen'	See *P.* **'Maori Queen'**
– 'Rainbow Sunrise'	See *P.* **'Maori Sunrise'**
– 'Variegatum' ♀	CFil CHEx IBlr LPal LPan MBal SAPC SArc SEND SRms WBrE WPat
– 'Veitchianum' (v)	IBlr WPGP
'Thumbelina'	CB&S EHoe MSte
'Tom Thumb'	CB&S IOrc WDin
'Yellow Wave' (v) ♀	CAbb CB&S CBlo CDoC CEnd CHEx CTrC EBrP EBre EHoe ELan EMil ENot IBlr IOrc LBre MBal SBre SPer SReu SRms WAbe WDin

PHOTINIA † (Rosaceae)

§ *arbutifolia*	CPle MAll
beauverdiana ♀	CB&S CPle CTho SRms WHCr WWat
§ *davidiana*	CPle CTrw ELan EMil GChr GRei IOrc LHop MBal MBar MBri MRav MWat SEas SPer SRms WNor WWat
– 'Palette' (v)	CB&S CEnd CHig CPle CTrw EAst EHoe ELan EMil GOrc IOrc LHop MBal MBar MBri MGos MPla MRav NFla NHol NSti SEas SPer SReu SRms SSta WBod WHar WStI WWeb
– var. *undulata*	CMHG LRHS MRav WBcn
– – 'Fructu Luteo'	CBlo CMHG CPle CTrG CTrw EHic EPfP EPla MBri MRav WFar WWat
– – 'Prostrata'	ELan EPfP MBar NHol SPer WFar WWat
× *fraseri*	CMCN ISea
– 'Birmingham'	CBlo CLan EHoe LPan MBal SCob SHBN SRms WDin WPyg WSHC WWeb
– 'Red Robin' ♀	Widely available
– 'Robusta' ♀	CBlo MBal WWat
§ – 'Rubens'	ELan MAsh MBri SDry SPer SPla SSta WPat WPyg WWat
§ *glabra* 'Parfait' (v)	CAbP ELan LHop MBal SDry SHBN SPer WFar WPat WPyg WWeb
– 'Pink Lady'	See *P. glabra* **'Parfait'**
– 'Rubens'	See *P.* × *fraseri* **'Rubens'**
– 'Variegata'	See *P. glabra* **'Parfait'**

glomerata	CHEx
lasiogyna	CMCN
¶ *lindleyana*	CPle
microphylla SF 92307	ISea
§ 'Redstart' ♀	CBlo CEnd CPle EPfP MGos SPer SSta SSto WWat
§ *serratifolia*	CBlo CBot CHEx CPle EPfP MBal SAPC SArc SDry SPer SSta WPGP WPat WPyg WWat
serrulata	See *P. serratifolia*
villosa ♀	CAbP CPle CTho GAri IOrc MBal MBar SPer
– var. *laevis*	CB&S

PHRAGMITES (Poaceae)

§ *australis*	CBen GBin NDea NGno SWat
– *giganteus*	See *P. australis* subsp. *altissimus*
¶ – subsp. *pseudodonax*	EMon LRHS
¶ – var. *striatopictus*	EMon
– 'Variegatus'	CBen CCuc CHEx CInt CRDP EHoe EMFW EMon EPPr EPla ESOG IBlr LHil MAvo MTed MWhi NSti SMad SWyc WChe WRus
communis	See *P. australis*
¶ – 'Variegatus'	CWat
karka 'Variegatus'	WChe

PHUOPSIS (Rubiaceae)

§ *stylosa*	CElw CLTr CSev EAst ECha ELan EMar LGan MFir MTis NBro NChi NRoo NSti SChu SHFr SMac SRms SSpe SVil WBea WHal WOve WPer WWhi WWin WWye
– 'Purpurea'	CBos CElw ELan LCot MNrw MRav NBrk NCat NChi SChu SDys WByw WFar WGwy WHal

PHYGELIUS † (Scrophulariaceae)

aequalis	CBot CFee CGle CKno CMHG CSev ELan EMil LFis MNrw MWgw SChu SDix SMac SSpi WCFE WPer WSHC WSan WWat WWhi
– *albus*	See *P. aequalis* **'Yellow Trumpet'**
– 'Aureus'	See *P. aequalis* **'Yellow Trumpet'**
– 'Cream Trumpet'	See *P. aequalis* **'Yellow Trumpet'**
– 'Indian Chief'	See *P.* × *rectus* **'African Queen'**
* – 'Pink Trumpet'	CLTr EFou GOrc NNor SCoo SMac SMrm
§ – 'Yellow Trumpet' ♀	Widely available
§ *capensis* ♀	Widely available
– × *aequalis*	See *P.* × *rectus*
◆ – *coccineus*	See *P. capensis*
– orange	CKno EGar LHop SVen
– *roseus*	CTrw
– S&SH 50	CHan SMac
'Golden Gate'	See *P. aequalis* **'Yellow Trumpet'**
* 'Janet's Jewel'	CKno SBid
§ × *rectus*	EPla
§ – 'African Queen' ♀	Widely available

– 'Devil's Tears'   CFee CKno CM&M CMHG
EAst EBar EMil ENot EPla
GGar LHop MAsh MBri MBro
NFai SAga SCro SMac WGwG
WHil WHoo WMer WPer
WWat WWeb

– 'Moonraker'   CKno CLTr CMHG EBar ECtt
ELan EMil ESis GGar GOrc
LFis MBro NFai NLar NRoo
SMac SMad SRms WBea WHoo
WMer WWat

– 'Pink Elf'   CKno ELan ERav ESis SMac
– 'Salmon Leap'   CKno CM&M CMHG CSpe
EAst EBar EOrc EPla GGar
LHop MAsh MBel MGrG NFai
SHFr SMac WFar WHal WHil
WOve WPer WWeb

¶ – 'Sunshine'   WWeb
§ – 'Winchester Fanfare'   Widely available
– 'Winton Fanfare'   See *P.* × *rectus* **'Winchester Fanfare'**
'Trewidden Pink'   CKno EHic EPri LHop MAvo
MMil NFai SMac SSpe WHal
WHoo WPbr WRus

PHYLA (Verbenaceae)
§ *canescens*   WCru WHal
§ *nodiflora*   CHal CNic ECha EEls SEND
WPer
– 'Alba'   CNic

PHYLICA (Rhamnaceae)
ericoides   MAll

× PHYLLIOPSIS (Ericaceae)
'Coppelia' ♀   CMHG EPot GGGa MAsh
MBal MDun NHar NHol SSta
WAbe WPat WPyg
hillieri 'Askival'   GCrs GGGa
– 'Pinocchio'   EPot GCrs GDra GGGa GTou
MAsh MBal MDun NHar NHol
WAbe WPat WPyg
¶ – 'Sprite'   MAsh
'Hobgoblin'   EPot MBal WPat
'Mermaid'   GGGa SSta WAbe
'Puck'   WAbe
'Sprite'   GCrs NHol WAbe WPat

PHYLLITIS See ASPLENIUM

PHYLLOCLADUS (Phyllocladaceae)
aspleniifolius var. *alpinus*   CDoC

PHYLLODOCE (Ericaceae)
aleutica   EPot GChr GCrs GGGa MBal
MBar MHig NHar WAbe
§ – subsp. *glanduliflora*   EPot GDra MBal NHol
– – 'Flora Slack'   CMHG GGGa MBal MHig
– – white   See *P. aleutica* subsp.
glanduliflora **'Flora Slack'**
× *alpina*   GDra
breweri   GDra GGGa
caerulea ♀   GDra GGGa MBal MHig NHar
NHol WAbe
– *japonica*   See *P. nipponica*
empetriformis   GChr GDra GGGa MBal MBar
MBri MGos MHig NHar NHed
NHol SRms WAbe
glanduliflora   See *P. aleutica* subsp.
glanduliflora
× *intermedia*   GDra MBal

– 'Drummondii'   CMHG GGGa
– 'Fred Stoker'   CMHG GGGa MHig NHol
§ *nipponica* ♀   GCrs GDra MBal WAbe
– var. *oblongo-ovata*   WAbe
¶ *tsugifolia*   GCrs

PHYLLOSTACHYS † (Poaceae - Bambusoideae)
angusta   EPla SDry WJun
arcana   EPla ISta SDry WJun
– 'Luteosulcata'   EPla SDry
§ *atrovaginata*   EPla SDry
aurea ♀   CB&S CEnd CHEx CTrC CTrG
EBee EFul EPfP EPla GAri
ISta LJus LNet LPan MWhi
NDov SArc SCha SCob SDry
SPar SPla WJun WNor
– 'Flavescens Inversa'   EPla ISta SDry WJun
– 'Holochrysa'   CB&S EFul EPla ISta SDry
WJun
– 'Koi'   EPla SDry
– 'Variegata'   EFul EPla SDry
aureosulcata   EBee EFul EPfP EPla ISta LBlo
SDry WJun
– f. *alata*   EPla SDry
– 'Aureocaulis'   CFil EFul EPla ISta MMoz
SCha SDry WJun WMul WPGP
– 'Harbin'   EPla SDry
– 'Spectabilis'   CFil EFul EOas EPfP EPla ISta
LJus LNet LRHS MMoz SCha
SDry WJun WPGP
bambusoides   CB&S EPla ISta SDix SDry
WJun
§ – 'Allgold'   EPla ERod SDry
– 'Castillonis' ♀   CB&S EFul EPla ERod ISta
LJus LNet MMoz SDix SDry
WJun WPGP
– 'Castillonis Inversa'   EPla ERod SDry WJun WPGP
– Holochrysa   See *P. bambusoides* **'Allgold'**
– 'Katashibo'   EPla
– 'Kawadana'   EPla SDry
¶ – f. *marliacea*   EPla
– f. *subvariegata*   SDry WPGP
– 'Sulphurea'   See *P. bambusoides* **'Allgold'**
– 'Tanakae'   SDry
bissetii   EFou EFul EOas EPla ERod
ISta LJus NDov SCha SDry
WJun WPGP
congesta hort.   See *P. atrovaginata*
decora   EPla ISta LJus SDry WJun
dulcis   EPla ERod LPJP WJun
§ *edulis*   CGre EFul EHoe ISta MBal
SDry WJun
– 'Bicolor'   SDry WJun
§ – var. *heterocycla*   SDry SMad
– f. *pubescens*   See *P. edulis*
– *subconvexa*   See *P. viridiglaucescens*
flexuosa   CFil CHEx EBee EFul EPla
ISta LNet SCob SDry WJun
WPGP
fulva   EPla
glauca   EPla
– 'Yunzhu'   EPla SDry WJun
§ *heteroclada*   SDry
– 'Solid Stem' misapplied   See *P. heteroclada* **'Straight Stem'**
§ – 'Straight Stem'   EPla SDry
heterocycla   See *P. edulis* var. *heterocycla*
– f. *pubescens*   See *P. edulis*
humilis   EBee EPla SDry WJun
iridescens   EPla SDry WJun
lithophila   WJun
* *lufoshanensis*   CFil WPGP

makinoi	WJun
mannii	EPla SDry WJun
meyeri	EFou EPla ISta SDry WJun
nidularia	EBee EPla ISta LJus SDry WJun
nigra ♀	CB&S CHEx CSWP CTrG EBee EFul EOas EPla LJus LNet LPal LPan MCCP MMoz NPal SArc SCha SCob SDry SPla SSoC WJun WMul
– 'Boryana'	CFil EFul EPla ISta LJus SDix SDry WJun WPGP
– var. *henonis* ♀	EBee EFul EPfP EPla ERod ISta LJus SDry WJun
– 'Megurochiku'	EPla SDry WJun
¶ – f. *nigra*	EPla
– f. *punctata*	CFil EPla ISta LJus LRHS SDry WJun WPGP
nuda	EPla ISta SDry WJun
– f. *localis*	SDry
parvifolia	EPla ERod WJun
¶ *platyglossa*	CFil WPGP
praecox	EPla WJun
propinqua	CDoC EPla ISta LJus MCCP MMoz WJun WMul
¶ – 'Li Yu Gai'	WPGP
purpurata	See *P. heteroclada*
rubicunda	WJun
rubromarginata	EPla SDry
stimulosa	EPla WJun
sulphurea 'Houzeau'	EPla SDry
– 'Robert Young'	CB&S EPla SDry WJun
– 'Sulphurea'	See *P. bambusoides* '**Allgold**'
§ – var. *viridis*	EFul EPla ERod ISta SDry WJun
– – 'Mitis'	See *P. sulphurea* var. *viridis*
violascens	CB&S EFul EPla ISta LJus SDry WJun WPGP
¶ *virella*	CFil WPGP
§ *viridiglaucescens* ♀	CB&S CFil CHEx EFul EPla ISta LJus MBrN SAPC SArc SCha SCob SDry SEND WCot WJun
◆ *viridis*	See *P. sulphurea* var. *viridis*
vivax	EFul EPla ISta MMoz SDry WJun
– 'Aureocaulis'	EFul EOas EPla ERod ISta LJus LPJP MMoz SDry WJun WPGP

× PHYLLOTHAMNUS (Ericaceae)

erectus	GCrs GGGa MHig NHar NHol WAbe WPat WPyg

PHYMOSIA (Malvaceae)

§ *umbellata*	CBot CGre LCns SOWG

PHYODINA See CALLISIA

PHYSALIS (Solanaceae)

alkekengi ♀	ERav MLan WOak
– var. *franchetii*	CArn CB&S ECED ELan ENot EPla GAbr GChr GLil MBri MCLN NBir NBro NFai NFla NMir NRoo SEas SHel SPer SRms WOve WPer WWin
– – 'Gigantea'	ECGP GBuc NNor
– – 'Variegata'	CDec CRDP EPla ERav EWes IBlr MTed NPro WPbr
¶ *edulis* (F)	LPVe

PHYSARIA (Brassicaceae)

¶ *alpina*	NWCA

PHYSOCARPUS (Rosaceae)

opulifolius	MSal
– 'Dart's Gold' ♀	EBrP EBre EHoe ELan EMil ENot IOrc LBre LBuc LHop MAsh MBar MHar MTis MWat NNor NSti SBre SCob SLPl SMac SPer SRms SSpi SSta WDin WWal WWin
– 'Diabolo'	CBlo EBee ECle ENot EPfP IOrc MAsh MBri MGos NBir NPSI SCoo SMur SPan SPer SPla SSta WWes
§ – 'Luteus'	CBot CPle CSam EPfP ESis ISea MBar MGos MRav NNor SPer SRms WBod WDin WFar
ribesifolius 'Aureus'	See *P. opulifolius* '**Luteus**'

PHYSOCHLAINA (Solanaceae)

orientalis	CRDP EBee EMan EMon MSal NChi

PHYSOPLEXIS (Campanulaceae)

§ *comosa* ♀	CLyd EPot MBro NTow SIng WAbe WHoo WPyg

PHYSOSTEGIA (Lamiaceae)

angustifolia	CHan EBee NLak
§ *virginiana*	CTri EBar EBee ECoo GBar GCHN GMaP LGan MHew NRoo SWat WByw WFar WRHF
– 'Alba'	CBot CGle EBrP EBre ECro GBri GMaP LBre LHop LWak MSte NOrc NRoo SBre SHel SUsu WEas WRHF WShe
§ – 'Crown of Snow'	CBot CFir CMdw CMil EBar ECoo ECtt GBur LPVe MCLN MSCN NHol NMir NPla SOkh WCot WHil WPer WRHF WWhi
– dwarf form	ECha
– 'Galadriel'	EMon
– 'Grandiflora'	CFir SIde WLRN
– pale pink	EFou LGan SUsu SWat
– 'Red Beauty'	CFir EBee EGar EHal EWll MTis SMrm WPyg WWin
– 'Rosea'	CB&S CBot EAst EWll GBur LWak MBel WOve WPer
– Schneekrone	See *P. virginiana* '**Crown of Snow**'
– 'Snow Queen'	See *P. virginiana* '**Summer Snow**'
– subsp. *speciosa*	EMon
§ – – 'Bouquet Rose'	CDec CHan EBrP EBre ECED ECha EMar ENot EOld LBre LFis LLWP MAus MBri MFir MRav MSte NCat NFla NMir NPri SBre SChu SPer SSea WHal WHoo WMow WPyg WRus
– – Rose Bouquet	See *P. virginiana* subsp. *speciosa* '**Bouquet Rose**'
§ – – 'Variegata'	Widely available

§ – 'Summer Snow' ♀ — CB&S CKel EAst ECha EFou ELan ENot LHop MAus MBel MBri MFir MWat NFla NHol SHFr SPer SRms WBea WHal WHoo WOld WOve WRus WWin

– 'Summer Spire' — ECha ECro ELan EMan MSte NHol SPer WBea WFar

– 'Vivid' ♀ — Widely available

PHYTEUMA (Campanulaceae)

balbisii — See *P. cordatum*
betonicifolium — WHil
charmelii — CPea
comosum — See *Physoplexis comosa*
§ *cordatum* — MFos
halleri — See *P. ovatum*
hemisphaericum — NGre NNrd SWas
nigrum — ELan GCal LBee MNrw WHoo WLin WPyg WThi
orbiculare — ECGN WPyg
§ *ovatum* — GAri
scheuchzeri — CHea CNic CPea CRDP ECha ECro ELan EMan GTou LFis LGan MBro MRav NMGW NOrc NPri SBla SRms SSca
sieberi — ELan GDra NBir WRHF
spicatum — NBro WWye
– subsp. *coeruleum* — GBin
tenerum — CKin
¶ *zahlbruckneri* — WLin

PHYTOLACCA (Phytolaccaceae)

acinosa — CArn IBlr LHol MHew MSal SWat WHer
§ *americana* — CArn CAvo CHEx CSev EBar ECha ELan ELau EMar GOrc GPoy IBlr LHol MChe MSal SIde SRms SWat WByw WEas WHer WPer WWye
clavigera — See *P. polyandra*
decandra — See *P. americana*
dioica — GBin
esculenta — EBee GBin NPSI
– B&SWJ 1000 — WCru
§ *polyandra* — ECGP ECha GBin GBuc GCHN LHol NBro NHex SAxl SRms WWye
¶ *tibetica* — GPoy MSal

PICEA † (Pinaceae)

§ *abies* — CPer CTri EHul ENot GChr GRei LBuc LCon MBar MBri MGos NBee NRoo NWea WDin WMou WWal
– 'Acrocona' — CDoC EHul EOrn LCon MBar MBri MGos MPla
¶ – 'Archer' — CKen
– 'Argenteospica' (v) — LCon NHol
– 'Aurea' — ECho EOrn LLin
– 'Aurea Magnifica' — LCon
– 'Capitata' — CBlo CKen GAri LCon MBar
* – 'Cinderella' — MAsh
– 'Clanbrassiliana' — CBlo CKen LCon MBar
– 'Columnaris' — GAri
– 'Compacta' — LBee
I – 'Congesta' — CKen
– 'Crippsii' — CKen
I – 'Cruenta' — CKen
– 'Cupressina' — CKen
– 'Diffusa' — CBlo CKen LCon MBar
– 'Elegans' — LCon MBar

– 'Ellwangeriana' — CBlo LCon
– 'Excelsa' — See *P. abies*
– 'Finedonensis' — LCon
– 'Formanek' — CKen LCon LLin
– 'Four Winds' — CAbP
– 'Frohburg' — CDoC COtt GAri LCon MBar MBri MGos NHol
– 'Globosa' — CBlo MBar WStI
– 'Globosa Nana' — MGos
– 'Gregoryana' — CDoC CKen EGra LCon MBar NHed WAbe
– 'Humilis' — LCon
¶ – 'Hystrix' — LCon
– 'Inversa' — CDoC EHul EOrn GAri IOrc LCon LLin LPan MBar
§ – 'J.W. Daisy's White' — CKen LLin LRHS SCoo SMur
– 'Little Gem' ♀ — CBlo CDoC CKen CMac EBrP EBre EHul EOrn LBee LBre LCon LLin MAsh MBar MBri MGos MPla MWat NBee NRoo SAga SBre SLim WAbe
¶ – 'Mariae Orffiae' — CKen LCon
– 'Maxwellii' — EHul MBar MGos
– 'Merkii' — GAri
– 'Nana' — MBar
– 'Nana Compacta' — CKen EHul ESis LCon LLin MBar MOne SLim
– 'Nidiformis' ♀ — Widely available
– 'Norrkoping' — CKen
– 'Ohlendorffii' — CKen EHul EOrn LCon LPan MBar MBri MPla MWat NHol NRoo SHBN SLim WStI
– 'Pachyphylla' — CKen
– 'Pendula Major' — SHBN
– 'Procumbens' — MBar
– 'Pseudomaxwellii' — CBlo LCon NHol
– 'Pumila' — EOrn NHed
– 'Pumila Nigra' — CMac EHul LCon LLin MAsh MBar MGos MPla NHar SLim
– 'Pusch' — CKen
– 'Pygmaea' — CKen GDra LCon MBar MGos MPla
– 'Reflexa' — EHul LCon LLin
– 'Repens' — MBar MBlu MGos NBee
– 'Rydal' — LCon MAsh
– 'Saint James' — CKen
– 'Tabuliformis' — MBar
– 'Tufty' — EOrn
– 'Veitchii' — See *P. abies* '**Gregoryana Veitchii**'
– 'Waugh' — CBlo MBar
– Will's Dwarf — See *P. abies* '**Wills Zwerg**'
§ – 'Wills Zwerg' — LCon MAsh
alcockiana 'Prostrata' — LCon MBal MBar NHol
asperata — ETen
§ *balfouriana* — LCon NHol WWes
bicolor — See *P. alcockiana*
brachytyla — LCon
breweriana ♀ — CB&S CDoC CMac EBrP EBre EHul ENot GChr GRei IHos IOrc ISea LBre LCon LLin LNet LPan MBar MBri NBee NHol NWea SBre SHBN SLim SPer SSta WNor
* – 'Frühlingsgold' — SMad
engelmannii — CBlo LCon MBar
– f. *glauca* — EHul LCon LPan MBar SSta
glauca — NWea
– 'Alberta Blue' — LLin LPan SCoo SLim WWeb

– var. **albertiana** 'Alberta Globe'	CBlo CDoC EBrP EBre EHul EOrn EPot GRei LBee LBre LCon LLin MAsh MBar MBri MGos MPla NBee NHed NRoo SAga SBre SLim SSmi WFar
– – 'Conica' ♀	Widely available
– – 'Gnome'	CKen
– – 'Laurin'	CDoC CKen EBrP EBre EOrn LBee LBre LCon MAsh MBar MBri SBre SSmi SSta WAbe
– – 'Tiny'	CKen EHul EOrn EPot ESis LCon LLin MBar MOne WAbe
– 'Arneson's Blue'	LCon SLim
– 'Coerulea'	LCon MBar
– 'Densata'	CBlo
– 'Echiniformis' ♀	CKen EHul EPot GAri LBee LCon LPan MBal MBar MBri
◆ – 'J.W. Daisy's White'	See *P. abies* '**J.W. Daisy's White**'
– 'Lilliput'	EHul EPot LCon MBar MBri MGos
– 'Nana'	CBlo CKen
– 'Piccolo'	CKen MBri SLim
– 'Rainbow's End'	CKen
– 'Sander's Blue'	CKen
– 'Zucherhut'	LRHS MBar MBri
glehnii 'Sasanosei'	CKen
– 'Shimezusei'	CKen
jezoensis	ETen GAri MGos NWea
– subsp. **hondoensis**	WNor
kosteri 'Glauca'	See *P. pungens* '**Koster**'
§ **koyamae**	CBlo CLnd ETen LCon
likiangensis	CBlo MBal
– var. **balfouriana**	See *P. balfouriana*
– var. **purpurea**	See *P. purpurea*
mariana 'Aureovariegata'	LCon
– 'Doumetii'	EOrn
– 'Ericoides'	GAri
– 'Fastigiata'	CKen EOrn
– 'Nana' ♀	CBlo CKen CMac EBrP EBre EGra EHul ELan ESis GDra LBre LCon LLin LNet MBar MBri MGos MNrw MPla MWat NBee NHed NHol SBre SLim SSmi SSta WDin
× **mariorika**	MBar
I **obovata** 'Glauca'	LCon
omorika ♀	CB&S CDoC CMCN CPer ENot GChr GRei LBuc LCon LNet MBal MBar MGos NBee NWea SIng SPer WCFE WCoo WDin WMou WWal
– 'Gnom'	See *P. × mariorika* '**Gnom**'
– 'Nana'	CMac EBrP EBre GAri LBre LCon LNet LPan MBar NBee SBre SLim
– 'Pendula' ♀	CBlo IOrc LCon MAsh MBar SHBN SSta
– 'Pimoko'	CKen LCon MBri
– 'Schneverdingen'	CKen
– 'Treblitsch'	CKen
orientalis ♀	CLnd ETen GChr LCon MBal STre WTro
§ – 'Aurea' ♀	CDoC CMac EBrP EBre EHul ELan IOrc LBre LCon LLin LPan MBar MBri SBre SHBN SLim
¶ – 'Aureospicata'	ECho
– 'Bergman's Gem'	CKen
– 'Gowdy'	MBar
– 'Kenwith'	CKen
– 'Pendula'	MGos

– 'Reynolds'	CKen
– 'Skylands'	CBlo CKen LCon MAsh MGos SLim
pungens	GChr MBar NWea SPer WDin WNor
– 'Blaukissen'	CKen
¶ – 'Corbet'	LCon
– 'Erich Frahm'	CDoC EBrP EBre GAri LBre LCon LPan MBri MGos SBre SCoo SLim SMad WWeb
– 'Fat Albert'	EBrP EBre LBre LPan SBre
– f. **glauca**	EHul GRei LBee MBal MBar NBee NWea WDin WMou WStI
– 'Glauca Globosa'	See *P. pungens* '**Globosa**'
– 'Glauca Procumbens'	LNet
§ – 'Glauca Prostrata'	EBrP EBre EHul LBre LCon MBal SBre SLim SSta
– 'Globe'	CKen LCon NHol
§ – 'Globosa' ♀	CDoC CKen EBrP EBre EHul ELan EOrn IOrc LBee LBre LCon LLin LPan MBar MBri MGos MWat NBee NHol SBre SHBN SLim SPer SRms WPyg WStI
I – 'Globosa Viridis'	EHul
– 'Gloria'	CKen LCon
– 'Hoopsii' ♀	CBlo CDoC CMac EBrP EBre EHul ELan ENot EOrn GChr IHos IOrc LBre LCon LNet LPan MBal MBar MWat NBee SBre SHBN SLim SPla WDin
– 'Hoto'	EHul EOrn IOrc LCon MBar WPyg WWeb
– 'Hunnewelliana'	EOrn
– 'Iseli Fastigiate'	COtt EBrP EBre LBre LCon MAsh SBre
§ – 'Koster' ♀	CDoC CMac EHul EOrn GRei IOrc LCon LLin LNet LPan MAsh MBar MGos NBee NWea SLim SMad SPer SRms SSta WDin WStI
– 'Koster Prostrate'	MBal
– 'Lucky Strike'	CKen LCon MAsh MGos
– 'Maigold'	CKen
– 'Moerheimii'	EHul LCon LNet MBar MGos
– 'Montgomery'	CBlo CKen LCon MBar NHol
– 'Procumbens' ♀	CKen LCon
– 'Prostrata'	See *P. pungens* '**Glauca Prostrata**'
– 'Saint Mary's Broom'	CKen
– 'Schovenhorst'	EHul EOrn
– 'Thomsen'	CKen EHul EOrn LCon MAsh MBal MBri
– 'Thuem'	EHul LCon MGos
– 'Wendy'	CKen
rubens	GAri LCon NWea
schrenkiana	ETen LCon
sitchensis	CPer GChr GRei LBuc LCon MGos NWea WMou
– 'Nana'	CDoC NHol
– 'Papoose'	See *P. sitchensis* '**Tenas**'
– 'Silberzwerg'	CKen
– 'Strypemonde'	CKen
§ – 'Tenas'	LCon MBri NHol
smithiana ♀	GAri ISea LCon MBal SLim WFro

PICRASMA (Simaroubaceae)

ailanthoides	See *P. quassioides*
§ **quassioides**	CMCN

PICRIS (Asteraceae)
echioides CKin EWFC WHer

PICRORHIZA (Scrophulariaceae)
¶ *kurrooa* GPoy

PIERIS † (Ericaceae)
'Bert Chandler' ELan LRHS SPer SSpi
'Flaming Silver' (v) ♀ Widely available
'Flamingo' CB&S CHig CTrh CTrw MAsh
MBal MBar MGos NHed NHol
SExb WAbe WPat WPyg
floribunda IOrc MBal SPer
'Forest Flame' ♀ Widely available
formosa CHig
¶ – B&SWJ 2257 WCru
– var. *forrestii* CDoC CTre CTrw GRei ISea
NWea SBrw SExb
– – 'Fota Pink' WHar WSHC
– – 'Jermyns' ♀ CB&S CEnd CHig IOrc MBal
SHBN
– – 'Wakehurst' ♀ CB&S CHig CLan CTrG IOrc
LHyd MAsh MBal MRav NWea
SAPC SArc SBrw SPer SReu
SSta WBod WFar WWal
♦ Havila See *P.* Havila = 'Mouwsvila'
japonica CB&S CHEx CHig CLan CTrw
MBal MBar MGos NWea SAPC
SArc SReu WDin
– 'Balls of Fire' CTrh
– 'Bisbee Dwarf' MBar MBro NHar NHol WAbe
WPat WPyg
– 'Blush' ♀ CHig NHol SBod SEas SHBN
WSHC
¶ – 'Brookside Miniature' WPat
– 'Cavatine' CMHG LRHS SBod
§ – 'Christmas Cheer' CLan IOrc MBal MGos NHed
SBrw SPer WDin WLRN
– 'Coleman' CMHG
– 'Compact Crimson' MBal
– 'Compacta' NHol WAbe
– 'Crispa' CHig
– 'Cupido' CBlo EMil MAsh MBar MGos
WLRN
– 'Daisen' CLan CTrw
§ – 'Debutante' ♀ CDoC ELan ENot EPfP
MAsh MPla NHol SBrw SSpi
WStI WWat
– 'Don' See *P. japonica* 'Pygmaea'
– 'Dorothy Wyckoff' CB&S CLan CMHG CTrG
NHed NHol SBrw SHBN SPer
SSta WCwm
– 'Firecrest' ♀ CB&S CHig CMHG CTrG
CTrh ENot IOrc MBal MBri
NHed SBrw SSpi WPat
– 'Flaming Star' ECot
– 'Geisha' WPat
– 'Glenroy Pink Plenty' MBal
– 'Grayswood' ♀ CHig CMHG CSam EPfP IOrc
MBri
– 'Little Heath' (v) ♀ Widely available
– 'Little Heath Green' ♀ CChe CDoC CHig CMHG
CTrG EPla GAri LHyd MAsh
MBar MBri MGos NHed SBrw
SPer SSta WBrE WFar WPic
WWeb
– 'Minor' MBar NHar NHol WPat WPyg

– 'Mountain Fire' ♀ CB&S CChe CDoC CMHG
CTrh ECle ENot GCHN GChr
GOrc IOrc MAsh MBal MBar
MBri MGos NHol SBod SBrw
SCoo SEas SHBN SPer SReu
WBrE WGwG WHar WPat
WWal WWeb
– 'Pink Delight' ♀ CAbP CB&S CHig MAsh MBal
MBar MGos MPla MRav SBid
SBrw SHBN SPer SRms WPat
– 'Prelude' ♀ CWSG GCHN MBri MRav
NHol WPat
– 'Purity' ♀ CB&S CBlo CDoC CHig
CMHG CTrh IOrc MBal MBar
MGos NHol SBrw SEas SPer
SReu SSta WDin WFar WLRN
WStI
§ – 'Pygmaea' GDra MBal MBro MHig NHar
NHol WPat WPyg
– 'Red Mill' CAbP CBlo CEnd CHig CMHG
EPfP GOrc MAsh NHol SBod
SPer SSpi WPat
– 'Robinswood' SBid WBcn
– 'Rosea' LHyd
– 'Rowallane' IBlr
– 'Sarabande' ♀ COtt MBri MGos NHol SBrw
SPer WPat WPyg
– 'Scarlett O'Hara' CB&S MGos
– 'Select' MGos
– 'Snowdrift' GCHN MSta SPer SSta
– 'Spring Candy' CB&S MGos SBid
– 'Spring Snow' LRHS
– Taiwanensis Group CGre CHig CMHG CTre CTrh
GCHN GRei IOrc LHyd MBal
MBar MRav NHol NWea SPer
SRms SSta WAbe WPat WWat
– 'Temple Bells' EHic ENot SBid SPar WFox
– 'Tickled Pink' CB&S EHic NHol
– 'Tilford' CHig MBal MBri MPla NHol
SSta WFox WPat
– 'Valley Fire' CTrh
– 'Valley Rose' CChe COtt CSam CTrh ENot
GCHN MAsh MBal MBel
MGos NBee SBid SPer SSpi
WGwG WStI
– 'Valley Valentine' ♀ CLan COtt EHic ENot EPfP
MAsh MBal MBri MGos NFla
NHed NHol SBid SBod SBrw
SPer SReu SSta WCwm WStI
WWeb
§ – 'Variegata' CHig CMHG ELan EPot GRei
(Carrière) Bean IOrc LHyd MBal MBar MGos
NBee NHed NHol SArc SExb
SHBN SPer SReu SSta WAbe
WDin WHar WPat WSHC
WWat
– 'Variegata' hort. See *P. japonica* 'White Rim'
– 'Wada's Pink' See *P. japonica* 'Christmas
Cheer'
– 'White Caps' MBal
– 'White Cascade' SBrw
– 'White Pearl' CAbP CLan MAsh MBal MBri
MGos SPer
§ – 'White Rim' (v) ♀ CB&S MAsh MGos MPla
– 'William Buchanan' GCrs MBar MBro MHig NHar
NHol WPat WPyg
– var. *yakushimensis* CBlo WSHC
§ Havila® = 'Mouwsvila' (v) CDoC CHig EHic IOrc MAsh
MBal MGos NHed NHol
SBrw WLRN
nana GAri MBal MBar NHar
– 'Redshank' MBal

PILEA (Urticaceae)
* 'Anette'	MBri
cadierei ♀	CHal MBri
nummulariifolia	CHal MBri
peperomioides ♀	CSev SRms
repens	MBri

PILEOSTEGIA (Hydrangeaceae)
viburnoides ♀	CB&S CGre CHEx CLan CMac CPlN CSPN CTrw EMil EPla GQui LHop MGos SArc SBid SBra SDix SHBN SPer SSpi SSta WBod WCru WPat WPyg WSHC WWat
¶ *viburnoides* B&SWJ 3565	WCru

PILOSELLA (Asteraceae)
§ *aurantiaca*	CLTr CNic CRow EBar ELan EWFC LWak MFir MHew MRav NOrc NSti SIde SIng SSmi WCer WCla WElm WHer
§ *officinarum*	CKin CRow EWFC WGwy
¶ × *stoloniflora*	CRow

PILULARIA (Marsileaceae)
globulifera	CNat NVic

PIMELEA (Thymelaeaceae)
arenaria	ECou
coarctata	See *P. prostrata*
drupacea	ECou
filiformis	ECou MAll
¶ *physodes*	MFiF
§ *prostrata*	CLyd CTri ECou EHyt EPot GCrs MAll MBar MHig NHar NMen NWoo SIng WAbe WPat WPer
– f. *parvifolia*	ECou
– Tennyson's form	SBla

PIMENTA (Myrtaceae) See Plant Deletions

PIMPINELLA (Apiaceae)
anisum	CArn LHol MSal SIde WHer WSel
¶ *brachycarpa* B&SWJ 863	WCru
major 'Rosea'	CHan CRDP CSpe EMan EMon GBri LHop MHlr SDix SMrm WBro WCot WFar WHal WPGP
saxifraga	EWFC LHol

PINELLIA (Araceae)
cordata	CMon CRDP EPot WCru
pedatisecta	CRDP EBee MRav SAxl SSoC WCot WCru
pinnatisecta	See *P. tripartita*
ternata	CMon CRDP EPar EPot MSal SIng WCru WOld WWye
¶ – B&SWJ 3532	WCru
§ *tripartita*	CMon EPot SAxl SUsu
– B&SWJ 1102	WCru

PINGUICULA † (Lentibulariaceae)
acuminata	WMEx
agnata	MHel WMEx
ehlersiae	EFEx MHel WMEx
emarginata	WMEx
esseriana	EFEx MHel WMEx
gracilis	WMEx
grandiflora	CRDP EFEx EPot GCrs MHel NGre NHar NMen NRya WAbe WHer WMEx WPGP
– subsp. *coenocantabrica* NS 307	NWCA
gypsicola	WMEx
hemiepiphytica	WMEx
'Kewensis'	MHel WMEx
laueana	MHel WMEx
longifolia subsp. *longifolia*	EFEx WPGP
macrophylla	WMEx
moranensis alba	MHel
– var. *caudata*	EFEx MHel WMEx
– *flos-mulionis*	MHel
– 'Kirkbright'	MHel
– var. *mexicana*	WMEx
– *moreana*	EFEx
– *superba*	EFEx
potosiensis	WMEx
primuliflora	MHel WMEx
reticulata	WMEx
rotundifolia	WMEx
'Sethos'	MHel WMEx
vulgaris	EFEx MHel WMEx
'Weser'	MHel WMEx
zecheri	MHel WMEx

PINUS † (Pinaceae)
albicaulis	WNor
– 'Flinck'	CKen
– 'Nana'	See *P. albicaulis* 'Noble's Dwarf'
§ – 'Noble's Dwarf'	CKen
aristata 'Cecilia'	CKen
– Engelm.	CAbP CBlo CDoC CMCN EBrP EBre EHul EOrn GChr LBre LCon LLin MAsh MBal MBar MGos MUlv NHol SBre SReu SSta STre WCoo WFro
– 'Sherwood Compact'	CKen
armandii	CB&S CDul CGre CMCN CSWP ETen LCon SMad
– SF 313	ISea
attenuata	CBlo STre
austriaca	See *P. nigra* subsp. *nigra*
N *ayacahuite*	LCon SMur
banksiana	CSam EHul ETen LCon MBal
– 'Chippewa'	CKen NHol
I – 'Compacta'	CKen
– 'H.J. Welch'	CKen
– 'Manomet'	CKen
– 'Neponset'	CKen LCon
– 'Wisconsin'	CKen
brutia	See *P. halepensis* subsp. *brutia*
bungeana	CAbP CDoC CLnd EHul LCon LLin MBal MBlu MUlv SLPl STre WFro WNor
¶ – 'Diamant'	CKen
canariensis ♀	EHul ISea
cembra ♀	CDoC CDul EHul GChr LCon MBal MBar NWea STre WCFE
– 'Aurea'	See *P. cembra* 'Aureovariegata'
§ – 'Aureovariegata'	CKen LLin
– 'Barnhourie'	CKen
– 'Blue Mound'	CKen
– 'Chalet'	CKen
– 'Compacta Glauca'	LRHS
* – 'Griffithii'	WDin
– 'Inverleith'	CKen MBri
– 'Jermyns'	CKen
– 'King's Dwarf'	CKen

– 'Nana'	See *P. pumila* 'Nana'
– 'Roughills'	CKen
– 'Stricta'	CKen
– Witches' broom	CKen
cembroides var. *edulis*	ETen
contorta	CB&S CBlo CDoC CDul CPer GChr GRei LCon MBal MBar MGos NWea STre WDin WMou
– 'Asher'	CKen
– 'Frisian Gold'	CKen
– var. *latifolia*	CLnd ETen MBal WTro
– 'Spaan's Dwarf'	CBlo CKen LCon LLin MBar MGos NHol SLim
coulteri ♀	CMCN ETen LCon MBal WNor WPGP
densiflora	CDul CMCN EHul ETen LCon MBal STre WFro WNor
– 'Alice Verkade'	CBlo LCon LLin LRHS SLim
– 'Aurea'	EBrP EBre LBre LCon MBar MGos NHol SBre SLim
– 'Jane Kluis'	CKen COtt LRHS MBri
– 'Oculus Draconis'	CDoC LCon MBar MGos SLim SMur
– 'Pendula'	CKen LLin MBal SLim
– 'Pygmy'	CKen
* – 'Pyramidalis'	ECho
– 'Umbraculifera'	CDoC IOrc LCon LLin LPan MBar MBri MGos MOne SLim SSta
edulis	LCon
flexilis	EBlo CDul ETen LCon MBal
– 'Firmament'	CDoC LCon LLin
– 'Glenmore Dwarf'	CKen
– 'Nana'	CKen
– 'Pendula'	LLin
– WB No. 1	CKen
– WB No. 2	CKen
gerardiana	LCon MBal
greggii	ISea
griffithii	See *P. wallichiana*
halepensis	CLnd ETen
hartwegii	ETen
§ *heldreichii* var.	CMac ETen LCon LNet MBal
leucodermis ♀	MBar SCoo WDin WNor
– – 'Aureospicata'	LCon LLin MBar SIng
– – 'Compact Gem'	CDoC CKen EBrP EBre IOrc LBre LCon LLin MBar MBri MGos SBre SCoo SLim SSta WPyg
– – 'Groen'	CKen
– – 'Malink'	CKen
– – 'Pygmy'	CKen
– – 'Satellit'	CDoC EOrn IOrc LBee LLin LPan MBri SLim
– 'Schmidtii' ♀	CDoC CKen EBrP EBre LBre LCon LLin MAsh MBar MBri SBre SLim
jeffreyi ♀	CAgr CBot CDul CLnd CMCN ETen ISea LCon MBal MBar WFro
– 'Joppi'	CKen
koraiensis	ETen LCon MBal WNor
– 'Bergman'	CKen
– 'Dragon Eye'	CKen
– 'Jack Corbit'	CKen
– 'Shibamichi'	CKen
– 'Silver Lining'	MAsh MBri
– 'Silvergrey'	CKen
– 'Winton'	CDoC CKen
lambertiana	ETen LCon
leucodermis	See *P. heldreichii* var. *leucodermis*

¶ – 'Zwerg Schneverdingen'	CKen
magnifica	See *P. montezumae*
massoniana	WNor
monophylla	ETen MBal
N *montezumae*	CB&S CGre CLnd CMCN IOrc ISea LCon LLin SAPC SArc SLim SMad WNor
monticola	CLnd
– 'Pendula'	MBar
– 'Pygmy'	See *P. monticola* 'Raraflora'
§ – 'Raraflora'	CKen
– 'Skyline'	MBar
– 'Windsor Dwarf'	CKen
mugo	CB&S CBlo CDul CTri EHul ENot GRei MAsh MBal MBar MGos SRms WDin WStI
* – 'Benjamin'	CKen
– 'Bisley Green'	LLin
– 'Brownie'	CKen
– 'Carsten'	CKen
– 'Carsten's Wintergold'	See *P. mugo* 'Winter Gold'
I – 'Columnaris'	LPan
– 'Corley's Mat'	CKen EBrP EBre LBre LCon LLin MAsh SBre SCoo SLim WWeb
– 'Gnom'	CBlo CKen CMac EHul EOrn LCon LLin MBar MBri MOne NBee WDin WFar
– 'Hoersholm'	CKen
– 'Humpy'	CKen EBrP EBre EOrn GAri LBee LBre LCon LLin MAsh MBar MBri MGos MOne NHol SBre SLim WAbe
– 'Jacobsen'	CKen
– 'Kissen'	CBlo CKen LCon MGos
– 'Klosterkotter'	MGos
– 'Knapenburg'	NHol
– 'Kobold'	CBlo NHol
– 'Krauskopf'	CKen
– 'Laarheide'	MBri
– 'Laurin'	CKen
– 'March'	CKen NHol
– 'Mini Mops'	CKen
– 'Minikin'	CKen
– 'Mops' ♀	CBlo CDoC CMac EBrP EBre EHul GChr IHos LBee LBre LCon LLin LPan MAsh MBar MBri MGos NBee NHol SBre SLim SPer SSta WPyg
– 'Mops Midget'	LLin MBri
– var. *mughus*	See *P. mugo* var. *mugo*
§ – var. *mugo*	CMCN EHic ESis GRei LPan MBar WWal
– 'Mumpitz'	CKen
– 'Ophir'	CKen EBrP EBre EHul EOrn IOrc LBee LBre LCon LLin LNet MAsh MBar MBri MGos NHol SBre SLim SPer SPla SSta WDin
– 'Pal Maleter'	CDoC LCon LLin MBri
¶ – 'Piggelmee'	CKen
– var. *pumilio* ♀	CBlo CDoC CDul CMac EHul ENot GRei IOrc LCon LLin LPan MBar MBro MGos NFla NWea SHBN SLPl STre WNor
– var. *rostrata*	See *P. mugo* subsp. *uncinata*
– 'Spaan'	CKen
¶ – 'Sunshine'	CKen
§ – subsp. *uncinata*	CLnd ETen GRei LCon NWea
– 'White Tip'	CKen

§ – 'Winter Gold'	CKen EBrP EBre EHul EOrn IOrc LBre LCon LLin MAsh SBre SSta
– 'Winzig'	CKen
– 'Zundert'	CBlo CKen LCon LLin MBar MBri MGos
¶ – 'Zwergkugel'	CKen
muricata ♀	CAbP CDoC CDul CLnd CPer ETen GChr LCon MBal MGos
nigra ♀	CB&S CBlo CDoC CDul GRei LCon LNet MBar MGos SHBN WDin WMou
* – 'Asterix'	CKen
– var. **austriaca**	See *P. nigra* subsp. *nigra*
– 'Black Prince'	CBlo CKen LBee LCon LLin NHol SCoo SLim
N – 'Cebennensis Nana'	CKen
– var. **corsicana**	See *P. nigra* subsp. *laricio*
– 'Hornibrookiana'	CKen LCon LPan
§ – subsp. **laricio** ♀	CDoC CKen ENot GChr GRei IHos LBuc LCon MBar NWea WMou
– – 'Bobby McGregor'	CKen LLin SLim
– – 'Globosa Viridis'	GAri LLin NHol
– – 'Goldfingers'	CKen LLin
§ – – 'Moseri' ♀	CKen GAri LCon LLin SLim SSta
– – 'Pygmaea'	CKen
– – 'Spingarn'	CKen
– – 'Talland Bay'	CKen
– – 'Wurstle'	CKen
– subsp. **maritima**	See *P. nigra* subsp. *laricio*
– 'Molette'	LCon
– 'Nana'	LPan MBri
§ – subsp. **nigra**	LBuc LPan NWea WStI
– – 'Bright Eyes'	CKen ECho EHul EOrn LBee LCon LLin
– – 'Helga'	CKen
– – 'Schovenhorst'	CKen
– – 'Strypemonde'	CKen
– – 'Yaffle Hill'	CKen
– 'Obelisk'	CKen
¶ – subsp. **pallasiana**	LCon
* – **serotina**	CMCN
– 'Uelzen'	CKen
palustris	LCon LLin
parviflora ♀	CMCN GAri LCon LPan NWea STre WCoo WDin WNor
– 'Adcock's Dwarf' ♀	CDoC CKen GAri LCon LLin MBar MGos NHol SCoo SLim WAbe
– 'Aizu'	CKen
– 'Al Fordham'	CKen
– 'Aoi'	CKen
¶ – 'Ara-kawa'	CKen
– 'Azuma-goyo'	CKen NHol
I – 'Baasch's Form'	CKen
– 'Bergman'	CBlo CDoC LCon MAsh MBar NHol
– 'Bonnie Bergman'	CKen
– 'Brevifolia'	GAri
– 'Dai-ho'	CKen
– 'Daisetsusan'	CKen
– 'Fukai Seedling'	CKen
– 'Fukiju'	CKen
– 'Fukushima-goyo'	CKen
– 'Fukuzumi'	LLin
– f. **glauca**	CDoC CMac EHul GAri IHos IOrc LCon LLin MBar MBri MGos NFla NHol NPal
I – 'Glauca Nana'	CKen
– 'Gyok-kan'	CKen
– 'Gyok-ke-sen'	CKen
– 'Gyo-ko-haku'	CKen
– 'Gyokuei'	CKen
– 'Gyokusen Seedling'	CKen
– 'Gyo-ku-sui'	CKen
– 'Hagaromo Seedling'	CKen
– 'Hakko'	CKen NHol
– 'Hatsumi'	NHol
– 'Ibo-can'	CKen
– 'Ichi-no-se'	CKen
– 'Iri-fune'	CKen
– 'Ishizuchi-goyo'	CKen
– 'Jyu-roko-ra-kan'	CKen
– 'Ka-ho'	CKen
– 'Kanzan'	CKen
– 'Kiyomatsu'	CKen
– 'Kobe'	CKen
– 'Kokonde'	CKen
– 'Kokonoe'	CBlo CKen LCon NHol
– 'Kokuho'	CKen NHol
– 'Koraku'	CKen
– 'Kusu-dama'	CKen
– 'Meiko'	CKen
– 'Michi-noku'	CKen
¶ – 'Myo-jo'	CKen
– 'Nasu-goyo'	CKen
– 'Negishi'	CKen EBrP EBre GAri LBre LCon LPan MBal MBri SBre
– 'Ogonjanome'	CKen
– 'Ryokuho'	CKen
– 'Ryuju'	CKen
– 'Sanbo'	CDoC CKen LCon MBar
§ – 'Saphir'	CKen LCon MBri
– 'Setsugekka'	CKen
– 'Shikashima'	CKen
– 'Shiobara'	CKen
– 'Shizukagoten'	CKen
– 'Shure'	CKen
– 'Tempelhof'	COtt GAri LNet MBar SLim
I – 'Zelkova'	LLin
– 'Zui-sho'	CKen
patula ♀	CAbb CDul CGre CSam ECre ISea LCon MBal MBlu SAPC SArc SCoo SIgm SLim WWat
peuce	CDul LCon MBar NWea STre WFro
– 'Arnold Dwarf'	CKen
pinaster ♀	CB&S CBlo CDoC CDul CLnd CPer EHul ISea LCon MBal
pinea ♀	CAgr CHEx CKen CMac GChr IOrc LCon LLin LPan MGos SAPC SArc SEND WNor
– 'Queensway'	CKen
ponderosa ♀	CDul CLnd ETen ISea LCon LLin LPan SIgm
pseudostrobus	MBal
pumila	CAgr LCon
– 'Buchanan'	CKen
– 'Draijer's Dwarf'	CDoC EOrn LLin SLim
– 'Dwarf Blue'	See *P. pumila* 'Glauca'
§ – 'Glauca' ♀	CBlo CKen LCon LLin LNet MBar MBri NHol
– 'Globe'	LCon LLin MBri
– 'Jeddeloh'	CKen
– 'Knightshayes'	CKen
§ – 'Nana'	SRms
– 'Säntis'	CDoC CKen
– 'Saphir'	See *P. parviflora* 'Saphir'
radiata ♀	CB&S CDoC CDul CHEx CPer CTrw ENot IHos IOrc LCon MBal SAPC SArc SHBN SLim STre WDin

– 'Aurea'	CBlo CKen LCon LLin MAsh SLim SMur
– 'Bodnant'	CKen
– 'Isca'	CKen
– 'Marshwood'	CKen
resinosa 'Don Smith'	CKen
– 'Joel's Broom'	CKen
– 'Nobska'	CKen
– 'Quinobequin'	CKen
– 'Watnong'	CKen
rigida	EHul LCon STre
¶ *roxburghii*	CGre
sabineana	CAgr LCon
× *schwerinii*	CDoC LCon LRHS
sibirica	See *P. cembra* subsp. *sibirica*
strobiformis	LCon
strobus	CDoC CDul CGre EHul GAri GChr IOrc ISea LCon MBar NWea SEND STre WNor
§ – 'Alba'	LCon MGos NHol
– 'Amelia's Dwarf'	CBlo CKen
– 'Anna Fiele'	CKen
– 'Bergman's Mini'	CKen
– 'Bergman's Pendula Broom'	CKen
I – 'Bergman's Sport of Prostrata'	CKen
* – 'Bloomer's Dark Globe'	CKen
– 'Blue Shag'	CBlo CKen COtt LLin MBri MGos SLim WPyg
– 'Densa'	CKen MBri
– 'Dove's Dwarf'	CKen
– 'Fastigiata'	CKen LLin
– 'Hillside Gem'	CKen
– 'Horsford'	CKen
– 'Jericho'	CKen
– 'Krügers Lilliput'	LCon LLin MBri SLim
– 'Macopin'	MGos
– 'Merrimack'	CBlo CKen
– 'Minima'	CDoC CKen LCon LLin MBar MBlu MBri SLim
– 'Minuta'	CKen LCon
– 'Nana'	See *P. strobus* 'Radiata'
– 'Nivea'	See *P. strobus* 'Alba'
– 'Northway Broom'	CKen LLin
§ – 'Radiata' ♀	EHul IHos IOrc LBee LNet MBar NBee SLim WAbe
– 'Reinshaus'	CKen LCon LLin
– 'Sayville'	CKen
– 'Sea Urchin'	CKen
– 'Uncatena'	CKen
– 'Verkade's Broom'	CKen
sylvestris ♀	Widely available
– 'Abergeldie'	CKen
– 'Andorra'	CKen
§ – 'Argentea'	LNet
– 'Aurea' ♀	CBlo CKen CMac EBrP EBre EHul IOrc LBee LBre LCon LLin LNet MAsh MBal MBar SBre SHBN SLim SPer SSta WLRN
– 'Avondene'	CKen
– 'Beuvronensis' ♀	CKen CMac EOrn GAri LBee LCon LLin LNet MAsh MGos NHol SLim SSta
– 'Brevifolia'	CBlo LCon MBar NHol
– 'Buchanan's Gold'	CKen
– 'Burghfield'	CBlo CKen LCon LLin NHol
– 'Chantry Blue'	CBlo EOrn LBee LCon LLin MAsh MBar MGos NHol SLim
– 'Clumber Blue'	CKen
– 'Compressa'	GAri

– 'Dereham'	CKen LLin
– 'Doone Valley'	CKen LLin
– 'Edwin Hillier'	See *P. sylvestris* 'Argentea'
– 'Fastigiata'	CDoC CEnd CKen EOrn LCon LLin MAsh MBar MGos SLim
– 'Frensham'	CBlo CKen EOrn LCon LLin MGos MOne
– 'Globosa'	GAri
– 'Gold Coin'	CBlo CDoC CKen EOrn LBee LCon LLin MBri MGos NHol SLim WPyg
– 'Gold Medal'	CKen LLin
– 'Grand Rapids'	CKen
– 'Green Flare'	CKen
– 'Hillside Creeper'	CBlo CKen LLin SLim
– 'Inverleith' (v)	GAri LCon LLin MAsh MBar MGos NHol SLim
– 'Jade'	See *P. sylvestris* 'Iceni'
– 'Jeremy'	CKen LCon LLin SLim WAbe
– 'Kelpie'	CKen
– 'Kenwith'	CKen NHol
– 'Lakeside Dwarf'	LLin
– 'Little Brolly'	CKen
– 'Lodge Hill'	CBlo CKen EBrP EBre EOrn LBre LCon LLin MAsh MOne SBre SLim WAbe
– 'Longmoor'	CDoC CKen
– 'Martham'	CKen
¶ – 'Moseri'	ECho
– 'Nana'	See *P. sylvestris* 'Watereri'
– 'Nana Compacta'	LLin
– 'Nisbet'	LLin
§ – 'Nisbet's Gem'	LLin
– 'Padworth'	CKen
– 'Pixie'	CKen LCon
– 'Pyramidalis Compacta'	NHol
– 'Reedham'	LLin
– 'Repens'	CKen
– 'Sandringham'	CBlo LCon LLin NHol
– 'Saxatilis'	CBlo EOrn LCon LLin
– 'Scott's Dwarf'	See *P. sylvestris* 'Nisbet's Gem'
– 'Sentinel'	CKen
I – 'Skjak I'	CKen
I – 'Skjak II'	CKen
– 'Spaan's Slow Column'	CKen
– 'Tage'	CKen LLin
– 'Tanya'	CKen
– 'Tilshead'	CKen
– 'Treasure'	CKen
– 'Variegata'	CBlo
§ – 'Watereri'	CDoC CMac EHul ENot IHos IOrc LBee LCon LLin LNet LPan MAsh MBar MBri MGos NHol SLim SPer WDin WWeb
– 'Westonbirt'	CKen LCon NHol
– 'Wishmoor'	LLin
* – 'Wolf Gold'	CKen
* – 'Yaff Hill'	LLin
tabuliformis	CLnd CMCN LCon MBlu
taiwanensis	ISea
thunbergii	CDoC CDul EHul LCon LLin MBal MGos SEND SPla STre WFro WNor
– 'Akame'	CKen
– 'Aocha-matsu'	CKen
– 'Banshosho'	CKen
– 'Compacta'	CKen
– 'Dainagon'	CKen
– 'Iwai'	CKen
– 'Kotobuki'	CKen
– 'Ko-yo-sho'	CKen
– 'Kujaku'	CKen

– 'Miyajuna'	CKen
– 'Nishiki-ne'	CKen
– var. *oculus draconis*	LLin
– 'Ogon'	CKen
§ – 'Sayonara'	CBlo CKen GAri LCon NHol
– 'Senryu'	CKen
– 'Shio-guro'	CKen
– 'Sunsho'	CKen
– 'Taihei'	CKen
I – 'Thunderhead'	CKen
– 'Yatsubusa'	See *P. thunbergii* 'Sayonara'
uncinata	See *P. mugo* subsp. *uncinata*
– 'Paradekissen'	CKen
virginiana	MBal
– 'Wate's Golden'	CKen
§ *wallichiana* ♀	CAbP CBlo CDoC CDul CKen
	EHul IOrc LCon LLin LPan
	MBal MBar MGos NBee SLim
	STre WCoo WNor WTro
¶ – CC 1740	SGre
– 'Densa'	MBri
– 'Nana'	CKen EHul MBar
– 'Umbraculifera'	LRHS MBal
– 'Zebrina' (v)	CBlo LCon MBar MGos
yunnanensis	ETen WNor

PIPER (Piperaceae)

¶ *auritum*	MSal
betle	CPlN MSal
excelsum	See *Macropiper excelsum*
¶ *methysticum*	NGno
nigrum	MSal

PIPTANTHUS (Papilionaceae)

forrestii	See *P. nepalensis*
laburnifolius	See *P. nepalensis*
§ *nepalensis*	CB&S CBot CHEx CHan CMac
	CPMA CPle ECha ELan EMil
	ENot EPla LHop MAll MGos
	MWat MWhi NChi NSti SDix
	SHBN SOWG SPer SRms SSpi
	WCru WDin WOMN WPat
¶ – B&SWJ 2241	WCru
¶ – SF 95180	ISea
tomentosus	SDry

PISONIA (Nyctaginaceae)

brunoniana	See *P. umbellifera*
§ *umbellifera*	CHEx
– 'Variegata'	CHEx

PISTACIA (Anacardiaceae)

chinensis	CB&S CMCN CPMA ELan
	EWes SSpi
¶ *terebinthus*	CFil

PISTIA (Araceae)

stratiotes	MSta WMul

PITTOSPORUM † (Pittosporaceae)

anomalum (m)	ECou
– (f)	ECou
–	ECou MAll SDry
¶ – 'Falcon'	ECou
¶ – 'Raven' (f)	ECou
¶ – 'Starling' (m)	ECou
* *argyrophyllum*	IOrc
'Arundel Green'	CBlo CDoC ECou LRHS MTed
	SDry
bicolor	CFil CPle ECou GQui MAll
	SAPC SArc WPGP

buchananii	CHid CPle
colensoi	ECou
– 'Wanaka'	ECou
crassifolium	CB&S CFil CPle ECou ERea
	IOrc WPGP
– 'Havering Dwarf'	ECou
– 'Napier'	ECou
– × *tenuifolium*	ECou MAll
– 'Variegatum'	CGre WSPU
dallii	CHEx
daphniphylloides var.	CFil CGre
adaphniphylloides	
¶ – ETE 275	WPGP
divaricatum	ECou
'Essex' (v)	ECou
eugenioides	CB&S CMHG IDee MAll
– 'Platinum'	CB&S
– 'Variegatum' ♀	CB&S CGre EPfP GQui IOrc
	SBid WSHC
'Garnettii' (v) ♀	CB&S CChe CDec CEnd CLan
	CMHG CPle CTrw EBrP EBre
	EHoe ELan EMil ENot GOrc
	IOrc LBre LHop MAll MBal
	MWgw SBre SMad SPer WAbe
	WDin WSHC
heterophyllum	CPle ECou MAll
– variegated	ECou
'Limelight' (v)	CB&S CBlo CGre EMil WWes
lineare	ECou
§ 'Margaret Turnbull' (v)	CB&S ECou EMil LHop MGos
michiei (m)	ECou
– (f)	ECou
–	ECou
¶ – 'Jill' (f)	ECou
'Nanum Variegatum'	See *P. tobira* 'Variegatum'
¶ *obcordatum*	ECou
– var. *kaitaiaense*	ECou
¶ *omeiense*	CGre
phillyreoides	MAll
pimeleoides var. *reflexum*	ECou
(m)	
ralphii	ECou
– 'Green Globe'	ECou
revolutum	MAll
¶ *rhombifolium*	MAll
'Saundersii' (v)	CBlo CMHG EMil MBal
tenuifolium ♀	CB&S EAst EBrP EBre ECou
	ELan EMil ENot GOrc ISea
	LBre LHop MAll MBal MBri
	MHlr SBre SPer SRms STre
	WAbe WBrE WDin WOMN
	WSHC WStI WWat
– 'Abbotsbury Gold' (v)	CAbb CChe CDoC CSam CTri
	CWSG ECou ELan EMil EWes
	GOrc MAll SDry SHBN SPer
	WSHC WStI
– 'Atropurpureum'	CB&S
– 'County Park Dwarf'	ECou WCru
– 'Deborah' (v)	CB&S ECou LHop SBid SSto
– 'Dixie'	CMHG ECou
§ – 'Eila Keightley' (v)	CBlo CMHG CSam IOrc MBal
* – 'French Lace'	ECou
– 'Gold Star'	CB&S CDoC ECou EMil SVen
– 'Golden King'	CB&S CDoC CMHG EBee
	MBal MRav SPla SRms
* – 'Green Elf'	CHan ECou
– 'Irene Paterson' (v) ♀	CAbb CB&S CGre CMHG
	CSam ECou ELan GOrc IOrc
	LHop MBal MGos SAga SDry
	SPer SPla SRms SSpi SSta
	WAbe WFar WSHC
– 'James Stirling'	ECou IOrc MAll WSHC

– 'John Flanagan'	See *P.* **'Margaret Turnbull'**	
– 'Katie'	CB&S	
¶ – 'Loxhill Gold'	LRHS	
– 'Marjory Channon' (v)	CB&S	
¶ – 'Mellow Yellow'	LRHS	
– 'Nigricans'	CB&S CLan	
¶ – 'Princess' (f)	ECou	
– 'Purpureum'	CPle CSam CTri CTrw ELan	
	EPfP IOrc LSpr MBal SDry	
	SHBN SPer SPla SRms WSHC	
* – 'Silver Dollar'	MBri	
– 'Silver Magic'	CB&S EMil	
¶ – 'Silver 'n' Gold'	LRHS	
– 'Silver Queen' (f/v) ♀	CB&S CEnd CMHG CSam	
	EBrP EBre ECou EHoe ELan	
	GOrc IOrc LBre MAll MBal	
	MNrw SBre SHBN SPer SPla	
	WAbe WBrE WSHC WStI	
	WWat	
– 'Stirling Gold' (v)	CB&S ECou EWes EWll	
– 'Sunburst'	See *P. tenuifolium* **'Eila**	
	Keightley'	
– 'Tiki'	CB&S ECou	
– 'Tom Thumb' ♀	CB&S CEnd CFee CMHG	
	CTrC CTrw ECou EHoe EMil	
	ENot IOrc LHop MAll MBal	
	MLan MPla SAga SDry SHBN	
	SPer SPla SSpi SSta WAbe	
	WBrE WSHC WWat	
– 'Tresederi' (f/m)	CTrw ECou MBal	
– 'Variegata'	CB&S ECou EMil SVen	
– 'Warnham Gold' ♀	CB&S CDoC CHan CMHG	
	COtt CTrw EBee ECou ELan	
	IOrc SDry SPla SSpi WAbe	
	WDin WWat	
– 'Wendle Channon' (v)	CB&S CDoC CEnd CMHG	
	CSam CWSG ECot ECou LHop	
	MAll MBal SPer SPla WSHC	
	WStI WWat	
– 'Winter Sunshine'	SSta	
tobira ♀	CB&S CBot CFil CHEx CHan	
	CLTr CPle CTrC ECou ELan	
	IOrc MAll MGos NPal SArc	
	SBid SHBN SPar SPer SSpi SSta	
	WAbe WBrE WCru WEas	
	WPat WPic WPyg WSHC WStI	
¶ – B&SWJ 4362	WCru	
– 'Nanum'	CB&S EBee ECou EPla ERea	
	IOrc SBid	
§ – 'Variegatum' ♀	CB&S CBot CGre CHEx CPle	
	ECou ERea GQui LHop MBri	
	NPal SBid SPer SSta WCru	
* – 'Variegatum	MAll	
Linearifolium' (v)		
undulatum	CB&S CHEx MAll	
– 'Variegatum'	CGre	

PITYROGRAMMA (Hemionitidaceae)
triangularis   CFil

PLAGIANTHUS (Malvaceae)

betulinus	See *P. regius*
¶ *divaricatus*	CFil WPGP
lyallii	See *Hoheria lyallii*
§ *regius*	ECou GQui LRHS SBid

PLAGIOMNIUM (Sphagnaceae) See Plant Deletions

PLAGIORHEGMA See JEFFERSONIA

PLANERA (Ulmaceae) See Plant Deletions

PLANTAGO (Plantaginaceae)

asiatica	MSal	
– 'Variegata'	CRow EBar EGoo EHoe ELan	
	GBuc LFlo MAus NBro NEgg	
	NSti WBea WHer WSan	
coronopus	CKin EWFC	
cynops	LRHS MTho WCot	
lanceolata	EWFC MHew	
¶ – 'Ballydowling	CNat	
Variegated' (v)		
* – 'Burren Rose'	CNat CRow WAlt	
¶ – 'Freaky'	WAlt	
– 'Streaker' (v)	CRow WCot WHal WHer	
major	EWFC	
– 'Atropurpurea'	See *P. major* **'Rubrifolia'**	
♦ – 'Bowles' Variety'	See *P. major* **'Rosularis'**	
¶ – 'Bract Act'	WAlt	
– 'Frills'	CNat CRow EPPr WAlt WCot	
	WHer	
* – 'Karmozijn'	EGoo	
§ – 'Rosularis'	CArn CInt CRow CSpe ECha	
	ECro ELan ILis LBay LHol	
	MFir MTho NBro NChi NEgg	
	NLar NRoo NSti WBea WBon	
	WHal WHer WPer WWye	
§ – 'Rubrifolia'	CArn CBos CKel CRow EBar	
	ECha ECoo EHoe ELan EMar	
	EPla LFis LHol LWak MFir	
	MNrw MRav NBro NChi NEgg	
	NFla NHar NMir NSti WBea	
	WCer WHer WPer WWye	
¶ – 'Subtle Streak' (v)	WAlt	
– 'Variegata'	LHol	
maritima	CKin GBin WHer	
media	CKin EWFC MHew	
nivalis	EHyt GBin GCLN MBro NNrd	
	NTow SMad WWin	
psyllium	CArn MSal	
raoulii	NHol WCot	
rosea	See *P. major* **'Rosularis'**	
sempervirens	ECro WHer	
uniflora	See *Littorella uniflora*	

PLATANTHERA (Orchidaceae)

hologlottis	EFEx
metabifolia	EFEx

PLATANUS † (Platanaceae)

x *acerifolia*	See *P.* x *hispanica*
§ x *hispanica* ♀	CB&S CBlo CKin CLnd CMCN
	CPer CTho EMil ENot GChr
	IOrc LBuc LPan MGos NWea
	SEND SHBN SPer WDin WFar
	WMou
¶ – 'Liberty'	SMad
– 'Pyramidalis'	CTho
– 'Suttneri' (v)	CBlo CDoC CEnd CLnd ERod
	LNet SMad
¶ – 'Tremonia'	SMad
occidentalis	CSto
orientalis ♀	CLnd CMCN EPfP IOrc SMad
	WDin WMou
– 'Cuneata'	LRHS MBri
§ – f. *digitata*	CLnd CTho SLPl WMou
– 'Laciniata'	See *P. orientalis* f. *digitata*
– 'Mirkovec'	CDoC MBri SMad SPer WMou

PLATYCARYA (Juglandaceae)
strobilacea   CMCN WCoo

PLATYCERIUM (Polypodiaceae)

alcicorne hort.	See *P. bifurcatum*
§ *bifurcatum* ♀	LCns MBri
grande hort.	See *P. superbum*
§ *superbum* ♀	LCns

PLATYCLADUS (Cupressaceae)

orientalis	See *Thuja orientalis*

PLATYCODON † (Campanulaceae)

grandiflorus ♀	CGle CNic ECha GLil LFis LHop MFir MHFP MSal NBro NFai NGre NOrc NVic SIng WCla WHoo WLin WOld WWye
– *albus*	CBro CRDP EAst ECro EFou EOld LHop MBri MBro NBro NFai NGre NOak SIng SPer SPla WHoo WOve WPer WWin
– 'Apoyama' ♀	CLyd LBee MBro MHar MHig SWas WAbe WHil WHoo WPer WWin
– *apoyama albus*	ECro LGre MBro NChi SIde SWas WCFE WCru WEas WHoo WPyg
– 'Baby Blue'	SRms
¶ – 'Blue Haze'	CMGP CMil EBee MMHG WLRN
– 'Blue Pearl'	WHoo
– 'Blue Surf'	SPla
– 'Florist Blue'	CMdw
– 'Florist Rose'	ECro NOak WWye
– 'Florist Snow'	CMdw ECro NOak WWye
– 'Fuji Blue'	CBlo EBrP EBre LBre LIck SBre
– 'Fuji Pink'	CBlo CBro CRDP EAst EBee MTis NSti SMrm SPer SPla SSte SUsu WAbe WGwG WLin
– 'Fuji White'	CBlo CMil MCCP NHol SMrm SPla
– 'Hakone'	CBlo CRDP EMan LHop MBro NCat SMrm WHoo WPyg WWal
* – 'Hakone Double Blue'	CBro CMGP ECGP ERic MMHG MMil SCro WGwG WLRN
– 'Hakone White'	MMHG WHil WHoo
– 'Mammoth Blue'	ECro
– 'Mammoth White'	ECro
– 'Mariesii' ♀	CBro CGle CLyd CNic EBrP EBre ECtt EFou ENot GMaP LBre LFis MBal MHig NBir NChi SBre SPer SRms WEas WHoo WPer WWin
– *mariesii albus*	MBro WHoo WPyg
– 'Misato Purple'	SMrm WBay WShe
– Mother of Pearl	See *P. grandiflorus* 'Perlmutterschale'
– 'Park's Double Blue' (d)	MHFP MLLN MTis NOak WHoo WPen WPyg WWhi
§ – 'Perlmutterschale'	CGle CMil EPfP GMac MBri WGwG WHoo WPyg WWeb
– *pumilus*	EBee MBro MHar NWCA WCFE WHoo WPyg
– *roseus*	ECro EFou MNrw WHoo
– 'Sentimental Blue'	SMrm WLRN WRHF
– 'Shell Pink'	See *P. grandiflorus* 'Perlmutterschale'
– 'Zwerg'	LGre

PLECOSTACHYS (Asteraceae)

§ *serpyllifolia*	CHal CLTr IHos LBlm

PLECTOCOLEA (Jungermanniaceae) See Plant Deletions

PLECTRANTHUS (Lamiaceae)

amboinicus	EOHP LHil
argentatus	CHad CSev EHic LHil SMrm
§ *australis*	CHal EOHP SLMG WEas
behrii	See *P. fruticosus*
ciliatus	LHil
coleoides 'Marginatus'	See *P. forsteri* 'Marginatus'
– 'Variegatus'	See *P. madagascariensis* 'Variegated Mintleaf'
excisus	EMon
§ *forsteri*	LHil
§ – 'Marginatus'	CHal CLTr ERea LHil MRav NFai SVen
§ *fruticosus*	CHal LHil
§ *madagascariensis*	CHal LHil MRav SHFr SRms
'Variegated Mintleaf'	
oertendahlii ♀	CHal EBak LHil MBEx SLMG
podena	CArn
purpuratus	EOHP
* *purpureus*	SVen
Swedish ivy	See *P. australis*
§ *thyrsoideus*	CHal
zatarhendii	LHil
zuluensis	CPle

PLEIOBLASTUS † (Poaceae - Bambusoideae)

akebono	EPla SDry
§ *auricomus* ♀	CCuc CHEx CRDP CRow EBee ECha EFul EGol EHoe ELan ENot ISta MBal MBar MBlu MBri MCCP MGos MRav NHol NVic SAxl SDix SDry SMad SPer WJun WPGP WPat WRus
– 'Bracken Hill'	EPla SDry WJun
– f. *chrysophyllus*	EPla SDry SMad WJun
§ *chino*	CHEx ISta SDry
§ – f. *angustifolius*	LHil SDry
– 'Aureostriatus' (v)	EPla ISta LJus NDov SDry
– *chrysanthus*	See *Sasa chrysantha*
– f. *elegantissimus*	CEnd COtt EBee EPla ISta LJus LRHS MMoz MWhi SCha SDry WJun
– 'Kimmei'	SDry
– 'Murakamianus'	EPla SDry
fortunei	See *P. variegatus*
'Gauntlettii'	See *P. humilis* var. *pumilus*
glaber 'Albostriatus'	See *Sasaella masamuneana* f. *albostriata*
gramineus	EPla ISta SDry WJun
§ *hindsii* hort.	EPla SAPC SArc SDry
§ *humilis*	CBlo ELan
§ – var. *pumilus*	CCuc CRow EHoe EPar EPla ISta LJus MBlu MBri NHol SCha SDry WBea WJun WNor WPat WPer
kongosanensis	EPla SDry
'Aureostriatus' (v)	
linearis	CB&S EFul EPla ISta LRHS MMoz SCha SDry WJun
longifimbriatus	WJun
oleosus	EPla SDry WJun

§ *pygmaeus* | CCuc CEnd CRow CWit EBrP
EBre ECro EFul EHoe ELan
EOas EPla ESis IOrc ISta LBre
LJus MBar MBrN MBri NBro
NFai SBre SDry SPer SRms
SSoC WJun WNor WPer
§ – var. *distichus* | EFul EPPr EPla GBin LHil
LJus SAPC SArc SDry WJun
* – – 'Mini' | WCot
§ – 'Mirrezuzume' | EPla GBin WWat
shibuyanus 'Tsuboi' | CEnd COtt EPla ISta LJus LPJP
MWhi NDov SCha SDry WJun
§ *simonii* | CHEx EBee EBrP EBre EFul
EPla GBin ISta LBre MWhi
SBre SDry
– var. *heterophyllus* | See *P. simonii* f. *variegatus*
§ – f. *variegatus* | CFil EPla ISta MBar MBlu
SDry SPer WJun
§ *variegatus* ♀ | Widely available
– var. *viridis* | SDry
viridistriatus | See *P. auricomus*

PLEIONE † (Orchidaceae)

¶ *albiflora* | SWes
§ – 'Pinchbeck Diamond' | EEve EPot LBut
g. *Alishan* | CNic GCrs LBut NSpr SWes
¶ – 'Foxhill' | NSpr
¶ – 'Merlin' | NSpr
– 'Mount Fuji' | LBut
– 'Soldier Blue' | LBut
g. *Asama* | LBut SWes
§ *aurita* | EFEx GCrs LAma NSpr SWes
g. *Bandai-san* | LBut
g. *Barcena* | LBut
g. *Beerenberg* | LBut
'Berapi' | EPot LBut SWes
g. *Brigadoon* | LBut
¶ – 'Stonechat' | LBut
g. *Britannia* | LBut
– 'Doreen' | LBut
§ *bulbocodioides* | EEve EPot ERos IBlr LBut
MBro MRPP NSpr WFar
– 'Lapwing' | LBut
§ – Limprichtii Group ♀ | EEve EFEx EPot LBut MRPP
NTow SWes
– Pricei Group | See *P. formosana* Pricei Group
§ – 'Yunnan' | EPot LBut NSpr SWes
g. *Captain Hook* | LBut NSpr
chunii | See *P. aurita*
× *confusa* | EEve EFEx EPot GCrs SWes
g. *Cotopaxi* | LBut
g. *Danan* | LBut SWes
g. *Deriba* | LBut
g. *Eiger* | EEve EPot LBut NSpr SWes
– cream form | EPot LBut
g. *El Pico* | GCrs LBut NSpr SWes
– 'Goldcrest' | LBut
– 'Kestrel' | GCrs LBut
– 'Pheasant' | LBut
– 'Starling' | LBut
g. *Erebus* | LBut SWes
– 'Quail' | LBut
* 'Erh Hai' | NSpr
* g. *Etna* | CNic GCrs LBut SWes
formosana ♀ | CNic EFEx EPot ETub GCrs
IBlr LAma NTow SDeJ SIng
SWes
– 'Achievement' | LBut
I – 'Alba' | EPot GCrs IBlr SWes
¶ – *alba* 'Lucy Diamond' | EEve EPot
¶ – g. *Polar Sun* | EEve
¶ – 'Red Spot' | EEve

– 'Avalanche' | EPot LBut NSpr
– 'Ben Nevis' | LBut
– 'Blush of Dawn' | EPot GCrs LBut NSpr
– 'Cairngorm' | NSpr SWes
– 'Christine Anne' | NSpr
– 'Clare' | EPot GCrs LBut NSpr
– g. *Eugene* | EEve EPot SWes
– 'Greenhill' | LBut
I – 'Iris' | LBut NSpr
– g. *Kate* | EEve EPot
– 'Lilac Beauty' | SWes
– 'Little Winnie' | EEve EPot SWes
– 'Lucy Diamond' | GCrs LBut
– g. *Lulu* | EEve EPot SWes
– 'Oriental Grace' | EPot LAma LBut SWes
– 'Oriental Jewel' | SWes
– 'Oriental Splendour' | EPot LBut NSpr SWes
– 'Polar Sun' | EPot GCrs NSpr SWes
§ – Pricei Group | EPot NTow WBor
– 'Serenity' | LBut
– 'Snow Cap' | SWes
– 'Snow White' | GCrs LBut
forrestii | EFEx EPot LAma SWes
g. *Fuego* | LBut NSpr SWes
– 'Wren' | LBut
g. *Fujiyama* | LBut
¶ 'Hallmark' | GCrs
g. *Hekla* | EPot LBut NSpr SWes
– 'Partridge' | LBut
hookeriana | SWes
humilis | SDeJ
¶ – 'Frank Kingdon Ward' | GCrs SWes
g. *Irazu* | GCrs LBut NSpr
¶ – 'Irazu Violet' | GCrs
g. *Jorullo* | LBut SWes
– 'Long-tailed Tit' | LBut
g. *Katla* | LBut SWes
g. *Katmai* | LBut
g. *Keith Rattray* | LBut
g. *Kilauea* | EPot LBut SWes
g. *Krakatoa* | LBut
g. *Lascar* | LBut
¶ *limprichtii* mauve | GCrs
¶ – pink | GCrs
g. *Lipari* | LBut
maculata | EFEx LAma SWes
g. *Marco Polo* | LBut NSpr
g. *Matupi* | LBut NSpr
¶ 'Mayfield' | GCrs
g. *Mayon* | LBut
g. *Mazama* | LBut
g. *Myojin* | LBut SWes
g. *Novarupta* | LBut
g. *Orinoco* | LBut SWes
– 'Gemini' | LBut
g. *Paricutin* | LBut
g. *Pavlof* | LBut
pinkepankii | See *P. albiflora*
g. *Piton* | EEve EPot LAma LBut SWes
pogonioides hort. | See *P. speciosa*
– Rolfe | See *P. bulbocodioides*
praecox | SWes
¶ g. *Rainier* | LBut
g. *Rakata* | LBut
– 'Shot Silk' | LBut
¶ g. *San Pedro* | LBut
scopulorum | EFEx LBut SWes
g. *Shantung* | EEve EPot GCrs LAma LBut
NSpr SWes
– 'Candyfloss' | NSpr
– 'Ducat' | EPot GCrs LAma LBut NSpr
– 'Gerry Mundey' | LBut NSpr

– 'Golden Jubilee'	NSpr
– 'Golden Plover'	LBut
¶ – 'Mikki'	NSpr
– 'Muriel Harberd' ♀	CRDP GCrs NSpr
– 'R6.7'	NSpr
– 'Ridgeway'	EPot LBut NSpr SWes
¶ – 'Stephanie Rose'	NSpr
g. *Sorea*	LBut
g. *Soufrière*	LBut NSpr SWes
§ *speciosa*	EEve EPot GCrs LBut MRPP SWes
– 'Blakeway Phillips'	LBut NSpr SWes
g. *Stromboli*	GCrs LBut NSpr SWes
– 'Fireball'	LBut NSpr
– 'Robin'	LBut
g. *Surtsey*	LBut
g. *Tacana*	LBut
g. *Tambora*	LBut
g. *Tarawera*	LBut SWes
g. *Tolima*	CNic EEve EPot LAma LBut NSpr SWes
¶ – 'Moorhen'	GCrs
g. *Tongariro*	EEve EPot LBut NSpr SWes
– 'Jackdaw'	LBut
g. *Versailles*	EEve EFEx EPot LAma LBut NSpr SWes
– 'Bucklebury' ♀	CNic EPot GCrs LBut NSpr
– 'Heron'	LBut
– 'Muriel Turner'	EEve EPot LAma LBut NSpr
g. *Vesuvius*	EPot LBut NSpr
– 'Aphrodite'	EPot
– 'Leopard'	LBut
* – 'Phoenix'	EPot LBut NSpr
g. *Volcanello*	GCrs LBut NSpr SWes
'Wunzen'	LBut
yunnanensis hort.	See *P. bulbocodioides* 'Yunnan'
– Rolfe	LAma LBut SWes
g. *Zeus Weinstein*	LBut
¶ – 'Desert Sands'	LBut

PLEOMELE See DRACAENA

PLEUROCHAETE (Sphagnaceae) See Plant Deletions

PLEUROSPERMUM (Apiaceae)

brunonis	EBee EDAr WHal

PLEXIPUS (Verbenaceae) See Plant Deletions

PLUMBAGO (Plumbaginaceae)

§ *auriculata* ♀	CB&S CEnd CHEx CLTr CPlN CPle CRHN CSpe EBak ELan ERav EREa ISea LBlm LHol LHop MBri MLan MRav NEgg NPal NRog SIde SLMG SOWG SPer SRms WBod
– var. *alba*	CB&S CBot CPlN CRHN CSev EBak ELan EMil ERav EREa IBlr ISea LBlm LHol MBEx MLan SLMG SOWG SPer
* – *aurea*	CSpe LIck
* – Royal Cape = 'Monott'	ERav
capensis	See *P. auriculata*
§ *indica*	CPle SLMG
– *rosea*	See *P. indica*
larpentiae	See *Ceratostigma plumbaginoides*

PLUMERIA (Apocynaceae)

§ *obtusa*	LChe

rubra	ECon LChe LRHS
– f. *lutea*	LChe
'Singapore'	See *P. obtusa*

PNEUMATOPTERIS See CYCLOSORUS

POA (Poaceae)

acicularifolia	ESOG NHol
alpina nodosa	GBin
¶ *buchananii*	EBee
bulbosa	EPPr
chaixii	CCuc EHoe EMan EMon EPPr EPla ESOG GBin NHol WFoF
cita	EBee EWes
colensoi	CCuc EBee EFou EHoe GBin GChr MCCP MHlr MWhi NHol NPSI WCot
eminens	EBee
– from Magadan, Siberia	EPPr
imbecilla	ESOG
× *jemtlandica*	EBee EHoe ESOG MCCP NHol
labillardierei	ECha EHoe EMan EPPr ESOG SApp WCot

PODALYRIA (Papilionaceae)

sericea	CSpe SIgm

PODANTHUS (Asteraceae)

ovatifolius G&K 4386	CGre

PODOCARPUS (Podocarpaceae)

acutifolius	CB&S CDoC ECou EPla MBar STre
andinus	See *Prumnopitys andina*
'Autumn Shades' (m)	ECou
'Blaze' (f)	ECou
chilinus	See *P. salignus*
'Chocolate Box' (*lawrencei* × *nivalis*) (f)	ECou
'County Park Fire' (*lawrencei* × *nivalis*) (f)	ECou LLin MGos
cunninghamii	See *P. hallii*
dacrydioides	See *Dacrycarpus dacrydioides*
elongatus	CTrC
ferrugineus	See *Prumnopitys ferruginea*
'Golden Dwarf'	See *Prumnopitys ferruginea* 'Golden Dwarf'
§ *hallii*	ECou WCwm
* – 'Kiwi' (f)	ECou
– × *nivalis* (f)	ECou
– 'Roro' (m)	ECou
'Havering' (f)	ECou
henkelii	CTrC
latifolius	CTrC
lawrencei	CBlo ECho EHul GAri IOrc
– 'Alpine Lass' (f)	ECou
– 'Blue Gem' (f)	ECou EOrn LCon MAsh MGos MUlv WBcn
– 'Bluey'	CBlo CDoC LBee LLin MBar MOne SLim WLRN WWat
– (f)	ECou MBar MGos MPla SSmi WWat
– 'Kiandra'	ECou
macrophyllus (m)	ECou
–	CDoC CGre EOrn SAPC SArc SMad STre WWat
– 'Angustifolius'	CHEx

nivalis	CMHG CMac EBrP EBre ECou EOrn EPla LBre LLin MBar MHig MPla SBre SIng SPla SRms SSmi WWat
– 'Arthur' (m)	ECou
– 'Bronze'	EPla
– 'Clarence' (m)	ECou
– 'Green Queen' (f)	ECou
– 'Jack's Pass' (m)	ECou
– 'Kaweka' (m)	ECou
– 'Little Lady' (f)	ECou
– 'Livingstone' (f)	ECou
– 'Lodestone' (m)	ECou
– 'Moffatt' (f)	ECou
– 'Otari' (m)	ECou
– 'Park Cover'	ECou
– 'Princess' (f)	ECou
– 'Ruapehu'	ECou EPla
salignus (m)	ECou
§ – ♀	CB&S CDoC CGre CHEx EPla IOrc ISea SAPC SArc WCoo WWat
spicatus	See *Prumnopitys taxifolia*
'Spring Sunshine'	ECou
totara	CGre CHEx CHan ECou STre WPic
– 'Aureus'	CB&S CDoC ECou EPla LLin MBal MBar SHBN WLRN WSHC
– 'Pendulus'	ECou
'Young Rusty'	ECou

PODOLEPIS (Asteraceae) See Plant Deletions

PODOPHYLLUM (Berberidaceae)

¶ *delavayi*	WCru
difforme	WCru
emodi	See *P. hexandrum*
– var. *chinense*	See *P. hexandrum* var. *chinense*
§ *hexandrum*	CBos CBro CHEx CRDP CRow EBrP EBre EOld EPot ERos GAbr GCal GCra GCrs GDra GPoy LAma LBre MBal MBri MHig MSal NChi NHar SBid SBre SSpi WWye
§ – var. *chinense*	CRow EHyt GBuc IBlr SMad WCru WWat
– 'Majus'	EBee WCru
peltatum	CArn CBro CRow EBee GPoy IBlr LAma MBri MSal NHar NSti SSpi WCru WThi WViv WWat
pleianthum	WCru
versipelle	WCru

PODRANEA (Bignoniaceae)

§ *ricasoliana*	CPlN ERea LChe LCns SLMG SOWG WMul

POGONATHERUM (Poaceae)

paniceum	See *P. saccharoideum*
§ *saccharoideum*	MBri

POGONIA (Orchidaceae)

ophioglossoides	SSpi

POGOSTEMON (Lamiaceae)

§ *cablin*	CArn GPoy MSal
¶ *heyneanus*	MSal
patchouly	See *P. cablin*

¶ sp. from An Veleniki Herb Farm, Pennsylvania	CArn

POLEMONIUM † (Polemoniaceae)

acutifolium var. *nipponicum*	See *P. caeruleum* subsp. *nipponicum*
'Apricot Beauty'	See *P. carneum* 'Apricot Delight'
N *archibaldiae*	CPea LBlm NFai
§ *boreale*	EBee GGar MNrw MSto NChi NPla SEas
brandegeei Greene	CHan ECro MHig NBro NGre WByw WPer
– subsp. *mellitum*	CArn GCHN LCot MSto WBea
§ *caeruleum*	Widely available
– var. *album*	See *P. caeruleum* subsp. *caeruleum* f. *album*
¶ – 'Bambino Blue'	WPer
– Brise d'Anjou = 'Blanjou' (v)	COtt EBrP EBre EOrc EWes LBre LRHS MCLN NRoo SBre SCoo SPer SWat WWeb
– 'Blue Bell'	ELau MAvo WPbr
§ – subsp. *caeruleum* f. *album*	CBre CGle CHan CHea EBar ECED ECha EFou ELan ELau EOrc GAbr LHop MMal MTis NBro NFai NOak SPer SRCN SSte WBea WCla WEas WHen WHil WPer WWin
– subsp. *dissectum* –	CBre
– var. *grandiflorum*	See *P. caeruleum* subsp. *himalayanum*
– Himalayan - misapplied	See *P. cashmerianum*
§ – subsp. *himalayanum*	GCra WPer
– 'Humile'	See *P.* 'Northern Lights'
– 'Newark Park'	EPPr
§ – subsp. *nipponicum*	GBin WPer
¶ – subsp. *villosum*	CStr
carneum	CGle CMea EAst ECha EMan EMon EOrc MCCP MFir MNrw MTho NHar WBea WOMN WPer WSan WWin
§ – 'Apricot Delight'	Widely available
§ *cashmerianum*	CLTr CMdw EBee ECGP ECro GAbr GBuc GCHN MBro NOak SMrm WBea WEas WHen WHoo WPyg
chartaceum	NGre NWCA
¶ – NNS 93-650	MRPP
'Churchills'	CBos CBre EBee NFai
confertum	See *P. viscosum*
§ 'Dawn Flight'	EBrP EBre LBre NCat SBre
delicatum	CVer MHar MTho NHar NWCA
¶ 'Eastbury Purple'	EBee
elegans	MSto
eximium	WFox
flavum	See *P. foliosissimum* var. *flavum*
foliosissimum A Gray	CBot CGle EBrP EBre ECha EPPr LBre MNrw SBre SRms SUsu WPer
– var. *albiflorum*	See *P. foliosissimum* var. *alpinum*
§ – var. *alpinum*	ECro LGan NBir WWal
§ – var. *flavum*	MHig
– hort.	See *P. archibaldiae*
'Glebe Cottage Lilac'	CElw CGle CHar CMil WBea WPGP
'Golden Showers' (v)	CPla CStr MCCP
'Hannah Billcliffe'	CLAP LCot
¶ 'Hidako White'	WPbr

'Hopleys'	CHan CLAP GBar GCal LBlm LFis LHop MAvo NBrk NRoo SAxl WByw WCot WFar WLin WPbr
× *jacobaea*	WBea WCot WPbr
¶ 'Katie Daley'	GBri
¶ *kiushianum*	EBee
§ 'Lambrook Mauve' ♀	Widely available
¶ 'Larch Cottage Variegated' (v)	NLar
liniflorum	EBee MSto
'Mary Mottram'	CBre
mellitum	MSto
§ 'Northern Lights'	ELan EMon EPPr GBri LGre MBri MCCP WFar
¶ 'Norwell Mauve'	MNrw
occidentale	See *P. caeruleum* subsp. *amygdalinum*
pauciflorum	Widely available
– form	LBlm
– subsp. *hinckleyi*	EBee NChi NGre
– silver-leaved	MHFP MSto WElm WOve WSan
§ 'Pink Beauty'	CBre CMGP ECro EFou ELan LRHS MArl NCat SCro WBea WCer WWal
'Pink Pearl'	WWhi
pulchellum Salisbury	See *P. reptans*
– Turczaninow	See *P. caeruleum*
pulcherrimum album	CGra
pulcherrimum Hooker	CHan ELan EPla GAbr GBar GCal GTou LHop NBro NHar NLak NTow SPer WBea WHen WPer WWye
¶ – subsp. *pulcherrimum*	WLin
pulcherrimum hort.	See *P. boreale*
– 'Tricolor'	NBus NLak
– 'Tricolor' hort.	See *P. boreale*
§ *reptans*	CAgr CArn CHea CLTr ECha ECoo ELau GBar GBri GCra GPoy LHol MSal NBro NRoo WBea WHil WPer WWye
– 'Album'	See *P. reptans* 'Virginia White'
– 'Blue Pearl'	CBre CGle CMea EMan EPPr EPar GAri LFis MLLN MNrw NBro NCat NChi NFla NHol NRoo SCro SHel SOkh SPer SUsu WBea WByw WHen WOve WRHF
– 'Dawn Flight'	See *P.* 'Dawn Flight'
– 'Lambrook Manor'	See *P.* 'Lambrook Mauve'
– 'Pink Beauty'	See *P.* 'Pink Beauty'
* – 'Sky Blue'	NBro
§ – 'Virginia White'	CBre CFis LRHS NChi
* – 'White Pearl'	WMow
richardsonii Graham	See *P. boreale*
– hort.	See *P.* 'Northern Lights'
'Sapphire'	CBre CDoC EMon MBel MBrN NFai NNor WBea
scopulinum	MSto NChi
'Sonia's Bluebell'	CElw CGle CLAP CMil EBee EWes MSte NLak WPbr
¶ 'Southern Skies'	CBre
'Theddingworth'	MAvo MTed WPbr
§ *viscosum*	CGra CNic EPot GBuc GCHN MSto NGre NTow WByw WCot WHen
– NNS 93-658	MRPP
yezoense	CBre CM&M GBri MHFP MNrw WCot WFar
– *hidakanum*	CPla NRoo

– 'Purple Rain'	CBre CPea EWes GBuc LFis MAus MAvo MCCP MCLN MLLN MNrw SUsu WHer WLin WSan

POLIANTHES (Agavaceae)

§ *geminiflora*	LAma
¶ *nelsonii*	CFir
tuberosa ♀	CAvo CB&S EBot NRog
– 'The Pearl' (d)	LAma

POLIOMINTHA (Lamiaceae)

bustamanta	CLon EBee LGre NBir WCot
¶ *incana*	EBee

POLIOTHYRSIS (Flacourtiaceae)

sinensis	CAbP CB&S CFil CGre SSpi WWes

POLYGALA (Polygalaceae)

calcarea	MBro MDun NHar NRya NWCA WPat
– Bulley's form	LBee SIng WAbe
– 'Lillet' ♀	CLyd ELan EPot MAsh MBro MTho NHar NMen SBla SWas WAbe WFar WPat WWin
chamaebuxus ♀	EBrP EBre GCrs GDra LBre MAsh MBal MDun MHig MPla NHar NHol NWoo SBre SHFr SRms WAbe WLin WWin
– *alba*	LBee MAsh WAbe
§ – var. *grandiflora* ♀	CB&S CNic ELan EPot GChr GDra LBee LHop MAsh MBal MBar MBro MDun MGos MHig MPla NHar NHol NMen NWCA SBla SChu SIng SSmi WAbe WBod WPat WSHC WWin
– 'Kamniski'	CMHG EPot MAsh NHar NMen
– 'Loibl'	EPot MAsh SBla SGre
– 'Purpurea'	See *P. chamaebuxus* var. *grandiflora*
– 'Rhodoptera'	See *P. chamaebuxus* var. *grandiflora*
§ × *dalmaisiana* ♀	CAbb CLTr CSpe EMil ERea GQui LBlm LHop MAsh SAga SBla
'Dolomite'	NHar
myrtifolia	CPle CSpe IBlr LCns MBEx SEND SHFr SMrm SUsu WWye
– 'Grandiflora'	See *P.* × *dalmaisiana*
vayredae	NRya WPat
virgata	CArn CSpe ECon ERea
vulgaris	EWFC IOrc

POLYGONATUM (Convallariaceae)

¶ *acuminatifolium*	CAvo
§ *biflorum*	CArn CBro CPou EBrP EBre EGar EGol ELan EMan EOrc EPot GCHN LBre LGan MSal NCat NRoo SBre SSpi WCot WCru WHer
– dwarf form	EPla WCot
canaliculatum	See *P. biflorum*
cirrhifolium	MDun WCru
commutatum	See *P. biflorum*
cryptanthum	WCru
curvistylum	CMea ECha LGre SWas WFar
cyrtonema B&SWJ 271	WCru
– hort.	See *Disporopsis pernyi*

§ *falcatum* — CBro CLyd CMea EBrP EBre EPla ERav LBre MBal MDun MHig NOak NWes SBre SIng WHer WWat WWin

§ – 'Variegatum' — CAvo CHad CLyd CRow CSpe ECha EFou ELan EPar LGre MBri MBro MCLN MDun NDea NFla NHol NSti SBla SCro SMac SPer WHoo WPyg WWat WWhi

'Falcon' — See *P. humile*

geminiflorum — SWas WFar

giganteum — See *P. biflorum*

§ *graminifolium* — CPBP EPot ERos LGre WCru

– GW 803 — SWas

§ *hirtum* — CLAP EMon EPla EPot NDov SAxl WCot WCru WFar

hookeri — CBro CLyd CMea EDAr EPla EPot ERos LBee LGre LHop MBal MHig MTho NGre NHar NHol NNrd NRya NSla NWCA SIng SMac WAbe WHal WHil WLin

§ *humile* — CGle CHan CLAP CRDP ELan EPla EPot ERos MBel NHar SAxl SBla SWas WAbe WCru WHal WRus

§ × *hybridum* ♀ — Widely available

– 'Flore Pleno' (d) — WHer

§ – 'Striatum' (v) — Widely available

– 'Variegatum' — See *P. × hybridum* 'Striatum'

¶ *inflatum* — NRya

¶ 'Langthorns Variegated' (v) — ELan

latifolium — See *P. hirtum*

multiflorum hort. — See *P. × hybridum*

multiflorum giganteum hort. — See *P. biflorum*

– Linnaeus — CMHG CRow EGar EPla SRms WSel

* 'Nymans Variety' — WHil

§ *odoratum* — CAvo CBro CRow CSWP ELau EOHP EPar EPla EPot EWFC MSal NRya SHDw SMac SSpi

– 'Flore Pleno' (d) ♀ — CLAP CMGP CRow NRar SBla SWas

– 'Grace Barker' — See *P. × hybridum* 'Striatum'

– Kew form — EPot

– var. *pluriflorum* — GBuc SSpi

– – 'Variegatum' — CBro EGol EPla LGan LGre MBal MBro MCli MRav NRoo SPer WCru WLin WRus WWat WWin

♦ – – 'Variegatum' misapplied — See *P. falcatum* 'Variegatum'

– 'Silver Wings' — ECha

officinale — See *P. odoratum*

¶ *oppositifolium* — WCru

B&SWJ 2537

pluriflorum — See *P. graminifolium*

¶ *prattii* — NRya

pubescens — MSto

pumilum — See *P. falcatum*

punctatum — WCru

¶ – B&SWJ 2395 — WCru

racemosum — SIng

roseum — WHer

sibiricum — NRya WCru

sp. Himalaya — WCru

stewartianum — CLAP NDov

---

verticillatum — CAvo CBro CHid CLyd CRow ECha EPla EPot MBal MTho NDov NHol SAxl SMad WCot WCru WWat

¶ – 'Himalayan Giant' — CHid

* *verticillatum rubrum* — CArn CBos CHid CRow EGar MSte MTho SAxl WCot

¶ – 'Serbian Dwarf' — CHid

POLYGONUM † (Polygonaceae)

affine — See *Persicaria affinis*

amplexicaule — See *Persicaria amplexicaulis*

aubertii — See *Fallopia baldschuanica*

baldschuanicum — See *Fallopia baldschuanica*

bistorta — See *Persicaria bistorta*

♦ *compactum* — See *Fallopia japonica* var. *compacta*

cuspidatum — See *Fallopia japonica*

equisetiforme hort. — See *P. scoparium*

¶ *japonica* var. *compacta* f. *rosea* — NLar

molle — See *Persicaria mollis*

multiflorum — See *Fallopia multiflora*

odoratum — See *Persicaria odorata*

polystachyum — See *Persicaria wallichii*

reynoutria — See *Fallopia japonica* var. *compacta*

♦ *runciforme* — See *Persicaria runcinata*

§ *scoparium* — CRow EPla LHil MFir NFai SDry SDys SVen WCot

POLYLEPIS (Rosaceae)

australis — SMad

POLYMNIA (Asteraceae) See Plant Deletions

POLYPODIUM † (Polypodiaceae)

australe — See *P. cambricum*

§ *cambricum* — NHar NMar WRic

§ – 'Barrowii' — CCuc NMar WRic

– 'Cambricum' ♀ — WRic

– 'Cristatum' — WRic

– 'Diadem' — WRic

– 'Grandiceps Forster' — WRic

– 'Grandiceps Fox' ♀ — WRic

– 'Hornet' — WRic

– 'Oakley' — SWas WAbe WPGP

– Omnilacerum Group — EMon

– 'Omnilacerum Oxford' — WRic

– Plumosum Group — EMon

– 'Prestonii' — WRic

– Pulcherrimum Group — EGol NHar SWas

– – 'Pulcherrimum Addison' — WRic

– Semilacerum Group — NMar WRic

– – 'Falcatum O'Kelly' — WRic

– – 'Jubilee' — NMar WRic

– – 'Robustum' — NMar WRic

– 'Wilharris' ♀ — CCuc CFil WPGP WRic

glycyrrhiza — WRic

– Grandiceps Group — WRic

– 'Longicaudatum' ♀ — EMon NMar WFib WRic

– 'Malahatense' (fertile) — WRic

– 'Malahatense' (sterile) — WRic

interjectum — EFer EFou NMar NOrc NVic SPer WAbe WFib WRic

– 'Bifidograndiceps' — WPGP WRic

– 'Cornubiense' ♀ — CBos CFil CRDP ECha EFer EMon GCal NBir NBro NHar NHol NMar NVic SSpi SWas WAbe WPGP WRic

– 'Ramosum Hillman' — WRic

× *mantoniae*	SWas
scouleri	NBro
vulgare	CBar CBlo CCuc CKin CTrC EBrP EBre EGoo EPfP GPoy LBre LHil LSyl MBal MBro NBro NEgg NHol NMar NOrc SApp SBre SChu SRms WFib WHil WRic
– 'Acutum'	NMar
– 'Bifidocristatum'	EMon GBin NHar NHol WFib WWat
– 'Bifidograndiceps'	NMar SChu
– 'Bifidomultifidum'	ETen
– 'Cornubiense Grandiceps'	CCuc SRms WFib WRic
– 'Cornubiense Multifidum'	NHar
– 'Crispum Cristatum'	See *P. vulgare* **'Congestum Cristatum'**
– (Cristatum Group) 'Forster'	CCuc
– 'Jean Taylor'	See *P. vulgare* **'Congestum Cristatum'**
– Ramosum Group	NMar

POLYPOGON (Poaceae) See Plant Deletions

POLYSCIAS (Araliaceae)

'Elegans'	MBri
fruticosa	MBri
sambucifolia	SBid
scutellaria 'Pennockii' (v)	MBri

POLYSTICHUM † (Aspidiaceae)

acrostichoides	CCuc GCal GQui IOrc MBri NHar WRic
aculeatum ♀	CCuc CTrC EBee EBrP EBre ECha EFer EFou EHon ELan EMon GQui IOrc LBre MBri NFla NHar NHol NMar NOak NOrc SAxl SBre SMer SRms WFib WHil WRic WWoo
– Grandiceps Group	NMar
andersonii	NHar NHol WRic
braunii	CB&S EBee EGol MLan NMar NOak WRic
californicum	CFil
caryotideum	See *Cyrtomium caryotideum*
falcatum	See *Cyrtomium falcatum*
falcinellum	CFil
fortunei	See *Cyrtomium fortunei*
* *fructuosum*	WRic
imbricans	NHar
makinoi	NHol NMar WFib WRic
¶ *mehrae*	WRic
mohrioides	CFil
munitum ♀	CBar CBlo CCuc CFil CMil IOrc LHil LRot MBri MTed NFla NHar NHol NOrc SAPC SArc SRms SSpi SWas WFib WPGP WRic WWoo
¶ – 'Incisum'	GCal
neolobatum	SWas WRic
polyblepharum ♀	CBlo CCuc CFil CHid EBrP EBre EFer ELan EMar EMon IOrc LBre MBri NHar NHol SBre SPla SRms SWas WAbe WFib WHal WRic
proliferum hort.	See *P. setiferum* **Acutilobum Group**
– (R.Br.) C. Presl.	SWas
retrorsopaleaceum	NMar WRic
¶ *richardii*	WRic
rigens	EHic GCal LHil NHar NHol NLak NMar SRms WFib WRic
§ *setiferum* ♀	Widely available
§ – Acutilobum Group	CB&S CFil CRDP ECha EHic EPot GAri MBal NCat NHar NVic SAxl SDix SMad SSpi WAbe WCot WCru WShe
– *angulare*	See *P. setiferum*
– 'Congestum'	EMon GCal WGor
– Congestum Group	CMil CRDP EHic IOrc MBri NHar NHol NMar SAxl SChu SPla SRms WFib WRic
§ – 'Cristatogracile'	NHar NMar
– 'Cristatopinnulum'	CFil EMon NHar NMar WPGP
– Cristatum Group	EMon SRms
¶ – Cruciatum Group	WRic
– Dahlem Group	CCuc CDoC ECha EFer ELan MBri MSte WAbe WRic
– Divisilobum Group	CCuc CDec CFee CFil CM&M CRow EBrP EBre EFer ELan EMon EPar LBre LSyl MBri MBro NHol NMar SApp SBre SMad SPla SRms WBon WEas WHoo WPGP WRic
– – 'Divisilobum Densum' ♀	MBal NMar NOrc SSoC SSpi
– – 'Divisilobum Iveryanum' ♀	NHol SRms
– – 'Herrenhausen'	CDoC EBee EBrP EBre ECha EFer ELan EMar EPfP LBre LHop MBri NFla NMar NOrc SBre SPer WAbe WFar WRic
– – 'Divisilobum Laxum'	CBlo EPar MHlr SChu
– – 'Madame Patti'	EMon
– – 'Mrs Goffy'	NMar
– – 'Ray Smith'	EMon
– Foliosum Group	EFer
– 'Gracile'	MBri
¶ – 'Grandidens'	WRic
– Lineare Group	CFil WFib WPGP
– Multilobum Group	WRic
– Percristatum Group	See *P. setiferum* **'Cristatogracile'**
– 'Plumosodensum'	See *P. setiferum* **'Plumosomultilobum'**
– Plumosodivisilobum Group	CCuc CMil CRow CSpe ECha EGol NHar SPla SWas WAbe WCru WFib
§ – 'Plumosomultilobum'	EMon NFla SRms WRic
– Plumosum Group	CBar CCuc CSam MBri NOrc SAxl SChu SPer SSoC WFib WStI
* – *plumosum grande* 'Moly'	WFib
– Proliferum Group	See *P. setiferum* **Acutilobum Group**
* – 'Proliferum Wollaston'	LSyl
– 'Pulcherrimum Bevis' ♀	EMon SDix WFib WRic
* – *ramopinnatum*	NMar
* – *ramulosum*	NMar
– Rotundatum Group	CRDP EMon NMar WFib
– – 'Cristatum'	EMon
– 'Wakeleyanum'	SRms
N – 'Wollaston'	NPla WAbe WWoo
silvaticum	WRic
stenophyllum	CFil WPGP
triangulum	NMar
tsussimense ♀	CCuc CRDP EFou GQui MSte MWgw NFla NHol NMar NOak SBla SEas SMad SPer SRms WAbe WFib WRic

POLYXENA (Hyacinthaceae)

§ *ensifolia*	LBow
odorata	CLyd MHig WAbe
pygmaea	See *P. ensifolia*

POMADERRIS (Rhamnaceae)

apetala	MAll
elliptica	MAll

PONCIRUS (Rutaceae)

§ *trifoliata*	CAgr CB&S CDoC CPle ELan EMil ENot EREa MBlu MWhi SArc SBid SMad SPar SPer STre WDin WFar WPGP WSHC
– 'Flying Dragon'	CAgr

PONERORCHIS (Orchidaceae) See Plant Deletions

PONTEDERIA (Pontederiaceae)

cordata ♀	CBen CRow CWat ECha ECtt EHon ELan EMFW LPBA MSta NDea SCoo SRms SWat SWyc WChe WMAq
– *alba*	CBen CRow EMFW SRms SWyc WChe
§ – var. *lancifolia*	CRow EMFW MSta SRms SWat SWyc
– 'Pink Pons'	CRow SWyc
dilatata	EMFW SRms SWyc
lanceolata	See *P. cordata* var. *lancifolia*

POPULUS † (Salicaceae)

x *acuminata*	WMou
alba	CBlo CDoC CKin CLnd CPer CTri EBrP EBre ENot GChr GRei IOrc LBre LBuc MBar MRav NBee NWea SBre SHBN SPer WDin WMou WStI
– 'Bolleana'	See *P. alba* f. *pyramidalis*
§ – f. *pyramidalis*	CB&S NBee SRms WMou
§ – 'Raket'	CBlo CLnd CTho ECrN ELan ENot EPfP IOrc MGos NWea SPer
§ – 'Richardii' ♀	CLnd CTho EBrP EBre ECtt EPla ESis IOrc LBre MBar SBre SPer WFar WMou
– Rocket	See *P. alba* 'Raket'
§ 'Balsam Spire' (f) ♀	CDoC CLnd CTho ENot GRei IOrc LBuc NWea WMou
§ *balsamifera*	CBlo CDoC CTho CTri ELan ENot MGos NWea SHBN SPer SRms WDin
x *berolinensis*	CDoC
x *canadensis* 'Aurea' ♀	CDoC CLnd CTho EMil ENot MDun MRav NWea SPer WDin WMou
¶ – 'Aurea' x *candicans* 'Aurora'	ECrN
– 'Eugenei' (m)	CTho WMou
– 'Robusta' (m)	CDoC CKin CLnd CTri EMil ENot IOrc LBuc NWea WDin WMou
– 'Serotina' (m)	CDoC GRei MAsh NWea WDin WMou
x *candicans*	WDin
– 'Aurora' (v)	CB&S CBlo CKin CPMA CTrw EBrP EBre ELan ENot GOrc GRei IOrc LBre LBuc MAsh MBar MBri MGos MWat NBee NWea SBre SHBN SPer SRms SSta WDin
x *canescens*	CDoC CPer ELan GChr WDin WMou
– 'De Moffart' (m)	ENot
– 'Tower'	WMou
x *euroamericana*	See *P.* x *canadensis*
x *interamericana* 'Beaupré'	CTho WMou
lasiocarpa ♀	CBot CHEx CLnd CTho EPfP MBlu MRav SLPl SMad WMou WPGP
§ – var. *tibetica*	WMou
maximowiczii	WMou
nigra	CPer ECrN ELan GChr NWea SPer WDin
– subsp. *betulifolia* ♀	CBlo CCVT CKin CTho LBuc MGos NWea WMou
– – (f)	WMou
– – (m)	WMou
– (f)	SLPl
– 'Italica' (m) ♀	CB&S CBlo CDoC CLnd CMHG CTho CTri EBrP EBre ELan ENot EPfP GChr IOrc LBre LBuc MBri MGos NBee NWea SBre SHBN SPer SRms WDin
– 'Italica Aurea'	See *P. nigra* 'Lombardy Gold'
§ – 'Lombardy Gold' (m)	CEnd CTho GRei SSpi WMou
– (m)	SLPl
– 'Pyramidalis'	See *P. nigra* var. *italica*
simonii 'Fastigiata'	NSti WMou
– 'Obtusata'	WMou
szechuanica	WMou
tacamahaca	See *P. balsamifera*
'Tacatricho 32'	See *P.* 'Balsam Spire'
tomentosa	WMou
tremula ♀	CBlo CKin CLnd CPer CTho EBrP EBre ELan ENot GChr GRei IOrc LBre LBuc LHyr MBar NBee NWea SBre SHBN SPer WDin WMou
§ – 'Erecta'	CLnd CTho EBee LPan WMou
– 'Fastigiata'	See *P. tremula* 'Erecta'
– 'Pendula' (m)	CLnd CTho EBee WDin WMou
trichocarpa	CBlo CTho SPer
– 'Fritzi Pauley' (f)	CTho WMou
violascens	See *P. lasiocarpa* var. *tibetica*
wilsonii	WMou
yunnanensis	WMou

PORTULACA (Portulacaceae)

grandiflora	MBri
oleracea	CArn ELau MChe MGra SIde WHer WJek
– var. *aurea*	ELau MChe MGra WJek

POTAMOGETON (Potamogetonaceae)

crispus	CBen EHon EMFW SAWi SRms
pectinatus	EHon

POTENTILLA † (Rosaceae)

alba	CGle CLyd CSev ECha EFou ELan EMar GCHN ISea LBlm LGro MHar MHig MRav MTho NChi NFai NRoo SCro SPer SUsu WByw WMow WPer

alchemilloides	MHig MNrw SMer SOkh WHil WPer
alpicola	WBro WPer
ambigua	See *P. cuneata*
¶ *andicola*	EBee
anserina	CArn CKin EEls EGoo EWFC GBar MHew WHer
– 'Golden Treasure'	CSpe EGoo MLLN WHer
anserinoides	EBee GCal MBel NTay WCot WPer
arbuscula D Don	See *P. fruticosa* var. *arbuscula* (**D. Don) Maxim.**
– hort.	See *P. fruticosa* '**Elizabeth**'
argentea	CBlo CSWP CSev EBar ELan LIck LPVe MTis NChi NFai WBea WCla WCru WPer
arguta	EBee
argyrophylla	See *P. atrosanguinea* var. *argyrophylla*
atrosanguinea	CBlo CBos CGle CHan CInt CMea ECGN ECha EOrc GCal GTou LBlm LHop MBal MBri MRav NChi NFai NNor NRoo NSti SUsu WHoo WMow WPyg WWal
§ – var. *argyrophylla*	Widely available
– – SS&W 7768	GDra MPla MSte NGre NMGW
– – CC 1384	CPou
– var. *leucochroa*	See *P. atrosanguinea* var. *argyrophylla*
aurea	CPea ECtt ELan EMNN MBri MHig NFla NGre NMen NMir NOrc NWCA SIng SRms SSmi WRHF
– 'Aurantiaca'	CElw ECGN MRav NNrd NRoo SBod SUsu
§ – subsp. *chrysocraspeda*	NHol NMen
§ – 'Goldklumpen'	EGar GAbr MRav NPro SCro
– 'Plena' (d)	GCHN GDra GTou MBro MHar MRav NGre NHar NHol SBod WWin
'Blazeaway'	EBee EBrP EBre EPPr LBre MBel MBri NCat NHol SBre SCoo WFar WLRN WMow
¶ *brevifolia*	NWCA
– NNS 94-25	MFos
calabra	ECha EDAr EMan SIgm SMer WByw WHer WWin
§ *cinerea*	CLyd CTri LBee NHar NMen SBla SIgm SSmi
¶ *collina*	EBee WUnu
§ 'Craigieburn Cochineal'	GCra
§ *crantzii*	CMea CTri EWFC GCHN GCrs GTou LBee MBar MHar MHig MSte NMen NNrd NTow NWCA SIng SRms WCla
– 'Nana'	See *P. crantzii* '**Pygmaea**'
§ – 'Pygmaea'	ECtt EPfP MOne MTPN NMen
§ *cuneata* ♀	CLyd CNic ELan ESis GBur GDra GTou MHig MPla MTho NHar NMen NRya NWCA SDys SIng SSmi WPer WWin
aff. – CC 1461	MRPP NGre
delavayi	MBro MNrw NBus
detommasii	WPer
dickinsii	NTow
dombeyi	GCHN WUnu
* 'Emilie'	EFou GCal MAvo MBri WFar
§ *erecta*	CArn CKin EOHP GBar GPoy LFis MChe MHew MSal
eriocarpa	CLyd EHyt EMNN GCHN GDra MBro MHar MHig MPla MWat NGre NHar NHol NMen NRoo SBod SSmi WAbe WCla WRHF
'Etna'	CBlo CElw CLon CStr ECtt EJud ELan GAbr GCal GCra GTou LFis LGre MAus MNrw NCat NFai NNor NRoo SAga SMad WByw WCru WHen WLin WMer WPer WWhi
'Everest'	See *P. fruticosa* '**Mount Everest**'
'Fireflame'	ECha LBlm
fissa	LBlm MNrw MSte NBir
'Flambeau'	MGed MRav
'Flamenco'	CB&S CSam CTri EBrP EBre EFou ELan LBre MArl MBri MNrw MRav NRoo SBre SUsu WAbb WByw WFar WHoo WMow WOld WPbr
fragiformis	See *P. megalantha*
fruticosa	GBur LBuc NMen NWea SHFr
– 'Abbotswood' ♀	CB&S CMHG EAst ELan ENot GChr GOrc LHop MAsh MBal MBar MBri MGos MRav NFla NHol NNor NRoo SPer WCFE WDin WGwG WHCG WHar WSHC WWal WWat WWeb
– 'Abbotswood Silver'	CB&S CBlo CLTr CLyd EBar ECtt ELan MAsh MRav NLon SPla WFar WHCG WHar WWal WWat
– 'Annette'	CBlo NPro WHCG WWeb
– var. *arbuscula* hort.	See *P. fruticosa* '**Elizabeth**'
– 'Argentea Nana'	See *P. fruticosa* '**Beesii**'
– 'Beanii'	NHol SPer WWeb
§ – 'Beesii' ♀	CDoC EHyt ELan ESis MAsh MBar MBlu MPla NHol NRoo SPer WAbe WDin WHCG WSHC WWeb WWin
– 'Beverley Surprise'	EHol NPro SPer WHCG WWeb
§ – Princess = 'Blink'	EBar EBrP EBre ELan ENot GRei LBre MBal MBar MBri MGos MHlr MWat NHol NRoo SBre SPer SReu SRms WDin WHar WStI WWat WWeb
– 'Buttercup'	NHol WHCG
– 'Cascade'	WBcn WHCG
* – 'Chelsea Star'	WHCG
* – 'Chilo'	MGos
– 'Clotted Cream'	MBar
– var. *dahurica*	WHCG
– – 'Hersii'	See *P. fruticosa* '**Snowflake**'
– – 'Rhodocalyx'	CPle WHCG WWat
– 'Dart's Cream'	MBri MRav
– 'Dart's Golddigger'	CB&S CTri ECtt ENot MBal NRoo SLPl WHCG
§ – 'Dart's Nugget'	WHCG WWeb
– 'Daydawn' ♀	CB&S CHar CLan CMHG EAst ELan EOrc GRei LHop MBal MBar MBri MPla MWat MWgw NBir NRoo SPer WAbe WDin WHCG WWat WWeb WWin
– 'Donard Orange'	See *P. fruticosa* '**Donard Gold**'
– 'Eastleigh Cream'	SPer
* – 'Eden Lemonlight'	NPro
§ – 'Elizabeth' ♀	CB&S CLan ELan ENot GDra ISea LGro LHop MBar MBri MGos MWat NFla NHol NNor NWea SHBN SPer SRms SSoC WBod WDin WHCG WWat
– 'Farreri'	See *P. fruticosa* '**Gold Drop**'

– 'Farreri Prostrata'	See *P. fruticosa* var. *pyrenaica*	
– 'Floppy Disc'	CBlo CFai ECtt ELan EPfP	
	MGos NCut NHol NWoo SEas	
	SHBN SPer SPla SSta	
– 'Frances Lady	ISea MPla	
Daresbury'		
– 'Friedrichsenii'	NHol	
– 'Glenroy Pinkie'	CFai CSam EBee MBal NPro	
	SAga SEas WAbe WHCG	
	WWeb	
– 'Glenroy Seashell'	MBal	
§ – 'Gold Drop'	EHol NHol WHCG WWeb	
– 'Golden Dwarf'	MBri MGos	
* – 'Golden Nugget'	WLRN	
– 'Golden Spreader'	EBrP EBre LBre NPro SBre	
– 'Goldfinger' ♀	CChe CDoC ELan ENot GChr	
	GOrc GRei IOrc MAsh MBri	
	MGos MRav SEas WAbe WDin	
	WHCG WHar WStI WWeb	
– Goldkugel	See *P. fruticosa* 'Gold Drop'	
– 'Goldstar'	CMHG EBee EBrP EBre ENot	
	EPla GAri GCHN IOrc LBre	
	MBri MGos SBre WHCG	
– 'Goldteppich'	LBuc MBar SHBN	
– 'Goscote'	MGos	
– 'Hopleys Little Joker'	WPat WPyg	
– 'Hopleys Orange'	CB&S CChe CDoC CMHG	
	EBee EWes GAri GCHN LHop	
	MBri SAga WGor WHCG	
	WWin	
– 'Hurstbourne'	WWeb	
– 'Jackman's Variety'	CSam ECtt ENot MAsh SPan	
	SPer SRms WBod WDin WStI	
	WWeb	
– 'Katherine Dykes' ♀	CChe CDoC ELan ENot GDra	
	MAsh MBal MBar MHlr SPer	
	SRms WBod WDin WGwG	
	WHCG WHar WStI WWeb	
* – 'King Cup'	WWeb	
– 'Klondike' ♀	CB&S CLan EBee ELan EPfP	
	MAsh NNor NWea SBid WDin	
§ – 'Knap Hill'	ENot EPar GDra NNor WWeb	
– 'Knap Hill Buttercup'	See *P. fruticosa* 'Knap Hill'	
– 'Kobold'	CBlo EBee GBur MBar WTro	
* – 'Lemon and Lime'	MBlu	
– 'London Town'	CMHG	
– 'Longacre Variety' ♀	CTri GDra MBar NHol NWea	
	SLPl WWat WWeb	
§ – 'Maanelys' ♀	CTrw ECtt ELan MBal MWat	
	NFla NWea SPer SPla SRms	
	WDin WHCG WWeb	
– 'Macpenny's Cream'	WHCG	
§ – 'Manchu'	ENot EPar GDra MBar MBri	
	MHlr MPla MRav NFla NHol	
	NNor NRoo SChu SHBN SMac	
	SPer SRms WWat WWin	
§ – Marian Red Robin =	CDoC EAst EBee EBrP EBre	
'Marrob'	ELan ENot EPfP GBur GCHN	
	GRei LBre MAsh MBri MGos	
	MWat NFla NHol NRoo SBre	
	SCoo SPer WDin WStI WWeb	
– 'Medicine Wheel	EHal ELan EWes MAsh NPro	
Mountain'	NTow SPer WHCG WWeb	
– 'Milkmaid'	WWeb	
– Moonlight	See *P. fruticosa* 'Maanelys'	
§ – 'Mount Everest'	CChe CDoC ELan MBar MWat	
	NCut NHol NWea SRms	
	WHCG WWeb	
– 'Nana Argentea'	See *P. fruticosa* 'Beesii'	
¶ – 'New Dawn'	ECle LRHS MAsh MBri WFar	
– 'Nugget'	See *P. fruticosa* 'Dart's Nugget'	
– 'Orange Star'	CBlo WHCG	

– 'Orange Stripe'	WWeb	
– 'Orangeade'	CBlo MAsh SMur SReu SSta	
	WWeb	
– 'Peaches and Cream'	EBee WHCG	
* – 'Peachy Proud'	NPro	
* – 'Pierce Ogon'	CBlo	
– 'Pink Glow'	GDra	
– 'Pink Pearl'	EBrP EBre LBre SBre WBcn	
	WWin	
– 'Pink Queen'	WRHF WWeb	
– 'Pretty Polly'	CDoC EAst ELan ENot IOrc	
	MBar MBri MGos NHol SHBN	
	SPer SSta WDin WHCG WHar	
	WStI WWal	
– 'Primrose Beauty' ♀	CLan EAst ELan ENot ISea	
	MBal MBar MGos MPla MRav	
	NFla NNor NRoo WAbe WDin	
	WGwG WHCG WHar WStI	
	WWat WWeb	
♦ – Princess	See *P. fruticosa* Princess =	
	'Blink'	
– 'Prostrate Copper'	NPro	
– var. *pumila*	WPat	
§ – var. *pyrenaica*	SGre	
– Red Ace	EBrP EBre ELan ENot GChr	
	GOrc GRei LBre LHop MBar	
	MBri MGos MWat NHol NRoo	
	NWea SBre SPer WDin WHCG	
	WHar WWal WWeb	
♦ – Red Robin	See *P. fruticosa* Marian Red	
	Robin = 'Marrob'	
– 'Royal Flush'	GAri LHop MAsh MBar MBri	
	SAga WHCG WStI	
– 'Silver Schilling'	LHop	
– 'Snowbird'	EBrP EBre EPfP LBre MBlu	
	MGos NLak NPro SBre WWeb	
§ – 'Snowflake'	CB&S WHCG	
– 'Sommerflor'	ENot	
– 'Sophie's Blush'	CLTr EAst MBal MRav NHol	
	NRoo NWea SBid WDin WRus	
	WSHC WWeb	
– 'Sunset'	CB&S CChe CDoC CSam ELan	
	ENot GChr GDra MAsh MBal	
	MBar MBri MGos MHlr MPla	
	MTis NNor NWea SPer SReu	
	SRms SSta WBod WGwG WStI	
	WWal WWeb	
– 'Tangerine' ♀	CB&S CLan CTrw EAst ELan	
	GOrc GRei ISea MAsh MBal	
	MBar MRav MWat NFla NHol	
	NWea SPer SRms WAbe WBod	
	WDin WGwG WHCG WHar	
	WWat WWeb WWin	
– 'Tilford Cream' ♀	Widely available	
– 'Tom Conway'	LBuc WHCG WWeb	
§ – var. *veitchii*	SHBN SPer WHCG WStI	
– 'Vilmoriniana'	CBot CHad CHar ELan EPfP	
	MRav NLon NNor SBid SMac	
	SSpi WAbe WGwG WHCG	
	WSHC WWat WWeb	
– 'Walton Park'	MBal	
– 'Wessex Silver'	CFai WHCG	
– 'Whirligig'	CFai WHCG	
– 'White Rain'	CLTr GDra NNor WWeb	
– 'Wickwar Trailer'	CLyd EPot ESis MBro MPla	
	WHCG WHoo	
– 'William Purdom'	EWll NHol WHCG	
– 'Yellow Bird'	MGos	
– 'Yellow Carpet'	WHCG	
– 'Yellow Giant'	WWeb	
fulgens	See *P. lineata*	

'Gibson's Scarlet' ♀ — CHad CKel CSam ECha ECtt EFou ELan GCal GMac MAus MBri MCLN MFir NDov NFai NFla NHol NRoo NVic SCro SHel SOkh SPer WHil WMer WMow WPer WSHC WWat

glandulosa — CAgr EBee MNrw

'Gloire de Nancy' — CBos EBrP EBre ELan GAri GCal LBre MRav NBir SBre SPer

'Gold Clogs' — See *P. aurea* 'Goldklumpen'

'Grace Darling' — CWit ECle GChr MTis NEgg NHol WGor WWeb

gracilis — EBee NNrd

§ – var. *glabrata* — EPPr

– subsp. *nuttallii* — See *P. gracilis* var. *glabrata*

'Helen Jane' — CGle EBrP EBre EFou GMac LBre LHop MBel MBri MBro NBir NBro NRoo SAga SBre SLod WFar WHoo WMer WPer

'Herzblut' — EBee EPfP GBuc

x *hopwoodiana* — CGle CHad CHea EPPr LBlm MBri NBir SAga SUsu SWas WAbb WByw

* x *hybrida* 'Jean Jabber' — EWll GBuc MRav WElm WUnu

hyparctica nana — CLyd GCrs LBee MBro NHol WAbe WPat WPyg

* 'Limelight' — ECle ELan EPla MAsh MRav SSta WFar WHCG

'Mandshurica' — See *P. fruticosa* 'Manchu'

¶ 'Master Floris' — WHer

§ *megalantha* ♀ — CBot CSam EAst EBar ECha EFou GCal GTou LFis LHop MBal MRav NBro NFai NGre NMen NMir NSti NWCA SBla SChu SHel SPer WPer WWhi WWin

'Melton' — EAst EBee ECoo EFou MNrw NBir NChi NOak SAga WElm WHen

* 'Melton Fire' — WGor

¶ *miyabei* — EBee

'Monarch's Velvet' — See *P. thurberi* 'Monarch's Velvet'

'Monsieur Rouillard' — CGle CLon EPPr LFis MBel MNrw MSCN MWat NNor NRoo SUsu WByw WCru WHoo WSan

'Mont d'Or' — LRHS MBri MRav

montana — GCHN MBel NHol WHer WPer

nepalensis — CNic CSam ECha EDAr GAbr GMac LHop LLWP MFir NBro NNor NPro SMac SWas

– 'Craigieburn' — GCra

– 'Craigieburn Cochineal' — See *P.* 'Craigieburn Cochineal'

– forms — EAst

– 'Kirsten' — WHil

§ – 'Miss Willmott' ♀ — Widely available

¶ – red — WLin

– 'Roxana' — CGle EBar EBee ECGP ELan GBuc MBel MRav NBro NFai SHel WAbb WByw WFar WHil WMow WPer

¶ – 'Shogran' — EBee

§ *neumanniana* — EWFC SGre SHel WAbe

– 'Goldrausch' — ECha MBri MRav SRms

§ – 'Nana' — CInt CSev EMNN EPot ESis LBee LHop MBro MHig MLLN MPla MRPP MWat NHar NMen NNrd NRoo SBla SIng SRms WEas WWin

nevadensis — CLyd CTri ECho MHig WPer

nitida — NGre NHar NMen

¶ – 'Alannah' — EHyt

– 'Alba' — EPot

– 'Lissadell' — CPBP

– 'Rubra' — CLyd CMea EHyt GCrs GTou MBro MWat NBir NMGW NNrd NTow NWCA SBla SRms SSmi WAbe WPat WWin

nivea — GTou

'Nunk' — CBlo MBar WWeb

* 'Olympic Mountains' — WPer

ovina — WPer

palustris — MSta NLar WCla WGwy

pamirica — EBee

pedata — LLWP NChi

peduncularis — WCot

– CC&McK 532 — GCHN

'Pink Panther' — See *P. fruticosa* Princess = 'Blink'

'Pyrenaica' — See *P. fruticosa* var. *pyrenaica*

recta — CBlo ELan EMan EWFC GTou MHew SIgm WHil

– 'Alba' — CBlo CPea EAst ECoo GMaP LGan LIck NFai NPri NRoo SMac WPer

– 'Citrina' — See *P. recta pallida*

¶ – HH&K 205 — CHan

– 'Macrantha' — See *P. recta* 'Warrenii'

– var. *sulphurea* ♀ — CGle CHad CLon CMil CPea CSam EBar ECoo GCal LHop MBel MCLN MFir MNrw MTis NCat NFai NRoo NSti SIgm SIng SUsu WAbe WHal WHer WHoo WPer WPyg

§ – 'Warrenii' — CHea CPea CSam EBar EBrP EBre ECro EFou GMaP LBre LGan MCLN MFir MRav MTis MWat NFai NMir NOrc NRoo SBre SCro SHel SPer WHal WHoo WMow WOve WPer WPyg

reptans — CArn CKin EWFC

– 'Pleniflora' (d) — MInt WAlt

rupestris — CAgr CGle CHan CInt CLTr CM&M CTri ECha EMan EWFC GCra GLil GMac MAus MCLN MFir MLLN MNrw NChi NRoo NSti SUsu WByw WCla WHal WPer WWin

speciosa — EHyt EMan WOMN

– var. *speciosa* — NWCA

– – NS 765 — MRPP

sterilis — CHid ELan EWFC WHer

– 'Turncoat' (v) — WAlt

'Sungold' — CBlo ECho ESis

tabernaemontani — See *P. neumanniana*

ternata — See *P. aurea* subsp. *chrysocraspeda*

thurberi — CGle EMan EWes GCal LGre MHar MNrw MRav WLin WMaN

§ – 'Monarch's Velvet' — CBot CLTr CMdw CMil CPou EBee MCli MOne NDov NFla WBro WGor WLRN

– 'White Queen' — See *P.* 'White Queen'

tommasiniana — See *P. cinerea*

x *tonguei* ♀ — CFee CHea CLyd ECha ECtt EFou ELan ESis GCHN GDra LHop MBal MBri MCLN MRav NChi NFai NHar NLon NNrd NRoo SBla SIng SSmi WLin WMer WMow WPer WWat

tormentilla	See *P. erecta*
tridentata	See *Sibbaldiopsis tridentata*
verna	See *P. neumanniana*
– 'Pygmaea'	See *P. neumanniana* **'Nana'**
'Versicolor Plena' (d)	CMea
villosa	See *P. crantzii*
'Volcan'	CBos EBar EPPr EWes GCal
	MBri SWas WAbb WFar
wallichiana 'Cream	EMon
Cracker'	
§ 'White Queen'	CMea EWll MNrw WBea WGor
'William Rollison' ♀	CB&S CBre CHad CSam EBar
	EBrP EBre ECro EFou ELan
	GChr GLil LBre LHop LRot
	MBel MBri MCLN MRav NHol
	NOrc NVic SBre SCro SOkh
	SPer SRms SUsu WMow WPer
willmottiae	See *P. nepalensis* **'Miss Willmott'**
'Yellow Queen'	CB&S CTri ELan EPfP MRav
	NFai NRoo NVic SCro SPer
	SWat WMer WMow WWeb

POTERIUM See SANGUISORBA

PRATIA (Campanulaceae)

§ *angulata*	CMea NGre NHar NHol SSmi
	WWeb
– 'Jack's Pass'	GAri NHar
– 'Messenger'	ECou
§ – 'Treadwellii'	ECha ELan LBee NPro NRoo
	SUsu WHal WHen WWin
– 'Woodside'	ECou
macrodon	NGre NNrd WCru
§ *pedunculata*	CHan CMHG CMea CRow
	ECha ECou ELan ESis GCHN
	GMac GTou LBee MBar NFla
	NGre NRoo NRya NVic SHFr
	SIng SRms SSmi WAbe WHen
	WHoo WPer WWhi WWin
– 'Blue Stars'	WCru
– 'County Park'	CBos CInt CMea CSpe CVer
	ECha ECou ELan EPot ESis
	GMac MBar NGre NHar NHol
	NMen NRoo NWCA SIng SRms
	SSmi WHal WHoo WOMN
	WPat WPer WPyg WWin
– 'Kiandra'	ECou
– 'Tom Stone'	CLTr EBar EPot NHar NNrd
§ *perpusilla*	ECou
– 'Fragrant Carpet'	ECou WFar
– 'Summer Meadows'	ECou WPer
§ *repens*	ECou

PRESLIA (Lamiaceae)

◆ *cervina*	See *Mentha cervina*

PRIMULA † (Primulaceae)

acaulis	See *P. vulgaris*
'Adrian Jones' (2)	EHyt NNrd WAbe
'Aire Mist' (*allionii* hybrid) (2)	CLyd EHyt GCLN MFie NGre NHar NHol WLin
§ 'Aire Waves' (2)	EHyt GCLN
'Alan Robb' (dPrim)(30)	EBar EHic MBri MBro MCLN NHol SIng SPer WHil
'Alexina' (*allionii* hybrid) (2)	EHyt NHar NHol
algida (11)	CPla ECho GCra NGre
§ *allionii* (2)	CTri EHyt EMNN EPot GTou ITim LBee MBro MFie MHig MRPP NCra NHar NHol NNrd NWCA WAbe
– 'A.K. Wells' (2)	EHyt EPot NGre WAbe
– 'Aire Waves'	See *P.* **'Aire Waves'**
– var. *alba* (2)	EMNN NHol
* – 'Alexander' (2)	WLin
– 'Anna Griffith' (2)	CGra EHyt EPot GCHN ITim MRPP NGre NHol NNrd NWCA WAbe WLin
– 'Anne' (2)	EHyt ITim
§ – 'Apple Blossom' (2)	CGra GAbr MDHE NNrd NTow SIng
– 'Archer' (2)	EMNN NGre NMen WLin
– x *auricula* 'Blairside Yellow' (2)	CLyd CPBP EMNN GCLN NGre
– x *auricula* 'Old Red Dusty Miller' (2)	MDHE MFie NHar NNrd
– 'Austen' (2)	EHyt EPot MHig NHol NMen NNrd WAbe
– 'Avalanche' (2)	CLyd EHyt GCLN ITim MHig NGre NHar NMen NTow WAbe WLin
– 'Bill Martin' (2)	EPot
– 'Brilliant' KRW 448/69 (2)	EHyt
– Burnley form (2)	EPot
¶ – CH 1989 (2)	WLin
¶ – 'Chris Norton' CCN/03 (2)	ITim
◆ – 'Clarence Elliott'	See *P.* **'Clarence Elliott' (allionii hybrid)**
– 'Claude Flight' (2)	EHyt NHar
– x *clusiana* (2)	NGre WLin
– 'Crowsley Variety' (2)	CLyd CPBP EHyt EPot MHig NGre NMen NSla NTow NWCA SBla WAbe WLin
– 'Crusader' (2)	EHyt WLin
* – 'E.G. Watson'	EHyt
§ – 'Edinburgh' (2)	CNic EHyt EMNN EPot ITim MFie MHig NHol NNrd
– 'Edrom' (2)	ITim MHig
– 'Elizabeth Baker' (2)	EHyt EMNN GCLN WAbe
– 'Elizabeth Earle' (2)	EPot NHol NMen WAbe
– 'Elliott's Large'	See *P. allionii* **'Edinburgh'**
– 'Elliott's Variety'	See *P. allionii* **'Edinburgh'**
– 'Fairy Rose' KRW 180/48 (2)	WAbe
– 'Fanfare' (2)	CGra EHyt WGwG
– 'Frank Barker' (2)	EPot NGre NHol
– 'Gavin Brown' (2)	EHyt EPot
– GFS 1984 (2)	CGra
§ – 'Gilderdale Glow' (2)	MFie NGre NHar
– 'Giuseppi's Form'	See *P. allionii* **'Mrs Dyas'**
– 'Grandiflora' (2)	NGre
– Hartside 383/12	See *P. allionii* **'Gilderdale Glow'**
– Hartside 383/3 (2)	EPot NHol NMen NNrd
– Hartside 383/6	NGre
– 'Hemswell' (2)	EMNN
– 'Hemswell Blush'	See *P.* **'Hemswell Blush'**
– 'Hemswell Ember'	See *P.* **'Hemswell Ember'**
– x *hirsuta* (2)	MFie
– 'Hocker Edge' (2)	NNrd
– 'Horwood' KD/KRW 397/60 (2)	EHyt
¶ – 'Huntsman'	MFie
– Ingwersen's form (2)	EPot GTou NHol
– JCA 4161/16 (2)	EPot
– JCA 4161/21	See *P. allionii* **'Travellers' JCA 4161/21**
– JCA 4161/22	See *P. allionii* **'Jenny' JCA 4161/22**
– JCA 4161/23	CGra EPot
§ – 'Jenny' JCA 4161/22 (2)	CGra EHyt EPot
¶ – 'Julia' JCA 4161/31	EHyt
– K R W	See *P. allionii* **'Ken's Seedling'**

§ – 'Kath Dryden' (2) — WHil
§ – 'Ken's Seedling' (2) — CLyd EHyt EMNN EPot NGre NHol NNrd WAbe
– KRW 392/56 (2) — EHyt
– KRW 455/70 (2) — EHyt
¶ – KRW 461/71 (2) — EHyt
– KRW 525/76 (thrum, white) (2) — EHyt
– 'Lindisfarne' (2) — EHyt WLin
¶ – Lismore 79/7 (2) — WLin
¶ – Lismore 81/19/3 — MFie
¶ – Lismore P85/16xx (2) — WLin
– × 'Lismore Treasure' (2) — CGra CPBP EHyt NWCA WLin
– 'Margaret Earle' (2) — NHol WAbe
– × *marginata* (2) — EBrP EBre EHyt EPot LBre MFie NHar SBre WLin
– 'Marion' (2) — EHyt EMNN EPot ITim NHed NHol NMen
– 'Marjorie Wooster' KRW 331/52 (2) — EHyt MRPP NGre NWCA
– 'Martin' (2) — EPot MHig NGre NHol NNrd
– 'Mary Berry' (2) — EMNN EPot MHig NGre WAbe
§ – 'Mrs Dyas' (2) — EHyt EMNN ITim NHar NHol NNrd WAbe WOMN
– Nettleton 8824 (2) — EPot
¶ – pale clone (2) — WLin
♦ – × *pedemontana* — See *P.* × *sendtneri*
– 'Peggy Wilson' (2) — EPot EWes NHol
– 'Pennine Pink' Hartside 383/7 (2) — EHyt EMNN EPot MRPP NGre NHol
– 'Perkie' JCA 4161/12 (2) — EHyt NNrd
– 'Picton's Variety' (2) — EPot NHed
– 'Pink Aire' — See *P.* 'Pink Aire'
– 'Pink Beauty' (2) — EPot
– 'Pinkie' KRW 271/51 (2) — CGra
– 'Praecox' (2) — EPot NHol NNrd NSla
– × *pubescens* 'Harlow Car' (2) — CLyd NHar
– 'Raymond Wooster' KRW 321/52 (2) — EPot
– 'Roger Bevan' (2) — EHyt
– × *rubra* (2) — MBro NHol
– 'Saint Dalmas' (2) — EPot
– 'Scimitar' (2) — EMNN NHar
– 'Serendipity' (2) — EHyt
– 'Snowflake' KRW 367/56 (2) — CGra CLyd CPBP EHyt EMNN EPot NHar NTow NWCA WAbe
– 'Stanton House' (2) — NHed NHol WAbe
– 'Stephen' JCA 4161/6 (2) — EHyt EMNN
¶ – 'Sylvia Martinelli' — EHyt
¶ – 'Tranquillity' (2) — WLin
– 'Tranquillity' Hartside 383/1 (2) — EHyt MFie NGre NHar NHol NMen NNrd
§ – 'Travellers' JCA 4161/21 (2) — CGra EPot
– 'Viscountess Byng' (2) — EMNN
¶ – W 1971 (2) — WLin
– 'William Earle' (2) — EHyt EMNN EPot NGre NHar NHed NHol NMen WAbe

alpicola (26) — CBot CFee CRow CSWP EBrP EBre GAbr GDra GFle GPot LBre LPBA MBal MFie NBro NCra NGre SBre SPer WAbe WHil WRus WWat
– var. *alba* (26) — CMil CNic CPla CRow CSWP GBin GCra GMac LSyl MBal MNrw NGre NRoo SWat
§ – var. *alpicola* — GBuc LSyl
♦ – var. *luna* — See *P. alpicola* var. *alpicola*

– var. *violacea* (26) — CPla CRow GAbr GDra GMac LSyl MBal MBri MFie MNrw NHar SWat WWhi
'Altaica' — See *P. elatior* subsp. *meyeri*
altaica grandiflora — See *P. elatior* subsp. *meyeri*
amoena — See *P. elatior* subsp. *meyeri*
♦ *anisodora* — See *P. wilsonii* var. *anisodora*
'April Rose' (dPrim)(30) — CMea SPer
× *arctotis* — See *P.* × *pubescens*
atrodentata (9) — WAbe
aurantiaca (4) — CPla GAbr GAri GFle LSyl MSta NGre SRms
aureata (21) — GCra GGGa NCra
¶ – subsp. *fimbriata* (21) — GCrs
¶ *auricula* hort. (B) — WLin
– 'A.H. Spring' (A) — MFie
– 'Adrian' (A) — MFie NCra NNrd SHya
– 'Aga Khan' — SHya
– 'Agamemnon' — NCra
– 'Alamo' — NCra SPop
– 'Alan Ravenscroft' (A) — MFie
– 'Albury' (d) — MFie
– 'Alfred Niblett' (S) — EMNN NNrd
– 'Alice Haysom' (S) — ELan MFie NNrd SHya WHil WLin
– 'Alicia' (A) — SHya SPop
– 'Alien' (S) — MFie
– 'Alison Jane' (A) — CLyd MFie NCra NOak SHya
– 'Allansford' — EMNN
– 'Almondbury' (S) — SHya
– Alpine mixed (A) — CNic GCra GDra MMal NCra SRms
– 'Amicable' (A) — SHya
– 'Andrea Julie' (A) — CNic EMNN MFie MOne NCra NHar NHol NNrd SHya WHil WLin
– 'Ann Taylor' (A) — NCra SHya
– 'Antoc' (S) — EMNN MFie
– 'Anwar Sadat' (A) — EMNN MFie
– 'Applecross' (A) — EMNN MFie NCra NHar NNrd SHya WLin
– 'Arctic Fox' — NCra
– 'Argus' (A) — CLyd MFie NBir NCra NHar NNrd SHya SUsu WHil WLin
¶ – 'Arundel Star' — GAbr
– 'Arundell' (S/St) — EMNN SHya WHil WLin
– 'Astolat' (S) — EMNN MFie NCra NNrd NOak SHya WLin
– 'Athur Delbridge' (A) — MFie
– 'Aurora' (A) — MFie SHya
– 'Austin' — NCra
– 'Avril Hunter' (A) — MFie SHya
– 'Aye Aye' — NCra
– 'Bacchus' (A) — MFie
– 'Ballet' (S) — MFie
– 'Barbara Mason' — NCra
– 'Barbarella' (S) — EMNN MFie
¶ – Barnhaven doubles — CSWP
– 'Basuto' (A) — EMNN MFie SHya
– 'Beatrice' (A) — CLyd EMNN GAbr MFie NCra NNrd SHya WLin
– 'Bedford Lad' (A) — SHya
– 'Beechen Green' (S) — EMNN NNrd SHya
¶ – 'Bellezana' — MFie
– 'Ben Lawers' (S) — SHya SPop
– 'Ben Wyves' (S) — SHya
– 'Bendigo' (S) — SHya
– 'Bilton' (S) — CLyd MFie NCra
– 'Blackfield' (S) — MFie
– 'Blackhill' (S) — EMNN MFie
– 'Blairside Yellow' (B) — CLyd EWes MRPP NHar NHol WAbe

– 'Blossom' (A)	EMNN MFie NCra NNrd SHya
¶ – 'Blue Bonnet' (A)	SPop
– 'Blue Heaven'	NCra
– 'Blue Jean' (S)	EMNN MFie NCra
– 'Blue Nile' (S)	EMNN MFie NCra
– 'Blue Steel' (S)	SHya
– 'Blue Velvet' (B)	EMNN MFie NBro SHya WHil WLin
– 'Bob Lancashire' (S)	EMNN MFie NHar NNrd SHya WHil
– 'Bolero' (A)	SHya
– 'Bookham Firefly' (A)	EMNN GAbr MBro MFie NCra NHar NHol NNrd SHya
– 'Bravura'	NCra
– 'Brazil' (S)	EMNN MFie NCra NHol NNrd NOak WHil WLin
– 'Brenda's Choice' (A)	MFie SHya
– 'Bright Eyes' (A)	MFie SHya
– 'Broad Gold' (A)	SHya
– 'Broadwell Gold' (B)	CLyd EPot MFie SHya WLin
– 'Brookfield' (S)	EMNN GCrs MFie NNrd SHya
– 'Broughton' (S)	MFie SHya
– 'Brown Bess' (A)	EMNN GCLN MFie NCra NNrd SHya WLin
– 'Buccaneer'	NCra
¶ – 'Bucks Green'	SPop
– 'Bunty' (A)	MFie
– 'Butterwick' (A)	MFie NHar NHol SHya WLin
– 'C.F. Hill' (A)	EMNN SHya
– 'C.G. Haysom' (S)	EMNN LRHS MFie NCra NHar NNrd SHya WLin
– 'C.W. Needham' (A)	EMNN MFie NCra NHol NNrd SHya WHil WLin
* – 'Cambodumun'	NCra SHya SPop
– 'Camelot' (d)	CLyd ELan EMNN GCrs MFie MOne NChi NCra NHar NHol NNrd SHya WFar WHil
– 'Candida' (d)	SHya
– 'Carole' (A)	MFie NNrd SHya
– 'Carreras'	NCra
– 'Catherine' (d)	MFie NCra
– 'Chaffinch' (S)	SHya
¶ – 'Chantilly Cream' (d)	WLin
– 'Chelsea Bridge'	EMNN
– 'Cherry' (S)	EMNN GAbr NCra SHya
– 'Cheyenne' (S)	EMNN GAbr MFie
– 'Chloë' (S)	SHya
– 'Chloris' (S)	NBir SHya
– 'Chorister' (S)	CLyd ELan EMNN EPot GAbr MBro MFie MOne NCra NHed NHol NNrd NOak NPri SHya SUsu WLin
– 'Cicero' (A)	SHya
– 'Cindy' (A)	MFie
* – 'Cinnamon' (S)	SHya
– 'Clare' (S)	SHya
¶ – 'Clatter-Ha'	GCrs
– 'Claudia Taylor'	NHar SHya WLin
– 'Clunie' (S)	GCLN WHil
– 'Clunie II' (S)	GCrs SHya WLin
– 'Coffee' (S)	MFie SHya
– 'Colbury' (S)	MFie NCra NHar SHya WLin
– 'Colonel Champney' (S)	MFie NNrd SHya WLin
– 'Comet' (S)	MFie NNrd
– 'Connie' (S)	MFie
– 'Conservative' (S)	MFie SHya
– 'Consett' (S)	EMNN MFie NCra NNrd SHya
– 'Coppernob' (S)	SHya
– 'Coral' (S)	MFie NCra NHed
– 'Corona' (S)	SHya
– 'Corrie Files' (d)	SHya

– 'Cortina' (S)	EMNN MOne NCra NHar NHol NNrd NOak WLin
– 'County Park Red' (B)	ECou
– 'Craig Vaughan' (A)	MFie NCra NNrd SHya
¶ – 'Cuckoo Fair'	SPop
– 'D.S.J.' (S)	SHya
– 'Daftie Green' (S)	EMNN GCLN NNrd SHya
– 'Dakota' (S)	EMNN MFie NCra
¶ – 'Dark Tiger' (St)	SHya
– 'Deep Wilson'	EWes
– 'Delilah' (d)	GCLN MFie WLin
– 'Denna Snufer'	EMNN
– 'Devon Cream' (d)	GCLN MFie NCra NHol WFar WLin
– 'Diane'	EMNN MFie SHya
– 'Divint Dunch' (A)	SHya SPop
– 'Doctor B. Sharma' (S)	SHya
– 'Doctor Duthie' (S)	SHya
– 'Doctor Lennon's White' (B)	MFie
– 'Donhead' (A)	MFie SHya
– 'Donna Clancy' (S)	MFie SHya
– 'Doris Jean' (A)	SHya
– double maroon (d)	WHil
– double yellow (d)	WHil
– 'Doublet' (d)	CLyd EMNN GAbr MFie NCra NHol NNrd NOak NSla SHya WHil WLin
– 'Doubloon' (d)	SHya
– 'Doublure' (d)	SHya
– 'Douglas Black' (S)	SHya
– 'Douglas Green' (S)	MFie SHya
– 'Douglas White' (S)	EMNN MFie SHya
– 'Dovedale' (S)	SHya
– 'Dowager' (A)	MFie
– 'Dubarii' (A)	NCra
– 'Dusky Maiden' (A)	EMNN GCLN NCra SHya WLin
– 'Dusky Yellow' (B)	MBro
– 'Dusty Lemon' (d)	SHya
– 'Dusty Miller' (B)	GPot
– 'Ed Spivey' (A)	SHya
– 'Edith Allen' (A)	SHya
– 'Eglinton'	NCra
– 'Eileen K' (S)	SHya
– 'Elegance' (S)	SHya
– 'Elizabeth Ann' (A)	EMNN MFie NCra SHya
– 'Ellen Thompson' (A)	MFie NNrd SHya WLin
– 'Elmor Vete' (S)	SHya
– 'Elsie' (A)	EMNN MFie
– 'Elsie May' (A)	EMNN GCLN MFie NCra NNrd SHya WHil WLin
– 'Embley' (S)	CLyd NCra SHya
– 'Emery Down' (S)	MFie NNrd SHya SPop
– 'Enlightened' (A)	NCra SHya
I – 'Erica' (A)	EMNN MFie NHar SHya WLin
¶ – 'Error' (S)	SHya
– 'Ettrick' (S)	SHya
– 'Eve Guest' (A)	SHya
– 'Everest Blue' (S)	SHya SPop
¶ – 'Eyeopener'	SPop
– 'Fairy' (A)	SHya
– 'Falcon' (S)	SHya
¶ – 'Falsefields' (S)	SHya
– 'Fanciful' (S)	CLyd MFie SHya WLin
– 'Fanny Meerbeck' (S)	EMNN MFie NCra NHol NNrd NOak WHil WLin
– 'Favorite'	EMNN NNrd SHya
– 'Figaro' (S)	SHya
¶ – 'Finavon'	GCrs
– 'Finchfield' (A)	EMNN MFie SHya
– 'Firenze'	NCra

– 'Flamingo' (S)	MFie
– 'Fleminghouse' (S)	SHya
– 'Forsinard' (S)	SHya
– 'Fradley' (A)	SHya
– 'Frank Crosland' (A)	MFie NCra NNrd SHya WHil
– 'Frank Faulkner' (A)	SHya
– 'Frank Taylor' (S)	SHya
¶ – 'Frittenden Yellow' (B)	WLin
– 'Frosty' (S)	SHya
– 'Fuller's Red' (S)	CLyd MFie
– 'Gaia' (d)	NHol SHya
– 'Galen' (A)	MFie NCra NNrd SHya
– 'Gay Crusader' (A)	EMNN MFie SHya
– 'Gee Cross' (A)	EMNN MFie
§ – 'Geldersome Green' (S)	EMNN MFie SHya WLin
– 'Generosity' (A)	SHya SPop
– 'George Rudd' (S)	SHya
– 'George Swinford's Leathercoat' (B)	SHya
– 'Geronimo' (S)	EMNN MFie SHya
– 'Gizabroon' (S)	CLyd EMNN MFie NCra NNrd WLin
– 'Gleam' (S)	EMNN GCrs MFie NNrd SHya WLin
– 'Glencoe' (S)	SHya
– 'Gleneagles' (S)	SHya
– 'Glenelg' (S)	MFie SHya SPop
– 'Glenluce' (S)	SHya
– 'Gnome' (B)	NHol
– 'Golden Chartreuse' (d)	WHil
– 'Golden Eagle'	NCra
– 'Golden Splendour' (d)	MFie SHya WLin
– 'Good Report'	NCra
– 'Gordon Douglas' (A)	EMNN MFie NCra SHya SUsu
– 'Gorey'	NCra
– 'Grace Ellen' (S)	SHya
– 'Green Isle' (S)	EMNN GAbr MFie NBir NNrd SHya WLin
– 'Green Jacket' (S)	SHya
¶ – 'Green Mansions' (S)	SHya
– 'Green Mouse' (S)	MFie SHya
– 'Green Parrot' (S)	CLyd EMNN SHya WHil WLin
– 'Green Shank' (S)	MFie NNrd SHya WLin
– 'Greenheart' (S)	EMNN GCLN SHya
– 'Greenpeace' (S)	LRHS NHar SHya
– 'Greensleeves' (S)	SHya
– 'Greta' (S)	ELan EMNN GCLN NHar NNrd NOak SHya WHil WLin
– 'Gretna Green' (S)	GCLN MFie SHya
– 'Grey Bonnet' (S)	SHya
– 'Grey Friar' (S)	SHya
– 'Grey Hawk' (S)	SHya
– 'Grey Lag'	EMNN GCLN MFie SHya
– 'Grey Monarch' (S)	GCLN MFie SHya
– 'Grey Shrike' (S)	SHya
– 'Grey Tarquin' (S)	SHya WLin
– 'Grizedale' (S)	MFie
– 'Guildersome Green'	See *P. auricula* 'Geldersome Green'
– 'Guinea' (S)	EMNN GAbr MFie NCra NNrd SHya
– 'Gwen' (A)	SHya
– 'Habanera'	NCra SPop
– 'Harmony' (B)	MFie
– 'Harrison Weir' (S)	SHya
– 'Harry 'O'' (S)	SHya
– 'Haughmond' (A)	EMNN MFie
– 'Hawkwood' (S)	EMNN NCra NHar NNrd WHil
– 'Hawkwood Fancy' (S)	SHya
* – 'Hazel' (A)	GAbr MFie NCra SHya
– 'Hazel's Fancy' (S)	SHya
– 'Headdress' (S)	MFie
– 'Heady'	NCra
– 'Hebers'	NCra
– 'Helen' (S)	SHya
– 'Helen Barter' (S)	SHya
– 'Helena' (S)	EMNN MFie NNrd NOak SHya
– 'Helena Brown' (S)	SHya
– 'Hetty Woolf'	EMNN NNrd
– 'Hew Dalrymple' (S)	SHya
– 'Hinton Admiral' (S)	SHya WLin
– 'Hinton Fields' (S)	MFie SHya
– 'Hoghton Gem' (d)	SHya
– 'Holyrood' (S)	MFie SHya
– 'Hopley's Double Mauve' (d)	MFie
– 'Humphrey' (S)	SHya
– 'Hurstwood Midnight'	MBro NHol WLin
* – 'Hyacinth' (S)	NWCA
– 'Ibis' (S)	MFie SHya
– 'Ice Maiden'	NCra
– 'Idmiston' (S)	SHya SPop
¶ – 'Immaculate'	SPop
– 'Impassioned' (A)	NCra
– 'Impeccable'	NCra
– 'Indian Love Call'	NCra
– 'Jack Dean' (A)	MFie SHya WHil
– 'Jack Stant' (S)	SHya
– 'James Arnot' (S)	MFie NCra NHar NOak SHya
– 'Jane Myers' (d)	MFie SHya
– 'Janet'	SHya
– 'Janie Hill' (A)	SHya
– 'Jeanne' (A)	SHya
– 'Jeannie Telford' (A)	NCra
– 'Jenny' (A)	EMNN GAbr MFie MYat NNrd SHya WHil
– 'Jessie' (d)	SHya
– 'Jezebel' (B)	SHya
– 'Joan Elliott' (A)	CLyd GAbr MFie MYat
– 'Joanne' (A)	SHya
– 'Joe Perks'	NCra
¶ – 'Joel'	MFie
– 'Johann Bach' (B)	MFie
– 'John Stewart' (A)	EMNN MFie
– 'John Wayne' (A)	EMNN MFie
– 'John Woolf' (S)	SHya
– 'Joy' (A)	CLyd EMNN MFie NCra NHol NNrd SHya WLin
– 'Joyce'	GAbr MFie NBir SHya WLin
– 'Julia' (S)	SHya
– 'July Sky' (A)	SHya
– 'Jupiter' (S)	SHya
– 'Karen Cordrey' (S)	WLin
– 'Kath Dryden'	See *P. allionii* 'Kath Dryden'
– 'Kathy' (A)	SHya
– 'Kelso' (A)	MFie
¶ – 'Kens Green' (S)	SHya
– 'Kercup' (A)	MFie NCra NNrd
– 'Khachaturian'	NCra
– 'Kim' (A)	EMNN MFie NNrd SHya
– 'Kincraig' (S)	SHya
– 'Kingcup' (A)	MFie NCra SHya
– 'Kiowa' (S)	MFie
– 'Kirklands' (d)	MFie SHya
¶ – 'Königin der Nacht' (St)	SHya
– 'Lady Daresbury' (A)	EMNN MFie NCra
– 'Lady Emma Monson' (S)	SHya
– 'Lady Joyful' (S)	SHya
– 'Lady Zoë' (S)	MFie NCra
– 'Lamplugh'	MFie NNrd
– 'Landy' (A)	GCrs SHya
– 'Langley Park' (A)	MFie SHya WHil
– 'Laverock' (S)	NBro SHya

– 'Laverock Fancy' (S)   EMNN MFie WLin
– 'Leather Jacket'   GAbr NHol
– 'Lechistan' (S)   EMNN MFie NHar NHol NNrd WLin
– 'Lee Paul' (A)   EMNN MFie NCra SHya WLin
– 'Lee Sharpe' (A)   SHya
– 'Lemon Drop' (S)   SHya
– 'Lemon Sherbet' (B)   MFie
– 'Lewis Telford' (A)   SHya
– 'Lich'   EMNN
– 'Lichfield' (A)   SHya
– 'Light Hearted'   NCra
– 'Lilac Domino' (S)   MFie NCra SHya WLin
– 'Lillian Hill' (A)   SHya
¶ – 'Lincoln Green' (S)   SHya
– 'Lindley' (S)   EMNN NHar
– 'Lindsey Moreno' (S)   SHya
– 'Ling' (A)   CLyd EMNN MFie NCra SHya
¶ – Lingen seedling No. 1   WLin
– 'Lisa' (A)   CLyd MBal MFie NCra NHar NNrd SHya WLin
– 'Lisa Clara' (S)   EMNN SHya
– 'Lisa's Smile' (S)   MFie NCra SHya
– 'Little Rosetta' (d)   WHil
¶ – 'Lord Saye-en-Sele' (St)   GCrs SHya
– 'Louisa' (d)   MFie
– 'Lovebird' (S)   EMNN GAbr GCLN MFie NCra NHar NNrd SHya SUsu WLin
– 'Madame Gina' (S)   MFie
– 'Maggie' (S)   EMNN SHya
– 'Magnolia' (B)   MFie
– 'Maid Marion' (d)   SHya
¶ – 'Mandarin'   SPop
– 'Manka' (S)   MFie NCra SHya
– 'Mansell's Green'   MFie NNrd SHya
– 'Margaret' (S)   SHya
– 'Margaret Faulkner' (A)   EMNN GCLN MFie NCra SHya
– 'Margaret Martin' (S)   SHya
– 'Margot Fonteyn'   NCra SPop
– 'Marigold' (d)   CLyd MFie NCra NNrd WFar WLin
– 'Mark' (A)   EMNN MFie NBro NCra NHol SHya WHil WLin
– 'Marmion' (S)   SHya
– 'Martin Luther King' (S)   MFie
– 'Mary' (d)   GCLN MFie SHya
– 'Mary of Dunoon' (S)   SHya
– 'Mary Taylor' (S)   SHya
– 'Mary Zac'   NNrd
– 'Matthew Yates' (d)   CHad GAbr LRHS MFie MOne NChi NCra NHol SHya WLin
– 'Maureen Millward'   EMNN MFie NNrd SPop
– 'May Tiger' (S)   SHya
¶ – 'Mazetta Stripe' (St)   WLin
– 'Meadow Lark'   NCra
– 'Mellifluous'   NCra
– 'Merlin' (A)   SHya
¶ – 'Merlin Stripe' (St)   SHya
– 'Mermaid'   GAbr MFie NCra SHya WHil WLin
– 'Merridale' (A)   EMNN MFie NCra SHya
– 'Metha'   NCra
– 'Mick' (A)   NCra
– 'Midnight' (S)   CBot CLyd EMNN MOne NCra NHar NNrd
– 'Mikado' (S)   MFie SHya
– 'Millicent' (A)   MFie SHya
– 'Mink' (A)   MFie SHya WHil
– 'Minley' (S)   EMNN GCLN GCrs ITim MFie NHar NNrd SHya WLin
– 'Minstrel' (S)   SHya

– 'Mipsie Miranda' (d)   MFie SHya
– 'Mirabella Bay'   NCra
– 'Miriam' (A)   SHya
– 'Mish Mish' (d)   SHya WHil
– 'Mojave' (S)   EMNN MBro MFie NCra NHar NHol WLin
¶ – 'Mollie Langford'   SPop
– 'Moneymoon' (S)   MFie
– 'Monica' (A)   MFie
– 'Monk' (A)   CLyd MFie NNrd
– 'Moonglow' (S)   EMNN LRHS MFie NCra
– 'Moonrise' (S)   EMNN MFie
– 'Moonstone' (d)   MFie
– 'Moscow' (S)   MFie
– 'Moselle' (S)   SHya
– 'Mr 'A'' (S)   CLyd GCrs WHil WLin
– 'Mrs L. Hearn'   EMNN MFie NCra NNrd SHya WLin
– 'Mrs R. Bolton' (A)   SHya WRha
– 'Murray Lakes'   NCra
– 'Nankenan'   WHil
– 'Neat and Tidy' (S)   CLyd EMNN MFie MHig NCra NHar NNrd NOak SHya WHil WLin
– 'Nefertiti'   NCra
– 'Neville Telford' (S)   EMNN GCLN MFie
– 'Nickity' (A)   SHya WLin
– 'Nigel' (d)   WLin
– 'Night and Day' (S)   EMNN MFie NCra
– 'Nocturne' (S)   EMNN GCLN LRHS MFie NBro NCra SHya WLin
– 'Norma' (A)   EMNN MFie NNrd
– 'Notability' (A)   NCra SHya
– 'Oake's Blue' (S)   NCra
– 'Oban' (S)   SHya
– 'Old Double Green' (d)   MFie
– 'Old England' (S)   SHya
– 'Old Gold' (S)   SHya
– 'Old Gold Dusty Miller' (B)   NNrd
– 'Old Irish Blue' (B)   CLyd MBro MFie NHol SHya
– 'Old Irish Scented' (B)   WHil WLin
– 'Old Lilac' (B)   MFie
– 'Old Mustard'   SWas
– 'Old Red Dusty Miller' (B)   ECha MFie MHig NBir SHya
– 'Old Red Elvet'   GCLN
– 'Old Suffolk Bronze' (B)   MFie NBro SHya
– 'Old Wine' (A)   CLyd MFie
– 'Old Yellow Dusty Miller' (B)   CLTr CLyd EMNN EWes GAbr MBro MFie MHig NBro NHol NNrd SHya WAbe WHil WLin WWin
– 'Olton' (A)   MFie SHya
– 'Orb' (S)   CLyd EMNN MFie SHya
¶ – 'Ordvic'   WLin
¶ – 'Orwell Tiger' (St)   SHya
– 'Osbourne Green' (B)   MFie SPop WHil WLin
– 'Overdale' (A)   SHya
– 'Paradise Yellow' (B)   EMNN MFie SHya SPop
– 'Paris' (S)   SHya
– 'Pastiche' (A)   MFie NCra
– 'Pat' (S)   EMNN MFie MOne NCra SHya
– 'Patience' (S)   NNrd
– 'Patricia Barras' (S)   SHya
– 'Pauline' (A)   MFie SHya
– 'Peggy' (A)   EPot MFie NNrd NWCA
– 'Petite Hybrid'   MFos
– 'Pharaoh'   NCra SPop
– 'Phyllis Douglas' (A)   EMNN MFie NCra SHya
– 'Pierot' (A)   MFie
– 'Piers Telford'   MFie NCra SPop

– 'Pink Lady' (A)	MFie
– 'Pinstripe'	NNrd
– 'Pippin' (A)	MFie SHya WLin
– 'Pixie' (A)	SHya
– 'Plush Royal' (S)	MFie
– 'Portree' (S)	EMNN SHya
– 'Pot o' Gold' (S)	MFie NCra NHar NOak SHya SPop
– 'Prague' (S)	MFie NBir SHya SPop
– 'Prince Charming' (S)	MFie
– 'Prince John' (A)	MFie NBro NCra NNrd SHya WHil WLin
– 'Purple Mermaid' (d)	MFie WLin
– 'Purple Sage' (S)	EMNN GCLN NHar
– 'Purple Velvet' (S)	EHyt
– 'Queen Bee' (S)	SHya
– 'Queen's Bower' (S)	EMNN SHya
– 'Quintessence'	NCra
– 'Quiquern' (S)	SHya
– 'Rabley Heath' (A)	CLyd EMNN MFie SHya
– 'Radiant' (A)	MFie SHya
– 'Rajah' (S)	ELan MFie NCra NHar SHya WHil WLin
– 'Ray's Grey' (S)	SHya
¶ – 'Red and White Stripe' (St)	WLin
– 'Red Beret' (S)	MFie NCra
– 'Red Gauntlet' (S)	EMNN MFie NCra NHar NNrd SHya
– 'Red Mark' (A)	MFie
– 'Red Rum' (S)	MFie NCra
¶ – 'Redstart' (S)	WHil
¶ – 'Redstart' (B)	WHil WLin
– 'Remus' (S)	ELan GAbr MFie NCra NHar NHol NNrd NWCA SHya WHil WLin
– 'Renata' (S)	MFie
– 'Rene'	EMNN
– 'Riatty' (d)	MFie
– 'Richard Shaw' (A)	MFie NNrd
– 'Rishworth' (S)	SHya
– 'Roberto' (S)	SHya
– 'Rock Sand' (S)	EMNN GCLN GCrs MFie NHar NNrd
– 'Rodeo' (A)	MFie NCra SHya
– 'Rolts' (S)	CLyd ELan EMNN GAbr MFie NBir NBro NCra NHar NHol NNrd NOak SHya WFar WHil
¶ – 'Rolt's Green Fly'	SSON
– 'Rondy' (S)	SHya
– 'Ronny Simpson'	NCra
– 'Rosalie Edwards' (S)	EMNN MFie NCra NNrd SHya
– 'Rosamund' (d)	SHya
– 'Rosemary' (S)	EMNN MFie NNrd
– 'Rowena' (A)	CLyd EMNN MFie MOne NCra NHar NHol SHya
– 'Roxburgh' (A)	EMNN SHya
– 'Royal Velvet' (S)	GAbr NNrd
– 'Ruby Hyde' (B)	MFie
– 'Rusty Dusty'	GAbr
– 'Sailor Boy' (S)	MFie SHya
– 'Saint Boswells' (S)	MFie SHya
– 'Saint Elmo' (d)	MFie
– 'Saint Gerrans' White' (B)	MFie
– 'Saint Quentin' (S)	SHya
– 'Salad' (S)	MFie SHya
– 'Sale Green' (A)	SHya
¶ – 'Sally'	WHil
– 'Sam Hunter'	NCra
– 'Sandhills' (A)	SHya
– 'Sandmartin' (S)	MFie
– 'Sandra' (A)	ELan EMNN GAbr MFie SHya WHil WLin
– 'Sandwood Bay' (A)	CLyd EMNN GAbr MFie NBro NCra NHar NNrd SHya WHil WPen
– 'Sarah Lodge' (d)	EMNN GAbr MFie
– 'Satchmo'	EMNN
– 'Scipio' (S)	SHya
– 'Seaton Burn' (S)	SHya
– 'Serenity' (S)	EMNN MFie SHya
– 'Shalford' (d)	MFie NHol SPop WLin
– 'Sharman's Cross' (S)	SHya
– 'Sheila' (S)	GAbr MFie NHar NNrd SBla SHya WLin
– 'Shere' (S)	EMNN MFie NCra SHya WLin
– 'Sherwood'	EMNN MFie NHar SHya
– 'Shirley Hibberd' (S)	SHya
– 'Shotley' (A)	EMNN
– 'Shrewton' (S)	SHya
– 'Silverway' (S)	SHya
– 'Sir Hardy Amies' (A)	SHya
– 'Sir John Hall'	NCra
– 'Sirius' (A)	CLyd MFie MOne NCra NHar NHol SHya WHil WLin
– 'Slioch' (S)	EMNN MFie NNrd SHya
– 'Snooty Fox' (A)	EMNN MFie NNrd WLin
– 'Snooty Fox II' (A)	SHya
– 'Snowy Owl'	GCLN MFie SHya
– 'Soncy Face'	NCra
– 'South Barrow' (d)	EMNN GAbr MFie WHil
– 'Splendour' (S)	SHya
– 'Spring Meadows' (S)	MFie MOne NCra NRoo SHya WLin
– 'Springtime'	NCra SPop
– SS TY 72 (S)	MFie
– 'Standish' (d)	GAbr MFie NCra NHol SHya
– 'Stant's Blue' (S)	EMNN LRHS MFie NBro NHol SHya
– 'Star Wars' (S)	SHya
– 'Starry' (S)	NHar NHol WLin
– 'Stella' (S)	MFie
– 'Stoke Poges' (A)	SHya
– 'Stonnal' (A)	MFie NHar SHya
– 'Streamlet' (S)	SHya
– 'Stubb's Tartan' (S)	NHar
– 'Sue' (A)	MFie
– 'Sue Douglas' (A)	SHya
– 'Sugar Plum Fairy'	EMNN NNrd
– 'Summer Sky' (A)	SHya
– 'Sumo'	NCra SPop
¶ – 'Sunburst' (S)	GCrs
I – 'Sunflower' (S)	MFie NHar NHol WLin
– 'Sunsal' (S)	MFie
– 'Sunstar' (S)	EMNN MFie
– 'Super Para' (S)	EMNN GCLN GCrs MFie NNrd SHya
– 'Superb' (S)	SHya
– 'Susan' (A)	MFie SHya
– 'Susannah' (d)	MFie MOne NChi NHol SHya WLin
– 'Sweet Pastures' (S)	EMNN MFie NCra NHol SHya
– 'Swift' (S)	MFie
– 'Swinley' (S)	SHya
– 'Sword'	NNrd SHya
– 'Symphony' (A)	SHya WHil
– 'Tall Purple Dusty Miller' (B)	MFie
– 'Tally-ho' (A)	SHya
– 'Tarantella' (A)	EMNN GCLN MFie NCra NNrd SHya
– 'Tawny Owl'	NBro
– 'Ted Roberts' (A)	EMNN MFie NCra SHya WLin

Name	Codes
– 'Teem' (S)	EMNN MFie NCra SHya WLin
– 'Tenby Grey' (S)	MFie
– 'The Baron' (S)	MFie MOne NHar WHil WLin
– 'The Bishop' (S)	MFie NCra
– 'The Bride' (S)	EMNN NCra
– 'The Cardinal' (d)	SAsh
– 'The Czar' (A)	SHya
¶ – 'The Marie Crousse'	WLin
– 'The Maverick' (S)	SHya
– 'The Raven' (S)	EMNN MFie
– 'The Sneeps'	NCra SHya WHil
– 'The Snods' (S)	EMNN MFie NCra
– 'Thebes'	NCra
– 'Thetis' (A)	MFie NCra SHya WHil WLin
– 'Thirlmere' (d)	MFie SHya
– 'Three Way Stripe'	SHya WHil
– 'Tinkerbell' (S)	MFie SHya
¶ – 'Tomato'	WLin
– 'Tomboy' (S)	MFie
– 'Tomma'	NCra
– 'Tosca' (S)	EMNN GCrs NNrd SHya WHil WLin
– 'Trojan' (S)	SHya WLin
– 'Trouble' (d)	CHad EMNN MFie MHlr MOne NChi NCra NHar SHya SMrm WLin
– 'Trudy' (S)	EMNN GAbr GCrs MFie NCra NNrd
– 'True Briton' (S)	MFie SHya
– 'Trumpet Blue' (S)	MFie
– 'Tumbledown' (A)	MFie SHya
– 'Tummel'	NCra
– 'Tuthmoses'	NCra
¶ – 'Two Tone' mauve (d)	WHil
– 'Tye Lea' (S)	MFie SHya
– 'Typhoon' (A)	MFie SHya
– 'Unforgetable'	NCra
– 'Valerie' (A)	MFie NCra NNrd SHya WHil
– 'Valerie Clare'	NCra
– 'Vee Too' (A)	MFie SHya SPop
– 'Velvet Moon'	NCra
– 'Venetian'	NCra
– 'Vera' (A)	MFie
– 'Verdi' (A)	EMNN MFie NCra SHya
– 'Victoria' (S)	SHya
– 'Victoria de Wemyss' (A)	MFie
– 'Vulcan' (A)	MFie NCra SHya
– 'Waincliffe Red' (S)	MFie
– 'Walhampton' (S)	EMNN MFie SHya
– 'Walton' (A)	MFie SHya
– 'Walton Heath' (d)	EMNN GAbr MFie SHya WHil WLin
– 'Warwick' (S)	SHya
– 'Wedding Day' (S)	MFie
¶ – 'Wendy'	WLin
– 'White Ensign' (S)	EMNN GAbr MFie NNrd NOak SHya WHil WLin
– 'White Water'	NCra
– 'White Wings' (S)	EMNN MFie NCra SHya WLin
– 'Wide Awake' (A)	MFie
– 'Wincha' (S)	GCrs MFie SHya
– 'Windways Mystery' (B)	MFie
– 'Winifrid' (A)	CLyd EMNN MFie MOne NCra NHar NHol SHya WHil
– 'Woodmill' (A)	SHya
– 'Wor Jackie' (S)	EMNN MFie NHar
¶ – 'Wycliffe Midnight'	GAbr
– 'Y.I. Hinney' (A)	EMNN MFie
– 'Yorkshire Grey' (S)	MFie NNrd SHya
– 'Zambia' (d)	CLyd MFie SHya WHil WLin
§ *auricula* L. (2) ♀	CArn ELan GCrs GDra GTou MBal MTho NBro NCra NSla NWCA SIng SPer SSmi WCla
– subsp. *auricula* (2)	GTou
♦ – subsp. *balbisii*	See *P. auricula* subsp. *ciliata*
– subsp. *bauhinii* (2)	MBro
§ – subsp. *ciliata* (2)	NNrd
'Barbara Midwinter' (30x6)	CMea NDov
Barnhaven Blues Group (Prim)(30)	GAbr NRya
Barnhaven doubles (dPoly)(30)	CSWP
♦ Barnhaven Gold-laced Group	See *P.* **Gold-laced Group Barnhaven**
Barnhaven Reds	See *P.* **Tartan Reds Group**
Barnhaven Traditional Group	CSWP
'Beamish Foam' (Poly)(30)	CVer MDHE
'Beatrice Wooster' (2)	CLyd CNic EHyt EMNN EPot LRHS MBro MFie NGre NHar NHed NHol NMen NNrd NWCA SIng WAbe
'Beeches' Pink'	GAbr
beesiana (4)	CInt CRow CSam EAst EBar EHon ELan GAbr GCHN GFle LPBA LSyl MBri MFie MSta MSte NHar NOak NSti SMrm SPer WChe WGwG WHil WLin WPer WPyg WWal
'Bellamy's Pride'	CLyd
bellidifolia (17)	CPla GAbr NGre
§ – subsp. *hyacinthina* (17)	NMen
beluensis	See *P.* × *pubescens* 'Freedom'
Bergfrühling Julianas Group (Prim)(30)	MFie
§ × *berninae* 'Windrush' (2)	CLyd EHyt NHar NNrd WAbe
'Betty Green' (Prim)(30)	MBri
'Bewerley White'	See *P.* × *pubescens* 'Bewerley White'
bhutanica	See *P. whitei* 'Sherriff's Variety'
× *biflora* (2)	CBlo
'Big Red Giant' (dPrim)(30)	CBlo EBar LFis MOne NHar
bileckii	See *P.* × *forsteri* 'Bileckii'
'Blue Riband' (Prim)(30)	CCot CGle GGar LSur MBri MHig WAbe WFar WHil
'Blue Sapphire' (dPrim)(30)	CBlo CMil GAbr LHop MOne NChi NRoo SLod
Blue Striped Victorians Group (Poly)(30)	GAbr
'Blutenkissen' (Prim)(30)	GAbr GMaP LSur
'Bon Accord Purple' (dPoly)(30)	CGle EJud WFar WRus
'Bonfire' (4)	GDra
boothii alba (21)	GGGa
¶ – subsp. *autumnalis* (21)	WAbe
¶ – subsp. *repens* (21)	MNrw
'Boothman's Ruby'	See *P.* × *pubescens* 'Boothman's Variety'
boveana (12)	MFie SBla
§ *bracteosa* (21)	GCrs ITim NHar WAbe
'Brimstone' (Poly)(30)	CGle
'Broadwell Pink' (2)	EHyt
¶ 'Broadwell Ruby' (2)	WLin
'Broxbourne'	CLyd NHar
'Buckland Wine' (Prim)(30)	CCot CVer LSur
× *bulleesiana* (4)	LFis NBro NPri SMrm SRms SWat WHil WPer WRha
¶ – Moerheim hybrids (4)	LIck

bulleyana (4) ♀ — Widely available
– ACE 2484 (4) — GGGa WAbe
burmanica (4) — CInt CPla CSam EBee GAbr GBuc GDra GFle GGar MBal MSta NCra NDea NHar NPri SRms WCru
'Butterscotch' (Prim)(30) — CGle CSWP GPot
'Caerulea Plena' (dPrim)(30) — GCal
calderiana (21) — GDra NHar WAbe
– subsp. *strumosa* BC 9347 (21) — GCra
Candelabra hybrids (4) — CBre CBro EMNN NCra
Candy Pinks Group (Prim)(30) — GAbr
capitata (5) — CBot CGle CInt CPla CSpe GDra GFle GTou LSyl MBal MBri NCra NGre NHar WBea WCla WFar WPer
– subsp. *crispata* AGS/ES 407 (5) — GCra
– dark forms (5) — MFie
– KEKE 274 (5) — MFie
– subsp. *mooreana* (5) — CFir CHan CPea GCan GFle GMac LPBA NLak WCla WHil
– subsp. *sphaerocephala* (5) — GCra NWCA
'Captain Blood' (dPrim)(30) — CBos ECGN GAbr NSti SUsu WRha
'Carmen' (Prim)(30) — CLyd
Carnation Victorians Group (Poly)(30) — CSWP GAbr MFie
'Casquet' — CSWP
cernua (17) — GCan GDra GFle MFie NGre NHar WAbe WCru
'Charlen' (dPrim)(30) — NHar
Chartreuse Group (Poly)(30) — CGle CSWP GAbr MFie
'Cherry' (Prim)(30) — CCot CVer GAbr
§ *chionantha* (18) ♀ — CBot CGle CPla GDra GFle GGGa GMaP GPot GTou LBee LSyl MBal MBri MFie MNrw NCra NDea NGre NHar NHed NNor NRoo SPer WGwG WHil WLin
§ – subsp. *melanops* (18) — CGle CPla ELan GCan GFle GMaP NGre NHar
§ – subsp. *sinoplantaginea* (18) — CPla GAbr
§ – subsp. *sinopurpurea* (18) — CGle CPla EBee EMNN EWes GAbr GCra GDra GFle GGGa GTou LSyl MBal NCra SPer WLin WPer WWhi
¶ – – ACE 1421 (18) — EPot
'Chocolate Soldier' (dPrim)(30) — GGar MBal
chungensis (4) — CGle CMea GCra GTou MBri MLLN NHar SRms WAbe
§ – × *pulverulenta* (4) — EBrP EBre LBre NPri SBre SMrm WAbe
× *chunglenta* — See *P. chungensis* × *pulverulenta*
§ 'Clarence Elliott' (2) — CGra CLyd EHyt NGre NHar SIng WLin
clarkei (11) — CLyd GCrs GFle GGGa GTou MHig NWCA
clusiana (2) — GDra MBal NGre NHol NSla WLin
¶ – 'Murray-Lyon' (2) — WLin
cockburniana (4) — CInt CRow GAbr GDra GFle GGGa GGar GMac GPot GTou MBal MBri MFie NCra NGre NHar NWCA SMrm SRms

concholoba (17) — CPla GAbr GCan GCra GFle GGGa GGar GTou MFie NGre NHar WAbe
'Corporal Baxter' (dPrim)(30) — EBar LHop MBri MOne SLod SMrm
cortusoides (7) — CPla EBee GCra GFle MNrw NCra SRms WHil
Cowichan (Poly)(30) — CCot CInt GAbr MBri NCra NSti
Cowichan Amethyst Group (Poly)(30) — CSWP GAbr
Cowichan Blue Group (Poly)(30) — CSWP EWoo GAbr LHop WPen
Cowichan Garnet Group (Poly)(30) — CSWP EWoo GAbr GCan MFie
Cowichan Venetian Group (Poly)(30) — CSWP GAbr GCan WFar
Cowichan Yellow Group (Poly)(30) — CMil GAbr NWoo WCot WPen
'Craven Gem' (Poly)(30) — GAbr LSur NRoo
Crescendo Series (Poly)(30) — GAbr
'Crimson Cushion' — NNrd
'Crimson Queen' (Prim)(30) — GAbr LSur
'Crimson Velvet' (2) — EMNN GAbr MBro MHig NNrd SRms
crispa — See *P. glomerata*
* *cuneata* — GTou
cuneifolia (8) — GCLN
* – *alba* (8) — GCLN
daonensis (2) — NMen
darialica (11) — CGle CPla ELan GDra MYat NChi NCra NMen
'David Green' (Prim)(30) — CVer SIng
'David Valentine' — GAbr LSur
'Dawn Ansell' (dPrim)(30) — Widely available
Daybreak Group (Poly)(30) — CSWP MFie
¶ *deflexa* (17) — GCrs GFle LSyl
denticulata (9) ♀ — Widely available
– var. *alba* (9) — CGle EBrP EBre ECha ELan EMNN EPot ERav GAbr GChr GPot GTou LBre LHop MBal MBri MFie MWat NCra NHar NHed NHol NOrc NRoo SBre WHen WPer
¶ – blue (9) — NLar
– 'Bressingham Beauty' (9) — EBrP EBre LBre SBre
– var. *cachemiriana* hort. (9) — EPfV WCla
– 'Glenroy Crimson' (9) — CRDP MBal SRms SVil
– 'Inshriach Carmine' (9) — GDra
– lilac (9) — EHon GTou MFie NPri
– purple (9) — GAbr IBlr
– red (9) — CRow EMNN EPar NOrc NPri
– 'Robinson's Red' (9) — EPot GBuc
– 'Ronsdorf' (9) — LHop
– rose (9) — NCut NHar
– 'Rubinball' (9) — EBrP EBre EPfP GAri LBre NHol NRoo SBre
– ruby (9) — CInt EHon GAbr GTou LWak MBri MCLN MFie NBro NOak SMrm SRms WHen WHil WPer WPyg
– 'Snowball' (9) — MCLN MFir NOak WHen WPyg
deorum (2) — CGra WLin
× *deschmannii* — See *P.* × *vochinensis*
'Desert Sunset' (Poly)(30) — CSWP GAbr MFie
'Devon Cream' (Prim)(30) — ECha GBuc

'Dianne' | See *P.* × *forsteri* 'Dianne'
'Doctor Mary' (Prim)(30) | GAbr
'Dora' | MDHE
'Dorothy' (Poly)(30) | GAbr LSur MRav
'Double Lilac' | See *P. vulgaris* 'Lilacina Plena'
drummondiana (21) | GFle
'Duchess of York' | CBos WBro
'Duckyls Red' (Prim)(30) | GBuc LSur
'Dusky Lady' | MTis WFar
'Early Irish Yellow' (Prim)(30) | LSur
'Easter Bonnet' | CBlo MOne NRoo
edelbergii (12) | GTou MFie
edgeworthii | See *P. nana*
elatior (30) ♀ | CBro CGle CKin CNic CPla CRow CSev EMou GDra GFle GLil LFox LSyl MHar MHew MMal MNrw MSal NChi NCra NMen NOrc NRoo NSti SPer SRms SSpi WCla WUnd
– hose in hose (30) | GAbr
– subsp. *intricata* (30) | CNic
* – 'Katy McSporran' (30) | SPer
– subsp. *leucophylla* (30) | ECho
ellisiae (21) | MFie NMen NSla
'Erin's Gem' (Poly)(30) | CGle
§ *erythra* (26) | NGre
'Ethel Barker' (2) | CLyd EHyt EMNN EPot ITim LFox MBro MHig NGre NHar NHed NHol NMen NNrd SIng WAbe
'Eugénie' (dPrim)(30) | CGle CSpe MOne NChi NHar NHol WLRN WWeb
farinosa (11) | CLyd CNic CPla GFle MBal MBri MSal NCra NGre NHar NMen NRya WCla WPer WUnd
– JCA 786.500 (11) | MFie
fasciculata (11) | EDAr LBee NSla
– CLD 345 (11) | NHar
'Fife Yellow' (dPoly)(30) | GBuc
'Fire Dance' (Poly)(30) | MFie
Firefly Group (Poly)(30) | GAbr LFox
firmipes (26) | EBee GFle NTow WLRN
§ *flaccida* (28) ♀ | GCra GDra GFle GGGa GMac MBal NCra NGre NHar WAbe WLin
× *flagellicaulis* | See *P.* × *polyantha*
Flamingo Group (Poly)(30) | CSWP GAbr MFie
§ × *floerkeana* (2) | NGre NHol WAbe
– f. *biflora alba* (2) | NGre SBla
florida (29) | GGGa
florindae (26) ♀ | Widely available
– hybrids (26) | CVer GAbr LFox MFie MSCN WHil WLin
– orange (26) | CSam GMac IBlr LSyl MNrw NChi WChe WCru WFar
– 'Ray's Ruby' (26) | GBuc MCLN MNrw NBir NBro WWhi
– red (26) | GAbr GGGa LSyl MSta SMrm WChe WFar
Footlight Parade Group (Prim)(30) | CSWP
forrestii (3) | GMaP MFie NGre NHar WAbe
– C&Cu 9431 (3) | GGGa
§ × *forsteri* (2) | EMNN ITim MHig NHed NHol WAbe
§ – 'Bileckii' (2) | EPot GCrs LBee MBal MBro MHig NBro NHar NHed NWCA SRms SSmi WAbe

§ – 'Dianne' (2) | EHyt EPot GAbr MBro MHig MYat NBro NHar NHol NNrd WAbe WGwG
'Freckles' (dPrim)(30) | ELan GGar MCLN MOne NHar NHol SPer
'Freedom' | See *P.* × *pubescens* 'Freedom'
frondosa ♀ | CGle CInt CLyd CPla GCra GCrs GPot LFox LHop MBal MBri MBro MFie NChi NCra NHar NMen NWCA SMrm WAbe WHoo
Fuchsia Victorians Group (Poly)(30) | CSWP MFie
¶ 'Garnet' (*allionii* hybrid) (2) | MFie
'Garryard Guinevere' | See *P.* 'Guinevere'
gaubana (12) | MFie NMen
gemmifera (11) | GGGa NHar
¶ – ACE 1375 (11) | EHyt
¶ – ACE 1427 (11) | EPot NHar NWCA
¶ – ACE 1541 (11) | IDac
– var. *zambalensis* (11) | WAbe
geraniifolia (7) | NRoo
§ 'Gigha' (Prim)(30) | CSWP CSpe GPot
glaucescens (2) | CLyd MBro MFie NHar NSla
– subsp. *calycina* | See *P. glaucescens* subsp. *glaucescens*
§ – subsp. *glaucescens* (2) | NHol
– JCA 786.900 (2) | MFie
'Glebe Grey' (Prim)(30) | CGle
§ *glomerata* (5) | CSWP GBuc GCrs GGGa
¶ 'Gloria' (Prim)(30) | LSur
'Gloriosa' (Prim)(30) | CCot LSur
'Glowing Embers' (4) | CGle ELan MBri MFie NBir
♦ *glutinosa* Allioni | See *P. allionii* (2)
– Lapeyrouse (2) | ITim
Gold-laced Group (Poly)(30) | CBre CCot CDec CGle CM&M CPla CRDP CSWP ELan EWoo GAbr GMac LFox MBri MBro NChi NCra NHar NNrd NWCA SUsu WHer WHil
§ Gold-laced Group Barnhaven | GAbr MFie
¶ Gold-laced Group Beeches strain (Poly)(30) ♀ | MAus
gracilipes (21) | CGle GFle GGGa MOne NHar SRms WAbe
– early form (21) | NHar WAbe
– L&S 1 (21) | NHar
– L&S 1166 (21) | NHar WAbe
– late form (21) | NHar WAbe
– 'Major' | See *P. bracteosa*
– 'Minor' | See *P. petiolaris*
– 'Winter Jewel' (21) | NHol
Grand Canyon Group (Poly)(30) | GPot MFie
griffithii (21) | GFle GGGa NGre
'Groeneken's Glory' (Prim)(30) | CGle CInt CNic CVer ELan GAbr LSur MBri MRav NBro NCra NFla SIng WFar WPbr
§ 'Guinevere' (Poly)(30) ♀ | Widely available
'Hall Barn Blue' | GAbr LSur
§ *halleri* (11) | CPea CPla GCHN GCan GCra GFle GTou MBal MFie NCra NHar NMen NWCA SSca WAbe WCla
– 'Longiflora' | See *P. halleri*
Harbinger Group (Prim)(30) | CGle GPot
'Harbour Lights' | CSWP MFie
Harlow Carr hybrids (4) | EHyt MLLN NCat NDea NRoo WPen

Harvest Yellows Group (Poly)(30) — GPot MFie
x *heeri* (2) — EPot NHol
'Helge' (Prim)(30) — GAbr LSur
helodoxa — See *P. prolifera*
§ 'Hemswell Blush' (2) — EMNN NGre NHol WLin
§ 'Hemswell Ember' (2) — EHyt EMNN MFie NHar NHed NMen WLin
heucherifolia (7) — CBot CPla GCan LFox LSyl MSCN
hirsuta (2) — CNic GCrs GTou MFie
– 'Lismore Snow' (2) — EHyt NHar
Hose in Hose (Poly)(30) — CCot CGle CSWP MNrw MOne NCra NPri WRus
'Hurstwood Midnight' — MFie
'Husky' ♀ — NRoo
§ 'Hyacinthia' (2) — CLyd EMNN EPot NGre WAbe
♦ *hyacinthina* — See *P. bellidifolia* subsp. *hyacinthina*
♦ *ianthina* — See *P. prolifera*
Indian Reds Group (Poly)(30) — MFie
'Ingram's Blue' (Prim)(30) — WPGP
Inshriach hybrids (4) — CMHG GAbr GCan GDra GGar LHop MBri MFie MSCN MSte SPer WWal
integrifolia (2) — GCLN GCrs NGre WAbe
x *intermedia* (2) — MHig
§ 'Inverewe' (4) ♀ — GAbr GAri GCal GDra GGar NHar NRoo
§ *involucrata* (11) — CBot GCLN GCan GFle GGGa NHar NWCA SWat WHil
¶ – CC 1422 (11) — MRPP
¶ – CC 1812 (11) — MRPP
§ – subsp. *yargongensis* (11) — CGle CInt CLyd CMea CNic CPla EWes GAbr GCHN GCrs GFle GGar GTou MBal MBri MFie MRPP NCra NGre NHar NNrd NWCA SBod SRms SWat WAbe WFar WPat
ioessa (26) — CPla EWes GCra GGGa MBal MBri NWCA
¶ – HWJCM 300 (26) — WCru
'Iris Mainwaring' (Prim)(30) — CVer EPot GAbr GMaP LSur MDHE NCra NNrd
irregularis — GCrs GGGa
Jack in the Green Group (Poly)(30) — CCot CDec CGle CMGP CNic CSWP LSur MNrw NChi NCra WHer WRus
Jackanapes Group (Poly)(30) — LSur
'Jackaroo' (4) — GFle
¶ 'Jackie Richards' (2) — WLin
japonica (4) ♀ — CGle CMHG CRow ECha GFle GPot GTou LPBA MFir NBro NChi NCra NHar NNor NRoo SUsu SWat WChe WCla WCru WPer
– 'Alba' (4) — GBin NPri WAbe WHil
– 'Apple Blossom' (4) — NHed
* – 'Carminea' — WHil
– 'Fromfield Pink' (4) — WWoo
– 'Fuji' (4) — CSWP CSam GCan GCra GDra MBal MBri MSta
– 'Miller's Crimson' (4) — Widely available
– 'Oriental Sunrise' (4) — CMil
– 'Postford White' (4) — Widely available
– red shades (4) — NSti WAbe
– 'Valley Red' (4) — GBin GBuc GCra GGar GMac LSyl NRoo
jesoana B&SWJ 618 (7) — WCru
Jewel Group — LSur

'Jill' — CVer LSur
'Joan Hughes' (*allionii* hybrid) (2) — CLyd NHar SIng WAbe
'Johanna' (11) — CGle GFle GGar LSyl NBro NGre NHar NLak NWCA
'Jo-Jo' (2) — CLyd
juliae (30) — CGle CPla CRDP GFle LSur MHlr NGre NMen WCot WEas
– white (30) — CGle NDov
x *juliana* — See *P.* x *pruhonicensis*
x *juribella* (2) — EHyt
'Kate Haywood' — CLyd
'Ken Dearman' (dPrim)(30) — CSpe EBar GGar MBal MCLN MHlr MOne MRav NEgg NHol NSti SIng SMrm
kewensis (12) ♀ — EBee MFie NWCA
'Kinlough Beauty' (Poly)(30) — CCot CDec CVer EPar GAbr LFox LSur NCra NRoo NSti NWes WEas WLin
kisoana (7) — CPla MTho WCru
– *alba* (2) — CLAP CPla MTho
'Lady Greer' (Poly)(30) ♀ — CCot CGle CInt CPla ECGN ELan GAbr ITim LFox LGan LSur MRav NBir NChi NCra NGre NHar NMen NRoo NRya NSti NWCA SIng SLod SMac SSmi WEas WHal WPbr WWat
'Lambrook Lilac' (Poly)(30) — CVer
§ *latifolia* (2) — NCra WLRN
– cream (2) — NGre NHed
latisecta (7) — GGGa
§ *laurentiana* (11) — EBee GFle NWCA
¶ 'Lea Gardens' (*allionii* hybrid) (2) — MFie
'Lee Myers' (*allionii* hybrid) (2) — CLyd CNic EHyt EMNN MFie NHar NHed NMen NNrd
'Lilac Fairy' — NHar NNrd
¶ 'Lilac Time' — SIng
'Lilian Harvey' (dPrim)(30) — CElw CGle MOne MRav NBir NHol SPer
Limelight Group (Poly)(30) — EWoo GAbr MFie
'Lingwood Beauty' (Prim)(30) — CVer GAbr LSur
'Linnet' (21) — ITim
'Lismore' (2) — EHyt
'Lismore Pink Ice' — NGre
'Lismore Yellow' (2) — EPot GTou NGre NHar NNrd SBla WAbe
Lissadel hybrids (4) — GMac
'Little Egypt' (Poly)(30) — EWoo
* 'Little Poppet' — GAbr
littoniana — See *P. vialii*
§ x *loiseleurii* (2) — EBrP EBre LBre MBro SBre
longiflora — See *P. halleri*
luteola (11) — GFle MFie MNrw NPri SRms WHil WWoo
macrophylla (18) — GFle GTou MBal
– H 78 (18) — GDra
magellanica (11) — WAbe
malacoides (3) — MBri
marginata (2) ♀ — EMNN EPot GAbr GCrs GDra GFle LFox LHop MBro MRPP MYat NCra NGre NHar NHed NHol SSmi WAbe
– *alba* (2) — EPot EWes MBro MHig MYat NBro NCra NGre NHar NHed NNrd SSmi WAbe
– 'Amethyst' (2) — EPot
– 'Arthur Branch' (2) — EPot WAbe
– 'Barbara Clough' (2) — CLyd MFie WAbe

– 'Beamish' (2) CLyd EPot NBro NRya
– 'Beatrice Lascaris' (2) EPot ITim MBro MFie MHig
MYat NHar NHol NMen NNrd
SIng WAbe WLin
– 'Beverley Reid' (2) EHyt
– 'Caerulea' (2) CLyd EPot MFos MHig MYat
WAbe
– 'Clear's Variety' (2) EHyt EMNN EPot MHig MYat
NHar NMen NNrd
– 'Correvon's Variety' (2) CLyd NCra WAbe
¶ – cut-leaved (2) NHol
– 'Doctor Jenkins' (2) NHar NHol WLin
– 'Drake's Form' (2) EPot ITim MHig NHol
– 'Earl L. Bolton' (2) EPot NHol NNrd WAbe
– 'Elizabeth Fry' (2) CLyd LFox MBro NNrd
– 'F.W. Millard' (2) MBro NHar
– 'Grandiflora' (2) MBro NHar NHol NNrd SIng
WLin
– 'Highland Twilight' (2) CNic CPBP NNrd
– 'Holden Variety' (2) EHyt EMNN MBal MBro MHig
NGre NHar NHed NHol NMen
NNrd WAbe WLin
– 'Hyacinthia' (2) See *P.* '**Hyacinthia**'
– 'Ivy Agee' CLyd EPot WAbe
– 'Janet' (2) CLyd EHyt EMNN EPot MHig
WAbe WLin
– 'Jenkins Variety' (2) CLyd EPot SIng
– 'Kesselring's Variety' CLyd EHyt ELan EPot MBro
MHig MRPP MYat NHar NHed
NNrd SIng SSmi WAbe WLin
WWin
* – 'Lilac' (2) EHyt LFox NHar NNrd
– 'Lilac Domino' WAbe
– 'Linda Pope' (2) ♀ CLyd CPBP EMNN EPot ITim
NCra NHar NHed NHol NMen
WAbe
– maritime form (2) NNrd
– 'Messingham' (2) EPot
– 'Millard's Variety' (2) CLyd NMen
– 'Nancy Lucy' (2) WAbe
– 'Napoleon' (2) ITim NHar NHol NNrd
– 'Prichard's Variety' (2) CLyd ELan EMNN EPot GDra
ITim LBee LFox MBro MFie
MYat NCra NGre NHar NHed
NMen NRya SSmi WAbe WCla
WEas WLin
– 'Rheniana' (2) EPot
– 'Rosea' (2) EPot NHol SIng
¶ – 'Rubra' SIng
– 'Sheila Denby' (2) EMNN GCLN NNrd
– 'Snowhite' (2) WAbe
– 'Violet Form' (2) EMNN MBro NHar
– 'Waithman's Variety' (2) EPot GTou
¶ 'Maria Talbot' NNrd
(*allionii* hybrid) (2)
'Marianne Davey' CGle EPri MBri MCLN MRav
(dPrim)(30) NMGW NSti SPer
'Marie Crousse' CGle EBar EHic GAbr LHop
(dPrim)(30) MBal MBro MFie MOne
MWgw NHar NHol SHya SMrm
SPer SSvw WHil WRha
Marine Blues Group CSWP GAbr MFie
(Poly)(30)
'Mars' (*allionii* hybrid) (2) MBro NGre NHar NNrd WLin
'Marven' (2) CLyd EPot MBro NCra NHol
NNrd NWoo WLin
'Mary Anne' LSur
¶ 'Mauve Jack in the Green' LSur
'Mauve Queen' (Prim)(30) LSur
Mauve Victorians Group CSWP MFie
'McWatt's Claret' CSWP CVer GAbr LSur NCra
(Poly)(30)

'McWatt's Cream' CSWP CVer GAbr GFle GGar
(Poly)(30) LHop LSur NBro NCra NHol
NMen WLin
✦ *melanops* See *P. chionantha* subsp.
melanops
'Mexico' MFie
Midnight Group CSWP MFie
'Miniera' (2) CLyd CPBP EPot SBla
minima (2) CGra CLyd GTou NBro NGre
NHar NWCA WAbe
– var. *alba* (2) CMea EPot GCLN GCrs GGGa
NSla
– × *glutinosa* (2) See *P.* × *floerkeana*
– × *hirsuta* (2) See *P.* × *forsteri*
– × *villosa* (2) See *P.* × *truncata*
– × *wulfeniana* (2) See *P.* × *vochinensis*
'Miss Indigo' (dPrim)(30) CGle CSam EBar EBrP EBre
LBre LFis MAus MBri MCLN
MOne MRav NEgg NHar NHol
NRoo NSti SBre SIng SLod
SMrm SPer SUsu WHil WPnn
'Miss Luck' CVer
✦ *mistassinica* var. See *P. laurentiana*
macropoda
¶ *miyabeana* B&SWJ 3407 (4) WCru
modesta alba (11) GCLN
– var. *faurieae* (11) GCLN MFie NGre
– 'Flore Pleno' (d) CPBP
– var. *samanimontana* NGre
(11)
'Morton' NGre
* 'Mrs Eagland' NGre
'Mrs McGillivray' GAbr LSur
(Prim)(30)
Munstead Strain (Poly)(30) LSur
× *murettiana* (2) WAbe
muscarioides (17) CGle CPla GAbr GCan GCra
GFle GTou LGan MFie NGre
NHar WAbe
Muted Victorians Group CSWP MFie
(Poly)(30)
nepalensis See *P. tanneri* subsp. *nepalensis*
New Pinks Group CSWP GAbr MFie
(Poly)(30)
'Nightingale' WAbe
✦ *nivalis* Pallas See *P. chionantha*
nutans Delavay See *P. flaccida*
§ – Georgi (25) GCra
obconica (19) MBri
'Old Port' (Poly)(30) GBin MBro WPat
Old Rose Victorians CSWP MFie
Group (Poly)(30)
'Olive Wyatt' (dPrim)(30) EPri
'Oriental Sunrise' (4) GPot MBri MFie
Osiered Amber Group CSWP GAbr GPot
(Prim)(30)
'Our Pat' (dPoly)(30) IBlr WRus
Pagoda hybrids (4) MBri
palinuri (2) MFie
palmata (7) GFle GGGa NHar WAbe
'Paris '90' (Poly)(30) CMil CSWP EWoo GAbr MFie
NNrd
parryi (20) CGra GCLN GCrs NCra NGre
NHar NWCA WHil
'Peardrop' (2) CGra NHol WLin
pedemontana (2) MSte NGre NHar NHol
– 'Alba' (2) EHyt
'Perle von Bottrop' GAbr MHig
(Prim)(30)
'Peter Klein' (11) EPot GAbr GDra GFle ITim
MBal NHar WOMN WPyg

§ *petiolaris* (21) — EHyt GCHN GCrs GFle GGGa ITim MOne NCra NHar NHol WAbe

– LS&H 19856 — See *P.* **'Redpoll'**

'Petticoat' — MOne NHol WWoo

§ 'Pink Aire' (2) — EHyt ITim MFie

¶ 'Pink Fairy' — EHyt

'Pink Gem' (dPrim)(30) — NWes

'Pink Ice' (*allionii* hybrid) (2) — CGra CLyd CPBP EHyt EMNN EPot GCLN MDHE MFie NMen NNrd WLin

'Pink Profusion' (Prim)(30) — NGre

pinnatifida (17) — GGGa

poissonii (4) — CBot CGle CHar CPla GAbr GCan GCra GFle GGar GMac IBlr LPBA MBal NGre WAbe

– CLD 193 (4) — LSyl

Polyanthus (30) — GDra NCra

polyneura (7) — CBot CNic CPla ECha GCra GFle GMac LSyl MBal MFie MHig MNes MNrw NDea NHol NWCA SRms

– ACE 1429 (7) — EPot SBla

¶ 'Port Wine' — GAbr

praenitens — See *P. sinensis*

prenantha (4) — WAbe

'Prince Silverwings' (dPoly)(30) — WEas

§ × *prolifera* (4) ♀ — CMHG CTrw ECha GCra GFle GGGa GGar GMaP GMac LGan LPBA LSyl MFir MLLN MNrw NLak NSti SBla SPer SRms SSpi SWat WAbe WHil WPer WWat

§ × *pubescens* (2) ♀ — CInt EMan EPot GAbr GDra LFox MBro MYat SMrm SSmi WLRN WPer

– 'Alba' (2) — NHar WAbe

– 'Alison Gibbs' (2) — MHig

– × *allionii* (2) — NNrd

– 'Apple Blossom' (2) — CLyd EHyt EMNN EPot MFie

– 'Balfouriana' (2) — CNic LFox MBro WLin

§ – 'Bewerley White' (2) — EHyt ELan EPot MBal MBro MRPP NCra NHed NMen NNrd WWin

– 'Blue Wave' (2) — MFie NNrd

§ – 'Boothman's Variety' (2) — CInt CLyd EMNN EPot ITim MBro MHig MRPP MYat NCra NGre NHar NHed NHol NMen NNrd NWCA SBla SIng SSmi WCla WWin

– 'Carmen' — See *P.* × *pubescens* **'Boothman's Variety'**

– 'Chamois' (2) — MFie

– 'Christine' (2) — CLyd EMNN EPot LBee MBro MFie MHig MYat NChi NCra NHar NHed NHol NMen NNrd SBod WLin

– 'Cream Viscosa' (2) — EMNN MBro MFie NHed NHol NMGW NMen NNrd

– 'Deep Mrs Wilson' (2) — EHyt SWas

– 'Ellen Page' (2) — MFie

– 'Elphenor' (2) — NNrd

– 'Faldonside' (2) — CInt CLTr CLyd EHyt EMNN EPot GCHN MBro MHig NCra NHed NHol NMGW NMen NNrd WWin

§ – 'Freedom' (2) — CLyd EHyt ELan EMNN EPot GTou ITim MBro MFie MHig MYat NCra NGre NHar NHed NHol NMen SBla SBod SRms SSmi WEas WLin WWin

– 'George Harrison' (2) — MFie

– 'Greenslacks Yellow' — NGre

– 'Harlow Car' (2) — CLyd EMNN EPot GMac ITim LFox MBro MFie MHig MYat NGre NHar NHed NMen NNrd SBla WAbe WLin

– 'Henry Hall' (2) — CLyd EWes MFie

– 'Herbert Beresford' (2) — NMen

– 'Hurstwood Red Admiral' (2) — EMNN

– 'Joan Danger' (2) — CLyd EMNN MFie NHol NNrd

– 'Joan Gibbs' (2) — CLyd ELan EPot LBee MBro MFie MHig NCra NHar NHed NMen NNrd

– 'Kath Dryden' (2) — MFie

– 'Lilac Fairy' (2) — EMNN NHed

– 'Mrs J.H. Wilson' (2) — CGra CLyd EHyt ITim MBal MBro MFie MHig NCra NGre NHed NHol NMen SBla WAbe

– 'Pat Barwick' (2) — EMNN EPot LFox MBro MFie NHed NHol NMen

– 'Peggy Fell' (2) — MDHE MFie

– 'Pink Freedom' (2) — NHed

– 'Roseille' (2) — EHyt

– 'Rufus' (2) — CGra CLyd EHyt GCLN GCrs ITim MBal NCra NHol NNrd WTin

– 'S.E. Matthews' (2) — EHyt

– 'Sid Skelton' (2) — EHyt EMNN

– 'Snowcap' — CGra

– 'Sonya' (2) — MFie

– 'The General' (2) — CLyd MBro MHig NCra NNrd WWin

– 'Victoria' (2) — EMNN

§ – 'Wedgwood' (2) — EMNN GCLN NNrd

¶ – × 'White Linda Pope' — MFie

– 'Winifred' — NHed NHol SSON

¶ *pulchra* (21) — GCLN

pulverulenta (4) ♀ — Widely available

– Bartley hybrids (4) ♀ — CBot CGle GBuc MFie SMur WChe

– 'Bartley Pink' (4) — CPla LSyl

'Purple Splendour' — LSur

'Purpurkissen' (Prim)(30) — NHol

'Quaker's Bonnet' — See *P. vulgaris* **'Lilacina Plena'**

¶ 'Rachael Kinnon' (2) — WLin

'Rachel Kinnen' (2) — EHyt MFie

'Ramona' (Poly)(30) — MFie

'Ravenglass Vermilion' — See *P.* **'Inverewe'**

'Red Sunset' (4) — GDra

'Red Velvet' (dPrim)(30) — CMil CSam LHop MOne SMrm WWeb

§ 'Redpoll' (21) — NHar WAbe

reidii (28) — MBri NCra

– var. *williamsii* (28) — EBrP EBre GDra GFle GGGa GTou LBre MBal MBri NGre NHar SBre

– var. *williamsii alba* (28) — GDra MBal MBri NGre

¶ *reptans* (16) — WAbe

'Reverie' (Poly)(30) — EWoo MFie

'Rhubarb and Custard' (Poly)(30) — CGle

'Romeo' (Prim)(30) — CVer LSur NCra

'Rose O'Day' (dPrim)(30) — ECGN MBal MCLN MOne NHol NRoo WWoo

rosea ♀ — CBot CPla CRow EPar GDra GFle GGGa GTou LHop MBal MFie NCra NDea NFla NGre NHar NSti NWes NIng SSpi WChe WEas WWeb
 – CC&McK 367 (11) — GCHN
 – 'Delight' — See *P. rosea* **'Micia Visser-de Geer'**
 – 'Gigas' (11) — MSta
 – 'Grandiflora' (11) — CGle CNic CPea EHon ELan EMNN ENot EPar GCrs GFle GPot LPBA LSyl MBri MRav NHed NMen NRoo SRms WPer
rotundifolia — See *P. roxburghii*
 'Rowallane Rose' (4) — CBro GBuc SSpi
§ *roxburghii* (25) — WCru
 'Roy Cope' (dPrim)(30) — CHad CLTr EBar EHic GGar MBal MBro MCLN MOne MRav NBir NEgg SIng WPnn
¶ 'Roydon Ruby' — WCot
rubra — See *P. erythra*
rusbyi (20) — MFie
 Rustic Reds Group (Poly)(30) — CSWP MFie
 'Sandy's Form' (21) — NHol
¶ 'Sapphire' — EHyt
saxatilis (7) — GGar MFie
scandinavica (11) — MFie
× *scapeosa* (21) — MBal NHar
§ 'Schneekissen' (Prim)(30) — CCot CHid GAbr LSur MBri MOne NBro NChi WHil WPbr WRus WViv
scotica (11) — GCrs GFle GTou LFox MBal MFie MRPP NCra NSla NWCA WAbe WCla WUnd
secundiflora (26) — CGle CInt CLTr CPla ELan GAbr GCra GDra GFle GGGa GTou LSyl MBal MBro MNrw NCra NMen NRoo NWoo SBla SPer SRms WAbe WHil WHoo WLin
§ × *sendtneri* (2) — MFie
× *serrata* — See *P.* × *vochinensis*
serratifolia (4) — GGGa GMaP SBla
sibirica — See *P. nutans* **Georgi**
sibthorpii — See *P. vulgaris* subsp. *sibthorpii*
sieboldii (7) ♀ — CBre CGle CRow EMNN GFle LFox MBal MBri MNrw NCra NHar NMen NRya NWCA SIng SRms SSpi WEas WHil
 – *alba* (7) — NBro WCru WFar
 – 'Carefree' (7) — NNrd
 – 'Cherubim' (7) — EBrP EBre ECtt GCHN LBre SBre
 – 'Dancing Ladies' (7) — CGle CMil
 – 'Galaxy' (7) — CMil WAbe
 – 'Geisha Girl' (7) — EBrP EBre ECtt GCHN LBre MRav SBre WFar
 – 'Lilac Sunbonnet' (7) — CGle
 – 'Manakoora' (7) — CDec CGle MFie SUsu
 – 'Mikado' (7) — EBrP EBre ECtt GCHN LBre MFie MRav NNrd SBre
 – 'Pago-Pago' (7) — CGle CInt CMea MFie
 – 'Seraphim' (7) — EBrP EBre LBre SBre
 – 'Snowflake' (7) — CGle CMea EBrP EBre GCHN LBre NSla SBre WAbe
 – 'Tah-ni' (7) — CNic GPot
 – 'Winter Dreams' (7) — CGle CInt MFie

§ *sikkimensis* (26) — CBot CBro CGle EBrP EBre EHon EMNN ENot GCHN GCrs GGGa GMac LBre LPBA LSyl MBal MBri MBro MNrw MSta NCra NDea NGre NHar SBre SIng SPer WAbe WChe WHil
¶ – ACE 1422 (26) — GBuc WCru
 – ACE 1822 (26) — NRya
¶ aff. – ACE 2176 (26) — GBuc
 – B&SWJ 2471 (26) — WCru
 – CC&McK 1022 (26) — GTou
 – crimson and gold (26) — MBro MFie
¶ – var. *hopeana* (26) — GCrs
¶ – MECC 82 (26) — SGre
 – 'Tilman Number 2' (26) — EWes GAbr GDra GFle WLin
¶ 'Silver Lining' — LRHS
 Silver-laced Group (Poly)(30) — CGle EPar
§ *sinensis* (27) — MBri
◆ *sinoplantaginea* — See *P. chionantha* subsp. *sinoplantaginea*
◆ *sinopurpurea* — See *P. chionantha* subsp. *sinopurpurea*
 'Sir Bedivere' (Prim)(30) — CElw GAbr
smithiana — See *P. prolifera*
 'Snow Carpet' — See *P.* **'Schneekissen'**
 'Snow Cushion' — See *P.* **'Schneekissen'**
 'Snow Queen' — LSur
 'Snow White' (Poly)(30) — LSur
¶ 'Snowcushion' — WRus
sonchifolia (21) — GGGa WAbe
◆ *sorachiana* — See *P. yuparensis*
¶ sp. ACE 1867 — NWCA
 sp. B&SWJ 2165 — WCru
 sp. BC 9331 — GCra
spectabilis (2) — NHar
 – JCA 789.400 (2) — MFie
 – JCA 789.401 (2) — MFie
¶ *specuicola* J&JA 1.768.600 (11) — NWCA
 Spice Shades Group (Poly)(30) — CSWP EWoo GAbr MFie
× *steinii* — See *P.* × *forsteri*
 'Stradbrook Charmer' (2) — EPot WLin
 'Stradbrook Dainty' (2) — EHyt WLin
¶ 'Stradbrook Dream' (2) — NHol
 'Stradbrook Gem' (2) — EHyt WAbe WLin
 'Stradbrook Lucy' (2) — EHyt ITim
 Striped Victorians Group — CMil CSWP GAbr MFie NChi
 'Sue Jervis' (dPrim)(30) — CSpe CVer EHic EPot GAbr LFis MBri MBro NEgg NHar NSti WHer WRha WRus
suffrutescens — CGra WAbe
 'Sunshine Susie' (dPrim)(30) — CGle CSam EBar ECGN EPri GAbr MAus MBri MOne MRav MYat NEgg NHol SIng SMrm WLRN WPnn
tanneri (21) — WAbe
§ – subsp. *nepalensis* (21) — ITim
 – subsp. *tsariensis* var. *alba* (21) — GGGa
¶ 'Tantallon' (21) — NHar WAbe
 'Tawny Port' (Poly)(30) — CBrd CCot CGle CLTr CMea CVer NBro NCra SRms
¶ 'The Grail' (Prim)(30) — LSur
tibetica (11) — GFle
¶ 'Tinney's Jewel' — EHyt
 'Tinney's Moonlight' — EHyt
 'Tipperary Purple' (Prim)(30) — GAbr

'Tomato Red' (Prim)(30) — CFee CVer GAbr LBee LSur NCra
'Tony' — ITim NHar WLin
'Torchlight' (dPrim)(30) — LHop
tosaensis (24) — NMen
'Tournaig Pink' (4) — GGar
uralensis — See *P. veris* subsp. *macrocalyx*
'Val Horncastle' (dPrim)(30) — CHad CSpe EBar ECGN MAus MCLN MOne MRav MWgw MYat NDov NEgg NHar NRoo NSti SMrm SPer SPla WCla WHil
Valentine Victorians (Poly)(30) — CSWP MFie
x *variabilis* — See *P.* x *polyantha*
veris (30) ♀ — CArn CBar CBre CBro CKin CPla ELan ENot GPoy GTou LFox LHol MBal MBri MHig MWat NCra NGre NHol NLan NMir SBla SIng SPer WChe WCla WHoo WLin WOak WRus
* – *alba* — CMea
  – hybrids (30) — WWal
  – red (30) — WRHF
¶ – red form — GFle
* – 'Rhandirmwyn Red' — WRha
vernalis — See *P. vulgaris*
verticillata (12) — MFie
§ *vialii* (17) ♀ — Widely available
§ *villosa* (2) — GCrs GFle GTou
  – var. *cottica* — See *P. villosa*
Violet Victorians Group (Poly)(30) — CSWP MFie
viscosa Allioni — See *P. latifolia*
§ x *vochinensis* (2) — CFee CLyd EPot MBro NHar NHol NNrd NWCA SIng WAbe
§ *vulgaris* (Prim)(30) — Widely available
  – *alba* (30) — CGle CRow ECha MHig NSla WAbe WLin
  – 'Alba Plena' (Prim)(30) — CGle CHad CRow CSWP GAbr GBuc GGar IBlr NChi WRus
  – Ballyrogan cream edge (Prim)(30) — IBlr
  – green-flowered — See *P. vulgaris* 'Viridis'
¶ – Jack in the Green (30) — WAlt
§ – 'Lilacina Plena' (dPrim)(30) — CBot CDec CGle CSam EBar GAbr IBlr LFis MAus MCLN NChi NSti SIng SMrm WCla WEas WHil WLin
§ – subsp. *sibthorpii* (Prim)(30) ♀ — CElw CGle CMHG EJud GAbr GTou LFox LSur MBro MFos MRav NBro NChi NCra NWCA SBla SRms SSvw WHoo WLin WPyg
¶ – subsp. *sibthorpii alba* from Lebanon — MFie
§ – 'Viridis' (Prim)(30) — CElw CSWP IBlr
  – white hose-in-hose (Prim)(30) — LSur
waltonii (26) — CBot CPla GCra GCrs GFle MBal MNrw
  – hybrids (26) — GGar
'Wanda' (Prim)(30) ♀ — CCot CGle CRow CVer ELan ENot GAbr LSur MWgw NGre NRoo NSti NVic SBla SIng SPer SRms WCFE WFar WHoo WMow
'Wanda Hose in Hose' (Prim)(30) — CGle CVer EMon GAbr LSur NChi WGwy WHer WHil
Wanda Jack in the Green (Prim)(30) — CRow MBro MLLN WFar

wardii — See *P. involucrata*
♦ *warshenewskiana* — See *P. involucrata* subsp. *yargongensis*
watsonii (17) — EWes GCan GCrs GGGa GTou MFie NHar
'Wedgwood' — See *P.* x *pubescens* 'Wedgwood'
'Wharfedale Bluebell' (2) — CLyd NHar WGwG
'Wharfedale Butterfly' (2) — NHar NNrd
'Wharfedale Crusader' (2) — MRPP NHol NNrd
'Wharfedale Gem' (*allionii* hybrid) (2) — EHyt EMNN MDHE MFie NGre NHar NHol NNrd WAbe
'Wharfedale Ling' (*allionii* hybrid) (2) — CGra CPBP EHyt EPot MFie MRPP NHar NHol WAbe
'Wharfedale Superb' (*allionii* hybrid) (2) — EMNN MFie NHar NHol NNrd WAbe
'Wharfedale Village' (2) — CLyd MDHE NHar NHol WGwG
'White Linda Pope' (2) — CLyd NHar WLin
'White Wanda' (Prim)(30) — CGle CRow CVer GAbr LSur WCru
whitei (21) — CBrd GCrs MBal MDun
§ – 'Sherriff's Variety' (21) — IBlr
¶ *wigramiana* (28) — WAbe
'William Genders' (Poly)(30) — GAbr LSur
wilsonii (4) — CPla GBuc GCra GFle GGGa GMac LSyl MBro MNes MNrw SWat WHer WHoo WPyg
§ – var. *anisodora* (4) — CPla EBee GCan GCra GFle GMaP MBal MFie
'Windrush' — See *P.* x *berninae* 'Windrush'
'Windward Blue' — SBla
'Winter White' — See *P.* 'Gigha'
'Wisley Crimson' — See *P.* 'Wisley Red'
wollastonii (28) — GGGa
¶ 'Woodland Blue' — NWoo
wulfeniana (2) — CGra GCLN MBro MFie NHol WAbe
yargongensis — See *P. involucrata* subsp. *yargongensis*
§ *yuparensis* (11) — CInt IDac NMen

PRINSEPIA (Rosaceae)

sinensis — CPle GBin MBlu
¶ *utilis* — CTrG

PRITCHARDIA (Arecaceae) See Plant Deletions

PRITZELAGO (Brassicaceae) See Plant Deletions

PROBOSCIDEA (Pedaliaceae)

louisianica — EFEx
parviflora — EFEx

PROSOPIS (Mimosaceae)

chilensis — See *P. glandulosa*

PROSTANTHERA (Lamiaceae)

aspalathoides — CPle ECon ECou LGre WCot
cuneata ♀ — Widely available
  – 'Alpine Gold' — CB&S CMHG CPle CTrC CWSG EHic LHop
  – 'Fastigiata' — CPle SPan
¶ – Kew form — WPGP
incisa — CTrw LBlm
  – 'Rosea' — CPle SChu WSHC
lasianthos — CB&S CPle CSev ECou LGre MAll SOWG WWye
  – var. *subcoriacea* — CPle

melissifolia	ECon ECre LCns
– var. *parvifolia*	CTrw ECre GCHN WAbe WSHC
nivea	CPle LGre MAll
ovalifolia	EBee ECou LHil LHop MAll MMil SMrm
'Poorinda Ballerina'	CLyn CPle CSev ECon LGre LHop LRHS SAga SMur
rotundifolia ♀	CAbb CB&S CInt CPle CSam CSev CSpe CTrG CTri ERea ISea MAll SAga SEND SMad SOWG WBod WKif WOld WWye
– 'Chelsea Girl'	See *P. rotundifolia rosea*
§ – *rosea*	CGre CPle CSpe CTrG ERea LHop MAll MLan SAga SVen WWye
saxicola var. *montana*	CPle LGre
walteri	CAbb CDoC CPle ECou LBlm LGre MAll

PROTEA (Proteaceae)

cynaroides	CB&S CHEx CTrC
eximia	CTrC
grandiceps	CTrC
¶ *lacticolor*	CTrC
¶ *magnifica*	CTrC
¶ *neriifolia*	CTrC

PRUMNOPITYS (Podocarpaceae)

§ *andina*	CGre WWat
elegans	See *P. andina*
§ *ferruginea*	ECou
§ – 'Golden Dwarf'	CLTr
§ *taxifolia*	ECou

PRUNELLA (Lamiaceae)

§ *grandiflora*	CAgr EBot EFer GBar MNrw MWat NGre NLon SRms SWat WBea WCHb WHoo WOve WWye
– 'Alba'	CDoC EPfP MAus NChi NCut NOrc NTay NWoo SPla WCHb WOve WPbr WWhi
– 'Blue Loveliness'	CLyd ELan EMan GAbr GDra GTou SPla WCHb
– 'Little Red Riding Hood'	See *P. grandiflora* 'Rotkäppchen'
– 'Loveliness' ♀	CDoC CLyd EBrP EBre ECha ECtt ELan EPar LBre LGro MBel MRav NBro NMir NSti NVic SBod SBre SPer SPla WMow WWeb WWin
– 'Pagoda'	EAst LIck NBrk NOak NTay SIng WCHb WElm
– 'Pink Loveliness'	CInt CLyd CNic EBrP EBre ECha EPar GCHN GDra GTou LBre LGro MBal MWgw NMir SBre SRms WByw WWin WWye
– *rosea*	CBlo EPfP LBuc MWat WByw WWhi
§ – 'Rotkäppchen'	EBrP EBre ECtt GCHN LBre SBre SPer WPbr
– 'White Loveliness'	CLyd EBrP EBre ECha EPar GCHN GDra GGar LBre NBrk NCat NMir NNrd SBre SPer SPla WByw WEas WLin WMow WPer WRus WWin WWye
hyssopifolia	EBee WHil
incisa	See *P. vulgaris*
* 'Inshriach Ruby'	NBir SPla WCHb

laciniata	CLyd CMCo LFis NChi WCHb WHil WPbr
¶ – pink form	NChi
– white form	GBin NChi
§ *vulgaris*	CAgr CArn CKin ELan EWFC GAbr GBar GPoy MChe MHew MSal NLan NMir NSti SIde WCHb WCla WHer WOak WWye
– *alba*	WAlt WHer
¶ – 'Inner Glow' (v)	WAlt
¶ – 'Ruth Wainwright' (v)	CNat WAlt
x *webbiana*	See *P. grandiflora*

PRUNUS † (Rosaceae)

'Accolade' ♀	CAbP CBlo CDoC CLnd COtt CSam CTho ECtt ENot IOrc LPan MAsh MBri NWea SEND SHBN SIgm SPer SSta WDin WJas WStI
§ 'Amanogawa' ♀	CB&S CBlo CLnd CSam EBrP EBre ELan ENot GChr GRei LBre LBuc LHyr LNet LPan MAsh MBal MBar MBri MGos NWea SBre SHBN SIgm SPer WJas
x *amygdalopersica* 'Pollardii'	CBlo ENot WJas
– 'Spring Glow'	CDoC MAsh MBri WJas
amygdalus	See *P. dulcis*
armeniaca 'Alfred' (F)	EMui ERea GTwe MBri SDea SIgm
¶ – 'Blenheim' (F)	ERea
– 'Bredase' (F)	SDea
– 'De Nancy'	See *P. armeniaca* 'Gros Pêche'
– 'Early Moor Park' (F)	ERea GBon GRei GTwe SDea SFam SIgm WWeb
– 'Farmingdale' (F)	ERea SDea SKee
– 'Goldcot' (F)	ERea SDea
¶ – 'Golden Glow' (F)	GTwe
§ – 'Gros Pêche' (F)	CMac
¶ – 'Hemskirke' (F)	ERea
– 'Hongaarse' (F)	SDea
– 'Moor Park' (F)	CEnd EMui ERea GTwe LBuc MGos NDal NRog SDea SKee WStI
– 'New Large Early' (F)	ERea GTwe SDea SEND SIgm SKee
– 'Royal' (F)	CMac
– 'Tross Orange' (F)	SDea
'Asano'	See *P.* 'Geraldinae'
avium ♀	CB&S CBlo CKin CLnd CPer ENot GChr GRei LBuc LHyr LPan MBar MBri MGos MRav NBee NRoo NWea SFam SHBN SKee SPer WDin WMou WOrn
– 'Amber Heart' (F)	SDea SKee
– 'Bigarreau Gaucher' (F)	SKee
§ – 'Bigarreau Napoléon' (F)	GTwe MGos SDea SKee
◆ – 'Birchenhayes'	See *P. avium* 'Early Birchenhayes'
– 'Black Eagle' (F)	CTho SKee
– 'Black Tartarian' (F)	SKee
◆ – 'Bottlers'	See *P. avium* 'Preserving'
– 'Bradbourne Black' (F)	SKee
– 'Bullion' (F)	CEnd CTho
– 'Burcombe' (F)	CEnd CTho
– 'Cherokee'	See *P. avium* 'Lapins'
¶ – 'Circassian'	SKee
– 'Colney' (F)	GTwe WJas
– 'Dun' (F)	CTho

§ – 'Early Birchenhayes' (F) CEnd CTho
– 'Early Rivers' (F) GTwe SDea SKee
– 'Elton Heart' (F) CTho SKee
– 'Fastigiata' CTho
¶ – 'Fice' (F) CEnd CTho
– 'Florence' (F) SKee
– 'Governor Wood' (F) GTwe
– 'Grandiflora' See *P. avium* **'Plena'**
– 'Greenstem Black' (F) CTho
– 'Hertford' (F) SKee
– 'Inga' (F) SKee
– 'Ironsides' (F) SKee
– 'Kassins Frühe Herz' (F) SKee
– 'Kentish Red' (F) SKee
§ – 'Lapins' (F) EMui GTwe SDea SFam SKee WJas
– 'May Duke' See *P.* × *gondouinii* **'May Duke'**
– 'Merchant' (F) ♀ GTwe SKee
– 'Mermat' (F) GTwe
– 'Merpet' (F) GTwe
– 'Merton Crane' (F) SKee
– 'Merton Favourite' (F) SKee
– 'Merton Glory' (F) CDoC GChr GTwe MGos
– 'Merton Premier' (F) SKee
♦ – 'Merton Reward' See *P.* × *gondouinii* **'Merton Reward'**
– 'Napoléon' See *P. avium* **'Bigarreau Napoléon'**
– 'Newstar' (F) EMui
– 'Noir de Guben' (F) GTwe
– 'Nutberry Black' (F) SKee
– 'Old Black Heart' (F) SKee
§ – 'Plena' (d) ♀ CB&S CBlo CLnd CSam CTho ELan ENot EPfP GChr IOrc LBuc LHyr LPan MBal MGos NBee NWea SFam SPer WDin WJas WOrn
§ – 'Preserving' (F) CTho
– 'Sasha' (F) GTwe
– 'Small Black' (F) CTho
– 'Starkrimson' (F) GTwe
– 'Stella' (F) ♀ CMac CSam EMui ERea GBon GChr GRei GTwe LBuc MBri MGos NBee NDal NRog SDea SFam SIgm SKee SPer WJas WWeb
– 'Stella Compact' (F) COtt GTwe MBri SKee
– 'Sunburst' (F) EMui GTwe LBuc MBri NDal SDea SFam SKee WJas WWeb
– 'Turkish Black' (F) SKee
* – 'Upright' CTho
– 'Van' (F) GTwe SKee
– 'Vega' (F) GTwe
– 'Waterloo' (F) CTho SKee
– 'White Heart' (F) CTho SKee
'Benden' CTho
* 'Beni-no-dora' SMur
* 'Beni-yutaka' CBlo CEnd LBuc MBri
♦ 'Blaze' See *P. cerasifera* **'Nigra'**
× *blireana* ♀ CBlo CDoC CLnd EBee ENot GChr MAsh MBri MRav MWat SPer SSta
'Blushing Bride' See *P.* **'Shôgetsu'**
bucharica JJH 98807 NWCA
¶ *campanulata* CTho
capuli See *P. salicifolia*
cerasifera CAgr CBlo CPer CTri GAri LBuc NWea SKee WDin WMou
– 'Cherry Plum' (F) SKee
– 'Crimson Dwarf' CBlo CDoC
* – 'Green Glow' CBlo
– 'Hessei' (v) CBlo CEnd MBri SPer

– 'Kentish Red' (F) SKee
§ – Myrobalan Group (F) CBlo CKin SDea SKee
§ – 'Nigra' L.H. Bailey ♀ CBlo CDoC CLnd EBee ELan GChr IOrc LBuc LNet LPan MAsh MBri MGos NBee SDea SHBN SPer SRms WDin WOrn WStI
§ – 'Pissardii' CBlo CTho CTri EBrP EBre ECrN GRei LBre MAsh MBar NNor NWea SBre SFam SIgm SPer WJas
– 'Rosea' MBri SLPl
– 'Spring Glow' CEnd
cerasus 'Montmorency' (F) SKee
– 'Morello' (F) ♀ CMac CSam EBrP EBre EMui GBon GChr GRei GTwe LBuc MBri MGos NBee NDal NRog SBre SDea SFam SIgm SKee SPer WJas WWeb
– 'Rhexii' (d) CBlo MAsh MGos SPer
– 'Wye Morello' (F) SKee
'Cheal's Weeping' See *P.* **'Kiku-shidare-zakura'**
§ 'Chôshû-hizakura' ♀ CBlo CLnd GChr GRei IOrc LNet SPer WDin WStI
§ × *cistena* ♀ CB&S CBlo CBot EBrP EBre ELan ENot IOrc LBre MBar MBri MGos MWat NBee SBre SEas SHBN SPer SPla WDin
– 'Crimson Dwarf' See *P.* × *cistena*
¶ 'Collingwood Ingram' MBri
conradinae See *P. hirtipes*
davidiana CTho
¶ *domestica* 'Allgroves Superb' (D) ERea
– 'Angelina Burdett' (D) ERea GTwe NRog SKee
– 'Anna Späth' (C/D) SKee
– 'Ariel' (C/D) SDea SKee
– 'Avalon' (D) GTwe SDea SIgm SKee
– 'Belgian Purple' (C) SKee
– 'Belle de Louvain' (C) CTho ERea GTwe NRog SDea SKee
– 'Birchenhayes' (F) CEnd
– 'Blue Tit' (C/D) ♀ EMui ERea GTwe SKee
– 'Bonne de Bry' (D) SKee
¶ – 'Bountiful' (C) ERea
– 'Brandy Gage' (C/D) SKee
– 'Bryanston Gage' (D) CTho SKee
– 'Burbank' (C/D) SDea
– 'Burcombe' CEnd
– 'Bush' (C) SKee
– 'Cambridge Gage' (D) CDoC CSam CTho EBrP EBre EMui ERea GBon GTwe LBre LBuc MBri MGos MWat NDal NRog SBre SDea SFam SIgm SKee SPer WJas WStI WWeb
– 'Chrislin' (F) CTho
– 'Coe's Golden Drop' (D) CTho EMui ERea GTwe MBri MGos SCoo SDea SFam SIgm SKee
– 'Count Althann's Gage' (D) ERea GTwe NRog SDea SFam SIgm SKee
– 'Cox's Emperor' (C) SKee
– 'Crimson Drop' (D) ERea SKee
– 'Cropper' See *P. domestica* **'Laxton's Cropper'**
– 'Curlew' (C) SDea
– 'Czar' (C) ♀ CDoC CSam CTri EBrP EBre EMui GTwe IOrc LBre LBuc MGos NRog SBre SDea SFam SIgm SKee SPer WWeb

– 'Delicious'	See *P. domestica* **'Laxton's Delicious'**
– 'Denniston's Superb'	See *P. domestica* **'Imperial Gage'**
– 'Diamond' (C)	SKee
– 'Dittisham Black' (C)	CTho
– 'Dittisham Ploughman' (C)	CSam CTho SKee
– 'Dunster Plum' (F)	CTho
– 'Early Laxton' (C/D) ♀	ERea GTwe SDea SFam SKee
– 'Early Orleans'	See *P. domestica* **'Monsieur Hâtif'**
– 'Early Prolific'	See *P. domestica* **'Rivers's Early Prolific'**
– 'Early Rivers'	See *P. domestica* **'Rivers's Early Prolific'**
– 'Early Transparent Gage' (C/D)	CTho CTri EMui ERea GTwe LBuc SDea SFam SIgm
¶ – 'Early Victoria' (C/D)	SDea
– 'Edwards' (C/D) ♀	GTwe LBuc NBee NDal SDea SFam SIgm SKee
– 'Excalibur' (D)	GTwe NDal SIgm
– 'Giant Prune' (C)	GTwe NRog SKee
– 'Godshill Blue' (C)	SDea
– 'Golden Transparent' (D)	CTho ERea GTwe NRog SFam
– 'Goldfinch' (D)	GTwe NRog SKee
§ – Green Gage Group (C/D)	EMui GTwe NRog SDea SFam SKee SPer
– – 'Old Green Gage' (D/C)	ERea SIgm WCFE WJas
§ – – 'Willingham Gage' (C/D)	ERea GTwe
– 'Grey Plum' (F)	CTho
– 'Grove's Late Victoria' (C/D)	SKee
– 'Guthrie's Late Green' (D)	SKee
– 'Herman' (C/D)	CSam GTwe SDea SIgm
– 'Heron' (F)	GTwe
– 'Imperial Epineuse' (D)	SKee
§ – 'Imperial Gage' (C/D) ♀	CTho EMui ERea GRei GTwe LBuc SDea SFam SIgm SKee
– subsp. *insititia*	See *P. insititia*
– 'Jan James' (F)	CEnd
– 'Jefferson' (D) ♀	EMui ERea GTwe NRog SDea SFam SIgm SKee
– 'Kea' (C)	CTho SKee
– 'Kirke's' (D)	CTho CWSG ERea GTwe MBri SDea SFam SIgm SKee
– 'Landkey Yellow' (F)	CTho
– 'Late Muscatelle' (D)	ERea SKee
– 'Laxton's Bountiful'	See *P. domestica* **'Bountiful'**
§ – 'Laxton's Cropper' (C)	GTwe NRog SKee
§ – 'Laxton's Delicious' (D)	GTwe
– 'Laxton's Delight' (D) ♀	GTwe
– 'Laxton's Gage' (D)	SDea SKee
– 'Manaccan' (C)	CTho
– 'Marjorie's Seedling' (C) ♀	CDoC CTho EBrP EBre EMui ERea GBon GTwe LBre LBuc MGos MWat SBre SDea SEND SFam SIgm SKee WJas
– 'McLaughlin' (D)	SKee
– 'Merton Gem' (C/D)	GTwe SFam SKee
– 'Monarch' (C)	GTwe SKee
– 'Ontario' (C/D)	GTwe SKee
– 'Opal' (D) ♀	CDoC EMui ERea GTwe IOrc LBuc MGos MWat SDea SEND SFam SIgm SKee WWeb
– 'Orleans' (C)	SKee

– 'Oullins Gage' (C/D) ♀	CMac EMui ERea GBon GTwe LBuc MBri MWat NRog SDea SFam SIgm SKee SPer WJas WWeb
– 'Pershore' (C) ♀	CTho ERea GTwe NRog SDea SFam SKee WStI
– 'Pond's Seedling' (C)	SDea SKee
– 'President' (C/D)	GTwe SDea
– 'Prince Englebert' (C)	SKee
– 'Priory Plum' (D)	SDea
– 'Purple Pershore' (C)	CTri CWSG ERea GTwe NRog SDea SFam SKee
– 'Quetsche d'Alsace'	See *P. domestica* **German Prune Group**
– 'Reeves' (C) ♀	GTwe SFam SIgm SKee
– 'Reine Claude de Bavais' (D)	CTho ERea GTwe NRog SFam SKee
– 'Reine Claude Dorée'	See *P. domestica* **Green Gage Group**
– 'Reine Claude Violette' (D)	CTho ERea SKee
§ – 'Rivers's Early Prolific' (C)	CTho ERea GTwe MWat NRog SCoo SDea SIgm SKee
– 'Royale de Vilvoorde' (D)	ERea SKee
– 'Sanctus Hubertus' (D) ♀	GTwe SDea SIgm SKee
– 'Severn Cross' (D)	GTwe SKee
– 'Stint' (C/D)	SKee
– 'Swan' (C)	GTwe SIgm
– 'Transparent Gage' (D)	ERea SKee
– 'Upright' (F)	CEnd
– 'Utility' (D)	SKee
– 'Victoria' (C/D) ♀	CMac CSam CTho EBrP EBre EMui ERea GBon GChr GRei GTwe IOrc LBre LBuc MBri MGos MWat NBee NDal NRog SBre SDea SFam SIgm SKee SPer WJas WWeb
– 'Warwickshire Drooper' (C)	CSam CTho ERea GBon GTwe SDea SFam SKee SPer
– 'Washington' (D)	CTho ERea SKee
– 'White Magnum Bonum' (C)	CTho SDea
♦ – 'Willingham'	See *P. domestica* **(Green Gage Group) 'Willingham Gage'**
– 'Wyedale' (C)	GTwe
§ *dulcis*	CLnd CTri ECrN EMui LHyr MWat NWea SDea SFam WBay WDin
– 'Balatoni' (F)	MBri
– 'Macrocarpa' (F)	ESim
– 'Roseoplena'	CBlo MBri
fruticosa 'Globosa'	CBlo CWSG
'Fugenzô'	CBlo
§ 'Geraldinae'	CLnd WPyg
glandulosa 'Alba Plena' (d) ♀	CB&S CBot CPMA CPle ECtt ELan ESis GChr GOrc MBal MGos MPla MTis MWat NBee NHol SHBN SPan SPer SPla SReu SRms SSpi SSta WDin WHCG WSHC
– 'Rosea Plena'	See *P. glandulosa* **'Sinensis'**
§ – 'Sinensis' (d) ♀	CBot CPMA CPle ELan ESis GChr GOrc MBal MGos MHlr MPla SHBN SPan SPer SPla SReu SRms SSpi SSta WHCG WSHC
§ × *gondouinii* 'May Duke' (F)	SKee
– 'Merton Reward' (F)	SKee
'Gyoikô'	CTho

'Hally Jolivette'	CEnd COtt ELan MAsh MBri SCoo SPla
'Hillieri'	MBar MGos
'Hillieri Spire'	See *P.* **'Spire'**
¶ 'Hilling's Weeping'	EBee
§ *hirtipes*	CTho
'Hisakura'	See *P.* **'Chôshû-hizakura'**
Hollywood	See *P.* **'Trailblazer'**
incisa	CTri GAri IOrc SLPl SPer SSpi
– 'Beniomi'	GAri MRav
– 'February Pink'	CPMA LBuc MPla MRav NPro WPGP
– 'Fujima'	EBee NHol SMur WPat WPyg WWat
– 'Kojo-no-mai'	CEnd CHar CMil CPMA EBrP EBre ECtt EPla ESis GAri GBin LBre MAsh MBlu MBri MGos NPro NTow SBre SPan WBay WFar WPat WWeb
– 'Mikinori'	MBri
– 'Oshidori'	MBri MGos MRav NHol WPat WPyg
* – 'Otome'	MBri
– 'Praecox' ♀	LRHS MBri
– 'The Bride'	CEnd MBri
§ – f. *yamadae*	CB&S CEnd
insititia 'Blue Violet Damson' (F)	SKee
§ – 'Bradley's King Damson' (F)	SKee
¶ – Bullace (C)	SDea
– 'Dittisham Damson' (C)	CTho
– 'Farleigh Damson' (C)	ECrN ERea GTwe SDea SFam SKee WJas
– 'Godshill Damson' (C)	SDea
– 'Golden Bullace'	See *P. insititia* **'White Bullace'**
– 'King of Damsons'	See *P. insititia* **'Bradley's King Damson'**
– 'Langley Bullace' (C)	CTho ERea SKee
– 'Merryweather Damson' (C)	CDoC CMac CTho EBrP EBre EMui ERea GBon GChr GRei GTwe LBre LBuc MBri NBee NDal NRog SBre SDea SFam SKee SPer WJas WStI WWeb
– 'Mirabelle de Nancy' (C)	CTho GTwe SDea SKee
– 'Mirabelle de Nancy (Red)' (C)	SDea
– 'Mirabelle Petite'	See *P. insititia* **'Mirabelle de Metz'**
§ – 'Prune Damson' (C)	CSam CTho EMui ERea GBon GTwe LBuc MBri MGos MWat NRog SDea SFam SIgm SKee WJas
– 'Shepherd's Bullace' (C)	CTho ERea SKee
– 'Shropshire Damson'	See *P. insititia* **'Prune Damson'**
– 'Small Bullace' (F)	SKee
§ – 'White Bullace' (F)	ERea SKee
– 'Yellow Apricot' (F)	SKee
¶ – 'Yellow Apricot Bullace' (C)	ERea
§ *jamasakura*	CTho
'Jô-nioi'	CEnd CLnd CTho
§ 'Kanzan' ♀	CB&S CBlo CLnd EBrP EBre ELan GRei LBre LBuc LHyr LPan MAsh MBal MBar MBri MGos NWea SBre SHBN SPer SSta WFar WJas
§ 'Kiku-shidare-zakura' ♀	CB&S CBlo CLnd EBrP EBre ELan ENot GChr GRei LBre LBuc LHyr LNet MBal MBar MBri MGos MRav NBee NWea SBre SFam SHBN SIgm SPer WDin WJas WStI
Korean Hill Cherry	See *P.* × *verecunda*
kurilensis	See *P. nipponica* var. *kurilensis*
'Kursar' ♀	CBlo COtt CTho EBee EPfP GRei IOrc LNet MAsh MBri SFam
laurocerasus ♀	CB&S CChe CKin ELan GRei LHyr LNet LPan MRav MWat NNor NWea SPer SReu WMou WStI
– 'Aureovariegata'	See *P. laurocerasus* **'Taff's Golden Gleam'**
– 'Camelliifolia'	CHan EPla ISea MBlu WHCG WPyg
N – 'Castlewellan' (v)	CBot CHan CLTr CPle CTrw EPla IOrc ISea MBar MGos NHol SEND SPer SPla SSta WGwG
¶ – 'Caucasica'	WStI
– 'Cherry Brandy'	ENot SPer WLRN WStI
♦ – Dart's Lowgreen™	See *P. laurocerasus* Low 'n' Green = **'Interlo'**
¶ – 'Etna'	EBee
– Green Carpet	See *P. laurocerasus* **'Grünerteppich'**
– 'Green Marble' (v)	CPMA CTri MUlv WSHC
§ – Low 'n' Green = 'Interlo'	ENot
§ – 'Latifolia'	CHEx EPla SAPC SArc SLPl SMad
♦ – Low 'n' Green	See *P. laurocerasus* Low 'n' Green = **'Interlo'**
– 'Magnoliifolia'	See *P. laurocerasus* **'Latifolia'**
– 'Marbled White'	See *P. laurocerasus* **'Castlewellan'**
– 'Mischeana'	ENot MBri SLPl
– 'Mount Vernon'	MBar MBri MGos NBee WDin
¶ – 'Otinii'	CHEx
– 'Otto Luyken' ♀	Widely available
– 'Reynvaanii'	EPla MBri MGos WBcn
– 'Rotundifolia'	CDoC CTri EBar ELan ENot LBuc MBar MBri MGos NFla SRms WDin WStI
– 'Rudolf Billeter'	EPla
– 'Schipkaensis'	NNor SLPl SPer WCot
§ – 'Taff's Golden Gleam' (v)	CEnd CPMA MGos SMad WWes
– 'Van Nes'	EMil IOrc
N – 'Variegata'	EHic MGos
– 'Zabeliana'	CDoC CLan CMHG CTrC ENot GChr MBar NWea SHBN SPer SRms WDin WPyg WRHF WWin
* *longipedunculata*	MBri
lusitanica ♀	Widely available
– subsp. *azorica* ♀	EPla SMad SPer WPGP WWat
– 'Myrtifolia'	EBee EPla MRav SMad WWat
– 'Variegata'	CB&S CBot CMHG EAst EBrP EBre EHoe ELan ENot EPla IOrc ISea LBre MBal MBri MGos MHlr MWat SBre SDix SHBN SPer SSta WDin WSHC WWat
maackii	CTho EPfP LPan SEND SSpi WDin WWat
– 'Amber Beauty'	CPMA GChr MBri MRav WPyg
mahaleb	CTho

* 'Mahogany Lustre' — MBlu
'Mount Fuji' — See *P.* **'Shirotae'**
mume — WNor
– 'Alboplena' — CChe
§ – 'Beni-chidori' — CB&S CBlo CEnd CPMA EPfP MBlu MBri SIgm SSpi SSta
– 'Beni-shidori' — See *P. mume* 'Beni-chidori'
* – 'Ken Kyo' — SSta
* – 'Kyo Koh' — SSta
§ – 'Omoi-no-mama' (d) — CEnd CPMA LRHS MAsh MBri MMHG
– 'Omoi-no-wac' — See *P. mume* 'Omoi-no-mama'
– 'Pendula' — CLnd MBri
myrobalana — See *P. cerasifera* Myrobalan Group
§ *nipponica* var. *kurilensis* — CB&S MAsh
– – 'Ruby' — CEnd COtt LRHS MBri MGos SMur
¶ – – 'Spring Joy' — MBri
'Okame' ♀ — CBlo CLnd CSam CTho EBee EBrP EBre LBre MAsh MBri MGos NBee NWea SBre SPer
§ 'Okumiyako' — CB&S CBlo CEnd SFam WDin
padus — CBlo CKin CLnd CPer GChr IOrc LBuc LHyr LNet MGos NBee NRoo NWea SSpi WDin WMou
– 'Albertii' — CTho LPan SLPl WJas
– 'Colorata' ♀ — CBlo CDoC CEnd CMHG CSam CTho ELan GChr IOrc LBuc LNet LPan NBee SHBN SPer SSpi WDin WJas
– 'Grandiflora' — See *P. padus* 'Watereri'
– 'Plena' (d) — CTho
– 'Purple Queen' — CBlo CEnd CTho ECrN ENot MGos WStI
§ – 'Watereri' ♀ — CB&S CBlo CDoC CLnd CTho ELan ENot IOrc LPan SHBN SPer SSta WDin WJas
'Pandora' ♀ — CBlo CLnd EBee ENot EPfP GChr LHyr LPan MAsh MBal MWat NBee NWea SEND SHBN SPer
§ *pendula* var. *ascendens* — CBlo CLnd
'Rosea'
§ – 'Pendula Rosea' ♀ — CB&S CBlo ECrN ENot LPan MAsh SPer WJas
§ – 'Pendula Rubra' ♀ — CBlo CDoC COtt CTho CTri ENot EPfP LNet MAsh MBri MGos SFam SHBN SPer
persica 'Amsden June' (F) — ERea GTwe SDea SFam
– 'Bellegarde' (F) — ERea GTwe SDea SFam SKee
– 'Bonanza' (F) — EMui ERea
– 'Doctor Hogg' (F) — SDea
– 'Duke of York' (F) — ERea GTwe SDea SFam SKee WWeb
– 'Dymond' (F) — ERea GTwe
– 'Early Rivers' (F) — CMac EMui ERea GTwe NRog SDea SFam
– 'Flat China' — ERea
– 'Francis' (F) — SKee
– 'Garden Anny' (F) — ERea
¶ – 'Garden Lady' (F) — EMui ERea GTwe WWeb
– 'Hale's Early' (F) — ERea GTwe SEND SFam SKee SPer
– 'Kestrel' (F) — GTwe
– 'Klara Mayer' (d/F) — CBlo WJas
– var. *nectarina* Crimson Gold (F) — SDea
– – 'Early Gem' (F) — ERea SDea
– – 'Elruge' (F) — ERea GTwe SEND SFam
– – 'Fantasia' (F) — ERea SDea

– – 'Fire Gold' (F) — SDea
¶ – – 'Garden Beauty' (F/d) — WWeb
– – 'Humboldt' (F) — ERea GTwe
– – 'John Rivers' (F) — ERea GTwe SFam
– – 'Lord Napier' (F) — CDoC CWSG EMui ERea LBuc MGos SDea SEND SFam SIgm SKee SPer WStI WWeb
– – 'Nectared' (F) — GTwe
– – 'Nectarella' (F) — EMui ERea GTwe
– – 'Pineapple' (F) — CTri ERea GTwe SDea SFam SIgm WWeb
– – 'Red Haven' (F) — GTwe SDea SIgm SKee
– – 'Ruby Gold' (F) — SDea
¶ – – 'Terrace Ruby' — WWeb
– 'Peregrine' (F) — CMac CTri CWSG EMui ERea GBon GRei GTwe LBuc MBri MGos NBee NDal NRog SDea SFam SIgm SKee SPer WJas WStI WWeb
– 'Reliance' (F) — SDea
– 'Robin Redbreast' (F) — SDea
– 'Rochester' (F) — CWSG EMui ERea GBon GTwe MBri SDea SEND SFam SIgm WStI
– 'Royal George' (F) — GTwe NRog SFam
– 'Rubira' (F) — EPla
– 'Saturne' (F) — EMui
– 'Springtime' (F) — ERea SDea
¶ – 'Terrace Amber' — WWeb
¶ – 'Terrace Diamond' — WWeb
¶ – 'Terrace Garnet' — WWeb
¶ – 'Terrace Pearl' — WWeb
'Pink Perfection' ♀ — CB&S CBlo CLnd EBee EBrP EBre ENot GChr LBre LBuc LHyr LPan MAsh MBri NBee SBre SFam SHBN SPer SSta WOrn
'Pink Shell' ♀ — CBlo CLnd CTho MAsh MBri SFam WStI
pissardii — See *P. cerasifera* 'Pissardii'
'Pissardii Nigra' — See *P. cerasifera* 'Nigra'
* *pissardii* 'Princess' — CBlo MAsh
prostrata — NHol WPat WWat
* – 'Anita Kistler' — ECho
* – var. *discolor* — WNor
* – 'Pygmaea' — EHyt
pumila — SEas
– var. *depressa* — CPMA CPle GAri MBar MBlu MPla MRav NPro
'Red Cascade' — SDea
rufa — CTho
¶ *salicina* 'Satsuma' (F) — ERea
sargentii ♀ — CBlo CDoC CLnd CSam CTho ELan ENot IHos IOrc LBuc LHyr LPan MAsh MBri MGos NWea SFam SHBN SPer SSta STre WDin
¶ – 'Columnaris' — MBri
– Rancho® — CLnd ENot SLPl SPer SSta WOrn
× *schmittii* — CLnd CTho ENot SPer WJas
'Sekiyama' — See *P.* **'Kanzan'**
serotina — NWea
§ *serrula* ♀ — CBar CBlo CDoC CEnd CLnd CTho ELan ENot GChr IOrc LPan MBal MBar MBlu MBri MGos NBee NBir NWea SHBN SPer SSta WDin WNor WWat
¶ – × *serrulata* — CTho
– var. *tibetica* — See *P. serrula*
serrulata 'Erecta' — See *P.* **'Amanogawa'**
– 'Grandiflora' — See *P.* **'Ukon'**

– var. **hupehensis**	SLPl
– 'Longipes'	See *P.* '**Okumiyako**'
– 'Miyak'	See *P.* '**Okumiyako**'
N – var. **pubescens**	See *P.* x **verecunda**
– 'Rosea'	See *P.* '**Kiku-shidare-zakura**'
– var. **spontanea**	See *P.* **jamasakura**
'Shidare-zakura'	See *P.* '**Kiku-shidare-zakura**'
'Shimizu-zakura'	See *P.* '**Okumiyako**'
'Shirofugen' ♀	CB&S CBlo CDoC CLnd CTho IOrc LBuc LPan MAsh MBri MWat SFam SPer SSta WDin WOrn
§ 'Shirotae' ♀	CBlo CDoC CEnd CLnd CSam CTho CTri EBee ELan ENot IOrc LBuc LHyr MAsh MBal MGos MRav NBee NWea SPer SSta WWeb
§ 'Shôgetsu' ♀	CLnd CTho ELan IOrc MBal MBri SFam SHBN SPer WDin WStI
'Shosar'	CBlo CEnd CLnd MBri SPer
'Snow Goose'	LPan MBri
spinosa	CDoC CKin CPer CSam CTri LBuc LHol MBri MHlr NBee NWea SPer STre WDin WHer WMou WNor
¶ – 'Plena' (d)	CTho
– 'Purpurea'	MBlu WHCG WMou WPat
§ 'Spire' ♀	CBlo CDoC CLnd CTho ENot GRei IOrc LBuc LHyr LPan SPer WJas
x **subhirtella**	WNor
– var. **ascendens**	See *P.* **pendula** var. **ascendens**
– 'Autumnalis' ♀	CB&S CBlo CEnd CLnd CTho EBrP EBre ELan ENot IHos LBre LPan MAsh MBal MBar MBri MGos NWea SBre SFam SHBN SIgm SPer SSpi SSta WDin WWat
– 'Autumnalis Rosea' ♀	CB&S CBlo CEnd CPMA CSam CTho ELan ENot GChr GRei LBuc LNet LPan MAsh MBar MBri MGos NBee NWea SHBN SIgm SPer WDin WHCG WHen WStI WWat
– 'Fukubana' ♀	CBlo CLnd CTho LPan MAsh MBri
– 'Pendula' hort.	See *P.* **pendula** '**Pendula Rosea**'
– 'Pendula Rubra'	See *P.* **pendula** '**Pendula Rubra**'
N – 'Rosea'	CLnd
– 'Stellata'	See *P.* **pendula** '**Stellata**'
¶ 'Sunset Boulevard'	MBri
'Taihaku' ♀	Widely available
'Takasago'	See *P.* x **sieboldii** '**Caespitosa**'
* **takesimensis**	CMCN
'Taoyame'	CLnd MBri WPyg
tenella	CB&S CEnd ELan NBee SIng WCot WHCG WWat
– 'Fire Hill' ♀	CEnd CPMA ELan LNet MBar MGos MPla NBee NFla SBod SHBN SPer SSpi SWas WCot WDin WJas WOrn WPat WPyg
tibetica	See *P.* **serrula**
tomentosa	EPla SBod
§ 'Trailblazer' (C/D)	CBlo CEnd CLnd CTho IOrc LPan MGos NWea SKee SSta WStI
triloba	CB&S CBlo CLnd LBuc LPan MBar MPla NFla NWea SHBN SIgm WDin WShe

– 'Multiplex' (d) ♀	EBrP EBre ENot GChr LBre MGos MRav SBre SPer SRms WJas
– Rosemund	MBri
§ 'Ukon' ♀	CB&S CBlo CDoC CLnd CTho CTri ENot IOrc LBuc LNet MBal MBar MBri NBee NWea SFam SPer SSta WDin WPyg WStI
'Umineko'	CBlo CDoC CLnd EBee ENot IOrc MGos SPer
§ x **verecunda**	CBlo CDoC CLnd EBee GChr NWea WJas
– 'Autumn Glory'	CTho SLPl
virginiana 'Schubert'	CBlo CDoC CLnd CTho EBee ENot EPla IOrc LPan SSta WJas
'Wood's Variety'	See *P.* **cerasifera** '**Woodii**'
♦ **yamadae**	See *P.* **incisa** f. **yamadae**
§ x **yedoensis** ♀	CLnd CSam CTho EBee ECrN ENot NWea SFam SPer WDin WJas WOrn WWat
– 'Ivensii'	CB&S CBlo CDoC MAsh MBri SFam SHBN SPer WStI
– 'Pendula'	See *P.* x **yedoensis** '**Shidare-yoshino**'
– 'Perpendens'	See *P.* x **yedoensis** '**Shidare-yoshino**'
§ – 'Shidare-yoshino'	CBlo CDoC CEnd CLnd EBee EPfP GChr LNet MBar MBri MRav MWat NWea SPer WOrn WPyg WWat
– 'Tsubame'	MBri
'Yoshino'	See *P.* x **yedoensis**
'Yoshino Pendula'	See *P.* x **yedoensis** '**Shidare-yoshino**'

PSEUDERANTHEMUM (Acanthaceae)

reticulatum 'Eldorado'	LChe

PSEUDOCYDONIA (Rosaceae)

§ **sinensis**	CB&S LNet

PSEUDOFUMARIA (Papaveraceae)

alba	See *Corydalis* **ochroleuca**
lutea	See *Corydalis* **lutea**

PSEUDOLARIX (Pinaceae)

§ **amabilis** ♀	CDoC CFil CGre CMCN EHul ISea LCon LNet MBal MBar MBlu MBri SMad STre WCoo WNor WWat
kaempferi	See *P.* **amabilis**

PSEUDOMERTENSIA (Boraginaceae) See Plant Deletions

PSEUDOMUSCARI See MUSCARI

PSEUDOPANAX † (Araliaceae)

(Adiantifolius Group) 'Adiantifolius'	CB&S CHEx GQui
– 'Cyril Watson' ♀	CB&S CHEx CTrC
arboreus	CAbb CHEx
chathamicus	CHEx MAll SAPC SArc
crassifolius	CAbb CBot CHEx ECou SAPC SArc SMad
discolor	ECou
ferox	CAbb CHEx SAPC SArc SMad
laetus	CAbb CHEx
lessonii	CB&S CHEx ECou

– 'Gold Splash' (v) ♀ CB&S
– hybrids CHEx
'Linearifolius' CTrC
¶ 'Purpureus' ♀ CHEx EOas
'Sabre' CTrC
'Trident' CTrC
¶ *valdiviensis* MAll

PSEUDOPHEGOPTERIS (Thelypteridaceae)
levingei CCuc EMon

PSEUDOPHOENIX (Arecaceae)
* *nativo* MBri

PSEUDOSASA (Poaceae - Bambusoideae)
§ *amabilis* LJus SDry
– hort. See *Arundinaria tecta*
§ *japonica* ♀ CB&S CHEx EBee EFul EOas
EPfP EPla ISta LBlo LJus MBal
MBrN SCha SDry SMad SPer
WDin WJun
§ – 'Akebonosuji' (v) CHEx EFul EPla ISta LJus
SCha SDry
– 'Tsutsumiana' CHEx EBee EPla ISta LJus
SCha SDry WJun
– 'Variegata' See *P. japonica* 'Akebonosuji'
owatarii SDry
pleioblastoides EPla SDry
usawai EPla WJun

PSEUDOTSUGA (Pinaceae)
§ *menziesii* ♀ CB&S CDoC CPer GChr IOrc
LBuc LCon MBar NRoo NWea
WMou
– 'Bhiela Lhota' CKen
– 'Blue Wonder' CKen MAsh
– 'Densa' CKen
– 'Fastigiata' CKen
– 'Fletcheri' CBlo CKen MBar SLim
– var. *glauca* CBlo LCon MBar STre
– 'Glauca Pendula' ♀ CDoC LCon MBar MGos
I – 'Gotelli's Pendula' CKen
– 'Graceful Grace' CKen
– 'Julie' CKen
– 'Little Jamie' CKen
– 'Little Jon' NHol
– 'Lohbrunner' CKen
– 'McKenzie' CKen
– 'Nana' CKen
– 'Stairii' CKen
– 'Tempelhof Compact' SLim
– f. *viridis* GRei
taxifolia See *P. menziesii*

PSEUDOWINTERA (Winteraceae)
§ *colorata* CB&S CDec CDoC CMCN
CPle CTrw IOrc ISea MAll
MBlu WCru WPat WPyg WWat

PSIDIUM (Myrtaceae)
cattleyanum See *P. littorale* var. *longipes*
¶ *guajava* (F) MPEx
littorale (F) ERea
§ – var. *longipes* (F) LBlo

PSILOSTROPHE (Asteraceae) See Plant Deletions

PSORALEA (Papilionaceae)
affinis CHEx
glandulosa CGre

pinnata CTrC CTrG LHil

PSYCHOTRIA (Rubiaceae)
capensis SLMG
viridis NGno

PTELEA (Rutaceae)
trifoliata ♀ CAgr CB&S CFil CLnd CMCN
CPMA ELan LHol SPer SRms
SSpi WCoo WFar WHCG
WNor WOMN
– 'Aurea' ♀ CAbP CBot CEnd CLnd CPMA
CPle ELan ICrw LHol MBlu
MBri MGos SHBN SPer SSpi
SSta WHCG WPat WPyg

PTERACANTHUS See STROBILANTHES

PTERIDIUM (Hypolepidaceae)
aquilinum Percristatum IOrc
Group

PTERIDOPHYLLUM (Papaveraceae)
racemosum EFEx EPot WCru

PTERIS (Pteridaceae)
argyraea MBri NMar
cretica ♀ MBri SAPC SArc
– var. *albolineata* ♀ GQui MBri SRms
– *cristata* MBri
– 'Gautheri' MBri
– 'Parkeri' MBri
– 'Rivertoniana' MBri
– 'Rowei' MBri
– 'Wimsettii' MBri
ensiformis MBri NMar
– 'Arguta' MBri
– 'Victoriae' MBri
longifolia NMar
tremula GQui MBri NMar SRms
umbrosa MBri
vittata SRms

PTEROCARYA (Juglandaceae)
fraxinifolia ♀ CAgr CB&S CDoC CLnd
CMCN CTho CTrG ENot ERod
IOrc MBlu SPer WDin WMou
– var. *dumosa* WMou
× *rehderiana* CTho WMou
rhoifolia WMou
stenoptera CB&S CLnd CMCN CTho SLPl
WMou
– 'Fern Leaf' WMou

PTEROCELTIS (Ulmaceae)
tatarinowii CMCN WHCr

PTEROCEPHALUS (Dipsacaceae)
¶ *hookeri* SIng
parnassi See *P. perennis*
§ *perennis* CLyd ELan ESis GCHN LBee
MBro NBir NHar NMen NTow
NWCA SBla SIng SMer SRms
WAbe WEas WHoo WOMN
WOld WPat WPyg WWin

PTEROSTYLIS (Orchidaceae)
alata SWes
g. *Bantam* SWes
coccinea SSpi SWes

¶ – red — SWes
concinna — SWes
¶ – yellow — SWes
curta — CFil
g. *Cutie* 'Harold's Pride' AM-OCSA — SWes
g. *Dunkle* — SWes
fischii — SWes
g. *Hookwink* — SWes
× *ingens* — SWes
g. *Joseph Arthur* — SWes
g. *Marelba* — SWes
g. *Mary Eleanor* — SWes
g. *Nodding Grace* — SWes
obtusa — SWes
ophioglossa — SWes
procera — SWes
robusta — SWes
russellii — SWes
g. *Sentinel* — SWes
stricta — SWes
g. *Talhood* — SWes
taurus — SWes
× *toveyana* — SWes
truncata — SSpi SWes

PTEROSTYRAX (Styracaceae)
corymbosa — CMCN WWat
hispida ♀ — CB&S CBrd CFil CHEx CLnd CMCN CPMA CPle EPfP MBel MBlu SSpi SSta WPGP WWat
psilophylla — CMCN CPle

PTILIMNIUM (Apiaceae)
¶ *capillaceum* — EBee

PTILOSTEMON (Asteraceae)
¶ *casabonae* — EBee
§ *diacantha* — ECGN

PTILOTRICHUM (Brassicaceae)
spinosum 'Roseum' — See *Alyssum spinosum* 'Roseum'

PTYCHOSPERMA (Arecaceae) See Plant Deletions

PUERARIA (Papilionaceae)
montana var. *lobata* — CAgr CArn CPlN
thunbergiana — SBra

PULICARIA (Asteraceae)
§ *dysenterica* — CArn CKin EWFC MChe MSal NMir SIde WBea WCHb WGwy WOak WWye

PULMONARIA † (Boraginaceae)
'Abbey Dore Pink' — CMea WAbb
affinis — EMon LRHS WPbr
angustifolia ♀ — CHad CRow CSam GDra MBro MSal NBrk NFla NHol NOrc SChu WByw WEas WFar WHil WWin
– subsp. *azurea* — CBro CElw CMil CRow CSpe CVer EAst EBar EFou EGol ELan EPla ERav LWak MBri MCLN MRav NBro NRoo NSti NTow SPer SPla SRms SSvw WHoo WMow WWye
– 'Blaues Meer' — CFir CMGP EBar GBuc NSti SWas WCru
– 'Blue Pearl' — EMon MBel NSti

– 'Munstead Blue' — CElw CGle CHea CLAP CWit ECha EFou EGol EPar LFis LSpr MTho NBrk NRya NSti SAga SRms WCru WRus
– 'Rubra' — See *P. rubra*
¶ 'Apple Frost' — NSti
'Barfield Regalia' — CGle EMon MBro NCat NChi NSti SAxl WByw WCer
¶ 'Berries and Cream' — NSti
'Beth's Blue' — ECha MBri MGrG WByw WCru WPbr
'Beth's Pink' — CElw ECha ERav MBel NCat WCHb WCru
¶ 'Blauer Hügel' — EMon
§ 'Blauhimmel' — CCot CLAP EMon MBro NSti WHoo
'Blue Crown' — CBos CElw CGle CLAP CSev EMon EPPr NSti NTow SSpe SWas WHal WLin WPGP
'Blue Ensign' — Widely available
* 'Blue Moon' — MBro WHoo WTin
'British Sterling' — WGle
Cally hybrid — CLAP GCal NSti WPbr
'Cedric Morris' — CElw NSti
'Chintz' — CLAP GBuc LGan MAvo SUsu WBay WCru WHal WPbr
'Cleeton Red' — NCat NSti WCru
¶ 'Coral Springs' — NSti
'Corsage' — CElw EBee WPbr
'Crawshay Chance' — SWas WPbr
¶ 'De Vroomen's Pride' — CChr CFir EBee EMan
¶ 'Diana Chappell' — MBel NCat SSpi
¶ 'Duke's Silver' — CElw
'Esther' — NSti WRus
'Excalibur' — CElw ECha GBuc
'Fiona' — NHaw
'Glacier' — CElw CGle CMea CMil ECha EMon EPPr LRHS MArl MBel NCat NChi SAxl WCer WCru WHal
'Hazel Kaye's Red' — NSti
'Highdown' — See *P. 'Lewis Palmer'*
'Joan's Red' — CElw WCot
§ 'Lewis Palmer' ♀ — Widely available
'Little Star' — EMon GBuc LGan LRHS MTed WGle
longifolia — CArn CBot CBro CFee CGle CHan CMHG CRow ECoo EGol ELan EPla GCal LFis MBri MHew MSal MUlv NBrk NCat NOrc NSti SChu SEas SMad WByw WCHb WCru WEas WRus
§ – 'Ankum' — CBos CGle CLAP CSpe CVer EFou EMan EPla GBuc MBel MCLN NCat SBid SSpe SUsu SWas WByw WCot WPbr WRus
– 'Bertram Anderson' — CBos CGle CHad CLAP EAst EBrP EBre EGol ERav GAbr GMaP LBre MBel MBri MLLN MUlv NFai NOrc NTow NVic SAga SBla SBre SMrm WCHb WCot WCru WHil
– subsp. *cevennensis* — SSpi
◆ – 'Coen Jansen' — See *P. longifolia* 'Ankum'
– 'Dordogne' — CGle CLAP CVer EBee ECha EFou EGle EPPr EPla GBuc MGrG MRav SBla SPla SUsu WCot WCru WPGP
– forms — ECha GAbr
– from France — EPPr
– wild-collected — WCot

'Lovell Blue'	CElw WRus
¶ 'Majesté'	CFil ECha EHoe SWas WCot
	WPGP
§ 'Margery Fish' ♀	CBro CGle COtt EGol LFis
	LGan MAvo MBri MLLN MUlv
	NBro NRoo NSti NWes SHFr
	SMad SMer SPer WByw WCHb
	WCru WEas WMer WPrP
	WWye
'Mary Mottram'	CCot CElw MBel MHFP MLLN
	MMil MUlv NBir SAxl SWas
	WByw WCer WCot WCru
	WGle WHal WMaN
'Mawson's Blue'	CGle CLAP CMea EBrP EBre
	ECha EMon LBre MAvo MBel
	MBri MWat NChi NRoo NSti
	SBre SPer WCHb WCot WCru
	WEas WElm WMaN WPbr
	WRHF WWat
'Merlin'	CLAP EBee EMon LRHS SSpi
	WCHb
mollis	CBot CMHG CSWP EMon
	EOrc EPla GCal MBri NBrk
	NCat NSti NWoo SAxl WByw
	WCot WPbr
– 'Royal Blue'	CMea EGol GCHN MRav SLod
	WCHb WPbr
– 'Samobor'	WCot
¶ 'Moonstone'	CElw WRus
'Mournful Purple'	CElw CGle CLAP CRow ECha
	EMon EPla ERav MHFP MUlv
	NBrk SWat WCot WCru
'Mrs Kittle'	CElw CMil EBee GBri MBro
	MCLN MGrG MRav NHaw
	NSti SAxl SSpi WByw WCHb
	WCot WHal WLin WMer WPbr
	WRus
'Nürnberg'	EFou EHoe EMon EPPr LFis
	LRHS MBel MBro NSti WCHb
	WCru WHal WPbr
obscura	EGar EMon LRHS MBel
Opal = 'Ocupol'	CLAP CMil GBuc LFis MGrG
	NHol NSti SWas WCot WFar
	WRha WRus WWeb
officinalis	CArn CBro CGle CRow ECED
	EHon EMon EOrc EPar EWFC
	GPoy LHol LLWP MChe MFir
	MHew NBrk NChi NVic SIde
	WCru WEas WHal WOak
	WWye
– 'Alba'	NCat WByw
– 'Blue Mist'	CElw CMil ECha EGar EMon
	EOrc NSti SAxl SMrm WByw
	WCru WHal WLin WPbr
– 'Bowles' Blue'	CElw CFis CGle CLAP CVer
	SHel SSpi WAbb WFox WPGP
	WPbr WRus
– Cambridge Blue Group	CElw CHan ECGN ECha EFou
	EGar EGol EMon EPla ERav
	MAus MCLN MRav NFai NSti
	WByw WCru WEas WHal
	WRus
– 'Plas Merdyn'	IBlr
– *rubra*	See *P. rubra*
– 'Sissinghurst White' ♀	Widely available
– 'White Wings'	CElw CHan CHea CMil EBar
	EFou EPPr EPla EPri MAvo
	MBro MCLN NDov NHol NPri
	NSti SSpi WCHb WCot WEas
	WFar WMaN WPbr
'Oliver Wyatt's White'	EMon
Opal	See *P.* Ocupol = '**Opal**'
'Patrick Bates'	MBel
'Paul Aden'	WGle
* 'Rowlatt Choules'	SSpi
'Roy Davidson'	Widely available
§ *rubra* ♀	CElw CGle CHan CSWP CStr
	ECha ELan EMar EOrc LFis
	MAus MFir MSCN NHol NOrc
	NSti SChu SEas SIng SRms
	SUsu WBon WByw WCHb
	WCru WElm WRha
– var. *alba*	See *P. rubra* var. *albocorollata*
§ – var. *albocorollata*	CBre CElw CGle CMHG CVer
	ECha EMon LRHS MAvo
	MBel MBro MCLN MFir MSte
	NCat NSti SAxl WByw WCru
	WPrP WRus
– 'Ann'	CElw EFou EMon IBlr LRHS
	MBro NSti SOkh
– 'Barfield Pink'	CElw CMil CRow ECtt EGol
	ELan EMon GCal MBel MBri
	MBro MCLN MHFP MMil
	NBro NRoo NSti SAga SAxl
	SChu SMrm SPer WCHb WCer
	WCru WHal WLin WPbr WRus
– 'Barfield Ruby'	CLAP EMon GBuc LRHS
	SOkh
– 'Bowles' Red'	CBot CBre CMea CWit EBrP
	EBre ECtt ENot ERav GAbr
	LBre LGan LHop MWgw NRoo
	NSti SBre SCro SMrm SPer
	WHal WMow
– 'David Ward' (v)	Widely available
– 'Prestbury Pink'	EMon
– 'Redstart'	Widely available
– 'Warburg's Red'	EMon
§ *saccharata*	CHEx CRow ECha ELan LGro
	MBro MFir NHol SChu SCro
	SSvw WCHb WCru WEas
	WHoo WPbr WPyg WWat
	WWin
– 'Alba'	CBro CRow ECha EGar GBuc
	MBel NOak SIng SRms WCru
– Argentea Group ♀	CBro CGle CRow CSev EAst
	ECha ECoo EFou EGol ELan
	EMar EOld EOrc EPla ERic
	GAbr GMaP MAus MCLN
	MTho NBro NChi NFla NLon
	NSti SPer SSpi WCru WSan
♦ – 'Blauhimmel'	See *P.* '**Blauhimmel**'
– 'Brentor'	CElw CRow
– 'Cotton Cool'	EGar SApp SBid WPGP
– 'Dora Bielefeld'	Widely available
– 'Frühlingshimmel'	CBro CElw CGle CMil ECha
	EFou EPla LGre MAvo MBel
	MHFP MRav MUlv NDov
	NTow SAxl SBla SMrm SUsu
	WCHb WHal WLin WPrP
	WRus
¶ – 'Glebe Cottage Blue'	CElw ECGP
– 'Jill Richardson'	EGar ELan WPbr
– 'Lady Lou's Pink'	LFis WCru
– 'Leopard'	CBos CElw CGle CLAP CMea
	CSam CSpe EBrP EBre ECtt
	EFou GMaP LBre LFis MBel
	MHFP NSti SBid SBla SBre
	SMrm SUsu WCru WMer WRus
– 'Mrs Moon'	Widely available
– 'Old Rectory Silver'	CLAP
– 'Picta'	See *P. saccharata*
– 'Pink Dawn'	CDoC EBee EMan EOrc LFis
	MBri NBus NPri NSti SPer
	WCru

– 'Reginald Kaye'	CElw CRow ECha EHic EMFP ERav EWes MBro NBrk NDov NSti SHBN
¶ – 'South Hayes'	CLAP
– 'White Leaf'	WRus
'Saint Ann's'	CElw CLTr EMon NSti
¶ 'Silver Spring'	WBon
'Skylight'	CElw
'Smoky Blue'	CBlo CLAP CSpe EAst EBee EFou EGol EPfP GBri MBro MCLN NPri NRoo NSti SMer SWat WByw WCot WFar WHal WMer WPbr WWeb WWoo
'Snowy Owl'	WGle
'Tim's Silver'	ECha NBrk WBcn
¶ 'Ultramarine'	EMon
♦ *vallarsae* 'Margery Fish'	See *P.* **'Margery Fish'**
'Weetwood Blue'	CBre CElw CLAP CVer MSte
¶ 'Wendy Perry'	CElw
'Wisley White'	CElw

PULSATILLA (Ranunculaceae)

alba	CBro GCLN MSto
albana	CBro MSto NTow SBla
– 'Lutea'	MSto SBla
– white	MSto
alpina	CBot NRoo SRms WAbe
§ – subsp. *apiifolia* ♀	CBot CLyd ELan GTou NGre NHar NRoo WCot WLin WOMN WSan
– subsp. *sulphurea*	See *P. alpina* subsp. *apiifolia*
ambigua	ESis MSto
aurea	GCrs MSto
bungeana	MSto
campanella	MSto
caucasica	CBro
cernua	GBuc MSto SIgm
chinensis	MSto
* *czerna*	MSto
dahurica	MFos
¶ x *gayeri*	MSto
georgica	MSto WLin
halleri ♀	ECGP EDAr EMan MMil MSto NSla SIgm
– subsp. *slavica* ♀	CBro GCrs MFos NNrd NWCA SWas WWin
koreana	CBro LRHS MSto
* *lutea*	WLin
montana	EWes MSto WLin
– var. *australis*	MSto
occidentalis	EBee GCLN MSto WOMN
§ *patens*	EBee GCLN MSto NTow WLin
¶ – subsp. *flavescens*	WAbe
¶ – var. *multifida* NNS 96221	IDac
* *pinnata*	MSto
pratensis	GTou MSto MTho
– subsp. *nigricans*	CBro LRHS
* *serotina*	MSto
turczaninovii	MSto SIgm
* *ucrainica*	MSto
§ *vernalis* ♀	EDAr EHyt EPot GCLN GCrs GDra GTou MSto NHar NRya NSla NTow NWCA SIng SRms WAbe
§ *vulgaris* ♀	Widely available
– 'Alba' ♀	Widely available
– 'Barton's Pink'	CMil EFou EWes EWll SBla SSON WRus
– 'Eva Constance'	CBro CLyd CRDP EBrP EBre EHyt ESis LBre LHop LRHS SBre SIng SWas WAbe
– 'Flore Pleno' (d)	CNic

– 'Gotlandica'	CLyd GDra NHol SIgm
– subsp. *grandis*	CLAP WLin
¶ – – 'Budapest'	WAbe
¶ – – f. *dissecta*	WAbe
¶ – – ex 'Budapest'	GCrs
– Heiler hybrids	EMan SSON
– 'Miss Beveridge'	NOak
– pale pink	NRoo
– 'Papageno'	CBot CGle EMan GCrs LGre NLar NRoo NSla SIgm SMrm WFar WHil WViv
I – 'Red Clock'	See *P. vulgaris* **'Röde Klokke'**
§ – 'Röde Klokke'	LGre MBro NRya WHil
¶ – *rosea*	WHoo
– Rote Glocke	See *P. vulgaris* **'Röde Klokke'**
– var. *rubra*	CB&S CGle CNic CSpe EFou EHyt ELan EOrc GAbr GLil LHop MBal MBri MBro MHig MSto NFla NHar NNrd NRoo SBla SUsu WHoo WPer WRus
§ – 'Weisse Schwan'	CBlo EHyt EOld LFis MBro MCLN NFla NMen
– White Swan	See *P. vulgaris* **'Weisse Schwan'**
* *wisetonensis*	MSto

PULTENAEA (Papilionaceae)

daphnoides	MAll

PUNICA (Punicaceae)

granatum	ECon EMil ERea GAri LPan MPEx SOWG STre WSHC
– 'Flore Pleno Rubro' (d)	LPan
– var. *nana*	CArn CHal CPle EPfP ERea GAri LHop LPan MPla SMrm SRms WPat WWat
– f. *plena* (d)	CB&S MRav WCFE
* – 'Striata'	SOWG

PURSHIA   (Rosaceae) See Plant Deletions

PUSCHKINIA (Hyacinthaceae)

§ *scilloides* var. *libanotica*	CAvo CBro ELan EPar EPot ETub GBur LAma MBal NEgg NRog WPer WShi
– – 'Alba'	CAvo EPar EPot LAma NRog
– Polunin 5238	CMon

PUTORIA (Rubiaceae)

calabrica	CLyd NWCA

PUYA (Bromeliaceae)

alpestris	CFil CHEx CTbh CTrC EOas SAPC SArc WCot WPGP
berteroniana	CHEx CTrC LLew WPic
chilensis	CAbb CB&S CHEx CTbh CTrC ECre EOas MAll SAPC SArc
coerulea	CFir CHEx GBin MAll SIgm
– var. *coerulea*	SAxl
¶ – F&W 8411	WLRN
¶ – JCA 14371	IDac
– RB 94100	LLew
§ – var. *violacea*	CGre CHEx
¶ – – F&W 7911	WLRN
laxa	CHEx
mirabilis	CHEx GCra LLew WPGP
raimondii	CHEx
venusta	CHEx GBin WPic
– JCA 14369	IDac
♦ *violacea*	See *P. coerulea* var. *violacea*
weberbaueri	CHEx

PYCNANTHEMUM (Lamiaceae)
montanum   WCot
muticum   MRav
pilosum   CArn CHal CSev ELau EMan
                          GBar GPoy LHol MSal NPri
                          SIde WHer WPer WWye
virginiana   ECha

PYCNOSTACHYS (Lamiaceae)
urticifolia   GCra

PYGMAEA See CHIONOHEBE

PYRACANTHA † (Rosaceae)
Alexander Pendula   CBlo EBee EHol ENot EPla
                          GAri LHop MGos MRav SEas
                          SRms WHar WWat
angustifolia   CB&S CBlo EHic WUnu
§ *atalantioides*   CB&S CBlo CMac CSam SPla
                          WCFE WWat
§ – 'Aurea'   CBlo CChe WWin
'Brilliant'   CB&S CBlo EPfP SLPl
'Buttercup'   EPla GAri WBcn
§ Saphyr® Orange =   CBlo COtt EPfP IOrc MBri
   'Cadange'   SBid SPer WLRN WWeb
§ Saphyr® Jaune =   CBlo CDoC EBar EPfP IOrc
   'Cadaune'   SPer WLRN WWeb
Saphyr® Rouge =   CBlo COtt EPfP IOrc MBri
   'Cadrou'   SBid SPer WLRN WWeb
coccinea   CTrw
§ – 'Lalandei'   CBlo CMac CSam EBee MGos
                          NNor SPer WGwG WWal
– 'Red Column'   CBlo CChe CMac EBar ECtt
                          ELan GChr GOrc GRei LBuc
                          MBar MGos MRav MWat NBee
                          NFla SAga SCoo SEas WDin
                          WGwG WHar WWal WWeb
– 'Red Cushion'   CBlo ENot IHos MGos MRav
                          SRms
– 'Rutgers'   SLPl
– 'Telstar'   CB&S CBlo
Dart's Red   CBlo MBri WLRN WWeb
gibbsii   See *P. atalantioides*
– 'Flava'   See *P. atalantioides* 'Aurea'
'Golden Charmer'   CBlo EBee EBrP EBre ECtt
                          ELan ENot EPfP LBre MBal
                          MGos SBre SHBN SPer SRms
                          WBod WDin WGwG WHar
'Golden Dome'   SEas
'Golden Glow'   CBlo
'Golden Sun'   See *P. 'Soleil d'Or'*
'Harlequin' (v)   CB&S CBlo ECtt EPla MBal
                          MBar NSti SBid SHBN SReu
                          WLeb WWeb
'John Stedman'   See *P. 'Stedman's'*
'Knap Hill Lemon'   CChe MBlu
'Mohave'   CB&S CBlo CChe CMac EBrP
                          EBre ELan ENot LBre MBal
                          MBar MGos MRav MWat
                          NHed NNor SBre SHBN SPer
                          SReu SRms WDin WStI WWal
'Mohave Silver' (v)   CBlo EAst EBar ELan MBar
                          MWat NNor SEas SPla WGwG
                          WWal
'Monrovia'   See *P. coccinea* 'Lalandei'
'Mozart'   WWeb
'Navaho'   CBlo EBee EPfP MPla MRav
'Orange Charmer'   CBlo CChe CTri ELan ENot
                          MAsh MBal MBar MGos MWat
                          NBee SHBN SPer WRHF WStI
                          WWeb
'Orange Giant'   See *P. coccinea* 'Kasan'

'Orange Glow' ♀   CBlo CChe CMac EBrP EBre
                          ECtt ENot GOrc GRei IHos
                          LBre LBuc MAsh MBar MGos
                          NFla NNor NWea SBre SPer
                          SRms WDin WHar WStI
* 'Red Pillar'   CBlo CDoC
'Renault d'Or'   SLPl
rogersiana ♀   CBlo EBee EHic ENot EPfP
                          MRav NNor WWal
– 'Flava' ♀   CBlo CLTr CTri EBee EHol
                          ENot EPfP MAsh MBal MBar
                          NFla NNor NWea WGwG
                          WWal
Saphyr Jaune   See *P.* Saphyr Jaune =
                          'Cadaune'
♦ Saphyr Orange   See *P.* Saphyr Orange =
                          'Cadange'
♦ 'Saphyr Rouge'   See *P.* Saphyr Rouge = 'Cadrou'
'Shawnee'   CB&S CBlo CMac ECot EHic
                          EPfP MAsh MRav MWat NHed
                          SPla WWeb
§ 'Soleil d'Or'   CBlo CMac CSam EBrP EBre
                          ECtt ELan ENot EPla IHos
                          LBre LBuc MBar MBri MPla
                          MRav NBee NCut NNor SBre
                          SPer SReu WDin WHCr WHar
                          WStI
'Sparkler' (v)   CBlo CMac CPMA EAst EBar
                          EHoe ELan LHop MAsh NHol
                          NLon NNor SAga SBid SEas
                          SPer SPla WHar
§ 'Stedman's'   MBri
'Teton'   CDec CMHG CMac ELan ENot
                          EPla LHop MAsh MBar MBri
                          MGos MRav NHed NHol SPla
                          SRms WBod WDin WFar
                          WLRN WStI
'Watereri' ♀   CBlo SBid SLPl SPer
'Yellow Sun'   See *P. 'Soleil d'Or'*

PYRACOMELES (Rosaceae) See Plant
Deletions

PYRETHROPSIS (Asteraceae)
§ *catananche*   ECho

PYRETHRUM (Asteraceae)
♦ *radicans*   See *Leucanthemopsis pectinata*
roseum   See *Tanacetum coccineum*

PYROCYDONIA (Rosaceae)
¶ 'Danielii' (F)   WMou

PYROLA (Ericaceae)
rotundifolia   WHer

PYROSTEGIA (Bignoniaceae)
venusta   CPlN LChe LCns SOWG WMul

PYRROCOMA (Asteraceae)
clementis   EBee

PYRROSIA (Polypodiaceae)
* *heterophylla*   NMar
¶ *lingua* 'Variegata' (v) EMon

PYRUS † (Rosaceae)
amygdaliformis   CTho
– var. *cuneifolia*   CTho
betulifolia   CMCN WJas

calleryana　CAgr
– 'Bradford'　CLnd
– 'Chanticleer' ♀　CB&S CBlo CDoC CEnd CLnd
　　CTho ENot IOrc LHyr LPan
　　MAsh MBlu NBee SHBN SLPl
　　SPer SSta WDin WJas WOrn
　　WWat
x *canescens*　CTho
communis (F)　CCVT CKin GChr LBuc MBlu
　　SKee SPer STre WMou
– 'Autumn Bergamot' (D)　CTho SKee
– 'Barland' (Perry)　WMou
– 'Barnet' (Perry)　CTho
– 'Baronne de Mello' (D)　CTho SFam SKee
– 'Beech Hill' (F)　CLnd CTho ENot EPfP
– 'Belle Guérandaise' (D)　SKee
– 'Belle Julie' (D)　SKee
– 'Bergamotte　SKee
　d'Automne' (D)
– 'Bergamotte Esperen'　SKee
　(D)
– 'Beth' (D) ♀　CDoC CWSG EMui GBon
　　GTwe LBuc MBri MGos NBee
　　NDal NRog SDea SFam SIgm
　　SKee SPer
– 'Beurré Alexandre　SKee
　Lucas' (D)
– 'Beurré Bedford' (D)　NRog SIgm
– 'Beurré Bosc' (D)　SKee
– 'Beurré Clairgeau'　SKee
　(C/D)
– 'Beurré d'Amanlis' (D)　SKee
– 'Beurré d'Avalon' (D)　CTho
¶ – 'Beurré de Beugny' (D)　SKee
– 'Beurré de Naghin'　SKee
　(C/D)
– 'Beurré Dumont' (D)　SFam
– 'Beurré Hardy' (D) ♀　CDoC CTho EMui ERea GTwe
　　MBri MWat NRog SDea SFam
　　SIgm SKee
– 'Beurré Mortillet' (D)　SKee
– 'Beurré Six' (D)　SKee
– 'Beurré Superfin' (D)　ERea GTwe SFam SIgm SKee
– 'Bianchettone' (D)　SKee
– 'Bishop's Thumb' (D)　SDea SKee
– 'Black Worcester' (C)　GTwe SDea SKee WJas
　　WMou WSPU
– 'Blakeney Red' (Perry)　CTho SDea WMou
– 'Blickling' (D)　SKee
– 'Brandy' (Perry)　CTho SDea WMou
– 'Bristol Cross' (D)　GTwe SKee
– 'Brown Bess' (Perry)　WMou
– 'Catillac' (C) ♀　CTho GTwe NRog SFam SKee
– 'Chalk'　See *P. communis* 'Crawford'
– 'Chaumontel' (D)　SKee
– 'Clapp's Favourite' (D)　CTho GTwe IOrc SIgm SKee
– 'Colmar d'Eté' (D)　CTho
– 'Comte de Lamy' (D)　SKee
– 'Concorde' (D) ♀　CDoC CWSG EMui ERea
　　GTwe LBuc MGos NBee
　　NDal SDea SFam SIgm SKee
　　WJas WWeb
– 'Conference' (D) ♀　CMac CSam CTho CWSG EBrP
　　EBre EMui ERea GBon GChr
　　GRei GTwe IOrc LBre LBuc
　　MBri MGos MWat NBee NDal
　　NRog SBre SDea SFam SIgm
　　SKee SPer WJas WWeb
– 'Craig's Favourite' (D)　GTwe
– 'Crassane'　CTho
§ – 'Crawford' (D)　SKee
– 'Deacon's Pear' (D)　SDea

– 'Docteur Jules Guyot'　SKee
　(D)
– 'Double de Guerre'　SKee
　(C/D)
– 'Doyenné Boussoch' (D)　SKee
– 'Doyenné d'Eté' (D)　ERea SFam SKee
– 'Doyenné du Comice'　CDoC CMac CSam CTho
　(D) ♀　　CWSG EBrP EBre EMui ERea
　　GBon IOrc LBre MBri MWat
　　NRog SBre SDea SFam SIgm
　　SKee SPer WJas WWeb
– 'Doyenné Georges　SKee
　Boucher' (D)
– 'Duchesse d'Angoulême'　SKee
　(D)
– 'Durondeau' (D)　CTho GTwe NRog SFam SIgm
　　SKee
– 'Easter Beurré' (D)　SKee
– 'Emile d'Heyst' (D)　CTho GTwe SIgm
– 'Eva Baltet' (D)　SKee
– 'Fertility Improved'　See *P. communis* 'Improved
　　Fertility'
– 'Fondante d'Automne'　CTho SKee
　(D)
– 'Forelle' (D)　ERea SKee
– 'Gansel's Bergamot' (D)　CTho
– 'Gin' (Perry)　CTho WMou
– 'Glou Morceau' (D)　CTho EMui GTwe MWat NRog
　　SDea SFam SIgm SKee
– 'Glow Red Williams'　SFam
　(D)
– 'Gorham' (D)　CTho GTwe NBee SFam SKee
– 'Gratiole de Jersey' (D)　CTho
– 'Green Horse' (Perry)　CTho WMou
– 'Green Pear of Yair'　SKee
　(D)
– 'Hacon's Imcomparable'　SKee
　(D)
– 'Hendre Huffcap'　WMou
　(Perry)
– 'Hessle' (D)　GTwe NRog SDea SFam SKee
– 'Highland' (D)　SKee
§ – 'Improved Fertility' (D)　CDoC GBon GTwe SDea SKee
– 'Jargonelle' (D)　GTwe NRog SDea SFam SKee
– 'Joséphine de Malines'　CTho GTwe SDea SFam SIgm
　(D) ♀　　SKee
– 'Judge Amphlett'　WMou
　(Perry)
– 'Laxton's Foremost' (D)　SKee
– 'Laxton's Satisfaction'　SFam
　(D)
– 'Le Lectier' (D)　SKee
– 'Louise Bonne of Jersey'　CDoC CTho CTri EMui GTwe
　(D)　　MBri NRog SDea SFam SIgm
– 'Maggie Duncan' (F)　GTwe
– 'Marguérite Marillat'　GTwe SDea
　(D)
– 'Marie-Louise' (D)　SKee
– 'Merton Pride' (D)　CTho GTwe MWat SDea SFam
　　SKee
– 'Merton Star' (D)　SKee
– 'Moorcroft' (Perry)　WMou
– 'Nouveau Poiteau'　CTho GTwe SKee
　(C/D)
– 'Oldfield' (Perry)　WMou
– 'Olivier de Serres' (D)　SFam SKee
– 'Onward' (D) ♀　EMui GTwe LBuc MGos NBee
　　NDal NRog SDea SFam SIgm
　　SKee
§ – 'Packham's Triumph'　CDoC GTwe NRog SDea SKee
　(D)

– 'Passe Colmar' (D)	CTho
– 'Passe Crassane' (D)	SKee
– 'Pear Apple' (D)	SDea
– 'Pitmaston Duchess' (C/D) ♀	CWSG GTwe SDea SKee
– 'Red Comice' (D/C)	GTwe SKee
– 'Robin' (C/D)	ERea SDea SKee
– 'Roosevelt' (D)	SKee
– 'Santa Claus' (D)	SDea SFam SKee
– 'Seckle' (D)	GTwe SFam SIgm SKee
– 'Soleil d'Automne' (F)	SKee
– 'Souvenir du Congrès' (D)	NRog
– 'Swan's Egg' (D)	CTho SKee
– 'Sweet Huffcap'	See *P. communis* **'Hellen's Early'**
– 'Thompson's' (D)	GTwe SFam SIgm
– 'Thorn' (Perry)	CTho WMou
– 'Triomphe de Vienne' (D)	SFam
– 'Triumph'	See *P. communis* **'Packham's Triumph'**
– 'Uvedale's St Germain' (C)	CTho SKee
– 'Vicar of Winkfield' (C/D)	GTwe SDea SKee
– 'Williams' Bon Chrétien' (D/C) ♀	CMac CWSG EBrP EBre EMui ERea GBon GChr GRei IOrc LBre LBuc MBri MGos MWat NDal NRog SBre SDea SFam SIgm SKee SPer WJas WStI WWeb
– 'Williams Red' (D/C)	GTwe SKee
– 'Winnal's Longdon' (Perry)	CTho WMou
– 'Winter Christie' (F)	GTwe
– 'Winter Nelis' (D)	CTho GTwe SDea SFam SKee
cordata	CTho
cossonii	CTho
elaeagnifolia	CTho WWat
– var. *kotschyana*	CBlo CEnd
nivalis	CLnd CTho ENot SHBN SLPl SPer
¶ *pashia* CLD 114	EPla
pyraster	CPer
pyrifolia '20th Century'	See *P. pyrifolia* **'Nijisseiki'**
– 'Chojura' (F)	IOrc
– 'Kumoi' (F)	ESim LBuc SDea
* – 'Nashi Kumoi'	LPan
– 'Shinseiki' (F)	EMui SDea
– 'Shinsui' (F)	SDea SKee
salicifolia 'Pendula' ♀	Widely available
ussuriensis	CBlo CMCN

QUERCUS † (Fagaceae)

acuta	CB&S CHEx CMCN
§ *acutissima*	CLnd CMCN SBir WDin WNor
– subsp. *chenii*	CMCN
aegilops	See *Q. macrolepis*
affinis	CMCN SBir
agrifolia	CB&S CMCN
alba	CMCN
¶ – f. *elongata*	LRHS
aliena	SBir
– var. *acuteserrata*	CMCN
alnifolia	CDul
arkansana	CMCN
austrina	CMCN
× *beadlei*	SBir
bicolor	CDul CMCN SBir WDin WNor
borealis	See *Q. rubra*
brantii	CMCN

breweri	CMCN
× *bushii*	CMCN MBlu
canariensis ♀	CFil CLnd CMCN CTho CTrG EPfP SBir WMou WPGP WTro
canbyi	CMCN
castaneifolia	CDul CLnd CMCN WMou
– 'Green Spire' ♀	CDoC CDul CLnd CMCN EBee EPfP MBlu MBri SMad SPer
cerris ♀	CB&S CBlo CDoC CDul CKin CLnd CMCN EMil ENot IOrc NWea SEND SPer SSta STre WDin WFro WMou WTro
§ – 'Argenteovariegata'	CDul CMCN CTho EPfP MBlu MBri SMad WMou
* – 'Marmorata'	CLyn
– 'Variegata'	See *Q. cerris* **'Argenteovariegata'**
– 'Wodan'	CMCN MBlu
chrysolepis	CMCN MBlu
coccifera	CDul CFil CMCN WPGP
coccinea	CAbP CB&S CDul CLnd CMCN CWSG EHic EPfP GChr IOrc NBee NWea SBir SPer SSta STre WNor
– 'Splendens' ♀	CDoC CDul CEnd CFil CMCN COtt CTho ELan IOrc LPan MBlu MBri NBee SHBN SMad SPer SSpi WDin WPGP
comptoniae	CMCN
crassipes	CMCN
dentata	CMCN EPfP
– 'Carl Ferris Miller'	CFil LRHS MBlu SMad WPGP
– 'Pinnatifida'	CMCN MBlu SMad
¶ – 'Sir Harold Hillier'	LRHS
douglasii	CAgr CMCN
dumosa	CMCN
ellipsoidalis	CAbP CDoC CDul CMCN MBri SBir WWat WWes
– 'Hemelrijk'	CFil MBlu
engelmannii	CMCN
faginea	CMCN MNes SBir
falcata	CDul CLnd CMCN
– var. *pagodifolia*	CMCN MBlu SBir
× *fernaldii*	CMCN
frainetto	CDoC CDul CLnd CMCN CTho EBee GChr IOrc LPan MBlu MBri SEND SMad SPer SSpi WDin WMou WShe WWat
– 'Trump'	MBlu
fruticosa	See *Q. lusitanica* **Lamarck**
gambelii	CMCN
garryana	CMCN MBlu
– × *turbinella*	SBir
georgiana	CMCN
glabra	See *Lithocarpus glaber*
glabrescens	CB&S
glandulifera	CMCN SBir
glauca	CMCN
hartwissiana	CMCN
× *hastingsii*	CMCN
hemisphaerica	CMCN SBir
× *heterophylla*	CDul CMCN SBir
× *hickelii*	CMCN
¶ *hinckleyi*	WDin
× *hispanica*	See *Q.* × *lucombeana*
– 'Lucombeana'	See *Q.* × *lucombeana* **'William Lucombe'**
ilex ♀	Widely available
ilicifolia	CDul CMCN MBlu WNor WWat
imbricaria	CDul CMCN MBlu SBir WWes
incana Bartram	CMCN

– Roxburgh	See *Q. leucotrichophora*
infectoria	CDul
– subsp. *veneris*	CMCN
ithaburensis	CMCN
kelloggii	CMCN WWes
× *kewensis*	CMCN WMou
laevis	CMCN MBlu
laurifolia	CDul CMCN
§ *leucotrichophora*	CMCN
liaotungensis	CMCN
¶ × *libanerris*	SBir
– 'Rotterdam'	CMCN
libani	CDul CMCN
lobata	CMCN
§ *lucombeana*	CLnd WPic
¶ – 'Ambrozyana'	LRHS SMad
– 'Diversifolia'	CMCN MBlu WMou
– 'Suberosa'	CTho
– 'Wageningen'	CMCN WMou
§ – 'William Lucombe' ♀	CDul CMCN CTho MBlu WMou
× *ludoviciana*	CMCN SAPC SArc
§ *lusitanica* Lamarck	CDul CMCN
lyrata	CMCN
macranthera	CMCN EMil EPfP
macrocarpa	CMCN WDin WNor
– × *gambelii*	SBir
– × *robur*	SBir
§ *macrolepis*	CMCN MBlu
¶ – from Lesbos, Greece	WPGP
marilandica	CDul CEnd CMCN SBir WWes
mexicana	CMCN
michauxii	CMCN SBir
mongolica var. *grosseserrata*	CMCN
§ *montana*	CMCN MBlu
muehlenbergii	CDul CMCN CTho SBir
myrsinifolia	CB&S CMCN SAPC SArc WNor
nigra	CMCN CMHG MBlu SBir
nuttallii	CMCN SBir
obtusa	CDul CMCN
palustris ♀	CAgr CDul CLnd CMCN CTho IOrc LPan MBal MBri SBir SPer SSpi WDin WNor WOrn
* – 'Compacta'	LRHS
– 'Pendula'	CEnd CMCN
* – 'Swamp Pygmy'	CMCN MBlu
pedunculata	See *Q. robur*
pedunculiflora	CMCN
§ *petraea* ♀	CDoC CDul CKin CLnd CPer EMil GChr GRei IOrc LBuc MBal NWea SPer WDin WFro WMou WTro
§ – 'Insecata'	CDoC CEnd CMCN
– 'Laciniata'	See *Q. petraea* 'Insecata'
– 'Mespilifolia'	CTho
– 'Purpurea'	CMCN MBlu
§ *phellos* ♀	CDul CLnd CMCN CTho GChr MBlu SLPl SSpi STre WCoo WDin WNor WWat WWes
* – *latifolia*	IOrc MBlu
phillyreoides	CB&S CDul CMCN SBir WCoo WNor
planipocula	CMCN
'Pondaim'	CMCN LRHS
pontica	CMCN MBlu
prinoides	SBir
prinus Engelm.	See *Q. montana*
§ – Linnaeus	CAgr CMCN MBlu
pubescens	CDul CMCN
pumila Michaux	See *Q. prinus* Linnaeus
– Walt.	See *Q. phellos*
pyrenaica	CMCN CTho
– 'Pendula'	CMCN MBlu MBri
§ *robur* ♀	Widely available
– 'Argenteomarginata'	CDul CMCN MBlu SMad SSta
– 'Atropurpurea'	EMil
* – 'Compacta'	MBlu
– 'Concordia'	CB&S CBlo CEnd CFil CMCN COtt EPfP LRHS MBlu SMad WPGP
– 'Cristata'	CDul CMCN
– 'Cucullata'	CMCN
* – *dissecta*	CMCN
– 'Facrist'	CBlo CDul CEnd
– f. *fastigiata*	CBlo CDoC CDul CLnd CTho EMil ENot GChr IOrc LBuc LPan MAsh MBar MWat NBee NWea SCoo SPer WOrn
– 'Fastigiata Koster' ♀	CDul CMCN COtt EMil EPfP MCoo SSta
– 'Fennessii'	CMCN MBlu SMad
– 'Fürst Schwarzenburg'	CMCN MBlu
– 'Hentzei'	CMCN
– 'Hungaria'	MBlu
– × *lobata*	SBir
– 'Pectinata'	MBlu
– f. *pendula*	CDul CEnd CMCN CTho
– 'Purpurascens'	CEnd CMCN MBlu
– 'Raba'	CMCN
– 'Strypemonde'	CMCN
– × *turbinella*	SBir
× *rosacea* 'Filicifolia'	CEnd WMou
§ *rubra* ♀	Widely available
– 'Aurea'	CDul CEnd CFil CMCN MBlu SMad SSpi
* – 'Sunshine'	CMCN LRHS MBlu MBri SMad
rugosa	CMCN
sadleriana	CMCN
sartorii	CMCN
× *saulii*	CMCN SBir
¶ × *schochiana*	CMCN
¶ *semecarpifolia*	ISea
serrata	See *Q. acutissima*
sessiliflora	See *Q. petraea*
shumardii	CDul CMCN SBir WDin WNor WWes
stellata	CMCN SBir
suber	CB&S CDoC CDul CLnd CMCN CTho GAri GChr ISea SAPC SArc SEND SSpi WDin WPGP
texana	CMCN WWes
trojana	CMCN
turbinella	CMCN
× *turneri*	CDoC CDul CLnd CMCN CTho MBri WMou
– 'Pseudoturneri'	CB&S EMil LRHS
vaccinifolia	CMCN MBal
variabilis	CDul CMCN MBlu WCoo WWes
velutina	CDul CGre CLnd CMCN SBir WCoo WWat
– 'Rubrifolia'	CMCN EPfP
virginiana	CMCN
'Warburgii'	CMCN
wislizenii	CMCN IOrc SBir

QUESNELIA (Bromeliaceae) See Plant Deletions

QUILLAJA (Rosaceae)
saponaria   CGre CPle CTrG

QUIONGZHUEA (Poaceae - Bambusoideae)
tumidinoda   See *Chimonobambusa*
                           tumidissinoda

RACOPILUM (Sphagnaceae) See Plant
Deletions

RACOSPERMA See ACACIA

RAMONDA (Gesneriaceae)
§ *myconi* ♀   CLAP CMea CPBP EHyt MBro
                           MHig NHar NSla NTow NWCA
                           SBla SIgm SIng SRms SWas
– var. *alba*   SIng
– 'Rosea'   CLAP
nathaliae ♀   CLAP CPBP GCLN NHar SIgm
– 'Alba'   SBla SWas WFar
pyrenaica   See *R. myconi*
serbica   GDra SIgm SIng

RANUNCULUS † (Ranunculaceae)
abnormis   SWas
aconitifolius   CGle EBrP EBre ECha EMFP
                           EPar LBre NChi NSti SBre
– 'Flore Pleno' (d) ♀   CHea CRow EBrP EBre EPar
                           EPri GBuc IBlr LBre LGre
                           NBir NTow SBla SBre SMrm
                           SWas WByw
acris   EWFC NLan WBro
* – *citrinus*   CBos CElw ECoo EPar EPri
                           EWoo WAlt WElm WFar
                           WRha WSan
¶ – 'Cricket' (v)   WAlt
– 'Farrer's Yellow'   CRow
– 'Flore Pleno' (d)   CAvo CElw CFee CFir CGle
                           CRow ECha ELan EMan EPar
                           GAbr MAus MInt NBro NChi
                           NFai NHex NHol NRya NSti
                           SMac WAlt WByw WHal WLin
                           WSan WWal
– 'Hedgehog'   EMon WCot
– 'Stevenii'   CBos CFee CRow SAxl SDix
                           WPbr
– 'Sulphureus'   CBre CGle EMon MSte NCat
                           SMrm WEas WHal
alpestris   NMen
amplexicaulis   CMon EPot ERos GCrs GDra
                           GTou NHar SBla WAbe
aquatilis   CBen EHon EMFW NDea
                           SWat SWyc WChe
asiaticus   CMon ETub WOMN
– Accolade   NNrd SCoo WStI
* – Tecolote hybrids   LAma
– white   SBla
– yellow   SBla
auricomus   CKin
¶ *baurii*   EBee
¶ *bilobus*   WAbe
bulbosus   CKin EWFC
§ – 'F.M. Burton'   CBos CRDP EGar GCal MAvo
                           MCLN MHlr NSti NTow WAlt
                           WCot WHal WRus
– *farreri*   See *R. bulbosus* **'F.M. Burton'**
– 'Speciosus Plenus'   See *R. constantinopolitanus*
                           'Plenus'
calandrinioides ♀   CMon SBla WAbe WCot
– dwarf form   SIgm
– SF 37   CMon

§ *constantinopolitanus*   CDec CElw CGle CRDP CRow
  'Plenus' (d)   ECha EMon GCal GGar MBri
                           MBro MInt NBro NChi NRya
                           WCot WEas WFar
cortusifolius   CRDP WCot
crenatus   CLyd EHyt ELan GTou ITim
                           LBee MBal NGre NHar NMen
                           NNrd NRya NSla NTow SBla
                           WAbe WHal WHil
creticus   EMon
eschscholtzii   NGre
¶ *extorris* 'Flore Pleno' EMon
ficaria   CArn CHid CJew CKin CNat
                           CRow EWFC GBar GCal MChe
                           MHew MSal WHer WOak WShi
                           WWye
I – 'Aglow in the Dark'   CNat
– var. *albus*   CElw CGle CMil CMon CRow
                           CVer EMon ERos NGre NRya
                           WByw
– anemone centred   See *R. ficaria* **'Collarette'**
– 'Ashen Primrose'   CRow
§ – var. *aurantiacus*   CMil CNic CRow CVer ECha
                           EMon EPar GDra MBro NGre
                           NHol NMen NNrd NRya SAxl
                           SBla SIng SRms SSvw WAbe
– 'Blackadder'   CRow
– 'Bowles' Double'   See *R. ficaria* **'Double Bronze'**,
                           'Picton's Double'
– 'Brambling'   CHea CLAP CRow EMon
                           WCot
– 'Brazen Daughter'   CRow
– 'Brazen Hussy'   CDec CFee CGle CMil CRow
                           ECha EFou EHyt EMar EMon
                           EPot ERos GAbr GCal MTho
                           NGre NSla NSti NTow SAxl
                           SBla SDix SIng SUsu SWas
                           WByw WCot WHal WHil
                           WOMN
– 'Bregover White'   CRow
– 'Bunch' (d)   CBre CRow
– 'Button Eye'   CMon
– 'Champernowne Giant'   CRow
– 'Chedglow'   WAlt
– 'Chocolate Cream'   CRow
§ – subsp. *chrysocephalus* CHid CRow CVer ECha EMon
                           NGre NRya SIng SSvw WCot
                           WHer
– 'Coffee Cream'   CRow
§ – 'Collarette' (d)   Widely available
– 'Coppernob'   CAvo CBos CHid CRDP CRow
                           CVer SWas WCot
– 'Coy Hussy' (v)   CNat
– 'Crawshay Cream'   SWas
– 'Cupreus'   See *R. ficaria* var. *aurantiacus*
– 'Damerham'   CRow EMon
– 'Double Bronze' (d)   CBos CMil CVer EMon EPar
                           ERos MTho NGre NRya NSti
                           SUsu
– double cream   See *R. ficaria* **'Double Mud'**
– double green eye (d)   CRow NGre
§ – 'Double Mud' (d)   CLAP CMil CRDP CVer EMon
                           ERos MAvo MBro MTho NNrd
                           NRya SBla SIng SUsu SWas
                           WCot WHal
– double yellow   See *R. ficaria flore-pleno*
– 'Dusky Maiden'   CRow EMon WFar
– 'E.A. Bowles' (d)   See *R. ficaria* **'Collarette'**
– 'Elan' (d)   CRow
– subsp. *ficariiformis*   EMon

§ – *flore-pleno* (d)	CAvo CFee CGle CInt CMil CMon CRow ECha ELan EMar EMon EPar ERos GAbr GDra MHig NDea NGre NHol NNrd NRya NSla NSti SAxl SIng SRms WCot WHil WWin
– 'Fried Egg'	CRow
– 'Green Petal'	CAvo CElw CMil CRDP CRow EMon EPar MS&S MTho NGre NNrd NRya NSla SIng SSvw SUsu SWas WCot WHal
I – 'Holly'	See *R. ficaria* 'Holly Green'
§ – 'Holly Green'	CRow
– 'Hoskin's Miniature'	NGre
¶ – 'Inky'	WAlt
¶ – 'James Dress'	CHid
– 'Ken Aslet' (d)	CRow EMon SWas WHal
– 'Lemon Queen'	NHol WCot
– 'Limelight'	CRow
– 'Little Southey'	CRow
– subsp. *major*	See *R. ficaria* subsp. *chrysocephalus*
¶ – 'Martin Gibbs'	CNat
– 'Mimsey' (d)	CRow
– 'Mobled Jade'	CNat
– 'Newton Abbot'	CRow
¶ – 'Norton'	WBon
¶ – 'Palest Cream'	CNic
– 'Picton's Double' (d)	CGle CRDP CRow CVer EHyt EMou GBar GCal LGan MTho NNrd NRya WAbe
– 'Primrose'	CRow EMon GGar MTho NCat NGre NHol NRya SUsu WCot
– 'Quillet' (d)	CBre CRow
– 'Randall's White'	CGle CRDP CRow CSWP ECha LSyl MRav MTho NTow SSvw WCot
– 'Rowden Magna'	CRow NGre
¶ – 'Ruby Baker'	EMon
– 'Salmon's White'	CAvo CBre CFee CRow CVer ELan EMar EPPr EPar EPot NGre NNrd NRya SBla SSvw WFar WHal WHil WLin
– 'Sheldon'	CNat
– 'Sheldon Silver'	CNat
– single cream	EMon GAbr
– 'Suffusion'	CHid CNat WAlt
– 'Sutherland's Double' (d)	CRow
– 'Sweet Chocolate'	CRow
– 'Tortoiseshell'	CHid CRow CVer MAvo WBro WCot
– 'Trenwheal' (d)	CRow
– 'Yaffle'	CBre CRow EMon MRav WAlt WCot
flammula	CArn CBen CKin CRow EHon EMFW GBar LPBA MSta NDea SWat SWyc WChe
¶ – subsp. *minimus*	CRow
¶ from NE China	MFos
gouanii	EPot NGre NTow
gramineus ♀	Widely available
– 'Pardal'	SBla WFar
¶ 'Granby Cream'	MAvo MGrG
hederaceus	EMFW SWyc
insignis	CRDP EHyt GCal
kochii	EPot
lanuginosus	WCot
– AL&JS 89066YU	EMon
lingua	CKin ECoo EMFW MHew WChe

– 'Grandiflorus'	CBen CRow EHon LPBA MSta NDea SWat SWyc WMAq WSan WWye
lyallii	CPla GCLN GCal SBla SIgm SSpi
¶ *macaulayi*	GCrs
macrophyllus	WCru
millefoliatus	EHyt ERos MTho NMen NRya WHil
montanus	MBal
– 'Molten Gold' ♀	ELan EPot GCrs MHig MRav MTho NBro NHar NHol NMen NRya NTow SBla SIng WLin
nivicola	EBee
ophioglossifolius	CNat
parnassiifolius	GCrs GTou NGre NHar NTow SBla WAbe
platanifolius	CBre LGre
repens	CKin EWFC
– 'Joe's Golden'	EHoe EMon NSti WAlt WCer
¶ – 'Just in Time' (v)	WAlt
– var. *pleniflorus* (d)	CDec CInt CNic CRow ECha ELan GCal NSti WAlt WEas
¶ – semidouble (d)	WAlt
– 'Timothy Clark' (d)	MInt WAlt WHil
rupestris	See *R. spicatus*
sceleratus	WHer
speciosus 'Flore Pleno'	See *R. constantinopolitanus* 'Plenus'
§ *spicatus*	CRDP WCot WHil WOMN

RANZANIA (Berberidaceae)

¶ *japonica*	SWas

RAOULIA (Asteraceae)

australis Hooker	CLTr CLyd ECou EHoe ELan EMNN EPot GAbr GCHN GDra ITim MBal MBar MHig MRPP MWat NBro NGre NHol NNrd NRoo NWCA SIng WAbe WHoo WPyg
– 'Calf'	ITim NHol
– 'Saxon Pass'	GCHN NHol
australis hort.	See *R. hookeri*
§ – Lutescens Group	ECha EPot GAri ITim LBee NTow
glabra	ECou GAbr
haastii	CLyd ECou EPot GDra NHol
§ *hookeri*	CLyd ECha ECou ELan EPot GCHN ITim LBee NHol NNrd NRya NTow NWCA SBla SIng WFar WLin
– var. *laxa*	EPot EWes
× *loganii*	See × *Leucoraoulia loganii*
lutescens	See *R. australis* Lutescens Group Hooker
monroi	ELan GCHN ITim NHol NTow GDra ITim
* *nova*	GDra ITim
petriensis	EPot GCrs NSla
× *petrimia* 'Margaret Pringle'	ITim NHar WAbe WLin
subsericea	CLyd CMHG ECou GCrs NGre NMen
tenuicaulis	ECha ECou GAbr GAri NHol WLin

RAOULIA × LEUCOGENES See × LEUCORAOULIA

RATIBIDA (Asteraceae)

columnifera	EBee

– f. *pulcherrima*   SDys
pinnata   EGar

RAUVOLFIA (Apocynaceae) See Plant
Deletions

RAVENALA (Musaceae)
madagascariensis   LBlo LPal WMul

RAVENEA (Arecaceae)
rivularis   LPal

RECHSTEINERIA See SINNINGIA

REEVESIA   (Sterculiaceae) See Plant Deletions

REGELIA (Myrtaceae)
velutina   SOWG

REHDERODENDRON (Styracaceae)
macrocarpum   CB&S EPfP

REHMANNIA (Scrophulariaceae)
angulata   See *R. elata*
§ *elata*   CBot CChr CGle CSev CSpe
    ECro ELan GMac LBlm LFis
    MCLN MNrw NPer SMrm
    WCru WFar WHer WPer WWal
    WWin WWye
glutinosa ♀   LGre LLew MSal MSto SMrm
    WOMN WWye

REINECKEA (Convallariaceae)
§ *carnea*   CHan CHid CNic ECha EGar
    ELan EMan EMar EOrc EPar
    EPla ERos GCal LFis LGan
    LWak MFir MRav MTho MUlv
    NNrd NRoo NSti SOkh WBon
    WCru WGwG WPer WWal
– 'Variegata'   WCot

REINWARDTIA (Linaceae)
§ *indica*   CGre CPle LHil
– S&SH 106   CHan
trigyna   See *R. indica*

RELHANIA   (Asteraceae) See Plant Deletions

RESEDA (Resedaceae)
alba   EMon
lutea   CKin EWFC MSal SIde
luteola   CJew CKin EJud EWFC GBar
    GPoy MChe MHew MSal SIde
    WCHb WHer WWye

RESTIO (Restionaceae)
¶ *quadratus*   WNor
subverticillatus   See *Ischyrolepis subverticillata*

RETAMA   (Papilionaceae) See Plant Deletions

REYNOUTRIA See FALLOPIA

RHABDOTHAMNUS (Gesneriaceae)
solandri   WCru

RHAGODIA (Chenopodiaceae)
triandra   ECou

RHAMNUS (Rhamnaceae)
alaternus   CFil SBid WPGP
– var. *angustifolia*   CFil WHCr WPGP WWat
§ – 'Argenteovariegata' ♀   Widely available
– 'Variegata'   See *R. alaternus*
    'Argenteovariegata'
cathartica   CCVT CKin ECrN GChr LBuc
    MPEx WDin WMou
frangula   CArn CCVT CKin CPer CSam
    ENot GChr LBuc STre WDin
    WMou
– 'Aspleniifolia'   EBee ENot EPfP EPla GChr
    LBuc MBri SMad SMur
– 'Columnaris'   EMil SLPl
× *hybrida* 'Billardii'   ESis
japonica   SPer

RHAPHIOLEPIS (Rosaceae)
× *delacourii*   CMHG EPfP GQui MAll SBid
    WBod
– 'Coates' Crimson'   CSPN EHic EMil EPfP GQui
    MBlu SBid SHBN SOWG SPer
    WSHC
– 'Enchantress'   EBrP EBre ENot LBre SBre
    SMur
– 'Spring Song'   EBee
indica   CGre ERom NPSI SEND
    WAbe WWat
ovata   See *R. umbellata*
§ *umbellata* ♀   CAbb CB&S CBot CHEx CSam
    CTri GQui LHop MAll MBlu
    SAga SAxl SOWG WHCG
    WPic WSHC WWat

RHAPHITHAMNUS (Verbenaceae)
cyanocarpus   See *R. spinosus*
§ *spinosus*   CGre CHan CPle EPla ERea
    SBid SMad WBod

RHAPIDOPHYLLUM (Arecaceae)
hystrix   LPal NPal

RHAPIS (Arecaceae)
§ *excelsa* ♀   LPal WMul
multifida   LPal

RHAZYA (Apocynaceae)
orientalis   See *Amsonia orientalis*

RHEKTOPHYLLUM See CERCESTIS

RHEUM † (Polygonaceae)
§ 'Ace of Hearts'   CBot CRow CWit EBrP EBre
    ECha EGol ELan EMFW EPar
    EPla GCal GTwe LBre LPBA
    MBri NDea NHol NSti SBre
    SChu SMrm SPer SSpi SWat
    WCot WRus
'Ace of Spades'   See *R.* **'Ace of Hearts'**
acuminatum   CRow EPla GBin WBay WCot
– HWJCM 252   WCru
alexandrae   GAri GCal GLil IBlr WBay
§ *australe*   CArn CRow MBro MLLN MSal
    NBro NLar SMrm WCot WHoo
    WPyg
× *cultorum*   See *R.* × *hybridum*
emodi   See *R. australe*
§ × *hybridum*   NVic
– 'Baker's All Season'   GTwe
– 'Canada Red'   GTwe
N – 'Cawood Delight'   GTwe SEND

– 'Champagne' GTwe
– 'Daw's Champion' GTwe
– 'Early Champagne' GTwe
– 'Early Cherry' GTwe
– 'Fenton's Special' GTwe
¶ – 'Fulton's Strawberry GTwe
Surprise'
– 'German Wine' GTwe
– 'Goliath' GTwe
– 'Grandad's Favorite' EBrP EBre LBre SBre
– 'Greengage' GTwe
– 'Hammond's Early' GTwe SEND
– 'Harbinger' GTwe
– 'Hawke's Champagne' GTwe
– 'Mac Red' GTwe
– 'Prince Albert' GTwe
– 'Red Prolific' GTwe
– 'Reed's Early Superb' GTwe
– 'Stein's Champagne' GTwe
– 'Stockbridge Arrow' GTwe
– 'Stockbridge Bingo' GTwe
– 'Stockbridge Emerald' GTwe
– 'Stockbridge GTwe
Guardsman'
* – 'Strawberry' EMui GTwe
– 'Sutton's Cherry Red' GTwe
– 'The Sutton' GTwe LBuc
– 'Timperley Early' CDoC CMac CSam CTri ECtt
EMui GChr GTwe LBuc NDal
NFai SDea WStI
– 'Tingley Cherry' GTwe
– 'Valentine' GTwe
– 'Victoria' GTwe
– 'Zwolle Seedling' GTwe
kialense EBee GCal NSti WChe WCot
* **maximum** WCot
nobile HWJCM 307 WCru
– SF 95170 ISea
officinale CAgr CHEx GCal IIve MBri
SWat
palmatum ♀ CArn CB&S CBlo CHEx EBee
ECha EHal ELan LHil LPBA
MAus MRav MSal NCut NDea
NFla NNor SPer SSpi SWat
WBea WHow WPyg WStI
WWal
– 'Atropurpureum' See *R. palmatum*
'Atrosanguineum'
§ – 'Atrosanguineum' CBot CHEx CRow EBrP EBre
ECha ECtt EGar EGol ELan
EPar GBuc LBlm LBre MWgw
NBro NHol NNor SBre SPer
SSoC SWat WCru WWin
– 'Bowles' Crimson' CHEx CHad LRHS MBri SAga
SSoC WBay WViv
– 'Hadspen Crimson' CHad
– 'Red Herald' MBri WCot
– **rubrum** CDoC COtt EBrP EBre EHic
GCHN LBre MCCP MHlr SBre
WCot
– 'Saville' MBri
– var. **tanguticum** CHEx CRow ECha EGar MBri
MSCN MSal MSta NCat NPri
NSti SPer SRms SSoC SWat
WCot WCru WHoo WWat
¶ **rhaponticum** EBee
tataricum CAgr GCal
tibeticum WWoo
¶ – SEP 20 EPot
undulatum CRow

RHEXIA (Melastomataceae) See Plant Deletions

RHINANTHUS (Scrophulariaceae) See Plant
Deletions

RHINEPHYLLUM (Aizoaceae)
broomii NGre

RHIPSALIS (Cactaceae)
cassytha See *R. baccifera*

RHODANTHE (Asteraceae)
§ **anthemoides** ECou

RHODANTHEMUM (Asteraceae)
atlanticum ECho ELan EWes
catananche CPBP ELan EPot EWes LHop
NTow SMrm WAbe
§ **gayanum** EBar ELan EMFP EOrc EWes
IHos LBee LFlo LHil NSty
NTow SCro SUsu WHen WKif
WOMN
– 'Flamingo' See *R. gayanum*
§ – 'Tizi-n-Test' LBee SBla
– 'Tizi-n-Tichka' CInt CPBP ELan EWes LBee
LHop LRHS NBir NTow SBla
SLod WAbe WLin
§ **hosmariense** ♀ CMHG CSam CSev ECha ELan
EPot LBee LFis LHop MBal
MTho NHol SBla SIng SPer
SRms SSmi SUsu WAbe WEas
WLin WOMN WRus

RHODIOLA (Crassulaceae)
alsia NGre
arctica NGre
bupleuroides CLD 1196 EMon
crassipes See *R. wallichiana*
§ **fastigiata** EMon GCal NGre NRoo
– x **kirilovii** NGre
gelida NGre
§ **heterodonta** ECha EGle ELan MRav MTPN
WCot
himalensis See *R. 'Keston'*
§ **ishidae** NGre
§ 'Keston' NGre SSmi
§ **kirilovii** EMon GBin GTou
– var. **rubra** EBrP EBre LBre NGre SBre
SSmi WFar
pachyclados See *Sedum pachyclados*
pamiroalaica NGre
§ **primuloides** CLyd NGre NMen
§ **quadrifida** NGre
¶ **recticaulis** EBee
rhodantha EBee NGre
§ **rosea** ECha ECro EHoe ELan EMan
GGar LBlm MBal MFir NGre
NNor NRoo NSti SCro SIng
SRms SSmi STre WAbb WEas
WFar WWhi
§ – subsp. **integrifolia** NGre
semenowii EBee GAri MHar WCot
sp. CC&McK 158 GCHN
sp. EMAK 0516 NHol
§ **trollii** CNic MHig NGre
§ **wallichiana** GAri GCrs NGre WCot

RHODOCHITON (Scrophulariaceae)
§ **atrosanguineus** ♀ CEnd CGle CHEx CMac CPlN
CRHN ELan ERea LHop MNes
NChi NEgg NFai SOWG SSoC
SUsu WEas
volubilis See *R. atrosanguineus*

RHODOCOMA (Restionaceae)
¶ *arida*   CTrC
¶ *gigantea*   CTrC IDac WNor

RHODODENDRON † (Ericaceae)
'A.J. Ivens'   See *R.* '**Arthur J. Ivens**'
'Abegail'   NMun SLeo
'Abendrot'   MBri
aberconwayi   IOrc MBal MDun NMun SLeo
    SReu
– 'His Lordship'   GGGa LHyd
– pink   NMun
'Accomplishment'   CWri
¶ ACE 2256   GCLN
¶ ACE 2384   GCLN
'Achilles'   SLeo
'Actress'   IOrc LHyd NMun SLeo
'Addy Wery' (EA) ♀   ENot GHCN IOrc LKna MBal
    MBar MGos NMun SBod SCog
    SExb SLeo SPer SReu WStI
adenogynum   GGGa MDun NMun SLeo
§ – Adenophorum Group   SLeo
– – F 20444   SLeo
– – 'Kirsty'   NMun
– – R 11471   NMun
– CLD 795   LMil
– PA Cox 6502   GGGa
– white   NMun SLeo
adenophorum   See *R. adenogynum*
    Adenophorum Group
adenopodum   GGGa MDun NMun SLeo
    SReu
¶ – A.M. form   SLeo
adenosum   LMil MDun NHol NMun
– Kuluense Group   NMun SLeo
– R 18228   GGGa
'Admiral Piet Hein'   SReu
'Adonis' (EA/d)   CMac IOrc MBar SPer
§ 'Adorable' (EA)   IOrc
'Adriaan Koster'   IOrc
adroserum USDAPI 52910   See *R. lukiangense* **R 11275***
'Advance' (O)   NMun SExb SLeo
aeruginosum   See *R. campanulatum* subsp.
    aeruginosum
aganniphum   GGGa NMun SLeo
§ – var. *aganniphum*   GGGa NMun SLeo
    Doshongense Group
– – Doshongense Group   GGGa
    C&V 9541
– – Doshongense Group   NMun
    KW 5863
– – F 16472   NMun
– – Glaucopeplum Group   GGGa
– – Schizopeplum Group   GGGa
– – SSNY 138   GGGa
¶ – CNW 1174   LMil
¶ – EGM 284   LMil
– var. *flavorufum*   GGGa MDun NMun SLeo
¶ – – EGM 160   LMil
– – PA Cox 5070*   GGGa
– – SSNY 143   GGGa
– PA Cox 6003   GGGa
– 'Rusty'   NMun
– SSNY 320a   GGGa
agapetum   See *R. kyawii* **Agapetum Group**
× *agastum*   NMun SLeo
– PW 98   GGGa LMil
'Aida' (R/d)   SReu
'Aksel Olsen'   ECho MBal MBar MDun NHol
'Aladdin' (EA)   ECho IOrc WFar
Aladdin Group & cl.   CWri SReu

Albatross Group & cl.   LHyd LKna LMil SLeo SPer
    SReu SSta
'Albatross Townhill Pink'   LMil
'Albert Schweitzer'   CWri GGGa LMil MBal MBar
    MBri SLeo SReu
albertsenianum   SLeo
albiflorum (A)   GGGa SReu
albrechtii (A) ♀   GGGa LHyd LMil NGre SReu
    WAbe
'Alena'   GGGa
'Alexander' (EA)   CB&S CTrh GQui IOrc LMil
    MBri MGos SBod SHBN
'Alfred'   LRHS
'Alice' (EA)   IHos LHyd LKna
'Alice' ♀   IOrc LHyd LKna MDun NMun
    SLeo SPer SReu
'Alice Street'   SLeo
'Alisa Nicole' (V)   CEqu
Alison Johnstone Group   CB&S GGGa ISea MBal MDun
  & cl.   MLea NMun SExb SLeo SPer
    SReu WAbe WPic
'Aloha'   CAbP MAsh MBar MDun
    MLea NHed SHBN SReu
Alpine Gem Group   GQui NHol
'Alpine Glow' ♀   NMun SLeo
alutaceum   NMun
– var. *alutaceum*   GGGa
§ – – Globigerum Group   LMil
– – Globigerum Group   GGGa NMun SLeo
    R 11100
§ – var. *iodes*   GGGa LMil NMun SLeo
§ – var. *russotinctum*   GGGa LMil SLeo
– – Triplonaevium Group   GGGa
    USDAPI 59442/ R10923
§ – – Tritifolium Group   GGGa
amagianum (A)   LMil
Amaura Group   WBod
ambiguum   CHig LMil SLeo SReu
– 'Jane Banks'   LMil
* – KR 185 select*   GGGa
'America'   CB&S IOrc MAsh MBal MBar
    MGos SLeo WWeb
amesiae   GGGa NMun SLeo
'Amethyst'   LHyd
§ 'Amethystinum' (EA)   LKna
¶ 'Amity'   CWri ECho
§ 'Amoenum' (EA/d)   CBlo CChe CMHG CMac CTrG
    CTrw IOrc LHyd LKna MBar
    MGos NMun SCog SExb SLeo
    WBod WFar
Amor Group & cl.   LHyd SLeo
'Analin'   See *R.* '**Anuschka**'
'Anatta Gold' (V)   GGGa
'Anchorite' (EA)   GQui LMil
'Andre'   NMun SLeo SReu
* 'Andrea'   NMun
Angelo Group & cl.   CWri LHyd LMil MDun SReu
Anita Group   SLeo
'Anita Dunstan'   LMil LRHS MLea
'Ann Lindsay'   SBrw SReu
'Anna Baldsiefen' ♀   CSam ENot LMil MAsh MBri
    NHol SPer SReu SSta WAbe
'Anna H. Hall'   IOrc MDun
'Anna Rose Whitney' ♀   CB&S CWri GChr GGGa GRei
    IOrc LHyd LKna LMil MBar
    MBri MDun MGos MLea
    NMun SHBN SLeo SPer SReu
    SSta
'Annabella' (K) ♀   MBri SLeo SReu
annae   GGGa LMil LRHS MDun
    NMun SLeo
¶ aff. – C&H 7185   LMil

§ – Hardingii Group — NMun
'Anne Frank' (EA) — EOrn MGos SReu WBod
'Anne George' — LHyd
'Anne Rothwell' — LHyd
¶ 'Anne Teese' — LMil
'Anneke' (K) — MBar MBri SLeo SReu SSta
'Anniversary Gold' — GGGa
'Anny' (EA) — IOrc LKna
anthopogon — LMil SLeo
– subsp. *anthopogon* — GGGa
  BL&M 332
– – Sch 2259 — GGGa
– 'Betty Graham' — LMil
– CH&M 2052 — GGGa
§ – subsp. *hypenanthum* — LMil MDun
– – 'Annapurna' — CSam GGGa NHol
§ *anthosphaerum* — GGGa NMun SLeo SReu
– F 26432 — SLeo
– Gymnogynum Group — NMun
§ – Heptamerum Group — NMun
– KW 5684 — NMun
§ 'Antilope' (Vs) — SReu SSta
§ 'Anuschka' — MBri SBrw
§ *anwheiense* ♀ — LHyd LMil NMun SLeo
aperantum — GGGa MDun
– F 26933 — SLeo
– F 27022 — GGGa
'Aphrodite' (EA) — GQui
apodectum — See *R. dichroanthum* subsp. *apodectum*
¶ 'Apple Blossom' — CMac
N 'Appleblossom' — See *R.* 'Ho-o'
'Apricot Fantasy' — LMil LRHS SMur
'April Dawn' — GGGa
'April Gem' — GGGa
§ 'April Glow' — LHyd SLeo
'April Showers' — ENot
'April Snow' (d) — GGGa
'April White' — GGGa
'Arabesque' — MBri
araiophyllum — GGGa SLeo
Arbcalo Group — SLeo
§ *arborescens* (A) — GGGa LKna LMil LRHS NMun SLeo SReu
arboreum — CB&S GGGa IOrc ISea LMil MDun NMun SLeo SReu WPic
– subsp. *arboreum* KR 966 — NMun
– B 708 — MBal
– 'Blood Red' — NMun
– C&S 1651 — NMun
– C&S 1695 — NMun
– subsp. *cinnamomeum* — GGGa NMun SLeo SReu
– – var. *album* — SReu
– – var. *cinnamomeum* — MBal
  BM&W 172
– – – Campbelliae Group — NMun SLeo
– – var. *roseum* — NMun
– – – BB 151* — NMun
– – – 'Tony Schilling' ♀ — LHyd LMil NMun SLeo
§ – subsp. *delavayi* — GGGa ISea NMun SLeo
– – C&H 7178 — GGGa
– – C&S 1515 — NMun
¶ – – CNW 994 — LMil
– – KW 21796 — NMun
– 'Heligan' — SReu
¶ – mid-pink — SLeo
* – *nigrescens* — SLeo
§ – subsp. *nilagiricum* — GGGa
¶ – var. *roseum* — SLeo
§ – subsp. *zeylanicum* — ISea NMun SLeo
¶ – – 'Rubaiyat' — NMun
'Arborfield' — SLeo

Arbsutch Group — SLeo
x *arbutifolium* — See *R.* Arbutifolium Group
§ Arbutifolium Group — SLeo
'Arcadia' (EA) — LKna
'Arctic Regent' (K) — GQui
'Arctic Tern' — See x *Ledodendron* 'Arctic Tern'
§ *argipeplum* — NMun SLeo
¶ – Bhutan form — MDun
'Argosy' ♀ — LMil NMun SBid SReu
argyrophyllum — MDun NMun SLeo
§ – subsp. *hypoglaucum* — NMun SLeo
§ – – 'Heane Wood' — GGGa
– – subsp. *nankingense* — GGGa IOrc LMil NMun
– – 'Chinese Silver' ♀ — LHyd LMil LRHS MDun NMun SLeo SReu
Ariel Group — SLeo
arizelum — GGGa LMil LRHS MDun NMun SLeo
¶ – R 25 — GGGa
¶ – Rubicosum Group — NMun SLeo
'Armantine' — LKna
armitii Woods 2518 (v) — GGGa
'Arneson Gem' (M) — GGGa LMil
§ 'Arpege' (Vs) — MBal SReu WWat
'Arthur Bedford' — CWri GGGa LHyd LKna SBrw SLeo SReu
¶ 'Arthur J. Ivens' — SLeo
'Arthur Osborn' — CHig GGGa SLeo
'Arthur Stevens' ♀ — SLeo
'Arthur Warren' — LKna
'Asa-gasumi' (EA) — LHyd
'Ascot Brilliant' — SLeo
asterochnoum C&H 7051 — GGGa
Asteroid Group — SLeo
¶ 'Astrid' — ENot
atlanticum (A) — GAri GGGa NMun SLeo SSpi
– 'Seaboard' (A) — LMil LRHS
'Atlantis' — CWri
'Audrey Wynniatt' (EA) — MAsh SExb
Augfast Group — CB&S CTrw IOrc MBal SBod WBod
'August Lamken' — SBid
augustinii — CB&S CSam CTrG CTrw CWri GGGa IOrc ISea LHyd LMil MBal MLea NMun SExb SLeo SPer SSpi SSta WBod WPic
– subsp. *augustinii* C 7008 — GGGa
– – C&H 7048 — GGGa
– – 'Smoke' — CGre
§ – subsp. *chasmanthum* — GGGa LMil SLeo
– – C&Cu 9407 white — GGGa
– – C&Cu 9418 pale pink — GGGa
§ – Electra Group & cl. — GGGa LHyd LMil MDun NMun SLeo
– EN 3527 — GGGa
– Exbury best form — SReu
§ – subsp. *hardyi* — GGGa SLeo
§ – subsp. *rubrum* — GGGa
– – 'Papillon' — NMun
I – 'Werrington' — SReu
§ *aureum* — GGGa LMil MDun NMun SLeo
auriculatum — GGGa LMil MBal NHol NMun SLeo SReu SSta
– PW 50 — GGGa
– Reuthe's form — SReu
auritum — CBlo GGGa NMun
'Aurora' (K) — NMun SLeo
§ *austrinum* (A) ♀ — LMil
'Autumn Gold' — COtt CWri LMil MBal NHol SBrw SLeo SMur
Avalanche Group & cl. — SReu

'Award'	GGGa LMil
'Ayah'	SReu
'Aya-kammuri' (EA)	LHyd
Azor Group & cl.	CHig LHyd NMun SLeo SReu
'Azorazie'	NMun SLeo
'Azuma-kagami' (EA) ♀	CB&S LHyd LKna LMil SCog WBod
'Azuray'	GGGa
'Azurika'	NHol
'Azurro'	GGGa LMil MDun SMur
'Baby Scarlet'	SSta
¶ 'Babylon'	SLeo
'Baden-Baden'	EPot GCHN GChr GCrs LKna MAsh MBal MBar MDun MGos NHol NMun NWea SBod SExb SHBN SLeo SPer SSta
'Bagshot Ruby' ♀	ENot LKna MDun NWea SBod
baileyi	GGGa LHyd LMil NMun
– LS&H 17359	NMun
¶ *bainbridgeanum* hybrid	LMil
– USDAPI 59184/ R11190	NMun SLeo
bakeri	See *R. cumberlandense*
balangense EN 3530	GGGa
balfourianum	GGGa MDun NMun SLeo
– var. *aganniphoides*	LMil NMun
– SSNY 224	GGGa
'Ballerina' (K)	MBal
'Balsaminiflorum'	See *R. indicum* 'Balsaminiflorum'
'Balzac' (K)	CSam IOrc MBri MGos
'Bambi'	LHyd NMun SLeo SReu
'Bambino'	CAbP COtt CWri LNet MAsh MLea SLeo
'Bandoola'	SReu
'Banzai' (EA)	SLeo
'Barbara Coates'	LHyd
'Barbara Reuthe'	SReu
barbatum	CWri GGGa LHyd LMil MDun NMun SLeo SReu
– BB 152	MBal
– BL&M 325	NMun
– DF 525	MBal
¶ 'Barbecue' (K)	LMil
Barclayi Group	LHyd
'Barclayi Helen Fox'	NMun SLeo
'Barclayi Robert Fox'	NMun SLeo
'Barmstedt'	CWri
'Barnaby Sunset'	CSam GAri GGGa LRHS NHol
'Bashful' ♀	EPfP GRei IOrc LHyd MAsh MBal MGos NMun SExb SLeo SReu
§ *basilicum*	GGGa IDee LMil NMun SLeo
¶ – AC 616	NMun
– SF 381	ISea
× *bathyphyllum*	NMun SLeo
– PA Cox 6542	GGGa
bauhiniiflorum	See *R. triflorum* var. *bauhiniiflorum*
beanianum	GGGa LMil NMun SLeo
– compact form	See *R. piercei*
– KW 6805	NMun
'Beatrice Keir' ♀	LHyd LMil NMun SLeo SReu
Beau Brummel Group & cl.	LMil LRHS
'Beaulieu Manor'	GQui
'Beauty of Littleworth' ♀	LHyd LKna LMil NMun SLeo SReu
'Beaver' (EA)	MBri
beesianum	GGGa LMil NMun SLeo
– F 10195	NMun
– SSNY 250	GGGa
– SSNY 303	GGGa

'Beethoven' (EA) ♀	CBlo CTrG LHyd LKna MBal NMun SBod SExb SLeo SReu WBod WGor
¶ Belkanto®	ENot
'Belle Heller'	CSam CWri MBal MBri SExb SLeo WGwG WLRN
Bellerophon Group	NMun
'Bengal'	ISea MAsh MBal MBar MBri MDun NHol SReu
'Bengal Beauty' (EA)	GQui LMil LRHS
'Bengal Fire' (EA)	CMac SExb
§ 'Benifude' (EA)	WBod
'Beni-giri' (EA)	CMac
I 'Benjamen'	GGGa
'Bergie Larson'	CWri LMil
bergii	See *R. augustinii* subsp. *rubrum*
'Berg's Yellow'	CWri GGGa MDun
'Bernard Shaw'	SReu
'Berryrose' (K) ♀	CB&S CTri ENot IOrc LHyd LKna LMil MBal MBar MBri MLea NMun SExb SLeo SPer WLRN
§ 'Beryl Taylor'	GGGa NMun
'Better Half'	GGGa
'Betty' (EA) ♀	CTrG LHyd SRms
'Betty Anne Voss' (EA)	LHyd LRHS MAsh SCoo SExb
'Betty Stewart'	SLeo
'Betty Wormald' ♀	CHig CWri IHos LKna LMil MGos MLea NMun SBid SCog SHBN SLeo SPer SReu SSta WGer WPic
beyerinckianum (V)	CEqu
bhutanense	MDun
– AC 119	NMun
– AC 124	NMun
– EGM 077	GGGa
'Big Punkin'	LMil
'Bijou de Ledeberg' (EA)	SSta
'Billy Budd'	SCog
'Binfield'	SLeo
'Birthday Girl'	COtt LMil SExb
'Birthday Greeting'	NMun SLeo
'Biscuit Box'	NMun SLeo
Biskra Group & cl.	GGGa NMun
'Blaauw's Pink' (EA) ♀	CHig CMac ENot GQui IOrc LHyd LKna LMil MAsh MBar MBri MGos NMun SBod SCog SExb SLeo SPer SReu SRms WFar
'Black Hawk' (EA)	CB&S CTrG
'Black Magic'	COtt CWri LMil SExb
'Black Satin'	COtt LMil
¶ 'Black Sport'	MLea
Blaue Donau	See *R. 'Blue Danube'*
'Blazecheck'	LRHS MGos SCoo
'Blewbury' ♀	LHyd LMil LRHS MDun NMun SLeo SReu SSta
'Blitz'	MBri SLeo
'Blizzard' (EA)	CTrh
'Blue Bell'	LKna
'Blue Boy'	LMil SMur
'Blue Carpet'	MAsh
'Blue Chip'	LHyd NMun SLeo
§ 'Blue Danube' (EA) ♀	CMac CTrG ENot IOrc LHyd LKna LMil MBal MBar MBri MRav NMun SBod SCog SExb SLeo SPer SReu SSta WBod WGwG WStI

Blue Diamond Group & cl.	CB&S CChe CMHG CWri ENot GRei LHyd LKna MAsh MBal MBar MDun MGos NHol NMun SBod SCog SHBN SLeo SReu SRms WBod WGwG
'Blue Gown'	LKna
'Blue Haze'	LHyd
'Blue Monday'	MBri WBod
'Blue Moon'	MBar
'Blue Mountain'	GDra MBal
'Blue Pacific'	SBod
'Blue Peter' ♀	CB&S CHig CWri ENot GGGa IHos IOrc LHyd LKna MAsh MBar MBri MDun MGos NMun SHBN SLeo SPer SReu SSta WStI
'Blue Pool'	LMil LRHS MBal MBar WBod
Blue Ribbon Group	CMHG CTrw ISea
'Blue Silver'	GGGa NHol
'Blue Star'	CMHG LHyd LRHS MBri MLea NHed SExb SReu WAbe
'Blue Steel'	See *R. impeditum* **'Blue Steel'**
Blue Tit Group	CB&S CSam CTrG CTre EPot GDra ITim LHyd LKna MAsh MBal MBar NHol NMun SHBN SLeo SReu SSta STre WBod
Bluebird Group & cl.	ECho ENot IOrc LKna MBal MBar MGos SPer SRms WBod
Bluestone Group	WBod
'Bluette'	ISea MBal MDun MLea NHed SLeo
'Blumiria'	GGGa
¶ 'Blurettia'	CWri
'Blushing Belle' (V)	CEqu
'Bob's Blue'	ISea
'Bob's Choice' (V)	CEqu
'Boddaertianum' ♀	LHyd SReu
bodinieri	NMun
USDAPI 59585/ R11281	
'Bodnant Yellow'	CSam
'Bonfire'	SReu
Bo-peep Group & cl.	CB&S CHig CSam LHyd LMil MBal MLea NMun SLeo
'Borderer'	SLeo
'Boskoop Ostara'	MBri
'Boule de Neige'	MDun SBod SLeo
'Bouquet de Flore' (G) ♀	LMil MBar MBri SLeo SPer SReu
¶ 'Bow Bells' ♀	NMun
Bow Bells Group & cl.	CSam EBrP EBre IOrc ISea LBre LHyd LKna LMil MAsh MBal MBar MBri MDun MGos MLea SBod SBre SCog SExb SHBN SPer SReu SRms
'Bow Street'	LHyd
brachyanthum	GGGa NMun SLeo
– subsp. *hypolepidotum*	GGGa LMil MBal MDun NMun SLeo
§ – – KW 7038	NMun
◆ – L&S 2764	See *R. glaucophyllum* var. *glaucophyllum* **L&S 2764**
brachycarpum	GGGa MBal NMun SLeo
– subsp. *brachycarpum* Tigerstedtii Group	SReu
§ – subsp. *fauriei*	NMun SLeo
– pink	NMun SLeo
– 'Roseum Dwarf'	GGGa NMun
brachysiphon	See *R. maddenii* subsp. *maddenii*
'Brazier' (EA)	LHyd NMun SLeo
'Brazil' (K)	LKna SBid SExb SReu
Break of Day Group & cl.	SLeo
¶ 'Bremen'	MOne WGwG
'Brentor'	SLeo
'Breslau' (EA)	SBrw SSta
'Brets Own'	NMun SLeo
Bric-a-brac Group & cl.	CB&S CSam CTrw LHyd MBal NMun SLeo SReu SRms
'Bride's Bouquet' (EA/d)	LRHS
'Bridesmaid' (O)	ENot SExb SLeo
'Brigadoon'	GGGa
'Bright Forecast' (K)	MBri SExb WGor
'Brigitte'	CWri GGGa LRHS
'Brilliant' (EA)	MGos
'Brilliant'	NHol
'Brilliant Blue'	MAsh
'Brilliant Crimson'	WWeb
'Brilliant Pink'	MAsh WWeb
'Britannia' ♀	CB&S CSam CWri IOrc ISea LHyd LKna LNet MAsh MBal MBar MBri MGos NMun NWea SBod SExb SHBN SLeo SPer SReu SSta WWeb
¶ 'Britannia' x *griersonianum*	SLeo
'Brocade' ♀	CSam LHyd LKna LMil MBri NMun SLeo SPer
'Bronze Fire' (A)	SReu
'Broughtonii'	CWri GGGa NMun SLeo
'Brown Eyes'	CWri
'Bruce Brechtbill'	CWri GGGa LMil MAsh MBal MLea NHol SExb SLeo SReu SSta
'Bruce Hancock' (Ad)	LMil
'Buccaneer' (EA)	IOrc LHyd MBal SBod SExb SPer
'Bud Flanagan'	LMil NMun
'Buketta'	GGGa MBri
bullatum	See *R. edgeworthii*
bulu C&V 9503	GGGa
'Bungo-nishiki' (EA/d)	CAbP GGGa IOrc LHyd LMil
bureaui ♀	MBal MDun NMun SLeo SReu SSta
– 'Ardrishaig'	GGGa
– C&H 7158	GGGa
– CNW 1039	GGGa
– CNW 957	GGGa
– CNW 965	GGGa
– CNW 969	GGGa
* – *cruentum* CNW 922	LMil
¶ – x Elizabeth Group	SReu
– F 15609	NMun
I – 'Lem's Variety'	LMil
– x *prattii* PA Cox 5066	GGGa
– R 25439	NMun
– SF 517	ISea
bureauoides	NMun SReu
– PA Cox 5039	GGGa
¶ – PA Cox 5076	GGGa
burmanicum ♀	GGGa LMil MDun NMun SLeo
Bustard Group	SLeo
'Butter Yellow'	ECho SLeo
'Buttercup' (K)	MBar
'Buttered Popcorn'	LMil
'Butterfly'	LKna NMun SExb SLeo
'Buttermint'	CSam CWri GAri ISea MAsh MBal MBri NMun SHBN SLeo SReu SSta
'Buttersteep'	SLeo
'Buttons and Bows' (K)	GGGa LMil
'Buzzard' (K)	LKna LMil
'C.I.S.'	MDun NMun SExb SLeo
'Caerhays Lavender'	CB&S IOrc

caesium — GGGa
calendulaceum (A) — LHyd LMil MBal SLeo SReu
– yellow — LMil
Calfort Group & cl. — NMun SLeo
caliginis (V) — CEqu
callimorphum — GGGa LMil NMun SLeo
– var. *myiagrum* F 21821a — NMun SLeo
– – KW 6962 — NMun
calophytum ♀ — CHEx CWri GGGa LHyd LMil MDun NMun SLeo
¶ – Knott 151 — NMun
¶ – var. *openshawianum* EGM 318 — LMil
calostrotum — GCrs LMil MBri SRms WAbe
– 'Gigha' ♀ — CSam CWri GGGa LMil MDun MOne NHar WAbe
§ – subsp. *keleticum* ♀ — CTrG GAri GDra LHyd MBal MBar MDun MGos NHol SBod SRms WAbe
– – F 19915 — NHol
– – F 21756 — NMun SLeo
– – R 58 — LMil NHol
§ – – Radicans Group — GCrs LHyd LMil MBar MBro MDun MLea NHol SRms WAbe WPat WPyg
– – Radicans Group mound form — NHol
– – Radicans Group USDAPI 59182/R 11188 — MLea
– subsp. *riparium* — MBal
– – Calciphilum Group — GGGa MDun WAbe WBod
– – Calciphilum Group Yu 19754 — GGGa
§ – – Nitens Group — CBlo CMHG GGGa LMil MDun NHed WAbe
¶ – – PA Cox 6157 — GGGa
♦ – – Rock's form R 178 — See *R. saluenense* subsp. *riparioides* **R 178**
– SF 357 — ISea
♦ – USDAPQ 03954/ R18453 — See *R. saluenense* subsp. *riparioides* **USDAPQ 03954/ R18453**
caloxanthum — See *R. campylocarpum* subsp. *caloxanthum*
'Calsap' — GGGa
Calstocker Group — SLeo
Calsutch Group — SLeo
calvescens var. *duseimatum* — NMun
camelliiflorum — GGGa LMil
'Cameronian' (Ad) — LKna
campanulatum — COtt IOrc LHyd LKna LMil MDun NMun SLeo SReu
§ – subsp. *aeruginosum* — GGGa LMil MDun NMun SReu
– – EGM 068 — LMil
– *album* — NMun SLeo
¶ – B&SWJ 2633 — WCru
– Bu 249 — GGGa
– Bu 258 — GGGa
– subsp. *campanulatum* B 643 — MBal
– – BL&M 283 — NMun
¶ – – 'Roland Cooper' — NMun
– DF 563 — MBal
– 'Graham Thomas' — SReu
– 'Knap Hill' ♀ — LHyd NMun SReu
¶ – 'Roland E. Cooper' — SLeo
¶ – SMM 41 — SLeo
– SS&W 9107 — GGGa SLeo
– TSS 11 — NMun SLeo
– TSS 7 — SLeo
– 'Waxen Bell' — LHyd NMun SLeo

§ 'Campfire' (EA) — SLeo
campylocarpum — CHig GGGa LHyd LMil NMun SLeo SReu
– BM&W 150 — MBal
§ – subsp. *caloxanthum* — GGGa IOrc
– – forms — NMun SLeo
¶ – – KR 3516 — LMil
§ – – Telopeum Group — NMun
§ – – Telopeum Group KW 5718B — NMun SLeo
– subsp. *campylocarpum* Elatum Group — MDun NMun
– – TSS 12 — NMun
– DF 558 — MBal
– LS&H 16495* — NMun
¶ *campylogynum* — LRHS SLeo SSpi
♦ – 'Album' — See *R.* **'Leucanthemum'**
– apricot — LMil
♦ – 'Beryl Taylor' — See *R.* **'Beryl Taylor'**
– Castle Hill form — LMil SReu
– Charopoeum Group — GCrs GGGa LMil MBal MBar MDun MGos NHar NHol WAbe
– – 'Patricia' — ECho MBal MBri MDun WBod
– claret — ECho GGGa LMil MBal MDun WAbe
§ – Cremastum Group — CTrG GGGa LHyd LMil NHol NMun SLeo
– – 'Bodnant Red' — CHig GGGa LHyd LMil MDun NMun SLeo
* – – 'Cerise' — GGGa
– KW 21481 — NHol
♦ – var. *leucanthum* — See *R.* **'Leucanthemum'**
– Myrtilloides Group — CB&S CHig CMHG CTrh CTrw EPot GAri GGGa GQui IOrc LHyd LMil MBal MBri MDun NMun SLeo SReu WAbe WBod
– – Farrer 1046 — EPot GGGa
– pink — CTrh MBar WAbe
– plum — GGGa WAbe
– salmon pink — ECho EPot MBal NHar NHol WAbe WBod
¶ – SF 95181 — ISea
camtschaticum — GAri GGGa MBal MLea SLeo WAbe
– var. *albiflorum* — GGGa
– red — GGGa
canadense (A) — GGGa MBal NHol SLeo SReu
– f. *albiflorum* (A) — GGGa LMil
– 'Deer Lake' (A) — SReu
'Canary' — LKna MBal SLeo SReu
'Canby' (K) — LMil
§ x *candelabrum* — NMun SLeo
¶ *canescens* (A) — LMil
'Cannon's Double' (K/d) — GGGa LMil
'Canzonetta' (EA) — GGGa MGos
capitatum — GGGa
'Captain Jack' — CWri GGGa SLeo
'Caractacus' — IOrc MBar SLeo WFar
'Carat' — MBri SLeo SReu
cardiobasis — See *R. orbiculare* subsp. *cardiobasis*
'Carillon Bells' — CEqu
Carita Group — LKna SReu
'Carita Golden Dream' ♀ — LKna LMil NMun SLeo
'Carita Inchmery' ♀ — LHyd LKna NMun SLeo
'Carmen' ♀ — CSam GChr GDra GGGa ISea LHyd LKna LMil MBal MBar MBri MDun MLea NHar NHol NMun NWea SBod SHBN SLeo SReu SRms WBod
carneum — GGGa

'Caroline Allbrook' ♀	CHig CSam CWri GGGa LHyd LMil MAsh MBri MGos MOne NHed NHol NMun SBrw SExb SLeo SReu
'Caroline de Zoete'	LHyd
carolinianum	See *R. minus* var. *minus* Carolinianum Group
'Cary Ann'	CSam CWri GCHN GChr GRei ISea MAsh MBal MLea NMun SBid SLeo SReu
'Cassley' (Vs)	LMil LRHS
catacosmum	GGGa SLeo
– R 11185	SLeo
catawbiense	CHig GGGa LHyd MDun NMun SLeo
'Catawbiense Album'	IOrc
'Catawbiense Boursault'	IOrc
'Catawbiense Grandiflorum'	CWri IOrc LRHS
'Catherine Hopwood'	NMun SLeo
caucasicum	LHyd MBal
§ – 'Cunningham's Sulphur'	MDun
– ex AC&H	GGGa NMun SLeo
'Caucasicum Pictum'	GGGa LHyd LMil MBar MBri
'Cayenne' (EA)	SExb
'Cecile' (K) ♀	CB&S GChr LHyd LKna LMil MAsh MBal MBar MBri MGos MLea NMun SExb SPer SReu SSpi
'Celestial' (EA)	CMac
I 'Celtic Cross'	CB&S
'Centennial'	See *R.* 'Washington State Centennial'
'Centennial Celebration'	IOrc MLea
cephalanthum	GGGa LMil
– subsp. *cephalanthum*	MBal
– – Crebreflorum Group	GAri GGGa LMil LRHS
¶ – – Nmaiense Group C&V 9513	GGGa
– – SBEC 0751	GGGa
– subsp. *platyphyllum*	GGGa
¶ – – CNW 835	LMil
cerasinum	GGGa ISea LMil MDun NMun SLeo
– C&V 9504	GGGa
– 'Cherry Brandy'	LHyd NMun
– 'Coals of Fire'	NMun SLeo
– deep pink	NMun SLeo
– x *forrestii* subsp. *forrestii*	MBal
– KW 11011	NMun SLeo
– KW 5830	SLeo
¶ – red form	SLeo
'Cetewayo'	SBrw SLeo SReu
chaetomallum	See *R. haematodes* subsp. *chaetomallum*
'Chaffinch' (K)	LKna
chamaethomsonii	GGGa LMil MBal NHar NMun SLeo
¶ – var. *chamaedoron* F 21768	LMil
– var. *chamaethauma* KW 5847	LMil
– var. *chamaethomsonii* Exbury form L&S	GGGa
§ – – F 21723	NMun
– – pink forms L&S	GGGa
– – Rock form	GGGa
'Chameleon' (EA)	IOrc
chameunum	See *R. saluenense* subsp. *chameunum*

§ 'Champagne' ♀	IOrc LHyd LMil MDun MGos MLea NMun SLeo SReu
championiae	GGGa
'Chanel' (Vs)	SReu SSta
'Chanticleer' (EA)	LRHS SCog SExb
◆ *chapaense*	See *R. maddenii* subsp. *crassum*
charitopes	GGGa LMil MBal MBri NMun SLeo
– subsp. *charitopes* F 25570	SReu
§ – subsp. *tsangpoense*	GGGa GQui LMil NHol
'Charlotte Currie'	SLeo
'Charlotte de Rothschild' ♀	LMil NMun
* 'Charlotte de Rothschild' (A)	SExb
Charmaine Group & cl.	CSam GGGa MBal MDun NHol WBod
'Charme La'	GGGa
'Charming Valentino' (V)	CEqu
chasmanthum	See *R. augustinii* subsp. *chasmanthum*
◆ 'Checkmate'	See *R.* (PJM Group) 'Checkmate'
'Cheer'	COtt CWri IOrc LMil MAsh MBal MBar MBri SExb WGor
'Cheerful Giant' (K)	LMil MLea
'Chelsea Reach' (K/d)	LKna SExb
'Chelsea Seventy'	COtt ENot IHos MBal NMun SLeo SReu
'Chenille' (K/d)	LKna
¶ 'Cherokee'	SLeo
'Chetco' (K)	LMil
'Chevalier Félix de Sauvage' ♀	CWri LMil MGos NMun SBod SLeo SReu
'Cheyenne'	SLeo
'Chicago' (M)	LKna
'Chiffchaff'	EPot LHyd MLea SLeo SPer WAbe
§ *chihsinianum* C&H 7189	GGGa
'Chikor'	CSam CTrG EPot GDra GGGa LKna MAsh MBal MBar MBri MDun MGos MLea NFla NHar NHol NMun SExb SLeo SReu SRms WBod WSHC
China Group & cl.	LKna SReu
'China A'	LKna SBrw SLeo
'Chinchilla' (EA)	GQui MBri
'Chink'	CB&S CGre CSam ENot LHyd MAsh MBal MBar MDun NMun SExb SLeo SPer WBod
'Chionoides'	GGGa IOrc LKna SBid
'Chippewa' (EA)	GGGa LMil LRHS MBri WGwG WWal
chlorops	SLeo
'Chocolate Ice' (K/d)	LKna
'Chopin' (EA)	WBod
'Choremia' ♀	CTrw MLea NMun SLeo SReu
'Chorister' (K)	LKna
¶ 'Chris Bagley'	SBrw
christi Sandham 61/86 (V)	GGGa
'Christina' (EA/d)	CMac GHCN MBri SLeo SPer WBod WWal
'Christmas Cheer' (EA)	See *R.* 'Ima-shojo'
'Christmas Cheer'	CHig CMac GGGa IOrc ISea LHyd LKna LMil MBri MGos MLea NMun SCog SExb SHBN SLeo SPer SReu WPic
'Christobel Maude'	LHyd
§ 'Christopher Wren' (K)	ELan GChr MBal
chrysanthum	See *R. aureum*
chryseum	See *R. rupicola* var. *chryseum*
chrysodoron	GGGa LMil NMun

chrysomanicum	See *R.* **Chrysomanicum Group & cl.**
§ Chrysomanicum Group & cl.	NMun SLeo
ciliatum ♀	CB&S CHig CSam EPot GGGa IOrc LHyd MBal NMun SLeo
– 'Multiflorum'	See *R.* **'Multiflorum'**
ciliicalyx subsp. *lyi*	See *R. lyi*
– SF 535	ISea
Cilpinense Group	CB&S CHig CSam CWri ENot GGGa IOrc ISea LHyd LKna LMil MAsh MBal MBar MDun NFla NHol NMun SCog SExb SLeo SPer SReu WAbe WBod
cinnabarinum	LMil LRHS MBal NMun SLeo
– Bu 268	GGGa
– 'Caerhays Lawrence'	MBal NMun SLeo
– 'Caerhays Philip'	MBal
– subsp. *cinnabarinum* 'Aestivale'	LMil MDun
– – B 652	MBal
– – BL&M 234	LMil
– Blandfordiiflorum Group	GGGa MBal MDun NMun SLeo
§ – – 'Conroy' ♀	GGGa LHyd LMil MBal MDun SReu
I – – 'Mount Everest'	SLeo
– – 'Nepal' ex LS&M 21283	LMil MDun SLeo
– – Roylei Group	GGGa LMil MBal MDun MLea NMun SExb SLeo SReu
– – 'Vin Rosé'	LMil MDun
§ – subsp. *tamaense*	GGGa NMun SLeo
– – KW 21003	NMun
– – KW 21021	GGGa NMun
§ – subsp. *xanthocodon* ♀	CHig ISea LMil MBal NMun SExb SLeo SReu
§ – – Concatenans Group	CB&S CSam GGGa MDun NMun SLeo WBod
– – – 'Amber'	LMil MDun
– – – C&V 9523	GGGa
– – – KW 5874	LMil LRHS
– – – LS&T 6560	NMun SLeo
– – – mustard form	NMun SLeo
– – 'Daffodilly'	SLeo
– – EGM 88	LMil
– – forms	NMun SLeo
¶ – – KW 8239	NMun
– – Purpurellum Group	GGGa MDun NMun SLeo
Cinnkeys Group & cl.	GGGa LMil SLeo
Cinzan Group	SReu
citriniflorum	NMun
– var. *citriniflorum*	LMil
– var. *horaeum*	NMun
– – F 21850*	GGGa LMil
– – F 25901	GGGa LMil NMun SLeo
– R 108	GGGa
'Clarissa' (EA/d)	IOrc
'Claydian Variegated'	GGGa
clementinae	GGGa LHyd MDun NMun SLeo SReu
– F 25705	LMil NMun SLeo
'Cliff Garland'	GQui LMil MDun
Clio Group	NMun SLeo
'Coccineum Speciosum' (G) ♀	GGGa IOrc LHyd LMil MBar MBri SReu SSta
'Cockade' (EA)	LKna
'Cockatoo' (K)	LKna
♦ *coelicum* F 21830	See *R. pocophorum* var. *pocophorum* F 21830
– F 25625	GGGa
§ – KW 21075	NMun
§ – KW 21077	NMun SLeo
coeloneuron	GGGa LMil MDun
'Colin Kenrick' (K/d)	LKna
collettianum H&W 8975	GGGa
'Colonel Coen'	CWri MBal SHBN
Colonel Rogers Group	LHyd NMun SLeo SReu
¶ 'Colyer' (EA)	LHyd
Comely Group	NMun SLeo
complexum F 15392	GGGa
– SSNY 296	GGGa
'Comte de Gomer'	CB&S
concatenans	See *R. cinnabarinum* subsp. *xanthocodon* Concatenans Group
concinnum	CHig CTrw LHyd LMil MBal NMun SLeo WAbe
– PA Cox 5011	GGGa
¶ – PA Cox 5085	GGGa
– Pseudoyanthinum Group ♀	GGGa GQui LMil MDun NMun SLeo WPic
'Concorde'	CHig LHyd MBri
'Congo'	See *R.* **'Robin Hill Congo'**
'Conroy'	See *R. cinnabarinum* 'Conroy'
'Consolini's Windmill'	LMil
'Constable'	LHyd NMun SLeo
'Constant Nymph'	LKna
'Contina'	GGGa
Conyan Group	LHyd
cookeanum	See *R. sikangense* Cookeanum Group
'Cora Grant' (EA)	SExb
'Coral Reef'	NMun SLeo SReu
'Coral Sea' (EA)	SReu
'Coral Velvet'	COtt
coriaceum	GGGa LMil NMun SLeo
– PA Cox 6531	GGGa
– R 120	NMun
– SF 348	ISea
'Corneille' (G/d) ♀	LKna LMil SBid SPer SReu
'Cornish Cracker'	NMun SLeo
Cornish Cross Group	LHyd NMun SLeo SReu
Cornish Early Red Group	See *R.* **Smithii Group**
'Cornish Red'	See *R.* **Smithii Group**
Cornubia Group	NMun SLeo
'Corona' ♀	LKna
'Coronation Day'	SLeo SReu
'Coronation Lady' (K)	ENot LKna MBri
'Corringe' (K) ♀	SExb
'Corry Koster'	LKna SBrw
coryanum	GGGa NMun SLeo
– 'Chelsea Chimes' ex KW 6311	GGGa LMil
'Cosmopolitan'	CWri GChr GGGa IOrc LMil MBar MDun MGos
'Costa del Sol'	NMun SLeo
¶ 'Cotton Candy'	LMil NMun
'Countess of Athlone'	IOrc LKna
'Countess of Derby'	IOrc SLeo SReu
'Countess of Haddington' ♀	CB&S ISea LMil NMun SLeo
'County of York'	See *R.* **'Catalode'**
cowanianum	GGGa
Cowslip Group	CSam LHyd LKna LMil MBal MBar MBri MDun MGos NHol NMun SHBN SLeo SReu
coxianum C&H 475B	GGGa
'Craig Faragher' (V)	CEqu
'Cranbourne'	SReu
'Crane'	GGGa GQui
crassum	See *R. maddenii* subsp. *crassum*
'Cream Crest'	GQui ISea MDun SHBN SLeo
'Cream Glory'	LHyd SReu

'Creamy Chiffon'	CSam CWri GCHN GGGa LHyd MBal MGos MLea SLeo SReu SSta WGwG
§ 'Creeping Jenny' ♀	GGGa LHyd MAsh MBal MBar MDun MLea NHol WBod
cremastum	See *R. campylogynum* **Cremastum Group**
§ 'Crest' ♀	CSam CWri GGGa IOrc ISea LHyd LKna LMil MAsh MBal MDun MGos MLea SHBN SLeo SPer SReu
'Crete'	COtt LMil LRHS MAsh MDun MGos SReu
'Crimson Glory'	See *R.* **'Natalie Coe Vitetti'**
'Crimson Pippin'	GGGa LMil LRHS
crinigerum	GGGa LMil LRHS MDun NMun SLeo
¶ – bicolored form	SLeo
– var. *crinigerum* KW 7123	NMun
– – KW 8164	NMun
– – R 100	NMun
– – R 38	NMun
– var. *euadenium*	NMun
'Crinoline' (K)	SCog SPer WWeb
Crossbill Group	CB&S CGre MBal SLeo
* *crossium*	SReu
'Crosswater Red'	LMil
cruttwellii (V)	GGGa
cubittii	See *R. veitchianum* **Cubittii Group**
cucullatum	See *R. roxieanum* var. *cucullatum*
cultivar FH 8	LMil
§ *cumberlandense* (A)	GGGa LMil
– 'Sunlight' (A)	LMil
cuneatum	GGGa LMil NMun
– F 27119*	NMun SLeo
– R 11392	NMun
§ – Ravum Group	CHig
'Cunningham's Blush'	GAri GGGa SHBN
'Cunningham's Sulphur'	See *R. caucasicum* **'Cunningham's Sulphur'**
'Cunningham's White'	CB&S CHig CPMA CSam CWri GChr GGGa GRei IOrc LKna LMil MAsh MBar MBri MDun MGos NMun NWea SExb SLeo SPer SReu WStI WWeb
'Cupcake'	GGGa
'Curlew' ♀	Widely available
'Cutie'	SLeo
cyanocarpum	GGGa LMil MDun NMun SLeo
¶ – AC 676	NMun
– Bu 294	GGGa
– EN 2458	GGGa
'Cynthia' ♀	CB&S CHig CWri ENot GGGa IOrc LHyd LKna LMil MAsh MBal MBar MBri MDun MGos NMun NWea SBod SHBN SLeo SPer SReu SSta
'Daimio' (EA)	SPer
'Dainty Drops' (V)	CEqu
'Dairymaid'	LHyd LKna NMun SLeo SReu
dalhousieae	GGGa SLeo
§ – var. *rhabdotum* ♀	GGGa SLeo
Damaris Group	NMun SLeo
'Damaris Logan'	See *R.* **'Logan Damaris'**
Damozel Group & cl.	SExb WStI
'Dandy'	LKna
Dante Group	SLeo
'Daphne'	SLeo
'Daphne Jewiss'	SReu
'Daphne Magor'	SLeo
'Daphnoides'	MLea
'Dartmoor Dawn'	MBal
* 'Dartmoor Rose'	GGGa
dasycladum	See *R. selense* subsp. *dasycladum*
dasypetalum .	ECho MBal MBar MDun
dauricum	EPot LMil MBal SLeo WBod
– 'Album'	See *R. dauricum* **'Hokkaido'**
– 'Arctic Pearl'	GGGa
– 'Dark St Andrews'	GGGa
– dwarf	LHyd
§ – 'Hokkaido'	GAri LHyd
– 'Hokkaido' x *leucaspis*	GGGa
– 'Midwinter' ♀	GGGa LHyd LMil MBri SLeo
– 'Nanum'	MBal
– 'Suzuki'	SLeo
'David' ♀	GGGa LHyd LKna NMun SLeo SReu
davidsonianum ♀	CB&S CTrw GGGa IOrc ISea LHyd LMil MBal NMun SLeo SPer WBod
– Bodnant Form	LMil
– 'Caerhays Pink'	GGGa
– 'Ruth Lyons'	LMil
'Daviesii' (G) ♀	CB&S ENot GGGa LHyd LKna LMil MAsh MBal MBri MLea SExb SLeo SPer SReu SSpi WWat WWeb
'Dawn's Delight'	NMun
* 'Dawn Dawn'	SReu
Day Dream Group & cl.	IOrc LKna SCog SReu
'Daybreak' (K)	GQui
N 'Daybreak' (EA/d)	See *R.* **'Kirin'**
'Dayspring' (EA)	ENot LMil
N 'Debutante'	IHos
¶ x *decipiens*	SLeo
decorum	COtt IOrc LHyd LMil MDun NMun SLeo SReu
¶ – AC 757	NMun
¶ – BU 286	NHol
– CNW 582	ISea
– 'Cox's Uranium Green'	SReu
– subsp. *decorum* SBEC 1060	NMun
– – SBEC 181	NMun
§ – subsp. *diaprepes*	CWri IOrc NMun
– – 'Gargantua'	NMun SLeo SReu
¶ – Farrer 979	NMun SLeo
– forms	GGGa NMun
– SF 252	ISea
degronianum	GGGa NMun SReu
§ – subsp. *degronianum*	NMun SLeo
– – 'Gerald Loder'	GGGa
§ – subsp. *heptamerum*	GGGa MDun NMun SLeo
– – 'Ho Emma'	LMil
– – var. *macranthum*	LMil
– 'Metternianum'	See *R. degronianum* subsp. *heptamerum* var. *kyomaruense*
¶ – 'Rae's Delight'	LMil
✦ *delavayi*	See *R. arboreum* subsp. *delavayi*
'Delicatissimum' (O) ♀	GGGa GQui MBri SExb WWeb
¶ 'Delta'	SBrw
dendricola KW 20981*	GGGa
dendrocharis	GGGa
– CC&H 4012	GGGa
– PA Cox 5016	GGGa NHol
'Denny's Scarlet'	SReu
'Denny's White'	SReu
denudatum C&H 7012	GGGa
– C&H 7118	GGGa
¶ – EGM 294	LMil
'Desert Orchid'	LHyd

'Desert Pink' (K) — LKna

desquamatum — See **R. rubiginosum Desquamatum Group**

x *detonsum* — LMil NMun SLeo

¶ – F13784 — SLeo

'Dexter's Spice' — LMil

'Diabolo' (K) — LKna

¶ 'Diadem' (V) — SBrw

Diamant Group (EA) — GAri GGGa

Diamant Group lilac (EA) — GGGa MBri

Diamant Group pink (EA) — ECho GGGa MGos WAbe

§ Diamant Group purple (EA) — ECho MGos

'Diamant Purpur' — See **R. Diamant Group purple**

§ Diamant Group red (EA) — WAbe

Diamant Group rosy red (EA) — COtt ECho GAri GGGa MBri

'Diamant Rot' — See **R. Diamant Group red**

Diamant Group white (EA) — ECho WAbe

'Diana Pearson' — LHyd NMun SLeo

¶ 'Diana van Herzeele' — SBrw

'Diane' — LKna NMun SLeo

diaprepes — See **R. decorum** subsp. *diaprepes*

dichroanthum — GGGa IOrc LHyd MBal NMun SLeo SReu

§ – subsp. *apodectum* — GGGa LMil MDun NMun SLeo

– subsp. *dichroanthum* F 6781 — NMun

– – SBEC 545 — GGGa

– – SBEC 601 — GGGa

– forms — NMun

§ – subsp. *scyphocalyx* — GGGa LMil MBal NMun SLeo

– – F 24546 — GGGa

– – F 27115 — GGGa

– – F 27137 — NMun

– – Farrer 1024 — GGGa

dictyotum — See **R. traillianum** var. *dictyotum*

¶ 'Dido' — LHyd

didymum — See **R. sanguineum** subsp. *didymum*

'Dietrich' — SBrw SReu SSta

dignabile C&V 9569 — GGGa

dimitrum — MDun

'Diny Dee' — MBal MGos SSta

'Diorama' (Vs) — CBlo MBri SReu SSta

diphrocalyx — NMun

¶ 'Direktor E. Hjelm' — SBrw

discolor — See **R. fortunei** subsp. *discolor*

'Doc' ♀ — CB&S ENot GRei IOrc ISea LHyd LMil MAsh MBal MBar MGos NHed NMun SLeo SReu WStI

'Doctor Arnold W. Endtz' — CWri IOrc MAsh MBri NMun SBrw SLeo

'Doctor Ernst Schäle' — GGGa MAsh

'Doctor H.C. Dresselhuys' — IOrc MBar SBrw SHBN

'Doctor M. Oosthoek' (M) ♀ — SReu

'Doctor Stocker' — NMun SLeo

'Doctor Tjebbes' — ISea

'Doctor V.H. Rutgers' — IOrc MBar MGos SBrw

¶ 'Donald Waterer' — SBrw

'Doncaster' — ENot IOrc LKna MAsh MBar MGos NMun NWea SBod SCog SHBN SLeo

'Dopey' ♀ — CDoC CSam CWri ENot GGGa GRei IHos IOrc ISea LHyd LMil MAsh MBal MBar MBri MDun MLea NHed NHol NMun SExb SHBN SLeo SPer SReu WAbe WGwG WWeb

'Dora Amateis' ♀ — COtt CSam GGGa ISea LHyd LMil MAsh MBal MBar MBri MGos MLea NHol NMun SBid SCog SLeo SPer SReu WAbe WBod WGwG WPic

Dormouse Group — LMil

'Dorothea' — SLeo

'Dorothy Corston' (K) — LKna

'Dorothy Hayden' (EA) — LHyd

doshongense — See **R. aganniphum** var. *aganniphum* **Doshongense Group**

'Double Beauty' (EA/d) — CTrh IOrc LKna SBod SPer SReu SSta WWal

'Double Damask' (K/d) ♀ — LHyd LKna

'Double Date' (d) — GGGa

'Double Delight' (K/d) — GGGa MLea

'Doubloons' — NMun SLeo

Dragonfly Group — MDun SLeo SReu

¶ Dragonfly Group x *serotinum* — SLeo

'Drake's Mountain' — ECho MBar MDun

'Dreamland' — COtt CWri ENot ISea LHyd LMil MAsh MBri SBid SBrw SExb SReu

'Driven Snow' (EA) — ENot SBod

drumonium — See **R. telmateium**

'Drury Lane' — GQui

dryophyllum Balfour & Forrest — See **R. phaeochrysum** var. *phaeochrysum*

– hort. — See **R. phaeochrysum** var. *levistratum*

¶ 'Duchess of Portland' — SReu

'Duchess of Rothesay' — NMun

'Duchess of Teck' — SReu

'Dusky Dawn' — NMun SLeo

'Dusky Orange' — SReu

'Dusty Miller' — CAbP CDoC COtt IHos ISea LHyd MBar MGos MLea NHed SExb SHBN SLeo WAbe

'Earl of Athlone' — LHyd SReu

'Earl of Donoughmore' ♀ — LHyd LKna SReu SSta

'Early Beni' (EA) — LHyd

Early Brilliant Group — LKna

'Eastern Fire' — See **R. kaempferi 'Eastern Fire'**

'Ebony Pearl' — GGGa MDun

eclecteum — LMil MDun NMun SLeo

– PA Cox 6054 — GGGa

– 'Rowallane Yellow' — NMun

'Eddy' (EA) — LKna NMun SExb SLeo

x *edgarianum* — LMil

§ *edgeworthii* ♀ — GGGa LHyd LMil MBal NMun SLeo WAbe WBod

¶ – AC 666 — NMun

– forms — GGGa WBod

– x *leucaspis* — CB&S

– x *moupinense* — CB&S GGGa

– SF 607 — ISea

¶ 'Edith Mackworth Praed' — SReu

'Edna Bee' (EA) — GQui LMil LRHS

'Egret' ♀ — CHig CSam EPot GAri GGGa ITim LHyd MAsh MBal MBar MBri MGos MLea NHar NHol SBid SExb SLeo WAbe WGer

'Ehrengold' — MBri

'Eider' — COtt GCHN GGGa ISea MAsh MBal NMun SLeo SReu WAbe
'Eileen' — SReu
'El Alamein' — SLeo
'El Camino' — COtt CWri MBal MLea NMun SHBN SLeo WGwG WWeb
'El Greco' — NMun SLeo
Eldorado Group — GQui
¶ 'Eleanor Habgood' — SLeo
Eleanore Group & cl. — IOrc
Electra Group & cl. — See *R. augustinii* **Electra Group & cl.**
elegantulum — GGGa LHyd LMil MDun NMun SLeo
'Elfin Gold' — GGGa SReu
'Elisabeth Hobbie' ♀ — GDra GGGa LKna LMil MBal MBar MDun MGos
N'Elizabeth' (EA) — ENot IOrc MGos
Elizabeth Group — CB&S CMHG CSam CTrw CWri EBee GDra GGGa IOrc LHyd LMil MAsh MBal MBar MGos NHol NMun NWea SBod SHBN SLeo SPer SReu WBod
'Elizabeth de Rothschild' — LMil MDun NMun
'Elizabeth Jenny' — See *R.* **'Creeping Jenny'**
'Elizabeth Lockhart' — CGre GGGa GQui MBal MBar MDun MGos MLea
'Elizabeth of Glamis' — GGGa
'Elizabeth Red Foliage' — GGGa LRHS MAsh MDun NHol
elliottii — GGGa NMun SLeo SReu
– KW 7725 — NMun
Elsae Group & cl. — NMun SLeo SReu
'Else Frye' — GGGa
'Elsie Lee' (EA) — CGre GGGa LMil MAsh SBod SCog SReu SSta
'Elsie Pratt' (K) — MBar MBri SReu SSta
'Elsie Straver' — CWri MBal NHol SBrw SExb SHBN SLeo SReu
'Elsie Watson' — LMil
'Elspeth' — LHyd LKna
§ 'Emasculum' ♀ — CGre COtt CSam LKna SPer SReu
'Ember Glow' — NMun
Emerald Isle Group — SReu
'Empire Day' — LKna SLeo
'Ems' — EPot
'Enborne' — LHyd NMun SLeo
'Endre Ostbo' — SLeo
'English Roseum' — IOrc
'Erato' — ENot GGGa LMil
eriogynum — See *R. facetum*
♦ *eritimum* — See *R. anthosphaerum*
'Ernest Inman' — LHyd NMun SLeo
erosum — NMun SLeo
erubescens — See *R. oreodoxa* var. *fargesii* **Erubescens Group**
§ × *erythrocalyx* — NMun SLeo
Panteumorphum Group
N'Esmeralda' — CMac CTrG SBod
Ethel Group & cl. — CHig WBod
¶ 'Etna' — SLeo
¶ 'Etoile de Sleidinge' — SBrw
'Etta Burrows' — CWri GGGa MBal MLea
'Euan Cox' — GGGa MBal NHar NHol
euchaites — See *R. neriiflorum* subsp. *neriiflorum* **Euchaites Group**
euchroum — NMun
eudoxum — GGGa MDun NMun
– var. *eudoxum* — GGGa
PA Cox 6036

♦ – – R 10950 — See *R. temenium* var. *mesopolium* **R 10950**
– – R 6c — NMun
– KW 5879* — NMun
'Eunice Updike' (EA) — LHyd
'Europa' — SReu
eurysiphon — NMun SLeo
– KW 21557* — NMun
'Eva Goude' (K) — LKna
'Evening Fragrance' (A) — SReu
'Evening Glow' — NHol
'Evensong' (EA) — LKna
'Everbloom' (EA) — NMun SCog SLeo
'Everest' (EA) — ENot LHyd MBri WBod
'Everestianum' — IOrc LKna MBar SLeo
exasperatum — NMun SLeo
– KW 8250 — GGGa
'Exbury Albatross' — LKna
¶ 'Exbury Calstocker' — LMil
'Exbury Fabia' — SReu
'Exbury May Day' — SReu
'Exbury Naomi' — LHyd LKna LMil NMun SExb SLeo SReu
'Exbury White' (K) — EPfP GQui SExb WWeb
excellens AC 146 — GGGa
– SF 92074 — ISea
– SF 92079 — ISea
– SF 92303 — ISea
eximium — See *R. falconeri* subsp. *eximium*
♦ *exquisitum* — See *R. oreotrephes* **Exquisitum Group**
'Exquisitum' (O) ♀ — EPfP GGGa LMil LRHS MBri SReu SSpi WWeb
F.C. Puddle Group & cl. — SLeo
§ *faberi* — GGGa MDun NMun SLeo
– EGM 111 — LMil
♦ – subsp. *prattii* — See *R. prattii*
Fabia Group & cl. — GCHN GGGa IOrc LHyd LKna LMil MDun NMun SCog SLeo SSpi
¶ 'Fabia' × *bureauii* — SLeo
¶ 'Fabia Roman Pottery' — MDun
§ 'Fabia Tangerine' — COtt MBal MDun MLea SReu SRms WBod
§ *facetum* — GGGa LMil NMun SLeo
– CLD 1522* — MDun
– Farrer 1022 — NMun
– SF 315 — ISea
'Faggetter's Favourite' ♀ — LKna LMil NMun SLeo SReu SSta
Fairy Light Group — ISea LMil MDun SRms
* 'Fairy Mary' — GGGa
♦ 'Falcon' — See *R.* **(Hawk Group) 'Hawk Falcon'**
falconeri ♀ — CHEx COtt GGGa IOrc ISea LHyd LMil MDun NMun SAPC SArc SLeo SPer SReu
¶ – B&SWJ 2437 — WCru
* – Cox's species — SReu
– DF 526 — MBal
§ – subsp. *eximium* — GGGa LMil LRHS MDun
– subsp. *falconeri* — MBal
BM&W 66
'Faltho' — SLeo
'Fanny' — See *R.* **'Pucella'**
'Fantastica' — CWri GGGa LHyd LMil MAsh MDun SReu
fargesii — See *R. oreodoxa* var. *fargesii*
'Fashion' — CChe CTrG SLeo
fastigiatum ♀ — GCrs GDra LMil MBal MBar MDun NMen NMun SLeo

§ – 'Blue Steel'   CB&S COtt CPMA CTri CWSG CWri GGGa LMil MAsh MBal MBri MBro MDun NHar NHol NMun SLeo SReu WAbe WPat WPyg
  – pink   GGGa
  – SBEC 804/4869   GGGa NHol
'Fastuosum Flore Pleno' (d) ♀   CWri GGGa IOrc ISea LHyd LKna LMil MBal MBar MBri MGos MLea NMun NWea SCog SLeo SPer SReu SSta
faucium   GGGa NMun SLeo
  – C&V 9508   GGGa
  aff. – KW 5732   NMun
§ – KW 6401   NMun
'Faulk Lemon'   CHig
fauriei   See *R. brachycarpum* subsp. *fauriei*
'Favorite' (EA)   CMac CTrw IOrc LHyd LKna MBri NMun SLeo
'Fedora' (EA) ♀   CB&S LHyd LKna MRav SLeo SPer
'Fernanda Sarmento'   SReu
ferrugineum   CHig GGGa LKna LMil MBal MBar MGos NMun SLeo SReu
  – Ascreavie form   NHol
* – *compactum*   ECho
  – Glenarn form   NHol
* – 'Hill of Tarvit'   NHol
'Festive'   LHyd
¶ 'Feuerwerk' (K)   SLeo
fictolacteum   See *R. rex* subsp. *fictolacteum*
fimbriatum   See *R. hippophaeoides* var. **hippophaeoides Fimbriatum Group**
Fire Bird Group   LHyd SLeo
'Fireball' (K)   CB&S CTri GGGa LHyd LMil MLea SExb SPer WWeb
'Fireball'   SLeo WLRN WWal
Firedrake Group   CWri SReu
'Firefly' (K)   ENot SExb
'Firefly' (EA)   See *R. 'Hexe'*
'Fireglow'   WFar
'Fireman Jeff'   CWri MBal SExb SPer
'Flamenco Dancer' (V)   ERea
'Flaming Bronze'   SReu
'Flaming June' (K)   LKna
§ *flammeum* (A)   LMil
Flashlight Group   SLeo
§ Flava Group & cl.   CWri LMil MAsh MBar MGos NHed SSta
¶ 'Flava Lackblatt'   MLea
flavidum   GGGa MBal
  – 'Album'   LHyd LMil MDun SBod SExb
  – PA Cox 5064   MDun
  – PA Cox 6143   GGGa
fletcherianum   MBal NMun WAbe
  – R 22302   NMun SLeo
  – 'Yellow Bunting'   GGGa
fleuryi KR 3286   GGGa
§ *flinckii*   GGGa LMil MDun NMun
  – CH&M 3080   GGGa
floccigerum   GGGa LMil NMun SLeo
  – bicolored   NMun
  aff. – F 20305   SLeo
'Floradora' (M)   SReu
'Floriade'   LHyd LKna
floribundum   LMil NMun SLeo
'Florida' (EA/d) ♀   CMac LKna LMil MAsh SBod SCog SPer SSta WBod WFar WWal
formosanum   GGGa

formosum ♀   CB&S CGre ERea GGGa GQui NMun
§ – var. *formosum* Iteaphyllum Group   GGGa SLeo
  – – 'Khasia' C&H 320   GGGa
  – var. *inaequale* C&H 301   GGGa
forrestii   GGGa NMun
◆ – subsp. *forrestii* F 21723   See *R. chamaethomsonii* var. *chamaethomsonii* F 21723
  – – LS&T 5582   NMun
  – – Repens Group   GGGa LMil MBal NMun SLeo WBod
  – Tumescens Group   GGGa NHol NMun SLeo
  – Tumescens Group C&V 9517   GGGa
Fortorb Group   NMun SLeo
Fortune Group & cl.   NMun SLeo
¶ *fortunea* subsp.   LMil
  Subsection Fortunea sp. PW 099*
fortunei   COtt GGGa IOrc ISea LHyd LKna LMil MDun NMun SLeo SReu
§ – subsp. *discolor* ♀   GGGa LMil NMun SLeo
¶ – – 'Hilliers Best'   SLeo
§ – – Houlstonii Group   LMil NMun SLeo
  – – 'Foxy'   NMun SLeo
¶ – – 'Lu-Shan'   MDun
  – 'Mrs Butler'   See *R. fortunei* **'Sir Charles Butler'**
§ – 'Sir Charles Butler'   LMil
'Fox Hunter'   LKna
¶ *fragariiflorum* C&V 9519   GGGa
  – hybrid LS&E 15828   GGGa
'Fragrantissimum' ♀   CB&S CDoC CGre CHad CTrG CTre CTrw ELan GGGa IOrc ISea LHyd LMil MBal MDun MRav NMun SReu
'Francis B. Hayes'   IOrc
Francis Hanger (Reuthe's) Group   NMun SLeo SReu
'Frank Baum'   CBlo CWri MBal NMun SLeo SReu SSta
'Frank Galsworthy' ♀   LKna LMil SExb SLeo SReu SSta
¶ 'Frans van der Bom' (M)   SLeo
¶ 'Fraseri' (M)   GGGa
¶ 'Fred Nutbeam' (EA)   MGos
'Fred Peste'   CAbP GGGa IOrc LMil MDun MLea SReu
'Fred Rose'   SLeo
'Fred Wynniatt' ♀   CWri ISea LHyd LMil LRHS MDun NMun SLeo SReu
'Fred Wynniatt Stanway'   See *R. 'Stanway'*
'Freya' (R/d)   LMil
¶ 'Fridoline' (EA)   GGGa
'Frigate'   WLRN
'Frilled Petticoats'   MLea NMun SLeo SReu
'Frills' (K/d)   LHyd
'Frilly Lemon' (K/d)   LMil
'Frome' (K)   LKna
'Frontier'   LMil
¶ 'Frosted Orange' (EA)   LMil
'Frosthexe'   GGGa
'Fudetsukasi'   SLeo
'Fuju-kaku-no-matsu'   MGos
'Fuko-hiko' (EA)   NMun SLeo
'Fulbrook'   NMun SLeo
'Fulgarb'   SLeo
fulgens   GGGa LHyd LMil MDun NMun SLeo SReu
  – DF 543   MBal

fulvum ♀	GGGa IOrc LHyd LMil MDun NMun SExb SLeo SReu SSta
¶ – subsp. *fulvoides*	NMun SLeo
– – PA Cox 6026	GGGa
– – PA Cox 6532	GGGa
– – R 143	NMun
– – R 180	NMun
– subsp. *fulvum* F 24110	SLeo
'Furnivall's Daughter' ♀	CSam CWri ENot GChr GGGa IOrc LHyd LKna LMil MBal MBar MBri MGos NMun SExb SLeo SPer SReu SSta
¶ 'Fusilier' ♀	SLeo
Fusilier Group & cl.	LHyd SReu
'Gabriele' (EA)	GQui SSpi
'Gabrielle Hill' (EA)	COtt
'Gaiety' (EA)	IOrc LMil SCog
'Galactic'	NMun SLeo
galactinum	LMil NMun SLeo
– EN 3537	GGGa
– W/A 4254	NMun
'Galathea' (EA)	LMil LRHS
'Gallipoli' (K)	CBlo
¶ 'Gandy Dancer'	CWri
'Garden State Glow' (EA/d)	SBod
'Gartendirektor Glocker'	CSam CWri EHic GGGa LMil MDun MOne SSta WWeb
'Gartendirektor Rieger'	CWri GGGa LMil MBri MDun NHol SReu
'Gauche'	GQui
'Gaugin'	GQui
'Geisha' (EA)	MBar
'Geisha Lilac' (EA)	COtt ECho MBar MBri WLRN WWeb
'Geisha Orange' (EA)	COtt GGGa MBar MBri MGos NHed WLRN WWeb
'Geisha Purple' (EA)	COtt MBar MOne WFar
'Geisha Red' (EA)	COtt EPfP MBar MBri STre WAbe WFar
'Gekkeikan' (EA)	CB&S
'Gena Mae' (A/d)	GGGa LMil
'General Eisenhower'	SBrw SReu
'General Eric Harrison'	LHyd NMun SLeo
'General Practitioner'	ENot NMun SLeo
¶ 'General Sir John du Cane'	NMun
'General Wavell' (EA)	CMac COtt GAri LKna SLeo
'Gene's Favourite'	SReu
'Genghis Khan'	MBri MLea NMun
'Geoffroy Millais'	LMil
'George Hardy'	CWri SExb
¶ 'George Hyde' (EA)	WLRN
'George Johnstone' ♀	MBal
'George's Delight'	CWri GGGa MLea
'Georgette'	LHyd NMun SLeo
§ × *geraldii*	SLeo
Gertrud Schäle Group	CTri MBal MBar MLea NHol SReu
'Getsutoku' (EA)	GAri
'Gibraltar' (K) ♀	CB&S CSam EBrP EBre ENot GChr GGGa GRei IOrc LBre LHyd LKna LMil MAsh MBal MBar MBri MGos MLea MRav SBre SPer SReu SSta WWal
giganteum	See *R. protistum* var. *giganteum*
'Gilbert Mullier'	MBri
'Ginger' (K)	EPfP LMil MBal NMun SExb SLeo WWeb
'Ginny Gee' ♀	CDoC COtt CSam CWri EPot GGGa ISea LHyd LMil MAsh MBal MBar MBri MDun MGos MLea NHar NHol NMun SExb SReu SSta WAbe WBod WFar WGwG
§ 'Girard's Hot Shot' (EA)	ECho GGGa GQui LMil SBod SVil
'Glad Tidings'	SLeo
Gladys Group & cl.	SCog
'Glamora' (EA)	LHyd
glanduliferum C&H 7131	GGGa
¶ – EGM 347	LMil
glaucophyllum	GGGa LHyd LMil NMun SLeo
¶ – var. *album*	GGGa
– BH form	LMil
* – 'Branklyn'	GGGa
§ – var. *glaucophyllum* L&S 2764	LMil
– 'Glenarn'	GGGa
– subsp. *tubiforme*	NMun SLeo
'Glencora' (EA)	LHyd
'Glenn Dale Adorable'	See *R.* 'Adorable'
§ *glischroides*	GGGa
glischrum	GGGa NMun SLeo
– C&Cu 9316	GGGa
¶ – CNW 398	ISea
– subsp. *glischroides*	LMil NMun SLeo
– subsp. *glischrum*	GGGa
§ – subsp. *rude*	GGGa LMil MDun NMun SLeo
– – C&V 9524	GGGa
globigerum	See *R. alutaceum* var. *alutaceum* Globigerum Group
'Glockenspiel' (K/d)	LKna
glomerulatum	See *R. yungningense* Glomerulatum Group
'Gloria'	LMil
'Glory of Leonardslee'	SLeo
'Glory of Penjerrick'	NMun SLeo
'Glowing Embers' (K)	CSam GAri GChr GRei MAsh MBal MBri MLea SBid SExb SLeo SPer SReu SSpi WFar WWeb
'Gloxineum'	CWri
¶ Goblin Group & cl.	SLeo
'Gog' (K)	LHyd LKna MBal SLeo WLRN
'Gold Crest' (K)	LKna
'Gold Dust' (K)	SExb
¶ 'Gold Mohur'	SBrw SLeo SReu
'Goldball'	See *R.* 'Christopher Wren'
'Goldbukett'	LHyd MBri
'Golden Bee'	GGGa NHol
'Golden Belle'	CWri LMil MBal MLea SLeo SMur
'Golden Coach'	COtt ISea LMil MBri MDun MLea NMun
'Golden Eagle' (K)	CB&S CBlo COtt MBri MGos SCoo
'Golden Eye' (K)	LKna
'Golden Flare' (K)	CB&S CBlo LHyd MBri SLeo WWeb
'Golden Fleece'	LKna SLeo SReu
'Golden Gate'	CDoC CWri MDun NMun SLeo WGor WGwG WWeb
'Golden Horn' (K)	GQui MAsh WGor WWeb
Golden Horn Group & cl.	IOrc MBal NMun SCog SLeo
'Golden Horn Persimmon'	See *R.* 'Persimmon'
'Golden Lights'	GChr LMil LRHS
'Golden Oriole' (K) ♀	LKna SReu
Golden Oriole Group	CB&S NHol NMun SLeo
§ – 'Talavera' ♀	CB&S MBal
'Golden Princess'	COtt LMil MDun NHol

'Golden Splendour'	LMil
'Golden Star'	GGGa LMil
'Golden Sunlight'	See *R.* **'Directeur Moerlands'**
'Golden Sunset' (K)	COtt MAsh MBar MBri MGos SExb
'Golden Torch' ♀	CAbP CMHG COtt CWri ENot GGGa IOrc ISea LHyd LMil LNet MBal MBri MDun MGos MLea NHed NMun SCog SExb SHBN SLeo SPer SReu SSta WWeb
'Golden Wedding'	CWri LMil LRHS MAsh MBal MLea
'Golden Wit'	ECho MBal SBod SBrw
'Goldfee'	LHyd
'Goldfinch' (K)	LKna
'Goldfinger'	MBal
'Goldflimmer' (v)	ENot GGGa MGos NHol SReu WWeb
'Goldfort'	CWri LKna SBrw SLeo SReu
'Goldika'	LMil
'Goldkrone'	CWri ENot GGGa ISea LHyd LMil MGos MLea NMun SCog SExb SReu
'Goldsworth Crimson'	LHyd SBrw
'Goldsworth Orange'	GGGa LHyd LKna MBal MGos NMun SLeo SPer SReu SSta
'Goldsworth Pink'	LKna SBrw SReu
'Goldsworth Yellow'	CBlo CSam LKna MGos SLeo SReu
'Gomer Waterer' ♀	CHig CWri GGGa IOrc LHyd LKna LMil MAsh MBal MBar MBri MDun MGos MLea NMun NWea SBod SLeo SPer SReu SSta
¶ 'Good News'	SLeo
¶ 'Goosander'	LHyd
'Gordon Jones'	GGGa
'Govenianum' (Ad)	LKna
'Grace Seabrook'	COtt CSam CWri GGGa ISea LHyd LMil MBri MDun MLea SExb SLeo SPer SReu
'Graciosum' (O)	LKna SReu
'Graf Zeppelin'	GGGa
grande	GGGa IOrc NMun SLeo
– DF 524	MBal
¶ aff. – KR 13649	NMun SLeo
– pink	NMun
– TSS 37	NMun
gratum	See *R. basilicum*
'Grayswood Pink'	CSam
'Graziella'	GGGa
'Greensleeves'	LKna LMil
'Greenway' (EA)	CB&S CGre CTre IOrc SPer
¶ Grenadier Group & cl.	SBrw
'Greta' (EA)	LHyd
'Gretzel'	MLea NMun SLeo SReu
griersonianum	CB&S GGGa IOrc LHyd MBal MDun NMun SLeo
– F 24116	NMun
griffithianum	GGGa LMil MDun NMun SLeo WPic
'Grisette'	SLeo
'Gristede'	COtt GGGa LMil MAsh MOne NHol SReu
¶ *groenlandicum*	GGGa
Grosclaude Group & cl.	NMun SLeo
'Grouse'	MBal MLea NHar
'Grouse' × *keiskei* 'Yaku Fairy'	ECho MDun

'Grumpy'	CDoC ENot GGGa GRei IHos IOrc LHyd LMil LNet MBal MBar MBri MGos MLea NHed NMun SHBN SLeo SReu WAbe
Guardsman Group	SLeo
§ 'Gumpo' (EA)	CMac EPot
'Gumpo Pink' (EA)	SLeo WAbe
'Gumpo White' (EA)	EPot SBod WBod
'Gwenda' (EA)	LHyd SCog
'Gwillt-king'	SLeo
gymnocarpum	See *R. microgynum* **Gymnocarpum Group**
'Gyokushin' (EA)	MBal
'H.H. Hume' (EA)	MBal
¶ 'H.O. Carre' (EA)	CMac
'H. Whitner'	NMun SLeo
habrotrichum	GGGa LMil NMun SLeo
– F 15778	NMun
'Hachmann's Brasilia'	CWri SBrw
'Hachmann's Charmant'	GGGa LMil
'Hachmann's Feuerschein'	ENot LMil
'Hachmann's Marlis'	ENot LHyd LMil SBrw SReu
'Hachmann's Polaris'	LMil
'Hachmann's Porzellan'	LHyd
§ 'Hachmann's Rokoko' (EA)	ECho GGGa
'Hachmann's Rosita'	MAsh WLRN
haematodes	GGGa MBal MBri MDun NMun SLeo SRms
¶ – AC 710	NMun
– Bu 290	GGGa
– C&Cu 9445	GGGa
§ – subsp. *chaetomallum*	GGGa LMil NMun
– – F 25601	NMun
♦ – – KW 21077	See *R. coelicum* **KW 21077**
– – R 18359	NMun SLeo
– – R 41	NMun
– CLD 1283	LMil
– subsp. *haemotodes* F 6773	NMun SLeo
– – McLaren S124A	NMun SLeo
– – SBEC 585	GGGa
'Haida Gold'	ISea MBal MBri MGos MLea NMun SLeo SReu SSta WWeb
Halcyone Group	SLeo
'Halfdan Lem'	CAbP CSam GGGa ISea LHyd LMil MBal MGos MLea NMun SCog SExb SHBN SLeo SPer SReu SSta
'Hallelujah'	CWri MBal SExb SMur WWeb
'Halton'	NMun
'Hamlet' (M)	LMil
'Hammondii' (Ad)	LKna
'Hana-asobi' (EA)	CB&S LHyd SLeo
hanceanum	CHig NMun SLeo
– 'Canton Consul'	EPot GGGa LHyd
– EN 2104	GGGa
– Nanum Group	CB&S EPot GGGa LMil MBal
'Handsworth Scarlet'	SLeo
¶ 'Hansel'	MDun
§ *haofui* Guiz 75	GGGa
Happy Group	IOrc SHBN
'Harbinger' (EA)	SBod SLeo
§ 'Hardijzer Beauty' (Ad) ♀	IOrc LKna MBal MBri
'Hardijzer's Beauty'	See *R.* **'Hardijzer Beauty'**
hardingii	See *R. annae* **Hardingii Group**
'Hardy Gardenia' (EA/d)	SCog
hardyi	See *R. augustinii* subsp. *hardyi*
'Harkwood Friendship'	LPan
'Harkwood Moonlight'	LPan MBri WWeb
'Harkwood Premiere'	GGGa LMil MBri MGos
'Harkwood Red'	GQui LMil

'Harry Tagg' CTrG GGGa LHyd SLeo
'Harumiji' (EA) SLeo
'Harvest Moon' LHyd MBal MBar MBri MDun
MGos SExb SLeo SReu
'Harvest Moon' (K) CSam IHos MBri MLea SCoo
SReu
'Hatsugiri' (EA) ♀ CHig CMac ENot EPfP IOrc
LHyd LKna LMil MBar SBid
SBod SCog SReu SSta
(Hawk Group) 'Crest' See *R.* **'Crest'**
¶ – 'Hawk Buzzard' SLeo
§ – 'Hawk Falcon' SReu
§ – 'Hawk Merlin' (EA) COtt LMil MBal SExb
– 'Jervis Bay' See *R.* **'Jervis Bay'**
'Haze' SLeo
'Hazel Fisher' LMil
headfortianum See *R. taggianum*
Headfortianum Group
'Heather Macleod' (EA) LHyd
heftii NMun
'Heidelberg' (K/d) WAbe
'Heiwa-no-kagami' (EA) GAri
'Helen Close' (EA) LRHS SExb
'Helen Curtis' (EA) SCog SReu
'Helene Schiffner' ♀ CWri GGGa NMun SLeo SReu
§ *heliolepis* GGGa IOrc LMil MBal SLeo
– Bu 292 GGGa
– C&Cu 9313 GGGa
◆ – var. *fumidum* See *R. heliolepis* var. *heliolepis*
¶ – var. *heliolepis* CNW 1038 ISea
¶ – – CNW 944 LMil
¶ – – F 6762 NMun SLeo
– – SSNY 66 GGGa NMun
– – SF 489 ISea
– – SF 516 ISea
– – SSNY 314 GGGa
¶ *heliopis* AC 759 NMun
hemidartum See *R. pocophorum* var.
hemidartum
× *hemigynum* NMun SLeo
hemitrichotum NMun SExb
§ – F 30940 NMun SLeo
– KW 4050 NMun
hemsleyanum GGGa IOrc MDun NMun SLeo
aff. – C&H 7189 GGGa LMil
– EN 2097 GGGa
¶ – × *ungernii* GGGa
'Henry Street' SLeo
heptamerum See *R. degronianum* subsp.
heptamerum
'Herbert' (EA) CMac
§ 'Hexe' (EA) WBod
hidakanum SReu
'Higasa' (EA) CHig GAri
'High Gold' LMil
'High Summer' LMil LRHS
'Hilda Margaret' SReu
himantodes (V) CEqu
'Hino-crimson' (EA) ♀ CGre CMac CTrG IOrc LKna
LMil MAsh MBar MBri MGos
SPer SReu SSta WFar WLRN
WStI WWeb
'Hinode-giri' (EA) ♀ CB&S CHig CMac CTrw ENot
LHyd LKna NMun SBod SCog
SExb SLeo SReu WBod
'Hinode-no-kumo' (EA) NMun SLeo
'Hinomayo' (EA) ♀ CB&S CMHG CMac CTrG
CTre GQui IOrc LHyd LKna
LMil MBar MBri NMun SCog
SExb SLeo SPer SReu SSta
WBod WPic WStI
'Hino-scarlet' See *R.* **'Campfire'**

'Hino-tsukasa' (EA) NMun SLeo
hippophaeoides CHig EHic EPfP LKna LMil
MBri MDun NMun SExb SLeo
SSta WAbe
– 'Bei-ma-shan' See *R. hippophaeoides* **'Haba Shan'**
– F 22197A SLeo
§ – 'Haba Shan' ♀ GGGa LMil MBri MDun MOne
– var. *occidentale* GGGa
C&Cu 9314
– Yu 13845 GGGa MDun
hirsutum GGGa LMil MBal SLeo SReu
WPyg
– f. *albiflorum* GGGa
– 'Flore Pleno' (d) ECho EPot GCrs GGGa MBal
MBar MDun WAbe
hirtipes GGGa
– C&V 9546 GGGa
– KW 10616 GGGa
– KW 5659 GGGa SLeo
– KW 6223 NMun SLeo
– LS&E 15765 GGGa
– LS&T 3624 NMun
× *hodconeri* NMun
◆ – LS&H 21296 See *R. hodgsonii* LS&H 21296
– 'pink' NMun
◆ – TSS 9 See *R. hodgsonii* TSS 9
hodgsonii GGGa IOrc LMil MDun NMun
SLeo SReu
– B 653 MBal
– DF 532 MBal
§ – LS&H 21296 NMun
– 'Poet's Lawn' NMun
– TSS 42A NMun SLeo
§ – TSS 9 NMun
'Hojo-no-odorikarako' NMun SLeo
(EA)
'Holden' CWri
'Hollandia' IOrc SHBN
'Homebush' (K/d) ♀ CB&S CMHG ENot GChr
GGGa IOrc ISea LHyd LKna
LMil MAsh MBal MBar MBri
SExb SPer SReu SSpi SSta
'Honey' LKna NMun SLeo
'Honey Bee' MAsh
'Honeymoon' NMun SLeo WLRN WWeb
'Honeysuckle' (K) IOrc MBar SLeo SReu
'Hong Kong' MDun
hongkongense GGGa NMun SLeo
§ 'Ho-o' (EA) CB&S CGre SCog SLeo
hookeri NMun SLeo SReu
– KW 13859 NMun
– Tigh-na-Rudha form GGGa
'Hope Findlay' LHyd
'Hoppy' CWri ENot LMil MAsh MBal
MDun MLea NMun SExb SLeo
SReu WGwG WWeb
'Horizon Lakeside' GGGa LMil
'Horizon Monarch' GGGa LMil MDun
horlickianum GGGa NMun SLeo
– KW 9403 NMun
'Hortulanus H. Witte' (M) SReu
'Hot Shot' See *R.* **'Girard's Hot Shot'**
'Hotei' ♀ CWri GCHN GChr GGGa ISea
LHyd LMil MAsh MBal MBar
MBri MDun MGos MLea
NMun SHBN SLeo SPer SReu
SSta WGer WWeb
Hotspur Group (K) ELan GGGa ISea SCoo SExb
SPer WLRN WWeb
¶ 'Hotspur' ♀ WGwG
'Hotspur Red' (K) ♀ CSam LKna LMil MBri SReu

'Hotspur Yellow' (K)	SReu
houlstonii	See *R. fortunei* subsp. *discolor* Houlstonii Group
huanum C&H 7073	GGGa
¶ – EGM 330	LMil
'Hugh Koster'	CB&S IOrc LKna MBri MGos NMun SLeo SPer
Humming Bird Group	CB&S CMHG CSam GGGa ISea LHyd LKna MBal MBar MBri MGos NHol NMun SHBN SLeo SPer SReu SRms WBod
hunnewellianum	GGGa
'Hurricane'	COtt MBri SLeo
'Huzzar'	MDun
'Hyde and Seek'	GQui
¶ 'Hydie' (EA/d)	MGos
'Hydon Ball'	LHyd
'Hydon Ben'	LHyd
'Hydon Comet'	LHyd
'Hydon Dawn' ♀	COtt GGGa ISea LHyd LMil MAsh MGos MLea NHed NMun SCog SExb SLeo SReu SSta WAbe
'Hydon Glow'	LHyd NMun SLeo
'Hydon Gold'	LHyd
'Hydon Haley'	LHyd
'Hydon Hunter' ♀	COtt GGGa IOrc ISea LHyd LMil LNet NHed NMun SBrw SCog SLeo SReu SSta
'Hydon Juliet'	LHyd
'Hydon Mist'	LHyd
'Hydon Pearl'	LHyd
'Hydon Pink'	LHyd
'Hydon Primrose'	LHyd
'Hydon Rodney'	LHyd
'Hydon Salmon'	LHyd NMun SLeo
'Hydon Velvet'	LHyd SReu
hylaeum	NMun
– KW 6401	See *R. faucium* KW 6401
– KW 6833	NMun SLeo
hypenanthum	See *R. anthopogon* subsp. *hypenanthum*
Hyperion Group	LKna LMil SReu SSta
hyperythrum	GGGa LMil MDun NHol NMun SLeo
* – *album*	NMun
– ETOT 183	ISea
– pink	NMun
hypoglaucum	See *R. argyrophyllum* subsp. *hypoglaucum*
– 'Heane Wood'	See *R. argyrophyllum* subsp. *hypoglaucum* 'Heane Wood'
Ibex Group & cl.	NMun
'Ice Cream'	LHyd
'Ice Cube'	CWri
'Ice Maiden'	SReu
'Iceberg'	See *R. 'Lodauric Iceberg'*
'Icecream Flavour'	See *R. 'Flavour'*
'Icecream Vanilla'	See *R. 'Vanilla'*
Idealist Group & cl.	CWri LHyd NMun SLeo SReu
'Ightham Gold'	SReu
'Ightham Peach'	SReu
¶ 'Ightham Purple'	SReu
'Ightham Yellow'	NMun SLeo SReu
¶ 'Igneum Novum' (G)	MBri
'Il Tasso' (R/d)	LKna
§ 'Ilam Melford Lemon'	LMil
§ 'Ilam Ming'	LMil
§ 'Ilam Red Velvet'	SLeo
'Ilam Violet'	LKna
'Imago' (K/d)	LKna
§ 'Ima-shojo' (EA/d) ♀	GAri IHos LHyd LMil
'Impala' (K)	LKna
impeditum ♀	CB&S CHig CSam ELan ENot GGGa GRei ISea LHyd LKna MBal MBar MDun MGos MLea MPla NBir NHar NHol NMun NWea SLeo SPer SReu SSta WPic
♦ – 'Blue Steel'	See *R. fastigiatum* 'Blue Steel'
– dark compact form	LKna
§ – F 29268	GGGa NMun
– 'Indigo'	CMHG MAsh MBri NHar
– 'Johnston's Impeditum'	LKna
– 'Moerheim'	See *R. 'Moerheim'*
– 'Pygmaeum'	MBro NHol WPat
– Reuthe's form	SReu
– 'Russell's Blue'	SReu
imperator	See *R. uniflorum* var. *imperator*
Impi Group & cl.	LKna NMun SLeo WAbe
'Ina Hair'	CB&S
¶ 'Independence Day'	CWri GGGa
§ *indicum* (EA)	MBal WBod
§ – 'Balsaminiflorum' (EA/d)	CMac
– var. *eriocarpum* 'Gumpo'	See *R. 'Gumpo'*
'Indigo Diamant'	See *R. Diamant Group indigo*
x *inopinum*	GGGa NMun
insigne ♀	CWri GGGa IOrc LHyd LMil MDun NMun SLeo
¶ – hybrid	SLeo
– Reuthe's form	SReu
¶ – X *yakushimanum*	SReu
Intermedium Group	MBal
x *intermedium* white	GGGa
¶ Intrepid Group	SReu
intricatum	GGGa
– KW 4184	NMun SLeo
– PA Cox 5060	GGGa
Intrifast Group	GAri GGGa LHyd MAsh MBal NHar NHol SLeo
iodes	See *R. alutaceum* var. *iodes*
¶ 'Irene'	SBrw
'Irene Koster' (O) ♀	CMHG ELan GGGa LHyd LKna LMil MBri SPer SReu WWeb
'Irohayama' (EA) ♀	CHig CMac CTrw GQui LHyd LKna LMil SCog SExb SLeo SPer SReu SSta
irroratum	CWri LMil NMun SLeo
– C&H 7185	GGGa
– subsp. *irroratum* C&H 7100	GGGa
¶ – subsp. *kontumense* var. *ningyuenense* EGM 339	LMil
¶ – 'Langbianense' KR 3295	LMil
– pale pink	NMun
§ – subsp. *pogonostylum*	NMun SLeo
– 'Polka Dot'	GGGa LHyd NMun SLeo
♦ – R 72	See *R. lukiangense* R 72
– SF 384	ISea
– SF 92304	ISea
'Isabel Pierce' ♀	CSam CWri LMil MBal SLeo
'Isabella Mangles'	LHyd
'Ishiyama' (EA)	SCog
Italia Group	SLeo
iteaphyllum	See *R. formosum* var. *formosum* Iteaphyllum Group
Ivanhoe Group & cl.	ISea
'Ivery's Scarlet'	IOrc
'Ivette' (EA)	CMac LHyd LKna
Iviza Group	SReu
¶ 'Ivory Coast'	LMil

'Iwato-kagami' (EA)	NMun SLeo
'Izayoi' (EA)	WBod
'J.C. Williams'	CB&S
'J.M. de Montague'	See *R.* **'The Hon Jean Marie de Montague'**
'Jabberwocky'	LHyd
'Jack A Sand' (K)	MLea
'Jacksonii'	IOrc ISea LKna MBal MBar NMun SLeo SReu
Jacques Group	NMun SLeo
'Jade'	SLeo
Jalisco Group & cl.	NMun SLeo
'Jalisco Eclipse'	LKna SLeo
'Jalisco Elect' ♀	CWri LKna LMil NMun SLeo
'Jalisco Goshawk'	SLeo
¶ 'Jalisco Janet'	NMun
¶ 'Jalisco Jubilant'	NMun
'James Barto'	IOrc LHyd NMun SLeo
'James Burchett' ♀	GGGa LKna LMil LRHS SLeo SReu
'James Gable' (EA)	MAsh
'Jan Bee'	MBal SLeo
'Jan Dekens'	SReu
¶ 'Jan Steen' (M)	SLeo
Jan Steen Group & cl.	NMun
'Jan Wellen' (EA)	IOrc
'Jane Abbott' (A)	GGGa
'Janelle Marie' (V)	CEqu
'Janet Blair'	CWri
'Janet Ward'	CBlo LHyd LKna SReu
'Janine Alexandre Debray'	NMun SLeo
japonicum (A Gray) Valcken	See *R. molle* subsp. *japonicum*
– var. *japonicum* Schneider	See *R. degronianum* subsp. *heptamerum*
– var. *pentamerum*	See *R. degronianum* subsp. *degronianum*
jasminiflorum (V)	ERea
'Jasorbit' (V)	CEqu
'Java Light' (V)	CDoC ERea
javanicum Sands 74 (V)	GGGa
'Jazz Band' (V)	CEqu GGGa
'Jean Mary Montague'	See *R.* **'The Hon Jean Marie de Montague'**
'Jean Read'	LHyd
'Jeanette' (EA)	LKna
'Jeff Hill' (EA)	ECho LMil LRHS MOne
'Jennie Dosser'	LMil
'Jenny'	See *R.* **'Creeping Jenny'**
§ 'Jervis Bay' ♀	SReu
'Jingle Bells'	CWri GGGa MAsh
'Joan Scobie'	SLeo
Jock Group	CB&S CMHG CTrw
'Jock Brydon' (O)	GGGa LMil
'Jock Coutts'	LKna
'Jock's White'	MBal SPer
'Johann Sebastian Bach' (EA)	WBod WWeb
'Johann Strauss' (EA)	WBod
'Johanna' (EA)	CMac GGGa GHCN LMil MAsh MBar MBri SExb SLeo SPer WBod
'John Barr Stevenson'	LHyd NMun SLeo
'John Cairns' (EA) ♀	CMac LHyd LKna LMil MBal MBar SCog SPer SReu
'John Eichelser'	LMil
¶ 'John Holms'	SLeo
'John Tremayne'	SLeo
'John Walter'	MBar MBri MGos SBid SLeo
'John Waterer'	CBlo CWri IOrc LKna SPer

Johnnie Johnston Group & cl.	SLeo
'Johnny Bender'	MLea SLeo
johnstoneanum ♀	CB&S CGre CSam GGGa LMil MBal NMun SLeo WBod
– 'Double Diamond' (d)	CGre LHyd
– 'Rubeotinctum' KW 7732	NMun SLeo
'Jolie Madame' (Vs)	CBlo MBri SReu
'Jonathan Shaw'	GGGa
'Joseph Hill' (EA)	ECho LMil LRHS SSpi WPat
'Joy's Delight' (Ad)	LKna
'Jubilee'	LKna SLeo
Jubilee Queen Group & cl.	SLeo
'Julischka'	MGos
'June Bee'	GGGa
'Juwel'	MGos
kaempferi (EA) ♀	CGre CHig GGGa LMil
– 'Damio'	See *R. kaempferi* **'Mikado'**
– dark form (EA)	SCog
– 'Firefly'	See *R.* **'Hexe'**
– light form (EA)	SCog
§ – 'Mikado' (EA)	LRHS SBod SCog SPer SReu SSta
– orange (EA)	IOrc
– pink (EA)	IOrc
'Kaho-no-hikari' (EA)	GAri
'Kakiemon' (EA)	SPer
'Kalinka'	LHyd MDun MGos NHol
'Kantilene'	LMil
'Kaponga'	CDoC MGos
'Karen Triplett'	LMil
'Karin'	COtt MBal MDun SBod SHBN SLeo
'Kasane-kagaribi' (EA)	LHyd
'Kate Waterer' ♀	IOrc LHyd LKna MBar MGos NMun SLeo SReu
N 'Kathleen' (A)	IOrc LHyd LKna
'Katinka' (EA)	MBal MGos
'Katisha' (EA)	LHyd
'Katy Watson'	SReu
kawakamii (V)	GGGa
'Keinohana' (EA)	NMun SLeo
keiskei	CHig LHyd MBal NMun SLeo
– 'Cordifolium'	NHol SLeo WAbe
– 'Ebino'	GGGa NHol WAbe
– var. *ozawae* 'Yaku Fairy' ♀	GAri GGGa LMil LRHS MBal NHar SIng SReu
¶ – – 'Yaku Fairy' × *campylogynum* var. *leucanthum*	NHol
– – 'Yaku Fairy' × *spinuliferum*	GGGa
keleticum	See *R. calostrotum* subsp. *keleticum*
§ 'Ken Janeck'	GGGa SLeo SMur WWeb
§ *kendrickii*	GGGa MDun NMun SLeo
– MH 62	GGGa
'Kermesinum' (EA)	CHig COtt GGGa MBar SReu WPat
'Kermesinum Album' (EA)	GGGa MBar MGos
I 'Kermesinum Rose' (EA)	GChr LRHS MBri SLeo
* 'Kermesinum Wit'	SReu
¶ *kesangiae* AC 110	NMun
– CH&M 3058	GGGa
¶ – CH&M 3099	GGGa
– EGM 061	LMil
– var. *kesangiae* KR 1136	NMun
aff. – KR 1640	GGGa MDun NMun
Kewense Group	See *R.* **Loderi Group**

keysii	GGGa LMil MBal MDun NMun SLeo
– KR 974	NMun
– KW 8101*	NMun
– 'Unicolor'	NMun SLeo
'Kijei'	CB&S
Kilimanjaro Group & cl.	LMil NMun SLeo SReu SSta
'Kimberly'	GGGa
'Kimbeth'	GGGa
'Kimigayo' (EA)	LHyd
'King Fisher'	NMun
♦ 'King George' Loder	See *R.* 'Loderi King George'
¶ 'King George' Van Nes	SReu
kingianum	See *R. arboreum* subsp. *zeylanicum*
'Kingston'	MAsh MDun MLea
§ 'Kirin' (EA/d) ♀	CGre CMac CTrw GHCN IOrc LHyd LKna LMil SBod SLeo WBod
'Kirishima' (EA)	LKna SRms
'Kiritsubo' (EA)	GAri IOrc LHyd
kiusianum (EA) ♀	GGGa LHyd NMun SReu SRms WAbe
– 'Album' (EA)	GAri LHyd LMil SReu WAbe
♦ – 'Amoenum'	See *R.* 'Amoenum' (EA/d)
– 'Hillier's Pink' (EA)	LMil
* – 'Mount Fuji' (EA)	LMil WAbe
'Kiwi Majic'	GGGa LMil
'Klondyke' (K) ♀	CB&S CTri EBrP EBre ELan ENot GChr GGGa IOrc LBre LMil MAsh MBri MGos MLea SBre SPer SReu
'Kluis Sensation' ♀	CB&S CWri ENot IOrc LHyd LKna LMil MDun MGos NMun SHBN SLeo SReu
'Kluis Triumph'	LKna SReu
'Knap Hill Apricot' (K)	CBlo LKna SMur
'Knap Hill Red' (K)	LKna LMil SMur
'Kobold' (EA)	NMun SLeo
'Koichiro Wada'	See *R. yakushimanum* 'Koichiro Wada'
'Kokardia'	SLeo
'Komurasaki' (EA)	NMun SLeo
kongboense	GGGa
¶ – C&V 9540	GGGa
¶ aff. – KR 3725	LMil
§ 'Koningin Emma' (M)	LMil MBri
§ 'Koningin Wilhelmina' (M)	IOrc SMer WBod
konori M Black (V)	GGGa
– var. *phaeopeplum* (V)	GGGa
'Koster's Brilliant Red' (M)	ENot MBal MBar SReu
kotschyi	See *R. myrtifolium*
'Kozan' (EA)	MBal
§ 'Kure-no-yuki' (EA/d) ♀	CMac CTrG LHyd LKna LMil MAsh SBod SExb WBod
'Kusudama' (EA)	GAri
kyawii	NMun SLeo
§ – Agapetum Group	NMun SLeo
'Lacs'	SLeo
lacteum	LMil MDun NMun SLeo
– bright yellow	NMun
– C 7164	GGGa
– CNW 930	GGGa
– CNW 936	GGGa
– CNW 966	GGGa
– forms	NMun SLeo
– KR 2760	GGGa
– SBEC 345	GGGa
– SF 374	ISea
'Lady Adam Gordon'	LHyd SLeo
'Lady Alice Fitzwilliam' ♀	CB&S CDoC CGre CMHG CTrG GGGa ISea LHyd LMil MBal NMun SLeo
'Lady Annette de Trafford'	LKna
'Lady Armstrong'	CWri
Lady Bessborough Group & cl.	SLeo
'Lady Bessborough Roberte'	See *R.* 'Roberte'
'Lady Bowes Lyon'	LHyd NMun SLeo
Lady Chamberlain Group & cl.	GGGa LMil MBal NMun SLeo
'Lady Chamberlain Exbury'	See *R.* 'Exbury Lady Chamberlain'
'Lady Chamberlain Golden Queen'	See *R.* 'Golden Queen'
'Lady Chamberlain Salmon Trout'	See *R.* 'Salmon Trout'
¶ 'Lady Clairmont'	SBrw
'Lady Clementine Mitford' ♀	CWri GGGa IHos LHyd LKna LMil MAsh MDun MGos MLea NMun SBid SExb SHBN SLeo SPer SReu SSta
'Lady Decies'	SReu
'Lady Eleanor Cathcart' ♀	CHig CWri EPfP GGGa IOrc LKna NMun SLeo
'Lady Elphinstone' (EA)	LHyd
'Lady Grey Egerton'	LKna
Lady Linlithgow Group	SLeo
'Lady Longman'	LHyd SSta
'Lady Louise' (EA)	LHyd
'Lady Primrose'	SLeo SReu
¶ 'Lady Robin' (EA)	LMil
'Lady Romsey'	LMil
'Lady Rosebery' (K)	LKna MBri
Lady Rosebery Group & cl.	MLea NMun SLeo
'Lady Rosebery Pink Delight'	See *R.* 'Pink Lady Rosebery'
Ladybird Group & cl.	SReu
laetum (V)	CEqu GGGa
Lamellen Group	LHyd SLeo
'Lampion'	ENot GGGa LHyd LMil
'Lamplighter' ♀	LMil SLeo SReu
lanatoides	NMun
– KW 5971	NMun
lanatum	LMil NMun SLeo
– BB 185b	NMun
– Cooper 2148	SLeo
– DF 538	MBal
– dwarf cream	GGGa
– Flinckii Group	See *R. flinckii*
– KR 873	GGGa
'Langmans'	LKna
'Langworth'	CWri ECho LKna MLea SBrw SLeo SReu
lanigerum	NMun SLeo SReu
– C&V 9530	GGGa
– KW 8251	GGGa
– pink	NMun SLeo
– red	NMun
– 'Round Wood' ex KW 6258	LHyd
lapponicum	LMil
– Japanese	GGGa
'Lapwing' (K)	GAri LKna MBri
'Lascaux'	SReu
¶ *lasiostylum* ETOT 135	ISea
– ETOT 136	ISea
'Late Love' (EA)	MGos SSpi
late pink Inverewe	WBod

§ *latoucheae* (EA) | MBal SLeo
– PW 86 (EA) | GGGa
laudandum var. *temoense* | GGGa LMil MDun
Laura Aberconway Group SLeo
& cl.
'Laura Morland' (EA) | LHyd
'Lava Flow' | LHyd NHol SCog
'Lavender Girl' ♀ | GGGa LHyd LKna LMil MBal
| MGos NMun SLeo SReu SSta
¶ 'Lavender Lady' (EA) | CTrG
'Lavender Princess' | LMil
'Lavender Queen' | CWri NMun SExb WWeb
'Lavendula' | CSam GGGa LMil
'Le Progrès' | SReu
'Lea Rainbow' | MLea
'Ledifolium' | See *R. mucronatum* var.
| *mucronatum*
'Ledifolium Album' | See *R. mucronatum* var.
| *mucronatum*
ledifolium 'Bulstrode' | See *R.* '**Bulstrode**'
– 'Magnificum' | See *R.* '**Magnificum**'
– 'Ripense' | See *R. ripense*
'Lee's Dark Purple' | CWri LMil MBar NMun SPer
| WGwG
'Lee's Scarlet' | LKna LMil SLeo
'Lemon Cloud' | GGGa
* 'Lemon Drop' (A) | GGGa
'Lemon Grove' | SReu
'Lemon Lodge' | CB&S CDoC
'Lemon Minuet' (V) | CEqu
'Lemonora' (M) | ELan MBri SLeo
'Lem's Cameo' ♀ | GGGa LHyd LMil NMun SReu
| SSta
'Lem's Monarch' ♀ | GGGa LMil LRHS MDun
| MGos MLea SReu SSta
'Lem's Stormcloud' | MLea SSta
'Lem's Tangerine' | LMil
'Lemur' (EA) | EPot GChr GGGa MAsh MBri
| MGos WAbe WPat
¶ 'Leni' | LRHS
'Leny' | NHol
'Leo' (EA) | GQui LHyd LKna LMil NMun
| SBod SExb SLeo SReu WWeb
'Leo' | EPfP NMun SLeo
'Leonardslee Brilliant' | SLeo
'Leonardslee Giles' | SLeo
'Leonardslee Pink Bride' | SLeo
'Leonardslee Primrose' | SLeo
Leonore Group & cl. | NMun SReu
lepidostylum ♀ | CB&S CWri EPot GGGa LHyd
| LMil MBar MBri MDun NHar
| NMun SLeo SReu WAbe
| WSHC
lepidotum | GGGa LHyd LMil NMun SLeo
| WAbe
¶ – var. *album* | GGGa
– Elaeagnoides Group | GGGa
– FMB 279 | MBal
– x *lowndesii* | WAbe
– M Black 602 | GGGa
– 'Reuthe's Purple' | See *R.* '**Reuthe's Purple**'
¶ – yellow form | NMun
leptocarpum | GGGa LMil
¶ – C&H 420 | NMun SLeo
leptothrium | GGGa NMun SLeo
Letty Edwards Group | LKna NMun SLeo SReu
& cl.
§ 'Leucanthemum' | CHig GGGa LMil
leucaspis ♀ | CGre CHig EPot ERea GGGa
| IOrc ISea LHyd MBal NMun
| SLeo SReu
– KW 7171 | NMun SLeo

'Leverett Richards' | LHyd SReu
levinei | GGGa
'Lila Pedigo' | COtt GGGa MBal MLea
'Lilac Time' (EA) | MBar
¶ 'Lilacinum' (EA) | WPic
liliiflorum Guiz 163 | CWri GGGa
'Lillie Maude' (EA) | CTrh
'Lilliput' | MAsh SBod SPer
'Lily Marleen' (EA) | CBlo CDoC CTri SCoo SLeo
| SReu WGwG
'Linda' | CSam CTri GChr GGGa MBal
| MBar MBri MDun MGos MLea
| SBod SLeo SReu WWeb
lindleyi ♀ | GQui LMil NMun SLeo
– 'Dame Edith Sitwell' | GGGa LMil
– L&S | GGGa MBal
'Linearifolium' | See *R. macrosepalum*
| '**Linearifolium**'
'Linnet' (K/d) | LKna
'Linwood Salmon' (EA/d) | SCog
Lionel's Triumph Group | LMil NMun SLeo
& cl.
'Lissabon Rosa' | SExb
litiense | See *R. wardii* var. *wardii*
| **Litiense Group**
'Little Beauty' (EA) | SExb SLeo
'Little Ben' | ECho MBal MBar MDun WAbe
'Little Bert' | SLeo
'Little Grace' (V) | CEqu
'Little Jock' | MBal
'Little One' (V) | CEqu
¶ 'Loch Earn' | GGGa
'Loch o'the Lowes' | GGGa LMil MOne
'Loch Rannoch' | GGGa
'Loch Tummel' | GGGa
lochiae (V) | CEqu GGGa
'Lochinch Spinbur' | GQui
Lodauric Group | SReu
§ 'Lodauric Iceberg' ♀ | LKna LMil LRHS SReu
'Lodbrit' | SReu
'Loderi Fairy Queen' | NMun SLeo
'Loderi Fairyland' | LHyd MDun NMun SLeo
§ 'Loderi Game Chick' | CB&S CWri LHyd LMil MBal
| NMun SLeo SPer SReu SSta
'Loderi Georgette' | NMun SLeo
'Loderi Helen' | NMun SLeo
§ 'Loderi Julie' | NMun SLeo SReu
§ 'Loderi King George' ♀ | CB&S CSam CWri GGGa ISea
| LHyd LKna LMil MBlu MDun
| MLea NMun SHBN SLeo SPer
| SReu SSta
'Loderi Patience' | LHyd NMun SLeo
'Loderi Pink Diamond' ♀ | LMil
'Loderi Pink Topaz' | CWri LHyd LMil LRHS MDun
| NMun SLeo
'Loderi Pretty Polly' | NMun SLeo
'Loderi Princess Marina' | NMun SLeo
'Loderi Sir Edmund' | LHyd NMun SLeo
'Loderi Sir Joseph | NMun SLeo
Hooker'
'Loderi Titan' | SReu
§ 'Loderi Venus' ♀ | GGGa IOrc LHyd LKna LMil
| MBal MDun MLea NMun
| SHBN SLeo SPer SReu SSta
'Loderi White Diamond' | LHyd NMun SLeo
'Loder's White' ♀ | CWri ENot GGGa IHos LHyd
| LKna LMil MBal MLea NMun
| SLeo SPer SReu SSta
§ 'Logan Damaris' | LHyd NMun SLeo SReu
'Loki' | SLeo
longesquamatum | GGGa LMil NMun SLeo

longipes var. *chienianum*	GGGa
EN 4074	
¶ – EGM 337	LMil
– var. *longipes* C&H 7072	GGGa
– – C&H 7113	GGGa
longistylum	GGGa NMun
'Longworth'	NMun
'Looking Glass'	SHBN
lopsangianum	See *R. thomsonii* subsp.
	lopsangianum
¶ – L S & T 5651	NMun
'Lord Roberts'	CB&S CHig CSam CWri ENot
	GChr GGGa GRei IOrc LKna
	LMil MAsh MBal MBar MBri
	MGos NMun SHBN SLeo SPer
	SReu SRms WWeb
'Lord Swaythling'	LHyd SLeo
'Lori Eichelser'	CSam LMil MAsh MBal MDun
	MLea NHar NHed
'Lorna' (EA)	ENot GQui LMil
'Louis Pasteur'	SReu
'Louisa' (EA)	SExb SSpi
'Louise Dowdle' (EA)	CTrh GChr LMil SExb SPer
'Lovely William'	CSam MBal SLeo
lowndesii	WAbe
– × *keiskei* var. *ozawae*	EPot
'Yaku Fairy'	
'Lucy Lou'	CSam GGGa NHol SExb
ludlowii	GGGa MBal
– × *viridescens*	NHol
ludwigianum	GGGa
lukiangense	NMun SLeo
§ – R 11275	NMun SLeo
§ – R 72	NMun
'Lullaby' (EA)	LKna
'Lunar Queen'	LHyd NMun SLeo
Luscombei Group	LHyd SLeo
luteiflorum	LMil
– KW 21040	GGGa NMun
– KW 21556	GGGa
lutescens	CB&S CGre CHig CTre CWri
	IBlr IOrc LMil MAsh MBal
	MBri MDun NMun SLeo SReu
	SSta WAbe WBod WWat
– 'Bagshot Sands' ♀	GGGa LHyd LMil LRHS SPer
	SReu
– C&H 7124	GGGa
– PA Cox 5092	GGGa NHol
¶ – PA Cox 5100	GGGa NHol
§ *luteum* (A) ♀	CB&S CPMA CTrG CTre CTri
	CWri GGGa ISea LKna LMil
	LPan MBal MBar MBri MGos
	MLea NMun SLeo SReu SRms
	SSta WBod WPic WWat
§ *lyi*	NMun SLeo
– KR 2861	GGGa
– KR 2962	GGGa
* 'Mac Ovata'	CMac
macabeanum ♀	CB&S CHEx GGGa LMil MBal
	MDun NMun SLeo SPer SReu
	SSta WPic
– DT 10	GGGa
– KW 7724	NMun SLeo
– Reuthe's form	SReu
– × *sinogrande*	MDun SReu
macgregoriae (V)	CEqu ERea
– P Woods 2646 (V)	GGGa
macranthum	See *R. indicum*
'Macranthum Roseum'	SBod SExb
(EA)	
macrophyllum	GGGa
◆ *macrosmithii*	See *R. argipeplum*

'Macrostemon'	See *R.* (Obtusum Group)
	'Macrostemon'
maculiferum	MDun NMun SLeo
◆ – subsp. *anwheiense*	See *R. anwheiense*
– Guiz 120*	GGGa
– Guiz 121	GGGa
'Madame Albert Moser'	LKna
'Madame de Bruin'	LKna MBal NWea SLeo
'Madame F.V. Chauvin'	ISea
'Madame Knutz'	SCog
'Madame Masson'	CHig CSam CWri GChr GGGa
	LMil MAsh MGos NMun SCog
	SExb SHBN SLeo SReu SSta
	WWeb
'Madame van Hecke'	COtt EPfP MAsh MBri SReu
(EA)	WFar
maddenii ♀	CGre LHyd LMil NMun SLeo
§ – subsp. *crassum* ♀	CTrw GGGa LMil MBal NMun
	SReu WBod
¶ – – AC 708	NMun
§ – – Obtusifolium Group	NMun SLeo
§ – subsp. *maddenii*	NMun SLeo
§ – – Polyandrum Group	GQui ISea MBal NMun SLeo
¶ 'Maestro'	LHyd
magnificum	LMil NMun SLeo SReu
N 'Magnificum' (A)	MBri
'Maharani'	GGGa
§ *makinoi* ♀	CHig GGGa LHyd LMil MDun
	NMun SLeo SReu SSta
mallotum	GGGa LHyd LMil MDun
	NMun SLeo SReu
'Malvaticum' (EA)	WBod
'Manda Sue'	LMil MAsh MBal MLea
Mandalay Group	MBri SLeo
¶ 'Manderley'	MDun
manipurense	See *R. maddenii* subsp. *crassum*
	Obtusifolium Group
¶ 'Manor Hill'	SLeo
'Marchioness of	MGos
Lansdowne'	
'Marcia'	LHyd SLeo
'Mardi Gras'	GGGa
Margaret Dunn Group	CWri SLeo
& cl.	
'Margaret Falmouth'	SReu
'Margaret George' (EA)	LHyd
'Maria Elena' (EA/d)	LMil
'Marianne' (EA/d)	LMil
'Marie' (EA)	CMac
'Marie Curie'	SReu
'Marilee' (EA)	MGos
Mariloo Group	NMun SLeo
'Marinus Koster' ♀	LKna MLea
'Marion Merriman' (K)	LKna
'Marion Street' ♀	LHyd LMil NMun SLeo SReu
'Markeeta's Prize' ♀	CBlo CSam CWri GAri GGGa
	LMil MBri MLea NMun
'Marlene Peste'	CAbP
'Mars'	SLeo SReu
'Martha Hitchcock' (EA)	LKna SRms
'Martha Isaacson' (Ad)	GGGa MBal MBri MGos MLea
	SReu
'Martine' (Ad)	LHyd LKna MBri MGos SLeo
martinianum	NMun SLeo
aff. – KW 21557	GGGa
'Mary Drennen'	LMil
'Mary Fleming'	MDun NMun SBod SExb SLeo
	SSta WLRN
'Mary Forte'	SLeo
'Mary Helen' (EA)	CDoC LHyd LRHS SCoo SExb
	WBod WGwG
'Mary Meredith' (EA)	LHyd

'Mary Poppins' GRei LRHS SCoo
¶ 'Maryke' LMil
'Master of Elphinstone' SCog
   (EA)
Matador Group & cl. NMun SReu WBod
'Mauna Loa' (K) LKna
'Maurice Skipworth' CB&S CDoC
¶ 'Mavis Davis' GGGa
maximum GGGa NMun SLeo
– 'Weeldon's Red' GGGa
'Maxine Childers' LMil
'Maxwellii' (EA) CMac
May Day Group & cl. CB&S CSam CTrw CWri ISea
   LHyd LKna MBal MBri MDun
   MGos NMun SCog SHBN SLeo
   SReu SSta WBod
'May Glow' MGos
May Morn Group & cl. SReu
'Mayor Johnstone' LRHS
'Mazurka' (K) LKna
meddianum GGGa NMun SLeo
– var. atrokermesinum NMun SLeo
– – F 26476 NMun SLeo
– – KW 21006a GGGa
Medusa Group GGGa SReu
megacalyx GGGa SLeo
'Megan' (EA) GGGa IOrc MAsh
megaphyllum See R. basilicum
megeratum GGGa NMun SLeo SReu
– 'Bodnant' WAbe WBod
'Meicho' (EA) GAri
mekongense GGGa
– var. mekongense SReu
§ – – KW 5829 NMun SLeo
– – Rubroluteum Group See R. viridescens Rubroluteum
   Group
– – Viridescens Group See R. viridescens
§ – var. melinanthum NMun SLeo
– var. rubrolineatum NMun SLeo
'Melford Lemon' See R. 'Ilam Melford Lemon'
¶ 'Melina' (EA/d) GGGa
melinanthum See R. mekongense var.
   melinanthum
'Merganser' ♀ GGGa LMil MAsh MBal MDun
   MLea NHol SReu WAbe WBod
♦ 'Merlin' See R. (Hawk Group) 'Hawk
   Merlin'
metternichii See R. degronianum subsp.
   heptamerum
¶ 'Mi Amor' LMil
'Michael Hill' (EA) CB&S COtt CTrh LHyd MAsh
   SExb SSpi
'Michael Waterer' ♀ MDun NMun SBod SLeo
'Michael's Pride' ♀ CB&S GQui MBal NMun
micranthum CGre GGGa MDun NMun
   SLeo
microgynum NMun SLeo
– F 14242 GGGa NMun SLeo
microleucum See R. orthocladum var.
   microleucum
micromeres See R. leptocarpum
¶ 'Midnight Mystique' GGGa
'Midori' (EA) SExb
'Midsummer' SLeo
'Mikado' (EA) See R. kaempferi 'Mikado'
mimetes LMil NMun SLeo
§ – var. simulans NMun SLeo
¶ – – F 20428 GGGa NMun
'Mimi' (EA) CMac LHyd
'Ming' See R. 'Ilam Ming'
'Minterne Cinnkeys' MBal
minus GQui

¶ – var. minus SLeo
§ – – Carolinianum Group LMil
§ – – Punctatum Group MBar
'Misomogiri' CHig
'Miss Muffet' (EA) SExb
'Mizu-no-yamabuki' (EA) SLeo
§ 'Moerheim' ♀ CSam MAsh MBal MBar MDun
   MOne MRav NHol SReu SSta
   WStI
§ 'Moerheim's Pink' LHyd LKna LMil MDun NHol
   SPer
'Moerheim's Scarlet' LKna
'Moidart' (Vs) LMil
'Moira Salmon' (EA) LHyd
'Molalla Red' LMil
§ molle subsp. japonicum GGGa LHyd
   (A)
– – JR 871 (A) GGGa
mollicomum NMun
– F 10347 NMun
♦ – F 30940 See R. hemitrichotum F 30940
Mollis orange (M) MBar SRms
Mollis pink (M) GGGa MBar SRms
Mollis red (M) MBar SRms
Mollis salmon (M) GGGa GQui
Mollis yellow (M) GQui MBar SRms
'Molly Ann' GGGa LRHS MAsh MDun
   MLea SReu
¶ 'Molly Miller' LMil
'Monaco' CWri SLeo
'Monica' SCog
♦ monosematum See R. pachytrichum var.
   monosematum
¶ montiganum ISea
montroseanum LMil MDun NMun SLeo WCru
* – 'Baravalla' CWri GGGa
– 'Benmore' NMun
'Moon Maiden' (EA) GQui LMil SVil
Moonbeam Group LKna
Moonshine Group & cl. SReu
'Moonshine Bright' LHyd MDun SReu
'Moonshine Crescent' SReu
'Moonshine Supreme' LKna SReu
Moonstone Group CHig EPot GAri MBal MBar
   MDun MLea NMun SLeo
   WAbe
Moonstone Group NHol
   pink-tipped
'Moonstone Yellow' GGGa
'Moonwax' CB&S CSam CWri MBal SMur
§ 'Morgenrot' ♀ GChr GGGa LMil LRHS MBri
   MGos SReu
morii ♀ CWri GGGa LHyd LMil MDun
   NMun SLeo
– ETOT 90 ISea
– W/A 10955 SLeo
'Morning Cloud' ♀ CAbP IOrc LHyd LMil MAsh
   MBar NHed NMun SLeo SReu
'Morning Magic' LHyd NMun SBrw SExb SLeo
Morning Red See R. 'Morgenrot'
'Morvah' SLeo
'Moser's Maroon' CWri LHyd LKna LMil MGos
   NMun SLeo WGwG
'Moser's Strawberry' LKna
'Motet' (K/d) LKna
'Moth' GGGa NHol
'Mother Greer' GGGa
'Mother of Pearl' LKna SCog SLeo SPer SReu
'Mother Theresa' LKna

'Mother's Day' (EA) ♀ — CB&S CGre CMac EBrP EBre ENot GChr GHCN GQui GRei IOrc LBre LHyd LKna LMil MBal MBar MBri MGos NMun SBod SBre SExb SPer SReu SSta WFar WLRN

§ *moulmainense* — SLeo
'Mount Everest' — LHyd LMil SLeo SReu SSta
'Mount Rainier' (K) — LMil
'Mount Saint Helens' — GGGa LMil
'Mountain Star' — SLeo
moupinense ♀ — CB&S CHig ERea GGGa IDee LHyd LMil NMun SLeo SPer SReu WBod

– C&K 140 — GGGa
– pink — GGGa WBod
'Mozart' (EA) — SBod WBod
'Mrs A.T. de la Mare' ♀ — ENot GGGa IOrc LHyd LKna LMil MBri NMun SLeo SPer SReu SSta
'Mrs Anthony Waterer' (O) — LKna
'Mrs Anthony Waterer' — CBlo LKna SSta
'Mrs Ashley Slocock' — SReu
'Mrs Betty Robertson' — CHig MBri MLea SReu
'Mrs C.B. van Nes' — SReu
Mrs C. Whitner Group — NMun SLeo
'Mrs Charles E. Pearson' ♀ — CB&S CWri ENot LHyd LKna LMil MLea NMun SCog SExb SHBN SLeo SPer SReu
'Mrs Davies Evans' ♀ — LHyd LKna MBar SReu SSta
'Mrs Dick Thompson' — SReu
'Mrs Donald Graham' — SReu
'Mrs Doorenbos' — CMac
'Mrs E.C. Stirling' — LHyd LKna SRms
'Mrs Emil Hager' (EA) — LHyd
'Mrs Furnivall' ♀ — CB&S CHig CWri EPfP LHyd LKna LMil MAsh MBri MGos SExb SReu WGer
'Mrs G.W. Leak' — CSam CWri ENot EPfP GGGa ISea LHyd LKna LMil MBri MLea NMun SCog SExb SHBN SLeo SPer SReu SSta
'Mrs Helen Koster' — LKna
'Mrs Henry Agnew' — NMun SLeo
'Mrs J.C. Williams' — LKna LMil NMun SLeo
'Mrs J.G. Millais' — LKna LMil NMun SLeo
'Mrs James Horlick' — NMun SLeo
¶ 'Mrs John Waterer' — SBrw
'Mrs Kingsmill' — SLeo
'Mrs Lindsay Smith' — LKna
¶ 'Mrs Lionel de Rothschild' ♀ — NMun
Mrs Lionel de Rothschild Group & cl. — LKna LMil SReu
'Mrs P.D. Williams' ♀ — LKna SReu
'Mrs Philip Martineau' — LKna
'Mrs R.S. Holford' ♀ — LKna NMun SLeo
'Mrs T.H. Lowinsky' ♀ — CHig CWri EPfP GCHN GGGa LKna LMil MAsh MBri MDun MGos MMun SLeo SReu SSta
'Mrs W.C. Slocock' — LKna MDun NMun SLeo SPer SReu SSta
'Mrs William Agnew' — LKna SLeo
X *mucronatum* — CHig NMun SLeo SPer SRms WBod WPic
'Mucronatum' — See R. mucronatum var. mucronatum
'Mucronatum Amethystinum' — See R. 'Amethystinum'
♦ *mucronatum* var. *ripense* — See R. ripense

mucronulatum — GGGa LHyd LMil NMun SLeo WAbe
¶ – B&SWJ 786 — WCru
♦ – var. *chejuense* — See R. mucronulatum var. taquetii
– 'Cornell Pink' ♀ — GGGa LMil
– 'Mahogany Red' — GGGa
§ – var. *taquetii* — GGGa
§ 'Multiflorum' — SReu
'Muncaster Bells' — NMun
'Muncaster Hybrid' — NMun
'Muncaster Mist' — NMun
'Muriel' — SLeo
'My Lady' — GGGa
myiagrum — See R. callimorphum var. myiagrum
§ *myrtifolium* — SLeo
nakaharae (EA) — MBal NMun SCog SLeo SReu WAbe
§ – 'Mariko' (EA) — EPot GGGa LHyd LMil MBal MBar MBro MGos NHol SCog SLeo WAbe WPat WPyg
– 'Mount Seven Stars' (EA) — CHig ECho GGGa LHyd LMil MBri MBro NHol SCog SLeo WAbe WPat
§ – orange (EA) — LMil LRHS MAsh MOne SCog SHBN SPer SReu SSta
– pink (EA) — CHig LHyd LMil MAsh SCog SPer SSta
'Nakahari Orange' — See R. nakaharae orange
'Nakahari-mariko' — See R. nakaharae 'Mariko'
¶ *nakotiltum* — NMun
'Nancy Evans' — COtt CSam GGGa ISea LMil MAsh MBal MDun MLea SBid SReu SSpi
'Nancy of Robinhill' (EA) — LHyd
'Nancy Waterer' (G) ♀ — MBri SLeo SReu
'Nanki Poo' (EA) — LHyd SPer
'Naomi' (EA) — GQui IOrc LKna LMil SHBN SLeo
Naomi Group & cl. — CSam CWri ISea LKna MLea SReu
'Naomi Astarte' — LKna MDun SLeo
'Naomi Early Dawn' — NMun
(Naomi Group) 'Paris' — See R. 'Paris'
'Narcissiflorum' (G/d) ♀ — CDoC ENot IOrc LHyd LKna LMil SPer SReu
'Naselle' — GGGa LMil
'Nassau' (EA/d) — LMil
¶ 'Nelly de Bruin' — SBrw
neriiflorum — GGGa ISea LMil MDun NMun SLeo SReu SSpi
– Bu 287 — GGGa
§ – subsp. *neriiflorum* Euchaites Group — NMun SLeo
– – L&S 1352 — GGGa
– – Phoenicodum Group Farrer 877 — GGGa NMun
§ – subsp. *phaedropum* — NMun SLeo
– – C&H 422 — NMun SLeo
– – KW 6845* — NMun SLeo
– – KW 8521 — SLeo
– SF 366 — ISea
– SF 375 — ISea
Neriihaem Group — NMun SLeo
nervulosum Argent (V) — GGGa
¶ 'Nestor' — SReu
'Nettie' (EA) — SCog
'New Comet' — LHyd LMil NMun SReu
'New Moon' — SLeo SReu
'Newcomb's Sweetheart' — LMil MDun SMur

'Niagara' (EA) ♀	CTrh ENot EPfP GQui LHyd LMil MBal SCog SExb WBod
'Nichola' (EA)	MAsh SBod
'Nico'	CMac MAsh MBri SPer WBod WPat
¶ 'Nicoletta'	GGGa LMil
'Night Sky'	GGGa LMil LRHS MOne NHol SLeo
'Nightingale'	LMil SReu
nigroglandulosum	GGGa
nigropunctatum	See *R. nivale* subsp. *boreale* **Nigropunctatum Group**
¶ x *nikomontanum*	LMil
nilagiricum	See *R. arboreum* subsp. *nilagiricum*
'Nimbus'	LKna LMil SLeo
Nimrod Group	CWri NMun SLeo
'Nishiki' (EA)	CMac
nitens	See *R. calostrotum* subsp. *riparium* **Nitens Group**
nitidulum	NMun
– var. *nitidulum* C 5059	GGGa
– – C 5107	GGGa
– var. *omeiense* KR 185	GGGa LMil NHol
nivale subsp. *boreale* Ramosissimum Group	GGGa
§ – – Stictophyllum Group	GGGa LMil
niveum ♀	GGGa LMil MBal MDun NMun SLeo SReu SSta
– 'Nepal'	LHyd
'Noble Mountain'	LMil SMur
nobleanum	See *R.* **Nobleanum Group**
§ Nobleanum Group	GGGa ISea LHyd LKna LMil NMun SCog SLeo SSta
'Nobleanum Album'	LHyd LKna LMil MBal NMun SLeo SReu SSta
'Nobleanum Coccineum'	ISea NMun SLeo SReu
'Nobleanum Lamellen'	SLeo
'Nobleanum Venustum'	ISea LHyd LKna LMil SReu SSpi SSta WBod
'Nofretete'	GGGa
N 'Norma' (R/d) ♀	ENot LMil MBri SReu
Norman Shaw Group & cl.	LHyd
'Northern Star'	SLeo
'Northlight'	MBri
notiale (V)	CEqu
'Nova Zembla'	GChr GGGa MAsh MBar MGos SHBN SLeo SReu SSta WGwG WStI
nudiflorum	See *R. periclymenoides*
* *nummularia* L&S 17294	GGGa
nuttallii ♀	GGGa LMil MBal
'Oban'	GGGa LMil NHol WAbe
Obtusum Group (EA)	CHig LHyd
♦ *obtusum* f. *amoenum*	See *R.* **'Amoenum' (EA/d)**
§ (Obtusum Group) 'Macrostemon' (EA)	WBod
occidentale (A) ♀	CGre GGGa LMil MBal SLeo SReu
– forms (A)	GGGa
ochraceum C&H 7052	GGGa
'Odee Wright' ♀	CWri GGGa LMil MAsh MDun MLea NMun SLeo SPer SReu SSta
¶ 'Oh-Too'	SBrw
'Oi-no-mezame' (EA)	LHyd
'Old Copper'	CWri LNet MBri MLea WGer
'Old Gold' (K)	SReu
'Old Port'	CWri LHyd MLea SHBN SReu SSta
Oldenburgh Group	SLeo
oldhamii (EA)	CTre NMun SLeo

– ETOT 60 (EA)	ISea
– ETOT 601 (A)	GGGa
'Olga'	LHyd LKna LMil NMun SPer SReu SSta
'Olga Mezitt'	GGGa LHyd NHol
'Olin O. Dobbs'	WGer
'Olive'	LHyd LKna LMil SLeo WAbe
'Olive Judson'	SLeo
'Oliver Cromwell'	SReu
Olympic Lady Group	LHyd MLea SLeo
'Olympic Sunrise'	LMil
Omar Group	MBar
§ 'One Thousand Butterflies'	COtt CWri GGGa MAsh MDun MLea
¶ 'Oporto'	SLeo
¶ 'Orange Beauty' (EA) ♀	CMac GGGa LHyd LKna MBal MBar MGos NMun SBod SCog SExb SLeo SPer SReu SSta WBod WFar WPic
¶ 'Orange King' (EA)	WLRN
'Orange Scout'	SLeo WGor WWal
'Orangengold'	GGGa
orbiculare	GGGa IDee LHyd LMil NMun SLeo SSta
– C&K 230	GGGa
§ – subsp. *cardiobasis*	NMun
– subsp. *orbiculare* W/V 1519	NMun SLeo
– Sandling Park form	SReu
Oreocinn Group	MBal
oreodoxa	LMil NMun SLeo SReu
§ – var. *fargesii* ♀	GGGa IOrc LMil NMun SLeo
§ – – Erubescens Group	NMun SLeo
¶ – – Knott 348	NMun
– var. *oreodoxa* EN 4212	GGGa
– – W/A 4245	NMun
– var. *shensiense*	GGGa
oreotrephes	IOrc LHyd LMil MBal MBri MDun NMun SLeo SReu
– C&Cu 9449	GGGa
aff. – C&V 9557	GGGa
§ – Exquisitum Group	ISea SReu
– F 20489	NMun
– F 20629	NMun
– KW 9509	NMun SLeo
– SF 640	ISea
– Timeteum Group	SReu
orthocladum	LHyd LMil
§ – var. *microleucum* ♀	GGGa ISea LMil MBal NMun SLeo
– var. *orthocladum* F 20488	GGGa NHol SLeo
'Oryx' (O)	LKna
'Osmar'	GGGa MDun MGos
'Ostara'	CB&S COtt MGos
'Ostfriesland'	SRms
'Ouchiyama'	LKna
'Oudijk's Favorite'	MBal MGos
'Oudijk's Sensation'	GCHN GGGa LKna MGos MOne SExb
'Ovation'	GGGa NHol
ovatum (A)	CB&S NMun SLeo WBod
¶ – CNW 548	ISea
¶ – red CNW 557	LMil
– W/A 1391 (A)	GGGa NMun SLeo
¶ – white CNW 548	LMil
Oxlip Group	SLeo
'Oxydol' (K) ♀	MLea
¶ 'P. Den Ouden' x *williamsianum*	SBrw
P J M Group	CSam CWri MAsh MBal MBri MLea SExb SSta
'P.J. Mezitt'	See *R.* **'Peter John Mezitt'**

§ *pachypodum* — GGGa
pachysanthum ♀ — LHyd LMil MDun NHol NMun SMur SPer SReu SSpi
  – 'Crosswater' — LMil
  – × *proteoides* — GGGa
  – RV 72/001 — GGGa NMun SLeo
pachytrichum — GGGa NMun SLeo
¶ – C&K 229 — NHol
§ – var. *monosematum* — ISea SLeo
¶ – – CNW 953 — LMil
  – – CNW 956 — GGGa
  – – W/V 1522 — NMun SLeo
  – var. *pachytrichum* — LMil
    'Sesame'
  – – W/A 1203 — NMun
'Palestrina' (EA) ♀ — CB&S CChe CMac EPot GHCN IOrc LHyd LKna MBal NMun SBod SCog SExb SLeo SPer SReu SSta WFar
'Pallas' (G) — MBri SReu
'Palma' — See *R. parmulatum* 'Palma'
'Pamela Miles' — LHyd
'Pancake' — CMac
'Panda' (EA) — CMac GGGa LHyd LMil MBar MBri NHed SCoo SReu WAbe WGwG
panteumorphum — See *R.* × *erythrocalyx* Panteumorphum Group
'Papaya Punch' — LMil
papillatum — NMun
'Paprika Spiced' — COtt CWri LMil MAsh MBal MDun MLea
'Parade' (A) — LMil
¶ 'Paradise Pink' (EA) — ENot
paradoxum C&K 228 — GGGa
  – CC&H 3906 — GGGa
'Paramount' (K/d) — LKna
§ 'Paris' — LMil MDun NMun SLeo
parmulatum — LMil MDun NMun SLeo
  – KW 5875 — NMun
  – mauve — NMun SLeo
  – 'Ocelot' — GGGa LHyd MDun NMun
¶ – 'Palma' — WBod
  – pink — GGGa NMun
'Party Pink' — CWri LMil
¶ 'Patricia's Day' — MDun
'Patty Bee' ♀ — CSam CWri EPot GChr GGGa LHyd LMil MAsh MBar MBri MDun MGos MLea NHar NHol SBod SExb SReu SSpi SSta WAbe
patulum — See *R. pemakoense* Patulum Group
'Pavane' (K) — LKna
'Peace' — GGGa MBal NMun SLeo WAbe
'Peach Blossom' — See *R.* 'Saotome'
'Peep-bo' (EA) — LHyd SPer
'Peeping Tom' — LMil MAsh MDun MLea NMun SBid SExb SHBN SLeo SReu
¶ 'Peggy Bannier' — SBrw
pemakoense — CMHG CTrG GGGa LHyd MBal MBar MGos NHol NMun SIng SLeo SReu SRms WAbe
§ – Patulum Group — GGGa MBar MDun NHol NMun SLeo WPat WPyg
'Pematit Cambridge' — SBod
pendulum — GGGa LMil
  – CH&M 3094 — GGGa
  – LS&T 6660 — GGGa
Penelope Group — SReu

'Penheale Blue' ♀ — CTre GGGa GOrc LMil NHed NHol SLeo WGer
'Penjerrick Cream' — NMun SLeo
'Penjerrick Pink' — NMun SLeo
pennivenium — See *R. tanastylum* var. *pennivenium*
'Penrose' — CB&S
peramoenum — See *R. arboreum* subsp. *delavayi* var. *peramoenum*
'Percy Wiseman' ♀ — CB&S CHig CSam CWri GGGa IHos IOrc LHyd LMil LNet MBal MBar MBlu MBri MDun MLea NHed NHol NMun SExb SLeo SPer SReu SSta WAbe
peregrinum — NMun SLeo
'Perfect' — MBal SPer
'Perfect Lady' — LMil LRHS
§ *periclymenoides* (A) — GGGa LMil LRHS
I 'Periwinkle' (V) — CEqu
'Persil' (K) ♀ — CB&S CSam ELan ENot GChr GGGa LHyd LKna MBar MBri MGos MLea SCoo SExb SLeo SPer SReu
§ 'Persimmon' — LKna NMun SLeo
'Peter Alan' — CWri MLea
'Peter Berg' — MGos
§ 'Peter John Mezitt' ♀ — LHyd LMil NMun SLeo SReu WGer WLRN
'Peter Koster' ♀ — CWri NMun SExb SHBN SLeo SMur WStI WWeb
'Petrouchka' (K) — LKna MAsh MBri
phaedropum — See *R. neriiflorum* subsp. *phaedropum*
phaeochrysum — GGGa MDun NMun SLeo
  – var. *agglutinatum* — GGGa NMun
  – – EGM 134 — LMil
§ – var. *levistratum* — NMun SLeo SReu
  – – EGM 143 — LMil
  – McLaren cup winner — NMun SLeo
  – var. *phaeochrysum* — LMil
    EGM 129
  – – 'Greenmantle' — NMun
  – USDAPI 59029/ R11323 — NMun
'Phalarope' — CSam GGGa MAsh MBal MBar MBri MDun MGos NHol SReu WAbe WBod
'Pheasant Tail' — NMun SLeo
'Phoebe' — SReu
phoenicodum — See *R. neriiflorum* subsp. *neriiflorum* Phoenicodum Group
pholidotum — See *R. heliolepis* var. *brevistylum* Pholidotum Group F 6762
'Phyllis Korn' — CAbP CHig CWri ISea LHyd LMil MDun MLea SExb SLeo SPer
'Piccolo' (K/d) — LKna
§ *piercei* — GGGa LMil NMun SLeo
  – KW 11040 — GGGa NMun SLeo
Pilgrim Group & cl. — LKna NMun
pingianum — NMun SLeo
¶ – EGM 304 — LMil
  – KR 150 — NMun
¶ – KR 184 — GGGa
'Pink and Sweet' (A) — LMil MLea
'Pink Bountiful' — LKna
'Pink Cherub' ♀ — ENot IHos LHyd MBal MBar MBri MOne NMun SLeo SReu
N 'Pink Delight' — ERea LKna SExb WBod

'Pink Drift'	ENot EPot GChr GDra ISea LKna MAsh MBal MBar MDun MGos NHar NHol NMun NWea SBod SExb SHBN SLeo STre WAbe WBod WGwG
'Pink Frills'	CB&S
'Pink Ghost'	NMun SLeo
'Pink Gin'	LMil
'Pink Glory'	NMun SLeo
'Pink Leopard'	ISea LMil MDun NMun SBid WWeb
'Pink Pancake' (EA)	CB&S CTrh GQui LMil MBri MGos MOne SCog SSpi SVil WLRN WWeb
'Pink Pearl'	CB&S CHig ENot GGGa ISea LHyd LKna LMil MAsh MBal MBar MDun MGos NHol NMun NWea SBod SCog SLeo SPer SReu SSta
'Pink Pebble' ♀	CTrw LHyd NMun SLeo SReu
'Pink Perfection'	MBar MGos NMun SLeo SReu
'Pink Poppet' (V)	CEqu
'Pink Rosette'	LKna
N 'Pink Ruffles'	ENot WBod
'Pink Sensation'	MBri
'Pinkerton'	LKna
'Pintail'	GGGa
'Pipaluk'	NMun
'Pipit'	GGGa MBal WAbe
'Pippa' (EA) ♀	CMac CTrG SRms
'PJM Elite'	GGGa
planetum	SLeo
pleistanthum F 15002	GGGa
◆ – R 11288	See *R. rigidum* **R 11288**
pocophorum	GGGa NMun SLeo
– forms	NMun SLeo
§ – var. *hemidartum*	GGGa NMun SLeo
◆ – KW 21075	See *R. coelicum* **KW 21075**
§ – var. *pocophorum* F 21830	SLeo
– – USDAPI 59190/R11201	NMun
pogonostylum	See *R. irroratum* subsp. *pogonostylum*
'Point Defiance'	CWri GGGa LMil MLea
'Polar Bear' (EA)	MBal MBar MDun MGos SLeo
Polar Bear Group & cl.	COtt CSam CWri GAri GGGa ISea LHyd LMil MLea NMun SLeo SReu WGer
'Polar Haven' (EA)	LKna
'Polar Sea'	CTrh SBod
'Polaris'	ENot LMil LRHS MBri MGos SReu
'Polgrain'	CB&S
§ *poluninii*	GGGa
polyandrum	See *R. maddenii* subsp. *maddenii* **Polyandrum Group**
§ *polycladum*	CSam GGGa LHyd LMil MBal MDun MLea
– Scintillans Group	GDra MBar MBri MLea NHol NMun SLeo WPic
polylepis	GGGa NMun SLeo
– C&K 284	GGGa
¶ – EGM 351	LMil
– EN 3619	GGGa
I 'Ponticum'	See *R. ponticum*
§ *ponticum*	GChr GGGa ISea LHyd LMil MBar MGos MLea NWea SLeo SPer
– (A)	See *R. luteum*
– AC&H 205	GGGa
– 'Cheiranthifolium'	NMun SLeo
– 'Foliis Purpureis'	SReu
– 'Silver Edge' (v)	LMil SMur
– 'Variegatum' (v)	CB&S CHig EBrP EBre ENot GChr GGGa IOrc ISea LBre MBal MBar MBri MGos NMun SBre SPer SReu SRms SSta WGer WWeb
'Pooh-Bah' (EA)	LHyd
'Pook'	LHyd
'Popacatapetl'	SReu
'Port Knap' (EA)	LKna
'Port Wine' (EA)	LKna
'Potlatch'	GGGa
poukhanense	See *R. yedoense* var. *poukhanense*
'Powder Puff'	LMil
§ 'Praecox' ♀	CB&S CHig CSam CTrw ENot GChr GGGa GRei ISea LHyd LKna LMil MAsh MBal MBar MBri MGos NHol NMun NWea SBod SHBN SPer SReu SSta WBod WGwG
praecox	See *R.* **'Praecox'**
– 'Emasculum'	See *R.* **'Emasculum'**
praestans	GGGa LMil MDun NMun SLeo
– KW 13369	NMun
– PA Cox 6025A	GGGa
praeteritum	SLeo
praevernum	GGGa LMil NMun SReu
§ *prattii*	CWri LMil MDun NMun SLeo
¶ – EGM 147	LMil
'Prawn'	LKna SReu
¶ Prelude Group & cl.	SLeo
preptum	GGGa SLeo
'President Roosevelt' (v)	IHos IOrc LKna LNet MBal MGos NMun SHBN SLeo SPer SReu SSta WWeb
'Pretty Girl'	LKna
'Pridenjoy'	LMil
'Prima Donna'	LMil SReu
primuliflorum	GGGa LMil LRHS MDun SReu
– Cephalanthoides Group	GGGa WAbe
– 'Doker-La'	LMil MDun
– KW 4160	NMun
'Prince Camille de Rohan'	LMil SMur
¶ 'Prince of Wales' (EA)	SBrw
'Princess Alice' ♀	CB&S CGre CHig COtt GGGa LHyd MBal NMun SCog WAbe WPic
'Princess Anne' ♀	CMHG CSam ENot EPot GDra GGGa GRei LHyd LMil MAsh MBal MBar MDun MGos MLea NHol NMun SBod SHBN SLeo SPer SReu SSta
'Princess Ida' (EA)	LHyd
'Princess Juliana'	WGor
'Princess Margaret of Windsor' (K)	GQui
principis	GGGa LMil MDun NMun
– C&V 9547	GGGa
– LS&E 15831	NMun
§ – Vellereum Group	NMun SLeo
¶ – Vellereum Group KW 5656	NMun
§ *prinophyllum* (A)	LMil
'Prins Bernhard' (EA)	IOrc LKna MAsh SLeo
'Prinses Juliana' (EA)	SExb SLeo SReu WFar
'Professor Hugo de Vries' ♀	LKna MGos SReu
'Professor J.H. Zaayer'	MGos SBrw SLeo
pronum	GGGa
¶ – × *proteoides*	GGGa
– R 151*	NMun
– R.B. Cooke form	GGGa

– Towercourt form — GGGa
§ 'Prostigiatum' — GDra MGos
prostigiatum — See *R.* **'Prostigiatum'**
prostratum — See *R. saluenense* subsp. *chameunum* **Prostratum Group**
proteoides — GGGa
* – 'Ascreavie' — GGGa
– C 6542a — GGGa
¶ – EGM 281 — LMil
– KGB 700 — GGGa
– R 151 — NMun
protistum — LMil NMun SLeo
§ – var. *giganteum* — CWri LMil NMun SLeo SReu
– KR 1986 — GGGa
– KW 8069 — NMun
pruniflorum — GGGa NMun SLeo
◆ – KW 7038 — See *R. brachyanthum* subsp. *hypolepidotum* **KW 7038**
prunifolium (A) — LMil SLeo
– 'Summer Sunset' (A) — NMun
przewalskii — GGGa NMun SLeo
– C&K 370 — GGGa
– CH&M 2545 — NHol
– subsp. *dabanshanense* — GGGa
– PA Cox 5073 — GGGa
pseudochrysanthum ♀ — CWri GGGa LHyd LMil MBal MDun NHol NMun SLeo SReu SSta
– ETE 442 — GGGa
– ETE 443 — GGGa
– ETOT 167 — ISea
¶ 'Psyche' (EA) — MDun
Psyche Group — See *R.* **Wega Group**
'Ptarmigan' ♀ — CB&S CMHG CSam EPot GChr GGGa LHyd LMil MBal MBar MDun MGos MLea NHar NHol NMun SBod SLeo SReu SSta WBod WPat
pubescens — LMil SLeo
– KW 3953 — GGGa
¶ *pubicostatum* — LMil
pudorosum — NMun SLeo
– L&S 2752 — GGGa
'Puget Sound' — SLeo
pumilum — GCrs GDra GGGa MBal MDun NMun WAbe
'Puncta' — GGGa NHol
punctatum — See *R. minus* var. *minus* **Punctatum Group**
* *purdomii* — GGGa SLeo
'Purple Diamond' — See *R.* **Diamant Group purple**
'Purple Emperor' — LKna
'Purple Gem' — NHar NHol
'Purple Heart' — ENot
'Purple Peterli' — GGGa
'Purple Queen' (EA/d) — MAsh
'Purple Splendor' (EA) — CMac IOrc LKna MGos
'Purple Splendour' ♀ — CB&S CHig CWri ENot GGGa LKna LMil MBal MBar MBri MDun MGos NMun NWea SCog SHBN SLeo SPer SReu SSta WWeb
'Purple Triumph' (EA) — CB&S IOrc LKna LMil NMun SLeo SReu SSta WBod
'Purpur Geisha' — GGGa
'Purpurtraum' (A) — GGGa
Quaver Group — SRms
'Queen Alice' — MDun
'Queen Anne's' — LMil MBal
'Queen Elizabeth II' ♀ — LHyd LMil SPer SReu SSta
Queen Emma — See *R.* **'Koningin Emma'**
'Queen Mary' — MBar

'Queen Mother' — See *R.* **'The Queen Mother'**
Queen of Hearts Group & cl. — LHyd NMun SLeo
'Queen Souriya' — SReu
Queen Wilhelmina — See *R.* **'Koningin Wilhelmina'**
quinquefolium (A) ♀ — LMil NMun SLeo
racemosum — CB&S CGre CSam LMil MBar MDun MTed NMun SLeo SPer SReu SSpi SSta
¶ – AC 719 — NMun
¶ – ACE 1367 — WAbe
– 'Glendoick' — GGGa
– 'Rock Rose' ex R 11265 ♀ — EPfP GGGa LHyd LMil NMun
– SF 365 — ISea
– SSNY 47 — GGGa
– × *tephropeplum* — MBal MBar
– × *trichocladum* SBEC — NHol
– 'White Lace' — LHyd
'Racil' — LHyd LKna MBal MBar MDun MGos MLea
'Racoon' (EA) — GGGa
radicans — See *R. calostrotum* subsp. *keleticum* **Radicans Group**
'Rainbow' — LKna NMun SLeo
'Ramapo' ♀ — CHig GChr GGGa LMil MAsh MBal MBar MDun MGos MLea MOne NHar NHol SPer SReu SSta WAbe WBod
ramsdenianum — GGGa NMun SLeo
'Rangoon' — GGGa
'Raphael de Smet' (G/d) — SReu
'Rashomon' (EA) — LHyd SLeo SReu WBod
'Raspberry Delight' (K/d) — SMur
'Raspberry Ripple' — LKna SReu
ravum — See *R. cuneatum* **Ravum Group**
'Razorbill' ♀ — EPot GGGa LHyd LMil MBri MGos MLea NHar SReu WAbe
recurvoides — GGGa LHyd LMil MDun NMun SReu
– Keillour form — GGGa
– KW 7184 — NMun SLeo
recurvum — See *R. roxieanum* var. *roxieanum*
Red Admiral Group — NMun SLeo
Red Argenteum Group — NMun SLeo
'Red Bird' (EA) — CMac
'Red Carpet' ♀ — LMil LRHS NMun
'Red Delicious' — LMil
'Red Diamond' — See *R.* **Diamant Group red**
'Red Dragon' — SLeo
'Red Fountain' (EA) — LMil LRHS SCog WLRN WWeb
'Red Glow' — LHyd NMun SLeo
'Red Red' — GGGa
'Red Riding Hood' — CWri LKna
'Red Velour' — CAbP
◆ 'Red Velvet' — See *R.* **'Ilam Red Velvet'**
'Red Wood' — GGGa
'Redmond' (EA) — LHyd
'Redshank' (K) — MBri
'Redwing' (EA) — SLeo SPer
'Reich's Schneewittchen' — GGGa
Remo Group — MBal SLeo
'Rendezvous' — ENot LMil SReu
'Renoir' ♀ — LHyd LMil SLeo SReu
Repose Group & cl. — LKna
¶ *reticulatum* — GGGa
– (A) ♀ — LMil NMun SLeo SReu SSta
* – *leucanthum* (A) — GGGa
– 'Sea King' (A) — LHyd
retusum (V) — GGGa

§ 'Reuthe's Purple' ♀ — GGGa MBal NHol NMun SLeo SReu
'Rêve d'Amour' (Vs) — SReu SSta
'Revlon' — LHyd
rex — COtt GGGa IDee IOrc LHyd LMil MBal MDun NMun SLeo
¶ – EGM 295 — LMil
§ – subsp. *fictolacteum* — GGGa LHyd LMil MBal MDun NMun SLeo SReu
– – 'Cherry Tip' R 11385 — NMun SLeo
– – var. *miniforme* F 25512 — GGGa
– – SF 649 — ISea
– – USDAPI 59104/ R11043 — NMun SLeo
– Sich 1037 — GGGa
– Sich 1134 — GGGa
– Sich 1154 — GGGa
– Sich 1159 — GGGa
– Sich 1236 — GGGa
– × Sincerity Group — NMun SLeo
rhabdotum — See *R. dalhousieae* var. *rhabdotum*
'Ria Hardijzer' — LKna MBri
Rickshaw Group — SLeo
rigidum — LHyd LMil NMun SLeo
* – *album* — CHig NMun
'Ring of Fire' — CWri LMil MDun MLea SReu
'Ripe Corn' — CBlo LKna NMun SLeo SReu
Riplet Group — EPot GAri GGGa MLea NHar SLeo WAbe
ririei — GGGa LHyd NMun SLeo
♦ – Guiz 75 — See *R. haofui* Guiz 75
– W/V 1808 — NMun
– W/V 5139 — NMun
'Robert Keir' ♀ — NMun SLeo
'Robert Korn' — LMil LRHS MDun
'Robert Seleger' — GGGa LMil LRHS MBri NHar
'Robert Whelan' (A) — SReu
'Robin Hill Frosty' (EA) — LHyd
'Robin Hill Gillie' (EA) — LHyd
Robin Hood Group — NMun
'Robin Redbreast' — NMun SLeo
'Rocket' — CAbP LMil MAsh MDun MLea NMun WGwG WWeb
♦ 'Rokoko' — See *R. 'Hachmann's Rokoko'*
Romany Chai Group — LHyd LMil MBal SLeo SPer
'Romy' — NMun SLeo
'Rosa Mundi' — ENot
* 'Rosabelle' — CEqu
'Rosata' (Vs) — MBri SLeo SReu SSta
'Rose Elf' — ECho MBal MDun NHar NHol
'Rose Glow' — SReu
'Rose Greeley' (EA) — CDoC CHig GQui IOrc SBod SExb SReu WFar WLRN WWeb
'Rose Haze' — SReu
'Rose Ruffles' (K) — SMur
'Rose Torch' — SReu
* *roseatum* F 17227 — GGGa
'Rosebud' (EA/d) ♀ — CB&S CGre CHig CMac CTrw ECho GGGa GHCN IOrc LHyd LKna MBar MGos NMun SBod SExb SLeo SPer SReu WBod WLRN
¶ 'Rosemary Hyde' (EA) — SLeo
roseotinctum — See *R. sanguineum* subsp. *sanguineum* var. *didymoides* **Roseotinctum Group**
♦ *roseum* — See *R. prinophyllum*
'Roseum Elegans' — ECho GChr LRHS MBar MDun NMun SLeo
* 'Rosie Posie' (V) — CEqu

'Rosiflorum' — See *R. indicum* **'Balsaminiflorum'**
'Rosy Bell' — LKna
'Rosy Cream' — SPer
'Rosy Dream' — CAbP CWri LMil MLea SMur
'Rosy Fire' (A) — SReu
'Rosy Lea' — MLea
'Rosy Lights' — CTri LMil LRHS
'Rothenburg' — LHyd SLeo SReu
rothschildii — GGGa LMil LRHS MDun NMun SLeo SMur
– C&Cu 9312 — GGGa
roxieanum — LMil NMun SLeo SReu
§ – var. *cucullatum* — ISea NMun
– – CNW 680 — GGGa
¶ – – CNW 690 — LMil
– – dwarf Dawyck — GGGa
– – R 10920 — NMun
– – SBEC 0345 — NMun SLeo
§ – – SBEC 350 — GGGa
– var. *oreonastes* ♀ — GGGa LHyd LMil LRHS MDun NMun SLeo SSta
– – CNW 307 — GGGa
– – CNW 723 — GGGa
– – CNW 740 — GGGa
– – CNW 743 — GGGa
– – Nymans form — SReu
– – USDAPI 59222/ R11312 — GGGa NMun
¶ – var. *parvum* — GGGa
– R 25422 — NMun SLeo
¶ – var. *recurvum* CNW 727 — LMil
§ – var. *roxieanum* — NMun
– – CNW 727 — GGGa
– – F 16508 — NMun
– USDAPI 59159/ R11141 — NMun SLeo
'Royal Blood' — SLeo
'Royal Command' (K) — COtt GAri LMil MAsh MBar SExb
Royal Flush Group — CB&S ISea
'Royal Lodge' (K) ♀ — SBid
'Royal Pink' — SBod
'Royal Ruby' (K) — MBri
'Roza Stevenson' ♀ — LHyd NMun SLeo SPer
'Rozanne Waterer' (K)/d — LKna
'Rubicon' — CB&S CWri
rubiginosum — CSam GGGa IOrc ISea LHyd LMil MBal NMun SCog SLeo SReu
§ – Desquamatum Group — LHyd NMun SLeo
¶ – Desquamatum Group EGM 272 — LMil
– SF 368 — ISea
– SF 404 — ISea
– white — LMil
Rubina Group — SLeo
'Rubinetta' (EA) — LRHS WFar
rubroluteum — See *R. viridescens* **Rubroluteum Group**
'Ruby F. Bowman' — CWri MDun MGos MLea NMun SLeo SReu
'Ruby Hart' — GGGa MDun NHol SReu
rude — See *R. glischrum* subsp. *rude*
¶ 'Ruffles and Frills' — CWri ECho MOne
rufum — GGGa NMun SLeo
– Sich 155 — GGGa
– W/V 1808* — SLeo
rugosum Sinclair 240 (V) — GGGa
'Rumba' (K) — LKna
¶ 'Rumpelstilzchen' — GGGa
rupicola — CHig GDra LMil MBal NMun
§ – var. *chryseum* — GGGa LHyd LMil NMun SLeo
– var. *muliense* — LMil NMun

– – Yu 14042	GGGa
russatum ♀	CSam ENot EPot GDra GGGa
	LMil MBri NGre NMun SLeo
– blue-black	LMil
– C&Cu 9315	GGGa
– 'Purple Pillow'	NHar
* – 'Tower Court'	NMun
russotinctum	See *R. alutaceum* var.
	russotinctum
'Sacko'	CHig ECho GGGa LMil MOne
	NHol
'Saffron Queen'	CB&S CGre CTrG CTrw ISea
	MBal
'Sahara' (K)	LKna
'Saint Breward'	CTrG GGGa LHyd MBal MLea
	NHol SBod SLeo SPer WAbe
¶ 'Saint Keverne'	SLeo
'Saint Merryn' ♀	CTrG EBee ENot GAri GGGa
	LHyd MAsh MBri MOne NHol
	NMun SLeo WGer WWeb
'Saint Michael'	SReu
'Saint Minver' ♀	LHyd
'Saint Tudy' ♀	CB&S EPfP LHyd LKna MBal
	NMun SBid SLeo SPer WAbe
	WBod
'Sakata Red' (EA)	CGre IOrc SExb WBod
'Sakon' (EA)	NMun SLeo
¶ 'Salmon Sander' (EA)	SLeo
'Salmon's Leap' (EA/v)	CB&S COtt GQui LMil MAsh
	MGos SCoo SHBN SLeo SPer
	WAbe WFar WWeb
saluenense	GGGa LHyd LMil MBal NMun
§ – subsp. ***chameunum*** ♀	GGGa LMil MBal NMun SLeo
	WAbe WGer
– – PA Cox 6112	GGGa
§ – – Prostratum Group	GGGa MBal WAbe
§ – subsp. ***riparioides*** R 178	GGGa NHol
§ – – USDAPQ 03954/ R18453	GGGa
¶ – subsp. ***saluenense***	LMil
Exbury form R 11005	
– – F 19479	NMun
'Sammetglut'	CWri
'Samuel Taylor Coleridge'	MBri
(M)	
sanctum	LMil SLeo
'Sang de Gentbrugge' (G)	SReu
sanguineum	GGGa LMil MDun NMun SLeo
§ – subsp. ***didymum***	GGGa NMun SLeo
¶ – var. ***himertum***	SLeo
– PA Cox 6056	GGGa
– subsp. ***sanguineum*** var.	NMun SLeo
cloiophorum R 10899	
– – – USDAPI 59553/ R11212	NMun SLeo
– – var. ***didymoides***	NMun SLeo
Consanguineum Group	
– – – Consanguineum	LMil
Group KW 6831	
§ – – – Roseotinctum Group	LMil
– – – Roseotinctum Group	GGGa LMil NMun SLeo
USDAPI 59038/ R10903	
– – var. ***haemaleum***	GGGa LMil NMun SLeo
– – – F 21732	NMun SLeo
– – – F 21735	GGGa NMun SLeo
– – – R 31	GGGa
– – – USDAPI 59303/ R10895	NMun SLeo
– – – USDAPI 59453/ R10938	NMun SLeo
¶ – – var. ***sanguineum***	LMil
F 25521	
¶ – – – R 10893	NMun SLeo
¶ – – – USDAPI 59096/R11029	NMun SLeo
'Santa Maria'	COtt SReu SSta
santapaui (V)	CEqu

§ 'Saotome' (EA)	LHyd
'Sapphire' ♀	CTrG EHic EPot LKna MBal
	MBar SBod SLeo SPer SRms
'Sappho' ♀	CB&S CWri ENot GGGa IHos
	IOrc ISea LHyd LKna LMil
	MBal MBar MGos NMun SBid
	SHBN SLeo SPer SReu SSta
	WGer WGwG WWeb
'Sapporo'	GGGa
¶ 'Sarah Boscawen'	SReu
sargentianum ♀	LMil MLea NMun SLeo
– 'Maricee'	GGGa MAsh MBri WGer
– 'Whitebait'	GGGa MBro NMun WPat
Sarita Loder Group & cl.	SLeo
Sarled Group	EPot GDra GGGa LHyd LMil
	MAsh MBal NHar NMun SBid
	SLeo SPer SReu SRms WAbe
	WWat
'Saroi' (EA)	NMun SLeo
'Saskia' (K)	LKna
'Satan' (K) ♀	COtt ELan GAri GGGa LKna
	MBri SReu
'Satsuki' (EA)	CGre ECho LNet MAsh WWeb
'Saturnus' (M)	ELan SLeo
scabrifolium	NMun SLeo
§ – var. ***spiciferum***	GGGa MBal NMun SLeo
	WAbe WPic
'Scarlet Wonder' ♀	CWri EPot GGGa GRei ISea
	LKna LMil MBal MBar MBri
	MGos MLea NHol NMun SBod
	SExb SLeo SReu SSta WBod
schlippenbachii (A) ♀	CGre GGGa LHyd LMil MBal
	NMun SLeo SPer SReu SSta
	WWat
– 'Sid's Royal Pink' (A)	LMil
'Schneekrone'	GGGa LMil NHol
¶ Schneespiegel®	ENot
'Schubert' (EA)	MBar MGos SLeo WBod
scintillans	See *R. polycladum*
'Scintillation'	CDoC CSam CWri EBee GGGa
	ISea LMil MBal MBar MLea
	NMun SBid SBrw SHBN SLeo
scopulorum	SLeo
– KW 6354	GGGa
scottianum	See *R. pachypodum*
scyphocalyx	See *R. dichroanthum* subsp.
	scyphocalyx
Seagull Group & cl.	NMun SLeo
searsiae	NMun SLeo
¶ 'Seashell'	SLeo
'Sea-Tac'	MLea
'Second Honeymoon'	CWri ISea MAsh MLea SHBN
	SReu SSta WWeb
¶ sect. Lapponica ACE 1787	GCLN
'Seikai' (EA)	CBlo
seinghkuense KW 9254	GGGa
selense	GGGa LMil NMun SLeo
¶ – CNW 690	ISea
§ – subsp. ***dasycladum***	MDun NMun SLeo
– – F 11312	NMun
– – KW 7189	NMun
– – R 11269	NMun
– subsp. ***jucundum***	GGGa LMil MDun NMun
¶ – – SF 660	ISea
– PA Cox 6041	GGGa
¶ – subsp. ***selense*** F 14458	NMun SLeo
– – PA Cox 6024	GGGa
§ – subsp. ***setiferum***	NMun
semnoides	GGGa NMun SLeo
– F 21870	NMun
– F 25639	NMun
– R 25388	NMun

'Senator Henry Jackson'	GGGa LMil
'Sennocke' ♀	GGGa LHyd
¶ 'September Morn'	CHig
'September Song'	CDoC COtt CWri GGGa LHyd
	LMil MAsh MBal MDun MLea
'Serendipity'	GGGa
¶ ser. *Taliensia* CNW 256	LMil
serotinum	LMil NMun SLeo SReu
serpyllifolium (A)	CB&S GGGa NMun SLeo
– var. *albiflorum* (A)	GAri
'Sesterianum'	CMHG
Seta Group & cl.	CB&S CHig LHyd MBal MLea
	NMun SLeo SReu WAbe
setiferum	See *R. selense* subsp. *setiferum*
setosum	GGGa LMil MBal MDun NMun
	SLeo
'Seven Stars' ♀	MDun NMun SLeo SReu WPyg
'Shamrock'	CSam EPfP GCrs ISea MAsh
	MBal MBar MDun MLea NHar
	NHol SLeo WAbe WBod
	WGwG
'Sham's Candy'	ERea
'Shanty' (K/d)	LKna
× *sheilae* (V)	CEqu
shepherdii	See *R. kendrickii*
¶ Shepherd's Delight Group	SLeo
sherriffii	GGGa MDun NMun SLeo
– L&S 2751	NMun
Shilsonii Group	NMun SLeo SReu
'Shinimiagagino' (EA)	NMun SLeo
'Shinnyo-no-hikari'	GAri
'Shi-no-noe' (EA)	NMun SBod SLeo
'Shinsei' (EA)	GAri
'Shin-seikai' (EA/d)	CB&S
'Shintoki-no-hagasane'	LHyd
(EA)	
'Shintsune' (EA)	NMun SLeo
Shot Silk Group	NMun
'Shrimp Girl'	ENot IHos ISea LHyd MBal
	MGos MLea NMun SLeo SReu
'Shukishima' (EA)	NMun SLeo
'Shuku-fuku' (EA)	GAri
shweliense	GGGa LMil SReu
sidereum	GGGa LMil NMun SLeo
– KR 2710*	GGGa
◆ – KW 13649	See *R. aff. grande* KR 13649
– KW 6792	NMun SLeo
– SF 314	ISea
– SF 318	ISea
siderophyllum	SLeo
¶ – EGM 346	LMil
sikangense	MDun NMun
– C&K 246	GGGa
§ – Cookeanum Group	NMun
¶ – Cookeanum Group	LMil
CNW 1060	
– EGM 108	LMil
¶ – var. *exquisitum* CNW 958	LMil
– R 18142	NMun
– var. *sikangense*	GGGa
PA Cox 5012	
– – PA Cox 5105	GGGa NHol
* *sikkimense* SD 1108	GGGa
§ 'Silberwolke'	ENot MBri SReu
'Silkcap'	WWeb
'Silky'	MBal
Silver Cloud	See *R. 'Silberwolke'*
'Silver Glow' (EA)	CMac
'Silver Jubilee'	GGGa LHyd LMil LRHS
'Silver Moon' (EA)	CBlo IOrc NMun SBod SCog
	SExb SLeo SPer
¶ 'Silver Queen'	ECho

'Silver Sixpence' ♀	CMHG ENot IHos IOrc MAsh
	MBal MBar MDun MLea NMun
	SExb SHBN SLeo SReu WWeb
'Silver Skies'	LMil
'Silver Slipper' (K) ♀	CGre GAri LHyd LKna LMil
	MBal MBar MBri MLea SExb
	SLeo SReu SSta WGor
'Silverwood' (K)	LMil
'Silvester' (EA)	COtt MBri WPat
simiarum	GGGa
'Simona'	CWri SReu
simsii (EA)	CMac LMil
– SF 431 (EA)	ISea
◆ *simulans*	See *R. mimetes* var. *simulans*
'Sinbad'	SLeo
sinofalconeri C&H 7183	GGGa
¶ – SEH 229	LMil
– SF 92142	ISea
sinogrande ♀	CB&S CHEx GGGa IOrc LMil
	MBal NMun SAPC SArc SLeo
	SPer WPic
– KW 21111	NMun SLeo
– SF 327	ISea
– SF 329	ISea
– SF 350	ISea
'Sir Charles Lemon' ♀	CWri LMil MDun NMun SLeo
	SPer SReu SSta
* 'Sir G.E. Simpson'	NMun SLeo
'Sir William Lawrence'	LKna SReu
(EA)	
Siren Group & cl.	MBal
'Skookum'	ECho LMil MGos SMur
¶ 'Sleeping Beauty'	WAbe
'Sleepy'	ENot IHos IOrc NHed NMun
	SExb SLeo SPer SReu WGwG
	WLRN
smirnowii	GGGa LMil MBal NMun SLeo
	SReu SSta
◆ *smithii*	See *R. argipeplum*
– Argipeplum Group	See *R. argipeplum*
'Sneezy'	CB&S ENot GGGa GRei IHos
	LHyd LMil MAsh MBal MBar
	MGos MLea NHol NMun SLeo
	SReu SSta WGwG
'Snipe' ♀	CSam ENot EPot GGGa LHyd
	LMil MAsh MBal MBar MBri
	MDun MGos MOne NHar
	NHol SReu
'Snow' (EA)	CMac MBar SLeo
'Snow Crown'	MAsh
'Snow Hill' (EA)	GQui LHyd LMil
'Snow Lady' ♀	ENot EPfP GCrs LMil MAsh
	MBal MBar MGos MLea NHar
	NHol SBid SCog SIng SLeo
	WAbe
Snow Queen Group & cl.	LKna LMil SExb SReu WWeb
'Snowbird'	GGGa
'Snowflake'	See *R. 'Kure-no-yuki'*
¶ 'Snowstorm'	CWri ECho
'Soho' (EA)	GAri GQui LNet
'Soir de Paris' (Vs)	MBar MBri NMun SReu SSta
'Soldier Sam'	SBrw SReu SSta
◆ 'Solent Queen'	See *R. (Angelo Group) 'Solent Queen'*
'Solidarity'	ECho MBal MBri WLRN
'Solway' (Vs)	LMil
'Sonata'	GAri GGGa MBal MBri MDun
	SReu
'Songbird'	CSam EPot GCHN GChr GDra
	LHyd LKna LMil MAsh MBal
	MBar MBri NMun SBid SReu
	WBod

'Songster'	SLeo
'Sophie Hedges' (K/d)	LKna
sororium KR 3080 (V)	GGGa
¶ – KR 3085	LMil
¶ – var. *wumengense*	LMil
CNW 990	
Souldis Group	LMil MDun SLeo SMur
souliei	GGGa IOrc LMil NMun SLeo
– C&K 371	GGGa
– PA Cox 5056	GGGa
– white	GGGa
'Southern Cross'	CSam CWri LMil MDun MLea
	NMun
¶ 'Souvenir de Congo'	SBrw
¶ 'Souvenir de D.A. Koster'	SLeo
'Souvenir de Doctor S.	CBlo CWri LKna MBal MBar
Endtz' ♀	
'Souvenir du Président	LKna
Carnot' (G/d)	
'Souvenir of Anthony	LKna SReu
Waterer' ♀	
'Souvenir of W.C.	CSam LKna NMun SHBN SLeo
Slocock'	SReu SSta
'Sparkler' (Vs)	GGGa
'Sparkler'	MGos MLea WWeb
♦ *speciosum*	See *R. flammeum*
'Spek's Orange' (M) ♀	LHyd MAsh MGos SReu
sperabile	NMun
– var. *sperabile* F 26446	SLeo
– var. *weihsiense*	GGGa LMil NMun SLeo
¶ – – CNW 564	ISea
– – F 26453	SLeo
sperabiloides	GGGa NMun
– R 125	NMun
sphaeranthum	See *R. trichostomum*
sphaeroblastum	GGGa LMil NMun SLeo
– F 20416	SLeo
– KR 1481*	NMun
– var. *wumengense*	ISea
CNW 510	
– – CNW 942	GGGa
– – CNW 963	GGGa
– – CNW 968	GGGa
– – SF 515	ISea
spiciferum	See *R. scabrifolium* var.
	spiciferum
'Spicy Lights'	LMil
spilotum	GGGa NMun SLeo
spinuliferum	GGGa NMun SLeo
– SF 247	ISea
'Spitfire'	MGos SLeo SReu
'Spoonbill' (K)	LKna
'Spring Beauty' (EA)	CMac SExb
'Spring Dream'	See *R.* 'Frühlingstraum'
'Spring Magic'	LMil MAsh NMun SLeo
'Spring Pearl'	See *R.* 'Moerheim's Pink'
'Spring Rose'	NMun SBid SLeo
'Spring Sunshine'	LMil
'Springbok'	LHyd
'Squirrel' (EA)	CDoC COtt GGGa LHyd LMil
	MAsh MBal MBri MGos NHed
	SCog SLeo SReu WAbe WPat
'Staccato'	GGGa
Stadt Essen Group & cl.	GGGa LMil
stamineum	NMun
¶ – SF 417	ISea
– W/V 887	NMun SLeo
'Stanley Rivlin'	LHyd SLeo
§ 'Stanway'	LMil LRHS NMun
'Starfish'	SReu
'Stella'	NMun SLeo
stenaulum	See *R. moulmainense*

stenosepalum	CMac ISea LMil NMun SLeo
'Linearifolium' (A)	SReu WAbe
stewartianum	GGGa MDun NMun SLeo
– CLD 1300*	LMil
– F 26921	NMun
– SF 370	ISea
'Stewartstonian' (EA) ♀	CMac CTrh IOrc LHyd LMil
	MBal MBar SBod SLeo SReu
	SSta WFar
stictophyllum	See *R. nivale* subsp. *boreale*
	Stictophyllum Group
'Stoat' (EA)	GQui MBri
'Stranraer'	MAsh MBri
'Strawberry Cream'	GGGa NHol
'Strawberry Ice' (K) ♀	CB&S CMHG ENot EPfP
	GGGa IOrc LKna LMil MAsh
	MBar MBri MGos MLea SExb
	SPer SReu
'Streatley' ♀	SLeo
strigillosum	GGGa MDun NMun SLeo
– C&H 7035	GGGa
– C&H 7047	GGGa
¶ – EGM 338	LMil
– Reuthe's form	SReu
'Striped Beauty'	MBal
'Suave'	SCog
subansiriense C&H 418	GGGa NMun SLeo
suberosum	See *R. yunnanense* Suberosum
	Group
¶ subsection *Triflora* PW 020*	LMil
¶ subsection *Triflora* PW 097	LMil
succothii	GGGa LHyd MDun NMun
	SLeo
– BB 185A	NMun
– CH&M 3109	NHol
– EGM 086	LMil
¶ – KW 13666	SLeo
– LS&H 21295	NMun SLeo
'Sugar Pink'	LMil LRHS
'Sugared Almond' (K) ♀	MBal
'Sugi-no-ito'	See *R.* 'Kumo-no-ito'
sulfureum	NMun
– SBEC 249	GGGa
'Summer Blaze'	SReu
'Summer Flame'	SLeo SReu
'Summer Fragrance' (O)	SReu SSta
♀	
'Sun Chariot' (K) ♀	CB&S LHyd LKna LMil MBri
	MLea MMHG SReu
'Sunbeam' (EA)	See *R.* 'Benifude'
'Sunbeam'	CBlo LKna SReu
'Sunny' (V)	GGGa
'Sunny Splendour' (V)	ERea
'Sunset Pink' (K)	CBlo LHyd LMil MAsh WWeb
¶ 'Sunstruck'	GGGa
'Sunte Nectarine' (K) ♀	GQui LHyd LMil MBri SCoo
'Superbum' (O)	SReu
superbum (V)	GGGa
'Surprise' (EA)	CTrh CTri MAsh NMun SCog
	SCoo SExb SLeo
'Surrey Heath' ♀	CB&S COtt CWri ENot GGGa
	GRei LMil LNet MAsh MBal
	MBar MBri MDun MGos MLea
	NHed NMun SExb SLeo SReu
	SSpi WAbe
'Susan' ♀	CHig CWri GGGa LHyd LKna
	LMil MDun MLea NMun SLeo
	SReu
'Susannah Hill' (EA)	CB&S CTrh LMil SBod SPer
	WPat
'Sussex Bonfire'	NMun SLeo

sutchuenense CB&S CHig GGGa IDee LMil
MDun NMun SLeo
– var. *geraldii* See *R.* × *geraldii*
'Swamp Beauty' CWri GGGa LMil
'Swansdown' CWri MDun SPer
'Swansong' (EA) CMac SCog
'Sweet Mac' (V) CEqu
'Sweet Simplicity' ♀ LKna MBal SBrw
'Sweet Sixteen' CWri NMun SLeo
'Sweet Sue' MAsh MBal NMun SLeo SReu
WLRN
'Swift' GGGa GQui MBri
¶ 'Sword of State' (K) LMil
'Sylphides' (K) GAri LKna MBri
'Sylvester' CDoC MGos SReu
taggianum 'Cliff Hanger' LMil
ex KW 8546
'Takasago' (EA/d) LHyd LMil
'Talavera' See *R.* **(Golden Oriole Group)**
'Talavera'
taliense GGGa LHyd LMil MDun
NMun SLeo
– F 6772 NMun SLeo
– KR 2765* GGGa
♦ – SBEC 350 See *R. roxieanum* var.
cucullatum **SBEC 350**
– SF 92069 ISea
– SSNY 352 GGGa
Tally Ho Group & cl. NMun SLeo SReu
tamaense See *R. cinnabarinum* subsp.
tamaense
'Tama-no-utena' (EA) LHyd
'Tan Crossing' SReu
'Tanager' (EA) CTrh LKna
§ *tanastylum* var. NMun SLeo
pennivenium
– – SF 593 ISea
'Tangerine' See *R.* **'Fabia Tangerine'**
'Tangiers' (K) SExb
tapetiforme GGGa
'Tara' SLeo
¶ Tarantella® ENot
¶ Tasco Group SLeo
tashiroi (EA) NMun
'Tatjana' ENot LMil
tatsienense GGGa
¶ – EGM 321 LMil
'Taurus' ♀ COtt CWri GGGa LMil MBri
MLea WGwG WWeb
'Teal' ♀ CSam CTri GGGa MBal MBar
MLea NHol NMun SLeo SPer
SReu
'Teddy Bear' GGGa LMil MDun SLeo SMur
§ *telmateium* NMun
telopeum See *R. campylocarpum* subsp.
caloxanthum **Telopeum Group**
¶ *temenium* MDun
– var. *dealbatum* LMil
¶ – – EGM 275 LMil
– – Glaphyrum Group NMun SLeo
F 21902
¶ – EGM 274 LMil
– var. *gilvum* 'Cruachan' GGGa LMil NMun SLeo
R 22272
– – R 101 NMun
– – R 22271 NMun
§ – var. *mesopolium* R 10950 NMun
– P Cox 6037B GGGa
– R 10909 NMun SLeo
– var. *temenium* F 21734 NMun SLeo
– – F 21809 NMun
¶ 'Temple Belle' ♀ MDun

Temple Belle Group CSam LHyd LKna MBal MLea
NHed NMun SLeo
¶ 'Tensing' SLeo
§ *tephropeplum* ♀ CB&S GGGa NMun SLeo
– Deleiense Group See *R. tephropeplum*
– KW 6303 NMun SLeo
¶ – SF 92069 ISea
– USDAPQ 3914/R 18408 GGGa
'Tequila Sunrise' LMil MBal MLea NMun SLeo
'Terra-cotta' LKna LMil SMur
'Terra-cotta Beauty' (EA) CTrG WPat
Tessa Group & cl. LKna LMil MGos MOne SBod
'Tessa Bianca' GGGa
'Tessa Roza' ♀ EPot GGGa GQui LHyd MAsh
thayerianum GGGa NMun
§ 'The Hon. Jean Marie de CAbP CWri EPfP IOrc LKna
Montague' ♀ LMil MBal MBri MDun MLea
NMun SLeo WWeb
'The Master' ♀ LKna NMun SBrw SLeo SReu
§ 'The Queen Mother' LHyd
¶ 'The Warrior' MDun
'Theme Song' SExb
thomsonii GGGa LHyd LMil MDun NHol
NMun SLeo
¶ – AC 113 NMun
– BL&M 153* MBal
– Bu 270 GGGa
– var. *candelabrum* See *R.* × *candelabrum*
– DF 540 MBal
§ – subsp. *lopsangianum* GGGa MDun SLeo
§ – LS&T 6561 NMun SLeo
– LS&H 1949* NMun
– MH 70 GGGa
– subsp. *thomsonii* NMun
BL&M 228
– – L&S 2847 GGGa NMun
Thomwilliams Group MBal
Thor Group & cl. GGGa SLeo SReu
'Thousand Butterflies' See *R.* **'One Thousand
Butterflies'**
'Thunderstorm' ♀ LHyd LKna SReu
thymifolium GGGa
'Tiana' GGGa
'Tibet' GQui LMil MBal MBar MDun
NHar SExb SHBN WWeb
'Tidbit' GGGa LHyd LKna LMil MAsh
MBal MBri MGos MLea NMun
SLeo WGer
'Tilford Seedling' LKna
'Timothy James' LRHS SReu
'Tit Willow' (EA) LHyd LRHS SCoo SPer WGwG
'Titian Beauty' ♀ CB&S COtt CWri GChr GGGa
IHos IOrc LMil LNet MBal
MBri MDun MGos MLea NHed
NMun SExb SLeo SPer SReu
WAbe WWeb
'Titipu' (EA) LHyd
'Tolkien' SReu SSta
¶ 'Tom Williams' NMun SLeo
'Tonkonatsu' (EA) SLeo
'Too Bee' GGGa MBri NHol WAbe
'Top Banana' LMil LRHS MBal MDun MLea
SMur SPer
'Top Hat' MLea
'Topsvoort Pearl' SReu
'Torch' LKna
'Toreador' (EA) CTrG SExb SLeo
'Torridon' (Vs) LMil
'Tortoiseshell Champagne' See *R.* **'Champagne'**
'Tortoiseshell Orange' ♀ LHyd LKna LMil MBri SBrw
SHBN SReu SSta WGer

'Tortoiseshell Pale Orange'	LKna
'Tortoiseshell Salome'	LKna SReu SSta
'Tortoiseshell Scarlet'	LKna SReu
'Tortoiseshell Wonder' ♀	LHyd LKna LMil MBal MGos NMun SLeo SPer SReu SSta
tosaense 'Ralph Clarke' (EA)	SLeo
'Totally Awesome' (K)	GGGa MLea
'Tottenham'	MBal
'Tower Beauty'	LHyd
'Tower Dainty'	LHyd
'Tower Daring'	LHyd
'Tower Dexter'	LHyd
'Tower Dragon'	LHyd
'Trail Blazer'	GGGa
traillianum	GGGa LMil NMun SLeo
¶ – *aberrans* aff. CNW 747	LMil
¶ – CNW 746	ISea
§ – var. *dictyotum*	NMun
– – 'Kathmandu'	NMun
– F 5881*	NMun SLeo
'Travis L'	SPer
Treasure Group	GDra IOrc LHyd MBal SLeo
'Trebah Gem'	NMun SLeo
'Tregedna'	NMun SLeo
¶ 'Tregedna Red'	SReu
'Tretawn'	SLeo
'Trewithen Orange'	CSam CTrw MBal MBar NMun SHBN SLeo SPer
'Trewithen Purple'	CTrw
'Trianon'	LMil NMun
trichanthum	CHig GGGa IOrc LMil NMun SLeo
– 'Honey Wood'	LHyd
trichocladum	LMil NMun SLeo
¶ – CNW 880	ISea
§ *trichostomum* ♀	GGGa LRHS NMun SSpi WAbe
– KW 4465	NMun
– Ledoides Group	LMil NMun SLeo SReu
– – 'Collingwood Ingram'	LMil SReu
– Radinum Group	SSta
triflorum	GGGa IOrc ISea LMil MBal MDun NMun SLeo
§ – var. *bauhiniiflorum*	LMil MDun NMun SLeo
– C&V 9573	GGGa
– var. *triflorum* Mahogani Group	NMun SLeo
'Trilby'	SLeo SReu
triplonaevium	See *R. alutaceum* var. *russotinctum* Triplonaevium Group
tritifolium	See *R. alutaceum* var. *russotinctum* Tritifolium Group
'Troll' (EA)	SLeo
'Troupial' (K)	LKna
'Trude Webster'	CHig CSam CWri GGGa MLea SExb SReu SSta
aff. *tsaii* C&H 7022	GGGa
aff. – H&M 1490	GGGa
tsangpoense	See *R. charitopes* subsp. *tsangpoense*
¶ aff. *tsariense*	LMil
–	GGGa LMil NHol NMun
– forms	NMun SLeo
– var. *magnum*	NMun
– Poluninii Group	See *R. poluninii*
– × *proteoides*	GGGa
– var. *trimoense*	GGGa NMun
– 'Yum Yum'	NMun SLeo
§ *tsusiophyllum*	GAri GGGa WAbe
'Tsuta-momiji' (EA)	LHyd
tubiforme	See *R. glaucophyllum* var. *tubiforme*
'Tulyar'	LKna
'Tunis' (K)	ECho MBri
'Turkish Delight'	MLea
N 'Twilight' (EA)	MBri
'Twilight Pink'	MLea NMun SExb
'Twilight Sky'	ENot MAsh WWeb
'Tyermannii' ♀	SLeo
'Ukamuse' (EA/d)	LHyd
'Uki Funei' (EA/v)	LMil
'Umpqua Queen' (K)	MLea
Ungerio Group	NMun SLeo
ungernii	GGGa NMun SLeo
uniflorum	GGGa LMil NHol NMun
§ – var. *imperator*	LMil
– – KW 6884	
– var. *uniflorum* KW 5876	NMun SLeo
'Unique' ♀	CB&S CHig CSam CWri GChr GGGa ISea LHyd LKna LMil LNet MAsh MBal MBri MDun MLea NMun SExb SHBN SLeo SPer SReu SSta WGwG WWeb
'Unique' (G)	LKna
'Unknown Warrior'	SReu
uvariifolium	GGGa NMun SLeo
¶ – CNW 127	ISea
¶ – CNW 1275	ISea
¶ – var. *griseum* KR 3423	LMil
¶ – – LS&E 15817	GGGa
– PA Cox 6519	GGGa
– 'Reginald Childs'	LMil
– var. *uvariifolium* USDAPI 59623/ R11391	NMun
– 'Yangtze Bend'	GGGa
¶ Valaspis Group & cl.	SLeo
'Valentine' (EA)	GGGa
valentinianum	CB&S CSam GGGa MBal NMun SLeo
– F 24347	NMun SLeo
¶ – var. *oblongilobatum* C&H 7186	LMil
Valpinense Group & cl.	WBod
'Van Nes Sensation'	LMil
¶ 'Van Weerden Poelman'	SBrw
Vanessa Group & cl.	LHyd LMil SCog SReu WBod
'Vanessa Pastel' ♀	CHig GGGa LHyd LMil MBal MDun MLea NMun SCog SLeo SReu WBod
§ 'Vanilla'	LKna
vaseyi (A) ♀	GGGa LHyd LMil MBal
veitchianum ♀	GGGa
§ – Cubittii Group ♀	GGGa NMun SLeo
– – 'Ashcombe'	LHyd
– KNE Cox 9001	GGGa
vellereum	See *R. principis* Vellereum Group
'Velvet Gown' (EA)	ENot IOrc LRHS MBri SBid
venator	GGGa MDun NMun SLeo
'Venetia' (K)	MBri
'Venetian Chimes'	ENot IHos IOrc ISea MBal MLea NMun SExb SLeo SPer SReu WWeb
vernicosum	GGGa LMil LRHS MDun NMun SLeo
– C&H 7009	GGGa
aff. – C&H 7150	GGGa
– Euanthum Group F 5880	NMun
– F 5881	NMun SLeo
– McLaren T 71	NMun
– SF 416	ISea

x *verruculosum*	SLeo
'Veryan Bay' ♀	CB&S LMil
vesiculiferum	NMun SLeo
'Vespers' (EA)	CTrh
'Victoria Hallett'	SReu
'Vida Brown' (EA/d)	CMac ENot LKna LMil MAsh
	MBri SBid SBod SCog SReu
	SSta WPat
'Viking' (EA)	LHyd
'Vincent van Gogh'	GGGa LMil
¶ 'Vinecourt Duke' (R/d)	ECho
¶ 'Vinecourt Troubador' (K/d)	ECho
¶ 'Vineland Dream' (K/d)	ECho
'Vineland Fragrance'	CWri MDun MLea
¶ 'Vinestar' AM	LMil
'Vinestar'	LHyd
'Vintage Rosé' ♀	LMil MBal MBri MLea NMun
	SLeo SReu WAbe
'Violet Longhurst'	LHyd
'Violetta' (EA)	GGGa WGwG
virgatum subsp. *oleifolium* KW 6279	SLeo
Virginia Richards Group & cl.	CHig GAri GChr GGGa LHyd
	MBal MBri MDun MGos MLea
	NMun SExb SLeo SReu SSta
	WGer
viridescens	LMil LRHS MBal MDun
– 'Doshong La'	LMil
◆ – KW 5829	See *R. mekongense* var. *mekongense* KW 5829
§ – Rubroluteum Group	GGGa LMil
viscidifolium	GGGa NMun
viscosum (A) ♀	GGGa GQui LHyd LKna LMil
	LRHS SReu
– 'Antilope'	See *R.* 'Antilope'
– 'Arpege'	See *R.* 'Arpege'
¶ – 'Grey Leaf' (Vs)	LMil
– var. *montanum* (A)	IBlr
– f. *rhodanthum* (A)	LMil
¶ – 'Roseum' (Vs)	LMil
'Viscount Powerscourt'	ENot SLeo
'Viscy'	CWri ECho GGGa GQui LHyd
	LMil WGer
'Vital Spark'	MBri
¶ 'Vivacious'	MDun
Volker Group	See *R.* Flava Group & cl.
'Vulcan' ♀	CB&S CWri ENot EPfP GGGa
	LMil MBal MLea SHBN SLeo
¶ 'Vulcan' x *yakushimanum*	SReu
'Vuyk's Rosyred' (EA) ♀	CB&S CHig CMac ENot GChr
	GQui GRei IOrc LHyd LKna
	LMil MBar MBri MGos SBod
	SExb SPer SReu WBod WFar
	WStI WWeb
'Vuyk's Scarlet' (EA) ♀	CB&S CChe CMac GGGa
	GQui IOrc ISea LHyd LKna
	LMil MBar MBri MGos NMun
	SExb SLeo SPer SReu SSta
	WFar WWeb
'W.E. Gumbleton' (M)	SReu
W.F.H. Group ♀	CWri LMil NMun SLeo
wadanum var. *leucanthum*	LMil
'Wagtail'	GGGa NHol WAbe
wallichii	GGGa SLeo
– Bu 249	GGGa
– Bu 262	GGGa
– Bu 290	GGGa
¶ – DM 21	LMil
– LS&H 17527	NMun SLeo
Walloper Group	NMun SLeo SReu
'Wallowa Red' (K)	ECho LMil

'Wally Miller'	SReu SSta
walongense	NMun
aff. – C&H 373	GGGa
wardii	IDee IOrc ISea LHyd LMil
	MBal MDun NMun SLeo
– C&V 9558	GGGa
– C&V 9606	GGGa
– L&S form*	GGGa SLeo SReu
– P Cox 6119	GGGa
– var. *puralbum*	GGGa NMun
– – F 10616	NMun
– SHEG 5672	NMun
– var. *wardii* C&V 9548	GGGa
– – F 21551	NMun
– – KW 5736	NMun
§ – – Litiense Group	NMun SLeo
– – LS&E 15764	NMun
– – LS&T 5679	NMun
– – LS&T 5686	NMun
– – LS&T 6591	NMun
– yellow	GGGa
'Ward's Ruby' (EA)	CTrh CTrw
¶ 'Warrior' (EA)	SBrw
§ 'Washington State Centennial'	GGGa
wasonii	GGGa LHyd LMil MDun NMun
– f. *rhododactylum*	NMun SLeo SReu
– – KW 1876	GGGa
¶ – var. *wenchuanense* C 5046	NHol
– white	SLeo SReu
¶ – yellow form	LMil
'Waterfall'	MBal
watsonii	GGGa MDun NMun SLeo SReu
– CC&H 3939	GGGa
– EGM 109	LMil
– PA Cox 5075	GGGa
'Waxwing'	LKna
websterianum EGM 146	LMil
– PA Cox 5123	GGGa
– PA Cox 5123a	MDun
'Wee Annie' (V)	CEqu
'Wee Bee'	EPot GCrs GGGa LMil MAsh
	MBri MDun MLea NHar NHed
	NHol SSpi WAbe
§ Wega Group	LHyd
'Wellesleyanum'	SLeo
'Werei'	NMun SLeo
'Werrington'	CGre
'Westminster' (O)	LKna LMil
'Weston's Innocence'	MLea
'Weston's Pink Diamond'	GGGa LMil NHol
'Weybridge'	NMun SLeo
weyrichii (A)	GGGa
'Whidbey Island'	LMil
'Whisperingrose'	CSam LMil MAsh MBal MBri
	MDun NHol
'White Frills' (EA)	LMil MBal SExb SMur
White Glory Group & cl.	NMun SLeo
'White Jade' (EA)	SExb SLeo
'White Lady' (EA)	LKna MBar SLeo SRms WGor
'White Lights'	GChr LMil LRHS MLea
'White Olympic Lady'	LKna
'White Swan' ♀	ENot LKna MBal SBrw SReu
'White Wings'	GQui SLeo WAbe WPic
'Whitethroat' (K/d) ♀	EPfP GQui IOrc LKna LMil
	MBri SExb
'Whitney's Dwarf Red'	SLeo
'Wigeon'	GGGa LMil NHol SPer
wightii	GGGa LMil MDun NMun SLeo

– BM&W 153*	MBal
– DF 542	MBal
'Wilbrit Rose'	SBod
'Wilgen's Ruby' ♀	CSam LKna MBar MBri MGos SBod SHBN SPer WStI
'Willbrit'	CDoC CHig CWri ECho LHyd MAsh MBri MDun MOne SExb WGor
williamsianum ♀	CB&S CHig CSam CTrG EPot GChr GGGa ISea LHyd LMil MBal MBar MDun MGos MLea NMun NWea SLeo SPer SReu SRms SSpi WAbe WBod WPic WSHC
– Caerhays form	MPla
– pink	WWat
– 'Special'	GGGa
– white	CPMA ISea MBal NMun SLeo WWat
'Willy' (EA)	LKna SLeo
wilsoniae	See *R. latoucheae*
'Wilsonii' (Ad)	LKna
¶ Wilsonii Group	CTrG
wiltonii	GGGa LMil LRHS MDun NMun SLeo
– CC&H 3906	GGGa
'Windbeam'	SBod
'Windlesham Scarlet' ♀	ENot LHyd LMil
'Windsor Lad'	LKna SBrw SReu
Winsome Group & cl.	CB&S CHig CSam CTrw CWri GCHN GGGa IOrc ISea LHyd LKna MBal MBar MDun MLea NHol NMun SBid SLeo SSta WBod
'Winston Churchill' (M)	MBar
'Wintergreen' (EA)	CB&S COtt CTrh
'Wishmoor' ♀	LMil NMun SLeo SReu
'Witch Doctor'	CDoC ECho LMil SBod SBrw
'Witchery'	GGGa
'Wojnar's Purple'	LMil
'Wombat' (EA)	CDoC COtt EPot GChr GGGa LHyd LMil MBal MBar MBri MGos NHed NHol SReu WAbe WPat
'Wonderland'	LKna
wongii	CSam GQui LMil NMun
'Woodcock'	GGGa
'Woodside'	SLeo
'Wren'	CSam EPot GCrs GGGa ISea MAsh MBal MBar MBri MDun MOne NHar NHol SExb SReu WAbe
'Wryneck' (K) ♀	LHyd LMil MBri SReu
xanthocodon	See *R. cinnabarinum* subsp. *xanthocodon*
xanthostephanum	NMun
¶ – KR 3095	LMil
'Yaku Angel'	MDun
'Yaku Prince'	CAbP IOrc SPer
'Yaku Princess'	CAbP IOrc MLea SLeo SPer
'Yaku Queen'	SLeo
yakushimanum	CB&S CMHG CSam CWri GGGa IOrc ISea LKna LMil MBar MBri MDun MGos NHol NMun SPer SReu SSta WAbe WGer
I – 'Angel'	MLea WWeb
– × *bureaui*	MBal MLea SReu
– × *campanulatum* 'Roland Cooper'	GGGa
– × *decorum*	GGGa SLeo SReu
– 'Edelweiss'	GGGa

– × 'Elizabeth'	GGGa
– Exbury form	SReu
– FCC form	CPMA EBee SBrw SReu
¶ – × 'Floriade'	SLeo
§ – 'Koichiro Wada' ♀	GGGa LHyd MBal MBri MGos NMun SLeo
– × *lanatum*	GGGa
– subsp. *makinoi*	See *R. makinoi*
– 'Mist Maiden'	MLea
– × *pachysanthum*	GGGa SLeo SReu
– × *ponticum*	GGGa
– × *proteoides*	GGGa
– × *rex*	GGGa SReu
– × 'Sappho'	GGGa
– × *tsariense*	GGGa
– subsp. *yakushimanum* 'Ken Janeck'	See *R.* 'Ken Janeck'
¶ 'Yellow Cloud' (K)	ECho
'Yellow Dane'	GGGa
¶ 'Yellow Hammer' ♀	CTrG MDun
Yellow Hammer Group	CB&S CHig CMHG CSam CWri GGGa ISea LKna LMil MBal MBar MGos NMun SBid SBod SExb SHBN SLeo SPer SReu SRms SSta WAbe WBod
'Yellow Petticoats'	MBri MLea SLeo
'Yellow Pippin'	CWri LMil
'Yellow Rolls Royce'	LMil MDun
'Yoga' (K)	LKna
'Youthful Sin'	MBal
'Yo-zakura' (EA)	NMun SLeo
yungningense	LMil NMun WAbe
◆ – F 29268	See *R. impeditum* F 29268
yunnanense	GGGa IOrc ISea LHyd LMil MDun NMun SLeo WGer
¶ – AC 751	NMun
¶ aff. – ACE 2097	GCLN
– C&H 7145	GGGa
– KGB 551	SReu
– KGB 559	SReu
– 'Openwood' ♀	GGGa LMil
– pink	GGGa
– SF 379	ISea
– SF 400	ISea
§ – Suberosum Group	NMun
– white	GGGa
'Yvonne Dawn'	NMun SLeo
¶ *zaleucum*	MDun
¶ – AC 685	NMun
– F 15688	GGGa
– F 27603	NMun SLeo
– Flaviflorum Group KW 20837	NMun SLeo
Zelia Plumecocq Group & cl.	CWri NMun SExb
zeylanicum	See *R. arboreum* subsp. *zeylanicum*
zoelleri (V)	CEqu
Zuiderzee Group	SLeo

RHODOHYPOXIS (Hypoxidaceae)

'Albrighton'	CAvo CBro CInt CRDP ELan EPot EWes LAma SBla SIng WAbe WPat
'Appleblossom'	CAvo EPot EWes GCrs SIng WAbe
baurii ♀	CAvo CElw CHea CInt CMHG CNic CRDP ELan EPot GCrs MBro MFos MHig MTho NNrd NRoo NTow WPyg WWin WWye
– 'Alba'	CBro CRDP CTri EDAr WWye

– var. **baurii**   EHyt EPot EWes GCrs LBee
– var. **confecta**   EPot EWes SIng
– 'Dulcie'   EDAr EPot EWes NTow SWas WAbe
* – × **parousia**   EWes
¶ – pink   WCru
– 'Pinkeen'   EPot WAbe
– var. **platypetala**   CRDP EHyt EPot EWes NHol NMen WAbe
– – × **milloides** , Burtt 6981   EWes
¶ – red   WCru
– 'Susan Garnett-Botfield'   EPot EWes SIng WAbe
¶ – white   WCru
'Confusion'   EHyt WAbe
'Dawn'   CAvo EHyt EPot EWes LAma NHol SBla SIng WAbe
deflexa   CGra EHyt EWes GCrs
'Donald Mann'   EHyt EWes
'Douglas'   CRDP EHyt EPot LAma NHol NNrd SBla WAbe WLRN WPat WPyg
'Dusky'   EPot
'E.A. Bowles'   EWes GCrs SIng WAbe
'Emily Peel'   EPot EWes WAbe
'Eva-Kate'   EPot EWes LAma SBla SIng WAbe WPat
'Fred Broome'   CBro ELan EPot EWes GCrs LAma NHol NTow SBla SIng WAbe WFar WPat WPyg
'Garnett'   EDAr EPot EWes GCrs NHol SBla WPat
'Great Scott'   ECho EPot EWes WAbe
'Harlequin'   CBro ELan EPot EWes LAma NHol SBla SIng WAbe
'Hebron Farm Biscuit'   EWes WAbe
* 'Hebron Farm Cerise'   EWes
'Hebron Farm Pink'   EWes GCrs WAbe
'Hebron Farm Red-eye'   EWes WAbe
§ 'Helen'   EPot EWes NHol SBla WAbe
hybrids   ELan
'Knockdolian Red'   NHol
'Margaret Rose'   EPot EWes GCrs WAbe
milloides   CRDP EHyt EPot EWes LBee NHol NMen NWCA SBla SSpi WAbe
– 'Claret'   CRDP
– 'Damask'   CRDP
'Monty'   EPot EWes WAbe
'New Look'   EWes WAbe
'Perle'   EPot EWes NMen NNrd WAbe
'Picta'   CAvo CRDP EHyt EPot EWes GCrs LAma NHol NNrd SBla SSpi WAbe WPat
'Pink Pearl'   EPot EWes NHol
'Pinkeen'   EWes GCrs
'Ruth'   EHyt EPot EWes LAma NHol SBla WAbe
'Shell Pink'   SBla
'Stella'   CAvo EPot EWes GCrs NHol SBla SIng WAbe
'Tetra Pink'   SIng
'Tetra Red'   EPot EWes NHol NMen SIng WAbe
'Tetra White'   See R. **'Helen'**
thodiana   CAvo CRDP EPot SIng SSpi

RHODOHYPOXIS × HYPOXIS (Hypoxidaceae)

R. **baurii** × H. **parvula**   EWes WAbe

RHODOMYRTUS (Myrtaceae) See Plant Deletions

RHODOPHIALA (Amaryllidaceae)

advena   WCot
§ **bifida**   CMon LBow
– **spathacea**   CMon LBow
chilensis   CLAP
elwesii   EHyt

RHODORA See RHODODENDRON

RHODOTHAMNUS (Ericaceae)

¶ **chamaecistus**   GCrs WAbe

RHODOTYPOS (Rosaceae)

kerrioides   See R. **scandens**
§ **scandens**   CB&S CBot CHan CPle EPfP GBin MPla MTis NTow SBid SSpi WCru WWin

RHOEO See TRADESCANTIA

RHOICISSUS (Vitaceae) See Plant Deletions

RHOPALOBLASTE (Arecaceae) See Plant Deletions

RHOPALOSTYLIS (Arecaceae)

baueri   CBrP LPal
¶ **cheesemanii**   CBrP
sapida   CBrP CHEx ECou LPal

RHUS (Anacardiaceae)

¶ **ambigua** B&SWJ 3656   WCru
¶ **chinensis**   EPfP
copallina   EPfP MWhi SMur
cotinus   See Cotinus **coggygria**
glabra   CAgr CArn CB&S CDoC MBlu NFla SPer WPGP
– 'Laciniata' hort.   See R. × **pulvinata** Autumn Lace Group
N **hirta**   See R. **typhina**
integrifolia   CArn
pendulina   CGre
potaninii   EPfP WWat
§ × **pulvinata** Autumn Lace   EPfP MBlu MGos SDix SHBN
    Group   WFar
– – 'Red Autumn Lace' ♀   MBlu SPer
§ **radicans**   CArn GPoy
toxicodendron   See R. **radicans**
trichocarpa   SMur SSpi
trilobata   CArn CFil WPGP
§ **typhina** ♀   CAgr CB&S CBlo CLnd EBrP EBre ECtt ELan ENot GChr GOrc IOrc ISea LBre MBar MBri MGos MWat NFla NNor NWea SBre SHBN SPer SSta WDin WStl WWal WWin
§ – 'Dissecta' ♀   CB&S CHEx CLnd CSpe ELan ENot GRei IOrc MAsh MBar MBri MWat NBee NFla SEND SEas SMad SPer WDin WTro
– 'Laciniata' hort.   See R. **typhina** 'Dissecta'
vernciflua   CFil SSpi

RHYNCHELYTRUM See MELINIS

RIBES † (Grossulariaceae)

alpinum   CAgr ELan ENot GRei IOrc LBuc NSti NWea SBid SPer SRms WDin WTro

– 'Aureum'	CMHG CTri EAst EBee EHoe ELan EPla MHig NNor NPro WCot WDin WSHC WTro
¶ – 'Schmidt'	MBar NFla
¶ *amarum*	CPle
americanum	EPla
– 'Variegatum'	EBee EHoe ELan EPla NHol SPan WPat WPyg
atrosanguineum	See *R. sanguineum* 'Atrorubens'
aureum hort.	See *R. odoratum*
* – 'Roxby Red'	MCoo
'Black Velvet' (F)	CBlo CMac COtt LRHS MBri MCoo SPer
bracteosum	CPle
californicum	CPle
× *culverwellii* Jostaberry (F)	CAgr EMui GTwe LBuc LRHS
divaricatum	CAgr
– 'Worcesterberry' (F)	CMac CWSG EMui MBri MGos NDal NRog SDea SPer
gayanum	CGre CPle LHop SLPl WHCG
glutinosum	See *R. sanguineum* var. *glutinosum*
× *gordonianum*	CGre CHan CMHG CPle CWSG EPla GBin LHop MBal MBel MRav SBid SEND SMrm WCot WHCG WPyg WWat
¶ *laurifolium* (m)	CPMA
¶ – (f)	CPMA
–	CB&S CBot CPle CSam IOrc MBal MBel MRav SBid SPer SSpi SSta WCot WCru WDin WHCG WPyg WSHC WWal WWat WWin
– 'Mrs Amy Doncaster'	EPla
lobbii	CPle
nigrum 'Amos Black' (F)	GTwe
– 'Baldwin' (F)	CMac GBon NDal SDea SPer WStI WWeb
* – 'Barchatnaja' (F)	CAgr
– 'Ben Alder' (F)	CBlo SDea
– 'Ben Connan' (F) ♀	COtt EMui GTwe MGos SCoo WLRN
– 'Ben Lomond' (F) ♀	CBlo CTri EMui GBon GChr GRei GTwe LBuc MBri MGos NBee NDal NRog SDea SPer WStI
– 'Ben Loyal' (F)	GTwe
– 'Ben More' (F)	CBlo GRei GTwe MBri NBee NDal SDea SPer WStI
– 'Ben Nevis' (F)	CBlo GTwe NDal NRog SDea
– 'Ben Sarek' (F) ♀	CBlo CSam CSut EBrP EBre EMui ERea GRei GTwe LBre LBuc MBri MGos NDal SBre SDea SPer WWeb
– 'Ben Tirran' (F)	CBlo CDoC LBuc MGos
– 'Blacksmith' (F)	WLRN
– 'Boskoop Giant' (F)	CMac GTwe NRog SPer
* – 'Byelorussian Sweet' (F)	CAgr
* – 'Consort' (F)	CAgr
– 'Daniel's September' (F)	GTwe
¶ – 'Farleigh' (F)	EMui
¶ – 'Foxendown'	EMui
* – 'Hystawneznaya' (F)	CAgr
– 'Jet' (F)	GTwe LRHS SPer
* – 'Kosmicheskaya' (F)	CAgr
– 'Laxton's Giant' (F)	GTwe
– 'Malling Jet' (F)	CBlo NRog WLRN
– 'Mendip Cross' (F)	CBlo GTwe NRog
* – 'Pilot Alek Mamkin' (F)	CAgr
– 'Wellington XXX' (F)	CBlo CTri ERea GTwe LBuc MBri NBee NRog WMow WStI WWeb
– 'Westwick Choice' (F)	GTwe
§ *odoratum*	CB&S CBlo CMHG CPle CSam ECoo ELan ENot EPla ERav GOrc GRei LHol MBar MBel MGos MHar MPla NBee NWea SEas SHBN SPer SRms SSpi WHCG WSHC WWat WWin
– 'Crandall'	CAgr
praecox	CB&S CBlo MBlu SEND
propinquum	CPlN
¶ *roezlii*	CPle
rubrum 'Blanka' (W)	CSut
¶ – 'Cascade' (R)	CAgr
– 'Fay's New Prolific' (R)	GTwe
– 'Hollande Rose' (P)	GTwe
– 'Jonkheer van Tets' (R) ♀	CAgr EMui GTwe LRHS MGos SDea WTro
– 'Junifer' (R)	CAgr CSut EMui GTwe
– 'Laxton Number One' (R)	CAgr CBlo CSam CTri EBrP EBre EMui GBon GRei GTwe LBre MBri NRog SBre SDea SPer WWeb
¶ – 'Laxton's Perfection' (R)	MCoo
– 'October Currant' (P)	GTwe
– 'Raby Castle' (R)	GTwe
– 'Red Lake' (R) ♀	CAgr CB&S CBlo CMac CSam EBrP EBre ERea GBon GChr GRei GTwe LBre LBuc MBri MGos NBee NDal NRog SBre SDea SPer WStI
– 'Redstart' (R)	CBlo COtt GTwe LBuc LRHS MBri SDea WWeb
– 'Rondom' (R)	SDea
– 'Rovada' (R)	CAgr CSut EMui
– 'Stanza' (R) ♀	GTwe SDea
§ – 'Versailles Blanche' (W)	CAgr CBlo CDoC CMac CSam CTri EMui GChr GTwe LBuc MBri MGos SDea SPer WWeb
¶ – 'White Dutch' (W)	MCoo
– 'White Grape' (W) ♀	CBlo CTri GTwe NRog
– 'White Pearl' (W)	CB&S GRei
– 'White Transparent' (W)	GTwe
– White Versailles	See *R. rubrum* (White Currant Group) 'Versailles Blanche'
– 'Wilson's Long Bunch' (R)	GTwe
sanguineum	CBlo CLTr CPle CSam GChr MBal MBar NCut NLon NNor WStI
– 'Albescens'	SPer WBcn
– 'Brocklebankii' ♀	CAbP CBlo CBrd EPar EPla LHop MGos MPla SAga SBid SHBN SPer SPla WFar WGwG WSHC
– double	See *R. sanguineum* 'Plenum'
– 'Flore Pleno'	See *R. sanguineum* 'Plenum'
– var. *glutinosum* 'Albidum'	SChu WWat
– 'King Edward VII'	CBlo CDoC ECtt GChr LBuc MBar MBri MGos MWat NBee NHol NNor NRoo NWea SHBN SPer SPla SReu SRms WDin WGwG WStI WTro WWeb
– 'Koja'	LRHS MBri NPro
– 'Lombartsii'	CBlo EPla MRav
§ – 'Plenum' (d)	CBot MBlu
– 'Porky Pink'	CLyn EBrP EBre GSki LBre LRHS MAsh MGos MRav SBre

– 'Pulborough Scarlet' ♀	CB&S CBlo CChe CDoC CLTr ELan ENot GOrc MAsh MBri MGos MPla MRav MWat NBee NBir NFla SPer SPla SRms WRHF WWeb
– 'Pulborough Scarlet Variegated'	CBlo CPMA EPla LHop MPla SBid
– 'Red Pimpernel'	EBar MBri WBcn WFar
– 'Roseum'	See *R. sanguineum* 'Carneum'
– 'Taff's Kim' (v)	CPMA
– 'Tydeman's White' ♀	CBlo CChe CPMA CPle EAst ECtt EPfP MBar MBlu SBid SSpi WStI
§ – White Icicle = 'Ubric'	CBlo CBot CMil CWSG EBee EBrP EBre ELan GSki LBre MAsh MGos MUlv NBir SBre SPla SSto WWat
◆ – White Icicle	See *R. sanguineum* White Icicle = 'Ubric'
speciosum ♀	CB&S CBot CBrd CMHG CPMA CPlN CPle CSam ELan ENot EOrc EPla EWes LHop MBal MBel MDun MPla SAga SPer WBod WDin WEas WHCG WPat WSHC WWat WWin
tenue	CPle EPla
uva-crispa var. *reclinatum*	GTwe
'Achilles' (C/D)	
– – 'Admiral Beattie' (F)	GTwe NRog
– – 'Alma' (D)	NRog
– – 'Annelii' (F)	SDea
– – 'Aston Red'	See *R. uva-crispa* var. *reclinatum* 'Warrington'
– – 'Australia' (F)	NRog
– – 'Bedford Red' (D)	GTwe NRog
– – 'Bedford Yellow' (D)	GTwe
– – 'Beech Tree Nestling' (F)	GTwe
– – 'Bellona' (C)	NRog
– – 'Blucher' (F)	NRog
– – 'Bright Venus' (D)	GTwe
– – 'Broom Girl' (D)	GTwe NDal NRog
– – 'Captivator' (F)	CSam GTwe
– – 'Careless' (C) ♀	CBlo CMac CSam CTri EMui ERea GBon GRei GTwe IOrc MBri MGos NBee NRog SDea SPer WMow WStI WWeb
– – 'Champagne Red' (F)	GTwe
– – 'Clayton' (F)	NRog
– – 'Cook's Eagle' (C)	GTwe
– – 'Cousen's Seedling' (F)	GTwe
– – 'Criterion' (C)	GTwe NRog
– – 'Crown Bob' (C/D)	GTwe LRHS NRog
– – 'Dan's Mistake' (D)	GTwe NRog
– – 'Drill' (F)	GTwe
– – 'Early Sulphur' (D/C)	CBlo GTwe LRHS NRog SDea WStI
– – 'Edith Cavell' (F)	GTwe
– – 'Firbob' (D)	GTwe NRog
– – 'Forester' (D)	GTwe
– – 'Freedom' (C)	GTwe LRHS NRog
– – 'Gipsey Queen' (F)	GTwe
– – 'Glenton Green' (F)	GTwe
– – 'Golden Ball' (D)	SDea
– – 'Golden Drop' (D)	GTwe LRHS
– – 'Green Gascoigne'	See *R. uva-crispa* var. *reclinatum* 'Early Green Hairy'
– – 'Green Gem' (C/D)	GTwe NRog
– – 'Green Ocean' (F)	GTwe NRog
– – 'Greenfinch' (F) ♀	CWSG EMui GTwe LRHS MGos SDea
– – 'Greengage' (D)	NRog
– – 'Gretna Green' (F)	GTwe
– – 'Guido' (F)	GTwe NRog
– – 'Gunner' (D)	CTri GTwe NRog
– – 'Heart of Oak' (F)	GTwe NRog
– – 'Hedgehog' (D)	GTwe
– – 'Hepburn Prolific' (D)	GTwe
– – 'Hero of the Nile' (C)	GTwe NRog
– – 'High Sheriff' (D)	GTwe
– – 'Hinnonmäki Röd' (F)	SDea
– – 'Howard's Lancer' (C/D)	GTwe NRog SDea
– – 'Invicta' (C) ♀	CBlo CDoC CMac CSut CTri CWSG EBrP EBre EMui GBon GChr GRei LBre LBuc MBri MGos NDal SBre SDea SPer WStI WWeb
– – 'Ironmonger' (F)	CBlo GTwe LRHS
– – 'Jubilee' (C/D)	COtt CTri LBuc MBri MGos NRog WStI
– – 'Keen's Seedling' (D)	GTwe
– – 'Keepsake' (C/D)	CBlo GTwe LRHS NRog SDea
– – 'King of Trumps' (F)	GTwe LRHS NRog
– – 'Lancashire Lad' (C/D)	GTwe LRHS NRog
– – 'Langley Gage' (D)	GTwe LRHS NRog
– – 'Laxton's Amber' (D)	GTwe
– – 'Leveller' (C/D) ♀	CBlo CMac CTri EBrP EBre EMui GBon GChr GTwe LBre LBuc MBri MGos NRog SBre SDea SPer WStI WWeb
– – 'London' (C/D)	GTwe LRHS NRog
– – 'Lord Derby' (C/D)	CBlo GTwe MBri NRog
– – 'Lord Kitchener' (F)	NRog
– – 'Macherauch's Seedling' (F)	NRog
– – 'Marigold' (F)	NRog
– – 'Matchless' (C)	NRog
– – 'May Duke' (C/D)	LRHS NRog SDea
– – 'Mitre' (C)	GTwe
– – 'Pax'	CDoC CWSG EMui GTwe LBuc SDea WLRN
– – 'Peru'	GTwe
– – 'Pitmaston Green Gage' (D)	GTwe
– – 'Plunder' (F)	NRog
– – 'Prince Charles' (F)	GTwe
– – 'Queen of Hearts' (F)	NRog
– – 'Queen of Trumps' (C)	GTwe NRog
– – 'Red Rough' (D)	GTwe
– – 'Rifleman' (D)	GTwe
– – 'Rokula'	CDoC GTwe
– – 'Roseberry' (D)	GTwe
– – 'Scottish Chieftan' (D)	GTwe
– – 'Sir George Brown' (D)	NRog
– – 'Snowdrop' (C)	GTwe
– – 'Speedwell' (F)	NRog
– – 'Spinefree' (F)	GTwe
– – 'Sultan Juror' (F)	NRog
– – 'Surprise' (C)	GTwe NRog
– – 'Suter Johnny' (F)	NRog
– – 'Telegraph' (F)	GTwe
– – 'The Leader' (F)	NRog
– – 'Tom Joiner' (F)	GTwe
– – 'Trumpeter' (C)	NRog
– – 'Victoria' (F)	GTwe LRHS NRog
§ – – 'Warrington' (D)	GTwe NRog

– – 'Whinham's Industry' (C/D) ♀	CBlo CMac CSam CSut EMui ERea GBon GChr GRei GTwe IOrc LBuc MBri MGos NBee NDal NRog SDea SPer WStI
– – 'White Eagle' (C)	NRog
– – 'White Lion' (C/D)	GTwe LRHS NRog
– – 'White Transparent' (C)	GTwe
– – 'Whitesmith' (C/D)	CTri GTwe LRHS NRog SDea WStI
– – 'Woodpecker' (F)	GTwe LRHS NRog
– – 'Yellow Champagne' (F)	GTwe LRHS NRog
viburnifolium	CPle LRHS SPan SSta SVen WPGP WWat

RICHEA (Epacridaceae)

dracophylla	CFil SAPC SArc
milliganii	CFil WPGP
scoparia	CFil MAll SAPC SArc

RICINUS (Euphorbiaceae)

¶ *communis*	CHEx
– 'Carmencita' ♀	LBlo
– 'Gibsonii'	EOas LBlo
– 'Impala'	LBlo MLan SSoC
¶ – 'Niger'	WMul
¶ – 'Zanzibariensis'	EOas LBlo WMul

RIVINA (Phytolaccaceae) See Plant Deletions

ROBINIA (Papilionaceae)

boyntonii	CTho
fertilis	SIgm WShe
hispida ♀	CEnd CHEx CLnd CTho ELan EPfP ICrw LNet MBlu MHlr SHBN SSpi SSta WPyg WSHC
– 'Macrophylla'	CBlo CEnd SSpi
N– 'Rosea'	CB&S CBlo CBot CHEx EBee ENot LRHS MGos NFla SPer WShe
kelseyi	CBlo IOrc SPer WPyg
× *margaretta* Casque Rouge	See *R.* × *margaretta* '**Pink Cascade**'
§ – 'Pink Cascade'	CBlo CDoC CEnd CTho EBee ECrN LNet LPan MBri MGos MMea SBid SHBN SPer WDin WPyg
neomexicana	CAgr CLnd
pseudoacacia ♀	CAgr CB&S CBlo CHEx CLnd CPer ELan ENot GAri LBuc LPan MCoo WFar WFox WNor
– 'Bessoniana'	CBlo CLnd CTho ECrN ENot
– 'Fastigiata'	See *R. pseudoacacia* '**Pyramidalis**'
– 'Frisia' ♀	Widely available
– 'Inermis' hort.	See *R. pseudoacacia* '**Umbraculifera**'
– 'Lace Lady'	EBee ELan ENot LPan MAsh MBri MRav SCoo SMad WWes
* – 'Mimosifolia'	MBri
§ – 'Pyramidalis'	CTho ENot
– 'Rozynskiana'	CTho
– 'Tortuosa'	CBlo CEnd CLnd CTho EBee ELan EMil EPfP LPan MAsh MBri MMea SPar SPer
§ – 'Umbraculifera'	CLnd EMil ENot LPan MGos SFam
– 'Unifoliola'	CLnd CTho
¶ *pseudocacia* 'Lacy Lady'	MGos

× *slavinii* 'Hillieri' ♀	CBlo CEnd CLnd CTho ELan IOrc LPan MAsh MWat SBid SPer SSpi WWat
* 'Twisty Baby'	EPfP

ROCHEA See CRASSULA

RODGERSIA † (Saxifragaceae)

aesculifolia ♀	CFil CGle CHEx CHad CHan CRow CSam EGol ELan EPar IBlr LFis MBal MBri NBee NDea NHar NHol SBla SMac SPer SRms SSoC SSpi SWat WByw WCru WWat
– 'Irish Bronze'	IBlr
– pink form	IBlr
¶ 'Die Anmutige'	CRow
henrici	CRow IBlr LBuc MCli SPer WRus
– hybrid	GAri MUlv NHol WCru
¶ 'Kupfermond'	CRow
nepalensis	IBlr
'Parasol'	CFil CHad ELan GBuc IBlr NHol SSpi WPGP
pinnata	CDoC CGle CHEx CHad CRow EBrP EBre EGol EHon ERav IBlr LBre LHil MBal MBri MCli MSta NDea NFla NHol NVic SAxl SBre SChu SPer WHil WHoo WPyg WWat WWhi
– 'Alba'	IBlr NHol
– 'Elegans'	CHEx CHad EBrP EBre EFou ELan EMan ENot EPar GCal GGar GMaP IBlr LBre MUlv NHol NOrc SBre SChu SMrm SSoC WGer WWat WWin
– 'Rosea'	IBlr
– 'Superba' ♀	CBos CHEx CHad CTrC EBar ECha ECtt EOld GAbr IBlr LBlm LFis LGro MBal MBri MBro MCLN MUlv NBee NFla NHar NPer NSti SSpi WAbe WCru WKif
¶ – white form	GCal
podophylla ♀	Widely available
– Donard form	CFil IBlr WCot
– 'Rotlaub'	CRow GCal IBlr MBri WCot
– 'Smaragd'	CLAP CRow GCal IBlr
purdomii hort.	CRow IBlr SSpi
¶ 'Rosenlicht'	CRow
sambucifolia	CB&S CDoC CHEx CRow EBee EMan LFis MBri MCli MFir MUlv NDea NFla NHar SMac SPer SSoC SSpi WCru WFar WGer WMer WWat
– dwarf pink-flowered	IBlr
– dwarf white-flowered	IBlr
– large green-stemmed	IBlr
– large red-stemmed	IBlr
– × *pinnata*	IBlr
– × *pinnata* 'Panache'	IBlr
sp. ACE 2303	GBuc SWas
sp. CLD 1329	NHol
sp. CLD 1432	NHol
sp. from Castlewellan	IBlr
tabularis	See *Astilboides tabularis*

ROELLA (Campanulaceae)

ciliata	CSpe
maculata	CSpe

ROHDEA † (Convallariaceae)

japonica	CFil WPGP
¶ – 'Gunjaku'	EMon
¶ – 'Lance Leaf'	SApp
– long-leaved form	WCru WPGP
– 'Talbot Manor' (v)	SApp WCot WPGP
– 'Tuneshige Rokujo'	WCot
– variegated	WCot
watanabei B&SWJ 1911	WCru

ROMANZOFFIA (Hydrophyllaceae)

§ *sitchensis*	CLyd CTri EBar SSca
suksdorfii Green	See *R. sitchensis*
– hort.	See *R. californica*
unalaschcensis	CNic ELan GTou MHig NBro
	NWCA SRms SSca WOMN
	WPer WWin

ROMNEYA (Papaveraceae)

coulteri ♀	CAbb CB&S CBot COtt CPle
	ELan GCal IBlr LHop MBlu
	MBri MGos MLan MWgw SBid
	SBla SPer SReu SSta SVil WDin
	WSHC WSpi WWat WWeb
– var. *trichocalyx*	IBlr SCro WAbe
§ – 'White Cloud'	ENot EREa IBlr MRav SMad
	SSoC
– 'White Sails'	IBlr
X *hybrida*	See *R. coulteri* 'White Cloud'

ROMULEA (Iridaceae)

battandieri AB&S 4659	CMon
bifrons AB&S 4359/4360	CMon
bulbocodium	CBro CMon CNic EHic MFos
	MHig
– var. *clusiana*	LAma
– – MS 239	EHyt
– – Serotina Group	EPot
– – SF 237	CMon
* – 'Knightshayes'	CLAP EHyt
* – var. *leichtliniana* MS 784	EHyt
campanuloides	CMon
columnae AB&S 4659	CMon
engleri SF 3	CMon
hirta	CMon
ligustica var. *rouyana*	CMon
SF 360	
linaresii	EPot LAma
– var. *graeca* CE&H 620	CMon
longituba	See *R. macowanii*
§ *macowanii*	MHig WAbe
– var. *alticola*	EHyt WAbe WOMN
minutiflora	NRog
monticola	CMon
nivalis	CAvo LAma LBow
ramiflora	CMon
– SF 63	CMon
requienii	WOMN
– L65	EHyt
rosea	NRog
sabulosa	CBro
saldanhensis	EHyt
sp. SF 367	CMon
tempskyana	CMon EHyt EPot
'Zahni'	CMon CNic LAma

RORIPPA (Brassicaceae)

nasturtium-aquaticum	MHew

ROSA † (Rosaceae)

A Shropshire Lad	See *R.* A Shropshire Lad = 'Ausled'
◆ Aalsmeer Gold®	See *R.* Aalsmeer Gold = 'Bekola'
'Abbandonata'	See *R.* 'Laure Davoust'
◆ Abbeyfield Rose	See *R.* Abbeyfield Rose = 'Cocbrose'
§ 'Abbotswood'	EBls MAus
(*canina* hybrid)	
◆ Aberdeen Celebration	See *R.* Aberdeen Celebration = 'Cocmystery'
◆ Abigaile®	See *R.* Abigaile = 'Taneliagib'
◆ Abraham Darby®	See *R.* Abraham Darby = 'Auscot'
◆ Acapulco	See *R.* Acapulco = 'Dicblender'
◆ Ace of Hearts	See *R.* Ace of Hearts = 'Korred'
acicularis	EPla
– var. *nipponensis*	EBls
'Adam' (ClT)	EBls MAus
'Adam Messerich' (Bb)	EBls MAus WHCG
'Adélaïde d'Orléans' (Ra) ♀	CRHN EBls MAus NPri SPer SRum SWCr WAct WHCG WPen
◆ Admirable	See *R.* Admirable = 'Searodney'
'Admiral Rodney' (HT)	MGan MJon NBat NRog
Adolf Horstmann® (HT)	MGan
'Agatha' (G)	EBls
◆ Agatha Christie	See *R.* Agatha Christie = 'Kormeita'
'Aglaia' (Ra)	WHCG
'Agnes' (Ru)	EBls ENot EPfP GCoc IHar IHos MAus MGan MMat NFla NSty SJus SPer SWCr WAct WHCG WOVN
'Aimée Vibert' (Ra)	EBls MAus MHlr NPri SMer SPer WAct WHCG WSHC
'Alain Blanchard' (G)	EBls MAus WHCG
X *alba* (A)	EBls MSto NRog
§ – 'Alba Maxima' (A) ♀	CHad EBls ENot GChr GCoc MAus MHlr MMat NFla NPri NSty SFam SPer WAct WHCG
§ – 'Alba Semiplena' (A) ♀	EBls MAus NSty SJus SPer WAct WGer WHCG WHow
– Celestial	See *R.* 'Céleste'
– 'Maxima'	See *R.* X *alba* 'Alba Maxima'
◆ Alba Meidiland®	See *R.* Alba Meidiland = 'Meiflopan'
'Albéric Barbier' (Ra) ♀	CHad CSam EBar EBls ENot IHos LHol LStr MAus MBri MGan MHlr MJon MMat NRog NSty SApu SJus SPer SRum SSea SWCr WAct WHCG WHow WOVN WSHC
'Albertine' (Ra) ♀	Widely available
'Alchymist' (S/Cl)	CHad EBee EBls ENot MAus MBri MGan MJon MMat SFam SPer SWCr WAct WHCG WHow
◆ Alec's Red®	See *R.* Alec's Red = 'Cored'
◆ Alex C. Collie	See *R.* Alex C. Collie = 'Cococrust'
◆ Alexander®	See *R.* Alexander = 'Harlex'
'Alexander Hill Gray' (T)	EBls
'Alexander von Humboldt' (Cl)	MGan
'Alexandre Girault' (Ra)	EBls EMFP MAus MHlr NPri SPer SWCr WAct WHCG WHow
§ 'Alfred Colomb' (HP)	EBls NSty
'Alfred de Dalmas' misapplied	See *R.* 'Mousseline'

'Alida Lovett' (Ra) — EBls MAus
♦ Alison — See *R.* Alison = **'Coclibee'**
§ 'Alister Stella Gray' (N) ♀ — EBls EMFP MAus MGan MHlr NPri SPer SSea SWCr WAct WHCG WHow
♦ All in One — See *R.* Exploit = **'Meilider'**
'Allen Chandler' (ClHT) — EBls MAus NSty
Allgold® (F) — CB&S CGro EBls GCoc LStr MAus MGan MJon SRum WStI
'Aloha' (ClHT) — Widely available
alpina — See *R. pendulina*
Alpine Sunset® (HT) — CTri EBee EBls GGre MGan SPer SRum
altaica hort. — See *R. pimpinellifolia* **'Grandiflora'**
♦ Altissimo® — See *R.* Altissimo = **'Delmur'**
'Amadis' (Bs) — EBls MAus SWCr WHCG
♦ Amanda — See *R.* Amanda = **'Beesian'**
'Amazing Grace' (HT) — GGre
♦ Amber Nectar — See *R.* Amber Nectar = **'Mehamber'**
♦ Amber Queen® — See *R.* Amber Queen = **'Harroony'**
§ Anvil Sparks® = 'Ambossfunken' (HT) — MGan
♦ Ambridge Rose — See *R.* Ambridge Rose = **'Auswonder'**
'Amélia' — See *R.* **'Celsiana'**
'American Pillar' (Ra) — CB&S CGro CSam EBls EBrP EBre ISea LBre LStr MAus MGan MHlr MMat NBat NRog NSty SApu SBre SPer SRum SSea WAct WFar WHCG
'Améthyste' (Ra) — NSty
♦ Amorette — See *R.* Snowdrop = **'Amoru'**
§ Snowdrop = 'Amoru' (Min/Patio) — MFry
§ Red Ace = 'Amruda' (Min) — MFry MJon
'Amy Robsart' (RH) — EBls MAus SJus
♦ Anabell — See *R.* Anabell = **'Korbell'**
'Anaïs Ségalas' (G) — MAus
§ Double Delight® = 'Andeli' (HT) — CGro ELan GCoc GGre LPlm LStr MBri MGan MJon NRog SApu SPer SRum
§ 'Andersonii' (*canina* hybrid) — EBls MAus WAct
§ Our Love = 'Andour' (HT) — GGre
§ With Love = 'Andwit' (HT) — MJon SApu
§ 'Anemone' (Cl) — EBls MAus
anemoniflora — See *R.* x *beanii*
anemonoides — See *R.* **'Anemone'**
– 'Ramona' — See *R.* **'Ramona'**
♦ Angela Rippon® — See *R.* Angela Rippon = **'Ocaru'**
'Angela's Choice' (F) — MGan
'Angèle Pernet' (HT) — EBls
'Angelina' (S) — EBls
♦ Anisley Dickson® — See *R.* Anisley Dickson = **'Dickimono'**
¶ 'Ann' — MAus
'Ann Aberconway' (F) — MJon MMat
'Anna de Diesbach' (HP) — EBls
♦ Anna Ford® — See *R.* Anna Ford = **'Harpiccolo'**
♦ Anna Livia — See *R.* Anna Livia = **'Kormetter'**
'Anna Olivier' (T) — EBls
'Anna Pavlova' (HT) — EBls
♦ Anna Zinkeisen — See *R.* Anna Zinkeisen = **'Harquhling'**
Anne Cocker® (F) — GCoc MGan
'Anne Dakin' (ClHT) — MAus

♦ Anne Harkness® — See *R.* Anne Harkness = **'Harkaramel'**
'Anne of Geierstein' (RH) — EBls MAus MGan
'Anne Watkins' (HT) — EBls
Antique — See *R.* Antique = **'Kordalen'**
♦ Antique '89® — See *R.* Antique '89 = **'Kordalen'**
'Antoine Rivoire' (HT) — EBls
'Antonia d'Ormois' (G) — EBls
♦ Anvil Sparks — See *R.* Anvil Sparks = **'Ambossfunken'**
Apothecary's Rose — See *R. gallica* var. *officinalis*
'Apple Blossom' (Ra) — EBls NSty WHCG
'Applejack' (S) — EBls
'Apricot Garnet' — See *R.* **'Garnette Apricot'**
'Apricot Nectar' (F) — LStr MAus MGan SPer SWCr
'Apricot Silk' (HT) — CB&S CGro CTri EBls IHar IHos MAus MGan NRog SPer WWeb
♦ Apricot Summer® — See *R.* Apricot Summer = **'Korpapiro'**
♦ Apricot Sunblaze® — See *R.* Apricot Sunblaze = **'Savamark'**
'Apricot Wine' (F) — IHar
¶ 'April Hamer' (HT) — NBat
Arc Angel — See *R.* Arc Angel = **'Fryyorston'**
Arcadian (F) — MJon
'Archiduc Joseph' misapplied — See *R.* **'Général Schablikine'**
'Archiduchesse Elisabeth d'Autriche' (HP) — EBls
'Ardoisée de Lyon' (HP) — EBls
♦ Ards Beauty — See *R.* Ards Beauty = **'Dicjoy'**
'Ards Rover' (ClHP) — EBls
'Arethusa' (Ch) — EBls
§ *arkansana* var. *suffulta* — EBls WHCG
♦ Armada® — See *R.* Armada = **'Haruseful'**
§ Golden Wedding = 'Arokris' (F/HT) — EBrP EBre ELan GCoc GGre IHar LBre LGod LPlm LStr MAus MBri MBur MFry MGan MJon MMat NBat SApu SBre SJus SPer SRum WStI WWeb
§ Strawberry Fayre = 'Arowillip' (Min/Patio) — COtt EBrP EBre GCoc LBre MFry MJon NBat SBre WWeb
¶ 'Arrillaga' (HP) — MAus
♦ Artful Dodger — See *R.* Artful Dodger = **'Sabbelief'**
'Arthur Bell' (F) ♀ — EBls EBrP EBre GChr GCoc GGre IHar IHos LBre LPlm LStr MAus MBur MGan MMat NBat NRog SApu SBre SPer SRum WWeb
'Arthur de Sansal' (DPo) — EBls MAus MRav
arvensis — CCVT CKin EBls LBuc MAus NWea SLPl WAct
§ Ash Wednesday = 'Aschermittwoch' (Cl) — EBls
§ Ash Wednesday — See *R.* Ash Wednesday = **'Aschermittwoch'**
'Assemblage des Beautés' (G) — EBls MAus
'Astrid Späth Striped' (F) — EBls
♦ Atco Royale — See *R.* Atco Royale = **'Frywinner'**
Atlantic Star (F) — MFry MJon
Audrey Gardner (Min/Patio) — SRum
Audrey Wilcox (HT) — MFry
'August Seebauer' (F) — EBls MAus
'Auguste Gervais' (Ra) — EBls IHar MAus SPer SRum WHCG
♦ Auguste Renoir® — See *R.* Auguste Renoir = **'Meitoifar'**

'Augustine Guinoisseau' (HT) — EBls MAus

'Augustine Halem' (HT) — EBls

§ Dapple Dawn = 'Ausapple' (S) — MAus SPer SWCr

§ The Wife of Bath = 'Ausbath' (S) — IHar MAus MBri

§ Moonbeam = 'Ausbeam' (S) — MAus

§ Bow Bells = 'Ausbells' (S) — MAus MHlr

§ The Dark Lady = 'Ausbloom' (S) — EBrP EBre EPfP IHar IHos LBre MAus MBri MJon MTis NBus NPri SBre SChu SJus SWCr

§ Peach Blossom = 'Ausblossom' (S) — MAus MHlr SWCr

§ Heritage® = 'Ausblush' (S) — CGro CSam EBar EBls ELan EMFP ENot GCoc GGre IHar IHos LGod LPlm LStr MAus MBri MFry MHlr MJon MMat NBat SApu SJus SMad SPer SRum WAct WHCG WHow WOVN

§ Gertrude Jekyll® = 'Ausbord' (S) ♈ — Widely available

§ Jayne Austin = 'Ausbreak' (S) — EBrP EBre LBre MAus MJon MTis SApu SBre SPer SWCr

§ Bredon® = 'Ausbred' (S) — IHar MAus MBri

§ Mayor of Casterbridge = 'Ausbrid' (S) — IHar MAus MJon NPri

§ English Garden® = 'Ausbuff' (S) — CAbP EBar EBrP EBre EMFP ENot IHar LBre LStr MAus MBri MMat SApu SBre SPer WAct WWeb

§ Emily = 'Ausburton' (S) — MAus SApu

§ Canterbury = 'Ausbury' (S) — MAus

§ Marinette = 'Auscam' (S) — MAus NPri SWCr

§ Winchester Cathedral® = 'Auscat' (S) — CDoC CGro CHad EBls EBrP EBre EMFP GChr GGre IHar LBre LGod LStr MAus MBri MHlr MJon SApu SBre SChu SJus SPer SPla SRum SSoC SWCr WOVN

§ John Clare = 'Auscent' — EBrP EBre LBre MAus NPri SBre

§ Chaucer® = 'Auscer' (S) — MAus MBri

§ Charity = 'Auschar' (S) — MAus

§ Fisherman's Friend® = 'Auschild' (S) — CDoC IHos MAus SChu SPer SRum

§ Kathryn Morley = 'Ausclub' (F) — CAbP EBrP EBre IHar LBre MAus MHlr MJon MTis NPri SBre SWCr

§ Red Coat = 'Auscoat' (F) — IHos MAus SWCr

§ Happy Child = 'Auscomp' (S) — EBrP EBre IHar LBre MAus MHlr MJon SBre SJus SPer WGer

§ Heather Austin = 'Auscook' — MAus NPri

§ Abraham Darby® = 'Auscot' (S) — CDoC CGro CSam EBrP EBre GGre IHar LBre LGod LStr MAus MFry MGan MHlr MJon MTis NPri SBre SPer SWCr WAct WHCG WHow WStI

§ Country Living® = 'Auscountry' (S) — EBls IHos MAus

§ Cressida = 'Auscress' (S) — MAus

§ L.D. Braithwaite® = 'Auscrim' (S) — CDoC CSam EBrP EBre ENot IHar LBre LGod LPlm LStr MAus MBri MFry MGan MHlr MJon MMat NFla SBre SJus SPer SRum SSoC SWCr WAct WHCG WHow WWeb

§ Windflower = 'Auscross' (S) — EBrP EBre LBre MAus NPri SBre

§ Ellen® = 'Auscup' (S) — MAus MBri

§ The Alexandra Rose = 'Ausday' (S) — MAus SWCr WHow

§ Bibi Maizoon® = 'Ausdimindo' — IHar IHos MAus SPer

§ Tradescant® = 'Ausdir' (S) — EBrP EBre IHar LBre MAus MGan MHlr NPri SBre

§ Doctor Jackson® = 'Ausdoctor' (S) — MAus

§ Mrs Doreen Pike = 'Ausdor' (S) — MAus WAct

§ Fair Bianca® = 'Ausea' (S) — IOrc MAus MBri MHlr

§ Belle Story® = 'Auselle' — MAus

§ Lucetta = 'Ausemi' (S) — MAus SPer WAct

§ Financial Times Centenary = 'Ausfin' — IHos MAus

§ Morning Mist = 'Ausfire' (S) — MAus

§ Cottage Rose® = 'Ausglisten' (S) — EPfP MAus MJon NPri SJus SWCr WHow

§ Brother Cadfael = 'Ausglobe' (S) — EBar EPfP IHar MAus MBri MHlr MJon NPri SPer SSoC WOVN

§ Golden Celebration® = 'Ausgold' (S) — EBee EBrP EBre GGre IHar LBre LStr MAus MBri MGan MHlr MJon NPri SApu SBre SJus SPer WGer

§ Geoff Hamilton® = 'Ausham' — MAus

§ Hero® = 'Aushero' (S) — MAus

§ Jacquenetta = 'Ausjac' (S) — MAus

§ Pretty Jessica = 'Ausjess' (S) — IHos MAus MHlr MJon SPer

§ Jude the Obscure = 'Ausjo' (S) — CAbP IHar MAus MJon

§ Mistress Quickly = 'Ausky' (S) — IHar MAus MJon NPri

§ Sceptre'd Isle® = 'Ausland' — CAbP EPfP MAus SPer

§ Leander® = 'Auslea' (S) — MAus MBri SWCr

§ English Elegance® = 'Ausleaf' (S) — MAus

§ Cymbeline = 'Auslean' (S) — MAus SPer SRum

§ Sweet Juliet® = 'Ausleap' (S) — CAbP EBls EBrP EBre IHar LBre LGod LPlm MAus MBri MHlr MJon NBat SApu SBre SJus SPer WAct WHow WOVN

§ A Shropshire Lad = 'Ausled' (S) — MAus MJon

§ Charles Austin® = 'Ausles' (S) — IHar MAus MBri NSty SJus WAct WHCG

§ Symphony® = 'Auslett' — CGro MJon WAct

§ Glamis Castle = 'Auslevel' (S) — CBlo EBls EBrP EBre IHar LBre MAus MBri MJon NPri SBre SJus SPer WAct WHCG WHow

§ Lilian Austin® = 'Ausli' (S) — IHos MAus MBri

§ Warwick Castle® = 'Auslian' (S) — EBar MAus NBus SPer

§ Claire Rose® = 'Auslight' (S) — CGro CSam EBar EBee IHar IHos MAus MJon NPri SPer SWCr

§ Othello® = 'Auslo' (S) — MAus SApu WAct

§ Sophy's Rose = 'Auslot' (S) — MAus

§ The Countryman® = 'Ausman' (S) — CAbP EBrP EBre IHar LBre MAus MFry MHlr NPri SBre SJus

§ Eglantyne = 'Ausmark' (S) — CAbP EBrP EBre IHar LBre MAus MHlr MJon SBre SJus SPer SWCr

§ Mary Rose® = 'Ausmary' (S) — CGro CHad CSam EBls EBrP EBre ELan ENot GCoc GGre IHos LBre LGod LStr MAus MBri MFry MGan MHlr MJon MMat NBat SApu SBre SJus SPer SRum WAct WOVN

§ Graham Thomas = 'Ausmas' (S) ♀ — Widely available

§ Heavenly Rosalind = 'Ausmash' — MAus

§ Charmian® = 'Ausmian' (S) — MAus

§ Saint Cecilia® = 'Ausmit' (S) — EBar EBee ELan IHos MAus MHlr MJon SJus SRum

§ Molineux = 'Ausmol' (S) — EBrP EBre GCoc IHar LBre LGod MAus MBri MHlr MJon NPri SBre WHCG

§ Pegasus = 'Ausmoon' (S) — IHar MAus MJon NPri SSoC SWCr

§ Pat Austin = 'Ausmum' (S) — MAus MJon NBus SJus SWCr

§ Hilda Murrell® = 'Ausmurr' (S) — MAus

§ The Nun = 'Ausnun' (S) — MAus

§ Troilus = 'Ausoil' (S) — MAus

§ Trevor Griffiths = 'Ausold' (S) — EBrP EBre LBre MAus SBre SWCr

§ Redouté = 'Auspale' (S) — CAbP EBrP EBre LBre MAus NPri SBre SJus SPer

§ Perdita® = 'Ausperd' (S) — EBee IHos IOrc MAus MBri MHlr MTis SPer SWCr WAct WHCG

§ Prospero® = 'Auspero' (S) — MAus MBri WAct

§ Charlotte = 'Auspoly' (S) — CAbP IHar MAus MHlr MJon NPri SApu SWCr WAct

§ Wise Portia = 'Ausport' (S) — MAus

§ The Squire® = 'Ausquire' (S) — MAus WAct

§ Francine Austin® = 'Ausram' (S/GC) — EPfP IHos MAus SPer WAct

§ Sharifa Asma® = 'Ausreef' (S) — CAbP EBrP EBre ENot EPfP IHar LBre LStr MAus MHlr MJon MMat NFla NPri SBre SJus SPer WAct

§ The Reeve® = 'Ausreeve' (S) — MAus

§ Charles Rennie Mackintosh® = 'Ausren' (S) — MAus MJon NPri SWCr WGer

§ William Shakespeare® = 'Ausroyal' (S) — CTri ELan GCoe GGre IHar IHos LStr MBri NBus SMad SPer SRum WStI

§ Windrush® = 'Ausrush' (S) — IHar MAus MBri SPer SWCr WAct WHCG

§ Radio Times = 'Aussal' (S) — EBrP EBre IHar LBre MAus MJon NPri SBre

§ Evelyn® = 'Aussaucer' (S) — CAbP EBee EBrP EBre EMFP GCoc IHar LBre LGod MAus MHlr MJon MMat SApu SBre SChu SPer SSoC WHow

§ The Herbalist® = 'Aussemi' (S) — MAus

§ Mountain Snow = 'Aussnow' (Ra) — MAus MBri

§ Sir Walter Raleigh® = 'Ausspry' (S) — MAus MBri

§ Tamora = 'Austamora' (S) — MAus

§ Constance Spry = 'Austance' (ClS) ♀ — Widely available

§ Barbara Austin = 'Austop' (S) — MAus

§ Rushing Stream = 'Austream' (GC) — MAus

Austrian Copper — See *R. foetida* 'Bicolor'

Austrian Yellow — See *R. foetida*

§ Emanuel® = 'Ausuel' (S) — MAus SPer

§ The Prince® = 'Ausvelvet' (S) — CAbP EBar EBrP EBre LBre MAus MJon MTis NPri SBre SWCr WHow

§ The Pilgrim = 'Auswalker' (S) — CAbP CHad EBrP EBre IHar LBre LFis MAus MBri MHlr MJon MTis SBre SChu SJus SPer WHCG WHow

§ Noble Antony = 'Ausway' (S) — MAus MJon NPri SWCr

§ Mary Webb® = 'Auswebb' (S) — MAus MBri

§ Wenlock® = 'Auswen' (S) — CSam EBar EBrP EBre GGre IHar LBre MAus SBre SPer

§ Swan® = 'Auswhite' (S) — MAus MJon

§ Saint Swithun = 'Auswith' (S) — EMFP GQui MAus MJon SWCr

§ Ambridge Rose = 'Auswonder' (S) — MAus MBri MTis

§ Yellow Charles Austin® = 'Ausyel' (S) — MAus MBri

'Autumn' (HT) — NRog

'Autumn Bouquet' (S) — EBls

'Autumn Delight' (HM) — EBls MAus WHCG

'Autumn Fire' — See *R.* 'Herbstfeuer'

'Autumn Sunlight' (ClHT) — MGan SPer

'Autumn Sunset' (S) — EBls

'Autumnalis' — See *R.* 'Princesse de Nassau'

'Aviateur Blériot' (Ra) — EBls MAus

◆ Avocet — See *R.* Avocet = 'Harpluto'

Avon — See *R.* Avon = 'Poulmulti'

◆ Awakening — See *R.* Awakening = 'Probuzini'

◆ Awareness — See *R.* Awareness = 'Frybingo'

'Ayrshire Splendens' — See *R.* 'Splendens'

'Baby Bio' (F) — CB&S MBri MGan NRog SRum

'Baby Darling' (Min) — MAus MGan

'Baby Faurax' (Poly) — MAus

'Baby Katie' (Min) — NBat

◆ Baby Love yellow (Min/Patio) — See *R.* Baby Love = 'Scrivluv'

◆ Baby Masquerade® — See *R.* Baby Masquerade = 'Tanba'

◆ Baby Sunrise (Min) — See *R.* Baby Sunrise = 'Macparlez'

'Bad Neuenahr' (Cl) — MGan

'Ballerina' (HM) ♀ — CB&S CHad EBrP EBre ELan ENot GCoc GGre LBre LGod LPlm LStr MAus MBri MBur MFry MGan MHlr MJon MMat NFla NRog SApu SBre SJus SPer SRum WAct WHCG WWeb

Ballindalloch Castle	See *R.* Ballindalloch Castle = **'Cocneel'**
'Baltimore Belle' (Ra)	EBls MAus WHCG
banksiae (Ra)	CGre GQui LPan SPer SRms
– *alba*	See *R. banksiae* var. *banksiae*
§ – var. *banksiae* (Ra/d)	CBot EPfP ERea LStr MAus NSty SBid SBra WWat
– 'Lutea' (Ra/d) ♀	CB&S CFee CGre CPlN CSPN CSam CTrw EBls ELan ENot ERea GQui ISea LStr MAus MHlr MMat NPSI NSty SBra SMad SPer SSoC SUsu WAct WBod WHCG WSHC WWat WWeb
– var. *normalis* (Ra)	CBot CGre MAus NSty
– 'Purezza'	See *R.* **'Purezza'**
¶ – SF 96051 (Ra)	ISea
Bantry Bay® (ClHT)	EBls LStr MGan MMat SJus SPla SRum SSea SWCr
◆ Barbara Austin	See *R.* Barbara Austin = **'Austop'**
'Barbara Carrera' (F)	EBls
◆ Barkarole®	See *R.* Barkarole = **'Tanelorak'**
'Baron de Bonstetten' (HP)	EBls
'Baron de Wassenaer' (CeMo)	EBls MGan
'Baron Girod de l'Ain' (HP)	CPou EBls MAus MHlr NSty SPer SPla SWCr WAct WHCG WHow
◆ 'Baroness Rothschild' (HT)	See *R.* Baronne Edmond de Rothschild = **'Meigriso'**
§ 'Baronne Adolph de Rothschild' (HP)	CPou EBee EMFP IHos IOrc MGan WHCG
'Baronne de Rothschild' (HP)	See *R.* **'Baronne Adolph de Rothschild'**
◆ Baronne Edmond de Rothschild®	See *R.* Baronne Edmond de Rothschild = **'Meigriso'**
'Baronne Henriette de Snoy' (T)	EBls
'Baronne Prévost' (HP) ♀	EBls MAus SFam WAct WHCG
§ Tranquility = 'Barout' (HT)	MBur
Barry Fearn	See *R.* Barry Fearn = **'Korschwana'**
§ Snowgoose = 'Barshifle' (F)	MAus MJon
'Bashful' (Poly)	MGan
◆ Basildon Bond	See *R.* Basildon Bond = **'Harjosine'**
◆ Battersby Beauty	See *R.* Battersby Beauty = **'Horbatbeauty'**
§ Myra = 'Battoo' (HT)	NBat
§ Norwich Cathedral = 'Beacath' (HT)	EBls
§ Dixieland Linda = 'Beadix' (ClHT)	EBls
§ × *beanii* (Ra)	EPla SMad
§ Twenty-fifth = 'Beatwe' (F)	EBls
¶ 'Beau Narcisse' (G)	MAus
'Beauté' (HT)	EBls MAus MGan
◆ Beautiful Britain	See *R.* Beautiful Britain = **'Dicfire'**
'Beauty of Rosemawr' (ClT)	EBls
◆ Beauty Star®	See *R.* Liverpool Remembers = **'Frystar'**
§ Pudsey Bear = 'Bedchild' (HT)	COtt GGre SCoo SPer
§ Amanda = 'Beesian' (F)	LStr MBri MJon SApu

§ Aalsmeer Gold® = 'Bekola' (HT)	MJon
¶ 'Bel Ange' (HT)	MGan
◆ Belfast Belle	See *R.* Belfast Belle = **'Dicrobot'**
¶ *bella*	EBee
'Belle Amour' (DxA)	EBls MAus NSty WHCG
'Belle Blonde' (HT)	MGan SPer
'Belle de Crécy' (G) ♀	EBls GCoc IOrc MAus MHlr MMat NSty SFam SJus SMer SPer SWCr WAct WHCG WHow
'Belle des Jardins'	See *R.* **'Centifolia Variegata'**
◆ Belle Epoque	See *R.* Belle Epoque = **'Fryyaboo'**
'Belle Isis' (G)	EBls MAus SPer
'Belle Lyonnaise' (ClT)	EBls
'Belle Poitevine' (Ru) ♀	EBls MAus NSty
'Belle Portugaise' (Cl)	EBls MAus
◆ Belle Story®	See *R.* Belle Story = **'Auselle'**
◆ Belle Sunblaze	See *R.* Belle Sunblaze = **'Meidanego'**
◆ Bellevue®	See *R.* Bellevue = **'Poulena'**
* 'Bengal Beauty'	WWat
Benita®	See *R.* Benita = **'Dicquarrel'**
§ Kristin™ = 'Benmagic' (Min)	NBat
'Bennett's Seedling' (Ra)	MAus
◆ Benson and Hedges Special	See *R.* Benson and Hedges Special = **'Macshana'**
◆ Berkshire	See *R.* Berkshire = **'Korpinka'**
Best Wishes	See *R.* Best Wishes = **'Chessnut'**
◆ Bettina®	See *R.* Bettina = **'Mepal'**
◆ Betty Driver	See *R.* Betty Driver = **'Gandri'**
'Betty Prior' (F)	GCoc MGan
'Betty Uprichard' (HT)	EBls NSty
'Beyreuth' (S)	MGan
◆ Bianco	See *R.* Bianco = **'Cocblanco'**
Bibi Maizoon®	See *R.* Bibi Maizoon = **'Ausdimindo'**
◆ Biddulph Grange	See *R.* Biddulph Grange = **'Frydarkeye'**
§ *biebersteinii*	EBls
'Big Chief' (HT)	MJon NRog
◆ Big Purple	See *R.* Big Purple = **'Stebigpu'**
◆ Birthday Girl	See *R.* Birthday Girl = **'Meilasso'**
¶ 'Birthday Wishes' (HT)	LPlm
'Bishop Darlington' (HM)	EBls
◆ Bishop Elphinstone	See *R.* Bishop Elphinstone = **'Cocjolly'**
'Bit o' Sunshine' (Min)	MGan
'Black Beauty' (HT)	MAus MJon
'Black Ice' (F)	MGan
◆ Black Jack	See *R.* Black Jack = **'Minkco'**
'Black Jack' (Ce)	See *R.* **'Tour de Malakoff'**
'Black Prince' (HP)	EBls
'Blairii Number One' (Bb)	EBls NSty
'Blairii Number Two' (ClBb) ♀	EBee EBls EMFP MAus MHlr NSty SFam SPer SWCr WAct WHCG WHow WSHC
'Blanche de Vibert' (DPo)	EBls MAus
'Blanche Double de Coubert' (Ru) ♀	CHad CSam EBls ELan ENot GCoc IHos IOrc LBuc LHol LStr MAus MFry MGan MHlr MJon MMat NRog NSty SApu SJus SPer SRum WAct WHCG WHow WOVN
'Blanche Moreau' (CeMo)	EBls IHar IHos MAus MGan MHlr NSty SPer WAct
'Blanchefleur' (CexG)	EBls IHos MAus NSty
blanda	EBls
'Blaydon Races'	NBat

Blenheim	See *R.* Blenheim = **'Tanmurse'**	§ 'Brenda Colvin' (Ra)	MAus
Blessings® (HT) ♀	CB&S CDoC CGro EBls EBrP	'Brennus' (China hybrid)	EBls
	EBre GCoc GGre IHos LBre	'Briarcliff' (HT)	EBls
	LGod LPlm LStr MAus MBri	◆ Bridal Pink	See *R.* Bridal Pink = **'Jacbri'**
	MBur MFry MGan MJon NBat	Bride	See *R.* Bride = **'Fryyearn'**
	NRog SApu SBre SPer SWCr	◆ Bright Fire	See *R.* Bright Fire = **'Peaxi'**
	WWeb	◆ Bright Smile®	See *R.* Bright Smile =
'Bleu Magenta' (Ra) ♀	EBee EBls MAus WHCG		**'Dicdance'**
'Bloomfield Abundance'	EBls MAus MMat NSty SPer	◆ Bright Spark	See *R.* Bright Spark =
(Poly)	SRum SWCr WHCG WHer		**'Rubrispa'**
	WHow	'Brindis' (ClF)	MGan
'Bloomfield Dainty' (HM)	EBls	¶ 'Britannia' (HT)	MFry
'Blossomtime' (Cl)	NRog SMad SPer	Broadlands	See *R.* Broadlands =
'Blue Diamond' (HT)	MGan		**'Tanmirson'**
◆ Blue Moon®	See *R.* Blue Moon = **'Tannacht'**	◆ Brother Cadfael	See *R.* Brother Cadfael =
◆ Blue Parfum®	See *R.* Blue Parfum =		**'Ausglobe'**
	'Tanfifum'	◆ Brown Velvet	See *R.* Brown Velvet =
◆ Blue Peter	See *R.* Blue Peter = **'Ruiblun'**		**'Macultra'**
'Blush Boursault' (Bs)	EBls MAus	'Browsholme Rose'	NSty
'Blush Damask' (D)	EBls WHCG	§ *brunonii* (Ra)	CHan EBls EWes MAus SBra
'Blush Noisette'	See *R.* **'Noisette Carnée'**		WLRN
'Blush Rambler' (Ra)	EBls MAus MHlr SPer SPla	¶ – 'Betty Sherriff' (Ra)	SSpi
	WHCG WHow	§ – 'La Mortola' (Ra)	MAus SMac
'Blushing Lucy' (Ra)	MAus SMrm WAct WSHC	¶ 'Bubbles' (GC)	MFry
'Bob Collard' (F)	SRum	Buck's Fizz (F)	GGre MBur MGan SApu SJus
¶ 'Bob Greaves' (F)	MFry	'Buff Beauty' (HM) ♀	CB&S CHad CSam EBls ENot
¶ Bob Grieves	MFry		GCoc GGre IHos IOrc LGod
'Bob Woolley' (HT)	NBat		LHol LStr MAus MBri MFry
'Bobbie James' (Ra) ♀	CHad EBls EBrP EBre IHos		MGan MHlr MJon MMat NRog
	LBre LStr MAus MGan MHlr		NSty SApu SJus SPer SPla
	MMat NBat NSty SBre SJus		SRum WAct WHCG WOVN
	SPer SRum WAct WHCG		WWeb
	WHow	'Bullata'	See *R.* × *centifolia* **'Bullata'**
'Bobby Charlton' (HT)	MFry MGan NRog	§ Katie Crocker =	MBur
'Bobolink' (Min)	MGan	'Burbrindley' (F)	
'Bon Silène' (T)	EBls	§ 'Burgundiaca' (G)	EBls LFis MAus WAct WHCG
Bonfire Night® (F)	CGro ENot MBur MGan	Burgundian Rose	See *R.* **'Burgundiaca'**
◆ Bonica®	See *R.* Bonica = **'Meidomonac'**	§ Grumpy = 'Burkhardt'	MGan
◆ Bonica 82	See *R.* Bonica = **'Meidomonac'**	(Poly)	
'Bonn' (HM)	CB&S MAus MGan NRog	'Burma Star' (F)	GCoc
'Bonnie Scotland' (HT)	MGan	Burnet, Double Pink	See *R. pimpinellifolia* double
◆ Bonsoir	See *R.* Bonsoir = **'Dicbo'**		pink
'Border Coral' (F)	NRog	Burnet, Double White	See *R. pimpinellifolia* double
§ Middlesex County =	NBat		white
'Bosanne' (F)		§ Good Luck = 'Burspec'	MJon SRum
§ Peppermint Ice =	MJon MRav SApu SRum	(F/Patio)	
'Bosgreen' (F)		◆ Bush Baby	See *R.* Bush Baby = **'Peanob'**
'Botzaris' (D)	EBls SFam	◆ Buttons	See *R.* Buttons = **'Dicmickey'**
'Boule de Nanteuil' (G)	EBls	◆ By Appointment	See *R.* By Appointment =
'Boule de Neige' (Bb)	CHad EBls EMFP ENot GCoc		**'Harvolute'**
	IHar LHol LStr MAus MHlr	'C.F. Meyer'	See *R.* **'Conrad Ferdinand**
	MMat NFla NSty SFam SJus		**Meyer'**
	SPer SPla SRum SWCr WAct	§ *caesia* subsp. *glauca*	MSto
	WHCG WOVN	'Café' (F)	WBcn
'Bouquet d'Or' (N)	EBls MAus WHCG	'Cairngorm' (F)	GCoc GGre
'Bouquet Tout Fait'	See *R.* **'Nastarana'**	'Caledonian' (HT)	NBat
misapplied		*californica* (S)	MAus
'Bourbon Queen' (Bb)	EBee EBls MAus MHlr NSty	– 'Plena'	See *R. nutkana* **'Plena'**
	WHCG	'Callisto' (HM)	MAus WHCG
◆ Bow Bells	See *R.* Bow Bells = **'Ausbells'**	◆ Calypso	See *R.* Calypso = **'Poulclimb'**
Boy O Boy	See *R.* Boy O Boy =	'Camaïeux' (G)	EBls MAus MHlr MMat SPer
	'Dicuniform'		SWCr WAct WHCG
◆ Boys' Brigade®	See *R.* Boys' Brigade =	◆ Cambridgeshire	See *R.* Cambridgeshire =
	'Cocdinkum'		**'Korhaugen'**
§ *bracteata*	EHol GQui MAus WHCG	'Camélia Rose' (Cl)	EBls WHCG
	WWat	'Cameo' (Poly)	EBls IHar MAus MGan SMer
◆ Brave Heart	See *R.* Brave Heart =	§ Mary Donaldson =	MGan
	'Horbondsmile'	'Canana' (HT)	
◆ Breath of Life	See *R.* Breath of Life =	'Canary Bird'	See *R. xanthina* **'Canary Bird'**
	'Harquanne'	Can-can	See *R.* Can-can = **'Legglow'**
◆ Bredon®	See *R.* Bredon = **'Ausbred'**	§ Goldstar = 'Candide'	EBee MGan SApu
'Breeze Hill' (Ra)	EBls MAus	(HT)	

§ Lady Rachel = 'Candoodle' (F) — EBee

◆ Candy Rose® — See *R.* Candy Rose = 'Meiranovi'

canina (S) — CB&S CCVT CKin CPer GChr LBuc MAus MHew NWea WMou

– 'Abbotswood' — See *R.* 'Abbotswood' (*canina* hybrid)

– 'Andersonii' — See *R.* 'Andersonii' (*canina* hybrid)

¶ – deep pink (S) — MAus

– 'Inermis' (S) — MSto

§ Sally's Rose = 'Canrem' (HT) — EBee GCoc GGre SApu SJus

§ Colchester Beauty = 'Cansend' (F) — EBee

§ Jenny's Rose = 'Cansit' (F) — EBee

§ Dame Wendy = 'Canson' (F) — GCoc LGod MAus MBri MGan MJon SApu

'Cantabrigiensis' (S) ♀ — EBee EBls ENot GChr MAus MHlr NBus NFla NRog SPer WAct WHCG WOVN WWat

Canterbury — See *R.* Canterbury = 'Ausbury'

'Capitaine Basroger' (CeMo) — EBls MAus

'Capitaine John Ingram' (CeMo) ♀ — EBee EBls MAus NSty SPer WHow

¶ 'Captain Christy' (HT) — MAus

◆ Captain Cook — See *R.* Captain Cook = 'Macal'

'Captain Hayward' (HP) — EBls

¶ 'Captain Scarlet' (MinCl) — WWeb

'Cardinal de Richelieu' (G) ♀ — CHad CPou EBls EMFP GCoc IOrc MAus MFry MHlr MMat NSty SApu SFam SPer WAct WHCG WHow

◆ Cardinal Hume® — See *R.* Cardinal Hume = 'Harregale'

'Carmen' (Ra) — EBls MAus

§ 'Carmenetta' (S) — EBls MAus

§ 'Carol' (Gn) — See *R.* 'Carol Amling'

§ 'Carol Amling' (Gn) — SWCr

carolina — CGre LHop SLPl WHCG

◆ Caroline de Monaco® — See *R.* Caroline de Monaco = 'Meipierar'

'Caroline Testout' — See *R.* 'Madame Caroline Testout'

§ Indian Sunblaze = 'Carol-Jean' (Min/Patio) — IHos

◆ Casino® — See *R.* Casino = 'Macca'

◆ Castle of Mey — See *R.* Castle of Mey = 'Coclucid'

◆ Catherine Cookson — See *R.* Catherine Cookson = 'Noscook'

'Catherine Mermet' (T) — EBls MAus NSty

'Catherine Seyton' (RH) — EBls

§ 'Cécile Brünner' (Poly) ♀ — CBos CHad EBls ELan EMFP ENot GCoc LHol LStr MAus MGan MHlr MMat NRog NSty SJus SPer SPla SRum SWCr WAct WHCG WHow WOVN WWat

◆ 'Cécile Brünner, White' — See *R.* 'White Cécile Brunner'

◆ Cecily Gibson — See *R.* Cecily Gibson = 'Evebright'

§ 'Céleste' (A) ♀ — EBls EMFP ENot GCoc IHar IHos MAus MFry MHlr MMat NFla NSty SApu SFam SJus SPer SRum SWCr WAct WGer WHCG WHow WOVN

'Celestial' — See *R.* 'Céleste'

'Célina' (CeMo) — EBls MGan

'Céline Forestier' (N) ♀ — EBls MAus SFam SPer SPla WAct WHCG

§ 'Celsiana' (D) — EBls IHar MAus MHlr SFam SPer WAct WHCG

◆ Centenaire de Lourdes® — See *R.* Centenaire de Lourdes = 'Delge'

◆ Centenary — See *R.* Centenary = 'Koreledas'

§ × *centifolia* (Ce) — CTri EBls IOrc MAus MHlr NRog SJus SMad WAct WHCG

§ – 'Bullata' (Ce) — EBls MAus

§ – 'Cristata' (Ce) ♀ — EBls EMFP ENot EPfP IHos MAus MMat NBus NRog SFam SJus SPer WAct WHCG

§ – 'Muscosa' (Ce) ♀ — CPou CTri EBls EMFP ENot GCoc IHos IOrc MAus MGan MMat NRog NSty SFam SJus WAct

– 'Parvifolia' — See *R.* 'Burgundiaca'

§ 'Centifolia Variegata' (Ce) — EBls MAus MGan

'Cerise Bouquet' (S) ♀ — EBls IHar MAus MMat NSty SJus SPer WAct WHCG WKif WWeb

◆ Cha Cha — See *R.* Cha Cha = 'Cocarum'

◆ Champagne® — See *R.* Champagne = 'Korampa'

◆ Champagne Cocktail — See *R.* Champagne Cocktail = 'Horflash'

'Champion' (HT) — MAus

'Champneys' Pink Cluster' (China hybrid) — EBls MAus

◆ Champs Elysées® — See *R.* Champs Elysées = 'Meicarl'

'Chanelle' (F) — EBls GCoc MAus MGan NRog SPer

Chapeau de Napoléon — See *R.* × *centifolia* 'Cristata'

'Chaplin's Pink Climber' (Cl) — EBls MGan

◆ Chardonnay — See *R.* Chardonnay = 'Macrealea'

◆ Charity — See *R.* Charity = 'Auschar'

◆ Charles Austin® — See *R.* Charles Austin = 'Ausles'

'Charles de Mills' (G) ♀ — CHad EBls ELan EMFP ENot GCoc IHar MAus MFry MHlr MJon MMat NSty SFam SJus SPer SRum SWCr WAct WHCG WHow WWeb

'Charles Gater' (HP) — EBls

'Charles Lefèbvre' (HP) — EBls

'Charles Mallerin' (HT) — EBls

◆ Charles Rennie Mackintosh® — See *R.* Charles Rennie Mackintosh = 'Ausren'

◆ Charleston — See *R.* Charleston = 'Meiridge'

◆ Charlotte — See *R.* Charlotte = 'Auspoly'

◆ Charmian® — See *R.* Charmian = 'Ausmian'

'Charter 700' (F) — MFry

'Château de Clos-Vougeot' (HT) — MGan

Chatsworth — See *R.* Chatsworth = 'Tanotax'

◆ Chaucer® — See *R.* Chaucer = 'Auscer'

◆ Chelsea Belle — See *R.* Chelsea Belle = 'Talchelsea'

◆ Chelsea Pensioner — See *R.* Chelsea Pensioner = 'Mattche'

Cherry Brandy (HT) — MBur MFry MGan MJon SRum

'Cherryade' (S) — MGan

§ Thank You = 'Chesdeep' (Patio) — GGre MJon

'Cheshire Life' (HT) — MAus MBur MFry MGan MJon NPri SRum WStI

§ Best Wishes = 'Chesnut' (Cl/v) — GCoc GGre LStr MJon SWCr

§ Golden Hands = 'Chessupremo' (Min/Patio) — CDoC GGre SPer

◆ Chester Cathedral — See *R.* Chester Cathedral = **'Franshine'**

§ Rosalie Coral = 'Chewallop' (Cl) — EBrP EBre LBre MBri MJon NBat NPer NPri SApu SBre SJus

§ Laura Ford® = 'Chewarvel' (ClMin) ♀ — EBrP EBre GGre IHar LBre LStr MAus MBri MBur MGan MJon MMat NBat NPri SApu SBre SJus SRum SWCr WWeb

§ Pillar Box = 'Chewaze' (F) — MGan

§ Donald Davis = 'Chewbeaut' (F) — MJon

§ Warm Welcome = 'Chewizz' (ClMin) ♀ — CDoC EBrP EBre GCoc GGre LBre LGod LStr MAus MBri MBur MFry MJon MMat NBat NPri SBre SJus SMad SPer SRum SSea SSoC WWeb

§ Edith Holden = 'Chewlegacy' (F) — LGod MAus MBri MJon SApu SJus

§ Open Arms = 'Chewpixcel' (ClMin) — LGod MFry MJon WGer

§ Pathfinder = 'Chewpobey' (GC) — MJon MMat

§ Little Rambler = 'Chewramb' (MinRa) — MJon MMat SApu

§ Nice Day = 'Chewsea' (ClMin) — EBrP EBre ENot GGre LBre LStr MBri MBur MFry MJon MMat NBat SApu SBre SJus WOVN

§ Good as Gold = 'Chewsunbeam' (ClMin) — EBrP EBre LBre LStr MBri MBur MFry MJon SApu SBre WGer WOVN

§ Golden Handshake = 'Chewsunford' (Patio) — MBri

'Chianti' (S) — EBls MAus MBri NSty WHCG

◆ Chicago Peace® — See *R.* Chicago Peace = **'Johnago'**

◆ Chilterns — See *R.* Chilterns = **'Kortemma'**

Chinatown® (F/S) ♀ — CB&S CGro EBls EBrP EBre ELan GCoc GGre IHos LBre LPlm LStr MAus MGan MJon NRog NSty SApu SBre SJus SPer SRum

◆ *chinensis* 'Minima' — See *R.* **'Rouletii'**

– 'Mutabilis' — See *R.* x *odorata* **'Mutabilis'**

– 'Old Blush' — See *R.* x *odorata* **'Pallida'**

'Chloris' (A) — EBls EMFP

'Chorus Girl' (F) — MGan

◆ Christian Dior — See *R.* Christian Dior = **'Meilie'**

'Christine Gandy' (F) — MGan

Christopher (HT) — See *R.* Christopher = **'Cocopher'**

◆ Christopher Columbus® (HT) — See *R.* Christopher Columbus = **'Meinronsse'**

§ 'Chromatella' (N) — EBls MAus

'Chrysler Imperial' (HT) — EBls MAus MGan

◆ Cider Cup — See *R.* Cider Cup = **'Dicladida'**

'Cinderella' (Min) — MGan

cinnamomea — See *R. majalis*

'Circus' (F) — MGan

City Lights — See *R.* City Lights = **'Poulgan'**

◆ City of Belfast® — See *R.* City of Belfast = **'Macci'**

◆ City of Birmingham — See *R.* City of Birmingham = **'Korholst'**

'City of Leeds' (F) — ENot GGre MGan MMat NRog SPer WStI

◆ City of London® — See *R.* City of London = **'Harukfore'**

¶ 'City of Newcastle' (HT) — NBat

'City of Portsmouth' (F) — CB&S MGan

◆ City of York — See *R.* City of York = **'Direktor Benschop'**

◆ Clair Matin® — See *R.* Clair Matin = **'Meimont'**

'Claire Jacquier' (N) — EBls MAus SPer WAct WHCG

◆ Claire Rayner — See *R.* Claire Rayner = **'Macpandem'**

◆ Clarissa® — See *R.* Clarissa = **'Harprocrustes'**

'Clementina Carbonieri' (T) — EBls

◆ Cleopatra — See *R.* Cleopatra = **'Korverpea'**

Climbing Alec's Red® (ClHT) — SPer SRum

'Climbing Allgold' (ClF) — EBls GGre IHos MGan SRum

'Climbing Arthur Bell' (ClF) — CTri NRog SApu SPer SRum

¶ 'Climbing Ballerina' (Ra) — SWCr

◆ Climbing Bettina® — See *R.* Climbing Bettina = **'Mepalsar'**

Climbing Blessings® (ClHT) — EBls SRum

'Climbing Blue Moon' (ClHT) — MBur MGan

'Climbing Captain Christy' (ClHT) — EBls MAus

'Climbing Cécile Brünner' (ClPoly) ♀ — CHad CHan EBls LGod LStr MAus NSty SApu SFam SJus SPer SWCr WAct WHCG WHow WSHC WWat

'Climbing Château de Clos-Vougeot' (ClHT) — EBls MAus

'Climbing Cherryade' (ClHT) — MGan

'Climbing Christine' (ClHT) — MAus

§ 'Climbing Columbia' (ClHT) — ERav ERea NSty WHCG

'Climbing Comtesse Vandal' (ClHT) — EBls MAus

'Climbing Crimson Glory' (ClHT) — EBls EMFP GCoc MAus MGan NRog SRum WStI

§ 'Climbing Devoniensis' (ClT) — CPou EBls MAus NSty

'Climbing Ena Harkness' (ClHT) — CB&S CGro CTri EBar EBls GCoc GGre IHos MAus MBri MBur MGan NRog SPer SPla SRum WStI WWeb

'Climbing Ernest H. Morse' (ClHT) — MGan

'Climbing Etoile de Hollande' (ClHT) ♀ — CPou CSam EBls EBrP EBre EMFP GCoc LBre LHol LStr MAus MGan MHlr MJon MRav NRog NSty SApu SBre SChu SJus SPer SPla SRum SWCr WHCG WHow WOVN WWeb

◆ Climbing Fragrant Cloud — See *R.* Climbing Fragrant Cloud = **'Colfragrasar'**

§ 'Climbing Frau Karl Druschki' (ClHP) — EBls MGan NRog

'Climbing General MacArthur' (ClHT) — EBls MAus

◆ Climbing Gold Bunny — See *R.* Climbing Gold Bunny = **'Meigro-Nurisar'**

'Climbing Golden Dawn' (ClHT) — MAus

'Climbing Grand-mère Jenny' (ClHT) — EBls

'Climbing Home Sweet Home' (ClHT) — MAus

'Climbing Iceberg' (ClF) ♀ — CGro EBls EBrP EBre ELan ENot GGre LBre LPlm LStr MAus MBri MGan MJon NRog SBre SPer SRum WHCG WOVN WSHC WWeb

'Climbing Irish Fireflame' (ClHT) — MAus

'Climbing Josephine Bruce' (ClHT) — MAus MGan

'Climbing la France' (ClHT) — CPou MAus

§ 'Climbing Lady Hillingdon' (ClT) ♀ — EBls EBrP EBre EMFP EPfP LBre MAus MGan MHlr NSty SApu SBre SFam SPer WAct WHCG WSHC

'Climbing Lady Sylvia' (ClHT) — EBls EMFP MAus MGan NRog SApu SPer WStI

'Climbing Little White Pet' — See R. 'Félicité Perpétue'

'Climbing Madame Abel Chatenay' (ClHT) — EBls MAus

'Climbing Madame Butterfly' (ClHT) — EBls EBrP EBre LBre MAus MGan SBre SJus SPer

'Climbing Madame Caroline Testout' (ClHT) — EBls MAus NRog NSty SPer SWCr WBcn WSHC

§ 'Climbing Madame Edouard Herriot' (ClHT) — EBls MAus MGan SPer

'Climbing Madame Henri Guillot' (ClHT) — EBls MAus

'Climbing Maman Cochet' (ClT) — EBls MAus

'Climbing Masquerade' (ClF) — EBls EBrP EBre GGre LBre LPlm MAus MGan MJon NRog SBre SRum WStI WWeb

'Climbing McGredy's Yellow' (ClHT) — MGan

§ 'Climbing Mevrouw G.A. van Rossem' (ClHT) — EBls MAus

'Climbing Mrs Aaron Ward' (ClHT) — EBls MAus

'Climbing Mrs G.A. van Rossem' — See R. 'Climbing Mevrouw G.A. van Rossem'

'Climbing Mrs Herbert Stevens' (ClHT) — EBee EBls EMFP MAus MHlr NRog NSty SPer WHCG WHow

'Climbing Mrs Sam McGredy' (ClHT) ♀ — CGro CTri EBls LPlm MAus MBri MGan MJon NRog SPla SRum

'Climbing My Love' (ClHT) — MGan NPri

¶ 'Climbing Niphetos' (ClT) — EBls MAus

'Climbing Ophelia' (ClHT) — EBee EBls MAus MHlr

♦ Climbing Orange Sunblaze — See R. Climbing Orange Sunblaze = 'Meijikatarsar'

'Climbing Pascali' (ClHT) — CB&S MGan

§ 'Climbing Paul Lédé' (ClT) — EBee EBls EBrP EBre EMFP IHar LBre MAus MHlr SBre WHCG WHow

'Climbing Picture' (ClHT) — EBls MAus MGan

§ 'Climbing Pompon de Paris' (ClCh) — CBot CDec CHan EBls LHop MAus MGan MRav NSty SMer SPer WHCG WSHC

'Climbing Richmond' (ClHT) — EBls MAus

'Climbing Roundelay' (Cl) — EBls

'Climbing Shot Silk' (ClHT) ♀ — EBee EBls MAus MGan SJus SPer SRum

§ 'Climbing Sombreuil' (ClT) — CHad EBls EBrP EBre EMFP LBre MAus MHlr MRav SBid SBre SChu SFam SJus SPer SPla SWCr WAct WHCG WHow

§ 'Climbing Souvenir de la Malmaison' (ClBb) — EBls MAus SPer WAct WHCG

'Climbing Spek's Yellow' (ClHT) — MAus

'Climbing Summer Sunshine' (ClHT) — MBri

♦ Climbing Super Star — See R. Climbing Super Star = 'Tangostar'

'Climbing Sutter's Gold' (ClHT) — MAus MGan

'Climbing Talisman' (ClHT) — EBls

'Climbing the Doctor' (ClHT) — MGan

'Climbing the Queen Elizabeth' (ClF) — EBls MGan SRum

'Clio' (HP) — MJon

♦ 'Cloth of Gold' — See R. 'Chromatella'

§ Wee Jock = 'Cocabest' (F/Patio) — GChr GCoc GGre LStr SWCr

§ Vital Spark = 'Cocacert' (F) — MGan

§ The Coxswain = 'Cocadilly' (HT) — GCoc

§ Golden Jubilee = 'Cocagold' (HT) — ELan GCoc GGre LPlm LStr MAus MBur NBat SRum

§ Dainty Dinah = 'Cocamond' (Min/Patio) — GCoc LStr SApu

§ Pink Posy = 'Cocanelia' (Min/Patio) — MAus

N Sweetheart = 'Cocapeer' (HT) — GCoc GGre MGan SWCr

§ Cha Cha = 'Cocarum' (Patio/Min) — SApu

Sunset Song = 'Cocasun' (HT) — GCoc

§ Crathes Castle = 'Cocathes' — GCoc

§ Doctor Dick = 'Cocbaden' (HT) — GCoc NBat

§ Fyvie Castle = 'Cocbamber' (HT) — GCoc GGre MGan

§ Bianco = 'Cocblanco' (Patio/Min) — GCoc MAus SJus

§ Ena Baxter = 'Cocbonne' (HT) — GCoc GGre

§ Abbeyfield Rose = 'Cocbrose' (HT) ♀ — ENot GCoc GGre NPri SApu SJus SPer

§ Rosabell® = 'Cocceleste' (F/Patio) — GCoc GGre LPlm MFry SApu

§ Ray of Sunshine = 'Cocclare' (Patio) — GCoc LPlm LStr MBri MFry

§ Gingernut = 'Coccrazy' (Patio) — EBrP EBre GCoc GGre LBre NBat SApu SBre

§ Royal Volunteer = 'Cocdandy' (HT) — GCoc

§ Scottish Special = 'Cocdapple' (Min/Patio) — GCoc MJon

§ Coral Reef = 'Cocdarlee' (Min/Patio) — GCoc GGre LStr SWCr

§ Remember Me® = 'Cocdestin' (HT) ♀ — EBrP EBre GCoc GGre LBre LGod LPlm LStr MBri MFry MGan MJon MMat NBat NRog SApu SBre SJus SPer SWCr

§ Conservation = 'Cocdimple' (Min/Patio) — GCoc GGre LStr MBri MJon NBat SApu WWeb

§ Boys' Brigade® = 'Cocdinkum' (Patio) — CGro GCoc MGan SApu

§ Roxburghe Rose = 'Cocember' (HT) — GCoc

§ Highland Laddie = 'Cocflag' — GCoc

§ Regal Red = 'Cocfoster' (S) — GCoc

§ Honey Bunch® = 'Cocglen' — GCoc LGod LStr MBri MJon NBat SApu

§ Toprose = 'Cocgold' (F) — EBrP EBre GCoc GGre LBre SBre SJus

§ Myriam® = 'Cocgrand' (HT) — GCoc MJon SApu

§ Shirley Spain = 'Cocharod' (F) — GCoc

§ Hello = 'Cochello' (Min/Patio) — GCoc

§ Ohshima Rose = 'Cochunter' (HT) — GCoc

§ Gordon's College = 'Cocjabby' (F) — GCoc SApu

§ UNICEF = 'Cocjojo' (F) — GCoc

§ Bishop Elphinstone = 'Cocjolly' (F) — GCoc

◆ Cocktail® — See *R.* Cocktail = **'Meimick'**

§ William Quarrier = 'Coclager' (F) — GCoc

§ Scotland's Trust = 'Coclands' (HT) — GCoc

§ Lady MacRobert = 'Coclent' (F) — GCoc

§ Alison = 'Coclibee' (F) — GCoc SApu

§ Castle of Mey = 'Coclucid' (F) — GCoc MJon

§ Wee Cracker = 'Cocmarris' (Patio) — GCoc

§ Aberdeen Celebration = 'Cocmystery' (F) — GCoc

§ Friend for Life = 'Cocnanne' (F) — GCoc MJon

§ Ballindalloch Castle = 'Cocneel' (F) — GCoc

§ Ray of Hope = 'Cocnilly' (F) — GCoc

§ Alex C. Collie = 'Cococrust' (F) — GCoc

§ Greer Garson = 'Cocoddy' (HT) — GCoc

§ Christopher = 'Cocopher' (HT) — GCoc

§ Heartbeat = 'Cocorona' (F) — NBat

§ Marguerite Anne = 'Cocredward' (F) — GCoc NBat SApu

§ Rob Roy® = 'Cocrob' (F) — GCoc MBur MGan SPer

§ Curiosity = 'Cocty' (HT/v) — GGre MJon

§ My Love = 'Cogamo' (HT) — MAus MBur MJon

◆ Colchester Beauty — See *R.* Colchester Beauty = **'Cansend'**

§ Climbing Fragrant Cloud = 'Colfragrasar' (ClHT) — CB&S ELan MGan

§ Colibre '79 (Min) — ELan LStr SWCr

Colibre '80 — See *R.* Colibre '79

◆ Colibri — See *R.* Colibri = **'Meimal'**

§ 'Colonel Fabvier' — EBls MAus

Colonial White — See *R.* **'Climbing Sombreuil'**

◆ Colorama — See *R.* Colorama = **'Meirigalu'**

◆ 'Columbian' — See *R.* **'Climbing Columbia'**

'Commandant Beaurepaire' (Bb) — EBls MAus NSty SWCr

Common Moss — See *R.* × *centifolia* **'Muscosa'**

Compassion® (ClHT) ♀ — Widely available

§ 'Complicata' (G) ♀ — EBls IHar MAus MBri MGan MHlr MMat MRav NRog NSty SApu SJus SPer SSpi WAct WHCG WOVN WSHC

N 'Comte de Chambord' — See *R.* **'Madame Knorr'**

'Comtesse Cécile de Chabrillant' (HP) — EBls MAus

'Comtesse de Lacépède' — See *R.* **'Du Maître d'Ecole'**

'Comtesse de Murinais' (DMo) — EBls IHar MAus SFam SWCr

§ 'Comtesse du Cayla' (Ch) — MAus

'Comtesse Vandal' (HT) — MAus

'Condesa de Sástago' (HT) — EBls

§ 'Conditorum' (G) — EBls SFam

◆ Congratulations — See *R.* Congratulations = **'Korlift'**

§ 'Conrad Ferdinand Meyer' (Ru) — EBls IHos MAus MGan NSty SPer SRum WAct

◆ Conservation — See *R.* Conservation = **'Cocdimple'**

Constance Fettes — See *R.* Constance Fettes = **'Cocnest'**

◆ Constance Spry — See *R.* Constance Spry = **'Austance'**

§ 'Cooperi' (Ra) — EBls MAus WAct WHow WSHC

Cooper's Burmese — See *R. laevigata* **'Cooperi'**

'Copenhagen' (ClHT) — EBls MAus MBri

'Copper Delight' (F) — NRog

◆ Copper Pot — See *R.* Copper Pot = **'Dicpe'**

'Coral Cluster' (Poly) — EBls MAus MGan SMer

'Coral Creeper' (ClHT) — EBls

Coral Dawn® (ClHT) — EBls IHar MFry MJon

◆ Coral Reef — See *R.* Coral Reef = **'Cocdarlee'**

'Coral Satin' (Cl) — EBls MGan

'Coralie' (D) — EBls

'Coralin' (Min) — LGod MGan

◆ Cordon Bleu — See *R.* Cordon Bleu = **'Harubasil'**

§ Alec's Red® = 'Cored' (HT) — CB&S CGro EBls GCoc IHar IHos LPlm LStr MAus MBri MGan MJon MMat NRog SPer WWeb

'Cornelia' (HM) ♀ — CB&S CHad CSam EBls ENot GCoc GGre IHos LHol LStr MAus MBri MFry MHlr MJon MMat NFla NRog NSty SApu SJus SPer SRum WAct WHCG WOVN WWeb

'Coronation Gold' (F) — GCoc

'Coryana' — EBls

I 'Corylus' — See *R.* **'Hazel Le Rougetel'**

corymbifera — EBls

corymbulosa — EBls

'Cosimo Ridolfi' (G) — EBls

Cottage Garden — See *R.* Cottage Garden = **'Haryamber'**

Cottage Maid — See *R.* **'Centifolia Variegata'**

◆ Cottage Rose™ — See *R.* Cottage Rose = **'Ausglisten'**

◆ Country Lady — See *R.* Country Lady = **'Hartsam'**

◆ Country Living™ — See *R.* Country Living = **'Auscountry'**

'Coupe d'Hébé' (Bb) — EBls MAus MBri

◆ Courage — See *R.* Courage = **'Poulduff'**

'Cramoisi Picotée' (G) — EBls MAus

'Cramoisi Supérieur' (Ch) — EBls MAus WHCG

'Cramoisi Supérieur Grimpant' (ClCh)	EBls
◆ Crathes Castle	See *R.* Crathes Castle = **'Cocathes'**
¶ 'Creme de la Creme' (Cl)	MGan
'Crépuscule' (N)	EBls NSty WHCG
Cressida	See *R.* Cressida = **'Auscress'**
Crested Moss	See *R.* × *centifolia* 'Cristata'
◆ Cricri	See *R.* Cricri = **'Meicri'**
◆ Crimson Cascade	See *R.* Crimson Cascade = **'Fryclimbdown'**
'Crimson Conquest' (ClHT)	EBls
Crimson Damask	See *R. gallica* var. *officinalis*
¶ 'Crimson Descant' (Cl)	EBee
'Crimson Gem' (Min)	MGan
'Crimson Globe' (Mo)	MGan
'Crimson Glory' (HT)	CTri EBls MBur MGan WAct
'Crimson Rambler' (Ra)	MAus MRav WBcn
'Crimson Shower' (Ra) ♀	EBrP EBre EMFP IHos LBre LPlm MAus MGan MHlr MJon MMat NRog SBre SPer SWCr WGer WHCG WHer WStI
'Cristata'	See *R.* × *centifolia* 'Cristata'
Crystal Palace®	See *R.* Crystal Palace = **'Poulrek'**
Cuisse de Nymphe	See *R.* 'Great Maiden's Blush'
'Cupid' (ClHT)	EBee EBls MAus SPer WAct
◆ Curiosity	See *R.* Curiosity = **'Cocty'**
◆ Cymbeline	See *R.* Cymbeline = **'Auslean'**
'Cynthia Brooke' (HT)	EBls
'D'Aguesseau' (G)	EBls MAus SPer
◆ Daily Express	See *R.* Daily Express = **'Frychambi'**
'Daily Mail'	See *R.* **'Climbing Madame Edouard Herriot'**
◆ Daily Post	See *R.* Daily Post = **'Frytrooper'**
◆ Daily Sketch	See *R.* Daily Sketch = **'Macai'**
'Dainty Bess' (HT)	EBls MAus MRav NSty
◆ Dainty Dinah	See *R.* Dainty Dinah = **'Cocamond'**
'Dainty Maid' (F)	EBls MAus
'Dairy Maid' (F)	MAus
'Daisy Hill' ('Macrantha' hybrid)	EBls
◆ Dalli Dalli®	See *R.* Dalli Dalli = **'Tanlilida'**
× *damascena* var. *bifera*	See *R.* × *damascena* var. *semperflorens*
§ – var. *semperflorens* (D)	EBls EMFP IHos MAus WAct WHCG WHow
N – 'Trigintipetala' misapplied	See *R.* **'Professeur Emile Perrot'**
§ – var. *versicolor* (D)	EBee EBls ENot IHos MAus MGan NSty SFam WAct WHCG
'Dame Edith Helen' (HT)	EBls
◆ Dame Wendy	See *R.* Dame Wendy = **'Canson'**
'Danaë' (HM)	EBls EMFP MAus MHlr WHCG
◆ Dancing Pink	See *R.* Dancing Pink = **'Hendan'**
◆ Danse Des Sylphes®	See *R.* Danse des Sylphes = **'Malcair'**
Danse du Feu® (Cl)	CB&S CGro EBls ELan ENot GCoc GGre IHos LGod LPlm LStr MAus MBri MFry MGan MJon MMat NRog SApu SPer SRum SSea WWeb
'Daphne Gandy' (F)	MGan
Dapple Dawn	See *R.* Dapple Dawn = **'Ausapple'**
◆ Darling Flame	See *R.* Darling Flame = **'Meilucca'**

'Dart's Defender'	SLPl
◆ David Whitfield	See *R.* David Whitfield = **'Gana'**
davidii	EBls MAus
Dawn Chorus	See *R.* Dawn Chorus = **'Dicquaser'**
'Daybreak' (HM)	EBls MAus NRog SWCr WAct WHCG
◆ Daylight	See *R.* Daylight = **'Interlight'**
◆ Dazzler	See *R.* Dazzler = **'Genpat'**
§ 'De Meaux' (Ce)	EBls EMFP ENot LFis MAus MMat NSty SPer SPla SWCr WHCG WHow
'De Meaux, White'	See *R.* **'White de Meaux'**
§ 'De Rescht' (DPo) ♀	CBos EBls ENot IHar LHol MAus MGan MJon MMat NFla NSty SPer WAct WGer WHCG WHow
'Dearest' (F)	CB&S CDoC GGre MBri MGan MJon NRog SRum WStI
◆ Deb's Delight	See *R.* Deb's Delight = **'Legsweet'**
'Debutante' (Ra)	EBls MAus MHlr SFam
'Deep Secret' (HT)	CDoC CGro EBrP EBre GCoc GGre LBre LPlm MBur MFry MGan MJon NRog SApu SBre SJus SPer SRum WWeb
§ Doc = 'Degenhard' (Poly)	MGan
'Delambre' (DPo)	EBls MAus MRav
§ Royal Baby = 'Delbrad' (F/Min)	MBur
§ Centenaire de Lourdes® = 'Delge' (F)	EBls
¶ 'Delicata' (Ru)	MAus
§ Altissimo® = 'Delmur' (Cl) ♀	CHad EBee EBls EMFP LPlm MAus MGan MHlr MJon MMat SPer SSea SWCr WAct WGer
§ Happy Anniversary = 'Delpre' (F)	CTri GChr GGre MJon WWeb
'Dembrowski' (HP)	EBls
◆ Denman	See *R.* Denman = **'Landen'**
'Dentelle de Malines' (S)	EBls MAus MHlr WAct
'Deschamps' (N)	EBls
'Desprez à Fleurs Jaunes' (N) ♀	CPou EBee EBls EMFP IHar MAus NPri NSty SFam SPla WHCG WHow WSHC
'Deuil de Paul Fontaine' (Mo)	EBls
'Devoniensis' (ClT)	See *R.* **'Climbing Devoniensis' (ClT)**
Diadem (F)	MFry MJon
'Diamond Jubilee' (HT)	EBls
§ Red Devil® = 'Dicam' (HT)	GGre LPlm MAus MGan MJon NBat NRog SRum
§ Memento® = 'Dicbar' (F)	IDic MBri MGan MMat
§ Acapulco = 'Dicblender' (HT)	EBee IDic MFry NBat
§ Bonsoir = 'Dicbo' (HT)	MGan
§ Bright Smile® = 'Dicdance' (F/Patio)	CDoC GCoc IDic IHar LStr MAus MFry MGan SPer SWCr
§ Pot o' Gold = 'Dicdivine' (HT)	EBee IDic IHos LStr MAus MFry MGan MJon SApu SPer SRum
§ Shona = 'Dicdrum' (F)	IDic SApu
§ Scarlet Queen Elizabeth® = 'Dicel' (F)	CB&S CGro EBls GGre MBur MJon NPri SRum WStI
§ Beautiful Britain = 'Dicfire' (F)	EBls GGre IDic IHos LStr MAus MBri MGan MJon NRog SJus SRum SWCr WFar
§ Peek A Boo = 'Dicgrow' (Min/Patio)	EBrP EBre ELan ENot IDic IHar IHos LBre LGod MFry MGan SApu SBre SPer WStI

§ Disco Dancer® = 'Dicinfra' (F) — IDic IHos

§ Elina® = 'Dicjana' (HT) ♀ — GCoc GGre IDic LGod LStr MAus MBur MFry MGan MJon MMat NBat NRog SApu SJus SPer

§ Len Turner = 'Dicjeep' (F) — IDic SApu

§ Freedom® = 'Dicjem' (HT) ♀ — ENot GCoc GGre IDic IHar LGod LPlm LStr MAus MBur MFry MGan MMat NBat NRog SApu SJus WWeb

Leslie's Dream = 'Dicjoon' (HT) — IDic MBri

§ Ards Beauty = 'Dicjoy' (F) — IDic MGan MJon SApu SPer

§ Lovely Lady™ = 'Dicjubell' (HT) ♀ — CTri EBee IDic LStr MGan MJon SApu SJus SWCr

§ Wishing = 'Dickerfuffle' (F/Patio) — GCoc IDic IHar MFry MJon SApu SPer WWeb

§ Anisley Dickson® = 'Dickimono' (F) ♀ — GCoc IDic LGod MGan MJon NBat SApu SPer

§ Tall Story® = 'Dickooky' (S/GC) ♀ — EBls IDic MJon SApu SRms SRum WHCG WOVN

'Dickson's Flame' (F) — MGan

§ Cider Cup = 'Dicladida' (Min/Patio) ♀ — CDoC GChr GCoc GGre IDic LGod LStr MAus MBur MFry MJon NBat SApu

§ Little Woman = 'Diclittle' (Patio) — IDic IHos LStr SApu SWCr

§ Gentle Touch = 'Diclulu' (Min/Patio) ♀ — CDoC CGro EBls EBrP EBre GGre IDic IHar LBre MBri MFry MJon MMat NBat SApu SBre SPer SRum

§ Sweet Magic = 'Dicmagic' (Min/Patio) ♀ — CDoC CGro EBrP EBre ENot GCoc GGre IDic IHar IHos LBre LGod LPlm LStr MBri MFry MGan MJon MMat NBat SApu SBre SJus SPer SRum WWeb

§ Buttons = 'Dicmickey' (Min/Patio) — IDic IHos MFry

§ Minilights = 'Dicmoppet' (Patio) — IDic SApu SPer

§ Empress Michiko = 'Dicnifty' (HT) — GCoc IDic SApu WOVN

§ Harvest Fayre = 'Dicnorth' (F) — CGro IDic LGod LStr MAus MBri MGan MMat NBat SApu SPer SRum

§ Tequila Sunrise = 'Dicobey' (HT) ♀ — CTri GGre IDic IHar LPlm LStr MBri MBur MFry MGan MJon MMat NBat SApu SJus SPer

§ Fragrant Dream = 'Dicodour' (HT) — GGre IDic LStr MBri SApu

§ Tear Drop = 'Dicomo' (Min/Patio) — IDic LStr MFry MGan MJon NBat SApu SPer SRum SWCr

§ Redgold = 'Dicor' (F) — GGre IDic

§ Painted Moon = 'Dicpaint' (HT) — GCoc IDic

§ Party Trick = 'Dicparty' (F) — IDic MBri

§ Copper Pot = 'Dicpe' (F) — MGan SPer

§ Quaker Star = 'Dicperhaps' (F) — IDic

§ New Horizon = 'Dicplay' (F) — IDic

§ Benita® = 'Dicquarrel' (HT) — EBee GCoc IDic LGod MJon

§ Dawn Chorus = 'Dicquasar' (HT) — CGro EBrP EBre GCoc GGre IHar LBre LGod LPlm LStr MBri MFry MGan MJon MMat NPri SApu SBre SJus SPer SRum WWeb

§ Melody Maker = 'Dicqueen' (F) — CDoC IDic MAus MBri MBur MGan MJon NBat SJus

§ Sunseeker = 'Dicracer' (F/Patio) — EPfP GGre IDic LGod MJon

§ Our Molly = 'Dicreason' (GC/S) — IDic MGan SApu

§ Flair = 'Dicrelax' (F) — IDic LStr MJon

§ Belfast Belle = 'Dicrobot' (HT) — IDic

§ Princess Royal = 'Dicroyal' (HT) — GCoc GGre IDic MBri

§ Mr J.C.B. = 'Dicsun' (S) — IDic

§ Shine On = 'Dictalent' (Patio) — COtt GCoc IDic MBri MFry MJon SJus WWeb

§ Pure Bliss = 'Dictator' (HT) — EBee GCoc IDic MJon NBat

§ Pretty in Pink = 'Dicumpteen' (GC) — IDic MJon

§ Wine and Dine = 'Dicuncle' (GC) — IDic

§ Boy O Boy = 'Dicuniform' (GC) — GCoc IDic

§ Tintinara = 'Dicuptight' (HT) — EBee GCoc IDic MFry

§ Happy Ever After = 'Dicvanilla' (F) — IDic MFry

§ Roche Centenary = 'Dicvintage' (Patio) — IDic

§ Glenshane = 'Dicvood' (S) — IDic

¶ Old John = 'Dicwillynilly' — ECle IDic

¶ Marry Me = 'Dicwonder' — ECle IDic

◆ Die Welt® — See R. Die Welt = 'Diekor'

§ Die Welt® = 'Diekor' (HT) — NBat

'Diorama' (HT) — MAus MGan NRog

'Directeur Alphand' (HP) — EBls WHCG

§ City of York = 'Direktor Benschop' (Ra) — EBls

◆ Disco Dancer® — See R. Disco Dancer = 'Dicinfra'

◆ Dixieland Linda — See R. Dixieland Linda = 'Beadix'

Doc — See R. Doc = 'Degenhard'

'Docteur Andry' (HP) — EBls

'Docteur Grill' (T) — EBls MAus

'Doctor A.J. Verhage' (HT) — MGan

'Doctor Abrahams' (HT) — MJon

◆ Doctor Dick — See R. Doctor Dick = 'Cocbaden'

'Doctor Eckener' (Ru) — EBls IHar MGan

'Doctor Edward Deacon' (HT) — EBls

◆ Doctor Goldberg — See R. Doctor Goldberg = 'Gandol'

◆ Doctor Jackson™ — See R. Doctor Jackson = 'Ausdoctor'

'Doctor John Snow' (HT) — MGan

◆ Doctor McAlpine — See R. Doctor McAlpine = 'Peafirst'

'Doctor W. Van Fleet' (Ra/Cl) — EBls MAus WSHC

'Don Charlton' (HT) — NBat

'Don Juan' (Cl) — MGan

◆ Donald Davis — See R. Donald Davis = 'Chewbeaut'

§ 'Doncasteri' — EBls MAus MSto

'Dopey' (Poly) — MGan

'Doreen' (HT) — NRog

Doris Tysterman (HT) — CGro EBls EBrP EBre GGre LBre LPlm LStr MAus MGan NRog SBre SRum WWeb

'Dorothy Perkins' (Ra) — CB&S CGro EBls GChr GGre GOrc LFis LPlm LStr MAus MGan MJon MMat NPer NRog NSty SApu SPer SRum WHCG

'Dorothy Wheatcroft' (F) — MGan

'Dorothy Whitney Wood' (HT) — MFry

'Dorothy Wilson' (F) — EBls

Dortmund® (ClHScB) — EBls LPlm MAus MGan MMat SPer WAct WHCG

◆ Double Delight® — See R. Double Delight = 'Andeli'

'Dream Girl' (Cl) ♀ — MAus MBri NSty

¶ 'Dream Lover' — GCoc

'Dreamglo' (Min) — NBat

'Dreaming Spires' (Cl) — IHos MBri MJon MMat SApu SJus SPer SRum

◆ Dreamland (HT) — See R. Dreamland = 'Resland' (HT)

◆ Dreamland (F) — See R. Dreamland = 'Träumland' (F)

'Dresden Doll' (MinMo) — EBls MAus SApu SPer

◆ Drummer Boy — See R. Drummer Boy = 'Harvacity'

§ 'Du Maître d'Ecole' (G) ♀ — EBls MAus WHCG

◆ Dublin Bay® — See R. Dublin Bay = 'Macdub'

'Duc de Fitzjames' (G) — EBls

'Duc de Guiche' (G) ♀ — CPou EBls MAus SFam SPer WAct WHCG

'Duchess of Portland' — See R. 'Portlandica'

◆ Duchess of York — See R. Sunseeker = 'Dicracer'

'Duchesse d'Albe' (T) — EBls

'Duchesse d'Angoulême' (G) — EBls MAus NSty SFam

'Duchesse d'Auerstädt' (N) — EBls

'Duchesse de Buccleugh' (G) — EBls MAus

§ 'Duchesse de Montebello' (G) ♀ — EBee EBls MAus MHlr SFam SPer SRms WHCG WHow

'Duchesse de Rohan' (CexHP) — EBls

'Duchesse de Verneuil' (CeMo) — EBls MAus SFam

◆ Duke Meillandina — See R. Duke Meillandina = 'Meipinjid'

'Duke of Edinburgh' (HP) — EBls MAus

'Duke of Wellington' (HP) — EBls WHCG

'Duke of Windsor' (HT) — IHar MGan NRog SPer

'Duke of York' (Ch) — EBls

Duke Sunblaze® — See R. Duke Meillandina

'Dundee Rambler' (Ra) — EBls MAus

'Dupontii' (S) — EBee EBls MAus SFam SPer WAct WHCG WHow WOVN

'Dupuy Jamain' (HP) — EBls WHCG

'Durham Prince Bishop' (HT) — NBat

'Dusky Maiden' (F) — EBls MAus WHCG

Dutch Gold® (HT) — CGro CTri LStr MAus MGan MJon NRog SPer

Dwarf King — See R. 'Zwergkönig'
(introduced 1957)

'E.H. Morse' — See R. 'Ernest H. Morse'

'Easlea's Golden Rambler' (Ra) — EBee EBls MAus NSty WAct WHCG

'Easter Morning' (Min) — ELan MAus MGan MJon SApu SPer SRum

'Eblouissant' (Poly) — MGan

ecae — EBls MAus

– 'Helen Knight' — See R. 'Helen Knight' (ecae hybrid)

'Eclair' (HP) — EBls

'Eddie's Jewel' — EBls IHar MAus MGan NSty
(moyesii hybrid)

Eden Rose® (HT) — EBls MGan SRum

◆ Eden Rose '88 — See R. Eden Rose '88 = 'Meiviolin'

'Edith Bellenden' (RH) — EBls

◆ Edith Holden — See R. Edith Holden = 'Chewlegacy'

eglanteria — See R. rubiginosa

Eglantyne — See R. Eglantyne = 'Ausmark'

'Elegance' (ClHT) — EBls MAus MGan

§ elegantula 'Persetosa' (S) — CHad EBls ENot MAus SPer WAct WHCG

◆ Elina® — See R. Elina = 'Dicjana'

'Eliza Boëlle' (HP) — WHCG

Elizabeth Harkness® (HT) — EBls MAus MBur MGan SPer

◆ Elizabeth Heather Grierson — See R. Elizabeth Heather Grierson = 'Mattnot'

◆ Elizabeth of Glamis® — See R. Elizabeth of Glamis = 'Macel'

'Elizabeth Philp' (F) — LPlm

◆ Ellen® — See R. Ellen = 'Auscup'

'Ellen Poulsen' (Poly) — MGan

'Ellen Willmott' (HT) — CHad EBee EBls MAus

'Elmshorn' (S) — CB&S MGan WHCG

◆ Elsie Warren — See R. Elsie Warren = 'Milsweet'

◆ Emanuel® — See R. Emanuel = 'Ausuel'

◆ Emily — See R. Emily = 'Ausburton'

'Emily Gray' (Ra) — CGro CPou EBls EBrP EBre ENot IHos LBre LStr MAus MBur MGan MHlr MJon NPri NRog NSty SBre SPer SRum SWCr WAct WHCG

◆ Emily Louise — See R. Emily Louise = 'Harwilla'

◆ Emma Mitchell — See R. Emma Mitchell = 'Horharpdos'

'Emma Wright' (HT) — MAus

'Emmerdale' (F) — WStI

'Empereur du Maroc' (HP) — EBls MAus MMat NSty WAct WHCG

'Empress Josephine' — See R. × francofurtana

◆ Empress Michiko — See R. Empress Michiko = 'Dicnifty'

◆ Ena Baxter — See R. Ena Baxter = 'Cocbonne'

'Ena Harkness' (HT) — CGro EBls ELan GChr GGre LStr MBur MGan NRog SRum WStI

§ 'Enfant de France' (HP) — EBls

¶ × engelmannii — EBls

◆ English Elegance® — See R. English Elegance = 'Ausleaf'

◆ English Garden® — See R. English Garden = 'Ausbuff'

'English Miss' (F) — CDoC EBls IHos LPlm LStr MAus MFry MGan MJon SApu SJus SPer SRum WStI WWeb

'Eos' (moyesii hybrid) — EBls MAus

'Erfurt' (HM) — EBls EMFP MAus MGan NSty SPla SRms SWCr WHCG

§ 'Erinnerung an Brod' (S) — WHCG

§ 'Ernest H. Morse' (HT) — CTri EBls GCoc GGre IHar IHos MAus MBur MGan MJon NRog SApu SPer SRum

Eroica (HT) — NRog

◆ Escapade®	See *R.* Escapade = **'Harpade'**	
'Especially for You'	See *R.* Especially For You = **'Fryworthy'**	
◆ Essex	See *R.* Essex = **'Poulnoz'**	
'Estrellita de Oro' (Min)	LPlm MAus MGan SPer	
§ 'Etendard'	MRav WAct	
· ◆ Eternally Yours	See *R.* Eternally Yours = **'Macspeego'**	
¶ 'Ethel' (Ra)	EMFP	
◆ Ethel Austin	See *R.* Ethel Austin = **'Frymestin'**	
'Etoile de Hollande' (HT)	CHad SSea	
'Etoile de Lyon' (T)	EBls	
'Eugène Fürst' (HP)	EBls WHCG	
'Eugénie Guinoisseau' (Mo)	EBls WHCG	
◆ Euphrates	See *R.* Euphrates = **'Harunique' (persica hybrid)**	
Europeana® (F)	CGro MAus MGan SWCr	
Eurostar	See *R.* Eurostar = **'Poulreb'**	
'Eva' (HM)	EBls	
'Evangeline' (Ra)	EBls MAus NSty WAct	
§ Cecily Gibson = 'Evebright' (F)	MJon	
◆ Evelyn®	See *R.* Evelyn = **'Aussaucer'**	
Evelyn Fison	See *R.* Evelyn Fison = **'Macev'**	
Evelyn Grace	See *R.* Evelyn Grace = **'Horavme'**	
◆ Evening Star®	See *R.* Evening Star = **'Jacven'**	
'Everest Double Fragrance' (F)	EBls	
'Excelsa' (Ra)	CTri EBls EMFP GChr GCoc GGre LGod LStr MAus MGan MJon NBus NRog NSty SRum SSea WAct WStI	
Exception (Ru)	WLRN	
◆ Exploit®	See *R.* Exploit = **'Meilider'**	
◆ Eye Paint	See *R.* Eye Paint = **'Maceye'**	
◆ Eyeopener	See *R.* Eyeopener = **'Interop'**	
'F.E. Lester'	See *R.* **'Francis E. Lester'**	
§ 'F.J. Grootendorst' (Ru)	EBls GOrc IHos IOrc LGod LStr MAus MGan MJon NRog NSty SRum WAct	
'Fabvier'	See *R.* **'Colonel Fabvier'**	
◆ Fair Bianca®	See *R.* Fair Bianca = **'Ausea'**	
◆ Fairhope	See *R.* Fairhope = **'Talfairhope'**	
◆ Fairy Changeling	See *R.* Fairy Changeling = **'Harnumerous'**	
◆ Fairy Damsel	See *R.* Fairy Damsel = **'Harneaty'**	
◆ Fairy Gold	See *R.* Fairygold = **'Frygoldie'**	
'Fairy Rose'	See *R.* **'The Fairy' (Poly) AGM**	
◆ Fairy Snow	See *R.* Fairy Snow = **'Holfairy'**	
◆ Fairyland®	See *R.* Fairyland = **'Harlayalong'**	
'Fantin-Latour' (*centifolia* hybrid) ♀	CHad EBls ELan ENot GCoc IHar IHos LStr MAus MBri MGan MHlr MMat NFla NRog NSty SApu SJus SPer SRum WAct WGer WHCG WHow WSHC WWeb	
fargesii hort.	See *R. moyesii* var. *fargesii*	
farreri	See *R. elegantula*	
– var. *persetosa*	See *R. elegantula* **'Persetosa'**	
◆ Fascination	See *R.* Fascination = **'Jacoyel' (HT)**	
◆ Favorite Rosamini	See *R.* Favorite Rosamini = **'Ruifaro'**	
fedtschenkoana	EBls MAus MGan NSty SPer WAct WHCG	
Fée des Neiges®	See *R.* Iceberg = **'Korbin'**	
'Felicia' (HM) ♀	CHad CSam EBls ENot GCoc IHar IHos LHol LStr MAus MBri MFry MHlr MJon MMat NFla NRog NSty SApu SJus SPer SRum WAct WHCG WHow WOVN	
'Félicité Parmentier' (AxD) ♀	EBls MAus NSty SFam SJus SPer WAct WHCG WOVN	
§ 'Félicité Perpétue' (Ra) ♀	EBls ELan GCoc IHar IHos ISea LHol LStr MAus MBri MGan MHlr MMat NFla NSty SApu SFam SJus SPer SWCr WAct WHCG WSHC	
◆ Felicity Kendal	See *R.* Felicity Kendal = **'Lanken'**	
'Fellenberg' (Ch)	EBls MAus WHCG	
◆ Fellowship	See *R.* Fellowship = **'Harwelcome'**	
'Femina' (HT)	MGan	
'Ferdinand Pichard' (Bb) ♀	EBls EMFP ENot IHar LFis MAus MBri MHlr MJon MMat NSty SJus SPer WAct WGer WHCG WHow WOVN	
◆ Ferdy®	See *R.* Ferdy = **'Keitoly'**	
◆ Fergie	See *R.* Fergie = **'Ganfer'**	
◆ Festival	See *R.* Festival = **'Kordialo'**	
Fiesta	See *R.* Fiesta = **'Macfirinlin'**	
◆ Fifi	See *R.* Fifi = **'Hanfif'**	
filipes 'Brenda Colvin'	See *R.* **'Brenda Colvin'**	
§ – 'Kiftsgate' (Ra) ♀	Widely available	
§ 'Fimbriata' (Ru)	EBls MAus MBri SPer WAct WHCG	
◆ Financial Times Centenary	See *R.* Financial Times Centenary = **'Ausfin'**	
◆ Fiona®	See *R.* Fiona = **'Meikeluxen'**	
'Firecracker' (F)	EBls	
◆ Firefly®	See *R.* Firefly = **'Macfrabro'**	
'First Love' (HT)	EBls MGan	
'Fisher and Holmes' (HP)	EBls MAus WAct WHCG	
◆ Fisherman's Friend®	See *R.* Fisherman's Friend = **'Auschild'**	
◆ Flair	See *R.* Flair = **'Dicrelax'**	
¶ 'Flamenco' (F)	EBee	
◆ Flamingo Meidiland	See *R.* Flamingo Meidiland = **'Meisolroz'**	
'Fleur Cowles' (F)	MBur	
'Flora' (Ra)	EBls MAus	
'Flora McIvor' (RH)	EBls MAus MGan	
Florence Nightingale (F)	MBri MBur MGan SApu SPer	
◆ Flower Carpet®	See *R.* Pink Flower Carpet = **'Noatraum'**	
◆ Flower Power	See *R.* Flower Power = **'Koredan'**	
§ *foetida* (S)	EBls MAus NSty	
§ – 'Bicolor' (S)	EBee EBls ENot IHar MAus MGan MMat NRog NSty SPer WAct	
§ – 'Persiana' (S)	EBls MAus MGan SPer	
foliolosa	EBls SLPl WHCG	
'Forgotten Dreams' (HT)	MJon	
forrestiana	EBls MAus MMat	
x *fortuneana*	EBls	
Fortune's Double Yellow	See *R.* x *odorata* **'Pseudindica'**	
'Fountain' (S/F)	CSam EBls LStr MAus MGan SApu SPer SRum	
◆ Fragrant Cloud	See *R.* Fragrant Cloud = **'Tanellis'**	
Fragrant Delight® (F) ♀	GCoc IHos LPlm LStr MFry MGan MJon NBat SApu SPer WWeb	
◆ Fragrant Dream	See *R.* Fragrant Dream = **'Dicodour'**	

◆ 'Fragrant Gold'　See *R.* Fragrant Gold = **'Tanduft'**

'Fragrant Hour' (HT)　MGan

'Francesca' (HM)　EBls LFis MAus MGan NSty SPer SWCr WAct WHCG

◆ Francine Austin®　See *R.* Francine Austin = **'Ausram'**

'Francis Dubreuil' (T)　EBls

§ 'Francis E. Lester' (HM/Ra) ♀　CHad CRHN CSam EBee EBls EBrP EBre LBre MAus MBri NSty SBre SFam SPer SWCr WAct WHCG WHow

§ × *francofurtana* ♀　EBls IHos MAus MRav SFam WAct WHCG

'François Juranville' (Ra) ♀　CRHN EBls LStr MAus MBri MGan MHlr MMat NBus NRog SApu SMad SPer SSoC WAct

§ Road to Freedom = 'Franlac' (F)　ECle

§ Summer Love = 'Franluv' (F)　IHar MJon

§ Chester Cathedral = 'Franshine' (HT)　MJon

'Frau Astrid Späth' (F)　NRog

§ 'Frau Karl Druschki' (HP)　EBls MAus MGan NSty WAct

'Fraulein Octavia Hesse' (Ra)　EBls

'Fred Loads' (S) ♀　CSam EBls MAus MFry MGan SApu

Freddie Mercury (HT)　NBat

◆ Free as Air　See *R.* Free as Air = **'Mehrbronze'**

◆ Freedom®　See *R.* Freedom = **'Dicjem'**

'Freiherr von Marschall' (T)　EBls

'Frensham' (F)　CB&S CGro EBls LStr MGan MMat

Fresh Pink (Min/Poly)　MGan

◆ Friend for Life　See *R.* Friend for Life = **'Cocnanne'**

'Fringette' (Min)　MGan

'Fritz Nobis' (S) ♀　EBls ENot GCoc IHar IHos LStr MAus MGan MHlr MRav NSty SJus SPer SWCr WAct WHCG WHow

◆ Frothy　See *R.* Frothy = **'Macfrothy'**

'Fru Dagmar Hastrup' (Ru) ♀　Widely available

'Frühlingsanfang' (PiH)　EBls MAus MBri WAct WHCG

'Frühlingsduft' (PiH)　EBee EBls NRog NSty

'Frühlingsgold' (PiH) ♀　CB&S CGro EBls EBrP EBre ELan ENot GCoc IOrc LBre LStr MAus MBri MFry MGan MMat NFla NRog NSty SApu SBre SJus SPer SRum SWCr WAct WHCG WOVN WWeb

'Frühlingsmorgen' (PiH)　EBls EBrP EBre ENot GCoc IHos LBre LFis LStr MAus MBri MGan MHlr MMat NFla NRog NSty SApu SBre SJus SPer SRum WAct WHCG WOVN

'Frühlingsschnee' (PiH)　EBls

'Frühlingszauber' (PiH)　EBls

§ Sightsaver = 'Fryaffair' (HT)　MFry SPer

¶ 'Fryamour' (HT)　MFry

§ Awareness = 'Frybingo' (HT)　MFry

§ Daily Express = 'Frychambi' (HT)　MFry

§ Crimson Cascade = 'Fryclimbdown' (Cl)　MAus MBri MFry NBat SApu SJus SWCr

§ Biddulph Grange = 'Frydarkeye' (S)　MFry

§ Fairygold = 'Frygoldie' (Patio)　MBri MFry SRum

§ Johnnie Walker = 'Frygran' (HT)　MFry SApu

§ The Flower Arranger = 'Fryjam' (F)　MFry MJon

§ Inner Wheel = 'Fryjasso' (F)　MFry

§ The Lady = 'Fryjingo' (S) ♀　EBee GCoc MAus MBur MFry MJon

§ Marianne Tudor = 'Frymartor' (HT)　MFry

§ Ethel Austin = 'Frymestin' (F)　MFry

§ Sweet Dream = 'Fryminicot' (Patio) ♀　CDoC CGro EBrP EBre ELan GCoc GGre LBre LGod LPlm LStr MAus MBri MBur MFry MGan MJon NBat SApu SBre SJus SPer SRum SWCr WOVN WWeb

§ Top Marks = 'Fryministar' (Min/Patio)　CDoC EBrP EBre GCoc LBre LGod LPlm LStr MBri MBur MFry MGan MJon MMat SApu SBre SCoo SJus SRum WStI WWeb

§ Arc Angel = 'Fryorst' (HT)　MFry

§ Velvet Fragrance = 'Fryperdee' (HT)　EBee GCoc LStr MAus MBur MFry MJon NBat SApu

§ Julie Cussons = 'Fryprincess' (F)　MFry

§ Pensioner's Voice = 'Fryrelax' (F)　MFry

§ Langdale Chase = 'Fryrhapsody' (F)　MFry

¶ 'Fryromeo' (HT)　MFry

§ Shrewsbury Show = 'Fryshrewby' (HT)　MFry

§ Liverpool Remembers = 'Frystar' (HT)　LGod MBri MBur MFry

§ Mary Gammon = 'Frysweetie' (Min/Patio)　MFry

§ Golden Moments = 'Frytranquil' (HT)　MBur MFry MJon

§ Daily Post = 'Frytrooper' (F)　MFry

§ Julie Andrews = 'Fryvivacious' (F)　MFry

§ Atco Royale = 'Frywinner' (HT)　MFry

§ Especially for You = 'Fryworthy' (HT)　LGod LStr MBur SApu

§ Warm Wishes = 'Fryxotic' (HT)　CTri EBee GCoc GGre LGod LPlm LStr MAus MBur MFry MGan MJon NPri SApu SJus SRum WWeb

§ Belle Epoque = 'Fryyaboo' (HT)　GCoc LStr MBur MFry MGan MJon MMat SApu

§ Bride = 'Fryyearn' (HT)　LPlm LStr MFry MJon SApu SWCr

§ Pomona = 'Fryyeh' (F)　MFry

§ Rosie Larkin = 'Fryyippee' (S)　MFry

§ Special Occasion = 'Fryyoung' (HT)　GCoc MFry SApu

§ The Cheshire Regiment = 'Fryzebedee' (HT)　MFry

'Fulgens'	See *R.* '**Malton**' (**China hybrid**)
Fulton Mackay (HT)	GCoc MFry MGan SApu
◆ Fyvie Castle	See *R.* Fyvie Castle =
	'**Cocbamber**'
'Gail Borden' (HT)	MAus MGan
§ *gallica* (G)	EBls
– 'Complicata'	See *R.* '**Complicata**'
– 'Conditorum'	See *R.* '**Conditorum**'
§ – var. *officinalis* (G) ♀	EBls GCoc GPoy LHol MAus
	MBri MMat NRog NSty SApu
	SFam SJus SPer WAct WHCG
	WHow
– 'Velutiniflora' (G)	EBls
§ – 'Versicolor' (G) ♀	CHad CSam EBls ELan ENot
	GChr GCoc GGre LStr MAus
	MBri MFry MGan MJon NRog
	NSty SApu SJus SPer SPla
	WHCG WHow WWeb
◆ Galway Bay®	See *R.* Galway Bay = '**Macba**'
§ David Whitfield = 'Gana' (R)	MGan MJon
§ Doctor Goldberg = 'Gandol' (HT)	MGan
§ Betty Driver = 'Gandri' (F)	MBri MGan SPer
§ Fergie = 'Ganfer' (F/Patio)	MGan
§ Moriah = 'Ganhol' (HT)	MGan
§ Spangles = 'Ganspa' (F)	MBur MGan
'Gardenia' (Ra)	MHlr SPer WHCG
§ 'Garnette' (Gn)	SRum
§ 'Garnette Apricot' (Gn)	SPla
'Garnette Carol'	See *R.* '**Carol Amling**'
'Garnette Golden'	See *R.* '**Golden Garnette**'
'Garnette Pink'	See *R.* '**Carol Amling**'
'Garnette Red'	See *R.* '**Garnette**'
◆ Gary Lineker	See *R.* Gary Lineker = '**Pearobin**'
'Gary Player' (HT)	NBat
'Gateshead Festival' (HT)	NBat
◆ 'Gaujard'	See *R.* Rose Gaujard = '**Gaumo**'
§ Rose Gaujard® = 'Gaumo' (HT)	EBls GGre LGod LPlm MAus MBur MGan SRum
◆ 'Gelbe Dagmar Hastrup'	See *R.* Yellow Dagmar Hastrup = '**Moryelrug**'
'Général Galliéni' (T)	EBls
'Général Jacqueminot' (HP)	EBls MAus WAct
'Général Kléber' (CeMo)	EBls MAus NSty SFam SPer WAct WHCG
§ 'Général Schablikine' (T)	EBls MAus WBcn
§ Dazzler = 'Genpat' (Patio)	MJon
N *gentiliana* (Ra)	EBls MAus WHCG
◆ Gentle Touch	See *R.* Gentle Touch = '**Diclulu**'
◆ Geoff Hamilton	See *R.* Geoff Hamilton = '**Ausham**'
◆ Geordie Lad	See *R.* Geordie Lad = '**Horkorblush**'
'Georg Arends' (HP)	EBls MAus
'George Dickson' (HT)	EBls MAus SRms
'George R. Hill' (HT)	NBat
'Georges Vibert' (G)	EBls MAus WHCG
◆ Geraldine	See *R.* Geraldine = '**Peahaze**'
§ 'Geranium' (*moyesii* hybrid) ♀	CB&S CGro EBrP EBre ELan ENot EPla GCoc IHar IOrc LBre LStr MAus MBri MGan MHlr NSty SApu SBre SPer SRum WAct WHCG WOVN WSHC WWeb
Gerbe d'Or	See *R.* Casino = '**Macca**'
'Gerbe Rose' (Ra)	EBls MAus NSty WAct

◆ Gertrude Jekyll®	See *R.* Gertrude Jekyll = '**Ausbord**'
'Ghislaine de Féligonde' (S/Ra)	EBls WHCG
gigantea	EBls ISea
– 'Cooperi'	See *R. laevigata* '**Cooperi**'
◆ Gilda	See *R.* The Daily Telegraph = '**Peahigh**'
Gingernut	See *R.* Gingernut = '**Coccrazy**'
◆ Ginny-Lou	See *R.* Ginny-Lou = '**Trobinka**'
Gipsy Boy	See *R.* '**Zigeunerknabe**'
◆ Glad Tidings	See *R.* Glad Tidings = '**Tantide**'
◆ Glamis Castle	See *R.* Glamis Castle = '**Auslevel**'
§ Lincoln Cathedral = 'Glanlin' (HT)	MGan MJon SApu SPer
§ Sir Neville Marriner = 'Glanmusic' (F)	NBat
§ Lincolnshire Poacher = 'Glareabit' (HT)	NBat
§ *glauca* (S) ♀	CHad CHan EBls ELan ENot GChr GGre IOrc LBuc LHop MAus MBri MFry MGan MJon MMat NChi NRog NRoo NSty NWea SApu SJus SPer SPla SRum WAct WEas WOVN WWat
'Glenfiddich' (F)	CGro GChr GCoc GGre IHar IHos LPlm LStr MAus MBri MGan MJon NRog SPer SRum SWCr WStI WWeb
◆ Glenshane	See *R.* Glenshane = '**Dicvood**'
'Gloire de Bruxelles' (HP)	EBls
'Gloire de Dijon' (ClT) ♀	Widely available
'Gloire de Ducher' (HP)	CPou EBee MAus MGan WAct WHCG
'Gloire de France' (G)	EBee EBls MAus
'Gloire de Guilan' (D)	EBls MAus NSty WAct
'Gloire des Mousseuses' (CeMo)	EBls MAus SFam WAct WHCG
'Gloire du Midi' (Poly)	MAus
'Gloire Lyonnaise' (HP)	EBee EBls WHCG
'Gloria Mundi' (Poly)	EBls MGan
¶ 'Gloriana' (Patio/Cl)	ECle
glutinosa	See *R. pulverulenta*
'Goethe' (CeMo)	EBls
◆ Gold Bunny	See *R.* Gold Bunny = '**Meifronuri**'
Gold Crown	See *R.* '**Goldkrone**'
◆ Gold Star (Cl)	See *R.* Gold Star = '**Tantern**'
'Goldbusch' (RH)	EBls MAus MGan SRms WAct
'Golden Anniversary' (Patio)	GGre SPer
◆ Golden Celebration®	See *R.* Golden Celebration = '**Ausgold**'
◆ Golden Chersonese	See *R.* Golden Chersonese = '**Hilgold**'
◆ Golden Days	See *R.* Golden Days = '**Rugolda**'
§ 'Golden Garnette' (Gn)	SRum
'Golden Glow' (Cl)	EBls MGan
Golden Hands	See *R.* Golden Hands = '**Chessupremo**'
◆ Golden Handshake	See *R.* Golden Handshake = '**Chewsunford**'
¶ 'Golden Hope' (F)	LStr
I Golden Jewel	See *R.* Goldjuwel = '**Tanledolg**'
◆ Golden Jubilee	See *R.* Golden Jubilee = '**Cocagold**'
'Golden Melody' (HT)	EBls
◆ Golden Moments	See *R.* Golden Moments = '**Frytranquil**' (HT)
'Golden Moss' (Mo)	EBls

'Golden Ophelia' (HT) — EBls

♦ Golden Penny — See *R*. Golden Penny = **'Rugul'**

Golden Quill — See *R*. Golden Quill = **'Tanellog'**

'Golden Rambler' — See *R*. **'Alister Stella Gray'**

♦ Golden Rosamini — See *R*. Golden Rosamini = **'Intergol' (Min/Patio)**

'Golden Salmon' (Poly) — MGan

'Golden Salmon Supérieur' (Poly) — EBls

'Golden Shot' (F) — MGan

¶ Golden Showers® — Widely available

'Golden Slippers' (F) — CB&S MGan

'Golden Sunblaze' — See **'Rise 'n' Shine'**

Golden Symphonie — See *R*. Golden Symphonie = **'Meilolcil'**

♦ Golden Times — See *R*. Kordes' Golden Times = **'Kortime'**

♦ Golden Wedding — See *R*. Golden Wedding = **'Arokris'**

'Golden Wings' (S) ♀ — CHad EBls EMFP ENot GCoc IHar IHos LFis LStr MAus MBri MFry MGan MJon MMat NFla NSty SApu SJus SPer SRum WAct WHCG WHow WOVN WWeb

♦ Golden Years® — See *R*. Golden Years = **'Harween'**

'Goldfinch' (Ra) — CHad EBls EBrP EBre EMFP GGre IHar LBre MAus MBri MHlr NSty SApu SBre SPer SWCr WAct WHCG WHow

Goldfinger (F) — See *R*. Goldfinger = **'Pearoyal'**

'Goldilocks' (F) — NRog

♦ Goldjuwel — See *R*. Goldjuwel = **'Tanledolg'**

♦ Goldstar (HT) — See *R*. Goldstar = **'Candide'**

♦ Goldstern® (Cl) — See *R*. Gold Star = **'Tantern'**

Good as Gold — See *R*. Good as Gold = **'Chewsunbeam'**

Good Luck — See *R*. Good Luck = **'Burspec'**

Gordon's College — See *R*. Gordon's College = **'Cocjabby'**

'Grace Abounding' (F) — NBat

'Grace Darling' (T) — EBls

♦ Grace de Monaco® — See *R*. Grace de Monaco = **'Meimit'**

♦ Graceland — See *R*. Graceland = **'Kirscot'**

♦ Graham Thomas — See *R*. Graham Thomas = **'Ausmas'**

Granada (HT) — EBls

♦ Grand Hotel® — See *R*. Grand Hotel = **'Mactel'**

'Grand-mère Jenny' (HT) — EBls MGan

'Grandpa Dickson' (HT) — EBls EBrP EBre GGre IHar IHos LBre LGod LPlm MAus MBur MGan MJon NBat NRog SApu SBre SPer SRum WWeb

§ 'Great Maiden's Blush' (A) — EBls GCoc MFry MMat NSty SFam WAct

'Great News' (F) — MAus

'Great Ormond Street' (F) — EBls

'Great Western' (Bb) — EBls

'Green Diamond' (Min) — MAus MFry MJon

♦ Greenall's Glory — See *R*. Greenall's Glory = **'Kirmac'**

'Greenmantle' (RH) — EBls MAus MGan WAct

♦ Greensleeves® — See *R*. Greensleeves = **'Harlenten'**

Greer Garson — See *R*. Greer Garson = **'Cocoddy'**

♦ 'Grootendorst' (S) — See *R*. **'F.J. Grootendorst' (Ru)**

'Grootendorst Supreme' (Ru) — MAus SPer

N 'Gros Choux de Hollande' (Bb) — EBls WHCG

♦ Grouse — See *R*. Grouse = **'Korimro'**

♦ Grumpy — See *R*. Grumpy = **'Burkhardt'**

'Gruss an Aachen' (Poly) — EBls LStr MAus MBri MGan NSty SPer SWCr WAct WHCG WHow

'Gruss an Teplitz' (China hybrid) — EBls LFis MAus SPer SWCr WHCG

♦ Guernsey Love — See *R*. Guernsey Love = **'Troblove'**

'Guinée' (ClHT) — CHad EBls EBrP EBre ELan IHar IHos LBre LStr MAus MBur MGan MMat NPri NSty SBre SChu SPer WHCG WHow

Guletta® — See *R*. Golden Penny = **'Rugul'**

'Gustav Grünerwald' (HT) — EBls MAus

♦ Gwent — See *R*. Gwent = **'Poulurt'**

§ *gymnocarpa* var. *willmottiae* — EBls ENot MAus MGan MMat NSty SPer WAct WBod WHCG

I Gypsy Boy — See *R*. **'Zigeunerknabe'**

§ Smooth Angel = 'Hadangel' (HT) — CGro ELan LGod LStr MGan SApu

§ Smooth Lady = 'Hadlady' (HT) — CGro ELan LGod LStr MGan

§ Smooth Melody = 'Hadmelody' (F) — LStr SPer

§ Smooth Prince = 'Hadprince' (HT) — ELan LGod LStr MGan

§ Smooth Romance = 'Hadromance' (HT) — LStr MGan SApu

§ Olde Romeo = 'Hadromeo' (HT) — LStr

§ Smooth Satin = 'Hadsatin' (HT) — LStr

§ Smooth Velvet = 'Hadvelvet' (HT) — CGro LGod LStr MGan

'Hakuun' (F/Patio) — MAus MGan

Hamburger Phönix® (Ra) — CGro EBls MGan SPer WAct

♦ Hampshire — See *R*. Hampshire = **'Korhamp'**

♦ Hand in Hand — See *R*. Hand in Hand = **'Haraztec'**

♦ Handel® — See *R*. Handel = **'Macha'**

§ Fifi = 'Hanfif' (F) — NBat

♦ Hannah Gordon — See *R*. Hannah Gordon = **'Korweiso'**

'Hannah Hauwxell' (Patio/F) — NBat SRum

'Hanne' (HT) — IHar NRog

'Hansa' (Ru) — EBls ENot IHar IHos LBuc MAus MGan MMat SPer WHCG WHow WOVN

'Happy' (Poly) — MGan

♦ Happy Anniversary — See *R*. Happy Anniversary = **'Delpre'**

'Happy Birthday' (Min/Patio) — GGre

♦ Happy Child — See *R*. Happy Child = **'Auscomp'**

♦ Happy Ever After — See *R*. Happy Ever After = **'Dicvanilla'**

'Happy Thought' (Min) — MJon

§ Hand in Hand = 'Haraztec' (Patio/Min) — MBri MJon NBat

§ Sunset Boulevard = 'Harbabble' (F) — CGro ENot GGre LGod LPlm LStr MAus MBur MFry NBat SApu SCoo SJus SPer SRum WWeb

§ Peacekeeper = 'Harbella' (F) — GGre SJus

§ Saint John℗ = 'Harbilbo' GGre
(F)

§ House Beautiful = SJus
'Harbingo' (Patio)

§ Ruby Anniversary = MFry SJus SWCr
'Harbonny' (Patio)

§ Saint Christopher = SJus
'Harcogent' (HT)

§ Highfield® = 'Harcomp' IHar LGod MAus MBri MJon
(Cl) SApu SJus SPer

§ Humanity℗ = 'Harcross' SRum
(F)

§ Princess of Wales = LStr MGan
'Hardinkum' (F)

§ Penny Lane = 'Hardwell' ECle ENot GCoc LGod LPlm
(Cl) LStr MBri MFry MGan NBat
SApu SJus

¶ Rising Star℗ = 'Hareast' SJus
(F)

§ Poetry in Motion = NBat SApu
'Harelan' (HT)

Harewood See *R.* Harewood = **'Taninaso'**

§ Marjorie Fair® = EBls LPlm MAus MGan MMat
'Harhero' (S/GC) SApu SRum WAct WOVN

§ x *harisonii* 'Harison's EBls MAus WAct
Yellow' (PiH) ♀

§ – 'Lutea Maxima' (PiH) EBls MAus

§ – 'Williams' Double EBls GChr GCoc MAus
Yellow' (PiH)

§ Basildon Bond = IHar MJon
'Harjosine' (HT)

§ Anne Harkness® = MAus MGan MJon NRog SPer
'Harkaramel' (F)

§ Judy Garland = 'Harking' SJus
(F)

§ Margaret Merril = CDoC EBls EBrP EBre GChr
'Harkuly' (HT/F) ♀ GCoc GGre IHos LBre LGod
LPlm LStr MAus MBri MBur
MFry MGan MJon MMat NBat
NRog SApu SBre SJus SPer
SRum WHCG WOVN WWeb

§ Fairyland® = EBls MAus MBur SApu
'Harlayalong' (Poly)

§ Greensleeves® = EBls LStr MAus SPer
'Harlenten' (F)

§ Alexander® = 'Harlex' CGro EBls ENot GCoc IHos
(HT) ♀ LGod LPlm LStr MFry MGan
MJon MMat NRog SApu SPer

§ L'Oréal Trophy = MAus MJon
'Harlexis' (HT)

§ Princess Michael of MGan WWeb
Kent® = 'Harlightly'
(F)

§ Mountbatten® = CB&S CGro EBls EBrP EBre
'Harmantelle' (F) ♀ ELan ENot GCoc GGre IHos
LBre LGod LPlm LStr MAus
MBri MFry MGan MJon MMat
NBat NRog SApu SBre SJus
SPer SRum WWeb

§ Radox Bouquet = GCoc MBur
'Harmusky' (F)

§ Fairy Damsel = 'Harneaty' EBls MAus MBur
(Poly/GC)

§ Fairy Changeling = MAus
'Harnumerous' (Poly)

§ Escapade® = 'Harpade' EBls MAus MGan NBat
(F) ♀

§ Anna Ford® = GGre IHar IHos LGod LPlm
'Harpiccolo' LStr MAus MGan MJon SApu
(Min/Patio) ♀ SRum SWCr

§ Avocet = 'Harpluto' (F) GGre MBri

§ Tigris® = 'Harprier' WAct
(*persica* hybrid) (S)

§ Clarissa® = IHos MAus
'Harprocrustes' (Min)

§ Breath of Life = CGro CSam EBls ELan GGre
'Harquanne' (ClHT) IHar LGod LStr MAus MBri
MFry MGan MJon NBat SApu
SJus SPer SRum SWCr

§ Paul Shirville = CDoC ENot GCoc GGre IHar
'Harqueterwife' (HT) IHos LPlm LStr MAus MFry
♀ MGan MMat NRog SApu SJus
SPer

§ Anna Zinkeisen = WAct WOVN
'Harquhling' (S)

§ Nigel Hawthorne = WAct
'Harquibbler' (S)

§ Wandering Minstrel = SApu
'Harquince' (S)

§ Cardinal Hume® = EBls LStr MGan SApu SPer
'Harregale' (S)

§ Amber Queen® = CDoC CGro EBls ELan GCoc
'Harroony' (F) ♀ GGre IHos LGod LPlm LStr
MAus MBri MBur MFry MGan
MJon MMat NRog SApu SJus
SPer SRum SWCr

§ Rosemary Harkness = IHos LStr MJon MMat SApu
'Harrowbond' (HT) SPer

'Harry Maasz' (GC/Cl) EBls

(Harry Wheatcroft CB&S CGro EBls GGre IHos
Group) 'Harry MAus MBri MBur MGan MJon
Wheatcroft' (HT) NRog

§ Sheila's Perfume = EBee GCoc GGre LPlm LStr
'Harsherry' (HT/F) MGan MJon NRog SApu SJus
SPer

§ Suma = 'Harsuma' (GC) EPfP GCoc GGre LGod MFry
♀ MJon SApu SJus SRum WAct
WOVN

§ Princess Alice = LGod MGan SApu
'Hartanna' (F)

§ Reconciliation℗ = GGre SJus
'Hartillery' (HT)

§ Country Lady = 'Hartsam' MBur SApu SJus SRum
(HT)

§ Cordon Bleu = 'Harubasil' MBur
(HT)

§ Queen Charlotte = MBri MBur
'Harubondee' (HT)

§ City of London® = EBls LStr MBur MJon SApu
'Harukfore' (F) ♀ SJus SPer

§ Euphrates = 'Harunique' MAus MGan WAct
(*persica* hybrid)

§ Armada® = 'Haruseful' GCoc SApu
(S)

§ Drummer Boy = GGre SJus SPer
'Harvacity' (F/Patio)

§ Samaritan = 'Harverag' MAus SApu SJus
(HT)

♦ Harvest Fayre See *R.* Harvest Fayre =
'Dicnorth'

§ Savoy Hotel = GCoc GGre LGod LStr MAus
'Harvintage' (HT) ♀ MBri MBur MFry MGan MJon
MMat SApu SJus SPer

§ By Appointment = GGre MJon SRum
'Harvolute' (F)

§ Rosy Future = SApu SJus
'Harwaderox' (F/Patio)

§ Jacqueline du Pré = GCoc IHar MAus MGan MHlr
'Harwanna' (S) ♀ MJon MMat SApu SChu SJus
SPer SWCr WAct WGer
WHCG WHow

§ Many Happy Returns = 'Harwanted' (F) ♥ — EBrP EBre ENot GCoc LBre LGod LPlm LStr MAus MBri MBur MFry MGan MJon MMat NBat SApu SBre SJus SPer SRum WOVN WWeb

§ Golden Years® = 'Harween' (F) — MAus MJon

§ Fellowship = 'Harwelcome' (F) — GCoc LGod LPlm LStr MAus MBri MBur MFry MGan MJon MMat SJus SRum WGer

§ Malcolm Sargent = 'Harwherry' (HT) — SPer

§ Emily Louise = 'Harwilla' (Patio) — NBat

§ Remembrance = 'Harxampton' (F) — LStr MBri SApu SRum SWCr

§ Cottage Garden = 'Haryamber' (Patio/Min) — GGre

§ High Hopes = 'Haryup' (Cl) — EBee GGre LGod LStr MBri MBur MFry MGan MJon SApu SJus SRum SWCr WHCG WWeb

§ Renaissance = 'Harzart' (HT) — ECle GCoc GGre LStr MBur MFry MJon NBat SJus SRum

§ Octavia Hill = 'Harzeal' (F/S) — LStr MFry MJon SApu SJus SPer SRum SWCr WAct WHCG WHow

§ Perception℗® = 'Harzippee' (HT) — GCoc SApu

§ The Compassionate Friends = 'Harzodiac' (F) — SJus

§ L'Aimant = 'Harzola' (F) — ECle GCoc LGod LStr MFry MJon NBat SApu SJus

§ Welwyn Garden Glory℗® = 'Harzumber' (HT) — SJus

'Headleyensis' — EBee EBls MAus
'Heart of England' (F) — MBur
♦ Heartbeat — See R. Heartbeat = 'Cocorona'
Heather Austin — See R. Heather Austin = 'Auscook'

§ 'Heather Muir' (sericea hybrid) (S) — EBls EHol MAus NSty
'Heaven Scent' (F) — MJon NBat
Heavenly Rosalind — See R. Heavenly Rosalind = 'Ausmarsh'

§ 'Hebe's Lip' (DxSwB) — EBls MAus WAct
'Hector Deane' (HT) — EBls MBur MGan NSty
'Heidi Jayne' (HT) — MBur SRum
'Heinrich Schultheis' (HP) — EBls

§ 'Helen Knight' (ecae hybrid) (S) ♥ — CHad EBls MAus MBri MMat NSty WHCG
'Helen Traubel' (HT) — EBls MGan
helenae — EBls GCal MAus SPer WHCG

§ Super Sparkle = 'Helhein' (Ra) — SApu

♦ Hello — See R. Hello = 'Cochello'
hemisphaerica (S) — EBls MAus WAct

§ Dancing Pink = 'Hendan' (F) — NBat
'Henri Fouquier' (G) — EBls

§ 'Henri Martin' (CeMo) ♥ — CTri EBls IOrc MAus NBus NRog SPer WAct WHCG
'Henry Nevard' (HP) — EBls MAus
'Her Majesty' (HP) — EBls
'Herbstfeuer' (RH) — EBls MAus NSty
♦ Heritage® — See R. Heritage = 'Ausblush'
'Hermosa' (Ch) — CBos EBls EMFP LFis MAus MHlr NBus NSty WAct WHCG
♦ Hero® — See R. Hero = 'Aushero'

♦ Hertfordshire — See R. Hertfordshire = 'Kortenay'
'Hiawatha' (Ra) — EBls MAus WHCG
× hibernica — MAus
'Hidcote Gold' (S) — EBls MAus
♦ High Hopes — See R. High Hopes = 'Haryup'
§ 'Highdownensis' (moyesii hybrid) (S) ♥ — EBls ELan MAus MMat SPer
♦ Highfield® — See R. Highfield = 'Harcomp'
♦ Highland Laddie — See R. Highland Laddie = 'Cocflag'
♦ Hilda Murrell® — See R. Hilda Murrell = 'Ausmurr'

§ Golden Chersonese = 'Hilgold' (S) — EBls MAus NRog NSty
§ 'Hillieri' (S) — EBls MAus
'Hippolyte' (G) — EBls MAus WSHC
♦ Hole-in-one — See R. Hole-in-one = 'Horeagle'
§ Fairy Snow = 'Holfairy' (S) — MFry

holodonta — See R. moyesii f. rosea
Holy Rose — See R. × richardii
'Home Sweet Home' (HT) — EBls MAus
'Homère' (T) — EBls MAus
Honey Bunch® — See R. Honey Bunch = 'Cocglen'
'Honey Favorite' (HT) — MAus
♦ Honeymoon — See R. 'Honigmond'
§ 'Honigmond' — CB&S GGre NPri SRum
'Honorine de Brabant' (Bb) — EBee EBls IHar LFis MAus MHlr MMat SFam SPer SPla WHCG

'Horace Vernet' (HP) — EBls
§ Evelyn Grace = 'Horavme' (F) — NBat
§ Battersby Beauty = 'Horbatbeauty' (HT) — NBat
§ Brave Heart = 'Horbondsmile' (F) — NBat
§ Hole-in-one = 'Horeagle' (F) — GGre
§ Isobel Derby = 'Horethel' (HT) — MJon
§ Champagne Cocktail = 'Horflash' (F) — GChr GGre MJon NBat SApu SRum
§ Emma Mitchell = 'Horharpdos' (Patio) — NBat
§ Whitley Bay = 'Horharryplus' (F) — NBat
§ Jack Collier = 'Horjack' (HT) — NBat
§ Geordie Lad = 'Horkorblush' (HT) — NBat
§ Ted Gore = 'Hormislac' (F) — NBat

horrida — See R. biebersteinii
§ Stacey's Star = 'Horstacey' (Patio) — NBat
'Horstmanns Rosenresli' (F) — EBls
§ Playgroup Rose = 'Horsun' (F) — IHar NBat
§ Voice of Thousands = 'Horsunsmile' (F) — NBat
§ Sir William Leech = 'Hortropic' (HT) — NBat
♦ House Beautiful — See R. House Beautiful = 'Harbingo'
'Hugh Dickson' (HP) — EBls MAus NSty SJus
hugonis — See R. xanthina f. hugonis
'Hula Girl' (Min) — LGod MBur MJon

◆ Humanity	See *R.* Humanity = **'Harcross'**
Hume's Blush	See *R.* × *odorata* **'Odorata'**
'Hunslet Moss' (Mo)	EBls
'Hunter' (Ru)	SWCr WAct
◆ Ice Cream	See *R.* Ice Cream = **'Korzuri'**
Iceberg	See *R.* Iceberg = **'Korbin'**
'Iced Ginger' (F)	MFry MGan SApu SPer
'Illusion' (Cl)	MGan
Ilse Krohn Superior® (Cl)	EBls
◆ Indian Summer (HT)	See *R.* Indian Summer = **'Peaperfume' (HT)**
◆ Indian Sunblaze	See *R.* Indian Sunblaze = **'Carol-Jean'**
'Indigo' (DPo)	EBls MAus WHCG
◆ Ingrid Bergman®	See *R.* Ingrid Bergman = **'Poulman'**
◆ Inner Wheel	See *R.* Inner Wheel = **'Fryjasso'**
§ Rosy Cushion® = 'Interall' (S/GC) ♀	CSam ENot GCoc IDic IHar IHos MAus MGan MHlr SApu SPer SRum SWCr WAct WHCG WOVN
§ White Diamond® = 'Interamon' (S)	IDic MAus SJus
§ Red Blanket® = 'Intercell' (S/GC) ♀	CGro EBls ENot GCoc IDic IHos MAus MGan NFla SPer SRum SWCr WAct WOVN
§ Pink Chimo® = 'Interchimp' (S/GC)	IDic MJon
¶ Euphoria = 'Intereup'	ECle GCoc IDic SApu
§ Petit Four® = 'Interfour' (Min/Patio)	IDic SApu
§ Golden Rosamini = 'Intergol' (Min/Patio)	MFry
§ Red Trail = 'Interim' (S/GC)	IDic MJon WOVN
§ Daylight = 'Interlight' (F)	IDic
'Intermezzo' (HT)	MBur MGan
§ Red Dot® = 'Intermunder' (S/GC)	IDic WOVN
§ Eyeopener = 'Interop' (S/GC)	CGro EBls IDic MGan MJon SRum
§ Robin Redbreast® = 'Interrob' (Min/GC)	EBls IDic IHar MJon SApu WWeb
§ Smarty = 'Intersmart' (S/GC)	EBls IDic IHar MAus MGan MJon SApu SPer WAct WOVN
◆ Intrigue	See *R.* Intrigue = **'Korlech'**
◆ Invincible	See *R.* Invincible = **'Runatru'**
'Invitation' (HT)	MBur MGan
'Ipsilanté' (G)	EBls MAus SMer SWCr WAct WHCG
'Irene Av Danmark'	EBls
'Irène Watts' (Ch) ♀	CHad EBls EMFP MAus MHlr SPla WAct WHCG WHow
'Irene's Delight' (HT)	NBat
'Irish Elegance' (HT)	EBls
'Irish Fireflame' (HT)	EBls
Irish Wonder	See *R.* Evelyn Fison = **'Macev'**
◆ Irresistible	See *R.* Irresistible = **'Tinresist'**
◆ Isabella	See *R.* Isabella = **'Poulisab'**
◆ Isis® (HT)	See *R.* Silver Anniversary = **'Poulari' (HT)**
'Isis' (F)	MBri
◆ Isobel Derby	See *R.* Isobel Derby = **'Horethel'**
'Ispahan' (D) ♀	EBls EPfP MAus MHlr NSty SApu SFam SJus SPer SWCr WAct WHCG WSHC
'Ivory Fashion' (F)	EBls
§ Red Rascal = 'Jacbed' (Patio)	IDic MBri MFry MJon SApu
§ Bridal Pink℠ = 'Jacbri' (F)	MJon
§ Tournament of Roses = 'Jacient' (HT)	IDic MAus MJon SSea
◆ Jack Collier	See *R.* Jack Collier = **'Horjack'**
§ × *jacksonii* White Max Graf = 'Korgram' (GC/Ru)	ENot IHos MAus WAct
§ – 'Max Graf' (GC/Ru)	EBls ENot IHos MAus MGan MJon NRog NSty SRum WAct
– Red Max Graf℠ (GC/Ru)	See *R.* Rote Max Graf = **'Kormax'**
◆ – White Max Graf	See *R.* × *jacksonii* White Max Graf = **'Korgram' (GC/Ru)**
§ Magic Carpet = 'Jaclover' (S/GC)	EPfP GCoc GGre IDic LGod LPlm LStr MAus MBri MFry MGan MJon MMat NBat SApu SCoo SJus SPla SRum
Jacobite rose	See *R.* × *alba* **'Alba Maxima'**
§ Fascination = 'Jacoyel' (HT)	ECle LStr
§ Pristine® = 'Jacpico' (HT)	IDic IHos LStr MAus MGan MJon SPer SRum
§ Purple Tiger = 'Jacpur' (F)	IDic LPlm MBri MBur MFry MJon SApu SRum
Jacqueline du Pré	See *R.* Jacqueline du Pré = **'Harwanna'**
◆ Jacquenetta	See *R.* Jacquenetta = **'Ausjac'**
N Jacques Cartier	See *R.* **'Marchesa Boccella'**
§ Summer Dream = 'Jacshe' (HT)	LStr MAus MFry SApu SJus SWCr
§ Evening Star® = 'Jacven' (HT)	MAus
'James Bourgault' (HP)	EBls
'James Mason' (G)	EBls MAus SWCr
'James Mitchell' (CeMo)	EBls MAus WHCG
'James Veitch' (DPoMo)	EBls MAus WHCG
◆ Jane Asher	See *R.* Jane Asher = **'Peapet'**
'Janet's Pride' (RH)	EBls MAus
◆ Janina®	See *R.* Janina = **'Tanija'**
'Japonica' (CeMo)	MAus
◆ Jardins de Bagatelle®	See *R.* Jardins de Bagatelle = **'Meimafris' (HT)**
Jayne Austin	See *R.* Jayne Austin = **'Ausbreak'**
◆ Jazz	See *R.* Jazz = **'Poulnorm'**
◆ Jean Kenneally℠	See *R.* Jean Kenneally = **'Tineally'**
'Jean Mermoz' (Poly)	MAus NRog NSty SRum WHCG
'Jean Rosenkrantz' (HP)	EBls
'Jean Sisley' (HT)	EBls
¶ 'Jeanie Deans'	MAus
'Jeanne de Montfort' (CeMo)	EBls MAus
§ Wee Barbie = 'Jelbar' (Min)	SApu
* 'Jemma' (Patio)	NBat
◆ Jennie Robinson	See *R.* Jennie Robinson = **'Trobette'**
Jenny Charlton	See *R.* Jenny Charlton = **'Simway'**
'Jenny Duval' misapplied	See *R.* **'Président de Sèze'**
'Jenny Wren' (F)	EBls MAus
◆ Jenny's Rose	See *R.* Jenny's Rose = **'Cansit'**
'Jens Munk' (Ru)	WAct
'Jersey Beauty' (Ra)	EBls MAus
¶ 'Jill's Rose' (F)	MGan
'Jiminy Cricket' (F)	EBls
'Jimmy Greaves' (HT)	MGan
'Joanna Hill' (HT)	EBls
'Joanne' (HT)	MJon
'Jocelyn' (F)	EBls
'Joe Longthorne' (HT)	NBat

John Clare   See *R.* John Clare = **'Auscent'**
'John Hopper' (HP)   EBls MAus NSty
John Keats   See *R.* John Keats = **'Meiroupis'**
§ Chicago Peace® =   EBls GGre IHos LGod LPlm
   'Johnago' (HT)   MAus MGan MJon NRog
                            SRum SWCr WStI
◆ Johnnie Walker   See *R.* Johnnie Walker =
                            'Frygran'
'Josephine Bruce' (HT)   CB&S CGro EBls LGod MAus
                            MBur MGan NRog SRum WStI
'Josephine Wheatcroft'   See *R.* **'Rosina'**
'Joseph's Coat' (S/Cl)   EBls IHos LGod LStr MFry
                            MGan SRum
'Journey's End' (HT)   MGan
'Jubilee Celebration' (F)   MJon
Jude the Obscure   See *R.* Jude the Obscure =
                            'Ausjo'
'Judy Fischer' (Min)   LGod
◆ Judy Garland   See *R.* Judy Garland = **'Harking'**
'Julia Mannering' (RH)   MAus
Julia's Rose® (HT)   CGro LStr MAus MBur MFry
                            MGan MJon SApu SPer
◆ Julie Andrews   See *R.* Julie Andrews =
                            'Fryvivacious'
◆ Julie Cussons   See *R.* Julie Cussons =
                            'Fryprincess'
'Juliet' (HP)   EBls
◆ June Laver   See *R.* June Laver = **'Lavjune'**
'Juno' (Ce)   EBls MAus WAct WHCG
'Just Jenny' (Min)   NBat
Just Joey® (HT) ♀   CGro EBls ELan GCoc GGre
                            IHos LGod LPlm LStr MAus
                            MBri MFry MGan MJon
                            MMat NRog SApu SJus SPer
                            SRum SSoC WWeb
◆ Just Magic   See *R.* Just Magic = **'Trobic'**
'Karl Foerster' (PiH)   EBls MAus
'Kassel' (S/Cl)   EBls MAus SPer WAct
'Katharina Zeimet' (Poly)   EBls MAus MGan NRog NSty
                            WAct WHCG
'Kathleen' (HM)   EBls
'Kathleen Ferrier' (F)   EBls MGan
'Kathleen Harrop' (Bb)   EBls ENot IHar LStr MAus
                            MBur MHlr MMat NSty SFam
                            SPer WAct WHCG WSHC
                            WWat
◆ Kathleen's Rose   See *R.* Kathleen's Rose =
                            'Kirkitt'
◆ Kathryn McGredy®   See *R.* Kathryn Mcgredy =
                            'Macauckland'
◆ Kathryn Morley   See *R.* Kathryn Morley =
                            'Ausclub'
'Katie' (ClF)   MGan
Katie Crocker   See *R.* Katie Crocker =
                            'Burbringley'
'Kazanlik' misapplied   See *R.* **'Professeur Emile Perrot'**
◆ Keepsake   See *R.* Keepsake = **'Kormalda'**
§ Ferdy® = 'Keitoly' (GC)   EBls ELan ENot MAus MGan
                            SApu SPer WOVN
◆ Kent®   See *R.* Kent = **'Poulcov'**
'Kew Rambler' (Ra)   EBls MAus MRav WHCG
'Kiese' (*canina* hybrid)   MJon
'Kiftsgate'   See *R. filipes* **'Kiftsgate'**
'Kilworth Gold' (HT)   MGan
'Kim' (Patio)   NRog
◆ Kind Regards   See *R.* Kind Regards =
                            'Pentiger'
King's Ransom® (HT)   CB&S CGro EBls GGre IHos
                            MBur MGan MJon SPer SRum
                            WWeb
§ Kathleen's Rose =   MJon
   'Kirkitt' (F)

§ Woman o'th' North =   WGer
   'Kirlon' (F/Patio)
§ Greenall's Glory =   LStr MAus MJon WHow
   'Kirmac' (F/Patio)
§ Owen's Pride = 'Kirpink' MJon
   (F)
§ Graceland = 'Kirscot'   MJon
   (Min/Patio)
§ Saint Dunstan's Rose =   MBri MJon NBat SApu SPer
   'Kirshru' (S)
'Kirsten Poulsen' (Poly)   EBls
§ Wor Jackie =   NBat
   'Kirworjackie' (HT)
◆ Kiss 'n' Tell   See *R.* Kiss 'n' Tell = **'Seakis'**
'Kitchener of Khartoum'   See *R.* **'K of K'**
× *kochiana*   EBls
'Köln am Rhein' (Cl)   MGan
§ 'Königin von Dänemark'   CHad EBls EMFP ENot GCoc
   (A) ♀   IHar MAus MBri MMat NFla
                            NSty SApu SJus SPer SRum
                            WAct WHCG WHow WSHC
§ Perfecta = 'Koralu' (HT) EBls MGan
§ Champagne® =   MJon
   'Korampa' (F)
§ Anabell = 'Korbell' (F)   MGan
§ Simba = 'Korbelma' (HT)   MBri MGan MMat SApu SJus
§ Iceberg = 'Korbin' (F) ♀ CB&S CDoC CGro EBls EBrP
                            EBre ENot GCoc GGre IHos
                            LBre LFis LGod LStr MAus
                            MFry MGan MJon MMat NRog
                            NSty SApu SBre SJus SPer
                            SRum SSea WWeb
§ Shocking Blue® =   EBee ENot LPlm MGan MJon
   'Korblue' (F)   MMat SPer
§ Mandarin® = 'Korcelin'   LStr MJon MMat NPri SWCr
   (Min)
§ The Valois Rose =   MMat
   'Kordadel' (Min/Patio)
§ Antique '89® = 'Kordalen' EBls MBri MJon MMat SJus
   (ClF)   WGer
§ Pheasant = 'Kordapt'   ELan ENot GCoc IHos MAus
   (GC)   MHlr MJon MMat SJus SPer
                            WAct WOVN
§ Malverns = 'Kordehei'   ENot MMat
   (GC)
Kordes' Golden Times   See *R.* Kordes' Golden Times =
                            'Kortimes'
◆ 'Kordes' Robusta'   See *R.* Robusta = **'Korgosa'**
§ Festival = 'Kordialo'   CDoC CGro EBrP EBre ENot
   (Patio)   GCoc GGre IHar LBre LGod
                            LPlm LStr MAus MBri MGan
                            MMat NPri SApu SBre SPer
                            SRum WGer WOVN WWeb
§ Flower Power = 'Koredan' MFry
   (Patio)
§ Valencia® = 'Koreklia'   ENot MBur MJon MMat NBat
   (HT)
§ Centenary = 'Koreledas'   ENot MMat
   (F)
§ Margaret Thatcher =   MJon
   'Korflüg' (HT)
§ Oxfordshire =   CDoC ENot LStr MMat SJus
   'Korfullwind' (GC)   SWCr
§ Robusta® = 'Korgosa'   EBls MAus MJon WHow
   (Ru)
§ Loving Memory =   ENot GCoc GGre LPlm LStr
   'Korgund' (HT)   MFry MGan MMat NPri SPer
                            SRum
§ Hampshire = 'Korhamp'   ENot IHos MAus MGan MMat
   (GC)   SApu SRum
§ The Compass Rose =   ENot MMat SPer
   'Korhassi' (S)

§ Cambridgeshire = 'Korhaugen' (GC) — ENot LGod LStr MAus MMat NBat NPri SPer SWCr WWeb

§ Perestroika = 'Korhitom' (F/Min) — ENot GCoc LStr MJon MMat SApu SJus WGer

§ City of Birmingham = 'Korholst' (S/HT) — MMat

§ Grouse = 'Korimro' (S/GC) — EBls ENot GCoc IHar IHos MAus MHlr MJon MMat SApu SPer WAct WOVN

§ Summer Wine = 'Korizont' (Cl) ♀ — EBee ENot IHos MBri MGan MJon MMat NBat SApu SJus SPer

§ Warwickshire = 'Korkandel' (GC) — ENot MHlr MMat NPri SJus SRum WOVN

§ Tradition '95® = 'Korkeltin' (Cl) — MMat SJus

§ Lady Rose® = 'Korlady' (HT) — MJon

§ Surrey = 'Korlanum' (GC) ♀ — EBrP EBre ELan ENot GCoc IHos LBre LFis LGod LPlm LStr MAus MFry MGan MHlr MJon MMat SApu SBre SJus SPer SPla SRum WAct WOVN WStI

§ Mary Pope = 'Korlasche' (HT) — ENot MMat

§ Intrigue = 'Korlech' (F) — ENot LStr MMat

§ Congratulations = 'Korlift' (HT) — EBee ENot GCoc GGre IHos LGod LPlm LStr MFry MGan MJon MMat NBat NPri SApu SJus SPer SRum SWCr

§ Lilli Marlene = 'Korlima' (F) — CB&S CTri EBls GCoc IHos LStr MAus MGan NPri NRog SPer SRum

§ Keepsake = 'Kormalda' (HT) — ENot LPlm MGan MMat NRog

§ Miss Pam Ayres = 'Kormarie' (S) — MMat

§ Sunrise = 'Kormarter' (Cl) — GCoc MBur MFry MJon MMat SApu WGer

§ Pink Pearl = 'Kormasyl' (HT) — LPlm MBri MJon MMat SApu

§ Saint Boniface = 'Kormatt' (F/Patio) — ENot MMat

§ Rote Max Graf® = 'Kormax' (GC) — EBls ENot MJon WAct

§ Agatha Christie = 'Kormeita' (ClF) — CGre MBri MJon MMat SApu SJus

§ Anna Livia = 'Kormetter' (F) ♀ — EBee ENot IHos MGan MJon MMat SApu SJus

§ Suffolk = 'Kormixal' (S/GC) — EBrP EBre ELan ENot GCoc IHos LBre LPlm LStr MAus MGan MHlr MMat NPri SApu SBre SJus SPer SRum WAct WHow WLRN WOVN WRHF WWeb

§ Wiltshire = 'Kormuse' (S/GC) — EBee ENot LFis LStr MFry MJon MMat SJus WHow WOVN

§ Korona® = 'Kornita' (F) — MGan NRog

§ Peer Gynt® = 'Korol' (HT) — EBrP EBre IHos LBre LPlm MGan NPri SBre

♦ Korona® — See R. Korona = 'Kornita'

§ Apricot Summer® = 'Korpapiro' (Patio) — ENot GCoc MJon MMat WGer

§ Patricia = 'Korpatri' (F) — SRum

§ The Times Rose = 'Korpeahn' (F) ♀ — ENot IHos LGod LStr MGan MJon MMat SJus SPer

§ Berkshire = 'Korpinka' (GC) — ENot LStr MGan MHlr MJon MMat SWCr WOVN WWeb

§ The Seckford Rose = 'Korpinrob' (S) — ENot MJon MMat

§ Selfridges = 'Korpriwa' (HT) — MMat NBat

§ Queen Mother = 'Korquemu' (Patio) ♀ — EBls ELan ENot GGre IHos LGod LStr MAus MBri MBur MFry MGan MJon MMat NPri SPer

§ Ace of Hearts = 'Korred' (HT) — MBur

'Korresia' (F) — EBls GCoc GGre IHar IHos LGod LStr MAus MBri MFry MGan MJon MMat NRog SJus SPer SRum

§ Playtime = 'Korsaku' (GC/Ru) — ENot MMat

§ Barry Fearn = 'Korschwama' (HT) — MMat

§ White Cloud = 'Korstacha' (S/ClHT) — ENot LGod MMat SJus

§ Chilterns = 'Kortemma' (GC) — ENot MMat SWCr

§ Hertfordshire = 'Kortenay' (GC) — EBrP EBre ENot LBre LPlm MMat SBre SPer SRum WOVN WRHF

§ Rosarium Uetersen® = 'Kortersen' (ClHT) — MJon WHow

§ Kordes' Golden Times = 'Kortime' (F) — MJon

§ Scarlet Patio = 'Kortingle' (Patio) — ENot MMat

§ Lady Mavis Pilkington = 'Kortlitze' (HT) — MMat

§ Cleopatra = 'Korverpea' (HT) — ENot MBur MMat

§ Partridge = 'Korweirim' (GC) — EBls IHos MAus MGan MJon MMat SApu SJus SPer WAct WOVN

§ Hannah Gordon = 'Korweiso' (F) — EBee ENot LStr MBur MGan MJon MMat NBat

§ Westerland® = 'Korwest' (F/S) ♀ — MGan MJon MMat WGer WHow

§ Toynbee Hall = 'Korwonder' (F) — ENot MMat

§ Romantic Hedgerose = 'Korworm' (F/S) — ENot MMat

§ Royal William = 'Korzaun' (HT) ♀ — CDoC CGro ELan GGre LGod LPlm LStr MAus MBur MGan MJon MMat SApu SJus SPer SRum

§ Ice Cream = 'Korzuri' (HT) — CTri ENot GGre LStr MGan MJon MMat NBat SApu SCoo SJus

♦ Kristin — See R. Kristin = 'Benmagic'

♦ Kronenbourg® — See R. Kronenbourg = 'Macbo'

'Kronprinzessin Viktoria' (Bb) — EBls MAus MHlr WHCG

♦ L.D. Braithwaite® — See R. L.D. Braithwaite = 'Auscrim'

'La Belle Distinguée' (RH) — EBls MAus WHCG

'La Belle Sultane' — See R. 'Violacea'

'La Follette' (Cl) — EBls

'La France' (HT) — EBls MAus

'La Mortola' — See R. brunonii 'La Mortola'

'La Noblesse' (Ce) — EBls

'La Perle' (Ra) — CRHN MAus

'La Reine' (HP) — EBls NSty

'La Reine Victoria' — See R. 'Reine Victoria'

'La Rubanée' — See R. 'Centifolia Variegata'

♦ La Sévillana — See R. La Sévillana = 'Meigekanu'

'La Ville de Bruxelles' (D) ♀ — EBls IHos MAus MRav NSty SFam SPer WAct WHCG WHow

'Lady Alice Stanley' (HT) — EBls
'Lady Barnby' (HT) — EBls
'Lady Belper' (HT) — EBls MBur
'Lady Curzon' (Ru) — EBls IHos MAus NSty SWCr
'Lady Elgin' — See *R.* Thaïs = **'Memaj'**
'Lady Forteviot' (HT) — EBls
'Lady Gay' (Ra) — MAus WHCG
'Lady Godiva' (Ra) — MAus
'Lady Hillingdon' (ClT) — See *R.* **'Climbing Lady Hillingdon' (ClT)**
'Lady Hillingdon' (T) — MAus NSty WHow
'Lady Iliffe' (HT) — MGan
◆ Lady in Red — See *R.* Lady in Red = **'Sealady'**
'Lady Love '95' (Patio) — GGre
◆ Lady MacRobert — See *R.* Lady MacRobert = **'Coclent'**
'Lady Mary Fitzwilliam' (HT) — EBls
◆ Lady Mavis Pilkington — See *R.* Lady Mavis Pilkington = **'Kortlitze'**
◆ Lady Meillandina® — See *R.* Lady Meillandina = **'Meilarco'**
¶ 'Lady Penelope' (MinCl) — WWeb
§ 'Lady Penzance' (RH) — CB&S EBls MAus MFry MGan NSty SApu SPer WAct
◆ Lady Rachel — See *R.* Lady Rachel = **'Candoodle'**
'Lady Romsey' (F) — EBls
◆ Lady Rose® — See *R.* Lady Rose = **'Korlady'**
'Lady Stuart' (Ch) — NSty
'Lady Sylvia' (HT) — EBls MAus MGan NRog NSty SPer WHow WStI
◆ Lady Taylor — See *R.* Lady Taylor = **'Smitling'**
'Lady Waterlow' (ClHT) — EBee EBls MAus SPer SWCr WHCG

laevigata (Ra) — CBot EBls MAus
– 'Anemonoides' — See *R.* **'Anemone'**
◆ – 'Cooperi' — See *R.* **'Cooperi' (Ra)**
'Lafter' (S) — EBls
'Lagoon' (F) — EBls
◆ L'Aimant — See *R.* L'Aimant = **'Harzola'**
'Lakeland' (HT) — MAus NRog
'Lamarque' (N) — MAus
Laminuette® (F) — MJon
◆ Lancashire Life — See *R.* Lancashire Life = **'Ruilanca'**
§ Denman = 'Landen' (HT) — MJon SApu
§ Snow White = 'Landisney' (HT) — MBri MJon
§ Sunblest = 'Landora' (HT) — CTri GGre IHos LPlm MBri MBur MFry NPri NRog SRum SWCr
'Lanei' (CeMo) — EBls
Langdale Chase — See *R.* Langdale Chase = **'Fryrhapsody'**
§ Felicity Kendal = 'Lanken' (HT) — MBri MJon
§ Torvill and Dean = 'Lantor' (HT) — MJon NRog
Laughter Lines (F) — IDic MGan
Laura Anne (HT) — GCoc
Laura Ashley (ClMin) — MAus MBur
◆ Laura Ford® — See *R.* Laura Ford = **'Chewarvel'**
'Laura Jane' (HT) — MGan
'Laura Louisa' (Cl) — EBls
◆ Laurence Olivier® — See *R.* Laurence Olivier = **'Meinagre'**
'Lavender Jewel' (Min) — IHar MAus MBur

'Lavender Lassie' (HM) ♀ — CHad EMFP IOrc MAus MFry MGan MHlr MMat SPer SRum WHCG WHow
'Lavender Pinocchio' (F) — MAus WAct
◆ Lavinia — See *R.* Lavinia = **'Tanklawi'**
§ June Laver® = 'Lavjune' (Min) — MBur
'Lawrence Johnston' (Cl) — EBls MAus NSty WAct
'Le Havre' (HP) — EBls
'Le Rêve' (Cl) — EBls MAus
'Le Vésuve' (Ch) — EBls MAus
◆ Leander® — See *R.* Leander = **'Auslea'**
◆ Leaping Salmon — See *R.* Leaping Salmon = **'Peamight'**
'Leda' (D) — EBls MAus SFam SPer WAct
§ Pearl Drift® = 'Leggab' — EBls LStr MAus MJon SPer WHCG
§ Can-can = 'Legglow' (HT) — MJon
§ News® = 'Legnews' (F) — MAus MGan
§ Deb's Delight = 'Legsweet' (F) — ELan MJon
'Lemon Pillar' — See *R.* **'Paul's Lemon Pillar'**
◆ Len Turner — See *R.* Len Turner = **'Dicjeep'**
§ Pink Surprise = 'Lenbrac' (Ru) — MAus
§ Pleine de Grâce = 'Lengra' (S) — EBls MAus SPer WAct
§ Pascali® = 'Lenip' (HT) — CGro EBls EBrP EBre ELan ENot GCoc GGre IHos LBre LStr MAus MBur MGan MJon NRog SBre SPer SRum SWCr
§ Rush® = 'Lenmobri' (S) — MAus
§ Running Maid® = 'Lenramp' (S/GC) — MAus WAct
'Léonie Lamesch' (Poly) — EBls
'Léontine Gervais' (Ra) — CAbP CRHN MAus MHlr SWCr WAct WHCG
◆ Leslie's Dream — See *R.* Leslie's Dream = **'Dicjoon'**
'Leuchtstern' (Ra) — EBls
'Leverkusen' (Cl) — CHad EBls EBrP EBre LBre LFis MAus MGan NSty SBre SPer SPla SRum SSea WAct WHCG WHow WSHC
'Leveson-Gower' (Bb) — EBls
'Ley's Perpetual' (ClT) — EBls WBcn
¶ x *l'heritieriana* (Bs) — EBee
'Lilac Charm' (F) — EBls MAus
Lilac Rose® (S) — MAus
◆ Lilian Austin® — See *R.* Lilian Austin = **'Ausli'**
◆ Liliana — See *R.* Liliana = **'Poulsyng'**
◆ Lilli Marlene — See *R.* Lilli Marlene = **'Korlima'**
'Lime Kiln' (S) — NSty
◆ Lincoln Cathedral — See *R.* Lincoln Cathedral = **'Glanlin'**
◆ Lincolnshire Poacher — See *R.* Lincolnshire Poacher = **'Glareabit'**
¶ 'Lions International' (HT) — MFry
◆ Little Artist® — See *R.* Little Artist = **'Macmanley'**
◆ Little Bo-peep — See *R.* Little Bo-peep = **'Poullen'**
'Little Buckaroo' (Min) — ELan LGod MGan SPer WStI
'Little Dorrit' (Poly) — NRog
'Little Flirt' (Min) — MAus MGan
'Little Gem' (DPMo) — EBls MAus MGan
◆ Little Jackie — See *R.* Little Jackie = **'Savor'**
'Little Len' (Min/Patio) — MJon
◆ Little Marvel — See *R.* Little Marvel = **'Ruigerdan'**

Little Rambler	See *R.* Little Rambler = 'Chewramb'	
◆ Little Russell	See *R.* Little Russell = 'Trobric'	
* 'Little White'	SRum	
'Little White Pet'	See *R.* 'White Pet'	
◆ Little Woman	See *R.* Little Woman = 'Diclittle'	
'Liverpool Echo' (F)	LPlm MJon	
◆ Liverpool Remembers	See *R.* Liverpool Remembers = 'Frystar'	
'Living Fire' (F)	MBur MGan	
'Lollipop' (Min)	MGan	
'Long John Silver' (Cl)	EBls	
longicuspis Bertoloni (Ra)	EBls	
– hort.	See *R. mulliganii*	
§ – var. *sinowilsonii* (Ra)	EBls GCal MAus	
◆ Lord Byron	See *R.* Lord Byron = 'Meitosier'	
'Lord Penzance' (RH)	EBee EBls MAus MGan NSty WAct WHow	
◆ L'Oréal Trophy	See *R.* L'Oréal Trophy = 'Harlexis'	
'Lorraine Lee' (T)	EBls	
'Los Angeles' (HT)	EBls	
'L'Ouche' misapplied	See *R.* 'Louise Odier'	
'Louis Gimard' (CeMo)	EBls IHos MAus SPer WAct WHCG	
'Louis Philippe' (Ch)	EBls	
'Louis XIV' (Ch)	CHad EBls WHCG	
§ 'Louise Odier' (Bb)	CBos EBls EBrP EBre EMFP IHar LBre LFis LStr MAus MBri MHlr MMat NSty SApu SBre SFam SJus SPer SPla SRum WAct WHCG WOVN	
'Love Token' (F)	MBur	
Lovely Fairy®	See *R.* Lovely Fairy = 'Spevu'	
◆ Lovely Lady	See *R.* Lovely Lady = 'Dicjubell'	
'Lovers' Meeting' (HT)	EBrP EBre GGre LBre LPlm MBri MBur MGan MJon NBat SApu SBre SPer SRum WStI	
◆ Loving Memory	See *R.* Loving Memory = 'Korgund'	
¶ LU 87	WCru	
'Lübeck'	See *R.* 'Hansestadt Lübeck'	
◆ Lucetta	See *R.* Lucetta = 'Ausemi'	
luciae	CMHG EBls	
– var. *onoei*	EPot NMen	
'Lucilla' (Patio)	NBat	
'Lucy Ashton' (RH)	MAus	
◆ Luis Desamero	See *R.* Luis Desamero = 'Tinluis'	
'Lutea Maxima'	See *R.* x *harisonii* 'Lutea Maxima'	
'Lykkefund' (Ra)	EBls MAus	
'Lyon Rose' (HT)	EBls	
'Ma Perkins' (F)	EBls	
'Ma Ponctuée' (DPMo)	EBls	
'Mabel Morrison' (HP)	EBls MAus SWCr	
§ Daily Sketch = 'Macai' (F)	MGan	
§ Captain Cook = 'Macal' (F)	NBat	
§ Snowball = 'Macangeli' (Min/GC)	MJon	
§ Piccadilly® = 'Macar' (HT)	CB&S CGro EBls GGre IHar LPlm MAus MGan MJon NRog SApu SBre SRum	
Macartney Rose	See *R. bracteata*	
§ Kathryn Mcgredy® = 'Macauckland' (HT)	MJon	
§ Galway Bay® = 'Macba' (ClHT)	EBrP EBre LBre MFry MGan MMat SBre SPer	
§ Young Quinn® = 'Macbern' (HT)	MBur	
§ Kronenbourg® = 'Macbo' (HT)	EBls LPlm MAus	
§ Casino® = 'Macca' (ClHT)	CGro EBls IHar LPlm MBur MFry MGan MJon SPer SRum WStI WWeb	
§ Snow Carpet® = 'Maccarpe' (Min/GC) ♥	EBls ENot GCoc IHos MAus MFry MJon MMat WAct	
§ Phantom = 'Maccatsun' (S/GC)	MBur MJon WGer	
§ City of Belfast® = 'Macci' (F)	EBls IHos MAus	
§ Dublin Bay® = 'Macdub' (Cl) ♥	CDoC CTri EBls EBrP EBre ELan ENot IHar IHos LBre LGod LPlm LStr MBri MBur MFry MGan MJon MMat NRog SApu SBre SPer SWCr WGer WHow	
§ Elizabeth of Glamis® = 'Macel' (F)	CGro CTri EBls GChr GCoc IHar IHos MBri MGan NRog SPer SRum	
§ Old Master = 'Macesp' (F)	MAus MGan	
§ Evelyn Fison = 'Macev' (F)	ELan ENot EPfP GCoc GGre IHos MAus MGan MJon NRog SApu SPer SRum	
§ Eye Paint = 'Maceye' (F)	MAus MGan MJon NRog SMrm	
§ Fiesta = 'Macfirinlin' (Patio)	LStr NBat SWCr WGer	
§ Tango = 'Macfirwal' (F) ♥	LPlm MBri MJon	
§ Firefly® = 'Macfrabro'	MJon	
§ Penelope Keith = 'Macfreego' (Min/Patio)	MJon SApu	
§ Frothy = 'Macfrothy' (Min)	MJon	
§ New Zealand = 'Macgenev' (HT)	MJon NBat SApu	
§ Handel® = 'Macha' (Cl) ♥	CGro EBls EBrP EBre ELan GGre IHos LBre LGod LPlm LStr MAus MBri MBur MFry MGan MJon MMat NBat NRog SApu SBre SPer SRum SWCr WWeb	
§ Violet Carson = 'Macio' (F)	MAus MGan	
§ Miss Ireland = 'Macir' (HT)	NRog	
§ Singin' in the Rain = 'Macivy' (F)	MFry MJon SApu	
§ Vidal Sassoon = 'Macjuliat' (HT)	EBee MBur MGan MJon MMat SApu	
§ Old Port = 'Mackati' (F)	GGre MBri MJon SApu	
§ Maestro® = 'Mackinja' (HT)	MAus	
§ Too Hot to Handle = 'Macloupri' (S)	MJon SApu WGer	
§ Matangi® = 'Macman' (F)	LGod MGan MMat	
§ Little Artist® = 'Macmanley' (Min)	MJon	
§ Mischief = 'Macmi' (HT)	EBls GCoc GGre MAus MGan NRog SPer SRum	
¶ 'Macmillan Nurse' (S)	EBls	
§ Penthouse = 'Macngaura' (HT)	MJon	
§ Uncle Walter = 'Macon' (HT)	EBls NPri NRog SRum WStI	
§ Oranges and Lemons® = 'Macoranlem' (F)	CGro ENot GCoc GGre LGod LPlm LStr MBri MBur MFry MGan MJon MMat SApu SJus SRum WGer WWeb	

§ Paddy McGredy = 'Macpa' (F) — CGro GChr GGre MAus MGan MJon NRog SRum

§ Claire Rayner = 'Macpandem' (F/Patio) — LPlm MJon WGer

§ Baby Sunrise = 'Macparlez' (Min) — MJon SJus

§ Picasso = 'Macpic' (F) — EBls MAus MGan

'Macrantha' (Gallica hybrid) — EBls MAus SLPl SPer WAct

× *macrantha* 'Raubritter' — See *R.* **'Raubritter' ('Macrantha' hybrid)**

§ Priscilla Burton® = 'Macrat' (F) — MAus

§ Chardonnay = 'Macrealea' (HT) — MBri MJon

§ Sexy Rexy® = 'Macrexy' (F) ♀ — CGro EBrP EBre ELan GGre IHar IHos LBre LStr MAus MBri MFry MGan MJon NBat SBre SJus SPer SRum SWCr WWeb

macrophylla — MAus MMat

¶ – B&SWJ 2603 — WCru

– 'Doncasteri' — See *R.* **'Doncasteri'**

§ – 'Master Hugh' ex SS&W 7822 ♀ — EBls MAus NSty

§ Royal Salute = 'Macros' (Min) — ENot MJon MMat NRog SPer

§ Benson and Hedges Special = 'Macshana' (Min) — ELan GGre MAus MJon

§ Sue Lawley = 'Macspash' (F) — MBri MGan MJon NRog

§ Eternally Yours = 'Macspeego' (HT) — MJon

§ Grand Hotel® = 'Mactel' (ClHT) — ENot IHos MBri MJon MMat SPer SWCr

§ The Painter = 'Mactemaik' (F) — EBee LStr MBur MFry MJon SApu

§ Trumpeter® = 'Mactru' (F) ♀ — ENot GCoc IHar IHos LGod LPlm LStr MAus MBri MFry MGan MJon MMat NBat SApu SPer

§ Brown Velvet = 'Macultra' (F) — MJon SApu

§ Regensberg® = 'Macyou' (F/Patio) — CTri ENot GGre IHos LPlm MAus MBri MFry MGan MJon MMat NRog SApu SPer WFar

¶ 'Madam Speaker' (HT) — SApu

§ Peace = 'Madame A. Meilland' (HT) ♀ — CB&S CGro EBls ELan GChr GCoc GGre IHos LGod LPlm LStr MAus MBri MBur MFry MGan MJon MMat NBat NRog SApu SPer SRum WWeb

'Madame Abel Chatenay' (HT) — EBls MAus

'Madame Alfred Carrière' (N) ♀ — Widely available

'Madame Alice Garnier' (Ra) — EBls SPer

'Madame Antoine Mari' (T) — EBls

'Madame Berkeley' (T) — EBls

'Madame Bravy' (T) — EBls MAus

'Madame Butterfly' (HT) — EBls MAus MBur MGan NSty SApu

§ 'Madame Caroline Testout' (HT) — MHlr

'Madame Charles' (T) — EBls

'Madame d'Arblay' (Ra) — EBls

'Madame de Sancy de Parabère' (Bs) — EBee EBls MAus SFam WHCG

'Madame de Watteville' (T) — EBls

'Madame Delaroche-Lambert' (DPMo) ♀ — EBls MAus WAct WHCG

'Madame Driout' (ClT) — EBls WHCG

'Madame Eliza de Vilmorin' (HT) — EBls

'Madame Ernest Calvat' (Bb) — EBls MAus NSty

'Madame Eugène Résal' hort. — See *R.* **'Comtesse du Cayla'**

'Madame Gabriel Luizet' (HP) — EBls

'Madame Georges Bruant' (Ru) — EBls MAus

§ 'Madame Grégoire Staechelin' (ClHT) ♀ — CSam EBls EBrP EBre EMFP ENot IHar LBre LStr MAus MBri MGan MHlr MJon MMat NBat NFla NRog NSty SApu SBre SChu SFam SJus SPer SRum WAct WHCG WOVN WWeb

'Madame Hardy' (ClD) ♀ — CPou EBls ENot GCoc IHar LStr MAus MBri MGan MHlr MJon MMat NFla NSty SApu SFam SJus SPer SRum WAct WHCG WHow WOVN

'Madame Isaac Pereire' (ClBb) ♀ — CHad EBls EBrP EBre ENot GCoc IHos IOrc LBre LHol LStr MAus MBri MFry MGan MHlr MJon MMat NRog NSty SApu SBre SFam SJus SMad SPer SSoC WAct WHCG

'Madame Jules Gravereaux' (ClT) — EBls MAus

'Madame Jules Thibaud' (Poly) — MAus

§ 'Madame Knorr' (DPo) ♀ — CBos CPou EBee EBls EBrP EBre EMFP IHos LBre MAus MMat NSty SBre SJus SPer SWCr WAct WHow WOVN

'Madame Laurette Messimy' (Ch) — EBls MAus WHCG WSHC

'Madame Lauriol de Barny' (Bb) — CPou EBls MAus MGan NSty SWCr WHCG

'Madame Legras de Saint Germain' (AxN) — EBls EMFP IHar MAus NSty SFam SJus SPer WAct WHCG

'Madame Lombard' (T) — EBls

'Madame Louis Laperrière' (HT) — EBls MAus MGan NSty SPer

'Madame Louis Lévêque' (DPMo) ♀ — EBls WHCG

'Madame Pierre Oger' (Bb) — EBls ENot GCoc IHos LHol LStr MAus MHlr MMat NSty SApu SPer SRum WAct WHCG WWeb

'Madame Plantier' (AxN) — EBee EBls IHar LHol MAus MHlr MMat SPer WHCG WOVN

'Madame Scipion Cochet' (T) — EBls WHCG

'Madame Victor Verdier' (HP) — EBls

'Madame Wagram, Comtesse de Turenne' (T) — EBls

'Madame William Paul' (PoMo) — EBls

'Madame Zöetmans' (D) — EBls MAus NSty

'Madeleine Selzer' (Ra) — EBls MAus MGan

♦ Maestro® — See *R.* Maestro = **'Mackinja'**

'Magenta' (S/HT) — EBls MAus SPer SWCr WAct WHCG

◆ Magic Carpet   See *R.* Magic Carpet = **'Jaclover'**

◆ Magic Carrousel®   See *R.* Magic Carrousel = **'Moorcar'**

'Magna Charta' (HP)   EBls

'Magnifica' (RH)   EBls MAus MGan

N 'Maiden's Blush' (A)   CSam EBls EBrP EBre ELan EMFP ENot IHar LBre LHol MAus MGan MHlr SApu SBre SChu SFam SJus SPer SRum SWCr WHCG WHow WWeb

'Maiden's Blush, Great'   See *R.* **'Great Maiden's Blush'**

'Maigold' (ClPiH) ♀   Widely available

§ *majalis*   MSto

◆ Make a Wish   See *R.* Make a Wish = **'Mehpat'**

'Malaga' (ClHT)   MMat

§ Danse des Sylphes® =   EBls
    'Malcair' (Cl)

◆ Malcolm Sargent   See *R.* Malcolm Sargent = **'Harwherry'**

Maltese rose   See *R.* **'Cécile Brünner'**

§ 'Malton' (China hybrid)   EBls

Malverns   See *R.* Malverns = **'Kordehei'**

◆ Mandarin®   See *R.* Mandarin = **'Korcelin'**

'Manettii' (N)   EBls

'Manning's Blush' (RH)   EBls MAus NSty WAct WHCG

◆ Manou Meilland®   See *R.* Manou Meilland = **'Meitulimon'**

Manuela® (HT)   MGan

'Manx Queen' (F)   MGan MJon

◆ Many Happy Returns   See *R.* Many Happy Returns = **'Harwanted'**

'Marbrée' (DPo)   EBls MAus

'Marcel Bourgouin' (G)   EBls

'Märchenland' (F/S)   EBls MAus

§ 'Marchesa Boccella' (DPo) ♀   EBee EBls EMFP EPfP IHar MAus MGan MMat NFla NPri SJus SMer SPer SPla WAct WWeb

'Marcie Gandy' (HT)   MGan

'Maréchal Davoust' (CeMo)   EBls MAus NSty SFam SPer

'Maréchal Niel' (N)   EBls ERea MAus MGan NSty SPer WHCG

'Margaret' (HT)   MBur MGan

◆ Margaret Merril   See *R.* Margaret Merril = **'Harkuly'**

◆ Margaret Thatcher   See *R.* Margaret Thatcher = **'Korflüg'**

'Margo Koster' (Poly)   EBls MAus NRog SRum

Marguerite Anne   See *R.* Marguerite Anne = **'Cockredward'**

'Marguérite Guillard' (HP)   EBls

'Marguerite Hilling' (S) ♀   EBls ENot GCoc GGre MAus MBri MGan MHlr MJon MMat NRog NSty SApu SPer SRum SWCr WAct WHCG WOVN

× *mariae-graebnerae*   SLPl WHCG

◆ Marianne Tudor   See *R.* Marianne Tudor = **'Frymartor'**

'Marie de Blois' (CeMo)   EBls

'Marie Louise' (D)   EBls IHar IHos MAus SFam WAct WHCG

¶ 'Marie Pavic' (Poly)   EBls MAus WHCG

'Marie van Houtte' (T)   EBls MAus

'Marie-Jeanne' (Poly)   EBls MAus

'Marijke Koopman' (HT)   MFry

◆ Marinette   See *R.* Marinette = **'Auscam'**

◆ Marjorie Fair®   See *R.* Marjorie Fair = **'Harhero'**

'Marlena' (F/Patio)   GCoc MAus MBri MGan

'Martha' (Bb)   EBls MAus

'Martian Glow' (F/S)   MGan

'Martin Frobisher' (Ru)   EBls MAus

'Mary' (Poly)   LStr

◆ Mary Donaldson   See *R.* Mary Donaldson = **'Canana'**

◆ Mary Gammon   See *R.* Mary Gammon = **'Frysweetie'**

'Mary Manners' (Ru)   EBls SPer

Mary Pope   See *R.* Mary Pope = **'Korlasche'**

◆ Mary Rose®   See *R.* Mary Rose = **'Ausmary'**

'Mary Wallace' (Cl)   EBls MAus

◆ Mary Webb®   See *R.* Mary Webb = **'Auswebb'**

'Masquerade' (F)   CB&S CGro EBls LGod LStr MAus MGan MJon NRog SRum WStI

'Master Hugh'   See *R. macrophylla* **'Master Hugh'**

◆ Matangi®   See *R.* Matangi = **'Macman'**

§ Chelsea Pensioner =   LPlm SApu
    'Mattche' (Min)

§ Northamptonshire =   ENot LGod MGan MMat SRum
    'Mattdor' (GC)

§ Pink Wave = 'Mattgro'   IHos MMat
    (GC)

§ Elizabeth Heather   MMat
    Grierson = 'Mattnot' (ClHT)

§ Tynwald = 'Mattwyt' (HT)   LStr MJon MMat SWCr

'Maurice Bernardin' (HP)   EBls

'Max Graf'   See *R.* × *jacksonii* **'Max Graf'**

'Maxima'   See *R.* × *alba* **'Alba Maxima'**

maximowicziana CC 541   WHCr

'May Queen' (Ra)   CRHN EBls EMFP MAus MHlr SFam SPer SWCr WAct WHCG WHow

Mayor of Casterbridge   See *R.* Mayor of Casterbridge = **'Ausbrid'**

'McGredy's Sunset' (HT)   NRog

'McGredy's Yellow' (HT)   EBls MBur MGan

§ Solitaire® = 'Mcyefre'   MBri MJon SApu WWeb
    (HT)

§ Message = 'Meban' (HT)   MGan

'Meg' (ClHT)   CHad EBee EBls MAus MBur MGan MHlr NSty SPer WAct WHCG

¶ 'Meg Merrilies' (RH)   EBls MAus MGan SWCr

§ Starina® = 'Megabi'   MGan
    (Min)

'Megiddo' (F)   MGan

§ Amber Nectar =   LStr
    'Mehamber' (F)

§ Free as Air = 'Mehbronze'   MBri
    (Patio)

§ Make a Wish = 'Mehpat'   LStr MBri SWCr
    (Min/Patio)

§ Pink Peace = 'Meibil'   CB&S GGre
    (HT)

§ Swany® = 'Meiburenac'   EBls ELan GGre IHos MAus
    (Min/GC) ♀   MGan SApu SPer SRum WAct WHCG WOVN

§ Champs Elysées® =   MGan
    'Meicarl' (HT)

§ Pigalle '84 = 'Meicloux'   SRum
    (F)

§ White Meidiland® =   MGan WOVN
    'Meicoublan' (S/GC)

§ Cricri = 'Meicri' (Min)   MAus MGan

§ Zambra® = 'Meicurbos'   CB&S
    (F)

§ Belle Sunblaze =   IHar
    'Meidanego' (Min)

§ Mimi = 'Meidesi' (Min) — MGan
§ Scarlet Gem® = 'Meido' (Min) — ELan MGan
§ Bonica® = 'Meidomonac' (GC) ♀ — CSam EBls EBrP EBre ELan ENot GCoc IHar IHos LBre LGod LStr MAus MBur MFry MGan MHlr MJon SApu SBre SJus SPer SRum SWCr WAct WHCG WOVN
§ Alba Meidiland® = 'Meiflopan' (S/GC) — WOVN
§ Gold Bunny = 'Meifronuri' (F) — MBri MGan MJon
§ La Sévillana = 'Meigekanu' (F/GC) — EBls SApu SPer SRum WOVN
§ Pink La Sevillana® = 'Meigeroka' (F/GC) — SRum
§ Tropico Sunblaze = 'Meiglassol' (Min/v) — MBri
§ Snow Sunblaze™ = 'Meigovin' (Min) — SPer WWeb
§ Baronne Edmond de Rothschild® = 'Meigriso' (HT) — MAus WAct
§ Climbing Gold Bunny = 'Meigro-Nurisar' (ClF) — MJon WGer
§ Sarabande = 'Meihand' (F) — MGan
§ Sparkling Scarlet = 'Meihati' (Ra) — EBrP EBre ELan LBre LPlm MGan SBre
§ Sweet Promise = 'Meihelvet' (GC) — MGan
§ Thomas Barton® = 'Meihirvin' (HT) — LStr SApu
§ Pink Sunblaze® = 'Meijidiro' (Min/Patio) — SApu
§ Orange Sunblaze® = 'Meijikatar' (Min) — EBls GGre IHos LStr MGan MJon SJus SPer WWeb
§ Climbing Orange Sunblaze = 'Meijikatarsar' (ClMin) — LStr MBri MJon NPri SApu SPer
§ Fiona® = 'Meikeluxen' (S/GC) — EBls GGre IHos SApu WHCG WOVN
§ Scarlet Meidiland® = 'Meikrotal' (S/GC) — MGan WOVN
§ Lady Meillandina® = 'Meilarco' (Min) — SApu
§ Birthday Girl = 'Meilasso' (F) — MJon SApu SRum
§ Exploit® = 'Meilider' (Cl) — GGre SCoo WWeb
§ Christian Dior = 'Meilie' (HT) — EBls
§ The Children's Rose = 'Meilivar' (F) — SApu SRum
♦ Meillandina® — See R. Meillandina = 'Meirov'
§ Repens Meidiland® = 'Meilontig' (S) — WOVN
§ Darling Flame = 'Meilucca' (Min) — ELan GGre MGan SApu
§ Jardins de Bagatelle® = 'Meimafris' (HT) — COtt MBur MJon SApu
§ Colibri = 'Meimal' (Min) — LGod MGan SPer
§ Cocktail® = 'Meimick' (S) — EBls MGan WAct
§ Grace de Monaco® = 'Meimit' (HT) — EBls MAus MGan
§ Clair Matin® = 'Meimont' (ClS) — CHad EBls MAus SPer SPla WAct
§ Laurence Olivier® = 'Meinagre' (F) — SApu
§ Susan Hampshire = 'Meinatac' (HT) — EBls MGan

§ Red Meidiland® = 'Meineble' (GC) — WOVN
§ Twenty-one Again® = 'Meinimo' (HT) — MBur MJon MRav SApu
§ Christopher Columbus® = 'Meinronsse' (HT) — MBri MJon MMat SApu
§ Caroline de Monaco® = 'Meipierar' (HT) — MJon
§ Duke Meillandina = 'Meipinjid' (Min) — SApu
§ Sunny Sunblaze™ = 'Meiponal' (Min) — SJus
§ Pink Meidiland® = 'Meipoque' (GC) — MGan WOVN
§ Candy Rose® = 'Meiranovi' (S) — GGre
§ Toulouse-Lautrec® = 'Meirevolt' (S) — SApu
§ Charleston = 'Meiridge' (F) — MGan
§ Paprika™ = 'Meiriental' (F) — MAus
§ Colorama = 'Meirigalu' (HT) — MBri
§ John Keats = 'Meiroupis' (S) — SApu
§ Meillandina® = 'Meirov' (Min) — MGan
§ Red Sunblaze = 'Meirutral' (Min) — IHos MJon WWeb
§ Papa Meilland® = 'Meisar' (HT) — CB&S CGro EBls MAus MGan MJon NRog SApu SPer SRum WOVN
§ Flamingo Meidiland = 'Meisolroz' — WOVN
§ Auguste Renoir® = 'Meitoifar' (HT) — GGre
§ Golden Symphonie = 'Meitoleil' (Min/Patio) — MJon
§ Pretty Polly® = 'Meitonje' (Min) — CGro CTri EBrP EBre GGre LBre LStr MBri MFry MGan MJon MMat NPri SApu SBre SJus WWeb
§ Lord Byron = 'Meitosier' (ClHT) — LStr MBri MJon SApu SWCr
§ Yellow Sunblaze = 'Meitrisical' (Min) — IHos WWeb
§ Manou Meilland® = 'Meitulimon' (HT) — MGan
§ Spirit of Youth = 'Meivestal' (HT) — SApu
§ Eden Rose '88 = 'Meiviolin' (ClHT) — MJon SApu SJus SPer
§ Peach Sunblaze = 'Meixerul' (Min) — MJon SApu SJus WWeb
§ The McCartney Rose = 'Meizeli' (HT) — GCoc GGre LPlm LStr MJon SApu SJus SPer
♦ Melina® — See R. Sir Harry Pilkington = 'Tanema'
'Melinda' (HT) — MBri
♦ Melody Maker — See R. Melody Maker = 'Dicqueen'
§ Thaïs = 'Memaj' (HT) — EBls
Memento® — See R. Memento = 'Dicbar'
'Memoriam' (HT) — MGan
Memory Lane — See R. Memory Lane = 'Peavoodoo'
§ Bettina® = 'Mepal' (HT) — MAus MGan NRog
§ Climbing Bettina® = 'Mepalsar' (ClHT) — EBls MAus
♦ Mercedes — See R. Mercedes = 'Merkor'
§ Mercedes = 'Merkor' (F) — MJon
'Mermaid' (Cl) ♀ — Widely available

'Merveille de Lyon' (HP) EBls
◆ Message See *R.* Message = **'Meban'**
Meteor® (F/Patio) MGan
§ 'Mevrouw Nathalie CHad EBee EBls IHar LStr
Nypels' (Poly) ♀ MAus SPer WAct WKif WOVN
'Mexico' (Min) LPlm
◆ Michael Crawford See *R.* Michael Crawford = **'Poulvue'**
'Michèle Meilland' (HT) EBls MAus MGan NSty
micrantha WUnd
x *micrugosa* EBls MAus
– 'Alba' EBls MAus
◆ Middlesex County See *R.* Middlesex County = **'Bosanne'**
§ Elsie Warren = 'Milsweet' NBat
(F)
◆ Mimi See *R.* Mimi = **'Meidesi'**
◆ Mini Metro See *R.* Mini Metro = **'Rufin'**
◆ Minilights See *R.* Minilights = **'Dicmoppet'**
§ Black Jack® = 'Minkco' MBur NBat
(Min/Patio)
'Minnehaha' (Ra) EBls EMFP LGod MAus
mirifica stellata See *R.* stellata var. *mirifica*
◆ Mischief See *R.* Mischief = **'Macmi'**
'Miss Edith Cavell' (Poly) EBls
◆ Miss Harp See *R.* Miss Harp = **'Tanolg'**
◆ Miss Ireland See *R.* Miss Ireland = **'Macir'**
'Miss Lowe' (Ch) EBls
◆ Miss Pam Ayres See *R.* Miss Pam Ayres = **'Kormarie'**
§ Mister Lincoln® (HT) EBls LGod MAus MBri MBur MGan SPer
Mistress Quickly See *R.* Mistress Quickly = **'Ausky'**
§ Mother's Day = NPri
'Moersdag' (Poly/F)
'Mojave' (HT) MAus MGan
Moje Hammarberg® (Ru) ENot IHos MJon WAct
Molineux See *R.* Molineux = **'Ausmol'**
§ *mollis* MSto
'Mona Ruth' (Min) MGan
'Monique' (HT) EBls MGan NSty
'Monsieur Tillier' (T) EBls
'Moon Maiden' (F) MMat
Moonbeam See *R.* Moonbeam = **'Ausbeam'**
'Moonlight' (HM) CTri EBls IHar IHos MAus MGan MMat NBus NRog NSty SJus SPer SRum SWCr WAct WHCG
§ Magic Carrousel® = LPlm MAus NPri WStI
'Moorcar' (Min)
'Morgengruss' (Cl) MGan SPer
◆ Moriah See *R.* Moriah = **'Ganhol'**
'Morlettii' (Bs) EBls EHol MRav
§ My Valentine® = MRav
'Mormyval' (Min)
Morning Jewel® CB&S GCoc LPlm MAus MFry MJon NBat NRog
◆ Morning Mist See *R.* Morning Mist = **'Ausfire'**
§ Sheri Anne = 'Morsheri' MAus
(Min)
§ Yellow Dagmar Hastrup = CTri EBee LFis MAus MBri
'Moryelrug' (Ru) MGan MHlr MJon SApu SJus SPer SRum WAct WHCG WOVN
moschata (Ra) EBls MAus MHlr MRav
– 'Autumnalis' See *R.* **'Princesse de Nassau'**
– var. *nastarana* See *R.* **'Nastarana'**
– var. *nepalensis* See *R.* *brunonii*
◆ Mother's Day See *R.* Mother's Day = **'Moersdag'**
I 'Mother's Day' ELan MJon

◆ Mountain Snow See *R.* Mountain Snow = **'Aussnow'**
◆ Mountbatten® See *R.* Mountbatten = **'Harmantelle'**
§ 'Mousseline' (DPoMo) EBls EMFP MAus NSty WAct WHCG
◆ 'Mousseuse du Japon' See *R.* **'Japonica'** (CeMo)
moyesii (S) CSam EBls ELan ENot GCoc IHar IHos IOrc ISea MAus MFry MGan MJon MMat NRog NSty NWea SPer WAct WOVN
– 'Evesbatch' (S) WAct
§ – var. *fargesii* (S) EBls
– 'Geranium' See *R.* **'Geranium'** (*moyesii* hybrid)
– 'Highdownensis' See *R.* **'Highdownensis'** (*moyesii* hybrid)
– 'Hillieri' See *R.* **'Hillieri'**
– f. *rosea* See *R. moyesii* f. *rosea*
§ – f. *rosea* (S) EBls GCal
– 'Sealing Wax' See *R.* **'Sealing Wax'** (*moyesii* hybrid)
'Mozart' (HM) MJon WHCG
'Mr Bluebird' (MinCh) MAus MGan WStI
'Mr Chips' (HT) MBur
◆ Mr J.C.B. See *R.* Mr J.C.B. = **'Dicsun'**
'Mr Lincoln' See *R.* Mister Lincoln
'Mrs Anthony Waterer' EBls IHos MAus NSty SPer WAct WHCG
(Ru)
'Mrs B.R. Cant' (T) EBls
◆ Mrs Doreen Pike See *R.* Mrs Doreen Pike = **'Ausdor'**
'Mrs Eveline Gandy' (HT) MGan
'Mrs Foley Hobbs' (T) EBls
'Mrs Honey Dyson' (Ra) CHad
'Mrs John Laing' (HP) EBls MAus MHlr NSty SJus SPer SWCr WHCG
'Mrs Oakley Fisher' (HT) CHad EBls MAus NSty WAct
♀ WCot
'Mrs Paul' (Bb) EBls MAus
'Mrs Pierre S. duPont' EBls
(HT)
'Mrs Sam McGredy' (HT) MAus MGan
'Mrs Walter Burns' MGan
(F/Patio)
'Mullard Jubilee' (HT) IHar MGan
§ *mulliganii* (Ra) ♀ EBls IHar MAus SBid SJus SPer SPla WHCG
multibracteata ♀ EBls MAus WHCG
multiflora EBls MAus WPic
– 'Carnea' EBls
– var. *cathayensis* EBls
§ – 'Grevillei' EBls MAus NSty SPer WHow
– 'Platyphylla' See *R. multiflora* **'Grevillei'**
– var. *watsoniana* See *R. watsoniana*
'München' (HM) MAus
mundi See *R. gallica* **'Versicolor'**
– 'Versicolor' See *R. gallica* **'Versicolor'**
'Mutabilis' See *R.* x *odorata* **'Mutabilis'**
'My Choice' (HT) MGan SWCr
'My Joy' (HT) NBat
'My Little Boy' (Min) MBur
◆ My Love See *R.* My Love = **'Cogamo'**
◆ My Valentine® See *R.* My Valentine = **'Mormyval'**
◆ Myra See *R.* Myra = **'Battoo'**
◆ Myriam® See *R.* Myriam = **'Cocgrand'**
'Nancy's Keepsake' (HT) NBat
'Narrow Water' (Ra) EBls LFis WAct WHCG
§ 'Nastarana' (N) EBls
'Nathalie Nypels' See *R.* **'Mevrouw Nathalie Nypels'**

'National Trust' (HT)	EBls GGre IHar IHos MGan MJon NBat NRog SPer SRum WStI	'Nyveldt's White' (Ru)	EBls IHos MAus
'Nestor' (G)	EBls MAus	§ Angela Rippon® = 'Ocaru' (Min)	IHos MFry MGan MJon SPer WGer
'Nevada' (S) ♀	CB&S EBrP EBre ELan ENot GCoc GGre IOrc LBre LGod LStr MAus MBri MFry MGan MHlr MJon MMat NFla NRog NSty SApu SBre SJus SPer SRum WAct WHCG WOVN WWeb	◆ Octavia Hill	See R. Octavia Hill = 'Harzeal'
		x odorata 'Fortune's Double Yellow'	See R. x odorata 'Pseudindica'
		§ – 'Mutabilis' (Ch) ♀	CGre EBls EMFP MAus MMat NSty SJus SMad SMrm SPer SPla WAct WHCG WHow WOVN WWat
§ 'New Dawn' (Cl) ♀	Widely available	§ – 'Ochroleuca' (Ch)	EBls
◆ New Fashion	See R. New Fashion = 'Poulholm'	§ – 'Odorata' (Ch)	EBls
◆ New Horizon	See R. New Horizon = 'Dicplay'	– Old Crimson China (Ch)	EBls WAct
'New Look' (F)	MGan	§ – 'Pallida' (Ch)	CHad EBls EMFP GCoc IHos MAus MMat NPri NSty SPla SWCr WHCG WHow
'New Penny' (Min)	IHar MGan		
◆ New Zealand	See R. New Zealand = 'Macgenev'	§ – 'Pseudindica' (ClCh)	EBls MAus WSHC
		§ – Sanguinea Group (Ch)	EBls WHCG
◆ News®	See R. News = 'Legnews'	§ – 'Viridiflora' (Ch)	CPou EBls MAus MBur MMat SMad SPer SRum SSoC WAct WHCG
◆ Nice Day	See R. Nice Day = 'Chewsea'		
'Nicola' (F)	MGan	'Oeillet Flamand'	See R. 'Oeillet Parfait'
◆ Nigel Hawthorne	See R. Nigel Hawthorne = 'Harquibbler'	'Oeillet Panaché' (Mo)	WAct
		§ 'Oeillet Parfait' (G)	EBls MAus
◆ Night Light®	See R. Night Light = 'Poullight'	officinalis	See R. gallica var. officinalis
Nina Weibull® (F)	MGan	'Ohl' (G)	EBls
nitida	EBls ELan ENot GChr MAus NSty NWea SLPl SPer WAct WHCG WHer WOVN	◆ Ohshima Rose	See R. Ohshima Rose = 'Cochunter'
		'Oklahoma' (HT)	MGan
§ White Flower Carpet® = 'Noaschnee' (GC)	IHar MFry MMat SCoo SPer WGer WWeb	Old Blush China	See R. x odorata 'Pallida'
		Old Cabbage	See R. x centifolia
§ Pink Flower Carpet® = 'Noatraum' (GC) ♀	CTri EBrP EBre ELan GGre IHar LBre MAus MFry MGan MJon MMat NPri SBre SCoo SJus SPer SPla SRum SWCr WWeb	◆ Old Master	See R. Old Master = 'Macesp'
		Old pink Moss rose	See R. x centifolia 'Muscosa'
		◆ Old Port	See R. Old Port = 'Mackati'
		Old Red Moss	See R. 'Henri Martin' (CeMo) AGM, R. 'Lanei' (CeMo)
Noble Antony	See R. Noble Anthony = 'Ausway'	Old Velvet Moss	See R. 'William Lobb'
		Old Yellow Scotch (PiH)	See R. x harisonii 'Williams' Double Yellow'
§ 'Noisette Carnée' (N)	CBos CHad EBls GChr MAus NSty SPer SSea WAct WHCG WHow WSHC		
		◆ Olde Romeo	See R. Olde Romeo = 'Hadromeo'
◆ Norfolk	See R. Norfolk = 'Poulfolk'		
◆ Northamptonshire	See R. Northamptonshire = 'Mattdor'	◆ Oliver Twist	See R. Oliver Twist = 'Sabbyron'
		'Omar Khayyám' (D)	EBls ENot MAus
Northern Lights® (HT)	GCoc	§ 'Ombrée Parfaite' (G)	EBls
¶ 'Northumberland WI' (HT)	NBat	omeiensis f. pteracantha	See R. sericea subsp. omeiensis f. pteracantha
'Norwich Castle' (F)	EBls		
◆ Norwich Cathedral	See R. Norwich Cathedral = 'Beacath'	Open Arms	See R. Open Arms = 'Chewpixcel'
'Norwich Pink' (Cl)	MAus	'Ophelia' (HT)	EBls MAus MBur MGan NSty SApu
¶ 'Norwich Salmon' (Cl)	MAus		
'Norwich Union' (F)	EBls	'Orange Honey' (Min)	MBur
§ Catherine Cookson = 'Noscook' (HT)	NBat	§ Orange Sensation® (F)	EBls ENot GChr MAus MGan MJon NRog SRum
§ Sunderland Supreme = 'Nossun' (HT)	NBat	◆ Orange Sunblaze®	See R. Orange Sunblaze = 'Meijikatar'
'Nova Zembla' (Ru)	EBls MAus NSty	Orange Triumph® (Poly)	EBls
'Nozomi' (GC) ♀	CGro EBls ELan ENot GCoc GGre IHos LPlm LStr MAus MFry MGan MHlr MJon MMat NMen SApu SJus SPer SRum WAct WHCG WOVN	Orangeade (F)	MGan
		◆ Oranges and Lemons®	See R. Oranges and Lemons = 'Macoranlem'
		'Oriana' (HT)	CGro
		'Orient Express' (HT)	MJon
'Nuits de Young' (CeMo)	CPou EBls GCoc IHar MAus MMat NSty SFam WHCG	'Orpheline de Juillet'	See R. 'Ombrée Parfaite'
		◆ Othello®	See R. Othello = 'Auslo'
'Nur Mahal' (HM)	EBls MAus WHCG	◆ Our Love	See R. Our Love = 'Andour'
nutkana (S)	EBls MAus	Our Molly	See R. Our Molly = 'Dicreason'
§ – var. hispida (S)	EBls	◆ Owen's Pride	See R. Owen's Pride = 'Kirpink'
§ – 'Plena' (S) ♀	CHan EBls ENot EPfP MAus NSty SWCr WGer WHCG	Oxfordshire	See R. Oxfordshire = 'Korfullwind'
'Nymphenburg' (HM)	EBls EMFP MAus SPer	◆ Paddy McGredy	See R. Paddy McGredy = 'Macpa'
'Nypels' Perfection' (Poly)	MAus		

◆ Painted Moon	See *R.* Painted Moon = **'Dicpaint'**	◆ Peace	See *R.* Peace = **'Madame A. Meilland'**
Paint-pot	See *R.* Paint-pot = **'Trobglow'**	◆ Peace Sunblaze (Min)	See *R.* Lady Meillandina = **'Meilarco' (Min)**
I 'Pam Ayres'	See *R.* Miss Pam Ayres = **'Kormarie'**	◆ Peacekeeper	See *R.* Peacekeeper = **'Harbella'**
Panache	See *R.* Panache = **'Poultop'**	◆ Peach Blossom	See *R.* Peach Blossom = **'Ausblossom'**
'Panorama Holiday' (F/HT)	MBur	◆ Peach Sunblaze	See *R.* Peach Sunblaze = **'Meixerul'**
'Papa Gontier' (T)	EBls MAus	'Peachy White' (Min)	MAus
'Papa Hémeray' (Ch)	EBls	§ Doctor McAlpine = 'Peafirst' (F/Patio)	MBri MJon SPer SWCr
◆ Papa Meilland®	See *R.* Papa Meilland = **'Meisar'**	§ Geraldine = 'Peahaze' (F)	MBri MGan MJon SWCr
'Papillon' (T)	EBls	§ Leaping Salmon = 'Peamight' (ClHT)	CGro ELan GCoc IHar IHos IOrc LGod LStr MAus MBri MGan MJon SApu SChu SPer SPla SRum WOVN WStI
◆ Paprika	See *R.* Paprika = **'Meiriental'**		
'Pâquerette' (Poly)	EBls		
§ Pour Toi = 'Para Ti' (Min)	ENot MAus MGan MJon NPri SPer		
'Parade' (Cl) ♀	MAus MFry MGan SJus WHCG	§ Bush Baby = 'Peanob' (Min)	LGod LStr MJon SApu SWCr WStI
◆ Paradise®	See *R.* Paradise = **'Weizeip'**	§ Royal Flush = 'Peapatio' (F/Patio)	MBri
Parkdirektor Riggers® (Cl)	CSam EBls LStr MAus MBri MGan SPer SRum WHCG WSHC	§ Indian Summer = 'Peaperfume' (HT) ♀	GCoc LGod MBri MFry MJon
Park's Yellow China	See *R.* × *odorata* **'Ochroleuca'**	§ Jane Asher = 'Peapet' (Min/Patio)	MBri MJon SApu
'Parkzierde' (Bb)	EBls	◆ Pearl Anniversary	See *R.* Pearl Anniversary = **'Whitson'**
Parson's Pink China	See *R.* × *odorata* **'Pallida'**		
◆ Partridge	See *R.* Partridge = **'Korweirim'**	◆ Pearl Drift®	See *R.* Pearl Drift = **'Leggab'**
Party Girl® (Min)	NBat	§ Gary Lineker = 'Pearobin' (F)	MBri
◆ Party Trick	See *R.* Party Trick = **'Dicparty'**	§ Goldfinger = 'Pearoyal' (F)	MBri
parvifolia	See *R.* **'Burgundiaca'**	◆ Peaudouce	See *R.* Elina = **'Dicjana'**
◆ Pascali®	See *R.* Pascali = **'Lenip'**	§ Stardust® = 'Peavandyke' (Patio/F)	GGre MJon
Passion (Ru)	WLRN		
◆ Pat Austin	See *R.* Pat Austin = **'Ausmum'**	§ Memory Lane = 'Peavoodoo' (F)	GGre
Pathfinder	See *R.* Pathfinder = **'Chewpobey'**	§ Ruby Celebration = 'Peawinner' (F)	GGre
◆ Patricia	See *R.* Patricia = **'Korpatri'**	§ Bright Fire = 'Peaxi' (Cl)	MBri
'Paul Crampel' (Poly)	EBls MAus MGan NRog NSty SPer	◆ Peek A Boo	See *R.* Peek A Boo = **'Dicgrow'**
		◆ Peer Gynt®	See *R.* Peer Gynt = **'Korol'**
'Paul Lédé'	See *R.* **'Climbing Paul Lédé'**	◆ Pegasus	See *R.* Pegasus = **'Ausmoon'**
Paul McCartney	See *R.* The McCartney Rose = **'Meizeli'**	'Pélisson' (CeMo)	EBls
'Paul Neyron' (HP)	EBls MAus MMat NSty SPer WAct WHCG	§ *pendulina*	EBls MAus WHCG
		'Penelope' (HM) ♀	CHad CSam EBls EBrP EBre ELan ENot GCoc GOrc IHos LBre LStr MAus MBri MFry MGan MHlr MJon MMat NRog NSty SApu SBre SJus SPer SRum WAct WHCG WKif WOVN
'Paul Ricault' (CexHP)	EBls MAus		
◆ Paul Shirville	See *R.* Paul Shirville = **'Harqueterwife'**		
'Paul Transon' (Ra) ♀	CRHN EBee EBls EMFP IHar MAus MBri MHlr SJus SPer WHCG WHow WOVN		
		◆ Penelope Keith	See *R.* Penelope Keith = **'Macfreego'**
'Paul Verdier' (Bb)	EBls	'Penelope Plummer' (F)	EBls
§ 'Paulii' (Ru)	EBls ELan ENot IHos LFis MAus MHlr SPer WAct WHCG WOVN	◆ Penny Lane	See *R.* Penny Lane = **'Hardwell'**
		◆ Pensioner's Voice	See *R.* Pensioner's Voice = **'Fryrelax'**
'Paulii Alba'	See *R.* **'Paulii'**		
'Paulii Rosea' (Ru/Cl)	EBls MAus MBri WAct WHCG	◆ Penthouse®	See *R.* Penthouse = **'Macngaura'**
'Paul's Early Blush' (HP)	EBls	§ Kind Regards = 'Pentiger' (F)	SRum
'Paul's Himalayan Musk' (Ra) ♀	CHad CRHN CSam EBls EBrP EBre EMFP IHar ISea LBre LHol LStr MAus MBri MHlr MJon NBat NSty SApu SBre SFam SJus SPer WAct WHCG WHow WKif WPic	× *penzanceana*	See *R.* **'Lady Penzance'**
		◆ Peppermint Ice	See *R.* Peppermint Ice = **'Bosgreen'**
		◆ Perception	See *R.* Perception = **'Harzippee' (HT)**
§ 'Paul's Lemon Pillar' (ClHT)	CHad EBee EBls EBrP EBre LBre MAus NRog NSty SBre SPer		
		◆ Perdita®	See *R.* Perdita = **'Ausperd'**
'Paul's Perpetual White' (Ra)	EBls WHCG	◆ Perestroika	See *R.* Perestroika = **'Korhitom'**
'Paul's Scarlet Climber' (Cl/Ra)	CGro EBls ELan ENot GGre IHos LGod LStr MAus MGan MJon MMat NSty SApu SPer SRum SWCr WWeb	◆ Perfecta	See *R.* Perfecta = **'Koralu'**
		'Perle des Jardins' (T)	EBls MAus
'Pax' (HM)	EBls EMFP MAus NSty SPer WHCG WKif	'Perle des Panachées' (G)	EBls

'Perle d'Or' (Poly) ♀ — CHad EMFP ENot GCoc MAus MHlr MMat NFla NRog NSty SChu SMer SPer SPla WAct WHCG WWat
'Perle von Hohenstein' (Poly) — EBls
Pernille Poulsen® (F) — EBls
Persian Yellow — See *R. foetida* 'Persiana'
¶ *persica* — MAus
◆ Petit Four® — See *R.* Petit Four = 'Interfour'
'Petite de Hollande' (Ce) — EBls MAus NSty SPer SWCr WAct WHCG WHow
'Petite Lisette' (CexD) — EBls MAus SPer
'Petite Orléannaise' (Ce) — EBls
¶ 'Phab Gold' (F) — MFry
◆ Phantom — See *R.* Phantom = 'Maccatsun'
'Pharisäer' (HT) — EBls
◆ Pheasant — See *R.* Pheasant = 'Kordapt'
¶ 'Philipa' — EBee
phoenicia — EBls
'Phyllis Bide' (Ra) ♀ — EBls EMFP LStr MAus MGan MHlr NSty SJus SPer SSea WHCG WHow
◆ Picasso — See *R.* Picasso = 'Macpic'
◆ Piccadilly® — See *R.* Piccadilly = 'Macar'
◆ Piccolo — See *R.* Piccolo = 'Tanolokip'
§ Valentine Heart = 'Picogle' (F) — CDoC EBee IDic LGod MFry MJon SApu SJus
'Picture' (HT) — EBls MAus MGan NRog NSty SPer
'Pierre Notting' (HP) — EBls
◆ Pigalle '84 — See *R.* Pigalle '84 = 'Meicloux'
◆ 'Pilgrim' — See *R.* The Pilgrim = 'Auswalker'
◆ Pillar Box — See *R.* Pillar Box = 'Chewaze'
§ *pimpinellifolia* — CKin EBls ENot LBuc MAus MGan MMat NFla NRoo NWea SPer WHCG WOVN
– 'Altaica' hort. — See *R. pimpinellifolia* 'Grandiflora'
§ – 'Andrewsii' ♀ — MAus WAct
– 'Bakewell Scots Briar' — NSty
§ – double pink — EBls
§ – double white — CNat EBls GCoc MAus WAct
– double yellow — See *R.* x *harisonii* 'Williams' Double Yellow'
§ – 'Dunwich Rose' — EBee EBls EBrP EBre ENot LBre MAus MBri MGan MMat SBre SPer WAct WHCG
– 'Falkland' — EBls MAus
§ – 'Glory of Edzell' — EBls MAus
§ – 'Grandiflora' — EBls MAus SJus
– 'Harisonii' — See *R.* x *harisonii* 'Harison's Yellow'
¶ – HH&K 328 — CHan
¶ – var. *hispida* — MAus
– 'Irish Marbled' — EBls
– 'Lutea' — See *R.* x *harisonii* 'Lutea Maxima'
– 'Marbled Pink' — EBls MAus
– 'Mary, Queen of Scots' — EBls MAus NSty SRms WAct
– 'Mrs Colville' — EBls MAus
– 'Ormiston Roy' — MAus NSty
– x *pendulina* — See *R.* x *reversa*
§ – 'Robbie' — MAus WAct
– 'Single Cherry' — EBls MAus
– 'Stanwell Perpetual' — See *R.* 'Stanwell Perpetual'
– 'Variegata' — CArn
– 'William III' — EBls LHop MAus NSty SChu SLPl
◆ Pink Bells® — See *R.* Pink Bells = 'Poulbells'
'Pink Bouquet' (Ra) — CRHN MAus

◆ Pink Chimo® — See *R.* Pink Chimo = 'Interchimp'
◆ Pink Drift — See *R.* Pink Drift = 'Poulcat'
'Pink Favorite' (HT) — IHos MGan NRog SPer SRum
◆ Pink Flower Carpet® — See *R.* Pink Flower Carpet = 'Noatraum'
'Pink Garnette' — See *R.* 'Carol Amling'
'Pink Grootendorst' (Ru) ♀ — CB&S EBls ENot IHos IOrc LStr MAus MGan MHlr MJon MMat NFla NRog NSty SPer SRum WAct WHCG
◆ 'Pink Hedgerose' — See *R.* Romantic Hedgerose = 'Korworm' (F/S)
I 'Pink Hedgrose' — See *R.* Romantic Hedgerose = 'Korworm'
Pink Hit® — See *R.* Pink Hit = 'Poulink'
◆ Pink la Sevillana® — See *R.* Pink La Sevillana = 'Meigeroka'
◆ Pink Meidiland® — See *R.* Pink Meidiland = 'Meipoque'
Pink Moss — See *R.* x *centifolia* 'Muscosa'
'Pink Parfait' (F) — EBls GCoc GGre MAus MGan NRog SPer SRum
◆ Pink Peace — See *R.* Pink Peace = 'Meibil'
Pink Pearl — See *R.* Pink Pearl = 'Kormasyl'
'Pink Perpétué' (Cl) — CDoC CGro EBls EBrP EBre ELan ENot GCoc GGre IHos LBre LGod LPlm MAus MBri MBur MFry MGan MJon MMat NBat NFla NRog NSty SApu SBre SPer SRum WWeb
◆ Pink Posy — See *R.* Pink Posy = 'Cocanelia'
'Pink Prosperity' (HM) — EBls MAus
¶ 'Pink Showers' (ClHT) — WAct
◆ Pink Sunblaze® — See *R.* Pink Sunblaze = 'Meijidiro'
◆ Pink Surprise — See *R.* Pink Surprise = 'Lenbrac'
◆ Pink Wave — See *R.* Pink Wave = 'Mattgro'
'Pinocchio' (F) — EBls
'Pinta' (HT) — EBls
◆ Piroschka® — See *R.* Piroschka = 'Tanpika'
'Pixie Rose' (Min) — IHos
◆ Playgroup Rose — See *R.* Playgroup Rose = 'Horsun'
◆ Playtime (GC/Ru) — See *R.* Playtime = 'Korsaku' (GC/Ru)
◆ Playtime (F) — See *R.* Playtime = 'Morplati' (F)
◆ Pleine de Grâce — See *R.* Pleine de Grâce = 'Lengra'
'Plentiful' (F) — EBls
◆ Poetry in Motion — See *R.* Poetry in Motion = 'Harelan'
◆ Polar Star — See *R.* Polar Star = 'Tanlarpost'
x *polliniana* — SLPl
'Polly' (HT) — EBls MGan NRog
polyantha grandiflora — See *R. gentiliana*
pomifera — See *R. villosa*
– 'Duplex' — See *R.* 'Wolley-Dod'
◆ Pomona — See *R.* Pomona = 'Fryyeh'
'Pompon Blanc Parfait' (A) — EBls MAus SFam
'Pompon de Bourgogne' — See *R.* 'Burgundiaca'
'Pompon de Paris' (ClCh) — See *R.* 'Climbing Pompon de Paris' (ClCh)
'Pompon Panaché' (G) — EBls MAus
Portland Rose — See *R.* 'Portlandica'
§ 'Portlandica' — EBls MAus SPer WAct WHCG
◆ Pot o' Gold — See *R.* Pot o' Gold = 'Dicidivine'
§ Silver Anniversary = 'Poulari' (HT) — COtt EBee ELan EPfP GGre LGod LStr MAus MFry MGan MJon MMat SApu SCoo SJus

§ Sussex = 'Poulave' (GC)   EBrP EBre ENot GCoc LBre
LPlm LStr MBur MFry MGan
MHlr MJon MMat SApu SBre
SJus SPer SPla SRum WHow
WOVN

§ Pink Bells® = 'Poulbells'   CGro EBls ENot GCoc IHos
(GC)   MAus MGan MHlr MMat NFla
SApu SPer SWCr WAct WHCG
WOVN

§ Pink Drift = 'Poulcat'   ENot MMat
(Min/GC)

§ Calypso = 'Poulclimb'   EBee

§ Kent® = 'Poulcov' (S/GC)   EBee ELan ENot GGre IHos
LPlm LStr MHlr MJon MMat
NBat NPri SPer SPla SRum
WHCG WOVN WRHF

§ Tiger Cub = 'Poulcub'   MMat
(Patio)

§ Tivoli = 'Poulduce' (HT)   MAus MJon

§ Courage = 'Poulduff'   SWCr
(HT)

§ Bellevue® = 'Poulena'   MJon
(HT)

§ Norfolk = 'Poulfolk' (GC)   EBls EBrP EBre ENot GCoc
LBre LStr MFry MGan MHlr
MMat SApu SBre SPer SPla
SRum WHCG WOVN

§ City Lights = 'Poulgan'   LGod MMat
(Patio)

§ New Fashion =   ENot MMat
'Poulholm' (Patio)

§ Pink Hit® = 'Poulink'   ENot MMat
(Min/Patio)

§ Isabella = 'Poulisab' (S)   EBee

§ White Knight = 'Poullaps'   EBee
(ClHT/S)

§ Little Bo-peep = 'Poullen' EBrP EBre ENot LBre MFry
(Min/Patio)   MJon MMat SBre

§ Night Light® = 'Poullight' LPlm MBri MBur MFry MGan
(Cl)   MJon SApu SJus

§ Ingrid Bergman® =   GCoc GGre LGod LStr MAus
'Poulman' (HT) ♥   MBri MBur MFry MGan MJon
MMat NBat SApu SJus

§ Avon = 'Poulmulti' (GC)   ELan ENot GCoc LGod LStr
MAus MGan MJon SApu SPer
SRum SWCr WHCG WOVN

§ Salmo = 'Poulnoev'   MBri MJon MMat NPri
(Patio)

§ Jazz = 'Poulnorm' (Cl)   EBee SApu

§ Essex = 'Poulnoz' (GC)   EBrP EBre ENot IHos LBre
MGan MMat SApu SBre SPer
WHCG WOVN

§ Eurostar = 'Poulreb' (F)   ENot MMat SApu

§ Red Bells® = 'Poulred'   CGro EBls ENot IHos LStr
(Min/GC)   MAus MGan MMat SPer
WHCG WOVN

§ Crystal Palace® =   MMat WHow
'Poulrek' (Patio)

§ Rutland = 'Poulshine'   ENot MMat WOVN
(Min/GC)

§ Susan = 'Poulsue' (S)   EBee

§ Sun Hit™® = 'Poulsun'   ENot GGre LGod MMat MRav
(Patio)

§ Liliana = 'Poulsyng' (S)   EBee

◆ 'Poultpie'   See R. Pink Hit = 'Poulink'

§ Panache = 'Poultop'   GGre LStr WGer
(Patio)

§ Gwent = 'Poulurt' (GC)   EBrP EBre ELan ENot LBre
LGod LPlm LStr MBur MFry
MGan MHlr MMat NPri SApu
SBre SPer SRum WOVN
WRHF

§ Michael Crawford =   LGod
'Poulvue' (HT)

§ White Bells® =   EBls ENot IHos MAus MGan
'Poulwhite' (Min/GC)   MMat SPer WAct WHCG
WOVN

§ Pzazz = 'Poulzazz'   LStr MJon
(Min/Patio)

§ Troika® = 'Poumidor'   ENot IHar LStr MAus MBur
(HT) ♥   MFry MGan MJon MMat SPer
SRum SWCr

◆ Pour Toi   See R. Pour Toi = 'Para Ti'
Prairie Rose   See R. setigera

'Precious Platinum' (HT)   IHar IHos LGod LStr MBri
MJon SJus SPer

§ Président de Sèze' (G) ♥   EBee EBls MAus NSty SFam
SPer WAct WHCG WHow

¶ 'President Heidar Aliyev'   GCoc
(HT)

'President Herbert   EBls
Hoover' (HT)

'Prestige' (S)   NRog

Pretty in Pink   See R. Pretty in Pink =
'Dicumpteen'

◆ Pretty Jessica   See R. Pretty Jessica = 'Ausjess'

◆ Pretty Lady   See R. Pretty Lady = 'Scrivo'

◆ Pretty Polly®   See R. Pretty Polly = 'Meitonje'

'Prima Ballerina' (HT)   CB&S CGro EBls GCoc GGre
IHos LPlm LStr MAus MBur
MGan MJon NBat NRog SPer
SRum

primula (S) ♥   CHad EBls EMFP ENot LHol
MAus MJon MMat NSty SPer
SSea WAct WHCG WHow

'Prince Camille de Rohan'   EBls MAus WHCG
(HP)

'Prince Charles' (Bb)   EBls MAus MHlr NSty SWCr
WHCG

◆ Prince Sunblaze® (Min)   See R. Red Sunblaze =
'Meirutral' (Min)

◆ Princess Alice   See R. Princess Alice =
'Hartanna'

'Princess Chichibu' (F)   SWCr

◆ Princess Margaret of   See R. Princess Margaret of
England   England = 'Meilista'

◆ Princess Michael of   See R. Princess Michael of Kent
Kent®   = 'Harlightly'

◆ Princess of Wales   See R. Princess of Wales =
'Hardinkum'

◆ Princess Royal   See R. Princess Royal =
'Dicroyal'

'Princesse Adélaïde' (Mo)   EBls

§ 'Princesse de Nassau' (Ra) EBls MAus WAct WHCG
WHow

'Princesse Louise' (Ra)   MAus SFam

'Princesse Marie' (Ra)   EBls MAus MBri SWCr WHCG

◆ Priscilla Burton®   See R. Priscilla Burton =
'Macrat'

◆ Pristine®   See R. Pristine = 'Jacpico'

§ Awakening = 'Probuzini'   EBls WHCG
(Cl)

N 'Professeur Emile Perrot' EBee EBls IHos MAus NSty
(D)

'Prolifera de Redouté'   See R. 'Duchesse de
hort.   Montebello'

'Prosperity' (HM) ♥   EBls EMFP ENot GCoc GOrc
IOrc MAus MFry MGan MHlr
MJon MMat NRog SJus SPer
WAct WHCG WHow WOVN
WWeb

◆ Prospero®   See R. Prospero = 'Auspero'

'Prudhoe Peach' (F)   NBat

× pruhoniciana 'Hillieri'   See R. moyesii 'Hillieri'

◆ Pudsey Bear   See *R.* Pudsey Bear = **'Bedchild'**
§ *pulverulenta*   EBls
  Pure Bliss   See *R.* Pure Bliss = **'Dictator'**
  'Purple Beauty' (HT)   MGan
  'Purple Splendour' (F)   MAus
◆ Purple Tiger   See *R.* Purple Tiger = **'Jacpur'**
  'Purpurtraum' (Ru)   WHCG
  Pzazz   See *R.* Pzazz = **'Poulzazz'**
◆ Quaker Star   See *R.* Quaker Star = **'Dicperhaps'**
  Quatre Saisons   See *R.* × *damascena* var. *semperflorens*
  'Quatre Saisons Blanche   EBls IHar
  Mousseuse' (DMo)
◆ Queen Charlotte   See *R.* Queen Charlotte = **'Harubondee'**
  Queen Elizabeth   See *R.* **'The Queen Elizabeth'**
◆ Queen Mother   See *R.* Queen Mother = **'Korquemu'**
  'Queen of Bedders' (Bb)   EBls
  Queen of Denmark   See *R.* **'Königin von Dänemark'**
  'Queen of Hearts'   See *R.* **'Dame de Coeur'**
◆ Queen of the Belgians   See *R.* **'Reine des Belges'**
  (Cl)
  Radio Times   See *R.* Radio Times = **'Aussal'**
◆ Radox Bouquet   See *R.* Radox Bouquet = **'Harmusky'**
¶ 'Ragtime' (Cl)   MFry
  'Rainbow' (T)   MMat
  'Rambling Rector' (Ra) ♀   CBar CSam EBar EBls ELan EMFP GChr GCoc GGre LGod LStr MAus MBri MBur MGan MHlr MMat NBrk NSty SApu SJus SPer SPla SRum WAct WHCG WSHC
§ 'Ramona'   EBls MAus WHCG WSHC
§ 'Raubritter'   EBee EBls IHos MAus MHlr
  ('Macrantha' hybrid)   NSty SApu SPer SWCr WAct WHCG
  Ray of Hope   See *R.* Ray of Hope = **'Cocnilly'**
◆ Ray of Sunshine   See *R.* Ray of Sunshine = **'Cocclare'**
  'Raymond Chenault' (Cl)   MGan
  'Rebecca Claire' (HT)   MJon SApu
◆ Reconciliation   See *R.* Reconciliation = **'Hartillery'**
◆ Red Ace   See *R.* Red Ace = **'Amruda'**
◆ Red Bells®   See *R.* Red Bells = **'Poulred'**
◆ Red Blanket®   See *R.* Red Blanket = **'Intercell'**
◆ Red Coat   See *R.* Red Coat = **'Auscoat'**
  'Red Dandy' (F)   MGan
◆ Red Devil®   See *R.* Red Devil = **'Dicam'**
◆ Red Dot®   See *R.* Red Dot = **'Intermunder'**
  'Red Garnette'   See *R.* **'Garnette'**
  'Red Grootendorst'   See *R.* **'F.J. Grootendorst'**
◆ 'Red Max Graf'   See *R.* Rote Max Graf = **'Kormax'**
◆ Red Meidiland®   See *R.* Red Meidiland = **'Meineble'**
  Red Moss   See *R.* **'Henri Martin'**
◆ Red New Dawn   See *R.* **'Etendard'**
◆ Red Rascal   See *R.* Red Rascal = **'Jacbed'**
  Red Rose of Lancaster   See *R. gallica* var. *officinalis*
◆ Red Sunblaze   See *R.* Red Sunblaze = **'Meirutral' (Min)**
◆ Red Trail   See *R.* Red Trail = **'Interim'**
§ 'Red Wing' (*hugonis* hybrid)   EBls MAus WAct
◆ Redgold   See *R.* Redgold = **'Dicor'**
◆ Redouté   See *R.* Redouté = **'Auspale'**
◆ Regal Red   See *R.* Regal Red = **'Cocfoster'**
◆ Regensberg®   See *R.* Regensberg = **'Macyou'**
§ 'Reine des Belges'   EBls

  'Reine des Centifeuilles'   EBls SFam
  (Ce)
  'Reine des Violettes' (HP)   CHad EBls IHar LStr MAus MHlr NSty SApu SChu SJus SPer WAct WHCG WHow
  'Reine Marie Henriette'   EBls
  (ClHT)
§ 'Reine Victoria' (Bb)   EBls EBrP EBre EMFP EPfP IHar IHos LBre LStr MAus MGan NSty SBre SJus SPer SPla WAct
◆ Remember Me®   See *R.* Remember Me = **'Cocdestin'**
◆ Remembrance   See *R.* Remembrance = **'Harxampton'**
◆ Rémy Martin®   See *R.* Rémy Martin = **'Starqueli'**
◆ Renaissance   See *R.* Renaissance = **'Harzart'**
  'René André' (Ra)   EBee EBls MAus
  'René d'Anjou' (CeMo)   EBls MAus
◆ Repens Meidiland®   See *R.* Repens Meidiland = **'Meilontig'**
  'Rescht'   See *R.* **'De Rescht'**
  'Rest in Peace' (Patio/F)   GGre
  'Rêve d'Or' (N)   EBee EBls EMFP MAus SPer WHow WSHC
  'Réveil Dijonnais' (ClHT)   EBls MAus
  'Reverend F.   EBls
  Page-Roberts' (HT)
  'Rhodes Rose' (S)   NSty
  Richard Buckley   See *R.* Richard Buckley = **'Smitshort'**
§ × *richardii*   EBls MAus WAct WHCG
§ 'Rise 'n' Shine' (Min)   CGro LGod MGan
◆ Rising Star   See *R.* Rising Star = **'Hareast'**
  'Ritter von Barmstede'   MGan
  (Cl)
  'Rival de Paestum' (T)   EBls MAus
  'River Gardens'   NPer
◆ Road to Freedom   See *R.* Road to Freedom = **'Franlac'**
◆ Rob Roy®   See *R.* Rob Roy = **'Cocrob'**
  'Robert le Diable' (Ce)   EBls MAus NSty SPer WAct WHCG
  'Robert Léopold' (DPMo)   EBls
  'Robin Hood' (HM)   EBls
◆ Robin Redbreast®   See *R.* Robin Redbreast = **'Interrob'**
◆ Robusta®   See *R.* Robusta = **'Korgosa' (Ru)**
  Roche Centenary   See *R.* Roche Centenary = **'Dicvantage'**
  'Roger Lambelin' (HP)   EBls ENot MAus MMat NSty SPer
◆ Romance®   See *R.* Romance = **'Tanezamor'**
◆ Romantic Hedgerose   See *R.* Romantic Hedgerose = **'Korworm' (F/S)**
◆ Rosabell®   See *R.* Rosabell = **'Cocceleste'**
◆ Rosalie Coral   See *R.* Rosalie Coral = **'Chewallop'**
◆ 'Rosamini Gold'   See *R.* Golden Rosamini = **'Intergol'**
◆ Rosarium Uetersen®   See *R.* Rosarium Uetersen = **'Kortersen'**
  'Rose à Parfum de l'Hay'   EBls
  (Ru)
§ 'Rose d'Amour' ♀   EBls ISea MAus SJus WHCG
  'Rose de Meaux'   See *R.* **'De Meaux'**
  'Rose de Meaux White'   See *R.* **'De Meaux, White'**
  'Rose de Rescht'   See *R.* **'De Rescht'**
  'Rose des Maures'   See *R.* **'Sissinghurst Castle'**
  'Rose d'Hivers' (D)   EBls

'Rose d'Orsay' (S)	EBls
'Rose du Maître d'Ecole'	See *R.* **'Du Maître d'Ecole'**
'Rose du Roi' (HP/DPo)	EBls MAus NSty WAct WHCG
'Rose du Roi à Fleurs Pourpres' (HP)	EBls MAus
'Rose Edouard' (Bb)	EBls
◆ Rose Gaujard®	See *R.* Rose Gaujard = **'Gaumo'**
'Rosecarpe' (HT)	NBat
§ 'Rose-Marie Viaud' (Ra)	CFee MAus WHCG
¶ 'Rosemary Foster'	SSpi
'Rosemary Gandy' (F)	MGan
◆ Rosemary Harkness	See *R.* Rosemary Harkness = **'Harrowbond'**
'Rosemary Rose' (F)	EBls MBri NRog SPer
'Rosenelfe' (F)	EBls
'Roseraie de l'Haÿ' (Ru) ♀	CB&S CDoC CGro EBls ELan ENot GCoc IHos IOrc LBuc LHol LPlm LStr MAus MBri MFry MGan MHlr MJon MMat NRog NSty SApu SJus SPer SRum WAct WHCG WOVN WWeb
'Rosette Delizy' (T)	EBls
Rosie Larkin	See *R.* Rosie Larkin = **'Fryyippee'**
§ 'Rosina' (Min)	MGan
'Rosy Cheeks' (HT)	LPlm MBur MGan
◆ Rosy Cushion®	See *R.* Rosy Cushion = **'Interall'**
◆ Rosy Future	See *R.* Rosy Future = **'Harwaderox'**
'Rosy Mantle' (Cl)	CB&S GCoc LPlm MGan SPer
◆ Rote Max Graf®	See *R.* Rote Max Graf = **'Kormax'**
§ 'Rouletii' (MinCh)	EBls
'Roundelay' (S)	EBls MAus
◆ Roxburghe Rose	See *R.* Roxburghe Rose = **'Cocember'**
roxburghii (S)	CB&S LFlo MMat NSty WAct WHCG
– f. *normalis* (S)	CFee EBls MAus
– 'Plena' (S)	See *R. roxburghii* f. *roxburghii*
§ – f. *roxburghii* (d/S)	MAus
'Royal Albert Hall' (HT)	EBls GCoc
◆ Royal Baby	See *R.* Royal Baby = **'Delbrad'**
◆ Royal Brompton Rose	See *R.* Royal Brompton Rose = **'Meivildo'**
¶ 'Royal Conquest' (HT)	SJus
◆ Royal Flush	See *R.* Royal Flush = **'Peapatio'**
'Royal Gold' (Cl)	EBls ENot IHos LPlm LStr MBri MFry MGan NPri NRog SRum WStI
'Royal Highness' (HT)	CGro EBls MGan SRum
'Royal Occasion' (F)	SPer
◆ Royal Salute	See *R.* Royal Salute = **'Macros'**
'Royal Smile' (HT)	EBls
◆ Royal Volunteer	See *R.* Royal Volunteer = **'Cocdandy'**
◆ Royal William	See *R.* Royal William = **'Korzaun'**
◆ Royal Worcester	See *R.* Royal Worcester = **'Trobroy'**
'Rubens' (HP)	EBls
§ *rubiginosa* ♀	CAgr CB&S CKin EBls ENot GChr GPoy ILis LBuc LHol MAus MMat NFla SPer WAct WMou
rubra	See *R. gallica*
rubrifolia	See *R. glauca*
– 'Carmenetta'	See *R.* **'Carmenetta'**
§ Bright Spark = 'Rubrispa' (Min)	MFry
'Rubrotincta'	See *R.* **'Hebe's Lip'**
rubus (Ra)	CRHN MAus WAct
– SF 579 (Ra)	ISea
Ruby Anniversary	See *R.* Ruby Anniversary = **'Harbonny'**
Ruby Celebration	See *R.* Ruby Celebration = **'Peawinner'**
'Ruby Wedding' (HT)	CB&S EBrP EBre ELan ENot GCoc GGre IHar LBre LGod LPlm LStr MAus MBri MFry MGan MJon MMat NBat NRog SApu SBre SJus SPer SRum WOVN WWeb
§ Mini Metro = 'Rufin' (Min)	MFry
'Ruga' (Ra)	EBls MAus
§ Golden Days = 'Rugolda' (HT)	MBri MFry
rugosa (Ru)	CAgr CPer EPla GChr IHos ISea LBuc LHol MAus MBri NWea SWCr WStI
– 'Alba' (Ru) ♀	CB&S CDoC CHad EBls ECGP ELan EMFP ENot GGre IHos LBuc LStr MAus MBri MMat NRoo NSty NWea SJus SPer SRum WAct WCFE WOVN
'Rugosa Atropurpurea' (Ru)	NRog
rugosa var. *kamtschatica*	See *R. rugosa* var. *ventenatia*
– 'Rubra' (Ru) ♀	CB&S CDoC CTri GGre LBuc MFry MMat NRoo NSty SPer SRum WAct
– 'Scabrosa'	See *R.* **'Scabrosa'**
'Rugspin' (Ru)	WAct
§ Golden Penny = 'Rugul' (Min)	MFry MGan MJon NPri WGer
'Ruhm von Steinfurth' (HP)	EBls
§ Blue Peter = 'Ruiblun' (Min)	IHos MFry MJon SApu WWeb
§ Favorite Rosamini = 'Ruifaro' (Min)	MFry
§ Little Marvel = 'Ruigerdan' (Min)	MBri
§ Lancashire Life = 'Ruilanca' (F)	LStr MBri
§ Royal Romance® = 'Rulis' (F)	SJus
§ Invincible = 'Runatru' (F)	MFry MGan
◆ Running Maid®	See *R.* Running Maid = **'Lenramp'**
◆ Rush®	See *R.* Rush = **'Lenmobri'**
◆ Rushing Stream	See *R.* Rushing Stream = **'Austream'**
'Ruskin' (RuxHP)	EBls MAus
'Russelliana' (Ra)	EBls EMFP MAus WAct WHCG WRha
◆ Rutland	See *R.* Rutland = **'Poulshine'**
§ Yorkshire Bank = 'Rutrulo' (HT)	MFry
§ Artful Dodger = 'Sabbelief' (Patio)	MBur
§ Oliver Twist = 'Sabbyron' (Patio)	MBur
§ Sweet Bouquet = 'Sabchurchill' (HT)	MBur
'Sadler's Wells' (S)	EBls
'Safrano' (T)	EBls
◆ Saint Boniface	See *R.* Saint Boniface = **'Kormatt'**
'Saint Catherine' (Ra)	CFee
◆ Saint Cecilia®	See *R.* Saint Cecilia = **'Ausmit'**

◆ Saint Christopher   See *R.* Saint Christopher = **'Harcogent'**

◆ Saint Dunstan's Rose   See *R.* Saint Dunstan's Rose = **'Kirshru'**

◆ Saint John   See *R.* Saint John = **'Harbilbo'**
   Saint John's Rose   See *R.* × *richardii*
   Saint Mark's Rose   See *R.* **'Rose d'Amour'**
'Saint Nicholas' (D)   EBls MAus WHCG
'Saint Prist de Breuze' (Ch)   EBls

◆ Saint Swithun   See *R.* Saint Swithun = **'Auswith'**

'Salet' (DPMo)   EBls MAus WHCG
Sally Holmes®   CHad EBls ENot GCoc IHar MAus MBri MFry MGan MJon MMat SApu SWCr WAct WHCG

◆ Sally's Rose   See *R.* Sally's Rose = **'Canrem'**
Salmo   See *R.* Salmo = **'Poulnoeu'**

◆ Samaritan   See *R.* Samaritan = **'Harverag'**
sancta   See *R.* × *richardii*
'Sanders' White Rambler' (Ra) ♀   CHad CRHN EBls EBrP EBre EMFP LBre LHol MAus MGan MJon NBat NRog NSty SBre SMad SPer SRum WAct WHCG WHow WWeb

'Sandringham Centenary' (HT)   EBls
'Sanguinea'   See *R.* × *odorata* Sanguinea Group

◆ Sarabande   See *R.* Sarabande = **'Meihand'**
◆ Sarah® (HT)   See *R.* Jardins de Bagatelle = **'Meimafris' (HT)**

◆ Sarah Robinson   See *R.* Sarah Robinson = **'Trobinette'**

'Sarah van Fleet'   CGro EBls EBrP EBre ENot GCoc LBre LStr MAus MFry MGan MHlr MMat NRog NSty SApu SBre SPer SRum WAct WOVN WWeb

◆ Sarah, Duchess of York   See *R.* Sunseeker = **'Dicracer'**
Satchmo® (F)   IHos
§ White Cloud = 'Savacloud' (Min)   MBri MFry SApu WHow
§ Apricot Sunblaze® = 'Savamark' (Min)   EBls IHos MJon SJus WWeb
§ Little Jackie™ = 'Savor' (Min)   NBat

◆ Savoy Hotel   See *R.* Savoy Hotel = **'Harvintage'**
§ 'Scabrosa' (Ru) ♀   EBls EMFP GCoc IHos MAus MGan MJon MMat WAct WHCG WOVN

Scarlet Fire   See *R.* **'Scharlachglut'**
◆ Scarlet Gem®   See *R.* Scarlet Gem = **'Meido'**
'Scarlet Glow'   See *R.* **'Scharlachglut'**
◆ Scarlet Meidiland®   See *R.* Scarlet Meidiland = **'Meikrotal'**
Scarlet Patio   See *R.* Scarlet Patio = **'Kortingle'**
◆ 'Scarlet Pimpernel'   See *R.* Scarlet Gem = **'Meido'**
◆ Scarlet Queen Elizabeth®   See *R.* Scarlet Queen Elizabeth = **'Dicel'**
'Scarlet Showers' (Cl)   MGan
Scarletta (Min)   IHos
'Scented Air' (F)   MGan SPer
◆ Sceptre'd Isle   See *R.* Sceptre'd Isle = **'Ausland'**
§ 'Scharlachglut' (ClS) ♀   EBls ELan ENot MAus MGan MMat NFla NSty SApu SPer SWCr WAct WHCG WOVN WSHC

* *schmidtiana*   CFee
'Schneelicht' (Ru)   EBls MAus
Schneewittchen   See *R.* Iceberg = **'Korbin'**
§ 'Schneezwerg' (Ru) ♀   EBls EBrP EBre ELan ENot GCoc IHar IHos IOrc LBre MAus MGan MJon MMat NSty SApu SBre SPer SPla WAct WHCG WOVN

'Schoolgirl' (Cl)   CB&S CGro EBls EBrP EBre ELan ENot GChr GGre IHos LBre LGod LPlm LStr MBri MFry MGan MJon MMat NRog SApu SBre SPer SRum SSea WFar WWeb

'Scintillation' (S/GC)   EBls MAus
   Scotch Rose   See *R. pimpinellifolia*
   Scotch Yellow (PiH)   See *R.* × *harisonii* **'Williams' Double Yellow'**
'Scotch Yellow' (HT)   MJon
◆ Scotland's Trust   See *R.* Scotland's Trust = **'Coclands'**
◆ Scottish Special   See *R.* Scottish Special = **'Cocdapple'**
§ Baby Love = 'Scrivluv' (Min/Patio)   MAus MFry MJon MMat
§ Pretty Lady = 'Scrivo' (F)   ECle LStr MJon
'Sea Pearl' (F)   ENot MGan
'Seagull' (Ra) ♀   EBls EBrP EBre ELan EMFP GGre LBre LGod LStr MAus MGan MHlr MJon NBus NPri NRog NSty SBre SPer SWCr WAct WGer WHCG
§ Kiss 'n' Tell = 'Seakis' (Min)   MBur
§ Lady in Red = 'Sealady' (Min)   MBur
§ 'Sealing Wax' (*moyesii* hybrid)   EBls MAus WAct
§ Admirable = 'Searodney' (Min)   MBur
◆ Selfridges   See *R.* Selfridges = **'Korpriwa'**
'Semiplena'   See *R.* × *alba* **'Alba Semiplena'**
'Sénateur Amic' (Cl)   EBls
sericea (S)   CFee MAus MBal NGre WHCG
   – BC 9355 (S)   GCra
   – 'Heather Muir'   See *R.* **'Heather Muir'** (*sericea* hybrid)
* – var. *morrisonensis* B&SWJ 1549   NGre
§ – subsp. *omeiensis* f. *pteracantha* (S)   CHad EBls ELan EMFP ENot MAus MGan MMat NRog NSty SApu SMad SPer WAct WOVN
   – 'Red Wing'   See *R.* **'Red Wing'** (*hugonis* hybrid)
¶ – SF 505   ISea
* – SF 95049   ISea
§ *setigera*   EBls MAus
setipoda   EBls MAus WAct WHCG WWat
'Seven Seas' (F)   MBur
   Seven Sisters Rose   See *R. multiflora* **'Grevillei'**
◆ Sexy Rexy®   See *R.* Sexy Rexy = **'Macrexy'**
§ 'Shailer's White Moss' (CeMo) ♀   EBls MAus MGan MMat NRog NSty SFam SJus WHCG
◆ Sharifa Asma®   See *R.* Sharifa Asma = **'Ausreef'**
¶ 'Sheelagh Baird' (S/Poly)   SWCr
◆ Sheila's Perfume   See *R.* Sheila's Perfume = **'Harsherry'**
'Shepherd's Delight' (F)   MGan
sherardii   WUnd
◆ Sheri Anne   See *R.* Sheri Anne = **'Morsheri'**

◆ Shine on	See *R.* Shine On = **'Dictalent'**	◆ Smooth Velvet	See *R.* Smooth Velvet = **'Hadvelvet'**
◆ Shirley Spain	See *R.* Shirley Spain = **'Cocharod'**	'Sneezy' (Poly)	MGan
◆ Shocking Blue®	See *R.* Shocking Blue = **'Korblue'**	◆ Snow Carpet®	See *R.* Snow Carpet = **'Maccarpe'**
◆ Shona	See *R.* Shona = **'Dicdrum'**	'Snow Dwarf'	See *R.* **'Schneezwerg'**
'Shot Silk' (HT)	EBls GCoc MAus MBur MGan	'Snow Queen'	See *R.* **'Frau Karl Druschki'**
◆ Shrewsbury Show	See *R.* Shrewsbury Show = **'Fryshrewby'**	◆ Snow Sunblaze®	See *R.* Snow Sunblaze = **'Meigovin'**
'Shropshire Lass' (S)	MAus SPer SWCr	◆ Snow White	See *R.* Snow White = **'Landisney'**
◆ Sightsaver	See *R.* Sightsaver = **'Fryaffair'**		
◆ Silver Anniversary	See *R.* Silver Anniversary = **'Poulari'**	◆ Snowball	See *R.* Snowball = **'Macangeli'**
		'Snowdon' (Ru)	EBls MAus
Silver Jubilee®	CB&S CDoC CGro EBls EBrP EBre ELan ENot GCoc GGre IHos LBre LGod LPlm LStr MAus MBri MBur MFry MGan MJon MMat NBat NRog SApu SBre SJus SPer SRum WWeb	'Snowdrift'	WHCG
		◆ Snowdrop	See *R.* Snowdrop = **'Amoru'**
		'Snowflake' (Ra)	WHCG
		◆ Snowgoose (F)	See *R.* Snowgoose = **'Barshifle'**
		'Snowline' (F)	MGan SPer
		'Soldier Boy' (Cl)	WHCG
'Silver Lining' (HT)	EBls MAus MBur SWCr	◆ Solitaire®	See *R.* Solitaire = **'Mcyefre'**
'Silver Moon' (Cl)	CRHN EBls MAus	'Sophie's Perpetual' (ClCh)	EBls ENot MAus MGan MHlr MMat NFla SJus SPer WAct WHCG
'Silver Tips' (Min)	MAus		
'Silver Wedding' (HT)	EBls EBrP EBre GCoc GGre IHar LBre LPlm MAus MBur MFry MGan MJon NRog SApu SBre SPer SRum SWCr WOVN	◆ Sophy's Rose	See *R.* Sophy's Rose = **'Auslot'**
		soulieana ♀	EBls MAus MMat WAct WKif
		'Soupert et Notting' (PoMo)	EBls MAus MHlr SBid SPer
◆ Simba	See *R.* Simba = **'Korbelma'**	'Southampton' (F) ♀	EBee EBls GGre IHar LStr MAus MGan NRog SApu SPer EBls WHCG
◆ Simon Robinson	See *R.* Simon Robinson = **'Trobwich'**		
§ Jenny Charlton = 'Simway' (HT)	NBat	'Souvenir d'Alphonse Lavallée' (ClHP)	
◆ Singin' in the Rain	See *R.* Singin' in the Rain = **'MacIvy' (F)**	'Souvenir de Brod'	See *R.* **'Erinnerung an Brod'**
sinowilsonii	See *R. longicuspis sinowilsonii*	'Souvenir de Claudius Denoyel' (ClHT) ♀	EBls MAus MMat NRog SPer SSoC
'Sir Cedric Morris' (Ra)	EBls ELan	'Souvenir de François Gaulain' (T)	EBls
'Sir Clough' (S)	MAus		
'Sir Edward Elgar' (S)	EBls EBrP EBre LBre MAus MJon NPri SBre SWCr	'Souvenir de Jeanne Balandreau' (HP)	EBls
'Sir Frederick Ashton' (HT)	EBls	'Souvenir de la Malmaison' (ClBb)	See *R.* **'Climbing Souvenir de la Malmaison' (ClBb)**
◆ Sir Harry Pilkington	See *R.* Sir Harry Pilkington = **'Tanema'**	'Souvenir de la Malmaison' (Bb)	EBls EBrP EBre ENot GCoc IHar IHos IOrc LBre MAus MGan MHlr MMat NFla NSty SBre SJus SPer WAct WWeb
¶ 'Sir Joseph Paxton' (Bb)	MAus		
'Sir Lancelot' (F)	MGan		
◆ Sir Neville Marriner	See *R.* Sir Neville Marriner = **'Glanmusic'**	'Souvenir de Madame Léonie Viennot' (ClT)	CPou EBls EHol MAus NSty
◆ Sir Walter Raleigh®	See *R.* Sir Walter Raleigh = **'Ausspry'**	'Souvenir de Philémon Cochet' (Ru)	EBls MAus
◆ Sir William Leech	See *R.* Sir William Leech = **'Hortropic'**	'Souvenir de Pierre Vibert' (DPMo)	EBls
§ 'Sissinghurst Castle' (G)	EBls SBid	'Souvenir de Saint Anne's' (Bb) ♀	CHad EBls IHar MAus WAct WHCG
'Sleepy' (Poly)	MGan		
◆ Smarty®	See *R.* Smarty = **'Intersmart'**	'Souvenir d'Elise Vardon' (T)	EBls
§ Summer Sérénade® = 'Smitfirst' (F)	MJon	'Souvenir di Castagneto' (HP)	MRav
§ Lady Taylor = 'Smitling' (F/Patio)	IHar MBur	'Souvenir du Docteur Jamain' (ClHP)	CHad EBls LStr MAus MHlr MMat NSty SFam SJus SPer SWCr WAct WHCG
§ Richard Buckley = 'Smitshort' (F)	MBur		
		'Souvenir du Président Carnot' (HT)	EBls MAus
◆ Smooth Angel	See *R.* Smooth Angel = **'Hadangel'**	'Souvenir d'un Ami' (T)	EBls
◆ Smooth Lady	See *R.* Smooth Lady = **'Hadlady'**	*spaldingii*	See *R. nutkana* var. *hispida*
◆ Smooth Melody	See *R.* Smooth Melody = **'Hadmelody'**	◆ Spangles	See *R.* Spangles = **'Ganspa'**
		'Spanish Beauty'	See *R.* **'Madame Grégoire Staechelin'**
◆ Smooth Prince	See *R.* Smooth Prince = **'Hadprince'**	◆ Sparkling Scarlet	See *R.* Sparkling Scarlet = **'Meihati'**
Smooth Romance	See *R.* Smooth Romance = **'Hadromance'**	◆ Special Occasion	See *R.* Special Occasion = **'Fryyoung'**
◆ Smooth Satin	See *R.* Smooth Satin = **'Hadsatin'**	'Spectabilis' (Ra)	EBls MAus WHCG

◆ Spek's Centennial (F)   See *R.* Singin' in the Rain = **'MacIvy'**

'Spek's Yellow' (HT)   CB&S EBls
'Spencer' misapplied   See *R.* **'Enfant de France'**
¶ Red Dagmar = 'Speruge'   IDic LBuc
§ Lovely Fairy® = 'Spevu'   IDic MBri MJon WAct
spinosissima   See *R. pimpinellifolia*
◆ Spirit of Youth   See *R.* Spirit of Youth = **'Meivestal'**
§ 'Splendens' (Ra)   CHad EBls ELan MAus SLPl WAct
'Spong' (G)   EBls MAus WAct
◆ Stacey's Star   See *R.* Stacey's Star = **'Horstacey'**
§ 'Stanwell Perpetual' (PiH)   EBls EMFP ENot GCoc IHos LStr MAus MHlr MMat NFla NSty SApu SPer SWCr WAct WHCG WOVN WWeb
'Star of Waltham' (HP)   WHCG
Stardust®   See *R.* Stardust = **'Peavandyke'**
Starina®   See *R.* Starina = **'Megabi'**
◆ Starlight Express   See *R.* Starlight Express = **'Trobstar'**
§ Rémy Martin® = 'Starqueli' (HT)   MBri
'Stars 'n' Stripes' (Min)   LGod LPlm MAus MFry
§ Big Purple = 'Stebigpu' (HT)   MJon SApu SRum
Stella (HT)   EBls MGan
¶ *stellata*   MAus
§ – var. *mirifica*   EBls MAus MGan MMat
'Stephanie Diane' (HT)   LPlm
Sterling Silver℠ (HT)   EBls LStr MAus MGan
◆ Strawberry Fayre   See *R.* Strawberry Fayre = **'Arowillip'**
'Strawberry Ice' (F)   MJon
subcanina   MSto
subcollina   MSto
◆ Sue Lawley   See *R.* Sue Lawley = **'Macspash'**
◆ Suffolk   See *R.* Suffolk = **'Kormixal'**
suffulta   See *R. arkansana* var. *suffulta*
◆ Suma   See *R.* Suma = **'Harsuma'**
¶ 'Summer Breeze' (Cl)   ENot
◆ Summer Dream (HT)   See *R.* Summer Dream = **'Jacshe'**
◆ Summer Fragrance   See *R.* Summer Fragrance = **'Tanfudermos'**
Summer Holiday® (HT)   MBur SPer
◆ Summer Lady®   See *R.* Summer Lady = **'Tanydal'**
◆ Summer Love   See *R.* Summer Love = **'Franluv'**
¶ 'Summer Palace' (Patio)   ECle
◆ Summer Sérénade®   See *R.* Summer Sérénade = **'Smitfirst'**
'Summer Sunrise' (GC)   EBls
'Summer Sunset' (GC)   EBls
◆ Summer Wine   See *R.* Summer Wine = **'Korizont'**
◆ Sun Hit℠   See *R.* Sun Hit = **'Poulsun'**
◆ 'Sunblaze'   See *R.* Orange Sunblaze = **'Meijikatar'**
◆ Sunblest   See *R.* Sunblest = **'Landora'**
◆ Sunderland Supreme   See *R.* Sunderland Supreme = **'Nossun'**
Sunmaid® (Min)   MJon
◆ Sunny Sunblaze℠   See *R.* Sunny Sunblaze = **'Meiponal'**
◆ Sunrise   See *R.* Sunrise = **'Kormarter'**
◆ Sunseeker   See *R.* Sunseeker = **'Dicracer'**
Sunset Boulevard (F)   See *R.* Sunset Boulevard = **'Harbabble'**
◆ Sunset Song   See *R.* Sunset Song = **'Cocasun'**

'Sunshine' (Poly)   MGan
'Sunsilk' (F)   MBri
◆ Super Sparkle   See *R.* Super Sparkle = **'Helhein'**
◆ Super Star®   See *R.* Super Star = **'Tanorstar'**
'Super Sun' (HT)   SWCr
'Surpasse Tout' (G)   EBls MAus MRav WHCG
§ 'Surpassing Beauty of Woolverstone' (ClHP)   EBls WHCG
◆ Surrey   See *R.* Surrey = **'Korlanum'**
◆ Susan   See *R.* Susan = **'Poulsue'**
◆ Susan Hampshire   See *R.* Susan Hampshire = **'Meinatac'**
◆ Sussex   See *R.* Sussex = **'Poulave'**
'Sutter's Gold' (HT)   EBls MAus MBur MGan NRog
◆ Swan®   See *R.* Swan = **'Auswhite'**
'Swan Lake' (Cl)   EBls EBrP EBre ELan ENot GGre IHos LBre LGod MAus MBri MBur MFry MGan MHlr MMat NBat SBre SPer SRum WWeb
◆ Swany®   See *R.* Swany = **'Meiburenac'**
◆ Sweet Bouquet   See *R.* Sweet Bouquet = **'Sabchurchill'**
◆ Sweet Dream   See *R.* Sweet Dream = **'Fryminicot'**
'Sweet Fairy' (Min)   LPlm
◆ Sweet Juliet®   See *R.* Sweet Juliet = **'Ausleap'**
◆ Sweet Magic   See *R.* Sweet Magic = **'Dicmagic'**
◆ Sweet Memories   See *R.* Sweet Memories = **'Whamemo'**
◆ Sweet Promise   See *R.* Sweet Promise = **'Meihelvet'**
'Sweet Repose' (F)   MAus MGan
Sweet Symphony (Min)   EBrP EBre ENot LBre MBri MFry MJon SBre
'Sweet Velvet' (F)   MGan
'Sweet Wonder' (Patio)   COtt
◆ Sweetheart   See *R.* Sweetheart = **'Cocapeer'**
sweginzowii   GCal MAus MMat
– 'Macrocarpa'   EBls
'Sydonie' (HP)   EBls
Sympathie® (ClHT)   IHar IHos LPlm MFry MGan MMat SJus SPer SRum
◆ Symphony®   See *R.* Symphony = **'Auslett'**
taiwanensis   CFil
§ Chelsea Belle = 'Talchelsea' (Min)   NBat
§ Fairhope = 'Talfairhope' (Min)   NBat
'Talisman' (HT)   EBls
◆ Tall Story®   See *R.* Tall Story = **'Dickooky'**
'Tallyho' (HT)   EBls
¶ 'Tambourine' (F)   GCoc
◆ Tamora   See *R.* Tamora = **'Austamora'**
§ The Dove = 'Tanamola' (F)   MGan
§ Baby Masquerade® = 'Tanba' (Min)   ELan GCoc IHos LGod LPlm MBur MGan MJon MMat NRog SWCr WStI
§ Fragrant Gold = 'Tanduft' (HT)   GCoc LStr SRum
§ Abigaile® = 'Taneliagib' (F)   MJon NBat
§ Golden Quill = 'Tanellelog' (F)   MJon
§ Fragrant Cloud = 'Tanellis' (HT)   CDoC CGro EBls EBrP EBre GCoc GGre IHar IHos LBre LStr MAus MBri MBur MFry MJon MMat NBat NRog SApu SBre SPer WWeb

§ Barkarole® = 'Tanelorak'   LStr MJon SApu SJus
  (HT)
§ Romance® = 'Tanezamor'   MJon MRav WWeb
  (S)
§ Blue Parfum® =   MAus MJon
  'Tanfifum'
§ Summer Fragrance =   GCoc GGre MGan MJon
  'Tanfudermos' (HT)
◆ Tango (F)   See *R*. Tango = **'Macfirwal'**
§ Climbing Super Star =   MAus
  'Tangostar' (ClHT)
§ Janina® = 'Tanija' (HT)   MJon
§ Harewood = 'Taninaso'   ECle MJon SApu
  (Patio/F)
§ Lavinia = 'Tanklawi' (Cl)   EBee LGod LStr MBri MGan
  ♀   SApu SJus SPer SRum
§ Whisky Mac = 'Tanky'   CB&S CGro EBls EBrP EBre
  (HT)   ELan GCoc GGre IHos LBre
    LGod LPlm LStr MAus MBri
    MBur MFry MGan MJon MMat
    NRog SApu SBre SPer SRum
    SWCr WWeb
§ Polar Star = 'Tanlarpost'   EBls GCoc GGre IHos LGod
  (HT)   LPlm LStr MFry MGan MJon
    NRog SApu SJus SPer SRum
    WWeb
§ Goldjuwel = 'Tanledolg'   NBat
  (F/Patio)
§ Dalli Dalli® = 'Tanlilida'   MJon
  (F)
§ Broadlands = 'Tanmirson'   CSam ECle LGod MAus MBur
  (GC)   MGan MJon SApu SChu WGer
    WHCG WHow
§ Blenheim = 'Tanmurse'   ECle MBur MGan MJon SApu
  (GC)   WOVN
§ Blue Moon® = 'Tannacht'   CGro EBls EBrP EBre ELan
  (HT)   GChr GCoc GGre IHos LBre
    LGod LPlm MAus MBur MGan
    MJon NRog SApu SBre SPer
    SRum WWeb
§ Miss Harp = 'Tanolg'   MGan NRog
  (HT)
§ Piccolo = 'Tanolokip'   GGre LStr MBri MFry MJon
  (F/Patio)   NPri SApu SRum WGer WWeb
§ Tip Top® = 'Tanope'   CB&S CGro CTri ELan GCoc
  (F/Patio)   IHos LFis MBri MFry MGan
    NRog SPer SRum WStI
§ Super Star® = 'Tanorstar'   CB&S CGro EBls EBrP EBre
  (HT)   ENot IHar LBre LPlm LStr
    MAus MGan MJon MMat NPri
    NRog SBre SRum WWeb
§ Chatsworth = 'Tanotax'   EBee ECle GCoc LGod LPlm
  (Patio/F)   LStr MBri MFry MGan MJon
    NBat SApu SCoo SPer SRum
    WWeb
§ Piroschka® = 'Tanpika'   MJon
  (HT)
§ Wimi® = 'Tanrowise'   MGan SApu
  (HT)
§ Glad Tidings = 'Tantide'   CGro GGre LPlm LStr MAus
  (F)   MBri MBur MGan MJon NBat
    SApu SJus SPer SRum WWeb
§ Summer Lady® =   MBri MBur MJon SApu
  'Tanydal' (HT)
◆ Tapis Jaune®   See *R*. Golden Penny = **'Rugul'**
◆ 'Tausendschön' (Ra)   EBls
  'Tea Rambler' (Ra)   EBls NSty
◆ Tear Drop   See *R*. Tear Drop = **'Dicomo'**
◆ Ted Gore   See *R*. Ted Gore = **'Hormislac'**
§ Teeny Weeny = 'Teeny'   MJon
  (Min)
◆ Teeny Weeny   See *R*. Teeny Weeny = **'Teeny'**

'Telstar' (F)   MGan
'Temple Bells' (Min/GC)   EBls MAus NRog
'Tenerife' (HT)   WStI
◆ Tequila Sunrise   See *R*. Tequila Sunrise =
    'Dicobey'
'Texas Centennial' (HT)   EBls
◆ Thaïs   See *R*. Thaïs = **'Memaj'**
'Thalia' (Ra)   MAus
Thank You   See *R*. Thank You = **'Chesdeep'**
◆ The Alexandra Rose (S)   See *R*. The Alexandra Rose =
    'Ausday'
'The Bishop' (CexG)   EBls MAus
'The Bride' (T)   EBls NSty
The Cheshire Regiment   See *R*. The Cheshire Regiment
    = **'Fryzebedee'**
◆ The Children's Rose   See *R*. The Children's Rose =
    'Meilivar'
'The Colwyn Rose'   See *R*. Colwyn Bay
◆ The Compass Rose   See *R*. The Compass Rose =
    'Korhassi'
◆ The Compassionate   See *R*. The Compassionate
  Friends   Friends = **'Harzodiac'**
◆ The Countryman®   See *R*. The Countryman =
    'Ausman'
◆ The Coxswain   See *R*. The Coxswain =
    'Cocadilly'
◆ The Daily Telegraph   See *R*. The Daily Telegraph =
    'Peahigh' (F)
◆ The Dark Lady   See *R*. The Dark Lady =
    'Ausbloom'
'The Doctor' (HT)   EBls MAus MGan
◆ The Dove   See *R*. The Dove = **'Tanamola'**
'The Ednaston Rose' (Cl)   WHCG
◆ 'The Fairy' (Poly) ♀   Widely available
◆ The Flower Arranger   See *R*. The Flower Arranger =
    'Fryjam' (F)
'The Garland' (Ra) ♀   EBls MAus MHlr MMat NSty
    SFam SPer SPla WAct WHCG
◆ The Herbalist™   See *R*. The Herbalist =
    'Aussemi'
'The Honorable Lady   NSty
  Lindsay' (S)
'The Knight' (S)   NSty
I The Lady   See *R*. The Lady = **'Fryjingo'**
¶ 'The Margaret Coppola   GCoc
  Rose' white gold
◆ The McCartney Rose   See *R*. The McCartney Rose =
    'Meizeli'
'The New Dawn'   See *R*. **'New Dawn'**
◆ The Nun   See *R*. The Nun = **'Ausnun'**
◆ The Painter   See *R*. The Painter =
    'Mactemaik'
◆ The Pilgrim   See *R*. The Pilgrim =
    'Auswalker'
◆ The Prince®   See *R*. The Prince = **'Ausvelvet'**
'The Prioress' (S)   MAus
§ 'The Queen Elizabeth' (F)   CB&S CDoC CGro EBls EBrP
  ♀   EBre ENot GCoc GGre IHos
    LBre LGod LPlm LStr MAus
    MBri MBur MFry MGan MJon
    MMat NRog SApu SBre SPer
    SRum WWeb
◆ The Reeve®   See *R*. The Reeve = **'Ausreeve'**
◆ 'The Royal Brompton   See *R*. Royal Brompton Rose =
  Rose'   **'Meivildo'**
◆ The Seckford Rose   See *R*. The Seckford Rose =
    'Korpinrob'
◆ The Squire®   See *R*. The Squire = **'Ausquire'**
◆ The Times Rose   See *R*. The Times Rose =
    'Korpeahn'
◆ The Valois Rose   See *R*. The Valois Rose =
    'Kordadel'

◆ The Wife of Bath	See *R.* The Wife of Bath = **'Ausbath'**
'Thelma' (Ra)	EBls MAus
'Thérèse Bugnet' (Ru)	EBls
'Thisbe' (HM)	EBls MAus SPer WAct WHCG
◆ Thomas Barton®	See *R.* Thomas Barton = **'Meihirvin'**
◆ Thora Hird	See *R.* Thora Hird = **'Tonybrac'**
Thousand Beauties	See *R.* **'Tausendschön'**
Threepenny Bit Rose	See *R. elegantula* **'Persetosa'**
'Tiara' (RH)	SRum
Tiger Cub	See *R.* Tiger Cub = **'Poulcub'**
◆ Tigris®	See *R.* Tigris = **'Harprier'** (**persica** hybrid)
'Till Uhlenspiegel' (RH)	EBls
'Tina Turner' (HT)	MBur MJon NBat
§ Jean Kenneally® = 'Tineally' (Min)	NBat
§ Luis Desamero = 'Tinluis' (Min)	NBat
§ Irresistible = 'Tinresist' (Min/Patio)	NBat
◆ Tintinara	See *R.* Tintinara = **'Dicuptight'**
◆ Tip Top®	See *R.* Tip Top = **'Tanope'**
'Tipo Ideale'	See *R.* × *odorata* **'Mutabilis'**
'Tipsy Imperial Concubine' (T)	EBls
Tivoli	See *R.* Tivoli = **'Poulduce'**
'Toby Tristam' (Ra)	CRHN WWat
'Tom Foster' (HT)	NBat
tomentosa	MSto
§ Thora Hird = 'Tonybrac' (F)	MAus
◆ Too Hot to Handle	See *R.* Too Hot to Handle = **'Macloupri'**
◆ Top Marks	See *R.* Top Marks = **'Fryministar'**
◆ Topaz Jewel	See *R.* Yellow Dagmar Hastrup = **'Moryelrug'**
'Topeka' (F)	SRum
Toprose	See *R.* Toprose = **'Cocgold'**
Topsi® (F/Patio)	IHos MJon NPri SPer SRum
◆ Torvill and Dean	See *R.* Torvill and Dean = **'Lantor'**
◆ Toulouse-Lautrec®	See *R.* Toulouse-Lautrec = **'Meirevolt'**
§ 'Tour de Malakoff' (Ce)	EBls IHar MAus MHlr SFam SPer WAct WHCG
◆ Tournament of Roses	See *R.* Tournament of Roses = **'Jacient'**
◆ Toynbee Hall	See *R.* Toynbee Hall = **'Korwonder'**
'Trade Winds' (HT)	MGan
◆ Tradescant®	See *R.* Tradescant = **'Ausdir'**
Tradition	See *R.* Tradition = **'Korbeltin'**
◆ Tradition '95®	See *R.* Tradition '95 = **'Korkeltin'**
◆ Tranquility	See *R.* Tranquility = **'Barout'**
§ Dreamland = 'Träumland' (F)	MFry MGan
'Treasure Trove' (Ra)	CRHN EBls EMFP IHar MAus MBur SWCr WAct
Trevor Griffiths	See *R.* Trevor Griffiths = **'Ausold'**
'Tricolore de Flandre' (G)	EBls MAus
Trier® (Ra)	EBls MAus MHlr MMat WHCG
'Trigintipetala' misapplied	See *R.* **'Professeur Emile Perrot'**
'Triomphe de l'Exposition' (HP)	MAus
'Triomphe du Luxembourg' (T)	EBls MAus

triphylla	See *R.* × *beanii*
§ Jennie Robinson = 'Trobette' (Min/Patio)	SApu
§ Just Magic = 'Trobic' (Min)	MJon
§ Sarah Robinson = 'Trobinette' (Min)	MJon
§ Ginny-Lou = 'Trobinka' (Min)	SJus
§ Woodland Sunbeam = 'Trobland' (Min/Patio)	MJon
§ Guernsey Love = 'Troblove' (Min)	MJon SJus
§ Little Russell = 'Trobric' (Min)	MJon
§ Royal Worcester = 'Trobroy' (S)	MJon WGer
§ Starlight Express = 'Trobstar' (Cl)	NBat SCoo SPer
§ Simon Robinson = 'Trobwich' (Min/GC)	MJon
◆ Troika®	See *R.* Troika = **'Poumidor'**
◆ Troilus	See *R.* Troilus = **'Ausoil'**
◆ Tropico Sunblaze	See *R.* Tropico Sunblaze = **'Meiglassol'**
◆ Trumpeter®	See *R.* Trumpeter = **'Mactru'**
¶ 'Tumbling Waters' (S)	ENot NFla
'Tuscany' (G)	GCoc MAus SJus SPer WAct WHCG
'Tuscany Superb' (G) ♀	CHad CPou EBls EMFP ENot IHar IHos LHol MAus MHlr MMat NPri NSty SPer WAct WHCG WHow WKif WSHC
tuschetica	MSto
◆ Twenty-fifth	See *R.* Twenty-fifth = **'Beatwe'**
◆ Twenty-one Again*	See *R.* Twenty-one Again* = **'Meinimo'**
◆ Tynwald	See *R.* Tynwald = **'Mattwyt'**
'Typhoon' (HT)	IHar MBur MJon
'Ulrich Brünner Fils' (HP)	EBls MAus
'Uncle Bill' (HT)	EBls
◆ Uncle Walter	See *R.* Uncle Walter = **'Macon'**
◆ UNICEF	See *R.* UNICEF = **'Cocjojo'**
§ 'Unique Blanche' (Ce)	CPou EBee EBls MAus WHow
◆ Valencia®	See *R.* Valencia = **'Koreklia'**
◆ Valentine Heart	See *R.* Valentine Heart = **'Picogle'**
'Vanguard' (Ru)	EBls
'Vanity' (HM)	EBls MAus SPer
'Variegata di Bologna' (Bb)	CHad EBee EBls LFis MAus MMat NSty WAct
Vatertag®	MJon
'Veilchenblau' (Ra) ♀	CHad EBls ELan LFis LGod LStr MAus MBri MBur MGan MHlr NSty SApu SJus SPer SRum SSea SWCr WAct WHCG WHow WKif WSHC
◆ Velvet Fragrance	See *R.* Velvet Fragrance = **'Fryperdee'**
'Venusta Pendula' (Ra)	EBls MAus
'Verschuren' (HT/v)	ELan
versicolor	See *R. gallica* **'Versicolor'**
'Vick's Caprice' (HP)	EBls MAus NSty
'Vicomtesse Pierre du Fou' (ClHT)	EBls MAus NSty
◆ Victor Hugo®	See *R.* Spirit of Youth = **'Meivestal'**
'Victoriana' (F)	MAus
◆ Vidal Sassoon	See *R.* Vidal Sassoon = **'Macjuliat'**
'Village Maid'	See *R.* **'Centifolia Variegata'**
◆ *villosa* Auct.	See *R. mollis*

§ *villosa* Linnaeus — EBls MAus MMat MSto NSty WAct

– 'Duplex' — See *R.* **'Wolley-Dod'**

§ 'Violacea' (G) — EBls WHCG

◆ Violet Carson — See *R.* Violet Carson = **'Macio'**

'Violette' (Ra) — EBls MAus NSty WAct WHCG WHer

'Violinista Costa' (HT) — EBls

virginiana ♀ — CTri EBls ENot GCal GChr IHar MAus MGan MSte NWea SPer WAct WHCG WHen WOVN

– 'Plena' — See *R.* **'Rose d'Amour'**

'Virgo' (HT) — EBls

'Viridiflora' — See *R.* x *odorata* **'Viridiflora'**

◆ Vital Spark — See *R.* Vital Spark = **'Cocacert'**

'Vivid' (Bourbon hybrid) — EBls

◆ Voice of Thousands — See *R.* Voice of Thousands = **'Horsunsmile'**

◆ *vosagiaca* — See *R. caesia* subsp. *glauca*

'W.E. Lippiat' (HT) — EBls

◆ Wandering Minstrel — See *R.* Wandering Minstrel = **'Harquince'**

wardii var. *culta* — MAus

◆ Warm Welcome — See *R.* Warm Welcome = **'Chewizz'**

◆ Warm Wishes — See *R.* Warm Wishes = **'Fryxotic'**

'Warrior' (F) — MGan SPer

◆ Warwick Castle® — See *R.* Warwick Castle = **'Auslian'**

◆ Warwickshire — See *R.* Warwickshire = **'Korkandel'**

§ *watsoniana* — EBls

webbiana — CBrd EBls MAus WHCG

'Wedding Day' (Ra) — CDoC CHad EBar EBls EBrP EBre ELan IHar LBre LHol LPlm MAus MBri MBur MGan MJon MMat NBat NSty SApu SBre SJus SPer SRum SSea WAct WHCG WHow WWeb

◆ Wee Barbie — See *R.* Wee Barbie = **'Jelbar'**

◆ Wee Cracker — See *R.* Wee Cracker = **'Cocmarris'**

◆ Wee Jock — See *R.* Wee Jock = **'Cocabest'**

'Weetwood' (Ra) — CRHN MAus SPer

'Weisse aus Sparrieshoop' (S) — MGan

Weisse Wolcke® — See *R.* White Cloud = **'Korstacha'**

§ Paradise® = 'Weizeip' (HT) — MGan

◆ Welwyn Garden Glory℗ — See *R.* Welwyn Garden Glory = **'Harzumber'**

'Wembley Stadium' (F/HT) — MGan

'Wendy Cussons' (HT) — CB&S CGro EBls GChr GCoc IHos LPlm MAus MBur MGan MJon NRog SApu SPer SRum WWeb

◆ Wenlock® — See *R.* Wenlock = **'Auswen'**

◆ Westerland — See *R.* Westerland = **'Korwest'**

'Westfield Star' (HT) — MAus

§ Sweet Memories = 'Whamemo' (Patio) — COtt CTri EBrP EBre EPfP GCoc LBre LStr MJon SBre SCoo SPla SWCr WGer

'Whisky Gill' (HT) — MGan

◆ Whisky Mac — See *R.* Whisky Mac = **'Tanky'**

'White Bath' — See *R.* **'Shailer's White Moss'**

◆ White Bells® — See *R.* White Bells = **'Poulwhite'**

§ 'White Cécile Brünner' (Poly) — EBls MAus SSea WHCG

'White Christmas' (HT) — ELan MBur MGan SRum

White Cloud (S/ClHT) — See *R.* White Cloud = **'Korstacha' (S/ClHT)**

White Cloud℗ (Min) — See *R.* White Cloud = **'Savacloud'**

White Cockade® (Cl) ♀ — CB&S EBls GCoc LPlm MFry MGan SApu SPer WHCG

§ 'White de Meaux' (Ce) — EBls MAus

◆ White Diamond® — See *R.* White Diamond = **'Interamon'**

◆ White Flower Carpet® — See *R.* White Flower Carpet = **'Noaschnee'**

'White Grootendorst' (Ru) — EBls MAus WAct

◆ White Knight — See *R.* White Knight = **'Poullaps'**

◆ White Max Graf — See *R.* x *jacksonii* White Max Graf = **'Korgram' (GC/Ru)**

◆ White Meidiland® — See *R.* White Meidiland = **'Meicoublan'**

White Moss — See *R.* **'Comtesse de Murinais'**, *R.* **'Shailer's White Moss'**

§ 'White Pet' (Poly) ♀ — CBos CHad EMFP ENot GCoc IHos LStr MBri MBur MGan MHlr MJon SApu SJus SPer SPla WAct WSHC

White Provence — See *R.* **'Unique Blanche'**

'White Queen Elizabeth' (F) — EBls SRum

White Rose of York — See *R.* x *alba* **'Alba Semiplena'**

'White Spray' (F) — EBls

¶ 'White Tausendschön' (Ra) — MAus

'White Wings' (HT) — CHad EBls MAus MGan NSty SPer WAct WHCG WKif

◆ Whitley Bay — See *R.* Whitley Bay = **'Horharryplus'**

§ Pearl Anniversary = 'Whitson' (Min/Patio) — GGre LStr SWCr

N *wichurana* (Ra) — EBls MAus WHCG

* – 'Nana' — MRav

– 'Variegata' (Ra) — CB&S CSWP EBar EHoe ELan EPot MAus MPla NHol SCoo WPyg

* – 'Variegata Nana' (Ra) — EAst LHop

¶ 'Wickham Highway' (F) — NBat

'Wickwar' (Ra) — CSWP EBls ELan EPla GCal MBri MHlr SSpi WAct WHCG

'Wilhelm' (HM) ♀ — EBls IHar MAus MRav NSty SWCr WHCG

'Will Scarlet' (HM) — MAus

'Willhire Country' (F) — EBls

'William Allen Richardson' (N) — EBls MAus WHCG

'William and Mary' (S) — EBls

§ 'William Lobb' (CeMo) ♀ — CHad CRHN EBls EBrP EBre ENot GCoc IHar IHos IOrc LBre MAus MGan MHlr MMat NFla NSty SApu SBre SChu SJus SPer SRum SSoC WAct WHCG WKif WWeb

◆ William Quarrier — See *R.* William Quarrier = **'Coclager'**

'William R. Smith' (T) — EBls

◆ William Shakespeare® — See *R.* William Shakespeare = **'Ausroyal'**

'William Tyndale' (Ra) — WHCG

'Williams' Double Yellow' — See *R.* x *harisonii* **'Williams' Double Yellow'**

◆ **willmottiae**   See *R.* gymnocarpa var. willmottiae

◆ Wiltshire   See *R.* Wiltshire = **'Kormuse'**
◆ Wimi®   See *R.* Wimi = **'Tanrowise'**
◆ Winchester Cathedral®   See *R.* Winchester Cathedral = **'Auscat'**
Windflower   See *R.* Windflower = **'Auscross'**
◆ Windrush®   See *R.* Windrush = **'Ausrush'**
◆ Wine and Dine   See *R.* Wine and Dine = **'Dicuncle'**
× **wintoniensis**   EHic WAct WHCG
◆ Wise Portia   See *R.* Wise Portia = **'Ausport'**
◆ Wishing   See *R.* Wishing = **'Dickerfuffle'**
◆ With Love   See *R.* With Love = **'Andwit'**
'Woburn Abbey' (F)   CGro EBls GGre IHar MJon NRog
§ 'Wolley-Dod' (S)   EBls MAus MRav
'Woman and Home' (HT)   CBlo
Woman o'th' North   See *R.* Woman o'th North = **'Kirlon'**
* 'Woman's Hour' (F)   EBls
◆ Woodland Sunbeam   See *R.* Woodland Sunbeam = **'Trobland'**
§ **woodsii**   EBls MAus MMat WHCG
– var. **fendleri**   See *R.* woodsii
'Woolverstone Church Rose'   See *R.* **'Surpassing Beauty of Woolverstone'**
◆ Wor Jackie   See *R.* Wor Jackie = **'Kirworjackie'**
§ **xanthina** 'Canary Bird' (S) ♀   Widely available
§ – f. **hugonis** ♀   EBls ECGP ELan MAus MGan MMat NRog SPer WAct WHCG
¶ – f. **spontanea**   EBls IHar MGan MMat
'Xavier Olibo' (HP)   EBls
Yellow Button® (S)   MAus MBri WAct
◆ Yellow Charles Austin®   See *R.* Yellow Charles Austin = **'Ausyel'**
'Yellow Cushion' (F)   MAus
◆ Yellow Dagmar Hastrup   See *R.* Yellow Dagmar Hastrup = **'Moryelrug'**
'Yellow Doll' (Min)   ELan MAus MGan
'Yellow Patio' (Min/Patio)   LStr SWCr
Yellow Scotch (PiH)   See *R.* × harisonii **'Williams' Double Yellow'**
◆ Yellow Sunblaze   See *R.* Yellow Sunblaze = **'Meitrisical'**
Yesterday® (Poly/F/S) ♀   EBls MAus MGan MMat SRum WHCG
'Yolande d'Aragon' (HP)   EBls
York and Lancaster   See *R.* × damascena var. versicolor
¶ 'Yorkshire' (GC)   LStr NBat
◆ Yorkshire Bank   See *R.* Yorkshire Bank = **'Rutrulo'**
'Yorkshire Lady' (HT)   NBat
◆ Young Quinn®   See *R.* Young Quinn = **'Macbern'**
◆ Yves Piaget®   See *R.* Royal Brompton Rose = **'Meivildo'**
'Yvonne Rabier' (Poly) ♀   EBls LStr MAus MHlr MMat NSty SPer WAct WHCG
◆ Zambra®   See *R.* Zambra = **'Meicurbos'**
'Zéphirine Drouhin' (Bb) ♀   Widely available
§ 'Zigeunerknabe' (S) ♀   EBee EBls EMFP GOrc MAus NSty SPer SWCr WAct WHCG
Zitronenfalter® (S)   MGan
'Zweibrücken' (Cl)   MGan
§ 'Zwergkönig' (Min)   MAus

◆ Zwergkönigin   See *R.* Zwergkönigin '82 = **'Korwerk'**

ROSCOEA (Zingiberaceae)

alpina   CBro CGra CPBP EBrP EBre EPot ERos GDra IBlr LBre MTho NHol NWCA SBla SBre SWas WCot WCru WOMN WSan
auriculata   CAvo CBro CFir CLAP CRDP IBlr MLLN MTho NHar NHol SBla SCro WCru WPyg
¶ **australis**   IBlr
'Beesiana'   CAvo CFir CHEx CRDP EBrP EBre ECha ERos IBlr LAma LBow LBre MBel MTho NHar NHol NPri SBre WCru WPyg
'Beesiana' white   CLAP EBar NHol
cautleyoides ♀   CAvo CBro CGle CRDP EBrP EBre EDAr EHyt EPot ERos GDra LAma LBow LBre MNrw MTho MUlv NHar NHol NRog SAxl SBre SMad SMrm SPer WCru WPyg WSan
¶ – Blackthorn strain   SBla
– 'Grandiflora'   CHEx
– × **humeana**   IBlr
– hybrid   MLLN NGre
– 'Kew Beauty'   CRDP EBrP EBre LBre MTho SAxl SBla SBre
humeana ♀   CBro CDec CFir CLAP EHyt GCrs LAma NHar SAxl WCru
§ **purpurea**   CBro CGle CHEx CRDP EBrP EBre EHyt ELan EMan ERos GCal LAma LBow LBre MFir NBir NHar NHol SBre SPer WCru WPyg WWin
– var. **procera**   See *R.* purpurea
§ **scillifolia**   CBro CFir CRDP EBee ERos GCal LAma LBow MTho NBir NGre NHar NMen NRog NTow SWas WCru
– pink form   IBlr WViv
tibetica   CFir SAxl

ROSMARINUS † (Lamiaceae)

* **calabriensis**   WCHb
corsicus 'Prostratus'   See *R.* officinalis **Prostratus Group**
¶ 'Green Ginger'   CChr NCut NPer WElm WWoo
× **lavandulaceus** hort.   See *R.* officinalis **Prostratus Group**
– Noë   See *R.* eriocalyx
¶ 'Loddon Pink'   ERav
officinalis   CArn CB&S CGle CLan CSev EBot ELan ELau ENot ERav ESis GPoy GRei ISea LBuc LHol MBar MChe MPla MWat NFla NNor NPer NSti SArc SIng SRCN SReu WOak WWin
– var. **albiflorus**   CArn CSev EFou ELau ESis GAbr GChr GPoy MBar MChe MPla NHHG NSti SChu SHDw SMac WCHb WEas WHer WOMN WSHC WWye
§ – **angustissimus** 'Corsican Blue'   CArn EBee EPla GBar GPoy SCro SHDw SIde SPer WPer
– 'Aureovariegatus'   See *R.* officinalis **'Aureus'**
§ – 'Aureus' (v)   CDec CLan CMil IBlr MHar NHHG SDry SEas SMad SUsu WByw WCHb WEas WHer WSel

§ – 'Benenden Blue'   CGle CSev EBar ECha EGoo
ELau GPoy LHop MChe MGos
MUlv NHHG SAxl SBid SChu
SDix SIde SPan SPer STre
WEas WSel WWat WWye
– 'Collingwood Ingram'   See **R. officinalis** '**Benenden Blue**'
– 'Corsicus Prostratus'   CB&S ELau SMac
– dwarf blue   ELau MGra
– 'Fastigiatus'   See **R. officinalis** '**Miss Jessopp's Upright**'
– 'Fota Blue'   CArn CBod CSWP ELau GBar
NHHG NHex NSti SAga SCro
SHDw SIde WJek WWye
– 'Frimley Blue'   See **R. officinalis** '**Primley Blue**'
* – 'Ginger-scented'   WRus
– 'Guilded'   See **R. officinalis** '**Aureus**'
– 'Gunnel's Upright'   GBar WRha
– 'Jackman's Prostrate'   CB&S ECtt
– 'Lady in White'   EAst ELan EPfP SPan SPer
WGwG WWat
– *lavandulaceus*   See **R. officinalis** Prostratus Group
– 'Lilies Blue'   GPoy
– 'Lockwood Variety'   WPer
– 'Majorca Pink'   CB&S CDec CSam EGoo ELau
GBar LHol MPla NSti SIde
SPer SSoC WCHb WOMN
WPer WWat WWye
– 'McConnell's Blue'   CArn CDoC CLTr CLan EBrP
EBre ELan ELau GAbr LBre
MAsh MGos MWat MWgw
NRoo SBre SDry SHDw SPan
WCHb WGer WPer WWat
WWye
* – 'Miss Jessopp's Prostrate'   MGra
§ – 'Miss Jessopp's Upright' ♀   CArn CB&S CHEx EAst EBrP
EBre ELan ENot GAbr GPoy
LBre LHol MBal MGos MWat
NMir NNor NSti SBre SIde
SMad SPer SPla SSta WAbe
WBod WGwG WSel WWal
WWat
¶ – 'Mrs Harding'   CBod
§ – 'Primley Blue'   CArn CFee CJew CSam CSev
CWSG ELau EMil GBar LHol
MChe MRav NHHG NSti SBid
SChu SIde SMac SMer WCHb
WHer WOak WPer WWye
§ – Prostratus Group ♀   CArn CB&S CLan CSev CTrw
ELau EMil MChe NHHG NSti
NWCA SArc SIde SPer SRms
SSoC SUsu SWas WHar
WOMN WPer WRus WWat
WWye
¶ – – 'Trewithen'   LFlo
– f. *pyramidalis*   See **R. officinalis** '**Miss Jessopp's Upright**'
– *repens*   See **R. officinalis** Prostratus Group
– 'Roseus'   CArn CHan CWit ELan ELau
EMil GChr GPoy LHop MChe
NHHG NSti SChu SEas SMad
SSoC SEas WGwG WHer
WPer WWat WWye
– 'Russell's Blue'   WHer
– 'Severn Sea' ♀   CArn CB&S CBot CGle CHan
CSev EBar ECtt ELan GOrc
GPoy LHol LHop NNor NSti
SIde SPer WAbe WEas WPGP
WPer WWat WWeb

– 'Sissinghurst Blue' ♀   CArn CMGP CSev ECha ELan
ELau EMil ERav LHol MAsh
SBid SIde SPer WCHb WGwG
WRHF WSel WWat WWye
– 'Sudbury Blue'   ELau GBar MChe MGra
NHHG NLon NRoo NSti
SHDw WEas WJek
– 'Trusty'   ECtt ELan ERav LHop LRHS
WPer
– 'Tuscan Blue'   CDoC CSWP ECGP ECot
ELau EMil EPri GBar MWat
NFla NHex SDry SIde SMer
WCHb WHer WJek WPer
WRha WWat WWye
– 'Variegatus'   See **R. officinalis** '**Aureus**'
– 'Vicomte de Noailles'   ERea
repens   See **R. officinalis** Prostratus Group

ROSTRINUCULA (Lamiaceae)

dependens Guiz 18   CBot SMac

ROSULARIA (Crassulaceae)

acuminata   See **R. alpestris** subsp. *alpestris*
§ *aizoon*   ESis MFos
alba   See **R. sedoides**
alpestris   MSte
§ – subsp. *alpestris*   WOMN
§ *chrysantha*   EBur ESis MBro NGre NMen
NNrd SIng SSmi WFar WPer
– Number 1   CWil
crassipes   See **Rhodiola wallichiana**
§ *muratdaghensis*   EBur MBro NGre NNrd
pallida A. Berger   See **R. chrysantha**
– Stapf   See **R. aizoon**
platyphylla hort.   See **R. muratdaghensis**
rechingeri   CWil EPot
§ *sedoides*   CMHG CWil EGoo ELan
GCHN MBar SChu SSmi WElm
WPer WWin
§ – var. *alba*   CMHG CWil ELan EPot GBur
GCHN MBar NFla NGre NVic
SChu SRms WHoo WOMN
WPyg WWin
sempervivum   CWil EWes NGre NMen
§ – subsp. *glaucophylla*   CWil NTow WPer
serpentinica   CWil
spatulata hort.   See **R. sempervivum** subsp. *glaucophylla*
turkestanica   CWil

ROTHMANNIA (Rubiaceae)

capensis   SOWG

RUBIA (Rubiaceae)

peregrina   CArn CKin EHic EWFC GBar
GPoy MHew MSal
tinctorum   CArn ELau GBar GPoy LHol
MHew MSal NHex SIde SWat
WHer WWye

RUBUS † (Rosaceae)

¶ 'Adrienne' (F)   EMui
alceifolius   CPMA
– Poiret   CGle
arcticus   CGle CInt ESim MBal MBro
MCCP MHig NCat NHar SRms
SSta WBea WCru WPat
– subsp. *stellarcticus* (F)   ESim
– – 'Anna' (F)   ESim
– – 'Beata' (F)   ESim

– – 'Linda' (F)	ESim
– – 'Sofia' (F)	ESim
australis	CPlN
x *barkeri*	ECou
§ 'Benenden' ♀	CB&S CBlo CBot CGle CMHG CSam EBar ELan ENot GChr ISea LHop MBal MBri MGos MHlr MRav MWat NBrk NFla NNor NSti SHBN SPer WCFE WDin WHCG WWal WWat WWin
'Betty Ashburner'	CAgr CBlo CDoC CHan CWit EBrP EBre EPfP EPla GCal GQui LBre LBuc MGos NFla SBre WHCG WTro WWat
biflorus	CB&S EMon EPla ERav WPGP
'Boysenberry, Thornless' (F)	EMui GTwe LBuc NDal SDea SPer
* *buergeri* 'Variegatus'	SMac
caesius 'Sidings'	CNat
* *calophyllus*	WCot
calycinoides Hayata	See *R. pentalobus*
chamaemorus	GPoy WUnd
cockburnianus (F) ♀	CB&S CBlo CGle CPle EBrP EBre ELan ENot EPla IOrc LBre LBuc MBal MRav MWat NHol NWea SAga SBre SPer SRms WDin WWat
– Goldenvale™ = 'Wyego'	CB&S CDoC CPle EAst EBee EBrP EBre EMil EPla GChr GQui LBre MBlu MLLN MPla MTis NEgg NHol SBre SEas SPer SSpi WDin WRus WWye
coreanus	CFil CPle
crataegifolius	MBro SMac WPat WWat
'Emerald Spreader'	LRHS SBod
flagelliflorus	MBar WHCG
fockeanus hort.	See *R. pentalobus*
¶ *formosensis* B&SWJ 1798	WCru
x *fraseri*	EPla
fruticosus	CKin
– 'Ashton Cross' (F)	EMui GRei GTwe LBuc SDea
– 'Bedford Giant' (F)	CBlo GChr GTwe MGos SPer WWeb
– 'Black Satin' (F)	CBlo CSam GRei MBri SDea SPer WWeb
– 'Dart's Ambassador'	ENot
– 'Fantasia' (F) ♀	EMui GTwe LBuc
– 'Godshill Goliath' (F)	SDea
¶ – 'Helen'	CSut EMui
– 'Himalayan Giant' (F)	CBlo CSam GTwe NRog SDea SPer
– 'John Innes' (F)	NRog
– 'Loch Ness' (F) ♀	CBlo COtt CSam EMui GTwe LBuc MBri MGos SDea SPer
– 'Merton Thornless' (F)	CBlo GTwe MGos NBee NRog
– 'No Thorn' (F)	SDea
– 'Oregon Thornless' (F)	CBlo EMui GTwe MBri NDal SDea SPer SRms
– 'Parsley Leaved' (F)	CBlo SDea
* – 'Sylvan' (F)	MGos
– 'Thornfree' (F)	CBlo NDal SDea WWeb
– 'Variegatus'	CBot CPMA CRDP EPla MBlu SAxl SMad WCot WPat
– 'Waldo'	CBlo COtt EMui LBuc MBri MGos SDea
henryi	CBot CPlN CSWP EPla MRav WCot WHCG WWal WWye
– var. *bambusarum*	CDec CFil CHan CMCN CPlN CPle EHic ELan EPar EPla SBid WCru WTin
hupehensis	SLPl

ichangensis	CBot CHan CMCN CPlN EPPr EPla MBal
idaeus	CKin
* – 'Allgold' (F)	EMui
– 'Augusta' (F)	EMui
– 'Aureus' (F)	ECha EHal ELan EPla LHop NSti SDry SMac WCot WLin WRus
– Autumn Bliss™ (F) ♀	CBlo CSam CSut CWSG EMui GChr GTwe LBuc MBri MGos NBee NEgg SDea SPer WBay WWeb
– 'Fallgold' (F)	GTwe
¶ – 'Galante' (F)	EMui
* – 'Glen Ample' (F)	CSut CWSG EMui GRei GTwe LBuc
– 'Glen Clova' (F)	CBlo GTwe NBee NRog SPer WBay WWeb
– 'Glen Coe' (F)	GTwe
– 'Glen Lyon' (F)	GRei GTwe LBuc MBri SCoo WBay
– 'Glen Magna' (F)	CSut CWSG EMui GRei GTwe LBuc
– 'Glen Moy' (F) ♀	CBlo CSut CWSG EMui GChr GTwe LBuc MGos NBee NRog SDea SPer
– 'Glen Prosen' (F) ♀	CSam CWSG EMui GTwe LBuc MBri NRog SDea SPer
– 'Glen Rosa' (F)	GTwe
– 'Glen Shee' (F)	GTwe
– 'Golden Everest' (F)	GTwe
– 'Heritage' (F)	EBee SPer WBay
– 'Julia' (F)	GTwe
– 'Leo' (F) ♀	CBlo EMui GTwe MGos SCoo WBay
– 'Malling Admiral' (F) ♀	CBlo COtt GTwe MBri NRog SPer
– 'Malling Delight' (F) ♀	CBlo GTwe NRog SCoo SPer WBay
– 'Malling Jewel' (F) ♀	CBlo COtt EMui GRei GTwe LBuc NBee SDea SPer WBay
– 'Malling Joy' (F)	GTwe
– 'Malling Orion' (F)	MGos
– 'Malling Promise' (F)	CBlo
– 'Redsetter' (F)	EMui
– 'Ruby' (F)	EMui
– 'September' (F)	CBlo
– 'Summer Gold' (F)	GTwe
¶ – 'Terri-Louise' (F)	EMui
¶ – 'Tulameen' (F)	EMui
– 'Zefa Herbsternte' (F)	GTwe WWeb
illecebrosus (F)	MBro SMac WBea
intercurrens	GCal
irenaeus	CFil CHan CPlN CPle WPGP WWat
'Kenneth Ashburner'	CDoC EPla MBri SLPl WWat
'King's Acre Berry' (F)	EMui
laciniatus	EHol EPla
lineatus	CAbb CBot CBrd CGre CHan CPle EPla LHop MBal MBlu SDix SDry SMad SSta WBea WCru WPat WWat WWye
(Loganberry Group) 'LY 59' (F) ♀	CDoC EMui GTwe NRog SDea SPer SRms
– 'LY 654' (F) ♀	CBlo CSam CSut GChr GRei GTwe LBuc MBri MGos SDea SPer WWeb
– 'New Zealand Black' (F)	SDea
– Thornless (F)	CBlo CTri ECot GTwe NDal NRog SDea
¶ *ludwigii*	LLew

'Margaret Gordon' — CBlo CPMA MRav NPro WHCG
microphyllus 'Variegatus' — MRav SBid WPat WWeb
§ *nepalensis* — CAgr CDoC CGle CLTr EGoo MBel NHol NPro NWoo WRHF
nutans — See *R. nepalensis*
◆ Odel — See *R.* Odel = **'Walberton Red'**
odoratus — CHEx CWit ELan EPfP LBlm MHlr NPal SBid SPer WCot WHCG WWat
palmatus var. *coptophyllus* — SLPl
parviflorus — CArn
¶ – double form — EMon
– 'Sunshine Spreader' — GAri LHop NPro
parvus — ECou
pectinellus var. *trilobus* B&SWJ 1669B — NDov SAxl WCru
¶ *peltatus* — CFil WPGP
§ *pentalobus* — CGle CTri CWit ELan ENot EPla ESis LHop MAll MBal MBar MWhi SMac SPer WAbe WCru WFar WWin
¶ – B&SWJ 3878 — WCru
– 'Emerald Carpet' — CAgr ESim SBod
– 'Green Jade' — WWat
phoenicolasius — CB&S ELan EMui EPla GTwe MBlu MBri NRog SDea SPer WAbb WBea WCru WHCG WPat WWat WWye
Japanese Wineberry (F)
¶ *rolfei* B&SWJ 3546 — WCru
rosifolius 'Coronarius' (d) — CHan CHid CMil CPle EHal ELan EOrc EPla GMac LHop MBel MHlr MLLN MMil MSCN MWhi NEgg NHaw NHol SAsh SBid SMad WCot WKif WLin WRus WSan
setchuenensis — CMCN CSWP
'Silvan' (F) ♀ — CDoC EMui GTwe
sp. B&SWJ 1735 — WCru
spectabilis — CPle CWit ELan EPla LFis LHop MBal MRav SEas SPan SRms WRha
– 'Flore Pleno' — See *R. spectabilis* **'Olympic Double'**
§ – 'Olympic Double' (d) — Widely available
* – 'Olympic Flame' — CEnd
splendidissimus B&SWJ 2361 — WCru
squarrosus — CPle ECou EHol EPla SMad
'Sunberry' (F) — GTwe NDal
taiwanicola B&SWJ 317 — CFee WCru
Tayberry Group ♀ — CSam CTri EMui GChr GRei GTwe MBri MGos NDal NRog SPer SRms WWeb
¶ – 'Buckingham' (F) — CSut EMui LBuc WLRN
– 'Medana Tayberry' (F) — SDea
§ *thibetanus* ♀ — CB&S CBot CDoC CHan CPle ELan EMil ENot GCal MBri MRav NBir NSti SBod SDix SDry SEas SMac SPer SUsu WBea WDin WHCG WWat WWye
– 'Silver Fern' — See *R. thibetanus*
tricolor — CAgr CB&S CChe CDec CGle CHEx CHan CPlN ECha ELan ENot EPla IHos LGro MBal NHol NNor SDix SHBN SLPl SPer WBod WDin WEas WHCG WWat WWin WWye
– 'Dart's Evergreen' — SLPl
– 'Ness' — SLPl

¶ 'Tridel' — WGwG
Tridel 'Benenden' — See *R.* **'Benenden'**
'Tummelberry' (F) — GTwe LRHS
ulmifolius 'Bellidiflorus' (d) — CBot CFis CSev ELan ENot EPla MBal MBlu MRav NNor SBid SChu SMac SPer WAbb WBea
* *variegatus* — NEgg
'Veitchberry' (F) — EMui GTwe NDal NRog
§ Odel = 'Walberton Red' — MBel SPer
'Youngberry' (F) — SDea

RUDBECKIA † (Asteraceae)

Autumn Sun — See *R.* **'Herbstsonne'**
californica — MNrw SSca WPer
◆ *deamii* — See *R. fulgida* var. *deamii*
echinacea purpurea — See *Echinacea purpurea*
§ *fulgida* var. *deamii* ♀ — Widely available
§ – var. *speciosa* — CM&M CMGP CSam ECGN ECha EHic ELan EPfP GMac MBel NRoo SHel SPer SRms WCot WOld WPer WRus
– var. *sullivantii* 'Goldsturm' ♀ — Widely available
gloriosa — See *R. hirta*
'Goldquelle' ♀ — ECED EFou EGar ELan EMan EPfP GMaP LHop MBel MLLN NOrc NPri SCro SMad SMrm SPer SRms WHil WWin
§ 'Herbstsonne' — CHea CTri ECGN ECGP ECha ECle LFis MAus MBel MWat NFla NOrc NPer NPri NVic SAga SMad SPer SPla SSoC SSvw WBor WEas WMow WRha
§ *hirta* — SCha
¶ – 'Irish Eyes' — EBee
¶ – var. *pulcherrima* — EFou EGar MUlv NCat SCro SMrm SSpe
§ 'Juligold'
July Gold — See *R.* **'Juligold'**
laciniata — CSam EBee ECGN ELan EMan EMon EPPr EPfP GCal LFis MArl MFir NOrc SMrm WByw
– 'Golden Glow' — See *R. laciniata* **'Hortensia'**
§ – 'Hortensia' — EMon MFir
maxima — CGle ECGN ECha EGar EMan EMon GBin LGre MBri MBro MCCP SAga SMrm SSoC WCot
* *mollis* — EBee
newmannii — See *R. fulgida* var. *speciosa*
occidentalis — CHan CPou LFis MAvo MLLN WPer
– 'Green Wizard' — CM&M CMil CPou EFou EGar GCal GCra MBro NBro SMad WBea WCot WElm WHer WHoo WWhi
purpurea — See *Echinacea purpurea*
◆ *speciosa* — See *R. fulgida* var. *speciosa*
subtomentosa — CHor CPou EBee EFou EGar EMan EMon GCal GMac MNrw NSti WOld
triloba — EBee ECGN EFou EMan NCut SGre WBea WCot WFar

RUELLIA (Acanthaceae)

amoena — See *R. graecizans*
caroliniensis — WCot
* 'Chi Chi' — WCot
devosiana — SLMG WMul
humilis — SIgm WCot WLRN
* 'Katie' — WCot

makoyana ♀	CHal IBlr MBri SLMG SRms WMul
strepens	WCot

RUMEX (Polygonaceae)

§ *acetosa*	CArn CKin CSev ECha EJud ELau GAbr GBar GPoy LHol MChe MHew MMal NBir SIde WHer WSel WWye
¶ – 'Crocodile' (v)	WAlt
– 'Redleaf'	See *R. acetosa* subsp. *vineatus*
§ – subsp. *vineatus*	WCot
acetosella	IIve MSal WSel
alpinus	WCot
flexuosus	CElw CRow EHoe EPPr GCal IBlr WCot
hydrolapathum	CArn EMFW EWFC LPBA MSta NDea
maritimus	EWFC
montanus 'Ruber'	See *R. alpestris* **'Ruber'**
rubrifolius	SIde
sanguineus	CHan EMFW EMan GGar LPBA MSCN SIng WCer WChe WFar WGwG WLRN WWal
– var. *sanguineus*	CArn CElw CRow CSev EHoe ELan EPar EPla LHol MNrw MRav MTho NBro NHol NLak NSti WFox WHer WOak WPer WSel WWye
scutatus	CArn CJew CSev EJud ELau GAbr GBar GPoy LHol MChe MHew MTho SIde WCer WGwG WHer WJek WSel WWye
– 'Silver Shield'	CJew CMil CRDP ELau EMar EMon EPPr IBlr LBlm NSti WCHb WHer WJek WOak WWye
venosus	MSal

RUMOHRA (Davalliaceae) See Plant Deletions

RUPICAPNOS (Papaveraceae)

africana	EPot NWCA SBla WAbe WOMN

RUSCHIA (Aizoaceae)

putterillii S&SH 64	CHan
uncinata	CTrC

RUSCUS † (Ruscaceae)

aculeatus	CArn CLTr CTri ECED ENot EPfP GPoy MFir MRav MWhi SAPC SArc SSta WDin WHer WOMN WPGP WRHF WSpi WStI WWye
– var. *angustifolius* (f)	EPla
– (f)	WMou
– hermaphrodite	EPla EWes GCal WWat
– (m)	EGoo WMou WWat
* – 'Wheeler's Variety' (f/m)	CPMA EBee MPla MRav
hypoglossum	GOrc MTed SAPC SArc WRHF
ponticus	EPla
racemosus	See *Danae racemosa*

RUSPOLIA (Acanthaceae) See Plant Deletions

RUSSELIA (Scrophulariaceae)

§ *equisetiformis* ♀	ERea SIgm
juncea	See *R. equisetiformis*

RUTA (Rutaceae)

chalepensis	CArn WCHb
§ – 'Dimension Two'	EMon WHer
– prostrate form	See *R. chalepensis* **'Dimension Two'**
corsica	CArn
graveolens	CArn CChr CGle CJew CWSG EFer GPoy MChe MHew NOak SIde SPar WGwG WHer WJek WOak WPer WShe
¶ – 'Harlequin'	SPil
– 'Jackman's Blue' ♀	CGle CMHG CSev EBrP EBre ECha EEls EHoe ELan ENot GChr LBre LGro LHol MBal MBar MCLN MPla MWat MWgw NNor NSti SBre SPer SRms WBod WEas WOak WOve WWin
* – *prostrata*	WOak
– 'Variegata'	CArn CBot ECha ELan MCLN MChe NNor NPSI NPer WHer WJek WPbr WWye
montana	CBot WHer
prostrata	See *R. chalepensis* **'Dimension Two'**

RUTTYA (Acanthaceae) See Plant Deletions

× RUTTYRUSPOLIA (Acanthaceae)

¶ 'Phyllis van Heerden'	CSpe

RYTIDOSPERMA (Poaceae)

* *arundinaceum*	EBee

SABAL (Arecaceae)

§ *bermudana*	CHEx LPal
¶ *etonia*	LPal
§ *mexicana*	NPal
minor	CHEx CTrC LPal NPal
palmetto	CArn CTrC LPal NPal WNor
♦ *princeps*	See *S. bermudana*
¶ *rosei*	LPal
texana	See *S. mexicana*
¶ *uresana*	LPal

SACCHARUM (Poaceae)

ravennae	EHoe EMon EWes GBin MSte NSti SAxl SMad WChe

SADLERIA (Blechnaceae)

¶ *cyatheoides*	WRic

SAGERETIA (Rhamnaceae)

§ *thea*	STre
theezans	See *S. thea*

SAGINA (Caryophyllaceae)

boydii	EMNN EWes GCLN ITim
subulata var. *glabra*	CMea EBar ECha EFer ELan LGro MOne MRav SIng SRms WEas WHal WPer WWin
'Aurea'	

SAGITTARIA (Alismataceae)

japonica	See *S. sagittifolia*
latifolia	CHEx EMFW LPBA NDea WChe
§ *sagittifolia*	CBen CHEx CRow EHon EMFW LPBA MHew MSta SRms SWat WChe WMAq WShi

* – 'Bloomin Baby' CRow
– 'Flore Pleno' (d) CRow CWat EHon EMFW
LPBA MBal MSta NDea SWat
WChe
– var. *leucopetala* WMAq
subulata CRow

SAINTPAULIA (Gesneriaceae) See Plant
Deletions

SALIX † (Salicaceae)
acutifolia ELan EPla IOrc
– 'Blue Streak' (m) ♀ CEnd EPla IOrc MAsh MBal
MBlu NBir SWat
– 'Pendulifolia' (m) IOrc
adenophylla Hooker See *S. cordata*
aegyptiaca CDoC CLnd MBlu NWea
WMou
alba CCVT CKin CLnd EOHP GChr
LBuc SPer WDin WMou
– f. *argentea* See *S. alba* var. *sericea*
– 'Aurea' CLnd CTho WMou
– subsp. *caerulea* CLnd EBee ENot LBuc NWea
WMou
– 'Chermesina' hort. See *S. alba* subsp. *vitellina*
'Britzensis'
– 'Dart's Snake' CBlo EBee ELan ENot MRav
SCoo SPer
– 'Hutchinson's Yellow' EPla MBri MGos
– 'Liempde' (m) ENot
§ – var. *sericea* ♀ CB&S CLnd CTho ENot IOrc
MBal MBlu MBri MRav NLon
NNor NWea SHBN SPer WDin
WGer WMou WTro WWat
– 'Splendens' See *S. alba* var. *sericea*
N – 'Tristis' CLnd CTri ELan GChr MAsh
MBri MRav NWea SRms WDin
WFar
– subsp. *vitellina* ♀ CBlo CKin CPer EBar ELan
GChr LBuc NHol NWea WDin
WOrn
§ – – 'Britzensis' ♀ CDoC CKin CLnd CTho CTri
ELan ENot EPla GRei IOrc
LBuc LHop MBal MBar MGos
MRav NNor NWea SHBN SPer
SPla SRms SSta WDin WMou
WWat
– 'Vitellina Pendula' See *S. alba* 'Tristis'
– 'Vitellina Tristis' See *S. alba* 'Tristis'
§ *alpina* CLyd EHyt EWes GAri MBal
MBro NHol NRoo NWoo
apoda (m) CLyd ESis EWes MBal NHar
NHol WPer
§ *arbuscula* CBlo CDoC EBar EHyt ESis
MBal MPla NHar NWCA
arctica var. *petraea* WPat
¶ *aurita* GChr
babylonica CBlo CTrG NBee SHBN WDin
WMou
– 'Annularis' See *S. babylonica* 'Crispa'
§ – 'Crispa' EHic ELan EPla ERav LHop
SHBN SMad SPla WLRN
– var. *pekinensis* 'Pendula' MUlv
§ – – 'Tortuosa' ♀ CArn CDec CLnd CTho ELan
ENot GChr IOrc LHop LPan
MAsh MBal MBar MGos MTis
MWat NHol NNor NPer NWea
SPer SRms WHar WWat
bockii CBlo MBar NWCA WPer
§ 'Bowles' Hybrid' LBuc MRav WMou

'Boydii' (f) ♀ CFee EHyt ELan EPot ESis
GBur GDra GTou MAsh MBal
MBri MBro MDun MGos MPla
NHar NHol NMen NNor NRoo
SIng SRms STre WAbe WPat
§ 'Boyd's Pendulous' (m) CFee CLyd EHyt GAri MBal
MBar SIng
breviserrata CLyd GDra NHol NWCA
calyculata EHyt
caprea CB&S CCVT CKin CLnd CPer
CTri ENot GChr GRei LBuc
LHyr NWea WDin WMou
WTro
– 'Curlilocks' CBlo COtt EBee MBlu MGos
§ – 'Kilmarnock' (m) ♀ CBlo CLnd ELan GRei LBuc
LHyr LPan MAsh MBar MGos
MWat NBee NHol NWea
SHBN SMad SPer WDin WMou
– var. *pendula* (f) See *S. caprea* 'Weeping Sally'
– – (m) See *S. caprea* 'Kilmarnock' (m)
cashmiriana CLyd MBro NHol WPat
× *cernua* NWCA
'Chrysocoma' See *S.* × *sepulcralis* var.
chrysocoma
cinerea CB&S CDoC CKin CPer ENot
GChr GRei NWea WDin
¶ – subsp. *oleifolia* GChr
– 'Tricolor' CArn CDoC GCHN
× *cottetii* CBlo
daphnoides CDoC CLnd CSam ELan ENot
GRei IHos IOrc LWak NWea
SHBN SPer SRms STre WDin
WMou WWat
– 'Aglaia' (m) ♀ CB&S CTri EPla MBal WPGP
– 'Meikle' CAgr
'E.A. Bowles' See *S.* 'Bowles' Hybrid'
× *ehrhartiana* CNat
§ *elaeagnos* ♀ CCVT CDoC CPle CTho EBar
EBee ENot MBlu SPan SPer
SWat WDin WMou
§ – subsp. *angustifolia* CLnd ELan IOrc LBuc LHop
MBal MTis NWea SMad SMrm
SRms STre WWat WWin
'Elegantissima' See *S. pendulina* var.
elegantissima
¶ × *erdingeri* EPla
§ 'Erythroflexuosa' CBlo CDoC CTho EBee EBrP
EBre ELan EPla LBre MAsh
MGos NHol NWea SBre SPla
SWat WDin WHer WOak
exigua CB&S CTho ELan ENot EWes
IOrc MBar MBlu MBri MGos
NWea SDry SMad SPer SSpi
WMou WWat
fargesii CBot CEnd CFee CFil CHan
CMHG ELan GOrc LHop MBal
MBlu MDun MGos MHlr NHar
SAxl SDix SMad SSpi SWas
WCru WPat WWat
§ × *finnmarchica* MBro
formosa See *S. arbuscula*
fragilis CCVT CKin CLnd CPer NWea
WDin WMou WTro
§ *fruticulosa* CGle CInt EPot GAri GCrs
GDra GGar GTou LLFlo MBal
MBro NWCA WWat
'Fuiri-koriyanagi' See *S. integra* 'Hakuro-nishiki'
furcata See *S. fruticulosa*
glauca CNat
glaucosericea EBee EHic WLRN WWat
'Golden Curls' See *S.* 'Erythroflexuosa'
gracilistyla CTho WMou WWat

subopposita	CDoC EBar EHic ELan EWes GOrc MBar MBlu MPla NPro SIng WWat
syrticola	See *S. cordata*
× *tetrapla* 'Hutchinson's Nigricans'	CNat
triandra	WMou
– 'Black Hollander'	CAgr
– 'Black Maul'	CAgr
– 'Semperflorens'	CNat
– 'Whissander'	CAgr
tristis	See *S. humilis*
× *tsugaluensis* 'Ginme' (f)	CMHG SLPl WTro WWat
§ *udensis* 'Sekka' (m)	CDec CLnd CTho ECtt ELan EPar EPla GChr IOrc MBal NChi NHol NWea STre SWat WMou WPyg
uva-ursi	CLyd GAri MBal
viminalis	CAgr CCVT CKin CPer ENot GChr GRei LBuc NWea WDin WMou
– 'Bowles' Hybrid'	See *S.* **'Bowles' Hybrid'**
– 'Brown Merrin'	CAgr
– 'Reader's Red' (m)	CAgr
– 'Yellow Osier'	CAgr
vitellina 'Pendula'	See *S. alba* **'Tristis'**
§ *waldsteiniana*	MBar
× *wimmeriana*	SRms
'Yelverton'	EPla MBri MRav

SALVIA † (Lamiaceae)

acetabulosa	See *S. multicaulis*
aethiopis	CPle CSev ECoo ELan EMar EOld LGre MLLN MSte NChi NSti SPil WPer WWye
afghanica	CPle WEas
§ *africana-caerulea*	CPle WWye
§ *africana-lutea*	CHal CPle CSev EGar ELan LHil MBEx MMil SBid WPen WPer WWye
– 'Kirstenbosch'	CPle MRav WCot WPer WWye
agnes	CPle
albimaculata	SBla
algeriensis	CPle
amarissima	CPle
ambigens	See *S. guaranitica* **'Blue Enigma'**
§ *amplexicaulis*	CPle WPer WWye
angustifolia Cavanilles	See *S. reptans*
– Michaux	See *S. azurea*
apiana	CPle SAga SIgm SPil WCot
argentea ♀	Widely available
arizonica	CPle GCal MLLN
atrocyanea	CPle CStr LHil SLod
aucheri	CPle EGar GBuc GCal
aurea	See *S. africana-lutea*
austriaca	CPle MBel SHFr WPer WWye
§ *azurea*	CArn CChr CLyd CPle MNrw MSte SMrm SPil
¶ – subsp. *pitcheri*	CStr
¶ – – var. *grandiflora*	EBee
bacheriana	See *S. buchananii*
§ *barrelieri*	CHan CPle MSto NChi SHFr SLod
'Belhaven'	GCal
bertolonii	See *S. pratensis* **Bertolonii Group**
bicolor Desfontaines	See *S. barrelieri*
blancoana	CArn CBot CFis CHan CPle ECha ELau EMan LHop MBEx MLLN MSte SAga SCro WSel
blepharophylla	CCan CHea CPle CSev CSpe GBri LHil LHop MWat SAga WPen WWye
brachyantha	CPle EGar
broussonetii	CPle
§ *buchananii* ♀	CHad CHal CHan CLon CPle CSWP CSam ELan EMil ERea GBri GQui LHop SAga SBid SCro SMrm SRCN SSoC WOld WPnn WWye
bulleyana	CFai CGle CHea CLyd CPle CSev ELan GBin GCal LHol MNrw NChi NSti SHFr SPil SSoC WBor WOve WPer WWin WWye
cacaliifolia ♀	CCan CHan CLTr CLon CPle CSpe EEls ERav LBlm LHil LHol MLLN MNrw MSte MWat SBid SHFr SPer WCHb WEas WHer WWye
caerulea hort.	See *S. guaranitica* **'Black and Blue'**
– Linnaeus	See *S. africana-caerulea*
caespitosa	CPle EHyt EPot MSto NWCA SBla SIng
campanulata	CPle CSev
¶ – CC&McK 1071	CFir
canariensis	CPle LHil MSte SAga SHFr WSan WWye
* – f. *alba*	CPle
– f. *candidissima*	CPle
candelabrum ♀	CHad CHan CLon CPle CSev EOrc LGre NLak SAga SAxl WCHb WHer WKif WSHC WWye
candidissima	CPle
canescens	CPle
cardinalis	See *S. fulgens*
carduacea	CPle
castanea	CPle
chamaedryoides	CCan CPle LHil WWye
– silver	CSpe LGre LHil
chapalensis	CPle SAga
chiapensis	CPle
chinensis	See *S. japonica*
cinnabarina	CPle CStr
¶ *cleistogama*	CStr
clevelandii	CPle SPil
¶ *coahuilensis*	SDys
coccinea	CBot CGle CMdw CPle EBar GBri MSte NBus SHFr WCHb WPen WPer WWye
* – 'Cherry Blossom'	SWat
– 'Coral Nymph'	CPle LIck SDys SLod SSoC WPen
– 'Indigo'	EGar ELan GBri
– 'Lactea'	CBot CPle
– 'Lady in Red' ♀	GBri LIck SMrm SWat
– pink	CPle
* – 'Snow Nymph'	LIck
columbariae	CPle
compacta	CPle
concolor hort.	See *S. guaranitica*
– Lamb.	CPle GCal LHil
confertiflora	CAbb CHal CPle CSev CWit ELan EOrc GBri GCal LHil LHop MLLN MSte SAga SBid SDys SLod SMrm WCHb WFar WOMN WWye
corrugata	CPle EPri LHil SDys
¶ *cryptantha*	CStr
cyanescens	CPle EPot

darcyi	CHan CKel CPle LGre LHop SIgm WPen WWye
davidsonii	CPle
'Dear Anja'	EFou LGre
deserta	See *S.* × *sylvestris*
digitaloides	CPle GBin
discolor ♀	CBot CDec CHad CPle CSam CSev CSpe CStr EBar ELan ERav ERea GQui LBlm LHil LHop MBEx MLLN MTho MWat SRCN SSoC WCHb WWye
* – *nigra*	CMdw
disermas	CPle CStr
divinorum	NGno
¶ – palatable strain	NGno
dolichantha	CPle
dolomitica	CPle
dombeyi	CPle
dominica	CPle
dorisiana	CArn CPle CSev ELan LBlm MSte WJek
eigii	CPle
§ *elegans*	CCan CPle CSev ELau EPri EWes LBlm MSCN MSte SBid SCro SIde WCer WMaN WOld
§ – 'Scarlet Pineapple'	CArn CBot CCan CFee CHal CInt CPle CSev EHol ELan ELau ERea GPoy LHol LHop MChe MMal SAga SIde SLMG SMac SMer SOWG SRCN WEas WHen WOak WPer WWye
* – 'Tangerine Sage'	CArn SPil WOak
fallax	CPle
farinacea 'Alba'	LBlm LGre
– 'Rhea'	LIck
– 'Silver'	CPle
– 'Strata'	CPle EHic
– 'Victoria' ♀	CPle ELau LBlm LPVe MWgw
forreri CD&R 1269	CPle
forsskaolii	CArn CGle CHal CHan CLTr CLyd CPle CSev ECro ECtt ELan LFis LLWP MBro MFir MNrw NHol NSti SAxl SChu WEas WHil WHoo WPer WWin WWye
frigida	CPle
§ *fruticosa*	CArn CHan CPle EEls ELau LHol SHFr SIde SPil
§ *fulgens* ♀	CGle CPle CSam CSev CStr CWit ERav LBlm LHil NBro NSti SBid SHFr SIde WCHb WEas WKif WWhi WWye
gesneriiflora	CAbb CPle CSev LHop MSCN MSte SBid SIde SMrm WPer WWye
glutinosa	CHad CHan CPle CSam ECha ELan GCal LHol MBel MNrw NBro NCat NChi NHex NSti SAga WPer WWye
– HH&K 294	CHan
grahamii	See *S. microphylla* var. *microphylla*
◆ *grandiflora* Etl. HH&K 210	See *S. tomentosa* Etl. HH&K 210
greggii	CFai CHan CPle EWes LHil MBEx MSCN MSte SAga SPer SWat WHil WOve WPer WWin WWye
– 'Alba'	CHal CPle LHop SBid WWye
– 'Blush Pink'	See *S. microphylla* 'Pink Blush'
– CD&R 1148	LHop SDys
– 'Keter's Red'	CPle
§ – × *lycioides*	CMdw CPle CSev LHil LHop SAga SBid SUsu WSHC
– 'Peach' ♀	CPle CSpe EWes MBEx MLLN MSCN NBrk SAga SAxl WAbe WFoF WPnn WWye
– 'Peach' misapplied	See *S.* × *jamensis* 'Pat Vlasto'
– 'Raspberry Royal'	See *S.* 'Raspberry Royale'
¶ – 'Sungold'	CPle
– yellow	LRHS
§ *guaranitica* ♀	CAbb CBot CGle CPle CSpe EBrP EBre ELan GCal LBre MRav SAga SBre SPer SRCN SUsu WCHb WEas WSan
– 'Argentine Skies'	CLon CPle LHil LHop SDys WWye
§ – 'Black and Blue'	CCan CGle CLTr CPle CSWP CSev CWit EPPr LBlm MSte MWat SSoC SVen WPer WPnn WWye
§ – 'Blue Enigma' ♀	CArn CBot CCan CHea CLon CSev ECha EFou EGar EMan EPPr GBri LHil LHop MBel SDix SDys SUsu WEas WHow WPen WWye
haematodes	See *S. pratensis* Haematodes Group
heldreichiana	CPle
hians	CFir CGle CHal CHan CHea CPle ECoo EMan EMar GBar GBri GCra MBro MNrw NLak NSti NWoo SBla SRms WCer WHoo WOve WPer WPyg WWye
hierosolymitana	CChr CPle SHFr SUsu
hirtella	CPle
hispanica	CPle
– hort.	See *S. lavandulifolia*
horminoides	CKin NMir WCla WWye
horminum	See *S. viridis*
hypargeia	CPle
indica	SRms
'Indigo Spires' ♀	CBrd CHan CLon CMdw ECha EPPr GBri LBlm LHil MLLN SAga SBid SMrm SUsu WKif WPen WWye
interrupta	CPle ECha EHal EHol EOHP EWes GBar LFis LHil SAga SChu SDix WCHb WEas WPen
involucrata ♀	CFir CHan CPle CSev EOrc GCal GQui LHil LHol NBro SBid SCro SMrm SRCN WEas WSHC
– 'Bethellii'	CArn CBot CCan CFee CGle CHal CPle CSev CWit EBar ELan EMil EPri GBri GCal LBlm LHop MBEx MWat SAga SBid SCro WEas WOMN WOld WPer WSHC WWye
– 'Boutin' ♀	CCan CPle ERav LBlm WEas GCal MSte
– dark form	GCal MSte
§ – 'Hadspen'	CBot CCan CHad CSam CStr MAvo
– 'Mrs Pope'	See *S. involucrata* 'Hadspen'
¶ – var. *puberula*	CHan CPle
¶ – – 'El Butano'	CPle
iodantha	CPle WWye
¶ × *jamensis* 'Cherry Queen'	CPle CStr
– 'Devantville'	CPle LHil SBid SLod
– 'El Duranzo'	CPle LGre

– 'Fuego'	CPle
– 'James Compton'	LHil MSte SAxl SBid SHFr SIgm
– 'La Luna'	CHan CLon CPle CSev EPPr EPri LGre LHil LHop MBEx MSCN MSte SLod SSoC SUsu WPen WPnn WWye
– 'La Siesta'	CPle CSev SAga WPnn
– 'La Tarde'	·CLon CPle MBEx MSte SAga
– 'Los Lirios' ♀	CHan CPle EPPr SLod SMrm SSoC SUsu
¶ – 'Moonlight Serenade'	CPle CStr
§ – 'Pat Vlasto'	CLon CPle GBri LGre MSte SAga SBid SMrm WEas WPen WWye
§ japonica	CPle WWye
judaica	CPle EBee MLLN
jurisicii	CFir CPle EBee EMan EWll MBro MLLN SBid SHFr SIgm SMrm SSca WHoo WPyg
karwinskyi	CPle
keerlii	CPle
koyamae	CPle
lanceolata	See S. reflexa
§ lavandulifolia	CArn CMHG CPle ECha EFou ELan ELau EMon EPri EWes NSti SAxl SIde SPan SPla SUsu WAbe WCHb WHer WLin WOak WPen WPer WWat WWye
lemmonii	See S. microphylla var. wislizenii
leptophylla	See S. reptans
leucantha ♀	CB&S CCan CHal CPle CSam CSev CSpe EBar ELan EPri ERea LHil LHop MBEx MLLN MSte SAxl SBid SCro SDys SHFr SIde SLMG SOWG SPer SRCN WEas WOMN WPer WWye
– 'Purple Velvet'	CPle
leucophylla	CPle EBee SIgm
longispicata	CPle WWye
¶ lycioides A. Gray	CPle
– hort.	See S. greggii x lycioides
lyrata	CPle EOHP MSal SHFr SPil SSca SUsu WWye
¶ macellaria	EBee
¶ – yellow form	EBee
madrensis	CPle
mellifera	CArn CPle LHop WWye
* meryama 'Mint-sauce'	CPla
mexicana	CPle GBri LBlm LHil WEas
– var. minor	CCan CPle LHop WPer
– T&K 550	CBot
microphylla	CArn CGle CLTr CMHG CPle CWit ELau EWes GBar LBay MAll MChe MSCN NFai SHFr SLMG SOkh WCru WHCG WPer
– 'Cerro Potosi'	CHan CLon CSev SHFr
* – 'Huntingdon Red'	ELau EOHP
¶ – 'Kew Red' ♀	CPle CStr
– 'La Foux'	CHea LGre NLak SMrm
– 'Maraschino'	WHil
§ – var. microphylla	Widely available
– – 'Newby Hall' ♀	CLon CPle LHil MBEx MBel WPer
– var. neurepia	See S. microphylla var. microphylla
– 'Oxford'	CPle

§ – 'Pink Blush' ♀	CAbP CBot CPle ELan EMan EPri LHil LHop MLLN MMil MSte SAga SSpi WOve WPen WSHC
¶ – 'Pleasant View' ♀	CPle
– purple form	GCal
* – 'Raspberry Ice'	LRHS
§ – 'Ruth Stungo' (v)	CPle SAga
– 'Variegata' splashed	See S. microphylla 'Ruth Stungo'
§ – var. wislizenii	CLyd CPle SCro WPer
microstegia	CPle
miniata	CPle
moelleri	MSCN WHal
moorcroftiana	CPle EBee NLak WOve WPer
§ multicaulis ♀	CHan CPle ECha EMan GCal MSCN NLak NTow SOkh SUsu WCHb WOld WPer WSHC
nemorosa	CHan MTPN SHFr WShe
– 'Amethyst' ♀	CHal CLon CPle EFou LGre MBel MBri MLLN SChu SHBN SHel SMrm SWas WCot
– East Friesland	See S. nemorosa 'Ostfriesland'
– HH&K 246	CHan
– 'Lubecca' ♀	CPle EBee EFou MLLN MMil NCat SMrm SOkh SPer WLRN WRus
§ – 'Ostfriesland' ♀	Widely available
– 'Plumosa' ♀	CHad ECha EMan LGre LRHS MCLN MLLN SCro SUsu WCot
– 'Rosenwein'	GBuc LGre
§ – subsp. tesquicola	CHan CMdw ECha
– 'Wesuwe'	CPle ECha
neurepia	See S. microphylla var. microphylla
nilotica	CPle EBee MSto SHFr WHer
nipponica	CPle WPer
* – 'Fuji Snow' (v)	WCot
nubicola	CHea CPle CStr EHic GPoy SLod WWye
nutans	CPle
officinalis	CArn CChe CHal ELau GBar GPoy MBal MBar MBri MChe MGos MWat NNor NPri SHBN SHFr SRCN WByw WDin WGwG WMow WOak WPer WWat WWye
– 'Alba'	See S. officinalis 'Albiflora'
§ – 'Albiflora'	CBot CPle ECha EFou ELan EOHP GBar LHol LLWP MLLN SIde WJek WPer
N– 'Aurea'	CPle EPar GPoy MBar MFir NFla NPri SUsu
– 'Berggarten'	EFou EGar EGoo EMon EPPr EPri GBar GCal LGre LHol WHer WLin
I – 'Blackcurrant'	NPri
§ – broad-leaved	CBot CJew CSWP EJud ELau MGra MLLN MMal NSti SIde SWat WJek WWye
¶ – 'Cedric'	MWgw
* – extrakta	EOHP
* – 'Giant'	MGra SPil
I – 'Ginger'	SPil
– 'Grandiflora'	CPle
– 'Grete Stolze'	EFou
– 'Herrenhausen'	CPle MSte WPen
§ – 'Icterina' (v) ♀	Widely available
– 'Kew Gold' ♀	EGar EMon GBar LHop MRav WJek
– latifolia	See S. officinalis broad-leaved
¶ – 'Minor'	EGoo WHer

* – 'Minor Alba'	WHil
– narrow-leaved	See *S. lavandulifolia*
– *prostrata* ♀	EOHP MGra
– Purpurascens Group ♀	Widely available
– 'Purpurascens Variegata'	GBar NSti WEas WJek
– 'Robin Hill'	CBod GBar
– 'Rosea'	CPle EGoo GBar SUsu
– 'Selsley Splash'	WSel
* – tangerine	NPri
– Tomentosa Group	CArn
– 'Tricolor' (v) ♀	Widely available
– 'Variegata'	See *S. officinalis* **'Icterina'**
oppositiflora ♀	CPle MLLN SAga
pachyphylla	SIgm WLin
patens ♀	CB&S CCan CHad CPle CSam
	CSev ELan EOrc EPri LHil
	LHol LHop NChi NFai NOrc
	NSti NWes SAga SBla SOWG
	WCHb WEas WOMN WOld
	WPer WRus WWin WWye
– 'Alba' misapplied	See *S. patens* **'White Trophy'**
– 'Cambridge Blue' ♀	CBot CHad CPle CRDP CSam
	CSev CSpe ECha ELan LBlm
	LHil LHol LHop MRav MWat
	NPer SAga SBla SCro SRCN
	WEas WMaN WOMN WOld
	WPer WPnn WWye
– 'Chilcombe'	CHan CPle CSpe CStr EBar
	EMan LBlm LHil LHop MBel
	SAga SChu SCro SDys SHFr
	SMrm SUsu WPen WPer WPnn
	WWye
– 'Guanajuato'	CPle CSam LGre LHil LHop
	SBid SCro SMad SMrm
– 'Lavender Lady'	CSam EWes MSCN WMaN
– 'Royal Blue'	ECha EGle
§ – 'White Trophy'	CBot CLon CPle ELan EOrc
	EPri LBlm LHil LHop MAvo
	NCut SBid SCro SLod SMad
	SUsu WRus WWye
penstemonoides	CPle
polystachya	CPle WWye
pratensis	CArn CKin CLon CPle EJud
	ELan GBar MHew MSal NChi
	SHFr WHil WOve WPer WWye
¶ – 'Albiflora'	EMon
§ – Bertolonii Group	CHan CPle EBee
§ – Haematodes Group ♀	CHad CPle EBrP EBre ECha
	ELan LBre MBel MBro MNrw
	NBro NBus SBre SHFr SRms
	WBea WHoo WOld WOve
	WPer WPyg WRus WWye
– 'Indigo' ♀	EBrP EBre EFou EWll LBre
	MRav SBre
– 'Lapis Lazuli'	CPle LGre WPGP
– 'Rosea'	CPle
– 'Tenorei'	WPer
przewalskii	CPle EBee ECro EGar MNrw
	MSal NChi SHFr WPer WWye
– ACE 1157	CPle
– CLD 247	CPle
♦ *puberula*	See *S. involucrata* var. *puberula*
pulchella	CPle
'Purple Majesty'	CLon CPle EFou WWye
purpurea	CPle EFou
§ 'Raspberry Royale' ♀	CHan CLon CPle ELan EPri
	EWoo LHil LHop MBel SAga
	SAxl SMrm SWat WPen WRus
	WWhi WWye
recognita	CBot CPle CStr GCal LGre
	MSto NChi
§ *reflexa*	CPle
♦ *regeliana* hort.	See *S. virgata* Jacq.
– Trautv.	CHar CPle EGar LFis MLLN
	NBir NChi NTow SSca WPer
	WRha
regla	CPle
repens	CPle WWye
§ *reptans*	CCan CPle CSam CSpe LHop
	SAga SLod WPer
ringens	CPle GCHN
§ *riparia*	CPle MLLN
roborowskii	CPle
roemeriana ♀	CPle EHic NWCA SSca WCru
	WOMN
rutilans	See *S. elegans* **'Scarlet Pineapple'**
scabiosifolia	EBee EHal MSto
scabra	CFir CPle MSto
sclarea	CArn CGle CPle EGoo EJud
	ELau GPoy LFis LHol MChe
	MHew MWat NChi NFai SIde
	SRCN WBea WCHb WHer
	WHoo WOak WPer WWye
* – 'Alba'	CPle
N – var. *turkestanica* hort.	CArn CB&S CHad CHan
	CMCo CPle CSam CSev EBar
	EBot EFou ELan EMon EOrc
	GMaP LHil LHop MFir NSti
	SHFr SMrm SPer SRms SSpi
	SUsu WByw WEas WHal WHil
	WPer
§ – 'Vatican White'	EMar
scutellarioides	CPle
♦ *semiatrata* hort.	See *S. chamaedryoides*
– Zucc.	CPle LHil MWat
sinaloensis	CPle MSte SAga SIgm
somalensis	CPle
sonomensis	CPle WWye
souliei	See *S. brevilabra*
sp. CC&McK 77	GTou
sp. Iran	WOMN
spathacea ♀	CPle GBar SIgm
spinosa	CPle
splendens	MSto
sprucei	CPle
squalens	CPle
§ *staminea*	CPle MNrw SSca
stenophylla	CPle EBee LFis WGwG WPer
stepposa	CPle EBee
x *superba* ♀	CBot CGle CHad CPle EBrP
	EBre ELan EOrc LBre LHil
	MBri MBro MWat NRoo SAxl
	SBre SCro SDix SMrm SRCN
	SRms SSvw WHoo WWhi
	WWye
– 'Adrian'	EFou SChu
– 'Forncett Dawn'	EFou SChu
– 'Rubin' ♀	CStr EFou SChu
– 'Superba'	CSev ECha EFou LGre MRav
x *sylvestris* 'Blauhügel' ♀	CLon CMGP CPle CSev EBrP
	EBre ECGN ECha EFou ELan
	EPPr EPar GCal LBre LGre
	MArl MBri MLLN MSte MTis
	MWat MWgw NRoo SBre SChu
	SMrm SUsu WPer
§ – 'Blaukönigin'	CGle EBrP EBre ECro EPPr
	GBri GCHN LBre LFis LWak
	MBro MWat NCat NMir NOak
	NRoo SBre SIgm SPar WBea
	WHoo WPer WPyg
– Blue Queen	See *S. x sylvestris* **'Blaukönigin'**
– 'Lye End'	CBos ECtt GCal LHop MRav
§ – 'Mainacht' ♀	Widely available

– May Night	See *S.* x *sylvestris* **'Mainacht'**
– 'Rose Queen'	Widely available
– 'Rügen'	LRHS NLak WRus
¶ – 'Schneehügel'	EBee EMan EPPr EPfP LBuc SCro SHel WLRN WMer
– 'Tänzerin' ♀	EFou LGre MBel SChu SMrm WLRN
– 'Viola Klose'	EFou LRHS MBri SUsu
– 'Wissalink'	SMad
tachiei	EBee MRav
taraxacifolia	CPle NWoo WWye
tarayensis	CPle
tesquicola	See *S. nemorosa* subsp. *tesquicola*
tiliifolia	CPle EBee SRms
tingitana	CPle
tomentosa	CPle SAga
§ – Etl. HH&K 210	CHan
transcaucasica	See *S. staminea*
transsylvanica	CArn CChr CHea CPle CSam EBee EMan EWll MAus NChi NLak SWat WHil WOld WPer
trijuga	CPle
triloba	See *S. fruticosa*
uliginosa ♀	Widely available
¶ – 'African Skies'	NBrk
urica	CPle
'Van-Houttei' ♀	CPle
♦ 'Vatican City'	See *S. sclarea* **'Vatican White'**
verbenaca	CPle EGar EWFC GCHN MHew MNrw MSal SPil WPer
– pink	CPle
verticillata	CArn CLTr CPle CStr EBar ECha ELan EOld EPri LHol MHew NNor NSti SDys SHFr WHoo WOve WPer WWhi WWye
– 'Alba'	CLTr CMGP CMea CPle CSev ECGN ECha EMon EPfP MAus MBel MGed NSti SBid SIde WHer WPer
– subsp. *amasiaca*	CPle
– HH&K 267	CHan
– 'Purple Rain'	Widely available
villicaulis	See *S. amplexicaulis*
virgata Jacq.	CPle LCot MNrw WHoo WPer
§ *viridis*	CArn CPle LHol LHop MChe MGra SIde SPil
– var. *alba*	CPle
¶ *viscosa*	WWye
– Jacquin	CPle
– Sesse & Moc.	See *S. riparia*
wagneriana	CPle
xalapensis	CPle

SALVINIA (Salviniaceae)

braziliensis	MSta

SAMBUCUS † (Caprifoliaceae)

¶ *adnata* B&SWJ 2252	WCru
– L 864	CPle
¶ *alba* 'Variegata'	WLRN
caerulea	EPla
canadensis 'Adams' (F)	ESim
– 'Aurea'	IOrc MBar NWea WHar
– 'Maxima'	CHEx EPfP GCal SBid SMad SMrm
– 'York' (F)	ESim
coraensis	See *S. sieboldiana* var. *coreana*
ebulus	CKin CRow
formosana B&SWJ 1543	WCru
¶ *javanica* B&SWJ 4047	WCru

nigra	CKin CPer ENot GChr GPoy GRei LBuc MBri NNor NWea SIde WMou WSel
– 'Albomarginata'	See *S. nigra* **'Marginata'**
– 'Albovariegata'	MGra WWeb
* – 'Ardwall'	GCal
N – 'Aurea' ♀	CB&S CInt CLnd CMHG CRow ELan EMon ENot EPla ERav GRei LHol MBar NFla NWea SPer WDin WSel
– 'Aureomarginata'	CInt CSam EBee ELan EPla GAri MBal MRav NNor NSti SHBN WCFE WFar
– 'Cae Rhos Lligwy'	WAlt WHer
¶ – 'Cannop'	WAlt
– 'Castledean'	EHal SMad WAlt WCot
¶ – 'Cool Head'	WAlt
– 'Din Dryfol' (v)	CNat
– 'Flex' (v)	CNat
* – 'Frances'	CNat WCot
– 'Greener Later' (v)	CNat
§ – 'Guincho Purple' ♀	Widely available
– 'Heterophylla'	See *S. nigra* **'Linearis'**
– f. *laciniata* ♀	CB&S CMHG CRow CSam ELan EMon EPla ERav LHol MBal MLLN NNor NRoo NSti SChu SDix SEas SMad SPer SSpi SSta WCot WSHC
§ – 'Linearis'	CPMA CPle EHal EHic ELan EPla MUlv SMad SPer WAbe WWat
¶ – 'Long Tooth'	CNat
– 'Madonna' (v)	CMHG CPMA EPla MGos NHol SAxl SEas SMad SPer WCot
§ – 'Marginata'	CMHG CRow EHoe ELan GChr GRei IOrc MBar MBri MGos MLLN MRav MUlv NRoo SDix SMad SPer WAbe WDin WHar WSHC WWat WWin
¶ – 'Nana'	EMon
– 'Pendula'	EPla ERav
– 'Plena' (d)	EMon EPla MInt WCot
– 'Pulverulenta' (v)	CBrd CDoC CHan CRow EBrP EBre ELan EPar EPla GCal LBre LHop MLLN NSti SAxl SBre SEas SPer WCot WSHC
¶ – 'Purple Pete'	CNat
– 'Purpurea'	See *S. nigra* **'Guincho Purple'**
– 'Pyramidalis'	CPMA EMon EPla MHlr SMad WCot
* – 'Thundercloud'	MBri NPro WPat
– 'Variegata'	See *S. nigra* **'Marginata'**
– 'Witches Broom'	EMon
racemosa	CAgr EPfP GRei NWea WRha
– 'Aurea'	EHoe GRei
– 'Goldenlocks'	EHal LHop MGos NHol NPro SPer WPyg
– 'Moerheimii'	EPla
– 'Plumosa Aurea'	CB&S CBot CMHG CRow CTrw EBrP EBre ELan ENot GOrc LBre LHop MBal MBri NBee NNor NWea SBre SDix SEas SHBN SMad SPer SRCN SReu SSpi SSta WDin WHCG WWin
§ – var. *sieboldiana*	CHan CPle EMon

– 'Sutherland Gold' ♀	CB&S CBot CHad CSam EAst EBrP EBre ELan ENot EPla IOrc LBre LNet MBar MBlu MGos MWat NBee NHol SBre SHBN SReu SSpi SSta WAbe WDin WHCG WPat WSHC WWat
– 'Tenuifolia' ♀	CPMA CSWP CWSG EHal ELan GSki MBro MGos MPla MUlv SMad SPer SSpi WCru WHCG WPat WPyg WWat
♦ sieboldiana	See S. racemosa var. sieboldiana
§ – var. coreana	EPla
tigrina	WWat
wightiana	See S. javanica

SAMOLUS (Primulaceae)

repens	ECou

SANCHEZIA (Acanthaceae)

nobilis hort.	See S. speciosa
§ speciosa	CHal

SANDERSONIA (Colchicaceae)

aurantiaca	CMon LAma LBow NRog

SANGUINARIA (Papaveraceae)

canadensis	CArn CBro CGle CSpe ECha EPot ERos GPoy IBlr LAma LHop LSyl MSte NRog NRya SMad SPer WAbe WCru WWat WWin
– f. multiplex (d)	CLAP CRDP EPot NEgg
– pink	SWas WThi
– 'Plena' (d) ♀	CBrd CBro CLyd CMea CRDP EHyt EMon EPar EPot GCLN LAma MBri MFos MHig MTho NHar NHol NMen NRya NWoo SBla SIgm SSpi SWas WAbe WEas WLin WSan
¶ 'Peter Harrison'	LGre

SANGUISORBA (Rosaceae)

§ albiflora	CBlo CRow EBee EBrP EBre ECro EFou ELan GAri GBuc LBre MCLN MRav NPro NRoo SBre WCot WFar WWin
armena	SSvw
benthamiana	CHEx
canadensis	CHan CRow ECha EGar EHic GAbr GCal GPoy MFir NHex SPer WCot WFar WOld WWye
* caucasica	EBee
hakusanensis	MNrw NBir NBro WWhi
magnifica alba	See S. albiflora
menziesii	EFou WCot WPGP
§ minor	CArn CKin EEls ELau EWFC GPoy LHol MBar MChe MHew NBro NMir SIde WCHb WCla WHer WOak WPer WWye WGwG WPbr
¶ – subsp. muricata	
¶ – – HH&K 289	CHan
obtusa	CHan CHea CInt CRow EBee ECha ECro EFou ELan EPar GBuc GCal LFis LHil LHol MCLN MLLN MRav MTis NBro NFla NHex NHol NRoo NSti SChu SPer SSoC WEas
– var. albiflora	See S. albiflora

SANICULA (Apiaceae)

elata B&SWJ 2250	WCru
europaea	CKin EWFC GBar GPoy MSal WHer

SANIELLA (Hypoxidaceae)

verna	ERos MHig NMen

SANSEVIERIA † (Dracaenaceae)

trifasciata 'Golden Hahnii' (v) ♀	MBri
– 'Laurentii' (v) ♀	MBri

SANTOLINA † (Asteraceae)

§ chamaecyparissus ♀	Widely available
– var. corsica	See S. chamaecyparissus var. nana
¶ – 'Double Lemon'	LFis SPla
– 'Lambrook Silver'	EBee ECtt EOHP EPPr ESis GAbr LFis NHol SAga SCoo SEas SPan SPla SSvw
– 'Lemon Queen'	CArn CDoC EAst EGoo ELau ESis GBar GOrc MBal MBel MGos NBir NFla NSti SAga SEas SIde SPla SWat WCHb WFar WOak WPer
¶ – subsp. magonica	MAll
§ – var. nana ♀	CB&S CLyd ECha ENot LHop MBar MDun NFai NNor SHFr SPer SRms SWat WAbe WPer WWye
– nana 'Weston'	CLyd EWes GBar
– 'Pretty Carol'	CABp EBrP EBre ELan EMil ESis GOrc LBre LHop MAsh NBrk NFai SAga SBre SEas SIde SPan WWeb
– 'Small-Ness'	CSWP EBrP EBre EDAr EGoo EPPr ESis EWes GCLN LBre LHop MAsh MBlu MBri MBro MSte NHol SBre SIng SMad WAbe WFar WPat WPyg
dentata	MGra
incana	See S. chamaecyparissus
'Oldfield Hybrid'	MBel MLan WCot
pectinata	See S. rosmarinifolia subsp. canescens
§ pinnata	CArn CSev CTri LHol WPer
§ – subsp. neapolitana ♀	CArn CMHG CSev ECha ELan ENot LHol LHop MAll MBri MCLN NNor NSti SDix SIde SSvw WEas WHCG WOak WWye
– – cream	See S. pinnata subsp. neapolitana 'Edward Bowles'

officinalis	CArn CChr CInt ECGN EPfP EWFC GBar MAus MBel NMir SSca SWat WCla WWin WWye
¶ – 'Arnhem'	LGre
– 'Tanna'	EMon EPPr GCal SLod SMrm WAlt WCot WMaN WPbr
pimpinella	See S. minor
sitchensis	See S. stipulata
§ stipulata	ECGN GCal IBlr
tenuifolia	EBee WGwy WWhi
– 'Alba'	CBlo ECha GBuc WCot
– 'Purpurea'	WCot

§ – – 'Edward Bowles'   CGle CLyd CMil EBar EFou
EJud ELan EMil ESis GCal
GOrc LHil LHop MCLN MRav
MWgw NBir NHol NPer NSti
SAga SAxl SChu SSvw WAbe
WBea WHen WHer WSHC

– – 'Sulphurea'   CMea EGoo EPfP LGre MBel
MBlu SPer WKif WPer WTro
WWhi

rosmarinifolia   CMil ELau ESis GChr LFlo
MBel MWhi SPan SRms WCHb
WRha WSel WWye

§ – subsp. *canescens*   LHol NCut WPer WWye

§ – subsp. *rosmarinifolia*   CChe CMHG CSev ECha EGoo
ELan ENot EOHP GCHN LHol
MAll MBri MCLN NFai NSti
SDix SSvw WCHb WEas WHoo
WSHC WTro WWin WWye

– – 'Primrose Gem' ♀   CB&S CSam ECha ELau EMil
ESis LHop MBal MCLN MPla
NSti SAxl SBod SEas SPer SPla
WPer WWal WWye

tomentosa   See *S. pinnata* subsp.
neapolitana

virens   See *S. rosmarinifolia* subsp.
rosmarinifolia

viridis   See *S. rosmarinifolia* subsp.
rosmarinifolia

SAPINDUS   (Sapindaceae) See Plant Deletions

SAPIUM   (Euphorbiaceae) See Plant Deletions

SAPONARIA   (Caryophyllaceae)

'Bressingham' ♀   CMea CPBP EBrP EBre ECha
EPot LBee LBre MTho NHar
NHol SBla SBre WPat WPyg
WWin

caespitosa   EPot EWes GTou MHig NMen
NNrd SIng WAbe WOMN

× *lempergii* 'Max Frei'   ECro GAbr GBuc SBla SDix
WCot

* 'Lilac Double'   MRav

lutea   NWCA WGor

ocymoides ♀   CB&S CLTr ECha ECtt EHon
ELan ELau EMNN ENot ESis
GAbr GBur GCHN GTou LGro
MPEx MWgw NFla NRoo NVic
SIng SRms WBea WHoo WOve
WPer WStI WWin

– 'Alba'   ECha WFar

– 'Rubra Compacta' ♀   MTho WPyg

officinalis   CAgr CArn CBre CKin CRow
EJud ELau EWFC GAbr GPoy
LHol MChe MHew MSal NFai
SIde SSea WGwG WHer WOak
WPer WWal WWye

– 'Alba Plena' (d)   CGle CJew CMil CRDP CSam
ECha ECoo ECro EJud EMon
GBar NBrk NSti WCHb WElm
WHer WPer WRha WWin

§ – 'Dazzler' (v)   ELau EMon LBlm LHol MRav
MTho NBir NBrk NFai NRoo
WBea WCHb WCot WHer
WPbr

– 'Rosea Plena' (d)   CBre CFee CHan CMHG CMil
CRDP CRow CSam ECoo ECro
EEls EJud ELan EMon GMac
LLWP MBel MBri MCLN NCat
NChi NFla NOrc SMrm SPer
WCHb WCot WOve WPbr
WPer

– 'Rubra Plena' (d)   CGle CHad CMHG CMil
CRDP ECha ELan EMon LBlm
LFis MCLN NSti WCHb WPbr
WRha

– 'Variegata'   See *S. officinalis* **'Dazzler'**

× *olivana* ♀   CLyd CMea ECha EPot ESis
LFis MHig MPla MTho NHol
NMen SBla SBod WOMN WPat
WPyg WWin

pamphylica   EBee MNrw

pulvinaris   See *S. pumilio*

§ *pumilio*   CLyd GCHN GTou NWCA

'Rosenteppich'   ESis SWas WLin WPat WPyg

sicula   WMow

zawadskii   See *Silene zawadskii*

SARCOCAPNOS   (Papaveraceae)

baetica   NWCA

SARCOCOCCA †   (Buxaceae)

confusa ♀   Widely available

hookeriana ♀   CBlo CTrG ECot EPfP GSki
IOrc WOMN

– B&SWJ 2585   WCru

– var. *digyna* ♀   Widely available

– – 'Purple Stem'   EHol EPla ERav MGos MRav
WDin

– var. *humilis*   Widely available

– Sch 2396   EPla

orientalis   CFil CMCN CPMA EPfP EPla
MAsh MGos SMac SSpi WWat
WWeb

'Roy Lancaster'   See *S. ruscifolia* **'Dragon Gate'**

ruscifolia   CB&S CDoC CMCN CPMA
CPle CWSG ELan ENot EPla
IHos IOrc LFis LHop MBel
MGos MPla MTis SPer SSpi
WPGP WWat

– var. *chinensis* ♀   CFil CSam EPfP EPla NHol
SBid SSta WCru

– – L 713   EPla

§ – 'Dragon Gate'   CFil EPla MAsh

saligna   CB&S CFil CPMA EPla WBod
WCru WPGP

SARCOPOTERIUM   (Rosaceae) See Plant Deletions

SARMIENTA   (Gesneriaceae)

repens ♀   WAbe WCru

SARRACENIA †   (Sarraceniaceae)

× *ahlsii* (*rubra* × *alata*   WMEx
'Red Lid')

alata   GTro WMEx

¶ – 'Citronelle'   WMEx

– copper lid   GTro

– × *flava* 'Maxima'   WMEx

¶ – 'Nicolson'   WMEx

¶ – pubescent form   WMEx

– purple lid   GTro

– 'Red Lid'   MHel

– 'Red Lid' × *flava*   WMEx
red pitcher

– red × *purpurea* subsp.   WMEx
venosa

– × *willisii*   WMEx

× *areolata*   GTro WMEx

× *catesbyi* ♀   CFil GTro MHel WMEx

– × *excellens*   WMEx

× *chelsonii* ♀   WMEx

× *courtii*	MHel
× *excellens* ♀	GTro MHel WMEx
× *exornata*	WMEx
× *farnhamii*	See *S.* × *readii* 'Farnhamii'
flava ♀	CFil CRDP EAnd GTro MHel
	WMEx WPGP
¶ – all green giant	WMEx
– 'Burgundy'	GTro WMEx
– copper lid	GTro
– 'Maxima'	WMEx WNor
– 'Maxima' × *purpurea*	MHel
subsp. *venosa*	
– 'Maxima' × *rubra* subsp.	MHel
jonesii	
¶ – var. *ornata*	WMEx
¶ – 'Prince George County'	WMEx
¶ – purple tube	WMEx
× *harperi*	WMEx
'Judy'	GTro MHel
leucophylla ♀	GTro MHel WMEx
– × *excellens*	MHel
¶ – white pitchers	WMEx
× *melanorhoda*	GTro MHel WMEx
× *miniata*	WMEx
minor	GTro MHel WMEx
– 'Okefenokee Giant'	WMEx
¶ – tall form	WMEx
× *mitchelliana* ♀	GTro MHel WMEx
× *moorei*	GTro MHel WMEx
– 'Brook's Hybrid'	GTro WMEx
oreophila	GTro WMEx
– × *leucophylla*	MHel
– × *purpurea*	MHel
× *popei*	WMEx
psittacina	EAnd GTro WMEx
purpurea	CFil
– subsp. *purpurea*	GTro MHel WMEx
– – f. *heterophylla*	WMEx
– subsp. *venosa*	GTro MHel WMEx
* – – f. *heterophylla*	MHel
– – × *oreophila*	WMEx
§ × *readii*	GTro WMEx
× *rehderi*	MHel WMEx
rubra	GTro WMEx
– subsp. *alabamensis*	WMEx
¶ – subsp. *gulfensis*	WMEx
¶ – subsp. *gulfensis*	WMEx
heterophylla	
strong green form	
– subsp. *jonesii*	MHel WMEx
× *swaniana*	GTro MHel WMEx
– × *popei*	WMEx
× *wrigleyana* ♀	GTro

SASA † (Poaceae - Bambusoideae)

borealis	See *Sasamorpha borealis*
chrysantha hort.	See *Pleioblastus chino*
disticha 'Mirrezuzume'	See *Pleioblastus pygmaeus*
	'Mirrezuzume'
glabra f. *albostriata*	See *Sasaella masamuneana* f.
	albostriata
kurilensis	EPla ISta LJus SCha SDry
	WJun
– 'Shimofuri' (v)	EPla ISta LJus SDry WJun
– short form	EPla
megalophylla 'Nobilis'	SDry
nana	See *S. veitchii* f. *minor*
nipponica	CEnd EPla SDry WJun
– 'Aureostriata'	SDry
oshidensis	EPla
§ *palmata* ♀	CB&S CHad CHan ENot GAri
	GOrc NRar

– f. *nebulosa*	CHEx EFul EOas EPla ISta
	LJus SAPC SArc SCha SDry
	WJun
– 'Warley Place' (v)	SDry
quelpaertensis	EPla GAri ISta SDry
senanensis	EPla SDry
tessellata	See *Indocalamus tessellatus*
tsuboiana	CB&S CHEx EBee EPla ISta
	SCha SDry
§ *veitchii*	CB&S CCuc CGre CHEx CWit
	EBrP EBre ECha EOld EPar
	EPla IOrc ISta LBlo LBre LJus
	LNet MBri MWhi SBre SCha
	SDry SPer WFar WHil WJun
	WWye
§ – f. *minor*	EPla

SASAELLA (Poaceae - Bambusoideae)

bitchuensis hort.	SDry
glabra	See *S. masamuneana*
§ *masamuneana*	EPla
§ – f. *albostriata* (v)	CFil COtt CPMA EBee EPPr
	EPla ISta LJus MMoz SCha
	SDry WJun
– f. *aureostriata* (v)	COtt EPla GCal LJus MAvo
	MMoz SDry
§ *ramosa*	EBee EPla GAri GBin GOrc
	ISta MBal MCCP NRya SCha
	SDry

SASSAFRAS (Lauraceae)

albidum	CArn CHEx CMCN

SASAMORPHA (Poaceae) See Plant Deletions

SATUREJA (Lamiaceae)

¶ *biflora*	CArn
§ *coerulea* ♀	EWes LFis NBir SIde WFar
hortensis	CBod GPoy ILis LHol MChe
	MHew MLan WHer WJek WSel
montana	CArn EEls EHyt ELau EWFC
	GMaP GPoy ILis LHol MBri
	MChe MPla NMen SDix SIde
	SRms WCHb WCer WHer
	WOak WPer WWye
* – *citriodora*	EOHP GPoy
– 'Coerulea'	See *S. coerulea*
§ – subsp. *illyrica*	SIgm WThi
– prostrate white	CRDP MHar
– 'Purple Mountain'	GPoy
– *subspicata*	See *S. montana* subsp. *illyrica*
parnassica	WPer WWye
repanda	See *S. spicigera*
seleriana	CInt EOHP
spicata	CLyd
§ *spicigera*	CArn CLyd CPBP EDAr ELau
	EPot LFis LHol MHig NBir
	NMen NPri NTow SIde WCHb
	WSel WWin WWye
thymbra	CArn EOHP GBar IIve SHDw
	SIde

SATYRIUM (Orchidaceae) See Plant Deletions

SAURAUIA (Actinidiaceae)

subspinosa	CHEx

SAUROMATUM (Araceae)

guttatum	See *S. venosum*
§ *venosum*	LAma MBri WCru

SAURURUS (Saururaceae)
cernuus   CBen CRow CWat EBrP EBre
EHon ELan EMFW LBre
LPBA MSta NDea SBre SRms
SWat WChe
chinensis   CRow

SAUSSUREA (Asteraceae)
auriculata HWJCM 490   WCru
¶ *ceratocarpa*   EBee
¶ – var. *depressa*   EBee

SAXEGOTHAEA (Podocarpaceae)
conspicua   CDoC CMCN ECou EPla LCon
LLin SMad WCwm

SAXIFRAGA † (Saxifragaceae)
'Aemula' (× *borisii*) (8)   CLyd WAbe
aizoides var. *atrorubens*   MBal MBro NGre
  (6)
aizoon   See *S. paniculata*
'Aladdin' (× *borisii*) (8)   NHol
'Alba' (× *apiculata*) (8)   CLyd ELan EMNN EPot GTou
LFox MBal MBro MHig NHol
NMen NRya SBla SChu SIng
SSmi WAbe WCla WHoo WPat
WWin
'Alba' (× *arco-valleyi*)   See *S.* 'Ophelia' (× *arco-valleyi*)
'Alba' (*oppositifolia*) (9)   CLyd ELan EMNN EWes GTou
MYat NGre NHar NMen WAbe
WWin
'Alba' (*sempervivum*)   See *S.* 'Zita'
'Albert Einstein' (×   NMen WAbe
  apiculata) (8)
* 'Albert Hawkins'   NBro
'Albertii' (*callosa*) (7)   CLyd GTou MHig NNrd SIng
SSmi WWin
'Albida' (*callosa*) (7)   NFla
'Aldebaran' (× *borisii*) (8)   EMNN MDHE NHar NMen
'Alfons Mucha' (8)   EPot MWat NGre WAbe
'Alpenglow' (8)   MWat NMen
alpigena (8)   EHyt NGre NSla
'Amitie' (× *gloriana*) (8)   MYat NMen
andersonii (8)   CLyd EHyt EMNN ITim MBal
MWat NGre NMen NNrd NRya
NTow WAbe
¶ *andersonii* McB 1475 (8)   NHol
× *andrewsii* (3×7)   MDHE MHig MTho SSmi
¶ × *anglica* 'Peggy   CGra
  Eastwood' (8)
angustifolia   NHar
'Anne Beddall' (×   CLyd MWat NGre WAbe
  goringiana) (8)
'Aphrodite' (*sempervivum*)   EPot
  (8)
× *apiculata*   See *S.* 'Gregor Mendel' (×
apiculata)
'Apple Blossom' (12)   GTou MOne NBro NFla WGor
'Archfield White' (*callosa*)   CNic NNrd
  (7)
§ 'Arco' (× *arco-valleyi*) (8)   CLyd EPot MWat NMen NRya
WAbe
× *arco-valleyi*   See *S.* 'Arco' (× *arco-valleyi*)
× *arendsii* (12)   WEas
§ 'Aretiastrum' (× *boydii*) (8)   EHyt EMNN EPot LFox MYat
NGre NHed NMen
aretioides (8)   GCHN NMen
'Ariel' (× *hornibrookii*) (8)   CNic LFox
'Assimilis' (× *petraschii*) (8)   CLyd MYat WAbe
'August Hayek' (×   MBro MWat NMen NNrd
  leyboldii) (8)

I 'Aureopunctata' (× *urbium*)   CMil CPri ECha EGoo ELan
  (3/v)   EMar EPla GBuc GCal GCra
LHop MBal MBro MWgw NHol
NLon NRoo SMrm SPer SRms
WFox WHen
'Backhousei' (12)   NHol
'Balcana'   See *S. paniculata* var. *orientalis*
'Baldensis'   See *S. paniculata* var. *baldensis*
'Ballawley Guardsman'   ECho EPar LFox MBal NRoo
  (12)   SIng
§ 'Beatrix Stanley' (× *anglica*)   EMNN GCLN LFox MBal
  (8)   MBro MYat NGre NHar NMen
NRya WAbe
'Becky Foster' (× *borisii*)   MWat
  (8)
'Beechcroft White'   LBee
¶ 'Berenika' (× *bertolonii*) (8)   NMen
'Bettina' (× *paulinae*) (8)   GCHN
× *biasolettoi*   See *S.* 'Phoenix' (× *biasolettoi*)
biflora (9)   NHol
'Birch Baby' (12)   SIng
'Birch Yellow'   See *S.* 'Pseudoborisii' (× *borisii*)
'Black Beauty' (12)   CMHG ECho LBee MBro
NRoo SSmi
* 'Blackhouse White' (7)   NGre
'Blütenteppich' (11)   WPer
'Bob Hawkins' (12/v)   CLyd CMHG ELan GBur
GCHN GDra LBee LFox NHar
SMer WRHF WWin
§ 'Bodensee' (× *hofmannii*)   WAbe WPat
  (8)
'Bohemia' (9)   CLyd EHyt ITim NMen SBla
WGle
'Boston Spa' (× *elisabethae*)   CLyd EMNN GCHN MBro
  (8)   MHig MYat NGre NHed NHol
NMen NNrd NRoo SChu WAbe
WPat
¶ × *boydii* 'White Cap' (8)   NHol
'Bridget' (× *edithiae*) (8)   CLyd CMea ELan ESis ITim
LFox MBal NGre NHed NMen
NRoo SSmi WAbe WWin
'Brookside' (*burseriana*) (8)   EPot NMen SIng
brunoniana   See *S. brunonis*
§ *brunonis* (2)   LFox WCru
– CC&McK 108 (2)   NWCA
bryoides (5)   GCrs GTou MHig
× *burnatii* (7)   CLyd LFox MBro MHig NHed
NMen NPro WGor
burseriana (8)   GCHN MBro WAbe WGor
WPyg
'Buttercup' (× *kayei*) (8)   CPBP EPot GTou MBro MWat
MYat NGre NHed NHol NNrd
NWCA WAbe WHoo WPat
WPyg
caesia (7)   NTow SRms
§ *callosa* (7) ♀   GCHN GTou MBro MWat
NGre NHar NHol SBla WPat
WTin
§ – var. *australis* (7)   CNic EPot ESis MBro MDHE
MHig MBro NHol NMen NNrd
– var. *bellardii*   See *S. callosa*
§ – subsp. *catalaunica* (7)   MBro
– var. *lantoscana*   See *S. callosa* var. *australis*
– *lingulata*   See *S. callosa*
'Cambria Jewel' (12)   NMen NNrd
'Cambridge Seedling' (8)   MWat MYat NMen
§ *camposii* (12)   GAbr SIng
'Camyra' (8)   MWat MYat NGre NHed NNrd
WAbe
canaliculata (12)   NNrd

× *canis-dalmatica* (7) — CLyd CMHG ECtt EGoo EMNN ESis GGar GTou LBee MBro MHig NHar NHed NHol NMen SIng WGor WPer WRHF

§ 'Carmen' (× *elisabethae*) (8) — ELan EMNN ITim MBro MHig MOne MYat NHed NMen NNrd NRya WAbe

'Carniolica' (*paniculata*) (7) — CInt CLyd LBee LFox MBar MDHE MHig NBro NMen NWCA SBla

'Castor' (× *bilekii*) (8) — MWat NHed NHol SIng WAbe

catalaunica — See *S. callosa* subsp. *catalaunica*

'Caterhamensis' (*cotyledon*) (7) — WEas

cebennensis ♀ — CLyd EPot EWes GCrs LFox NHed NMen NRya NTow SIgm SIng

– dwarf form (12) — NMen

cespitosa — NWCA

'Chambers' Pink Pride' — See *S. 'Miss Chambers'* (× *urbium*)

§ *cherlerioides* (5) — EBar ELan NRya NVic WCla WEas WWin

'Cherrytrees' (× *boydii*) (8) — CLyd MBro NMen NNrd

'Chetwynd' (*marginata*) (8) — MWat WAbe

'Chez Nous' (× *gloriana*) (8/v) — NGre NMen

'Christine' (× *anglica*) (8) — LFox MWat NMen NNrd NRya SIng

chrysospleniifolia — See *S. rotundifolia* subsp. *chrysospleniifolia*

'Clare' (× *anglica*) (8) — MDHE

'Clare Island' (12) — SIng

§ 'Clarence Elliott' (*umbrosa* var. *primuloides*) (3) ♀ — CNic ELan EWes GCal GCrs GDra MBro MHig NHol NRya NVic WCla WHoo WPat WWin

§ 'Cloth of Gold' (*exarata* subsp. *moschata*) (12) — CLyd CMea EAst ECha ELan GDra GTou LBee MBal MBar MPla MWhi MMen NRoo NRya NWCA SBla SBod SSmi WAbe WFar WRHF WWin

cochlearis (7) — CMea ESis LBee MBal MOne MWat NBro NHed NMen NNor SSmi WPer WPyg WWin

'Cockscomb' (*paniculata*) (7) — MDHE

¶ *columnaris* (8) — NSla WLin

'Compacta' (*exarata* subsp. *moschata*) (12) — MBro

corbariensis — See *S. fragilis*

'Corona' (× *boydii*) (8) — LFox MDHE MWat NGre NHol NMen

* 'Corrennie Claret' — GTou

'Correvoniana' (*paniculata*) (7) — EBrP EBre ECtt ESis GCHN LBre MBro MOne NBus NBre NNrd NRya SBre WGor WRHF WWin

'Corrie Fee' (*oppositifolia*) (9) — GCrs GTou NHar NHol

corsica subsp. *cossoniana* (11) — WOMN

§ *cortusifolia* (4) — CHEx MBal NHar SSpi WAbe

– var. *fortunei* — See *S. fortunei*

§ *corymbosa* (8) — NGre

cotyledon (7) — CLyd GBur GDra LBee NHol NNor WCla WEas WPer

§ 'Cranbourne' (× *anglica*) (8) ♀ — CLyd EBrP EBre EHyt EMNN EPot LBre LFox MBro MWat MYat NGre NHar NHol NMen SBla SBre SSmi WAbe WPat

'Cream' (*paniculata*) (7) — SSmi

'Cream Seedling' (*elisabethae*) × (8) — EBrP EBre ESis LBre MDHE MWat NGre NHed NMen SBre

'Crenata' (*burseriana*) (8) — CGra CLyd CNic EPot GCHN LFox MBro MFos MWat MYat NGre NHar NHed NMen NNrd WAbe WHoo

'Crimson Rose' (*paniculata*) — NNrd

§ *crustata* (7) — EHyt GCHN MDHE NWCA SIng

– var. *vochinensis* — See *S. crustata*

'Crystalie' (× *biasolettoi*) (8) — EPot MBro MDHE NGre NMen WAbe WPat

'Cultrata' (*paniculata*) (7) — NBro

'Cumulus' (*iranica* hybrid) (8) ♀ — EHyt WAbe

cuneata (12) — NHol

cuneifolia (3) — CHEx CLyd EAst GDra GGar LBee MBal MWat NFla NGre NHed NRoo NSti NWCA SSmi

– var. *capillipes* — See *S. cuneifolia* subsp. *cuneifolia*

§ – subsp. *cuneifolia* (3) — SGre

– var. *subintegra* (3) — ECho

cuscutiformis (4) — CInt GCal MHlr MRav NTow WCot WCru WOve

cymbalaria (13) — CInt EBur WCla

– var. *huetiana* (13) — CNic

'Dainty Dame' (× *arco-valleyi*) (8) — CLyd LFox MWat NGre NHed NMen SIng WAbe

'Dana' (× *megaseiflora*) (8) — CLyd EMNN MWat NHol NMen

'Dartington Double' (12/d) — EBrP EBre EWes GBur GCHN GDra GTou LBre MBal MOne NHar NNrd SBre

'Dawn' (8) — NNrd

'Dawn Frost' (9) — EHyt

'Delia' (× *hornibrookii*) (8) — CNic CPBP NMen

§ 'Denisa' (× *pseudokotschyi*) (8) — MBal NMen WAbe

densa — See *S. cherlerioides*

§ 'Dentata' (× *polita*) (3) — CHan ECha EPPr EPla GAbr GGar NVic

'Dentata' (× *urbium*) — See *S. 'Dentata'* (× *polita*)

desoulavyi (8) — GTou MHig NGre WLin

diapensioides (8) — CLyd NGre NMen

'Doctor Clay' (7) — MDHE NMen WAbe

'Doctor Ramsey' (7) — ELan ESis EWes GTou ITim LBee MBro MHig MRPP NBro NHed NNrd SIng SSmi WGor WHoo

aff. *doyalana* SEP 45 — CGra EHyt

'Drakula' (*ferdinandi-coburgi*) (8) — CLyd LRHS MDHE MWat NHed NMen WAbe

'Dubarry' (12) — ECho EWes SIng

'Duncan Lowe' (*andersonii*) (8) ♀ — EHyt NGre

'Dwight Ripley' (8) — LFox

'Edgar Irmscher' (8) — LFox MWat WAbe

'Edie Campbell' (12) — NGre

'Edith' (× *edithiae*) (8) — LRHS MBro NNrd

'Edward Elgar' (× *megaseiflora*) (8) — MWat NHol NMen

'Elf' (12) — ELan EMNN LBee MOne NBro NMen NNrd NRoo SIng SRms SSmi WCla WFar WGor

'Eliot Hodgkin' (× *millstreamiana*) (8) — LFox NNrd WAbe

¶ × *elisabethae* 'Brno' (8) — NHol

– hort. — See *S. 'Carmen'* (× *elisabethae*)

'Elizabeth Sinclair' (× *elisabethae*) (8) — EPot NMen NNrd

'Ellie Brinckerhoff' (× *hornibrookii*) (8) — CLyd NGre

'Ernst Heinrich' (× *heinrichii*) (8) — NMen NRya

'Esther' (× *burnatii*) (7) — CLyd CMea EBrP EBre EHyt ELan ESis LBee LBre MHig NMen SBla SBre SMer SSmi WAbe

§ 'Eulenspiegel' (× *geuderi*) (8) — CLyd EPot MBro NNrd

exarata (12) — ITim LBee LFox NMen

§ – subsp. *moschata* (12) — NGre

– *pyrenaica* — See *S. androsacea*

Fair Maids of France — See *S. 'Flore Pleno'* (*granulata*)

'Fairy' (*exarata* subsp. *moschata*) (12) — ELan NFla

'Faldonside' (× *boydii*) (8) ♀ — CLyd LFox MBro MWat NGre NHed NHol NMen SBla WAbe WHoo WPat WPyg

'Falstaff' (*burseriana*) (8) — EPot LFox MDHE MWat MYat SBla SIng

× *farreri* (7) — NGre NHed NNrd

§ 'Faust' (× *borisii*) (8) — EMNN NGre NMen SBla SIng

federici-augusti — See *S. frederici-augusti*

'Ferdinand' (× *hofmannii*) (8) — NMen NNrd WAbe

ferdinandi-coburgi ♀ — CLyd EPot LFox NGre NHed NNrd NWCA WAbe

– var. *pravislavii* — See *S. ferdinandi-coburgi* var. *rhodopea*

– var. *radoslavoffii* — See *S. ferdinandi-coburgi* var. *rhodopea*

§ – var. *rhodopea* (8) — EPot LRHS NHed NMen SIng

'Findling' (12) — CMHG GCHN LGro MBro MOne NGre NMen NNrd NRoo SBod SIng WAbe WWin

'Flavescens' (*paniculata*) (7) — NBro

× *fleischeri* (8) — NMen

§ 'Flore Pleno' (*granulata*) (d) — CBos CFir CMil CRDP CVer ELan EWes GAbr GBri LBay LFox MHlr MTed NBir NHar NPro NRya NWoo SIng WAbe WCot WHil

'Florissa' (*oppositifolia*) (9) — EBrP EBre GCHN LBre LRHS SBre WAbe

'Flowers of Sulphur' — See *S. 'Schwefelblüte'*

§ *fortunei* ♀ — CHEx CLTr CMea MRav NBir NHol SPer SSpi WCru

¶ – var. *incisolobata* (4) — SSpi

'Foster's Gold' (× *elisabethae*) (8) — NMen

'Four Winds' (12) — EGle EWes GAbr LBee NMen NNrd SBla SIng SSmi

'Francis Cade' (7) — ELan ITim NGre

'Franzii' (× *paulinae*) (8) — MDHE MYat NHed

§ *frederici-augusti* (8) — SBla

§ – subsp. *grisebachii* (8) ♀ — GTou MFos MYat NGre NSla NTow WCla

'Friar Tuck' (× *boydii*) (8) — MWat NMen

'Friesei' (× *salmonica*) (8) — CLyd EHyt EMNN EPot MYat NHar NHed NMen

§ × *fritschiana* (7) — MDHE NHol NNrd SIng

'Funkii' (× *petraschii*) (8) — MWat NMen

'Gaiety' (12) — ECho ELan GDra LBee NFla NRoo SIng

'Galaxie' (× *megaseiflora*) (8) — CLyd LFox MDHE NGre NHol NMen WAbe

'Gelber Findling' (8) — EPot LRHS MDHE WAbe

'Gem' (× *irvingii*) (8) — EMNN MBro NHar NMen NNrd

'Geoides' — See *S. hirsuta* subsp. *paucicrenata*

georgei (8) — EPot NGre

¶ – ENF 5 (8) — EHyt

¶ – McB 1379 (8) — NHol

geranioides (11) — GCHN

'Gertie Pritchard' (× *megaseiflora*) — See *S. 'Mrs Gertie Prichard'* (× *megaseiflora*)

× *geuderi* — See *S. 'Eulenspiegel'* (× *geuderi*)

§ × *geum* (3) — CHid ECha ELan EPar MRav NWoo SDys

– Dixter form (3) — ECha EPPr EPla

* 'Gladys' — ELan

§ 'Glauca' (*paniculata* var. *brevifolia*) (7) — MDHE NGre

'Gleborg' — EGoo EWes

'Gloria' (*burseriana*) (8) ♀ — CLyd EHyt GCrs LFox MBal MBro MRPP MYat NGre NMen NNrd NSla SBla SRms WPat

× *gloriana* (8) — EMNN NMen

'Gloriosa' (× *gloriana*) — See *S. 'Godiva'* (× *gloriana*)

§ 'Godiva' (× *gloriana*) (8) — ITim MWat WAbe

'Goeblii' (8) — MDHE NGre WAbe

'Gold Dust' (× *eudoxiana*) (8) — CLyd CNic EMNN GTou LFox MHig MOne MWat MYat NHar NMen NNrd SBod SIng WAbe WWin

'Golden Falls' (12/v) — CMea EWes GTou LBee LHop MBro NGre NMen SIng WPat WRHF

Golden Prague (× *pragensis*) — See *S. 'Zlatá Praha'* (× *pragensis*)

¶ 'Gothenburg' — EHyt

'Grace Farwell' (× *anglica*) (8) — CLyd EMNN EPot GCHN ITim MBar MBro MYat NGre NHed NHol NMen NWCA SIng WAbe WHoo WPyg

'Gracilis' (× *geum*) — See *S. 'Gracilis'* (× *polita*)

§ 'Gracilis' (× *polita*) (3) — CNic

granulata — CNic EWFC MHew MMal NMen NRya WCla WOMN

'Gratoides' (× *grata*) (8) — MYat NGre WAbe

'Greenslacks Claire' (*oppositifolia*) (9) — NGre

'Greenslacks Heather' (*oppositifolia*) (9) — NGre

'Greenslacks Valerie' (*oppositifolia*) (9) — NGre

§ 'Gregor Mendel' (× *apiculata*) (8) ♀ — CMea ELan EMNN EPot GDra GTou MBal MBro MHig MNrw MPla MYat NGre NHed NHol NMen SBla SBod SIng SSmi WAbe WHoo WPyg

grisebachii — See *S. frederici-augusti* subsp. *grisebachii*

– *montenegrina* — See *S. frederici-augusti*

'Gustav Hegi' (× *anormalis*) (8) — WAbe

'Haagii' (× *eudoxiana*) (8) — CInt CLyd ELan EMNN GCHN GCrs GTou MBal MBro MOne NGre NHed NMen SIng SSmi WAbe WRHF WWin

hallii — GCHN WWin

'Harlow Car' (8) — CLyd LFox NMen

¶ 'Harlow Car' × *poluniniana* (8) — CPBP

'Hartside Pink' (*umbrosa*) (3) — NWoo

'Hartswood White' (12) — MWat SIng

'Hedwig' (× *malbyana*) (8) — MWat NMen

'Herbert Cuerden' (× *elisabethae*) (8) — NGre NHed NNrd

'Hi-Ace' (12/v) — ELan GTou LBee LFox MBro NBro NGre NRoo NWCA SBla SBod SSmi WFar WWin

'Highdownensis' (7) — MDHE

'Hindhead Seedling' (× *boydii*) (8) — CLyd EMNN LRHS MDHE MWat NHar NHed NMen WAbe

hirsuta (3) — CLyd MDHE NRya WCru

'Hirsuta' (× *geum*) — See *S.* × *geum*

'Hirtella' (*paniculata*) (7) — MDHE

'His Majesty' (× *irvingii*) (8) — EMNN LFox MDHE NHar NMen WAbe

'Hocker Edge' (× *arco-valleyi*) (8) — ITim LFox MHig MWat MYat NHed NMen WAbe

'Holden Seedling' (12) — EMNN EPot EWes

hostii (7) — CLyd GTou ITim LBee MHig SIng WTin

§ – subsp. *hostii* (7) — MDHE

– – var. *altissima* (7) — STre

– subsp. *rhaetica* (7) — MDHE NBro NMen

¶ hybrid JB 11 — NMen

hypnoides (12) — GAbr MOne SSmi

§ – var. *egemmulosa* (12) — MBal

hypostoma (8) — NGre

'Icelandica' (*cotyledon*) (7) — NHol

'Icicle' (× *elisabethae*) (8) — MWat

'Ingeborg' (12) — ECha LBee SIng

iranica (8) — EHyt EMNN GCHN GCrs MWat MYat NGre NMen NNrd

'Irene Bacci' (× *baccii*) (8) — MWat NMen

'Iris Prichard' (× *hardingii*) (8) — CLyd EPot ESis MBro MYat NGre NMen NNrd WAbe WHoo WPyg

irrigua (11) — EWes NChi SSca

× *irvingii* — See *S.* 'Walter Irving' (× *irvingii*)

'Ivana' (× *caroliquarti*) — MWat

'James Bremner' (12) — GGar LBee MOne NBro NFla SBod SIng

'Jason' (× *elisabethae*) (8) — MWat

'Jenkinsiae' (× *irvingii*) (8) ♀ — Widely available

§ 'Johann Kellerer' (× *kellereri*) (8) — CNic EPot GCrs LFox MHig MYat NGre NHed WAbe

'John Tomlinson' (*burseriana*) (8) — NSla WAbe

'Josef Capek' (× *megaseiflora*) (8) — EPot NMen

'Josef Mánes' (× *borisii*) (8) — MDHE NMen

'Joy' — See *S.* 'Kaspar Maria Sternberg' (× *petraschii*)

'Judith Shackleton' (× *abingdonensis*) (8) — CLyd EHyt MWat NGre NMen NNrd WAbe

'Juliet' — See *S.* 'Riverslea' (× *hornibrookii*)

§ *juniperifolia* (8) — ELan EMNN GBur GCHN GTou ITim MOne MWat NGre NHar NHed NMen NNrd NRoo NWCA SChu SMer SRms SSmi

– var. *macedonica* — See *S. juniperifolia*

'Jupiter' (× *megaseiflora*) (8) — CLyd EMNN MWat NGre NHar NMen NNrd WAbe

'Karasin' (9) — NNrd

'Karel Capek' (× *megaseiflora*) (8) — CGra CLyd CMea CNic EHyt EPot MWat NGre NHed NHol NMen NNrd WAbe

'Karel Stivín' (× *edithiae*) (8) — EMNN MWat NGre NMen

'Karlstejn' (× *borisii*) (8) — NRya WAbe

§ 'Kaspar Maria Sternberg' (× *petraschii*) (8) — EMNN GCHN ITim LFox MBro NGre NHar NHol NMen NNrd WPat

'Kath Dryden' (× *anglica*) (8) — CLyd MDHE NHol SIng WAbe

'Kathleen Pinsent' (7) ♀ — EPot MBro NGre NHar NNrd NVic NWCA SIng SSmi WAbe

'Kathleen' (× *polulacina*) (8) — CLyd EHyt NGre NHol

× *kellereri* — See *S.* 'Johann Kellerer' (× *kellereri*)

'Kestoniensis' (× *salmonica*) (8) — MWat NNrd

'Kewensis' (× *kellereri*) (8) — MWat NMen SIng WAbe

'King Lear' (× *bursiculata*) (8) — EPot LFox LRHS MWat NMen NRya SIng

'Kingii' — See *S. hypnoides* var. *egemmulosa*

'Kingscote White' — SIng

'Klondike' (× *boydii*) (8) — MDHE

'Knapton Pink' (12) — CMHG LBee NRya SIng SSmi

'Knapton White' (12) — LBuc NBro SIng WCla

§ × *kochii* (9) — EHyt NHar NTow

§ 'Kolbiana' (× *paulinae*) (8) — CLyd MDHE MWat MYat

'Koprvnik' (*paniculata*) (7) — MDHE

'Krasava' (× *megaseiflora*) (8) — CGra CLyd CPBP EHyt EMNN GCLN NGre NHar NHol NMen WAbe

'Kyrillii' (× *borisii*) (8) — NMen

'Labe' (× *arco-valleyi*) (8) — CLyd CNic EPot LRHS NMen WAbe

'Labradorica' (*paniculata*) — See *S. paniculata neogaea*

'Lady Beatrix Stanley' — See *S.* 'Beatrix Stanley' (× *anglica*)

'Lagraveana' (*paniculata*) (7) — ELan NGre NHed WRHF WWin

× *landaueri* — See *S.* 'Leonore' (× *landaueri*)

'Lenka' (× *byam-groundsii*) (8) — EHyt EMNN ITim NGre NHar NMen NNrd NSla WAbe

'Leo Gordon Godseff' (× *elisabethae*) (8) — CLyd MHig MOne MYat NMen SBla SIng

§ 'Leonore' (× *landaueri*) (8) — MDHE MWat SIng WAbe

'Letchworth Gem' (× *urbium*) (3) — GCal

× *leyboldii* (8) — GTou NMen

'Lidice' (8) — EMNN NGre NHar NMen NNrd WAbe

lilacina (8) — CLyd EMNN NGre NHar NMen NNrd SIng WPat

'Lindau' (8) — MWat

lingulata — See *S. callosa*

'Lismore Carmine' (× *lismorensis*) (8) — CGra CLyd EHyt MWat NGre NMen

¶ 'Lismore Gem' — EHyt

¶ 'Lismore Mist' (9) — EHyt

'Lismore Pink' (× *lismorensis*) (8) — CLyd EHyt EPot MWat NGre NMen

'Lohengrin' (× *hoerhammeri*) (8) — MWat NNrd

'Lohmuelleri' (× *biasolettoi*) (8) — MWat

longifolia (7) — ELan GCrs NSla NWCA SIng SBla

– JJA 861600 (7) — SBla

Love Me — See *S.* 'Miluj Mne' (× *poluanglica*)

'Lowndes' (*andersonii*) (8) — WAbe

'Ludmila Šubrová' (× *bertolonii*) (8) — NGre

'Luna' (× *millstreamiana*) (8) — WAbe

'Lusanna' (× *irvingii*) (8) — MDHE NGre NHol

'Lutea' (*marginata*) — See *S.* 'Faust' (× *borisii*)

'Lutea' (*paniculata*) (7) ♀ CNic ESis GBur GDra GTou LBee MBal MBro MRPP NBro NGre NHed NMen NNrd NRoo SBla SChu SIng SSmi
'Lutea' (× *stuartii*) (8) MDHE
§ 'Luteola' (× *boydii*) (8) ♀ MDHE WAbe
luteoviridis See **S. corymbosa**
'Luznice' (× *poluluteopurpurea*) (8) MWat NGre NHed
¶ 'Magna' (*burseriana*) (8) EHyt
'Major' (*cochlearis*) (7) ♀ LRHS MBro NMen NNrd WAbe WGor
'Major Lutea' See **S. 'Luteola' (× boydii)**
manshuriensis (1) GDra
'Margarete' (× *borisii*) (8) MWat NHed NNrd WAbe
marginata (8) CLyd LFox MYat NGre
– var. **balcanica** See **S. marginata** var. **rocheliana**
– var. **boryi** (8) EHyt EPot MDHE MWat MYat NGre NMen SIng WAbe
– var. **coriophylla** (8) EPot MDHE MYat NWCA
– var. **karadzicensis** (8) EMNN NMen
§ – var. **rocheliana** (8) CGra CLyd CMHG CPBP ELan EPot NGre NMen SIng
'Maria Luisa' (× *salmonica*) (8) CLyd CNic CPBP EMNN EPot GCrs LFox MBro MWat NGre NHed WAbe WPat
'Marianna' (× *borisii*) (8) CLyd CNic MYat NGre NHed NMen NNrd
'Marie Stivínová' (× *borisii*) (8) MWat
'Mars' (× *elisabethae*) (8) MWat
* 'Marshal Joffre' (12) LBuc NPri
§ 'Martha' (× *semmleri*) (8) CLyd EMNN NGre NMen NNrd
matta-florida MWat
'May Queen' (9) MWat NHol
media (8) CLyd EHyt MWat NGre
× **megaseiflora** See **S. 'Robin Hood' (× megaseiflora)**
mertensiana (1) CLyd EBee GTou NBir
– var. **bulbifera** (1) CNic
'Meteor' (8) NNrd NRya
micranthidifolia (1) WThi
'Millstream Cream' (× *elisabethae*) (8) CGra CLyd MDHE MWat NNrd
§ 'Miluj Mne' (× *poluanglica*) (8) EHyt LFox NGre NHar NNrd
'Minehaha' (× *elisabethae*) (8) MDHE WAbe
'Minor' (*cochlearis*) (7) ♀ CInt EMNN ESis GDra GTou LBee LFox MBal MBro MHig MRPP NHol NMen NVic NWCA SChu SIng SSmi WCla WHoo WLin WPat
'Minor Glauca' (*paniculata*) See **S. paniculata** var. **brevifolia 'Glauca'**
'Minor' (*paniculata*) See **S. paniculata** var. **brevifolia**
'Minutifolia' (*paniculata*) (7) CNic EPot ESis LBee LFox MBal MBro MDHE NHed NWCA SIng
§ 'Miss Chambers' (× *urbium*) (3) CBos EGoo EMon SUsu WCot
'Mona Lisa' (× *borisii*) (8) MDHE MWat MYat SIng WAbe WPat
§ 'Mondscheinsonate' (× *boydii*) (8) NHol
'Moonlight' See **S. 'Sulphurea' (× boydii)**
'Moonlight Sonata' (× *boydii*) See **S. 'Mondscheinsonate' (× boydii)**
moschata See **S. exarata** subsp. **moschata**
* 'Mossy Irish' EPot

'Mother of Pearl' (× *irvingii*) (8) EMNN NHar NMen WAbe
'Mother Queen' (× *irvingii*) (8) MBro MDHE NHol WHoo WPat WPyg
'Mount Nachi' (*fortunei*) (4) CBos CFil EHyt EWes NHar NMen SSpi SWas WAbe WCot WFar WPer
'Mrs E. Piper' (12) LBuc
§ 'Mrs Gertie Prichard' (× *megaseiflora*) (8) LFox MWat NHol NMen WAbe
'Mrs Helen Terry' (× *salmonica*) (8) CLyd EPot LRHS MDHE MYat NHed NMen
'Mrs Leng' (× *elisabethae*) (8) EMNN NMen
'Myra' (× *anglica*) (8) EMNN LFox MBro MWat MYat NHol NMen NWCA WAbe WHoo WPat WPyg
'Myra Cambria' (× *anglica*) (8) GCHN MWat MYat NGre NHol NMen NNrd WAbe
'Nancye' (× *goringiana*) (8) CGra CLyd EHyt MDHE NGre NMen WAbe
§ **nelsoniana** (1) NHol NNrd
¶ 'Niobe' (9) EHyt
nivalis (1) NHol NWCA
'Norvegica' (*cotyledon*) (7) CLyd GTou MDHE NGre WWin
'Notata' (*paniculata*) (7) NMen NNrd
'Nottingham Gold' (× *boydii*) (8) CLyd EPot MDHE MWat NGre NHol NMen NNrd WAbe
¶ × **novacastelensis** 'Allendale Pearl' (8) EHyt
'Nugget' (8) SIng
'Obristii' (× *salmonica*) (8) ITim NHol NMen WAbe
§ **obtusa** (8) NMen
'Obtusocuneata' (*fortunei*) (4) ECho EHyt ELan NHar SBla WAbe
'Ochroleuca' (× *elisabethae*) (8) CLyd EMNN ITim NMen WAbe
¶ 'Odysseus' NMen
'Opalescent' (8) CLyd LFox MWat NNrd WAbe
§ 'Ophelia' (× *arco-valleyi*) (8) MWat NGre NHol
oppositifolia (9) EBrP EBre GTou ITim LBre MOne MYat NHol NSla SBre SRms WAbe WWin
¶ – subsp. **asiatica** EHyt
♦ – × **biflora** See **S. × kochii**
– subsp. **latina** (9) CLyd ELan EMNN GCrs GDra GGar GTou NHar
'Oriole' (× *boydii*) (8) NMen
'Orjen' (*paniculata* var. *orientalis*) (7) NNrd
§ **paniculata** (7) ELan ESis GTou LBee LPVe MBal MBro MWat NHed NMen NRoo NSla NVic WCla WHoo WPyg
§ – var. **baldensis** (7) CLyd ELan GDra GTou ITim MBar MBro MWat NBro NGre NHed NHol NMen NNrd SBla SIgm SSmi WAbe WCla WRHF WWin
§ – var. **brevifolia** (7) CNic NNrd SIng SSmi
§ – subsp. **cartilaginea** (7) NHol SBla
– subsp. **kolenatiana** See **S. paniculata** subsp. **cartilaginea**
§ – **neogaea** (7) MDHE
§ – var. **orientalis** (7) MBro MDHE SSmi WCla
paradoxa (14) CLyd EPot SBla WGor
'Parcevalis' (× *finnisiae*) (8×6) CLyd WAbe
'Parsee' (× *margoxiana*) (8) EPot WAbe
'Paula' (× *paulinae*) (8) NGre

'Peach Blossom' (8) — CLyd CNic EPot GCrs MWat MYat NGre NMen NRya SBla SIng WAbe

'Pearl Rose' (× *anglica*) (8) — LFox NGre

'Pearly Gates' (× *irvingii*) (8) — CLyd MWat NGre NMen WAbe

'Pearly Gold' (12) — CMea NRoo NRya SSmi

'Pearly King' (12) — CLyd ECho ELan LBee MBal NMen NVic WAbe WFar

× **pectinata** — See S. × *fritschiana*

'Penelope' (× *boydilacina*) (8) — CLyd CPBP EHyt EPot GCrs ITim LBee MBro MFos MYat NGre NHed NHol SBla WAbe WHoo WPat WPyg

'Peter Burrow' (× *poluanglica*) (8) ♀ — CLyd CPBP EHyt MDHE NHar NMen NNrd WAbe

'Peter Pan' (12) — ELan EMNN EPot GDra GTou LBee LFox LGro MBro NFla NGre NMen NNrd NRoo SBod SSmi WPat

'Petra' (8) — CLyd EPot MBro NHol NNrd WAbe

× **petraschii** (8) — ITim

§ 'Phoenix' (× *biasolettoi*) (8) — LRHS NMen

'Pilatus' (× *boydii*) (8) — MWat NMen SIng

¶ 'Pink Pearl' — CMea

'Pixie' (12) — EBrP EBre EMNN LBee LBre MBal MPla MWat NFla NGre NMen NNrd NRoo NRya SBre SIng SRms SSmi

'Pixie Alba' — See S. 'White Pixie'

'Plena' (*granulata*) — See S. 'Flore Pleno' (*granulata*)

'Pluto' (× *megaseiflora*) (8) — MDHE

'Pollux' (× *boydii*) (8) — EPot NHol

¶ × **poluanglica** 'Maria Callas' — CGra

poluniniana (8) — CLyd EHyt EMNN ITim LFox NGre NHar NHol NMen NWCA WAbe

'Pompadour' — LBee

porophylla (8) — EHyt GDra NGre WAbe

aff. – (8) — NWCA

– var. **thessalica** — See S. *sempervivum* f. *stenophylla*

'Portae' (*paniculata*) (7) — NNrd SIng

'Primrose Bee' (× *apiculata*) (8) — EHyt EPot WAbe

'Primrose Dame' (× *elisabethae*) (8) — EMNN ESis ITim MBal MWat MYat NHol NMen SIng WAbe WFar

× **primulaize** (6x3) — CLyd MBro MHlr NMen NRya SRms WOMN

'Primulina' (× *malbyana*) (8) — LFox NHed WAbe

primuloides — See S. *umbrosa* var. *primuloides*

'Prince Hal' (*burseriana*) (8) — EHyt EMNN EPot ESis GCrs ITim MDHE NHar NHed NMen NNrd

'Princess' (*burseriana*) (8) — EHyt NMen

'Probynii' (*cochlearis*) (7) — EPot MDHE MWat

'Prometheus' (× *prossenii*) (8) — NGre NNrd

'Prospero' (× *petraschii*) (8) — MWat NGre WAbe

× **prossenii** — See S. 'Regina' (× *prossenii*)

§ 'Pseudoborisii' (× *borisii*) (8) — ITim

¶ × 'Pseudofranzii' (× *paulinae*) (8) — NWCA

× **pseudokotschyi** — See S. 'Denisa' (× *pseudokotschyi*)

'Pseudoscardica' (× *wehrhahnii*) (8) — MWat

'Pseudovaldensis' (*cochlearis*) (7) — MDHE

pubescens subsp. **iratiana** (12) — NMen

punctata — See S. *nelsoniana*

'Pungens' (× *apiculata*) (8) — NHed NHol NMen WAbe

'Purpurea' (*fortunei*) — See S. 'Rubrifolia' (*fortunei*)

'Purpurteppich' (11) — WPer

§ 'Pygmalion' (× *webrii*) (8) — CLyd CPBP ESis MYat NGre NHol NMen WAbe WPat

'Pyramidalis' (*cotyledon*) (7) — EPfP SRms

'Pyrenaica' (*oppositifolia*) (9) — EMNN GCLN NHar NMen

¶ **quadrifaria** — NHol

'Quarry Wood' (× *anglica*) (8) — ITim NMen

'Rainsley Seedling' (*paniculata*) (7) — MDHE NBro NMen

ramulosa — NMen

'Red Poll' (× *poluanglica*) (8) — CLyd EHyt MDHE MWat NGre NMen WAbe

§ 'Regina' (× *prossenii*) (8) — GCHN ITim NNrd SIng WAbe

retusa (9) — CLyd EHyt EMNN NGre NMen NSla NWCA SSca

'Rex' (*paniculata*) (7) — GCHN LBuc NHol NMen

¶ **rhodopetala** (8) — EHyt

§ 'Riverslea' (× *hornibrookii*) (8) ♀ — CGle CLyd CPBP EMNN LFox MBro MWat NGre NHar NHol NMen SIng WAbe WPat

§ 'Robin Hood' (× *megaseiflora*) (8) — CLyd EMNN EPot ITim LFox MWat MYat NGre NHar NHol NMen NNrd SBla SIng WAbe WPat

'Rokujô' (*fortunei*) (4) — LRHS

rosacea subsp. **hartii** (12) — SIng

'Rosea' (*cortusifolia*) (4) — NHar

'Rosea' (*paniculata*) (7) ♀ — GDra GTou LBee MBal MBro NBro NGre NHed NHol NRoo NSla SBla SIng SSmi STre WCla WHoo WPyg WWin

'Rosea' (× *stuartii*) (8) — NHed NMen WAbe

'Rosemarie' (× *anglica*) (8) — CLyd ITim MHig MYat NHol WAbe

'Rosenzwerg' (12) — LBee

'Rosina Sündermann' (× *rosinae*) (8) — EPot NHed NSla WAbe

rotundifolia — CLyd GBin NHol SSpi WCot

§ – subsp. **chrysospleniifolia** (10) — WCot WCru WPer

'Rubella' (× *irvingii*) (8) — MDHE MWat

§ 'Rubrifolia' (*fortunei*) (4) — CFil CMil EBrP EBre ECha LBre MBri NHar NRoo SBre SSpi SWas WCot WCru WFar WFox WGer WSan

* 'Ruby Red' — NPro

¶ 'Russell Vincent Prichard' (× *irvingii*) (8) — NHol

'Ruth Draper' (*oppositifolia*) (9) — EMNN GCHN NGre NHar NWCA SBla WAbe

'Ruth McConnell' (12) — CMea LBee LBuc

'Sabrina' (× *fallsvillagensis*) (8) — CLyd MWat

'Saint John's' (*caesia*) (7) — EBur MBro MDHE NNrd WWin

'Saint Kilda' (*oppositifolia*) (9) — CLyd GCrs GTou

'Salmon' (× *primulaize*) (6x3) — ESis LBee MHig NHed NWoo WPer

'Salomonii' (× *salmonica*) (8) — CLyd EPot ITim MBro MHig MOne NHed NMen NNrd SIng SRms WAbe

sancta (8) | CLyd EPot GCHN LFox MBal
MHig NMen SRms SSmi

– subsp. *pseudosancta* var.
macedonica | See *S. juniperifolia*

'Sanguinea Superba' (x
arendsii) (12) ♀ | GDra NNrd SIng

'Sara Sinclair' (x
arco-valleyi) (8) | MYat

sarmentosa | See *S. stolonifera*
'Sartorii' | See *S.* x **'Pygmalion'** (x *webrii*)
'Saturn' (x *megaseiflora*) (8) | MBro MWat NGre NHol NMen
'Sázava' (x
poluluteopurpurea) (8) | ITim MDHE MWat NGre
NHed

scardica | CPBP EHyt EMNN MBro
MDHE MWat NBro NMen
WAbe

– var. *dalmatica* | See *S. obtusa*
– f. *erythrantha* (8) | NNrd
– var. *obtusa* | See *S. obtusa*
¶ – 'Olymp' (8) | NMen
'Schelleri' (x *petraschii*) | See *S.* **'White Star'** (x
petraschii)
'Schleicheri' (x *kellereri*) | See *S.* **'Schleicheri'** (x
landaueri)
§ 'Schleicheri' (x *landaueri*)
(8) | EMNN
'Schneeteppich' (11) | WPer
§ 'Schwefelblüte' (12) | GTou LBee MBal NRoo SIng
SSmi WPat WRHF
scleropoda | NGre WLin
'Seaspray' (x *arendsii*)
(12/v) | EWes
'Seissera' (*burseriana*) (8) | NHol
x *semmleri* | See *S.* **'Martha'** (x *semmleri*)
sempervivum | EPot LFox MBro NMen NSla
NWCA WLin

– JCA 864.003 (8) | CPBP MBro
§ – f. *stenophylla* | GCHN GTou MDHE NHed
NRya
sibirica (11) | GTou
'Silver Cushion' (12/v) | CMea EAst ELan GTou LBee
MBar MBro NRoo SIng SMer
SSmi WAbe
'Silver Edge' (x *arco-valleyi*)
(8) | NMen WAbe
'Silver Mound' | See *S.* **'Silver Cushion'**
'Sir Douglas Haig' (12) | NNrd SIng
'Snowcap' (*pubescens*) (12) | CGra EHyt LBee NHed NMen
NWCA
'Snowdon' (*burseriana*) (8) | MWat
'Snowflake' (7) | GCLN MHig NHed
§ 'Sofia' (x *borisii*) (8) | EPot LFox NGre NNrd WAbe
§ 'Southside Seedling' ♀ | CLyd CPri ELan EPot ESis
GBur GTou LHop MBar MBro
MFos MTho NBro NGre NHar
NHol NMen NNrd NRoo SIng
SRms SSmi WAbe WCla WHoo
WLin WPat WPyg WWin
sp. BM&W 118 | GDra
sp. SEP 22 | MWat NGre
'Spartakus' (x *apiculata*) (8) | NRya WAbe
spathularis | MHlr WCot WEas WWin
'Speciosa' (*burseriana*) (8) | MDHE NHed
'Splendens' (*oppositifolia*)
(9) ♀ | ELan EMNN EPot ITim LFox
MBal NHed NMen SMer SRms
SSmi WAbe WGor WPat
'Sprite' (12) | GCHN LBee
spruneri | EHyt MYat NMen
– var. *deorum* (8) | NGre
'Stansfieldii' (12) | EBrP EBre EMNN LBre NGre
NMen NNrd SBod SBre SSmi
WWin

§ 'Stella' (x *stormonthii*) (8) | SBla
stellaris (1) | GTou
stolitzkae | CLyd EMNN EPot GCrs NGre
NMen
§ *stolonifera* (4) ♀ | CArn CHEx CHal CHan ECho
ELan GAri NBro SDix WEas
WFar
¶ – B&SWJ 1980 | WCru
'Stormonth's Variety' | See *S.* **'Stella'** (x *stormonthii*)
stribrnyi (8) | MWat NMen NTow
– JCA 861-400 | NWCA
'Sturmiana' (*paniculata*) (7) | MBro NMen SRms
'Suendermannii' (x
kellereri) (8) | MWat NHed NWCA SIng
WAbe
'Suendermannii Major' (x
kellereri) (8) | CLyd SIng
'Suendermannii Purpurea' | GCHN
(x *kellereri*) (8)
§ 'Sulphurea' (x *boydii*) (8) | EMNN ESis LFox MBro MYat
NGre NHar NHed NHol NMen
NNrd NWCA SChu WAbe
WHoo WPat WPyg
'Sun Dance' (x *boydii*) (8) | MDHE NHol
'Superba' (*callosa australis*)
(7) | GBur GCra GDra GTou MBro
MDHE SGre SSmi
'Sylva' (x *elisabethae*) (8) | MWat NGre
taygetea (10) | GBur NTow
'Theoden' (*oppositifolia*) (9)
♀ | CGra EHyt EMNN EPot EWes
GCrs GTou MBro NGre NHar
NHol NPro NWCA SBla WAbe
WSan
'Thorpei' (8) | GCrs ITim NMen SIng
'Timballii' (x *gaudinii*) (7) | SIng
'Timmy Foster' (x *irvingii*)
(8) | NGre NHol
x *tiroliensis* (7) | NHed
'Tom Thumb' (12) | MBro NMen NNrd
tombeanensis | NGre
'Tricolor' (*stolonifera*) (4) ♀ | EBak ELan SLMG
'Triumph' (x *arendsii*) (12) | ECtt EMNN GCHN GDra
GTou LBee NMen NRoo NVic
SBod
'Tully' (x *elisabethae*) (8) | ESis NHol WPat
'Tumbling Waters' (7) ♀ | CInt GAbr LHop MBro MTho
NMen SIng SRms SSca WAbe
WGor WPat WWin
§ 'Tvůj Den' (x *poluanglica*)
(8) | CGra EHyt NHed NMen WAbe
§ 'Tvuj Píseň' (x *poluanglica*)
(8) | EHyt MDHE NGre NHar
NHed WAbe
§ 'Tvuj Polibek' (x
poluanglica) (8) | CGra EHyt MDHE NHar NHed
NMen
§ 'Tvuj Přítel' (x *poluanglica*)
(8) | EHyt MDHE NGre NHar
NHed WAbe
§ 'Tvuj Úsměv' (x
poluanglica) (8) | CGra EHyt MDHE MWat
NGre NHar NHed NMen NNrd
WAbe
§ 'Tvuj Úspěch' (x
poluanglica) (8) | CGra EHyt MDHE NGre NHed
NMen WAbe
'Tycho Brahe' (x *doerfleri*)
(8) | CLyd NMen WAbe
umbrosa | CLyd EBrP EBre EPar LBre
NNor SBre SPer SRms WHen
WWin
§ – var. *primuloides* (3) ♀ | CGle GCHN LFox MBro MYat
NMen NPri SRms WBon WEas
WFox
* – *subinteger* | SGre
'Unique' | See *S.* **'Bodensee'** (x *hofmannii*)
x *urbium* (3) ♀ | EAst EGoo EJud ELan EPfP
GBur GDra LGro MBal NDov
NSti SIng WBon WFar WPer

urbium primuloides | See *S. umbrosa* var. *primuloides*
'Elliott's Variety' | **'Clarence Elliott'**
'Vaccarina' (*oppositifolia*) (9) | EBrP EBre ECho LBre MRPP SBre WAbe
'Václav Hollar' (× *gusmusii*) (8) | MWat NGre NMen
'Vahlii' (× *smithii*) (8) | WAbe
'Valborg' | See *S.* **'Cranbourne'** (× *anglica*)
'Valentine' | See *S.* **'Cranbourne'** (× *anglica*)
'Valerie Finnis' | See *S.* **'Aretiastrum'** (× *boydii*)
'Variegata' (*cuneifolia*) (3) | CNic ECho ECtt ELan EPPr ESis GBur GCHN MBar MBro NChi NMen NPri NRoo NVic SHFr SSmi WHil WPer
'Variegata' (*umbrosa*) | See *S.* **'Aureopunctata'** (× *urbium*)
'Variegata' (× *urbium*) (3) | CDec EAst ELan EPar GDra GGar LBee LGro MBal NCat NNor NSti SRms SSmi WCla WEas WWal WWin
vayredana (12) | CLyd
veitchiana | EPla MHig NBro NCat NNrd WCot WCru
'Venetia' (*paniculata*) (7) | MDHE NNrd SSmi
'Vesna' (× *borisii*) (8) | CLyd EMMN GCHN MHig MOne MWat NGre NMen NNrd WAbe WWin
'Vincent van Gogh' (× *borisii*) (8) | ITim LBuc NHol NNrd
'Vladana' (× *megaseiflora*) (8) | CLyd EHyt EMNN EPot GCLN MDHE NGre NHar NHol NMen NRya WAbe
'Vlasta' (8) | MWat WAbe
'Vltava' (8) | NGre
'W.A. Clark' (*oppositifolia*) (9) | MBal WAbe
'Wada' (*fortunei*) (4) | CFil CGle CWit EPar GAbr GCHN MBal NBir NHar NRoo SCro SSpi WAbe WCot WFar WWin
'Waithman's Variety' (7) | NNrd
§ 'Wallacei' (12) | ECho
'Walpole's Variety' (*longifolia*) (7) | NHar NNrd WPer
§ 'Walter Irving' (× *irvingii*) (8) | EHyt EMNN EPot MDHE MYat NHar NHol NMen NRya WAbe
'Welsh Dragon' (12) | WAbe
'Welsh Red' (12) | WAbe
'Welsh Rose' (12) | WAbe
wendelboi | CLyd EHyt EMNN LFox MWat MYat NGre NMen NNrd WAbe
'Wendrush' (× *wendelacina*) (8) | MDHE NMen WAbe
'Wendy' (× *wendelacina*) (8) | CLyd NGre NMen WAbe
'Wetterhorn' (*oppositifolia*) (9) | MBal NMen WAbe
'Wheatley Lion' (× *borisii*) | MDHE NMen
'Wheatley Rose' (8) | CLyd LRHS NHol
§ 'White Pixie' (12) | EMNN EPfP LBee LFox LGro NGre NNrd NPri SBla SIng SRms SSmi WCla
'White Spire' (12) | MBro
§ 'White Star' (× *petraschii*) (8) | NNrd WAbe
'Whitehill' (7) | CLyd EBrP EBre ELan ESis GCHN GTou LBee LBre LFox MBal MBro MHig NBro NEgg NGre NHol NMen SBre SIng SSmi WHoo WPat WPer WPyg WTin WWin

'Whitlavei Compacta' (*hypnoides*) (12) | MTPN NMen NWoo
'Wilhelm Tell' (× *malbyana*) (8) | NMen
'William Boyd' (× *boydii*) (8) | MDHE MWat NRya WAbe
¶ 'Winifred' | GCrs
'Winifred' (× *anglica*) (8) | CLyd EPot LFox MWat NGre NMen WAbe WFar
'Winifred Bevington' (7x3) | CInt CLyd EBrP EBre ELan EMMN ESis GBur GDra GTou LBee LBre LHop MBro NBro NHar NHed NMen NNrd NRoo NRya SBre SIng WCla WHoo WPat WPer WPyg WRHF
'Winston Churchill' (12) | EPfP SIng
'Winter Fire' | See *S.* **'Winterfeuer'** (*callosa*)
* 'Winton' (× *paulinae*) | MDHE
'Wisley' (*frederici-augusti* subsp. *grisebachii*) (8) ♀ | GCHN MBal MBro NHar NMen WHoo WPat WPyg
'Wisley Primrose' | See *S.* × **'Kolbiana'** (× *paulinae*)
¶ 'Woodside Ross' | MOne
'Yellow Rock' (8) | WAbe
Your Day | See *S.* **'Tvůj Den'** (× *poluanglica*)
Your Friend | See *S.* **'Tvuj Přítel'** (× *poluanglica*)
Your Good Fortune | See *S.* **'Tvuj Úspěch'** (× *poluanglica*)
Your Kiss | See *S.* **'Tvuj Polibek'** (× *poluanglica*)
Your Smile | See *S.* **'Tvuj Úsměv'** (× *poluanglica*)
Your Song | See *S.* **'Tvuj Píseň'** (× *poluanglica*)
Your Success | See *S.* **'Tvuj Úspěch'** (× *poluanglica*)
× *zimmeteri* (7x3) | EWes NNrd SSmi
§ 'Zlatá Praha' (× *pragensis*) (8) | NGre NMen SIng WAbe

SCABIOSA † (Dipsacaceae)

africana | WCot
alpina L. | See *Cephalaria alpina*
anthemifolia | CHan
atropurpurea | CLTr GBur MSto SMrm SUsu
¶ – 'Peter Ray' | EWes LRHS
banatica | See *S. columbaria*
* 'Black Prince' | NBir
'Butterfly Blue' | EBar EBee EMan EPfP MBri MWgw SCoo SPer WWeb
caucasica | CSam EAst ECha EPfP GBur GChr LGan MBro NCat NChi NLak SBla WHoo WOld WPyg WWin
– var. *alba* | CBot CM&M EPfP MBri NCut NNor NRoo WHoo
– Blue Seal = 'Blausiegel' | EBrP EBre EFou LBre SBre
– 'Blue Lace' | MBri
– 'Bressingham White' | EBrP EBre EWes LBre SAsh SBre
– 'Challenger' | MBri
– 'Clive Greaves' ♀ | CB&S CDoC CHad CMGP CRDP EAst ECED ECha EFou ENot LHop LRot MAus MBri MBro NFla NMir NNor SPer WEas WMow
– 'Fama' | EBar EMan NBir NRoo SMrm SRms WGor WHoo WPyg
– 'Goldingensis' | EBar EOld GMac NPri WFar WPer

– House's hybrids .... NVic SRms
– 'Isaac House' .... SIde SWat
– 'Kompliment' .... EFou ENot WShe
– 'Miss Willmott' ♀ .... CDoC CGle CHad CRDP CSev
EAst ECha EFou LHop MAus
MBel MBri MBro NCut NFla
SPer SRms SUsu WRus
– 'Moerheim Blue' .... ECha MBri NFla SPer
– 'Mount Cook' .... LHop SAsh
– 'Nachtfalter' .... LRHS MBri
– 'Perfecta' .... EOrc GMaP MTis NRoo SWat
WWhi
– 'Perfecta Alba' .... EMan GMaP LFis MBro MWat
NOrc NPri NTay SWat WPyg
WWhi
– 'Stäfa' .... CDoC EFou LHop MBel MBri
MTed MWat SMrm
'Chile Black' .... CHan CMea GBri GCal LGre
NCut SUsu WCot WElm WRus
* 'Chile Red' .... GCal
cinerea .... WWin
§ *columbaria* .... CKin EWFC MChe MHew
MLLN NLan NMir NTow
NWCA WCla WGor WHer
WHoo WJek WPyg
* – *alba* .... SSpi
– 'Nana' .... NBir NMen NPri SSmi WPyg
§ – var. *ochroleuca* .... CBot CChr CGle CHan CMea
CRDP CSam EBar ECha GMac
LLWP MBro MCLN MLLN
NBir NChi NPla NPri NSti
SMrm SRms SSca SSpi SWas
WBro WHoo WOld WPGP
WWin
¶ – subsp. *portae* .... EBee
¶ 'Crimson Cushion' .... CFis
farinosa .... CBot CHan SSca WAbe WPer
– 'Schofield's Variegated' .... WAbe
gigantea .... See *Cephalaria gigantea*
graminifolia .... EDAr ELan EMan GBuc NBir
NMen NTow NWCA WOld
– *rosea* .... EWes
holosericea .... MSto
¶ *incisa* 'Pink Cheer' .... WSPU
japonica .... MSto WPer
– var. *alpina* .... CInt CLTr EFou ESis GDra
GTou LIck MBel MSCN WHoo
WRha
¶ *lachnophylla* .... EBee
lucida .... CGle CSev ELan EPar GDra
GMac GTou LGan LHop MBro
MHig NPri NRoo SBla SMrm
WAbe WEas WMow WPat
WPer
minoana .... MSto
ochroleuca .... See *S. columbaria* var.
ochroleuca
parnassi .... See *Pterocephalus perennis*
* 'Perfecta Lilac Blue' .... CSev
* 'Perpetual Flowering' .... EFou MRav
'Pink Mist' .... CGle MBri NBir SCoo SPer
SRms WWeb
pterocephala .... See *Pterocephalus perennis*
rhodopensis .... MSto
rumelica .... See *Knautia macedonica*
succisa .... See *Succisa pratensis*
tatarica .... See *Cephalaria gigantea*
triandra .... CHan

SCADOXUS (Amaryllidaceae)

'König Albert' .... See *Haemanthus* 'König Albert'
multiflorus .... LAma MBri NRog

natalensis .... See *S. puniceus*
§ *puniceus* .... ERea NRog SLMG

SCAEVOLA (Goodeniaceae)

aemula 'Blue Fan' .... CHal CSpe EMan MBEx SBid
SHFr SMrm
– 'Blue Wonder' .... CLTr LHil LHop
– 'New Wonder' .... WLRN
– 'Petite' .... CHal CLTr LHil
¶ *crassifolia* .... MFiF
hookeri .... ECou
suaveolens .... See *S. calendulacea*

SCANDIX (Apiaceae)

pecten-veneris .... EWFC

SCHEFFLERA (Araliaceae)

actinophylla ♀ .... EBak MBri SRms
arboricola ♀ .... MBri
– 'Compacta' .... MBri
– 'Gold Capella' ♀ .... MBri
– 'Jacqueline' .... MBri
– 'Trinetta' .... MBri
digitata .... CHEx
¶ sp. B&SWJ 3872 .... WCru

SCHIMA (Theaceae)

argentea .... See *S. wallichii* subsp. *noronhae*
var. *superba*
§ *wallichii* subsp. *noronhae* .... CHEx
var. *superba*
– subsp. *wallichii* var. .... ISea
khasiana

SCHINUS (Anacardiaceae)

molle .... IDee
patagonicus .... MAll
polygamus .... CGre
¶ *terebinthifolius* .... SMad

SCHISANDRA (Schisandraceae)

¶ *arisanensis* B&SWJ 3050 .... WCru
chinensis .... CArn CHan CPlN ETen WSHC
grandiflora .... ECot ELan EPfP SSta
– B&SWJ 2245 .... WCru
– var. *cathayensis* .... See *S. sphaerandra*
propinqua var. *sinensis* .... CBot
rubriflora .... CBar CRHN CWSG EHic EPfP
MUlv SHBN SSpi
– (f) .... CB&S CPlN ELan MBlu MGos
SBid SBra WSHC WWat
– (m) .... CPlN EMil NHol
§ *sphaerandra* .... CPlN
sphenanthera .... EFou EHic ELan EMil EPfP
ETen MDun NPal SSto WSHC

SCHIZACHYRIUM (Poaceae)

§ *scoparium* .... CRow EBee EBrP EBre EHoe
EPPr EWes GBin LBre SApp
SBre WRHF

SCHIZANTHUS (Solanaceae)

candidus RB 94104 .... MSto
gilliesii .... MSto
grahamii JCA 12365 .... MSto
hookeri .... MSto

SCHIZOCENTRON See HETEROCENTRON

SCHIZOCODON See SHORTIA

SCHIZOLOBIUM (Papilionaceae)
¶ *parahybum* — LBlo WMul

SCHIZOPHRAGMA (Hydrangeaceae)
¶ *corylifolium* — WCru
hydrangeoides — CFil CHEx CPlN CPle EBrP
EBre ELan EMil GChr LBre
MBal MBri MGos SBra SBre
SMur SRms SSpi SSta WCru
WDin WSHC
– 'Brookside Littleleaf' — WCru
– 'Moonlight' (v) — EPfP LRHS SSpi SSta WCru
– 'Roseum' — CBot CFil MBlu SBla SSpi
WCru
integrifolium ♀ — CB&S CFil CHEx CMac CPlN
EMil MBal SDix SHBN WSHC
WWat
– *fauriei* B&SWJ 1701 — WCru
* – var. *molle* — CPlN

SCHIZOSTACHYUM (Poaceae - Bambusoideae)
§ *funghomii* — SDry WJun

SCHISTOSTEGA (Sphagnaceae) See Plant
Deletions

SCHIVERECKIA (Brassicaceae) See Plant
Deletions

SCHIZOPETALON (Brassicaceae) See Plant
Deletions

SCHIZOSTYLIS † (Iridaceae)
coccinea — CArn CAvo CB&S CBro CNic
CPea CRDP EAst ECGN ELan
ERos ETub LAma LPBA MBal
MFir MNrw NChi NHol NNor
NRoo NSti SOkh WBro WHal
WHoo WOld WWhi WWye
– f. *alba* — CB&S CElw CMHG CMea
CMil EAst ECha ELan GMac
LHop LWak MAus MAvo
MNrw MRav SApp SDix SMad
SPer SUsu WEas WHal WHil
WPbr WRus WSHC WWat
– 'Ballyrogan Giant' — CMil IBlr WPGP
– 'Cardinal' — CDec CPea NPla
– 'Fenland Daybreak' — EBee EBrP EBre ECro EFou
EGar EMan GMac IBlr LBre
LIck MLan NHol SBre SSpe
– 'Gigantea' — See *S. coccinea* **'Major'**
– 'Grandiflora' — See *S. coccinea* **'Major'**
– 'Hilary Gould' — CRDP GBuc IBlr MAvo NBrk
SUsu WFar WHal
– 'Jennifer' ♀ — CAvo CBro CGle CHid CMHG
COtt CRDP CSpe CTri ECha
EFou ERos IBlr MBri NHol
SApp SCro SRms SUsu WRus
WWat
– 'Maiden's Blush' — ECGP EFou EWll GMac LIck
MBel NHol SPer
§ – 'Major' ♀ — Widely available
¶ – 'Molly Gould' — EBee
– 'Mrs Hegarty' — CB&S CHid CMHG EAst EFou
ELan EPot GChr GMac LAma
LHop LPBA LRot MAus NFla
NHol NRog NRoo SDeJ SMad
SPer SSea SSoC WBod WBrE
WEas WHoo WOld WPer
WWat

– 'November Cheer' — CDec CMHG ECot EPPr IBlr
LIck MSte NRoo SSpe WOld
– 'Pallida' — CMil CSam EBee ECha EGar
ELan GBuc IBlr LHop
– 'Professor Barnard' — CFee CGle GCal GMac IBlr
LGan MBri MSte NBrk SApp
WOld WPnn WPyg WWat
– 'Salmon Charm' — EFou IBlr
¶ – seedling — WHil
– 'Snow Maiden' — CFai CRDP EBar LIck LRHS
§ – 'Sunrise' ♀ — CB&S CFee CHea CMHG
CRDP CSam ECha ELan GCal
LHop LIck MAvo NHol NLon
NNor NRoo SIng SOkh SPer
SSpi SWas WAbe WBod
WOMN WOld WPer WRus
– 'Sunset' — See *S. coccinea* **'Sunrise'**
– 'Tambara' — CDec CMHG CPou EGar
GMac IBlr LGre MHFP SApp
WElm WOld WWat
– 'Viscountess Byng' — CB&S CBro CGle CHea EGar
EMon EPot GCal MAvo MBri
NRog SAga SPer WHal WPer
WWat
* – 'Zeal Blush' — IBlr
– 'Zeal Salmon' — CBro CPou ECha EGar GMac
IBlr NBrk SApp SCro SSpi
WHil
* 'Marietta' — ETub
¶ 'Tambara' — WPGP

SCHOENOPLECTUS (Cyperaceae)
§ *lacustris* — EMFW MMoz WChe
– subsp. *tabernaemontani* — CBen EBrP EBre EHon EMFW
'Albescens' (v) — LBre LPBA MSta MTed SBre
SRms SWat SWyc WChe WCot
– – 'Zebrinus' (v) — CBen CInt EBrP EBre EHon
ELan EMFW GBin LBre LPBA
MSta MTed NDea SBre SWat
SWyc WChe WCot WWeb

SCHOENUS (Cyperaceae)
pauciflorus — CCuc CFil ECou EHoe EPot
ESOG GOrn WPGP

SCHOTIA (Caesalpiniaceae)
brachypetala — SOWG

SCIADOPITYS (Sciadopityaceae)
verticillata ♀ — CB&S CDoC CKen EHul IOrc
LCon LLin LNet LPan MBar
MBlu MBri MDun SLim WCoo
WCwm WDin WNor
¶ – 'Firework' — CKen
¶ – 'Globe' — CKen
– 'Gold Star' — CKen
¶ – 'Jeddeloh Compact' — CKen
– 'Picola' — CKen
¶ – 'Pygmy' — CKen
¶ – 'Shorty' — CKen

SCILLA † (Hyacinthaceae)
adlamii — See *Ledebouria cooperi*
× *allenii* — See × *Chionoscilla allenii*
amethystina — See *S. litardierei*
amoena — CMon LAma LRHS
autumnalis — CAvo CMon EPot EWFC
LAma WOMN WShi
– *fallax* AB&S 4345 — CMon
bifolia ♀ — CAvo CBro EPar EPot LAma
NRog WShi

– 'Rosea'	EPar EPot LAma NRog WPer
bithynica	SSpi WShi WWat
campanulata	See *Hyacinthoides hispanica*
chinensis	See *S. scilloides*
cilicica	CBro CMon EPot LAma
hanburyi S&L 78	CMon
¶ *hohenackeri*	EPot
– BSBE 811	CMon
hyacinthoides	CMon EHyt
italica	See *Hyacinthoides italica*
japonica	See *S. scilloides*
libanotica S&L 113	CMon
liliohyacinthus	CAvo CBro CRDP CRow EHyt
	IBlr SSpi
lingulata ciliolata	CBro
– MS 320	CMon
– S&L 253	CMon
– SF 288/281	CMon
§ *litardierei*	CAvo CMon EPot ERos LAma
	MFos NEgg
mauretanica alba	CMon
– SF 65	CMon
messeniaca	SHel
§ *mischtschenkoana*	CAvo CBro CMon EBrP EBre
	EHyt EPot ETub LAma LBow
	LBre MBri NRog SBre
monophyllos	CFil LAma
– SB 184	CMon
morrisii M 4015	CMon
non-scripta	See *Hyacinthoides non-scripta*
numidica MS&CL 288	CMon
nutans	See *Hyacinthoides non-scripta*
obtusifolia AB&S 4410	CMon
ovalifolia	See *Ledebouria ovalifolia*
paucifolia	SLMG
¶ *persica*	CAvo LRHS
– BSBE 1054	CMon
peruviana	CAvo CB&S CBrd CBro CFee
	CHEx CHad CMil CSpe EBrP
	EBre EPar EPot ERos LAma
	LBre MTho NRog SApp SBre
	SMrm SSpi SUsu WAbe WWhi
– 'Alba'	CAvo CMon EBrP EBre LAma
	LBre MTho NRog SBre
– *elegans*	CMon
– var. *venusta*	CMon
pratensis	See *S. litardierei*
puschkinioides	LAma
ramburei	LAma
– B&S 406	CMon
– MS 417	CMon
reverchonii	EHyt ERos
– MS 418	CMon
§ *scilloides*	CBro EPot ERos MHig WCot
– MSF 782	SSpi
siberica ♀	CAvo ETub LAma NEgg NRog
	WPer WShi
– 'Alba'	CBro EPar EPfP EPot LAma
	NEgg NRog WPer
¶ – subsp. *armena*	CHEx
– 'Spring Beauty'	CAvo CBro EPar EPot LAma
	MBri MHlr NRog
¶ – var. *taurica*	ERos
– – M&T 4148	CMon
tubergeniana	See *S. mischtschenkoana*
verna	CMon ERos WHer WShi
– JCA 878.000	CNic
– MS 483	CMon
vicentina	See *Hyacinthoides italica vicentina*
violacea	See *Ledebouria socialis*

SCINDAPSUS (Araceae)

aureus	See *Epipremnum aureum*
pictus (v)	MBri

SCIRPOIDES (Poaceae) See Plant Deletions

SCIRPUS (Cyperaceae)

cernuus	See *Isolepis cernua*
◆ *cespitosus*	See *Trichophorum cespitosum*
§ *fauriei* var. *vaginatus*	CRow EHoe ESOG SWyc
'Golden Spear'	SRms
holoschoenus	See *Scirpoides holoschoenus*
lacustris	See *Schoenoplectus lacustris*
– 'Spiralis'	See *Juncus effusus* 'Spiralis'
¶ *maritimus*	LPBA
mucronatus	MSta
sylvaticus	CKin MTed SWyc
tabernaemontani	See *Schoenoplectus lacustris* subsp. *tabernaemontani*
variegatus	CBot

SCLERANTHUS (Caryophyllaceae)

biflorus	CPea ECou EGle ELan EPPr EWes MBro SSca WPer
perennis	CNat
singuliflorus	ECou NHol WPat WPyg
uniflorus	CLyd EWes GAbr GAri GCLN NHed NWCA
– CC 466	NWCA
¶ – CC 556	MRPP

SCLEROCHITON (Acanthaceae) See Plant Deletions

SCOLIOPUS (Trilliaceae)

bigelowii	MS&S SWas WFar
¶ *hallii*	SWas

SCOLOPENDRIUM See ASPLENIUM

SCOLYMUS See CYNARA

SCOPOLIA (Solanaceae)

carniolica	CAvo CFir EGle EMon EPar GCal GDra GPoy MBel MBlu MHar MSal NSti WCru WHal
– forms	ECha IBlr
– subsp. *hladnikiana*	CAvo CBlo EBrP EBre ECro EPPr LBre LSpr SBre WBcn WTin
– *podolica*	CMea
¶ – yellow form	MHar
¶ – 'Zwanenburg'	CAvo EPar
lurida	MNrw MSal WWye
physaloides	MSal
sinensis	See *Atropanthe sinensis*

SCORZONERA (Asteraceae)

¶ *hispanica*	WCot
humilis	GPoy
suberosa subsp. *cariensis*	EBee NTow

SCROPHULARIA (Scrophulariaceae)

aquatica	See *S. auriculata*
§ *auriculata*	ELau EWFC MSal NDea NOrc WHer WWye
– 'Burdung' (v)	EMon

§ – 'Variegata' | CGle CRow EHoe ELan ENot LHop LPBA MBri MCLN MSta MWat NRoo NSti SPer SRms WBea WEas WFar WHal WOve WRus WWin

buergueriana 'Lemon and Lime' (v) | EMon NSti WCot

canina subsp. *bicolor* | WHer

¶ *macrantha* | EBee

nodosa | CArn CJew CKin ELau MChe MSal NMir SIde WCla WHer

– *tracheliodes* | CNat

– *variegata* | See *S. auriculata* 'Variegata'

sambucifolia | EJud GBin MNrw NChi

¶ *scopolii* | EBee

scorodonia | SRms

umbrosa | MSal

vernalis | EBee EWFC

SCUTELLARIA (Lamiaceae)

¶ *albida* | EBee

§ *alpina* | CLyd CPBP EBrP EBre GCHN LBee LBre MAvo NWCA SBla SBre SRms WGor WPer WWye

¶ – 'Greencourt' | EBee

altissima | CGle EBee ECGN EGar EMan EMar EPPr GBuc LBay LFis MAvo MSal NBro NPla SSca WLin WPbr WPer WWin WWye

baicalensis | CArn CHan EBee IBlr LHop MSal SBla WOve WPer WWye

barbata | MNrw MSal

brevibracteata | SHFr

brittonii | EBee

canescens | See *S. incana*

¶ *columnae* | EBee

diffusa | CPBP WPer WWye

galericulata | CKin EWFC GPoy MHew MSal WHer WJek

– 'Corinne Tremaine' (v) | WHer

hastata | See *S. hastifolia*

§ *hastifolia* | CPBP CTri ECot ECtt EMNN NSti SSea WCot WOMN WPer

§ *incana* | CGle EBee ECGN EFou ELan EMan EPPr LFis LGre MNrw NSti SMrm SUsu SWas WCot WEas WWoo

indica var. *japonica* | See *S. indica* var. *parvifolia*

§ – var. *parvifolia* | CPBP EBee EBur EHyt ELan EWes LBee MTho NMen NTow NWCA SSca SUsu WCru WPbr WWye

– – 'Alba' | CMHG LBee

integrifolia | MSal

lateriflora | CArn CBod CJew EFou ELau ESis GBar GPoy LHol MChe MHew MSal NSti SIde WCer WJek WPer WSel WWye

minor | CKin EWFC MSal WWye

nana var. *sapphirina* | CPBP MRPP

– – JJA 1840650 | NWCA

novae-zelandiae | ECou LBee MTho SSca SUsu WWye

orientalis | CGra EBee LBee NWCA SBla WCot WCru WPat WWin

– subsp. *carica* | CMHG WOMN WWye

– subsp. *pinnatifida* | EHyt NWCA WLin

pontica | NWCA

prostrata | ESis SSca WOMN WWin

¶ *resinosa* | EBee

---

scordiifolia | CLyd CMea CMil CSam CSpe ECha EFou ELan EPot LFis MBro MNrw NMen NRya SBla SUsu WCla WCot WHoo WPyg WRus WWin WWye

supina | See *S. alpina*

tournefortii | WBor WPbr

SECURIGERA See CORONILLA

SECURINEGA (Euphorbiaceae)

ramiflora | CPle MAll

SEDASTRUM See SEDUM

SEDUM † (Crassulaceae)

acre | CTri ECot EFer ELan GPoy LHol MBar NGre SIde WLRN

– 'Aureum' | CInt CNic ELan EPfP MBar MHlr MOne MWat NHol NVic WCot WHoo WPat WPyg

– 'Elegans' | ECtt GDra GTou MBal NGre

§ – var. *majus* | CChe NGre SIde SSmi

– 'Minus' | MOne NGre SIde SSmi WFar

aggregatum | See *Orostachys aggregata*

§ *aizoon* | EPfP NGre SChu SIde WEas WOve WUnu WWal

– 'Aurantiacum' | See *S. aizoon* 'Euphorbioides'

§ – 'Euphorbioides' | EBrP EBre ECED ECha ECro ECtt EGoo ELan EMon ESis LBre MBel MRav NFai NPro SBre SPer WCot WFar

albescens | See *S. forsterianum* f. *purpureum*

§ *alboroseum* | EBrP EBre LBre MTho SBre

§ – 'Mediovariegatum' | CBot EBee ECro EGar EGoo ELan EMan EMon EOld LHop MBri MCLN MRav MSCN NEgg NFai NRoo SHBN WEas WPer WWal

§ *album* | CHal EBar NBro SIde WPer

§ – 'Chloroticum' | NGre SIde SSmi

– subsp. *clusianum* | See *S. gypsicola glanduliferum*

– 'Coral Carpet' | CNic ELan EPfP EPot GDra MBar MWat NGre NMen NVic SChu SSmi

– var. *micranthum* | See *S. album* 'Chloroticum'

§ – subsp. *teretifolium* 'Murale' | CTri MBar NGre

algidum | See *S. alsium*

alpestre | NGre

§ *alsium* | NGre

altissimum | See *S. sediforme*

altum | EBee EMon EPPr WPer

amplexicaule | See *S. tenuifolium*

§ *anacampseros* | CHEx CNic EGoo GCHN NGre NHol SIde SSmi WCla WEas WPer

anglicum | NGre WCla

anopetalum | See *S. ochroleucum*

– alpine form | See *S. ochroleucum* subsp. *montanum*

athoum | See *S. album*

atlanticum | See *S. dasyphyllum* subsp. *dasyphyllum* var. *mesatlanticum*

atuntsuense | CBlo NGre

Autumn Joy | See *S.* 'Herbstfreude'

batesii | See *S. hemsleyanum*

§ 'Bertram Anderson' ♀ | Widely available

beyrichianum hort. | See *S. glaucophyllum*

bithynicum 'Aureum' | See *S. hispanicum* var. *minus* 'Aureum'

¶ *bodinieri* EBee
brevifolium MDHE
* – *potsii* NGre
§ – var. *quinquefarium* NGre
¶ bronze-leaved WHil
¶ *caeruleum* CInt EJud
'Carl' EGoo EMon
§ *caucasicum* NGre SUsu WAbb WEas
– DS&T 89001T EMon MTPN
cauticola ♀ CLyd CMHG CPri GCal LHop
  MBro MFos MHar MHig MRav
  NGre NNor NRoo SBod SRms
  SSca SSmi WWin
– Lida ECho
§ – 'Lidakense' CMea CSam EBar EBrP EBre
  ELan EMon GBur LBre MBar
  MBri MBro MCLN MTis NFai
  NGre NHar NVic SBla SBre
  SChu SHel SIng SSmi
– 'Robustum' EMon
– × *tatarinowii* EGoo EWes NGre
clusianum See *S. gypsicola glanduliferum*
crassipes See *Rhodiola wallichiana*
crassularia See *Crassula milfordiae*
cyaneum hort. See *S. ewersii* var. *homophyllum*
– Rudolph GCHN MDHE NGre NWCA
dasyphyllum ELan ESis GTou MBal MBar
  MOne MRPP MWat NGre
  NHol NRoo NVic SSmi WCla
  WRHF
– subsp. *dasyphyllum* var. CHEx CHal
  glanduliferum
– – var. *macrophyllum* MDHE NGre SSmi
§ – – var. *mesatlanticum* CNic MDHE NBir NGre
– *mucronatis* See *S. dasyphyllum* subsp.
  dasyphyllum var. *mesatlanticum*
– subsp. *oblongifolium* NGre
debile NGre
divergens NGre
– large form NGre
douglasii See *S. stenopetalum* 'Douglasii'
'Dudley Field' CLyd GCHN NGre NMen
'Eleanor Fisher' See *S. telephium* subsp.
  ruprechtii
ellacombeanum See *S. kamtschaticum* var.
  ellacombeanum
erythrostichum See *S. alboroseum*
§ *ewersii* CHEx CMHG CNic EBee EBrP
  EBre EGoo ELan EMNN ESis
  GCHN GTou LBre MHar NBro
  NGre NMen SBre SSmi WEas
  WOMN WUnu
§ – var. *homophyllum* CLyd MHig MTPN NGre SSmi
§ *fabaria* MCLN NGre WCot WEas
farinosum MHig
fastigiatum See *Rhodiola fastigiata*
floriferum See *S. kamtschaticum*
forsterianum subsp. EMFP LGro
  elegans
* 'Frosty Morn' EBee EFou EGar LRHS MMil
  NEgg NRoo NSti SPer WCot
  WElm
¶ *furfuraceum* NMen
'Gooseberry Fool' CLon EGoo EMon LGre SUsu
gracile NGre SSmi
* 'Green Expectations' EFou
gypsicola CHEx MDHE NGre WPer
'Harvest Moon' EBur
§ 'Herbstfreude' ♀ Widely available
heterodontum See *Rhodiola heterodonta*

hidakanum CLyd EBee ECha EMFP GBur
  GCrs GTou MBro NBro NMen
  NTay WHoo WPat
hillebrandtii See *S. urvillei* **Hillebrandtii**
  Group
himalense See *Rhodiola* 'Keston'
§ *hispanicum* CTri ECho
– 'Albescens' CNic NGre
– var. *bithynicum* NGre
– *glaucum* See *S. hispanicum* var. *minus*
§ – var. *minus* ECtt EGoo GAri GTou MBar
  NGre NNrd NPri SChu SIde
  SSmi STre
§ – – 'Aureum' ECha MBar MHig MRPP NGre
  NMen SBod SSmi
humifusum EBur EHyt MFos MHig NMen
  NTow SIng SSmi WOMN
hybridum NGre
hyperaizoon NGre
integrifolium See *Rhodiola rosea* subsp.
  integrifolia
ishidae See *Rhodiola ishidae*
jaeschkei See *S. oreades*
japonicum NGre
'Joyce Henderson' EBee EFou ERav MGrG
  MSCN SUsu WCot WEas WOld
§ *kamtschaticum* ♀ CLyd ESis GBur MBar NGre
§ – var. *ellacombeanum* ♀ CNic EGoo ELan EMon ESis
  NGre NMen
§ – var. *floriferum* Widely available
  'Weihenstephaner
  Gold'
– var. *kamtschaticum* CHEx CPri CTri ECro ELan
  'Variegatum' ♀ ESis GCHN LBee LHop MHig
  MWat NFla NGre NPri NRoo
  SBla SBod SRms SSmi WEas
  WPyg
– var. *middendorffianum* See *S. middendorffianum*
* – 'Takahira Dake' NGre
kirilovii See *Rhodiola kirilovii*
kostovii See *S. grisebachii* subsp.
  kostovii
lanceolatum NGre
laxum NGre
– subsp. *heckneri* NGre
lineare ELan SLMG
– 'Variegatum' ESis MBri
litorale NGre
§ *lydium* CLyd CNic CTri EMNN GTou
  MBal MBar MHig MOne MRPP
  NGre NMen NNrd NRoo SSmi
– 'Aureum' See *S. hispanicum* var. *minus*
  'Aureum'
– 'Bronze Queen' See *S. lydium*
'Lynda et Rodney' CRDP EGoo EMon
makinoi 'Variegatum' EBrP EBre LBre SBre
'Matrona' See *S. telephium* 'Matrona'
maweanum See *S. acre* var. *majus*
maximowiczii See *S. aizoon*
mexicanum MBri
§ *middendorffianum* CLyd ECho EGoo ELan EMon
  GTou LHop MDHE MHig
  MWat NGre NMen SBod SRms
  WHoo WWin
– var. *diffusum* NGre SSmi
¶ – 'Striatum' CNic
'Mohrchen' CRDP EBee EFou LRHS
monregalense NGre
'Moonglow' NGre NMen
moranense CHal CNic NGre NTow SIde
  SSmi

'Morchen'	CHad CLon CMGP LBuc MLLN MTed NSti SChu SMrm SUsu SWas WCot WFar
morganianum ♀	CHal EBak LCns MBri
morrisonense	NGre
multiceps	NGre SSmi
murale	See *S. album* subsp. *teretifolium*
	'Murale'
N *nevii*	CLyd EGle
nicaeënse	See *S. sediforme*
obcordatum	NGre
§ *obtusatum*	CPri EGle MBro MHig NBro NFla NGre NNrd NSla NTay SSmi
§ – subsp. *retusum*	NGre
obtusifolium	NGre
ochroleucum 'Green Spreader'	SSmi
§ – subsp. *ochroleucum* glaucum	NGre
oppositifolium	See *S. spurium* var. *album*
§ *oreganum*	CInt CMHG ECha EMNN ESis GBur GTou MBar MHig MWat NGre NMen NRoo NVic SBod SHel SIng SRms SSmi WPer WPyg WWin
– 'Procumbens'	See *S. oreganum* subsp. *tenue*
§ – subsp. *tenue*	CNic MBro WPat
§ *oregonense*	EBur GTou NGre NMen NNrd
oryzifolium	NGre
– 'Minor'	EBur
§ *pachyclados*	CInt CLyd EBur EGoo EHoe ELan ESis GAbr GBur GTou LBee MBar MDHE MOne NBir NGre NNrd SChu SIde SIng SSmi WCla WPat WPer
pallidum	NGre
palmeri	CFis EOas NBir NTow SSmi WCot
pilosum	EBur NGre NWCA SBla WOMN
§ *pluricaule*	EHyt GCHN GDra MBro NGre NMen NNrd SBod SChu SRms WCla WRHF
– Rose Carpet	See *S. pluricaule* **'Rosenteppich'**
polytrichoides	See *Rhodiola komarovii*
populifolium	CLyd CMHG ECha EGoo GCHN GCal MBel MHar NGre SDry SDys SSmi STre WEas WPer
praealtum	EOas SEND SPar
primuloides	See *Rhodiola primuloides*
pruinatum	NGre
pruinosum	See *S. spathulifolium* subsp. *pruinosum*
pulchellum	NGre
purdyi	NGre NMen
'Purple Emperor'	CRDP EFou EPPr SUsu SWas WCot
quadrifidum	See *Rhodiola quadrifida*
quinquefarium	See *S. brevifolium* var. *quinquefarium*
ramosissimum	See *Villadia ramosissima*
'Red Bead'	NGre
reflexum L.	See *S. rupestre* L.
reptans var. *carinatifolium*	NGre
retusum	See *S. obtusatum* subsp. *retusum*
rhodiola	See *Rhodiola rosea*
rosea	See *Rhodiola rosea*
rubroglaucum hort.	See *S. oregonense*
– Praeger	See *S. obtusatum*

x *rubrotinctum*	CHEx CHal SLMG
§ 'Ruby Glow' ♀	Widely available
§ *rupestre* L.	CAgr CNic EBar EBot EGoo ELan EPfP MBar MWhi NGre NPri SChu SIde SSmi WCla WEas WHer
– 'Minus'	CNic NGre
– 'Monstrosum Cristatum'	MBal NBir SIde SMad
ruprechtii	See *S. telephium* subsp. *ruprechtii*
sarcocaule	See *Crassula sarcocaulis*
sarmentosum	NGre SSmi
§ *sediforme*	LHop MBro NGre
– *nicaeense*	See *S. sediforme*
selskianum	GDra GTou MOne NPri
sempervivoides	EBur NGre
sexangulare	EMNN ESis GDra MBar MOne NGre NMen SSmi WFar
sibiricum	WEas
sichotense	NGre
§ *sieboldii*	CSam GBur LCns LGro MBri MBro MDHE NGre SSmi
– 'Mediovariegatum' ♀	ELan EMan LHop NGre SCro SSmi WEas WPer
'Silver Moon'	EBur EGoo ESis GCHN MDHE NGre SSmi
sp. B&SWJ 054	WCru
spathulifolium	ECha ELan ESis GTou MOne MRPP NBus SChu SRCN WEas WMow
– 'Aureum'	EBur ECtt EMNN GTou MBar MHig MWat NGre SBod
– 'Cape Blanco' ♀	Widely available
§ – subsp. *pruinosum*	MDHE NGre
– 'Purpureum' ♀	Widely available
– 'Roseum'	CBlo CLyd SSmi
§ *spectabile* ♀	CArn CDoC ELan EPfP GMaP MAus NBee NPla NSti SHFr SRms WBea WHil WWin
– 'Abendrot'	EMon
– 'Album'	CHEx
– 'Brilliant' ♀	CDoC CM&M EBrP EBre ECED ECha EFou EGoo ELan EMon ENot LBlm LBre MBri NGre NOrc NRoo SBre SMad SPer SPla SSoC WEas
– 'Iceberg'	CM&M CRDP CSev EBee ECha EFou EGoo EMan EMon EPPr ERav LBlm LGre LHop MAus MCLN NHaw NLar SMad SSoC WCot WHil
– 'Indian Chief'	CBlo NRoo SCro WCot WElm WFar WLRN
– 'Meteor'	EBar ECha EGoo MLLN MWat NCat NFai NGre SCro WAbe WCot WPer
* – 'Mini'	ELan
¶ – 'Pink Fairy'	WHil
– 'Rosenteller'	EFou EMon NGre SMrm
– September Glow	See *S. spectabile* **'Septemberglut'**
§ – 'Septemberglut'	EMan EMon
– 'Stardust'	CBlo EBar EGar EGoo EMil EPfP GMaP MBri MLLN MTis NCut NGre SIde SPla WAbe WGor WViv WWeb
– 'Variegatum'	See *S. alboroseum* **'Mediovariegatum'**
spinosum	See *Orostachys spinosa*
spurium	EGoo EJud ELan GBur LGro NGre NNor SBod SRms STre

§ – var. *album*	EGoo ELan ESis MHar NGre SIde
* – 'Atropurpureum'	CLyd ECha NNor NRoo
– 'Coccineum'	MBar
– Dragon's Blood	See *S. spurium* **'Schorbuser Blut'**
– 'Erdblut'	CTri EBrP EBre LBre MHig NFla NGre NMen NRoo SBre
– 'Fuldaglut'	CHal CNic CPri EBrP EBre EHoe LBre MBel MWat NGre NHar SBre SChu SMac WPer WWin
– 'Glow'	CTri STre
– 'Green Mantle'	CBlo ECha SMer
– Purple Carpet	See *S. spurium* **'Purpurteppich'**
– 'Purpureum'	CHan CInt EGoo ELan GDra
§ – 'Purpurteppich'	CPri EBrP EBre ESis LBre LGro MHig MRav NBro NGre NHol SBre SHel SRms
– 'Roseum'	CLyd SRms
– 'Ruby Mantle'	CBlo NPro WCot
§ – 'Schorbuser Blut' ♀	CMea EBar ELan EPot LHop MBal MBro MWat NBro NChi NGre NVic SHel SRms WEas WHoo WPat WPyg WRHF
– 'Splendens Roseum'	LGro
– 'Tricolor'	See *S. spurium* **'Variegatum'**
§ – 'Variegatum'	CHan CLyd CMHG CNic CSam ECha EHoe ELan ESis GBur LHop MBar MHig NGre NRoo SBod SHel SIng SPla SSmi STre WAbe WCla WEas WOve WPat WPyg WWin
stenopetalum	NGre
§ – 'Douglasii'	CNic MOne NNrd SRms SSmi
stephanii	See *Rhodiola crassipes* var. *stephanii*
'Stewed Rhubarb Mountain'	CLon CMil EBee EGoo EMon GAri MRav WBea WCot
stoloniferum	NGre SSmi
* 'Strawberries and Cream'	LRHS MRav SUsu
stribrnyi	See *S. urvillei* **Stribrnyi Group**
'Sunset Cloud'	CLyd CMHG CSam EMon GCal MRav NGre WOld
takesimense	NGre
§ *tatarinowii*	CLyd EDAr NGre NTow
§ *telephioides*	WCot
§ *telephium*	CAgr CArn CMea EBar EMon EWFC MHlr NSti SRms WCla WCot WUnu
– 'Abbeydore'	EGoo EMon NSti
– 'Arthur Branch'	CElw CMil EHal EMon GBuc MNrw MSte MTho NChi SUsu WCot WLin
¶ – var. *borderi*	EMon
– subsp. *fabaria*	See *S. fabaria*
* – 'Hester'	EFou EMan MAus
* – 'Leonore Zuutz'	WCot
§ – 'Matrona'	ECha EFou EGoo EJud EMon EWes SMrm SUsu WCot WWhi
§ – subsp. *maximum*	ECha EMon MBel SChu
– – 'Atropurpureum' ♀	CBot CGle CHad CMea CSev ECha ECoo ELan EMan EMar EMon MBri MCLN MFir MRav NRoo SChu WEas WWhi WWin
– 'Munstead Red'	CLyd CMil EBee EFou EGoo EJud EMan EMar EMon ERic LFis LHop MAus MRav NGre SPla SSpe SUsu WCot
– 'Roseovariegatum'	EMon
– 'Roseum'	LHop

§ – subsp. *ruprechtii*	CLyd CMHG CMea CMil EBee ECha EGoo EMan EMon EOld EOrc MBri NGre SPer SUsu SWas WCot WEas WLin WPer WViv WWhi
– 'Variegatum'	CMHG COtt ECoo LFis MBel NRoo SPar WHal WWin
* – Washfield purple selection	EWes
§ *tenuifolium*	EBur SSmi
– subsp. *ibericum*	NGre
– subsp. *tenuifolium*	EBur
ternatum	NGre
trollii	See *Rhodiola trollii*
§ 'Vera Jameson' ♀	CLon CLyd CSam ECha ECro EGoo EHoe EMar ENot MBri MCLN MFir MHlr MRav MTis NGre NHol NSti SBla SChu SHBN SPer SUsu WEas WHil WOve WPer WWat WWhi
verticillatum	NGre
'Weihenstephaner Gold'	See *S. kamtschaticum* var. *floriferum* **'Weihenstephaner Gold'**
weinbergii	See *Graptopetalum paraguayense*
yezoense	See *S. pluricaule*
yunnanense	See *Rhodiola yunnanensis*

SEEMANNIA See GLOXINIA

SELAGINELLA (Selaginellaceae)

apoda	MBri
braunii	NMar
douglasii	NMar
emmeliana	See *S. pallescens*
helvetica	NHol
¶ *involvens*	WCot
kraussiana ♀	CHal MBal MBri NMar WRic
– 'Aurea'	CHal GGar MBri NMar SMad
– 'Brownii' ♀	MBri NMar NVic
– 'Variegata' ♀	MBri
martensii 'Watsoniana'	NMar
§ *pallescens*	NMar
– 'Aurea'	NMar
¶ *tamariscina*	WRic
vogelii	NMar

SELAGO (Selaginellaceae)

¶ *flanaganii*	MHig

SELINUM (Apiaceae)

tenuifolium	See *S. wallichianum*
¶ *wallichianum*	CBos CHad ECGN
§ – EMAK 886	CGle CMil CPou EPla MBri NSti SDix SMrm WEas

SELLIERA (Goodeniaceae)

radicans	NHol SSca
– forms	ECou
– 'Lake Ellerman'	NHol

SEMELE (Ruscaceae)

androgyna	CHEx CPlN

SEMIAQUILEGIA † (Ranunculaceae)

§ *adoxoides*	CLyd GBin NRya WPer
¶ 'Early Dwarf'	NCut

§ *ecalcarata* — CBot CGle CMil ECro GBin GMac LGan MAvo MNrw NHar NHol NOak NWoo SIng SMrm SRms WCru WLin WPGP WPer WWhi WWin

– 'Flore Pleno' (d) — CNic ECGN LGan NPSI NRoo WRha WWhi

simulatrix — See *S. ecalcarata*

SEMIARUNDINARIA (Poaceae - Bambusoideae)

§ *fastuosa* ♀ — CHEx EBee EFul EOas EPfP EPla ERod GOrc ISta LJus SAPC SArc SDry WJun WMul

– var. *viridis* — EPfP EPla ERod ISta LPJP SDry WJun

kagamiana — CDoC EPla ERod ISta LJus MMoz SCha SDry WJun

§ *lubrica* — ISta WPGP

makinoi — EPla WJun

nitida — See *Fargesia nitida*

§ *okuboi* — EPla WJun

¶ *sinica* — ISta

villosa — See *S. okuboi*

yamadorii — EPla ERod ISta SDry WJun

– 'Brimscombe' — EPla SDry

yashadake — EPla ISta SDry WJun

– *kimmei* — EBee EPla ERod ISta LJus SDry WJun

SEMPERVIVELLA See ROSULARIA

SEMPERVIVUM † (Crassulaceae)

'Abba' — MOne WHal WPer

acuminatum — See *S. tectorum* var. *glaucum*

'Aglow' — CWil MOne SSmi

'Alcithoë' — CWil

'Aldo Moro' — CWil MOne NMen SSmi

allionii — See *Jovibarba allionii*

'Alluring' — GAbr MOne

'Alpha' — CWil ESis LBee NGre NHol SIng SSmi STre WHal

altum — CWil NMen SIng SSmi

'Amanda' — CWil MBro MOne NMen SSmi WHoo WPer

'Ambergreen' — CWil NMen SSmi

andreanum — CWil MOne NBro NGre NHol SSmi

'Apache' — CWil MOne NNrd SSmi

'Apple Blossom' — CWil MOne NBus SIng SSmi

arachnoideum ♀ — CMea CWil EGoo ELan EPot ESis GAbr LBee MBar MBro MOne MWat NHed NHol NNrd NRoo NWCA SBla SIng SLMG SSmi WAbe WEas WHal WHoo WPyg WWin

¶ – 'Abruzzii' — SIng

– var. *bryoides* — CWil GCHN MBro NMen

– × *calcareum* — CWil MBro MOne NGre NMen SSmi

– 'Clairchen' — MBro MOne NMen

– subsp. *doellianum* — See *S. arachnoideum* var. *glabrescens*

– 'Form No. 1' — SSmi

§ – var. *glabrescens* — NMen SSmi

¶ – – 'Album' — SIng

¶ – 'Gusseri' — SIng

♦ – 'Kappa' — See *S.* 'Kappa'

– 'Laggeri' — See *S. arachnoideum* subsp. *tomentosum*

– × *nevadense* — CWil SDys SIng SSmi

– × *pittonii* — CWil MBro NGre NHol NMen SSmi

¶ – 'Red Variety' — NMen

– 'Rubrum' — MOne

– 'Sultan' — MOne

– subsp. *tomentosum* — NHol SIng
  'Minor'

♦ – – misapplied — See *S.* × *barbulatum* 'Hookeri'

– – Schinz & Thell ♀ — EBrP EBre EMNN GCHN LBre MBro MOne MRPP NGre NHol NMen NPer NWCA SBre SChu SMer SSmi WPer WWin

§ – – 'Stansfieldii' — GAbr MOne NGre NMen STre WHal

arenarium — See *Jovibarba arenaria*

¶ *armenum* — NMen

'Aross' — CLyd CWil GAbr MOne NMen SSmi

'Arrowheads Red' — MOne SSmi

arvernense — See *S. tectorum*

'Ashes of Roses' — CWil EGoo MBro NMen NTow SSmi WAbe

'Asteroid' — CWil NMen SSmi

¶ *atlanticum* — MOne

¶ – — CWil MOne NMen NNrd SSmi

– 'Edward Balls' — MOne SDys

– from Oukaimaden — CWil MBro MOne NHol NMen

'Atlantis' — MOne NHol

'Atropurpureum' — CWil ELau GAbr MBro MOne

'Aureum' — See *Greenovia aurea*

¶ *balcanicum* — MBro MOne NMen

ballsii — CWil GCHN NHed NMen

– from Smólikas — MOne NMen SSmi

– from Tschumba Petzi — SDys SSmi

'Banderi' — CWil MOne

§ × *barbulatum* — GCHN MOne NMen SDys SIng SSmi WHoo WPer WPyg

§ – 'Hookeri' — CWil ESis EWes MOne NHol NRoo SSmi WAbe WPer

'Bascour Zilver' — CWil GAbr MOne SIng WHal

* 'Beaute' — CWil

* 'Bedazzled' — CWil

'Bedivere' — CWil MOne NGre NMen SSmi

* 'Bedivere Cristate' — CWil NMen

'Bella Meade' — CHEx CWil MOne NGre SSmi

I 'Belladonna' — CWil MDHE NHol NMen NTow WPer

'Bellotts Pourpre' — CWil

'Bennerbroek' — MDHE

'Bernstein' — CWil MBro NHed NMen SIng WHal

'Beta' — NHol NMen NRoo SIng SSmi WAbe

'Bethany' — MOne NMen WHal

'Bicolor' — EPfP

'Big Slipper' — NHol SSmi

'Birchmaier' — CWil NMen

¶ 'Black Knight' — LBee WHal

'Black Mini' — CWil MOne NBir NHed NMen

'Black Mountain' — CWil MOne

'Black Prince' — CLyd GBur SWas

'Black Velvet' — CWil MBro MOne SSmi

'Bladon' — WPer

'Blari' — SSmi

'Blood Tip' — CHEx CLyd ESis GAbr GCHN LBee MBro NHar NMen NRoo SChu SSmi WGor WHal WHoo

'Blue Boy' — CWil ESis GAbr NHol SIng

'Blue Moon' — MOne

¶ 'Blue Time' — MOne

'Blush' — SSmi

'Boissieri' — See *S. tectorum* subsp. *tectorum* 'Boissieri'

¶ 'Bold Chick' — SSmi

'Booth's Red' — CHEx MOne SIng SSmi
borisii — See *S. ciliosum* var. *borisii*
borissovae — CWil NMen SSmi
'Boromir' — CWil MOne SSmi
* 'Bowles' Variety' — WPer
'Brock' — CWil MOne MRPP NHol
'Bronco' — CWil ELan MOne NMen SSmi
'Bronze Pastel' — CWil MBro MOne NGre NMen SSmi
'Brown Owl' — CWil MOne
'Brownii' — GAbr NMen WPer
* 'Brunette' — GAbr
'Burnatii' — CWil
'Butterbur' — CWil
'Café' — CWil MBro MOne NMen NNrd SIng SSmi WPer
x *calcaratum* — LBee SIng
calcareum — CWil ELau MBro MOne NBro NGre SSmi WPer
* – 'Atropurpureum' — MBro
¶ – 'Benz' — SDys
– from Colle St Michael — CWil
– from Gleize — CWil NMen
– from Gorges du Cains — CWil SSmi
– from Guillaumes, Mont Ventoux, France — GAbr NMen
– from Mont Ventoux, France — SSmi
– from Queyras — CWil MOne SSmi
– from Route d'Annôt — CWil SSmi
– from Triora — CWil MBro NMen
– 'Greenii' — CWil MRPP NGre NHed NMen SSmi
§ – 'Grigg's Surprise' — CInt CWil NMen
– 'Limelight' — CWil ESis EWes MBro NMen SIng SSmi WHal
– 'Monstrosum' — See *S. calcareum* **'Grigg's Surprise'**
– 'Mrs Giuseppi' — ESis GAbr GCHN LBee MBro MOne NOak NRoo SChu SSmi STre WPer
– 'Pink Pearl' — CWil MOne NMen WTin
– 'Sir William Lawrence' — CPBP CWil ESis NRoo SChu WHal
* 'Caldera' — CWil
californicum — NHed
'Caliph's Hat' — CWil MTPN
'Canada Kate' — CWil SSmi WPer
'Cancer' — CLyd MOne SSmi
'Candy Floss' — CWil SSmi
cantabricum — CWil MDHE SIng SSmi
– subsp. *cantabricum* from Leitariegos — CWil NMen
– from Navafria — CWil SIng
– from Peña Prieta — MOne NMen SSmi
– from Piedrafita, Spain — SSmi
– from Riaño, Spain — CWil GAbr
– from San Glorio — CWil GAbr MBro NMen
– from Santander, Spain — SSmi
– from Ticeros — CWil MOne NMen
– from Valvernera — CWil MOne
– subsp. *guadarramense* from Lobo No 1 — CWil MBro SSmi
– – from Lobo No 2 — SSmi
– – from Navafria No 1 — SSmi WTin
– – from Valvanera No 1 — NMen SSmi
– x *montanum* subsp. *stiriacum* — CWil NGre SSmi WEas
¶ – subsp. *urbionense* from Picos de Urbión, Spain — MBro NMen
'Canth' — CWil
'Caramel' — CWil

'Carmen' — CHal CWil GAbr MBro MOne
'Carneus' — MOne
'Carnival' — CHal MBro MOne SSmi WPer
caucasicum — CWil MOne NMen SSmi
'Cavo Doro' — CWil MDHE NGre
charadzeae — CWil
'Cherry Frost' — MOne NGre NNrd SSmi
'Cherry Tart' — CWil
'Chocolate' — SSmi
x *christii* — NHol SSmi
chrysanthum — NMen
¶ *ciliosum* — CPBP NMen
§ – var. *borisii* — CNic ESis GCal GTou MBro MRPP NGre NHed NMen NNrd NRoo SSmi WHal
– x *ciliosum* var. *borisii* — CHal CWil EPot
* – from Ochrid — CWil NMen
– var. *galicicum* 'Mali Hat' — CWil NHol NMen
– x *marmoreum* — CWil MBro NMen SSmi
'Cindy' — CWil
'Circlet' — CWil NMen SSmi
* *cistaceum* — WEas
'Clara Noyes' — MOne SSmi WPer
'Clare' — MOne NGre NNrd SSmi
'Cleveland Morgan' — CWil GAbr MOne NBro NHar SSmi
'Climax' — MOne
'Cobweb Capers' — MOne
¶ 'Cobweb Centre' — MOne
'Collage' — CWil
'Collecteur Anchisi' — MOne NGre SDys SSmi
'Commander Hay' ♀ — CHEx CLyd CPri ESis EWes LHop MRPP NGre NHol NMen NPer NTow SAxl WEas WFar WHal
'Compte de Congae' — MOne NMen
'Congo' — CWil MOne SSmi
'Cornstone' — CWil
'Corona' — WPer
'Correvons' — See *S.* **'Aymon Correvon'**
'Corsair' — CWil MBro MOne NMen SIng WPer
¶ 'Cresta' — SSmi
'Crimson Velvet' — CWil MDHE MOne NGre SSmi WPer
§ 'Crispyn' — CLyd CWil MBro MOne MRPP NHol NMen SIng SSmi WEas
'Croton' — SIng WPer
'Cupream' — CWil MDHE NGre NHed
'Dakota' — CWil
'Dallas' — CWil MOne
'Damask' — CWil GAbr MBro MDHE MOne NGre SSmi
'Dark Beauty' — CWil MBro MOne NMen SIng SSmi WHal
'Dark Cloud' — CWil GAbr MOne
'Dark Point' — CWil MOne NMen SSmi
'Darkie' — CWil
'Deep Fire' — CWil GBin MOne SSmi
x *degenianum* — GAbr MBro
densum — See *S. tectorum*
'Director Jacobs' — CWil GAbr GCHN MOne NGre NMen SSmi WEas
'Disco Dancer' — CWil
dolomiticum — MOne
* – from Rif Sennes — CWil
– x *montanum* — CWil NBro NHed NMen SSmi
¶ 'Donarrose' — SIng
'Downland Queen' — CWil
'Duke of Windsor' — CWil MOne MRPP NGre NMen SSmi

'Dusky'	CWil SSmi
'Dyke'	CWil GAbr MBro WHal
dzhavachischvilii	CWil MOne
'Edge of Night'	CWil
'El Greco'	CWil
'El Toro'	SIng
'Elgar'	CWil SIng
'Elizabeth'	WPer
'Elvis'	CWil GAbr MBro MOne NMen SSmi
'Emerald Giant'	CWil MOne
'Emerson's Giant'	CWil MOne
¶ 'Emma Jane'	MOne
¶ 'Engles'	WHal
'Engle's 13-2'	CLyd CWil MOne NBro NHar NHol SChu
¶ 'Engles No. 1'	MBro
'Engle's Rubrum'	CPBP ESis GAbr GTou LBee NHol NMen
erythraeum	CWil NGre NMen WAbe WHal
– from Pirin, Bulgaria	NGre NMen
'Excalibur'	CWil MBro NMen SSmi
'Exhibita'	CWil MBro SDys SSmi
'Exorna'	CWil NMen SIng SSmi WEas
'Fair Lady'	CWil MOne NMen SSmi
'Fame'	CWil MDHE
x *fauconnettii*	CWil MBro MOne NHol SSmi
– *thompsonii*	NGre NHol SSmi
'Festival'	CWil NMen
¶ 'Feu de Printemps'	MOne
'Fiesta'	CWil WHal
fimbriatum	See *S.* x *barbulatum*
'Finerpointe'	MBro SSmi
'Fire Glint'	CWil GAbr MOne
'Firebird'	CWil
'First Try'	CWil MOne
'Flaming Heart'	CWil NMen SSmi WPer
'Flander's Passion'	ELau LBee WPer
'Flasher'	CWil MBro WEas WPer
* 'Fluweel'	CWil
¶ 'Fontanae'	MOne
'Forden'	CHEx WGor
'Ford's Amability'	CWil ESis NGre SSmi
'Ford's Giant'	CWil
'Ford's Shadows'	SDys SSmi
'Ford's Spring'	CWil MOne NHol SSmi WPer
¶ 'Freckles'	MOne
'Freeland'	WPer
'Frigidum'	NHed
'Frosty'	CWil MOne
'Fuego'	CWil MOne SIng
x *funckii*	CWil ELau MBro NGre NHol NMen SDys SIng WPer
'Fuzzy Wuzzy'	CWil SSmi
'Galahad'	CWil MTPN
¶ 'Gambol'	SIng
'Gamma'	CHEx LBee MOne NHol NMen SChu SDys
'Garnet'	MOne
'Gay Jester'	CWil GAbr MBro MOne NGre SSmi WHoo
'Gazelle'	SSmi
'Georgette'	CWil MBro SSmi
'Ginnie's Delight'	CWil SSmi
'Gipsy'	CWil MBro
giuseppii	CWil MBro MOne MRPP NGre NHol NMen SIng SRms SSmi
– from Peña Espigüete, Spain	CWil MOne NHol NMen SSmi
– from Peña Prieta, Spain	CWil MOne NMen
'Gizmo'	CWil
'Gloriosum'	GAbr MBro MOne NBus NGre NRoo SIng SSmi
'Glowing Embers'	CWil MBro SSmi WHal
'Gollum'	MOne SSmi
'Granada'	MBro NGre
'Granat'	CPri CWil GCal NLak WPer
'Granby'	MOne NMen SSmi
grandiflorum	CWil GCHN MBro MRPP NGre NHed NMen SSmi WPer
– x *ciliosum*	CWil NMen
– 'Fasciatum'	CWil NMen SSmi
– 'Keston'	NGre SSmi
'Grape Idol'	CWil
'Grapetone'	CWil NGre SDys SSmi WHal
'Graupurpur'	CWil
'Gray Dawn'	CWil MOne SSmi
'Green Apple'	CWil NGre SSmi
'Green Gables'	CWil MBro SSmi
'Greenwich Time'	CWil MOne NMen SSmi
* *greigii*	EPot NNrd
'Grey Ghost'	CWil
'Grey Green'	CWil MOne
'Grey Lady'	CWil SSmi
'Greyfriars'	CWil MBro NMen SSmi WPer
'Greyolla'	CWil MOne SSmi WPer
¶ 'Grunspecht'	MOne
* 'Hades'	CWil
'Hall's Hybrid'	GAbr MOne NBro NHar NNrd SIng
¶ 'Hall's Seedling'	MOne
'Happy'	CWil MBro MOne
* 'Hart'	CWil MOne
'Havana'	CWil MOne NMen
'Hayling'	CWil MOne NHol NMen SSmi
'Heigham Red'	CWil ESis MOne NGre SIng SSmi
¶ 'Heliotroop'	MOne SDys
helveticum	See *S. montanum*
'Hester'	CWil ESis GAbr MBro MDHE MOne NBro NHar NMen SSmi
'Hey-Hey'	ELau LBee MBro MOne NMen WAbe WPer
'Hidde'	CWil MOne SSmi
'Hiddes Roosje'	SSmi
hirtum	See *Jovibarba hirta*
'Hookeri'	See *S.* x *barbulatum* 'Hookeri'
'Hopi'	CWil NHol
'Hortulanus Smit'	SSmi
'Hot Peppermint'	CWil
'Hot Shot'	CLyd
¶ 'Hullabaloo'	MOne
'Hurricane'	MOne
'Icicle'	CWil NBro NGre NHol NMen SIng SSmi WGor
imbricatum	See *S.* x *barbulatum*
'Imperial'	CWil MOne SSmi
ingwersenii	MOne NGre SIng SSmi
'Interlace'	CWil SSmi
'Iophon'	SSmi
'Irazu'	CWil GAbr MBro SDys
ispartae	CWil
italicum	CWil
'Itchen'	NMen SIng SSmi
'IWO'	CWil GAbr NMen
'Jack Frost'	CWil MOne NBro NGre NMen SChu SIng SSmi
'Jane'	MOne
'Jasper'	MOne
* 'Jaspis'	CWil MOne
'Jelly Bean'	CWil MOne NMen SSmi
'Jet Stream'	CWil GAbr MOne NMen SDys SSmi
'Jewel Case'	CWil ELau MOne SIng SSmi
¶ 'John T.'	MOne

'Jolly Green Giant'	CWil MOne
'Jo's Spark'	CWil
'Jubilee'	CLyd ELan GAbr MOne NHol NMen NRoo SSmi WEas WGor WPer WWin
'Jubilee Tricolor'	MBro MOne SSmi
'Jungle Fires'	CWil
'Jupiter'	EHyt ESis
'Justine's Choice'	CWil MOne
'Kalinda'	NGre
§ 'Kappa'	CWil MBro MOne NBro NHol SDys SIng SSmi
'Katmai'	CWil
'Kelly Jo'	CWil MOne NBro NGre NHar NMen SIng SSmi
'Kermit'	MOne SSmi
'Kibo'	CWil
'Kilt'	CWil
'Kimble'	CWil WPer
kindingeri	CWil GTou NMen NWCA SSmi
'King George'	CWil ESis GAbr GBin LBee MBro NGre NMen NPer SChu SSmi WGor WHal WHoo WPer WPyg
'Kip'	CWil NMen SSmi
'Kismet'	CWil MOne NGre SSmi
'Kolibri'	GAbr MDHE
kosaninii	CWil ELau MBro MOne NGre NMen SIng SSmi WPer
– from Koprivnik	CWil MOne NMen SDys SSmi WAbe
– from Visitor	CWil MOne
'Krakeling'	CWil MOne
'Kramers Purpur'	CWil
'Kramers Spinrad'	CHEx CWil ESis GAbr MBro MOne NGre NMen SDys SIng SSmi WEas WHoo
'Lady Kelly'	CLyd CWil ESis SIng
'Launcelot'	MOne WPer
'Lavender and Old Lace'	CWil ELau GAbr MOne MRPP NGre NMen SChu SMer
'Laysan'	CWil
¶ Le Clair's hybrid No. 4	MOne
'Leneca'	NGre SSmi
'Lennik's Glory'	See *S.* **'Crispyn'**
* 'Lennik's Glory No. 1'	CWil MBro
'Lennik's Time'	MBro MOne SSmi
'Lentevur'	CWil
'Lentezon'	CWil MOne
'Leocadia's Nephew'	CWil MOne
'Lilac Time'	CWil GAbr MBro MOne NGre NNrd SChu SSmi WHal
'Lipari'	CWil
'Lipstick'	CWil ELau NGre
'Lively Bug'	CWil MBro MOne NNrd SDys SIng SSmi WPer
'Lloyd Praeger'	See *S. montanum* subsp. *stiriacum*
* 'Lonzo'	CWil
'Lou Bastidou'	SSmi
'Lowe's Rubicundum'	MOne
'Lynne's Choice'	CWil SIng WHal
macedonicum	CWil MBro NGre SSmi
– from Ljuboten	NMen SSmi
'Magic Spell'	CWil MOne
'Magical'	CWil MOne SSmi
'Magnificum'	CWil NMen
* 'Mahogany'	CHEx GBin LBee MBro MOne NHol NMen NRoo WGor WHal
'Maigret'	CWil MOne SIng
'Majestic'	CWil MOne NGre NMen SSmi
'Malabron'	CWil MOne

'Malby's Hybrid'	See *S.* **'Reginald Malby'**
'Marella'	CWil SIng WPer
'Marijntje'	SSmi
'Marjorie Newton'	CWil
'Marmalade'	MOne SSmi
§ *marmoreum*	CMea CWil LBee NMen STre WEas WHal WPer
– 'Brunneifolium'	CWil EGoo ESis MBro NGre NHol NMen SChu SSmi WPer
– from Kanzas Gorge	NGre NHol SSmi
– from Monte Tirone	CWil SDys SSmi
– from Okol	CWil NMen SSmi
– from Sveta Peta	NGre
– subsp. *marmoreum* var. *dinaricum*	MBro MOne NMen
§ – – 'Rubrifolium'	GCal MRPP
§ – 'Ornatum'	NGre NHed SRms
'Marshall'	MBro
'Mary Ente'	CWil
'Mate'	NMen SSmi
'Maubi'	CPri CWil
'Mauna Kea'	MOne SSmi
'Mavbi'	NNrd
'Medallion'	CWil MOne
'Meisse'	MOne SSmi
'Melanie'	CWil
'Mercury'	CWil MDHE NBro NHol SSmi
'Merlin'	CWil SSmi
'Midas'	CWil
'Mila'	CWil
'Mini Frost'	CLyd CWil GAbr MOne NMen SIng
* 'Minuet'	CWil
'Moerkerk's Merit'	CWil GAbr SSmi
'Mondstein'	CWil GAbr MOne SIng
* 'Montague'	CWil MOne
§ *montanum*	CWil ESis SMer WPer
– subsp. *burnatii*	NGre SIng SSmi
– *carpaticum* 'Cmiral's Yellow'	MBro MOne
– from Anchisis	CWil MBro MOne
– from Arbizion	CWil MBro
– from Windachtal	CWil MBro MOne NMen
– subsp. *montanum* var. *braunii*	MOne MRPP
– 'Rubrum'	See *S.* **'Red Mountain'**
§ – subsp. *stiriacum*	CWil MBro MOne NMen
– – from Mauterndorf, Austria	SSmi
– – 'Lloyd Praeger'	CWil MOne NGre SDys SSmi
'More Honey'	CWil MOne
¶ 'Morning Glow'	MOne WGor WHal
'Mount Hood'	CWil WHal
¶ 'Mrs Elliott'	MOne
'Mulberry Wine'	CLyd CWil
'Myrrhine'	CWil MOne
'Mystic'	CWil MBro MOne NMen NNrd SIng WPer
¶ 'Nell'	MOne
'Neptune'	CWil
nevadense	CWil MBro MOne MRPP NGre NMen SRms SSmi
– var. *hirtellum*	CWil NMen SSmi
'Nico'	CWil MOne
'Night Raven'	CLyd CWil MOne NMen SIng SSmi
'Nigrum'	See *S. tectorum* **'Nigrum'**
'Niobe'	CWil MOne
'Nixes 27'	MOne
'Noir'	CWil GAbr MOne NBro NGre NMen SSmi WRHF
'Norbert'	CWil MOne
¶ 'Nortofts Beauty'	MOne

'Nouveau Pastel'	CWil MBro WHal
'Octet'	MOne NMen SIng
octopodes	CLyd ESis MDHE NBir NHed SIng
– var. *apetalum*	CWil GAbr NMen SIng SSmi
'Oddity'	CPBP CWil WCot WPer
¶ 'Ohio'	ELau
'Ohio Burgundy'	CWil ELau MDHE MOne NMen SSmi WAbe WPer
'Olivette'	SSmi WPer
'Omega'	MBro MOne SSmi WPer
'Opitz'	CLyd CWil WPer
'Ornatum'	EPot NGre SSmi WAbe WEas WHal
ossetiense	CWil GAbr MOne NMen SSmi
'Othello'	CHEx CHal EBrP EBre GAbr LBre MRPP NBir NLak NVic SBre SIng
'Packardian'	CWil MOne NMen SSmi
'Painted Lady'	CWil SSmi
'Palissander'	CWil MBro MOne NGre SSmi
'Paricutin'	CWil SDys
'Pastel'	CWil MOne NMen SSmi
patens	See *Jovibarba heuffelii*
'Patrician'	CWil EBrP EBre ESis LBee LBre SBre
'Peach Blossom'	CWil
'Pekinese'	CWil EWes MBro MOne NBro NMen NNrd SIng SSmi WEas WPer WWin
'Peterson's Ornatum'	MOne NGre SSmi
¶ 'Petsy'	MOne
'Pilatus'	CWil
'Pilosella'	MOne
'Pink Cloud'	CWil MBro SSmi
'Pink Dawn'	CWil MOne
'Pink Delight'	CWil
¶ 'Pink Flamingoes'	SSmi
* 'Pink Mist'	WPer
'Pink Puff'	CWil MOne SSmi
'Pippin'	CWil GAbr MBro WPer
'Piran'	CWil MOne
pittonii	CMea CWil ESis GAbr NLak NMen SSmi WHal
'Pixie'	CWil MOne NHed
'Plumb Rose'	CWil MBro MOne SChu
'Pluto'	CWil GBur SSmi
'Poke Eat'	MOne SSmi
'Polaris'	CWil SSmi
'Pottsii'	CWil GAbr MOne NHed
¶ 'Powellii'	MOne
* 'Prairie Sunset'	CWil MOne
'Precious'	CWil SSmi
'President Arsac'	SSmi
'Proud Zelda'	CWil MOne SSmi
'Pruhonice'	CWil
'Pseudo-ornatum'	EPfP LBee SChu
'Pumaros'	CWil NMen SDys SSmi
pumilum	CWil MBar NGre NMen
– from Adyl Su No 1	CWil SSmi
– from Adyl Su No 2	SSmi
– from Armchi	CWil MRPP SDys SIng SSmi
– from Armchi X *ingwersenii*	NMen
– from El'brus No 1	CWil MOne MRPP NMen SIng SSmi
– from El'brus No 2	SSmi
– from Techensis	CWil NMen
– X *ingwersenii*	CWil MBro
'Purdy'	WAbe
'Purdy's 50-6'	CWil MOne
'Purdy's 90-1'	MOne
'Purple Beauty'	CWil MOne
'Purple King'	CWil
'Purple Passion'	MBro
'Purpurriese'	CWil GAbr
'Queen Amalia'	See *S. reginae-amaliae*
'Quintessence'	CWil MOne
¶ 'R.H.I.'	MOne
'Racy'	CWil
'Radiant'	CWil
'Ramses'	MOne
'Raspberry Ice'	CLyd CWil GCrs MBro MOne NBro NHol NMen WAbe WPer
'Red Ace'	CWil GAbr NBro NMen SSmi
'Red Beam'	CWil MDHE NGre SSmi
'Red Delta'	CWil MOne NBir SSmi
'Red Devil'	CWil MBro MOne NMen SSmi
'Red Indian'	CWil
¶ 'Red King'	SSmi
§ 'Red Mountain'	CHal CPri CWil ELau MBro MOne MWat NLak SSmi
'Red Prince'	CWil
'Red Rum'	WPer
'Red Shadows'	CInt CWil ESis WPer
'Red Skin'	CWil
'Red Spider'	NBro
'Red Wings'	NGre SRms
'Regal'	MOne
'Regina'	MOne
reginae	See *S. reginae-amaliae*
§ *reginae-amaliae*	NHol SSmi STre
– from Kambeecho No 1	SSmi
– from Kambeecho No 2	MDHE NMen SDys
– from Mavri Petri	CWil MBro MOne SDys SSmi
– from Peristéri, Greece	MBro SSmi
– from Sarpun	CWil MOne NMen SSmi
¶ – from Vardusa	SDys
§ 'Reginald Malby'	CWil ITim MDHE NGre SSmi
'Reinhard'	CWil GAbr ITim MOne NMen NNrd NRoo SIng SSmi WHal WPer
'Remus'	CWil MBro NMen SDys SIng
'Rex'	NMen
'Rhone'	CWil GAbr MBro
* *richardii*	MBar NBus
'Risque'	CWil WPer
'Rita Jane'	CLyd CWil NMen SSmi
'Robin'	CLyd CWil MOne NBro NHol
'Ronny'	CWil MOne
'Roosemaryn'	MBro
* 'Rose Splendour'	CWil
X *roseum* 'Fimbriatum'	MBro NHed NHol NLak SSmi WEas
'Rosie'	CMea CWil GAbr MBro MOne NBus NGre NMen NRoo SIng SSmi WHal WHoo WPer WPyg
'Rotkopf'	CWil
'Rotmantel'	MOne SSmi
'Rotund'	CWil
'Rouge'	CWil MOne NMen SRms
'Royal Flush'	CWil SSmi
'Royal Opera'	CWil NGre SSmi
'Royal Ruby'	CWil GCHN LBee MOne NRoo SChu SSmi
¶ 'Rubellum'	MOne
'Rubin'	EGoo EPfP ESis MBro MOne MRPP NGre NMen NNrd SSmi WAbe WEas WHoo WPer WPyg
'Rubrifolium'	See *S. marmoreum* subsp. *marmoreum* 'Rubrifolium'
'Rubrum Ash'	CWil MBro MOne NMen
'Rubrum Ray'	CWil SSmi
* 'Ruby Glow'	ESis

'Ruby Heart'	NGre SSmi
'Rusty'	CWil WFar
¶ 'Ruth'	MOne
ruthenicum	NGre
¶ 'Sabanum'	MOne
* 'Safara'	CWil
'Saffron'	CLyd CWil MOne
'Saga'	CWil MOne
'Sanford's Hybrid'	MOne
'Santis'	MBro
¶ 'Sassy Frass'	MOne
'Saturn'	CWil GAbr NMen SSmi
schlehanii	See *S. marmoreum*
'Seminole'	CWil MOne SSmi
'Sharon's Pencil'	CWil
'Shawnee'	CWil
'Sheila'	GAbr
'Shirley's Joy'	CHal CWil GAbr MOne NMen SSmi WEas
* 'Sideshow'	CWil MOne
'Sigma'	MOne
'Silberkarneol'	See *S.* 'Silver Jubilee'
'Silberspitz'	CWil MOne NBro NMen WPer
§ 'Silver Jubilee'	CWil GAbr MDHE NBro NGre NHed SSmi
'Silver Spring'	MOne
'Silver Thaw'	CWil MOne NMen
'Simonkaianum'	See *Jovibarba hirta*
'Sioux'	CWil MOne NGre NMen SIng SSmi WPer
'Skrocki's Bronze'	NMen WPer
'Skrocki's Purple Rose'	CWil
'Slabber's Seedling'	CWil
'Smokey Jet'	CWil
'Snowberger'	CWil ELau ESis GAbr MOne NHar SIng WHal WPer
soboliferum	See *Jovibarba sobolifera*
'Soothsayer'	CWil MOne
'Sopa'	CWil MOne
sosnowskyi	CWil MOne NMen SSmi
sp. from Figaua Dhag	NGre
sp. Sierra del Cadi	MOne NHol
sp. Sierra Nova	NHed
'Spanish Dancer'	CWil MOne SSmi
'Spherette'	CWil MBro MOne NMen SSmi WPer
'Spice'	CWil SSmi
'Spinnelli'	MBro NHed
¶ 'Spiver's Velvet'	MOne
'Spode'	SSmi
'Spring Mist'	CWil GCHN MBro NHar WPer
'Sprite'	CLyd CWil GAbr MOne NMen SDys SSmi
stansfieldii	See *S. arachnoideum* subsp. *tomentosum* 'Stansfieldii'
'Starion'	CWil SSmi
'Starshine'	CWil MBro MOne NMen SSmi
'State Fair'	CWil MBro NGre SSmi WPer
* 'Strawberry Fields'	CWil MOne
'Strider'	GAbr MBro
'Stuffed Olive'	CWil MOne SDys SSmi
'Sun Waves'	CWil SSmi
'Super Dome'	CWil
'Superama'	CWil
'Supernova'	CWil
'Syston Flame'	MOne
'Tamberlane'	CWil
'Tambimuttu'	CWil
* 'Tambora'	CWil
'Tarn Hows'	CWil
'Teck'	CWil

§ *tectorum* ♀	CArn CNic CPri CWil EJud ELan EWFC GAbr GPoy GTou MBar MDHE SIde SIng STre WAbe WJek WOak WWye
* – 'Alp Gasson'	SIng
– subsp. *alpinum*	CWil MBro NMen SIng SSmi
– 'Atropurpureum'	ELan
– 'Atroviolaceum'	CPri CWil ESis GCal SIng WFar
– from Sierra del Cadi	SSmi
§ – var. *glaucum*	CWil ESis SSmi
§ – 'Nigrum'	CWil ESis LBee MBro MOne NBro NGre NHol NMen SIng SSmi
– 'Red Flush'	CWil NHar NMen SDys SIng SSmi
¶ – 'Robustum'	MOne
– 'Royanum'	ESis GAbr WEas
– 'Sunset'	CWil ESis MOne NMen SIng SSmi WEas WHal
– subsp. *tectorum*	MOne NGre
§ – – 'Atropurpureum'	CWil SIng SSmi
§ – – 'Boissieri'	CWil MBro NGre SSmi
– – 'Triste'	CWil ESis LBee MBro SSmi
– 'Violaceum'	MOne SIng WAbe
* 'Telfan'	SSmi
'Thayne'	NMen
thompsonianum	CWil ESis MRPP NGre NHed NHol NMen SIng SSmi
'Tiffany'	NHol WPer
¶ 'Tiger Bay'	MOne
'Tina'	MOne WPer
'Titania'	CWil MBro NBro NHar WHal
'Tombago'	CWil
'Topaz'	CWil GAbr LBee MOne SChu
'Tordeur's Memory'	CWil NGre NMen SSmi
'Traci Sue'	CWil MOne SSmi
* 'Trail Walker'	CWil
transcaucasicum	CWil SSmi
* 'Tree Beard'	CWil
'Tristesse'	CWil NMen WGor
'Tristram'	SSmi
'Truva'	CWil MOne SIng SSmi
'Twilight Blues'	CWil MOne
'Unicorn'	CWil
x *vaccarii*	MOne NGre NMen SSmi
'Vanbaelen'	CWil MOne SDys SSmi
'Vaughelen'	CWil MBro MOne
* 'Velvet Prince'	CWil MOne
x *versicolor*	NHol
vicentei	CWil MBro NHed NMen
¶ – from Gaton	MOne
'Video'	CWil MOne NMen SSmi
'Violet Queen'	CWil
'Virgil'	CWil MBro SDys SIng SSmi WPer
'Virginus'	CWil MBro
'Vulcano'	CWil GAbr
¶ 'Watermelon Rind'	MOne
webbianum	See *S. arachnoideum* subsp. *tomentosum*
'Webby Flame'	CWil
'Webby Ola'	MOne SSmi
'Weirdo'	CWil
'Wendy'	CLyd CWil MOne NMen
'Westerlin'	CWil GAbr MOne NGre SIng SSmi
'Whitening'	CWil GAbr NGre NMen SSmi
x *widderi*	SSmi
'Wollcott's Variety'	ELau GAbr MOne MRPP NBir NHar WPer
wulfenii	CWil NMen
'Zaza'	CWil

¶ *zeleborii* — MOne WHal
'Zenith' — CWil GAbr MOne
'Zenocrate' — CWil WHal
'Zeppelin' — CWil MBro
'Zircon' — NMen
'Zone' — CWil MOne NMen SSmi
'Zulu' — CWil NHed SSmi

SENECIO (Asteraceae)

§ *abrotanifolius* — MHar NNrd NTow
– var. *tiroliensis* — See *S. abrotanifolius*
aquaticus — CKin
§ *articulatus* — CHal
aschenbornianus — GCal
aureus — See *Packera aurea*
bicolor subsp. *cineraria* — See *S. cineraria*
bidwillii — See *Brachyglottis bidwillii*
buchananii — See *Brachyglottis buchananii*
candicans — See *S. cineraria*
cannabifolius — EBee
¶ *canus* — WLin
¶ *chionophila* — EBee
chrysanthemoides — See *Euryops chrysanthemoides*
§ *cineraria* — CHEx IBlr MBri
– 'Ramparts' — LHop WEas
¶ – 'Silver Dust' ♀ — ENot
– 'White Diamond' ♀ — CLTr ECha LGro
compactus — See *Brachyglottis compacta*
confusus — CPlN ECon ERea LCns SOWG
  WMul
doria — EBee EPPr SCro WCot WFar
  WLRN
doronicum — EMan
elaeagnifolius — See *Brachyglottis elaeagnifolia*
¶ *elegans* — LHil
fuchsii HH&K 318 — CHan
glastifolius — EBee ERea GBri LHil
'Gregynog Gold' — See *Ligularia* 'Gregynog Gold'
greyi Hooker — See *Brachyglottis greyi*
– hort. — See *Brachyglottis* (Dunedin
  Group) 'Sunshine'
¶ *harbourii* RMRP 96596 — IDac
hectoris — See *Brachyglottis hectoris*
heritieri — See *Pericallis lanata*
herreanus — MBri
¶ *jacquemontianus* — EBee
kirkii — See *Brachyglottis kirkii*
laciniatus — CHEx
laxifolius Buchanan — See *Brachyglottis laxifolia*
– hort. — See *Brachyglottis* (Dunedin
  Group) 'Sunshine'
'Leonard Cockayne' — See *Brachyglottis* 'Leonard
  Cockayne'
leucophyllus — LHil
leucostachys — See *S. viravira*
macroglossus — CPlN
– 'Variegatus' ♀ — CB&S CHal CPlN ERea
¶ *macrospermus* — CTrC
maritimus — See *S. cineraria*
mikanioides — See *Delairea odorata*
monroi — See *Brachyglottis monroi*
¶ *nemorensis* subsp. *fuchsii* — EMan
petasitis — CHEx LHil
polyodon — CInt EWes GBri MAvo MNrw
  SUsu WFar
– S&SH 29 — CFir CHan CRDP EBee SAga
  WCot WCru WHoo WWhi
populifolius — See *Pericallis appendiculata*
przewalskii — See *Ligularia przewalskii*

pulcher — CFil CGle CHan CSam GBri
  MAvo MMil MNrw MTho
  NTow SMrm SUsu WCot WCru
  WPGP
reinholdii — See *Brachyglottis rotundifolia*
rowleyanus — EBak
scandens — CB&S CFil CMac CPlN CPle
  ELan ERea ISea MCCP MNrw
  MTho SBra SUsu WCru WHer
  WPGP
seminiveus — WCot
serpens — MBri
§ *smithii* — CHan CRDP CRow ECha ELan
  NChi WBcn WCot WCru
¶ *speciosus* — NBir NTow
spedenii — See *Brachyglottis spedenii*
'Sunshine' — See *Brachyglottis* (Dunedin
  Group) 'Sunshine'
takedanus — See *Tephroseris takedanus*
tamoides 'Variegatus' — ERea WPyg
tanguticus — See *Sinacalia tangutica*
§ *viravira* ♀ — CDec CGle CHan CPle EHol
  ELan EMFP EMar ERea GBri
  LIck MBel MLLN MRav SMac
  SMad SPer WOve WSHC
  WWat
werneriifolius — See *Packera werneriifolius*

SENNA (Caesalpiniaceae)

alexandrina — CB&S MSal
artemisioides ♀ — CTrC SOWG
¶ *candolleana* — SPan
N *corymbosa* — CB&S CBot CHEx CPlN CPle
  (Lam.) Irwin & Barneby — ERea LChe LCns LHil SLMG
  SOWG
didymobotrya — SOWG WMul
hebecarpa — MSal
marilandica — CB&S EBee MSal WCru WSHC
obtusa Clos — See *S. candolleana*
– (Roxb.) Wight — CGre SBid
§ *obtusifolia* — CPlN MSal
tomentosa — See *S. multiglandulosa*

SEQUOIA (Taxodiaceae)

sempervirens ♀ — CB&S CDoC CGre CMCN
  CTrG EHul EPfP GChr IOrc
  ISea LCon LPan MBlu WDin
  WMou WNor
– 'Adpressa' — CDoC CMac EBrP EBre EGra
  EHul EOrn EPla LBre LCon
  LLin MAsh MBal MBar MBri
  MGos MPla NHol NWea SAga
  SBre SLim WPyg
– 'Prostrata' — EBrP EBre EOrn EPla LBee
  LBre LCon LLin MAsh MBar
  MBri MOne SBre

SEQUOIADENDRON (Taxodiaceae)

giganteum ♀ — CB&S CDoC CMCN CMac
  EBrP EBre EHul ELan ENot
  GChr GRei IOrc ISea LBre
  LCon LNet LPan MBar MBlu
  MBri NBee NPal NWea SBre
  SMad SPer WFro WMou WNor
– 'Barabits' Requiem' — LRHS MBlu SMad WMou
– 'Glaucum' — CBlo LCon LPan MBlu MBri
  SMad WMou
– 'Hazel Smith' — MBlu WMou
– 'Pendulum' — CBlo CDoC ERod LCon LPan
  MBlu WMou
– 'Variegatum' — WMou

SERAPIAS (Orchidaceae)
   lingua   LAma SBla SSpi

SERENOA (Arecaceae)
   ¶ *repens*   LPal

SERIPHIDIUM (Asteraceae)
   § *caerulescens* subsp.   EEls MAvo
     gallicum
   § *canum*   EEls IIve
   § *ferganense*   EEls
   § *maritimum* ♀   GBar GGar GPoy ILis NSti
    – var. *maritimum*   EEls
   ¶ *novum*   EEls
   § *nutans*   EEls MWat NSti
   § *tridentatum*   CArn
    – subsp. *tridentatum* EEls
    – subsp. *wyomingense* EEls
   tripartitum rupicola EEls
   § *vallesiacum* ♀   CJew EEls GBar SAga WEas
   vaseyanaum   EEls

SERISSA (Rubiaceae)
   foetida   See *S. japonica*
   § *japonica*   STre
    – *rosea*   STre
    – 'Variegata'   CPle ECon STre

SERRATULA (Asteraceae)
   ¶ *coronata*   EBee
   § *seoanei*   CBos CMea CNic CRDP CSev
                    CSpe CTri ECha EDAr EMan
                    EMon LHop MHig MWat NNrd
                    SDix SIng SRms WByw WCot
                    WHil WPat WWin
   shawii   See *S. seoanei*
   tinctoria   CArn CKin ELau EMan GBar
                    MHew MSal
    – subsp. *macrocephala* EPPr MTPN WFar

SESAMUM (Pedaliaceae)
   indicum   CArn MSto

SESBANIA (Papilionaceae)
   punicea   MFiF SOWG

SESELI (Apiaceae)
   dichotomum   SIgm
   elatum subsp. *osseum* SIgm
   globiferum   SIgm
   gummiferum   CArn CBot CGle CSpe EWes
                    LGre SIng SMrm WCot
   hippomarathrum   CGle
   libanotis   SIgm
   pallasii   SIgm SMrm
   varium   SIgm

SESLERIA (Poaceae)
   § *albicans*   EPPr
   caerulea   CCuc CElw EGar EHoe ELan
                    EMon EPla GBin LWak MBel
                    MLLN MWgw MWhi
    – subsp. *calcarea*   See *S. albicans*
   cylindrica   See *S. argentea*
   glauca   EHoe MAvo MSCN NSti WPer
   heufleriana   CSte EHoe EMan EMon EPPr
                    EPla ESOG LRHS
   insularis   CMea CSWP EMon EPPr
                    ESOG LRHS

   nitida   CCuc CElw EGar EHoe EMar
                    EMon EPPr LRHS MAvo
   sadleriana   EBee EPPr EPla ESOG EWes

SETARIA (Poaceae)
   palmifolia   CHEx LHil SApp WMul
   ¶ *sphacelata*   EBee

SETCREASEA See TRADESCANTIA

SEVERINIA (Rutaceae)
   buxifolia   SCit

SHEPHERDIA (Elaeagnaceae)
   argentea   CAgr CB&S CPle MAll
   ¶ *canadensis*   CAgr

SHERARDIA (Rubiaceae)
   arvensis   EWFC MHew MSal

SHIBATAEA (Poaceae - Bambusoideae)
   ¶ *chinensis*   EPla
   kumasasa   CB&S CCuc CPMA CWit EBee
                    EPla GCal IOrc ISta LJus LNet
                    MBal MBrN MCCP MGos
                    MUlv MWhi SCha SDry WJun
                    WNor
    – *aureastriata*   EPla ISta SDry
   lancifolia   EPla SDry WJun

SHORTIA (Diapensiaceae)
   galacifolia   IBlr
   soldanelloides   IBlr WCru
    – f. *alpina*   IBlr
    – var. *ilicifolia*   IBlr
   ¶ – – 'Askival'   IBlr
    – var. *magna*   GCrs IBlr
   ¶ *uniflora*   IBlr
    – 'Grandiflora'   GCrs IBlr

SIBBALDIA   (Rosaceae) See Plant Deletions

SIBBALDIOPSIS (Rosaceae)
   ¶ *tridentata* 'Lemon Mac' SIng
    – 'Nuuk'   GAri MGos

SIBIRAEA (Rosaceae)
   altaiensis   See *S. laevigata*

SIDA (Malvaceae)
   hermaphrodita   EMon
   ¶ *petrophila*   MFiF

SIDALCEA (Malvaceae)
   'Brilliant'   CM&M EBar EBee EPfP MBel
                    MTis NFai WMer WMow
   candida   Widely available
    – 'Bianca'   CBot CPea EAst EBar EBee
                    LFis MBel WFar WMow WPer
   'Crimson King'   LFis MAvo
   'Croftway Red'   CB&S CSpe EBrP EBre ELan
                    LBre LFis MFir NRoo SAga
                    SBre SChu SCro SHel SOkh
                    SPer WMaN WMow
   Crown hybrids   CTri
   'Elsie Heugh'   Widely available
   hendersonii   EBee
   ¶ *hickmanii* subsp. *anomala* IDac
    NNS 95462
   'Interlaken'   NFla NOrc WMow

'Loveliness' — CGle CRDP ECED ELan EMan MAvo MTis NCat WCot
malviflora — CBre MFir NSti SChu SRms
– dark form — GMac WMow
'Monarch' — NCut
'Mr Lindbergh' — EBrP EBre LBre SBre SPer WCot WMow WRus
'Mrs Borrodaile' — CBos EBrP EBre ECGN GBuc LBre MCLN MTis MUlv NHaw SBre WCot WMow WRus
'Mrs Galloway' — LFis WMow
'Mrs T. Alderson' — EMan WMow
neomexicana — EBee GCal NCat WBea WMow
'Oberon' — CHan GBuc NHol SPer WEas WFar WMow
¶ *oregana* — CSam
¶ – subsp. *spicata* — WLin
'Party Girl' — CHar CM&M CSam EAst EBrP EBre ECot ECtt EFou EHal EMar EOld GGar LBre LGan MCLN MPEx MTis NCat NLak NOrc NPri NRoo NVic SBre SHel WHoo WOve WPer
* *purpetta* — CPea NChi NCut NPSI SMac WBea
'Reverend Page Roberts' — CMCo LFis MMHG MRav SMrm WMaN WMow
'Rosaly' — WHoo
'Rosanna' — NCut WBea
'Rose Bouquet' — MHlr WCot
¶ 'Rose Bud' — CStr
'Rose Queen' — CGle CMGP CSpe EBrP EBre ECha EMan EMar ENot GChr LBre LGan LHop MAus MCLN MRav NFla NLon NRoo SAga SBre SChu SOkh SPer SRms WMow
'Rosy Gem' — CBlo GLil NCat NCut WMow
Stark's hybrids — SRms WBea
'Sussex Beauty' — CRDP ECha EFou LFis MLLN MRav NCat SChu SPer WCot WMow
¶ 'Sweet Joy' — EFou
'The Duchess' — LFis MAvo WMow
'Twixt' — WMow
'William Smith' ♀ — CHea COtt CRDP CSam EAst EBrP EBre ECED ECha EMan EPfP EWes LBre LFis LGan LHop MCLN MLLN NCat NFla NHol NOrc NPla SAga SBre SPer SUsu WCot WMow

SIDERITIS (Lamiaceae)

candicans — NSty
¶ *clandestina* — EBee
¶ *glacialis* — EBee
macrostachys — LHil
¶ *scardica* — WLin
scordioides — CFis SHFr
syriaca — CBot EBot ECha EMan EOHP SHFr SIgm
– subsp. *syriaca* — EBee

SIEVERSIA (Rosaceae) See Plant Deletions

SILAUM (Apiaceae)

silaus — CKin EWFC

SILENE (Caryophyllaceae)

acaulis — ESis GCHN GTou ITim LBee LFis MBro MPla MTho NMen NRoo NWCA SBla SIng SRms SSmi WAbe
§ – subsp. *acaulis* — CGra CMHG EPot GDra NCat SRms
– 'Alba' — EHyt EPot EWes GDra LBee NHar NNrd WAbe
– subsp. *elongata* — See *S. acaulis* subsp. *acaulis*
– subsp. *exscapa* — See *S. acaulis* subsp. *bryoides*
– 'Frances' — EHyt GAbr GCHN GCrs GDra GTou ITim MHig NHar NRya NSla NWCA WAbe WPat
– 'Francis Copeland' — ECho ELan
– 'Helen's Double' (d) — EHyt EPot NNrd WAbe
* – *minima* — CLyd EPot
– 'Mount Snowdon' — CInt EBrP EBre ELan EWes LBee LBre MTho NBus NHar NHol NMen NPri NWCA SBre WAbe WPat
– 'Pedunculata' — See *S. acaulis* subsp. *acaulis*
– 'Plena' (d) — NBrk
alba — See *S. latifolia*
alpestris — CMea ELan EPfP ESis LFis MBar MHig MNrw MPla MTho NGre NNrd NWCA SRms WCla WFar
– 'Flore Pleno' (d) ♀ — CMil ESis EWes LBee LBlm MHig WOMN WWin
argaea — EHyt
× *arkwrightii* — See *Lychnis* × *arkwrightii*
armeria — EMar WHer
asterias — CBre CSam EBar EJud GBuc MBel MNrw NBrk NBro NSti WPer WWin
– NS 657 — NWCA
¶ *bellidioides* — MAvo
¶ *campanula* — EBee
caroliniana — SSca
¶ – subsp. *pensylvanica* — EBee
¶ *chungtienensis* — EBee
ciliata — EPot
§ *compacta* — WCot WEas
conica — EWFC
delavayi — CNic
¶ cf. – ACE 2466 — EBee
¶ *densiflora* HH&K 326 — CHan
dinarica — SIng
§ *dioica* — CArn CKin ELan EWFC MChe MHew MRav NFai NLan SWat WCla WHen WHer WJek WShi
– 'Clifford Moor' (v) — EHoe LRHS NSti SCoo
– 'Compacta' — See *S. dioica* 'Minikin'
¶ – 'Dorset' — WBon
§ – 'Flore Pleno' (d) — CBot CJew ECha LFis LLWP MNrw MTho NBro SMrm WByw WCot WEas WHoo WPer WWin
§ – 'Graham's Delight' (v) — EMon GBri NCat WBea WCHb WCot WHer
– 'Inane' — CNat MAvo WAlt WCot WRHF
§ – 'Minikin' — CLyd ECha ELan EMon LRHS MAvo NBrk NCat WAlt WCot WTin
– 'Pat Clissold' (v) — EMon
– 'Richmond' (d) — ECha EMon GBuc MNrw
§ – 'Rosea Plena' (d) — CBre CGle CSam ELan EMan EMon MTho SChu SMrm WByw WHer WPer
– 'Rubra Plena' — See *S. dioica* 'Flore Pleno'

– 'Thelma Kay' (v)	CMil CSev GBuc LBay MAvo MLLN WCHb WCot WHer WPGP WPbr
– 'Variegata'	See *S. dioica* **'Graham's Delight'**
elisabethae	MRPP NWCA
– 'Alba'	WCla
§ *fimbriata*	CBrd CHad CHan EEls EJud ELan EPPr GCal LFis MFir MWat SAxl SMrm SUsu SWas WAbb WCot WRHF
– 'Marianne'	MNrw
fortunei B&SWJ 296	WCru
¶ – var. *kiruninsularis* B&SWJ 296	WCru
¶ *frivaldskyana* HH&K 214	CHan
gallica	EWFC
hookeri	EMar MTho NMGW NWCA
– Ingramii Group	CGra WAbe
¶ – JCA 1855400	CPBP
ingramii	CPBP MHew
italica	CKin
keiskei	ECha ELan NTow WPer
– var. *minor*	EWes MTho NWCA SSca WAbe WWin
§ *latifolia*	CArn EWFC NMir WCla WHen WHer WJek
maritima	See *S. uniflora*
¶ *morrisonmontana* B&SWJ 3149	WCru
multifida	See *S. fimbriata*
noctiflora	CKin EBee WCla
nutans	CArn CKin EJud EWFC MNrw WGwy WHer WUnd
* – var. *salmoniana*	WUnd
– var. *smithiana*	WUnd
orientalis	See *S. compacta*
* *parishii* var. *viscida* NNS 95-474	MRPP
pendula	LLWP
– 'Compacta'	CInt
petersonii	NWCA WLin
pusilla	CHal CLyd CNic NMen NWCA
¶ *regia*	EBee
rubra 'Flore Pleno'	See *S. dioica* **'Flore Pleno'**
saxatilis	NHol
schafta ♀	CHal ECha ELan EMNN GCHN MBro MFir MPla MWat NFla NGre NNrd NRoo NWCA SRms WCla WHoo WPer WWin
– 'Abbotswood'	See *Lychnis* × *walkeri* **'Abbotswood Rose'**
§ – 'Shell Pink'	CInt EPot EWes LHop MHig NWCA WAbe WHoo WOMN WThi
sieboldii	See *Lychnis coronata* var. *sieboldii*
¶ sp. ACE 1573	EHyt
suksdorfii	CPea EPot MBro MHig NHol WHoo WPyg
* *surortii*	WPer
¶ *tenuis* ACE 2429	GBuc
¶ *thessalonica*	EBee MBro
¶ *undulata*	EBee
§ *uniflora*	ELan EMNN EMar EWFC GCHN MFir MHew MWat NBro NOak NWCA SBod WCla WHen WHer WWin
– 'Alba Plena'	See *S. uniflora* **'Robin Whitebreast'**
§ – 'Druett's Variegated'	Widely available
– 'Flore Pleno'	See *S. uniflora* **'Robin Whitebreast'**

§ – 'Robin Whitebreast' (d)	CMHG CMil CPBP CVer EBar ECha ECtt ELan GCal MBar MRav MTho MWat NBro NHol NOak SRms WEas WHoo WOve WPer WPyg WWin
– 'Rosea'	CGle CMil CNic ECtt EMNN EMar MRav SIng SMrm SSca SUsu WCot WPer
– 'Silver Lining' (v)	ELan GBuc
– 'Variegata'	See *S. uniflora* **'Druett's Variegated'**
– Weisskehlchen	See *S. uniflora* **'Robin Whitebreast'**
– 'White Bells'	CMea CTri EBee WBea WHoo WPyg WSHC
vallesia	WPer WRHF
§ *vulgaris*	CKin EWFC MChe NLan NMir
– subsp. *alpina*	See *S. uniflora* subsp. *prostrata*
– subsp. *maritima*	See *S. uniflora*
¶ – – 'Flore Pleno' (d)	GMac
wallichiana	See *S. vulgaris*
'Wisley Pink'	CHal NMen
§ *zawadskii*	EBar EHal GBuc MNrw NGre SSca WPer

SILPHIUM (Asteraceae)

laciniatum	CArn ECro EMon
perfoliatum	CArn ECro GPoy NSti WCot

SILYBUM (Asteraceae)

marianum	CArn CGle CInt ECoo EFer ELan EMan EMar EPar GPoy LGan LHol MSal MWgw NFai SIde SRCN SSoC WCer WEas WFar WHer WHil WOak WWye

SIMMONDSIA (Simmondsiaceae)

chinensis	MSal

SINACALIA (Asteraceae)

§ *tangutica*	CGle CHEx CHan CRow EBar ELan EMan GGar MBal MHlr MNrw NBro NDea NSti SDix SMrm WAbb WCot WCru WFar WHil

SINARUNDINARIA (Poaceae - Bambusoideae)

anceps	See *Yushania anceps*
jaunsarensis	See *Yushania anceps*
maling	See *Yushania maling*
murieliae	See *Fargesia murieliae*
nitida	See *Fargesia nitida*

SINNINGIA (Gesneriaceae)

'Arion'	NMos
'Blanche de Méru'	NMos SDeJ
'Blue Wonder'	MBri
'Boonwood Yellow Bird'	NMos
canescens ♀	CHal
§ *cardinalis*	CHal EBak MLan WDib
§ × *cardosa*	MBri
'Cherry Belle'	NMos
'Diego Rose'	MBri
'Duchess of York'	CSut
'Duke of York'	CSut
'Etoile de Feu'	LAma MBri NMos
'Hollywood'	LAma NMos SDeJ
'Island Sunset'	NMos
'Kaiser Friedrich'	LAma MBri NMos NRog
'Kaiser Wilhelm'	LAma MBri NMos NRog

'Medusa'	NMos
'Mont Blanc'	CSut LAma MBri NMos SDeJ
'Pegasus'	NMos
'Princess Elizabeth'	SDeJ
'Red Tiger'	CSut
'Reine Wilhelmine'	SDeJ
'Royal Crimson'	CSut
Royal Pink Group	CSut
'Royal Tiger'	CSut
Tigrina Group	NMos SDeJ
tubiflora	CMon
'Violacea'	MBri NMos NRog
'Waterloo'	NMos NRog

SINOBAMBUSA (Poaceae - Bambusoideae)

¶ *intermedia*	LJus SCha
¶ *orthotropa*	WPGP
¶ *rubroligula*	WPGP
tootsik	SDry WJun
§ – f. *albostriata*	SDry
– 'Variegata'	See *S. tootsik* f. *albostriata*

SINOCALYCANTHUS (Calycanthaceae)

chinensis	CMCN CPMA EPfP LNet
	LRHS SMad SSpi WWoo

SINOFRANCHETIA (Lardizabalaceae)

chinensis	CPlN WCru WWat

SINOJACKIA (Styracaceae)

¶ *xylocarpa*	MBel

SINOWILSONIA (Hamamelidaceae)

henryi	CB&S CMCN

SISYMBRIUM (Brassicaceae)

§ *luteum*	MAvo WHer

SISYRINCHIUM † (Iridaceae)

x *anceps*	See *S. angustifolium* **Miller**
¶ *angustifolium*	EBot WWeb
– *album*	CInt MSCN NCut SMad WLin
	WRHF
§ *angustifolium* Miller	CHan EBar EBur ECha ELan
	GCHN MBal MBar MSal MWat
	NDea NFla NHol NNrd SRms
	SSmi WCla WEas WPer WWin
§ *arenarium*	EBur EHyt MDHE SBla
atlanticum	CPea EHyt ESis MDHE NBro
	WAbe WPer
bellum hort.	See *S. idahoense* var. *bellum*
¶ *bermudiana*	GBin
bermudianum 'Album'	See *S. graminoides* **'Album'**
– Linnaeus	See *S. angustifolium* **Miller**
birameum	See *S. graminoides*
'Biscutella'	CHad CHan CInt CLyd CMea
	EAst EBur ECtt ELan LHop
	NDea NMen SAxl SChu SLod
	SOkh SSea SSmi SSvw SUsu
	WCla WEas WGwG WHal
	WLRN WOMN
* 'Blue Ice'	CCuc CInt CMea CPBP CSpe
	CVer EBur EGar LWak MBro
	MDHE MHig NCat NHol
	WAbb WAbe WFar WHal
	WHoo WPat WPer WPyg
boreale	See *S. californicum*
brachypus	See *S. californicum* **Brachypus Group**
¶ *brevipes* F&W 7946	MSto

'Californian Skies'	CBro CElw CGle CHan CLon
	CMil CRDP EBur ECha EHyt
	LBee LBlm LGre LWak MDHE
	MHig NFla NHol SAsh SHBN
	SMrm SSmi SSvw SUsu SWas
	WKif WPat WRus WWhi
	WWye
§ *californicum*	CBen CBro CInt CLon EBur
	EHon ESis GBur LPBA MBar
	MFir MSta MWat NBro NHol
	NMen NNrd SSmi SWyc WCla
	WPer WWin WWye
§ – Brachypus Group	CBro CMea EAst EBar ECtt
	EPot GCHN GCra GTou LPVe
	MNrw NDea NMen NWes SWat
	WBea WBrE WCer WEas
	WOak
§ *chilense*	MSto SIng
coeleste	EBur MDHE
coeruleum	See *Gelasine coerulea*
commutatum	CInt EBar GBuc MNrw WElm
	WSan WWye
convolutum	LBuc
cuspidatum	See *S. arenarium*
demissum	CLyd CNic EBur
depauperatum	CLyd EBur EMar ESis NWCA
	WHer WPer
'Devon Skies'	CHid CInt CMHG EBur MNrw
	WSan WWin
douglasii	See *Olsynium douglasii*
¶ 'Dragon's Eye'	SUsu
'E.K. Balls'	CHea CInt CVer EAst EBur
	ELan EPla EPot LBee LWak
	MBro MHew MTho NBro NCat
	NFai NHol NMen NRya SBla
	SSmi SSvw SUsu WAbe WCla
	WHen WPat WWin
elmeri	EBur MSto
filifolium	See *Olsynium filifolium*
§ *graminoides*	EBur NBro WPer
§ – 'Album'	EBur GAri NBro WCla WPer
¶ – sterile form	LBee
grandiflorum	See *Olsynium douglasii*
'Hemswell Sky'	CLyd EBur MDHE MMil
	WWye
¶ 'Iceberg'	SWas
idahoense	NRoo
§ – 'Album'	Widely available
§ – var. *bellum*	CBro CInt CMHG EBar EBrP
	EBre EBur ECha ELan EPfP
	GCHN GTou LBee LBre MBal
	MNrw NCut NMen NRya
	NWCA SBre WBea WCla
	WHen WPat WPer
– – 'Rocky Point'	EBur LBee
– blue	ELan
iridifolium	See *S. micranthum*
junceum	See *Olsynium junceum*
littorale	EBur MSto WCla WPer
macrocarpon ♀	CBro CGra CInt CPBP EBur
	EHyt EPot ERos ESis GTou
	ITim LBee MHig NMen NWCA
	SSpi WAbe WCla WCot WHal
	WHoo WLin WOMN WPer
	WWye
'Marie'	EBur MDHE
'Marion'	CMil NHar SAsh SUsu SWas
	WWye
'May Snow'	See *S. idahoense* **'Album'**
§ *micranthum*	CBro EBur ECGP EWes
montanum	EBur ERos MSto NHol WHer
	WThi

– var. *crebrum*	CInt MSto
– var. *montanum*	NHol
'Mrs Spivey'	EBar EBur ECtt EMNN ESis MBal MBal MBro NMen NOak SIng WCla WRHF
mucronatum	EBur MSto
'North Star'	See *S.* 'Pole Star'
nudicaule	EBur
– × *montanum*	CFee EBur EMNN ESis GCal ITim MDHE MNrw NHar NHol NNrd NRya WAbe WPer
patagonicum	EBur ERos GBuc MSto NCat NNrd WCla WLRN WPer
pearcei	MSto
§ 'Pole Star'	CFee CInt CLyd CNic CSpe EBur GTou IBlr MFir NBro NHar NHol NMen SSmi SSvw WHal WPer
'Quaint and Queer'	CHea CInt CMil EBur ECha EMar ERav GCra LBlm LGan LWak MBrN MCLN MTho NBro NPer NRoo SHBN SSmi WAbe WBea WLin WPer WRus WWhi WWin
* 'Raspberry'	EBur NHol WAbe
scabrum	See *S. chilense*
'Sisland Blue'	EBur EHic EWes MDHE
sp. from Tierra del Fuego	CRow
¶ 'Stars and Stripes'	LPBA
§ *striatum*	Widely available
§ – 'Aunt May' (v)	CB&S CBot CBro CGle CM&M CRow EBur ECED ECha EHoe ELan ERav MBri MHlr MTho MWat NEgg NHol NSti SApp SMad SPer SUsu WAbe WEas WRus WWat WWye
– 'Variegatum'	See *S. striatum* 'Aunt May'

SIUM (Apiaceae)

sisarum	ELau GBar GPoy LHol MSal SIde WGwy WOak

SKIMMIA † (Rutaceae)

anquetilia	EPla MBar WBod WWat
× *confusa*	EHol MAll
– 'Kew Green' (m) ♀	CB&S CGre CHan CMHG CTrG ELan ENot EPfP EPla IOrc LHop MAsh MBal MBar MBri MGos NHol SAga SPer SPla SReu SSta WBod WFoF WPyg WWat
¶ *dulcamara*	ISea
japonica (f)	CTrG CTri ELan SRms
§ –	CHEx CLan CMHG CTrw EBrP EBre EMil ENot GChr GQui LBre MBri MGos SBre SDix SReu SSta STre WGwG WHCG WStI
– 'Alba'	See *S. japonica* 'Wakehurst White' (f)
– 'Bowles' Dwarf Female' (f)	CHig EBee EMon EPla MBar MBri MPla MRav NHol SPer WWat
– 'Bowles' Dwarf Male' (m)	EBee EPla MBar MBri MPla SBid SPer WWat
* – 'Bronze Beauty'	SBid SReu
– 'Bronze Knight' (m)	EBee EHic EMil ENot GBin IHos MAsh MBar MGos NHol SEas SPan SSta WGwG
– 'Cecilia Brown' (f)	WWat
¶ – 'Claries Repens'	SPer
¶ – var. *distincte-venulosa*	WCru B&SWJ 3544
– 'Emerald King'	MAsh MBar MBri
N – 'Foremanii'	See *S. japonica* 'Veitchii' (f)
– 'Fragrans' (m) ♀	CDoC CHig CSam CTrw EMil ENot IOrc MAll MAsh MBal MBar MBel MBri MGos SEas SHBN SPer SReu SSta WBod WFar
– 'Fragrantissima' (m)	EPla LRHS MBri
– 'Fructu Albo'	See *S. japonica* 'Wakehurst White' (f)
– 'Highgrove Redbud' (f)	MBar MBri MGos SSta
¶ – 'Keessen'	CDec
– 'Kew White' (f)	CBlo CSam EBrP EBre EPfP LBre MAll MBal MBel NHol SBre WHCG WLRN WWat
– 'Nymans' (f) ♀	CDoC CEnd EBrP EBre ELan EMil IOrc LBre MAll MAsh MBal MBar MBri MRav NHed NHol SBre SHBN SPer SPla SReu SSpi SSta WStI WWal WWat WWeb
– 'Oblata'	MBar
– 'Obovata' (f)	EPla
– 'Red Princess' (f)	EPla LRHS MBri
* – 'Red Riding Hood'	CLyn NHol
– 'Redruth' (f)	CB&S CLan EPla IOrc MAll
§ – subsp. *reevesiana*	CDec CPMA EBrP EBre EPla GQui IOrc ISea LBre MAsh MBal MBar MBri MGos MPla NHol SBre SHBN SPer SReu SSpi SSta WBod WDin WStI WWal
¶ – – B&SWJ 3763	WCru
¶ – – B&SWJ 3895	WCru
– – 'Chilan Choice'	SAga SSta
– – 'Robert Fortune' ♀	MBar SCoo WWat
§ – Rogersii Group	CTri GRei IHos IOrc MBal MBar MWat SPla
– – 'Dunwood'	MBar
– – 'George Gardner'	MBar
– – 'Helen Goodall' (f)	MBar
§ – – 'Nana Femina' (f)	IHos
§ – – 'Nana Mascula' (m)	CTri
– – 'Rockyfield Green'	MBar
– – 'Snow Dwarf' (m)	EPla LRHS MBar MBri
– 'Rubella' (m) ♀	CB&S CLan EBrP EBre EMil ENot GChr GRei IHos IOrc LBre LNet MBal MBar MBri MGos MWat NHed NHol SBre SHBN SPer SReu SSpi SSta WBod WDin WGwG WHCG WWat
– 'Rubinetta' (m)	IOrc MAll MAsh MBar MGos NHol SSto WWeb
– 'Ruby Dome' (m)	MBar MBri WWat
– 'Ruby King'	CSam EHic MAll MBal MBar MBri MGos NHol SSta WStI
– 'Scarlet Dwarf' (f)	MBar MBri
– 'Tansley Gem' (f)	ELan EPfP MAsh MBar
– 'Thelma King'	LRHS MBri
§ – 'Veitchii' (f)	CChe CTri EBee ENot MAll MAsh MBar MGos NBee NHol SHBN SPer WBod WDin WStI WWal WWeb
§ – 'Wakehurst White' (f)	CDec CPle CTrw MBar MBri MPla SAga SHBN SPer SReu SSta WWat
¶ – 'White Gerpa'	MGos
– 'Winifred Crook' (f)	CDec MBar WWat

'Royal Robe' CB&S CRHN GQui
seaforthianum CPlN LPan SOWG
¶ sessiliflorum (F) LBlo
sisymbriifolium WKif
wendlandii CB&S CPlN ERea SLMG
 SOWG

SOLDANELLA (Primulaceae)

alpina ELan GDra GTou MBal MTho
 NHar NHol NMen NRoo
 NWCA SBla SIng SRms WAbe
¶ austriaca GCrs
carpatica ♀ GCal GTou MBal MHig NCat
 NNrd NRya NTow WAbe
– 'Alba' EDAr NHar SBla SWas WAbe
cyanaster EPot MBal NBir NRya WAbe
dimoniei CFee EPot ITim MHig SBla
 WAbe
hungarica CLyd EDAr MBal MHig MTho
 NGre NWCA WAbe
minima CLyd NHar NSla WAbe
– 'Alba' ITim
montana CVer GCrs GTou MHig MTho
 NMen NNrd WAbe WRHF
 WRha
pindicola EHyt ELan EWes LBee MBal
 MBro MOne NHar NMen NNrd
 NWCA SIng SSmi WAbe
pusilla GDra ITim WAbe
villosa CRDP CTri MBal MHig MTho
 NHar NNrd NRya NSla NTow
 WAbe WFar WOMN WRHF
 WRus

SOLEIROLIA (Urticaceae)

soleirolii CHEx CHal EPot LPBA MBri
 SHFr SIng STre WHer WMow
 WOak
– 'Argentea' See S. soleirolii 'Variegata'
§ – 'Aurea' CHal EPot STre WOak
– 'Golden Queen' See S. soleirolii 'Aurea'
– 'Silver Queen' See S. soleirolii 'Variegata'
§ – 'Variegata' CHal WOak

SOLENOMELUS (Iridaceae)

chilensis See S. pedunculatus
§ pedunculatus CFee
¶ segethii EBee
sisyrinchium EHyt

SOLENOPSIS (Campanulaceae)

♦ axillaris See Laurentia axillaris
– alba CLTr CSpe LHop LIck
– pink LHop LIck
* 'Fairy Carpet' CInt
fluviatilis CLTr ECou

SOLENOSTEMON (Lamiaceae)

aromaticus CHal CInt
'Autumn' CHal MBEx
'Beauty' (v) CHal MBEx
'Beauty of Lyons' MBEx
'Beckwith's Gem' CHal
'Bizarre Croton' MBEx
'Black Prince' CHal MBEx WDib
'Blackheart' MBEx
'Brilliant' (v) MBEx WDib
'Bronze Gloriosus' MBEx
'Buttercup' WDib
'Buttermilk' (v) ♀ CHal MBEx
'Carnival' (v) CHal MBEx

'Chamaeleon' (v) MBEx WDib
'Cream Pennant' (v) MBEx
'Crimson Ruffles' (v) ♀ MBEx WDib
'Crimson Velvet' CHal
'Dairy Maid' (v) MBEx
'Dazzler' (v) CHal MBEx
'Display' CHal MBEx
'Etna' CHal
'Firebrand' (v) ♀ CHal MBEx
'Firedance' MBEx
'Freckles' (v) MBEx
'Funfair' (v) MBEx
¶ 'Gloriosum' CHal MBEx
'Glory of Luxembourg' CHal MBEx
 (v) ♀
'Goldie' MBEx
* 'Holly' (v) MBEx
'Inky Fingers' (v) MBEx
'Jean' (v) MBEx
'Joseph's Coat' (v) MBEx
'Juliet Quartermain' MBEx WDib
'Jupiter' CHal
'Kentish Fire' MBEx
'Kiwi Fern' (v) CHal CInt MBEx WDib
'Klondike' CHal MBEx
'Laing's Croton' (v) MBEx
'Lemon Dash' MBEx
'Lemondrop' CHal
'Leopard' (v) MBEx
'Lord Falmouth' ♀ CHal MBEx WDib
'Luminous' MBEx
'Melody' MBEx
'Mission Gem' MBEx
'Mrs Pilkington' (v) MBEx
'Nettie' (v) MBEx
'Ottoman' CHal
'Paisley Shawl' (v) ♀ CHal MBEx WDib
pentheri CHal
'Percy Roots' MBEx
'Picturatum' (v) ♀ CHal MBEx WDib
'Pineapple Beauty' (v) ♀ CHal MBEx WDib
'Pineapplette' ♀ CHal MBEx
'Pink Showers' MBEx
'Primrose Cloud' MBEx
'Primrose Spray' (v) MBEx
'Raspberry Ripple' CHal
'Red Croton' MBEx
'Red Heart' MBEx
'Red Mars' MBEx WDib
'Red Nettie' (v) MBEx
'Red Paisley Shawl' (v) MBEx
'Red Velvet' MBEx
'Roseblush' WDib
'Rosie' MBEx
'Royal Scot' (v) ♀ CHal MBEx WDib
'Salmon Plumes' (v) CHal MBEx
'Scarlet Ribbons' MBEx
scutellarioides MBri
'Spire' MBEx
'Stawberry Blush' CHal
'Surprise' MBEx
thyrsoideus See Plectranthus thyrsoideus
'Treales' (v) CHal MBEx
'Vesuvius' CHal MBEx
'Walter Turner' (v) ♀ CHal MBEx WDib
'White Gem' (v) CHal MBEx
'White Pheasant' (v) MBEx
'Winsome' (v) CHal MBEx WDib
'Winter Sun' (v) CHal MBEx
'Wisley Flame' MBEx
'Wisley Tapestry' (v) ♀ MBEx WDib
'Yellow Croton' MBEx

SOLIDAGO (Asteraceae)

altissima	See *S. canadensis* var. *scabra*
◆ Babygold	See *S.* **'Goldkind'**
brachystachys	See *S. cutleri*
caesia	ECha EGar EMan EMon EWes LRHS WCot
canadensis	CTri ELan WByw WFar
'Cloth of Gold'	CB&S COtt EBrP EBre ECro GChr LBre MBri NPro NSti SBre WCot WLRN WOld WOve
§ 'Crown of Rays'	CLyd EBrP EBre ECtt EFou LBre MArl MRav NFla SBre WFar WWin
§ *cutleri*	CLyd CNic ELan EMon MBar MTho MWat NGre NNrd SIng WHoo WPat WPer WPyg WWin
– *nana*	EPPr EWes
¶ 'Early Bird'	EFou
¶ 'Early Sunrise'	EFou
§ *flexicaulis*	GMaP
§ – 'Variegata'	CBos CM&M EBee EBrP EBre ECoo EGar EJud ELan EMan EMar EMon ERav GBin LBre LFis LGan LHop MHar NSti SBre SEas SMad WCot WHer WPbr
gigantea	ECGN EMon
glomerata	CHan WPer
◆ Golden Baby	See *S.* **'Goldkind'**
§ 'Golden Dwarf'	CDoC EBrP EBre EFou LBre MCLN SBre
'Golden Fleece'	See *S. sphacelata* **'Golden Fleece'**
'Golden Rays'	See *S.* **'Goldstrahl'**
'Golden Shower'	MWat
'Golden Thumb'	See *S.* **'Queenie'**
'Golden Wings'	CBre MWat
'Goldenmosa' ♀	CDec EBrP EBre ECGN EHal EMan EMon ENot EPfP GMaP LBre MBel MWat NFla SBre SChu SPer WCot
'Goldilocks' (Prim)	NPri
I 'Goldkind'	CLTr CM&M CTri ECtt EGar EMan ESis GAbr GChr GLil LWak MBri MFir MMal NCut NFai NOak NOrc SPla WBea WByw WRHF
§ 'Goldstrahl'	WLRN
Goldzwerg	See *S.* **'Golden Dwarf'**
graminifolia	EMon
hybrida	See *x Solidaster luteus*
latifolia	See *S. flexicaulis*
'Laurin'	EPfP NFai NHol WHoo WPyg WTin
'Ledsham'	CMGP EMFP MMil WLRN
'Lemore'	See *x Solidaster luteus* 'Lemore'
* *leuvalis*	CStr
microcephala	EMon
multiradiata	ESis
odora	MSal
* 'Peter Pan'	NFla
§ 'Queenie'	CHan CPea ECha ECro ELan ESis GCHN MBri MCLN MWat NPro NVic SEas SPer SRms WGwG WHal WLRN
randii	EMon
rigida	MRav WCot
¶ – subsp. *humilis*	EBee
– JLS 88002WI	EMon LFis
rugosa 'Fireworks'	CBre EFou WCot WOve

sempervirens	CBlo EBrP EBre EMon LBre SBre WCot
shortii	NSti
'Spätgold'	EFou
spathulata f. *nana*	CMHG WPer
§ *sphacelata* 'Golden Fleece'	WLRN WPbr WThi WWoo
Strahlenkrone	See *S.* **'Crown of Rays'**
'Tom Thumb'	EGle MRav SRms WEas WRHF
virgaurea	CArn CBod CKin GPoy LHol SIde WHer WJek WPer WSel WWye
– subsp. *alpestris* var. *minutissima*	CInt CNic MHig MTPN WAbe WPat
– var. *cambrica*	See *S. virgaurea* var. *minuta*
§ – var. *minuta*	GAri WCla
– 'Praecox'	CM&M NHol WLRN
§ – 'Variegata'	EHoe EPla NPro WAlt WLin WOld
vulgaris 'Variegata'	See *S. virgaurea* 'Variegata'

× SOLIDASTER (Asteraceae)

hybridus	See *× S. luteus*
§ *luteus*	CB&S CHan CMil CTri EFou GBri MBri NSti SPla SRms WEas WHal WHil WOld
§ – 'Lemore' ♀	CDec EBrP EBre ECGN ECha EFou ELan EMan EMon EPPr LBre LFis MCli MRav MWat NBus NFla NSti NVic SBre SEas SPer WCot WFar
'Super'	EFou LGre WCot

SOLLYA (Pittosporaceae)

fusiformis	See *S. heterophylla*
§ *heterophylla* ♀	Widely available
– 'Alba'	CB&S CPle LGre
– mauve	ECou
– pink	CPlN
– 'Pink Charmer'	ERea LRHS SBra
parviflora	CPlN ECou EWes

SONCHUS (Asteraceae)

palustris	EMon
platylepsis	CHEx

SOPHORA (Papilionaceae)

§ *davidii*	CPle SOWG WPGP
flavescens	ISea
japonica ♀	CAbP CB&S CLnd CPMA ELan EMil ENot EPfP GAri IOrc ISea MBlu MWhi NBee SHBN WDin WNor
– 'Pendula'	LPan SMad
– 'Regent'	LPan
§ 'Little Baby'	EMil EPfP ERea MBlu SHFr SMur
macrocarpa	CHan GQui ISea SBid
microphylla	CHEx CPle CTrC ECou LHop MAll MBlu SAPC SArc SIgm SMad SPar SRCN SVen SVil
– 'Dragon's Gold'	ECou ELan EMil EPfP LRHS
– 'Early Gold'	CB&S ERea GQui SBid
– var. *fulvida*	ECou
¶ – Sun King = 'Hilsop'	LRHS MGos SCoo WWeb
– var. *longicarinata*	ECou
prostrata Buch.	CBot ECou
◆ – misapplied	See *S.* **'Little Baby'**
– Pukaki form	ECou

tetraptera ♀ — CAbP CB&S CBot CHEx CHan CLnd CMac CPle CWit ECou ECre EMil GQui IOrc ISea LHil LHop MBlu MLan NPSI SEND SIgm SRms
– 'Gnome' — CB&S
– 'Goughensis' — WCru
viciifolia — See *S. davidii*

SORBARIA (Rosaceae)

aitchisonii — See *S. tomentosa* var. *angustifolia*
arborea — See *S. kirilowii*
§ *kirilowii* — IOrc SMad SPer
* – 'Glauca' — SMad
lindleyana — See *S. tomentosa*
¶ SF 95205 — ISea
sorbifolia — CAbP EHic EMil EPla MBar MTis MWhi NPro SEND SLPl SMac SPer STre WCot WDin WWat
– var. *stellipila* — SLPl WPGP
– *stellipila* B&SWJ 776 — WCru
§ *tomentosa* — CAbP CPle EBrP EBre LBre SBid SBre SHBN WCru WHCG
§ – var. *angustifolia* ♀ — CTri EBee ELan ENot EPfP MBal MBar MGos MRav SHFr SMac SPer SPla WEas WHer WWat

SORBUS † (Rosaceae)

§ *alnifolia* — CLnd CMCN LSyl SLPl WWat
americana — CLnd CMCN NWea
– 'Belmonte' — LSyl MBri
– *erecta* — See *S. decora*
anglica — WMou
'Apricot Lady' — CLnd MBri WJas
arachnoidea — LSyl
aria — CBlo CKin CLnd CPer CTri EBrP EBre GChr GRei LBre LBuc LHyr MBar NRoo NWea SBre WDin WMou WOrn
¶ – 'Aurea' — MBlu
– 'Chrysophylla' — CDul CLnd CTho CWSG ECrN LSyl MAsh MBri NWea SPer
– 'Decaisneana' — See *S. aria* 'Majestica'
– 'Gigantea' — CDul
– 'Lutescens' ♀ — CB&S CDul CLnd CSam CTho EBrP EBre ELan GChr GRei LBre LBuc LHyr LPan LSyl MAsh MBar MBri MGos NBee NWea SBre SHBN SPer SReu SSta WDin WHar WJas
– 'Magnifica' — CDoC CDul CTho ENot LPan WDin WJas
§ – 'Majestica' ♀ — CDoC CDul CLnd CTho ELan LPan LSyl MAsh MGos NWea SPer WJas WOrn
– 'Mitchellii' — See *S. thibetica* 'John Mitchell'
– var. *salicifolia* — See *S. rupicola*
× *arnoldiana* 'Apricot Queen' — CDul MAsh
– 'Brilliant Yellow' — MBlu
– 'Chamois Glow' — WJas
aronioides — LSyl
¶ *arranensis* — WMou
aucuparia — CB&S CDul CKin CLnd CPer ELan ENot GRei ISea LBuc LHyr LPan MAsh MBal MBar MBri MGos NBee NRoo NWea SHBN SReu WDin WHar WMou

– 'Apricot Lady' — LSyl SSta
– 'Aspleniifolia' — CB&S CDul CLnd CTho EBrP EBre ENot LBre LHyr LPan MGos NBee NWea SBre SPer WDin WJas WOrn
§ – 'Beissneri' — CLnd CTho MGos WWat
– 'Dirkenii' — CBlo CDul CLnd COtt GChr LSyl MAsh WJas
– 'Edulis' (F) — CDul CLnd CTho ESim IOrc LBuc MGos WDin
§ – 'Fastigiata' — CBlo CDoC CDul CEnd CSam CTho CTri EPfP EPla IOrc LSyl MAsh MBri MGos SHBN WDin WStl
§ – 'Fructu Luteo' ♀ — CBlo ENot LSyl MGos WBay
– 'Hilling's Spire' — CBlo CTho SLPl
– 'Pendula' — CDul
– *pluripinnata* — See *S. scalaris*
– 'Red Copper Glow' — MBlu
– 'Rossica Major' — CDoC CDul CTho GQui LSyl
– 'Rowancroft Coral Pink' — CTho LSyl
– 'Scarlet King' — MBlu
– 'Sheerwater Seedling' ♀ — CB&S CDul CDoC CDul CLnd CTho EBee EBrP EBre ELan ENot IOrc LBre LHyr LSyl MGos NBee SBre SCoo SPer SSta WDin WOrn
– 'Winterdown' — CNat
– 'Xanthocarpa' — See *S. aucuparia* 'Fructu Luteo'
bristoliensis — CTho EMon LSyl WMou
caloneura — CFil LSyl SBid WAbe WHCr WPGP
'Cardinal Royal' — CBlo CEnd GQui MBri WJas
'Carpet of Gold' — CBlo CLnd CTho LSyl
cashmiriana ♀ — Widely available
¶ – 'Rosea' — LSyl
– 'Rosiness' — LRHS MBri
chamaemespilus — GDra LSyl WPat
'Chinese Lace' — CEnd CLnd CTho EBee ECot LSyl MAsh MBlu MBri MDun MGos SFam SHBN SMad WBay WGor WJas WOrn WPyg WWat
§ *commixta* — CB&S CDul CEnd CLnd CMCN CTho IOrc LSyl MBar MBri MGos SPer WDin WJas WOrn
* – 'Creamlace' — CBlo
– 'Embley' ♀ — CB&S CBlo CDul CLnd CMCN CSam CTho EBee ELan ENot LSyl MBar MBri MGos NBee SLPl SSpi SSta WOrn
– var. *rufoferruginea* — GChr GQui LSyl MBlu WAbe WHCr
* – 'Serotina' — LSyl
conradinae hort. — See *S. pohuashanensis* (Hance) Hedlund
– Koehne — See *S. esserteauana*
'Coral Beauty' — CLnd
cuspidata — See *S. vestita*
× *decipiens* — WMou
§ *decora* — CDul CLnd CTho LSyl SPer
* – 'Grootendorst' — CDul
– var. *nana* — See *S. aucuparia* 'Fastigiata'
devoniensis — CDul CTho LSyl WMou
discolor Hedlund — CLnd ELan GRei LSyl MGos MWat NWea WJas
– hort. — See *S. commixta*
domestica — CAgr CDul CTho ENot LBuc SLPl SPer WMou
– 'Maliformis' — See *S. domestica* var. *pomifera*
§ – var. *pomifera* — EHol WMou

'Schouten' — ENot MBlu MBri
scopulina hort. — See *S. aucuparia* 'Fastigiata'
semi-incisa — LSyl
setschwanensis — GAri
'Signalman' — MBri SPer
sp. CLD 237 — LSyl
sp. Ghose — LSyl
sp. Harry Smith 12732 — LSyl
sp. KR 3595 — LSyl
sp. KR 3733 — LSyl
sp. nova — LSyl
'Sunshine' — CDoC LSyl MAsh MBri WJas
thibetica — LSyl
§ – 'John Mitchell' ♀ — CDul LLnd CMCN CSam CTho EBee ENot GChr GQui LPan LSyl MAsh MBlu MBri MGos NWea SPer WJas WOrn WWat
§ × *thuringiaca* — LSyl WMou
§ – 'Fastigiata' — CB&S CDoC CDul LLnd EBee ENot MGos WDin WJas
torminalis — CAgr CCVT CDul CKin LLnd CPer CSWP CSam CTho CTri LBuc NWea SPer WCoo WDin WMou
umbellata var. *cretica* — See *S. graeca*
ursina — CAbP LLnd CTho LSyl
× *vagensis* — LLnd WMou
§ *vestita* — LLnd CTho LSyl WWat
vilmorinii ♀ — Widely available
wardii — LLnd CTho LSyl
'White Wax' — CBlo MGos NEgg WDin WFar
'Wilfrid Fox' — LLnd EBee SHBN SLPl
willmottiana — WMou
wilsoniana — LSyl
'Winter Cheer' — LSyl
zahlbruckneri hort. — See *S. alnifolia*

SORGHASTRUM (Poaceae)
§ *avenaceum* — EBee ECha EHoe EMan
– 'Indian Steel' — EBee EMan MAvo MCCP MMoz MSte SVil
nutans — See *S. avenaceum*

SORGHUM (Poaceae)
halepense — MSte
nigrum — MLan

SPARAXIS (Iridaceae)
bulbifera — NRog
elegans — NRog
– 'Coccinea' — LBow
fragrans subsp. *acutiloba* — NRog
– subsp. *fimbriata* — LBow
hybrids — LAma
tricolor — EPar GSki MBri NRog
§ *variegata* — LBow NRog

SPARGANIUM (Sparganiaceae)
§ *erectum* — CRow ECoo EHon EMFW LPBA MHew MSta NDea SWat SWyc WHer
ramosum — See *S. erectum*

SPARRMANNIA (Tiliaceae)
africana ♀ — CAbb CHEx CPle ERea GQui LBlm LCns LHil MBri SAPC SArc SVen WOak
– 'Variegata' — ERea LCns
♦ *palmata* — See *S. ricinocarpa*
§ *ricinocarpa* — CHEx

SPARTINA (Poaceae)
pectinata — CHan GBin
– 'Aureomarginata' — CCuc CInt CRow ECha ECoo EGol EHoe ELan EMon EPar EPla ESOG GCHN GCal GOrn LHil MAvo MBar MSta MSte MWhi NDea NHol NSti SPer WRus WWye

SPARTIUM (Papilionaceae)
junceum ♀ — CB&S CPle ELan EMil ENot ISea MBal MBri MGos MWat SArc SDix SHBN SPer SPla SRCN SRms WBod WGwG WKif WOMN WUnu

SPARTOCYTISUS See CYTISUS

SPATHANTHEUM (Araceae)
orbignyanum — WCot

SPATHICARPA   (Araceae) See Plant Deletions

SPATHIPAPPUS See TANACETUM

SPATHIPHYLLUM (Araceae)
'Viscount' — MBri
wallisii — CHal EOHP MBri

SPEIRANTHA (Convallariaceae)
§ *convallarioides* — CFil CLAP CRDP EBee WCot WCru WPGP
gardenii — See *S. convallarioides*

SPERGULARIA (Caryophyllaceae)
rupicola — CKin EWFC

SPHACELE See LEPECHINIA

SPHAERALCEA (Malvaceae)
ambigua — ELan MLLN
coccinea — EMan MFos WCot
fendleri — CB&S CBot CLTr CMHG CSam EBar EOrc LFlo MBEx MSCN WOMN WWye
– *venusta* — CFir EBee
'Hopley's Lavender' — CSpe EBar EMan LHil LHop
'Hyde Hall' — EHic GBri MCCP MLLN WRus WWeb
incana — CSev MCCP MLLN SMrm
malviflora — WPer
miniata — CMHG ELan GBri LGre LHil LHop MLLN SAga SMrm
munroana — CBot CMHG CSev CSpe ELan LBlm LHil LHop MCCP MSCN SMrm SSpi WEas WOMN WSHC
– 'Dixieland Pink' — WEas
– pale pink — CSpe ECtt EMan LGre LHop SMrm
* – 'Shell Pink' — ECGP
¶ 'Newleaze Coral' — LHop
¶ *remonta* — MNrw
¶ *rivularis* — CGen EBee EMan
umbellata — See *Phymosia umbellata*

SPHAEROMERIA (Asteraceae)
argentea — See *Tanacetum nuttallii*
§ *capitata* — NWCA
compacta — CPBP

SPHAGNUM (Sphagnaceae) See Plant Deletions

SPHENOTOMA (Epacridaceae) See Plant Deletions

SPIGELIA (Loganiaceae)
  marilandica — CRDP EMan

SPILANTHES (Asteraceae) See Plant Deletions

SPIRAEA † (Rosaceae)
¶ 'Abigail' — CDoC
albiflora — See *S. japonica* var. *albiflora*
arborea — See *Sorbaria kirilowii*
arcuata — CTri MBri
§ 'Arguta' — Widely available
× *arguta* 'Bridal Wreath' — See *S.* **'Arguta'**
– 'Compacta' — See *S.* × *cinerea*
– 'Nana' — See *S.* × *cinerea*
bella — CPle MBar WHCG
betulifolia — EBee MRav SMac WHCG WPat WPyg
– var. *aemiliana* — CBot CMHG CPle EBrP EBre ECtt EHal EPla ESis LBre LHop MGos MPla MUlv NHol SBre SLPl SPan SSta WWat
× *billiardii* 'Macrothyrsa' — CB&S
– 'Triumphans' — CBlo ENot NCut NNor SHFr WWin
× *bumalda* — See *S. japonica* **'Bumalda'**
– 'Wulfenii' — See *S. japonica* **'Walluf'**
callosa 'Alba' — See *S. japonica* var. *albiflora*
cantoniensis — CPle
§ – 'Flore Pleno' (d) — CPle EMon MBlu
– 'Lanceata' — See *S. cantoniensis* **'Flore Pleno'**
chamaedryfolia — CPle
§ × *cinerea* — EPfP SSta WRHF
– 'Grefsheim' ♀ — CB&S CBlo CDoC COtt ECtt ENot GOrc MBri MGos MMil SPer SPla SSta WTro
– 'Variegata' — MPla
crispifolia — See *S. japonica* **'Bullata'**
decumbens — CPle WDin
densiflora — EPot
douglasii — GOrc MBar NRoo SMac
– subsp. *menziesii* — CBlo NLon
× *fontenaysii* 'Rosea' — CBlo CPle
formosana — CPle
– CC 1597 — WHCr
fritschiana — CMCN CPle SLPl WHCG
hendersonii — See *Petrophytum hendersonii*
henryi — CPle
§ *japonica* — CPle SBod
– 'Alba' — See *S. japonica* var. *albiflora*
§ – var. *albiflora* — CB&S CPle CTri ESis MBal MBar MWat NRoo SPer SRms WHCG
– 'Allgold' — NBee
– 'Alpina' — See *S. japonica* **'Nana'**
¶ – 'Alpine Gold' — SPan
– 'Anthony Waterer' (v) ♀ — CB&S CChe CPle EBrP EBre ELan ENot GRei LBre MBal MBar MBri MGos MRav NBee NFla NNor NRoo NWea SBre SHBN SPer SRms WBod WDin WFox WGwG WHar WSHC WWin
– 'Blenheim' — SRms
§ – 'Bullata' — CFee CMHG ELan ESis MBal MBar MBri MHig MPla NFla NHol NRoo NWCA SRms WBod WHCG

– 'Candle Light' — CAbP CBlo CWSG EAst EBrP EBre ECle EGra EMil EPfP LBre MAsh MGos NHol SBre SCoo SPla WRHF
– 'Country Red' — CBlo WRHF
§ – 'Crispa' — EPfP MBar MBlu MBri NPro
– 'Dart's Red' — CBlo GCHN IOrc MAsh MBlu MBri SCoo SEas SSta WWeb
– 'Fire Light' — CAbP CBlo EBrP EBre ELan EPfP LBre MAsh MGos NHol SBre SCoo SPer SPla SSta WWeb
– var. *fortunei* — WHCG
  'Atrosanguinea'
– 'Froebelii' — ISea LBuc WFox WRHF
– 'Glenroy Gold' — MBal WHen
– 'Gold Mound' ♀ — CMHG EBrP EBre ELan ESis GChr GOrc LBre MBal MBar MBel MBlu MBri MGos MRav MWat NBee NNor NRoo SBre SChu SEas SHBN SHFr SPer SRms WHar WSHC WTro WWat
– 'Gold Rush' — CMHG EBar WHCG WRus
– 'Golden Dome' — EHic WHCG
– 'Goldflame' ♀ — Widely available
– Golden Princess = — EAst EBrP EBre ECle ELan 'Lisp' — GRei IOrc LBre MAsh MBal MBar MBlu MGos MPla NHol NRoo SBre SEas SPer SReu SSta WWeb
– 'Little Princess' — CB&S ELan EMil ENot EPot ISea LHop MAsh MBal MBar MBri MRav MWat NBee NHol NRoo NWCA SPer SSta WDin WHar WWal WWat
– 'Magnifica' — WHCG
¶ – 'Manon Red Princess' — EBee
§ – 'Nana' ♀ — CMHG EHyt ELan ENot ESis MBal MBar MBri MPla MRav MTho NHar SReu SRms WEas WHCG WPat WPer WPyg
– 'Nyewoods' — See *S. japonica* **'Nana'**
– 'Pamela Harper' — EHic
N – 'Shirobana' ♀ — CB&S CHar CPle EBrP EBre ELan ENot ESis GOrc GRei IOrc LBre LHop MAsh MBal MBar MBri MGos MPla MWat NHol NRoo SBre SHBN SMac SPer SPla SRms SSta
– Magic Carpet = — LRHS MAsh SCoo 'Walbuma'
§ – 'Walluf' — COtt CPle EHic NNor SPan WHCG
'Margaritae' — CPle NPro SHBN SLPl SPer
mollifolia — CPle
myrtilloides — CPle
nipponica — CB&S MBar
– 'Halward's Silver' — CBlo CFai MGos MRav NHol NPro SLPl WBcn
– 'June Bride' — CBlo NHol WRHF
§ – 'Snowmound' ♀ — Widely available
– var. *tosaensis* hort. — See *S. nipponica* **'Snowmound'**
– – (Yatabe) Makino — LHop MWat SReu
palmata elegans — See *Filipendula palmata* **'Elegantissima'**
prunifolia (d) — CFai CPle EBee ELan ENot EPla LHop MBlu MPla SEas SPer WHCG WWin
◆ – 'Plena' — See *S. prunifolia*
salicifolia — CPle
stevenii — GAri

'Summersnow'	SLPl	
tarokoensis	CPle	
thunbergii ♀	CChe CPle CTri EBee ELan	
	ENot IOrc LHop MPla MRav	
	NFla NNor NWea SCoo SMer	
	SPer SRms WDin WGwG	
	WHCG WWal	
– 'Mount Fuji'	CAbP CFai EBrP EBre EHoe	
	ELan EPla GSki LBre MBri	
	MGos NLak NPro SBre SCoo	
	SMac WFar WTro	
* – 'Variegata'	EBee	
¶ *tomentosa*	WShe	
trichocarpa	CMCN	
trilobata	CPle WLRN	
ulmaria	See *Filipendula ulmaria*	
× *vanhouttei* ♀	CB&S CTri ELan ENot IOrc	
	MBal MBar MRav MWat NFla	
	NNor SHBN SHFr SMac SPer	
	SRms WDin WWal WWat	
– Pink Ice (v)	CAbP CDoC COtt CPMA CWit	
	EAst EBrP EBre ECle EHoe	
	ELan EMil LBre LHop MAsh	
	MBal MGos MLLN MPla MTis	
	SBre SHBN SPer SPla WDin	
	WHar	
veitchii	MBal MRav	
venusta 'Magnifica'	See *Filipendula rubra* 'Venusta'	
¶ *wilsonii*	CHan	
'Wyndbrook Gold'	NHol	

SPIRANTHES (Orchidaceae)

aestivalis	SWes
cernua	EFEx
– f. *odorata* 'Chadd's Ford'	WCot
spiralis	SSpi WHer

SPIRODELA (Lemnaceae)

§ *polyrhiza*	MSta

SPODIOPOGON (Poaceae)

sibiricus	ECha EMon EPPr EPla ESOG
	LRHS MCCP MSte SApp WCot

SPOROBOLUS (Poaceae)

heterolepis	EBee

SPRAGUEA (Portulacaceae)

§ *umbellata*	MFos WAbe
§ – *glandulifera*	NGre

SPREKELIA (Amaryllidaceae)

formosissima ♀	CMon EBot ETub GCra LAma
	LBow NRog

STACHYS (Lamiaceae)

§ *affinis*	CFir ELau GPoy
alopecuros	CMGP EBee WWin
alpina	CNat
× *ambigua*	EWFC NSti
betonica	See *S. officinalis*
§ *byzantina*	Widely available
§ – 'Big Ears'	ECha EGoo EMon MAus
	MCLN SAga SAxl SMrm WCot
§ – 'Cotton Boll'	CMGP ECha EFou GCal
	MCLN MHar MTho MWat NSti
	SAxl SPer WCot WGwG WPbr
	WWal WWat
– 'Countess Helen von Stein'	See *S. byzantina* 'Big Ears'

– gold-leaved	See *S. byzantina* 'Primrose Heron'
– large-leaved	See *S. byzantina* 'Big Ears'
– 'Limelight'	WCot
§ – 'Primrose Heron'	CMGP COtt ECha ECot EMan
	EPla GMaP MAus MFir NOrc
	NSti SMer SPer
– 'Sheila McQueen'	See *S. byzantina* 'Cotton Boll'
– 'Silver Carpet'	CB&S CGle ECha EFou EGoo
	EHoe ENot GCra GMaP LGro
	MAus MBel MBri MCLN MFir
	NBro NFla NOrc NRoo NSti
	SPar SPer SPla SRms WPyg
	WWat
§ – 'Striped Phantom' (v)	CHan EGoo MBel WCot WPbr
– 'Variegata'	See *S. byzantina* 'Striped Phantom'
candida	CLyd EHyt MSto NMen WThi
chrysantha	CPBP LGre
citrina	CLyd CMea GCal LBee WCot WPbr
coccinea	CElw CGle CHan CInt CLTr
	CPle CSpe EBar EBrP EBre
	GCra LBre LGre LHop LLWP
	MFir NBir NFai SBre SHFr
	SSca WEas WHil WOve WSan
	WWye
– apricot	WEas
¶ – 'Avondale Peach'	MAvo
– 'Axminster Lemon'	SAga
– 'Axminster Variegated'	SAga
– 'El Salto'	SAga
cretica	EOrc MAus SIgm SRCN WHer
densiflora	See *S. monieri*
§ *discolor*	CBos GBri MBri MLLN WCot
	WCru WHil WPbr WPer
germanica	CNat EMan
grandiflora	See *S. macrantha*
* 'Hidalgo'	LHop
iva	ESis LGre NTow WLin
lanata	See *S. byzantina*
lavandulifolia	EBee
§ *macrantha*	Widely available
* – 'Hummelo'	EFou
– 'Nivea'	CElw EBee EBrP EBre ELan
	EMan GCal LBre MRav SBre
	WPat WPbr WWal
§ – 'Robusta' ♀	CGle ELan EPPr MBri NBro
	SCro SHel SUsu WRHF WWye
– 'Rosea'	CNic EBee EFou ELan MArl
	MCLN MGed NWes SCro SHel
	WEas WOld WPer WRha WViv
	WWye
– 'Superba'	CDoC CGle CHan CRDP EBar
	EGar GCHN MAus MBel MBri
	NFai NMGW SMrm SPla WByw
	WFar
¶ – 'Violacea'	CStr EMon
§ *monieri*	CMGP CRDP EBrP EBre
	EMan ESis LBre LFis MCLN
	MRav SBre SIgm SMrm WLin
	WPer WSan
¶ – 'Hummelo'	LGre
nivea	See *S. discolor*
§ *officinalis*	CArn CKin CSev CStr EWFC
	GPoy MChe MHew MHig
	MPEx MSal NLan NMir SIde
	SIng WBea WCla WGwG WHal
	WHer WWye
– 'Alba'	CGle CJew CMGP CRDP
	MCLN MHig NBro NHol SUsu
	WAlt WFar WPbr WRha

¶ – 'Rosea' WPrP
– 'Rosea Superba' CGle CMil EBee ECha MCLN
SDix WCot WFar WPbr
olympica See **S. byzantina**
palustris CKin ECoo LPBA MSta WChe
¶ *plumosa* EBee
¶ *setifera* EBee
spicata See **S. macrantha**
sylvatica CArn CKin EMan EWFC GPoy
MHew MMal WCla WHer
¶ – 'Shade of Pale' WAlt
thirkei EBee EOrc
tuberifera See **S. affinis**

STACHYTARPHETA (Verbenaceae)
mutabilis SOWG

STACHYURUS (Stachyuraceae)
chinensis CB&S CMCN CPMA CRos
MBri WFar
himalaicus CFil WPGP
¶ – HWJCM 009 WCru
¶ *lancifolius* B&SWJ 2817 WCru
leucotrichus CPMA
'Magpie' (v) CFil CPMA EPfP SBid SSpi
WCru WSpi WWat
praecox ♀ CB&S CBot CDoC CEnd CFil
CPMA CPle CRos ELan EMil
ENot IOrc MBar MBlu MBri
MRav NPal SHBN SPer SReu
SSpi SSta WCoo WDin WSHC
WWat
– var. *matsuzakii* CFil WPGP
* – 'Rubriflora' CPMA ELan LRHS SPer

STAEHELINA (Asteraceae) See Plant Deletions

STANLEYA (Brassicaceae)
¶ *albescens* EBee
¶ *elata* EBee
¶ *integrifolia* EBee
¶ *pinnata* EBee

STAPHYLEA (Staphyleaceae)
bumalda CMCN
colchica ♀ CB&S CHan CMHG IOrc SPer
WPGP WSHC WWat
emodi CPle
holocarpa CPMA CPle WWat
N– var. *rosea* CPMA ENot EPfP LHop SMad
SPer
N– 'Rosea' ♀ CBot MBlu MGos SMur SSpi
WSHC
pinnata EPfP WHCr WNor
trifolia CAgr

STATICE See LIMONIUM

STAUNTONIA (Lardizabalaceae)
hexaphylla CDoC CHEx CPlN CSam EHol
EMil EPfP GQui SBid SBra
SPer SReu SSpi SSta WSHC
¶ *purpurea* B&SWJ 3690 WCru

STEGNOGRAMMA (Thelypteridaceae) See
Plant Deletions

STEIRODISCUS (Asteraceae)
* *euryopoides* NSty

STELLARIA (Caryophyllaceae)
graminea CKin
holostea CKin EMan EWFC MChe NMir
WHer

STEMODIA (Scrophulariaceae) See Plant
Deletions

STENANTHIUM (Melanthiaceae)
¶ *robustum* WPGP

STENOCARPUS (Proteaceae)
sinuatus CTrC

STENOCHLAENA (Blechnaceae)
palustris MBri

STENOGLOTTIS (Orchidaceae)
¶ *fimbriata* GCrs
¶ *longifolia* ♀ GCrs
¶ *woodii* GCrs

STENOMESSON (Amaryllidaceae)
§ *miniatum* EPot
variegatum CMon

STENOTAPHRUM (Poaceae)
secundatum 'Variegatum' CHEx CHal CInt IBlr LHil
♀ WMul

STENOTUS (Asteraceae) See Plant Deletions

STEPHANANDRA (Rosaceae)
incisa CB&S CBlo CGle CPle EMil
GChr IOrc SChu SPla WHCG
WWal
§ – 'Crispa' CGle CMHG CPle ELan EMil
ENot GOrc GRei LHop MBar
MBlu MWat NHol NNor SHBN
SHel SPer WCFE WDin WFar
WHCG WWat
– 'Prostrata' See **S. incisa** 'Crispa'
tanakae CDoC CGle CPle ELan GOrc
IOrc MBar MBlu MRav MUlv
MWat NFla NHol NNor SChu
SHBN SLPl SPer SPla STre
WDin WHCG WPat WPic

STEPHANIA (Menispermaceae)
glandulifera CPlN

STEPHANOTIS (Asclepiadaceae)
floribunda ♀ CB&S EBak GQui LCns MBri
SOWG

STERNBERGIA (Amaryllidaceae)
candida CBro CMon LAma
¶ – JCA 933000 SSpi
§ *clusiana* CMon LAma
colchiciflora EPot
fischeriana CBro CMon EHyt LAma
greuteriana EPot
lutea CAvo CBro CHan CTri EBrP
EBre ECha EHyt ELan EPot
EWes LAma LBre MBri MWat
NRog SBre SDix SSpi WEas
– Angustifolia Group CBro CMea CMon EMon
– var. *lutea* MS 971 CMon
macrantha See **S. clusiana**
sicula CBro EHyt EPot ETub

– var. *graeca*	CMon EHyt EPot
– MS 796	CMon

STEVIA (Asteraceae)
rebaudiana	EOHP GPoy

STEWARTIA † (Theaceae)
'Korean Splendor'	See *S. pseudocamellia* Koreana Group
koreana	See *S. pseudocamellia* Koreana Group
malacodendron	ELan EPfP LRHS MBri SSpi
monadelpha	CPMA SSpi WCoo WNor WWat
ovata	CGre EPfP SSpi WWat
N– var. *grandiflora*	CB&S LRHS SPer
pseudocamellia ♀	CB&S CDoC CGre COtt CPMA ELan GChr ICrw IOrc ISea LPan MBel MBlu MBri MDun MLan SBrw SHBN SMur SPer SReu SSpi SSta WCru WNor WWat
– var. *koreana*	See *S. pseudocamellia* Koreana Group
§ – Koreana Group ♀	CBlo CGre CMCN ISea MBri SReu SSpi SSta WDin WNor
pteropetiolata	CWSG
– var. *koreana*	LRHS
serrata	CGre EPfP LRHS SSpi
sinensis ♀	CPMA EPfP SSpi WNor WPGP WWat

STICTOCARDIA (Convolvulaceae)
beraviensis	CPIN

STIGMAPHYLLON (Malpighiaceae)
cilliatum	CPIN

STIPA (Poaceae)
barbata	EBrP EBre EGar EGle EPPr LBre LGre SBre SUsu WCot WHal
¶ *boysterica*	CFee
♦ *brachytricha*	See *Calamagrostis brachytricha*
§ *calamagrostis*	CCuc CElw CHan CVer EBrP EBre ECGN ECha EHoe EMon EPPr EPla ESOG GAbr GMaP GOrn LBre LHil MBrN MBri NBro NCat NSti SBre SMrm WHal WWoo
¶ – 'Lemperg'	EPPr
capillata	EBee ECGN EGle ESOG GBin MAvo SMrm WCot WHal
elegantissima	CInt LHil
extremiorientalis	EGle LGre
gigantea ♀	Widely available
¶ – 'Gold Fontaene'	EMon
¶ – 'Variegata'	CHEx
¶ *grandis*	WPer
lasiagrostis	See *S. calamagrostis*
offneri	LGre SBla
patens	CCuc EBee EHoe EPPr ESOG
pennata	CB&S ECGN EMan EPPr GBin MFir SAxl SMad WCot WLRN
pulcherrima	EPPr ESOG GCal SIgm
– 'Windfeder'	CFir ECGN SMrm
pulchra	GBin MCCP
robusta	NGno SApp
§ *splendens*	CCuc ECoo EFou EHoe EPPr MBrN SDix

tenacissima	CSte EFou EHoe EMon EPPr EPla LLWP MHlr
tenuifolia	CCuc CMea CMil CSam EBee ECED EGar EMan MBri MCLN MRav NBir NBro NChi NHol NVic SIng SPla WHal WWoo
tenuissima	Widely available
¶ *turkestanica*	LGre

STOEBE (Asteraceae)
plumosa	CTrC

STOKESIA (Asteraceae)
♦ *cyanea*	See *S. laevis*
§ *laevis*	CDoC CGen CHea CMea EAst ECGP ECha EHic GMac LFis MAus MBro NBro NNor SAga SAxl WBrE WCot WFar WPGP WPer WWeb
– 'Alba'	CHan CHea CM&M CMGP CRDP EAst EBrP EBre ECGP ECha EPar LBre LGre MBri MCLN NBrk NHol SAga SBre SChu SMrm SPer SUsu SVil WMow WRus
– 'Blue Star'	CB&S CElw CGle CRDP CSam EFou ELan LGre LHop MBri MCLN MFir MTho MWgw NHol NOak NRoo SChu SEas SMrm SPer WMow WRus WWin
– 'Mary Gregory'	CFir EBee EHic NHol SOkh WCot
– mixed	CPou
* – 'Omega Skyrocket'	WCot
– 'Träumerei'	CRDP EAst EFou EHic EMan GMac LFis MBro MGrG NHol SOkh WCot WLRN WWal

STRANSVAESIA See PHOTINIA

STRATIOTES (Hydrocharitaceae)
aloides	CBen CHEx CWat ECoo EHon EMFW LPBA MSta NDea SAWi SWat SWyc WChe

× STRAVINIA See PHOTINIA

STRELITZIA (Musaceae)
¶ *alba*	WMul
nicolai	CTrC LBlo LPal WMul
reginae ♀	CB&S CBrP CHEx CTrC ECon ELan ERea GQui IBlr LCns LPal LPan NPal SAPC SArc SRms WMul
– 'Kirstenbosch Gold'	LBlo

STREPTOCARPELLA See STREPTOCARPUS

STREPTOCARPUS † (Gesneriaceae)
'Albatross' ♀	WDib
'Amanda'	WDib
'Anne'	WDib
'Athena'	WDib
'Beryl'	WDib
'Bethan'	WDib
* 'Black Panther'	WDib
'Blue Gem'	WDib
'Blue Heaven'	WDib
'Blue Moon'	WDib

'Blue Nymph' WDib
'Blue Pencil' CSpe
* 'Blushing Bride' WDib
* 'Boysenberry Delight' CSpe LHil WDib
'Branwen' WDib
candidus WDib
'Carol' MBri WDib
'Catrin' WDib
caulescens LHil WDib
– var. *pallescens* WDib
'Chorus Line' WDib
'Clouds' CSpe
'Cobalt Nymph' MBri
'Concord Blue' MBri WDib
'Constant Nymph' WDib
cyaneus MSto WDib
'Cynthia' ♀ MBri WDib
'Diana' ♀ WDib
dunnii CFir WDib
'Elsi' WDib
'Falling Stars' ♀ CSpe MBri WDib
'Festival Wales' WDib
'Fiona' WDib
gardenii WDib
¶ – JCA 3790400 CPBP
glandulosissimus CHal LCns LHil SVen WDib
'Gloria' ♀ CSpe WDib
'Good Hope' ERea
'Happy Snappy' WDib
'Heidi' ♀ MBri WDib
'Helen' ♀ WDib
holstii CHal CSpe LHil
'Huge White' CSpe
'Jennifer' WDib
'Joanna' MBri WDib
'Julie' WDib
* 'Karen' WDib
¶ *kentaniensis* WDib
'Kim' ♀ CSpe WDib
¶ *kirkii* WDib
'Laura' WDib
'Lisa' ♀ CSpe MBri WDib
* 'Louise' WDib
'Lynette' WDib
'Lynne' WDib
'Maassen's White' ERea WDib
'Mandy' WDib
'Marie' WDib
* 'Maureen' CSpe
'Megan' WDib
'Mini Nymph' WDib
'Myba' MBri
'Neptune' MBri
'Nicola' MBri WDib
'Olga' WDib
¶ 'Party Doll' WDib
'Paula' ♀ MBri WDib
pentherianus SBla WDib
'Pink Fondant' CSpe
'Pink Upstart' CSpe
'Plum Crazy' CSpe
primulifolius subsp. WDib
  formosus
* 'Purple Passion' CSpe
rexii MSto WDib
* 'Rhiannon' WDib
'Rosebud' WDib
¶ 'Rosemary' WDib
'Ruby' ♀ MBri WDib
'Sally' WDib
'Sandra' MBri WDib
'Sarah' ♀ WDib

saxorum ♀ CHal CInt CSWP EMan LCns
LHil LIck MBEx MBri NTow
SRms WDib
– compact form LCns WDib
¶ 'Sian' WDib
'Snow White' ♀ CSpe WDib
* 'Something Special' WDib
'Stella' ♀ WDib
stomandrus WDib
* 'Sugar Almond' CSpe
'Susan' ♀ WDib
* 'Sweet Violet' CSpe
'Tina' ♀ MBri WDib
'Tracey' WDib
'Upstart' CSpe
'Violet Lace' CSpe
'Wiesmoor Red' MBri WDib
'Winifred' WDib

STREPTOLIRION (Commelinaceae)
volubile CPIN

STREPTOPUS (Convallariaceae)
amplexifolius EMan
roseus LAma

STREPTOSOLEN (Solanaceae)
jamesonii ♀ CHal CPIN CPle CSev EBak
ELan ERea IBlr LCns LHil
NRog SLMG WBod
– yellow ERea MBEx

STROBILANTHES (Acanthaceae)
anisophyllus CSpe
atropurpureus CBos CBot CGle CGre CHan
CHea CPle ECGN ECha EFou
EHal ELan GCal LHil MHar
NSti SAxl SMrm SUsu WCot
WCru WHer WMow WOMN
WOld WPer WWin WWye
attenuatus SWas WCru WFar
– subsp. *nepalensis* WWye
– – TSS CGle CHan EBee EMar WPbr
WRHF
dyerianus ♀ CHal WMul
violaceus ERea LFis SAga SMac WPer

STROMANTHE (Marantaceae)
amabilis See *Ctenanthe amabilis*
'Freddy' MBri
sanguinea CHal MBri
'Stripestar' MBri

STROPHANTHUS (Apocynaceae)
kombe CPIN MSal SLMG
preussii CPIN
speciosus CPIN MSal

STRUTHIOPTERIS (Blechnaceae)
niponica See *Blechnum niponicum*

STRYCHNOS (Loganiaceae)
¶ *cocculoides* LBlo
¶ *madagascariensis* LBlo
¶ *spinosa* LBlo

STUARTIA See STEWARTIA

STYLIDIUM (Stylidiaceae)
¶ *macranthum* MFiF

STYLOMECON   (Papaveraceae) See Plant
Deletions

STYLOPHORUM (Papaveraceae)
  diphyllum   CGen CHan CPBP CPou
                                          ECGN ECha EMar EMon EPar
                                          LAma MBel MSal WCot WCru
                                          WWhi
  lasiocarpum   EMar EMon GMac MBel MHlr
                                          NCat SSca SWas WCot WCru
                                          WFar

STYPHELIA (Epacridaceae)
  colensoi   See *Cyathodes colensoi*

STYRAX (Styracaceae)
  americanus   CB&S
  ¶ *formosanus*   WPGP
  hemsleyanus ♀   CAbP CFil CTho EPfP MBlu
                                          SPer SSpi SSta WPGP WWat
  japonicus ♀   Widely available
  § – Benibana Group   MAsh SReu SSta
  – – 'Pink Chimes'   CAbP CEnd CPMA ELan EPfP
                                          MAsh MBlu SPer SSta WWat
                                          WWes
  – 'Carillon'   CEnd ELan EPfP LRHS MAsh
                                          SPer
  – 'Fargesii'   LRHS SSpi SSta WFar
  – 'Roseus'   See *S. japonicus* **Benibana
                                          Group**
  obassia ♀   CArn CB&S CGre CMCN
                                          CPMA CTho CWSG EPfP
                                          SReu SSpi SSta WNor WWat
  odoratissimus   CArn

SUCCISA (Dipsacaceae)
  § *pratensis*   CArn CKin ECoo EMan EWFC
                                          MChe MFir MHew MHig NLan
                                          SSpi WGwG WGwy WHer
                                          WJek WOak
  – *alba*   SSpi
  ¶ – 'Corinne Tremaine' (v)   WHer
  – dwarf form   CLyd GDra LBlm MBro NGre
                                          NTow
  ¶ – 'Peddar's Pink'   EWes
  – *rosea*   SSpi

SUTERA (Scrophulariaceae)
  ¶ *breviflora* JCA 3-810-200   EHyt
  cordata   EBar LHop
  – 'Knysna Hills'   EHic EMan LIck MBEx NPri
  – 'Lilac Pearls'   EMan LHop
  – 'Pink Domino'   WLRN
  § – 'Snowflake'   CBar CHal CSpe LHil LPVe
                                          MBEx MLan NPri SCoo SMer
                                          WLRN
  grandiflora   CSpe
  ¶ *halimifolia* JCA 3-812   EHyt
  jurassica   EHyt NMen
  ¶ – H&B 19148   EHyt

SUTHERLANDIA (Papilionaceae)
  frutescens   CAbb CSam CSpe CTrC LHop
                                          SHFr SUsu SWat
  – Edinburgh strain   LLew
  – 'Prostrata'   SIgm
  microphylla   LLew
  – S&SH 56/61   CHan
  montana   CFir CTrC LLew SIgm

SWAINSONA (Papilionaceae)
  formosa   MSto
  galegifolia 'Albiflora'   CSpe EWes LGre SMrm SOWG
  tephrotricha   MSto

SWERTIA (Gentianaceae)
  kingii   WThi

SYAGRUS (Arecaceae)
  § *romanzoffiana*   CBrP EOas LPJP LPal

× SYCOPARROTIA (Hamamelidaceae)
  semidecidua   CFil CPMA CPle EPla LRHS
                                          SBid SSta WWat

SYCOPSIS (Hamamelidaceae)
  sinensis   EPfP ICrw SBid SSpi SSta
                                          WSHC WWat
  tutcheri   See *Distylium racemosum
                                          tutcheri*

SYMPHORICARPOS (Caprifoliaceae)
  albus   CChe CKin CPer ENot GChr
                                          NWea WDin
  – 'Constance Spry'   MTed MUlv SRms
  § – var. *laevigatus*   CB&S ENot GRei LBuc MBar
                                          WDin
  – 'Variegatus'   See *S. albus* **'Taff's White'**
  × *chenaultii* 'Hancock'   ELan ENot EPfP GRei MBar
                                          MGos MRav MWat NLon NPro
                                          SHBN SLPl SPer WDin WFar
  × *doorenbosii* 'Magic   CBlo EBee ENot LBuc MBar
    Berry'   NWea
  – 'Mother of Pearl'   CBlo ECha ELan ENot EPfP
                                          LBuc MBar MGos NWea SPer
                                          WDin WTro
  – 'White Hedge'   EBee ELan ENot LBuc NWea
                                          SPer WDin
  orbiculatus   WGwG
  – 'Albovariegatus'   See *S. orbiculatus* **'Taff's Silver
                                          Edge'**
  – 'Argenteovariegatus'   See *S. orbiculatus* **'Taff's Silver
                                          Edge'**
  – 'Bowles' Golden   See *S. orbiculatus* **'Foliis
    Variegated'   Variegatis'**
  § – 'Foliis Variegatis'   CTri EHal EHoe ELan ENot
                                          EPla LHop MBal MGos MRav
                                          SHBN SPer WAbe WDin WEas
                                          WGwG WHCG WSHC WWal
                                          WWat WWin
  § – 'Taff's Silver Edge' (v)   EHoe ELan EPla IOrc ISea
                                          MBar MPla NSti WWat
  – 'Variegatus'   See *S. orbiculatus* **'Foliis
                                          Variegatis'**
  rivularis   See *S. albus* var. *laevigatus*

SYMPHYANDRA † (Campanulaceae)
  armena   CLTr CPea EBur ECro ELan
                                          GBuc GDra MHar NPer SWat
                                          WBea
  asiatica   CHan WWat
  cretica   EBee EWll NTow SWat
  hofmannii   CGle EBur ELan LGan MBro
                                          MTho NBrk NFai NWCA SRms
                                          SSca SWat WBea WOve WPer
                                          WSan WWin
  § *ossetica*   CGle NWoo SSvw WCot
  § *pendula*   CFir EBar ECro EMan EWes
                                          GBri GBuc GCra LGan SCro
                                          SSca WFar WPer WThi
  – *alba*   See *S. pendula*

wanneri	EBur ECro EMan EPfP GCra	*orientale*	CElw CGle EJud EMon WCHb
	LGan MCCP NMen WOMN	*peregrinum*	See *S.* × *uplandicum*
	WWin	'Roseum'	See *S.* 'Hidcote Pink'
zanzegura	CNic EBee EBur ECro EEls	'Rubrum'	EAst ECot ELan ELau EOrc
	EMan LCot MHar SUsu SWat		EPfP EWes MAus MCli MSte
			NOrc NRoo SMrm SPer WCru
		tuberosum	CBre CJew CRDP EGar ELau
SYMPHYTUM (Boraginaceae)			EOHP GPoy LGan MFir MMal
asperum	ECha EGar ELan EMon EPPr		NCat NHol NSti SSvw WCHb
	MHew MRav MSal MTed		WFar WHer WRha WWat
	WCHb WCer		WWye
* *azureum*	EAst LRHS MAus MBri MSte	– JMH 8106	MDun
	WCHb WGwy	§ × *uplandicum*	CSev EJud ELan ELau EMar
¶ 'Belsay'	GBuc		MHew MSal SIde WCHb WCer
'Boking'	GAbr		WGwG WJek WOak WWye
caucasicum	CBre CElw CHan CSam ECED	– 'Axminster Gold' (v)	CLAP CRDP CRow IBlr SAga
	ECha ELau EPar GPoy LHol	– 'Bocking 14'	CAgr CBod CJew MGra
	MBri MHar NFai NSti SAxl	¶ – 'Denford Variegated'	MInt
	SIde SSvw WCHb WHer WHil	– 'Jenny Swales'	EMon
	WRha WWye	– 'Variegatum' ♀	CBot CGle CLAP ECha ELau
– 'Eminence'	CGle CRDP EBee EGoo EMon		EOrc EWes GCal GPoy LHop
	MGra MHlr WCHb WCot		MCLN MTho NRoo SSpi WBea
– 'Norwich Sky'	CDoC CInt EJud NMir WCHb		WCHb WEas WFar WLin
	WPGP		WWat WWin
'Denford Variegated'	WCot		
§ 'Goldsmith' (v)	CArn CMil CRDP EAst ECha	**SYMPLOCARPUS** (Araceae) See Plant
	ELan EMon EOrc LHop MAus	Deletions
	MBri MCLN MRav MTho		
	MUlv MWat NDov NLar NOrc	**SYMPLOCOS** (Symplocaceae)
	NPer NRoo NSti SAxl SSpi	*paniculata*	SSpi
	WHer WHoo WLin WPbr WPer	¶ *pyrifolia*	CFil WPGP
	WRus		
grandiflorum	See *S. ibericum*	**SYNADENIUM** (Euphorbiaceae) See Plant
'Hidcote Blue'	CBre CHan CMGP CTri ECha	Deletions
	ELan ELau EPla ILis LHop		
	MBri MSte NBro NHol NSti	**SYNEILESIS** (Asteraceae)
	SIde SLPl SPer WCru WElm	*aconitifolia* B&SWJ 879	WCru
	WPrP WWeb WWin	*intermedia* B&SWJ 298	WCru
§ 'Hidcote Pink'	CGle EAst ECha ELau ENot	*palmata* B&SWJ 1003	WCru
	EPla LHol LHop MSte NFla		
	NRoo NSti SLPl SUsu WCer	**SYNGONIUM** (Araceae)
	WFar	'Maya Red'	MBri
'Hidcote Variegated'	CGle SIng WCHb WRha	*podophyllum* ♀	LBlo
§ *ibericum*	CArn CGle CHan CNic ECha	– 'Emerald Gem'	CHal
	ELau GPoy LGan LGro LHol	– 'Silver Knight'	MBri
	MAus MDun MFir MNrw	– 'Variegatum'	MBri
	MWgw NSti SAWi SIde WCHb	'White Butterfly'	CHal MBri
	WOve WWat		
– 'All Gold'	EBee ECha ELau LGan MBri	**SYNNOTIA** See SPARAXIS
	WCru		
– 'Blaueglocken'	CSev EBee ECha NCat NRoo	**SYNTHYRIS** (Scrophulariaceae)
	WHow WSan	¶ *missurica*	NTow
¶ – dwarf form	SGre	*pinnatifida*	NWCA
– 'Gold in Spring'	EGoo EMon WCHb WCer	– var. *canescens*	MFos
	WFar WRha	– var. *lanuginosa*	CGra GCLN MFos
– 'Jubilee'	See *S.* 'Goldsmith'	– var. *pinnatifida*	WLin
– 'Langthornes Pink'	WPbr	*reniformis*	IBlr WCot WHil
– 'Lilacinum'	MBro SAga WCer WHer WWat	*stellata*	CLAP EBrP EBre GCal GGar
– 'Pink Robins'	EMon WCHb		LBre LFis SBre WHal WOMN
– 'Variegatum'	See *S.* 'Goldsmith'		WPGP WPbr
– 'Wisley Blue'	ELan EPfP NCat WCer WWoo		
'Lambrook Sunrise'	CFis EBrP EBre EPPr EPla	**SYRINGA** † (Oleaceae)
	LBre NBus NRoo NSti SBre	*afghanica*	See *S. protolaciniata*
	WCot WSan	*amurensis*	See *S. reticulata* var. *amurensis*
'Langthorns Pink'	ELan EMar EMon GBar GBri	× *chinensis*	WWat
	GBuc GCal NRoo WCHb WCer	– 'Saugeana'	SPer WPyg
'Mereworth' (v)	EMon WCHb WPbr	'Correlata'	IOrc
officinale	CArn CKin CSev EJud EPla	(graft-chimaera)	
	GPoy LHol MChe MHew	*debelderorum*	SSta
	MNrw MSal NFai NHex NMir	*emodi*	CBot WHCG
	NPer SIde SRms WHer WWye	– 'Aureovariegata'	CEnd CPMA
* – blue	MGra WWat		
– *ochroleucum*	WCHb WHer		

¶ × *henryii* 'Alba' WBcn
× *hyacinthiflora* WStI
– 'Esther Staley' ♀ ENot MRav SFam
– 'Laurentian' SSta
– 'Sunset' (d) SSta
– 'The Bride' SSta
× *josiflexa* 'Bellicent' ♀ CEnd CHan CPle ELan ENot
  ISea MAsh MBal MBar MGos
  MHlr MRav MTis NSti SChu
  SHBN SMur SPer SPla SRms
  SSta WHCG WPat
– 'Lynette' EPla WBcn
josikaea CBlo CPMA CPle LPan MBar
  SPer WHCG
julianae See *S. pubescens* subsp. *julianae*
§ *komarovii* subsp. *reflexa* EPfP LBuc LPan MBar MGos
  ♀ WWat
§ × *laciniata* Miller CBot CPMA CPle EHol MBri
  MRav SMad SMur SPer WGor
  WSHC WWat
§ *meyeri* var. *spontanea* CBlo CBot CPle CSam ENot
  'Palibin' ♀ ESis GOrc LBuc LHop MBar
  MBel MBri MGos MPla MTis
  NFla NHar NHol SBla SBod
  SHBN SPer SSpi WDin WGwG
  WHCG WPat WRus WSHC
  WWat
microphylla See *S. pubescens* subsp.
  microphylla
– 'Superba' See *S. pubescens* subsp.
  microphylla 'Superba'
¶ *oblata* WWoo
– var. *donaldii* SSta
palibiniana See *S. meyeri* 'Palibin'
patula hort. See *S. meyeri* 'Palibin'
◆ *patula* (Palibin) Nakai See *S. pubescens* subsp. *patula*
pekinensis See *S. reticulata* subsp.
  pekinensis
× *persica* ♀ EHal EPfP ERav ISea MGos
  MWat SPer SPla WPyg WSpi
– 'Alba' ♀ CBot CMil GQui SMad SPla
  WHCG WSHC WWat
– var. *laciniata* See *S.* × *laciniata* Miller
pinnatifolia CBot CPle WHCG
× *prestoniae* 'Agnes MGos
  Smith'
– 'Audrey' MGos
¶ – 'Coral' COtt
– 'Desdemona' CB&S
– 'Elinor' ♀ CBlo CMHG CPMA CPle ENot
  ISea NSti SPer
– 'Isabella' MGos NFla
– 'Redwine' COtt MGos
¶ – 'Royalty' COtt
§ *protolaciniata* CMHG EPla MBlu MPla NPro
  SSta WFar
§ *pubescens* subsp. MHlr
  microphylla
§ – – 'Superba' ♀ CPle ELan ENot GChr IOrc
  MAsh MBel MBri MBro MGos
  NBee NFla NHol NRoo SHBN
  SPer SPla SSpi SSta WHCG
  WPat WPyg WSHC WWal
  WWat
– subsp. *patula* EAst ELan IHos IOrc LNet
  MBal MWat NBee NRoo SPla
  WStI
§ – – 'Miss Kim' ♀ CBlo EBee EBrP EBre ECle
  LBre MAsh MBel MBri MGos
  NPro SBre SHBN SSta WGwG
  WHCG WPyg
reflexa See *S. komarorii* subsp. *reflexa*

§ *reticulata* subsp. MBal
  amurensis
– var. *mandschurica* See *S. reticulata* var. *amurensis*
§ – subsp. *pekinensis* CBot
sweginzowii LBuc MBal SPer WRus WWat
tomentella CPle CWSG NWea
velutina See *S. patula* (Palibin) Nakai
¶ *villosa* MWhi
vulgaris CBlo GOrc GRei LBuc MBar
  NWea
– var. *alba* MBar
– 'Albert F. Holden' SSta
§ – 'Andenken an Ludwig CB&S CBot CTho CTri ECtt
  Späth' ♀ ENot IOrc MBar MBri MGos
  NWea SHBN SPer WPyg WWal
  WWeb
– 'Arthur William Paul' MRav
  (d)
– 'Aurea' EPla MRav WBcn
– 'Avalanche' SSta
– 'Belle de Nancy' (d) ECtt EHic ELan MAsh MBri
  MWat SHBN WDin WLRN
  WPyg
– 'Charles Joly' (d) ♀ CB&S CBlo CTho ELan ENot
  GChr GRei IHos IOrc LNet
  MAsh MBal MBar MBri MGos
  MRav MTis NBee NWea SHBN
  SPer WDin WShe WStI
– 'Condorcet' (d) LNet
– 'Congo' ENot SCoo
– 'Edward J. Gardner' (d) ENot SPer
– 'Ellen Willmott' (d) MRav
– 'Firmament' ♀ ELan ENot SCoo SHBN SPer
  SRms
– 'Glory of Horstenstein' See *S. vulgaris* 'Ruhm von
  Horstenstein'
– 'Katherine Havemeyer' CB&S CBot CDoC CSam CTri
  (d) ♀ ELan ENot GChr GRei LBuc
  MAsh MBri MGos MHlr MRav
  SHBN SPer SReu WDin WStI
– 'Krasavitsa Moskvy' SSta
– 'Lucie Baltet' SSta
– 'Madame Antoine ENot MRav SPer
  Buchner' (d) ♀
– 'Madame Florent CBlo
  Stepman'
– 'Madame Lemoine' (d) CB&S CBot CTho ELan ENot
  ♀ GChr GRei LBuc LNet MAsh
  MBal MBar MBri MGos MHlr
  MRav NBee NWea SFam
  SHBN SPer SReu WDin WStI
– 'Masséna' ENot MRav SCoo SPer WWeb
– 'Maud Notcutt' ENot SCoo
– 'Michel Buchner' (d) CB&S ECtt ENot GRei IHos
  IOrc MAsh MBar MBri MRav
  MWat
– 'Mrs Edward Harding' ECtt ENot LBuc LNet MBal
  (d) ♀ MBri MGos SPer WLRN
– 'Olivier de Serres' SSta
– 'Président Grévy' (d) CDoC ECle SPer
– 'Primrose' CBlo CBot CTho EHic ELan
  ENot EPfP MBal SPer SSta
  WDin WLRN
– 'Romance' SSta
– 'Sensation' CPle EBee EHic ENot MRav
  SCoo SHBN SPer SSta
– 'Silver King' SSta
– 'Souvenir de Louis See *S. vulgaris* 'Andenken an
  Spaeth' Ludwig Späth'
– variegated double (d) MBal
– 'Vestale' ♀ CBlo ENot SCoo SRms
¶ *wolfii* CPle

yunnanensis	ELan
¶ – 'Rosea'	ISea

SYZYGIUM (Myrtaceae) See Plant Deletions

TABERNAEMONTANA (Apocynaceae)
coronaria	See *T. divaricata*

TACITUS See GRAPTOPETALUM

TAGETES (Asteraceae)
lemmonii	SMac
lucida	EOHP MSal

TAIWANIA (Taxodiaceae) See Plant Deletions

TALBOTIA (Velloziaceae)
elegans	WCot

TALINUM (Portulacaceae)
calycinum	NGre
okanoganense	CGra MFos NGre NTow NWCA WAbe WOMN
rugospermum	WAbe
teretifolium	WThi
'Zoe'	SIng WAbe WFar

TAMARINDUS (Caesalpiniaceae)
¶ *indica* (F)	LBlo

TAMARIX (Tamaricaceae)
africana	SEND WWin
gallica	CBlo ENot GCHN NWea SAPC SArc SEND WSHC
germanica	See *Myricaria germanica*
§ *parviflora*	CB&S CBlo EMil IOrc MGos SSoC WWal
pentandra	See *T. ramosissima*
§ *ramosissima*	CSpe EBrP EBre ELan EPla GChr LBre SBre SEND SMrm SRms SSoC SSta WDin WTro WWeb
– 'Pink Cascade'	CTri EBee EMil ENot EPfP GChr MBri MRav SEas SPer WDin WGwG WStI WWal
§ – 'Rubra' ♀	CBlo CChe CDoC EMil ENot EPfP IOrc MBlu MGos MMHG WPyg
– 'Summer Glow'	See *T. ramosissima* 'Rubra'
tetrandra ♀	CMHG EAst EBrP EBre ELan ENot GChr GOrc LBre LNet LPan MWat NBee NNor NPer SBre SHBN SPer SReu SRms WBod WBrE WFar WHar WRHF WStI WTro WWeb
– var. *purpurea*	See *T. parviflora*

TAMUS (Dioscoreaceae)
communis	CArn

TANACETUM † (Asteraceae)
§ *argenteum*	LRHS MRav MTho NTow SIng
– subsp. *canum*	ELan EWes LRHS MAsh
§ *balsamita*	CArn CSev EJud ELan ELau EOHP ERav GPoy LBay MBri MSal WHer WJek WOak WPer WSel WWye
§ – subsp. *balsametoides*	CBod EJud ELau LHol MChe MGra NPri SIde WGwy WJek WWye

§ – subsp. *balsamita*	EOHP GPoy LHol MRav MSal SIde
– var. *tanacetoides*	See *T. balsamita* subsp. *balsamita*
– *tomentosum*	See *T. balsamita* subsp. *balsametoides*
capitatum	See *Sphaeromeria capitata*
§ *cinerariifolium*	CArn CBod CInt GPoy SIde SPil WPer
§ *coccineum*	CChr EOHP GBar GPoy MSal NVic SRms WWin
– 'Aphrodite'	SMrm
– 'Brenda' ♀	EFou MRav SMrm
* – 'Duplex'	EPfP
– 'Duro'	CMdw GBuc NCut
– 'Eileen May Robinson' ♀	EBee ECED ECot EPfP NCut NFla SMrm
– 'Evenglow'	CM&M CMGP EFou MRav MTis SMrm
¶ – 'H.M. Pike'	CMGP EBee
– 'James Kelway' ♀	ECot ENot EPfP EWll GChr MBri MRav NBir NFai SMrm SRms
¶ – 'K.M. Price'	MRav
– 'Kelway's Glorious'	NCut
– 'King Size'	CSam NFla NMir WFar
– 'Laurin'	EBrP EBre LBre SBre
¶ – 'Madeleine' (d)	EBee MAvo MTis
– 'Queen Mary'	CMGP EMan MAvo
– Robinson's giant flowered	WRHF
– 'Robinson's Pink'	EMan GMaP NFla NOrc NPla NPri NRoo SMrm SRms
– 'Robinson's Red'	GBur GMaP LIck MAvo MGrG NOrc NPla NPri NRoo SMrm SPla WRus
– 'Salmon Beauty'	EFou EMan LRHS
– 'Scarlet Glow'	MWat
– 'Snow Cloud'	EBee EFou EMan MWat SMrm
– 'Vanessa'	EBee EMan SMrm
¶ *coccineus* 'Robinson's Roseum'	NCut
§ *corymbosum*	CGle CSpe EMon GCal LFis NCat WCot
– 'Festafel'	ECha MRav
densum	ECho EPot WCFE
– subsp. *amani*	ECha ELan EMFP GTou LBee LGro MPla MWat NRoo NWCA SEND SRms SSmi WWin
§ *haradjanii*	CGle ELan EMNN GCHN MBro MHar NNor SBla SChu WByw WEas WHer WHoo WOld WSHC
herderi	See *Hippolytia herderi*
¶ 'Jackpot'	EWes LRHS WMow
§ *macrophyllum*	EMon GCal WCot WPer
niveum	CArn CHad EBee EGar EOHP MSal SPil WBea WCot
pallidum	See *Leucanthemopsis pallida*
§ *parthenium*	CArn CHEx CKin EEls EJud ELau EWFC GBar GPoy LHol MChe MHew NFai NHex NPer NRoo SIde WGwG WHer WOak WWye
– 'Aureum'	CM&M CRow ECha EEls ELan ELau EOld GPoy LGro MBri MChe NFai NHex SIng SMad SPer SRms WBea WEas WHer WOak WOve WPer WWin
– 'Ball's Double White' (d)	SRms

– double white (d)	CM&M CSWP GBar GPoy NPer SEND
– 'Golden Ball'	NTow SPil WCot
– 'Plenum' (d)	LBlm MBri SIng
§ – 'Rowallane' (d)	EHol ELan GBuc MBri WCot WSan
¶ – 'Silver Ball'	LPVe
– 'Sissinghurst White'	See *T. parthenium* 'Rowallane'
¶ – 'Snowball' (d)	SPil
– 'White Bonnet' (d)	CGle ECGP ELan NBrk WEas
¶ *poteriifolium*	LFis
§ *praeteritum*	LGre
¶ – subsp. *massicyticum* MP 95277	IDac
§ *ptarmiciflorum*	SMer
¶ – 'Silver Feather' sp. CC&McK 460	EPPr SPil GTou
vulgare	CAgr CArn CKin CSev ECtt EEls EJud ELau EWFC GPoy LHol MChe MHew MSal NLan NMir SIde SPer WByw WCla WOak WWye
– var. *crispum*	CJew EBot ELan ELau EOHP EPla GBar GCal GPoy LBay LFis MAvo MBri NHex NLon NVic SIde WBea WCot WFar WGwy WHer WJek WRha WSel
– 'Isla Gold'	CBod CBos CSpe EFou EMon EWes GCal LFis MMil NSti SMad WCHb WCot WFar WPbr WRha WWye
– 'Silver Lace' (v)	ECha EHoe EMon LFis MAvo NBrk NHex NSti WAlt WBea WCHb WCot WFar WHer WPbr

TANAKAEA (Saxifragaceae)

radicans	NHol WCru

TAPEINOCHILOS (Zingiberaceae) See Plant Deletions

TAPISCIA (Staphyleaceae)

¶ *sinensis*	CLyn

TARASA (Malvaceae)

¶ *humilis*	CPBP

TARAXACUM (Asteraceae)

albidum B&SWJ 509	EBee
carneocoloratum	EPPr
I *officinale*	MHew SIde
¶ – white-flowered	WAlt
pamiricum JJH 395	EHyt EPPr

TASMANNIA See DRIMYS

TAXODIUM (Taxodiaceae)

ascendens	See *T. distichum* var. *imbricatum*
§ *distichum* ♀	CB&S CDoC CLnd CMCN CMac CWSG EHul ELan ENot GChr ISea LCon LNet MBal MBar MBlu MBri MRav NHol NPal NWea SHBN SPer SReu WDin WFro WGer WHar WNor WWat
– var. *imbricatum* 'Nutans' ♀	CEnd IOrc LPan MBlu MBri SMur
mucronatum	LCon WFro

TAXUS † (Taxaceae)

baccata ♀	Widely available
baccata 'Adpressa Aurea'	CKen EPla ESis GAri MPla
– 'Adpressa Variegata' ♀	EHul LCon MAsh SLim
– 'Aldenham Gold'	CKen
– 'Amersfoort'	EOrn EPla LCon SSpi
– 'Argentea Minor'	See *T. baccata* 'Dwarf White'
§ – Aurea Group	CBlo EPot SRms
I – 'Aurea Pendula'	EBrP EBre EOrn LBre SBre
I – 'Aureomarginata'	CB&S EOrn WStI
– 'Cavendishii'	ECho
– 'Compacta'	EPla
– 'Corley's Coppertip'	CBlo CFee CKen CSam EHul EPot LCon LLin MAsh MBar MOne NHol WGwG WLRN WWal
– 'Cristata'	LCon
¶ – 'David'	LBee
– 'Dovastoniana' ♀	CDoC CMac LCon MBar NWea
– 'Dovastonii Aurea' (v) ♀	CDoC CMac EHul EOrn EPla LBee LCon LHol MBar MBri SLim WDin
– 'Drinkstone Gold'	EHul EPla WBcn
§ – 'Dwarf White'	EOrn LCon NHol
– 'Elegantissima' (f/v) ♀	EHul LBuc MPla NWea
– 'Erecta' (m)	EHul SHBN
§ – 'Fastigiata' (f) ♀	CB&S CDoC CMac EAst EBrP EBre EHul ENot EREa GChr GRei IOrc ISea LBre LCon LLin LNet MBar MBri MGos NBee SBre SLim SPer WDin WHar WMou WStI
– 'Fastigiata Aurea'	CKen CLnd EAst EHul ELan IHos LBuc LLin NBee NHol NPer NRoo SRms WBrE WHar WLRN
– 'Fastigiata Aureomarginata' (m) ♀	CDoC CKen CMac EAst EBrP EBre EHul EOrn EPot GRei IOrc ISea LBee LBre LCon LPan MBal MBar MBri MGos MWat NHol NWea SBre SLim WGwG WMou WWal
– 'Fastigiata Robusta' (f)	EBrP EBre EPla LBre MBar SBre WGer WPyg
– 'Glenroy New Penny'	MBal
¶ – 'Golden Elise'	CKen WLRN
– 'Green Diamond'	CKen
– 'Hibernica'	See *T. baccata* 'Fastigiata' (f)
– 'Ivory Tower'	CB&S MGos
¶ – 'Lori'	LBee
– 'Melfard'	EHul
– 'Nutans'	CKen CNic EHul ESis LCon LLin MBar MOne WLRN
– 'Overeynderi'	EHul
– 'Pendula'	MBal MRav
– 'Pumila Aurea'	ELan MAsh
– 'Pygmaea'	CKen IOrc
– 'Repandens' (f) ♀	CDoC EHul LCon LPan MBar SHBN WCFE WFar WGer
– 'Repens Aurea' (v) ♀	CDoC CHig CKen EHul ELan EOrn GCHN LCon LLin MAsh MBar MBri MGos MPla NRoo SAga
– 'Semperaurea' (m) ♀	CB&S CMac EBrP EBre EHul ELan EOrn EPla GCHN LBee LBre LCon LPan MBal MBar MBri MGos NBee NWea SAga SBre SLim SPla WDin
– 'Silver Spire' (v)	CB&S CKen

– 'Standishii' ♀   CDoC CKen EHul ELan EPla GCHN IOrc ISea LBee LCon LLin LNet MAsh MBal MBar MBri MGos MPla MRav MWat NHol SAga SHBN SLim WDin
– 'Summergold' (v)   CDoC EBrP EBre EHul ELan ENot GCHN GChr GRei IOrc LBre LCon MBar MGos NHol NRoo SBre SLim WPyg WStI
– 'Variegata'   See *T. baccata* Aurea Group
– 'Washingtonii'   SHBN
¶ – 'White Icicle'   WWeb
brevifolia   EPla LCon
cuspidata   CMCN ETen
– 'Aurescens'   CKen EPla LCon MAsh SRms
– f. *nana*   EHul EOrn GAri LCon MBar NBee NHol WGwG WLRN WWal
– 'Robusta'   EHul LLin
– 'Straight Hedge'   EHul WLRN
x *media* 'Brownii'   EHul LBuc
– 'Hicksii' ♀   CEnd CLnd EHul LBuc LNet LPan MBar NRoo NWea SLim WLRN
– 'Hillii'   CBlo MBar NHol

TECOMA (Bignoniaceae)
capensis ♀   CB&S CHEx CPlN CPle CSev CTrC EBak EHol ELan EMil ERea SLMG SOWG SSoC
¶ – 'Apricot'   CSpe EHol
– 'Aurea'   CPle CSev CSpe ERea SLMG SOWG
¶ – 'Lutea'   WMul
– subsp. *nyassae*   ERea
¶ 'Coccinea'   CSpe
garrocha   CPlN
¶ 'Orange Glow'   SOWG
ricasoliana   See *Podranea ricasoliana*
¶ 'Salmon'   CSpe
* x *smithii*   CPlN
stans   CPlN

TECOMANTHE (Bignoniaceae)
dendrophila   CPlN
speciosa   CPlN ECou

TECOMARIA See TECOMA

TECOPHILAEA (Tecophilaeaceae)
cyanocrocus ♀   CAvo CBro EPot LAma LRHS WCot
– 'Leichtlinii' ♀   CAvo CBro EHyt EPot LAma LRHS SSpi
– 'Purpurea'   See *T. cyanocrocus* 'Violacea'
§ – 'Violacea'   CAvo CBro EPot LRHS
violiflora   LAma

TECTARIA (Dryopteridaceae)
gemmifera   GQui NMar

TELANTHOPHORA (Asteraceae)
grandifolia   SAPC SArc

TELEKIA (Asteraceae)
§ *speciosa*   CHan CSam ECro ELan LFis MFir MRav NBro NBus NPSl SDix WBea WByw WHer WOld WPer WPrP WRHF

TELESONIX See BOYKINIA

TELINE See GENISTA

TELLIMA (Saxifragaceae)
grandiflora   Widely available
– 'Delphine'   CElw
* – 'Forest Frost'   WCot
– Odorata Group   CBre CHid ECha EGoo EPPr EPla NBrk NCat NLak WGwG WHen WPrP WWal WWat WWye
– 'Purpurea'   See *T. grandiflora* Rubra Group
– 'Purpurteppich'   CDec CGle ECha EGoo MRav NCat
§ – Rubra Group   Widely available

TELOPEA (Proteaceae)
speciosissima   CHEx CTrC
truncata   CFil CHEx IDee ISea MAll SSpi

TEMPLETONIA (Papilionaceae)
¶ *retusa*   MFiF

TEPHROSERIS (Asteraceae)
integrifolia   EBee WHer

TERNSTROEMIA (Theaceae)
gymnanthera   See *T. japonica*
§ *japonica*   EPfP SBid

TETRACENTRON (Tetracentraceae)
sinense   CFil CGre CPle CWSG EPfP GQui SBid SSpi WWat

TETRACLINIS (Cupressaceae) See Plant Deletions

TETRADIUM (Rutaceae)
§ *daniellii*   CDoC CFil CMCN GChr NPal SSpi WPGP WWat
§ – Hupehense Group   CMCN GGGa MBri SSpi WDin
velutinum   CMCN

TETRAGONOLOBUS See LOTUS

TETRANEURIS (Asteraceae)
§ *grandiflora*   CPBP
– JCA 11422   SBla
§ *scaposa*   EPot

TETRAPANAX (Araliaceae)
§ *papyrifer* ♀   CHEx CTrC SAPC SArc

TETRAPATHAEA See PASSIFLORA

TETRASTIGMA (Vitaceae)
voinierianum ♀   CHEx CPlN ECon LCns MBri SAPC SArc

TETRATHECA (Tremandraceae) See Plant Deletions

TEUCRIDIUM (Lamiaceae)
¶ *parvifolium*   MAll

TEUCRIUM (Lamiaceae)
* *ackermannii*   CLyd EGoo EHyt ESis LBee LHop MBro SBla SCro SMac WAbe WHoo WPat

* *arabii*	NChi
arduinoi	CPle
aroanium	CLyd CMea CPBP EGle EPot LBee MBro MHig MWat NGre NMen NTow SBla SHFr WAbe
asiaticum	EGoo SSca
bicolor	CGre CPle SSta WWye
botrys	MHew MSal
canadense	LHop
chamaedrys hort.	See *T.* × *lucidrys*
– Linnaeus	CHal CSam EGoo ESis GBar LFis NHol NRoo NWCA SRms SSea SVen WCer WHoo WSel WTro
– 'Nanum'	CLyd CNic MBro WPat WPyg WWye
– 'Rose Carpet'	CMGP EGoo EOrc MHar
¶ – subsp. *tauricolum* MP 95278	IDac
– 'Variegatum'	CDec EGoo GBar LLWP MAll MAvo MHar NHol WBea WCHb WCot WHer WOve WPer WRha WSel
¶ *cyprium*	EHyt
flavum	EJud LFlo LGan WHer WPGP WPbr
fruticans	CB&S CBot CChe CHan CLyd CPle EAst EBrP EBre EEls EHoe ENot LBre LHop NFai NSti SAxl SBre SHBN SIng SPer SSta WDin WEas WHCG WHar WSHC WWin WWye
– 'Album'	CPle
– 'Azureum' ♀	CB&S CBot CPle CSpe ERav MBro SAga SBra SPer WAbe WBod WPat WPyg WSpi
¶ – 'Collingwood Ingram'	EBee
– 'Compactum'	CMil EGoo EHic ESis LHop SMad SMrm SPer SPla WAbe WBay WSHC WWat
– dark form	SMrm
¶ *halacysanum*	EBee
hircanicum	CFis CPle CSam ECoo EGoo EHic EJud ELan EMan EMon GBin LHop LLWP MBro MFir MNrw MSte WCot WPbr WWye
§ × *lucidrys*	CArn CChe CMea CSev EAst EGoo EHyt ELan ELau EPla EPot ERea GAbr GPoy IOrc LHol MBal MCLN MChe MPla SIde SMad SPer SRCN SRms WCla WDin WEas WWin
lucidum	GBin WCla WOak
majoricum	See *T. polium* f. *pii-fontii*
marum	CArn EOHP LHol MSal NMen SIgm SVen
massiliense hort.	See *T.* × *lucidrys*
– Linnaeus	EOrc WHer
montanum	CMea MHig
musimonum	CLyd EHyt EPot MHig NNrd
polium	CLyd ESis MBro MWat SIgm WPat
– *aureum*	NWCA SBla SIng
pulverulentum	See *T. cossonii*
pyrenaicum	CHal CMea EGoo EPot GCrs LBee MBro MHig NSla NWCA WOld WPat WPyg WWin WWye
rosmarinifolium	See *T. creticum*
scordium	CNat WWhi
scorodonia	CArn CKin CSev EGoo ELau EWFC GPoy MChe MHew MSal NMir SIde WCla WHer WJek WSel WWye
– 'Crispum'	CB&S CHan CInt ECGN ELan ELau EOrc GOrc LBay LHol MBri MFir MHar MLLN MSCN MWat MWgw NBro NFai SMrm WBod WCHb WKif WPer WSel
* – 'Crispum Aureomarginatum'	MLLN
§ – 'Crispum Marginatum' (v)	CBot ECha ECoo EFou EGoo EHoe ELan EMar EMon EPla ESis GAbr IBlr ILis LFis MBro MNrw MTis NBrk NFai NOak NRoo NSti SPar WBea WBon WEas WHoo WOve WPyg
– 'Winterdown' (v)	CMea CNat WAlt WCHb WCot WHer WLin WPbr
subspinosum	CMea CPle ITim LBee MBro NMen NTow SBla WPat WPyg
webbianum	ECho

THALIA (Marantaceae)

dealbata	CHEx MSta WMul

THALICTRUM † (Ranunculaceae)

actaeifolium	EBee
adiantifolium	See *T. minus adiantifolium*
angustifolium	See *T. lucidum*
aquilegiifolium	Widely available
– var. *album*	CBot CMil EBrP EBre ECGN ECha EFou ELan EPla LBre LFis LGan MBri MBro MCLN MCli MHlr MNrw MWgw NPSI NSti NTow SBre SCro SSpi WEas WHil WHoo WPer
– dwarf form	ECha
* – 'Hybridum'	CHad EHic WPer
– Purple Cloud	See *T. aquilegiifolium* 'Thundercloud'
– 'Purpureum'	CHid CSev ECGN LFis MBro NLar NPSI SPla WCru WHoo
§ – 'Thundercloud' ♀	CBro CFir EBrP EBre ECro ECtt EFou GCal LBre MBel MBri MUlv NHol SBre WAbe WCot WMer
¶ *baicalense*	EBee
calabricum	EMon
§ *chelidonii*	EBee
– dwarf form	GDra
clavatum	EBee
coreanum	See *T. ichangense*
¶ *coriaceum*	EBee
¶ *cultratum* HWJCM 367	WCru
¶ *dasycarpum*	LFis MLLN
§ *delavayi* ♀	Widely available
– 'Album'	CGle CSpe ECha EFou ELan GCra LGan LGre MBro NDea NOak WBro WHoo WMaN
– 'Hewitt's Double' (d) ♀	Widely available
diffusiflorum	GCrs NHar SBla
dipterocarpum hort.	See *T. delavayi*
fendleri	GBuc
¶ *filamentosum* B&SWJ 777	WCru
finetii	EMon
flavum	CGle CHan EBee EBrP EBre EFou ELan EOld GGar LBre NBro NDea NPri SBre SSpi WHil WRha
– 'Chollerton'	See *T.* sp. **Afghanistan**
I – 'Glauca'	LSyl

§ – subsp. *glaucum* ♀ — Widely available
– 'Illuminator' — CHad ECle MArl MAus MBel MCLN MOne NHol NPri SBid WCot
◆*flexuosum* — See *T. minus* subsp. *minus*
foetidum — EMon
¶ *foliolosum* B&SWJ 2705 — WCru
§ *ichangense* — CBos CRDP SMrm
isopyroides — CLTr CLon CPBP CSev CVer EAst EBee ECro EHic EMan EMon GBin GMac MHar MRav SMrm WAbe WCru WLRN WLin WPrP
javanicum B&L 12327 — EMon
kiusianum — CLyd CMGP CMea EBee ECha EDAr EGar EHyt EPot ESis EWes GAri LFis LGre MBel MRav MTho NBir NDov NHar NHol NMGW NMen NTow SAga WAbe WFar
– Kew form — CBos CRDP SWas
koreanum — See *T. ichangense*
§ *lucidum* — CBos CPou ELan EMan SSca
minus — CAgr CBos CHan ELan EMan EMon GAbr GBuc MBel MBri MUlv NHol NOak NRoo NSti SPla WBea WHil WWye
§ – *adiantifolium* — CMGP EAst EBee ECro EHic EJud EPla LRHS MFir NOak NPSI SMrm SRms WMer WPer WShe WWat
§ – subsp. *minus* — EBee
§ – subsp. *olympicum* — WPer
– subsp. *saxatile* — See *T. minus* subsp. *olympicum*
occidentale JLS 86255 — EMon MNrw
orientale — SBla
¶ *polycarpum* — NHol
polygamum — EBee EBrP EBre LBre LFis MHew MSal MUlv SBre WCot
punctatum B&SWJ 1272 — LGre WCru
ramosum — EMon
¶ *reniforme* B&SWJ 2610 — WCru
rhynchocarpum — LLew
rochebruneanum — CGle CHan EBee ECGN EMan EWes MBri MNrw MTed MTis MUlv SMrm SSca WCru WPen WRus WSHC
* *rugosum* — GBuc
¶ *simplex* — NHol
¶ sp. ACE 1612 — EPPr
sp. B&SWJ 2622 — WCru
sp. CLD 564 — EMon
§ sp. from Afghanistan — ELan EPot GBuc GTou MPEx WCot WHil WSan
speciosissimum — See *T. flavum* subsp. *glaucum*
sphaerostachyum — MBri WGer
tuberosum — CHan CRDP EMon EPot LGre SAga SBla SWas WCot
uchiyamae — WCot
¶ *venulosum* — EBee
¶ *virgatum* B&SWJ 2964 — WCru

THAMNOCALAMUS (Poaceae - Bambusoideae)
aristatus — EPla ISta LJus
crassinodus — EPla SCha SDry
– dwarf from — EPla
– 'Kew Beauty' — EFul EPla ERod ISta LJus MMoz SDry WJun
– 'Lang Tang' — EPla WJun
– 'Merlyn' — CHEx EPla ERod SDry WJun
falcatus — See *Drepanostachyum falcatum*
falconeri — See *Himalayacalamus falconeri*

funghomii — See *Schizostachyum funghomii*
khasianus — See *Drepanostachyum khasianum*
maling — See *Yushania maling*
spathaceus hort. — See *Fargesia murieliae*
§ *spathiflorus* — EFul EPla ISta SDry WJun
§ *tessellatus* — EFul EPla ISta LJus MMoz SDry WJun

THAMNOCHORTUS (Restionaceae)
¶ *insignis* — WNor
¶ *lucens* — IDac
¶ *rigidus* — CTrC
¶ *spicigerus* — CTrC

THAPSIA (Apiaceae)
decipiens — See *Melanoselinum decipiens*
garganica — SIgm WCot

THEA See CAMELLIA

THELYMITRA (Orchidaceae)
¶ 'Goldfingers' 410 — SWes
¶ 'Melon Glow' — SWes
¶ *nuda* — SWes
¶ *rubra* — SWes
¶ 'Spring Delight' 458 — SWes

THELYPTERIS † (Thelypteridaceae)
limbosperma — See *Oreopteris limbosperma*
palustris — EBee EMon MLan NHol SRms WFib WRic
phegopteris — See *Phegopteris connectilis*

THEMEDA (Poaceae) See Plant Deletions

THERMOPSIS (Papilionaceae)
caroliniana — See *T. villosa*
fabacea — See *T. lupinoides*
lanceolata — CHad CSam CTri ECGP EMan GBin LSpr MAus MBel MBri MLLN MMil MTis SAga SMac SMrm SOkh WFar WLin WMow WPer
§ *lupinoides* — ECha ECro NOrc SLod WCot WCru WPer
mollis — MUlv
montana — CGen CMGP CRDP ELan ERav GAbr MGed MNrw NOrc NSti WAbb WByw WGwG WLRN WOve WPer WRus WWal WWat
§ *villosa* — CGle CHan EBee MLLN MRav MSte NFai SBla SDix SPer WCot WPGP

THEVETIA (Apocynaceae)
peruviana — MSal SOWG

THLADIANTHA (Cucurbitaceae)
dubia — CPlN SDix
oliveri (f) — MSCN

THLASPI (Brassicaceae)
alpinum — CMHG EPot MPla MWat NMen NNrd NWCA
bellidifolium — GDra NBir
biebersteinii — See *Pachyphragma macrophyllum*
bulbosum — GTou

cepaeifolium subsp.	GTou NGre
rotundifolium	
fendleri	MNrw
stylosum	NWCA

THRINAX (Arecaceae) See Plant Deletions

THUJA † (Cupressaceae)

§ *koraiensis*	LCon MBar WCwm WHCr
occidentalis	NWea WDin
– 'Aurea'	MBar
– 'Aureospicata'	EHul
– 'Beau Fleur'	LLin
– 'Beaufort' (v)	CKen EHul MAsh MBar MPla WWal
– 'Caespitosa'	CBlo CKen CNic EGra ESis LLin MOne NHol
– 'Cristata Aurea'	CKen
– 'Danica' ♀	CMac EBrP EBre EHul ENot EOrn GRei IOrc LBre LCon LLin MAsh MBar MGos MPla MWat SBod SBre SLim SRms WGwG WStI WWal WWeb
– 'Dicksonii'	EHul
– 'Douglasii Aurea'	CKen
– 'Ellwangeriana Aurea'	LBee MGos
– 'Emerald'	See *T. occidentalis* 'Smaragd'
– 'Ericoides'	CDoC CTri EHul LCon MAsh MBal MBar SRms SSmi WStI
– 'Europa Gold'	CDoC EHul IOrc LBee MBar MGos SLim WLRN
– 'Fastigiata'	MBar
– 'Filiformis'	CKen EPla
– 'Globosa'	CBlo CMac MBar MGos SBod WGor WGwG WWal
– 'Globosa Variegata'	CBlo CKen MBar
– 'Golden Globe'	CBlo EHul ENot LCon LNet LPan MBar MGos NHol SBod SLim SPla WDin WLRN
* – 'Golden Minaret'	EHul
– 'Hetz Midget'	CBlo CKen EHul EOrn EPfP ESis LCon LLin MBar MGos MOne NHol SLim SMer WLRN
– 'Holmstrup' ♀	CDoC CMac CNic EBrP EBre EGra EHul ENot EOrn IOrc LBre LCon LLin MAsh MBal MBar MBri MWat NBee NHol SBre SLim SRms SSmi WStI WWeb
– 'Holmstrup's Yellow'	CBlo CDoC CKen EGra EHul LCon MAsh MOne MPla WCFE WWeb
– 'Hoveyi'	CTri EGra EHul LCon WLRN
¶ – 'Linesville'	CKen
– 'Little Champion'	EHul GRei NHol
– 'Little Gem'	EHul MGos NHol NPro SRms WDin WGor
– 'Lutea Nana' ♀	CMac EHul EOrn MBal MBar
¶ – 'Malonyana'	WCwm
– 'Marrisen's Sulphur'	CBlo EHul LCon SLim WLRN
– 'Meineckes Zwerg'	CKen EPla SSmi
– 'Miky'	CKen WBcn
– 'Milleri'	EPot
– 'Ohlendorffii'	CBlo CKen EHul EOrn LCon LLin MBar MWat NHol SSmi
– 'Orientalis Semperaurescens'	See *T. orientalis* 'Semperaurea'
I – 'Pumila Sudworth'	NHol
– 'Pygmaea'	CKen MBar
– 'Pyramidalis Compacta'	EHul LNet WGor
– 'Recurva Nana'	EHul LLin MBal MBar NHol
– 'Rheingold' ♀	CB&S CDoC CKen CMHG CMac EHoe EHul ENot EOrn GRei LBee LCon LLin MBal MBar MGos MPla MWat NEgg NHol NRoo NWea SBod SLim SPer SSmi WAbe WDin WGwG
– 'Silver Beauty' (v)	CMHG
§ – 'Smaragd' ♀	EBrP EBre EHul ENot IOrc LBre LBuc LCon LLin LNet LPan MAsh MBar MGos MPla SBod SBre SPer WCFE WStI
– 'Southport'	CBlo CKen MBri
– 'Sphaerica'	MPla
– 'Spiralis'	CBlo CMHG MBar WCFE
§ – 'Stolwijk'	CBlo EHul MBar MGos SLim
– 'Sunkist'	CKen CMHG CMac EBrP EBre EHul ENot EOrn GRei IHos IOrc LBre LCon LLin LNet LPan MAsh MBar MBri MGos MPla MWat NHol SBod SBre SLim SPla WFar WWeb
– 'Suzie'	LLin
– 'Tiny Tim'	CBlo CMac EGra EHul ESis LCon LLin MBar MGos MOne SIng WGor WLRN WWal WWeb
– 'Trompenburg'	CBlo ECho EHul MAsh WBcn
– 'Wansdyke Silver' (v)	CBlo CMac EHul EOrn EPla LCon MBar MPla SLim SPla
– 'Wareana'	CMac
– 'Wareana Aurea'	See *T. occidentalis* 'Wareana Lutescens'
§ – 'Wareana Lutescens'	CMHG CMac EHul EOrn GRei LCon MBal MBar MGos MPla
– 'Woodwardii'	EHul MBar MOne SMer WDin WGor
– 'Yellow Ribbon'	CBlo EBrP EBre EHul LBre LCon NHol SBre SLim SMer SPla
§ *orientalis*	NWea
§ – 'Aurea Nana' ♀	CDoC CKen CMac EBrP EBre EHul ENot EPot ISea LBee LBre LCon LLin LNet LPan MBal MBar MBri MGos MPla MWat NBee NWea SBod SBre SLim SSmi WAbe WDin WStI
– 'Autumn Glow'	CBlo CKen
– 'Bergmanii'	CBlo WWeb
– 'Beverleyensis'	LLin
– 'Blue Cone'	MBar
– 'Carribean Holiday'	MAsh
– 'Collen's Gold'	CTri EHul MBar SPla
– 'Conspicua'	CKen EHul LBee LCon MAsh MBar MWat
– 'Elegantissima' ♀	CMac EHul EOrn LBee LCon MBar MGos SBod
– 'Flame'	CBlo MGos
– 'Golden Minaret'	WBcn
– 'Golden Pygmy'	CKen EOrn MAsh WBcn
– 'Juniperoides'	CBlo EHul EPla LCon LLin MBar WLRN
– 'Madurodam'	EGra LLin
– 'Magnifica'	EHul WCwm
– 'Meldensis'	CTri EBrP EBre EHul LBre LLin MBal MBar SBre WDin
– 'Miller's Gold'	See *T. orientalis* 'Aurea Nana'
– 'Minima'	CDoC EPot ESis MWat
– 'Minima Glauca'	CKen MBar SRms
– 'Purple King'	EPla LCon SLim
I – 'Pyramidalis Aurea'	LPan

– 'Rosedalis'	CKen CMac EBrP EBre EHul EOrn EPla ESis LBee LBre LCon LLin MAsh MBal MBar MBri MPla MWat SBod SBre SLim SRms
– 'Sanderi'	CKen EBrP EBre EOrn LBre MBar SBre WCFE
§ – 'Semperaurea'	CMac WGor
– 'Shirley Chilcott'	MBri
– 'Sieboldii'	EHul
– 'Southport'	LBee LLin MAsh
– 'Spaethii'	EOrn
– 'Summer Cream'	CBlo CKen EHul MBar MGos
– 'Westmont'	CKen EOrn
plicata	CPer EHul GChr GRei IOrc LHyr MBal MBar MGos NEgg NWea SBod SPer WFro WMou WStI WTro
– 'Atrovirens' ♀	CTri EBrP EBre EGra ENot LBee LBre LBuc LCon LPan MAsh MBre SMer SRms WHar WMou WWal WWeb
– 'Aurea' ♀	CBlo EHul MAsh SRms
– 'Can-can'	CBlo EPla MBri
I – 'Cole's Variety'	CBlo MBar MBlu
– 'Collyer's Gold'	EGra EHul LCon SRms
– 'Copper Kettle'	CBlo CKen CNic EGra EHul LCon MAsh MBar MBri MPla NHol NPro SLim WLRN
– 'Cuprea'	CKen EHul ESis LLin MBar
– 'Doone Valley'	CKen CMHG EHul EOrn MBar NHol WAbe
– 'Dura'	CDoC
– 'Fastigiata' ♀	CMac
– 'Gelderland'	EHul
– 'Gracilis Aurea'	CBlo ECho EHul MPla WBcn
– 'Hillieri'	EHul MBar
– 'Irish Gold' (v) ♀	CAbP CBlo CMac EPla LCon LLin SAga
– 'Rogersii'	CDoC CKen CMHG CMac EBar EBrP EBre EHul EOrn EPot ESis IOrc LBre LCon LLin MAsh MBar MGos MPla NHol SBod SBre SIng SLim SPer SRms SSmi WAbe
– 'Semperaurescens'	CBlo
¶ – × *standishii*	WCwm
– 'Stolwijk's Gold'	See *T. occidentalis* 'Stolwijk'
– 'Stoneham Gold' ♀	CDoC CKen CMHG CMac EBrP EBre EHul EOrn IOrc LBee LBre LCon LLin MAsh MBar MPla MBod SBre SLim SMer SPer SRms SSmi WCFE
¶ – 'Sunshine'	CKen
– 'Winter Pink' (v)	CBlo CKen
– 'Zebrina' (v)	CB&S CDoC CMHG CMac EHul EOrn LBee LCon LLin MAsh MBal MBar MGos MWat NBee NEgg NWea SBod SLim SPer WHar WWal WWin
¶ *standishii*	WCwm

THUJOPSIS (Cupressaceae)

dolabrata ♀	CB&S CGre CTrG EHul IOrc MBar NHed NWea SHBN SPer WBrE WCwm WFar WTro WWat
– 'Aurea' (v)	CDoC CKen EHul EOrn LCon MBar MGos SAga SHBN SLim
– 'Laetevirens'	See *T. dolabrata* 'Nana'

§ – 'Nana'	CDoC CKen CMac EGra EHul EOrn ESis LCon LLin MBar MPla SLim SRms STre WFar
– 'Variegata'	CDoC CMac EHul EOrn ESis LCon LLin MBal MBar NHed NHol SHFr SLim WDin WLRN
koraiensis	See *Thuja koraiensis*

THUNBERGIA (Acanthaceae)

alata	CPlN MBri
coccinea	CPlN LCns SOWG
erecta	CPlN ELan EREa LChe LCns SOWG
– 'Alba'	LChe
fragrans	CPlN EREa LCns SOWG
grandiflora ♀	CPlN ECon ELan EREa LChe LCns SLMG SOWG WMul
– 'Alba'	CPlN LChe SLMG
gregorii	CPlN LChe LCns SOWG
laurifolia	CPlN
mysorensis ♀	CPlN ECon EREa LCns SOWG WMul
natalensis	CHan LChe LLew
petersiana	CPlN

THYMUS † (Lamiaceae)

'Anderson's Gold'	See *T.* × *citriodorus* 'Bertram Anderson'
azoricus	See *T. caespititius*
¶ 'Caborn Lilac Gem'	LLWP
§ *caespititius*	CArn CInt CLyd ELau EPar EPot GAbr GDra GGar GPoy ILis LHol LLWP MBro MHig MRPP NHex NMen NRya SDys SSmi WCHb WPer
¶ *caespitosus*	NRoo
camphoratus	CBod CMea EHyt ELau EOHP EWes LHop MWat NHex WJek
carnosus Boiss.	LFis NHol SAxl SIng SSmi
♦ – misapplied	See *T. vulgaris* 'Erectus'
'Carol Ann' (v)	CBod EWes LLWP NLak
cephalotos	EHyt
ciliatus	LLWP WPer
cilicicus	CLyd EHyt EWes GCHN LBee MChe MHig SBla WCHb WJek WMow WWye
× *citriodorus*	CArn CDoC ELau GAbr GCHN GPoy LGro MBrN MChe NHex NMen NOak WHen WJek WOMN WOak WPer WWye
– 'Archer's Gold'	EAst EBrP EBre EHoe ELau EPot ESis GAbr LBee LBre LGro LHop LLWP MBri MHig MRPP NHex NSti SBre SChu SIde SMer SRms SSmi WCHb WJek WPat WPer
– 'Argenteus'	LLWP MBro
– 'Aureus' ♀	EBrP EBre EMNN ESis GBar GBur GDra GTou LBre LLWP MBal MBar MBri MBro MFos NFla NMen NRoo NWCA SBla SBre SRms WHen WHoo WPyg
§ – 'Bertram Anderson' ♀	Widely available
§ – 'Golden King' (v)	EBrP EBre ECha ELan EPar LBee LBre LHop LLWP MBar MBri MBro MChe NGre NHex NSti SAga SBre WCHb WHoo WPer WSel WStI
§ – 'Golden Lemon' (v)	CArn EOHP GPoy LLWP WJek WWye

– 'Golden Lemon' misapplied	See *T.* × *citriodorus* **'Golden Lemon'**
– 'Golden Queen' (v)	CLTr CMea EOHP EPot ESis GBar NFla NLak NPri NRoo NSla SMrm WRHF WWin
– 'Nyewoods'	GAbr MGra SIde SPil
– *repandus*	SIde
– 'Silver Posie'	See *T. vulgaris* **'Silver Posie'**
– 'Silver Queen' (v) ♀	CB&S CLyd ECha ELan EOHP EPar GDra GPoy MBal MBar MBro MChe MHig NGre NHex NLon NRoo SSmi WHoo WPyg WShe WStI
* – 'Variegatus'	CJew ESis LGro LHol LHop MBri MBro MChe MPla NGre NMen WEas WWin
– 'Variegatus' misapplied	See *T.* × *citriodorus* **'Golden King'**
* 'Coccineus' ♀	CArn ECha ELan ELau EMNN ESis GDra GTou LGro LHol LLWP MBal MBar MBri MBro MChe MHig MRPP MWat NHol NNrd NRoo SBla SIng WCla WHen WHoo WOak WPat WWin
comosus	CNic CPBP LLWP MChe MGra NTow WHoo WPat WPer
¶ *compactus albus*	ELau
¶ 'Creeping Orange'	LLWP
¶ 'Dartmoor'	GCal LLWP
'Desboro'	GAbr LLWP NHex NHol NNrd
doerfleri	CLyd ECha EOHP GBar LLWP NMen SIde WSel WWye
– 'Bressingham'	Widely available
'Doone Valley' (v)	Widely available
'Dorcas White'	LLWP WPer
drucei	See *T. polytrichus* subsp. *britannicus*
'E.B. Anderson'	See *T.* × *citriodorus* **'Bertram Anderson'**
¶ 'Elf'	MTPN
* 'Emma's Pink'	LLWP NHex
erectus	See *T. vulgaris* **'Erectus'**
* *ericoides*	MGra
'Fragrantissimus'	CArn CChr CJew ELau EOHP ESis GAbr GPoy LHol LLWP MChe MWat NHex NPri NRoo SIde WJek WPer WWye
* 'Golden Icing'	MGra
§ 'Hartington Silver' (v)	Widely available
herba-barona	CArn CHad CTri EBot ECha ELau EOHP ESis GAbr GBar GDra GPoy LHol LLWP MBal NHex NHol NNor NRoo SIde SRms SSmi WOak WPer WWye
– *citrata*	See *T. herba-barona* **'Lemon-scented'**
§ –'Lemon-scented'	CArn ELau GPoy LLWP MOne NHex NHol NLon SHDw SIde
'Highland Cream'	See *T.* **'Hartington Silver'**
I *hirsutus minus*	CNic
hyemalis	LLWP SIde
integer	SBla
lanuginosus hort.	See *T. pseudolanuginosus*
'Lavender Sea'	EWes LLWP
'Lemon Caraway'	See *T. herba-barona* **'Lemon-scented'**
leucotrichus	CLyd GAbr ILis MBro MHig SDys SSmi WPat
'Lilac Time'	EWes LLWP
longicaulis	CArn EBar ECha EGoo ELau LGan LLWP NHex SIde WJek WWye
marschallianus	See *T. pannonicus*
mastichina	CArn ESis GBar LHop MChe SBla SChu SMac SSca WWye
– 'Didi'	LLWP NHex
membranaceus	CLyd EHyt EWes
micans	See *T. caespititius*
I *minus*	See *Calamintha nepeta*
montanus Waldstein & Kitaibel	See *T. pulegioides*
neiceffii	CArn CLyd ECha EGoo ELau GAbr GBar LHol LLWP MHig NHex NTow
* *nummularius*	ELau LGro SSca
odoratissimus	See *T. pallasianus* subsp. *pallasianus*
'Onyx'	CLyd NHex NMen
pallasianus	ELau LLWP
§ – subsp. *pallasianus*	CBod GBar SIde SPil WOak
§ *pannonicus*	LLWP MGra NHex WPer
'Peter Davis'	CArn CBod CMea EBar EOHP ESis LHop LLWP MChe MGed MGra MPla NHex NMen SBla SChu SIde WJek
'Pink Ripple'	CBod ELau EWes LLWP MChe
'Pinkushion'	LLWP NHol SIng
§ *polytrichus*	LLWP NHol NMir
§ – subsp. *britannicus*	CKin EEls EPot EWFC GPoy LLWP MFos MHew NMen NSti WJek WPer
– – 'Minor'	EPot LLWP SIde WPer
§ – – 'Thomas's White' ♀	ELan LBee LLWP
'Porlock'	CDoC CMea CSev EBar ELau ESis GPoy LLWP MChe NHex NHol SIde SRms WHoo WJek WPer WPyg
praecox subsp. *arcticus*	See *T. polytrichus* subsp. *britannicus*
¶ 'Provence'	LLWP
§ *pseudolanuginosus*	CArn CMea EBar ECha ELau GTou LBee LGro LHol LLWP MBar MBri MBro MRPP NFla NGre NHex NHol NRya NSti NVic SHFr SRms SSmi WAbe WHoo WOak WPer WPyg
– 'Hall's Variety'	CHal ELau
§ *pulegioides*	CArn CBod CJew ELau GBar GPoy LHol LLWP MBri NHex NPri NRoo SHDw SIde WJek WOak WPer WWye
¶ – 'Foxley'	ELau LLWP
'Redstart'	ELau LBee LLWP
richardii subsp. *nitidus*	LHol MGra WWye
– – 'Compactus Albus'	See *T. richardii* subsp. *nitidus* **'Snow White'**
rotundifolius	ELau LLWP SIde
¶ – 'Ruby Glow'	ELau
'Ruby Glow'	EBrP EBre EWes LBre LLWP MChe MGra NHex NRoo SBre
serpyllum	CArn ELan ELau GAbr GCHN LLWP MBri MChe MPla MWat NOak SIde SRms WJek WMow WPer
– var. *albus* (Ghose & Bhattacharyya) H.B.Naithani	CHal ECha ELau EMNN ENot ESis GDra GPoy GTou LLWP MBal MBro MHar NNrd NRoo NVic SBla SChu SIde SMac SRms WHoo WOak WWye
– 'Albus Variegatus'	See *T.* **'Hartington Silver'**

– 'Annie Hall'	CDoC CHal EBrP EBre ELau EMNN EPot ESis GAbr LBee LBre LGro LHol LLWP MBro MChe NHex NHol NMen NNor NRoo SBod SBre SDys SIde SIng SSmi WPer WWye
– *coccineus* 'Major'	GDra SIde WJek
– 'Minor'	EBrP EBre GAri GTou LBre LLWP MChe NRoo SBre SIde
– 'East Lodge'	LLWP
– 'Elfin'	CArn CLyd EPot ESis EWes GBar GTou LBee LHol MBri MBro MHar NGre NMen NNrd SIng WAbe WCla WHoo
– 'Flossy'	LLWP NNrd
– 'Fulney Red'	EWes LLWP
– 'Goldstream'	CDoC CHal CLyd CMea ELau EMNN GAbr LBee LBuc LHop LLWP MBar MBri MChe NHol NNrd NRoo NSti SIde SRms WCHb WPer
¶ – 'Iden'	SIde
– subsp. *lanuginosus*	See *T. pseudolanuginosus*
– 'Lavender Sea'	See *T.* 'Lavender Sea'
– 'Lemon Curd'	CBod EOHP GAbr GBar LLWP MChe NSti SIde SMer WCHb WJek WRha WSel WWye
– 'Minimus'	CArn CDoC CHal CLyd ECha ELau ESis GAbr LHol LLWP MBri MChe NSti NTow SIde WOMN WPat WPer WRHF WSel WWye
§ – 'Minor'	CArn ELan EMNN ESis GDra LBee LHol MBro MChe MHig NHol NMen NRya NSla SIde SIng SSmi WAbe WCla WHoo WLin WPyg WWin
* – 'Minor Albus'	GBar
I – 'Minus'	See *T. serpyllum* 'Minor'
– 'Petite'	EWes LLWP
– 'Pink Chintz' ♀	CHal ECha ELau EMNN ESis GAbr GDra GPoy GTou LGro LHol LLWP MBar MBri MHig NHol NRoo SBla SChu SIng SSmi WAbe WHoo WOak WPer WPyg WWin WWye
– 'Pink Ripple'	See *T.* 'Pink Ripple'
– subsp. *pulchellus*	LLWP
– 'Rainbow Falls' (v)	CBod EWes GAbr GBar GMaP LLWP MChe NCat NHex NRoo SHDw SIde
– 'Roseus'	EOHP GBar SIde
– 'Ruby Glow'	See *T.* 'Ruby Glow'
– 'Russetings'	CDoC CHal CLyd EGoo EMNN EPot ESis LHol LLWP MBar MBro MChe NHex NHol NMen NNrd NRoo SIde SRms WOak WWin WWye
– 'September'	LLWP NHol WAbe
– 'Snowdrift'	CHal CMea EGar EOHP GBar LHol MBar MBro MChe NHex NSti SIde SSmi WAbe WJek WPat WPer WRHF
– 'Splendens'	GMaP LLWP
– 'Variegatus'	See *T.* 'Hartington Silver'
– 'Vey'	EGle ESis EWes GBar LLWP MChe NHex NHol SIng SSmi WMaN
sibthorpii	CArn
N 'Silver Posie'	See *T. vulgaris* 'Silver Posie'

'Snow White'	EWes GBar LLWP MPla NBus NMen WJek
sp. from Turkey	EPPr EWes LLWP
* *taeniensis*	CArn
§ *villosus*	CBot ESis
vulgaris	CArn CChe CSev ECha ELau GPoy LLWP MBar MBri MChe MHew NFla NHex NRoo NVic SDix WJek WPer
– *albus*	EOHP GBar LLWP NHex SIde
* – 'Aureus' hort.	GBar LGro LLWP MChe NRoo WJek WSel
¶ – 'English Winter'	SPil
§ – 'Erectus'	CArn CLyd ELan GBar LHol LLWP NTow SRms WHer WPer WWye
– French	ELau LLWP
¶ – 'French Summer'	SIde
– 'Golden Pins'	CArn ECha EGar EHal EPot GBar SBla
¶ – 'Lemon Queen'	ELau
– 'Lucy'	GBar LLWP SIde WJek
– 'Pinewood'	GPoy LLWP
– pink	LLWP
– 'Silver Pearl' (v)	EWes LLWP
§ – 'Silver Posie'	Widely available
zygis	CArn

THYSANOTUS (Anthericaceae) See Plant Deletions

TIARELLA (Saxifragaceae)

collina	See *T. wherryi*
cordifolia ♀	Widely available
– 'Oakleaf'	GCal MLLN SAxl SMrm WPbr
'Darkeyes'	WCot
'Eco Red Heart'	WPbr
'Elizabeth Oliver'	WThi
'Filigree Lace'	WThi
'Glossy'	GBuc SAxl SDys WCot WPbr
* lanciniate runner	WPbr
'Martha Oliver'	WPbr WThi WTin
¶ 'Ninja'	EBee EHic LRot NHol WCot
'Pinwheel'	MRav NCat WCot
polyphylla	CLyd ELan EMar EPar GAbr GBin GMac LGro MLLN MRav NBro NMor NOrc NSti WBea WCla WCru WFar WWhi WWye
¶ – 'Filigran'	NLar
– 'Moorgrün'	GCal MBel WWat
– pink	CGle CLTr EPar SAxl
¶ – pink form	MBel
'Slick Rock'	EMon WThi
'Tiger Stripe'	EBee WCot WThi
trifoliata	ELan LGan MRav SBla WPbr
– 'Incarnadine'	EMon
unifoliata	NCat
¶ 'Vivid Selection'	WTin
§ *wherryi* ♀	CGle CHea CLyd CRow ECGN ECha ELan GAbr GCHN LSyl MBri MTho NBrk NBro NFla NNor NOrc NSti SBla SMac SPer SRCN WAbe WEas WHoo WPer WShe WWat WWin WWye
– 'Bronze Beauty'	CMea CMil CRDP EBee ECha EPar GBuc MCLN MRav NLak NPro SAga SAxl SUsu SWas WAbe WCot WFar WPGP WPbr
– fig-leaved	WPbr WThi

- 'George Schenk' WThi
- 'Pink Foam' ECha

TIBOUCHINA (Melastomataceae)

grandifolia LHil
graveolens ERea
* *holosericea* 'Elsa' ERea
'Jules' ECon ERea
laxa 'Noelene' ECon
organensis CB&S ERea GQui IBlr LBlm LChe LHil
paratropica CLTr CPle CSev ERea LChe LHil
semidecandra hort. See *T. urvilleana*
§ *urvilleana* ♀ CAbb CB&S CDoC CGre CHEx CPIN CPle CSPN CSpe CWit EBak ECre ELan ERea IOrc ISea LBlm LCns LHop LPan SArc SBid SLMG SOWG SPer SRms
- 'Edwardsii' CBar CSev LChe LHil MLan NPSI SMrm

TIGRIDIA (Iridaceae)

hybrids SDeJ
lutea SDeJ
pavonia CGre EBot ERea GMac LAma LBow MBri NCut NRog

TILIA † (Tiliaceae)

americana CLnd CMCN ENot WMou
- 'Dentata' WMou
- 'Fastigiata' ECrN WMou
- 'Nova' CDoC CTho ECrN WMou
- 'Redmond' CTho WMou
amurensis CMCN WMou
argentea See *T. tomentosa*
begoniifolia See *T. dasystyla*
caucasica WMou
- 'Select' WMou
- 'Winter Red' WMou
'Chelsea Sentinel' SMad WMou
chenmoui WMou
chinensis WMou
chingiana CMCN SSta WMou
cordata ♀ CDul CKin CLnd CPer ELan ENot GChr GRei IOrc LBuc LHyr MBal MWat NBee NWea SHBN SPer WDin WMou WStI WWye
- 'Erecta' GChr WMou
- 'Greenspire' ♀ CDoC CDul CLnd CTho ENot IOrc LPan SLPl WMou WOrn
- 'Len Parvin' WMou
- 'Lico' WMou
- 'Morden' WMou
- 'Plymtree Gold' CTho WMou
- 'Rancho' WMou
- 'Roelvo' WMou
- 'Swedish Upright' CTho WMou
- 'Umbrella' WMou
- 'Westonbirt Dainty Leaf' WMou
- 'Winter Orange' MBlu WMou
§ *dasystyla* WMou
x *euchlora* ♀ CDoC CDul CLnd EBee ENot EPfP GChr LPan MBri MGos MWat NWea SPer SSta WDin WFar WMou WOrn
x *europaea* CDul CLnd ELan WMou
- 'Pallida' CDul CTho WMou
- 'Pendula' WMou

- 'Wratislaviensis' ♀ CBlo CDoC CDul CTho LBuc MBlu SMad WMou
- 'Zwarte Linde' WMou
x *flavescens* 'Glenleven' WMou
'Harold Hillier' WMou
henryana CEnd CLnd CMCN CTho ERod MBlu SMad WMou
- var. *subglabra* WMou
§ *heterophylla* CTho WMou
- var. *michauxii* SSta WMou
'Hillieri' See *T.* 'Harold Hillier'
insularis MBlu WMou
intonsa WMou
japonica CMCN WMou
kiusiana CMCN WMou
¶ *koreana* WMou
¶ *laetevirens* SSta
ledebourii WMou
mandshurica WMou
maximowicziana SSta WMou
mexicana WMou
miqueliana CMCN WMou
'Moltkei' CMCN WMou
mongolica ♀ CDul CLnd CMCN ENot EPfP GAri SSta WMou
monticola See *T. heterophylla*
neglecta WMou
oliveri CMCN WMou
'Orbicularis' WMou
paucicostata WMou
'Petiolaris' ♀ CDoC CDul CEnd CLnd CMCN CTho EBee ELan ENot EPfP IOrc LHyr NBee NWea SHBN SMad SPer SSta WDin WMou
platyphyllos CDoC CDul CKin CMCN ENot GChr GRei LBuc NWea SPer WDin WMou
- 'Aurea' CTho ECrN WMou
- 'Corallina' See *T. platyphyllos* 'Rubra'
- 'Delft' WMou
- 'Erecta' See *T. platyphyllos* 'Fastigiata'
§ - 'Fastigiata' CDul CTho ECrN ENot MAsh SLPl WMou
- 'Grandiflora' WMou
- 'Laciniata' CEnd CMCN CTho SMad WMou
- 'Orebro' SLPl WMou
- 'Pannonia' WMou
* - 'Pendula' CTho
- 'Prince's Street' WMou
§ - 'Rubra' ♀ CBlo CDoC CLnd CTho EBee ENot EPfP GChr IOrc LHyr MBri MGos NBee NWea WDin WMou
- 'Tortuosa' CBlo SMad WMou
- 'Vitifolia' WMou
tarquetii WMou
§ *tomentosa* CAgr CDul CLnd CMCN CTho ENot NWea SEND WDin
- 'Brabant' ♀ CDoC ENot IOrc WMou
- 'Erecta' WMou
- 'Silver Globe' WMou
- 'Szeleste' WMou
- 'Van Koolwijk' MBlu WMou
tuan SSta WMou

TILLAEA See CRASSULA

TILLANDSIA (Bromeliaceae)

abdita MBri

acostae	MBri
argentea	MBri
baileyi	MBri
balbisiana	MBri
benthamiana	See *T. erubescens*
brachycaulos	MBri
– var. *multiflora*	MBri
bulbosa	MBri
butzii	MBri
caput-medusae	MBri
circinnatoides	MBri
cyanea	MBri
× *erographica*	MBri
* *fasciculata* 'Tricolor' (v)	MBri
filifolia	MBri
flabellata	MBri
ionantha	MBri
– var. *scaposa*	See *T. kolbii*
juncea	MBri
§ *kolbii*	MBri
magnusiana	MBri
§ *matudae*	MBri
oaxacana	MBri
polystachia	MBri
punctulata	MBri
seleriana	MBri
sphaerocephala	MBri
tenuifolia var.	See *T. tenuifolia* var. *tenuifolia*
surinamensis	
tricolor var. *melanocrater*	MBri
valenzuelana	See *T. variabllis*
velickiana	See *T. matudae*
vicentina	MBri
wagneriana	MBri
xerographica	MBri

TINANTIA   (Commelinaceae) See Plant
Deletions

TIPUANA   (Papilionaceae) See Plant Deletions

TITHONIA (Asteraceae)

rotundifolia 'Torch'	SMrm

TOFIELDIA (Melanthiaceae)

calyculata	NHol

TOLMIEA (Saxifragaceae)

'Goldsplash'	See *T. menziesii* 'Taff's Gold'
menziesii ♀	CGle CHEx EBar ECha GAri
	LGro MBri NHol NOrc WByw
	WFox
– JLS 86284CLOR	EMon
– 'Maculata'	See *T. menziesii* 'Taff's Gold'
§ – 'Taff's Gold' (v) ♀	CGle CMHG CRow ECha
	EHoe ELan EOHP EPar GMac
	MBri MCLN MRav NChi NHol
	NMir NNor NRoo NSti NVic
	SHel WBea WByw WEas
	WHoo WOve WPyg WWye
– 'Variegata'	See *T. menziesii* 'Taff's Gold'

TOLPIS   (Asteraceae) See Plant Deletions

TONESTUS (Asteraceae)

§ *lyallii*	MHar WMow WPer WWin

TOONA (Meliaceae)

§ *sinensis*	CMCN CPle CTho CTrC EMil
	EPfP ISea
– 'Flamingo' (v)	CB&S CPMA EMil

TORENIA (Scrophulariaceae)

concolor formosana	WCru
B&SWJ 124	
* 'Summerwave'	SCoo

TORREYA   (Taxaceae) See Plant Deletions

TORTULA   (Sphagnaceae) See Plant Deletions

TOVARA See PERSICARIA

TOWNSENDIA (Asteraceae)

condensata	MFos
exscapa	MFos
– NNS 93-74	MRPP
florifera	CLyd MFos
formosa	CInt CLyd NBir NMen NNrd
	WOMN WWin
hookeri	CGra MFos
incana	CGra EHyt MFos WLin
leptotes	CGra
mensana	NMen
montana	CGra WLin
¶ *nuttallii*	CGra
parryi	MFos
§ *rothrockii*	CPBP NMen NWCA
sp. from California	CGra
spathulata	CGra EHyt MFos
wilcoxiana hort.	See *T. rothrockii*

TRACHELIUM (Campanulaceae)

§ *asperuloides*	CPBP EHyt EPot
caeruleum ♀	CLTr EHol ERea SBid WBrE
	WCot
– 'Purple Umbrella'	CSam EMan
– 'White Umbrella'	CLTr EMan
jacquinii subsp.	CPBP MBro NTow NWCA
rumelianum	WPat WPyg
rumelianum	WHoo

TRACHELOSPERMUM (Apocynaceae)

§ *asiaticum* ♀	Widely available
* – 'Aureum'	LRHS
– 'Goshiki'	CB&S GQui MGos SPer SSpi
– var. *intermedium*	CFil WPGP
* *bodinieri* 'Cathayensis'	GCal
jasminoides ♀	Widely available
§ – 'Japonicum'	GCal LRHS NSti SBra
– 'Major'	CSPN CTrG SSpi
* – 'Oblanceolatum'	GCal
– 'Tricolor' (v)	CRHN SMur SSta
– 'Variegatum' ♀	CB&S CBot CMac COtt CTrw
	EBar ELan ERav ERea GCal
	GQui LHop MRav NHol NPal
	SApp SArc SHBN SLMG SPer
	SReu SSpi SSta WPat WSHC
	WWat
– 'Wilsonii' W 776	CBot CHEx CMac CPlN CPle
	CRHN CSPN EBrP EBre EHic
	ELan EMil ETen GCal IOrc
	LBre MCCP SArc SBre SLMG
	SPer SReu SSpi SSta WCru
	WHar WPGP WWat
majus hort.	See *T. jasminoides* 'Japonicum'
– Nakai	See *T. asiaticum*
sp. from Nanking, China	CHan

TRACHYCARPUS (Arecaceae)

§ *fortunei* ♀	Widely available
¶ *latisectus*	LPJP LPal
martianus	LPJP LPal

nanus	LPal
* *oreophilus*	LPal
¶ *takil*	LPJP LPal NPal
wagnerianus	LPJP LPal NPal SDry

TRACHYMENE   (Apiaceae) See Plant Deletions

TRACHYSTEMON (Boraginaceae)

orientalis	CBre CGle CHEx CRDP CSev EBrP EBre ECha EFou EGol ELan EPar EPla ERav LBre MFir MRav MUlv NChi NPSl SAxl SBre SIng WCru WHer WWal WWat WWin

TRADESCANTIA (Commelinaceae)

albiflora	See *T. fluminensis*
× *andersoniana*	ECGN MBro MFir MSal NNor WEas WFox WHil WPer WRHF WWin
– 'Bilberry Ice'	EFou LFis MBri NCat NTow WSan
– 'Blaby Blue'	MTed
– 'Blue Stone'	CMea ECha EFou EPla MAus NFai NPri NRya SRms WFar WThi
– 'Caerulea Plena'	See *T. virginiana* '**Caerulea Plena**'
– Carmine Glow	See *T.* × *andersoniana* '**Karminglut**'
– 'Charlotte'	MAvo MGrG NCut
– 'Croftway Blue'	SCro
– 'Domaine de Courson'	CHan
– 'Innocence'	CBos CSpe EBrP EBre ECGN ECha ECtt EFou ELan EOrc EPla GCHN GMaP LBre LHop MBel MBri MCLN MHFP MTho NCat NFai NOrc NRoo SBre SPer WHoo WMer WRHF WRus
– 'Iris Prichard'	CHan CM&M CMGP CMil EBee ELan EPar EPla GMaP LHop MHFP NWoo SChu SCro SEas WWal
– 'Isis' ♀	CB&S CHar CKel EBrP EBre ECED ECGN ECtt EFou ELan EPar EPla GCHN LBre LFis LHop MRav MWgw NFai NOrc NRoo SBre SChu SLMG SPer SSoC WCer WMow WWin
– 'J.C. Weguelin' ♀	CBlo EMil EPfP MAus MBri NFai SRms WHoo WPnn WPyg
§ – 'Karminglut'	CB&S ELan EPar EPla GCHN MAus MHFP MNrw NHol NOrc NRoo NVic WCer WHoo WPbr WPnn WRHF WRus
– 'Leonora'	CDoC EAst ENot EPfP NCut NFai WRHF WThi
* – 'Little Doll'	WCot
– 'Maiden's Blush'	CHal CSpe NCut SVen WFoF
– 'Osprey' ♀	CRDP CSpe CVer EBar ECha EFou ELan ENot EPla GChr LWak MAus MNrw MTho NBro NDea NOak NOrc NPri NSti NVic NWes SPer WEas WMer WMow WPbr WPnn WWin
– 'Pauline'	EBrP EBre ECGN ECro ECtt EFou EMan EPla GCHN LBre MBel MRav NBir NFai NRoo SBre SChu SUsu WCer WHoo WPyg WSan WWal WWin
– 'Purewell Giant'	CTri ECot EPla NBro NCat SChu SPer WGor WKif WPyg
– 'Purple Dome'	CHan CKel CMGP CNic CRDP CStr EBrP EBre ECED ECtt EFou EOld EPla GCHN GMaP LBre MRav NBir NCat NFai NMir NWes SBre WCer WHoo WMow WPbr WPyg
– 'Rubra'	CDoC CMea EBee EPfP LFis MBel MOne NDea NFai NOrc NPri SChu SCro SLod SRms WViv
– 'Valour'	CBlo NCut WMow
– 'Zwanenburg Blue'	CMGP EBrP EBre ECha ECro EFou EOrc EPla GCHN LBre LFis MUlv NFai SBre SEas WMer WPnn
¶ 'Blue and Gold'	EMan
bracteata	NTow
– *alba*	SEas WThi
brevicaulis	CMon ECha ECro EFou EMFP EPar EPla GBuc GDra MAvo MBel MTho NBro
canaliculata	See *T. ohiensis*
¶ *cerinthoides*	SLMG
'Chedglow'	LHop
fluminensis 'Albovittata'	CHal SLMG
– 'Aurea' ♀	CHal MBri
– 'Laekenensis' (v)	MBri
– 'Quicksilver' (v) ♀	CHal MBri
multiflora	See *Tripogandra multiflora*
navicularis	See *Callisia navicularis*
§ *ohiensis*	EMan LPBA MHFP
§ *pallida*	CHal IBlr
pendula	See *T. zebrina*
sillamontana ♀	CHal LChe MBri
¶ *spathacea*	CHEx
tricolor	See *T. zebrina*
virginiana	GBur MWhi SMrm
– 'Alba'	GCal WPer WThi
§ – 'Caerulea Plena' (d)	CHan CM&M CMGP ECED EFou ELan EMan EPla LHop NHol NLar SChu SLod WThi WWal
– 'Rubra'	CHan CM&M EAst NCut WThi
§ *zebrina* ♀	CHal
– *pendula*	See *T. zebrina*

TRAGOPOGON (Asteraceae)

porrifolius	CJew ILis NLak
pratensis	CArn CKin CPou EWFC NMir
roseus	See *T. ruber*

TRAPA (Trapaceae)

natans	CHEx MSta

TREVESIA   (Araliaceae) See Plant Deletions

TRICHOCEREUS (Cactaceae)

¶ *pachanoi*	NGno

TRICHOCOLEA   (Trichocoleaceae) See Plant Deletions

TRICHOPETALUM (Anthericaceae)

§ *plumosum*	CBro

TRICHOPHORUM (Cyperaceae)

§ *cespitosum*	MBal

TRICHOSANTHES (Cucurbitaceae)
cucumerina CPlN

TRICHOSTEMA (Lamiaceae)
lanatum SHFr

TRICUSPIDARIA See CRINODENDRON

TRICYRTIS (Convallariaceae)
'Adbane' CBro ELan MBri WCru WFar
WPbr
affinis GBuc
¶ – B&SWJ 2804 WCru
– 'Variegata' SAxl WCru WFar
bakeri See *T. latifolia*
♦ *dilatata* See *T. macropoda*
formosana ♀ Widely available
– B&SWJ 306 WCru
¶ – B&SWJ 355 WCru WFar
* – 'Dark Beauty' GSki MCLN WFar
¶ – dark form WFar
– forms SEas WCru
¶ – pale form WFar
– 'Shelley's' GCal NBro
§ – Stolonifera Group CAvo CB&S CBro CHan
CM&M ECha EFou EGol ELan
EOld LHop MBal MRav NDea
NFai SAxl SCro SPer WFar
WHil WOld WPbr WRus WThi
WWat WWin
¶ – 'Variegata' WCru
* 'Golden Gleam' WCot
§ *hirta* CB&S CBro CHan CHid CSam
EBrP EBre ECtt EFou EOld
GMaP LBre MBri MBro MRav
MTho NBro NHol SBre SCro
WAbe WBea WCru WFar
WHoo WMow WOMN WOld
WRus
§ – *alba* CBro CHan CSam ELan MBal
MBel MBro NNrd WCru WFar
WHoo WPbr WThi WWat
WWin
– hybrids CM&M WCru WFar WPbr
¶ – 'Kinkazan' WFar
– 'Makinoi Gold' MRav
¶ – var. *masamunei* WCru
¶ – 'Matsukaze' WFar
– 'Miyazaki' CFir CHan EAst EFou EGar
EGle ELan EMan EOld EPar
GBuc GCra MBel MBro NLak
NLar SCro WCru WFar WHoo
WPbr WThi WWat
* – 'Nana' ELan WFar
– 'Variegata' CLon ECha EGol EWes GBuc
SMad SUsu WCot WCru WHil
WPbr
– 'White Flame' (v) WCot
N Hototogisu CMea Egle EMon EPar MTho
WCot WCru WFar WHil WPbr
¶ *ishiiana* 'Sunngensis' WFar
¶ *ishiiana* WCru WPbr
japonica See *T. hirta*
¶ – 'Kinkazan' WFar
'Kohaku' WCru WFar WPbr
§ *latifolia* CBro CGle CHad CHan EFou
ELan GCra GMaP MNrw NLar
SAxl SWas WCot WCru WFar
WHil WOld WPbr WThi WWat
WWye
¶ 'Lemon Lime' WCru
'Lilac Towers' CHan EPar WCru WKif WPbr

macrantha MBal
– subsp. *macranthopsis* SWas WCru WFar
§ *macropoda* CGle CLon CMGP CPea CSam
EGar ELan EMan EPar GBuc
GGar GMaP NBus SAga WFar
WThi
– B&SWJ 1271 WCru
¶ – variegated WCru
maculata HWJCM 470 WCru
nana WCru
ohsumiensis CGle CHan EBee ECha ELan
EPar EPot MTho WCot WCru
WFar WThi
perfoliata SWas WCru WFar WThi
'Shimone' CBro CHan CHid ELan GBuc
LRHS MBri WCru WFar WKif
WPbr
stolonifera See *T. formosana* Stolonifera
Group
'Tojen' CAvo CBro CHan ECha EGar
ELan EWes GBuc LRHS MBri
MMil NBro NTay WCru WFar
WPbr
'White Towers' CFee CHid ECha EPar GCra
MBel NBus NCut SAga SSON
SWas WBea WCru WFar WPbr
WSan WThi
¶ 'White Towers' SDys
spotted form

TRIDENS (Poaceae) See Plant Deletions

TRIENTALIS (Primulaceae)
europaea rosea CNat

TRIFOLIUM (Papilionaceae)
alpinum GDra SIng
campestre CKin
¶ *eximea* WAbe
incarnatum SIde WHer
ochroleucum EWFC
pannonicum EMon GCal MBel MHlr MSte
SMrm SUsu WCot WRus
pratense EWFC
– 'Chocolate' See *T. pratense* 'Purple Velvet'
– 'Dolly North' See *T. pratense* 'Susan Smith'
– 'Ice Cool' See *T. repens* 'Green Ice'
¶ – 'Nina' (v) WAlt
* – 'Speech House' WAlt
¶ – 'Sprite' (v) WAlt
§ – 'Susan Smith' (v) CElw CLyd CRow ECha EMan
EMar EMon EWes IBlr LHop
MCLN MHar MLLN MNrw
MSCN MTho SUsu WAlt WHer
WHil WPic
repens CHEx EWFC LWak NCat
NGre
– 'Aureum' MBal
– 'Gold Net' See *T. pratense* 'Susan Smith'
– 'Good Luck' CRow MTho WAlt
§ – 'Green Ice' CBre CHor CInt CRow CSev
EJud EMan EMar LHop MTho
NBir WAlt WCot WHer WRus
* – 'Harlequin' CBre CLTr
¶ – 'Hiccups' (v) WAlt
* – 'Pale Centre' WAlt
¶ – 'Peach Pink' WElm
– 'Pentaphyllum' See *T. repens* 'Quinquefolium'
¶ – 'Purp' (v) WAlt
¶ – 'Purple Velvet' EPPr

– 'Purpurascens'	CArn CBre CHEx CInt CLyd CRow EBar GCal GDra GMac ILis LWak MBal NRoo SSea WHen WKif WOak WWhi	– var. *hibbersonii*	CBro GBuc GDra MBal NHar NMen NTow WAbe
§ – 'Purpurascens Quadrifolium'	CDec CNic CSev EAst ECha ELan EPla EWes MBel NMir NNrd NPer SIde SIng SPer WAlt WOve WPbr WPic WRHF WRus WWin	¶ – 'Roy Elliott'	NBir
		parviflorum	GCrs MSto SSpi
		¶ *pusillum*	EPot
		– var. *pusillum*	GCrs NHar
		– var. *virginianum*	CBro LAma WCru
		recurvatum	CB&S EBee EPar EPot LAma NFai NRog SSON WAbe WCru
– 'Quadrifolium'	EHoe EPar	*rivale* ♀	CBro CElw GCrs LAma SBla WAbe
§ – 'Quinquefolium'	WPer		
¶ – 'Shannel Pinnate'	WAlt	*rugelii*	GCrs LAma WCru
– 'Tetraphyllum Purpureum'	See *T. repens* '**Purpurascens Quadrifolium**'	*sessile*	CHEx ELan EPot GBuc LAma LBow NBir NHar NHol SPer WCru WFar WSHC WShi
* – 'Velvet and Baize' (v)	CNat		
– 'Wheatfen' (v)	CBre CNat CRow EMan EWes LFlo LHop MTho NCat NPer SUsu WAlt WCot WRus	– var. *luteum*	See *T. luteum*
		¶ – purple	WPGP
		smallii	LAma WCru
rubens	CSpe EBee ECGN EMan EMar EMon GBri MSte SMrm SSca SUsu WCot WRus WWeb	*stylosum*	See *T. catesbyi*
		sulcatum	CAvo CBro CLAP EPot GDra MDun SSpi WCru
		tschonoskii	GCrs LAma
		undulatum	CHEx LAma WCru
		vaseyi	CBro EHyt EPot GCrs LAma SSpi
TRIGONELLA (Papilionaceae)			
foenum-graecum	CArn MSal SIde	*viride*	ELan LAma WCru

TRINIA (Apiaceae) See Plant Deletions

TRIGONOTIS (Boraginaceae)	
rotundifolia	EBee

TRIOSTEUM (Caprifoliaceae)

¶ *himalayanum*	EBee

TRILLIUM † (Trilliaceae)	
albidum	CBro SSpi
apetalon	GCrs WCru
§ *catesbyi*	CBro EBee EPot GCrs LAma MGrG MSal SSON SSpi WCru
cernuum	EPot GCrs LAma MGrG NRog SBid WCot WCru
chloropetalum	CBro EBrP EBre GCra GDra LBre NHol SAxl SBre SSpi WAbb WCru
¶ – var. *giganteum* ♀	MSto
– *rubrum*	CFil SSpi SWas WPGP
cuneatum	CB&S CBro EHyt ELan EPar EPot GAbr ITim LAma MDun MTho NRog SBid SDeJ SPer SSpi WAbe WCot WCru
§ – f. *albiflorum*	CBro CRDP EPot LAma MSal SSpi WCot WCru
– f. *luteum*	GCrs LAma SSpi
flexipes	GCrs
grandiflorum ♀	CAvo CB&S CBro CFil CGle CHEx CLAP CRDP EBrP EBre EHyt ELan EPot GAbr GDra LAma LBow LBre MDun NHar NHol NRog NSti SBid SBre SDeJ SPer WAbe WSHC WShi
– 'Flore Pleno' (d) ♀	EBrP EBre GBuc LBre NHar SBre SWas
kamtschaticum	CAvo GCrs LAma WCru
kurabayashii	SSpi
§ *luteum* ♀	CB&S CBro EHyt ELan EPar EPot GAbr GBuc GCrs LAma LBow MDun NFai NHar NRog SBid SPer WAbe WCru WFar
nivale	GCrs
ovatum	GCrs GDra LAma MSto

TRIPETALEIA (Ericaceae) See Plant Deletions

TRIPLEUROSPERMUM (Asteraceae) See Plant Deletions

TRIPOGANDRA (Commelinaceae)	
§ *multiflora*	CHal

TRIPTEROSPERMUM (Gentianaceae)	
¶ *cordifolium* B&SWJ 081	WCru
japonicum B&SWJ 1168	WCru
lanceolatum B&SWJ 085	WCru
taiwanense B&SWJ 1205	WCru

TRIPTERYGIUM (Celastraceae)	
regelii	CPlN

TRISETUM (Poaceae)	
¶ *dictophyllum*	EHoe
flavescens	CKin

TRISTAGMA (Alliaceae)	
'Rolf Fiedler'	See *Ipheion* '**Rolf Fiedler**'
uniflorum	See *Ipheion uniflorum*

TRISTANIA (Myrtaceae)	
conferta	See *Lophostemon confertus*
♦ *laurina*	See *Tristaniopsis laurina*

TRISTANIOPSIS (Myrtaceae)	
laurina	CPle CTrC

TRISTELLATEIA (Malpighiaceae)	
australasiae	CPlN

TRITELEIA (Alliaceae)	
californica	See *Brodiaea californica*
§ 'Corrina'	GBur

grandiflora	WCot
hyacintha	ETub GBur LAma MFos WCot
ixioides	ERos
– 'Splendens'	ETub
¶ – 'Starlight'	CAvo EPot
§ *laxa*	CAvo CMea EHic ELan GBur
	LAma NRog WBea WCot
§ – 'Koningin Fabiola'	CTri EBee ETub GBur LAma
	MBri NRog
– Queen Fabiola	See *T. laxa* **'Koningin Fabiola'**
§ *peduncularis*	LAma MFos
x *tubergenii*	LAma WCot
uniflora	See *Ipheion uniflorum*

TRITHRINAX (Arecaceae)

acanthocoma	LPal
¶ *campestris*	LPal

TRITICUM   (Poaceae) See Plant Deletions

TRITOMA See KNIPHOFIA

TRITONIA (Iridaceae)

crocata	CPou LBow NRog
– *hyalina*	LBow
§ *disticha* subsp.	CAvo CBro CElw CFil CHan
rubrolucens	CMil CPou CSev EBrP EBre
	ECha EMan GCHN LBre MBel
	MBri NRoo SAga SBre SOkh
	WFar WGer WPGP WRHF
'Orange Delight'	LBlm MHlr
¶ 'Prince of Orange'	CPou
rosea	See *T. disticha* subsp.
	rubrolucens
securigera	CMon
squalida	LBow

TROCHETIOPSIS (Sterculiaceae)

melanoxylon	LHil

TROCHOCARPA (Epacridaceae)

¶ *thymifolia*	WAbe

TROCHODENDRON (Trochodendraceae)

aralioides	CB&S CFil CGre CMCN ENot
	EPfP MBlu MGos SAPC SArc
	SMad SPer SReu SSpi SSta
	WCoo WCot WCru WSHC
	WWat

TROLLIUS (Ranunculaceae)

acaulis	EGle EWes GDra LHop MTho
	NGre SMrm WPat WPyg
asiaticus	CRDP GBuc
§ *chinensis*	CGle ECha EPot GCal LSyl
	NChi NCut NDov SWat
– 'Golden Queen' ♀	Widely available
– 'Imperial Orange'	CGle WWal WWin
¶ 'Cressida'	EBee
x *cultorum* 'Alabaster'	CHea CLon CRDP CRow ECha
	MRav SMad WSan
– 'Baudirektor Linne'	ECtt GCHN MRav NRoo WFar
– Bressingham hybrids	EBrP EBre LBre NRoo SBre
– 'Bunce'	NCut
– 'Canary Bird'	CHea EGol ELan NFla SMur
	SRms WCot WRus
– 'Cheddar'	COtt EBee EFou MCLN MRav
– 'Commander-in-chief'	COtt EBee EBrP EBre EMan
	LBre MUlv SBre
– 'Earliest of All'	CDoC CGle EGol MBri NRoo
	SPla SRms WGor
– 'Etna'	MBri NRoo
§ – 'Feuertroll'	CDoC CMGP ECha MBri NPro
	SMur
– Fireglobe	See *T.* x *cultorum* **'Feuertroll'**
– 'Golden Cup'	ECot NRoo
– 'Golden Monarch'	CBlo EPar
– 'Goldquelle' ♀	EHon NVic SMur
– 'Goliath'	CGle CMGP NRoo WFar
– 'Helios'	CGle CHea CSam ECha
– 'Lemon Queen'	EMan EPar GCal LSyl MBri
	MUlv NCut NNor NRoo SCro
	SWat WCot WRus
– 'Maigold'	MBri
¶ – new hybrids	WHil
– 'Orange Crest'	GCal
¶ – 'Orange Globe'	NPri WHil
– 'Orange Princess' ♀	EBee EBrP EBre ENot EPfP
	GCHN LBre LSyl MBal MBel
	NBro NDea NHol SBre SPer
	SRms
– 'Prichard's Giant'	LBuc WCot
– 'Salamander'	SMur
– 'Superbus' ♀	COtt CRDP ELan EPar EPfP
	MBri NHol NRoo SPer SSpi
	WCot
¶ – 'T. Smith'	NHol
europaeus	CBot CRow CSam ECha EPot
	LHil LHop LSyl MBal MBro
	MNrw NDea NMir NRya SRms
	SWat WCla WHoo WLin WPer
	WPyg
◆ – 'Superbus'	See *T.* x *cultorum* **'Superbus'**
hondoensis	EBee GBin NLar WSan
ledebourii hort.	See *T. chinensis*
pumilus	CGle ECha ELan EPar LBee
	MBro MHig NMGW NNrd
	NWCA WHil WViv
¶ – ACE 1818	GBuc
* – *albidus*	SIng
– 'Wargrave'	EPot NMen
stenopetalus	EBee ECha
yunnanensis	CGle GBuc MBal NGre NSti
	NWoo SMac
¶ – CD&R 2097	WCru

TROPAEOLUM †   (Tropaeolaceae)

azureum	CPla MSto
brachyceras	MSto
ciliatum ♀	CAvo CFir CHan CLAP
	CMHig CMon CPlN CPla
	CSWP CSam EBrP EBre ELan
	EOrc GCal LBow LBre MSto
	MTho SBre SLMG WCru WHer
	WNor WPGP
incisum	MSto
majus	CHEx EMFW LHol SBid WSel
– 'Alaska' (v)	CBod SBid SIde WJek
¶ – 'Apricot Trifle'	CSpe
* – 'Clive Innes'	ERea GCra
– 'Crimson Beauty'	CSpe MAvo MHlr MLLN MMil
– 'Darjeeling Double' (d)	WCru
¶ – 'Darjeeling Gold' (d)	CSpe LHil
– 'Empress of India'	SBid WEas WJek
– 'Hermine Grashoff' (d)	CSWP CSpe CTbh ECtt ERea
♀	GCal LBlm LHil LHop NPer
	SAxl SBid SLod SUsu WEas
	WHer WLRN
– 'Margaret Long' (d)	CSpe LHil MLLN WEas WLRN
* – 'Peaches and Cream'	WJek
– 'Red Wonder'	CHad CSWP CSpe GCal LHil
	SBid SUsu
– Tom Thumb mixed	WJek

peltophorum	MSto
pentaphyllum	CAvo CLAP ECha GCal IBlr MSto MTho WCot
polyphyllum	CPlN GBuc GCLN MSto SDix SWas WOMN
sessilifolium	EHyt MSto
speciosum ♀	Widely available
sylvestre	WCru
tricolorum ♀	CAvo CLAP CMon CPlN EPot MTho SDix WCot
tuberosum	CB&S CGle CMHG ETub GPoy MBal NSti WWye
– var. *lineamaculatum* 'Ken Aslet' ♀	CAvo CBro CGle CPlN CRDP CRHN CSam CWit ECha ELan EOrc EPot ERea ERos GBur GCHN IBlr LAma LBow LFis LHop MBal MTho NPSI NRog SSpi WCru WHer WPGP WWat
– P.J. Christian's form	NRog
– var. *piliferum* 'Sidney'	CFil CGle IBlr WCru

TSUGA (Pinaceae)

canadensis	EHul GAri GChr LCon MBar NWea SHBN SPer WDin
– 'Abbot's Dwarf'	CKen LCon MGos
§ – 'Abbott's Pygmy'	CKen
– 'Albospica'	ESis LBee LCon
– 'Aurea' (v)	LCon MBar
– 'Baldwin Dwarf Pyramid'	MBar
– 'Bennett'	EHul LCon MBar MUlv
– 'Brandley'	CKen
§ – 'Branklyn'	CKen
– 'Cinnamonea'	CKen
– 'Coffin'	CKen
– 'Cole's Prostrate'	CKen EBrP EBre LBre LCon MAsh MBar NHol SBre SHBN
– 'Curley'	CKen
– 'Curtis Ideal'	CKen
– 'Dwarf Whitetip'	EPla LCon
– 'Everitt Golden'	CKen
– 'Fantana'	EHul LBee LCon LLin MBar NHol SBod SLim WLRN
– 'Gentsch Snowflake'	CKen EPla MGos
¶ – 'Greenwood Lake'	EPla
– 'Horsford'	CKen
– 'Hussii'	CKen
– 'Jacqueline Verkade'	CKen
– 'Jeddeloh' ♀	CDoC EBar EBrP EBre EHul ENot EOrn EPot ESis GChr LBre LCon LLin MAsh MBal MBar MBri MGos MPla NBee SBre SLim WPyg WStI
– 'Jervis'	CKen LCon
– 'Kingsville Spreader'	CKen
I – 'Lutea'	CKen
¶ – 'Minima'	CKen
– 'Minuta'	CKen EHul EOrn ESis LBee LCon MBar MGos
– 'Nana'	CMac EHul IOrc WLRN
– 'Nana Gracilis'	See *T. canadensis* 'Gracilis'
– 'Palomino'	CKen MBar
– 'Pendula' ♀	CDoC CKen EHul ENot EOrn LBee LCon MBar MBri MOne SLim WCwm
¶ – 'Pincushion'	CKen
– 'Prostrata'	See *T. canadensis* 'Branklyn'
– 'Pygmaea'	See *T. canadensis* 'Abbott's Pygmy'
– 'Rugg's Washington'	CKen
– 'Verkade Petite'	CKen
– 'Verkade Recurved'	CKen LCon MBar MUlv WBcn

– 'Von Helms'	CKen
– 'Warnham'	CKen ECho LBee LCon MAsh MBri
caroliniana 'La Bar Weeping'	CKen
diversifolia	EPot LCon
– 'Gotelli'	CKen
heterophylla ♀	CDoC CPer ENot GAri GChr GRei IOrc LBuc LCon MBar NWea SHBN SMad SPer STre WDin
– 'Iron Springs'	CKen EOrn
¶ – 'Laursen's Column'	CKen
menziesii	See *Pseudotsuga menziesii*
¶ *mertensiana*	WCwm
– 'Elizabeth'	CKen
I – 'Glauca Nana'	CKen
– 'Quartz Mountain'	CKen
sieboldii 'Nana'	CKen

TSUSIOPHYLLUM (Ericaceae)

tanakae	See *Rhododendron tsusiophyllum*

TUBERARIA (Cistaceae)

guttata	SSpi WCru
lignosa	CInt CMHG SSpi WAbe WCla WLin

TULBAGHIA † (Alliaceae)

acutiloba	CAvo LLew
alliacea	CFee LHil WCot
capensis	CFee LGre
cepacea	LHil NBir
§ – var. *maritima*	CAvo CMon LLew
coddii	CAvo CFee CHan LGre
cominsii	CAvo CMon LGre
¶ *dregeana*	LLew
'Fairy Star'	WCot
fragrans	See *T. simmleri*
galpinii	CMon WCot
¶ – 'John Rider'	CAbb
* 'John May's Special'	WCot
'John Rider'	WPer
leucantha	ERos LHil LLew WCot
ludwigiana	WCot
♦ *maritima*	See *T. cepacea* var. *maritima*
natalensis	CAvo CHan CMon CPou LGre
– pink	WCot
§ *simmleri*	CAvo CMon EWes LAma LBlm LHil LLew SSpi WCot
violacea	CB&S CBro CHan CMon CPea CPou CSev ECha ERav ETub IBlr LAma LPan MTho SMrm SSpi SWat WPGP
* – 'Alba'	CPea LLew
– *pallida*	CAvo CRDP LGre LHil SAxl SLod SMrm SUsu WCot
§ – 'Silver Lace' (v)	CAvo CBos CFee CGle CHan CRDP CSWP CSpe ELan EMon ERav ERea EWes LGre LHop MBEx MTho SIgm SSpi WCot WPGP
– *tricolor*	CMon
– 'Variegata'	See *T. violacea* 'Silver Lace'

TULIPA † (Liliaceae)

'Abu Hassan' (3)	ETub LAma
acuminata (15)	CBro EBot ETub LAma LBow
'Ad Rem' (4)	LAma
'Addis' (14)	LAma

'African Queen' (3)	LAma
aitchisonii	See *T. clusiana*
'Aladdin' (6)	EWal LAma NRog
'Alaska' (6)	LAma
albertii (15)	LAma
'Albino' (3)	LAma
aleppensis (15)	LAma
'Aleppo' (7)	LAma
'Alfred Cortot' (12) ♀	LAma
'Ali Baba' (14)	MBri
'Alice Leclercq' (2)	LAma
'All Bright' (5)	LAma
'Allegretto' (11)	LAma NRog
altaica (15)	EPot LAma
amabilis PF 8955	See *T. hoogiana* PF 8955
'Ancilla' (12) ♀	CBro LAma
'Angélique' (11)	CAvo ETub EWal LAma MBri NBir
anisophylla (15)	MSto
'Anne Claire' (3)	LAma
'Antwerp' (3)	LAma
'Apeldoorn' (4)	ETub EWal LAma MBri NRog
'Apeldoorn's Elite' (4) ♀	EWal LAma NRog
'Apricot Beauty' (1)	CAvo ETub EWal LAma MBri NBir NRog WBro
'Apricot Jewel'	See *T. linifolia* (**Batalinii Group**) **'Apricot Jewel'**
'Apricot Parrot' (10) ♀	LAma NRog
'Arabian Mystery' (3)	CAvo LAma NBir
'Aristocrat' (5) ♀	LAma
'Arma' (7)	LAma
'Artist' (8) ♀	CAvo LAma NBir
'Athleet' (3)	LAma
'Attila' (3)	LAma NRog
aucheriana (15) ♀	CBro CMea CMon EHyt EPot ERos ETub LAma LBow
'Aurea'	See *T. greigii* **'Aurea'**
'Aureola' (5)	LAma
australis (15)	CMon
bakeri	See *T. saxatilis* **Bakeri Group**
'Balalaika' (5)	LAma
'Ballade' (6) ♀	ETub LAma
'Ballerina' (6) ♀	CAvo LAma
batalinii	See *T. linifolia* **Batalinii Group**
'Beauty of Apeldoorn' (4)	LAma NRog
'Belcanto' (3)	LAma
'Bellflower' (7)	LAma
'Bellona' (3)	ETub LAma
'Berlioz' (12)	LAma
biebersteiniana (15)	LAma
§ *biflora* (15)	CBro EPot ETub LAma NRog
bifloriformis (15)	MSto
'Big Chief' (4) ♀	LAma MBri
'Bing Crosby' (3)	ETub LAma
'Bird of Paradise'	See *T. 'Mrs Keightley'*
'Black Parrot' (10) ♀	CAvo LAma
'Blenda' (3)	ETub
'Bleu Aimable' (5)	CAvo ETub LAma
'Blue Heron' (7) ♀	LAma
'Blue Parrot' (10)	CSWP EWal LAma NRog
'Blushing Lady' (5)	LAma
'Bonanza' (11)	LAma
'Boule de Neige' (2)	LAma
'Bravissimo' (2)	MBri
'Brilliant Star' (1)	LAma MBri
'Burgundy' (6)	ETub LAma
'Burgundy Lace' (7)	LAma
'Burns' (7)	LAma
butkovii (15)	LAma
I 'Calypso' (14)	ETub
'Candela' (13)	LAma
'Cantata' (13)	CBro LAma
'Cantor' (5)	LAma
'Cape Cod' (14)	LAma NRog
'Caprice' (10)	LAma
'Captain Fryatt' (6)	LAma
carinata (15)	LAma
'Carlton' (2)	ETub LAma NRog
'Carnaval de Nice' (11/v)	ETub LAma MBri
'Cassini' (3)	LAma
§ *celsiana* (15)	CMon EBot EPot LAma
'César Franck' (12)	LAma
'Charles' (3)	LAma
'China Pink' (6) ♀	CAvo ETub LAma NRog
'Chopin' (12)	LAma NRog
'Christmas Marvel' (1)	ETub LAma
chrysantha Boiss.	See *T. montana*
– Boiss. ex Baker	See *T. clusiana* var. *chrysantha*
'Clara Butt' (5)	LAma NRog
§ *clusiana* (15)	CBro LAma
§ – var. *chrysantha* (15) ♀	CAvo LAma LBow MSto NRog
– – 'Tubergen's Gem' (15)	CSWP LAma MBri SUsu
– 'Cynthia' (15)	CAvo CSWP EHyt EPot LAma
§ – var. *stellata* (15)	LAma
'Concerto' (13)	CBro ETub LAma
'Cordell Hull' (5)	NRog
'Corona' (12)	ETub LAma
'Corsage' (14) ♀	LAma
'Couleur Cardinal' (3)	EBot ETub EWal LAma NRog
cretica (15)	CMon MSto
'Crystal Beauty' (7)	NRog
'Dancing Show' (8)	CAvo LAma
dasystemon (15)	EBar LAma MRPP
'Diana' (1)	LAma NRog
'Diantha' (14)	LAma
didieri	See *T. passeriniana*
'Dillenburg' (5)	LAma
'Dix' Favourite' (3)	LAma
'Doctor Plesman' (3)	LAma
'Doll's Minuet' (8)	LAma
'Don Quichotte' (3) ♀	LAma
'Donna Bella' (14) ♀	LAma
'Douglas Bader' (5)	CAvo LAma NRog
'Dreaming Maid' (3)	LAma
'Dutch Gold' (3)	LAma
'Dyanito' (6)	EWal LAma
'Early Harvest' (12) ♀	LAma
'Easter Parade' (13)	EWal LAma
'Easter Surprise' (14)	LAma
§ *edulis* (15)	CMon LAma LRHS
eichleri	See *T. undulatifolia*
'Electra' (5)	EWal LAma MBri
'Elegant Lady' (6)	ETub
'Elizabeth Arden' (4)	LAma
'Elmus' (5)	LAma
'Esperanto' (8/v)	LAma NRog
'Estella Rijnveld' (10)	ETub LAma NBir NRog
'Fair Lady' (12)	LAma
'Fancy Frills' (7) ♀	LAma
'Fantasy' (10) ♀	LAma
'Fashion' (12)	LAma
ferganica (15)	CMon LAma
'Feu Superbe' (13)	LAma
'Fireside'	See *T. 'Vlammenspel'*
'First Lady' (3) ♀	LAma
'Flair' (1)	LAma
'Flaming Parrot' (10)	LAma
'Flying Dutchman' (5)	LAma
fosteriana (13)	MBri
'Franz Léhar' (12)	LAma
'Frasquita' (5)	LAma
'Fresco' (14)	LAma
Fringed Group (7)	ETub
'Fringed Apeldoorn' (7)	NRog

'Fringed Beauty' (7)	ETub MBri
'Fringed Elegance' (7)	LAma
'Fritz Kreisler' (12)	LAma
'Fulgens' (6)	LAma
'Gaiety' (12)	LAma
'Galata' (13)	LAma
galatica (15)	LAma
'Garden Party' (3)	ETub LAma
'Generaal de Wet' (1)	ETub LAma MBri
'General Eisenhower' (4)	LAma
'Georgette' (5)	EWal LAma MBri NRog
'Giuseppe Verdi' (12)	EWal LAma LBow MBri NRog
'Glück' (12)	EWal LAma
'Gold Medal' (11)	LAma MBri
'Golden Age' (5)	LAma
'Golden Apeldoorn' (4)	EWal LAma MBri NRog
'Golden Artist' (8)	LAma MBri NRog
'Golden Emperor' (13)	LAma
'Golden Harvest' (5)	LAma
'Golden Melody' (3)	ETub LAma NRog
'Golden Oxford' (4)	LAma
'Golden Parade' (4)	LAma
'Golden Springtime' (4)	LAma
'Gordon Cooper' (4)	EWal LAma
'Goudstuk' (12)	LAma
'Grand Prix' (13)	LAma
'Green Eyes' (8)	LAma
'Green Spot' (8)	LAma
greigii (14)	CBro CMon
§ – 'Aurea' (14)	CMon
grengiolensis (15)	EPot LAma
'Greuze' (5)	LAma
'Grével' (3)	CAvo LAma
'Groenland' (8)	LAma
'Gudoshnik' (4)	LAma
hageri (15)	CMon LAma
– 'Splendens' (15)	ETub LAma
'Halcro' (5) ♀	ETub LAma
'Hamilton' (7) ♀	LAma
'Happy Family' (3)	LAma
'Heart's Delight' (12)	CBro ETub EWal LAma LBow NRog
'Hibernia' (3)	LAma
'Hit Parade' (13)	LAma
'Hoangho' (2)	LAma
'Hollands Glorie' (4) ♀	LAma
'Hollywood' (8)	LAma
hoogiana (15)	LAma
§ – PF 8955 (15)	CMon
§ *humilis* (15)	CAvo CBro EPar EPot LAma LBow MBri
– 'Eastern Star' (15)	LAma MBri
§ – 'Lilliput' (15)	CBro EPot GCrs
– 'Odalisque' (15)	EPot LAma
– 'Persian Pearl' (15)	EPot LAma MBri NRog
§ – var. *pulchella* Albocaerulea Oculata Group (15)	EPot LAma
§ – Violacea Group (15)	CAvo CMea EPar EWal LAma MBri
§ – Violacea Group black base (15)	CBro LRHS
– Violacea Group yellow base (15)	CBro LAma LBow LRHS
'Humming Bird' (8)	LAma
'Hytuna' (11)	LAma NRog
'Ibis' (1)	LAma
'Ile de France' (5)	LAma
¶ 'Inferno'	NBir
ingens (15)	LAma
'Inzell' (3)	ETub LAma
'Jeantine' (12) ♀	LAma

'Jewel of Spring' (4) ♀	LAma
'Jimmy' (3)	NRog
'Jockey Cap' (14)	LAma
'Joffre' (1)	LAma MBri
'Johann Strauss' (12)	CBro EWal LAma MBri
'Johanna' (3)	LAma
'Juan' (13)	LAma MBri
'Kansas' (3)	LAma
'Karel Doorman' (10)	LAma
'Kareol' (2)	LAma
kaufmanniana (12)	CAvo CBro EPot LBow NRog SRms
§ 'Kees Nelis' (3)	LAma MBri NRog
'Keizerskroon' (1) ♀	EBot EWal LAma NRog
'Kingsblood' (5) ♀	LAma
kolpakowskiana (15) ♀	LAma MBri NRog
kurdica (15)	LAma
'La Tulipe Noire' (5)	LAma
* 'Lady Diana' (14)	MBri
lanata (15)	LAma
'Large Copper' (14)	LAma
'Leen van der Mark' (3)	LAma
'Lefeber's Favourite' (4)	LAma
'Lilac Time' (6)	LAma
'Lilac Wonder'	See *T. saxatilis* (Bakeri Group) 'Lilac Wonder'
'Lilliput'	See *T. humilis* 'Lilliput'
linifolia (15) ♀	CAvo EHyt EPar EPot ETub LAma LBow NRog SUsu WAbe
§ – Batalinii Group (15) ♀	CBro LAma NRog WOMN
§ – – 'Apricot Jewel' (15)	CAvo CBro
– – 'Bright Gem' (15) ♀	CAvo CBro EPot LAma LBow MBro NRog WHoo WPyg
– – 'Bronze Charm' (15)	CAvo CBro CMea CSWP EPot ETub LAma SUsu
– – 'Red Gem' (15)	CBro LAma
¶ – – 'Red Jewel' (15)	CMea
– – 'Yellow Gem' (15)	CBro
– – 'Yellow Jewel' (15)	LAma
§ – Maximowiczii Group	CBro LAma LBow
'London' (4)	LAma
'Lucifer' (5)	EWal LAma
'Lucky Strike' (3)	LAma
§ 'Lustige Witwe' (3)	ETub EWal LAma
§ 'Madame Lefeber' (13)	CBro EWal LBow MBri
'Magier' (5)	LAma
'Maja' (7)	LAma
'Mamasa' (5)	LAma
'March of Time' (14)	MBri
'Maréchal Niel' (2)	LAma
'Mariette' (6)	LAma
'Marilyn' (6)	ETub LAma
marjolletii (15)	CBro LAma NRog
'Mary Ann' (14)	LAma
'Maureen' (5) ♀	CMea ETub LAma
mauritiana (15)	LAma
maximowiczii	See *T. linifolia* Maximowiczii Group
'Maytime' (6)	LAma
'Maywonder' (11)	LAma
'Melody d'Amour' (5)	ETub
'Menton' (5)	ETub
Merry Widow	See *T.* 'Lustige Witwe'
'Mickey Mouse' (1)	NRog
'Minerva' (3)	NRog
'Miss Holland' (3)	MBri
'Mona Lisa' (6)	LAma
§ *montana* (15)	CBro EPot ETub LAma
'Monte Carlo' (2) ♀	ETub EWal LAma
'Mount Tacoma' (11)	ETub EWal LAma MBri NRog
'Mr Van der Hoef' (2)	LAma MBri
'Murillo' (2)	LAma

Name	Suppliers
'My Lady' (4) 🏆	LAma
'Negrita' (3)	LAma
neustreuvae	CBro EPot GCrs
'New Design' (3/v)	ETub EWal LAma MBri NRog
'New Look' (7)	ETub
'Orange Bouquet' (3) 🏆	LAma NRog
'Orange Elite' (14)	LAma MBri
'Orange Emperor' (13)	LAma MBri NRog
'Orange Favourite' (10)	LAma
'Orange Sun'	See *T.* 'Oranjezon'
'Orange Triumph' (11)	MBri
'Oranje Nassau' (2) 🏆	LAma MBri NRog
§ 'Oranjezon' (4) 🏆	LAma
'Oratorio' (14)	LAma MBri
'Oriental Beauty' (14)	LAma NRog
'Oriental Splendour' (14) 🏆	EWal LAma
orphanidea (15)	EPot LAma LBow WCot
– 'Flava' (15)	CBro CMon ETub LAma
§ – Whittallii Group (15)	CAvo CBro CMea CMon LAma NRog
ostrowskiana (15)	LAma
'Oxford' (4) 🏆	LAma
'Oxford's Elite' (4)	LAma
'Page Polka' (3)	LAma
'Palestrina' (3)	LAma
'Pandour' (14)	LAma MBri
'Parade' (4) 🏆	LAma MBri
passeriniana (15)	LAma
'Paul Richter' (3)	LAma
'Pax' (3)	LAma
'Peach Blossom' (2)	ETub LAma MBri NRog
'Peerless Pink' (3)	LAma
'Perlina' (14)	LAma
persica	See *T. celsiana*
'Philippe de Comines' (5)	LAma
'Picture' (5) 🏆	LAma
'Pimpernel' (8/v)	CAvo LAma
'Pink Beauty' (1)	LAma
'Pink Impression' (4)	LAma
'Pink Trophy' (1)	LAma
'Pinkeen' (13)	LAma
'Pinocchio' (14)	EWal NRog
'Plaisir' (14) 🏆	LAma MBri
platystigma (15)	LAma
polychroma	See *T. biflora*
praestans (15)	LAma
– 'Fusilier' (15) 🏆	CBro EPot ETub EWal LAma LBow MBri NBir NRog
– 'Unicum' (15/v)	EWal LAma MBri NRog
– 'Van Tubergen's Variety' (15)	LAma NRog
'Preludium' (3)	LAma
'President Kennedy' (4) 🏆	LAma
primulina (15)	CMon
'Prince Karl Philip' (3)	NRog
'Prince of Austria' (1)	LAma
'Princeps' (13)	CBro EWal LAma MBri
'Princess Margaret Rose' (5)	EWal LAma
'Prinses Irene' (3) 🏆	CMea ETub LAma MBri NBir
'Professor Röntgen' (10)	LAma
pulchella	See *T. humilis* var. *pulchella* Albocaerulea Oculata Group
– *humilis*	See *T. humilis*
§ 'Purissima' (13)	CAvo CBro ETub EWal LAma LBow
'Queen' (4)	LAma
'Queen Ingrid' (14)	LAma
'Queen of Bartigons' (5) 🏆	LAma NRog
'Queen of Night' (5)	CAvo CMea ETub EWal LAma MBri
'Queen of Sheba' (6) 🏆	CAvo LAma
'Queen Wilhelmina'	See *T.* 'Koningin Wilhelmina'
'Recreado' (5)	ETub
'Red Champion' (10)	LAma
'Red Emperor'	See *T.* 'Madame Lefeber'
'Red Georgette' (5) 🏆	MBri
'Red Matador' (4)	LAma
'Red Parrot' (10)	LAma
'Red Riding Hood' (14) 🏆	CBro ETub EWal LAma LBow MBri NBir NRog
'Red Shine' (6) 🏆	LAma
'Red Wing' (7) 🏆	LAma
Rembrandt Mix	ETub MBri
rhodopea	See *T. urumoffii*
'Ringo'	See *T.* 'Kees Nelis'
'Rosario' (3)	ETub
* 'Rose Emperor' (13)	LAma
'Rosy Wings' (3)	LAma
'Safari' (14)	ETub
saxatilis (15)	CAvo CBro CNic LAma MBri NRog
§ – Bakeri Group (15)	LAma MRPP
§ – – 'Lilac Wonder' 🏆	CAvo CBro EPot ETub LAma MBri NRog
– MS 769 (15)	CMon
'Scarlett O'Hara' (5)	LAma
'Schoonoord' (2)	ETub LAma MBri
schrenkii (15)	LAma LRHS
'Scotch Lassie' (5)	LAma
'Shakespeare' (12)	CBro LAma LBow NRog
'Shirley' (3)	CAvo ETub EWal LAma MBri NRog
'Showwinner' (12) 🏆	CBro ETub LAma MBri
'Sigrid Undset' (5)	LAma
'Silentia' (5)	LAma
'Smiling Queen' (5)	LAma
'Snowflake' (3)	LAma
'Snowpeak' (5)	LAma
sogdiana (15)	LAma
'Sorbet' (5) 🏆	LAma
'Sparkling Fire' (14)	LAma
'Spectacular Gold'	See *T.* 'Goldenes Deutschland'
sprengeri (15) 🏆	CAvo CBro CFil CLAP CMon CNic EHyt EPar LAma SSpi Wlvy WPGP
– Trotter's form (15)	WCot
'Spring Green' (8) 🏆	CAvo CMea ETub EWal LAma MBri NRog
'Spring Pearl' (13)	LAma
'Spring Song' (4)	LAma
stellata	See *T. clusiana* var. *stellata*
'Stockholm' (2) 🏆	LAma
'Stresa' (12) 🏆	CBro LAma
'Striped Apeldoorn' (4)	LAma NRog
¶ 'Striped Bellona' (3)	CSWP
subpraestans (15)	EPot LAma
'Summit' (13)	LAma
'Sundew' (7)	LAma NRog
'Sunray' (3)	LAma
'Susan Oliver' (8)	LAma
'Swan Wings' (7)	LAma
'Sweet Harmony' (5) 🏆	LAma MBri NRog
'Sweet Lady' (14)	LAma NRog
'Sweetheart' (5)	See *T.* 'Princess Juliana'
'Sweetheart' (13)	CBro LAma NRog
sylvestris (15)	CAvo CBro CMea EPar EWFC LAma LBow NRog WCot WRHF WShi
'Tango' (14)	LAma

tarda (15) ♀	CAvo CBro CMea EPar EPot
	ETub EWal LAma LBow MBri
	MBro MSto NMGW NRog
	WPat WPyg
'Temple of Beauty' (5) ♀	LAma
'Tender Beauty' (4)	LAma
tetraphylla (15)	LAma
'Texas Flame' (10)	LAma
'Texas Gold' (10)	LAma
'The First' (12)	CBro LAma
'Toronto' (14) ♀	ETub LAma MBri
'Toulon' (13)	MBri
'Towa' (14)	LAma
'Trinket' (14)	LAma
'Triumphator' (2)	LAma
tschimganica (15)	LAma
tubergeniana (15)	LAma
– 'Keukenhof' (15)	LAma
turkestanica (15) ♀	CAvo CBro CSWP EPar EPot
	ETub LAma LBow MBri MBro
	NRog SUsu WHoo WOMN
	WRHF
'Uncle Tom' (11)	LAma MBri
§ *undulatifolia* (15)	CBro LAma
'Union Jack' (5) ♀	EWal LAma
urumiensis (15) ♀	CAvo CBro EHyt EPot LAma
	MBri MBro NRog WAbe
	WHoo WPat WPyg
§ *urumoffii* (15)	LAma
'Valentine' (3)	LAma
'Van der Neer' (1)	LAma
'Varinas' (3)	LAma
violacea	See *T. humilis* Violacea Group
'Viridiflora' (8)	ETub
'Vivaldi' (12)	LAma
'Vivex' (4)	LAma
§ 'Vlammenspel' (1)	LAma
'Vuurbaak' (2)	LAma
vvedenskyi (15)	CBro LAma NRog
– 'Blanka' (15)	EPot
– 'Hanka' (15)	EPot
– 'Lenka' (15)	EPot
– 'Tangerine Beauty' (15)	MBri
'West Point' (6) ♀	CAvo ETub EWal LAma
* 'White Bouquet' (5)	NRog
'White Dream' (3)	EWal LAma
'White Emperor'	See *T.* 'Purissima'
'White Parrot' (10)	CAvo LAma NRog
'White Swallow' (3)	NRog
'White Triumphator' (6) ♀	CAvo CMea ETub EWal LAma
	NBir NRog
'White Virgin' (3)	LAma
whittallii	See *T. orphanidea* Whittallii Group
'Willem van Oranje' (2)	LAma
'Willemsoord' (2)	LAma MBri
wilsoniana	See *T. montana*
'Yellow Dawn' (14)	LAma
'Yellow Emperor' (5)	MBri
'Yellow Empress' (13)	LAma
'Yellow Present' (3)	LAma
'Yellow Purissima' (13)	NRog
'Yokohama' (3)	LAma
'Zampa' (14) ♀	EWal LAma
zenaidae (15)	MSto
'Zombie' (13)	LAma
'Zomerschoon' (5)	EBot ETub

TUNICA See PETRORHAGIA

TURBINA (Convolvulaceae)
corymbosa	NGno

TURNERA (Turneraceae)
¶ *ulmifolia*	MSal

TURRAEA (Meliaceae)
obtusifolia	CSpe

TUSSILAGO (Asteraceae)
farfara	CArn CJew CKin ELau EWFC
	GPoy MHew MSal SIde WHer

TUTCHERIA (Theaceae) See Plant Deletions

TWEEDIA (Asclepiadaceae)
§ *caerulea* ♀	CChr CGle CInt CRHN CSev
	CSpe ELan EMil ERea GCal
	IBlr LGre LHop LLWP SAxl
	SHFr SPer SUsu WEas

TYLOPHORA (Asclepiadaceae)
ovata	CPlN

TYPHA (Typhaceae)
angustifolia	CBen CKin CRow CWat EHon
	EMFW ESOG GBin LPBA
	MSta SWat SWyc WChe WWye
latifolia	CBen CHEx CRow CWat EHon
	EMFW LPBA MSta SWat SWyc
	WChe WHer WMAq WWye
– 'Variegata'	CBen CRow CWat EGar ELan
	EMFW LPBA MSta SWyc
	WChe WCot
§ *laxmannii*	CBen EHon EMFW LPBA
	MSta SRms
minima	CBen CRDP CRow EHoe
	EHon EMFW ESOG GBin
	LPBA MSta NDea SCoo SMad
	SWat SWyc WChe WFar
	WMAq
shuttleworthii	CRow
stenophylla	See *T. laxmannii*

UGNI (Myrtaceae)
§ *molinae*	CDec CGre CMHG CPle CSam
	CTrC ESim GAri ISea MBal
	MBel SHFr SOWG WCHb
	WJek WPic WSHC WWal
	WWat WWye

ULEX (Papilionaceae)
europaeus	CCVT CDoC EMil ENot
	EWFC GRei LBuc MCoo
	NWea SEND WDin WHar
	WMou
– 'Aureus'	CB&S
§ – 'Flore Pleno' (d) ♀	CB&S CDoC CInt CTri ENot
	GChr MBal SHBN SMad SPer
	WBcn WCot
– 'Plenus'	See *U. europaeus* 'Flore Pleno'
– 'Prostratus'	MBar
¶ *gallii*	IIve
– 'Mizen'	EHic ESis GCal GGGa GSki
	LRHS MPla NHar SMad
nanus	See *U. minor*

ULMUS (Ulmaceae)
'Dodoens'	LBuc MGos NBee
§ *glabra*	CPer GChr GRei NWea WDin
	WMou
– 'Camperdownii'	CDoC CTho ECrN ELan SPer
– 'Exoniensis'	CTho

– 'Gittisham'	CTho
– 'Horizontalis'	See *U. glabra* **'Pendula'**
¶ – 'Lutescens'	CTri
– 'Nana'	WPat
– 'Pendula'	LPan
x *hollandica* 'Commelin'	EMil
– 'Groeneveld'	EMil
– 'Jacqueline Hillier'	CBar CInt CTre EBrP EBre
	ELan ESis GDra LBre LHop
	MBal MBar MBro MPla NHar
	NHol SBre SHFr SIng SRms
	SSpi STre SVil WAbe WHCG
	WPat WPyg
– 'Lobel'	MGos
– 'Wredei'	See *U. minor* **'Dampieri Aurea'**
minor 'Cornubiensis'	CBlo CDoC CTho
§ – 'Dampieri Aurea'	CBlo CBot CEnd CLnd ECrN
	ELan LBuc LNet LPan MAsh
	MBar MBlu MBro NBee SHBN
	SMad SPer SSta WDin WPat
– 'Variegata'	EPot
montana	See *U. glabra*
parvifolia	ECrN EHal EHic GAri NWea
	STre WFro WHCr WNor
– 'Frosty' (v)	ECho ELan EPot
– 'Geisha' (v)	CBlo CPMA ELan MGos SBla
	SMad WPat WPyg
§ – 'Hokkaido'	EHyt LBee MBro SBla WAbe
	WPat WPyg
– 'Pygmaea'	See *U. parvifolia* **'Hokkaido'**
– 'Yatsubusa'	CLyd EHyt EPot ESis EWes
	MBro SIng STre WAbe WGle
	WPat WPyg
¶ *procera*	SMad
'Argenteovariegata'	
pumila	CAgr GAri WNor
'Sapporo Autumn Gold'	CDoC

UMBELLULARIA (Lauraceae)

californica	CArn SAPC SArc WSHC

UMBILICUS (Crassulaceae)

erectus	CRDP
rupestris	ELan EWFC GAri GBar IIve
	NGre NWCA WCla WCot
	WHer WShi WWye

UNCINIA (Cyperaceae)

N *rubra*	Widely available
* – 'Dunn Valley'	GBri WCot
sp. from Chile	EBee EWes GCal
uncinata	CFil CSpe EBee ECGN ECha
	EHoe EMan EOas GOrn MBal
	NHol NWCA SDix SUsu
* – *rubra*	CFir CTrC ECot LRHS MMHG

UNGNADIA (Sapindaceae) See Plant Deletions

UNIOLA (Poaceae)

latifolia	See *Chasmanthium latifolium*

URCEOLINA (Amaryllidaceae)

miniata	See *Stenomesson miniatum*
peruviana	See *Stenomesson miniatum*

URECHITES See PENTALINON

URGINEA (Hyacinthaceae)

fugax SF 62	CMon
maritima	EBot EOHP GPoy LAma
	MNrw MSal

– SF 275	CMon
ollivieri MS&CL 281	CMon
undulata SF 2	CMon

UROSPERMUM (Asteraceae)

delachampii	CGle CHan COtt CSam EMan
	SAga SUsu

URSINIA (Asteraceae) See Plant Deletions

URTICA (Urticaceae)

¶ *dioica* 'Brightstone Bitch'	WAlt
(v)	
* – 'Chedglow'	CNat
¶ – 'Danae' (v)	CNat
¶ – 'Dusting' (v)	WAlt
galeopsifolia	CNat

UTRICULARIA (Lentibulariaceae)

alpina	WMEx
australis	EFEx
biloba	GTro
bisquamata	GTro WMEx
calcyfida	GTro WMEx
capensis	WMEx
dichotoma	EFEx GTro MHel WMEx
exoleta	See *U. gibba*
§ *gibba*	EFEx
intermedia	EFEx
laterifolia	EFEx GTro MHel WMEx
livida	EFEx GTro MHel WMEx
longifolia	GTro WMEx
menziesii	EFEx GTro
monanthos	EFEx
nephrophylla	GTro
novae-zelandiae	GTro
ochroleuca	EFEx
praelonga	GTro
prehensilis	GTro WMEx
pubescens	WMEx
reniformis	EFEx GTro MHel WMEx
– *nana*	EFEx
sandersonii	GTro MHel WMEx
– blue	GTro
subulata	EFEx WMEx
tricolor	GTro WMEx
vulgaris	EFEx SAWi WMEx

UVULARIA (Convallariaceae)

disporum	LAma
grandiflora ♀	Widely available
– var. *pallida*	CBos CRDP ECha EMon EPar
	GBuc IBlr LGre SAxl SWas
	WCru
perfoliata	CHid ECha EHyt EPar EPfP
	EPot GCrs LAma MBro MRav
	SBla SIng WAbe WCru WPGP
	WWat
pudica	See *U. caroliniana*
§ *sessilifolia*	EBee EPar EPot GCrs LAma
	LGan WCru

VACCARIA (Caryophyllaceae)

segetalis	See *V. hispanica*

VACCINIUM † (Ericaceae)

arctostaphylos	SSta
caespitosum	GDra
corymbosum ♀	CB&S CBlo EPfP MBal MBar
	MGos MHlr NBee SReu SSta
	WDin WGer

– 'Berkeley' (F)	CTrh GTwe LBuc LRHS
– 'Bluecrop' (F)	CDoC CMac CTrh ELan EMui GChr GTwe LBuc MBri MGos WStI WWeb
¶ – 'Bluegold'	CTrh
– 'Bluejay' (F)	CTrh LRHS
– 'Bluetta' (F)	CTrh GTwe LRHS
– 'Concord' (F)	EBee ENot
– 'Coville' (F)	CTrh EMui
– 'Duke' (F)	CTrh ELan EPfP LRHS
– 'Earliblue' (F)	EMui MGos
– 'Elliott' (F)	CTrh
– 'Goldtraube' (F)	CDoC MBlu MBri MGos NDal
– 'Herbert' (F)	CTrh EMui GTwe MGos
¶ – 'Ivanhoe' (F)	CTrh
– 'Jersey' (F)	LRHS
– 'Nelson'	CTrh
– 'Northland' (F)	GAri GTwe
– 'Patriot' (F)	CTrh GAri GTwe LRHS
– 'Pioneer' (F)	MBar
– 'Spartan' (F)	GAri GTwe LRHS
– 'Sunrise' (F)	GTwe
– 'Toro' (F)	GTwe
– 'Trovor' (F)	ELan
crassifolium 'Well's Delight' (F)	LRHS MAsh
cylindraceum ♀	NHol WAbe WBod WPat WPyg
– 'Tom Thumb'	WAbe
delavayi	EPot GCHN MAsh MBal MBar MBlu MHig SReu SSta WAbe
donianum	See *V. sprengelii*
duclouxii	CB&S
dunalianum	CB&S
¶ – var. *caudatifolium* B&SWJ 1716	WCru
emarginatum	SSta
floribundum	CFil CMHG EPfP GDra GSki GTou MBal SBrw SPer SSta WAbe WPGP WPic
glaucoalbum ♀	CAbP EPfP GGGa MBar MBlu MRav SPer SReu SSpi SSta WAbe WDin
– B 173	MBal
§ *macrocarpon*	CMac ELan ESim GTwe MBal MBar MBri SRms
– 'CN' (F)	ESim MGos
– 'Early Black' (F)	CB&S
– 'Franklin' (F)	CTrh EPot ESim
– 'Hamilton' (F)	EPot GDra NHol WAbe WPat WPyg
¶ – 'McFarlin' (F)	EMui
– 'Pilgrim' (F)	ESim
* 'McMinn'	GAri MBal
moupinense	ITim MAsh MBal MBlu MGos SPer SSta WAbe
– small-leaved	MBal
– 'Variegatum'	WPyg
myrtillus	GPoy IIve MBal WDin
'Nimo Pink'	MBar
nummularia	EPot GDra LRHS MBal MHig NHar SSpi WAbe
ovatum	CMHG GSki LRHS MBal MBar SPer SSta
§ *oxycoccos*	CArn
* – *rubrum*	LRHS
padifolium	CFil CGre MBal WPGP
pallidum	IBlr
palustre	See *V. oxycoccos*
praestans	GAri NHol
retusum	CGre CTrw LRHS MBal WAbe
sikkimense	EHyt GGGa
virgatum	MBal

vitis-idaea	CAgr CNic ESim GPoy MBal MBar MGos MHig SReu WPyg
– 'Compactum'	EWes MBal NHar
– Koralle Group ♀	EPfP MAsh MBal MBar MBri MGos MRav NHol SPer SReu SSta WAbe WPat WPyg
– subsp. *minus*	GAri MAsh MBal MHig SSta
– 'Red Pearl'	MAsh MGos
* – 'Variegatum'	EWes WPat
¶ *wrightii* var. *formosanum* B&SWJ 1542	WCru

VAGARIA (Amaryllidaceae)

ollivieri SF 266	CMon

VALERIANA (Valerianaceae)

'Alba'	See *Centranthus ruber albus*
alliariifolia	EBee EMon GCal NBro NSti WCot WGwy
arizonica	CLyd EGoo EMan LFis MSte MTho NCat
'Coccinea'	See *Centranthus ruber*
dioica	CRDP
¶ *jatamansi*	GPoy
montana	EHyt GTou MBro NBro NRya SRms SWat
officinalis	CArn CKin CRDP CSev ELau EWFC GPoy ILis LHol MChe MHew NBro NRoo SIde SWat WHer WOak WPer WShi WWye
– subsp. *sambucifolia*	CHan SHel WCot WPbr
* – 'Variegata'	WCHb
phu 'Aurea'	Widely available
* – 'Purpurea'	ECoo
pyrenaica	ECha EMon WCot
saxatilis	NRoo NRya
supina	CGra NWCA
tatamana	WEas

VALERIANELLA (Valerianaceae)

§ *locusta*	GPoy
olitoria	See *V. locusta*

VALLEA (Elaeocarpaceae)

¶ *stipularis*	CB&S
– *pyrifolia*	CGre CPle

VALLOTA (Amaryllidaceae)

♦ *speciosa*	See *Cyrtanthus elatus*

VANCOUVERIA (Berberidaceae)

chrysantha	CElw CFil CVer ECha EMon EPla GBuc SLod SSpi SUsu WCru WPbr WSHC
hexandra	CFil CHEx CNic CVer ECha EMan EMon EPla ERos GBuc GCal LHop MBal NCat NRya NSti SSpi WBea WCru WPbr WRus WWin

VANIA (Brassicaceae) See Plant Deletions

VEITCHIA (Arecaceae)

¶ *merrillii*	LPal

VELLA (Brassicaceae) See Plant Deletions

VELTHEIMIA (Hyacinthaceae)
§ *bracteata* ♀ — CHal CMon EBak ETub IBlr LBow NRog WCot
§ *capensis* ♀ — CSev SLMG
  viridifolia hort. — See *V. capensis*
  – Jacquin — See *V. bracteata*

× VENIDIOARCTOTIS See ARCTOTIS

VENIDIUM See ARCTOTIS

VERATRUM (Melanthiaceae)
  album — CBot CFil CFir ECha NLar SBla WCot WCru
¶ – var. *flavum* — LGre
  – var. *oxysepalum* — WCru
  californicum — ECha
  formosanum B&SWJ 1575 — WCru
  nigrum ♀ — CBot CBro CFir CHEx GCal GDra LGre MNrw SAxl SChu WByw WCot WFar WTin
  stamineum — WCru
  viride — CBot EBee ECha GCal GCal IBlr

VERBASCUM † (Scrophulariaceae)
  acaule — EBee GCLN
* – 'Album' — WCru
  adzharicum — EWll MAvo MBro SWat WHoo WOve WRHF WSan
  Allstree hybrids — CFee EHol
  'Arctic Summer' — See *V. bombyciferum* 'Polarsommer'
  arcturus — ESis MSto WPer
* *bakerianum* — WEas
  blattaria — CGle CPou EBee EBot ECGN ELan EPPr EWFC LIck MGed NBir SWat WEas WHer WPer
  – f. *albiflorum* — CLon CNic CSpe ECGN EMar LGan LGre MBro MCLN NSti SUsu WBon WHer WHoo WKif WPer WPyg WRus
  – pink — CChr CLTr EWll GAbr GBur NLak WOve
  – yellow — EWll SWat
§ *bombyciferum* ♀ — CSWP CSam CSev IIve NSti NVic SIng SRms SSvw WByw WEas WHer
¶ – BSSS 232 — WCru
§ – 'Polarsommer' — CSam EBrP EBre EMan GAbr LBre MBri MHlr MRav NBir SBre SRCN SRms WCot WFar
  – 'Silver Lining' — NFla NNor NPer SRCN
  'Broussa' — See *V. bombyciferum*
¶ 'Butterscotch' — GMac
  chaixii — CHea ECha GBuc LRot MRav NBir NCut WPer WPyg
  – 'Album' — CGle CSpe ECED ECGN ECoo EFou EPar LGre LHop MBri MBro MCLN MFir NBir NBrk NBro NChi NSti NVic SMrm SUsu SWil WHen WHoo WMow WPer WRus WWin
¶ – subsp. *austriacum* — EBee
  – × *phoeniceum* 'Clent Sunrise' — CHan
  (Cotswold Group) — CFai CHad CLon COtt CSam
  'Cotswold Beauty' ♀ — EAst EMan LBuc MBel MMil MTis NLak NLar NSti SChu WLRN WPGP
  – 'Cotswold King' — CGle WCot WGle WSan
  – 'Cotswold Queen' — CGle CLon CM&M EBrP EBre ECED EFou ELan EMan LBre MAus MMil MWat NCut NFla NSti SBre SChu SMrm SPer WEas WPGP WRHF WRus WSan WWin
  – 'Gainsborough' ♀ — CDoC CGle CHad CLon EAst EBar EBrP EBre ECha ECtt EFou ELan EPar GMac LBre MAus MBri MCLN MWat NLar SBla SBre SChu SMrm SPer SSvw SUsu SWat WRus
  – 'Mont Blanc' — CGle EBee EBrP EBre ECot EFou EMan LBre MLLN NRoo SBre WRus
  – 'Pink Domino' ♀ — CBot CDoC CGle CHad CLon EBrP EBre EFou ELan GBri LBre MAus MBri MTis MWat NCut NLak NSti SBre SChu SMrm SPer SSca SWat WMow WRus WViv
  – 'Royal Highland' — CGle CHad CLon EAst EBee ECot EFou ELan EMan GBri MTis MWat NCut NLak NLar SChu SMrm SWat WCot WRus
  – 'White Domino' — EBar EFou MAus WRus
  creticum — ECoo EPri GCra NLak WCla WPer
§ *densiflorum* — CArn ECoo EMan LHol NCut SIde SPer WCla WPer
  dumulosum ♀ — EDAr EHyt EPot GCal MAvo MHar NWCA SBla SHFr WAbe WSan
¶ 'Ellenbank Rose' — GMac
  'Frosted Gold' — LGre WCot
  'Golden Wings' — CPBP EPot ITim NMen NTow WAbe WPat
  'Helen Johnson' ♀ — Widely available
  'Jackie' — LGre SBla SPer
  'Letitia' ♀ — CSpe EBrP EBre ELan EPot EWes GCal LBee LBre MTho NTow SBla SBre SIng SSmi SWas WAbe WEas WHoo WKif WPyg WWin
¶ *longifolium* — EBee
  – var. *pannosum* — See *V. olympicum*
  lychnitis — CArn CLTr EBee WHer
  nigrum — CArn CGle CJew EBar EPfP EWFC MAus MChe MHew MSto NChi SEND SRCN WHer WOak WPer
  – var. *album* — ECGN MBel WWhi
§ *olympicum* — CGle CLTr CSam EBar ECha EGoo ELan ENot MOne NOak SEND WCot WPer
  phlomoides — CHea MSto WHil WKif
  phoeniceum — CArn CGle ECoo ELan GMac MSCN MWgw NBro NCut NMir NOak SRms WBro WCla WEas WHen WHil WOve WPer WWin
* – 'Album' — GMac LIck SSvw
¶ – 'Candy Spires' — WGwG
  – 'Flush of White' — CBot CM&M ECoo EMan EWll MLLN NCut SMrm WHen WWhi
  – hybrids — CBot CSpe EBrP EBre EGoo EMan LBre NChi NVic SBre SSea WFar WGor WPer
  pulverulentum — CKin EWFC
  rorippifolium — EMan
¶ 'Silberkandelaber' — SSvw

sinuatum	CArn WCot
* 'Spica'	CGle EMan NCut SSvw
spicatum	CBot
spinosum	CGle SHFr SIng
* Sunset shades	WGor
thapsiforme	See *V. densiflorum*
thapsus	CJew CKin CSam CSev EBot
	EGoo EOld EWFC GPoy MChe
	MHew MMal NLak NMir NNor
	WOak WSel WWye
'Vernale'	CBot
wiedemannianum	CBrd CSpe EWll GAbr SRCN
	WLin WPen

VERBENA (Verbenaceae)

¶ 'Adonis'	CAsh
'Aphrodite'	CAsh
'Apple Blossom'	WCot
'Aveyron'	CAsh SChu SMrm
* 'Batesville Rose'	WCot
'Blue Cascade'	CAsh LPVe
¶ 'Blue Knight'	CAsh
¶ 'Blue Moon'	CAsh
'Blue Prince'	CAsh CSpe
§ *bonariensis*	CArn CAsh CHad CHan
	CM&M CSam ECha EFou
	EMon GCal GMac LBlm LHil
	LHol LHop MBri MFir MUlv
	NBro NSti SDix SMad SPer
	SSvw SUsu WEas WHal
	WOMN WSHC WWat
¶ 'Boon'	SVil
¶ 'Booty'	CAsh SVil
'Boughton House'	CAsh MSte
'Bramley'	CAsh SChu SUsu
¶ *brasiliensis*	EBee
¶ *canadensis*	CAsh
– 'Perfecta'	CAsh EBar
'Candy Carousel'	CAsh CB&S CElw CSev EBar
	LIck NPri SCro SUsu
'Carousel'	CAsh NPri
chamaedrifolia	See *V. peruviana*
corymbosa	CAsh CGre CM&M ECGP
	ECha EGar LLWP MAvo
	SMrm SUsu WCot WPer
	WRHF
– 'Gravetye'	CAsh GBuc GCal GMac LGan
	NChi WAbe WFar
'Crimson Star'	CAsh
¶ 'Cupido'	CAsh
'Edith Eddleman'	CAsh MNrw WCot
* 'Fiesta'	WCot
* 'Foxhunter'	CAsh EMan
hastata	CAsh CHan CJew CSev EBot
	ECot EMan EMon EOrc GBar
	GCal LHol MChe MHew MNrw
	NChi NSti WCot WPer
– 'Alba'	CAsh CSWP EHal EMan EMon
	GBuc MBel WCot WPer
– JLS 88010WI	CAsh EMon
– 'Rosea'	CAsh ECGN EFou EMon GBuc
'Hecktor'	CAsh EMan
'Hidcote Purple'	CAsh GCal MBEx MSte
'Homestead Purple'	CAsh CSev EAst EBrP EBre
	ECGP EHic EMan GCal GMac
	LBre LFis LHop LLWP MBEx
	MCLN MFir MLLN MMil NFai
	NFla SBid SBre SCoo SUsu
	WCot WOve WWeb WWoo
'Huntsman'	CAsh GBuc GCal MSte WEas
¶ 'Jugend'	CAsh
N 'Kemerton'	CAsh CSev EMan MBEx MTis

'Kurpfalz'	CAsh IHos
* 'La France'	CAsh CElw CSam ECha EMan
	MRav SChu SDix SMrm SUsu
'Lawrence Johnston' ♀	CAsh GCal MBEx SLMG WEas
	WHen
'Loveliness'	CAsh EMan GCal IBlr SMer
	SMrm WEas
¶ *macdougalii*	EBee
× *maonettii*	CAsh WCot
'Nero'	CAsh NPri SMrm
officinalis	CArn CAsh EJud EWFC GPoy
	LHol MChe MHew MSal SIde
	WGwy WHer WJek WOak
	WPer WSel WWye
¶ 'Ophelia'	CAsh
¶ 'Paradiso'	CAsh
patagonica	See *V. bonariensis*
* 'Peach Blossom'	WCot
¶ 'Peaches and Cream'	CAsh LIck
§ *peruviana*	CAsh EBrP EBre LBre LHop
	MBEx MRav SBre SChu SCro
	SDix SIng SRms WAbe WOMN
– 'Alba'	CAsh GCal MBEx NTow SCro
phlogiflora	CAsh MBEx
¶ 'Piccolo'	CAsh
'Pink Bouquet'	See *V. 'Silver Anne'*
'Pink Parfait'	CHal EBar ELan EMan EOrc
	LHop MBEx MRav SCro SMer
	SUsu
'Pink Pearl'	CAsh ECtt
* 'Pink Perfection'	SMrm
pulchella	See *V. tenera*
'Purple Kleopat'	CAsh IHos
¶ 'Purple Sissinghurst'	CAsh
¶ 'Raspberry Crush'	CAsh
¶ 'Red Cascade'	CAsh
'Red Sissinghurst'	CAsh NPri SBid
§ *rigida* ♀	CAsh CFai CFir CHea CMea
	ECGP ECha LHil MHlr NCat
	SRms SUsu WCot WEas WOve
¶ – 'Polaris'	SMrm SUsu
* 'Royal Purple'	CAsh EMan
§ *scabridoglandulosa*	CAsh
§ 'Silver Anne' ♀	CAsh CB&S CHad CSam ECtt
	GCal LFis LHop MBEx MRav
	NFai NPri NTow SChu SCro
	SDix SMer SMrm SRms SUsu
	WCot WEas WHen WHoo
	WOve
§ 'Sissinghurst' ♀	CArn CAsh CB&S CGle CHad
	CSam CSpe ECtt GCal LFis
	LHop MBEx NFai NPri SBid
	SCro SLMG SRms SUsu WEas
	WHen WHoo WPyg WWin
* 'Snow Flurry'	CAsh EWll WCot
* *spicata* 'Pam' (v)	WCot
stricta	CAsh EMan GBar
¶ Temari Pink = 'Sunmaripi'	NPri
¶ Temari Scarlet =	CAsh NPri
'Sunmarisu'	
§ Tapien Pearl = 'Sunvat'	CAsh
§ Tapien Pink = 'Sunver'	CAsh LIck NPri
§ Tapien Violet = 'Sunvop'	CAsh LIck NPri
¶ 'Tapien Lilac'	CAsh
Tapien Pearl	See *V.* Tapien Pearl = 'Sunvat'
Tapien Pink	See *V.* Tapien Pink = 'Sunver'
Tapien Violet	See *V.* Tapien Violet = 'Sunvop'
¶ Temari Violet	NPri
§ *tenera*	CAsh
'Tenerife'	See *V. 'Sissinghurst'*
tenuisecta	CAsh CM&M MBEx WPer
– f. *alba*	WCot

– 'Edith'	CAsh LHop WCot WPen
venosa	See *V. rigida*
¶ 'Violet Profusion'	CAsh
'White Cascade'	CAsh ECtt
* 'White Knight'	CAsh MBEx NPri
'White Sissinghurst'	CAsh LIck SBid

VERBESINA (Asteraceae)
¶ *alternifolia*	EMan

VERNONIA (Asteraceae)
crinita	CHan ECha ECro EMon GCal
	LFis SDix SIgm
¶ – 'Mammuth'	LGre
fasciculata	EMan GCal LFis
noveboracensis	ECGN SMrm WCot WPer
– 'Albiflora'	WCot WPer

VERONICA † (Scrophulariaceae)
amethystina	See *V. spuria*
armena	CLyd EWes LBee MBro MSte
	MWat SBla
§ *austriaca*	MLLN SMac SMrm
– Corfu form	CLyd CMea CMil EMan EWes
	LGre LHop MSCN NBrk SLod
	WPer
– var. *dubia*	See *V. prostrata*
– 'Ionian Skies'	CLon CLyd CPBP CRDP CSpe
	EBrP EBre ESis GBuc LBee
	LBre MBel SAga SBla SBre
	SChu SHel SIgm SPer SWas
	WCru WFar WKif
§ – subsp. *teucrium*	CArn CHan EBee EHal LHol
	LPVe MLLN MWgw NNor
	NRoo NWCA SRms WPer
– – 'Blue Blazer'	SCro
– – 'Crater Lake Blue' ♀	CHea CKel CLon CRDP ECha
	ECtt EFou ELan ENot ESis
	LGre MFir MRav NFai NNor
	SMac SMrm SRms WByw WCot
	WEas WPat WPer WWin
– – 'Kapitän'	ECha EGar ELan GBuc LHop
	MFir SMrm WFar WPer
– – 'Knallblau'	EBee EFou EMil MBri SUsu
	WLRN
¶ – – 'Königsblau'	SGre WBea
– – 'Royal Blue' ♀	CLTr CMil EBee ECot EFou
	EPfP ESis GBuc MArl NOak
	NSti SIng SPla WBea WBro
	WHoo WPyg
– – 'Shirley Blue'	See *V.* '**Shirley Blue**'
beccabunga	CArn CBen CKin CWat EBrP
	EBre EHon ELan EMFW
	EWFC GPoy LBre LPBA
	MHew MSta NDea NMir SBre
	SRms SWat WChe WHer
	WMAq
– 'Don's Dyke' (v)	CRow
bellidioides	CLyd GTou NGre
Blue Bouquet	See *V. longifolia* '**Blaubündel**'
'Blue Spire'	SWat WPer
bombycina	CLyd EHyt EPot NMen NTow
	NWCA
– Mac&W 5840	EHyt
bonarota	See *Paederota bonarota*
caespitosa subsp.	CLyd EHyt
caespitosa	
– Mac&W 5849	EHyt NTow
candida	See *V. spicata* subsp. *incana*
× *cantiana* 'Kentish Pink'	EGoo EGoo LGan MBel MBro
	SHel SPla SSca SUsu WHoo
	WPer

* 'Catforth Border Guard'	NCat
caucasica	EHal ELan EMon LGre MSCN
chamaedrys	CKin NMir
§ – 'Miffy Brute' (v)	CHan EGoo ELan LFis LHop
	MAvo MHar MLLN MRav
	NHol NPro WAlt WHer WLRN
	WPbr WRus WWeb
– 'Variegata'	See *V. chamaedrys* '**Miffy Brute**'
– 'Waterrow'	EMon
¶ – 'Yorkley Wood'	WAlt
cinerea ♀	CLyd CMHG ECha MBro
	MHar NHol NTow SIgm WAbe
	WEas WPat
coreana	CLon
dichrus	EGoo ELan
¶ 'Ellen Mae'	MAus
exaltata	CBrd EBee ECGN EHal EMFP
	EMan EMon GBuc LFis LGre
	LRHS MLLN MNrw MSte
	NChi SAxl WCot WOve WPer
– white	CBrd
filifolia	MHar
filiformis	MWhi
¶ – 'Fairyland' (v)	EWes
formosa	See *Hebe formosa*
§ *fruticans*	CLyd CNic GTou NCat NMen
	WCla
fruticulosa	NWCA
* *galactites*	LLew
gentianoides ♀	Widely available
– 'Alba'	CMea CRDP EOrc GCal NChi
	NSti
– 'Barbara Sherwood'	EBee EBrP EBre GMac LBre
	MFir MLLN MTed SBre
– 'Nana'	EOrc MMil
– 'Pallida'	EBee EMan EPfP MRav NPri
– 'Robusta'	ECha GCra GMac WPbr
– 'Tissington White'	CBos CBre CLon CVer EFou
	EMar LRot MAus MCLN
	MLLN MTis NCut NRoo NWes
	SAga SBla SHel SMac SOkh
	SWat WAbb WBea WLin WPbr
	WPen
– 'Variegata'	Widely available
× *guthrieana*	MAll MHar WCru WFar WPer
hendersonii	See *V. subsessilis hendersonii*
incana	See *V. spicata* subsp. *incana*
¶ 'Inspiration'	EFou
* *keiskei* pink form	NLar
kellereri	See *V. spicata*
kiusiana	CStr EBrP EBre LBre MBel
	MTis SBre
kotschyana	NGre
* 'Lila Karina'	WPer
liwanensis	ELan ESis EWes GCHN NTow
	WThi
– Mac&W 5936	EPot MHig
longifolia	CHan CKel ECro EGar ELan
	EOld EPfP MBel MCLN MFir
	NCat WBea WEas WLRN
– 'Alba'	CHea EGar ELan EPfP MBel
	SIde SSca WBea WShe
– 'Blaubündel'	EFou NFai
– 'Blauer Sommer'	CMGP EBee EFou EGar NHol
	SPer
§ – 'Blauriesin'	CM&M CTri ECtt GMaP MBri
	MCLN MUlv NCut NHol NSti
– Blue Giantess	See *V. longifolia* '**Blauriesin**'
– 'Fascination'	SMrm
– 'Foerster's Blue'	See *V. longifolia* '**Blauriesin**'
– 'Joseph's Coat' (v)	EBee EMon LFis NBrk WBro
	WCot WPbr

– 'Oxford Blue'	WRHF
– pink shades	EPfP
– 'Rose Tone'	ECha MRav MTis SMrm WWhi
– 'Rosea'	CTri MBel WCru WPer
– 'Schneeriesin'	CMGP EBee EBrP EBre ECha ECtt GMaP LBre MBri MCLN MWgw NHol NWoo SBre SCro SPer
lyallii	See *Parahebe lyallii*
¶ *macrostachya* RMRP 95188	IDac
¶ 'Martje'	SMrm
montana	CKin
– 'Corinne Tremaine' (v)	CElw CNat EMon MAvo MLLN WCot WHer WPbr
morrisonicola B&SWJ 086	NBro
nipponica	NLak WPer
'Noah Williams' (v)	WCot
nummularia	NGre NTow WOMN WPer
officinalis	CArn CKin EWFC
oltensis	CLyd CMHG CPBP EHyt EPot ESis EWes MHig NMen WAbe WLin WPat WWin
– JCA 984.150	NTow
orientalis subsp. *orientalis*	EPot NMen
ornata	ECha SVen WPer
pectinata	EHic ESis GDra MBel NCat NMen SHel
– 'Rosea'	CMHG CMea CNic ESis EWes GDra NBus NMen SHel WPer WWin
peduncularis	CNic EOrc LBee LRHS SBla WEas
¶ – 'Alba'	WPer
§ – 'Georgia Blue'	Widely available
– 'Oxford Blue'	See *V. peduncularis* 'Georgia Blue'
perfoliata	See *Parahebe perfoliata*
petraea 'Madame Mercier'	LRHS MMil SMrm
'Pink Damask'	CHad CLon EBee EFou LGre SCro SOkh WRus
pinnata 'Blue Eyes'	ESis LBee LHop WPbr
prenja	See *V. austriaca*
§ *prostrata* ♀	CLyd CSam CSpe ECGN ELan EMNN EPot ESis GDra LBee MBar MHig MPla MWat NFla NGre NHol NNrd NRoo SHel SIng SRms SSmi SSoC WEas WHil WHoo WWin
– 'Alba'	CSpe MBro MWat WHoo WPyg
§ – 'Blauspiegel'	CLon CPBP ECGP SBla SIgm SWas WCru
– 'Blue Ice'	SSmi
– Blue Mirror	See *V. prostrata* 'Blauspiegel'
– 'Blue Sheen'	ECtt EHic ESis LGre NBus NPri SChu SIng SMer WAbe WLin WPer WRHF WWin
– 'Loddon Blue'	NRoo NVic SBla SMer WPer
– 'Miss Willmott'	See *V. prostrata* 'Warley Blue'
– 'Mrs Holt'	CLyd CMea CSam EBrP EBre EMNN ESis LBre LGan LGre NCat NFla NMen NNor NRoo SBla SBre SIng SRms SSmi SWas WWin
– 'Nana'	EMNN EPot ESis EWes LBee MHig MPla MWat NHol NMen
– 'Rosea'	CLyd ELan ESis MPla MWat SIgm WKif WPer
* – 'Shirley Holt'	CHar
– 'Silver Queen'	SRms
– 'Spode Blue' ♀	CLTr CMea ELan ESis LGre LHop MHar MHig MMil NCat NWCA SBla SRms WLin
– 'Trehane'	CHea CLyd EBrP EBre ECha ELan ESis LBee LBre LFis LGan LGro LHop MBro MCCP NGre NHar NOak NRoo NRya SBre SCro SRms SSmi SWat WAbe WLin WWhi
§ – 'Warley Blue'	CMGP
* 'Red Georgia'	LFis
repens	See *V. reptans*
§ *reptans*	EHal LWak MOne NCat WBea WPer
'Rosalinde'	CBot EBrP EBre GBuc LBre NCat SBre SPla WPer
rupestris	See *V. prostrata*
saturejoides	CNic CPBP MBro SRms WPer
saxatilis	See *V. fruticans*
schmidtiana	GTou WPer
– 'Nana'	CLyd MBro NHol WOMN WPat
selleri	See *V. wormskjoldii*
§ 'Shirley Blue' ♀	EBar EBrP EBre ECro EFou GCHN GChr LBre LFis LWak MBel MCLN MFir MWat NChi NFla NHol NMir NRoo SBre SHel SPer SRms SWat WHen WPer WWhi
§ *spicata*	EBar ELan EWFC GDra LWak MAus MBro NLon NNor SRms SSea WCla WCot WOve WPer WWhi
– 'Alba'	EBar EBee EMan EMil MRav NCut WBea WHil WPer
– 'Barcarolle'	EBee ELan MLLN WPbr
§ – 'Blaufuchs'	CBlo CMHG CSam EBrP EBre LBre NRoo SBre
– Blue Fox	See *V. spicata* 'Blaufuchs'
§ – 'Erika'	ECha ECtt GBuc GMac MBro MLLN MWat NOak NRoo SIde SUsu WCla WHil
– 'Heidekind'	CGle CLon CMea CSam ECha EFou ELan EOrc ESis GBur GDra LHop MCLN MRav NHar NNor NVic SBla SHel SIng SWat WEas WOMN WOve WWin
¶ – subsp. *hybrida*	WHer
§ – 'Icicle'	CLon EFou EOrc LRHS MAus SLod WPGP WRus
§ – subsp. *incana* ♀	CBot CGle CLon CSpe ECGN EHoe ELan ENot ESis GMaP LFis LGan MBri MBro MWat NChi NMir NNor SBla SPer WAbe WBea WLin WPer WPyg
– – 'Mrs Underwood'	ECha
– – 'Nana'	ECha ESis SAxl SRms
– – 'Saraband'	EBrP EBre LBre SBre WCot WPer
– – 'Silver Carpet'	CMil EBee EBrP EBre EFou LBre MTis NHol NSti SBre SCoo
– – 'Wendy' ♀	GCal
– 'Minuet'	WByw
– 'Nana Blauteppich'	EMan WBea
– 'Pink Damask'	LFis
– red	WBea WHil
– Red Fox	See *V. spicata* 'Rotfuchs'
– 'Romiley Purple'	ECGP EFou EMon LGre MBrN MBro MLLN MRav MSte NFla NSti SAxl SChu SHel SLod WCot WHoo WPyg
¶ – 'Rosalind'	NLar
– *rosea*	See *V. spicata* 'Erika'
¶ – 'Rosenrot'	EMan

§ – 'Rotfuchs'   CGle CMHG CSam EBrP EBre ECha ECtt EFou ELan EOld EPar LBre MRav MWat NFla NRoo NSti SBre SCro SMrm SPer WByw WEas WHoo WOve WPer WWeb WWin
– 'Sightseeing'   GMac NBus NCut NRoo SWat WBea
– subsp. *spicata* 'Nana'   SSmi
– *variegata*   MLLN NBir WPbr
§ *spuria*   CStr EMon NWes WPer
stelleri   See *V. wormskjoldii*
¶ *subsessilis* 'Blau Pyramide'   ECGN
§ – *hendersonii*   EHal
'Sunny Border Blue'   EPfP LBuc WCot
surculosa   MFos SBla
tauricola   NTow
– JJH 92101536   LGre
– Mac&W 5835   EPot SIgm
¶ – MP 93236   IDac
telephiifolia   CLyd EGoo EHoe EHyt EMNN ESis EWes MPla NMen NTow NWCA WAbe WPyg WWin
teucrium   See *V. austriaca* subsp. *teucrium*
thessalica   EPot NTow
¶ *thessalonica*   MTPN
thymoides subsp. *pseudocinerea*   NWCA
– subsp. *thymoides*   ESis
* Ulster blue dwarf   WCot
virginica   See *Veronicastrum virginicum*
¶ *waldsteiniana*   CStr
'Waterperry Blue'   EGoo ELan MBel MHig MRav NWoo SBod SMer WPer
wherryi   WPer
'White Icicle'   See *V. spicata* '**Icicle**'
'White Spire'   CBot
whitleyi   CLyd CNic CTri MHar WWin
§ *wormskjoldii*   CHan ELan ESis LHop MBrN MBro MCLN MHar MHig NMen SBla SHel SRms WCla WFar WHil WOMN WPer WWin
– 'Alba'   WPer

VERONICASTRUM (Scrophulariaceae)
§ *virginicum*   CArn CHea CPou CRow ECGN ECha EFou EMon MBel MFir MUlv NSti WPer WWhi WWin
– 'Alboroseum'   ECGN WCot
– *album*   CBot CDoC CHan EBrP EBre ECGN ELan GCal LBlm LBre LFis LGan MAus MBri MBro MRav MWat NFai NFla NRoo NSti SAxl SBre SCro SHel SPer SRms WEas WHoo WRus
¶ – 'Apollo'   EFou MBri
¶ – 'Diana'   LGre
– 'Fascination'   CLon EFou GCal LGre WCot
§ – var. *incarnatum*   CLon ECGN LRHS MBri NFla SCro SHel SPer SUsu WCot
– 'Lavendelturm'   CLon LGre WCot
* – 'Lila Karina'   EPfP
– 'Pink Glow'   EBrP EBre EFou ELan EMil EPfP LBre SBre SMrm SOkh
– *roseum*   See *V. virginicum* var. *incarnatum*
– var. *sibiricum*   EMon WCot·
¶ – 'Spring Dew'   EFou MBri
¶ – 'Temptation'   MBri

VESTIA (Solanaceae)
§ *foetida* ♀   CB&S CGre CHEx CHan CPle ELan ERea IBlr IDee MHar MNrw NChi SLod SOWG WPer WSHC
lycioides   See *V. foetida*

VETIVERIA (Poaceae)
zizanioides   GPoy MSal

VIBURNUM † (Caprifoliaceae)
acerifolium   CFil WHCG WWat
'Allegheny'   WWat
alnifolium   See *V. lantanoides*
atrocyaneum   CFil CPle WHCG WPGP WPat WWal WWat
awabuki   CFil EPfP
betulifolium   CB&S CBrd CFil CPle CTrw EPfP MBal SMad WAbe WHCG WPGP WWat
bitchiuense   CPle ELan
x *bodnantense*   CBot CTri CTrw ELan ENot GRei MRav MWat NHed NLon NNor WStl WWat WWin
– 'Charles Lamont' ♀   CBot CEnd CSam ECtt EMil IBlr LPan MAsh MBri MGos MPla NHol SEND SHBN SPer SSpi WPat WPyg WWat WWeb
– 'Dawn' ♀   Widely available
– 'Deben' ♀   EBee ENot EPfP LRHS MBri SPer WDin WWat
bracteatum   CFil CPle EPfP
buddlejifolium   CEnd CHan CPle WHCG WWat
burejaeticum   CPle
x *burkwoodii*   CB&S CBot CLan CMHG EAst ELan ENot GRei ISea LHop LPan MBal MBel MBri MGos MRav MWat NWea SHBN SPer SReu SSpi SSta WAbe WDin WHCG WPat
– 'Anne Russell' ♀   CB&S CPMA CTri EBrP EBre ELan EPfP EWes IOrc LBre MAsh MGos NSti SBre SHBN SPer SPla WFar
– 'Chenaultii'   EHal ELan EPfP SPer WCru
– 'Fulbrook' ♀   CMHG CRos EPfP MBri SSpi WWat
– 'Park Farm Hybrid' ♀   CBlo CPMA CSam CTri EBrP EBre ELan ENot IOrc LBre MAsh MBal MRav SBre SLPl SPan SPer SRms WCru WWat
x *carlcephalum* ♀   CB&S CEnd EBrP EBre ELan EMil ENot IOrc LBre LPan MAsh MBri MGos MHlr MRav MTis MWat NHol NNor SBre SPer SSpi WBod WDin WHCG WPGP WPat WSHC WWat
* – 'Variegatum'   CPMA
carlesii   CB&S ENot EPfP GRei IOrc LHol MBlu NBee SCoo SPer SReu WShe WStl
* – 'Aurea'   LPan SHBN
– 'Aurora' ♀   CB&S CEnd CPMA EBrP EBre ELan ENot IOrc LBre MBar MBri MGos MWat NHol NLon SBre SPan SPer SReu SSpi SSta WBod WDin WHCG WPat WWat
– 'Charis'   CMHG WBod

– 'Diana'	CBlo CEnd CMHG CPMA CRos EPfP MMil SBid SSpi SSta WPat WWat
* – *sieboldii* (v)	CPMA
cassinoides	CPle WPat WWat
'Chesapeake'	CPMA CPle EWes MTis NTow SBid SEND SSpi WWat WWes
chingii	CFil CPle ELan GGGa WPGP WWat
cinnamomifolium ♀	CBlo CFil CHEx CLan CPle ELan ISea LNet MAsh MHlr SAPC SArc SBid SPer SSpi WHCG WLRN WSHC WWat
congestum	CPle ELan EMon
cotinifolium	CPle
cylindricum	CBot CFil CGre CPle ELan EPfP SBid WCru WWat
dasyanthum	CPle EPfP EPla
davidii ♀	CChe CDec CHEx EBrP EBre ELan EMil ENot GChr GRei LBre LHop MBal MBar MBri MGos MHlr MRav MWat NHol NNor NWea SBre SHBN SSpi WDin WGwG WHCG WWal WWin
– (f)	CB&S CBot CDoC CHEx ELan EPfP MAsh MBal MGos MUlv SHBN SPer SPla SReu SRms SSta WBod WHar WPat WWat WWeb
÷ (m)	CB&S CBot CDoC ELan EPfP MBal MGos MUlv SPer SPla SReu SRms SSta WBod WHar WPat WWat WWeb
dentatum	CFil CPle WPGP
§ – var. *pubescens*	CPle
dilatatum	CBlo ELan WWat WWes
erosum	CFil EPla
erubescens	CPle WWat
– var. *gracilipes*	CHan CPle WWat
'Eskimo'	CBlo CEnd CPMA LHop MBlu MBro SSpi WHCG WPat WPyg WWes
§ *farreri* ♀	CB&S CPle EAst EBar ECtt ELan ENot GRei ISea LBuc LHol MBal MBar MGos MPla MRav NHol NWea SHBN SPer WCFE WDin WGwG WHCG WWat
– 'Album'	See *V. farreri* 'Candidissimum'
§ – 'Candidissimum'	CBot CFil ELan EPfP LHop SBid SSpi WPat WPyg WWat
– 'Farrer's Pink'	CPMA WWat
– 'Nanum'	CBlo CFil CPMA CPle EPfP LHop MAsh MBar MPla NHol SChu SSta WHCG WPat WPyg WWat
foetidum	CPle WHCr
– var. *ceanothoides*	CPle
¶ – var. *rectangulatum* B&SWJ 3637	WCru
fragrans Bunge	See *V. farreri*
furcatum ♀	EPfP SSpi WHCG WWat
× *globosum* 'Jermyns Globe'	CB&S CBlo CDoC CMHG CPle EBee MAll MBar MGos SEas WAbe WHCG WWat
¶ *grandiflorum* f. *foetens*	EPfP
harryanum	CFil CPle EBee EPla IOrc MBal WCru WPGP WWat
henryi	CFil CPle EPfP MBri SPer WHCG WWat

× *hillieri*	CAbP CFil CHan CPle MWhi WHCG WKif WWat
– 'Winton' ♀	CAbP CDoC CGre EBee EPfP ISea MAsh MBri SBid SHBN WCru WFar WWat
japonicum	CFil CHEx CPle CSam SBid SHBN WWat
× *juddii* ♀	CB&S CBot CEnd CPMA CPle EBrP EBre ELan EMil ENot IOrc LBre MAsh MBal MBar MBlu MBri MGos MRav NBee SBre SPer SReu SSta WAbe WDin WHCG WPat WWat
lantana	CKin CPer CTri EHic ENot IOrc LBuc NWea SPer WDin WMou WTro
– 'Aureum'	EHoe EPla MBlu WBcn
– 'Mohican'	NPro
§ *lantanoides*	EPfP SSpi
lentago	CAbP CPle
lobophyllum	CPle EPfP
¶ *luzonicum* B&SWJ 3930	WCru
macrocephalum	CPMA WPGP
– f. *keteleeri*	CPMA WWes
mariesii	See *V. plicatum* 'Mariesii'
'Mohawk'	CAbP CRos ELan LRHS MAsh MBri SCoo SMur SSpi WWat
¶ *mullaha*	CPle
¶ *nervosum* B&SWJ 2251a	WCru
nudum 'Pink Beauty'	CPMA CPle WShe WWat
odoratissimum	CB&S CFil CGre CHEx CPle SBid SHBN SMad WSHC
opulus	CB&S CKin CPer CSam ECtt ELan EGhr GPoy IOrc LBuc MBar MBlu MBri MRav MWat NBee NNor NWea SHBN SHFr SMac SPer WDin WHar WMou
– 'Aureum'	CMHG CSam EBrP EBre EHoe ELan EMil IOrc LBre MAsh MBal MGos MPla NFla NHol SBre SEas SHBN SPer SSta WHCG WPat WWeb
– 'Compactum' ♀	CB&S CHan EBrP EBre ELan ENot GChr IOrc LBre LHop MAsh MBar MBri MGos MPla MWat NHol SBre SDix SLPl SPer SReu WDin WGwG WHCG WPat WWat
N – 'Fructu Luteo'	ELan
– 'Nanum'	CAbP CBlo CPle ELan EPla ESis MBal MBar MBri MPla NHol NMen WDin WGwG WHCG WPat WWat
– 'Notcutt's Variety' ♀	ENot EPfP NTow SHBN SHFr SMur SRms
– 'Park Harvest'	CPle CRos CSWP EBee EPla MBri NSti SAga SLPl
§ – 'Roseum' ♀	CB&S CBot CPle ELan ENot IOrc LPan MBar MBlu MBri MGos MPla MWat NBee NFla NWea SHBN SPer SPla WCFE WDin WStI WWal
– 'Sterile'	See *V. opulus* 'Roseum'
N – 'Xanthocarpum' ♀	CMHG CSam EBrP EBre ELan EMon IOrc LBre LHop MBar MGos MHlr MRav MUlv MWat NHol SBre SEas SLPl SMac SPer SRms WDin WSHC WWat WWin
N *plicatum*	CB&S EBee ENot MBar WDin
– 'Cascade'	MUlv NHol SHBN

– 'Dart's Red Robin'	CEnd ECtt EHic GChr MBri MGos MPla NHol
– 'Grandiflorum' ♀	CBlo CPle EBee EPfP MBar SSta WAbe WHCG
– 'Lanarth'	CB&S CSam CTre ECtt EMil ENot IOrc LHop MBri MHlr NFla SPer SPla SSta WBod WDin WHCG WPat WWat
¶ – 'Magician'	NHol
§ – 'Mariesii' ♀	Widely available
– 'Nanum'	See *V. plicatum* **'Nanum Semperflorens'**
§ – 'Nanum Semperflorens'	CBar ECtt ELan EPla ESis IOrc LHop MAsh MBal MBlu MGos MPla SHBN SPer WFar WHCG WPat WSHC WWal WWat
– 'Pink Beauty' ♀	CAbP CB&S CEnd CPle EBrP EBre ECtt ELan EPla LBre LHop MBal MBlu MBri MGos MPla MRav NBee NHol SBre SHBN SPer SSpi SSta WAbe WHCG WPat WSHC WWat WWeb
* – 'Prostratum'	ESis
– 'Rotundifolium'	MBri NHol SHBN
– 'Rowallane' ♀	EPfP MBel WWat
– 'Saint Keverne'	NHol SHBN
N – 'Sterile'	GOrc
– 'Summer Snowflake'	EBee ELan ENot EPfP IOrc MAsh MBal MBri MPla MWat NHol SHBN SPer SPla SVil WDin WHCG WPat WWeb
– f. *tomentosum*	CLan ELan EPla MRav WDin WHCG WStI
– 'Watanabe'	See *V. plicatum* **'Nanum Semperflorens'**
'Pragense' ♀	CMCN CPle EBee EPfP EPla MBar MGos NHol SPer WHCG WLRN WPat WPyg WWat
¶ *propinquum*	WWat
¶ – B&SWJ 4009	WCru
pubescens	See *V. dentatum* var. *pubescens*
recognitum	CPle
x *rhytidophylloides*	CPle NNor WWat
– 'Dart's Duke'	ENot MBri SLPl
rhytidophyllum	CHEx CLan EBrP EBre ELan ENot GChr GRei ISea LBre LPan MBal MBar MGos SBre SHBN SMad SPer SReu SRms SSpi WBod WDin WGwG WWat WWin
¶ – 'Holland'	EPla
– 'Roseum'	CBot MRav
– 'Variegatum'	CBot CPMA ELan EPla SPer
– 'Willowwood'	ELan MAsh SMad SPer SSpi SSta WPat WShe WWat
rigidum	CFil
sargentii	CBlo GBin IOrc WWoo
– 'Onondaga' ♀	CB&S CBot CMHG CPMA CSam CTre EBrP EBre ELan EPla IOrc LBre LGre LHop MBri MPla MWat NHol SBre SHBN SMad SPan SPer SSpi SSta WDin WHCG WKif WPat WWat
¶ – 'Susquehanna'	EPfP
semperflorens	See *V. plicatum* **'Nanum Semperflorens'**
§ *setigerum*	CPle EPfP EPla SLPl SSpi
'Shasta'	CBlo CDoC CMCN COtt CRos EHic EPfP MBri NHol NPro SPla SSpi SSta

sieboldii	CB&S CPle
¶ – B&SWJ 2837	WCru
suspensum	CPle
¶ *taiwanianum* B&SWJ 3009	WCru
theiferum	See *V. setigerum*
tinus	CB&S CBot CLan CTrG CTrw ELan EMil ENot ISea LBuc LNet MBal MBar MGos MWat NBee NFla NNor SArc SHFr SReu SRms SSta WDin WHCG WPat WWin
– 'Bewley's Variegated'	CB&S EBee EMil MGos SCoo
– 'Compactum'	EHic
– 'Eve Price' ♀	Widely available
– 'French White'	CBlo CEnd EHic ELan EPfP EPla SBid SCoo SEas SRms WGwG WRHF WWal WWat
– 'Gwenllian' ♀	CDoC CEnd CHan CHar EBrP EBre ECtt ELan EMil ENot EPla LBre MAsh MBal MGos MPla MRav NTow SBre SEas SLPl SPer SPla SRms SSpi WAbe WPat WWat WWeb
– *hirtellum*	CTre
– 'Israel'	EBee EHic EMil SPan SPer SPla
– 'Lucidum'	CB&S CBlo CPle CSam EHic MGos SBid SHBN SPla
– 'Lucidum Variegatum'	CFil CLan CPMA EHol SDry WPGP
* – 'Macrophyllum'	EHic LPan
* – 'Pink Parfait'	MRav
– 'Pink Prelude'	ENot SEas
– 'Purpureum'	CB&S EBee EHal EHoe ELan EPla GChr MAsh MRav SBid SEas SHBN SLPl SMac SPer SPla WGwG WWal
– 'Pyramidale'	See *V. tinus* **'Strictum'**
* – *rigidum*	CPle
– 'Sappho'	EHic
* – var. *subcordatum* C 2002	GGGa
– 'Variegatum'	CB&S CBot CTre EBrP EBre ELan GOrc IOrc LBre LHop MBal MBar MBel MBri MHlr MWat SBre SHBN SPer SPla SReu SSta WAbe WCFE WDin WHCG WPat WSHC WWat WWin
tomentosum	See *V. plicatum*
utile	CPle EPfP WHCG WWat
wrightii	CPle EPfP NHol WHCG WPat WPyg
– var. *hessei*	MUlv

VICIA (Papilionaceae)

angustifolia	See *V. sativa* subsp. *nigra*
cracca	CKin EWFC NLan
orobus	MSCN NChi WGwy
§ *sativa* subsp. *nigra*	CKin
sepium	CKin EWFC
sylvatica	WGwy

VICTORIA (Nymphaeaceae)

regia	See *V. amazonica*

VIGNA (Papilionaceae)

§ *caracalla*	CPlN

VIGUIERA (Asteraceae)

¶ *multiflora*	EMan

VILLADIA (Crassulaceae)
hemsleyana   See *Sedum hemsleyanum*

VILLARESIA See CITRONELLA

VILLARSIA (Menyanthaceae)
bennettii   See *Nymphoides peltata*
    'Bennettii'

VIMINARIA (Papilionaceae)
¶ *juncea*   MAll MFiF

VINCA † (Apocynaceae)
difformis   CGle CHar CLTr CTri ECha
    ELan EPla LBlm LHop LLWP
    NCat SDix SDry WCru WFox
    WHer WPic WWat
– subsp. *bicolor* 'Alba'   EBar
– var. *bicolor* 'Jenny Pym'   EMon LHop SCoo SMad
¶ – subsp. *bicolor* 'Ruby   EMon
    Baker'
– subsp. *difformis*   EMon
– Greystone form   EBar EPla LHop SCoo SEND
    WRus WWat
– 'Oxford'   SLPl
– 'Snowmound'   MRav WFox WWat
'Hidcote Purple'   See *V. major* var. *oxyloba*
major   CB&S CChe CDoC ELan ENot
    EOrc GChr GPoy GRei LBuc
    MBri MFir MGos MWat SBod
    SHBN SIde SPer WDin WGwG
    WMow WOak WStI
– var. *alba*   EPla GBuc IBlr
– 'Caucasian Blue'   CFil WPGP
– 'Elegantissima'   See *V. major* 'Variegata'
§ – subsp. *hirsuta*   EMon EOrc WFox WWye
    (Boiss.) Stearn
– *hirsuta* hort.   See *V. major* var. *oxyloba*
¶ – 'Honeydew'   EMon
– 'Jason Hill'   EMon MBel
§ – 'Maculata' (v)   ELan EMar EMon ENot EPla
    LHop MBar MBri MSCN NPla
    NRoo NSti SDry SPar SPer
    WAlt WCru WHer WStI WWeb
§ – var. *oxyloba*   CHid CLyd CNic ECGN ECtt
    ELan EMon EPla GSki LHop
    MRav SLPl SRms WHen WPic
– var. *pubescens*   See *V. major* subsp. *hirsuta*
    (Boiss.) Stearn
– 'Reticulata'   ELan EMon MBel MSCN NSti
– 'Surrey Marble'   See *V. major* 'Maculata'
§ – 'Variegata' ♀   CB&S CBlo CGle CHEx ECha
    EFou EHoe ELan ENot ERav
    GCHN GPoy GRei LBuc LGro
    LHop LLWP MBal MBar MBel
    MBri MGos NNor NRoo SHBN
    SIde SPer WDin WEas WOak
minor   CDoC CKin CLyd ELan ENot
    EPar ERav GCHN GChr GPoy
    GRei MBar MBro MFir MSCN
    MWat SIde WDin WMow
    WOak WWye
– f. *alba*   CB&S CBot CDoC EAst EBrP
    EBre ECha EGoo ELan EPla
    LBre LHol LHop MBar MBri
    MGos NNor NOak SBre SEas
    SHBN SPer STre WCot WOak
    WStI WWat WWye
– 'Alba Aureavariegata'   See *V. minor* 'Alba Variegata'

§ – 'Alba Variegata'   CGle EAst EBot EBrP EBre
    EGoo EHoe EJud EPPr EPla
    LBre MBar MFir NHol NPro
    NRoo SBre SPer SRms STre
    WEas WHer WWat
§ – 'Argenteovariegata' ♀   Widely available
§ – 'Atropurpurea' ♀   CB&S CSam ECGN ECha
    EGoo ELan ENot EPla GChr
    LBuc LHol MAus MBar MBri
    MGos MRav MSCN NFla NHol
    NRoo NSti SBod SChu SHBN
    SPer WEas WOak WWeb
    WWhi
– 'Aurea'   EGoo EPla WRHF
§ – 'Aureovariegata'   CB&S CBot EAst ELan EOrc
    EPla GPoy LHol MBal MBar
    MFir MRav NHol NNor NRoo
    WHen WWye
§ – 'Azurea Flore Pleno' (d)   Widely available
    ♀
* – 'Blue and Gold'   EGoo
– 'Blue Cloud'   MLLN NHol SBod
– 'Blue Drift'   CBlo EBar EFou EMon MLLN
    NHol SBod
– 'Blue Moon'   ECtt EHic NHol SPla
– 'Bowles' Blue'   See *V. minor* 'La Grave'
– 'Bowles' Variety'   See *V. minor* 'La Grave'
– 'Burgundy'   EPar GChr GGar LLWP MBal
    SMac SRms WWat WWye
– 'Caerulea Plena'   See *V. minor* 'Azurea Flore
    Pleno'
– 'Dartington Star'   See *V. major* var. *oxyloba*
– 'Dart's Blue'   MBri
– 'Double Burgundy'   See *V. minor* 'Multiplex'
– 'Gertrude Jekyll' ♀   CLTr EBee ELan EMon ENot
    EPla GChr ILis LBay MAsh
    MAus MBri NHol NRoo SBod
    SChu SCoo SEND SPer SVil
    WHer
– Green Carpet   See *V. minor* 'Grüner Teppich'
§ – 'Grüner Teppich'   EMon SPla
§ – 'La Grave' ♀   CChe CSev ECGP ECha ELan
    ENot EPla GAbr MBri MBro
    NHol SBod SPer SRms SSvw
    STre WPyg WWat
– 'Maculata' (v)   EGoo ELan EPPr SCoo WAlt
    WBcn
– 'Marion Cran'   CEnd GSki
§ – 'Multiplex' (d)   CHid CNic ECtt EMon EPPr
    EPar EPla ERav MBri MInt
    NHol NLon NNor NRoo SRms
    WCru WRHF WWat
* – 'Persian Carpet'   EMon
– 'Purpurea'   See *V. minor* 'Atropurpurea'
– 'Rubra'   See *V. minor* 'Atropurpurea'
– 'Sabinka'   CHid EGoo EMon EPla
– 'Silver Service' (v)   CElw CHid EMon EPPr EPla
    GBuc LBlm MAvo MBel MInt
    NHol WCot WPbr
– 'Variegata'   See *V. minor*
    'Argenteovariegata'
– 'Variegata Aurea'   See *V. minor* 'Aureovariegata'
– 'White Gold'   CChe EBee EHic MPla NHol
    NPro WFox

VINCETOXICUM (Asclepiadaceae)
¶ *forrestii* ACE 1615   IDac
§ *hirundinaria*   EEls GPoy
nigrum   CPlN EMon NChi WThi WTin
officinale   See *V. hirundinaria*
¶ sp. HH&K 142   CHan

VIOLA † (Violaceae)

'Abigail' (Vtta)	LPVe
'Achilles' (Va)	LPVe
'Adelina' (Va)	GHCN LPVe
'Admiral Avellan'	See *V.* **'Amiral Avellan'**
'Admiration' (Va)	CFul GHCN GMac LPVe NPla WBou
adunca	NWCA
– 'Alba'	WLRN
– var. *minor*	See *V. labradorica*
aetolica	CInt
'Agnes Cochrane' (ExVa)	GHCN
'Agneta' (Va)	LPVe
'Alanta' (Va)	LGre LPVe SAga WWhi
§ *alba*	CPla EFou ELan EWes NHol NSti NWes SCro WEas WWin
albanica	See *V. magellensis*
I 'Alcea' (Va)	LPVe
'Alethia' (Va)	LPVe
'Alexander Rayfield' (Va)	LPVe
'Alexia' (Va)	LPVe
'Alice Witter' (Vt)	CDev CGro
'Alice Wood' (ExVa)	GHCN
'Alice Woodall' (Va)	LPVe
* 'Alison'	GMaP GMac WBou
'Alma' (Va)	GHCN
altaica	LPVe
'Alwyn' (Va)	LPVe
'Amelia' (Va)	GMac LPVe WWhi
'Amethyst' (C)	CDoC LHop
§ 'Amiral Avellan' (Vt)	CCot CDev CGro NBro WRus
'Andrena' (Va)	LPVe
'Angela' (Va)	LPVe
'Anita' (Va)	LPVe
'Ann' (SP)	GHCN
'Ann Kean' (Vtta)	LPVe NRoo
'Anna' (Va)	LPVe
* 'Anna Leyns' (Va)	LPVe
'Annabelle' (Va)	LPVe
'Annaliese' (C)	LPVe
'Anne Mott' (Va)	LPVe
'Annette Ross' (Va)	LPVe
I 'Annona' (Va)	LPVe
'Anthea' (Va)	LPVe
'Antique Lace' (Va)	GMac NBrk NPla
'Aphrodite' (Va)	LPVe
'Apollo' (Va)	LPVe
¶ 'Apricotta'	NHaw
'Arabella' (Va)	GHCN LBee LPVe SChu SIng SLod SMrm WBou WFar WHer WLRN
arborescens	MSCN SIng
'Ardross Gem' (Va)	CFul CGle CMHG CPla CSam GCHN GHCN GMac LBee LHop LPVe MCLN NRoo WBou WEas WIvy WKif WPer WWhi WWin
arenaria	See *V. rupestris*
'Arkwright's Ruby' (Va)	CArn CLTr LPVe
'Artemis' (Va)	LPVe
'Aspasia' (Va) ♀	CFul GMac LBee LPVe WBou
'Astrid' (Va)	LPVe
'Atalanta' (Vtta)	LPVe
'Athena' (Va)	LPVe
athois	LPVe
'Aurelia' (Va)	LPVe
'Aurora' (Va)	LPVe
'Avril' (Va)	LPVe
'Avril Lawson' (Va)	GHCN GMac NNrd WBou
¶ 'Baby Blue'	WOMN
'Baby Lucia' (Va)	CElw

'Barbara' (Va)	CFul GHCN LPVe NRoo WBou
'Barbara Cawthorne' (C)	LPVe
'Baronne Alice de Rothschild' (Vt)	CDev LHop WLRN
¶ 'Beatrice' (Vtta)	WBou
'Becka' (Va)	LPVe
* *bella*	EWll LPVe WEas
§ 'Belmont Blue' (C)	CFul CLon CLyd EFou EWes GMac LBee LPVe MBel MCLN MRav NChi NHol NRoo SAga SChu SHel SMrm WBou
§ *bertolonii*	LPVe WBou
'Beshlie' (Va) ♀	CMea GMaP GMac LPVe MArl MGrG SChu WBou WEas WKif
'Bessie Cawthorne' (C)	LPVe SChu
'Bessie Knight' (Va)	LPVe
betonicifolia	LPVe
* – *albescens*	NHar
'Bettina' (Va)	LPVe
'Betty' (Va)	GHCN LPVe
'Bianca' (Vtta)	LPVe
biflora	CMHG CPla EPar GDra MTho NChi NGre NRya
'Bishop's Belle' (FP)	GHCN
'Bishop's Gold' (FP)	GHCN
'Black Ace' (Va)	LPVe
* 'Black Beauty'	WCot
'Blue Carpet' (Va)	GMac
'Blue Cloud' (Va)	LPVe NChi
'Blue Moon' (C)	SChu SMrm WBou
'Blue Moonlight' (C)	CBos GBuc GMac NChi NSti SMrm
'Blue Tit' (Va)	SChu WBou
'Bonna Cawthorne' (Va)	LPVe
bosniaca	See *V. elegantula bosniaca*
'Boughton Blue'	See *V.* **'Belmont Blue'**
'Bournemouth Gem' (Vt)	CDev CGro
§ 'Bowles' Black' (T)	CArn CDev CHan CSWP ECha ELan GAbr LPVe NBro NLak NRoo NSti SBla SHBN SIng SRms WBea WBou WEas WOve
'Boy Blue' (Vtta)	EHal LPVe
'Brenda Hall' (Va)	LPVe
'Bronwen' (Va)	LPVe
* 'Bryony' (Vtta)	LPVe WBou
'Bullion' (Va)	EWll LPVe WMer
'Burnock Yellow' (Va)	GHCN
'Buttercup' (Vtta)	CFul CInt EWll GHCN GMac LBee LPVe NHar NRoo SChu SIng WBou WLRN WWin
¶ 'Butterpat' (C)	NBrk
'Buxton Blue' (Va)	CFul LPVe SHBN WBou
calaminaria	LPVe
'Calantha' (Vtta)	LPVe
calcarata	ELan LPVe SIng
§ – subsp. *zoysii*	EWes GCHN GDra NGre
'California' (Vt)	CDev
'Callia' (Va)	LPVe
I 'Calliandra' (Vtta)	LPVe
I 'Calypso' (Va)	LPVe
§ *canadensis* var. *rugulosa*	CRDP
'Candida' (Vtta)	LPVe
canina	CKin NBro WUnd
* – *alba*	CBre
'Carberry Seedling' (Va)	LPVe
'Carina' (Vtta)	LPVe
'Carnival' (Va)	NBrk
'Carola' (Va)	LPVe
'Caroline' (Va)	SMrm
I 'Cassandra' (Vtta)	LPVe

* 'Catforth Gold'	NCat
'Catherine Williams' (ExVa)	GHCN
'Cat's Whiskers'	CElw GBri GMac NBrk NSti
¶ *cazorlensis*	CGra
chaerophylloides	See *V. dissecta* var. *chaerophylloides*
'Chandler's Glory' (Va)	LPVe
'Chantal' (Vtta)	LPVe NRoo
'Chantreyland' (Va)	CMdw NBir SRms
'Charity' (Va)	LPVe
'Charlotte Mott' (Va)	LPVe
'Chelsea Girl' (Va)	SMrm
'Chloe' (Vtta)	LPVe
* 'Christina'	LBee WLRN
'Christmas' (Vt)	CDev CGro
'Christobel' (Va)	LPVe
'Cinderella' (Va)	CFul GHCN
'Citrina' (Va)	LPVe
¶ 'Claire' (Va)	LPVe
* 'Clare Harrison' (Va)	LPVe
'Clementina' (Va) ♀	GCHN LPVe MRav NRoo
'Cleo' (Va)	GMac WBou
'Clive Groves' (Vt)	CDev CGro
'Clodagh' (Va)	LPVe
'Clover' (Va)	LPVe
'Coeur d'Alsace' (Vt)	CCot CDev CHan CMea CNic EFou ELan EPar GMac LPVe NBro WEas WRus
'Colette' (Va)	LPVe
'Colleen' (Vtta)	LPVe
'Columbine' (Va)	CBos CElw CInt CLTr CLon CMHG CRDP CSam GHCN GMac LBee LPVe MCLN NSti SAga SChu SHBN SLod SMrm WBou WEas WLRN WMaN WWhi
§ 'Comte de Brazza' (dPVt)	CDev CGro CTri GBar GMac WRha
¶ 'Comte de Chambord' (dVt)	WRha
'Connie' (Va)	CBos LPVe
¶ 'Connigar'	CSam
'Coralie' (Vtta)	LPVe
'Cordelia' (Va)	CElw LPVe NBro
* 'Cornish White'	CDev
cornuta ♀	CElw CFul CGle CHad CMea CPla EOrc EPot LHop LPVe MBro MFir MHig MWat NBro NRoo NSti SDix SMrm SPer SRms WAbe WBou WHen WHoo WPyg
– Alba Group ♀	Widely available
§ – 'Alba Minor'	CFul CLyd CMHG ELan EWes GMac LPVe MBro MCLN MFir NBro NRoo SChu WAbe WCot WFar WHoo WPyg
– blue	LPVe WWat
¶ – 'Blue Butterfly' (C)	GMac
* – 'Bluestone Gold'	WCot
¶ – 'Eastgrove Elizabeth'	WEas
¶ – 'Eastgrove Ice Blue'	WEas
¶ – 'Eastgrove Twinkle'	WEas
¶ – 'Gypsy Moth'	GMac
– Lilacina Group (C)	CFul CGle ECha EWes GMac LPVe MBro NCat NChi NFla SChu SMrm SWat WFar WHoo
¶ – 'Maiden's Blush'	GMac
– 'Minor' ♀	CFul CInt CPla CSam ECGP GMac LPVe MFir NBro SBla WAbe WBou WBro WRus
– 'Minor Alba'	See *V. cornuta* 'Alba Minor'
* – 'Paris White'	EPfP
– Purpurea Group	CMea ECha GBuc WRus
– 'Rosea'	CBos CFul CLyd LPVe NSti
– 'Seymour Pink'	CFul
– 'Variegata'	LPVe NHol WLin
* – 'Victoria's Blush'	NHar NRoo NSti SMrm WBou WWhi
¶ – 'Violacea'	CBos GMac
¶ – 'Yellow King'	EFou
corsica	CInt EMan LPVe
* 'Cottage Garden' (Va)	GHCN SHBN WFar
'Countess of Shaftsbury' (dVt)	CDev
'Cox's Moseley' (ExVa)	GHCN
¶ 'Cream Princess'	EPfP
'Cressida' (Va)	LPVe
§ *cucullata* ♀	CGro SChu WPrP
§ – 'Alba'	ECGP LLWP
– *rosea*	EWes
* – 'Striata Alba'	MWgw
cunninghamii	GDra
– CC 463	MRPP
curtisii	See *V. tricolor* subsp. *curtisii*
'Cyril Bell' (Va)	LPVe
§ 'Czar' (Vt)	CBre ILis NRya
§ 'Czar Bleu' (Vt)	CDev
'Daena' (Vtta)	LPVe
'Daisy Smith' (Va)	CFul GHCN GMac NChi SChu WBou
'Dartington Hybrid' (Va)	LPVe
'Daveron' (C)	LPVe NRoo
'David Rhodes' (FP)	GHCN
'David Wheldon' (Va)	GHCN LPVe
'Davina' (Va)	LPVe SChu SDys
'Dawn' (Vtta)	CCot CFul GHCN GMac LPVe MMil WBou
'Deanna' (Va)	LPVe
'Decima' (Va)	LPVe
'Delia' (Va)	GMac LPVe WBou
'Delicia' (Vtta)	LPVe NChi NRoo
'Delmonden' (Va)	CRDP SAsh
'Delphine' (Va)	LPVe NPla NRoo SChu
'Demeter' (Va)	LPVe
'Desdemona' (Va)	CMHG GMac LBee LGre WBou
'Desmonda' (Va)	LPVe SChu
'Devon Cream' (Va)	GMac WBou
'Dimity' (Va)	LPVe
'Dione' (Vtta)	LPVe
I 'Diosma' (Va)	LPVe
§ *dissecta*	WCot WPer
§ – var. *chaerophylloides* f. *eizanensis*	ECro EHyt MTho NWCA
– var. *sieboldiana*	CRDP
'Dobbie's Bronze' (Va)	LPVe
'Dobbie's Buff' (Va)	LPVe
'Dobbie's Red' (Va)	LPVe WLRN
'Doctor Smart' (C)	LPVe
doerfleri	LPVe
'Dominique' (Va)	LPVe
'Dominy' (Vtta)	LPVe
'Donau' (Vt)	CDev CGro
'Double White' (dVt)	CGle
dubyana	EAst GBuc MTPN SSca
'Duchesse de Parme' (dVt)	CDev CGle CGro GBar GMac WHer
'D'Udine' (dVt)	CDev CGro GBar GMac WBou
'Dusk'	WBou
'E.A. Bowles'	See *V. 'Bowles' Black'*
'Eastgrove Blue Scented' (Va)	CLTr GMac MCLN WAbe WBou WCot WEas WIvy WRHF

eizanensis	See *V. dissecta* var. *chaerophylloides* f. *eizanensis*
'Elaine Cawthorne' (C)	LPVe
* 'Elaine Quin'	SChu WBou
§ *elatior*	CElw CHea CMea CMil CPla CSWP EAst EBar EMon EPar EPla GBri LGan LPVe MBel MHar NHol NSti SChu SSca SUsu WFar WLin WPer WWye
§ *elegantula*	GCrs LPVe SSca
§ – *bosniaca*	LPVe
'Elisha' (Va)	LPVe NRoo
'Elizabeth' (Va)	GHCN LPVe NPri SChu SMrm SRms WBou WLRN
'Elizabeth Cawthorne' (C)	LPVe
'Elizabeth Lee'	CGro
'Elizabeth McCallum' (FP)	GHCN
'Elliot Adam' (Va)	GHCN
'Elsie Coombs' (Vt)	CDev WPer
'Emily Mott' (Va)	LPVe
'Emma' (Va)	CMea LPVe NHar
'Emma Cawthorne' (C)	CLTr GHCN LPVe
'Enterea' (Va)	LPVe
erecta	See *V. elatior*
'Eris' (Va)	LPVe NRoo
'Eros' (Va)	LPVe NRoo
'Etain' (Va)	ECha ELan GHCN GMaP LGre LPVe MMil NBrk NRoo SHBN WBou WLRN
'Ethena' (Va)	LPVe
'Etienne' (Va)	LPVe
'Evelyn Cawthorne' (C)	LPVe NRoo
'Fabiola' (Vtta)	GMac LBee LPVe NBir WBou
'Felicity' (Va)	LPVe
¶ 'Felix'	CChr
'Finola Galway' (Va)	LPVe
'Fiona' (Va)	CBos CLon CMHG GHCN GMac LPVe MCLN NBrk NCat NRoo NSti SChu SHel SUsu WBou
* 'Fiona Lawrenson' (Va)	LPVe
'Florence' (Va)	LPVe NRoo
'Foxbrook Cream' (C)	CFul CLTr CMea GBuc GHCN GMac LPVe MBel NBrk NPla SHel WAbe WBou WCot WHoo WRus
'Frances' (Va)	LPVe
'Francesca' (Va)	LPVe
'Freckles'	See *V. sororia* 'Freckles'
'Gatina' (Va)	LPVe
I 'Gazania' (Va)	CMea LPVe WBou
'Gazelle' (Vtta)	LPVe MCLN WPen
'Genesta Gambier' (Va)	CFul CSam
¶ 'George Lee'	CGro
'Georgina' (Va)	LPVe
'Geraldine' (Vtta)	LPVe
'Geraldine Cawthorne' (C)	GHCN LPVe
'Gina' (Vtta)	LPVe
'Giselle' (Va)	LPVe
glabella	CLTr SUsu WOMN
'Gladys Findlay' (Va)	GHCN GMac LPVe WBou
'Glenroyd Fancy' (ExVa)	GHCN
'Governor Herrick' (Vt)	CDev CGro EFou NSti WPer
'Grace' (Va)	NRoo
§ *gracilis*	CElw ECha ELan LPVe MRav
– × *cornuta*	LPVe
– 'Lutea'	CLon CSam NRoo SMrm
* – 'Magic'	CElw SMrm SUsu SWat WCot
¶ – 'Major'	WBou
¶ 'Green Jade'	CPla

'Grey Owl' (Va)	CLon CMea LBee LGre LPVe NBrk NCat SChu SLod WBou WKif WRHF
grisebachiana	GCLN NGre
* – *alba*	GCLN
'Griselda' (Vtta)	LPVe
'Grovemount Blue' (C)	CMea NCat WPen
§ *grypoceras* var. *exilis*	CDec CInt EHyt EWes GBri NBus SMad WBor
– 'Variegata'	EHoe NBir
'Gustav Wermig' (C)	GAbr LPVe MBel WBou
'Gwen Cawthorne' (C)	LPVe
'H.H. Hodge' (ExVa)	GHCN
¶ 'Hackpen'	CSam
'Hadria Cawthorne' (C)	GHCN LPVe
'Hansa' (C)	CHid WMer
'Haslemere'	See *V.* 'Nellie Britton'
¶ 'Hazeldene Blue'	CChr
* 'Heaselands'	SMrm
I 'Hebe' (Vtta)	LPVe
§ *hederacea*	CArn CBos CCot CDev CGro CHan CMHG CPla ECou ELan ESis GCHN GMac GQui LPVe MNrw NBro NHar NOak SUsu WHer WOMN WWhi WWye
– blue	CFee CLTr CPla SIng WPer
– 'Putty'	ECou EWes
– var. *sieberi*	See *V. sieberiana*
'Helen Dillon'	EWes GMac NHaw WWhi
'Helen W. Cochrane' (ExVa)	GHCN
'Helena' (Va)	LPVe SChu
'Hera' (Va)	LPVe
'Hespera' (Va)	LPVe
I 'Hesperis' (Va)	LPVe
heterophylla subsp. *epirota*	See *V. bertolonii*
'Hextable' (C)	LPVe
hirta	CKin WCla
hispida	LPVe
'Hopley's White'	CGro
'Hudsons Blue'	WEas
'Hugh Campbell' (ExVa)	GHCN
'Huntercombe Purple' (Va) ♀	CBos CFul CGle GHCN GMac LBee LPVe MWat NPla SAga SBla SChu SUsu WBou WKif SMrm
'Hunter's Pride'	SMrm
'Hyperion' (Va)	LPVe
¶ 'I.G. Sherwood'	GHCN
'Iantha' (Vtta)	LPVe
'Iden Gem' (Va)	CFul GHCN LPVe
'Inkie' (Va)	CFul
'Inverurie Beauty' (Va) ♀	EJud GMaP LPVe MFir NBrk NCat SChu WBou WKif
'Inverurie Mauve' (Va)	LPVe
'Iona' (Va)	LPVe
'Irina' (Va)	LPVe
'Irish Elegance' (Vt)	CDev CGro NBro WHal
'Irish Mary' (Va)	LPVe SChu
'Irish Molly' (Va)	CBot CElw CFul CLon CMHG CSam CSpe EAst ECha ELan GCal GHCN GMac LBee LBlm LPVe MCLN NRoo SBla SMrm WBou WEas WHer WSHC WWhi WWin
'Isata' (Vtta)	LPVe
'Isla' (Vtta)	LGre LPVe
'Isobel'	EWes
'Ita' (Va)	LPVe
'Iver Grove' (Va)	LPVe
'Ivory Queen' (Va)	CFul GHCN GMac LPVe NBrk WBou WPen

'Ivory White' (Va) — CDev LPVe WOMN
* 'Jack Sampson' — CDev
'Jackanapes' (Va) ♀ — CBot CFul CMHG ECha ECtt ELan GHCN GMac LPVe MHig NBrk NRoo SHBN SMrm SRms SUsu WBou WFar WWin
'James' — EWes
'James Pilling' (Va) — CFul GHCN GMac
'Jane Askew' (Va) — LPVe
'Jane Mott' (Va) — LPVe
'Janet' (Va) — GHCN LPVe SMrm WLRN
'Janine' (Vtta) — LPVe
'Janna' (Va) — LPVe
japonica — EGar
¶ – 'Rodney Davey' — MCCP
'Jean Arnot' — CGro
'Jeannie Bellew' (Va) — GHCN GMac LPVe NCat NHar NPri SChu WBou WLRN
'Jemma' (Va) — LPVe
'Jenelle' (Vtta) — LPVe
'Jenny' (Vtta) — LPVe
'Jersey Gem' (Va) — GMac LPVe
'Jessica' (Va) — LPVe
'Jessie East' — WEas
'Jessie Taylor' (FP) — GHCN
'Jimmie's Dark' (ExVa) — GHCN
'Joanna' (Va) — GHCN WBou
I 'Jocunda' (Va) — LPVe
'Joella' (Va) — LPVe
¶ 'John Rodger' (SP) — GHCN
'John Wallmark' (c) — WMer
'John Yelmark' (Va) — LPVe
'John Zanini' (Vtta) — LPVe
'Johnny Jump Up' (T) — EWll
jooi — CInt CLyd GTou NBir NBro NMen SBla SIng SSca WOMN WRha
¶ *jordanii* — LPVe
'Jordieland Gem' (c) — GMac WAbe
'Josie' (Va) — LPVe
'Joyce Gray' (Va) — GHCN GMac NRoo WBou
* 'Judy Goring' (Va) — LPVe
'Julia' (Va) — LPVe WBou
'Julian' (Va) — CFul CLTr GDra GHCN GMac MOne NRoo SBla SRms WBou WIvy
'Juno' (Va) — GMac LPVe
'Jupiter' (Va) — LPVe SMrm
'Kate' (Va) — CElw CFul
'Katerina' (Va) — LPVe
'Kathy' (Vtta) — LPVe
* 'Katie Grayson' (C) — LPVe
'Katinka' (Va) — LPVe
keiskei — GCHN
'Kerrie' (Va) — LPVe
* 'Kerry Girl' — CDev
'Kiki McDonough' (C) — CBos LPVe NBrk SChu
'Kilruna' (Va) — LPVe
* 'King of the Blacks' (T&M) — ECoo
'King of the Blues' (Va) — LPVe
'Kinvarna' (Va) — LPVe
'Kirsty' (Va) — LPVe
'Kitten' — GMac NRoo NSti SChu WAbe WBou
'Kitty White' (Va) — LPVe
koraiensis — NWCA
koreana — See *V. grypoceras* var. *exilis*
§ *labradorica* — CGro EOld EPot GBur GLil LSyl SMer
N– hort. — See *V. riviniana* Purpurea Group

N– *purpurea* misapplied — See *V. riviniana* Purpurea Group
♦ 'Lady Saville' — See *V.* 'Sissinghurst'
'Lady Tennyson' (Va) — GMac LPVe SBla
'Lamorna' (Vtta) — LPVe
lanceolata — GCra
'Larissa' (Va) — LPVe
'Latona' (Va) — LPVe
'Laura' (C) — CFul GBuc GMac NBrk
¶ 'Lavender Lady' — CGro
'Laverna' (Va) — LPVe
'Lavinia' (Va) — GCrs GHCN LBee LPVe WBou
'Lawrence' (c) — WMer
'Leander' (Va) — LPVe
'Leda' (Va) — LPVe
'Leora' (Vtta) — CFul GMac LPVe NRoo
'Leora Hamilton' (C) — CMHG LPVe NPla
'Lerosa' (Va) — LPVe
'Leta' (Vtta) — LPVe
'Letitia' (Va) — CFul EFou GHCN GMac LPVe MMil NPri SMrm WBou WLRN
'Leto' (Va) — LPVe
'Lewisa' (Va) — LPVe
'Lianne' (Vt) — CDev WPer
'Lilac Rose' (Va) — CFul GMac SAga WBou
'Liliana' (Va) — LPVe
'Liriopa' (Va) — LPVe
'Lisa Cawthorne' (C) — LPVe
'Little David' (Vtta) ♀ — CBos CFul CInt CSam EAst EHal GHCN GMac LBee LPVe MCLN NRoo NSti WBou WEas
'Livia' (Vtta) — LPVe
'Lola' (Va) — LPVe
'Lord Nelson' (Va) — EMou EWll LPVe WMer
'Lord Plunket' (Va) — CFul LPVe WBou
'Lorna' (Va) ♀ — LPVe SUsu
'Lorna Cawthorne' (C) — CElw GHCN LPVe NCat
'Lorna Moakes' (Va) — LPVe SAga
'Louisa' (Va) — LPVe
'Louise Gemmell' (Va) — LPVe NBrk SChu
'Luca' (Va) — LPVe
'Lucinda' (Va) — LPVe
'Lucy' (Va) — LPVe
'Ludy May' (Va) — LPVe
'Luna' (Va) — LPVe
§ *lutea* — EBot LPVe WBou WGwy WUnd
– subsp. *elegans* — See *V. lutea*
'Luxonne' (Vt) — CBre WLRN
'Lydia' (Va) — LPVe SChu WBou
'Lydia Groves' — CDev CGro
'Lynn' (Va) — GHCN LPVe
'Lysander' (Va) — LPVe
macedonica — See *V. tricolor* subsp. *macedonica*
¶ *macloskeyi* var. *pallens* — WLRN
'Madame Armandine Pagès' (Vt) — CBre CDev
'Madelaine' (Va) — LPVe
'Madge' (Va) — LPVe
'Maera' (Vtta) — LPVe
¶ *magellanica* — NWoo
§ *magellensis* — NChi
'Magenta Maid' (Va) — CFul MArl NCat
'Maggie' (Va) — LPVe
'Maggie Mott' (Va) ♀ — CCot CFul CGle CSam ECha ECtt EOrc GHCN GMac LBee LBlm LHop LPVe MBri MCLN MHig NBrk NHol NRoo SBla SHBN WBou WEas WKif WRus WWhi WWin

'Magic'	GMac LBee MArl NPla SChu WBou WCru
'Maid Marion'	SRms
'Majella' (Vtta)	LPVe
'Malise' (Va)	LPVe
'Malvena' (Vtta)	LPVe
¶ *mandshurica*	LPVe
¶ *– triangularis bicolor*	CInt
¶ 'Margaret' (Va)	WBou
'Margaret Cawthorne' (C)	LPVe
'Marian' (Va)	LPVe
'Marie-Louise' (dPVt)	CCot CDev CGro CPla CTri EPar
'Marika' (Va)	LPVe
'Mark Talbot' (Va)	GHCN
'Maroon Picotee'	ELan GHCN
'Mars' (Va)	CLon LPVe
'Marsland's Yellow' (Vtta)	LPVe
'Martin' (Va) ♀	CFul CInt CMHG CNic CSam ECha EWes GCHN GHCN GMac LBee LHop LPVe NBrk SChu SDys WBou WIvy WKif WWin
'Mary Cawthorne' (C)	LPVe
'Mary Ellen' (Va)	CFul GHCN
¶ 'Mary Wyllie'	GHCN
'Mauve Beauty' (Va)	LPVe
'Mauve Haze' (Va)	GMac WBou WEas
'Mauve Radiance' (Va)	CFul GMac LPVe NVic WBou
'May Mott' (Va)	GMac NBrk WBou
'Mayfly' (Va)	GHCN GMac NBrk WBou
'Meena' (Vtta)	LPVe
'Megumi' (Va)	LPVe
'Melinda' (Vtta)	LPVe WBou
* 'Melissa' (Va)	CFul LPVe SChu WBou
'Mercury' (Va)	GHCN LPVe
'Midnight Turk' (Va)	GBuc
'Milkmaid' (Va)	CGle ECha EFou EWll GCrs GHCN LBee NBir NHaw SIng WFar WKif
'Mina Walker' (ExVa)	GHCN
'Minerva' (Va)	LPVe
* *minor* subsp. *calcarea*	WUnd
'Miranda' (Vtta)	LPVe
'Miss Brookes' (Va)	CFul GHCN GMac LPVe WBou
'Miss Helen Mount'	WShe
'Mistral' (Va)	LPVe
'Misty Guy' (Vtta)	NChi WBou
'Mitzel' (Vtta)	LPVe NRoo
'Molly Sanderson' (Va) ♀	CB&S CBos CBot CGle CMea CSam CSpe EAst ECha ECtt ELan ENot EPot GHCN GMac LBee LHop LPVe MCLN MHig MRav NRoo SChu SMrm SSoC WBou WEas WWhi WWin
I 'Mona' (Va)	LPVe
'Monica' (Va)	LPVe SChu
'Moonlight' (Va) ♀	CFul CMea EAst ECha ELan GCHN GMac LBee LHop LPVe MOne NRoo NSti SAga SBla SChu SUsu WBou WMaN
'Moonraker'	CBos CCot NCat
'Morvana' (Va)	LPVe
'Morwenna' (Va)	LPVe NRoo WWhi
'Moscaria' (Va)	LPVe
'Moseley Ideal' (ExVa)	GHCN
'Moseley Perfection' (Va)	LPVe
'Mrs Chichester' (Va)	GHCN GMac LPVe NBrk WBou

'Mrs David Lloyd George' (dVt)	CDev
'Mrs Lancaster' (Va)	CFul CMea CSam EAst EWes GHCN GMac LPVe MCLN NBir NRoo SChu SMrm SRms WBou WLRN
'Mrs M.B. Wallace' (ExVa)	GHCN
'Mrs R. Barton' (Vt)	CCot CDev CGro NBro WLRN
'Myfawnny' (Va)	CBos ELan EWes GHCN GMac LBee LPVe NPla NPri NRoo SAga SChu SHBN SRms WBou WKif WLRN
'Mylene' (Va)	LPVe
'Myntha' (Vtta)	LPVe
'Mysie' (Va)	CFul
'Nadia' (Va)	LPVe
'Naomi' (Va)	LPVe
'Natasha' (Va)	LPVe
'Neapolitan'	See *V.* **'Pallida Plena'**
'Nell' (Va)	CFul
§ 'Nellie Britton' (Va) ♀	CFul CGle EAst GBur GHCN GMac LHop LPVe NRoo NSti SBla SChu WBou WEas WRus WWin
'Nemesis' (Va)	LPVe
'Neptune' (Va)	LPVe
'Nerena' (Vtta)	LPVe
'Nesta' (Vtta)	LPVe
'Netta Statham'	See *V.* **'Belmont Blue'**
'Nicole' (Va)	LPVe
'Nigra' (Va)	LPVe
'Nina' (Va)	LPVe
'Nona' (Va)	LPVe
¶ 'Nora May' (Va)	GHCN
'Norah Church' (Vt)	CCot CDev CGro
'Norah Leigh' (Va)	NRoo WBou
obliqua	See *V. cucullata*
¶ *– alba*	NChi
occulta striata albe	EMar NBro
'Octavia' (Va)	LPVe
'Odile' (Va)	LPVe
odorata	CArn CB&S CDev CGle CGro CJew CKin CSWP EWFC GBar GMac GPoy LHol LPVe MRav MWat NFla NLak NRoo NSti SIde SIng SSea WCla WOak WWye
– 'Alba'	CBre CDev CGle CGro CKin CSWP CVer EAst EFou ELan EMan GMac ILis MCLN MWgw NCat NOak NRoo NSti SIde WBon WCla WOve WRus WWat WWye
– 'Alba Plena' (d)	CVer EBot ELan EPar SBla
– apricot	See *V.* **'Sulphurea'**
– dumetorum	See *V. alba*
– flore-pleno	EBot EPar
– pink	EOld EPar WCla
– rosea	CBre GBar GMac MRav SIng WOMN
* *– subsp. subcarnea*	WUnd
– 'Sulphurea'	See *V.* **'Sulphurea'**
'Olive Edmonds' (Va)	LPVe
'Olwyn' (Va)	LPVe
oreades	LPVe NTow
'Oriana' (Va)	LPVe
orphanidis	LPVe
ossea	LPVe
¶ 'Painted Lady' (Va)	GMac
§ 'Pallida Plena' (dPVt)	CDev
¶ *palmata*	LPVe

'Palmer's White' (Va)	CFul LPVe
palustris	CKin EWFC WHer WShi
'Pamela Zambra' (Vt)	CDev
'Pandora' (Va)	LPVe
papilionacea	See *V. sororia*
'Parme de Toulouse' (dPVt)	CDev
'Pat Creasy' (Va)	GHCN GMac WBou
'Pat Kavanagh' (C)	CMea GHCN GMac LPVe MWat SMrm WBou
'Patricia Brookes' (Va)	LPVe
pedata	CBro CFai EMan EPot MBri NHar SMad WAbe
– 'Bicolor'	SBla WAbe
pedatifida	EBar ECro ELan MBel MBro MTho NMGW NNrd SChu WWye
¶ 'Peggy Morgan'	LPVe
'Penelope' (SP)	GHCN
pensylvanica	See *V. pubescens* var. *eriocarpa*
¶ 'Peppered-palms'	CPla
'Perle Rose' (Vt)	CDev CGro
'Pete'	SChu
'Petra' (Vtta)	LPVe
'Philippa Cawthorne' (C)	LPVe
'Phoebe' (Va)	LPVe
'Phyllida' (Va)	LPVe
'Pickering Blue' (Va)	CFul GHCN GMac LPVe WBou
'Pilar' (Va)	LPVe SChu SUsu
'Pippa' (Vtta)	LPVe SChu
'Poppy' (Va)	CLTr LPVe
'Priam' (Va)	LPVe
'Primrose Cream' (Va)	LPVe
'Primrose Dame' (Va)	CDoC GHCN GMac LPVe NBrk NCat WBou WMer
'Primrose Pixie' (Va)	WBou
¶ 'Prince Henry' (T)	LPVe
'Prince John' (T)	EGar LPVe
'Princess Mab' (Vtta)	CFul GHCN LPVe NBrk NRoo WBou
'Princess of Prussia' (Vt)	CBre CDev
'Princess of Wales'	See *V.* **'Princesse de Galles'**
* 'Princess Yellow'	EPfP
§ 'Princesse de Galles' (Vt)	CB&S CDev CM&M EOld EPar NSti WRus
§ *pubescens* var. *eriocarpa*	CBro
'Purity' (Vtta)	GHCN LPVe NRoo
'Purple Dove' (Va)	SMrm
'Purple Wings' (Va)	GMac WBou
'Putty'	WCru
'Queen Charlotte' (Vt)	CDev CFai CM&M GCHN ILis NBro NFai NHar NMen NWCA WCot WGwG
'Queen Disa' (Vtta)	CMHG LPVe
'Queen Victoria'	See *V.* **'Victoria Regina'**
'Quink' (Va)	CFul
'R.N. Denby' (ExVa)	GHCN
'Ramona' (Va)	LPVe
'Rave' (Vtta)	GMac
* 'Raven'	NCat NHar NRoo SAga SChu WBou WWhi
'Ravenna' (Va)	LPVe
'Rebecca' (Vtta)	CFul CGle CInt CMHG CPla CRDP CSam CSpe EBar ECtt EFou ELan GHCN GMac LBee LPVe MCLN NBir NBrk NHar NRoo SChu SRms SSoC SUsu WBou WHer WKif
'Rebecca Cawthorne' (C)	LPVe NRoo
'Red Charm' (Vt)	CM&M EWll NBro NCat NPla WHow WLRN

'Red Lion'	CDev
'Red Queen' (Vt)	CCot NSti
reichenbachiana	ELan EPar EWFC
'Reine des Blanches' (dVt)	EFou
'Reliance' (Va)	CFul GHCN
'Remora' (Vtta)	LPVe
reniforme	See *V. hederacea*
'Rhoda' (Va)	LPVe
'Richard Vivian' (Va)	LPVe
'Richard's Yellow' (Va)	GHCN LPVe
riviniana	CArn CKin EJud MMal NChi WHer WJek WOak WShi
§ – Purpurea Group	Widely available
¶ – *purpurea* × *verecunda* *yakusimana*	SIng
– white	EWes NWoo
'Rodney Davey' (Vt/v)	CDec CPla EGar GBri MCLN MOne NBro NCut NFai NWes WElm WLRN
¶ 'Rodney Marsh'	NBir
'Romilly' (Va)	LPVe
'Rosalie' (Va)	LPVe
* 'Rosanna'	CDev
'Roscastle Black'	NPla WBou WCot WWhi
'Rosemary Cawthorne' (C)	LPVe
'Rowan Hood' (ExVa)	GHCN
'Rowena' (Va)	LPVe
'Royal Delft'	GCHN
'Royal Robe' (VT)	CDev
'Rubra' (Vt)	WPer
rugulosa	See *V. canadensis* var. *rugulosa*
¶ *rupestris*	WOak
§ – *rosea*	CDev CInt CLTr CNic CPla LLWP MNrw NCat NGre NSti NWCA STre WCla WOMN WPrP
'Russian Superb' (Vt)	WLRN
'Ruth Blackall' (Va)	LPVe
'Ruth Elkans' (Va)	GHCN GMac LPVe NBrk
'Saint Helena' (Vt)	CDev CGro
'Saint Maur' (Va)	CFul
'Sally' (Vtta)	LPVe
'Samantha' (Vtta)	LPVe
'Sammy Jo' (Va)	WBou
* 'Sandra Louise' (C)	LPVe
'Sarah' (Va)	CFul
'Saughton Blue' (Va)	LPVe
saxatilis	See *V. tricolor* subsp. *subalpina*
selkirkii	CInt CNic CPla LPVe NBro NBus NWCA WHal
– 'Variegata'	GBri GBuc NBir NWes WLin
¶ *sempervirens*	CInt
septentrionalis	CCot CRDP ECha EGol ELan MNrw MOne NBro NGre NNrd NRya SSmi WHal WRus
– *alba*	CHid CM&M CMHG CSWP CVer EBee EFou MWgw NPla WHow WLRN WPer
'Septima' (Va)	LPVe
'Serena' (Va)	LPVe WBou
'Sheila' (Va)	WBou
'Sidborough Poppet'	CInt CNic CPBP EWes NHar SSca WAbe WOMN WPer
'Sigrid' (Va)	LPVe
* 'Sir Fred Warner' (Va)	LPVe
'Sissinghurst' (Va)	GMac LPVe NBir
'Sky Blue' (Va)	LPVe
¶ 'Smugglers Moon'	SChu
¶ 'Snow Queen'	GMac
'Sophie' (Vtta)	LPVe SChu

§ *sororia*	EMan GCHN GSki LPVe MSCN WBro WLRN WOMN WWal
– 'Albiflora'	CSpe EBar EMil EPPr EPar EPfP GMaP GSki NHar NPro WLin WPer WRus
§ – 'Freckles'	CBro CDev CElw CHad CMHG CRDP ECha EFou EGoo ELan EOrc ESis GCal GMac ILis LBee LHop MTho NFai NHar NNrd NRoo SBla SIng SSmi SUsu WEas WGwG WHil
– 'Priceana'	CM&M CNic EAst EBee EMan EOrc NCat NPla SLod SMrm WHow WLRN WPer WWal WWat
'Soula' (Vtta)	LPVe
* 'Stacey Proud' (v)	NPro
'Steyning' (Va)	LPVe
stojanovii	CMea ELan SBla WCot WEas WOMN
striata	CInt WWat
§ 'Sulphurea' (Vt)	CBre CDev CHid CPla CSWP ELan LPVe MHar SUsu WHil WOMN WPer
'Susanah' (Vtta)	GHCN GMac LPVe NPla
'Susie' (Va)	GHCN
'Swanley White'	See *V.* **'Comte de Brazza'**
'Sybil' (SP)	GHCN
'Sylvia Hart'	EWes MTho WBon
'Talitha' (Va)	GMac LPVe
'Tamsin' (Va)	LPVe
* 'Tanith' (Vt)	CBre CDev
'Tara' (Va)	LPVe
'Thalia' (Vtta)	CFul LPVe MCLN WBou
'The Czar'	See *V.* **'Czar'**
'Thea' (Va)	LPVe
'Thelma' (Va)	LPVe
'Thetis' (Va)	GHCN LPVe
'Thierry' (Va)	LPVe
'Tiffany' (Va)	LPVe
'Tina' (Va)	GHCN LPVe WBou
'Titania' (Va)	LPVe
'Tom' (SP)	GHCN
'Tom Tit' (Va)	LPVe WBou
'Tomose' (Va)	CFul
'Tony Venison' (C/v)	CCot CElw CStr EHal EHoe LHop MBel MTho NBus NHaw NSti WBou WCot
tricolor	CKin CNic CSWP EFer EWFC GBar GPoy LHol MHew SIde WHer WJek WSel
§ – subsp. *curtisii*	LPVe
– 'Sawyer's Blue'	WPer
¶ – subsp. *saxatilis*	LPVe
'Tullia' (Vtta)	LPVe
'Una' (Va)	LPVe
'Unity' (Vtta)	LPVe
¶ 'Valerie Proud'	NBrk
'Velleda' (Vtta)	LPVe
velutina	See *V. gracilis*
'Venetia' (Va)	LPVe
'Venus' (Va)	LPVe
§ *verecunda* var. *yakusimana*	CNic CRDP ESis EWes NGre
'Victoria'	See *V.* **'Czar Bleu'**
'Victoria Cawthorne' (C)	CElw CMea GBuc GHCN GMac LPVe MBel MBro NChi NRoo SBla SChu SUsu WBou WHoo WPyg
§ 'Victoria Regina' (Vt)	CDev CRow EMon
'Violacea' (C)	GHCN LPVe

'Virginia' (Va)	CFul GMac LPVe SChu WBou
'Virgo' (Va)	LPVe
'Vita' (Va)	CFul CLTr CMea CSpe EBar GBuc GMac LBee LGre LPVe NRoo NSti SBid SBla SChu SRms WBou WIvy WLin WWhi
vourinensis	LPVe
'Wanda' (Va)	LPVe
¶ 'Wendy' (SP)	GHCN LPVe
¶ 'Westacre' (Va)	EWes
'White Gem' (Va)	LBee
'White Ladies' (Vt)	See *V. cucullata* **'Alba'**
'White Pearl' (Va)	GBuc GMac LGre WBou
'White Superior'	CB&S
'White Swan' (Va)	EAst GMac LPVe
'William Fife' (ExVa)	GHCN
'William Wallace' (Va)	LPVe
'Windward' (Vt)	CCot NCat
'Winifred Jones' (Va)	GHCN
* 'Winifred Warden' (Va)	GHCN
'Winifred Wargent' (Va)	LPVe NPri SAga WLRN
'Winona' (Vtta)	LPVe NRoo
'Winona Cawthorne' (C)	GHCN GMac LPVe NChi SChu WAbe WBou
'Woodlands Cream' (Va)	GHCN GMac NBrk NPla WBou
'Woodlands Lilac' (Va)	GHCN LPVe NRoo SChu WBou
'Woodlands White' (Va)	LPVe
'Xantha' (Va)	LPVe
yakusimana	See *V. verecunda* var. *yakusimana*
yezoensis	CPla
'Zalea' (Va)	LPVe
'Zara' (Va)	GMaP WBou
'Zenobia' (Vtta)	LPVe
'Zepherine' (Va)	LPVe
'Zeta' (Va)	LPVe
'Ziglana' (Va)	LPVe
'Zoe' (Vtta)	GHCN GMac LPVe MMil NPri NRoo SChu SDys SMrm WBou WLRN
'Zona' (Va)	LPVe
zoysii	See *V. calcarata* subsp. *zoysii*

VISCARIA (Caryophyllaceae)

vulgaris	See *Lychnis viscaria*

VITALIANA (Primulaceae)

§ *primuliflora*	CLyd GCrs GTou MBro NSla WHoo WPyg
– subsp. *canescens*	NHol
– subsp. *praetutiana*	EHyt EPot GDra MBro MHig MRPP NHar NHol NMen NNrd NTow NWCA WLin WPat WPyg
– subsp. *praetutiana chionantha*	EPot
– subsp. *tridentata*	EPot NMen NNrd

VITEX (Verbenaceae)

agnus-castus	CAgr CArn CB&S EEls ELan ELau EOas GPoy LHol LLew SBid SIgm SMad SPer WFar WHil WWye
¶ – 'Chaste Tree'	MCCP
– var. *latifolia*	MBri
– 'Silver Spire'	SBid
lucens	CHEx
negundo	CArn LLew
– *cannabifolia*	See *V. incisa*

VITIS † (Vitaceae)

'Abundante' (F)	WSuF
amurensis	CPlN EHic EPfP EPla ETen WCru WWat
'Baco Noir' (O/B)	GTwe WSuF
Black Hamburgh	See *V. vinifera* **'Schiava Grossa'**
§ 'Boskoop Glory' (F)	CMac GTwe LBuc SCoo SDea WSuF
'Brant' (O/B) ♀	CAgr CB&S CBlo CMac CPlN EBrP EBre ELan ENot ERea GTwe LBre LPri MAsh MBri MGos MWat NBea NPer NRog SBre SDea SHBN SPer SRms WStI WSuF WWeb
californica (F)	ERea
§ 'Cascade' (O/B)	ERea SDea WSuF
'Chambourcin' (B)	WSuF
Claret Cloak	See *V. coignetiae* Claret Cloak = **'Frovit'**
coignetiae ♀	Widely available
§ – Claret Cloak = 'Frovit'	ELan LRHS MAsh SMur SPer SSpi
* – 'Rubescens'	CPlN
'Dalkauer' (W)	WSuF
ficifolia	See *V. thunbergii*
'Fiesta'	WSuF
§ 'Fragola' (O/R)	CAgr CMac CPlN EBrP EBre EHic EPfP EPla ERea GTwe LBre SBre SDea SEND SRms WSuF WWat
henryana	See *Parthenocissus henryana*
'Himrod' (O/W)	ERea GTwe SDea WSuF
inconstans	See *Parthenocissus tricuspidata*
'Kuibishevski' (O/R)	WSuF
labrusca 'Concord' (O/B)	ERea
Landot 244 (O/B)	WSuF
'Léon Millot' (O/G/B)	CAgr EMui ERea NDal SDea WSuF
'Maréchal Foch' (O/B)	WSuF
'Maréchal Joffre' (O/B)	GTwe WSuF
Oberlin 595 (O/B)	WSuF
'Orion'	WSuF
parsley leaved	See *V. vinifera* **'Ciotat'**
parvifolia	CPlN WPat
'Phönix' (O/W)	WSuF
¶ *piasezkii*	WCru
* 'Pink Strawberry' (O)	WSuF
'Pirovano 14' (O/B)	ERea GTwe SDea WSuF
§ 'Plantet' (O/B)	WSuF
* 'Polaske Muscat' (W)	WSuF
pseudoreticulata	CFil CPlN WPGP
'Pulchra'	WCru
quinquefolia	See *Parthenocissus quinquefolia*
Ravat 51 (O/W)	WSuF
riparia	CPlN GAri WCru
'Schuyler' (O/B)	WSuF
Seibel (F)	EMui GTwe
Seibel 13053	See *V.* **'Cascade'**
Seibel 5455	See *V.* **'Plantet'**
Seibel 7053	WSuF
Seibel 9549	WSuF
'Seneca' (W)	WSuF
§ 'Seyval Blanc' (O/W)	ERea GTwe SDea WSuF
Seyve Villard 12.375	See *V.* **'Villard Blanc'**
Seyve Villard 5276	See *V.* **'Seyval Blanc'**
'Tereshkova' (O/B)	ERea SDea WSuF
'Thornton'	WSuF
§ *thunbergii*	WCru
'Triomphe d'Alsace' (O/B)	NPer SDea WSuF
'Trollinger'	See *V. vinifera* **'Schiava Grossa'**
§ 'Villard Blanc' (O/W)	WSuF

vinifera 'Abouriou' (O/B)	WSuF
§ – 'Alicante' (G/B)	ERea GTwe WSuF
– 'Apiifolia'	See *V. vinifera* **'Ciotat'**
– 'Appley Towers' (G/B)	ERea
– 'Auxerrois' (O/W)	WSuF
– 'Bacchus' (O/W)	SDea WSuF
– 'Black Alicante'	See *V. vinifera* **'Alicante'**
– 'Black Corinth' (G/B)	ERea
– 'Black Frontignan' (G/O/B)	ERea WSuF
– Black Hamburgh	See *V. vinifera* **'Schiava Grossa'**
– 'Black Monukka' (G/B)	ERea WSuF
– 'Blauburger' (O/B)	WCru
– 'Blue Portuguese'	See *V. vinifera* **'Portugieser'**
– 'Buckland Sweetwater' (G/W)	ERea GTwe MBri SDea WSuF
– 'Cabernet Sauvignon' (O/B)	SDea WSuF
– 'Canon Hall Muscat' (G/W)	ERea
– 'Cardinal' (F)	ERea
– 'Chaouch' (G/W)	ERea
– 'Chardonnay' (O/W)	SDea WSuF
§ – 'Chasselas' (G/O/W)	CMac ERea WSuF WWeb
– 'Chasselas d'Or'	See *V. vinifera* **'Chasselas'**
– 'Chasselas Rosé' (G/R)	ERea WSuF
– 'Chasselas Vibert' (G/W)	ERea WSuF
– 'Chenin Blanc' (O/W)	WSuF
§ – 'Ciotat' (F)	EHic EPla ERea SDea WCru WSuF WWat
§ – 'Cot' (O/B)	WSuF
– 'Csabyongye' (W)	WSuF
– 'Dornfelder' (O/R)	CWSG WSuF
– 'Dunkelfelder' (O/R)	WSuF
– 'Early Van der Laan' (F)	LHol
– 'Ehrenfelser' (O/W)	WSuF
– 'Elbling' (O/W)	WSuF
– 'Excelsior' (W)	SDea WSuF
– 'Faber' (O/W)	WSuF
– 'Findling' (W)	WSuF
– 'Forta' (O/W)	WSuF
– 'Foster's Seedling' (G/W)	CBlo ERea GTwe SDea WSuF
– 'Gagarin Blue' (O/B)	ERea GTwe NPer SDea WSuF
– 'Gamay Hatif' (O/B)	ERea
– 'Gamay Hatif des Vosges'	WSuF
– 'Gamay Noir' (O/B)	WSuF
– Gamay Teinturier Group (O/B)	WSuF
– 'Gewürztraminer' (O/R)	SDea WSuF
– 'Glory of Boskoop'	See *V.* **'Boskoop Glory'**
– 'Golden Chasselas'	See *V. vinifera* **'Chasselas'**
– 'Golden Queen' (G/W)	ERea
– 'Goldriesling' (O/W)	WSuF
– 'Gros Colmar' (G/B)	ERea
– 'Gros Maroc' (G/B)	ERea
– 'Grüner Veltliner' (O/W)	WSuF
– 'Gutenborner' (O/W)	WSuF
– 'Helfensteiner' (O/R)	WSuF
– 'Huxelrebe' (O/W)	WSuF
– 'Incana' (O/B)	CPlN EPla MRav WCot WCru WPen WSHC
– 'Interlaken' (F)	ERea
– 'Jubiläumsrebe' (O/W)	WSuF
– 'Kanzler' (O/W)	WSuF
– 'Kerner' (O/W)	WSuF
– 'Kernling' (F)	WSuF
– 'King's Ruby' (F)	ERea

- 'Lady Downe's Seedling' ERea
  (G/B)
- 'Lady Hastings' (G/B)   ERea
- 'Lady Hutt' (G/W)   ERea
- 'Madeleine Angevine'   CDoC ERea GTwe NDal SDea
  (O/W)   WSuF WWeb
- 'Madeleine Royale'   ERea WSuF
  (G/W)
- 'Madeleine Silvaner'   EMui ERea GTwe LBuc MGos
  (O/W)   NPer SDea SPer WSuF
- 'Madresfield Court'   ERea GTwe WSuF
  (G/B)
- 'Malbec'   See *V. vinifera* **'Cot'**
- 'Mireille' (F)   GTwe SDea WSuF
- 'Morio Muscat' (O/W)   WSuF
- 'Mrs Pearson' (G/W)   ERea
- 'Mrs Pince's Black   ERea
  Muscat' (G/B)
§ – 'Müller-Thurgau' (O/W)   CBlo EMui ERea GChr GTwe
  LBuc MBri MGos SDea WSuF
  WWeb
- 'Muscadet'   See *V. vinifera* **'Melon de
  Bourgogne'**
- 'Muscat Blanc à Petits   WSuF
  Grains' (O/W)
- 'Muscat Bleu' (O/B)   ERea
- 'Muscat Champion'   ERea
  (G/R)
- 'Muscat de Saumur' (W)   WSuF
- 'Muscat Hamburg'   EMui ERea MGos SDea WSuF
  (G/B)
- 'Muscat of Alexandria'   CB&S CMac CRHN CSam
  (G/W)   EHol EMui ERea MWat NDal
  SPer
- 'Muscat of Hungary'   ERea
  (G/W)
- 'Muscat Ottonel' (O/W)   WSuF
- 'New York Muscat'   ERea
  (O/B)
- 'No. 69' (W)   WSuF
- 'Noir Hatif de   ERea
  Marseilles' (O/B)
- 'Oliver Irsay' (O/W)   ERea WSuF
- 'Optima' (O/W)   WSuF
- 'Ortega' (O/W)   WSuF
- 'Perle' (O/W)   WSuF
- 'Perle de Czaba'   ERea
  (G/O/W)
- 'Perlette' (O/W)   WSuF
- 'Pinot Blanc' (O/W)   WSuF
- 'Pinot Gris' (O/B)   SDea WSuF
- 'Pinot Noir' (F)   WSuF
§ – 'Portugieser' (O/B)   WSuF
- 'Précoce de Bousquet'   WSuF
  (O/W)
- 'Précoce de Malingre'   ERea SDea
  (O/W)
- 'Primavis Frontignan'   WSuF
  (G/W)
- 'Prince of Wales' (G/B)   ERea
- 'Purpurea' (O/B) ♀   Widely available
- 'Reichensteiner'   SDea WSuF
  (O/G/W)
- 'Reine Olga' (O/R)   ERea
- 'Rembrant' (R)   WSuF
- 'Riesling' (O/W)   WSuF
- Riesling-Silvaner   See *V. vinifera* **'Müller-Thurgau'**
- 'Royal Muscadine' (F)   See *V. vinifera* **'Chasselas'**
- 'Saint Laurent' (G/O/W) ERea WSuF
- 'Sauvignon Blanc'   WSuF
  (O/W)
- 'Scheurebe' (O/W)   WSuF

§ – 'Schiava Grossa' (G/B)   CMac CRHN CSam ELan ERea
  GChr GRei GTwe LBuc LHol
  MBlu MBri MGos MWat NBea
  NDal NPer NRog SPer WSuF
- 'Schönburger' (O/W)   SDea WSuF
- Seibel 138315 (R)   WSuF
- Seibel 5409 (W)   WSuF
- 'Septimer' (O/W)   WSuF
- Seyve Villard 20.473 (F)   WSuF
- 'Siegerrebe' (O/W)   EMui ERea GTwe SDea WSuF
  WWeb
- 'Silvaner' (O/W)   WSuF
- 'Spetchley Red'   WCru
- Strawberry Grape   See *V.* **'Fragola'**
§ – 'Sultana'   ERea GTwe WSuF
- 'Syrian' (G/W)   ERea
- Teinturier Group (F)   ERea
- 'Thompson Seedless'   See *V. vinifera* **'Sultana'**
- 'Trebbiano' (G/W)   ERea
- 'Wrotham Pinot' (O/B)   SDea WSuF
- 'Würzer' (O/W)   WSuF
- 'Zweigeltrebe' (O/B)   WSuF
* 'White Strawberry' (O/W) WSuF

VITTADINIA (Asteraceae)
cuneata   See *V. australis*

VRIESEA (Bromeliaceae)
carinata   MBri
hieroglyphica   MBri
× *poelmanii*   MBri
× *polonia*   MBri
saundersii ♀   MBri
splendens ♀   MBri
'Vulkana'   MBri

WACHENDORFIA (Haemodoraceae)
thyrsiflora   CFir CGre CHEx CTrC IBlr
  WCot
- Trengwainton Form   GCal

WAHLENBERGIA (Campanulaceae)
albomarginata   ECou EMan GTou NHar
  NWCA WRHF
- 'Blue Mist'   ECou
congesta   LBee
gloriosa   CPBP CSpe EHyt EPPr GCrs
  LBee MBro NHol NSla WAbe
  WFar WPat WPyg WWin
matthewsii   EPot
pumilio   See *Edraianthus pumilio*
¶ *pygmaea*   WHoo
§ *saxicola*   CLyd CRow EHyt GTou NSla
  NWCA SSca WPer
serpyllifolia   See *Edraianthus serpyllifolius*
simpsonii   GTou
species   ECou
tasmanica   See *W. saxicola*
undulata   CMdw CSpe

WALDHEIMIA See ALLARDIA

WALDSTEINIA (Rosaceae)
fragarioides   ECro NWoo WPer
geoides   EMan EPPr EPfP NPro SPer
  WLRN
ternata   Widely available
* – 'Variegata'   IBlr SApp

WALLICHIA (Arecaceae)
¶ *densiflora*   LPal

¶ *disticha* — LPal

WASABIA (Brassicaceae)
japonica — GPoy

WASHINGTONIA (Arecaceae)
filifera ♀ — CAbb CBrP CHEx CTbh CTrC LPal MBri SAPC SArc
robusta — CHEx CTrC LPal

WATSONIA (Iridaceae)
aletroides — LBow LLew SIgm
angusta — GCal IBlr LLew
ardernei — See *W. borbonica* subsp. *ardernei*
beatricis — See *W. pillansii*
§ *borbonica* — IBlr LBow LLew
§ – subsp. *ardernei* — CHan GCal IBlr LLew
– pink form — CPou
brevifolia — See *W. laccata*
bulbillifera — See *W. meriana*
coccinea — LLew
– Baker — See *W. spectabilis*
densiflora — CB&S CPou LLew
distans — LLew
fourcadei — LLew
¶ – S&SH 89 — CHan
fulgens — CHan GCal LLew MSte
¶ *galpinii* — CFir
§ *humilis* — CFil CHan WPGP
hysterantha — IBlr
§ *laccata* — LLew
¶ *lepida* — LLew
marginata — CHan CPou GCal LLew SIgm
§ *merianiae* — CHan GCal IBlr LLew WCot
* 'Mount Congreve' — SVen
§ *pillansii* — CHan CPou EBrP EBre GCal IBlr LBre SAxl SBre SMrm
pyramidata — See *W. borbonica*
roseoalba — See *W. humilis*
'Stanford Scarlet' — CPou IBlr SBla WEas WPGP WSHC
¶ *stenosiphon* — LLew
tabularis — CHan GCal IBlr LLew
'Tresco Dwarf Pink' — GCal
vanderspuyae — IBlr LLew
versfeldii — CHan
¶ *watsonioides* — LLew
wilmaniae — CPou IBlr

WATTAKAKA See DREGEA

WEIGELA † (Caprifoliaceae)
'Abel Carrière' ♀ — CTri ECtt EHic ENot EPfP MRav ECtt EHic ENot EPfP MRav ECtt WCFE
'Avalanche' hort. — See *W.* 'Candida'
'Avalanche' Lemoine — See *W. praecox* 'Avalanche'
'Boskoop Glory' — GQui MBri SPer
◆ Briant Rubidor — See *W.* Briant Rubidor = 'Olympiade'
'Bristol Ruby' — CChe ELan ENot GChr GRei LHop MBar MGos MPla MWhi NBee NNor NRoo NWea SHBN SPer SRms WDin WGwG WMow WWal WWin
§ 'Candida' — CTri EAst ELan EWes GSki MBar MBri NHol SEas SMac SPan SPer SPla WGor
'Centennial' — MGos
coraeensis — EHic IDee MBlu

Carnaval = 'Courtalor' — CBlo COtt EBee EHic GAri LPan MBri WLRN
decora — CPle GQui
'Eva Rathke' — CB&S CBlo CTri EPla ISea NWea SCoo
* 'Eva Supreme' — EHic
'Evita' — CMHG EHic IOrc MBar MGos MPla SEas SPer SPla
Feline — COtt SPer
florida — CTrw EPfP MBar MWat SMer
– f. *alba* — CB&S MBar
§ – 'Aureovariegata' — CDec CMHG CTri GQui ISea MBal SPla SRms WHCG
– 'Bicolor' — CB&S
– 'Bristol Snowflake' — CSWP EHic EPfP LHop MAsh MBar WLRN
– 'Foliis Purpureis' ♀ — Widely available
◆ – Rubigold — See *W.* Briant Rubidor = 'Olympiade'
¶ – 'Samabor' — WFar
¶ – 'Sunny Princess' — NHol WRHF
– 'Suzanne' (v) — MBri NPro WWeb
– 'Tango' — CPMA ECtt MAsh MBri NPro WBcn
'Florida Variegata' ♀ — Widely available
* *florida* 'Variegata Aurea' — See *W. florida* 'Aureovariegata'
– 'Versicolor' — CMHG GQui LHop MBel
¶ 'Gold Rush' — CBlo
'Gustave Malet' — GQui
hortensis 'Nivea' — CPle MBri
japonica — CPle
– Dart's Colourdream — EBee EBrP EBre ECtt EHal EHic EPla IOrc LBre MBel MCCP MGos MRav SBre SCoo SEas SLPl
¶ 'Java Red' — MBri
¶ 'Jean's Gold' — MGos
'Kosteriana Variegata' — CBlo EHic NHol NRoo WFar WLRN
'Looymansii Aurea' — CMHG CPle CTri EAst ELan LHop MPla MRav SEas SMac SPer SPla WAbe WDin WGwG WHCG WHar WWal WWat WWin
Lucifer — CBlo CDoC MHlr NHol WDin WLRN
¶ 'Marjorie' — WLRN
maximowiczii — CPle GOrc GQui GSki WHCG WLRN
§ *middendorffiana* — CB&S CBot CGre CMHG CPle CWit ELan EMil ENot GChr ISea LHop MBal MBar MDun MNrw MPla MWat NHol NSti SMac SPer SSpi WCwm WDin WHCG WSHC WWin
'Minuet' — CBlo CMHG EHic GSki MBar MRav NPro SBid SEas SPla WPat WShe
'Mont Blanc' ♀ — CBot MMHG SEND
Nain Rouge — CBlo COtt NHol WLRN
'Nana Variegata' — EAst EHal GChr MBar MBri NBee NHol
'Newport Red' — CBlo EBar EBee EHic ENot MRav MWat NBee NWea SMer SPla WGwG WLRN WStI WWal
§ Briant Rubidor = 'Olympiade' — EBar ECtt EHoe ENot GRei IOrc MAsh MBal MBar MBel MBri MGos MRav MWhi NFla NNor SEas SPer WBay WBod WHCG WStI WWeb
§ *praecox* 'Avalanche' — ECtt MRav WStI

– 'Espérance'	EPla
'Praecox Variegata' ♀	CMHG CTri ELan EPfP MBri SMac SPer SPla SReu SRms SSta WCru WHCG WSHC
'Red Prince'	CBlo EBee ELan MAsh MBri MGos SEas
* 'Rosabella'	EHic
◆ Rubidor	See *W.* Briant Rubidor = **'Olympiade'**
◆ Rubidor Variegata	See *W.* Briant Rubidor = **'Olympiade'**
◆ Rubigold	See *W.* Briant Rubidor = **'Olympiade'**
'Rumba'	EHic EMil GSki MMHG NPro NRoo
¶ *sessifolia splendens*	ENot
'Snowflake'	EBee ECtt EPla MPla SEas SRms WDin
sp. CC 1279	WHCr
subsessilis CC 1289	WHCr
'Victoria'	CBlo CLTr CMHG CSWP EBrP EBre ECtt ELan LBre MAsh MBel MBri NBee NRoo SBre SCoo WDin WGor WHar WLRN WWeb
* 'Wessex Gold'	CFai

WEINMANNIA (Cunoniaceae)
trichosperma	CGre CHEx IBlr ISea MAll SAPC SArc

WELDENIA (Commelinaceae)
candida	NHar SIng

WESTRINGIA (Lamiaceae)
angustifolia	ECou
brevifolia	ECou
– Raleighii Group	ECou
§ *fruticosa* ♀	CInt CPle LHil MAll SBid WJek
– 'Variegata'	CPle GQui MAll SBid WJek WLRN WSHC
– 'Wynyabbie Gem'	LHop
rosmariniformis	See *W. fruticosa*

WETTINIA (Arecaceae)
¶ *kalbreyeri*	LPal
¶ *maynensis*	LPal
¶ *quinaria*	LPal

WIDDRINGTONIA (Cupressaceae)
cedarbergensis	IBlr
cupressoides	See *W. nodiflora*
§ *nodiflora*	IBlr MBri
schwarzii	CTrC
whytei	See *W. nodiflora*

WIGANDIA (Hydrophyllaceae)
urens	CHEx

WIKSTROEMIA (Thymelaeaceae)
¶ *nutans* B&SWJ 4081	WCru

WISTERIA † (Papilionaceae)
* 'Captain Fuji'	CMCN SPla
'Caroline'	CB&S CEnd CMCN CPMA CSam ERea GChr GOrc LNet MGos MMea SPer SPla SReu SSpi SSta
¶ 'Consequa'	SBra

floribunda	CB&S CRHN ELan MAsh SHBN WDin WNor
§ – 'Alba' ♀	CB&S CBot CDoC CEnd CPMA EBrP EBre ELan GChr LBre LNet LPan MAsh NEgg NHol SBra SBre SHBN SPer SSpi SSta WDin WStI
– 'Burford'	CBlo CEnd CTri EBee MAsh MBri MMea MWat NHol WHar WWeb
– 'Fragrantissima'	CBlo
* – 'Harlequin'	LRHS MGos
– 'Hichirimen'	EBee LNet MMea
– 'Honko'	See *W. floribunda* **'Rosea'**
– Jakohn-fuji	See *W. floribunda* **'Reindeer'**
§ – 'Kuchi-beni'	CB&S CPMA EBee ELan EPfP LNet MGos MMea SBra SPer WWeb
* – 'Lavender Lace'	CPMA EPfP
– 'Lipstick'	See *W. floribunda* **'Kuchi-beni'**
– 'Longissima Alba'	EBee LPan MBar MGos
– 'Macrobotrys'	See *W. floribunda* **'Multijuga'**
§ – 'Multijuga' ♀	CDoC CEnd CPMA ELan GOrc IOrc LNet LPan MBri MGos MMea MWat NHol SBra SMad SPer SPla SSoC SSpi SSta WSHC WWat WWeb
– Murasaki-naga	See *W. floribunda* **'Purple Patches'**
– 'Murasaki-noda'	MGos
– 'Nana Richin's Purple'	LNet
– 'Peaches and Cream'	See *W. floribunda* **'Kuchi-beni'**
– 'Pink Ice'	See *W. floribunda* **'Rosea'**
§ – 'Purple Patches'	CPMA ELan LNet MGos MMea MWat NPri SPer WWeb
* – 'Purple Tassle'	LNet
§ – 'Reindeer'	NHol WWeb
§ – 'Rosea' ♀	CB&S CEnd CMac CPMA EBrP EBre ELan ENot EPfP IOrc LBre LNet MAsh MBar MBri MGos MMea MWat NHol SBra SBre SHBN SPer WStI WWat WWeb
– 'Royal Purple'	CBlo ERea MMea WGor
– Shiro-nagi	See *W. floribunda* **'Snow Showers'**
§ – 'Snow Showers'	CHad CPMA ELan EPfP IHos LNet MBri MGos MMea NPri SPer SPla WGer WGor WWeb
* – 'Variegata'	CPMA
≙ – 'Violacea Plena' (d)	CBlo EBee MBri MGos MMea NPal SHBN SPar
floridunda 'Honbeni'	See *W. floribunda* **'Rosea'**
× *formosa*	CPMA ETen WFro WWat
– Black Dragon	See *W.* × *formosa* **'Kokuryû'**
– Domino	See *W.* × *formosa* **'Issai'**
§ – 'Issai'	CB&S CBlo CEnd CHad CPMA EBee LNet MBar MGos MMea NEgg NHol NSti SBra SPla WWat WWeb
§ – 'Kokuryû' (d)	CB&S CDoC CEnd CPMA ELan EPfP GChr IOrc LNet MAsh MGos MMea NHol SBra SHBN SMad SPer SPla SReu SSpi SSta WGor WPyg WWat WWeb
frutescens	WNor
– 'Nivea'	CMCN
¶ 'Jako'	SBra
* 'Kofuji'	LNet
multijuga 'Alba'	See *W. floribunda* **'Alba'**
¶ 'Shironoda'	SBra

'Showa-beni'	LNet
sinensis ♀	Widely available
§ – 'Alba' ♀	CB&S CBlo ELan ENot EPfP IOrc ISea LNet LPan MBar MMea MWat SSto WDin
– 'Amethyst'	CPMA EPfP ERea SBra SPla
– 'Blue Sapphire'	CPMA
– 'Plena' (d)	CPMA
– 'Prematura'	MAsh NHol WSHC
– 'Prolific'	CDoC CPMA CPlN EBee ELan EPfP LBuc LPan MBri MGos MMea SBra SPer SPla SSpi SSto
* – 'Rosea'	LPan
– Shiro-capital	See *W. sinensis* **'Alba'**
venusta	CEnd CPMA CTri ELan ENot EPfP LNet MAsh MBri MGos MMea NHol SBra SHBN SMad SPer WWat
– *purpurea*	See *W. venusta* var. *violacea*
§ – var. *violacea*	CEnd
* – 'Violacea Plena'	LRHS
* – 'White Silk'	CPMA

WITHANIA (Solanaceae)
somnifera	CArn GPoy

WITTSTEINIA (Alseuosmiaceae)
vacciniacea	MAll WCru

WODYETIA (Arecaceae)
¶ *bifurcata*	LPal

WOODSIA (Aspidiaceae)
fragilis	EMon
intermedia	NBro
obtusa	EBee GMaP NHar NHol WAbe WRic
polystichoides ♀	EMon GQui NHar

WOODWARDIA † (Blechnaceae)
fimbriata	NHol SPer
martinezii	CFil
orientalis var. *formosana*	NMar
radicans ♀	CAbb CFil CGre CHEx GQui ISea LBlm NMar SAPC SArc SMad WAbe
unigemmata	NWoo WAbe

WULFENIA (Scrophulariaceae)
carinthiaca	CNic GAbr MBro MHig MRav NBir NMen

WYETHIA (Asteraceae)
helianthoides	EMan

× LEUCORAOULIA (Asteraceae)
§ x *Leucoraoulia* hybrid (*Raoulia hectorii* × *Leucogenes grandiceps*)	EPot GTou MHig NSla SIng

XANTHOCERAS (Sapindaceae)
sorbifolium ♀	CAbb CAgr CB&S CBlo CBot CFil CLnd CMCN ELan MTis MWhi SBid SIgm SMad SWhi WCoo WDin WLRN WNor WPGP WWat

XANTHOPHTHALMUM (Asteraceae)
¶ *coronarium*	CArn EEls WJek
segetum	EWFC MHew WHer WOak

XANTHORHIZA (Ranunculaceae)
simplicissima	CFil CRow EPfP GCal SDys SPer SSpi WIvy WThi WWat

XANTHORRHOEA (Xanthorrhoeaceae)
australis	CTrC SMad WGer
preisii	LPan

XANTHOSOMA (Araceae)
lindenii	See *Caladium lindenii*
sagittifolium	CHEx
¶ *violaceum*	LHil WMul

XERODRABA (Brassicaceae)
¶ *mendocinensis*	ITim

XERONEMA (Phormiaceae)
callistemon	ECou

XEROPHYLLUM (Melanthiaceae) See Plant Deletions

XYLORHIZA See MACHAERANTHERA

XYLOSMA (Flacourtiaceae)
quichensis	CPle

YPSILANDRA (Liliaceae)
¶ *thibetica*	WCru

YUCCA † (Agavaceae)
aloifolia	CHEx CTrC SAPC SArc SIgm
– 'Variegata'	CHEx LPal LPan SAPC SArc
angustifolia	See *Y. glauca*
angustissima	CTbh
arizonica	CTbh
baccata	CHEx CTbh
brevifolia	CFil
carnerosana	CTbh
elata	CTbh
§ *elephantipes* ♀	CHEx MBri
¶ *faxoniana*	EOas
¶ – × *glauca*	CHEx
filamentosa ♀	Widely available
– 'Bright Edge' (v) ♀	CB&S CDoC CHEx CMHG CTrC EBrP EBre ECtt ELan ENot EPla GChr IHos IOrc LBre LPan MAsh MBri MGos MTis MUlv MWat SArc SBre SHBN SPer WAbe WMow WStI WWin
– 'Variegata' ♀	CB&S CBot EBrP EBre ELan ENot IOrc LBre LHop MBal MGos SAga SBre SPer SRms WDin WFar WStI
flaccida	MAsh MAus NBee NFla SDix SPar
– 'Golden Sword' (v) ♀	CAbb CDoC CMHG CTrC EBrP EBre ELan GChr IHos IOrc LBre LHop MAsh MBal MBri MHlr MSCN NCut NPSI SBre SCoo SPer SPla WAbe WBay WMow
– 'Ivory' ♀	CB&S CDoC CEnd CHEx CTrC ECtt ELan ENot GAbr GCal GMaP IOrc MAsh MBri MRav NPSI SEas SMad SPer SPla SRms SSoC SSta STre WPic WWeb WWin
× *floribunda*	SAPC SArc

'Garland's Gold' (v)	CDoC CHEx COtt ELan GQui MAsh MBri MGos SMad
§ *glauca*	CB&S CBrP CHEx CMHG CTbh CTrC EHic GCal NCut SAPC SArc
gloriosa ♀	CB&S CDoC CHEx ENot EPla LNet LPan NFla NPal SAPC SArc SHBN SMad SPer SSpi WBrE WStI
– 'Aureovariegata'	See *Y. gloriosa* **'Variegata'**
– 'Nobilis'	SDix
§ – 'Variegata' ♀	CBot CDoC CHEx EBrP EBre ELan ENot LBre MRav NPal SAPC SArc SBre SCro SDry SEas SHBN SRms SSto WCot WPat WWeb
guatemalensis	See *Y. elephantipes*
harrimaniae	CTbh SIgm
kanabensis	CTbh
neomexicana	CTbh
recurvifolia ♀	CB&S CHEx MBal SAPC SArc
rigida	CBrP
rostrata	CBrP CHEx SAPC SArc
schidigera	CTbh
schottii	CBrP CTbh EOas
thompsoniana	CTbh
¶ *toftiae* JCA 1993500	EMon
* *torcelli*	CTbh
torreyi	CTbh EOas SLMG
'Vittorio Emanuele II'	SAPC SArc SMad
whipplei	CAbb CBot CBrP CDoC CFil CHEx CTrC EOas GCra SAPC SArc SLMG SMad SSpi
¶ – subsp. *caespitosa* JCA 1993600	EMon
– var. *parishii*	SIgm

YUSHANIA (Poaceae - Bambusoideae)

§ *anceps* ♀	CDoC CFil CHEx CHad EFul EPla GAri IOrc ISta LJus MBri MGos MMoz NBee SAPC SArc SCha SDry SMad SPer SPla WCru WPGP
§ – 'Pitt White'	EOas EPla SDry WJun
¶ *chungii*	WPGP
maculata	EPla ISta SDry WJun
§ *maling*	EPla ISta SDry WJun

ZALUZIANSKYA (Scrophulariaceae)

'Katherine'	EBee GCal MTPN SIng WPen
ovata	CPBP EHyt EPot EWes GCal LHop LSpr MAvo MTho NBir NWCA SAga SBla SHFr WAbe WLRN WOve WPat
* cf. *rostrata* DBG 219	NTow
¶ sp. JCA 15665	EHyt
¶ sp. JCA 15758	IDac

ZAMIA (Zamiaceae)

floridana	LPal
furfuracea	CBrP LPal
¶ *integrifolia*	CBrP
¶ *muricata*	LPal
¶ *skinneri*	LPal
¶ *vazquezii*	CBrP

ZAMIOCULCAS (Araceae) See Plant Deletions

ZANTEDESCHIA (Araceae)

§ *aethiopica* ♀	CBen CHEx CMHG CTrC CWat EHon EOas EWes ISea LAma LCns LPBA MBro MNrw MSta NDea NOrc NRog SDix SSoC SSpi SWat WBrE WChe WEas WFar WPic WWal
– 'Apple Court Babe'	CRow SApp
¶ – 'Childsiana'	SApp
– 'Crowborough' ♀	Widely available
– 'Gigantea'	SLMG
– 'Green Goddess' ♀	CB&S CBro CDec CFir CHEx CHan CMon COtt CRow CTrC EBee ECha EGar ELan EMFW GCra GQui LPBA MHlr NPSI SDeJ SPar SRms SSoC SUsu WCot WFib WWat
– 'Little Gem'	ECha
* – 'Pershore Fantasia'	WSPU
– 'Snow White'	CDec
– 'White Sail'	CRow GCal MTed WFib
albomaculata	CMon CTrC LAma NPSI NRog
– S&SH 35	CHan
¶ 'Apricot'	WViv
'Best Gold'	LAma
'Black Eyed Beauty'	CBro LAma NRog WWeb
'Black Magic'	CHEx LAma WViv WWeb
'Bridal Blush'	LAma
'Cameo'	LAma
elliottiana ♀	CB&S CFir CHal CSut GQui LAma NRog SLMG
¶ 'Galaxy'	WViv
'Harvest Moon'	CWit LAma
'Helen O'Connor'	SLMG
¶ 'Kiwi Blush'	CFir CMil CRow EBee NPSI SSpi SVil WSan
'Lavender Petite'	LAma NRog
* 'Little Suzy'	WViv
'Majestic Red'	WWeb
'Mango'	EBrP EBre LBre SBre
'Maroon Dainty'	LAma NRog
'Pacific Pink'	LAma
pentlandii	See *Z. angustiloba*
'Pink Persuasion'	WWeb
rehmannii ♀	CB&S CBlo CMon GQui LAma SRms WViv
* – *alba*	CBlo SLMG
* – *superba*	SLMG
* 'Romeo'	SLMG
'Ruby'	WWeb
'Shell Pink'	CBlo LAma NRog
'Solfatare'	CBlo LAma
* 'Sweet Suzie'	EBrP EBre LBre SBre
'Treasure'	WWeb

ZANTHORHIZA See XANTHORHIZA

ZANTHOXYLUM (Rutaceae)

americanum	CFil CLnd WPGP
¶ *armatus*	CFil WPGP
coreanum	CFil WPGP
oxyphyllum	CFil WPGP
piperitum	CAgr CFil
planispinum	MRav
simulans	CB&S WCoo

ZAUSCHNERIA (Onagraceae)

arizonica	See *Z. californica* subsp. *latifolia*
§ *californica*	CGen GQui MAll
– 'Albiflora'	EPot

§ – subsp. *cana*	CLTr CSam ECGP ECha ELan IOrc MHar MPla SAga SChu SIgm SUsu WCru WEas
– – 'Sir Cedric Morris'	ELan
– 'Clover Dale'	CMHG LGre
– 'Dublin' ♀	ECha EFou ELan EPot ERea LHop MBel MBro MFos MHar MHig MPla MWat SBla SChu SIng WAbe WEas WHer WHil WHoo WOld WPat WSHC WWat WWin
§ – subsp. *garrettii*	LHop NWCA
– 'Glasnevin'	See *Z. californica* **'Dublin'**
§ – subsp. *latifolia*	CPle LHop MBro NMen SAga SIgm WHoo
§ – subsp. *mexicana*	CLyd EPot SRms WAbe
– 'Olbrich Silver'	LGre LHop MSCN NWCA WAbe WCot WCru
– 'Sierra Salmon'	LGre
– 'Solidarity Pink'	CLTr ELan MTho SAga
¶ – var. *villosa*	IDac
– 'Western Hills'	CFir EBee LGre LHop NWCA SAga SBla SIgm SIng SUsu WAbe WPGP
cana subsp. *garrettii*	SIgm
– *villosa*	See *Z. californica* subsp. *mexicana*
* *septentrionalis*	SIgm

ZEBRINA See TRADESCANTIA

ZELKOVA † (Ulmaceae)

¶ *abelicea*	CTho
carpinifolia	CLnd CMCN CTho LRHS WNor WWoo
hyrcana	SBir
schneideriana	CMCN WWoo
serrata ♀	CB&S CBlo CDoC CLnd CMCN CTho ELan EMil GChr IOrc ISea MBal MBar NPal NWea SBir SPer SSpi STre WDin WFro WMou WNor WWat
– 'Goblin'	MBro NHol SSta WPat
– 'Nira'	WWes
– 'Variegata'	CPMA MBlu MGos SSta WBcn
– 'Yatsubusa'	STre
– 'Yrban Ruby'	MGos SSta
sinica	CDoC CLnd CMCN GAri SSpi STre WNor
× *verschaffeltii*	GAri

ZENOBIA (Ericaceae)

pulverulenta	CAbP CB&S CGre CTrG ELan GOrc GQui IOrc MBal MBar MBlu MBri MBro MUlv NHol SBrw SHBN SPer SReu SSpi SSta WDin WNor WPGP WPat WPyg WSHC WWat
– f. *nitida*	SSta

ZEPHYRANTHES (Amaryllidaceae)

candida	CAvo CBro EMan ERea ERos ITim LAma LHop NMen NRog SApp SDeJ SDix WCot WFox
citrina	LAma NMen NRog
drummondii	WCot
flavissima	CBro WCot
× *lancasterae*	CMon
robusta	See *Habranthus robustus*
rosea	LAma
sulphurea	LAma

ZIERIA (Rutaceae) See Plant Deletions

ZIGADENUS (Melanthiaceae)

elegans	ECha EHyt EMan EPar GCrs LGre MBro NDov NHol NWCA SMad SSpi WHoo WPyg
¶ *fremontii*	EBee WLin
nuttallii	CLyd EMan LBee LGre MSte NHol WCot
venenosus	CHan EBee

ZINGIBER (Zingiberaceae)

officinale	MSal NHex

ZINNIA (Asteraceae) See Plant Deletions

ZIZANIA (Poaceae)

caducifolia	See *Z. latifolia*
§ *latifolia*	MSta

ZIZIA (Apiaceae)

aurea	EBee

ZIZIPHUS (Rhamnaceae)

§ *jujuba* (F)	CAgr LPan
¶ – 'Lang' (F)	LHol
¶ – 'Li' (F)	LHol
sativa	See *Z. jujuba*

Nursery-Code Index

Nurseries that are included in **THE RHS PLANT FINDER** for the first time this year (or have been reintroduced) are marked in **Bold Type.**
Full details of the nurseries with a four letter Code will be found in the **Code-Nursery** Index on page 739.
Nurseries with a number are detailed in the **Additional Nursery** Index on page 842.
Nurseries marked **SEED, SUCC** or **ORCH** are listed in the **Seed Suppliers, Cactus & Succulent** or **Orchid Specialist Index**

Note: the first letter of each nursery Code indicates the main area of the country in which the nursery is situated, as follows: **C** = South West England, **E** = Eastern England, **G** = Scotland, **I** = Northern Ireland & Republic of Ireland, **L** = London area, **M** = Midlands, **N** = Northern England, **S** = Southern England, **W** = Wales & Western England, **X** = Abroad. For further details refer to page 8.

39 Steps	**WThi**	**Balmer Grove Plants**	**118**
A La Carte Daylilies	**SDay**	T H Barker & Sons	**NBrk**
Abbey Dore Court Gardens	**WAbb**	Barncroft Nurseries	**MBar**
Abbey Plants	**CAbP**	Barnsdale Gardens	**EBar**
Abbotsbury Sub-Tropical Gardens	**CAbb**	Barters Farm Nurseries Ltd	**CBar**
Aberconwy Nursery	**WAbe**	Barwinnock Herbs	**GBar**
Abriachan Nurseries	**GAbr**	Battersby Roses	**NBat**
Acton Beauchamp Roses	**WAct**	**Bay Tree Cottage Plants**	**LBay**
Agar's Nursery	**SAga**	**Bayleys Garden Centre**	**WBay**
Agroforestry Research Trust	**CAgr**	Beacons' Botanicals	**WBea**
Agroforestry Research Trust	**SEED**	Beacon's Nurseries	**WBcn**
Alderton Plant Nursery	**MAld**	Peter Beales Roses	**EBls**
Paul Allanson	**MAll**	Beamish Clematis Nursery	**NBea**
Allwood Bros	**SAll**	Beechcroft Nurseries	**NBee**
Allwood Bros	**SEED**	Beechcroft Nursery	**LBee**
Alternatives	**WAlt**	Beeches Nursery	**EBee**
Jacques Amand Ltd	**LAma**	**Bees of Chester**	**SEED**
Anders Nursery	**EAnd**	Bellhouse Nursery	**MBel**
Apple Court	**SApp**	Bennett's Water Lily Farm	**CBen**
Apuldram Roses	**SApu**	**Betwys-Y-Coed Garden Nursery**	**116**
Arcadia Nurseries Ltd	**NArc**	Biddenden Nursery at Garden Crafts	**SBid**
Anthony Archer-Wills Ltd	**SAWi**	Binny Plants	**GBin**
Architectural Plants	**SArc**	Birchfleet Nursery	**SBir**
Architectural Plants (Chichester) Ltd	**SAPC**	Birchwood Farm Nursery	**33**
Arivegaig Nursery	**GAri**	Birkheads Cottage Garden Nursery	**NBir**
Arley Hall Nursery	**MArl**	Blackmore & Langdon Ltd	**CBla**
Arne Herbs	**CArn**	Blackmore & Langdon Ltd	**SEED**
Ashenden Nursery	**SAsh**	**Blacksmiths Cottage Nursery**	**119**
Ashfield Court Nurseries	**CAsh**	Blackthorn Nursery	**SBla**
Ashwood Nurseries Ltd	**MAsh**	Terence Bloch - Plantsman	**LBlo**
Ashwood Nurseries	**SEED**	Bloomsbury	**LBlm**
Askew's Nursery	**MAsk**	Blounts Court Nurseries	**CBlo**
Asterby Nurseries	**EAst**	Bluebell Nursery	**MBlu**
Aultan Nursery	**130**	R J Blythe	**EBly**
David Austin Roses Ltd	**MAus**	Bodiam Nursery	**SBod**
Avon Bulbs	**CAvo**	Bodmin Plant and Herb Nursery	**CBod**
Avondale Nursery	**MAvo**	Bodnant Garden Nursery Ltd	**WBod**
Axe Valley Penstemons	**CAxe**	S & E Bond	**WBon**
Axletree Nursery	**SAxl**	Bonhard Nursery	**GBon**
Aylett Nurseries Ltd	**LAyl**	**Bordervale Plants**	**WBor**
B & T World Seeds	**SEED**	Bosvigo Plants	**CBos**
Steven Bailey Ltd	**SBai**	The Botanic Nursery	**CBot**
B & H M Baker	**EBak**	**Botanicus**	**EBot**
Ballagan Nursery	**3**	Bouts Cottage Nurseries	**WBou**
Ballalheannagh Gardens	**MBal**	Ann & Roger Bowden	**CBdn**
Ballydorn Bulb Farm	**IBal**	Rupert Bowlby	**LBow**
Ballyrogan Nurseries	**IBlr**	S & N Brackley	**SEED**

Granby Gardens	**MGrG**	Hill Farmhouse Plants	**MHFP**
Grange Farm Nursery	**32**	The Hiller Garden	**MHlr**
Grange Cottage Herbs	**MGra**	Hillside Cottage Plants	**CHil**
Grasmere Plants	**EGra**	Hillview Hardy Plants	**WHil**
Peter Grayson (Sweet Pea Seedsman)	**SEED**	Hoecroft Plants	**EHoe**
Great Dixter Nurseries	**SDix**	Hofflands Daffodils	**EHof**
Green Farm Plants	**LGre**	Holden Clough Nursery	**NHol**
Greenhead Roses	**GGre**	**Holkham Gardens**	**EHol**
Greenslacks Nurseries	**NGre**	Hollington Nurseries	**LHol**
Greenway Gardens	**CGre**	Holly Gate Cactus Nursery	**SUCC**
Greenwood Plants	**SGre**	Holly Gate Cactus Nursery	**SEED**
C W Groves & Son	**CGro**	Honeysome Aquatic Nursery	**EHon**
Growing Carpets	**LGro**	**Honeymyrtles & Paperbarks**	**CHon**
Gwydir Plants	**WGwy**	Hoo House Nursery	**WHoo**
Gwynfor Growers	**WGwG**	Hopleys Plants Ltd	**LHop**
Hadspen Garden & Nursery	**CHad**	Horton Vale Nursery	**CHor**
Hall Farm Nursery	**EHal**	Hosford's Geraniums & Garden Centre	**IHos**
Hall Farm Nursery	**WHal**	The Hosta Garden	**LHos**
Halls of Heddon	**NHal**	How Caple Court Gardens	**WHow**
Halsway Nursery	**CHal**	Diana Hull	**MHul**
Hanging Gardens Nurseries Ltd	**122**	Diana Hull	**SEED**
The Hannays of Bath	**CHan**	Hull Farm	**EHul**
Hardstoft Herb Garden	**NHHG**	Hunts Court Garden & Nursery	**WHCG**
Hardy Exotics	**CHEx**	Brenda Hyatt	**SHya**
Hardy Orchids Ltd	**ORCH**	Hydon Nurseries	**LHyd**
Hardy's Cottage Garden Plants	**SHar**	Hyrons Trees	**LHyr**
Harley Nursery	**WHar**	Hythe Alpines	**EHyt**
Harlow Garden Centre	**EHGC**	Iden Croft Herbs	**SIde**
Harry Byrne's Garden Centre	**IHar**	Iden Croft Herbs	**SEED**
Sue Hartfree	**SHFr**	Tim Ingram	**SIgm**
Harts Green Nursery	**MHar**	W E Th. Ingwersen Ltd	**SIng**
Hartside Nursery Garden	**NHar**	W E Th. Ingwersen Ltd	**SEED**
Harvest Nurseries	**SUCC**	Intakes Farm	**MInt**
Harvest Nurseries	**SEED**	International Animal Rescue Nursery	**CInt**
The Hawthornes Nursery	**NHaw**	The Iris Garden	**LIri**
Hayward's Carnations	**SHay**	**Iverna Herbs**	**IIve**
Heather Bank Nursery	**CHea**	Ivycroft Plants	**WIvy**
Hedgerow Nursery	**NHed**	Jackson's Nurseries	**MJac**
Heldon Nurseries	**MHel**	Jasmine Cottage Gardens	**2**
Heldon Nurseries	**SUCC**	**Jasmine Cottage Gardens**	**SEED**
Hellyer's Garden Plants	**SHel**	Paul Jasper - Fruit & Ornamental Trees	**WJas**
James Henderson & Sons	**SEED**	Jekka's Herb Farm	**WJek**
Henllys Lodge Plants	**WHen**	Jekka's Herb Farm	**SEED**
Henllys Lodge Plants	**SEED**	Jean Jewels	**CJew**
The Herb Garden & Historical Plant	**WHer**	C & K Jones	**MJon**
Nursery		Judy's Country Garden	**EJud**
Hergest Croft Gardens	**WHCr**	Jungle Giants	**WJun**
Herterton House Garden Nursery	**36**	**Just Bamboo Ltd**	**LJus**
Hewthorn Herbs & Wild Flowers	**MHew**	Just Phlomis	**WPhl**
Hexham Herbs	**NHex**	Just Roses	**SJus**
Hickling Heath Nursery	**EHic**	Kayes Garden Nursery	**63**
Hidden Valley Nursery,	**CHid**	Keepers Nursery	**SKee**
High Banks Nurseries	**SHBN**	Kelways Ltd	**CKel**
The High Garden	**CHig**	Kent Cacti	**SUCC**
Highcroft Nursery	**GHCN**	Kent Street Nurseries	**SKen**
Highdown Nursery	**SHDw**	Kenwith Nursery (Gordon Haddow)	**CKen**
Highfield Hollies	**SHHo**	Kiftsgate Court Gardens	**WKif**
Highgates Nursery	**MHig**	Kingfisher Nurseries	**10**
Brian Hiley	**LHil**	Kingsfield Conservation Nursery	**CKin**

Code-Nursery Index

Please note that all these nurseries are listed in alphabetical order of their Codes. All nurseries are listed in alphabetical order of their name in the **Nursery-Code Index** on page 731.
Addresses printed in **bold type** provide a Mail Order Service to the EU.
For a description of the headings used, refer to the section 'Supporting Information about Nurseries' on page 11.

CAbb **Abbotsbury Sub-Tropical Gardens, Abbotsbury, Nr Weymouth, Dorset, DT3 4LA**

TEL: (01305) 871344/412 *FAX:* (01305) 871344 *CONTACT:* David Sutton
OPENING TIMES: 1000-1800 daily mid Mar-1st Nov. 1000-1500 Nov-mid Mar.
MIN. MAIL ORDER UK: £10.00 + p&p *MIN. VALUE EC:* £20.00 + p&p
CAT. COST: £2 + A4 Sae + 42p stamp *W/SALE or RETAIL:* Retail *CREDIT CARDS:* not for telephone orders
SPECIALITIES: Less common & tender Shrubs. *MAP PAGE:* 2

CAbP **Abbey Plants,** Chaffeymoor, Bourton, Gillingham, Dorset, SP8 5BY

TEL: (01747) 840841 *CONTACT:* K Potts
OPENING TIMES: 1000-1300 & 1400-1700 Tue-Sat Mar-Nov. Dec-Feb by appt.
No mail order
CAT. COST: 2 x 2nd class *W/SALE or RETAIL:* Retail *CREDIT CARDS:* none
SPECIALITIES: Flowering Trees & Shrubs. Shrub Roses incl. many unusual varieties.
MAP PAGE: **2**

CAgr **Agroforestry Research Trust,** 46 Hunters Moon, Dartington, Totnes, Devon, TQ9 6JT

TEL: *E-MAIL:* agrorestr@aol.com *CONTACT:* Martin Crawford
OPENING TIMES: Not open - Mail Order only.
MIN. MAIL ORDER UK: No minimum charge *MIN. VALUE EC:*
CAT. COST: 3 x 1st class *W/SALE or RETAIL:* Retail *CREDIT CARDS:* None
SPECIALITIES: Mostly Trees, some Perennials, Alnus, Berberis, Citrus, Eucalyptus, Juglans & Salix. See also SEED Index.

CArn **Arne Herbs, Limeburn Nurseries, Limeburn Hill, Chew Magna, Avon, BS40 8QW**

TEL: (01275) 333399 *FAX:* (01275) 333399 *CONTACT:* A Lyman-Dixon & Jenny Thomas
OPENING TIMES: Most times - please check first.
MIN. MAIL ORDER UK: No minimum charge *MIN. VALUE EC:* Nmc   *EXPORT:* Yes
CAT. COST: £2.00 UK, 6 x IRC *W/SALE or RETAIL:* Both *CREDIT CARDS:* None
SPECIALITIES: Herbs, Wild Flowers & Cottage Flowers. *MAP PAGE:* 2

CAsh **Ashfield Court Nurseries, Farringdon, North Petherton, Somerset, TA6 6PF**

TEL: (01278) 663438 *FAX:* (01278) 663438 *CONTACT:* Michael Michieli
OPENING TIMES: By appt. - Shows.
MIN. MAIL ORDER UK: No minimum charge *MIN. VALUE EC:* Nmc   *EXPORT:* Yes
CAT. COST: 2 x 1st class *W/SALE or RETAIL:* Retail *CREDIT CARDS:* none
SPECIALITIES: Verbena. *MAP PAGE:* 1/2

CAvo **Avon Bulbs, Burnt House Farm, Mid-Lambrook, South Petherton, Somerset, TA13 5HE**

TEL: (01460) 242177 *CONTACT:* C Ireland-Jones
OPENING TIMES: Thu, Fri, Sat mid Sep-end Oct & mid Feb-end Mar for collection of pre-booked orders.
MIN. MAIL ORDER UK: £10.00 + p&p *MIN. VALUE EC:* £20.00 + p&p   *EXPORT:* Yes
CAT. COST: 4 x 2nd class *W/SALE or RETAIL:* Retail *CREDIT CARDS:* Visa, Access
SPECIALITIES: Smaller & unusual Bulbs. *MAP PAGE:* 1/2

CAxe **Axe Valley Penstemons,** Blue Firs, Wessiters, Seaton, Devon, EX12 2PJ

TEL: (01297) 625342 *FAX:* (01297) 24085 *CONTACT:* Mrs S K Reynolds
OPENING TIMES: 1400-1700 Thurs mid April-mid Sept. Other times by appt.
No mail order
CAT. COST: Free plant list *W/SALE or RETAIL:* Retail *CREDIT CARDS:* None
SPECIALITIES: Penstemons *MAP PAGE:* 1/2

◆ **See also Display Advertisements**

CB&S **Burncoose & South Down Nurseries, Gwennap, Redruth, Cornwall, TR16 6BJ**
TEL: (01209) 861112 *FAX:* (01209) 860011 *WEB SITE:* http://www.eclipse.co.uk/burncoose
CONTACT: C H Williams & D Knuckey NDH
OPENING TIMES: 0800-1700 Mon-Sat & 1100-1700 Sun.
MIN. MAIL ORDER UK: No minimum charge *MIN. VALUE EC:* Nmc*   *EXPORT:* Yes
CAT. COST: £1.00 inc p&p *W/SALE or RETAIL:* Both *CREDIT CARDS:* Visa, Access, AmEx, Switch
SPECIALITIES: Extensive range of over 2500 Ornamental Trees & Shrubs and Herbaceous. 30 acre garden. *NOTE: Individual quotations for EC sales. *MAP PAGE:* 1

CBar **Barters Farm Nurseries Ltd,** Chapmanslade, Westbury, Wiltshire, BA13 4AL
TEL: (01373) 832694 *FAX:* (01373) 832677 *CONTACT:* D Travers
OPENING TIMES: 0900-1700 Mon-Sat & 1000-1700 Sun & Bank Hols.
No mail order
CAT. COST: A4 Sae *W/SALE or RETAIL:* Both *CREDIT CARDS:* Visa, Switch
SPECIALITIES: Wide range of Shrubs. Ground Cover, Patio plants, container & open-ground Trees. Ferns, half-hardy Perennials, Grasses & Herbaceous. *MAP PAGE:* 2

CBdn **Ann & Roger Bowden, Cleave House, Sticklepath, Okehampton, Devon, EX20 2NL**
TEL: (01837) 840481 *FAX:* (01837) 840482 *CONTACT:* Ann & Roger Bowden
♦ *OPENING TIMES:* Appt. only.
MIN. MAIL ORDER UK: No minimum charge *MIN. VALUE EC:* Nmc   *EXPORT:* Yes
CAT. COST: 3 x 1st class *W/SALE or RETAIL:* Retail *CREDIT CARDS:* Visa, Access, EuroCard
SPECIALITIES: Hosta only. *MAP PAGE:* 1

CBen **Bennett's Water Lily Farm,** Putton Lane, Chickerell, Weymouth, Dorset, DT3 4AF
TEL: (01305) 785150 *FAX:* (01305) 781619 *CONTACT:* J Bennett
OPENING TIMES: Tue-Sun Apr-Aug, Tue-Sat Sep, Oct & Mar.
No mail order
CAT. COST: None issued *W/SALE or RETAIL:* Both *CREDIT CARDS:* Visa, Access
SPECIALITIES: Aquatic plants. NCCPG Collection of Water Lilies. *MAP PAGE:* 2

CBla **Blackmore & Langdon Ltd, Pensford, Bristol, Avon, BS39 4JL**
TEL: (01275) 332300 *FAX:* (01275) 332300 *CONTACT:* J S Langdon
OPENING TIMES: 0900-1700 Mon-Sat, 1000-1600 Sun.
MIN. MAIL ORDER UK: No minimum charge *MIN. VALUE EC:* Nmc   *EXPORT:* Yes
CAT. COST: Sae *W/SALE or RETAIL:* Retail *CREDIT CARDS:* None
SPECIALITIES: Phlox, Delphinium & Begonias. See also SEED Index. *MAP PAGE:* 2

CBlo **Blounts Court Nurseries,** Studley, Calne, Wiltshire, SN11 9NH
TEL: (01249) 812103 *FAX:* (01249) 812103 *CONTACT:* Mrs P E Rendell & Mr S N Fox
OPENING TIMES: 1030-1630 Sun, 0900-1700 Nov-Feb, 0900-1800 Apr-Jul, 0900-1730 Mon, Tue, Fri & Sat Aug-Oct.
No mail order
CAT. COST: 2 x 1st or 2nd class *W/SALE or RETAIL:* Retail *CREDIT CARDS:* Visa, Access, Switch
SPECIALITIES: Wide range of Shrubs, Fruit & Ornamental Trees, Conifers, Roses, container & open ground. Clematis, Climbers, Herbaceous, incl. unusual varieties. *MAP PAGE:* 2

CBod **Bodmin Plant and Herb Nursery,** Laveddon Mill, Laninval Hill, Bodmin, Cornwall, PL30 5JU
TEL: (01208) 72837 *FAX:* (01208) 76491 *CONTACT:* Sarah Wilks
OPENING TIMES: 0900-1800 (or dusk if earlier) daily.
No mail order
CAT. COST: 2 x 1st class for herb list. *W/SALE or RETAIL:* Both *CREDIT CARDS:* MasterCard, Visa
SPECIALITIES: Herbs, & good range of Shrubs & Herbaceous Plants. *MAP PAGE:* 1

Nursery ADDRESSES in BOLD do Mail Order to EU

CBos   Bosvigo Plants, Bosvigo House, Bosvigo Lane, Truro, Cornwall, TR1 3NH
TEL: (01872) 275774 *FAX:* (01872) 275774 *CONTACT:* Wendy Perry
OPENING TIMES: 1100-1800 Wed-Sat Mar-end Sep.
No mail order
CAT. COST: 4 x 2nd class *W/SALE or RETAIL:* Retail *CREDIT CARDS:* None
SPECIALITIES: Rare & unusual Herbaceous. *MAP PAGE:* 1

CBot   The Botanic Nursery, Bath Road, Atworth, Nr Melksham, Wiltshire, SN12 8NU
TEL: (01225) 706597, 0850 328756 mobile *FAX:* (01225) 700953 *CONTACT:* T & M Baker
OPENING TIMES: 1000-1700 Wed-Mon, Closed Jan.
MIN. MAIL ORDER UK: 30p Sae for mail order lists.* *MIN. VALUE EC:*
CAT. COST: 5 x 1st class *W/SALE or RETAIL:* Both *CREDIT CARDS:* Visa, Access
SPECIALITIES: Rare hardy Shrubs & Perennials for lime soils. *Note: mail order to UK only.
MAP PAGE: 2

CBrd   Broadleas Gardens Ltd, Broadleas, Devizes, Wiltshire, SN10 5JQ
TEL: (01380) 722035 *CONTACT:* Lady Anne Cowdray
OPENING TIMES: 1400-1800 Wed, Thu & Sun Apr-Oct.
No mail order
CAT. COST: 1 x 1st class *W/SALE or RETAIL:* Both *CREDIT CARDS:* None
SPECIALITIES: General range. *MAP PAGE:* 2

**CBre   Bregover Plants, Hillbrooke, Middlewood, North Hill, Nr Launceston, Cornwall, PL15
7NN**
TEL: (01566) 782661 *CONTACT:* Jennifer Bousfield
OPENING TIMES: 1100-1700 Wed-Fri Mar-mid Oct and by appt.
MIN. MAIL ORDER UK: No minimum charge *MIN. VALUE EC:* Nmc
CAT. COST: 2 x 1st class *W/SALE or RETAIL:* Retail *CREDIT CARDS:* None
SPECIALITIES: Unusual Hardy Perennials. *MAP PAGE:* 1

CBro   Broadleigh Gardens, Bishops Hull, Taunton, Somerset, TA4 1AE
TEL: (01823) 286231 *FAX:* (01823) 323646 *CONTACT:* Lady Skelmersdale
OPENING TIMES: 0900-1600 Mon-Fri for viewing ONLY. Orders collected if prior notice given.
MIN. MAIL ORDER UK: No minimum charge *MIN. VALUE EC:* Nmc
CAT. COST: 2 x 1st class *W/SALE or RETAIL:* Retail *CREDIT CARDS:* Visa, Access
SPECIALITIES: Two Catalogues. (Jan) - Bulbs in growth, (Galanthus, Cyclamen etc.) &
Herbaceous. (June) - Dwarf & unusual Bulbs. *MAP PAGE:* 1/2

CBrP   Brooklands Plants, Palm & Cycad Nursery, 25 Treves Road, Dorchester, Dorset, DT1
2HE
TEL: (01305) 265846 *CONTACT:* Ian Watt
OPENING TIMES: By appt. for collection of plants.
MIN. MAIL ORDER UK: £25.00 + p&p* *MIN. VALUE EC:*
CAT. COST: 2 x 2nd class *W/SALE or RETAIL:* Both *CREDIT CARDS:* None
SPECIALITIES: Palms & Cycads from Temperate & Sub-tropical regions & other distinctive
foliage plants. *Note: mail order to UK only. *MAP PAGE:* 2

CCan   Cannington College Mail Order Centre, Cannington, Bridgwater, Somerset, TA5 2LS
TEL: (01278) 655000 *FAX:* (01278) 655055 *E-MAIL:* admin@cannington.ac.uk
WEB SITE: http://www.cannington.ac.uk *CONTACT:* Peter Elliman
OPENING TIMES: 1400-1700 daily Easter-Oct.
MIN. MAIL ORDER UK: £15.00 *MIN. VALUE EC:* By quotation   *EXPORT:* Yes
CAT. COST: Free *W/SALE or RETAIL:* Retail *CREDIT CARDS:* None
SPECIALITIES: Abutilon, Argyranthemum, Osteospermum, Salvia, Felicia & Euryops.
MAP PAGE: 1/2

◆ **See also Display Advertisements**

CCAT Cider Apple Trees, (Off.) 12 Tallowood, Shepton Mallet, Somerset, BA4 5QN

TEL: (01749) 343368 *CONTACT:* Mr J Dennis
OPENING TIMES: By appt. only.
MIN. MAIL ORDER UK: £6.00 + p&p *MIN. VALUE EC:* £6.00 + p&p
CAT. COST: Free *W/SALE or RETAIL:* Both *CREDIT CARDS:* None
SPECIALITIES: Malus (speciality standard trees). NB Nursery at Corkscrew Lane, Woolston.
Visits BY APPT. ONLY. *MAP PAGE:* 2

CChe Cherry Tree Nursery, (Sheltered Work Opportunities), off New Road Roundabout, Northbourne, Bournemouth, Dorset, BH10 7DA

TEL: (01202) 593537 *FAX:* (01202) 590626 *CONTACT:* Stephen Jailler
OPENING TIMES: 0830-1600 Mon-Fri, 0900-1200 most Sats.
No mail order
CAT. COST: A4 Sae + 2 x 2nd class *W/SALE or RETAIL:* Both *CREDIT CARDS:* None
SPECIALITIES: Hardy Shrubs. *MAP PAGE:* 2

CChr Christina's Cottage Plants, Friars Way Nursery, Church Street, Upwey, Weymouth, Dorset, DT3 5QE

TEL: (01305) 813243 *FAX:* (01305) 813243 *CONTACT:* Christina Scott
OPENING TIMES: 1100-1700 Wed-Sun incl.
No mail order
CAT. COST: 3 x 1st class *W/SALE or RETAIL:* Retail *CREDIT CARDS:* None
SPECIALITIES: Hardy Perennials. *MAP PAGE:* 2

CCot Cottage Garden Plants Old & New, Cox Cottage, Lower Street, East Morden, Wareham, Dorset, BH20 7DL

TEL: (01929) 459496 *FAX:* (01929) 459496 *CONTACT:* Mrs Alex Brenton
OPENING TIMES: Mainly Mail Order. Visitors by appt. only.
MIN. MAIL ORDER UK: £5.00 + p&p *MIN. VALUE EC:* £10.00 + p&p
CAT. COST: 2 x 1st class *W/SALE or RETAIL:* Retail *CREDIT CARDS:* None
SPECIALITIES: Pinks, Primroses, Cheiranthus, Viola & Violets. *MAP PAGE:* 2

CCuc Cuckoo Mill Nursery, Rose Ash, South Molton, Devon, EX36 4RQ

TEL: (01769) 550530 *CONTACT:* P A Woollard
OPENING TIMES: By appt. only. Please phone before 1000 or after 1800.
No mail order
CAT. COST: 3 x 1st class *W/SALE or RETAIL:* Retail *CREDIT CARDS:* None
SPECIALITIES: Hardy Ferns, Grasses & Astilbe. Shade & moisture loving plants.
MAP PAGE: 1

CCVT Chew Valley Trees, Winford Road, Chew Magna, Bristol, BS40 8QE

TEL: (01275) 333752 *FAX:* (01275) 333746 *CONTACT:* J Scarth
OPENING TIMES: 0800-1700 Mon-Fri all year. 0900-1600 Sat 1st Oct-30th Jun. Other times by appt.
MIN. MAIL ORDER UK: No minimum charge* *MIN. VALUE EC:*
CAT. COST: 1 x 1st class *W/SALE or RETAIL:* Both *CREDIT CARDS:* None
SPECIALITIES: Native British Trees and Shrubs, Apple Trees & Hedging. *Note: mail order to UK only; max. plant height 2.7m. *MAP PAGE:* 2

CDec Decorative Foliage, Higher Badworthy, South Brent, Devon, TQ10 9EG

TEL: (01548) 821493 evening, (01364) 72768 daytime only. *FAX:* (01364) 72768
CONTACT: Amanda Hansford
OPENING TIMES: By appt. only.
MIN. MAIL ORDER UK: No minimum charge* *MIN. VALUE EC:*
CAT. COST: 2 x 1st class *W/SALE or RETAIL:* Retail *CREDIT CARDS:* None
SPECIALITIES: Flower arrangers plants & rarities. *Note: mail order to UK only.
MAP PAGE: 1

Nursery ADDRESSES in BOLD do Mail Order to EU

CDev **Devon Violet Nursery, Rattery, South Brent, Devon, TQ10 9LG**
TEL: (01364) 643033 *FAX:* (01364) 643033 *CONTACT:* Joan & Michael Yardley
♦ *OPENING TIMES:* Oct-June. Please ring first.
MIN. MAIL ORDER UK: 6 plants *MIN. VALUE EC:* 6 plants   *EXPORT:* Yes
CAT. COST: 2 x 2nd class *W/SALE or RETAIL:* Both *CREDIT CARDS:* None
SPECIALITIES: Violets & Parma Violets. *MAP PAGE:* **1**

CDoC **Duchy of Cornwall,** Penlyne Nursery, Cott Road, Lostwithiel, Cornwall, PL22 0HW
TEL: (01208) 872668 *FAX:* (01208) 872835 *CONTACT:* Andrew Carthew
OPENING TIMES: 0900-1700 Mon-Sat, 1000-1700 Sun. Closed Bank Hols.
MIN. MAIL ORDER UK: Ask for details *MIN. VALUE EC:*
CAT. COST: £2.00 *W/SALE or RETAIL:* Retail *CREDIT CARDS:* Visa, AmEx, Access, Switch, Delta
SPECIALITIES: Very wide range of all garden plants incl. Trees, Shrubs, Conifers, Roses, Perennials, Fruit & half-hardy Exotics. *MAP PAGE:* **1**

CDul **Dulford Nurseries,** Cullompton, Devon, EX15 2DG
TEL: (01884) 266361 *FAX:* (01884) 266663 *CONTACT:* David & Mary Barrow
OPENING TIMES: 0730-1630 Mon-Fri
MIN. MAIL ORDER UK: £10.00 + p&p *MIN. VALUE EC:*
CAT. COST: Free *W/SALE or RETAIL:* Both *CREDIT CARDS:* None
SPECIALITIES: Native, Ornamental & unusual Trees & Shrubs, incl. Oaks, Maples, Beech, Birch, Chestnut, Ash, Lime, Sorbus & Pines. *MAP PAGE:* **1**

CElm **Elm Tree Nursery,** Court Farm, Sidbury, Sidmouth, Devon, EX10 0QG
TEL: (01395) 597790 *FAX:* (01395) 597790 *CONTACT:* M Saunders
OPENING TIMES: Not open to the public.
MIN. MAIL ORDER UK: £7.50 + p&p *MIN. VALUE EC:*
CAT. COST: 1 x 2nd class *W/SALE or RETAIL:* Retail *CREDIT CARDS:* None
SPECIALITIES: Cyclamen species. See also SEED Index.

CElw **Elworthy Cottage Plants,** Elworthy Cottage, Elworthy, Lydeard St Lawrence, Taunton, Somerset, TA4 3PX
TEL: (01984) 656427 *CONTACT:* Mrs J M Spiller
OPENING TIMES: 1100-1700 Tue, Thu & Fri mid Mar-mid Oct & by appt.
No mail order
CAT. COST: 3 x 2nd class *W/SALE or RETAIL:* Retail *CREDIT CARDS:* None
SPECIALITIES: Unusual Herbaceous plants esp. Hardy Geranium, Geum, Grasses, Campanula, Erysimum, Pulmonaria, Origanum & Viola. *MAP PAGE:* **1/2**

CEnd **Endsleigh Gardens,** Milton Abbot, Tavistock, Devon, PL19 0PG
TEL: (01822) 870235 *FAX:* (01822) 870513 *CONTACT:* Michael Taylor
♦ *OPENING TIMES:* 0800-1700 Mon-Sat, 1400-1700 Sun. Closed Sun Dec & Jan.
MIN. MAIL ORDER UK: £12.00 + p&p *MIN. VALUE EC:*
CAT. COST: 2 x 1st class *W/SALE or RETAIL:* Both *CREDIT CARDS:* Visa, Access
SPECIALITIES: Choice & unusual Trees & Shrubs incl. Acer & Cornus cvs. Old Apples & Cherries. Grafting service. *MAP PAGE:* **1**

CEqu **Equatorial Plant Co. (Vireyas), The White Cottage, Three Gates, Leigh, Nr Sherborne, Dorset, DT9 6JQ**
TEL: (01963) 210309 *FAX:* (01833) 690519 *CONTACT:* Blair & Jackie Sibun
OPENING TIMES: By appt.
MIN. MAIL ORDER UK: No minimum charge *MIN. VALUE EC:* Nmc
CAT. COST: Free *W/SALE or RETAIL:* Retail *CREDIT CARDS:* Visa, Access
SPECIALITIES: Vireya Rhododendrons

♦ **See also Display Advertisements**

Code-Nursery Index

CFai   **Fairhaven Nursery,** Clapworthy Cross, Chittlehampton, Umberleigh, Devon, EX37 9QT

TEL: (01769) 540528   *CONTACT:* Derek & Pauline Burdett
♦   *OPENING TIMES:* 1000-1600 all year, but please check first.
MIN. MAIL ORDER UK: £10.00 + p&p* *MIN. VALUE EC:*
CAT. COST: 2 x 1st class *W/SALE or RETAIL:* Retail *CREDIT CARDS:* None
SPECIALITIES: Wide selection of more unusual Hardy Trees, Shrubs & Perennials. *Note: mail order to UK only. *MAP PAGE:* 1

CFee   **Feebers Hardy Plants,** 1 Feeber Cottage, Westwood, Broadclyst, Nr Exeter, Devon, EX5 3DQ

TEL: (01404) 822118 *FAX:* (01404) 822118 *CONTACT:* Mrs E Squires
♦   *OPENING TIMES:* 1000-1700 Thur & 1400-1800 Sat Mar-Jul & Sep-Oct
No mail order
CAT. COST: Sae + 36p stamp *W/SALE or RETAIL:* Retail *CREDIT CARDS:* None
SPECIALITIES: Plants for wet clay soils, Alpines & Hardy Perennials incl. those raised by Amos Perry. *MAP PAGE:* 1

CFil   **Fillan's Plants, Pound House Nursery, Buckland Monachorum, Yelverton, Devon, PL20 7LJ**

TEL: (01822) 855050 *FAX:* (01822) 614351 *CONTACT:* Mark Fillan
OPENING TIMES: By appt. only.
MIN. MAIL ORDER UK: £20.00 + p&p *MIN. VALUE EC:* £50.00 + p&p   *EXPORT:* Yes
CAT. COST: 3 x 1st class *W/SALE or RETAIL:* Both *CREDIT CARDS:* None
SPECIALITIES: Ferns, Hydrangea & less usual plants. *MAP PAGE:* 1

CFir   **Fir Tree Farm Nursery,** Tresahor, Constantine, Falmouth, Cornwall, TR11 5PL

TEL: (01326) 340593 *FAX:* (01326) 340593 *E-MAIL:* ftfnur@aol.com
WEB SITE: http://members.aol.com/ftfnur *CONTACT:* Jim Cave
OPENING TIMES: 1000-1700 Thu-Sun 1st Mar-30th Sep.
MIN. MAIL ORDER UK: £25.00 + p&p *MIN. VALUE EC:*
CAT. COST: 6 x 1st class *W/SALE or RETAIL:* Retail *CREDIT CARDS:* Visa, Access, Delta, Switch
SPECIALITIES: Over 1500 varieties of Cottage Garden & rare Perennials & 100 types of Clematis. *MAP PAGE:* 1

CFis   **The Margery Fish Plant Nursery, East Lambrook Manor, East Lambrook, South Petherton, Somerset, TA13 5HL**

TEL: (01460) 240328 *FAX:* (01460) 242344 *CONTACT:* Mr M Stainer
OPENING TIMES: 1000-1700 Mon-Sat Mar-Oct, 1000-1700 Mon-Fri Nov-Feb.
MIN. MAIL ORDER UK: £10.00 + p&p *MIN. VALUE EC:* £25.00 + p&p   *EXPORT:* Yes
CAT. COST: 4 x 1st class *W/SALE or RETAIL:* Retail *CREDIT CARDS:* None
SPECIALITIES: Hardy Geranium, Euphorbia, Helleborus, Primula vulgaris, Penstemon, Salvia & Herbaceous. *MAP PAGE:* 1/2

CFul   **Rodney Fuller,** Coachman's Cottage, Higher Bratton Seymour, Wincanton, Somerset, BA9 8DA

TEL: CONTACT: Rodney Fuller
OPENING TIMES: Not open.
MIN. MAIL ORDER UK: £25.00 *MIN. VALUE EC:*
CAT. COST: Sae *W/SALE or RETAIL:* Retail *CREDIT CARDS:* None
SPECIALITIES: Violas & Violettas. Buxus 'Suffruticosa'.

CGen   **Genus Plants, Crudwell Road, Malmesbury, Wiltshire, SN16 9JL**

TEL: (01666) 823075 *FAX:* (01666) 825567 *E-MAIL:* genusplants@mcmail.com
WEB SITE: http://www/mcmail/genusplants *CONTACT:* Cliff Cowling
OPENING TIMES: Not open to public.
MIN. MAIL ORDER UK: 6 plants (plugs)* + p&p *MIN. VALUE EC:* 6 plants (plugs)* + p&p
CAT. COST: 2 x 1st class *W/SALE or RETAIL:* Retail *CREDIT CARDS:* Access, AmEx, Connect, Delta, Diners, EuroCard, JCB, MasterCard, Switch, Visa
SPECIALITIES: Hardy & tender unusual Perennials. *Note: mail order of large plugs only.

Nursery ADDRESSES in BOLD do Mail Order to EU

CGle   **Glebe Cottage Plants,** Pixie Lane, Warkleigh, Umberleigh, Devon, EX37 9DH
TEL: FAX: (01769) 540544 *CONTACT:* Carol Klein
OPENING TIMES: 1000-1300 Tue, Wed, Thur & Fri.
No mail order
CAT. COST: £1.50 *W/SALE or RETAIL:* Retail *CREDIT CARDS:* none
SPECIALITIES: Extensive range of hard-to-find Perennials. *MAP PAGE:* **1**

CGOG **Global Orange Groves UK,** Horton Road, Horton Heath, Wimborne, Dorset, BH21 7JN
TEL: (01202) 826244 *CONTACT:* P K Oliver
♦   *OPENING TIMES:* 1030-1700 7 days a week, unless exhibiting.
MIN. MAIL ORDER UK: No minimum charge *MIN. VALUE EC:* Nmc   *EXPORT:* Yes
CAT. COST: Sae *W/SALE or RETAIL:* Both *CREDIT CARDS:* none
SPECIALITIES: Citrus trees, Citrus fertiliser & book 'Success with Citrus'.

CGra   **Graham's Hardy Plants,** Southcroft, North Road, Timsbury, Bath, Avon, BA3 1JN
TEL: (01761) 472187 *E-MAIL:* graplant@aol.com *CONTACT:* Graham Nicholls
OPENING TIMES: 1000-1600 Wed, Thur & Fri 1st Apr-30th Sep. Please phone first.
MIN. MAIL ORDER UK: £1.50 + p&p *MIN. VALUE EC:* £1.50 + p&p
CAT. COST: 2 x 1st class or 2 x IRC *W/SALE or RETAIL:* Retail *CREDIT CARDS:* None
SPECIALITIES: North American Alpines esp. Lewisia, Eriogonum, Penstemon, Campanula, Kelseya, Phlox. *MAP PAGE:* **5**

CGre   **Greenway Gardens,** Churston Ferrers, Brixham, Devon, TQ5 0ES
TEL: (01803) 842382 *CONTACT:* Roger Clark (Manager)
OPENING TIMES: 1400-1700 (Nov-Feb 1630) Mon-Fri, 1000-1200 Sat, ex Bank Hols. Also by appt.
MIN. MAIL ORDER UK: No minimum charge* *MIN. VALUE EC:*
CAT. COST: 3 x 1st class *W/SALE or RETAIL:* Retail *CREDIT CARDS:* None
SPECIALITIES: Unusual Trees & Shrubs particularly from temperate Southern hemisphere.
*Note: mail order by Carrier only. *MAP PAGE:* **1**

CGro   **C W Groves & Son,** West Bay Road, Bridport, Dorset, DT6 4BA
TEL: (01308) 422654 *FAX:* (01308) 420888 *CONTACT:* C W Groves
OPENING TIMES: 0830-1700 Mon-Sat, 1030-1630 Sun.
MIN. MAIL ORDER UK: No minimum charge* *MIN. VALUE EC:* £10.00 + p&p *EXPORT:* Yes
CAT. COST: Free *W/SALE or RETAIL:* Retail *CREDIT CARDS:* Access, Visa, Switch
SPECIALITIES: Nursery & Garden Centre specialising in Parma & Hardy Viola. *Note: Violets Mail Order ONLY. *MAP PAGE:* **1/2**

CHad   **Hadspen Garden & Nursery,** Hadspen House, Castle Cary, Somerset, BA7 7NG
TEL: (01749) 813707 *FAX:* (01749) 813707 *CONTACT:* N & S Pope
OPENING TIMES: 1000-1700 Thu-Sun & Bank Hols. 1st Mar-1st Oct. Garden open at the same time.
No mail order
CAT. COST: 3 x 1st class *W/SALE or RETAIL:* Retail *CREDIT CARDS:* None
SPECIALITIES: Large leaved Herbaceous. Old fashioned and shrub Roses. *MAP PAGE:* **2**

CHal   **Halsway Nursery,** Halsway, Nr Crowcombe, Taunton, Somerset, TA4 4BB
TEL: (01984) 618243 *CONTACT:* T A & D J Bushen
OPENING TIMES: Most days - please telephone first.
MIN. MAIL ORDER UK: £2.00 + p&p *MIN. VALUE EC:*
CAT. COST: 2 x 1st class* *W/SALE or RETAIL:* Retail *CREDIT CARDS:* None
SPECIALITIES: Coleus & Begonias (excl. tuberous & winter flowering). Also good range of Greenhouse & garden plants. *Note: List for Coleus & Begonias only, no nursery list.
MAP PAGE: **1/2**

♦ **See also Display Advertisements**

CHan   The Hannays of Bath, Sydney Wharf Nursery, Bathwick, Bath, Avon, BA2 4ES
TEL: (01225) 462230   *CONTACT:* Mr V H S & Mrs S H Hannay
OPENING TIMES: 1000-1700 Wed-Sun (but open Bank Hols.) 1st Mar-12th Oct or by appt. esp in Winter.
No mail order
CAT. COST: £1.00 + 40p p&p   *W/SALE or RETAIL:* Retail   *CREDIT CARDS:* None
SPECIALITIES: Uncommon Perennials & Shrubs, many grown from seed collected abroad by ourselves. *NOTE: For Export items, Certificates arranged but collection only.   *MAP PAGE:* 2

CHar   West Harptree Nursery, Bristol Road, West Harptree, Bath & North East Somerset, BS40 6HG
TEL: (01761) 221370   *FAX:* (01761) 221989   *CONTACT:* Bryn & Helene Bowles
OPENING TIMES: Daily from 10.00 except Mondays, 1st Mar-30th Nov.
MIN. MAIL ORDER UK: No minimum charge   *MIN. VALUE EC:* Nmc   *EXPORT:* Yes
CAT. COST: £1 coin or p. order + 1 x 1st class   *W/SALE or RETAIL:* Both   *CREDIT CARDS:* None
SPECIALITIES: Unusual Herbaceous Perennials & Shrubs. Lilies.   *MAP PAGE:* 2

CHea   Heather Bank Nursery, Woodlands, 1 High Street, Littleton Panell, Devizes, Wiltshire, SN10 4EL
TEL: (01380) 812739   *CONTACT:* Mrs B Mullan
OPENING TIMES: 1000-1500 Mon, Wed & Thurs. Other times by appt.
MIN. MAIL ORDER UK: £10.00 + p&p*   *MIN. VALUE EC:*
CAT. COST: 3 x 1st class   *W/SALE or RETAIL:* Retail   *CREDIT CARDS:* none
SPECIALITIES: Campanula, Polemonium & Cottage Garden Plants. *Note: mail order to UK only.   *MAP PAGE:* 2

CHEx   Hardy Exotics, Gilly Lane, Whitecross, Penzance, Cornwall, TR20 8BZ
TEL: (01736) 740660   *FAX:* (01736) 741101   *CONTACT:* C Shilton/J Smith/Ian Lowe
OPENING TIMES: 1000-1700 1st Apr-31st Oct. 1000-1600 Mon-Sat 1st Nov-31st Mar. Please phone first Nov-Mar.
MIN. MAIL ORDER UK: £13.00 carriage   *MIN. VALUE EC:* P.O.A.
CAT. COST: £1.00 postal order   *W/SALE or RETAIL:* Retail   *CREDIT CARDS:* Visa, Access, MasterCard, Connect, Delta
SPECIALITIES: Trees, Shrubs & Herbaceous plants to create tropical & desert effects. Hardy & half-Hardy for gardens patios & conservatories. *Note: mail order payment by cheque only.   *MAP PAGE:* 1

CHid   Hidden Valley Nursery, Umberleigh, Devon, EX37 9YY
TEL: (01769) 560567   *CONTACT:* Linda & Peter Lindley
OPENING TIMES: By appt. only.
MIN. MAIL ORDER UK: No minimum charge   *MIN. VALUE EC:* Nmc   *EXPORT:* Yes
CAT. COST: 2 x 1st class   *W/SALE or RETAIL:* Retail   *CREDIT CARDS:* None
SPECIALITIES: Hardy Perennials, esp. shade lovers.

CHig   The High Garden, Courtwood, Newton Ferrers, South Devon, PL8 1BW
TEL: (01752) 872528   *CONTACT:* F Bennett
OPENING TIMES: By appt.
MIN. MAIL ORDER UK: No minimum charge   *MIN. VALUE EC:* £20.00 + p&p
CAT. COST: 60p   *W/SALE or RETAIL:* Both   *CREDIT CARDS:* None
SPECIALITIES: Pieris & Rhododendron.   *MAP PAGE:* 1

CHil   Hillside Cottage Plants, Hillside, Gibbet Lane, Whitchurch, North East Somerset, BS14 0BX
TEL: (01275) 837505   *CONTACT:* Josephine Pike
◆   *OPENING TIMES:* Normally here but please phone first in case at show.
MIN. MAIL ORDER UK: £15.00 + p&p*   *MIN. VALUE EC:*
CAT. COST: 4 x 1st class   *W/SALE or RETAIL:* Retail   *CREDIT CARDS:* None
SPECIALITIES: Hardy Geraniums & wide range of Hardy Perennials. *Note: mail order to UK only.   *MAP PAGE:* 2

Nursery ADDRESSES in BOLD do Mail Order to EU

CHon **Honeymyrtles & Paperbarks, Hebrody, Herland Road, Godolphin Cross, Nr Helston, Cornwall, TR13 9RD**

TEL: (01736) 763612 *FAX:* (01736) 763612 *CONTACT:* Janette & Michael Knowles
OPENING TIMES: By appt. for collection only.
MIN. MAIL ORDER UK: £10.00 + p&p *MIN. VALUE EC:* £10.00 + p&p
CAT. COST: 2 x 1st class *W/SALE or RETAIL:* Both *CREDIT CARDS:* none
SPECIALITIES: Melaleuca & Callistemon species, plus a selection of other Australian Myrtaceae for milder gardens or containers.

CHor **Horton Vale Nursery,** Horton Heath, Wimborne, Dorset, BH21 7JN

TEL: (01202) 813473 *CONTACT:* David Wright
OPENING TIMES: 0900-1700 daily exc. Wed, Feb-Nov.
No mail order
CAT. COST: None issued *W/SALE or RETAIL:* Retail *CREDIT CARDS:* None
SPECIALITIES: Perennials *MAP PAGE:* 2

CInt **International Animal Rescue Nursery,** Animal Tracks, Ash Mill, South Molton, Devon, EX36 4QW

TEL: (01769) 550277 *FAX:* (01769) 550917 *CONTACT:* Jo Hicks
OPENING TIMES: 1000-1800 or dusk 365 days a year.
No mail order
CAT. COST: 3 x 1st class *W/SALE or RETAIL:* Retail *CREDIT CARDS:* None
SPECIALITIES: Alpines, Grasses & Hardy Perennials. *MAP PAGE:* 1

CJew **Jean Jewels,** Millmoor Cottage, Burrington, Umberleigh, Devon, EX37 9EF

TEL: (01769) 520285 *CONTACT:* Jean Jewels & Peter Charnley
OPENING TIMES: Phone call first appreciated.
No mail order
CAT. COST: 3 x 1st class *W/SALE or RETAIL:* Retail *CREDIT CARDS:* None
SPECIALITIES: Herbs, culinary, medicinal & dye plants. Scented foliage plants & plants for the wild garden. *MAP PAGE:* 1

CKel **Kelways Ltd, Langport, Somerset, TA10 9EZ**

TEL: (01458) 250521 *FAX:* (01458) 253351 *CONTACT:* Mr David Root
OPENING TIMES: 0900-1700 Mon-Fri, 1000-1700 Sat, 1000-1600 Sun.
MIN. MAIL ORDER UK: £4.00 + p&p* *MIN. VALUE EC:* £8.00 + p&p   *EXPORT:* Yes
CAT. COST: Free *W/SALE or RETAIL:* Both *CREDIT CARDS:* Visa, Access
SPECIALITIES: Paeonia, Iris, Hemerocallis & Herbaceous perennials. *Note: mail order for Paeonia, Iris & Hemerocallis only. *MAP PAGE:* 1/2

CKen **Kenwith Nursery (Gordon Haddow), Blinsham, Nr Torrington, Beaford, Winkleigh, Devon, EX19 8NT**

♦ *TEL:* (01805) 603274 *FAX:* (01805) 603663 *CONTACT:* Gordon Haddow
OPENING TIMES: 1000-1630 Wed-Sat Nov-Feb & by appt. 1000-1630 daily Mar-Oct.
MIN. MAIL ORDER UK: £10.00 + p&p *MIN. VALUE EC:* £50.00 + p&p   *EXPORT:* Yes
CAT. COST: 3 x 1st class *W/SALE or RETAIL:* Retail *CREDIT CARDS:* Visa, MasterCard, EuroCard
SPECIALITIES: All Conifer genera. Grafting a speciality. Many new introductions to UK. Also provisional National Collection of Dwarf Conifers. *MAP PAGE:* 1

CKin **Kingsfield Conservation Nursery,** Broadenham Lane, Winsham, Chard, Somerset, TA20 4JF

TEL: (01460) 30070 *FAX:* (01460) 30070 *CONTACT:* Mrs M White
OPENING TIMES: Please phone for details.
MIN. MAIL ORDER UK: No minimum charge* *MIN. VALUE EC:*
CAT. COST: 31p stamps *W/SALE or RETAIL:* Both *CREDIT CARDS:* None
SPECIALITIES: Native Trees, Shrubs, Wild flowers & Wild flower Seeds. *Note: mail order to UK only. See also SEED Index under Y.S.J. Seeds. *MAP PAGE:* 1/2

♦ **See also Display Advertisements**

CKno   Knoll Gardens, Hampreston, Stapehill, Nr Wimborne, Dorset, BH21 7ND
TEL: (01202) 873931 *FAX:* (01202) 870842 *CONTACT:* N R Lucas
OPENING TIMES: 1000-1730 every day Easter-October only. For Nov-Easter please phone.
MIN. MAIL ORDER UK: * *MIN. VALUE EC:*
CAT. COST: None issued *W/SALE or RETAIL:* Retail *CREDIT CARDS:* Visa, Access
SPECIALITIES: Deciduous Ceanothus & Phygelius National Collections (list available).
Herbaceous & Grasses. Half-hardy Perennials. *Note: UK mail order of Phygelius only.
MAP PAGE: **2**

CLan   The Lanhydrock Gardens (NT), Lanhydrock, Bodmin, Cornwall, PL30 5AD
TEL: (01208) 72220 *FAX:* (01208) 72220 *CONTACT:* Mr N.R. Teagle
OPENING TIMES: Daily - Easter (or Apr 1st)-31st Oct.
No mail order
CAT. COST: Free *W/SALE or RETAIL:* Both *CREDIT CARDS:* None
SPECIALITIES: Shrubs, especially Camellia, Azalea, Rhododendron, Magnolia & Ceanothus.
MAP PAGE: **1**

**CLAP   Long Acre Plants, South Marsh, Charlton Musgrove, Nr Wincanton, Somerset, BA9
8EX**
TEL: (01963) 32802 *FAX:* (01963) 32802 *CONTACT:* Nigel Rowland
OPENING TIMES: 1000-1600 Fri & Sat Mar-Oct. Other days by appt.
MIN. MAIL ORDER UK: £10.00 + p&p *MIN. VALUE EC:* £20.00 + p&p
CAT. COST: 3 x 1st class *W/SALE or RETAIL:* Both *CREDIT CARDS:* None
SPECIALITIES: Paeonia, Lilium, Ferns, Climbers, shade tolerant Perennials & Rare Bulbs.
MAP PAGE: **2**

**CLCN   Little Creek Nursery, 39 Moor Road, Banwell, Weston-super-Mare, North Somerset,
BS29 6EF**
TEL: (01934) 823739 *FAX:* (01934) 823739 *CONTACT:* Rhys & Julie Adams
OPENING TIMES: 1000-1630 Thu & Fri March & April. Other times by appt. Please ring first.
MIN. MAIL ORDER UK: No minimum charge *MIN. VALUE EC:* Nmc   *EXPORT:* Yes
CAT. COST: 3 x 1st class *W/SALE or RETAIL:* Retail *CREDIT CARDS:* None
SPECIALITIES: Species Cyclamen (from seed) & Helleborus. *MAP PAGE:* **2**

CLit   Littleton Nursery, Littleton, Somerton, Somerset, TA11 6NT
TEL: (01458) 272356 *FAX:* (01458) 272065 *CONTACT:* G & R Seymour
◆ *OPENING TIMES:* 0900-1700 Mon-Sat.
MIN. MAIL ORDER UK: £5.00 + p&p* *MIN. VALUE EC:*
CAT. COST: 3 x 1st + A5 Sae *W/SALE or RETAIL:* Both *CREDIT CARDS:* None
SPECIALITIES: Fuchsia, Pelargoniums & half-hardy Perennials. *Note: mail order to UK only.
MAP PAGE: **1/2**

CLnd   Landford Trees, Landford Lodge, Landford, Salisbury, Wiltshire, SP5 2EH
TEL: (01794) 390808 *FAX:* (01794) 390037 *CONTACT:* C D Pilkington
OPENING TIMES: 0800-1700 Mon-Fri.
No mail order
CAT. COST: Free *W/SALE or RETAIL:* Both *CREDIT CARDS:* None
SPECIALITIES: Deciduous ornamental Trees. *MAP PAGE:* **2**

CLoc   C S Lockyer, Lansbury, 70 Henfield Road, Coalpit Heath, Bristol, BS36 2UZ
TEL: (01454) 772219 *FAX:* (01454) 772219
WEB SITE: http://ourworld.compuserve.com/homepages/terrydavies1 *CONTACT:* C S Lockyer
◆ *OPENING TIMES:* Appt. only. (Many open days & coach parties).
MIN. MAIL ORDER UK: 6 plants + p&p *MIN. VALUE EC:* £12.00 + p&p
CAT. COST: 4 x 1st class *W/SALE or RETAIL:* Both *CREDIT CARDS:* none
SPECIALITIES: Fuchsia. *MAP PAGE:* **5**

Nursery ADDRESSES in BOLD do Mail Order to EU

CLon   **Longhall Nursery, Stockton, Nr Warminster, Wiltshire, BA12 0SE**

TEL: (01985) 850914 *FAX:* (01985) 850914 *E-MAIL:* www.designbywire.com
CONTACT: H V & J E Dooley
OPENING TIMES: 0930-1700 Fri-Sat only, from 3rd Fri in Mar-last Sat in Sept.
MIN. MAIL ORDER UK: 10 plants + p&p *MIN. VALUE EC:* 10 plants + p&p
CAT. COST: 3 x 1st class *W/SALE or RETAIL:* Both *CREDIT CARDS:* None
SPECIALITIES: Many chalk tolerant plants, esp. Digitalis, Eryngium, Euphorbia & Salvia.
MAP PAGE: **2**

CLTr   **Little Treasures, Wheal Treasure, Horsedowns, Cornwall, TR14 0NL**

TEL: (01209) 831978 *FAX:* (01209) 831978 *CONTACT:* Bernadette Jackson
OPENING TIMES: 1000-1700 Wed-Sat Mar-end Sep. Other times by appt. only
MIN. MAIL ORDER UK: £15.00 + p&p *MIN. VALUE EC:* £25.00 + p&p
CAT. COST: 4 x 1st class *W/SALE or RETAIL:* Retail *CREDIT CARDS:* None
SPECIALITIES: Cottage garden plants, Shrubs & tender Perennials. *MAP PAGE:* **1**

CLyd   **Lydford Alpine Nursery,** 2 Southern Cottages, Lydford, Okehampton, Devon, EX20 4BL

TEL: (01822) 820398 *CONTACT:* Julie & David Hatchett
OPENING TIMES: 1000-1700 Tue & Thu Apr-Oct & by appt. Nov-Mar by appt. only. Closed 6-22 July.
No mail order
CAT. COST: 3 x 1st class *W/SALE or RETAIL:* Retail *CREDIT CARDS:* None
SPECIALITIES: Dianthus, Primula & Saxifraga. Very wide range of choice & unusual Alpines in small quanities. See also SEED Index. *MAP PAGE:* **1**

CLyn   **Lynash Nurseries,** Culhaven, Wall Ditch Lane, Boozer Pit, Merriott, Somerset, TA16 5PW

TEL: (01460) 76643, (01460) 77764 *FAX:* (01460) 76643
CONTACT: Lynn Wallis & Ashley Wallis
OPENING TIMES: 0900-1700 Thur-Sat, 1000-1600 Sun.
No mail order
CAT. COST: None issued. *W/SALE or RETAIL:* Retail *CREDIT CARDS:* none
SPECIALITIES: Hebe. *MAP PAGE:* **1/2**

CM&M   **M & M Plants,** Lloret, Chittlehamholt, Umbesleigh, Devon, EX37 9PD

TEL: (01769) 540448 *CONTACT:* Mr M Thorne
OPENING TIMES: 0930-1730 Tue-Sat Apr-Oct & 1000-1600 Tue-Sat Nov-Mar.
No mail order
CAT. COST: £1.00 (incl. p&p) *W/SALE or RETAIL:* Retail *CREDIT CARDS:* None
SPECIALITIES: Perennials. We also carry a reasonable range of Alpines, Shrubs, Trees & Roses.
MAP PAGE: **1**

CMac   **Macpennys Nurseries, 154 Burley Road, Bransgore, Christchurch, Dorset, BH23 8DB**

TEL: (01425) 672348 *CONTACT:* T & V Lowndes
OPENING TIMES: 0800-1700 Mon-Fri, 0900-1700 Sat 1400-1700 Sun.
MIN. MAIL ORDER UK: No minimum charge *MIN. VALUE EC:* Nmc
CAT. COST: A4 Sae with 3x1st class *W/SALE or RETAIL:* Retail *CREDIT CARDS:* Access,
AmEx, Delta, Access, EuroCard, MasterCard, Visa
SPECIALITIES: General. *MAP PAGE:* **2**

CMCN   **Mallet Court Nursery, Curry Mallet, Taunton, Somerset, TA3 6SY**

TEL: (01823) 480748 *FAX:* (01823) 481009 *CONTACT:* J G S & P M E Harris F.L.S.
OPENING TIMES: 0900-1300 & 1400-1700 Mon-Fri. Sat & Sun by appt.
MIN. MAIL ORDER UK: No minimum charge *MIN. VALUE EC:* Nmc *EXPORT:* Yes
CAT. COST: 31p Sae *W/SALE or RETAIL:* Both *CREDIT CARDS:* MasterCard
SPECIALITIES: Maples, Oaks, Magnolia, Hollies & other rare and unusual plants including those from China & South Korea. *MAP PAGE:* **1/2**

◆ **See also Display Advertisements**

CMCo **Meadow Cottage Plants,** Pitt Hill, Ivybridge, Devon, PL21 0JJ

TEL: (01752) 894532 *CONTACT:* Mrs L P Hunt
OPENING TIMES: By appt. only.
No mail order
CAT. COST: 2 x 2nd class *W/SALE or RETAIL:* Both *CREDIT CARDS:* none
SPECIALITIES: Hardy Geraniums & other Hardy Perennials. *MAP PAGE:* 1

CMdw **Meadows Nursery,** 5 Rectory Cottages, Mells, Frome, Somerset, BA11 3PA

TEL: (01373) 813025 *CONTACT:* Sue Lees
OPENING TIMES: 1000-1800 Tue-Sun 1st Mar-31st Oct & Bank Hols.
No mail order
CAT. COST: 2 x 1st class *W/SALE or RETAIL:* Retail *CREDIT CARDS:* None
SPECIALITIES: Hardy Cottage garden plants & some Conservatory plants. *MAP PAGE:* 2

CMea **The Mead Nursery,** Brokerswood, Nr Westbury, Wiltshire, BA13 4EG

TEL: (01373) 859990 *CONTACT:* Steve Lewis-Dale
OPENING TIMES: 0900-1700 Wed-Sat, 1200-1700 Sun, 0900-1700 Bank Hols. 1st Feb-31st Oct.
Closed Easter Sunday.
No mail order
CAT. COST: 5 x 1st class *W/SALE or RETAIL:* Retail *CREDIT CARDS:* None
SPECIALITIES: Perennials & Alpines incl. Bulbs. *MAP PAGE:* 2

CMGP **Milton Garden Plants,** Milton-on-Stour, Gillingham, Dorset, SP8 5PX

TEL: (01747) 822484 *FAX:* (01747) 822484 *CONTACT:* Sue Hardy & Richard Cumming
♦ *OPENING TIMES:* 0830-1700 Tue-Sat & Bank Hol Mons, 1000-1630 Sun. Closed Jan.
MIN. MAIL ORDER UK: No minimum charge* *MIN. VALUE EC:*
CAT. COST: £1.50 *W/SALE or RETAIL:* Retail *CREDIT CARDS:* Visa, Access, Switch, Delta
SPECIALITIES: Very wide range of Perennials. Ever changing selection of Trees, Shrubs,
Conifers, Alpines & Herbs. *Note: mail order to UK only. *MAP PAGE:* 2

CMHG **Marwood Hill Gardens,** Barnstaple, Devon, EX31 4EB

TEL: (01271) 342528 *CONTACT:* Dr Smart
OPENING TIMES: 1100-1700 daily.
No mail order
CAT. COST: 5 x 2nd class *W/SALE or RETAIL:* Retail *CREDIT CARDS:* None
SPECIALITIES: Large range of unusual Trees & Shrubs. Eucalyptus, Alpines, Camellia, Astilbe
& Bog plants. *MAP PAGE:* 1

CMil **Mill Cottage Plants, The Mill, Henley Lane, Wookey, Somerset, BA5 1AP**

TEL: (01749) 676966 *CONTACT:* Sally Gregson
OPENING TIMES: 1000-1800 Wed Mar-Sep or by appt. Ring for directions.
MIN. MAIL ORDER UK: £5.00 + p&p *MIN. VALUE EC:* £10.00 + p&p
CAT. COST: 4 x 1st class *W/SALE or RETAIL:* Retail *CREDIT CARDS:* None
SPECIALITIES: Unusual & period Cottage plants especially 'old' Pinks, Campanula, Papaver
orientale, Hardy Geranium, Euphorbia, Ferns, Pulmonaria & Grasses. *MAP PAGE:* 1/2

CMon **Monocot Nursery, Jacklands, Jacklands Bridge, Tickenham, Clevedon, Avon, BS21 6SG**

TEL: (01275) 810394 *CONTACT:* M R Salmon
OPENING TIMES: 1000-1800 Mon-Fri, Sat & Sun by appt.
MIN. MAIL ORDER UK: No minimum charge *MIN. VALUE EC:* Nmc   *EXPORT:* Yes
CAT. COST: Sae *W/SALE or RETAIL:* Retail *CREDIT CARDS:* None
SPECIALITIES: Rare & unusual Bulbous plants. Narcissus, Colchicum, Scilla, Crocus, Aroids, S.
African & S. American species. See also SEED Index. *MAP PAGE:* 2

CNat **Natural Selection,** 1 Station Cottages, Hullavington, Chippenham, Wiltshire, SN14 6ET

TEL: (01666) 837369 *E-MAIL:* @worldmutation.demon.co.uk *CONTACT:* Martin Cragg-Barber
OPENING TIMES: Wed afternoon Easter-end June. Other times please telephone first.
MIN. MAIL ORDER UK: £8.00 + p&p *MIN. VALUE EC:*
CAT. COST: 2 x 1st class *W/SALE or RETAIL:* Retail *CREDIT CARDS:* None
SPECIALITIES: Unusual British natives, Pelargoniums & others. See also SEED Index.
MAP PAGE: 2/5

Nursery ADDRESSES in BOLD do Mail Order to EU

CNCN Naked Cross Nurseries, Waterloo Road, Corfe Mullen, Wimborne, Dorset, BH21 3SR
TEL: (01202) 693256 *FAX:* (01202) 693256 *CONTACT:* Mr P J French & Mrs J E Paddon
OPENING TIMES: 0900-1700 daily.
MIN. MAIL ORDER UK: No minimum charge *MIN. VALUE EC:*
CAT. COST: 2 x 1st class *W/SALE or RETAIL:* Both *CREDIT CARDS:* Visa, Access, AmEx,
Switch
SPECIALITIES: Heathers. *MAP PAGE:* **2**

CNic Nicky's Rock Garden Nursery, Broadhayes, Stockland, Honiton, Devon, EX14 9EH
TEL: (01404) 881213 *FAX:* (01404) 881213 *CONTACT:* Diana & Bob Dark
OPENING TIMES: 0900-dusk daily. Please telephone first to check & for directions.
No mail order
CAT. COST: 3 x 1st class *W/SALE or RETAIL:* Retail *CREDIT CARDS:* None
SPECIALITIES: Plants for Rock gardens, Alpine house, Scree, Troughs, Banks, Walls & front of
border & Dwarf Shrubs. Many unusual. *MAP PAGE:* **1/2**

COCH Otters' Court Heathers, Otters' Court, West Camel, Yeovil, Somerset, BA22 7QF
TEL: (01935) 850285 *CONTACT:* Mrs D H Jones
OPENING TIMES: By appt. only.
MIN. MAIL ORDER UK: £3.00 + p&p *MIN. VALUE EC:* No minimum charge
CAT. COST: 3 x 1st class *W/SALE or RETAIL:* Both *CREDIT CARDS:* None
SPECIALITIES: Lime-tolerant Heathers - Erica, & Daboecia. *MAP PAGE:* **2**

COtt Otter Nurseries Ltd, Gosford Road, Ottery St. Mary, Devon, EX11 1LZ
TEL: (01404) 815815 *FAX:* (01404) 815816 *CONTACT:* Mr K Owen
OPENING TIMES: 0800-1730 Mon-Sat, 1030-1630 Sun. Closed Xmas & Boxing day & Easter Sun.
No mail order
CAT. COST: Free *W/SALE or RETAIL:* Retail *CREDIT CARDS:* Visa, Access, AmEx, Diners,
Switch
SPECIALITIES: Large Garden Centre & Nursery with extensive range of Trees, Shrubs, Conifers,
Climbers, Roses, Fruit & hardy Perennials. *MAP PAGE:* **1/2**

CPas Passiflora (National Collection), Lampley Road, Kingston Seymour, Clevedon, North
Somerset, BS21 6XS
TEL: (01934) 833350 *FAX:* (01934) 877255 *E-MAIL:* passion@3wa.co.uk
CONTACT: John Vanderplank or Jane Lindsay
OPENING TIMES: 0900-1300 & 1400-1700 Mon-Sat
MIN. MAIL ORDER UK: No minimum charge *MIN. VALUE EC:* £20.00 + p&p *EXPORT:* Yes
CAT. COST: 3 x 1st class *W/SALE or RETAIL:* Both *CREDIT CARDS:* Visa, Access, EuroCard
SPECIALITIES: Passiflora. National Collection of over 200 species & varieties. Note: Retail
nursery now at Kingston Seymour. See also SEED Index. *MAP PAGE:* **2**

CPBP Parham Bungalow Plants, Parham Lane, Market Lavington, Devizes, Wiltshire, SN10
4QA
TEL: (01380) 812605 *CONTACT:* Mrs D E Sample
OPENING TIMES: Please ring first.
MIN. MAIL ORDER UK: No minimum charge *MIN. VALUE EC:* Nmc
CAT. COST: Sae *W/SALE or RETAIL:* Retail *CREDIT CARDS:* None
SPECIALITIES: Alpines & dwarf Shrubs. *MAP PAGE:* **2**

CPea Pear Tree Cottage Plants, Pear Tree Cottage, Prestleigh, Shepton Mallet, Somerset,
BA4 4NL
TEL: (01749) 831487 *CONTACT:* PJ & PM Starr
OPENING TIMES: 0900-1900 1st Mar-31st Oct.
MIN. MAIL ORDER UK: £12.50 + p&p *MIN. VALUE EC:* £20.00 + p&p
CAT. COST: 3 x 1st class *W/SALE or RETAIL:* Both *CREDIT CARDS:* None
SPECIALITIES: Wide General Range with many unusual plants. *MAP PAGE:* **2**

◆ **See also Display Advertisements**

CPer   **Perrie Hale Forest Nursery,** Northcote Hill, Honiton, Devon, EX14 8TH
TEL: (01404) 43344 *FAX:* (01404) 47163 *CONTACT:* N C Davey & Mrs J F Davey
OPENING TIMES: 0800-1630 Mon-Fri, 0900-1230 Sat, Mar-Nov. Retail sales please telephone
first.
No mail order
CAT. COST: Sae 1 x 1st class. *W/SALE or RETAIL:* Both *CREDIT CARDS:* None
SPECIALITIES: Forest Trees, native Hedging plants & Shrubs. *Note: no mail order but will send
trees (TNT) if customers cannot collect. *MAP PAGE:* 1/2

CPev   **Peveril Clematis Nursery,** Christow, Exeter, Devon, EX6 7NG
TEL: (01647) 252937 *FAX:* (01647) 252937 *CONTACT:* Barry Fretwell
OPENING TIMES: 1000-1300 & 1400-1730 Fri-Wed, 1000-1300 Sun. Dec-Mar by appt.
No mail order
CAT. COST: 2 x 1st class *W/SALE or RETAIL:* Retail *CREDIT CARDS:* None
SPECIALITIES: Clematis. *MAP PAGE:* 1

CPla   **Plant World Botanic Gardens,** St Marychurch Road, Newton Abbot, South Devon,
TQ12 4SE
TEL: (01803) 872939 *FAX:* (01803) 872939 *CONTACT:* Ray Brown
♦   *OPENING TIMES:* 0930-1700 open 6 days (incl. Sun), closed Weds. Easter-end Sept.
MIN. MAIL ORDER UK: * *MIN. VALUE EC:*
CAT. COST: 3 x 1st class or $2 *W/SALE or RETAIL:* Both *CREDIT CARDS:* Visa, Access,
EuroCard, MasterCard
SPECIALITIES: Alpines & unusual Herbaceous plants. 4 acre world botanic map. NCCPG
Primula collections. *Note: mail order for seed only. See also SEED Index for choice seed list
(Aquilegia, Geranium, Gentian, Viola). *MAP PAGE:* 1

CPle   **Pleasant View Nursery,** Two Mile Oak, Nr Denbury, Newton Abbot, Devon, TQ12
6DG
TEL: Please write with Sae *WEB SITE:* http://www.pview.demon.co.uk
CONTACT: Mrs B D Yeo
OPENING TIMES: 1000-1700 Wed-Sat mid Mar-mid Oct. (Closed for lunch 1245-1330). Garden
open 1400-1700 Wed & Fri May-Sep.
MIN. MAIL ORDER UK: £20.00 + p&p *MIN. VALUE EC:* £20.00 + p&p
CAT. COST: 5 x 2nd class or 2 x IRC *W/SALE or RETAIL:* Retail *CREDIT CARDS:* None
SPECIALITIES: Salvias & unusual shrubs for garden & conservatory incl. Buddleja, Viburnum,
Ceanothus, Berberis, Lonicera, Spiraea. Nat. Collections Salvia & Abelia. 2 books on Salvias - the
first to be devoted to the genus. Off A381 at T.M. Oak Cross towards Denbury. See also in SEED
Index. *MAP PAGE:* 1

CPlN   **The Plantsman Nursery,** North Wonson Farm, Throwleigh, Okehampton, Devon,
EX20 2JA
TEL: (01647) 231618 *FAX:* (01647) 231618 *CONTACT:* Guy & Emma Sisson
♦   *OPENING TIMES:* Strictly by appt.
MIN. MAIL ORDER UK: 2 plants + p&p *MIN. VALUE EC:* £45.00 + p&p   *EXPORT:* Yes
CAT. COST: £1.50 *W/SALE or RETAIL:* Both *CREDIT CARDS:* None
SPECIALITIES: Unusual hardy & tender Climbers. Also SEEDS for exchange only.
MAP PAGE: 1

CPMA   **P M A Plant Specialities,** Lower Mead, West Hatch, Taunton, Somerset, TA3 5RN
TEL: (01823) 480774 *FAX:* (01823) 481046 *CONTACT:* Karan or Nick Junker
OPENING TIMES: STRICTLY by appt. only.
MIN. MAIL ORDER UK: No minimum charge *MIN. VALUE EC:* Nmc   *EXPORT:* Yes
CAT. COST: 5 x 2nd class *W/SALE or RETAIL:* Both *CREDIT CARDS:* None
SPECIALITIES: Choice & unusual Shrubs incl. grafted Acer palmatum cvs, Cornus cvs, Magnolia
cvs. and a wide range of Daphne. *MAP PAGE:* 1/2

Nursery ADDRESSES in BOLD do Mail Order to EU

CPor **Porth Veor Fuchsias,** 54 Arundel Way, Newquay, Cornwall, TR7 3AG
TEL: (01637) 877207 *CONTACT:* Mrs Mavis Morris
OPENING TIMES: By appt.
MIN. MAIL ORDER UK: £6.00 + p&p* *MIN. VALUE EC:*
CAT. COST: 2 x 1st class *W/SALE or RETAIL:* Retail *CREDIT CARDS:* None
SPECIALITIES: Fuchsia. *Note: mail order to UK only. *MAP PAGE:* 1

CPou **Pounsley Plants, Poundsley Combe, Spriddlestone, Brixton, Plymouth, Devon, PL9 0DW**
TEL: (01752) 402873 *FAX:* (01752) 402873 *CONTACT:* Mrs Jane Hollow
OPENING TIMES: Normally 1000-1700 Mon-Sat but please phone first.
MIN. MAIL ORDER UK: £10.00 + p&p* *MIN. VALUE EC:* £20.00 + p&p
CAT. COST: 2 x 1st class *W/SALE or RETAIL:* Both *CREDIT CARDS:* None
SPECIALITIES: Unusual Herbaceous Perennials & 'Cottage plants'. Selection of Clematis & Old Roses. *Note: mail order Nov-Feb only. *MAP PAGE:* 1

CPri **David Price,** 24 Crantock Drive, Almondsbury, Bristol, BS12 4HG
TEL: (01454) 615578 *CONTACT:* David Price
OPENING TIMES: Not open.
MIN. MAIL ORDER UK: £10.00 +p&p *MIN. VALUE EC:*
CAT. COST: 2 x 1st class *W/SALE or RETAIL:* Retail *CREDIT CARDS:* none
SPECIALITIES: Wide range of Rock & Herbaceous plants incl. Dianthus, Helianthemum, Lavender, Hebe. *MAP PAGE:* 2/5

CQua **Quality Daffodils, 14 Roscarrack Close, Falmouth, Cornwall, TR11 4PJ**
TEL: (01326) 317959 *CONTACT:* R A Scamp
OPENING TIMES: Mail Order only.
MIN. MAIL ORDER UK: No minimum charge *MIN. VALUE EC:* Nmc *EXPORT:* Yes
CAT. COST: 2 x 1st class *W/SALE or RETAIL:* Both *CREDIT CARDS:* None
SPECIALITIES: Narcissus Hybrids & Species.

CRDP **R D Plants,** Homelea Farm, Chard Road, Tytherleigh, Axminster, East Devon, EX13 7BG
TEL: (01460) 220206* *CONTACT:* Rodney Davey & Lynda Windsor
OPENING TIMES: 0900-1300 & 1400-1700 Mon-Fri & most weekends, Mar-end Sep. Please check first. Feb by appt. for Hellebores.
No mail order
CAT. COST: 4 x loose 2nd class *W/SALE or RETAIL:* Retail *CREDIT CARDS:* None
SPECIALITIES: Choice & unusual Herbaceous, retentive shade & woodland plants, Helleborus, plus rarities. *NOTE Please 'phone between 0830 & 0930 ONLY. *MAP PAGE:* 1/2

CRHN **Roseland House Nursery,** Chacewater, Truro, Cornwall, TR4 8QB
TEL: (01872) 560451 *CONTACT:* C R Pridham
OPENING TIMES: 1200-1800 Tue Mar-Jul.
MIN. MAIL ORDER UK: £10.00 + p&p *MIN. VALUE EC:*
CAT. COST: 2 x 1st class *W/SALE or RETAIL:* Retail *CREDIT CARDS:* Visa, Access
SPECIALITIES: Climbing Plants. See also SEED Index. *MAP PAGE:* 1

CRos **Royal Horticultural Society's Garden,** Rosemoor, Great Torrington, Devon, EX38 8PH
TEL: (01805) 624067 *FAX:* (01805) 622422 *CONTACT:* Plant Sales Manager
OPENING TIMES: 1000-1800 Apr-Sep, 1000-1700 Oct-Mar.
No mail order
CAT. COST: None issued *W/SALE or RETAIL:* Retail *CREDIT CARDS:* Visa, Access, AmEx
SPECIALITIES: National Cornus and part Ilex Collections. Many rare & unusual plants. *MAP PAGE:* 1

◆ **See also Display Advertisements**

CRow   Rowden Gardens, Brentor, Nr Tavistock, Devon, PL19 0NG
TEL: (01822) 810275 *CONTACT:* John R L Carter
OPENING TIMES: 1000-1700 Sat-Sun & Bank Hols 26th Mar-end Sep. Other times by appt.
MIN. MAIL ORDER UK: No minimum charge *MIN. VALUE EC:* Nmc   *EXPORT:* Yes
CAT. COST: £1.50 *W/SALE or RETAIL:* Both *CREDIT CARDS:* None
SPECIALITIES: Aquatics, Bog, unusual & rare specialist plants. NCCPG Polygonum &
Ranunculus ficaria Collection. *MAP PAGE:* 1

CSam   Sampford Shrubs, Sampford Peverell, Tiverton, Devon, EX16 7EW
TEL: (01884) 821164 *WEB SITE:* http://freespace.virgin.net/martin.h
CONTACT: M Hughes-Jones & S Proud
OPENING TIMES: 0900-1700 (dusk if earlier) Thu, Fri, Sat. 1000-1600 Sun. Closed 3rd Dec-3rd
Feb.
MIN. MAIL ORDER UK: £15.00 + p&p* *MIN. VALUE EC:*
CAT. COST: Sae *W/SALE or RETAIL:* Retail *CREDIT CARDS:* None
SPECIALITIES: Extensive range of good common & uncommon plants including Herbaceous,
Shrubs, Trees & Fruit. *Note: mail order to UK only. *MAP PAGE:* 1

CSCl   Scott's Clematis, Birchbrook, Birch Lane, Landkey, N Devon, EX32 7PE
TEL: (01271) 831032 *CONTACT:* John & Marianne McLellan-Scott
OPENING TIMES: Not open.
MIN. MAIL ORDER UK: £20.00 + p&p *MIN. VALUE EC:* £40.00 + p&p   *EXPORT:* Yes
CAT. COST: A5 Sae *W/SALE or RETAIL:* Retail *CREDIT CARDS:* none
SPECIALITIES: Clematis only. Note: will also be supplying wholesale from spring 1999.
MAP PAGE: 1

CSev   Lower Severalls Nursery, Crewkerne, Somerset, TA18 7NX
TEL: (01460) 73234 *FAX:* (01460) 76105 *CONTACT:* Mary R Cooper
OPENING TIMES: 1000-1700 Fri-Wed, 1400-1700 Sun 1st Mar-20th Oct.
MIN. MAIL ORDER UK: £10.00 + p&p *MIN. VALUE EC:*
CAT. COST: 4 x 1st class *W/SALE or RETAIL:* Retail *CREDIT CARDS:* None
SPECIALITIES: Herbs, Herbaceous & Conservatory plants. *MAP PAGE:* 1/2

CSil   Silver Dale Nurseries, Shute Lane, Combe Martin, Illfracombe, Devon, EX34 0HT
TEL: (01271) 882539 *CONTACT:* Roger Gilbert
♦   *OPENING TIMES:* 1000-1800 daily
MIN. MAIL ORDER UK: No minimum charge *MIN. VALUE EC:* Nmc
CAT. COST: 3 x 1st class *W/SALE or RETAIL:* Retail *CREDIT CARDS:* Visa, MasterCard,
EuroCard
SPECIALITIES: Fuchsia. *MAP PAGE:* 1

**CSpe   Special Plants, Hill Farm Barn, Greenways Lane, Cold Ashton, Chippenham,
Wiltshire, SN14 8LA**
TEL: (01225) 891686 *E-MAIL:* derry@sclegg.demon.co.uk
WEB SITE: http://www.sclegg.demon.co.uk/cat.html *CONTACT:* Derry Watkins
OPENING TIMES: 1100-1500 daily Mar-Sep. Other times please ring first to check.
MIN. MAIL ORDER UK: £10.00 + p&p* *MIN. VALUE EC:* £10.00 + p&p
CAT. COST: 4 x 2nd class *W/SALE or RETAIL:* Retail *CREDIT CARDS:* None
SPECIALITIES: Tender Perennials, Felicia, Diascia, Lotus, Pelargonium, Salvia, Streptocarpus,
Osteospermum etc. New introductions of South African plants. *Note: mail order Sep-Mar only.
See also SEED Index. *MAP PAGE:* 2/5

CSPN   Sherston Parva Nursery Ltd, Malmesbury Road, Sherston, Wiltshire, SN16 0NX
TEL: (01666) 841066 *FAX:* (01666) 841132 *CONTACT:* Martin Rea
OPENING TIMES: 1000-1700 every day.
MIN. MAIL ORDER UK: No minimum charge *MIN. VALUE EC:* Nmc   *EXPORT:* Yes
CAT. COST: 4 x 1st class *W/SALE or RETAIL:* Retail *CREDIT CARDS:* none
SPECIALITIES: Clematis, wall Shrubs & Climbers. *MAP PAGE:* 5

Nursery ADDRESSES in BOLD do Mail Order to EU

CSte **Stewarts Country Garden Centre,** God's Blessing Lane, Broomhill, Holt, Wimborne, Dorset, BH21 7DF

TEL: (01202) 882462 *FAX:* (01202) 842127 *E-MAIL:* nsy@stewarts.co.uk
WEB SITE: http://www.stewarts.co.uk *CONTACT:* Richard Loader
OPENING TIMES: 0900-1730 Mon-Sat & 1000-1630 Sun.
No mail order
CAT. COST: None issued *W/SALE or RETAIL:* Both *CREDIT CARDS:* Visa, Access, MasterCard, Switch
SPECIALITIES: Wide range of Shrubs, Trees, Climbers, Perennials, Grasses & Conifers. Some unusual. *MAP PAGE:* **2**

CSto **Stone Lane Gardens, Stone Farm, Chagford, Devon, TQ13 8JU**

TEL: (01647) 231311 *FAX:* (01647) 231311 *CONTACT:* Kenneth Ashburner
OPENING TIMES: By appt. only.
MIN. MAIL ORDER UK: No minimum charge *MIN. VALUE EC:* Nmc
CAT. COST: See below* *W/SALE or RETAIL:* Both *CREDIT CARDS:* None
SPECIALITIES: Wide range of wild provenance Betula and Alnus. Also interesting varieties of Rubus, Sorbus etc. *£3.00 for descriptive Catalogue. *MAP PAGE:* **1**

CStr **Sue Strickland Plants,** The Poplars, Isle Brewers, Taunton, Somerset, TA3 6QN

TEL: (01460) 281454 *FAX:* (01460) 281808 *CONTACT:* Sue Strickland
OPENING TIMES: 0930-1430 Mon-Wed Apr-Jul & Sep. Other times by appt.
No mail order
CAT. COST: 2 x 1st class *W/SALE or RETAIL:* Retail *CREDIT CARDS:* none
SPECIALITIES: Salvia & unusual Herbaceous Perennials incl. Nepeta, Helianthus, Origanum & Monarda. *MAP PAGE:* **1/2**

CSut **Suttons Seeds,** Hele Road, Torquay, South Devon, TQ2 7QJ

TEL: (01803) 614455 *FAX:* (01803) 615747 *CONTACT:* Customer Services
OPENING TIMES: (Office) 0830-1700 Mon-Fri. Answerphone also.
MIN. MAIL ORDER UK: No minimum charge* *MIN. VALUE EC:*
CAT. COST: Free *W/SALE or RETAIL:* Retail *CREDIT CARDS:* Visa, MasterCard
SPECIALITIES: Over 1,000 varieties of flower & vegetable seed, bulbs, plants & sundries. *Note: mail order to UK only. See also SEED Index.

CSWP **Sonia Wright Plants, Grove Farm, Stitchcombe, Marlborough, Wiltshire, SN8 2NG**

TEL: (01672) 514003 *FAX:* (01672) 541047 *CONTACT:* Sonia Wright
OPENING TIMES: 1000-dusk all year. Closed Wed & Sun.
MIN. MAIL ORDER UK: £15 Primulas only *MIN. VALUE EC:* £15 Primulas only
CAT. COST: 4 x 1st class *W/SALE or RETAIL:* Retail *CREDIT CARDS:* None
SPECIALITIES: Barnhaven Polyanthus & Primula. Grasses, grey-leaved plants, Iris, Euphorbia, Penstemon. *MAP PAGE:* **2**

CTbh **Trebah Enterprises Ltd,** Trebah, Mawnan Smith, Falmouth, Cornwall, TR11 5JZ

TEL: (01326) 250448 *FAX:* (01326) 250781 *CONTACT:* Plant Sales Staff
OPENING TIMES: 1030-1700 every day of the year.
No mail order
CAT. COST: *W/SALE or RETAIL:* Retail *CREDIT CARDS:* Visa, Access, EuroCard, AmEx, Switch
SPECIALITIES: Agave, Tree Ferns, Palms, Camellias, Gunnera & Conservatory Climbers. *MAP PAGE:* **1**

CTho **Thornhayes Nursery, St Andrews Wood, Dulford, Cullompton, Devon, EX15 2DF**

TEL: (01884) 266746 *FAX:* (01884) 266739 *CONTACT:* K D Croucher
OPENING TIMES: By appt. only.
MIN. MAIL ORDER UK: No minimum charge *MIN. VALUE EC:* Nmc   *EXPORT:* Yes
CAT. COST: 5 x 1st class *W/SALE or RETAIL:* Both *CREDIT CARDS:* None
SPECIALITIES: A broad range of forms of Broadleaved, Ornamental, Amenity & Fruit Trees, including West Country Apple varieties. *MAP PAGE:* **1**

♦ **See also Display Advertisements**

CThr   **Three Counties Nurseries,** Marshwood, Bridport, Dorset, DT6 5QJ

TEL: (01297) 678257 *FAX:* (01297) 678257 *CONTACT:* A & D Hitchcock
OPENING TIMES: Not open.
MIN. MAIL ORDER UK: No minimum charge* *MIN. VALUE EC:*
CAT. COST: 2 x 2nd class *W/SALE or RETAIL:* Both *CREDIT CARDS:* None
SPECIALITIES: Pinks & Dianthus. * Mail order to UK only.

CTor   **The Torbay Palm Farm, St Marychurch Road, Coffinswell, Nr Newton Abbot, South Devon, TQ12 4SE**

TEL: (01803) 872800 *FAX:* (01803) 213843 *CONTACT:* T A Eley
OPENING TIMES: 0900-1730 Mon-Fri, 1030-1700 Sat & Sun.
MIN. MAIL ORDER UK: £3.50 + p&p *MIN. VALUE EC:* Poa   *EXPORT:* Yes
CAT. COST: Free *W/SALE or RETAIL:* Both *CREDIT CARDS:* None
SPECIALITIES: Cordyline australis, Trachycarpus fortuneii & new varieties of Cordyline.
 MAP PAGE: **1**

CTrC   **Trevena Cross Nurseries, Breage, Helston, Cornwall, TR13 9PS**

TEL: (01736) 763880 *FAX:* (01736) 762828 *CONTACT:* Graham Jeffery
 ◆   *OPENING TIMES:* 0900-1700 Mon-Sat, 1030-1630 Sun.
MIN. MAIL ORDER UK: No minimum charge *MIN. VALUE EC:* Nmc
CAT. COST: A4 Sae with 2 x 1st class *W/SALE or RETAIL:* Both *CREDIT CARDS:* Access, Visa
SPECIALITIES: South African & Australasian Plants, Aloe, Protea, Tree Ferns, Palms, wide range of Hardy Exotics. *MAP PAGE:* **1**

CTre   **Trewidden Estate Nursery, Trewidden Gardens, Penzance, Cornwall, TR20 8TT**

TEL: (01736) 362087 *FAX:* (01736) 3331470 *CONTACT:* Mr M G Snellgrove
OPENING TIMES:
MIN. MAIL ORDER UK: No minimum charge *MIN. VALUE EC:* Nmc
CAT. COST: 2 x 1st class *W/SALE or RETAIL:* Both *CREDIT CARDS:* None
SPECIALITIES: Camellia & unusual Shrubs. *MAP PAGE:* **1**

CTrG   **Tregothnan Nursery, Estate Office, Tregothnan, Truro, Cornwall, TR2 4AN**

TEL: (01872) 520584 *FAX:* (01872) 520291 *CONTACT:* Jonathon Jones
OPENING TIMES: By appt. for collection only.
MIN. MAIL ORDER UK: No minimum charge *MIN. VALUE EC:* Nmc   *EXPORT:* Yes
CAT. COST: Sae *W/SALE or RETAIL:* Both *CREDIT CARDS:* MasterCard, Visa, Delta, EuroCard
SPECIALITIES: Unusual and rare plants from own stock. Large specimens available.
 MAP PAGE: **1**

CTrh   **Trehane Camellia Nursery, J Trehane & Sons Ltd, Stapehill Road, Hampreston, Wimborne, Dorset, BH21 7NE**

TEL: (01202) 873490 *FAX:* (01202) 873490 *CONTACT:* Chris, Lorraine or Jeanette
OPENING TIMES: 0900-1630 Mon-Fri all year (ex. Xmas & New Year) 1000-1600 Sat-Sun late Feb-May & Autumn, & by special appt.
MIN. MAIL ORDER UK: No minimum charge *MIN. VALUE EC:* Nmc   *EXPORT:* Yes
CAT. COST: Cat/Book £1.50 *W/SALE or RETAIL:* Both *CREDIT CARDS:* Visa, Access, MasterCard
SPECIALITIES: Extensive range of Camellia species, cultivars & hybrids. Many new introductions. Evergreen Azalea, Pieris, Magnolia, Blueberries & Cranberries. *MAP PAGE:* **2**

CTri   **Triscombe Nurseries,** West Bagborough, Nr Taunton, Somerset, TA4 3HG

TEL: (01984) 618267 *CONTACT:* S Parkman
 ◆   *OPENING TIMES:* 0900-1300 & 1400-1730 Mon-Sat. 1400-1730 Sun & Bank Hols.
No mail order
CAT. COST: None issued *W/SALE or RETAIL:* Retail *CREDIT CARDS:* None
SPECIALITIES: Rock plants & Alpines, Herbaceous, Conifers and unusual Shrubs.
 MAP PAGE: **1/2**

Nursery ADDRESSES in BOLD do Mail Order to EU

CTrw   Trewithen Nurseries, Grampound Road, Truro, Cornwall, TR2

TEL: (01726) 882764   *FAX:* (01726) 882764   *CONTACT:* M Taylor
OPENING TIMES: 0800-1630 Mon-Fri.
No mail order
CAT. COST: £1.25   *W/SALE or RETAIL:* Both   *CREDIT CARDS:* None
SPECIALITIES: Shrubs, especially Camellia & Rhododendron.   *MAP PAGE:* 1

CVer   Veryans Plants, The Barn, Coryton House, Coryton, Okehampton, Devon, EX20 4PB

TEL: (01822) 860302 day*   *CONTACT:* Miss R V Millar
OPENING TIMES: Essential to telephone first for appt. *Note: (01822) 860130 evenings.
MIN. MAIL ORDER UK: No minimum charge*   *MIN. VALUE EC:*
CAT. COST: 3 x 1st class   *W/SALE or RETAIL:* Both   *CREDIT CARDS:* None
SPECIALITIES: Range of hardy Perennials inc. Aster, Ornamental Grasses, Geranium & large
selection of Primroses, many rare. *Note: mail order to UK only.   *MAP PAGE:* 1

CWat   The Water Garden, Hinton Parva, Swindon, SN4 0DH

TEL: (01793) 790558   *FAX:* (01793) 791298   *CONTACT:* Mike & Anne Newman
OPENING TIMES: 1000-1700 Wed-Sun.
MIN. MAIL ORDER UK: £10.00 + p&p   *MIN. VALUE EC:*
CAT. COST: 4 x 1st class   *W/SALE or RETAIL:* Retail   *CREDIT CARDS:* Visa, Access, Switch
SPECIALITIES: Water Lilies, Marginal & Moisture plants, Oxygenators & Alpines.
MAP PAGE: 2/5

CWDa   Westdale Nurseries, Holt Road, Bradford-on-Avon, Wiltshire, BA15 1TS

TEL: (01225) 863258   *FAX:* (01225) 863258   *CONTACT:* Mr Clarke
OPENING TIMES: 0900-1800 7 days a week.
MIN. MAIL ORDER UK: £10.00 + p&p   *MIN. VALUE EC:* £10.00 + p&p   *EXPORT:* Yes
CAT. COST: 4 x 1st class   *W/SALE or RETAIL:* Both   *CREDIT CARDS:* MasterCard, Visa
SPECIALITIES: Bougainvillea, Geranium, Conservatory Plants.   *MAP PAGE:* 2

CWhi   Whitehouse Ivies, Eggesford Gardens, Chulmleigh, Devon, EX18 7QU

TEL: (01769) 580250   *FAX:* (01769) 581041   *CONTACT:* Joan Burks
OPENING TIMES: 0900-1700 daily exc. Xmas, Boxing and N.Year's Day.
MIN. MAIL ORDER UK: £17.70 + p&p   *MIN. VALUE EC:* £17.70 + p&p
CAT. COST: £1.50 or 6 x 1st class   *W/SALE or RETAIL:* Retail   *CREDIT CARDS:* Visa,
MasterCard, Switch, Delta
SPECIALITIES: Ivy - over 350 varieties.   *MAP PAGE:* 1

CWil   Howard & Sally Wills, Fernwood, Peters Marland, Ilfracombe, Devon, EX38 8QG

TEL: (01805) 601446   *FAX:* (01805) 601446   *E-MAIL:* hjwills@aol.com   *CONTACT:* H Wills
OPENING TIMES: By appt. only.
MIN. MAIL ORDER UK: £5.00 + p&p   *MIN. VALUE EC:* £5.00 + p&p
CAT. COST: 3 x 1st class   *W/SALE or RETAIL:* Retail   *CREDIT CARDS:* None
SPECIALITIES: Sempervivum, Jovibarba & Rosularia.

CWin   Winfrith Hostas, 5 Knoll Park, Gatemore Road, Winfrith Newburgh, Dorchester, Dorset, DT2 8LD

TEL: (01305) 852935   *CONTACT:* John Ledbury
OPENING TIMES: By appt.
MIN. MAIL ORDER UK: No minimum charge*   *MIN. VALUE EC:*
CAT. COST: 2 x 1st class   *W/SALE or RETAIL:* Both   *CREDIT CARDS:* none
SPECIALITIES: Hostas. *Note: mail order to UK only.   *MAP PAGE:* 2

CWit   Withleigh Nurseries, Quirkhill, Withleigh, Tiverton, Devon, EX16 8JG

TEL: (01884) 253351   *CONTACT:* Chris Britton
OPENING TIMES: 0900-1730 Mon-Sat Mar-Jun, 0900-1730 Tue-Sat Jul-Feb.
No mail order
CAT. COST: None issued   *W/SALE or RETAIL:* Retail   *CREDIT CARDS:* None
SPECIALITIES: Shrubs & Herbaceous.   *MAP PAGE:* 1

◆ **See also Display Advertisements**

CWoo   Ian and Rosemary Wood, Newlands, 28 Furland Road, Crewkerne, Somerset, TA18 8DD

TEL: (01460) 74630   *CONTACT:* Ian and Rosemary Wood
OPENING TIMES: By appt. only. Primarily mail order service.
MIN. MAIL ORDER UK: No minimum charge*   *MIN. VALUE EC:*
CAT. COST: 1 x 1st class   *W/SALE or RETAIL:* Retail   *CREDIT CARDS:* none
SPECIALITIES: Erythronium. *Note: mail order to UK only.   *MAP PAGE:* **1/2**

CWri   Nigel Wright Rhododendrons, The Old Glebe, Eggesford, Chumleigh, Devon, EX18 7QU

TEL: (01769) 580632   *CONTACT:* Nigel Wright
OPENING TIMES: By appt. only.
No mail order
CAT. COST: 2 x 1st class   *W/SALE or RETAIL:* Both   *CREDIT CARDS:* None
SPECIALITIES: Rhododendron only. 200 varieties field grown. Root-balled, not potted - for collection only. Specialist grower.   *MAP PAGE:* **1**

CWSG   West Somerset Garden Centre, Mart Road, Minehead, Somerset, TA24 5BJ

TEL: (01643) 703812   *FAX:* (01643) 706470   *E-MAIL:* wsgardencentre@compuserve.com
CONTACT: Mrs J K Shoulders
OPENING TIMES: 0800-1700 Mon-Sat, 1100-1700 Sun (Winter times vary, please phone).
MIN. MAIL ORDER UK: No minimum charge   *MIN. VALUE EC:* Nmc
CAT. COST: 2 x 1st class   *W/SALE or RETAIL:* Retail   *CREDIT CARDS:* Access, Visa
SPECIALITIES: Wide general range.   *MAP PAGE:* **1**

EAnd   Anders Nursery, 20 East Hall, Lodge Road, Feltwell, Thetford, Norfolk, IP26 4DP

TEL: (01842) 827676   *CONTACT:* Timothy Anders
OPENING TIMES: Please call for appt.
MIN. MAIL ORDER UK: £10.00 + p&p*   *MIN. VALUE EC:*
CAT. COST: Sae   *W/SALE or RETAIL:* Retail   *CREDIT CARDS:* none
SPECIALITIES: Carnivorous plants. *Note: mail order to UK only.   *MAP PAGE:* **8**

EAst   Asterby Nurseries, Dairy Farm, Church Lane, Asterby, Louth, Lincolnshire, LN11 9UF

TEL: (01507) 343549   *CONTACT:* Edwin & Elizabeth Aldridge
OPENING TIMES: Generally open but please phone first.
No mail order
CAT. COST: 2 x 1st class   *W/SALE or RETAIL:* Retail   *CREDIT CARDS:* None
SPECIALITIES: Hardy Shrubs & Herbaceous.   *MAP PAGE:* **8**

EBak   B & H M Baker, Bourne Brook Nurseries, Greenstead Green, Halstead, Essex, CO9 1RJ

TEL: (01787) 472900/476369   *CONTACT:* B, HM and C Baker
OPENING TIMES: 0800-1630 Mon-Fri, 0900-1200 & 1400-1630 Sat & Sun.
No mail order
CAT. COST: 20p + stamp   *W/SALE or RETAIL:* Both   *CREDIT CARDS:* None
SPECIALITIES: Fuchsia & Conservatory Plants.   *MAP PAGE:* **6**

EBar   Barnsdale Gardens, Exton Avenue, Exton, Oakham, Rutland, LE15 8AH

TEL: (01572) 813200   *FAX:* (01572) 813346   *E-MAIL:* barnsdale@dial.pipex.com
CONTACT: Nick Hamilton
OPENING TIMES: 1000-1700 1st Mar-31st Oct, 1000-1600 1st Nov-28/29th Feb. Closed Xmas & New Year.
No mail order
CAT. COST: A5 + 5 x 2nd class   *W/SALE or RETAIL:* Retail   *CREDIT CARDS:* Visa, Access
SPECIALITIES: Choice & unusual Garden Plants & Trees.   *MAP PAGE:* **8**

Nursery ADDRESSES in BOLD do Mail Order to EU

EBee   Beeches Nursery, Village Centre, Ashdon, Saffron Walden, Essex, CB10 2HB
TEL: (01799) 584362 *FAX:* (01799) 584362 *E-MAIL:* beenurs@argonet.co.uk
CONTACT: Alan Bidwell
OPENING TIMES: 0830-1700 Mon-Sat, 1000-1700 Sun incl. Bank Hols.
MIN. MAIL ORDER UK: See catal.* *MIN. VALUE EC:*
CAT. COST: 3 x 2nd class *W/SALE or RETAIL:* Retail *CREDIT CARDS:* Visa, Access,
MasterCard, EuroCard
SPECIALITIES: Herbaceous specialists & extensive range of other garden plants. *Note: see
catalogue for mail order details. *MAP PAGE:* 6

EBls   Peter Beales Roses, London Road, Attleborough, Norfolk, NR17 1AY
TEL: (01953) 454707 *FAX:* (01953) 456845 *E-MAIL:* sales@classicroses.co.uk
WEB SITE: http://www.classicroses.co.uk *CONTACT:* Customer advisors
OPENING TIMES: 0900-1700 Mon-Fri, 0900-1630 Sat, 1000-1600 Sun. Jan closed Sun.
MIN. MAIL ORDER UK: No minimum charge *MIN. VALUE EC:* Nmc   *EXPORT:* Yes
CAT. COST: Free *W/SALE or RETAIL:* Retail *CREDIT CARDS:* Visa, EuroCard, MasterCard
SPECIALITIES: Old fashioned Roses & Classic Roses. *MAP PAGE:* 8

EBly   R J Blythe, Potash Nursery, Cow Green, Bacton, Stowmarket, Suffolk, IP14 4HJ
TEL: (01449) 781671 *CONTACT:* R J Blythe
OPENING TIMES: 1000-1700 Sat, Sun & Mon mid Feb-end June.
No mail order
CAT. COST: 3 x 1st class *W/SALE or RETAIL:* Retail *CREDIT CARDS:* Visa, Access
SPECIALITIES: Fuchsia. *MAP PAGE:* 6

EBot   Botanicus, The Nurseries, Ringland Lane, Old Costessey, Norwich, NR8 5BG
TEL: (01603) 742063 *CONTACT:* A S Murphy
OPENING TIMES: 1000-1700 Fri-Sun & B/Hol Mons Apr-Oct. 1000-1600 Sats Nov & Mar.
MIN. MAIL ORDER UK: £15.00 + p&p *MIN. VALUE EC:* £50.00 + p&p
CAT. COST: £2.50 *W/SALE or RETAIL:* Retail *CREDIT CARDS:* none
SPECIALITIES: Historic garden plants grown in Britain from Roman times to 1850, particularly
Bulbs, Herbaceous Perennials & Shrubs. *MAP PAGE:* 8

EBre   Bressingham Plant Centre, Bressingham, Diss, Norfolk, IP22 2AB
TEL: (01379) 687464/688133 *FAX:* (01379) 688034 *CONTACT:* Tony Fry
◆   *OPENING TIMES:* 0900-1730 daily. (Direct retail Plant Centre).
No mail order
CAT. COST: None issued *W/SALE or RETAIL:* Retail *CREDIT CARDS:* Visa, Delta, Switch,
MasterCard
SPECIALITIES: Very wide general range. Many own varieties. Focus on Hardy Ornamental plants
& grasses. *MAP PAGE:* 6/8

EBrP   Bressingham Plant Centre, Elton, Peterborough, PE8 6SH
TEL: (01832) 280058 *FAX:* (01832) 280081 *CONTACT:* Tom Green
◆   *OPENING TIMES:* 0900-1730 daily. (Direct retail Plant Centre).
No mail order
CAT. COST: None issued *W/SALE or RETAIL:* Retail *CREDIT CARDS:* Delta, Switch,
MasterCard, Visa
SPECIALITIES: Very wide general range. Many own varieties. Focus on Hardy Ornamental plants
& Grasses. *MAP PAGE:* 8

EBSP   Brian Sulman, 54 Kingsway, Mildenhall, Bury St Edmunds, Suffolk, IP28 7HR
TEL: (01638) 712297 *FAX:* (01638) 515052 *CONTACT:* Brian Sulman
OPENING TIMES: Mail Order only. Special open weekend 6/7th June 1998, 12/13th June 1999.
MIN. MAIL ORDER UK: £12.00 + p&p *MIN. VALUE EC:* £12.00 + p&p
CAT. COST: 2 x 1st class *W/SALE or RETAIL:* Retail *CREDIT CARDS:* None
SPECIALITIES: Regal Pelargoniums.

◆ **See also Display Advertisements**

EBur **Jenny Burgess, Alpine Nursery, Sisland, Norwich, Norfolk, NR14 6EF**
TEL: (01508) 520724 *CONTACT:* Jenny Burgess
OPENING TIMES: Any time by appt.
MIN. MAIL ORDER UK: £5.00 + p&p* *MIN. VALUE EC:* £10.00 + p&p *EXPORT:* Yes
CAT. COST: 3 x 1st class *W/SALE or RETAIL:* Retail *CREDIT CARDS:* None
SPECIALITIES: Alpines, Sisyrinchium & Campanula. National Collection of Sisyrinchium. *Note:
only Sisyrinchium by mail order. *MAP PAGE:* 8

ECED **C E & D M Nurseries, The Walnuts, 36 Main Street, Baston, Peterborough,**
Lincolnshire, PE6 9PB
TEL: (01778) 560483 *CONTACT:* Mr C E Fletcher
OPENING TIMES: 0900-1700 Fri-Tue 1st Feb-30th Nov & by appt.
MIN. MAIL ORDER UK: See Cat. for details *MIN. VALUE EC:* See Cat. *EXPORT:* Yes
CAT. COST: 2 x 1st class *W/SALE or RETAIL:* Retail *CREDIT CARDS:* None
SPECIALITIES: Hardy Herbaceous Perennials. *MAP PAGE:* 8

ECGN **The Contented Gardener - Nursery,** The Garden House, 42 Wragby Road, Bardney,
Lincolnshire, LN3 5XL
TEL: (01526) 397307 *FAX:* (01526) 397280 *CONTACT:* Lee Heykoop
OPENING TIMES: By appt.
No mail order
CAT. COST: A4 Sae + 2 x 1st class *W/SALE or RETAIL:* Both *CREDIT CARDS:* None
SPECIALITIES: Prairie/Steppe Perennials for Dry & Damp; Woodland Edge Perennials; Grasses,
Aconitum, Digitalis, Eryngium, Geranium, Hemerocallis, Nepeta, hardy Salvia, Veronicastrum.
MAP PAGE: 8

ECGP **Cambridge Garden Plants,** The Lodge, Clayhithe Road, Homingsea, Cambridgeshire,
CB5 9JD
TEL: (01223) 861370 *CONTACT:* Mrs Nancy Buchdahl
OPENING TIMES: 1100-1730 Thu-Sun mid Mar-31st Oct. Other times by appt.
No mail order
CAT. COST: 4 x 1st class *W/SALE or RETAIL:* Retail *CREDIT CARDS:* None
SPECIALITIES: Hardy Perennials incl. wide range of Geraniums, Alliums, Euphorbia,
Penstemons, Digitalis. Some Shrubs, Roses & Clematis. *MAP PAGE:* 6

ECha **The Beth Chatto Gardens Ltd, Elmstead Market, Colchester, Essex, CO7 7DB**
TEL: (01206) 822007 *FAX:* (01206) 825933 *CONTACT:* Beth Chatto
OPENING TIMES: 0900-1700 Mon-Sat 1st Mar-31st Oct. 0900-1600 Mon-Fri 1st Nov-1st Mar.
Closed Sun & Bank Hols.
MIN. MAIL ORDER UK: See Cat. for details *MIN. VALUE EC:* Ask for details
CAT. COST: £2.50 incl p&p *W/SALE or RETAIL:* Retail *CREDIT CARDS:* Visa, Access, Switch
SPECIALITIES: Predominantly Herbaceous. Many unusual for special situations. *MAP PAGE:* 6

ECho **Choice Landscapes, Priory Farm, 101 Salts Road, West Walton, Wisbech, Cambs,**
PE14 7EF
TEL: (01945) 585051 *FAX:* (01945) 585051 *CONTACT:* Michael Agg & Jillian Agg
OPENING TIMES: 1000-1700 Thur-Sat, Bank Hols between 1st Apr & 31st Oct. Other times by
appt.
MIN. MAIL ORDER UK: No minimum charge *MIN. VALUE EC:* £10.00 + p&p *EXPORT:* Yes
CAT. COST: 4 x 1st class *W/SALE or RETAIL:* Retail *CREDIT CARDS:* None
SPECIALITIES: Dwarf Conifers, Heathers, Alpines & Rhododendrons. *MAP PAGE:* 8

ECle **Cley Nurseries Ltd,** Holt Road, Cley-Next-the-Sea, Holt, Norfolk, NR25 7TX
TEL: (01263) 740892 *FAX:* (01263) 741138 *CONTACT:* Alec or Gill Mellor
OPENING TIMES: 1000-1600 daily.
MIN. MAIL ORDER UK: £10.00 + p&p *MIN. VALUE EC:*
CAT. COST: List 2 x 1st class *W/SALE or RETAIL:* Retail *CREDIT CARDS:* Visa, Access,
Switch
SPECIALITIES: Roses. *MAP PAGE:* 8

Nursery ADDRESSES in BOLD do Mail Order to EU

ECon **Conservatory PlantLine, Nayland Road, West Bergholt, Colchester, Essex, CO6 3DH**
TEL: (01206) 242533 FAX: (01206) 242530 E-MAIL: 100724.3432@compuserve.com
CONTACT: Caroline Clements & Paul Holt
OPENING TIMES: By appt. only.
MIN. MAIL ORDER UK: No minimum charge MIN. VALUE EC: Nmc EXPORT: Yes
CAT. COST: £2.00 W/SALE or RETAIL: Both CREDIT CARDS: Access, MasterCard,
EuroCard, Visa
SPECIALITIES: Conservatory Plants. MAP PAGE: 6

ECoo **Patricia Cooper,** Magpies, Green Lane, Mundford, Norfolk, IP26 5HS
TEL: (01842) 878496 CONTACT: Patricia Cooper
OPENING TIMES: 0900-1700 Mon, Tue, Thu & Fri 1200-1700 Sat & Sun.
No mail order
CAT. COST: Free W/SALE or RETAIL: Retail CREDIT CARDS: None
SPECIALITIES: Unusual hardy Perennials, Grasses, Wild Flowers, Bog, Aquatic & Foliage plants.
MAP PAGE: 8

ECot **Cottage Gardens,** Langham Road, Boxted, Colchester, Essex, CO4 5HU
TEL: (01206) 272269 CONTACT: Alison Smith
OPENING TIMES: 0800-1730 daily Spring & Summer. 0800-1730 Thu-Mon Sept-Feb.
No mail order
CAT. COST: Free W/SALE or RETAIL: Retail CREDIT CARDS: Visa, Access
SPECIALITIES: 400 varieties of Shrubs, 390 varieties of Herbaceous. Huge range of Trees,
Alpines, Herbs, Hedging - all home grown. Garden antiques. MAP PAGE: 6

ECou **County Park Nursery,** Essex Gardens, Hornchurch, Essex, RM11 3BU
TEL: (01708) 445205 CONTACT: G Hutchins
OPENING TIMES: 0900-dusk Mon-Sat ex Wed, 1000-1700 Sun Mar-Oct. Nov-Feb by appt. only.
No mail order
CAT. COST: 3 x 1st class W/SALE or RETAIL: Retail CREDIT CARDS: None
SPECIALITIES: Alpines & rare and unusual plants from New Zealand, Tasmania & Falklands.
MAP PAGE: 6

ECre **Creake Plant Centre,** Nursery View, Leicester Road, South Creake, Fakenham,
Norfolk, NR21 9PW
TEL: (01328) 823018 CONTACT: Mr T Harrison
OPENING TIMES: 1000-1300 & 1400-1730 every day exc. Xmas.
No mail order
CAT. COST: None issued W/SALE or RETAIL: Retail CREDIT CARDS: none
SPECIALITIES: Unusual Shrubs, Herbaceous, Conservatory Plants. Huge selection of Hardy
Geraniums. MAP PAGE: 8

ECrN **Crown Nursery,** High Street, Ufford, Woodbridge, Suffolk, IP13 6EL
TEL: (01394) 460755 FAX: (01394) 460142 CONTACT: Jill Proctor
OPENING TIMES: 0900-1700 Mon-Sat
MIN. MAIL ORDER UK: No minimum charge* MIN. VALUE EC:
CAT. COST: Free W/SALE or RETAIL: Both CREDIT CARDS: Visa, Delta, MasterCard,
EuroCard, JCB, Switch
SPECIALITIES: Mature & semi-mature Native & Ornamental Trees. *Note: mail order to UK
only. MAP PAGE: 6

ECro **Croftacre Hardy Plants,** Croftacre, Ellingham Road, Scoulton, Norfolk, NR9 4NT
TEL: (01953) 850599 FAX: (01953) 851399 CONTACT: Mrs V J Allen
OPENING TIMES: Please phone.*
No mail order
CAT. COST: 2 x 1st class W/SALE or RETAIL: Retail CREDIT CARDS: None
SPECIALITIES: Rare & uncommon Perennials. *Note: The nursery is moving to a new site in
March & will be closed for a short time. All phone & mail enquiries will be re-directed.
MAP PAGE: 8

◆ **See also Display Advertisements**

ECtt   Cottage Nurseries, Thoresthorpe, Alford, Lincolnshire, LN13 0HX

TEL: (01507) 466968 *FAX:* (01507) 466968 *CONTACT:* W H Denbigh
OPENING TIMES: 0900-1700 daily 1st Mar-31st Oct, 1000-1600 Thu-Sun Nov-Feb.
MIN. MAIL ORDER UK: £5.00 + p&p* *MIN. VALUE EC:*
CAT. COST: 3 x 1st class *W/SALE or RETAIL:* Both *CREDIT CARDS:* None
SPECIALITIES: Wide general range. *Note: mail order to UK only. *MAP PAGE:* 8

EDAr   D'Arcy & Everest, (Off.) St Ives Road, Somersham, Huntingdon, Cambridgeshire, PE17 3ET

TEL: (01487) 843650 *FAX:* (01487) 840096 *E-MAIL:* angalps@martex.com.uk
CONTACT: Barry Johnson
OPENING TIMES: By appt. ONLY.
MIN. MAIL ORDER UK: £10.00 + p&p *MIN. VALUE EC:* £50.00 + p&p
CAT. COST: 5 x 1st class *W/SALE or RETAIL:* Both *CREDIT CARDS:* None
SPECIALITIES: Alpines & Herbs *MAP PAGE:* 6

EDen   Denbeigh Heather Nurseries, All Saints Road, Creeting St. Mary, Ipswich, Suffolk, IP6 8PJ

TEL: (01449) 711220 *FAX:* (01449) 711220 *E-MAIL:* heathers@zetnet.co.uk
CONTACT: D J & A Small
OPENING TIMES: By appt. only.
MIN. MAIL ORDER UK: No minimum charge *MIN. VALUE EC:* Nmc   *EXPORT:* Yes
CAT. COST: Free *W/SALE or RETAIL:* Retail *CREDIT CARDS:* None
SPECIALITIES: Rooted Heather cuttings. *MAP PAGE:* 6

EEls   Elsworth Herbs, Avenue Farm Cottage, 31 Smith Street, Elsworth, Cambridgeshire, CB3 8HY

TEL: (01954) 267414 *FAX:* (01954) 267414 *CONTACT:* Drs J D & J M Twibell
OPENING TIMES: Advertised weekends & by appt. only.
MIN. MAIL ORDER UK: £10.00 + p&p *MIN. VALUE EC:* £10.00 + p&p
CAT. COST: 2 x 1st class *W/SALE or RETAIL:* Retail *CREDIT CARDS:* None
SPECIALITIES: Herbs, Artemisia (NCCPG Collection), Cottage garden plants & Nerium oleanders (NCCPG Collection). *MAP PAGE:* 6

EEve   R G & A Evenden, 25 Penway Drive, Pinchbeck, Spalding, Lincolnshire, PE11 3PJ

TEL: (01775) 767857 *FAX:* (01775) 713878 *CONTACT:* Richard Evenden
OPENING TIMES: By appt. only, weekends May-Jul.
MIN. MAIL ORDER UK: No minimum charge *MIN. VALUE EC:* Nmc   *EXPORT:* Yes
CAT. COST: Sae *W/SALE or RETAIL:* Both *CREDIT CARDS:* None
SPECIALITIES: Bletilla species & hybrids. Pleiones. *MAP PAGE:* 8

EFer   The Fern Nursery, Grimsby Road, Binbrook, Lincolnshire, LN3 6DH

TEL: (01472) 398092 *CONTACT:* R N Timm
OPENING TIMES: 0900-1700 Sat & Sun Apr-Oct or by appt.
MIN. MAIL ORDER UK: No minimum charge *MIN. VALUE EC:* Nmc
CAT. COST: 2 x 1st class *W/SALE or RETAIL:* Both *CREDIT CARDS:* None
SPECIALITIES: Ferns & Hardy Perennials. *MAP PAGE:* 9

EFEx   Flora Exotica, Pasadena, South-Green, Fingringhoe, Colchester, Essex, CO5 7DR

TEL: (01206) 729414 *CONTACT:* J Beddoes
OPENING TIMES: Not open to the public.
MIN. MAIL ORDER UK: No minimum charge *MIN. VALUE EC:* Nmc   *EXPORT:* Yes
CAT. COST: 6 x 1st class *W/SALE or RETAIL:* Both *CREDIT CARDS:* None
SPECIALITIES: Insectivorous plants, esp. Pinguicula, Drosera & rare & exotica Flora incl. Orchids.

EFlo   Flor do Sol, Copenore Lodge, South Hanningfield Road, Wickford, Essex, SS11 7PF

TEL: (01268) 710499 *CONTACT:* Mrs M Heaton
OPENING TIMES: By appt. only from 1st Apr- 31st Oct
No mail order
CAT. COST: Sae + 1 x 1st class *W/SALE or RETAIL:* Retail *CREDIT CARDS:* None
SPECIALITIES: Conservatory plants esp. Nerium oleanders. *MAP PAGE:* 6

Nursery ADDRESSES in BOLD do Mail Order to EU

EFou **Four Seasons, Forncett St Mary, Norwich, Norfolk, NR16 1JT**

TEL: (01508) 488344 *FAX:* (01508) 488478 *E-MAIL:* four.seasons@dial.pipex.com
WEB SITE: http://ds.dial.pipex.com/four.seasons *CONTACT:* J P Metcalf & R W Ball
OPENING TIMES: No callers.
MIN. MAIL ORDER UK: £15.00 + p&p *MIN. VALUE EC:* £15.00 + p&p
CAT. COST: 4 x 1st class *W/SALE or RETAIL:* Retail *CREDIT CARDS:* Visa, MasterCard,
Switch
SPECIALITIES: Herbaceous Perennials. Aquilegia, Aconitum, Anemone, Aster, Campanula,
Dendranthema, Digitalis, Erigeron, Geranium, Helenium, Iris, Salvia & Grasses.

EFul **Fulbrooke Nursery, Home Farm, Westley Waterless, Newmarket, Suffolk, CB8 0RG**

TEL: (01638) 507124 *FAX:* (01638) 507124 *E-MAIL:* fulbrook@clara.net
CONTACT: Paul Lazard
OPENING TIMES: By appt. most times incl. weekends.
MIN. MAIL ORDER UK: £6.00 + p&p *MIN. VALUE EC:* £6.00 + p&p
CAT. COST: 2 x 1st class *W/SALE or RETAIL:* Both *CREDIT CARDS:* None
SPECIALITIES: Bamboos & Grasses. *MAP PAGE:* 6

EGar **Gardiner's Hall Plants, Braiseworth, Eye, Suffolk, IP23 7DZ**

TEL: (01379) 678285 *FAX:* (01379) 678192 *CONTACT:* Raymond Mayes or Joe Stuart
OPENING TIMES: 1000-1800 Wed-Sat 1st Apr-31st Oct.
MIN. MAIL ORDER UK: £15.00 + p&p *MIN. VALUE EC:* £15.00 + p&p *EXPORT:* Yes
CAT. COST: 5 x 1st class *W/SALE or RETAIL:* Retail *CREDIT CARDS:* None
SPECIALITIES: Herbaceous Perennials, incl. Crocosmia, Euphorbia, Kniphofia, Monarda &
Grasses. *MAP PAGE:* 6

EGle **Glen Chantry,** Ishams Chase, Wickham Bishops, Essex, CM8 3LG

TEL: (01621) 891342 *CONTACT:* Sue Staines & Wol Staines
OPENING TIMES: 1000-1600 Fri & Sat Apr 3rd-mid Oct. Also Sun & Mon on NGS open days.
No mail order
CAT. COST: 4 x 1st class *W/SALE or RETAIL:* Retail *CREDIT CARDS:* None
SPECIALITIES: A wide & increasing range of Perennials & Alpines, many unusual.
MAP PAGE: 6

EGol **Goldbrook Plants, Hoxne, Eye, Suffolk, IP21 5AN**

TEL: (01379) 668770 *FAX:* (01379) 668770 *CONTACT:* Sandra Bond
OPENING TIMES: 1030-1800 or dusk if earlier, Thu-Sun Apr-Sep; Sat & Sun Oct-Mar, or by
appt. Closed during Jan, & Chelsea & Hampton Court shows.
MIN. MAIL ORDER UK: £15.00 + p&p *MIN. VALUE EC:* £100.00 + p&p *EXPORT:* Yes
CAT. COST: 4 x 1st class *W/SALE or RETAIL:* Retail *CREDIT CARDS:* None
SPECIALITIES: Very large range of Hosta (over 700), Hemerocallis & Bog Iris. Interesting Hardy
plants esp. for shade & bog. *MAP PAGE:* 6

EGoo **Elisabeth Goodwin Nurseries,** Elm Tree Farm, 1 Beeches Road, West Row, Bury St.
Edmunds, Suffolk, IP28 8NP

TEL: (01638) 713050 *CONTACT:* Elisabeth Goodwin
OPENING TIMES: 1000-1700 (dusk if earlier) Thur-Sat 19th Mar-12th Sept, or any time by prior
arrangement.
MIN. MAIL ORDER UK: No minimum charge *MIN. VALUE EC:*
CAT. COST: £1 coin or 4 x 1st class *W/SALE or RETAIL:* Retail *CREDIT CARDS:* None
SPECIALITIES: Drought tolerant plants esp. Dianthus, Helianthemum, Sedum, Teucrium &
Vinca. See also SEED Index. *MAP PAGE:* 6

EGou **Gouldings Fuchsias, West View, Link Lane, Bentley, Nr Ipswich, Suffolk, IP9 2DP**

TEL: (01473) 310058 *FAX:* (01473) 310058 *CONTACT:* Mr E J Goulding
OPENING TIMES: 1000-1700 everyday 2nd Sat in Jan-Aug B/Hol Mon.
MIN. MAIL ORDER UK: See Cat. for details *MIN. VALUE EC:* See Cat. for details.
EXPORT: Yes
CAT. COST: 4 x 1st class *W/SALE or RETAIL:* Both *CREDIT CARDS:* None
SPECIALITIES: Fuchsia - new introductions, Basket, Hardy, Upright, Terminal flowering
(Triphylla), Species, Encliandras & Paniculates. *MAP PAGE:* 6

◆ **See also Display Advertisements**

EGra **Grasmere Plants, Grasmere, School Road, Terrington St. John, Wisbech, Cambs, PE14 7SE**

TEL: (01945) 880514 *CONTACT:* Angela Fleming
OPENING TIMES: 1000-1700 daily Apr-July & Sept; 1000-dusk Sat & Sun Oct, Nov, Feb & Mar. Other times by appt. Garden open.
MIN. MAIL ORDER UK: £10.00 + p&p *MIN. VALUE EC:* £20.00 + p&p
CAT. COST: 2 x 1st class *W/SALE or RETAIL:* Retail *CREDIT CARDS:* none
SPECIALITIES: Hardy Perennials incl. Geraniums & Grasses; Shrubs incl. Cytisus, dwarf & hedging Conifers. *MAP PAGE:* **8**

EHal **Hall Farm Nursery,** Harpswell, Nr Gainsborough, Lincolnshire, DN21 5UU

TEL: (01427) 668412 *FAX:* (01427) 667478 *E-MAIL:* hfnursery@aol.com
WEB SITE: http://members.aol.com/hfnursery *CONTACT:* Pam & Mark Tatam
OPENING TIMES: 0930-1730 daily. Please telephone in winter to check.
No mail order
CAT. COST: 4 x 1st class *W/SALE or RETAIL:* Retail *CREDIT CARDS:* Visa, MasterCard, Access, Switch
SPECIALITIES: Wide range of Shrubs, Perennials & old Roses. *MAP PAGE:* **8/9**

EHGC **Harlow Garden Centre,** M11 J7, (A414 Chelmsford turn-off), Nr Harlow, Essex, CM17 9LD

TEL: (01279) 419039 *FAX:* (01279) 428319 *CONTACT:* David Albone or Steve Lee
♦ *OPENING TIMES:* 0830-1745 Mon-Sat, 1030-1630 Sun (closed Easter Sun).
No mail order
CAT. COST: 1 x 1st class for Clematis list. *W/SALE or RETAIL:* Retail *CREDIT CARDS:* Access, Visa
SPECIALITIES: 200 varieties of Clematis and wide general range of plants. *MAP PAGE:* **6**

EHic **Hickling Heath Nursery,** Sutton Road, Hickling, Norwich, Norfolk, NR12 0AS

TEL: (01692) 598513 *CONTACT:* Brian & Cindy Cogan
OPENING TIMES: 0930-1700 Tue-Sun & Bank Hol Mons. Please ring before visiting.
No mail order
CAT. COST: 4 x 1st class *W/SALE or RETAIL:* Retail *CREDIT CARDS:* Visa, Delta, MasterCard, EuroCard
SPECIALITIES: Shrubs & Herbaceous, many unusual inc. wide variety of Diascia, Euphorbia, Hydrangea, Lonicera, Penstemon & Viburnum. *MAP PAGE:* **8**

EHoe **Hoecroft Plants, Severals Grange, Holt Road, Wood Norton, Dereham, Norfolk, NR20 5BL**

TEL: (01362) 684206 *FAX:* (01362) 684206 *CONTACT:* M Lister
♦ *OPENING TIMES:* 1000-1600 Thur-Sun 1st Apr-1st Oct.
MIN. MAIL ORDER UK: No minimum charge *MIN. VALUE EC:* Nmc
CAT. COST: 5 x 2nd class/£1coin *W/SALE or RETAIL:* Retail *CREDIT CARDS:* None
SPECIALITIES: 240 varieties of Variegated and 300 varieties of Coloured-leaved plants in all species. 220 Grasses. *MAP PAGE:* **8**

EHof **Hofflands Daffodils, Bakers Green, Little Totham, Maldon, Essex, CM9 8LT**

TEL: (01621) 788678 *FAX:* (01621) 788445 *E-MAIL:* sales@hoffdaff.kemc.co.uk
CONTACT: John Pearson
OPENING TIMES: By appt. only. Normally Mail Order only.
MIN. MAIL ORDER UK: No minimum charge *MIN. VALUE EC:* Nmc   *EXPORT:* Yes
CAT. COST: Free *W/SALE or RETAIL:* Retail *CREDIT CARDS:* None
SPECIALITIES: Narcissus.

EHol **Holkham Gardens,** Holkham Park, Wells-next-the-Sea, Norfolk, NR23 1AB

TEL: (01328) 711636 *FAX:* (01328) 711117 *CONTACT:* Mr G F T Biddle & Mrs M Gill
OPENING TIMES: 1000-1700 (or dusk if earlier) daily. Closed Xmas & Boxing Day.
No mail order
CAT. COST: 2 x 1st class *W/SALE or RETAIL:* Retail *CREDIT CARDS:* Access, Visa, Switch
SPECIALITIES: Wide range of Shrubs, Herbaceous Perennials & Alpines, many unusual. *MAP PAGE:* **8**

Nursery ADDRESSES in BOLD do Mail Order to EU

EHon **Honeysome Aquatic Nursery,** The Row, Sutton, Nr Ely, Cambridgeshire, CB6 2PF
TEL: (01353) 778889 *CONTACT:* D B Barker & D B Littlefield
OPENING TIMES: At all times by appt. ONLY.
MIN. MAIL ORDER UK: No minimum charge *MIN. VALUE EC:*
CAT. COST: 2 x 1st class *W/SALE or RETAIL:* Both *CREDIT CARDS:* None
SPECIALITIES: Hardy Aquatic, Bog & Marginal. *MAP PAGE:* **6/8**

EHul **Hull Farm,** Spring Valley Lane, Ardleigh, Colchester, Essex, CO7 7SA
TEL: (01206) 230045 *FAX:* (01206) 230820 *CONTACT:* J Fryer & Sons
OPENING TIMES: 1000-1600 daily ex Xmas.
No mail order
CAT. COST: None issued *W/SALE or RETAIL:* Both *CREDIT CARDS:* None
SPECIALITIES: Conifers. *MAP PAGE:* **6**

EHyt **Hythe Alpines, Methwold Hythe, Thetford, Norfolk, IP26 4QH**
TEL: (01366) 728543 *CONTACT:* Mike Smith
OPENING TIMES: 1000-1700 Tue & Wed, Mar-Oct inclusive.
MIN. MAIL ORDER UK: No minimum charge *MIN. VALUE EC:* Nmc   *EXPORT:* BO
CAT. COST: 4 x 1st class *W/SALE or RETAIL:* Retail *CREDIT CARDS:* None
SPECIALITIES: Rare & unusual Alpines, Rock garden plants & Bulbs for enthusiasts &
exhibitors. *Export of dry Bulbs ONLY. *MAP PAGE:* **8**

EJud **Judy's Country Garden,** The Villa, Louth Road, South Somercotes, Louth,
Lincolnshire, LN11 7BW
TEL: (01507) 358487 *FAX:* (01507) 358487 *E-MAIL:* jcg@mharry.demon.co.uk
WEB SITE: http://www.mharry.demon.co.uk *CONTACT:* M J S & J M Harry
OPENING TIMES: 0900-1800 most Fri, Sat, Sun, Mon mid Mar-end Sep. Other times by appt.
No mail order
CAT. COST: 3 x 1st class *W/SALE or RETAIL:* Retail *CREDIT CARDS:* None
SPECIALITIES: Perennials and Herbs, incl. several scarce & old varieties. *MAP PAGE:* **9**

EJWh **Jill White,** St. Davids', Recreation Way, Brightlingsea, Essex, CO7 ONJ
TEL: (01206) 303547 *CONTACT:* Jill White
OPENING TIMES: By appt. only
MIN. MAIL ORDER UK: No minimum charge *MIN. VALUE EC:*
CAT. COST: Sae *W/SALE or RETAIL:* Both *CREDIT CARDS:* None
SPECIALITIES: Cyclamen species especially Cyclamen parviflorum. See also SEED index.
MAP PAGE: **6**

EKMF **Kathleen Muncaster Fuchsias, 18 Field Lane, Morton, Gainsborough, Lincolnshire,
DN21 3BY**
TEL: (01427) 612329 *E-MAIL:* 101713.730@compuserve.com *CONTACT:* Kathleen Muncaster
OPENING TIMES: 1000-dusk Fri-Mon incl. After mid-July please phone for opening times.
MIN. MAIL ORDER UK: See Cat. for details *MIN. VALUE EC:* See Cat.   *EXPORT:* Yes
CAT. COST: 2 x 1st class *W/SALE or RETAIL:* Retail *CREDIT CARDS:* None
SPECIALITIES: Fuchsia. *Note: mail orders to be received before April 1st. *MAP PAGE:* **9**

ELan **Langthorns Plantery,** High Cross Lane West, Little Canfield, Dunmow, Essex, CM6
1TD
TEL: (01371) 872611 *FAX:* (01371) 872611 *CONTACT:* P & D Cannon
OPENING TIMES: 1000-1700 or dusk (if earlier) daily ex Xmas fortnight.
No mail order
CAT. COST: £1.50 *W/SALE or RETAIL:* Retail *CREDIT CARDS:* Visa, Access, Switch,
MasterCard
SPECIALITIES: Wide general range with many unusual plants. *MAP PAGE:* **6**

♦ **See also Display Advertisements**

ELau   Laurel Farm Herbs, Main Road, Kelsale, Saxmundham, Suffolk, IP13 2RG

TEL: (01728) 668223 *CONTACT:* Chris Seagon
OPENING TIMES: 1000-1700 Wed-Mon 1st Mar-31st Oct. 1000-1500 Wed-Fri only 1st Nov-28th Feb.
MIN. MAIL ORDER UK: * *MIN. VALUE EC:*
CAT. COST: 4 x 25p *W/SALE or RETAIL:* Retail *CREDIT CARDS:* None
SPECIALITIES: Herbs, esp. Rosemary, Thyme, Lavender, Mint, Comfrey & Sage. *Note: mail order to UK avail. from May; please phone for details. *MAP PAGE:* 6

EMan   Manor Nursery, Thaxted Road, Wimbish, Saffron Walden, Essex, CB10 2UT

TEL: (01799) 513481 *FAX:* (01799) 513481 *E-MAIL:* flora@gardenplants.co.uk
WEB SITE: http://www.gardenplants.co.uk *CONTACT:* William Lyall
♦   *OPENING TIMES:* 0900-1700 Summer. 0900-1600 Winter. Closed Xmas.
MIN. MAIL ORDER UK: No minimum charge* *MIN. VALUE EC:*
CAT. COST: 2 x 1st class *W/SALE or RETAIL:* Both *CREDIT CARDS:* Visa, Access, Switch
SPECIALITIES: Uncommon Perennials, Grasses & Fuchsia. *Note: mail order to UK only.
MAP PAGE: 6

EMar   Lesley Marshall, Islington Lodge Cottage**, Tilney All Saints, King's Lynn, Norfolk, PE34 4SF

TEL: (01553) 765103** *CONTACT:* Lesley & Peter Marshall
OPENING TIMES: 1000-1700 weekends Mar-Oct. Othertimes by appt.
MIN. MAIL ORDER UK: 4 plants* *MIN. VALUE EC:*
CAT. COST: £1 refundable *W/SALE or RETAIL:* Retail *CREDIT CARDS:* None
SPECIALITIES: Uncommon garden plants, hardy Perennials & plants for Foliage effect. *Note: mail order to UK only. **Note: nursery moving March 1998. Existing address to remain for mailing. Please phone for details after 6pm. *MAP PAGE:* 8

EMFP   Mills' Farm Plants & Gardens, Norwich Road, Mendlesham, Suffolk, IP14 5NQ

TEL: (01449) 766425 *FAX:* (01449) 766425 *CONTACT:* Peter & Susan Russell
OPENING TIMES: 0900-1730 daily except Tue. (Closed Jan).
MIN. MAIL ORDER UK: No minimum charge* *MIN. VALUE EC:* Nmc   *EXPORT:* Yes
CAT. COST: 5 x 2nd class *W/SALE or RETAIL:* Retail *CREDIT CARDS:* Access, Visa, Switch
SPECIALITIES: Pinks, Old Roses, Wide general range. *Note: mail order for Pinks & Roses only.
MAP PAGE: 6

EMFW   Mickfield Fish & Watergarden Centre, Debenham Road, Mickfield, Stowmarket, Suffolk, IP14 5LP

TEL: 01449 711336 *FAX:* 01449 711018 *E-MAIL:* mike@mickfield.co.uk
WEB SITE: http://www.mickfield.co.uk *CONTACT:* Mike & Yvonne Burch
♦   *OPENING TIMES:* 0930-1700 daily
MIN. MAIL ORDER UK: No minimum charge *MIN. VALUE EC:* £25.00 + p&p *EXPORT:* Yes
CAT. COST: £1.00 *W/SALE or RETAIL:* Both *CREDIT CARDS:* Visa, Access, MasterCard
SPECIALITIES: Hardy Aquatics, Nymphaea & moisture lovers. *MAP PAGE:* 6

EMic   Mickfield Hostas, The Poplars, Mickfield, Stowmarket, Suffolk, IP14 5LH

TEL: (01449) 711576 *FAX:* (01449) 711576 *CONTACT:* Mr & Mrs R L C Milton
OPENING TIMES: By appt. only.
MIN. MAIL ORDER UK: See Cat. for details *MIN. VALUE EC:* See Cat.
CAT. COST: 4 x 1st class* *W/SALE or RETAIL:* Retail *CREDIT CARDS:* None
SPECIALITIES: Hosta, over 425 varieties (subject to availability) mostly from USA. *Catalogue cost refundable with order. *MAP PAGE:* 6

EMil   Mill Race Nursery, New Road, Aldham, Colchester, Essex, CO6 3QT

TEL: (01206) 242521 *FAX:* (01206) 241616 *CONTACT:* Bill Mathews
OPENING TIMES: 0900-1730 daily.
No mail order
CAT. COST: Sae + 2 x 1st class *W/SALE or RETAIL:* Both *CREDIT CARDS:* Access, Visa, Diners, Switch
SPECIALITIES: Over 400 varieties of Herbaceous & many unusual Trees, Shrubs & Climbers.
MAP PAGE: 6

Nursery ADDRESSES in BOLD do Mail Order to EU

EMNN Martin Nest Nurseries, Grange Cottage, Harpswell Lane, Hemswell, Gainsborough, Lincolnshire, DN21 5UP

TEL: (01427) 668369 *FAX:* (01427) 668080 *E-MAIL:* mary@martin-nest.demon.co.uk
WEB SITE: http://www.martin-nest.demon.co.uk *CONTACT:* M & M A Robinson
OPENING TIMES: 1000-1600 daily
MIN. MAIL ORDER UK: No minimum charge *MIN. VALUE EC:* £30.00 + p&p *EXPORT:* Yes
CAT. COST: 3 x 2nd class *W/SALE or RETAIL:* Both *CREDIT CARDS:* Visa, Access, Switch
SPECIALITIES: Alpines especially Primula, Auricula & Saxifraga. *MAP PAGE:* **9**

EMon Monksilver Nursery, Oakington Road, Cottenham, Cambridgeshire, CB4 4TW

TEL: (01954) 251555 *E-MAIL:* monksilver@dial.pipex.com
WEB SITE: http://dialspace.dial.pipex.com/monksilver/ *CONTACT:* Joe Sharman & Alan Leslie
OPENING TIMES: 1000-1600 Fri & Sat 1st Mar-30th Jun, 20th Sept, & Fri & Sat Oct.
MIN. MAIL ORDER UK: £15.00 + p&p *MIN. VALUE EC:* £30.00 + p&p
CAT. COST: 6 x 1st class *W/SALE or RETAIL:* Retail *CREDIT CARDS:* None
SPECIALITIES: Herbaceous plants, Grasses, Anthemis, Arum, Helianthus, Lamium, Nepeta, Monarda, Salvia, Vinca, Sedges & Variegated plants. Many NCCPG 'Pink Sheet' plants. See also SEED index. *MAP PAGE:* **6**

EMor John Morley, North Green Only, Stoven, Beccles, Suffolk, NR34 8DG

TEL: CONTACT: John Morley
OPENING TIMES: By appt. ONLY.
MIN. MAIL ORDER UK: Details in Catalogue *MIN. VALUE EC:* Details in Cat.
CAT. COST: 6 x 1st class *W/SALE or RETAIL:* Retail *CREDIT CARDS:* None
SPECIALITIES: Galanthus, species & hybrids. See also SEED Index.

EMou Frances Mount Perennial Plants, 1 Steps Farm, Polstead, Colchester, Essex, CO6 5AE

TEL: (01206) 262811 *CONTACT:* Frances Mount
OPENING TIMES: 1000-1700 Tue Wed Sat & Bank Hols. 1400-1800 Fri. Check weekends & Hols.
MIN. MAIL ORDER UK: £5.00 + p&p *MIN. VALUE EC:* £5.00 + p&p
CAT. COST: 3 x 1st class *W/SALE or RETAIL:* Retail *CREDIT CARDS:* None
SPECIALITIES: Hardy Geraniums. *MAP PAGE:* **6**

EMui Ken Muir, Honeypot Farm, Rectory Road, Weeley Heath, Essex, CO16 9BJ

TEL: (01255) 830181 *FAX:* (01255) 831534 *CONTACT:* Ken Muir
OPENING TIMES: 1000-1600.
MIN. MAIL ORDER UK: No minimum charge *MIN. VALUE EC:*
CAT. COST: 3 x 1st class *W/SALE or RETAIL:* Both *CREDIT CARDS:* Visa, Access, Switch
SPECIALITIES: Fruit. *MAP PAGE:* **6**

ENor Norfolk Lavender, Caley Mill, Heacham, King's Lynn, Norfolk, PE31 7JE

TEL: (01485) 570384 *FAX:* (01485) 571176 *E-MAIL:* admin@norfolk-lavender.co.uk
WEB SITE: http://www.norfolk-lavender.co.uk *CONTACT:* Henry Head
OPENING TIMES: 0930-1700 daily.
MIN. MAIL ORDER UK: £15.00 + p&p *MIN. VALUE EC:* £15.00 + p&p   *EXPORT:* Yes
CAT. COST: 2 x 1st class *W/SALE or RETAIL:* Retail *CREDIT CARDS:* Visa, Access, Switch
SPECIALITIES: National collection of Lavandula. *MAP PAGE:* **8**

ENot Notcutts Nurseries, Woodbridge, Suffolk, IP12 4AF

TEL: (01394) 383344 *FAX:* (01394) 445440 *E-MAIL:* sales@notcutts.demon.co.uk
WEB SITE: http://notcutts.co.uk *CONTACT:* Plant Adviser
◆ *OPENING TIMES:* Garden Centre varies between 0830-1800 Mon-Sat & 1030-1630 Sun.
MIN. MAIL ORDER UK: £150.00 + p&p *MIN. VALUE EC:* £300.00 + p&p   *EXPORT:* Yes
CAT. COST: £4.00 + £1.00 postage *W/SALE or RETAIL:* Both *CREDIT CARDS:* Visa, Access, Switch, Connect
SPECIALITIES: Wide general range. Specialist list of Syringa. National Collection of Hibiscus. Note: please also see advertisement. *MAP PAGE:* **6**

◆ See also Display Advertisements

EOas   Oasis, 42 Greenwood Avenue, South Benfleet, Essex, SS7 1LD
TEL: (01268) 757666 *FAX:* (01268) 795646 *E-MAIL:* exotic@globalnet.co.uk
WEB SITE: http://user.globalnet.co.uk/~exotic *CONTACT:* Paul Spracklin
OPENING TIMES: Strictly by appt. ONLY.
MIN. MAIL ORDER UK: No minimum charge *MIN. VALUE EC:*
CAT. COST: 2 x 1st class *W/SALE or RETAIL:* Retail *CREDIT CARDS:* None
SPECIALITIES: Small nursery offering a range of Hardy & Half-hardy Exotic plants esp.
Bamboos, Palms, Tree Ferns, Bananas & unusual Xerophytes. *MAP PAGE:* **6**

EOHP   Old Hall Plants, 1 The Old Hall, Barsham, Beccles, Suffolk, NR34 8HB
TEL: (01502) 717475 *CONTACT:* Janet Elliott
OPENING TIMES: By appt. most days - please phone first.
No mail order
CAT. COST: 3 x 1st class *W/SALE or RETAIL:* Retail *CREDIT CARDS:* None
SPECIALITIES: Herbs, over 450 varieties grown. *MAP PAGE:* **8**

EOld   Old Mill House Garden Nursery, Guithavon Valley, Witham, Essex, CM8 1HF
TEL: (01376) 512396 *FAX:* (01376) 512396 *CONTACT:* Kirsty Bishop & Sheila Bates
OPENING TIMES: 1000-17.30 (dusk in winter) all year except 25th Dec-31st Jan. Garden open as
nursery.
No mail order
CAT. COST: 2 x 1st class *W/SALE or RETAIL:* Retail *CREDIT CARDS:* none
SPECIALITIES: Herbaceous Perennials, plus large range of Shrubs, Alpines, Herbs, Bog & Water
Plants; also Seasonal Bedding. *MAP PAGE:* **6**

EOrc   Orchard Nurseries, Tow Lane, Foston, Grantham, Lincolnshire, NG32 2LE
TEL: (01400) 281354 *FAX:* (01400) 281354 *CONTACT:* Margaret Rose
OPENING TIMES: 1000-1800 Wed-Mon 1st Feb-30th Sep.
No mail order
CAT. COST: 5 x 2nd class *W/SALE or RETAIL:* Retail *CREDIT CARDS:* none
SPECIALITIES: Unusual herbaceous & small flowered Clematis both hardy & for the
Conservatory. See also SEED Index. *MAP PAGE:* **7/8**

EOrn   Ornamental Conifers, 22 Chapel Road, Terrington St Clement, Kings Lynn, Norfolk,
PE34 4ND
TEL: (01553) 828874 *CONTACT:* Peter Rotchell
♦   *OPENING TIMES:* 0930-1700 7 days a week, 1st Feb-20th Dec.
No mail order
CAT. COST: None issued *W/SALE or RETAIL:* Retail *CREDIT CARDS:* None
SPECIALITIES: Conifers & Heathers. *MAP PAGE:* **8**

EPar   Paradise Centre, Twinstead Road, Lamarsh, Bures, Suffolk, CO8 5EX
TEL: (01787) 269449 *FAX:* (01787) 269449 *CONTACT:* Cees & Hedy Stapel-Valk
OPENING TIMES: 1000-1700 Sat-Sun & Bank Hols or by appt. Easter-1st Nov.
MIN. MAIL ORDER UK: £7.50 + p&p *MIN. VALUE EC:* £25.00 + p&p   *EXPORT:* Yes
CAT. COST: 5 x 1st class *W/SALE or RETAIL:* Retail *CREDIT CARDS:* Visa, Access, Diners
SPECIALITIES: Unusual bulbous & tuberous plants including shade & bog varieties. See also
SEED Index. *MAP PAGE:* **6**

EPfP   The Place for Plants, East Bergholt Place, East Bergholt, Suffolk, CO7 6UP
TEL: (01206) 299224 *FAX:* (01206) 299224 *CONTACT:* Rupert & Sara Eley
OPENING TIMES: 1000-1700 (dusk if earlier) daily. Closed Xmas fortnight. Garden open
Mar-Oct.
No mail order
CAT. COST: Free list *W/SALE or RETAIL:* Retail *CREDIT CARDS:* Visa, Access, MasterCard,
EuroCard, Delta, Switch
SPECIALITIES: Wide range of specialist & popular plants. 15 acre mature garden.
MAP PAGE: **6**

Nursery ADDRESSES in BOLD do Mail Order to EU

EPGN **Park Green Nurseries, Wetheringsett, Stowmarket, Suffolk, IP14 5QH**

TEL: (01728) 860139 *FAX:* (01728) 861277 *CONTACT:* Richard & Mary Ford
OPENING TIMES: 1000-1700 daily Mar-Sep.
MIN. MAIL ORDER UK: No minimum charge *MIN. VALUE EC:* Nmc   *EXPORT:* Yes
CAT. COST: 4 x 1st class *W/SALE or RETAIL:* Retail *CREDIT CARDS:* Visa, MasterCard,
Delta, Switch
SPECIALITIES: Hosta, Astilbe, ornamental Grasses & Herbaceous. *MAP PAGE:* 6

EPla **P W Plants, Sunnyside, Heath Road, Kenninghall, Norfolk, NR16 2DS**

TEL: (01953) 888212 *FAX:* (01953) 888212 *CONTACT:* Paul Whittaker
◆   *OPENING TIMES:* Every Friday & last Saturday in every month.
MIN. MAIL ORDER UK: No minimum charge *MIN. VALUE EC:* Nmc
CAT. COST: 5 x 1st class *W/SALE or RETAIL:* Retail *CREDIT CARDS:* Visa, MasterCard,
Switch, JCB
SPECIALITIES: Choice Shrubs, Perennials, Grasses, Climbers, Bamboos, Hedera. Wide range of
unusual hardy ornamental Shrubs. *MAP PAGE:* 8

EPot **Potterton & Martin, Moortown Road, Nettleton, Caistor, Lincolnshire, LN7 6HX**

TEL: (01472) 851714 *FAX:* (01472) 852580 *E-MAIL:* pottin01@globalnet.co.uk
WEB SITE: http://www.users.globalnet.co.uk/~pottin01 *CONTACT:* Mr or Mrs Potterton
OPENING TIMES: 0900-1700 daily.
MIN. MAIL ORDER UK: No minimum charge *MIN. VALUE EC:* Nmc   *EXPORT:* Yes
CAT. COST: £1 in stamps only *W/SALE or RETAIL:* Both *CREDIT CARDS:* Visa, Access,
MasterCard, EuroCard
SPECIALITIES: Alpines, Dwarf Bulbs, Conifers & Shrubs. See also SEED Index.
MAP PAGE: 9

EPPr **The Plantsman's Preference, Lynwood, Hopton Road, Garboldisham, Diss, Norfolk,
IP22 2QN**

TEL: (01953) 681439 *CONTACT:* Jenny & Tim Fuller
OPENING TIMES: 0900-1700 Fri & Sun Mar-Oct. Other times by appt.
MIN. MAIL ORDER UK: No minimum charge *MIN. VALUE EC:* Nmc
CAT. COST: 4 x 1st class *W/SALE or RETAIL:* Retail *CREDIT CARDS:* None
SPECIALITIES: Hardy Geraniums, Grasses and unusual & interesting Perennials.
MAP PAGE: 6/8

EPri **Priory Plants,** 1 Covey Cottage, Hintlesham, Nr Ipswich, Suffolk, IP8 3NY

TEL: (01473) 652656 *CONTACT:* Sue Mann
OPENING TIMES: 0930-1700 Fri-Mon 1st Mar-31st Oct
MIN. MAIL ORDER UK: £10.00 + p&p *MIN. VALUE EC:*
CAT. COST: 3 x 1st class *W/SALE or RETAIL:* Retail *CREDIT CARDS:* None
SPECIALITIES: Penstemon, hardy Geranium, Euphorbia, Campanula, Salvia. Small range of
Shrubs & hardy Herbaceous. *MAP PAGE:* 6

ER&R **Rhodes & Rockliffe, 2 Nursery Road, Nazeing, Essex, EN9 2JE**

TEL: (01992) 463693 *FAX:* (01992) 440673 *CONTACT:* David Rhodes or John Rockliffe
OPENING TIMES: By appt.
MIN. MAIL ORDER UK: £2.50 + p&p *MIN. VALUE EC:* £5.00 + p&p   *EXPORT:* Yes
CAT. COST: 2 x 1st class *W/SALE or RETAIL:* Retail *CREDIT CARDS:* None
SPECIALITIES: Begonia species & hybrids. *MAP PAGE:* 6

ERav **Raveningham Gardens, Norwich, Norfolk, NR14 6NS**

TEL: (01508) 548222 *FAX:* (01508) 548958 *CONTACT:* Carol Clutten
◆   *OPENING TIMES:* Mail Order only. Gardens open - Sun & B/Hol Mon May-July. Please phone
for details.
MIN. MAIL ORDER UK: No minimum charge *MIN. VALUE EC:* Nmc   *EXPORT:* Yes
CAT. COST: 4 x 1st class *W/SALE or RETAIL:* Both *CREDIT CARDS:* None
SPECIALITIES: Plants noted for Foliage. Variegated & coloured leaf plants, Herbaceous,
Galanthus & Hardy Agapanthus. *MAP PAGE:* 8

◆ **See also Display Advertisements**

ERea **Reads Nursery, Hales Hall, Loddon, Norfolk, NR14 6QW**

TEL: (01508) 548395 *FAX:* (01508) 548040 *CONTACT:* Stephen Read
◆ *OPENING TIMES:* 1000-1700 (or dusk if earlier) Tue-Sat, 1100-1600 Sun & Bank Hols
Easter-27th Sep & by appt.
MIN. MAIL ORDER UK: £10.00 + p&p *MIN. VALUE EC:* £10.00 + p&p *EXPORT:* Yes
CAT. COST: 4 x 1st class *W/SALE or RETAIL:* Retail *CREDIT CARDS:* Visa, Access, Diners, Switch
SPECIALITIES: Conservatory plants, Vines, Citrus, Figs & unusual Fruits & Nuts. Wall Shrubs & Climbers. Scented & Aromatic Hardy plants. Box & Yew hedging & topiary. UK grown.
MAP PAGE: 8

ERic **J W Rickeard,** The Gables, Station Road, Yoxford, Saxmundham, Suffolk, IP17 3LA

TEL: (01728) 668451 *CONTACT:* Michael Rickeard
OPENING TIMES: 0900-1800 daily except Thurs, Xmas & New Year.
No mail order
CAT. COST: None issued *W/SALE or RETAIL:* Retail *CREDIT CARDS:* none
SPECIALITIES: Hardy Perennials, particularly Geraniums. *MAP PAGE:* 6

ERob **Robin Savill Clematis Specialist, (Off.) 2 Bury Cottages, Bury Road, Pleshey, Chelmsford, Essex, CM3 1HB**

TEL: (01245 237380) *CONTACT:* Robin Savill
OPENING TIMES: Mail order only.
MIN. MAIL ORDER UK: 1 plant + p&p *MIN. VALUE EC:* 1 plant + p&p *EXPORT:* Yes
CAT. COST: £1.00 or 4 x 1st class *W/SALE or RETAIL:* Both *CREDIT CARDS:* None
SPECIALITIES: Over 450 varieties of Clematis, incl. many unusual species & cultivars from around the world.

ERod **The Rodings Plantery, Plot 3, Anchor Lane, Abbess Roding, Essex, CM5 0JW**

TEL: (01279) 876421 *CONTACT:* Jane & Andy Mogridge
◆ *OPENING TIMES:* By appt. only. Occasional Open Days, please phone for details.
MIN. MAIL ORDER UK: £15.00 + p&p *MIN. VALUE EC:* £500.00 + p&p *EXPORT:* Yes
CAT. COST: 3 x 1st class *W/SALE or RETAIL:* Both *CREDIT CARDS:* none
SPECIALITIES: Bamboo. Rare & unusual Trees. *MAP PAGE:* 6

ERom **The Romantic Garden, Swannington, Norwich, Norfolk, NR9 5NW**

TEL: (01603) 261488 *FAX:* (01603) 871668 *CONTACT:* John Powles
◆ *OPENING TIMES:* 1000-1700 Wed, Fri & Sat all year.
MIN. MAIL ORDER UK: £5.00 + p&p *MIN. VALUE EC:* £30.00 + p&p *EXPORT:* Yes
CAT. COST: 4 x 1st class *W/SALE or RETAIL:* Both *CREDIT CARDS:* Visa, Access, AmEx
SPECIALITIES: Half-hardy & Conservatory. Buxus topiary, Ornamental standards, large specimen. *MAP PAGE:* 8

ERos **Roseholme Nursery, Roseholme Farm, Howsham, Lincoln, Lincolnshire, LN7 6JZ**

TEL: (01652) 678661 *FAX:* (01472) 852450 *CONTACT:* P B Clayton
OPENING TIMES: By appt. for collection of orders.
MIN. MAIL ORDER UK: No minimum charge *MIN. VALUE EC:* Nmc *EXPORT:* Yes
CAT. COST: 2 x 2nd class *W/SALE or RETAIL:* Both *CREDIT CARDS:* None
SPECIALITIES: Underground Lines - Bulbs, Corms, Rhizomes & Tubers (esp. Crocus, Iris).
MAP PAGE: 9

ERou **Rougham Hall Nurseries, Ipswich Road, Rougham, Bury St. Edmunds, Suffolk, IP30 9LZ**

TEL: (01359) 270577 *FAX:* (01359) 271149 *CONTACT:* A A & K G Harbutt
OPENING TIMES: 1000-1600 Thu-Mon Easter-31st Oct.
MIN. MAIL ORDER UK: No minimum charge *MIN. VALUE EC:* Nmc *EXPORT:* Yes
CAT. COST: 4 x 1st class *W/SALE or RETAIL:* Both *CREDIT CARDS:* MasterCard, Visa
SPECIALITIES: Hardy Perennials, esp. Aster (n-a, n-b & species), Delphinium, Hemerocallis, Iris, Kniphofia, Papaver & Phlox. See also SEED Index. *MAP PAGE:* 6

Nursery ADDRESSES in BOLD do Mail Order to EU

ESCh   **Sheila Chapman Clematis,** Crowther Nurseries, Ongar Road, Abridge, Romford, Essex, RM4 1AA

TEL: (01708) 688581 (temporary) *FAX:* (01708) 688677 *CONTACT:* Sheila Chapman
OPENING TIMES: 0900-1700 daily Summer, 0900-1700 or dusk daily Winter, excl. Xmas week. No mail order
CAT. COST: 4 x 1st class *W/SALE or RETAIL:* Retail *CREDIT CARDS:* Visa, Access, Switch, Connect, Delta, Discover, EuroCard, Electron, JCB, Laser, MasterCard
SPECIALITIES: Over 400 varieties of Clematis. *MAP PAGE:* **6**

ESim   **Clive Simms,** Woodhurst, Essendine, Stamford, Lincolnshire, PE9 4LQ

TEL: (01780) 755615 *CONTACT:* Clive & Kathryn Simms
OPENING TIMES: By appt. for collection only.
MIN. MAIL ORDER UK: No minimum charge *MIN. VALUE EC:*
CAT. COST: 2 x 1st class *W/SALE or RETAIL:* Retail *CREDIT CARDS:* None
SPECIALITIES: Uncommon nut Trees & unusual fruiting plants.

ESis   **Siskin Plants, April House, Davey Lane, Charsfield, Woodbridge, Suffolk, IP13 7QG**

TEL: (01473) 737567 *FAX:* (01473) 737567 *CONTACT:* Chris & Valerie Wheeler
OPENING TIMES: 1000-1700 Tue-Sat Feb-Oct.
MIN. MAIL ORDER UK: No minimum charge *MIN. VALUE EC:* Nmc
CAT. COST: £1.00 *W/SALE or RETAIL:* Retail *CREDIT CARDS:* Access, Visa
SPECIALITIES: Alpines, miniature Conifers & dwarf Shrubs, esp. plants for Troughs. National Collection of Dwarf Hebe. See also SEED Index. *MAP PAGE:* **6**

ESOG   **Smallworth Ornamental Grasses,** Fourwynds, Smallworth, Garboldisham, Diss, Norfolk, IP22 2QW

TEL: (01953) 681536 *CONTACT:* Wally Thrower
OPENING TIMES: 1000-1600 Thu & Fri, 1330-1730 Sat 1st Mar-31st Oct. Other days by appt.
MIN. MAIL ORDER UK: No minimum charge* *MIN. VALUE EC:*
CAT. COST: 3 x 2nd class *W/SALE or RETAIL:* Retail *CREDIT CARDS:* None
SPECIALITIES: An increasing range of Grasses, Sedges & Rushes. *Note: mail order to UK only.
MAP PAGE: **6/8**

ESul   **Pearl Sulman, 54 Kingsway, Mildenhall, Bury St Edmunds, Suffolk, IP28 7HR**

TEL: (01638) 712297 *FAX:* (01638) 515052 *CONTACT:* Pearl Sulman
OPENING TIMES: Not open. Mail Order only. Open weekend June 6/7th 1998 & 12/13th June 1999.
MIN. MAIL ORDER UK: £9.00 + p&p *MIN. VALUE EC:* £9.00 + p&p
CAT. COST: 4 x 1st class *W/SALE or RETAIL:* Retail *CREDIT CARDS:* None
SPECIALITIES: Miniature, Dwarf & Scented-leaf Pelargoniums.

ETen   **Tennyson Nurseries, Chantry Farm, Campsea Ashe, Wickham Market, Suffolk, IP13 0PZ**

TEL: (01728) 747113 *FAX:* (01728) 747725 *CONTACT:* Sales Office
OPENING TIMES: 1000-1700 daily British Summer time, 0900-1600 daily Winter time.
MIN. MAIL ORDER UK: No minimum charge *MIN. VALUE EC:* £20.00 + p&p
CAT. COST: 3 x 1st class *W/SALE or RETAIL:* Both *CREDIT CARDS:* None
SPECIALITIES: Range of rare & unusual Hardy Plants. *MAP PAGE:* **6**

ETho   **Thorncroft Clematis Nursery, The Lings, Reymerston, Norwich, Norfolk, NR9 4QG**

TEL: (01953) 850407 *CONTACT:* Ruth P Gooch
OPENING TIMES: 1000-1630 Thu-Tue 1st March-31st Oct.
MIN. MAIL ORDER UK: No minimum charge *MIN. VALUE EC:* Nmc
CAT. COST: 4 x 2nd class *W/SALE or RETAIL:* Retail *CREDIT CARDS:* None
SPECIALITIES: Clematis. *MAP PAGE:* **8**

◆ **See also Display Advertisements**

ETub   **Van Tubergen UK Ltd, Bressingham, Diss, Norfolk, IP22 2AB**
TEL: (01379) 688282 *FAX:* (01379) 687227 *E-MAIL:* sales@vantub.flexnet.co.uk
CONTACT: General Manager
OPENING TIMES: Not open to the public.
MIN. MAIL ORDER UK: No minimum charge *MIN. VALUE EC:* Nmc
CAT. COST: Free *W/SALE or RETAIL:* Both *CREDIT CARDS:* Visa, Access
SPECIALITIES: Bulbs. *Note: Retail & Wholesale sales by Mail Order only (wholesale bulbs not listed in Plant Finder).

EWal   **J Walkers Bulbs, Washway House Farm, Holbeach, Spalding, Lincolnshire, PE12 7PP**
TEL: (01406) 426216 *FAX:* (01406) 425468 *E-MAIL:* walkers@taylors-bulbs.demon.co.uk
CONTACT: J W Walkers
OPENING TIMES: Not open to the public.
MIN. MAIL ORDER UK: See Cat. for details *MIN. VALUE EC:* See Catalogue
CAT. COST: 2 x 1st class *W/SALE or RETAIL:* Both *CREDIT CARDS:* Visa, Access
SPECIALITIES: Daffodils & Fritillaria.

EWes   **West Acre Gardens,** West Acre, Kings Lynn, Norfolk, PE32 1UJ
TEL: (01760) 755562/755989 *FAX:* (01760) 755989 *CONTACT:* J J Tuite
OPENING TIMES: 1000-1700 daily 1st Mar-31st Oct. Other times by appt.
No mail order
CAT. COST: 4 x 1st class *W/SALE or RETAIL:* Retail *CREDIT CARDS:* None
SPECIALITIES: Unusual Shrubs, Herbaceous & Alpines. Large selection of Rhodohypoxis & Grasses. *MAP PAGE:* **8**

EWFC   **The Wild Flower Centre,** Church Farm, Sisland, Loddon, Norwich, Norfolk, NR14 6EF
TEL: (01508) 520235 *FAX:* (01508) 528294 *CONTACT:* D G Corne
OPENING TIMES: 0900-1700 Fri, Sat, Sun & Tue. By appt. please.
MIN. MAIL ORDER UK: £3.80 + p&p *MIN. VALUE EC:*
CAT. COST: 2 x 2nd class *W/SALE or RETAIL:* Retail *CREDIT CARDS:* None
SPECIALITIES: British native and naturalised Wild Flower plants. 283+ varieties.
MAP PAGE: **8**

EWll   **The Walled Garden,** Park Road, Benhall, Saxmundham, Suffolk, IP17 1JB
TEL: (01728) 602510 *FAX:* (01728) 602510 *CONTACT:* J R Mountain
♦   *OPENING TIMES:* 0930-1700 Tue-Sun Mar-Oct, Tue-Sat Nov-Feb.
No mail order
CAT. COST: 2 x 1st class *W/SALE or RETAIL:* Retail *CREDIT CARDS:* Visa, MasterCard, Switch
SPECIALITIES: Tender & hardy Perennials & wall Shrubs. *MAP PAGE:* **6**

EWoo   **Wootten's Plants,** Wenhaston, Blackheath, Halesworth, Suffolk, IP19 9HD
TEL: (01502) 478258 *CONTACT:* M Loftus
OPENING TIMES: 0930-1700 daily.
No mail order
CAT. COST: £2.50 illus. *W/SALE or RETAIL:* Retail *CREDIT CARDS:* Access, Visa, AmEx, Switch
SPECIALITIES: Pelargonium, Salvia, Penstemon, Viola, Aquilegia, Digitalis, Campanula & Polemonium. *MAP PAGE:* **6**

GAbr   **Abriachan Nurseries, Loch Ness Side, Inverness, Invernesshire, Scotland, IV3 6LA**
TEL: (01463) 861232 *FAX:* (01463) 861232 *CONTACT:* Mr & Mrs D Davidson
OPENING TIMES: 0900-1900 daily (dusk if earlier) Feb-Nov.
MIN. MAIL ORDER UK: No minimum charge *MIN. VALUE EC:* Nmc
CAT. COST: 4 x 1st class *W/SALE or RETAIL:* Retail *CREDIT CARDS:* None
SPECIALITIES: Herbaceous, Primula, Helianthemum, Hardy Geranium & Sempervivum.
MAP PAGE: **10**

Nursery ADDRESSES in BOLD do Mail Order to EU

GAri **Arivegaig Nursery,** Aultbea, Acharacle, Argyll, Scotland, PH36 4LE

TEL: (01967) 431331 *E-MAIL:* arivegaignursery@btinternet.com *CONTACT:* E Stewart
OPENING TIMES: 0900-1700 daily Easter-end Oct.
MIN. MAIL ORDER UK: £10.00 + p&p* *MIN. VALUE EC:*
CAT. COST: 4 x 1st class *W/SALE or RETAIL:* Both *CREDIT CARDS:* None
SPECIALITIES: A wide range of unusual plants, including those suited for the milder parts of the country. *Note: mail order to UK only. *MAP PAGE:* 10

GBar **Barwinnock Herbs, Barrhill, by Girvan, Ayrshire, Scotland, KA26 0RB**

TEL: (01465) 821338 *FAX:* (01465) 821338 *E-MAIL:* 101344.3413@compuserve.com
CONTACT: Dave & Mon Holtom
OPENING TIMES: 1000-1800 daily 1st April-31st Oct.
MIN. MAIL ORDER UK: No minimum charge *MIN. VALUE EC:* Nmc   *EXPORT:* Yes
CAT. COST: 3 x 1st class *W/SALE or RETAIL:* Retail *CREDIT CARDS:* None
SPECIALITIES: Culinary, Medicinal & fragrant leaved plants organically grown.
 MAP PAGE: 10

GBin **Binny Plants,** West Lodge, Binny Estate, Ecclesmachen Road, Nr Broxbourn, West Lothian, Scotland, EH52 6NL

TEL: (01506) 858931 *FAX:* (01506) 858931 *E-MAIL:* binnycrag@aol.com
CONTACT: Billy Carruthers
◆   *OPENING TIMES:* 1000-1700 Thur-Mon last week Mar-middle Oct.
MIN. MAIL ORDER UK: No minimum charge* *MIN. VALUE EC:*
CAT. COST: 3 x 1st class *W/SALE or RETAIL:* Retail *CREDIT CARDS:* Visa, MasterCard, EuroCard
SPECIALITIES: Euphorbia, Grasses, hardy Geranium & many lesser known Shrubs. Herbaceous, Ferns, Alpines & Aquilegias. *Note: mail order to UK only. *MAP PAGE:* 10

GBon **Bonhard Nursery,** Murrayshall Road, Scone, Perth, Tayside, Scotland, PH2 7PQ

TEL: (01738) 552791 *FAX:* (01738) 552791 *CONTACT:* Mr & Mrs Hickman
OPENING TIMES: 1000-1800, or dusk if earlier, daily.
No mail order
CAT. COST: Free (fruit trees & roses) *W/SALE or RETAIL:* Retail *CREDIT CARDS:* Access, AmEx, EuroCard, MasterCard, Switch, Visa
SPECIALITIES: Herbaceous, Conifers & Alpines. Fruit & ornamental Trees. Shrub & species Roses. *MAP PAGE:* 10

GBri **Bridge End Nurseries,** Gretna Green, Dumfries & Galloway, Scotland, DG16 5HN

TEL: (01461) 800612 *FAX:* (01461) 800612 *CONTACT:* R Bird
OPENING TIMES: 0930-1700 all year. Evenings by appt.
No mail order
CAT. COST: None issued *W/SALE or RETAIL:* Retail *CREDIT CARDS:* None
SPECIALITIES: Hardy cottage garden Perennials. Many unusual & interesting varieties.
 MAP PAGE: 10

GBuc **Buckland Plants, Whinnieliggate, Kirkcudbright, Scotland, DG6 4XP**

TEL: (01557) 331323 *FAX:* (01557) 331323 *CONTACT:* Rob or Dina Asbridge
OPENING TIMES: 1000-1700 Thu-Sun Mar-Nov.
MIN. MAIL ORDER UK: £15.00 + p&p *MIN. VALUE EC:* £50.00 + p&p
CAT. COST: 3 x 1st class *W/SALE or RETAIL:* Retail *CREDIT CARDS:* None
SPECIALITIES: A very wide range of scarce Herbaceous & Woodland plants incl. Anemone, Cardamine, Crocosmia, Erythronium, Hellebore, Meconopsis, Tricyrtis & Trillium etc.
 MAP PAGE: 10

GBur **Burnside Nursery, by Girvan, Ayrshire, Scotland, KA26 9JH**

TEL: (01465) 714290 *FAX:* (01465) 714290 *CONTACT:* Mrs C Walker
OPENING TIMES: 1000-1900 daily except Weds, 1st Mar-31st Oct.
MIN. MAIL ORDER UK: No minimum charge *MIN. VALUE EC:* Nmc
CAT. COST: 4 x 1st class *W/SALE or RETAIL:* Both *CREDIT CARDS:* None
SPECIALITIES: Rare plants & Hardy Geraniums. *MAP PAGE:* 10

◆ **See also Display Advertisements**

GCal   **Cally Gardens, Gatehouse of Fleet, Castle Douglas, Scotland, DG7 2DJ**

TEL: Not on phone. *FAX:* Only (01557) 815029 *CONTACT:* Michael Wickenden
OPENING TIMES: 1000-1730 Sat-Sun, 1400-1730 Tue-Fri 11th Apr-25th Oct.
MIN. MAIL ORDER UK: £15.00 + p&p *MIN. VALUE EC:* £50.00 + p&p
CAT. COST: 3 x 1st class *W/SALE or RETAIL:* Both *CREDIT CARDS:* None
SPECIALITIES: Unusual perennials. Agapanthus, Crocosmia, Eryngium, Euphorbia, Hardy
Geraniums & Grasses. Some rare Shrubs, Climbers & Conservatory plants. *MAP PAGE:* **10**

GCan   **Candacraig Gardens,** Strathdon, Aberdeenshire, Scotland, AB3 8XT

TEL: (01975) 651226 *FAX:* (01975) 651391 *E-MAIL:* candacraig@buchanan.co.uk
CONTACT: Mrs E M Young
OPENING TIMES: 1000-1700 Mon-Fri & 1400-1800 Sat & Sun May-Sep or by appt.
MIN. MAIL ORDER UK: No minimum charge *MIN. VALUE EC:*
CAT. COST: Sae or 1st class for list. *W/SALE or RETAIL:* Retail *CREDIT CARDS:* None
SPECIALITIES: A wide variety of Hardy Perennials, Meconopsis & Primula. *MAP PAGE:* **10**

GCHN   **Charter House Nursery, 2 Nunwood, Dumfries, Dumfries & Galloway, Scotland, DG2
0HX**

TEL: (01387) 720363 *CONTACT:* John Ross
OPENING TIMES: 0900-1700 Mar-Oct. Other times by appt.
MIN. MAIL ORDER UK: No minimum charge *MIN. VALUE EC:* Nmc
CAT. COST: 3 x 1st class *W/SALE or RETAIL:* Retail *CREDIT CARDS:* None
SPECIALITIES: Aquilegia, Hypericum, Geranium, Erodium, Saxifraga and Campanula. Erodium
National Collection. *MAP PAGE:* **10**

GChr   **Christie Elite Nurseries,** The Nurseries, Forres, Moray, Scotland, IV36 0TW

TEL: (01309) 672633 *FAX:* (01309) 676846 *CONTACT:* Dr S Thompson
OPENING TIMES: 0800-1700 daily.
MIN. MAIL ORDER UK: No minimum charge *MIN. VALUE EC:*
CAT. COST: Free *W/SALE or RETAIL:* Both *CREDIT CARDS:* Visa, Access
SPECIALITIES: Hedging & screening plants. Woodland & less common Trees, Shrubs & Fruit.
MAP PAGE: **10**

GCLN   **Craig Lodge Nurseries, Balmaclellan, Castle Douglas, Kirkcudbrightshire, Scotland,
DG7 3QR**

TEL: (01644) 420661 *CONTACT:* Sheila & Michael Northway
♦   *OPENING TIMES:* 1000-1700 Wed-Mon late Mar-mid Oct.
MIN. MAIL ORDER UK: £10.00 + p&p *MIN. VALUE EC:* £10.00 + p&p (normally 48 hr priority
rate).
CAT. COST: A5 Sae + 4 x 2nd class *W/SALE or RETAIL:* Retail *CREDIT CARDS:* None
SPECIALITIES: Alpines, Auriculas, dwarf Rhododendron, Bulbs & Conifers. Bulbs & Alpines are
largely grown from wild seed. *MAP PAGE:* **10**

GCoc   **James Cocker & Sons, Whitemyres, Lang Stracht, Aberdeen, Scotland, AB9 2XH**

TEL: (01224) 313261 *FAX:* (01224) 312531 *CONTACT:* Alec Cocker
OPENING TIMES: 0900-1730 daily.
MIN. MAIL ORDER UK: No minimum charge *MIN. VALUE EC:* £4.15 + p&p
CAT. COST: Free *W/SALE or RETAIL:* Both *CREDIT CARDS:* Visa, Access
SPECIALITIES: Roses. *MAP PAGE:* **10**

GCra   **Craigieburn Classic Plants, Craigieburn House, by Moffat, Dumfries, Scotland, DG10
9LF**

TEL: (01683) 221250 *FAX:* (01683) 221250 *CONTACT:* Janet Wheatcroft & Bill Chudziak
OPENING TIMES: 1230-1800 Tue-Sun Easter-end Oct. Nov-Apr by appt.
MIN. MAIL ORDER UK: £10.00 + p&p *MIN. VALUE EC:* £25.00 + p&p
CAT. COST: £1.00 *W/SALE or RETAIL:* Retail *CREDIT CARDS:* None
SPECIALITIES: Codonopsis, Digitalis, Meconopsis & Primula. National Meconopsis Collection.
MAP PAGE: **10**

Nursery ADDRESSES in BOLD do Mail Order to EU

GCrs   Christie's Nursery, Downfield, Westmuir, Kirriemuir, Angus, Scotland, DD8 5LP

TEL: (01575) 572977 *FAX:* (01575) 572977 *E-MAIL:* christiealpines@btinternet.com
WEB SITE: http://www.btinternet.com/~christiealpines
CONTACT: Ian & Ann Christie & Ian Martin
♦   *OPENING TIMES:* 1000-1700 daily except Tue (closed) & 1300-1700 Sun, 1st Mar-31st Oct.
MIN. MAIL ORDER UK: 5 plants + p&p *MIN. VALUE EC:* On request   *EXPORT:* Yes
CAT. COST: 2 x 1st class *W/SALE or RETAIL:* Both *CREDIT CARDS:* Access, AmEx, Delta,
Diners, EuroCard, JCB, MasterCard, Switch, Visa
SPECIALITIES: Alpines, esp. Gentians, Cassiope, Primula, Lewisia, Orchids, Trillium &
Ericaceous. *MAP PAGE:* 10

GDra   Jack Drake, Inshriach Alpine Nursery, Aviemore, Invernesshire, Scotland, PH22 1QS

TEL: (01540) 651287 *FAX:* (01540) 651656 *CONTACT:* J C Lawson
OPENING TIMES: 0900-1700 Mon-Fri, 0900-1600 Sat & Bank Hol Suns.
MIN. MAIL ORDER UK: No minimum charge *MIN. VALUE EC:* £50.00 + p&p *EXPORT:* Yes
CAT. COST: £1.00 *W/SALE or RETAIL:* Both *CREDIT CARDS:* None
SPECIALITIES: Rare and unusual Alpines & Rock plants. Especially Primula, Meconopsis,
Gentian, Heathers etc. See also SEED Index. *MAP PAGE:* 10

**GFle   Fleurs Plants, 2 Castlehill Lane, Abington Road, Symington, Biggar, Scotland, ML12
6SJ**

TEL: (01889) 308528 *CONTACT:* Jim Elliott
OPENING TIMES: Please phone to arrange a visit.
MIN. MAIL ORDER UK: £8.00 + p&p *MIN. VALUE EC:* £20.00 + p&p
CAT. COST: Sae *W/SALE or RETAIL:* Retail *CREDIT CARDS:* None
SPECIALITIES: Primula. *MAP PAGE:* 10

GGar   Garden Cottage Nursery, Tournaig, Poolewe, Achnasheen, Highland, Scotland, IV22
2LH

TEL: (01445) 781339 *CONTACT:* R & L Rushbrooke
OPENING TIMES: 1200-1900 Mon-Sat (Mar-Oct) or by appt.
MIN. MAIL ORDER UK: £10.00 + p&p *MIN. VALUE EC:*
CAT. COST: 4 x 2nd class *W/SALE or RETAIL:* Retail *CREDIT CARDS:* None
SPECIALITIES: Large range of Herbacous & Alpines esp. Primula, Hardy Geraniums & moisture
lovers. Range of West Coast Shrubs. *MAP PAGE:* 10

GGGa   Glendoick Gardens Ltd, Glencarse, Perth, Scotland, PH2 7NS

TEL: (01738) 860205 *FAX:* (01738) 860630 *E-MAIL:* sales@glendoick.com
CONTACT: P A, E P & K N E Cox
OPENING TIMES: By appt. only. Garden Centre open 7 days.
MIN. MAIL ORDER UK: £35.00 + p&p *MIN. VALUE EC:* £100.00 + p&p   *EXPORT:* Yes
CAT. COST: £1.50 or £1 stamps *W/SALE or RETAIL:* Retail *CREDIT CARDS:* not for mail
orders
SPECIALITIES: Rhododendron, Azalea and Ericaceous, Primula & Meconopsis. Many Catalogue
plants available at Garden Centre. *MAP PAGE:* 10

**GGre   Greenhead Roses, Greenhead Nursery, Old Greenock Road, Inchinnan, Renfrew,
Strathclyde, PA4 9PH**

TEL: (0141) 812 0121 *FAX:* (0141) 812 0121 *CONTACT:* C N Urquhart
OPENING TIMES: 1000-1700 daily.
MIN. MAIL ORDER UK: No minimum charge* *MIN. VALUE EC:* Nmc
CAT. COST: Sae *W/SALE or RETAIL:* Both *CREDIT CARDS:* Visa, Switch
SPECIALITIES: Roses. Wide general range, dwarf Conifers, Heather, Azalea, Rhododendron,
Shrubs, Alpines, Fruit, hardy Herbaceous & Spring & Summer bedding. *Note: mail order for bush
roses only. *MAP PAGE:* 10

♦ **See also Display Advertisements**

Code-Nursery Index

GHCN Highcroft Nursery, By Coylton, Ayrshire, Scotland, KA6 6LX
TEL: (01292) 570209 *CONTACT:* Rose & Malcolm Macgregor
OPENING TIMES: 0900-1700 Mon-Sat & 1000-1700 Sun Apr-Aug. Other times by arrangement.
MIN. MAIL ORDER UK: No minimum charge *MIN. VALUE EC:*
CAT. COST: 2 x 1st class *W/SALE or RETAIL:* Both *CREDIT CARDS:* None
SPECIALITIES: Pansies & Violas, plus range of quality Shrubs. *MAP PAGE:* **10**

GLil Lilliesleaf Nursery, Garden Cottage, Linthill, Melrose, Roxburghshire, Scotland, TD6 9HU
TEL: (01835) 870415 *FAX:* (01835) 870415 *CONTACT:* Teyl de Bordes
OPENING TIMES: 0900-1700 Mon-Sat, 1000-1600 Sun. In Dec-Feb please phone first.
No mail order
CAT. COST: None issued *W/SALE or RETAIL:* Both *CREDIT CARDS:* Visa, Access
SPECIALITIES: Epimedium & wide range of common & uncommon plants. *MAP PAGE:* **10**

GMac Elizabeth MacGregor, Ellenbank, Tongland Road, Kirkcudbright, Dumfries & Galloway, Scotland, DG6 4UU
TEL: (01557) 330620 *CONTACT:* Elizabeth MacGregor
OPENING TIMES: Please phone.
MIN. MAIL ORDER UK: 6 plants £11.40 + p&p *MIN. VALUE EC:* £40.00 + p&p *EXPORT:* Yes
CAT. COST: 4 x 1st class or 5 x 2nd class *W/SALE or RETAIL:* Retail *CREDIT CARDS:* None
SPECIALITIES: Violets, Violas & Violettas, old and new varieties. Campanula, Geranium, Penstemon & other unusual Herbaceous *MAP PAGE:* **10**

GMaP Macplants, Berrybank Nursery, 5 Boggs Holdings, Pencaitland, E Lothian, Scotland, EH34 5BA
TEL: (01875) 341179 *FAX:* (01875) 340797 *CONTACT:* Claire McNaughton
OPENING TIMES: 1030-1700 daily mid-March-Oct
No mail order
CAT. COST: 4 x 2nd class *W/SALE or RETAIL:* Both *CREDIT CARDS:* None
SPECIALITIES: Herbaceous Perennials, Alpines, Hardy Ferns, Violas & Grasses.
MAP PAGE: **10**

GOrc Orchardton Nurseries, Gardeners Cottage, Orchardton House, Auchencairn, Castle Douglas, Kircudbrightshire, DG7 1QL
TEL: (01556) 640366 *CONTACT:* Fred Coleman
OPENING TIMES: 1200-1800 Sun, Mon & Tues Apr-end Oct.
No mail order
CAT. COST: None issued *W/SALE or RETAIL:* Retail *CREDIT CARDS:* None
SPECIALITIES: Unusual Shrubs & Climbers. *MAP PAGE:* **10**

GOrn Ornamental Grasses, 14 Meadowside of Craigmyle, Kemnay, Inverurie, Aberdeenshire, Scotland, AB51 5LZ
TEL: (01467) 643544 *CONTACT:* John & Lois Frew
OPENING TIMES: By appt.
MIN. MAIL ORDER UK: No minimum charge *MIN. VALUE EC:* Nmc
CAT. COST: 3 x 1st class *W/SALE or RETAIL:* Retail *CREDIT CARDS:* None
SPECIALITIES: Ornamental Grasses. *MAP PAGE:* **10**

GPot The Potting Shed, Upper Scotstown, Strontian, Acharacle, Argyll, Scotland, PH36 4JB
TEL: (01967) 402204 *CONTACT:* Mrs Jo Wells
OPENING TIMES: By appt. only.
MIN. MAIL ORDER UK: £1.80 + p&p *MIN. VALUE EC:* £1.80 + p&p
CAT. COST: 4 x 1st class *W/SALE or RETAIL:* Retail *CREDIT CARDS:* None
SPECIALITIES: Primula. *MAP PAGE:* **10**

Nursery ADDRESSES in BOLD do Mail Order to EU

GPoy **Poyntzfield Herb Nursery, Nr Balblair, Black Isle, Dingwall, Ross & Cromarty, Highland, Scotland, IV7 8LX**
TEL: (01381) 610352* *FAX:* (01381) 610352 *CONTACT:* Duncan Ross
OPENING TIMES: 1300-1700 Mon-Sat 1st Mar-30th Sep, 1300-1700 Sun June-Aug.
MIN. MAIL ORDER UK: £5.00 + p&p *MIN. VALUE EC:* £10.00 + p&p   *EXPORT:* Yes
CAT. COST: 4 x 1st class *W/SALE or RETAIL:* Retail *CREDIT CARDS:* None
SPECIALITIES: Over 350 popular, unusual & rare Herbs, esp. Medicinal. See also SEED Index.
*Note: Phone only 1200-1300 & 1800-1900. *MAP PAGE:* **10**

GQui **Quinish Garden Nursery, Dervaig, Isle of Mull, Argyll, Scotland, PA75 6QL**
TEL: (01688) 400344 *FAX:* (01688) 400344 *CONTACT:* Nicholas Reed
OPENING TIMES: By appt. only.
MIN. MAIL ORDER UK: No minimum charge *MIN. VALUE EC:* Nmc
CAT. COST: 2 x 1st class *W/SALE or RETAIL:* Both *CREDIT CARDS:* None
SPECIALITIES: Specialist garden Shrubs & Conservatory plants. *MAP PAGE:* **10**

GRei **Ben Reid and Co,** Pinewood Park, Countesswells Road, Aberdeen, Grampian, Scotland, AB15 7AL
TEL: (01224) 318744 *FAX:* (01224) 310104 *CONTACT:* John Fraser
OPENING TIMES: 0900-1700 Mon-Sat, 1000-1700 Sun.
MIN. MAIL ORDER UK: £10.00 + p&p *MIN. VALUE EC:*
CAT. COST: Free *W/SALE or RETAIL:* Both *CREDIT CARDS:* Visa, Access, Switch
SPECIALITIES: Trees & Shrubs. *MAP PAGE:* **10**

GSki **Skipness Plants, The Gardens, Skipness, Nr Tarbert, Argyll, Scotland, PA29 6XU**
TEL: (01880) 760201 *FAX:* (01880) 760201 *E-MAIL:* skipnessplants@geocities.com
WEB SITE: http://www.geocities.com/eureka/7627/ *CONTACT:* Bill & Joan McHugh
OPENING TIMES: 0900-1800 Mon-Fri, 0900-1600 Sat-Sun, Feb-Nov.
MIN. MAIL ORDER UK: No minimum charge *MIN. VALUE EC:* Nmc
CAT. COST: £1.00* *W/SALE or RETAIL:* Both *CREDIT CARDS:* None
SPECIALITIES: Unusual Herbaceous Perennials, Shrubs, Climbers & Grasses. *Catalogue cost refundable on first order. *MAP PAGE:* **10**

GTou **Tough Alpine Nursery, Westhaybogs, Tough, Alford, Aberdeenshire, Scotland, AB33 8DU**
TEL: (01975) 562783 *FAX:* (01975) 563561 *CONTACT:* Fred & Monika Carrie
OPENING TIMES: 1st Mar-31st Oct. Please check first.
MIN. MAIL ORDER UK: £15.00 + p&p *MIN. VALUE EC:* £15.00 + p&p   *EXPORT:* Yes
CAT. COST: 3 x 2nd class *W/SALE or RETAIL:* Both *CREDIT CARDS:* None
SPECIALITIES: Alpines *MAP PAGE:* **10**

GTro **Tropic House, Langford Nursery, Carty Port, Newton Stewart, Wigtownshire, Scotland, DG8 6AY**
TEL: (01671) 402485, (01671) 404050 *CONTACT:* Mrs A F Langford
OPENING TIMES: 1000-1700 daily Easter-end Oct. Other times by appt.
MIN. MAIL ORDER UK: No minimum charge *MIN. VALUE EC:* £20.00 + p&p *EXPORT:* Yes
CAT. COST: Sae *W/SALE or RETAIL:* Retail *CREDIT CARDS:* None
SPECIALITIES: Carnivorous. *MAP PAGE:* **10**

GTwe **J Tweedie Fruit Trees,** Maryfield Road Nursery, Maryfield, Nr Terregles, Dumfries, Dumfrieshire, Scotland, DG2 9TH
TEL: (01387) 720880 *CONTACT:* John Tweedie
◆ *OPENING TIMES:* Saturdays, 0930-1400 from 21st Oct-Mar. Other times by appt.
MIN. MAIL ORDER UK: No minimum charge *MIN. VALUE EC:*
CAT. COST: Sae *W/SALE or RETAIL:* Retail *CREDIT CARDS:* None
SPECIALITIES: Fruit trees & bushes. A wide range of old & new varieties. *MAP PAGE:* **10**

◆ **See also Display Advertisements**

IBal   Ballydorn Bulb Farm, Killinchy, Newtownards, Co. Down, N Ireland, BT23 6QB
TEL: (01238) 541250 *CONTACT:* Sir Frank & Lady Harrison
OPENING TIMES: Not open.
MIN. MAIL ORDER UK: £15.00 + p&p *MIN. VALUE EC:* £25.00 + p&p   *EXPORT:* Yes
CAT. COST: 4 x 1st class *W/SALE or RETAIL:* Retail *CREDIT CARDS:* None
SPECIALITIES: New Daffodil varieties for Exhibitors and Hybridisers.

IBlr   Ballyrogan Nurseries, The Grange, Ballyrogan, Newtownards, Co. Down, N Ireland, BT23 4SD
TEL: (01247) 810451 eves *CONTACT:* Gary Dunlop
OPENING TIMES: Only open, by appt., for viewingof national collections of Crocosmia, Celmisia & Euphorbia.
MIN. MAIL ORDER UK: £10.00 + p&p *MIN. VALUE EC:* £20.00 + p&p
CAT. COST: 2 x 1st class *W/SALE or RETAIL:* Both *CREDIT CARDS:* None
SPECIALITIES: Choice Herbaceous & Shrubs. Agapanthus, Celmisia, Crocosmia, Euphorbia, Hardy Geraniums, Meconopsis, Grasses & Iris. *MAP PAGE:* 11

IBro   Brookwood Nurseries, 18 Tonlegee Road, Coolock, Dublin 5, Rep. of Ireland
TEL: (00) 353-1-847 3298 *CONTACT:* Jim Maher
OPENING TIMES: For Collection ONLY. 1st Feb-30th Apr.
MIN. MAIL ORDER UK: £5.00 + p&p *MIN. VALUE EC:* £5.00 + p&p
CAT. COST: 2 x 1st class *W/SALE or RETAIL:* Retail *CREDIT CARDS:* None
SPECIALITIES: Hybrid Crocosmia rarities & hardy Cyclamen.

ICar   Carncairn Daffodils, Broughshane, Ballymena, Co. Antrim, N Ireland, BT43 7HF
TEL: (01266) 861216 *FAX:* (01266) 861216 (please phone first)
CONTACT: Mr & Mrs R H Reade
OPENING TIMES: 1000-1700 Mon-Fri. Please phone in advance.
MIN. MAIL ORDER UK: No minimum charge *MIN. VALUE EC:* Nmc   *EXPORT:* Yes
CAT. COST: Free *W/SALE or RETAIL:* Both *CREDIT CARDS:* None
SPECIALITIES: Old and new Narcissus cultivars, mainly for show. *MAP PAGE:* 11

ICrw   Carewswood Garden Centre, Carewswood House, Castlemartyr, Co. Cork, Rep. of Ireland
TEL: 00 353 (0)21 667283 *FAX:* 00 353 (0)21 667673 *CONTACT:* Gillian Hornibrook
OPENING TIMES: 0900-1800 Mon-Sat & 1200-1800 Sun.
MIN. MAIL ORDER UK: £20.00 + p&p *MIN. VALUE EC:* £20.00 + p&p   *EXPORT:* Yes
CAT. COST: £1.00 *W/SALE or RETAIL:* Retail *CREDIT CARDS:* Visa, Access, AmEx
SPECIALITIES: Rare & unusual Shrubs, Alpines & Herbaceous plants. *MAP PAGE:* 11

IDac   Dacus Plants, P O Box No. 5326, Dunlaoghaire, Co. Dublin, Ireland
TEL: FAX: 01 2809602 *CONTACT:* Carl Dacus
OPENING TIMES: Not open to public.
MIN. MAIL ORDER UK: £10.00 + p&p *MIN. VALUE EC:* £10.00 + p&p   *EXPORT:* Yes
CAT. COST: Free *W/SALE or RETAIL:* Both *CREDIT CARDS:* none
SPECIALITIES: Alpines, Perennials & Shrubs, many rare & unusual, growing from collected seed. South American & South African plants.

IDee   Deelish Garden Centre, Skibbereen, Co. Cork, Rep. of Ireland
TEL: 00 353 (0)28 21374 *FAX:* 00 353 (0)28 21374 *CONTACT:* Bill & Rain Chase
OPENING TIMES: 1000-1300 & 1400-1800 Mon-Sat, 1400-1800 Sun.
MIN. MAIL ORDER UK: IR£50.00 + p&p *MIN. VALUE EC:* IR£100.00 + p&p
CAT. COST: Sae *W/SALE or RETAIL:* Retail *CREDIT CARDS:* Visa, Access
SPECIALITIES: Unusual plants for the mild coastal climate of Ireland. Conservatory plants. Sole Irish agents for Chase Organic Seeds. *MAP PAGE:* 11

Nursery ADDRESSES in BOLD do Mail Order to EU

IDic   **Dickson Nurseries Ltd, Milecross Road, Newtownards, Co. Down, N Ireland, BT23 4SS**

TEL: (01247) 812206 *FAX:* (01247) 813366 *CONTACT:* A P C Dickson OBE.
OPENING TIMES: 0800-1230 & 1300-1700 Mon-Thur. 0800-1245 Fri.
MIN. MAIL ORDER UK: One plant *MIN. VALUE EC:* £25.00 + p&p   *EXPORT:* Yes
CAT. COST: Free *W/SALE or RETAIL:* Both *CREDIT CARDS:* None
SPECIALITIES: Roses, especially modern Dickson varieties. *MAP PAGE:* 11

IDun   **Brian Duncan, Novelty & Exhibition Daffodils, 15 Ballynahatty Road, Omagh, Co. Tyrone, N Ireland, BT78 1PN**

TEL: (01662) 242931 *FAX:* (01662) 242931 *CONTACT:* Brian Duncan
OPENING TIMES: By appt. only.
MIN. MAIL ORDER UK: £20.00 + p&p *MIN. VALUE EC:* £20.00 + p&p   *EXPORT:* Yes
CAT. COST: £1.00 inc p&p *W/SALE or RETAIL:* Both *CREDIT CARDS:* None
SPECIALITIES: New hybrid & Exhibition Daffodils & Narcissus. *MAP PAGE:* 11

IHar   **Harry Byrne's Garden Centre,** Castlepark Road, Sandycove, Dublin, Eire

TEL: 01 2803887 *FAX:* 01 2801077 *E-MAIL:* dburn@indigo.ie *CONTACT:* H Byrne
OPENING TIMES: 0900-1730 Mon-Sat 1200-1730 Sun & Public Hols.
MIN. MAIL ORDER UK: £20.00 + p&p* *MIN. VALUE EC:*
CAT. COST: £1.00 Roses & Clematis only. *W/SALE or RETAIL:* Retail *CREDIT CARDS:* Visa, MasterCard
SPECIALITIES: Roses, Clematis, Patio & Basket Plants. Wide variety of Trees, Shrubs, Herbaceous, Alpines. *Note: mail order to UK & Eire only. *MAP PAGE:* 11

IHos   **Hosford's Geraniums & Garden Centre, Cappa, Enniskeane, Co. Cork, Rep. of Ireland**

TEL: 00 353 (0)2339159 *FAX:* 00 353 (0)2339300 *CONTACT:* John Hosford
OPENING TIMES: 0900-1800 Mon-Sat, 1400-1730 Sun March-Xmas.
MIN. MAIL ORDER UK: £10.00 + p&p *MIN. VALUE EC:* £10.00 + p&p   *EXPORT:* Yes
CAT. COST: IR£1.50 *W/SALE or RETAIL:* Retail *CREDIT CARDS:* Visa, Access, AmEx, Diners, Laser
SPECIALITIES: Hardy Geraniums, Pelargoniums, Basket & Window box plants, Bedding & Roses. NOTE: Express Courier service available within Ireland. *MAP PAGE:* 11

IIve   **Iverna Herbs, Glenmalure, Rathdrum, Co. Wicklow, Rep. of Ireland**

TEL: CONTACT: Peter O'Neill
OPENING TIMES: Mail order, or write for appt.
MIN. MAIL ORDER UK: No minimum charge *MIN. VALUE EC:* Nmc   *EXPORT:* Yes
CAT. COST: 3 x IRCs or £1.50 (refundable). *W/SALE or RETAIL:* Retail *CREDIT CARDS:* none
SPECIALITIES: Organically grown Herbs - Culinery, Medicinal & Aromatic. *MAP PAGE:* 11

ILis   **Lisdoonan Herbs,** 98 Belfast Road, Saintfield, Co. Down, N Ireland, BT24 7HF

TEL: (01232) 813624 *CONTACT:* Barbara Pilcher
OPENING TIMES: Most days - please phone to check.
No mail order
CAT. COST: 2 x 1st class *W/SALE or RETAIL:* Both *CREDIT CARDS:* None
SPECIALITIES: Aromatics, Herbs, kitchen garden plants, some native species. Freshly cut herbs & salads. *MAP PAGE:* 11

IOrc   **Orchardstown Nurseries, 4 Miles Out, Cork Road, Waterford, Rep. of Ireland**

TEL: 00 353 51384273 *FAX:* 00 353 51384422 *E-MAIL:* otown@iol.ie *CONTACT:* Ron Dool
OPENING TIMES: 0900-1800 Mon-Sat, 1400-1800 Sun.
MIN. MAIL ORDER UK: No minimum charge* *MIN. VALUE EC:* Nmc   *EXPORT:* Yes
CAT. COST: List £1.50 *W/SALE or RETAIL:* Retail *CREDIT CARDS:* none
SPECIALITIES: Unusual hardy plants incl. Shrubs, Shrub Roses, Trees, Climbers, Rhododendron species & Water plants. *Note: Only SOME plants Mail Order. *MAP PAGE:* 11

◆ **See also Display Advertisements**

Code-Nursery Index

ISea   **Seaforde Gardens, Seaforde, Co. Down, N Ireland, BT30 8PG**
  TEL: (01396) 811225   *FAX:* (01396) 811370   *CONTACT:* P Forde
  OPENING TIMES: 1000-1700 Mon-Fri all year. 1000-1700 Sat & 1300-1800 Sun mid Feb-end Oct.
  MIN. MAIL ORDER UK: No minimum charge   *MIN. VALUE EC:* Nmc   *EXPORT:* Yes
  CAT. COST: Free   *W/SALE or RETAIL:* Both   *CREDIT CARDS:* None
  SPECIALITIES: Over 700 varieties of self-propagated Trees & Shrubs. National Collection of
  Eucryphia.   *MAP PAGE:* **11**

ISta   **Stam's Nurseries,** The Garden House, Cappoquin, Co. Waterford, Rep. of Ireland
  TEL: 00 353 (0)5854787   *FAX:* 00 353 (0)5852083   *E-MAIL:* stam@iol.ie
  WEB SITE: http://www.se_growers.ie   *CONTACT:* Peter Stam
  OPENING TIMES: By appt. only.
  No mail order
  CAT. COST: Sae   *W/SALE or RETAIL:* Both   *CREDIT CARDS:* None
  SPECIALITIES: Bamboos.   *MAP PAGE:* **11**

ITim   **Timpany Nurseries, 77 Magheratimpany Road, Ballynahinch, Co. Down, N Ireland,
  BT24 8PA**
  TEL: (01238) 562812   *FAX:* (01238) 562812   *CONTACT:* Susan Tindall
  OPENING TIMES: 1100-1800 Tue-Fri, 1000-1800 Sat & Bank Hols.
  MIN. MAIL ORDER UK: No minimum charge   *MIN. VALUE EC:* £30.00 + p&p   *EXPORT:* Yes
  CAT. COST: 75p in stamps   *W/SALE or RETAIL:* Retail   *CREDIT CARDS:* Visa, Access,
  MasterCard
  SPECIALITIES: Celmisia, Androsace, Primula, Saxifraga, Helichrysum & Dianthus.
  MAP PAGE: **11**

LAma   **Jacques Amand Ltd, The Nurseries, 145 Clamp Hill, Stanmore, Middlesex, HA7 3JS**
  TEL: (0181) 427 3968   *FAX:* (0181) 954 6784   *CONTACT:* Sales Office
  OPENING TIMES: 0900-1700 Mon-Fri, 0900-1400 Sat-Sun. Limited Sun opening in Dec & Jan.
  MIN. MAIL ORDER UK: No minimum charge   *MIN. VALUE EC:* Nmc   *EXPORT:* Yes
  CAT. COST: Free   *W/SALE or RETAIL:* Both   *CREDIT CARDS:* Visa, AmEx, Access
  SPECIALITIES: Rare and unusual species Bulbs.   *MAP PAGE:* **6**

LAyl   **Aylett Nurseries Ltd,** North Orbital Road, London Colney, St Albans, Hertfordshire,
  AL2 1DH
  TEL: (01727) 822255   *FAX:* (01727) 823024   *E-MAIL:* aylett_nurseries@compuserve.com
  CONTACT: Roger S Aylett
  OPENING TIMES: 0830-1730 Mon-Fri, 0830-1700 Sat, 1030-1600 Sun.
  No mail order
  CAT. COST: Free   *W/SALE or RETAIL:* Both   *CREDIT CARDS:* MasterCard, Switch, Visa,
  Connect
  SPECIALITIES: Dahlias.   *MAP PAGE:* **6**

LBay   **Bay Tree Cottage Plants,** Bay Tree Cottage, Callow Hill, Virginia Water, Surrey,
  GU25 4LH
  TEL: (01344) 844320   *CONTACT:* Linda Regel
  OPENING TIMES: Open by appt.
  MIN. MAIL ORDER UK: £5.00 + p&p*   *MIN. VALUE EC:*
  CAT. COST: 3 x 1st class   *W/SALE or RETAIL:* Retail   *CREDIT CARDS:* none
  SPECIALITIES: Interesting & old fashioned Cottage Garden Perennials incl. Aquilegia, Dianthus,
  Geranium, Lavender & Herbs. *Note: mail order to UK only.   *MAP PAGE:* **3**

LBee   **Beechcroft Nursery,** 127 Reigate Road, Ewell, Surrey, KT17 3DE
  TEL: 0181 393 4265   *FAX:* 0181 393 4265   *CONTACT:* C Kimber
  OPENING TIMES: 1000-1700 May-Sept. 1000-1600 Oct-Apr, Bank Hols & Suns. Closed
  Xmas-New Year & August.
  No mail order
  CAT. COST: 2 x 1st class   *W/SALE or RETAIL:* Both   *CREDIT CARDS:* Visa, Access, Switch
  SPECIALITIES: Conifers & Alpines   *MAP PAGE:* **3**

Nursery ADDRESSES in BOLD do Mail Order to EU

LBlm **Bloomsbury,** Upper Lodge Farm, Padworth Common, Reading, Berkshire, RG7 4JD
TEL: (0118) 970 0239 *CONTACT:* Susan Oakley
OPENING TIMES: By appt. and NGS days incl. 1st Tues monthly, May-Oct.
MIN. MAIL ORDER UK: £15.00 + p&p* *MIN. VALUE EC:*
CAT. COST: 5 x 1st class *W/SALE or RETAIL:* Retail *CREDIT CARDS:* None
SPECIALITIES: Selected range of good Conservatory and Garden perennials, esp. Geranium, Iris, Salvia, White flowers & borderline-hardy Exotics. *Note: mail order to UK only. *MAP PAGE:* 2

LBlo **Terence Bloch - Plantsman,** 9 Colberg Place, Stamford Hill, London, N16 5RA
TEL: (0181) 802 2535 *CONTACT:* Mr T Bloch
OPENING TIMES: Mail order only.
MIN. MAIL ORDER UK: £15.00 + p&p* *MIN. VALUE EC:*
CAT. COST: 6 x 1st class *W/SALE or RETAIL:* Retail *CREDIT CARDS:* None
SPECIALITIES: Tropical Plants for the conservatory/home; plants for sub-tropical summer bedding; some rare fruiting species. *Note: mail order to UK only.

LBow **Rupert Bowlby, Gatton, Reigate, Surrey, RH2 0TA**
TEL: (01737) 642221 *FAX:* (01737) 642221 *CONTACT:* Rupert Bowlby
OPENING TIMES: Sat & Sun pm in Mar & Sep-Oct.
MIN. MAIL ORDER UK: No minimum charge *MIN. VALUE EC:* Nmc
CAT. COST: 3 x 2nd class *W/SALE or RETAIL:* Retail *CREDIT CARDS:* None
SPECIALITIES: Unusual Bulbs & Corms. *MAP PAGE:* 3

LBre **Bressingham Plant Centre,** Dorney, Windsor, Buckinghamshire, SL4 6QP
TEL: (01628) 669999 *FAX:* (01628) 669693 *CONTACT:* Peter Freeman
◆ *OPENING TIMES:* 0900-1730 daily. (Direct retail Plant Centre).
No mail order
CAT. COST: None issued *W/SALE or RETAIL:* Retail *CREDIT CARDS:* Delta, Switch, MasterCard, Visa
SPECIALITIES: Very wide general range. Many own varieties. Focus on Hardy Ornamental plants & Grasses. *MAP PAGE:* 3

LBro **Mrs P J Brown, V H Humphrey-The Iris Specialist, Westlees Farm, Logmore Lane, Westcott, Dorking, Surrey, RH4 3JN**
TEL: (01306) 889827 *FAX:* (01306) 889371 *CONTACT:* Mrs P J Brown
◆ *OPENING TIMES:* Open days 1100-1500 Sat 16th & Sun 17th May 1998. Otherwise by appt.
MIN. MAIL ORDER UK: No minimum charge *MIN. VALUE EC:* Nmc *EXPORT:* Yes
CAT. COST: Sae or 3 x 1st class *W/SALE or RETAIL:* Both *CREDIT CARDS:* None
SPECIALITIES: Bearded, Spuria, Siberian, Pacific Coast, species & Japanese Iris.
MAP PAGE: 3

LBuc **Buckingham Nurseries, 14 Tingewick Road, Buckingham, Buckinghamshire, MK18 4AE**
TEL: (01280) 813556 *FAX:* (01280) 815491 *CONTACT:* R J & P L Brown
◆ *OPENING TIMES:* 0830-1730 (1800 in summer) Mon-Fri, 0930-1730 (1800 in summer) Sun.
MIN. MAIL ORDER UK: No minimum charge *MIN. VALUE EC:* Nmc
CAT. COST: Free *W/SALE or RETAIL:* Retail *CREDIT CARDS:* Visa, Access
SPECIALITIES: Bare rooted and container grown hedging. Trees, Shrubs, Herbaceous Perennials, Alpines, Grasses & Ferns.. *MAP PAGE:* 5

LBut **Butterfields Nursery, Harvest Hill, Bourne End, Buckinghamshire, SL8 5JJ**
TEL: (01628) 525455 *CONTACT:* I Butterfield
OPENING TIMES: 0900-1300 & 1400-1700. Please telephone beforehand in case we are attending shows.
MIN. MAIL ORDER UK: No minimum charge *MIN. VALUE EC:* £30.00 + p&p *EXPORT:* Yes
CAT. COST: 2 x 2nd class *W/SALE or RETAIL:* Both *CREDIT CARDS:* None
SPECIALITIES: Only Pleione by Mail Order. Dahlia for collection. *MAP PAGE:* 6

◆ **See also Display Advertisements**

LChe   **Chessington Nurseries Ltd, Leatherhead Road, Chessington, Surrey, KT19 2NG**
TEL: (01372) 744490 *FAX:* (01372) 740859 *CONTACT:* Jim Knight
OPENING TIMES: 0900-1800 Mon-Sat, 1000-1600 Sun.
MIN. MAIL ORDER UK: No minimum charge *MIN. VALUE EC:* Nmc   *EXPORT:* Yes
CAT. COST: 6 x 1st class *W/SALE or RETAIL:* Retail *CREDIT CARDS:* MasterCard, Visa
SPECIALITIES: Conservatory plants esp. Citrus, Hoya & Passiflora. *MAP PAGE:* **3**

LCla   **Clay Lane Nursery,** 3 Clay Lane, South Nutfield, Nr Redhill, Surrey, RH1 4EG
TEL: (01737) 823307 *CONTACT:* K W Belton
OPENING TIMES: 0900-1700 Tue-Sun 1st Feb-30th Jun & Bank Hols. From 1st Jul-31st Aug
please telephone.
No mail order
CAT. COST: 2 x 1st class *W/SALE or RETAIL:* Retail *CREDIT CARDS:* None
SPECIALITIES: Fuchsia. *MAP PAGE:* **3**

LCns   **The Conservatory, Gomshall Gallery, Gomshall, Surrey, GU5 9LB**
TEL: (01483) 203019 *FAX:* (01483) 203282 *CONTACT:* Marceline Siddons
OPENING TIMES: 1000-1730 Mon-Sat all year; 1400-1700 Sun Apr-Oct.
MIN. MAIL ORDER UK: No minimum charge *MIN. VALUE EC:* Nmc
CAT. COST: 3 x 2nd class *W/SALE or RETAIL:* Retail *CREDIT CARDS:* Visa, MasterCard
SPECIALITIES: Wide range of Conservatory & House plants. *MAP PAGE:* **3**

LCon   **The Conifer Garden,** Hare Lane Nursery, Little Kingshill, Great Missenden,
Buckinghamshire, HP16 0EF
TEL: (01494) 890624 (11-4), (01494) 862086 (9-6) *FAX:* (01494) 862086
CONTACT: Mr & Mrs M P S Powell
OPENING TIMES: Usually 1100-1600 Tue-Sat & Bank Hol Mons. (1100-1300 Dec/Jan &
July/Aug.) Please phone first.
MIN. MAIL ORDER UK: No minimum charge *MIN. VALUE EC:*
CAT. COST: 2 x 1st class *W/SALE or RETAIL:* Retail *CREDIT CARDS:* None
SPECIALITIES: Conifers only - over 500 varieties always in stock. *MAP PAGE:* **5/6**

LCot   **Cottage Garden Plants,** 9 Buckingham Road, Newbury, Berkshire, RG14 6DH
TEL: (01635) 31941 *CONTACT:* Mrs Hannah Billcliffe
OPENING TIMES: 1000-1700 Tue-Sat Mar-Jul & Sep-Oct, 1400-1700 Sun & Bank Hols Jun-Jul.
No mail order
CAT. COST: Sae + 1 x 1st class *W/SALE or RETAIL:* Retail *CREDIT CARDS:* None
SPECIALITIES: Wide range of unusual Perennials. *MAP PAGE:* **2**

LCTD   **CTDA, 174 Cambridge Street, London, SW1V 4QE**
TEL: (0171) 976 5115 *CONTACT:* Basil Smith
OPENING TIMES: Not open.
MIN. MAIL ORDER UK: £10.00 + p&p *MIN. VALUE EC:* £20 + p&p   *EXPORT:* SO
CAT. COST: Free *W/SALE or RETAIL:* Retail *CREDIT CARDS:* None
SPECIALITIES: Hardy cyclamen for the garden & named hellebores. See also SEED Index.

LDea   **Derek Lloyd Dean, 8 Lynwood Close, South Harrow, Middlesex, HA2 9PR**
TEL: (0181) 864 0899 *CONTACT:* Derek Lloyd Dean
OPENING TIMES: Mail Order only.
MIN. MAIL ORDER UK: £2.50 + p&p *MIN. VALUE EC:* £2.50+p&p   *EXPORT:* Yes
CAT. COST: 2 x 1st class *W/SALE or RETAIL:* Retail *CREDIT CARDS:* None
SPECIALITIES: Regal, Angel, Ivy & Scented Leaf Pelargoniums.

LFis   **Kaytie Fisher Nursery,** South End Cottage, Long Reach, Ockham, Surrey, GU23 6PF
TEL: (01483) 282304 *FAX:* (01483) 282304 *CONTACT:* Kaytie Fisher
OPENING TIMES: 1000-1700 daily May-Jul, Wed-Fri Mar & Oct, Wed-Sun Apr, Aug & Sep.
Oct-Feb by appt. only.
MIN. MAIL ORDER UK: £11.95. Courier up to 20kg. *MIN. VALUE EC:*
CAT. COST: 3 x 1st class *W/SALE or RETAIL:* Retail *CREDIT CARDS:* None
SPECIALITIES: Mainly hardy Herbaceous, Alpines, Clematis species, Shrubs. Old Shrub Roses &
Climbing Roses. Nursery 1 mile South East of RHS Wisley. *MAP PAGE:* **3**

Nursery ADDRESSES in BOLD do Mail Order to EU

LFli **Flittvale Garden Centre & Nursery,** Flitwick Road, Westoning, Bedfordshire, MK45 5AA

TEL: (01525) 712484 *FAX:* (01525) 718412 *CONTACT:* Bernie Berry
OPENING TIMES: 0830-1800 Mon-Sat, 1030-1630 Sun.
MIN. MAIL ORDER UK: £10.00 + p&p *MIN. VALUE EC:*
CAT. COST: 4 x 1st class *W/SALE or RETAIL:* Retail *CREDIT CARDS:* Visa, Access, Switch, Delta, MasterCard
SPECIALITIES: Fuchsia. *MAP PAGE:* 6

LFlo **Flora Arcana,** 8 Flitwick Road, Maulden, Bedfordshire, MK45 2BJ

TEL: (01525) 403226 *CONTACT:* Mark Todhunter
OPENING TIMES: 0900-1600 Fri & 1300-1700 Sat Mar-Nov. Please phone first.
No mail order
CAT. COST: 2 x 1st class *W/SALE or RETAIL:* Both *CREDIT CARDS:* None
SPECIALITIES: Plants for dry gardens & scented plants.

LFox **Foxgrove Plants, Foxgrove, Enborne, Nr Newbury, Berkshire, RG14 6RE**

TEL: 01635 40554 *CONTACT:* Miss Louise Vockins
OPENING TIMES: 1000-1700 Wed-Sun & Bank Hols.
MIN. MAIL ORDER UK: No minimum charge* *MIN. VALUE EC:* Nmc
CAT. COST: £1.00 *W/SALE or RETAIL:* Retail *CREDIT CARDS:* None
SPECIALITIES: Hardy & unusual plants. Alpines & good selection of Saxifraga & Galanthus.
*Note: mail order for Galanthus only. *MAP PAGE:* 2

LGan **Gannock Growers, Gannock Green, Sandon, Buntingford, Hertfordshire, SG9 0RH**

TEL: (01763) 287386 *FAX:* (01763) 287795 *E-MAIL:* ppi@globalnet.co.uk
CONTACT: Penny Pyle
OPENING TIMES: Usually 1000-1600 Thur-Sat Apr-Sept but please ring first. Other times by appt.
MIN. MAIL ORDER UK: No minimum charge *MIN. VALUE EC:* £25.00 + p&p
CAT. COST: 3 x 1st class *W/SALE or RETAIL:* Retail *CREDIT CARDS:* None
SPECIALITIES: Unusual & some rare herbaceous plants. *MAP PAGE:* 6

LGod **Godly's Roses, Redbourn, St Albans, Hertfordshire, AL3 7PS**

TEL: (01582) 792255 *FAX:* (01582) 794267 *CONTACT:* Colin Godly
OPENING TIMES: 0900-1900 Summer, 0900-dusk Winter Mon-Fri. 0900-1800 Sat & Sun.
MIN. MAIL ORDER UK: £3.95 + p&p *MIN. VALUE EC:* £50.00 + p&p
CAT. COST: Free *W/SALE or RETAIL:* Both *CREDIT CARDS:* Visa, Access, AmEx, Switch
SPECIALITIES: Roses. *MAP PAGE:* 6

LGre **Green Farm Plants,** Bury Court, Bentley, Farnham, Surrey, GU10 5LZ

TEL: (01420) 23202 *FAX:* (01420) 22382 *CONTACT:* M Christopher & J Coke
OPENING TIMES: 1000-1800 Wed-Sat, end Mar-end Oct.
No mail order
CAT. COST: 3 x 1st class *W/SALE or RETAIL:* Retail *CREDIT CARDS:* Visa, MasterCard, JCB, Switch, Visa, Delta, Electron, Solo
SPECIALITIES: Small Shrubs, Sub-shrubs & Perennials. Many uncommon. Cistus, Prostanthera, Achillea, Eryngium, Monarda, Phlox, Grasses. *MAP PAGE:* 2/3

LGro **Growing Carpets,** Christmas Tree House, High Street, Guilden Morden, Nr Royston, Hertfordshire, SG8 0JP

TEL: (01763) 852705 *CONTACT:* Mrs E E Moore
♦ *OPENING TIMES:* 1100-1700 Mon-Sat 14th Mar-31st Oct 1998. (Closed 2nd-4th May incl.) 1100-1700 Mon-Sat 13th Mar-30th Oct 1999. (Closed 3rd-5th May incl.)
MIN. MAIL ORDER UK: £5.00 + p&p *MIN. VALUE EC:*
CAT. COST: 5 x 2nd class *W/SALE or RETAIL:* Retail *CREDIT CARDS:* None
SPECIALITIES: Wide range of Ground-covering plants. *MAP PAGE:* 6

♦ **See also Display Advertisements**

LHil   Brian Hiley, 25 Little Woodcote Estate, Wallington, Surrey, SM5 4AU

TEL: (0181) 647 9679   *CONTACT:* Brian & Heather Hiley
OPENING TIMES: 0900-1700 Wed-Sat (ex Bank Hols). Please check beforehand.
MIN. MAIL ORDER UK: No minimum charge   *MIN. VALUE EC:* Nmc
CAT. COST: 3 x 1st class   *W/SALE or RETAIL:* Retail   *CREDIT CARDS:* None
SPECIALITIES: Penstemon, Salvia, Canna, Pelargoniums, tender & unusual plants.
MAP PAGE: **3**

LHol   Hollington Nurseries, Woolton Hill, Newbury, Berkshire, RG20 9XT

TEL: (01635) 253908   *FAX:* (01635) 254990   *E-MAIL:* hnherbs@netcomuk.co.uk
WEB SITE: http://www.netcomuk.co.uk/~hnherbs/hollingt.htm   *CONTACT:* S & J Hopkinson
OPENING TIMES: 1000-1700 Mon-Sat, 1100-1700 Sun & Bank Hols Mar-Sep. Please enquire for
winter hours.
MIN. MAIL ORDER UK: No minimum charge*   *MIN. VALUE EC:* Nmc
CAT. COST: 3 x 2nd class   *W/SALE or RETAIL:* Both   *CREDIT CARDS:* Visa, Access, AmEx,
Switch
SPECIALITIES: Herbs, Thymes, Old fashioned Roses, Salvia & Lavandula. *Note: Ltd mail order
service.   *MAP PAGE:* **2**

LHop   Hopleys Plants Ltd, High Street, Much Hadham, Hertfordshire, SG10 6BU

TEL: (01279) 842509   *FAX:* (01279) 843784   *E-MAIL:* hopleys@compuserve.com
CONTACT: Aubrey Barker
OPENING TIMES: 0900-1700 Mon & Wed-Sat, 1400-1700 Sun. Closed Jan & Feb.
MIN. MAIL ORDER UK: No minimum charge*   *MIN. VALUE EC:*
CAT. COST: 5 x 1st class   *W/SALE or RETAIL:* Both   *CREDIT CARDS:* Visa, Access, Switch
SPECIALITIES: Wide range of Hardy & Half-hardy Shrubs & Perennials. *Note: mail order in
Autumn only.   *MAP PAGE:* **6**

LHos   The Hosta Garden, 47 Birch Grove, London, W3 9SP

TEL: (0181) 248 1300   *FAX:* (0181) 248 1300   *E-MAIL:* 101534.3273@compuserve.com
CONTACT: Ian Toop
OPENING TIMES: Mail order only. Visiting by appt. 1st May-31st Oct.
MIN. MAIL ORDER UK: No minimum charge   *MIN. VALUE EC:* £20.00 + p&p   *EXPORT:* Yes
CAT. COST: 4 x 1st class   *W/SALE or RETAIL:* Retail   *CREDIT CARDS:* None
SPECIALITIES: Hosta.   *MAP PAGE:* **3/6**

LHyd   Hydon Nurseries, Clock Barn Lane, Hydon Heath, Godalming, Surrey, GU8 4AZ

TEL: (01483) 860252   *FAX:* (01483) 419937   *CONTACT:* A F George & Rodney Longhurst
◆   *OPENING TIMES:* 0800-1245 & 1400-1700 Mon-Sat. Sun during May and by appt. Open Bank
Hols.
MIN. MAIL ORDER UK: No minimum charge   *MIN. VALUE EC:* £25.00 + p&p   *EXPORT:* Yes
CAT. COST: £1.50   *W/SALE or RETAIL:* Both   *CREDIT CARDS:* None
SPECIALITIES: Large and dwarf Rhododendron, Yakushimanum hybrids & evergreen Azalea, &
Camellias.   *MAP PAGE:* **3**

LHyr   Hyrons Trees, The Green, Sarratt, Rickmansworth, Hertfordshire, WD3 6BL

TEL: (01923) 263000   *FAX:* (01923) 270625   *CONTACT:* Graham Peiser
OPENING TIMES: 0900-1300 Mon-Fri, but please check first. Other times by appt.
No mail order
CAT. COST: 4 x 1st class   *W/SALE or RETAIL:* Both   *CREDIT CARDS:* Visa, Delta, Switch
SPECIALITIES: Broadleaved TREES (from Whips to Extra Heavy Standards), TOPIARY (incl.
Bay & Box) and HEDGING - all in containers.   *MAP PAGE:* **6**

LIck   **Lower Icknield Farm Nurseries,** Meadle, Princes Risborough, Aylesbury, Buckinghamshire, HP17 9TX

TEL: (01844) 343436   *CONTACT:* S Baldwin
◆   *OPENING TIMES:* 0900-1730 daily ex. Xmas-New Year
MIN. MAIL ORDER UK: *   *MIN. VALUE EC:*
CAT. COST: Sae for Argy. list   *W/SALE or RETAIL:* Retail   *CREDIT CARDS:* None
SPECIALITIES: Argyranthemum. Patio & Basket plants. Tender & hardy Perennials. *Note: collection of 10 Argyranthemums £12.50 for mail order to UK only. Sae for details.
MAP PAGE: 6

LIri   **The Iris Garden, 47 Station Road, New Barnet, Hertfordshire, EN5 1PR**

TEL: (0181) 441 1300   *FAX:* (0181) 441 1300   *E-MAIL:* iris1992@aol.com
CONTACT: Clive Russell
◆   *OPENING TIMES:* Show Garden at Roan Cottage, Dukes Kiln Drive, Gerrards Cross, Bucks SL9 7HD. Open by appt. only from mid-May-mid June.*
MIN. MAIL ORDER UK: £15.00 + p&p   *MIN. VALUE EC:* £25.00 + p&p
CAT. COST: £1.50 inc. Full colour   *W/SALE or RETAIL:* Retail   *CREDIT CARDS:* none
SPECIALITIES: Modern Tall Bearded Iris from breeders in UK, USA, France & Australia. *Tel. for Garden appt. (01753) 884308 after 1700.

LJus   **Just Bamboo Ltd, 109 Hayes Lane, Bromley, Kent, BR2 9EF**

TEL: (0181) 462 1800   *FAX:* (0181) 462 1800   *E-MAIL:* mike_james_justbamboo@compuserve.com
WEB SITE: http://www.rsl.ox.ac.uk/users/djh/ebs/ebsgbn.htm   *CONTACT:* Mike James
OPENING TIMES: Thurs-Sun - by appt. please.
MIN. MAIL ORDER UK: £20.00 + p&p   *MIN. VALUE EC:* £60.00 + p&p   *EXPORT:* Yes
CAT. COST: Sae + 2 x 1st class   *W/SALE or RETAIL:* Both   *CREDIT CARDS:* none
SPECIALITIES: Bamboo.   *MAP PAGE:* 3

LKna   **Knap Hill & Slocock Nurseries, Barrs Lane, Knaphill, Woking, Surrey, GU21 2JW**

TEL: (01483) 481214/5   *FAX:* (01483) 797261   *CONTACT:* Mrs Joy West
OPENING TIMES: 0900-1700 Mon-Fri by appt. only
MIN. MAIL ORDER UK: No minimum charge   *MIN. VALUE EC:* Nmc   *EXPORT:* Yes
CAT. COST: 3 x 1st class   *W/SALE or RETAIL:* Both   *CREDIT CARDS:* Visa, Access
SPECIALITIES: Wide variety of Rhododendron & Azalea.   *MAP PAGE:* 3

LLew   **Michael Lewington Gardener - Plantsman,** 12a Tredown Road, Sydenham, London, SE26 5QH

TEL: 0181-778 4201, 0958 476214   *CONTACT:* Michael Lewington
OPENING TIMES: May-Oct by appt. only.
MIN. MAIL ORDER UK: Please phone for details.*   *MIN. VALUE EC:*
CAT. COST: 3 x 1st class   *W/SALE or RETAIL:* Both   *CREDIT CARDS:* None
SPECIALITIES: Datura & Brugmansia. Rare Perennials, Shrubs, Conservatory plants & South African Bulbs. *Note: mail order to UK only.   *MAP PAGE:* 3

LLin   **Lincluden Nursery, Bisley Green, Bisley, Woking, Surrey, GU24 9EN**

TEL: (01483) 797005   *FAX:* (01483) 474015   *CONTACT:* Mr & Mrs J A Tilbury
◆   *OPENING TIMES:* 0930-1630 Mon-Sat all year. 1000-1500 Sun & Bank Hols Easter-end Sept.
MIN. MAIL ORDER UK: No minimum charge   *MIN. VALUE EC:* Nmc   *EXPORT:* Yes
CAT. COST: 3 x 1st class   *W/SALE or RETAIL:* Both   *CREDIT CARDS:* Visa, MasterCard
SPECIALITIES: Dwarf, slow-growing & unusual Conifers.   *MAP PAGE:* 3

LLWP   **L W Plants,** 23 Wroxham Way, Harpenden, Hertfordshire, AL5 4PP

TEL: (01582) 768467   *CONTACT:* Mrs M Easter
OPENING TIMES: 1000-1700 most days, but please phone first.
MIN. MAIL ORDER UK: £15 + p&p*   *MIN. VALUE EC:*
CAT. COST: A5 Sae + 5 x 2nd class*   *W/SALE or RETAIL:* Retail   *CREDIT CARDS:* None
SPECIALITIES: Unusual Hardy Perennials & Herbs. Especially Diascia, Penstemon & Thymus. National Collection of Thymus. *Note:mail order to UK only, late Sept-April. *Sae for list.
MAP PAGE: 6

◆ **See also Display Advertisements**

LMil   Millais Nurseries, Crosswater Lane, Churt, Farnham, Surrey, GU10 2JN

TEL: (01252) 792698 *FAX:* (01252) 792526 *CONTACT:* David Millais
OPENING TIMES: 1000-1300 & 1400-1700 Mon-Fri. Sats Mar, Apr, Oct & Nov. Also daily in May.
MIN. MAIL ORDER UK: £25.00 + p&p *MIN. VALUE EC:* £60.00 + p&p   *EXPORT:* Yes
CAT. COST: 4 x 1st class *W/SALE or RETAIL:* Both *CREDIT CARDS:* Visa, Access
SPECIALITIES: Rhododendron & Azalea.   *MAP PAGE:* 2/3

LMor   Morehavens, 28 Denham Lane, Gerrards Cross, Buckinghamshire, SL9 0EX

TEL: (01494) 871563 *CONTACT:* B Farmer
OPENING TIMES: Only for collection.
MIN. MAIL ORDER UK: £10.25 incl. p&p *MIN. VALUE EC:*
CAT. COST: Free *W/SALE or RETAIL:* Both *CREDIT CARDS:* None
SPECIALITIES: Camomile 'Treneague'.   *MAP PAGE:* 6

LNet   Nettletons Nursery, Ivy Mill Lane, Godstone, Surrey, RH9 8NF

TEL: (01883) 742426 *FAX:* (01883) 742426 *CONTACT:* Jonathan Nettleton
OPENING TIMES: 0900-1300 & 1400-1700 Mon Tue Thu-Sat.
No mail order
CAT. COST: 2 x 1st class *W/SALE or RETAIL:* Both *CREDIT CARDS:* Visa, Access
SPECIALITIES: Trees & Shrubs. Especially Conifers, Azalea, Camellia, Rhododendron, Climbers.
100 Japanese Acer. 27 Wisteria.   *MAP PAGE:* 3

LPal   The Palm Centre, Ham Central Nursery, opposite Riverside Drive, Ham Street, Ham, Richmond, Surrey, TW10 7HA

TEL: (0181) 255 6191 *FAX:* (0181) 255 6192 *E-MAIL:* mail@palmcentre.co.uk
WEB SITE: http://www.palmcentre.co.uk *CONTACT:* Martin Gibbons
OPENING TIMES: 1000-1800 daily.
MIN. MAIL ORDER UK: £10.00 + p&p *MIN. VALUE EC:* £10.00 + p&p   *EXPORT:* Yes
CAT. COST: £1.95 *W/SALE or RETAIL:* Both *CREDIT CARDS:* Visa, MasterCard
SPECIALITIES: Palms & Cycads, exotic & sub-tropical, hardy, half-hardy & tropical. Seedlings to mature trees. Also Bamboo, Tree Ferns, Citrus & other Exotics. Colour Catalogue for Palms & Cycads £1.95.   *MAP PAGE:* 3/6

LPan   Pantiles Plant & Garden Centre, Almners Road, Lyne, Chertsey, Surrey, KT16 0BJ

TEL: (01932) 872195 *FAX:* (01932) 874030 *CONTACT:* Brendan Gallagher
OPENING TIMES: 0900-1730 Mon-Sat, 0900-1700 Sun.
MIN. MAIL ORDER UK: £100.00 + p&p *MIN. VALUE EC:* £100.00 + p&p   *EXPORT:* Yes
CAT. COST: Free *W/SALE or RETAIL:* Both *CREDIT CARDS:* Visa, Switch, MasterCard
SPECIALITIES: Large Trees, Shrubs, Conifers & Climbers in containers. Australasian & other unusual plants.   *MAP PAGE:* 3

LPBA   Paul Bromfield - Aquatics, Maydencroft Lane, Gosmore, Hitchin, Hertfordshire, SG4 7QD

TEL: (01462) 457399 *FAX:* (01462) 422652 *CONTACT:* P Bromfield
OPENING TIMES: 0900-1300 & 1400-1730 daily Feb-Oct. 1000-1300 Sat-Sun Nov-Jan. Please ring first.
MIN. MAIL ORDER UK: £10.00 incl. *MIN. VALUE EC:* £50.00 incl.   *EXPORT:* Yes
CAT. COST: 2 x 1st class *W/SALE or RETAIL:* Both *CREDIT CARDS:* Visa, MasterCard, Delta, JCB, Switch
SPECIALITIES: Water Lilies, Marginals & Bog.   *MAP PAGE:* 6

LPen   Penstemons by Colour, 76 Grove Avenue, Hanwell, London, W7 3ES

TEL: (0181) 840 3199 *FAX:* (0181) 840 6415 *CONTACT:* Debra Hughes
OPENING TIMES: Any time by appt.
MIN. MAIL ORDER UK: £5.00 + p&p* *MIN. VALUE EC:*
CAT. COST: Free *W/SALE or RETAIL:* Retail *CREDIT CARDS:* None
SPECIALITIES: Penstemons. *Note: mail order to UK only.   *MAP PAGE:* 3/6

Nursery ADDRESSES in BOLD do Mail Order to EU

LPJP   **PJ's Palms and Exotics, 41 Salcombe Road, Ashford, Middlesex, TW15 3BS**
TEL: (01784) 250181   *CONTACT:* Peter Jenkins
OPENING TIMES: Mail order only. Visits by arrangement.
MIN. MAIL ORDER UK: No minimum charge   *MIN. VALUE EC:* Nmc
CAT. COST: Sae for list.   *W/SALE or RETAIL:* Retail   *CREDIT CARDS:* none
SPECIALITIES: Palms and other Exotic Foliage plants, hardy & half hardy.   *MAP PAGE:* 3

LPlm   **A J Palmer & Son, Denham Court Nursery, Denham Court Drive, Denham, Uxbridge, Middlesex, UB9 5PG**
TEL: (01895) 832035   *FAX:* (01895) 832035   *CONTACT:* Sheila Palmer
OPENING TIMES: 0900-dusk daily Jul-Oct, Rose field viewing. 0900-1700 Mon-Sat, 1000-1300 Sun Nov. Dec-Jun phone.
MIN. MAIL ORDER UK: No minimum charge   *MIN. VALUE EC:* Nmc
CAT. COST: Free   *W/SALE or RETAIL:* Both   *CREDIT CARDS:* None
SPECIALITIES: Roses.   *MAP PAGE:* 6

LPri   **Priorswood Clematis, Priorswood, Widbury Hill, Ware, Hertfordshire, SG12 7QH**
TEL: (01920) 461543   *FAX:* (01920) 461543   *CONTACT:* G S Greenway
OPENING TIMES: 0800-1700 Tue-Sun & Bank Hol Mondays.
MIN. MAIL ORDER UK: £8.75 + p&p   *MIN. VALUE EC:* £10.00 + p&p   *EXPORT:* Yes
CAT. COST: 4 x 1st class   *W/SALE or RETAIL:* Both   *CREDIT CARDS:* Visa, Access
SPECIALITIES: Clematis & other climbing plants. Lonicera, Parthenocissus, Solanum, Passiflora, Vitis etc.   *MAP PAGE:* 6

LPVe   **Planta Vera, Lyne Hill Nursery, Farm Close, Lyne Crossing Road, Chertsey, Surrey, KT16 0AT**
TEL: (01932) 563011   *FAX:* (01932) 563011   *CONTACT:* Morris May
OPENING TIMES: Bank Holiday weekends in May. Otherwise ring for an appt.
MIN. MAIL ORDER UK: £24.00 (12 plants)   *MIN. VALUE EC:* £24 (12 plants)   *EXPORT:* Yes
CAT. COST: 5 x 2nd class   *W/SALE or RETAIL:* Both   *CREDIT CARDS:* None
SPECIALITIES: Largest Viola collection in the world (415 named Violas & Violettas). NCCPG status (provisional).   *MAP PAGE:* 3

LRHS   **Wisley Plant Centre,** RHS Garden, Wisley, Woking, Surrey, GU23 6QB
TEL: (01483) 211113   *FAX:* (01483) 212372   *CONTACT:*
◆   *OPENING TIMES:* 1000-1800 Mon-Sat 1100-1700 Sun Summer, 1000-1730 Mon-Sat 1000-1600 Sun Winter. Closed Easter Sun.
No mail order
CAT. COST: None issued   *W/SALE or RETAIL:* Retail   *CREDIT CARDS:* MasterCard, Access, AmEx, Switch, Visa
SPECIALITIES: Very wide range, many rare & unusual.   *MAP PAGE:* 3

LRot   **Rotherstone Plants, 70 Long Lane, Tilehurst, Reading, Berkshire, RG31 6YJ**
TEL: (01189) 615889   *CONTACT:* J H Over
OPENING TIMES: 1000-1800 all year. Please ring first.
MIN. MAIL ORDER UK: No minimum charge   *MIN. VALUE EC:* Nmc
CAT. COST: Free   *W/SALE or RETAIL:* Retail   *CREDIT CARDS:* none
SPECIALITIES: Perennials, Grasses & Ferns   *MAP PAGE:* 2/5

LSpr   **Springlea Nursery,** Springlea, Seymour Plain, Marlow, Bucks, SL7 3BZ
TEL: (01628) 473366   *CONTACT:* Mary Dean
OPENING TIMES: 1000-1700 Tue-Sun Mar-Oct. Please check before visiting. Garden open, see NGS for details.
No mail order
CAT. COST: None issued   *W/SALE or RETAIL:* Retail   *CREDIT CARDS:* none
SPECIALITIES: Wide range of rare & unusual Shrubs & Perennials incl. Hardy Geranium, Pulmonaria, Primula, Bog plants, Ground Cover & Shade loving plants.   *MAP PAGE:* 5/6

◆ **See also Display Advertisements**

LStr   **Henry Street Nursery, Swallowfield Road, Arborfield, Reading, Berkshire, RG2 9JY**
TEL: 0118 9761223 *FAX:* 0118 9761417 *CONTACT:* Mr M C Goold
OPENING TIMES: 0900-1730 Mon-Sat, 1000-1600 Sun.
MIN. MAIL ORDER UK: No minimum charge *MIN. VALUE EC:* Nmc
CAT. COST: Free *W/SALE or RETAIL:* Both *CREDIT CARDS:* Visa, Access
SPECIALITIES: Roses. *MAP PAGE:* **2/3**

LSur   **Surrey Primroses, Merriewood, Sandy Lane, Milford, Godalming, Surrey, GU8 5BJ**
TEL: (01483) 416747 *CONTACT:* Val & Geoff Yates
OPENING TIMES: Not open to the public.
MIN. MAIL ORDER UK: No minimum charge *MIN. VALUE EC:* Nmc
CAT. COST: Sae *W/SALE or RETAIL:* Retail *CREDIT CARDS:* None
SPECIALITIES: Primroses, old named varieties.

LSyl   **Sylvatica Nursery,** Crosswater Farm, Crosswater Lane, Churt, Farnham, Surrey, GU10 2JN
TEL: (01252) 792775 *FAX:* (01252) 792526 *CONTACT:* John Millais
OPENING TIMES: By appt.
MIN. MAIL ORDER UK: No minimum charge* *MIN. VALUE EC:*
CAT. COST: 5 x 1st class *W/SALE or RETAIL:* Retail *CREDIT CARDS:* None
SPECIALITIES: Sorbus & Woodland Perennials. *Note: mail order to UK only. *MAP PAGE:* **3**

LTor   **Torhill Nursery, 3 The Avenue, Hertford, Hertfordshire, SG14 3DG**
TEL: (01992) 503311 *FAX:* (01992) 534310 *E-MAIL:* torhill.topiary@dial.pipex.com
WEB SITE: http://dspace.dial.pipex.com/town/square/kcr31/ *CONTACT:* Chris Gates
◆   *OPENING TIMES:* By appt. only.
MIN. MAIL ORDER UK: No minimum charge *MIN. VALUE EC:* Nmc
CAT. COST: Free *W/SALE or RETAIL:* Both *CREDIT CARDS:* none
SPECIALITIES: Yew (Taxus) Hedging & Topiary, Box (Buxus) Hedging, Gunnera manicata.

LVER **The Vernon Geranium Nursery, Cuddington Way, Cheam, Sutton, Surrey, SM2 7JB**
TEL: (0181) 393 7616 *FAX:* (0181) 786 7437 *E-MAIL:* mrgeranium@aol.com
CONTACT: Philip James & Liz Sims
OPENING TIMES: 0930-1730 Mon-Sat, 1000-1600 Sun, 1st Mar-31st July.
MIN. MAIL ORDER UK: No minimum charge *MIN. VALUE EC:* Nmc
CAT. COST: £2.00 UK* *W/SALE or RETAIL:* Retail *CREDIT CARDS:* Visa, MasterCard, Switch
SPECIALITIES: Pelargonium & Fuchsia. *NOTE: Illustrated colour Catalogue. £2.50 for overseas.
MAP PAGE: **3**

LWak   **N & J Wake, 27 Clifton Road, Henlow, Bedfordshire, SG16 6BL**
TEL: (01462) 815223 *FAX:* (01462) 815223 *CONTACT:* N K Wake
OPENING TIMES: By appt. only.
MIN. MAIL ORDER UK: No minimum charge *MIN. VALUE EC:* Nmc
CAT. COST: 4 x 1st class *W/SALE or RETAIL:* Both *CREDIT CARDS:* None
SPECIALITIES: Herbaceous Perennials. *MAP PAGE:* **6**

MAld   **Alderton Plant Nursery,** Spring Lane, Alderton, Towcester, Northamptonshire, NN12 7LW
TEL: (01327) 811253 *CONTACT:* Tom Hutchinson
OPENING TIMES: 1000-1630 Tue-Sun & Bank Hol Mons. Closed Jan 1998.
No mail order
CAT. COST: 2 x 1st class *W/SALE or RETAIL:* Retail *CREDIT CARDS:* None
SPECIALITIES: Fuchsia. *MAP PAGE:* **5**

Nursery ADDRESSES in BOLD do Mail Order to EU

MAll **Paul Allanson,** Rhendhoo, Jurby, Isle of Man, IM7 3HB

TEL: (01624) 880766 *FAX:* (01624) 880649 *CONTACT:* Paul Allanson
OPENING TIMES: By appt. only. Closed Dec & Jan.
MIN. MAIL ORDER UK: £10.00 + p&p *MIN. VALUE EC:*
CAT. COST: £1.50 cheque/PO* *W/SALE or RETAIL:* Retail *CREDIT CARDS:* None
SPECIALITIES: Shrubs for seaside locations, west coast & southern England. Particularly Australian, Tasmanian & New Zealand. *Note: English stamps not accepted in IoM.
MAP PAGE: 4

MArl **Arley Hall Nursery,** Northwich, Cheshire, CW9 6NA

TEL: (01565) 777479/777231 *FAX:* (01565) 777465 *CONTACT:* Jane Foster
OPENING TIMES: 1200-1730 Tue-Sun Easter to end Sept. Also Bank Hol Mons.
No mail order
CAT. COST: 4 x 1st class *W/SALE or RETAIL:* Retail *CREDIT CARDS:* None
SPECIALITIES: Wide range of Herbaceous. *MAP PAGE:* 7

MAsh **Ashwood Nurseries Ltd,** Greensforge, Kingswinford, West Midlands, DY6 0AE

TEL: (01384) 401996 *FAX:* (01384) 401108 *CONTACT:* John Massey & Philip Baulk
OPENING TIMES: 0900-1800 Mon-Sat & 1100-1700 Sun. ex Xmas & Boxing day.
MIN. MAIL ORDER UK: * *MIN. VALUE EC:*
CAT. COST: 4 x 1st class *W/SALE or RETAIL:* Both *CREDIT CARDS:* Visa, Access
SPECIALITIES: Large range of hardy plants & dwarf Conifers; Lewisia, Cyclamen species (NCCPG Collection Holder for both) & Hellebores. * Note: mail order for seeds, & special offers only. See also SEED Index. *MAP PAGE:* 7

MAsk **Askew's Nursery,** South Croxton Road, Queniborough, Leicestershire, LE7 3RX

TEL: (01664) 840557 *CONTACT:* Mrs Longland
OPENING TIMES: 0900-1800 Mon-Fri Feb-Sep. 10000-1800 Sat & Sun. Oct-Jan please telephone first.
MIN. MAIL ORDER UK: No minimum charge *MIN. VALUE EC:*
CAT. COST: 3 x 1st class *W/SALE or RETAIL:* Retail *CREDIT CARDS:* None
SPECIALITIES: Fuchsia. *MAP PAGE:* 7

MAus **David Austin Roses Ltd, Bowling Green Lane, Albrighton, Wolverhampton, West Midlands, WV7 3HB**

TEL: (01902) 376300 *FAX:* (01902) 372142 *E-MAIL:* ken@david-austin.simplyonline.co.uk
CONTACT: Office Reception
OPENING TIMES: 0900-1700 Mon-Fri, 1000-1800 Sat, Sun & Bank Hols. Until dusk Nov-Mar.
MIN. MAIL ORDER UK: No minimum charge *MIN. VALUE EC:* £25.00 + p&p *EXPORT:* Yes
CAT. COST: Free *W/SALE or RETAIL:* Both *CREDIT CARDS:* Access, Switch, Visa
SPECIALITIES: Roses, Paeonia, Iris & Hemerocallis & hardy plants. Also Roses & Herbaceous perennials at Nursery. *MAP PAGE:* 7

MAvo **Avondale Nursery,** (Off.) 3 Avondale Road, Earlsdon, Coventry, Warwickshire, CV5 6DZ

TEL: (01203) 673662 *CONTACT:* Brian Ellis
OPENING TIMES: 1000-1230, 1400-1700 daily Mar-Oct. Other times by appt.
No mail order
CAT. COST: 4 x 1st class *W/SALE or RETAIL:* Retail *CREDIT CARDS:* None
SPECIALITIES: Rare & unusual Perennials, esp. Campanula, Centaurea, Eryngium, Leucanthemum Pulmonaria, Sidalcea & Grasses. NOTE: Nursery at Smith's Nursery, 3 Stoneleigh Road, Baginton, Nr Coventry CV8 3BA. *MAP PAGE:* 5

MBal **Ballalheannagh Gardens,** Glen Roy, Lonan, Isle of Man, IM4 7QB

TEL: (01624) 861875 *FAX:* (01624) 861114 *CONTACT:* Clif & Maureen Dadd
OPENING TIMES: 1000-1300 & 1400-1700 or dusk if earlier in Winter. Closed w/ends Nov-Mar. Please telephone first.
No mail order
CAT. COST: £1.50 *W/SALE or RETAIL:* Retail *CREDIT CARDS:* None
SPECIALITIES: Rhododendron & Ericaceous Shrubs. Small number of rare trees and shrubs not in catalogue. *MAP PAGE:* 4

◆ **See also Display Advertisements**

MBar   **Barncroft Nurseries,** Dunwood Lane, Longsdon, Nr Leek, Stoke-on-Trent, Staffordshire, ST9 9QW

TEL: (01538) 384310 *FAX:* (01538) 384310 *CONTACT:* S Warner
OPENING TIMES: 0900-1900 or dusk if earlier Fri-Sun.
No mail order
CAT. COST: None issued *W/SALE or RETAIL:* Both *CREDIT CARDS:* None
SPECIALITIES: Very large range of Heathers, Conifers & Shrubs. *MAP PAGE:* **7**

MBel   **Bellhouse Nursery,** Bellhouse Lane, Moore, Nr Warrington, Cheshire, WA4 6TR

TEL: (01925) 740874* *FAX:* (01925) 740672 *CONTACT:* Elaine Soens & Doreen Scott
OPENING TIMES: 1000-1700 Wed-Mon Mar-Oct. 1000-1600 Wed-Mon Feb. Closed Nov-Jan & every Tue.
No mail order
CAT. COST: t£1.00 *W/SALE or RETAIL:* Retail *CREDIT CARDS:* None
SPECIALITIES: Wide range of Herbaceous plants & Shrubs. Good selection of unusual varieties.
*NOTE: New telephone no. *MAP PAGE:* **7**

MBEx   **Brockings Exotics,** Rosedene, Nottingham Road, Woodborough, Nottingham, NG14 6EH

TEL: (0115) 951 3381 *CONTACT:* Ian K S Cooke
OPENING TIMES: Strictly by appt. ONLY. Apr-Sep.
MIN. MAIL ORDER UK: £15.00 + p&p* *MIN. VALUE EC:*
CAT. COST: 3 x 1st class *W/SALE or RETAIL:* Both *CREDIT CARDS:* None
SPECIALITIES: Tender Perennials, Canna, Coleus & Conservatory plants. *Note: mail order within UK only. *MAP PAGE:* **7**

MBlu   **Bluebell Nursery, Annwell Lane, Smisby, Nr Ashby de la Zouch, LE65 2TA**

TEL: (01530) 413700 *FAX:* (01530) 417600 *E-MAIL:* castell@bigfoot.com
CONTACT: Robert & Suzette Vernon
OPENING TIMES: 0900-1700 Mon-Sat & 1030-1630 Sun Mar-Oct, 0900-1600 Mon-Sat (not Sun) Nov-Feb. Closed Xmas-New Year.
MIN. MAIL ORDER UK: No minimum charge *MIN. VALUE EC:* Nmc   *EXPORT:* Yes
CAT. COST: £1.00 + 2 x 1st class *W/SALE or RETAIL:* Retail *CREDIT CARDS:* Visa, Access
SPECIALITIES: Uncommon Trees & Shrubs. Display Garden & Arboretum. *MAP PAGE:* **7**

MBri   **Bridgemere Nurseries,** Bridgemere, Nr Nantwich, Cheshire, CW5 7QB

TEL: (01270) 521100 *FAX:* (01270) 520215 *CONTACT:* Keith Atkey
♦   *OPENING TIMES:* 0900-2000 Mon-Sat, 1000-2000 Sun summer, until 1700 in winter.
No mail order
CAT. COST: None issued *W/SALE or RETAIL:* Both *CREDIT CARDS:* Visa, Access, MasterCard, Switch
SPECIALITIES: Perennials, Shrubs, Trees, Roses, Rhododendrons & Azaleas, Alpines, Heathers & Houseplants. *MAP PAGE:* **7**

MBrN   **Bridge Nursery,** Tomlow Road, Napton-on-the-hill, Nr Rugby, Warwickshire, CV23 8HX

TEL: (01926) 812737 *CONTACT:* Christine Dakin & Philip Martino
OPENING TIMES: 1000-1600 Fri-Sun Apr-July, Sept & Oct.
MIN. MAIL ORDER UK: £10.00 + p&p *MIN. VALUE EC:*
CAT. COST: 3 x 1st class *W/SALE or RETAIL:* Both *CREDIT CARDS:* none
SPECIALITIES: Ornamental Grasses, Sedges & Bamboos. Also range of Shrubs & Perennials.
*Note: nursery has moved from Cambs where it was called Simply Plants. *MAP PAGE:* **5**

MBro **Broadstone Nurseries,** 13 The Nursery, High Street, Sutton Courtenay, Abingdon, Oxfordshire, OX14 4UA

TEL: (01235) 847557 (day/eve) *CONTACT:* J Shackleton
OPENING TIMES: 1400-1700 Tue, 1400-1800 Sat (except Show days). By appt on other days/times.
No mail order
CAT. COST: 3 x 1st class *W/SALE or RETAIL:* Retail *CREDIT CARDS:* None
SPECIALITIES: Plants for rock garden, scree, troughs & borders. Lime tolerant hardy Alpines, Perennials & unusual plants. *MAP PAGE:* 5

MBur **Burrows Roses, Meadow Croft, Spondon Road, Dale Abbey, Derby, Derbyshire, DE7 4PQ**

TEL: (01332) 668289 *FAX:* (01332) 668289 *CONTACT:* Stuart & Diane Burrows
OPENING TIMES: Mail Order only.
MIN. MAIL ORDER UK: £3.50 + p&p *MIN. VALUE EC:* £3.50 + p&p
CAT. COST: 2 x 1st class *W/SALE or RETAIL:* Retail *CREDIT CARDS:* None
SPECIALITIES: Roses

MCad **Caddick's Clematis Nurseries, Lymm Road, Thelwall, Warrington, Cheshire, WA13 0UF**

TEL: (01925) 757196 *CONTACT:* H Caddick
♦ *OPENING TIMES:* 1000-1700 Tue-Sun 1st Feb-31st Oct. Nov by arrangement. 1000-1700 Bank Hols. Closed Dec & Jan.
MIN. MAIL ORDER UK: £12.60 + p&p *MIN. VALUE EC:* £12.60 + p&p
CAT. COST: £1.20 cheque/PO UK, £1.50 EC & Eire. *W/SALE or RETAIL:* Both *CREDIT CARDS:* Visa, Access, MasterCard, Switch
SPECIALITIES: Clematis. *MAP PAGE:* 7

MCCP **Collectors Corner Plants,** 33 Rugby Road, Clifton-under-Dunsmore, Rugby, Warwickshire, CV23 0DE

TEL: (01788) 571881 *CONTACT:* Pat Neesam
♦ *OPENING TIMES:* By appt. only.
MIN. MAIL ORDER UK: No minimum charge *MIN. VALUE EC:*
CAT. COST: 4 x 1st class *W/SALE or RETAIL:* Retail *CREDIT CARDS:* None
SPECIALITIES: General range of choice Herbaceous Perennials, Grasses & Shrubs.
MAP PAGE: 5

MChe **Cheshire Herbs,** Fourfields, Forest Road, Nr Tarporley, Cheshire, CW6 9ES

TEL: (01829) 760578 *FAX:* (01829) 760354 *CONTACT:* Mr & Mrs Ted Riddell
♦ *OPENING TIMES:* 1000-1700 daily 3rd Jan-24th Dec.
No mail order
CAT. COST: 1 x 1st class *W/SALE or RETAIL:* Both *CREDIT CARDS:* Access, Visa, Switch
SPECIALITIES: Display Herb garden & Elizabethan knot garden. See also SEED Index.
MAP PAGE: 7

MCli **Clipston Nursery,** Naseby Road, Clipston, Market Harborough, Leicestershire, LE16 9RZ

TEL: (01858) 525567 *CONTACT:* Kate Hayward
OPENING TIMES: 1000-1800 daily Mar-Sep.
No mail order
CAT. COST: 2 x 2nd class *W/SALE or RETAIL:* Retail *CREDIT CARDS:* None
SPECIALITIES: Perennials including many unusual varieties. *MAP PAGE:* 5/7

MCLN **Country Lady Nursery,** Lilac Cottage, Chapel Lane, Gentleshaw, Nr Rugeley, Staffordshire, WS15 4ND

TEL: (01543) 675520 *CONTACT:* Mrs Sylvia Nunn
OPENING TIMES: 1000-1700 Wed-Sun & Bank Hols Mar-Oct. Other times by appt.
No mail order
CAT. COST: A5 Sae + 2 x 1st class *W/SALE or RETAIL:* Retail *CREDIT CARDS:* None
SPECIALITIES: Wide range of unusual Perennials, incl. Hardy Geranium, Campanula, Penstemon. 1 acre show garden. *MAP PAGE:* 7

♦ **See also Display Advertisements**

MCol **Collinwood Nurseries,** Mottram St. Andrew, Macclesfield, Cheshire, SK10 4QR
TEL: (01625) 582272 *CONTACT:* A Wright
OPENING TIMES: 0830-1730 Mon-Sat 1300-1730 Sun. Closed Sun in Jan-Mar.
MIN. MAIL ORDER UK: No minimum charge *MIN. VALUE EC:*
CAT. COST: 1 x 1st class *W/SALE or RETAIL:* Retail *CREDIT CARDS:* None
SPECIALITIES: Chrysanthemums (Dendranthema). *MAP PAGE:* **7**

MCoo **Cool Temperate, 5 Colville Villas, Nottingham, NG1 4HN**
TEL: (0115) 947 4977 *FAX:* (0115) 947 4977 *CONTACT:* Phil Corbett
OPENING TIMES: Not open.
MIN. MAIL ORDER UK: No minimum charge *MIN. VALUE EC:* Nmc
CAT. COST: Sae *W/SALE or RETAIL:* Both *CREDIT CARDS:* none
SPECIALITIES: Tree Fruit, Soft Fruit, Nitrogen-fixers, Hedging, Own-root Fruit Trees.

MDHE **DHE Plants,** (Off.) Rose Lea, Darley House Estate, Darley Dale, Matlock,
Derbyshire, DE4 2QH
TEL: (01629) 732512 *CONTACT:* Peter M Smith
OPENING TIMES: 1000-1700 Tue-Sat, 1030-1630 Sun. Advance telephone call desirable - see note
below.
MIN. MAIL ORDER UK: No minimum charge* *MIN. VALUE EC:*
CAT. COST: 2 x 1st class *W/SALE or RETAIL:* Retail *CREDIT CARDS:* None
SPECIALITIES: Alpines; esp. Erodium, Helianthemum, Saxifraga & Sisyrinchium. *Note: mail
order Oct-Mar only. Nursery stock at Robert Young GC, Bakewell Rd, Matlock. *MAP PAGE:* **7**

MDun **Dunge Valley Gardens,** Windgather Rocks, Kettleshulme, High Peak, SK23 7RF
TEL: (01663) 733787 *FAX:* (01663) 733787 *E-MAIL:* xon74@dial.pipex.com
CONTACT: David Ketley
OPENING TIMES: 1030-1800 daily 1st Apr-31st Aug or by appt.
No mail order
CAT. COST: A4 Sae *W/SALE or RETAIL:* Retail *CREDIT CARDS:* None
SPECIALITIES: Rhododendron species & hybrids. Trees, Shrubs & Perennials, some rare & wild
collected. Meconopsis & Trillium. *MAP PAGE:* **7**

MFie **Field House Nurseries, Leake Road, Gotham, Nottinghamshire, NG11 0JN**
TEL: (0115) 9830278 *CONTACT:* Doug Lochhead & Valerie A Woolley
OPENING TIMES: 0900-1700 Fri-Wed or by appt.
MIN. MAIL ORDER UK: No minimum charge *MIN. VALUE EC:* 4 plants   *EXPORT:* Yes
CAT. COST: 4 x 1st or 4 x IRCs *W/SALE or RETAIL:* Retail *CREDIT CARDS:* Visa, Access
SPECIALITIES: Auriculas, Primula, Alpines & Rock plants. *Note: mail order for Auriculas,
Primula & Seeds ONLY. See also SEED Index. *MAP PAGE:* **7**

MFiF **Field Farm Nursery, Gotham Lane, Osbaston, Leicestershire, CV13 0DR**
TEL: 0410 702347 *FAX:* (01283) 217377 *CONTACT:* Aubrey Wood
OPENING TIMES: 1200-1700 Sun Apr-end Oct.
MIN. MAIL ORDER UK: £15.00 + p&p *MIN. VALUE EC:* £25.00 + p&p   *EXPORT:* Yes
CAT. COST: 4 x 1st class *W/SALE or RETAIL:* Both *CREDIT CARDS:* none
SPECIALITIES: New nursery with increasing range of unusual Trees, Shrubs & Pot plants for
garden, greenhouse & conservatory - mainly from Australasia. 15 acre garden & nature trail.
 MAP PAGE: **7**

MFir **The Firs Nursery,** Chelford Road, Henbury, Macclesfield, Cheshire, SK10 3LH
TEL: (01625) 426422 *CONTACT:* Fay J Bowling
OPENING TIMES: 1000-1700 Mon, Tue, Thu, Fri, Sat Mar-Sep.
No mail order
CAT. COST: 2 x 1st class *W/SALE or RETAIL:* Retail *CREDIT CARDS:* None
SPECIALITIES: Wide range of Herbaceous Perennials, many unusual. *MAP PAGE:* **7**

Nursery ADDRESSES in BOLD do Mail Order to EU

MFos **Fosse Alpines, 33 Leicester Road, Countesthorpe, Leicestershire, LE8 5QU**
TEL: (0116) 2778237 *FAX:* (0116) 2778237 *CONTACT:* T K West
OPENING TIMES: By appt. only
MIN. MAIL ORDER UK: £8.00 + p&p *MIN. VALUE EC:* £8.00 + p&p
CAT. COST: 4 x 1st class *W/SALE or RETAIL:* Retail *CREDIT CARDS:* None
SPECIALITIES: Alpines including specialist species in small quantities. *MAP PAGE:* **7**

MFry **Fryer's Nurseries Ltd, Manchester Road, Knutsford, Cheshire, WA16 0SX**
TEL: (01565) 755455 *FAX:* (01565) 653755 *E-MAIL:* garethfryer@fryers-roses.co.uk
WEB SITE: http://www.fryers-roses.co.uk *CONTACT:* Gareth Fryer
OPENING TIMES: 0900-1730 Mon-Sat & 1030-1630 Sun & 1000-1730 Bank Hols.
MIN. MAIL ORDER UK: No minimum charge *MIN. VALUE EC:* Nmc   *EXPORT:* Yes
CAT. COST: Free *W/SALE or RETAIL:* Both *CREDIT CARDS:* Visa, Access, Switch
SPECIALITIES: Extensive Rose Nursery & Garden Centre producing over half a million bushes annually. Rose fields in bloom Jun-Oct. *MAP PAGE:* **7**

MGan **Gandy's (Roses) Ltd, North Kilworth, Nr Lutterworth, Leicestershire, LE17 6HZ**
TEL: (01858) 880398 *FAX:* (01858) 880433 *CONTACT:* Miss R D Gandy
OPENING TIMES: 0900-1700 Mon-Sat & 1400-1700 Sun.
MIN. MAIL ORDER UK: No minimum charge *MIN. VALUE EC:* £25.00 + p&p
CAT. COST: Free *W/SALE or RETAIL:* Both *CREDIT CARDS:* None
SPECIALITIES: 580 Rose varieties. *MAP PAGE:* **5/7**

MGed **Geddington Gardens,** The Spinney, Grafton Road, Geddington, Northants, NN14 1AJ
TEL: (01536) 461020 *CONTACT:* Christine Sturman
OPENING TIMES: daily 1st Mar-31st Oct 1998 & 3rd Mar-31st Oct 1999.
No mail order
CAT. COST: 2 x 1st class *W/SALE or RETAIL:* Retail *CREDIT CARDS:* none
SPECIALITIES: Hardy Perennials, Cottage Garden plants. *MAP PAGE:* **5/6**

MGos **Goscote Nurseries Ltd, Syston Road, Cossington, Leicestershire, LE7 4UZ**
TEL: (01509) 812121 *FAX:* (01509) 814231 *CONTACT:* D C & R C Cox & F J Toone
♦ *OPENING TIMES:* 7 days a week.
MIN. MAIL ORDER UK: £10.00 + p&p *MIN. VALUE EC:* £50.00 + p&p
CAT. COST: 5 x 1st class *W/SALE or RETAIL:* Retail *CREDIT CARDS:* Visa, Access, MasterCard, Delta, Switch
SPECIALITIES: Japanese Maple, Rhododendron, Azalea, Magnolia, Camellia, Pieris & other Ericaceae. Ornamental Trees & Shrubs, Conifers, Heathers, Alpines, Herbaceous, Clematis & unusual Climbers. Showground to visit. *MAP PAGE:* **7**

MGra **Grange Cottage Herbs, 4 Grange Cottages, Nailstone, Nuneaton, Warwicks, CV13 0QN**
TEL: (01530) 262072 *CONTACT:* Alec Duthie
OPENING TIMES: Not open to the public, except for National Garden Scheme Open Days on 16/5/98 & 18/7/98.
MIN. MAIL ORDER UK: £10.00 + p&p *MIN. VALUE EC:* Tba.
CAT. COST: Phone for details *W/SALE or RETAIL:* Both *CREDIT CARDS:* None
SPECIALITIES: Herbs - Culinary, Medicinal & Aromatic. Wild Flowers. *MAP PAGE:* **7**

MGrG **Granby Gardens,** Granby House, 8 Long Acre, Bingham, Nottinghamshire, NG13 8BG
TEL: (01949) 837696 *FAX:* (01949) 837696 *CONTACT:* Maureen Gladwin
OPENING TIMES: 0900-1800 Mon-Fri, 0900-1600 Sat & Sun, Mar-Oct.
No mail order
CAT. COST: *W/SALE or RETAIL:* Retail *CREDIT CARDS:* None
SPECIALITIES: A wide range of Herbaceous Perennials, Shrubs & Climbers. Some rare & unusual. *MAP PAGE:* **7**

♦ **See also Display Advertisements**

MHar **Harts Green Nursery,** 89 Harts Green Road, Harborne, Birmingham, B17 9TZ
TEL: (0121) 427 5200 *CONTACT:* B Richardson
OPENING TIMES: 1400-1730 Wed Apr-July & Sep. Closed Aug. Other times by appt.
No mail order
CAT. COST: 2 x 1st class *W/SALE or RETAIL:* Retail *CREDIT CARDS:* None
SPECIALITIES: Alpines & Hardy Perennials. *MAP PAGE:* 5/7

MHel **Heldon Nurseries, Ashbourne Road, Spath, Uttoxeter, Staffordshire, ST14 5AD**
TEL: (01889) 563377 *FAX:* (01889) 563377 *CONTACT:* Mrs J H Tate
OPENING TIMES: 1000-sunset daily.
MIN. MAIL ORDER UK: £2.00 + p&p *MIN. VALUE EC:* £50.00 + p&p   *EXPORT:* Yes
CAT. COST: Sae *W/SALE or RETAIL:* Retail *CREDIT CARDS:* None
SPECIALITIES: Carnivorous plants, Cactus & Succulents. See also in Cactus & Succulent Index.
MAP PAGE: 7

MHew **Hewthorn Herbs & Wild Flowers, 82 Julian Road, West Bridgford, Nottingham, NG2 5AN**
TEL: (0115) 981 2861 *CONTACT:* Julie Scott
OPENING TIMES: By appt, only.
MIN. MAIL ORDER UK: No minimum charge *MIN. VALUE EC:* £10.00 + p&p
CAT. COST: 3 x 1st class *W/SALE or RETAIL:* Retail *CREDIT CARDS:* None
SPECIALITIES: Native Wild Flowers, Dye Plants, Native Medicinal Herbs. All organically grown.
MAP PAGE: 7

MHFP **Hill Farmhouse Plants,** Hill Farmhouse, Cottingham, Market Harborough, Leicestershire, LE16 8XS
TEL: (01536) 770994 *CONTACT:* R Cain
OPENING TIMES: 0930-1800 Sats only from 1st Mar-18th July. Other times by appt.
No mail order
CAT. COST: 2 x 1st class *W/SALE or RETAIL:* Retail *CREDIT CARDS:* None
SPECIALITIES: Hardy Geraniums & Cottage Garden plants. *MAP PAGE:* 7/8

MHig **Highgates Nursery,** 166a Crich Lane, Belper, Derbyshire, DE56 1EP
TEL: (01773) 822153 *CONTACT:* R E & D I Straughan
OPENING TIMES: 1030-1630 Mon-Sat mid Mar-mid Oct. Closed Sun.
No mail order
CAT. COST: 2 x 1st class *W/SALE or RETAIL:* Retail *CREDIT CARDS:* None
SPECIALITIES: Alpines. *MAP PAGE:* 7

MHlr **The Hiller Garden,** Dunnington, Nr Alcester, Warwickshire, B49 5PD
TEL: (01789) 490991 *FAX:* (01789) 490439 *CONTACT:* David Carvill & Brian Meredith
♦   *OPENING TIMES:* 1000-1700 daily.
No mail order
CAT. COST: 2 x 1st class *W/SALE or RETAIL:* Retail *CREDIT CARDS:* Visa, Access, Switch
SPECIALITIES: Two acre garden displaying Herbaceous Perennials, Old-fashioned & Shrub Roses, & Shrubs. All available for sale during the season. *MAP PAGE:* 5

MHul **Diana Hull, Fog Cottages, 178 Lower Street, Hillmorton, Rugby, Warwickshire, CV21 4NX**
TEL: (01788) 536574 after 1600 *CONTACT:* Diana Hull
OPENING TIMES: Not open. Mail order only.
MIN. MAIL ORDER UK: No minimum charge *MIN. VALUE EC:* Nmc
CAT. COST: Sae or IRC for list. *W/SALE or RETAIL:* Retail *CREDIT CARDS:* None
SPECIALITIES: Pelargonium species. See also SEED Index. *MAP PAGE:* 5

MInt **Intakes Farm,** Sandy Lane, Longsdon, Stoke-on-Trent, Staffordshire, ST9 9QQ
TEL: (01538) 398452 *CONTACT:* Mrs Kathleen Inman
OPENING TIMES: By appt. only.
No mail order
CAT. COST: None issued *W/SALE or RETAIL:* Retail *CREDIT CARDS:* None
SPECIALITIES: Double, Variegated & unusual forms of British natives & Cottage Garden plants.
MAP PAGE: 7

MJac **Jackson's Nurseries,** Clifton Campville, Nr Tamworth, Staffordshire, B79 0AP
TEL: (01827) 373307 *FAX:* (01827) 373307 *CONTACT:* N Jackson
OPENING TIMES: 0900-1800 Mon Wed-Sat, 1000-1700 Sun.
No mail order
CAT. COST: 2 x 1st class *W/SALE or RETAIL:* Both *CREDIT CARDS:* None
SPECIALITIES: Fuchsia. *MAP PAGE:* 7

MJon **C & K Jones, Golden Fields Nurseries, Barrow Lane, Tarvin, Cheshire, CH3 8JF**
TEL: (01829) 740663 *FAX:* (01829) 741877 *CONTACT:* Keith Jones/P Woolley
OPENING TIMES: 0800-1700 daily Mar-Sep, 0900-1600 daily Oct-Feb.
MIN. MAIL ORDER UK: 1 plant + p&p *MIN. VALUE EC:* 1 plant + p&p   *EXPORT:* Yes
CAT. COST: £1.00 *W/SALE or RETAIL:* Both *CREDIT CARDS:* not for telephone orders
SPECIALITIES: Roses. *MAP PAGE:* 7

MLan **Lane End Nursery,** Old Cherry Lane, Lymm, Cheshire, WA13 0TA
TEL: (01925) 752618 *E-MAIL:* sawyer@laneend.u-net.com *CONTACT:* I Sawyer
OPENING TIMES: 0930-1730 Thu-Tue Mar-Dec.
No mail order
CAT. COST: None issued *W/SALE or RETAIL:* Retail *CREDIT CARDS:* None
SPECIALITIES: Award of Garden Merit plants with a wide range of choice & unusual Shrubs,
Trees, Perennials & Ferns. *MAP PAGE:* 7

MLea **Lea Rhododendron Gardens Ltd, Lea, Matlock, Derbyshire, DE4 5GH**
TEL: (01629) 534380/534260 *FAX:* (01629) 534260 *CONTACT:* Jon Tye
OPENING TIMES: 1000-1900 daily.
MIN. MAIL ORDER UK: £15.00 + p&p *MIN. VALUE EC:* £15.00 + p&p   *EXPORT:* Yes
CAT. COST: 30p + Sae *W/SALE or RETAIL:* Retail *CREDIT CARDS:* None
SPECIALITIES: Rhododendron, Azalea & Kalmia. *MAP PAGE:* 7

MLLN **Lodge Lane Nursery & Gardens,** Lodge Lane, Dutton, Nr Warrington, Cheshire, WA4
4HP
TEL: (01928) 713718 *CONTACT:* Rod or Diane Casey
OPENING TIMES: 1000-1700 Wed-Sun & Bank Hols, mid Mar-early Oct.
No mail order
CAT. COST: 3 x 1st class *W/SALE or RETAIL:* Retail *CREDIT CARDS:* None
SPECIALITIES: Unusual Perennials & Shrubs. Many Aquilegia, Allium, Aster, Campanula,
Diascia, Nepeta, Penstemon & Salvia. See also SEED Index. *MAP PAGE:* 7

MLov **Lovers Knot Nursery, Woodside, Langley Road, Langley, Macclesfield, Cheshire, SK11
0DG**
TEL: (01260) 252179 *FAX:* (01260) 252179 *CONTACT:* Ian Coppack
OPENING TIMES: Mail order only.
MIN. MAIL ORDER UK: £5.00 + p&p *MIN. VALUE EC:* £5.00 + p&p
CAT. COST: 2 x 1st class *W/SALE or RETAIL:* Retail *CREDIT CARDS:* none
SPECIALITIES: Hostas.

MMal **Malcoff Cottage Garden Nursery,** Malcoff, Chapel-en-le-Frith, High Peak, Derbyshire,
SK23 0QR
TEL: (01663) 751969 *FAX:* Please phone first *E-MAIL:* malcoffcot@aol.com
CONTACT: Mrs J Norfolk
OPENING TIMES: 1200-1700 Fri-Wed Mar-Sept. Other times by appt. only. NB Visitors please
phone for directions.
MIN. MAIL ORDER UK: £10.00 + p&p* *MIN. VALUE EC:*
CAT. COST: 3 x 1st class *W/SALE or RETAIL:* Retail *CREDIT CARDS:* none
SPECIALITIES: Herbs, Wild Flowers & hardy Cottage Garden plants. *Note: mail order to UK
only. *MAP PAGE:* 7

◆ **See also Display Advertisements**

MMat   Mattock's Roses, The Rose Nurseries, Nuneham Courtenay, Oxford, Oxfordshire, OX44 9PY

> *TEL:* (01865) 343265, 0345 585652 retail order line *FAX:* (01865) 343267 *CONTACT:* Sales Office
> *OPENING TIMES:* 0900-1730 Mon-Sat, 1100-1700 Sun. Closes 1700 Nov-Feb.
> *MIN. MAIL ORDER UK:* No minimum charge *MIN. VALUE EC:* Nmc   *EXPORT:* Yes
> *CAT. COST:* Free *W/SALE or RETAIL:* Both *CREDIT CARDS:* Visa, MasterCard
> *SPECIALITIES:* Roses. *MAP PAGE:* **5**

MMea   Mears Ashby Nurseries Ltd, Glebe House, Glebe Road, Mears Ashby, Northamptonshire, NN6 0DL

> *TEL:* (01604) 812371/811811 *FAX:* (01604) 812353 *E-MAIL:* 106612.1047@compuserve.com
> *CONTACT:* John B & J E Gaggini
> *OPENING TIMES:* 0800-1730 Mon-Fri (Wholesale & Retail). 0900-1730 Sat & Sun (Retail only).
> *MIN. MAIL ORDER UK:* * *MIN. VALUE EC:*   *EXPORT:* Yes
> *CAT. COST:* £1.00** *W/SALE or RETAIL:* Both *CREDIT CARDS:* Visa, Access, Switch,
> MasterCard, Diners
> *SPECIALITIES:* Specialist growers of container Trees, Shrubs, Conifers & Fruit, esp. Wisteria.
> *Note: UK mail order for Wisteria only. **Note: Please state retail or w/sale catalogue.
> *MAP PAGE:* **5/6**

MMHG Morton Hall Gardens, Morton Hall, Ranby, Retford, Nottingham, DN22 8HW

> *TEL:* (01777) 702530 *CONTACT:* Gill McMaster
> *OPENING TIMES:* 0900-1600 Mon-Fri, 1400-1700 Sat-Sun & Bank Hols, Mar-Nov incl.
> *MIN. MAIL ORDER UK:* £5.00 + p&p *MIN. VALUE EC:* £10.00 + p&p
> *CAT. COST:* 3 x 1st class *W/SALE or RETAIL:* Retail *CREDIT CARDS:* None
> *SPECIALITIES:* Shrubs & Perennials. *MAP PAGE:* **7**

MMil   Mill Hill Plants, Mill Hill House, Elston Lane, East Stoke, Newark, Nottinghamshire, NG23 5QJ

> *TEL:* (01636) 525460 *CONTACT:* G M Gregory
> ◆ *OPENING TIMES:* 1000-1800 Wed-Sun & Bank Hols Mar-Sep, Fri-Sun in Oct & by appt.
> *MIN. MAIL ORDER UK:* No minimum charge* *MIN. VALUE EC:*
> *CAT. COST:* Sae for Iris list. *W/SALE or RETAIL:* Retail *CREDIT CARDS:* None
> *SPECIALITIES:* Hardy Perennials - many unusual & Bearded Iris. *Note: mail order Iris only, UK
> only. *MAP PAGE:* **7**

MMiN   Millfield Nurseries, Mill Lane, South Leverton, Nr Retford, Nottinghamshire, DN22 0DA

> *TEL:* (01427) 880422 *FAX:* (01427) 880422 *CONTACT:* Mr S G Clark
> *OPENING TIMES:* By appt. only.
> *MIN. MAIL ORDER UK:* £10.00 + p&p *MIN. VALUE EC:* £25.00 + p&p
> *CAT. COST:* £1.00* *W/SALE or RETAIL:* Both *CREDIT CARDS:* None
> *SPECIALITIES:* Hosta. *Catalogue cost discounted against any order placed. *MAP PAGE:* **7**

MMoz   Mozart House Nursery Garden, 84 Central Avenue, Wigston Magna, Leicestershire, LE18 2AA

> *TEL:* (0116) 288 9548 *CONTACT:* Des Martin
> ◆ *OPENING TIMES:* By appt. only.
> *MIN. MAIL ORDER UK:* £15.00 + p&p* *MIN. VALUE EC:*
> *CAT. COST:* 5 x 2nd class *W/SALE or RETAIL:* Retail *CREDIT CARDS:* none
> *SPECIALITIES:* Bamboo, Ornamental Grasses, Rushes & Sedges, Hosta. *Note: mail order to UK
> only. *MAP PAGE:* **7**

MNes   Ness Gardens, Univ. of Liverpool Botanic Gdns., Ness, Neston, South Wirral, Cheshire, L64 4AY

> *TEL:* (0151) 353 0123 *FAX:* (0151) 353 1004 *E-MAIL:* peter.cunnington@liverpool.ac.uk
> WEB SITE: http://www.merseyworld.com/nessgardens/. *CONTACT:* D Maher
> *OPENING TIMES:* 0930-1700 Apr-Oct, 1000-1600 Nov-Mar daily.
> No mail order
> *CAT. COST:* None issued *W/SALE or RETAIL:* Retail *CREDIT CARDS:* Delta, Switch, Visa
> *SPECIALITIES:* Rhododendron, Primula, Meconopsis & Penstemon. *MAP PAGE:* **7**

Nursery ADDRESSES in BOLD do Mail Order to EU

MNFA **The Nursery Further Afield, Evenley Road, Mixbury, Nr Brackley, Northamptonshire, NN13 5YR**

TEL: (01280) 848808/848539 *FAX:* (01280) 848864 *CONTACT:* Gerald Sinclair
OPENING TIMES: 1000-1700 Wed-Sat & Bank Hol Mons Apr-early Oct. Please check opening arrangements during August.
MIN. MAIL ORDER UK: £15.00 + p&p* *MIN. VALUE EC:* £15.00 + p&p*
CAT. COST: Sae *W/SALE or RETAIL:* Retail *CREDIT CARDS:* None
SPECIALITIES: Hardy Perennials esp. Geranium, Hemerocallis, Aster & Anemone. *Note: mail order for Hemerocallis only. *MAP PAGE:* 5

MNrw **Norwell Nurseries,** Woodhouse Road, Norwell, Newark, Nottinghamshire, NG23 6JX

TEL: (01636) 636337 *CONTACT:* Dr Andrew Ward
◆ *OPENING TIMES:* 1000-1700 Mon, Wed-Fri & Sun (daily exc. Tue during May & June). By appt. in Aug & 20th Oct-1st Mar.
MIN. MAIL ORDER UK: £10.00 + p&p *MIN. VALUE EC:*
CAT. COST: 3 x 1st class *W/SALE or RETAIL:* Both *CREDIT CARDS:* None
SPECIALITIES: New nursery with increasing range of unusual & choice herbaceous Perennials & Alpines. Esp. Penstemon, hardy Geranium, Campanula, Geum, Primula & Grasses.
MAP PAGE: 7

MOke **Okell's Nurseries,** Duddon Heath, Nr Tarporley, Cheshire, CW6 0EP

TEL: (01829) 741512 *FAX:* (01829) 741587 *CONTACT:* Tim Okell
OPENING TIMES: 0900-1730 daily.
No mail order
CAT. COST: Free *W/SALE or RETAIL:* Both *CREDIT CARDS:* Visa, Access, MasterCard, AmEx, Switch
SPECIALITIES: Heathers. *MAP PAGE:* 7

MOne **One House Nursery,** Buxton New Road, Macclesfield, Cheshire, SK11 0AD

TEL: (01625) 427087 *CONTACT:* Miss J L Baylis
◆ *OPENING TIMES:* 1000-1700 Tue-Sun Mar-Sep & B/Hol Mons. Nov-Feb ring for opening times.
MIN. MAIL ORDER UK: No minimum charge* *MIN. VALUE EC:*
CAT. COST: 3 x 1st class *W/SALE or RETAIL:* Retail *CREDIT CARDS:* None
SPECIALITIES: Alpines & Perennials. Good range of Primula, Sempervivum, Dwarf Rhododendron, Dwarf Conifers, Bulbs & Gentians *Note: mail order for Sempervivum only.
MAP PAGE: 7

MPEx **Planta Exotica, 11 Heath Close, Banbury, Oxon, OX15 4RZ**

TEL: (01295) 721989 *FAX:* (01295) 721989 *E-MAIL:* chris_hill@dial.pipex.com
CONTACT: Mrs M Hill
OPENING TIMES: Mar-Sept by appt.
MIN. MAIL ORDER UK: £3.95 + p&p *MIN. VALUE EC:* £3.95 + p&p
CAT. COST: 1 x 1st class *W/SALE or RETAIL:* Both *CREDIT CARDS:* none
SPECIALITIES: Rain forest plants, Alpines. *MAP PAGE:* 5

MPhe **Phedar Nursery, Bunkers Hill, Romiley, Stockport, Cheshire, SK6 3DS**

TEL: (0161) 430 3772 *FAX:* (0161) 430 3772 *CONTACT:* Will McLewin
OPENING TIMES: Frequent, esp. in Spring but very irregular. Please telephone to arrange appt.
MIN. MAIL ORDER UK: No minimum charge *MIN. VALUE EC:* Nmc   *EXPORT:* Yes*
CAT. COST: A5 Sae + 1 x 1st class *W/SALE or RETAIL:* Both *CREDIT CARDS:* None
SPECIALITIES: Helleborus, Paeonia. *Note: exports subject to destination. See also SEED Index.
MAP PAGE: 7/9

MPla **E L F Plants,** Cramden Nursery, Harborough Road North, Northampton, Northamptonshire, NN2 8LU

TEL: (01604) 846246 Eve. *CONTACT:* E L Fincham-Nichols
OPENING TIMES: 1000-1700 Thu-Sat ex Nov, Dec & Jan.
No mail order
CAT. COST: 3 x 1st class *W/SALE or RETAIL:* Retail *CREDIT CARDS:* None
SPECIALITIES: Dwarf and slow growing Shrubs & Conifers, many unusual. Some Alpines, Daphne & Heathers. *MAP PAGE:* 5

◆ **See also Display Advertisements**

MRav Ravensthorpe Nursery, 6 East Haddon Road, Ravensthorpe, Northamptonshire, NN6 8ES
TEL: (01604) 770548 *FAX:* (01604) 770548 *CONTACT:* Jean & Richard Wiseman
OPENING TIMES: 1000-1800 (dusk if earlier) Tue-Sun. Also Bank Hol Mons.
MIN. MAIL ORDER UK: No minimum charge *MIN. VALUE EC:* Nmc
CAT. COST: 4 x 1st class *W/SALE or RETAIL:* Retail *CREDIT CARDS:* Visa, Access
SPECIALITIES: Over 2,600 different Trees, Shrubs, & Perennials with many unusual varieties.
Search & delivery service for large orders - winter months only. *MAP PAGE:* 5

MRPP R P P Alpines, 6 Bentley Road, Bushbury, Wolverhampton, West Midlands, WV10 8DZ
TEL: (01902) 784508 *CONTACT:* R Smallwood
OPENING TIMES: 1000-1700 Fri, Sat & Sun only.
MIN. MAIL ORDER UK: No minimum charge *MIN. VALUE EC:* £50.00 + p&p
CAT. COST: 2 x 1st class *W/SALE or RETAIL:* Retail *CREDIT CARDS:* None
SPECIALITIES: Rare & choice Alpines from Europe, Himalaya & other regions. A selection of
Bulbs & Hardy Perennials. All in small quantities but ever changing. *MAP PAGE:* 7

MS&S S & S Perennials, 24 Main Street, Normanton Le Heath, Leicestershire, LE67 2TB
TEL: (01530) 262250 *CONTACT:* Shirley Pierce
OPENING TIMES: Afternoons only - otherwise please telephone.
No mail order
CAT. COST: 2 x 1st class *W/SALE or RETAIL:* Retail *CREDIT CARDS:* None
SPECIALITIES: Erythronium, Fritillaria, hardy Cyclamen, Iris, dwarf Narcissus, Hepatica,
Anemone & Ranunculus. *MAP PAGE:* 7

MSal Salley Gardens, 32 Lansdowne Drive, West Bridgford, Nottinghamshire, NG2 7FJ
TEL: (0115) 9233878 evenings *CONTACT:* Richard Lewin
OPENING TIMES: Mail Order only.
MIN. MAIL ORDER UK: No minimum charge *MIN. VALUE EC:* Nmc   *EXPORT:* Yes
CAT. COST: Sae *W/SALE or RETAIL:* Retail *CREDIT CARDS:* None
SPECIALITIES: Medicinal plants, esp. from North America & China. Dye plants. See also SEED
Index.

MSCN Stonyford Cottage Nursery, Stonyford Lane, Cuddington, Northwich, Cheshire, CW8 2TF
TEL: (01606) 888128 *E-MAIL:* sales@stonyford.u-net.com *CONTACT:* F A Overland
OPENING TIMES: 1000-1730 Tues-Sun & Bank Hol Mons 1st Mar-30th Nov.
No mail order
CAT. COST: 4 x 1st class *W/SALE or RETAIL:* Both *CREDIT CARDS:* None
SPECIALITIES: Wide range of Herbaceous Perennials, Diascia, Salvia & Hardy Geranium.
MAP PAGE: 7

MSta Stapeley Water Gardens Ltd, London Road, Stapeley, Nantwich, Cheshire, CW5 7LH
TEL: (01270) 623868 *FAX:* (01270) 624919 *E-MAIL:* stapeleywg@btinternet.com
CONTACT: Mr R G A Davies (Chairman)
◆ *OPENING TIMES:* Open 0900 Mon-Fri, 1000 Sat, Sun & Bank Hols all year. Please check closing
times (Closed Xmas day).
MIN. MAIL ORDER UK: £15.00 + p&p *MIN. VALUE EC:* No minimum charge *EXPORT:* Yes
CAT. COST: £1.00 *W/SALE or RETAIL:* Both *CREDIT CARDS:* Visa, Access
SPECIALITIES: World's largest Water Garden Centre. Full range of Hardy & Tropical Water
Lilies, Aquatic, Bog & Poolside plants. Also large general stock. Curators of National Collection of
Nymphaea (UK & France). *MAP PAGE:* 7

MSte   Steventon Road Nurseries, Steventon Road, East Hanney, Wantage, Oxfordshire, OX12 0HS

TEL: (01235) 868828 *FAX:* (01235) 763670 *CONTACT:* John Graham
OPENING TIMES: 1000-1630 Wed-Fri, 1000-1700 Sat & Sun 7th Mar-25th Oct 1998, 6th Mar-31st Oct 1999.
MIN. MAIL ORDER UK: £15.00 + p&p *MIN. VALUE EC:* £30.00 + p&p
CAT. COST: 4 x 1st class *W/SALE or RETAIL:* Retail *CREDIT CARDS:* None
SPECIALITIES: Tender & Hardy Perennials. *MAP PAGE:* 5

MSto   Richard Stockwell, 64 Weardale Road, off Hucknall Road, Sherwood, Nottinghamshire, NG5 1DD

TEL: (0115) 969 1063 *FAX:* (0115) 969 1063 *CONTACT:* Richard Stockwell
OPENING TIMES: Not open - mail order only.
MIN. MAIL ORDER UK: £20.00 + p&p *MIN. VALUE EC:* £20.00 + p&p   *EXPORT:* SO
CAT. COST: 4 x 2nd class or 2 x IRC *W/SALE or RETAIL:* Retail *CREDIT CARDS:* none
SPECIALITIES: Very rare climbing species, also dwarf species. Available in small numbers. See also SEED Index. *MAP PAGE:* 7

MTed   Ted Brown Unusual Plants, 1 Croftway, Markfield, Leicester, Leicestershire, LE67 9UG

TEL: (01530) 244517 *CONTACT:* Ted Brown
OPENING TIMES: From 1000 Sat-Sun Mar-Nov. Other times by appt.
No mail order
CAT. COST: None issued *W/SALE or RETAIL:* Retail *CREDIT CARDS:* None
SPECIALITIES: Mainly Herbaceous - many unusual. *MAP PAGE:* 7

MTho   A & A Thorp, Bungalow No 5, Main Street, Theddingworth, Leicestershire, LE17 6QZ

TEL: (01858) 880496 *CONTACT:* Anita & Andrew Thorp
OPENING TIMES: Dawn to Dusk all year.
No mail order
CAT. COST: 50p + Sae *W/SALE or RETAIL:* Retail *CREDIT CARDS:* None
SPECIALITIES: Unusual plants or those in short supply. *MAP PAGE:* 7

MTis   Tissington Nursery, Tissington, Nr Ashbourne, Derbyshire, DE6 1RA

TEL: (01335) 390650 *FAX:* (01335) 390693 *CONTACT:* Mrs Sue Watkins
OPENING TIMES: 1000-1800 Wed-Sun Mar-Oct & Bank Hols.
No mail order
CAT. COST: 2 x 1st class *W/SALE or RETAIL:* Retail *CREDIT CARDS:* Visa, MasterCard
SPECIALITIES: Perennials, Shrubs & Climbers incl. unusual varieties. *MAP PAGE:* 7

MTPN   The Plant Nursery, Sandy Hill Lane, Off Overstone Road, Moulton, Northampton, NN3 7JB

TEL: (01604) 491941 after 6pm *CONTACT:* Mrs B Jeyes
OPENING TIMES: 1000-1700 Thur-Sun & B/Hols Mar-Oct. 1000-1600 Sun only Nov & Dec.
MIN. MAIL ORDER UK: No minimum charge* *MIN. VALUE EC:*
CAT. COST: 2 x 1st class *W/SALE or RETAIL:* Retail *CREDIT CARDS:* none
SPECIALITIES: Wide range of Herbaceous, Alpines, Shrubs, Grasses, Hardy Geranium, Sempervivum & Succulents. *Note: mail order of Sempervivum, Succulents only, to UK.
MAP PAGE: 5

MUlv   Ulverscroft Grange Nursery, Priory Lane, Ulverscroft, Markfield, Leicestershire, LE67 9PB

TEL: (01530) 243635 *CONTACT:* David Sewell
OPENING TIMES: From 1000 7 days Mar-Nov. Other times by appt.
No mail order
CAT. COST: None issued *W/SALE or RETAIL:* Retail *CREDIT CARDS:* none
SPECIALITIES: Herbaceous & Shrubs, many unusual. *MAP PAGE:* 7

◆ **See also Display Advertisements**

MWar   Ward Fuchsias, 5 Pollen Close, Sale, Cheshire, M33 3LS
TEL: (0161) 282 7434   *CONTACT:* K Ward
OPENING TIMES: 0930-1700 Tue-Sun Feb-Jun incl Bank Hols.
MIN. MAIL ORDER UK: No minimum charge   *MIN. VALUE EC:*
CAT. COST: Free*   *W/SALE or RETAIL:* Retail   *CREDIT CARDS:* None
SPECIALITIES: Fuchsia. *Includes cultural information.   *MAP PAGE:* **7/9**

MWat   Waterperry Gardens Ltd, Waterperry, Nr Wheatley, Oxfordshire, OX33 1JZ
TEL: (01844) 339226/254   *FAX:* (01844) 339883   *CONTACT:* Mr R Jacobs
OPENING TIMES: 0900-1730 Mon-Fri, 0900-1800 Sat & Sun Summer. 0900-1700 Winter.
MIN. MAIL ORDER UK: No minimum charge*   *MIN. VALUE EC:* Nmc
CAT. COST: 75p   *W/SALE or RETAIL:* Retail   *CREDIT CARDS:* None
SPECIALITIES: General plus National Reference Collection of Saxifraga (Porophyllum). *Note:
ltd mail order, please phone for further information and credit card facilities.   *MAP PAGE:* **5**

MWgw   Wingwell Nursery, Top Street, Wing, Oakham, Rutland, LE15 8SE
TEL: (01572) 737727   *FAX:* (01572) 737788   *CONTACT:* Rose Dejardin
OPENING TIMES: 1000-1700 Wed-Sun Mar-Dec exc. August. Mail order Oct-Mar.
MIN. MAIL ORDER UK: No minimum charge*   *MIN. VALUE EC:*
CAT. COST: Sae for plant list.   *W/SALE or RETAIL:* Retail   *CREDIT CARDS:* none
SPECIALITIES: Herbaceous Perennials. *Note: mail order to UK only.   *MAP PAGE:* **7/8**

MWhe   A D & N Wheeler, Pye Court, Willoughby, Rugby, Warwickshire, CV23 8BZ
TEL: (01788) 890341   *CONTACT:* Mrs N Wheeler
OPENING TIMES: 1000-1630 daily mid Feb-late Jun. Other times please phone first for appt.
No mail order
CAT. COST: 3 x 1st class   *W/SALE or RETAIL:* Retail   *CREDIT CARDS:* None
SPECIALITIES: Fuchsia, Pelargonium & Hardy Geranium.   *MAP PAGE:* **5**

MWhi   Whitehill Farm Nursery, Whitehill Farm, Burford, Oxon, OX18 4DT
TEL: (01993) 823218   *FAX:* (01993) 822894   *CONTACT:* P J M Youngson
OPENING TIMES: 0900-1800 daily 1st Feb-31st Nov.
MIN. MAIL ORDER UK: £5.00 + p&p   *MIN. VALUE EC:* £5.00 + p&p
CAT. COST: Free   *W/SALE or RETAIL:* Retail   *CREDIT CARDS:* none
SPECIALITIES: Grasses & Bamboos, less common Shrubs, Perennials & Trees.   *MAP PAGE:* **5**

MWoo   Woodfield Bros, Wood End, Clifford Chambers, Stratford-on-Avon, Warwickshire,
CV37 8HR
TEL: (01789) 205618   *CONTACT:* B Woodfield
OPENING TIMES: 1000-1630 Mon-Fri, 1000-1600 Sat & 0900-1200 Sun for plant collection
ONLY.
MIN. MAIL ORDER UK: See list for details   *MIN. VALUE EC:*
CAT. COST: Sae   *W/SALE or RETAIL:* Both   *CREDIT CARDS:* None
SPECIALITIES: Carnations, Lupins & Delphinium. UK Mail Order for Carnations only. See also
SEED Index.   *MAP PAGE:* **5**

**MYat   R J Yates, The Gardens, Roecliffe Manor, Woodhouse Eaves, Leicestershire, LE12
8TN**
TEL: (0116) 230 3422   *CONTACT:* R J Yates
OPENING TIMES: 0930-1630 Sat & Sun only. Please phone before visit.
MIN. MAIL ORDER UK: £10.00 + p&p   *MIN. VALUE EC:* £20.00 + p&p
CAT. COST: Large (A4) Sae   *W/SALE or RETAIL:* Retail   *CREDIT CARDS:* None
SPECIALITIES: Primula & Kabschia Saxifrages.   *MAP PAGE:* **7**

Nursery ADDRESSES in BOLD do Mail Order to EU

NArc **Arcadia Nurseries Ltd, Brasscastle Lane, Nunthorpe, Middlesborough, Cleveland, TS8 9EB**

TEL: (01642) 310782 *FAX:* (01642) 300817 *CONTACT:* Mrs M E Phillips
OPENING TIMES: Garden Centre 0900-1700 Spring-Autumn, 0900-1500 Winter. Mail Order office 0900-1700 all year.
MIN. MAIL ORDER UK: 6 plants or 1 collection *MIN. VALUE EC:* 6 plants or £2 handling charge. *EXPORT:* Yes
CAT. COST: 4 x 1st class *W/SALE or RETAIL:* Retail *CREDIT CARDS:* Visa, Access, EuroCard, Switch, MasterCard
SPECIALITIES: Fuchsia. *MAP PAGE:* 9

NBat **Battersby Roses, Peartree Cottage, Old Battersby, Great Ayton, Cleveland, TS9 6LU**

TEL: (01642) 723402 *CONTACT:* Eric & Avril Stainthorpe
OPENING TIMES: 1000-dusk most days.
MIN. MAIL ORDER UK: n/a *MIN. VALUE EC:* No min. charge
CAT. COST: Sae *W/SALE or RETAIL:* Both *CREDIT CARDS:* None
SPECIALITIES: Exhibition Roses. *MAP PAGE:* 9

NBea **Beamish Clematis Nursery,** Burntwood Cottage, Stoney Lane, Beamish, Co. Durham, DH9 0SJ

TEL: (0191) 370 0202 *FAX:* (0191) 370 0202 *CONTACT:* Colin Brown or Jan Wilson
OPENING TIMES: 0900-1700 daily Feb-Nov.
MIN. MAIL ORDER UK: £50.00 + p&p* *MIN. VALUE EC:*
CAT. COST: 3 x 1st class *W/SALE or RETAIL:* Retail *CREDIT CARDS:* none
SPECIALITIES: Clematis, Climbers, Shrubs & ornamental Trees. *Note: mail order to UK only. *MAP PAGE:* 10

NBee **Beechcroft Nurseries,** Bongate, Appleby-in-Westmorland, Cumbria, CA16 6UE

TEL: (01768) 351201 *FAX:* (01768) 351201 *CONTACT:* Roger Brown
OPENING TIMES: 0800-1800 Mon-Sat, 1100-1800 Sun.
MIN. MAIL ORDER UK: No minimum charge* *MIN. VALUE EC:*
CAT. COST: £2.50* *W/SALE or RETAIL:* Retail *CREDIT CARDS:* None
SPECIALITIES: Hardy field-grown Trees & Shrubs. *Note: mail order Trees Nov-Mar only. *Sae for Tree list only. *MAP PAGE:* 9

NBir **Birkheads Cottage Garden Nursery,** Birkheads Lane, Nr Sunniside, Newcastle upon Tyne, Tyne & Wear, NE16 5EL

TEL: (01207) 232262 *FAX:* (01207) 232262 *CONTACT:* Mrs Christine Liddle
OPENING TIMES: 1000-1800 Sat & Sun & Bank Hols Apr-mid Oct & by appt.
No mail order
CAT. COST: None issued *W/SALE or RETAIL:* Retail *CREDIT CARDS:* None
SPECIALITIES: Allium, Campanula, Digitalis, Euphorbia, Hardy Geraniums, Meconopsis, Primula & Herbs. *MAP PAGE:* 10

NBrk **T H Barker & Sons,** Baines Paddock Nursery, Haverthwaite, Ulverston, Cumbria, LA12 8PF

TEL: (015395) 58236 *E-MAIL:* rachel@thbarker.demon.co.uk *CONTACT:* W E Thornley
◆ *OPENING TIMES:* 0930-1730 Wed-Mon all year.
MIN. MAIL ORDER UK: 2 plants + p&p *MIN. VALUE EC:*
CAT. COST: £1.00 (Clematis & Climbers) *W/SALE or RETAIL:* Retail *CREDIT CARDS:* None
SPECIALITIES: Clematis, Lonicera, Passiflora & other climbers; Cottage Garden Plants esp. Hardy Geranium, Aster, Ranunculus, Iris & Viola. Many rare. Most stock grown on the nursery. *MAP PAGE:* 9

NBro **Brownthwaite Hardy Plants,** Fell Yeat, Casterton, Kirkby Lonsdale, Lancashire, LA6 2JW

TEL: (015242) 71340*　*CONTACT:* Chris Benson
OPENING TIMES: Tue-Sun 1st Apr-30th Sep.
No mail order
CAT. COST: 3 x 1st class　*W/SALE or RETAIL:* Retail　*CREDIT CARDS:* None
SPECIALITIES: Herbaceous Perennials & Grasses incl. Geranium, Campanula & Penstemon.
*Note: Tel. No. (015242) 71340 after 1800.　*MAP PAGE:* **9**

NBus **Bush Green Cottage Nursery,** Foxfield Road, Broughton-in-Furness, Cumbria, LA20 6BY

TEL: (01229) 716724　*CONTACT:* Jim Haunch
OPENING TIMES: 1000-1700 Tues, Sun & Bank Hols. Garden open at same time.
MIN. MAIL ORDER UK: No minimum charge　*MIN. VALUE EC:*
CAT. COST: 4 x 1st class　*W/SALE or RETAIL:* Both　*CREDIT CARDS:* None
SPECIALITIES: Hardy Geraniums, Hostas, interesting hardy perennials. See also SEED index.
MAP PAGE: **9**

NCat **Catforth Gardens,** Roots Lane, Catforth, Preston, Lancashire, PR4 0JB

TEL: (01772) 690561/690269　*CONTACT:* Judith Bradshaw & Chris Moore
OPENING TIMES: 1030-1700 14th Mar 1998-13th Sep 1998.
No mail order
CAT. COST: 5 x 1st class　*W/SALE or RETAIL:* Retail　*CREDIT CARDS:* None
SPECIALITIES: National Collection of Hardy Geraniums. Gardens open every day. Over 1500 varieties of Herbaceous plants.　*MAP PAGE:* **9**

NChi **Chipchase Castle Nursery,** Chipchase Castle, Wark, Hexham, Northumberland, NE48 3NT

TEL: (01434) 230083　*CONTACT:* Suzanne Newell & Janet Beakes
OPENING TIMES: 1000-1700 Thu-Sun & Bank Hol Mons from Easter (1st Apr)-mid Oct.
No mail order
CAT. COST: A5 Sae for list　*W/SALE or RETAIL:* Retail　*CREDIT CARDS:* None
SPECIALITIES: Unusual Herbaceous esp. Campanula, Codonopsis, Erodium, Eryngium, Geranium, Penstemon, Salvia & Viola.　*MAP PAGE:* **10**

NCLN **Crags Lewisia Nursery, Rosley, Wigton, Cumbria, CA7 8DD**

TEL: (016973) 42527　*FAX:* (016973) 42527　*CONTACT:* E & E Parkinson
OPENING TIMES: By arrangement. Please phone.
MIN. MAIL ORDER UK: £10.00 + p&p　*MIN. VALUE EC:* £10.00 + p&p
CAT. COST: 2 x 2nd class　*W/SALE or RETAIL:* Both　*CREDIT CARDS:* None
SPECIALITIES: Lewisia Cotyledon Crags hybrids.　*MAP PAGE:* **9/10**

NCra **Craven's Nursery, 1 Foulds Terrace, Bingley, West Yorkshire, BD16 4LZ**

TEL: (01274) 561412　*FAX:* (01274) 561412　*CONTACT:* S R Craven & M Craven
OPENING TIMES: By appt. only.
MIN. MAIL ORDER UK: £10.00 + p&p　*MIN. VALUE EC:* £50.00 + p&p　　　*EXPORT:* Yes
CAT. COST: 4 x 1st class　*W/SALE or RETAIL:* Both　*CREDIT CARDS:* None
SPECIALITIES: Show Auricula, Primula, Pinks, Alpines and specialist Seeds. See also SEED Index.　*MAP PAGE:* **9**

NCut **Cutting Edge Nursery,** Highfield Farm, Knowle Road, off Upper Sheffield Road, Barnsley, Yorkshire, S70 4AW

TEL: (01226) 730292　*FAX:* (01226) 280256　*E-MAIL:* cen@cockerline.newnet.co.uk
CONTACT: Brian B Cockerline
◆　*OPENING TIMES:* 0900-1700 daily all year round,
No mail order
CAT. COST: 2 x 1st class　*W/SALE or RETAIL:* Retail　*CREDIT CARDS:* None
SPECIALITIES: Wide selection of Perennials & Shrubs, many uncommon.　*MAP PAGE:* **9**

NDal **Daleside Nurseries Ltd,** Ripon Road, Killinghall, Harrogate, North Yorks, HG3 2AY
TEL: (01423) 506450 *FAX:* (01423) 527872 *CONTACT:* Messrs Darley & Townsend
OPENING TIMES: 0900-1700 Mon-Sat, 1000-1200 & 1330-1630 Sun.
No mail order
CAT. COST: None issued *W/SALE or RETAIL:* Retail *CREDIT CARDS:* Visa, Access, Delta, Switch
SPECIALITIES: Many plants & trees not generally available. Container grown Fruit, Apples, Pears & Soft Fruit. *MAP PAGE:* 9

NDea **Deanswood Plants,** Potteries Lane, Littlethorpe, Ripon, North Yorkshire, HG4 3LF
TEL: (01765) 603441 *CONTACT:* Jacky Barber
OPENING TIMES: 1000-1700 Tue-Sun 1st Apr-30th Sep.
No mail order
CAT. COST: List 2 x 25p *W/SALE or RETAIL:* Retail *CREDIT CARDS:* None
SPECIALITIES: Pond, Marginals & Bog plants. *MAP PAGE:* 9

NDov **Dove Cottage Plants,** 23 Shibden Hall Road, Halifax, West Yorkshire, HX3 9XA
TEL: (01422) 203553 *CONTACT:* Stephen & Kim Rogers
OPENING TIMES: 1000-dusk Tues-Sun & B/Hols.
MIN. MAIL ORDER UK: No minimum charge* *MIN. VALUE EC:*
CAT. COST: Sae + 1 x 1st class *W/SALE or RETAIL:* Retail *CREDIT CARDS:* none
SPECIALITIES: Helleborus, Pulmonaria, Epimedium, Hardy Geranium, Bamboo, Hosta & Grasses & other Perennials. *Note: mail order to UK only. *MAP PAGE:* 9

NEgg **Eggleston Hall,** Barnard Castle, Co. Durham, DL12 0AG
TEL: (01833) 650403 *FAX:* (01833) 650378 *CONTACT:* Mrs R H Gray
OPENING TIMES: 1000-1700 daily
No mail order
CAT. COST: £1.50 + Sae *W/SALE or RETAIL:* Retail *CREDIT CARDS:* None
SPECIALITIES: Rare & Unusual plants with particular emphasis to Flower Arrangers.
MAP PAGE: 9

NFai **Fairy Lane Nurseries,** Fairy Lane, Sale, Greater Manchester, M33 2JT
TEL: (0161) 905 1137, (0161) 969 5594 *CONTACT:* Mrs J Coxon
OPENING TIMES: 1200-1700 Thur-Mon Mar-Oct.
MIN. MAIL ORDER UK: No minimum charge *MIN. VALUE EC:*
CAT. COST: None issued. *W/SALE or RETAIL:* Retail *CREDIT CARDS:* Access, Visa
SPECIALITIES: Hardy & tender Perennials, Herbs, Hebe & less usual Shrubs. National garden gift tokens. *MAP PAGE:* 7/9

NFla **Flaxton House Nursery,** Flaxton, York, North Yorkshire, Y06 7RJ
TEL: (01904) 468753 *CONTACT:* Mrs H Williams
OPENING TIMES: 1000-1700 Tues-Sun 1st Mar-31st Oct.
MIN. MAIL ORDER UK: £3.50 + p&p* *MIN. VALUE EC:*
CAT. COST: 3 x 1st class *W/SALE or RETAIL:* Retail *CREDIT CARDS:* None
SPECIALITIES: Wide General Range of Shrubs & Herbaceous with many unusual plants. *Note: mail order to UK only. *MAP PAGE:* 9

NGno **Gnostic Garden, PO Box 242, Newcastle Upon Tyne, NE99 1ED**
TEL: *E-MAIL:* info@gnosticgarden.ndirect.co.uk
WEB SITE: http://www.gnosticgarden.ndirect.co.uk *CONTACT:* Dan Gibson
OPENING TIMES: Mail order only
MIN. MAIL ORDER UK: No minimum charge *MIN. VALUE EC:* Nmc   *EXPORT:* Yes
CAT. COST: 4 x 2nd class (refundable) *W/SALE or RETAIL:* Retail *CREDIT CARDS:* none
SPECIALITIES: Ethnobotanical Plants, Seeds, Spores & Research Literature.

◆ **See also Display Advertisements**

NGre   Greenslacks Nurseries, Ocot Lane, Scammonden, Huddersfield, Yorkshire, HD3 3FR
TEL: (01484) 842584   *CONTACT:* Mrs V K Tuton
OPENING TIMES: 1000-1600 Wed-Sun 1st Mar-31st Oct.
MIN. MAIL ORDER UK: No minimum charge   *MIN. VALUE EC:* £20.00 + p&p   *EXPORT:* Yes
CAT. COST: 4 x 1st class or 2 x IRCs   *W/SALE or RETAIL:* Retail   *CREDIT CARDS:* None
SPECIALITIES: Unusual & Hardy plants esp. Succulents - Sedum, Sempervivum, Lewisia,
Saxifraga & Primula.   *MAP PAGE:* 9

**NHal   Halls of Heddon, (Off.) West Heddon Nurseries, Heddon-on-the-Wall,
Newcastle-upon-Tyne, Northumberland, NE15 0JS**
TEL: (01661) 852445   *CONTACT:* Judith Lockey
OPENING TIMES: 0900-1700 Mon-Sat 1000-1700 Sun.
MIN. MAIL ORDER UK: No minimum charge*   *MIN. VALUE EC:* £25.00 + p&p*
EXPORT: Yes
CAT. COST: 2 x 2nd class   *W/SALE or RETAIL:* Both   *CREDIT CARDS:* None
SPECIALITIES: Chrysanthemum & Dahlia. Wide range of Herbaceous. *Note: Mail Order Dahlia
& Chrysanthemum only. *EC & Export Dahlia tubers ONLY.   *MAP PAGE:* 10

NHar   Hartside Nursery Garden, Nr Alston, Cumbria, CA9 3BL
TEL: (01434) 381372   *FAX:* (01434) 381372   *CONTACT:* S L & N Huntley
OPENING TIMES: 0900-1630 Mon-Fri, 1230-1600 Sat, Sun & B/Hols, 1st Mar-31st Oct. By appt.
1st Nov-28th Feb.
MIN. MAIL ORDER UK: No minimum charge   *MIN. VALUE EC:* £50.00 + p&p   *EXPORT:* Yes
CAT. COST: 4 x 1st class or 3 x IRC   *W/SALE or RETAIL:* Retail   *CREDIT CARDS:* Visa,
Access, AmEx
SPECIALITIES: Alpines grown at altitude of 1100 feet in Pennines. Primula, Ferns, Gentian &
Meconopsis.   *MAP PAGE:* 9/10

**NHaw   The Hawthornes Nursery, Marsh Road, Hesketh Bank, Nr Preston, Lancashire, PR4
6XT**
TEL: (01772) 812379   *CONTACT:* Irene & Richard Hodson
OPENING TIMES: 0900-1800 daily 1st Mar-30th Jun, Thurs & Fri July-Sep. Gardens open for
NGS.
No mail order
CAT. COST: 5 x 1st class   *W/SALE or RETAIL:* Both   *CREDIT CARDS:* none
SPECIALITIES: Bedding & Basket plants. Fuchsia, Clematis, Diascia, Penstemon,
Argyranthemum, Osteospermum & other Perennials.   *MAP PAGE:* 9

NHed   Hedgerow Nursery, 24 Braithwaite Edge Road, Keighley, West Yorkshire, BD22 6RA
TEL: (01535) 606531   *CONTACT:* Nigel Hutchinson
OPENING TIMES: 1000-1700 Wed-Sun & Bank Hols.
MIN. MAIL ORDER UK: No minimum charge   *MIN. VALUE EC:* Nmc   *EXPORT:* Yes
CAT. COST: 4 x 2nd class   *W/SALE or RETAIL:* Both   *CREDIT CARDS:* Visa
SPECIALITIES: NCCPG Collection of dwarf Hebe. Saxifraga, Primula, Rhododendron &
Conifers.   *MAP PAGE:* 9

**NHex   Hexham Herbs, Chesters Walled Garden, Chollerford, Hexham, Northumberland,
NE46 4BQ**
TEL: (01434) 681483   *FAX:* (01434) 681483   *CONTACT:* Susie & Kevin White
◆   *OPENING TIMES:* 1000-1700 Mar-end Oct daily. Please phone for Winter opening times.
No mail order
CAT. COST: £1.50 inc. p&p   *W/SALE or RETAIL:* Retail   *CREDIT CARDS:* None
SPECIALITIES: Extensive range of Herbs & National Collections of Thymus & Origanum. Wild
flowers, Grasses & unusual Perennials, esp. Geranium, Epilobium & Variegated plants.
MAP PAGE: 10

Nursery ADDRESSES in BOLD do Mail Order to EU

NHHG Hardstoft Herb Garden, Hall View Cottage, Hardstoft, Pilsley, Nr Chesterfield, Derbyshire, S45 8AH

TEL: (01246) 854268 *CONTACT:* Lynne & Steve Raynor
OPENING TIMES: 1000-1800 daily, 15th Mar-15th Sep.
No mail order
CAT. COST: Free *W/SALE or RETAIL:* Retail *CREDIT CARDS:* None
SPECIALITIES: Very wide range of Herb Plants. Over 40 Lavenders & 12 Rosemary. Scented Pelargoniums. *MAP PAGE:* **7**

NHol Holden Clough Nursery, Holden, Bolton-by-Bowland, Clitheroe, Lancashire, BB7 4PF

TEL: (01200) 447615 *FAX:* (01200) 447615 *CONTACT:* P J Foley
◆ *OPENING TIMES:* 0900-1630 Tue-Sat all year (closed some Fri), 0900-1630 B/Hol Mons, 1300-1630 Easter Sun + 1 Sun in Apr & 1 in May each year.
MIN. MAIL ORDER UK: No minimum charge *MIN. VALUE EC:* Nmc   *EXPORT:* Yes
CAT. COST: £1.40 *W/SALE or RETAIL:* Both *CREDIT CARDS:* None
SPECIALITIES: Large general list incl. Primula, Saxifraga, Pulmonaria, Astilbe, Gentiana, Grasses, Hosta & Rhododendron. NOTE: Closed 24th Dec-1st Jan 1999 & Good Friday.
MAP PAGE: **9**

NLak Lakes' Hardy Plants, (Off.) 4 Fearns Building, Penistone, Sheffield, South Yorkshire, S30 6BA

TEL: (01226) 370574, (0370) 544679 mobile *FAX:* (01226) 370574 *CONTACT:* Dr P A Lake
OPENING TIMES: 0930-1730 Sat 1st Apr-31st Sept. Other times by appt. Please phone first if making long journey.
MIN. MAIL ORDER UK: No minimum charge *MIN. VALUE EC:* Nmc
CAT. COST: 4 x 1st class/Sae for list *W/SALE or RETAIL:* Both *CREDIT CARDS:* none
SPECIALITIES: Unusual Herbaceous & Cottage garden plants esp. Diascia, Digitalis, Eryngium, Euphorbia, Penstemon & Grasses. Note: Nursery is at Royd Moor Garden Nursery, Mill House Green. *MAP PAGE:* **9**

NLan Landlife Wildflowers Ltd, National Wildflower Centre, Court Hey Park, Liverpool, Merseyside, L16 3NA

TEL: (0151) 737 1819 *FAX:* (0151) 737 1820 *E-MAIL:* info@landlife.u-net.com
WEB SITE: http://www.merseyworld.com/landlife *CONTACT:* Gillian Watson
OPENING TIMES: By appt. for collection only.
MIN. MAIL ORDER UK: £14.00* *MIN. VALUE EC:*
CAT. COST: Sae + 2 x 2nd class *W/SALE or RETAIL:* Both *CREDIT CARDS:* Visa, AmEx
SPECIALITIES: Wild herbaceous plants. *Note: mail order to UK only. See also SEED Index.
MAP PAGE: **7/9**

NLar Larch Cottage Nurseries, Melkinthorpe, Penrith, Cumbria, CA10 2DR

TEL: (01931) 712404 *FAX:* (01931) 712727 *CONTACT:* Joanne McCullock or Briony Stott
◆ *OPENING TIMES:* 1000-1900 daily.
No mail order
CAT. COST: 4 x 1st class *W/SALE or RETAIL:* Retail *CREDIT CARDS:* Visa, Access, Switch, Delta, AmEx
SPECIALITIES: Unusual & Old fashioned Perennials. Rare & dwarf Conifers. Unusual Shrubs & Trees. Aquatics & Water Lilies. *MAP PAGE:* **9**

NLon Longframlington Gardens, Swarland Road, Longframlington, Morpeth, Northumberland, NE65 8DB

TEL: (01655) 570382 *FAX:* (01655) 570382 *CONTACT:* Hazel Huddleston
◆ *OPENING TIMES:* 1000-1900 (or dusk) daily all year, or by appt.
No mail order
CAT. COST: £2.50 incl. (available late 1998) *W/SALE or RETAIL:* Retail *CREDIT CARDS:* Access, Visa
SPECIALITIES: Hardy Ornamental Trees, Shrubs, Perennials, Herbs, Ground cover & Alpines.
MAP PAGE: **10**

◆ **See also Display Advertisements**

NMar   **J & D Marston, Culag, Green Lane, Nafferton, Driffield, East Yorkshire, YO25 0LF**
♦   *TEL:* (01377) 254487   *CONTACT:* J & D Marston
OPENING TIMES: 1350-1700 Easter-mid Sep, Sat, Sun & other times by appt.
MIN. MAIL ORDER UK: £15.00 + p&p   *MIN. VALUE EC:* Price on application
CAT. COST: 5 x 1st class   *W/SALE or RETAIL:* Retail   *CREDIT CARDS:* None
SPECIALITIES: Hardy & Greenhouse Ferns only.   *MAP PAGE:* 9

NMen   **Mendle Nursery, Holme, Scunthorpe, DN16 3RF**
TEL: (01724) 850864   *CONTACT:* Mrs A Earnshaw
OPENING TIMES: 1000-1600 daily
MIN. MAIL ORDER UK: No minimum charge   *MIN. VALUE EC:* Nmc
CAT. COST: 2 x 1st class   *W/SALE or RETAIL:* Retail   *CREDIT CARDS:* None
SPECIALITIES: Many unusual Alpines esp. Saxifraga & Sempervivum.   *MAP PAGE:* 9

NMGW   **MGW Plants,** 45 Potovens Lane, Lofthouse Gate, Wakefield, Yorkshire, WF3 3JE
TEL: (01924) 820096   *CONTACT:* Michael G Wilson
OPENING TIMES: 1000-dusk Wed-Sat 1st Mar-31st Oct. (Closed only 11/12th July.)
MIN. MAIL ORDER UK: £10.00 + p&p   *MIN. VALUE EC:*
CAT. COST: 1 x 1st class   *W/SALE or RETAIL:* Retail   *CREDIT CARDS:* None
SPECIALITIES: Alpines incl. Campanula & Geranium. Bulbs incl. Colchicum & Crocus.
Herbaceous incl. Geranium & Iris.   *MAP PAGE:* 9

NMir   **Mires Beck Nursery, Low Mill Lane, North Cave, Brough, North Humberside, HU15 2NR**
TEL: (01430) 421543   *CONTACT:* Irene Tinklin & Martin Rowland
OPENING TIMES: 1000-1600 Thur-Sat 1st Mar-31st July. 1000-1500 Thur-Fri 1st Aug-28th Feb & by appt.
MIN. MAIL ORDER UK: £15.00 + p&p   *MIN. VALUE EC:* £15.00 + p&p
CAT. COST: 3 x 1st class   *W/SALE or RETAIL:* Both   *CREDIT CARDS:* None
SPECIALITIES: Wild flower plants of Yorkshire provenance. See also SEED index.
MAP PAGE: 9

NMos   **Stanley Mossop, Boonwood Garden Centre, Gosforth, Seascale, Cumbria, CA20 1BP**
TEL: (01946) 725330   *FAX:* (01946) 725829   *CONTACT:* Stanley & Gary Mossop.
OPENING TIMES: 1000-1700 daily.
MIN. MAIL ORDER UK: No minimum charge   *MIN. VALUE EC:* £50.00 + p&p   *EXPORT:* Yes
CAT. COST: Free   *W/SALE or RETAIL:* Both   *CREDIT CARDS:* None
SPECIALITIES: Achimenes, Achimenantha, Eucodonia, Gloxinia (incl. species) & Smithiantha.
MAP PAGE: 9

NMun   **Muncaster Castle, Ravenglass, Cumbria, CA18 1RQ**
TEL: (01229) 717357   *FAX:* (01229) 717010   *CONTACT:* Susan Clark
OPENING TIMES: 1000-1700 daily 1st Apr-31st Oct. All other times by appt.
MIN. MAIL ORDER UK: £20.00 + p&p   *MIN. VALUE EC:* £50.00 + p&p   *EXPORT:* Yes
CAT. COST: 3 x 1st class   *W/SALE or RETAIL:* Retail   *CREDIT CARDS:* Access, Visa, not for telephone orders
SPECIALITIES: Rhododendron & Azalea.   *MAP PAGE:* 9

NNor   **Northumbria Nurseries, Castle Gardens, Ford, Berwick-upon-Tweed, Northumberland, TD15 2PZ**
♦   *TEL:* (01890) 820379   *FAX:* (01890) 820594   *CONTACT:* Hazel M Huddleston & Paul Tunnard
OPENING TIMES: 0900-1800 Mon-Fri all year, & 1000-1800 Sat-Sun & Bank Hols Mar-Oct & by appt. (Or till dusk).
MIN. MAIL ORDER UK: Nmc*   *MIN. VALUE EC:* No minimum charge
CAT. COST: £2.30 PO/Chq.   *W/SALE or RETAIL:* Both   *CREDIT CARDS:* Visa, Access
SPECIALITIES: Over 1600 different species of container grown hardy ornamental Shrubs, Perennials & Alpines. *Please phone for further info. on mail order prices.   *MAP PAGE:* 10

Nursery ADDRESSES in BOLD do Mail Order to EU

NNrd   **Norden Alpines, Hirst Road, Carlton, Nr Goole, Humberside, DN14 9PX**
TEL: 01405 861348   *CONTACT:* Norma & Denis Walton
OPENING TIMES: 1000-1700 Fri-Mon incl. or by appt.
MIN. MAIL ORDER UK: £10.00 + p&p   *MIN. VALUE EC:* £10.00 + p&p
CAT. COST: 3 x 2nd class   *W/SALE or RETAIL:* Both   *CREDIT CARDS:* None
SPECIALITIES: Many unusual Alpines - over 2000 esp. Auricula, Campanula, Primula, Saxifraga & dwarf Iris.   *MAP PAGE:* 9

NOak   **Oak Tree Nursery,** Mill Lane, Barlow, Selby, North Yorkshire, YO8 8EY
TEL: (01757) 618409   *CONTACT:* Gill Plowes
OPENING TIMES: 1000-1630 Tue-Sun mid Feb-mid Oct.
No mail order
CAT. COST: 2 x 1st class   *W/SALE or RETAIL:* Retail   *CREDIT CARDS:* None
SPECIALITIES: Cottage Garden plants.   *MAP PAGE:* 9

NOrc   **Orchard House Nursery,** Orchard House, Wormald Green, Nr Harrogate, North Yorks, HG3 3PX
TEL: (01765) 677541   *FAX:* (01765) 677541   *CONTACT:* Mr B M Corner
OPENING TIMES: 0800-1630 Mon-Fri.
No mail order
CAT. COST: £1.00   *W/SALE or RETAIL:* Both   *CREDIT CARDS:* None
SPECIALITIES: Herbaceous, Ferns, Grasses, Water Plants & unusual cottage garden plants.
MAP PAGE: 9

NPal   **The Palm Farm, Thornton Hall Gardens, Station Road, Thornton Curtis, Nr Ulceby, Humberside, DN39 6XF**
TEL: (01469) 531232   *FAX:* (01469) 531232   *CONTACT:* W W Spink
◆   *OPENING TIMES:* 1400-1700 daily ex Winter when advised to check by phone first.
MIN. MAIL ORDER UK: £11.00 + p&p   *MIN. VALUE EC:* £25.00 + p&p   *EXPORT:* Yes
CAT. COST: 1 x 2nd class   *W/SALE or RETAIL:* Both   *CREDIT CARDS:* None
SPECIALITIES: Hardy & half-Hardy Palms, unusual Trees, Shrubs & Conservatory plants.
MAP PAGE: 9

NPer   **Perry's Plants,** The River Garden, Sleights, Whitby, North Yorkshire, YO21 1RR
TEL: (01947) 810329   *FAX:* (01947) 810940   *CONTACT:* Pat & Richard Perry
◆   *OPENING TIMES:* 1000-1700 Easter to October.
No mail order
CAT. COST: Large (A4) Sae   *W/SALE or RETAIL:* Retail   *CREDIT CARDS:* None
SPECIALITIES: Lavatera, Malva, Erysimum, Euphorbia, Anthemis, Osteospermum & Hebe. Also uncommon Hardy & Container plants.   *MAP PAGE:* 9

NPin   **Pinks & Carnations, 22 Chetwyn Avenue, Bromley Cross, Bolton, Lancashire, BL7 9BN**
TEL: (01204) 306273   *FAX:* (01204) 306273   *CONTACT:* R & T Gillies
◆   *OPENING TIMES:* Appt. only.
MIN. MAIL ORDER UK: No minimum charge   *MIN. VALUE EC:* £15.00 + p&p
CAT. COST: 1 x 1st class   *W/SALE or RETAIL:* Both   *CREDIT CARDS:* Visa, MasterCard
SPECIALITIES: Pinks, Perpetual Flowering Carnations. See also SEED Index.   *MAP PAGE:* 9

NPla   **Plantations Perennials,** Cicely's Cottage, 43 Elmers Green, Skelmersdale, Lancashire, WN8 6SG
TEL: (01695) 720790/724448   *CONTACT:* Maureen Duncan/Jennifer Madeley
OPENING TIMES: By appt. only. Please phone.
No mail order
CAT. COST: 4 x 1st class   *W/SALE or RETAIL:* Retail   *CREDIT CARDS:* None
SPECIALITIES: Perennials & Shrubs incl. Diascia, Osteospermum, Penstemon, Viola, Hedera & Hebe.   *MAP PAGE:* 9

◆ **See also Display Advertisements**

NPri   **Primrose Cottage Nursery,** Ringway Road, Moss Nook, Wythenshawe, Manchester, M22 5WF

    TEL: (0161) 437 1557 *FAX:* (0161) 499 9932 *CONTACT:* Caroline Dumville
◆ *OPENING TIMES:* 0815-1800 Mon-Sat, 0930-1730 Sun.
    No mail order
    CAT. COST: 1 x 1st class *W/SALE or RETAIL:* Retail *CREDIT CARDS:* Visa, Access, Switch
    SPECIALITIES: Hardy Herbaceous Perennials, Alpines, Herbs, Roses, Patio & Hanging Basket Plants. *MAP PAGE:* **7**

NPro   **ProudPlants,** Shadyvale Nurseries, Ainstable, Carlisle, Cumbria, CA4 9QN

    TEL: (01768) 896604 *CONTACT:* Roger Proud
    OPENING TIMES: 0900-1800 daily Mar-Nov. Other times by appt.
    No mail order
    CAT. COST: None issued *W/SALE or RETAIL:* Retail *CREDIT CARDS:* None
    SPECIALITIES: Interesting & unusual Shrubs & Perennials esp. Dwarf & Ground cover plants.
    MAP PAGE: **9/10**

NPSI   **Plants of Special Interest,** 4 High Street, Braithwell, Nr Rotherham, South Yorkshire, S66 7AL

    TEL: (01709) 812328 *FAX:* (01709) 790342 *CONTACT:* Rita Ann Dunstan
◆ *OPENING TIMES:* 1000-1700 Tue-Sun Mar-Nov.
    No mail order
    CAT. COST: 3 x 1st class *W/SALE or RETAIL:* Retail *CREDIT CARDS:* Access, Switch
    SPECIALITIES: Wide selection of Herbaceous plants, esp. Aquilegia, Zantedeschia & Grasses.
    MAP PAGE: **9**

NRar   **Rarer Plants,** Ashfield House, Austfield Lane, Monk Fryston, Leeds, North Yorkshire, LS25 5EH

    TEL: (01977) 682263 *CONTACT:* Anne Watson
    OPENING TIMES: 1000-1600 Sat & Sun 1st Feb-1st May.
    No mail order
    CAT. COST: Sae *W/SALE or RETAIL:* Retail *CREDIT CARDS:* None
    SPECIALITIES: Helleborus & unusual plants. *MAP PAGE:* **9**

NRog   **R V Roger Ltd, The Nurseries, Pickering, North Yorkshire, YO18 7HG**

    TEL: (01751) 472226 *FAX:* (01751) 476749 *E-MAIL:* ian@clivia.demon.co.uk
    CONTACT: J R, A G & I M Roger
    OPENING TIMES: 0900-1700 Mon-Sat, 1300-1700 Sun. Closed Dec 25th-Jan 2nd each year.
    MIN. MAIL ORDER UK: No minimum charge *MIN. VALUE EC:* Nmc   *EXPORT:* Yes
    CAT. COST: £1.50 *W/SALE or RETAIL:* Both *CREDIT CARDS:* Visa, Access
    SPECIALITIES: General list, hardy in North of England. Co-holders of National Erodium & Erythronium Collection. See also SEED Index. *MAP PAGE:* **9**

NRoo   **Rookhope Nurseries,** Rookhope, Upper Weardale, Co. Durham, DL13 2DD

    TEL: (01388) 517272 *CONTACT:* Karen Blackburn
    OPENING TIMES: 0900-1600 mid Mar-end Sept.
    No mail order
    CAT. COST: 3 x 1st class *W/SALE or RETAIL:* Retail *CREDIT CARDS:* Visa, Access, MasterCard
    SPECIALITIES: Wide range of Hardy plants grown at 1,100 feet in the northern Pennines.
    MAP PAGE: **9/10**

NRya   **Ryal Nursery, East Farm Cottage, Ryal, Northumberland, NE20 0SA**

    TEL: (01661) 886562 *FAX:* (01661) 886918 *E-MAIL:* stevehadden@globalnet.co.uk
    CONTACT: R F Hadden
    OPENING TIMES: 1300-1600 Tue, 1000-1600 Sun Mar-Jul & by appt.
    MIN. MAIL ORDER UK: £5.00 + p&p *MIN. VALUE EC:* £5.00 + p&p
    CAT. COST: Sae *W/SALE or RETAIL:* Both *CREDIT CARDS:* None
    SPECIALITIES: Alpine & Woodland plants. *MAP PAGE:* **10**

Nursery ADDRESSES in BOLD do Mail Order to EU

NSla   **Slack Top Alpines,** Hebden Bridge, West Yorkshire, HX7 7HA
TEL: (01422) 845348   *CONTACT:* M R or R Mitchell
OPENING TIMES: 1000-1800 Wed-Sun & Bank Hol Mons 1st Mar-31st Oct.
No mail order
CAT. COST: Sae   *W/SALE or RETAIL:* Both   *CREDIT CARDS:* None
SPECIALITIES: Alpine & Rockery plants.   *MAP PAGE:* **9**

NSpr   **Springwood Pleiones, 35 Heathfield, Leeds, W Yorkshire, LS16 7AB**
TEL: (0113) 261 1781   *CONTACT:* Ken Redshaw
OPENING TIMES: By appt. only.
MIN. MAIL ORDER UK: £2.00 + p&p   *MIN. VALUE EC:* £2.00 + p&p
CAT. COST: 1 x 1st class   *W/SALE or RETAIL:* Retail   *CREDIT CARDS:* None
SPECIALITIES: Pleione.   *MAP PAGE:* **9**

NSti   **Stillingfleet Lodge Nurseries,** Stillingfleet, Yorkshire, YO4 6HW
TEL: (01904) 728506   *FAX:* (01904) 728506   *CONTACT:* Vanessa Cook
OPENING TIMES: 1000-1600 Tue Wed Fri & Sat 1st Apr-18th Oct.
MIN. MAIL ORDER UK: No minimum charge   *MIN. VALUE EC:*
CAT. COST: 7 x 2nd class   *W/SALE or RETAIL:* Retail   *CREDIT CARDS:* None
SPECIALITIES: Foliage & unusual perennials. Hardy Geraniums, Pulmonaria, variegated plants &
Grasses. Holder of National Pulmonaria Collection.   *MAP PAGE:* **9**

NSty   **Stydd Nursery, Stonegate Lane, Ribchester, Nr Preston, Lancashire, PR3 3YN**
TEL: (01254) 878797   *FAX:* (01254) 878254   *CONTACT:* Mrs C Walker
OPENING TIMES: 1330-1700 Tue-Fri, 1330-1700 Sat. Please check first.
MIN. MAIL ORDER UK: No minimum charge   *MIN. VALUE EC:* £50.00 + p&p
CAT. COST: (£1) 4 x 1st class   *W/SALE or RETAIL:* Retail   *CREDIT CARDS:* None
SPECIALITIES: Old Roses & ornamental foliage. Half-hardy Perennials, Conservatory Plants.
  MAP PAGE: **9**

NTay   **Taylors Nurseries,** Sutton Road, Sutton, Doncaster, Yorkshire, DN6 9JZ
TEL: (01302) 700716   *FAX:* (01302) 708415   *CONTACT:* John Taylor
◆   *OPENING TIMES:* 0800-1800 Summer, 0800-1700 Winter daily. Closed Xmas & Boxing day &
New Year's day.
MIN. MAIL ORDER UK: 2 plants + p&p   *MIN. VALUE EC:*
CAT. COST: 2 x 1st class   *W/SALE or RETAIL:* Retail   *CREDIT CARDS:* Visa, Access
SPECIALITIES: Clematis (over 150 varieties) & Herbaceous Perennials.   *MAP PAGE:* **9**

NTow   **Town Farm Nursery,** Whitton, Stillington, Stockton on Tees, Cleveland, TS21 1LQ
TEL: (01740) 631079   *CONTACT:* F D Baker
◆   *OPENING TIMES:* 1000-1800 Fri-Mon Mar-Oct.
MIN. MAIL ORDER UK: £5.00 + p&p   *MIN. VALUE EC:*
CAT. COST: Sae   *W/SALE or RETAIL:* Retail   *CREDIT CARDS:* None
SPECIALITIES: Unusual Alpines, Border Perennials & Shrubs. See also SEED Index.
  MAP PAGE: **9**

NVic   **The Vicarage Garden,** Carrington, Urmston, Manchester, M31 4AG
TEL: (0161) 775 2750   *FAX:* (0161) 775 3679   *CONTACT:* Mr R Alexander
OPENING TIMES: 1000-1200 & 1330-1700 Fri-Wed Sep-Mar. 1000-1200 & 1330-1830 Apr-Aug.
MIN. MAIL ORDER UK: £10.00 + p&p*   *MIN. VALUE EC:*
CAT. COST: 5 x 1st class   *W/SALE or RETAIL:* Both   *CREDIT CARDS:* Visa, Access
SPECIALITIES: Herbaceous. *Note: mail order to UK only.   *MAP PAGE:* **9**

NWCA   **White Cottage Alpines,** Sunnyside Nurseries, Hornsea Road, Sigglesthorne, East
Yorkshire, HU11 5QL
TEL: (01964) 542692   *FAX:* (01964) 542692   *CONTACT:* Sally E Cummins
OPENING TIMES: 1000-1700 (or dusk) Thu-Sun & Bank Hol Mons. Closed Dec & Jan.
MIN. MAIL ORDER UK: £7.50 + p&p   *MIN. VALUE EC:*
CAT. COST: 4 x 1st class   *W/SALE or RETAIL:* Retail   *CREDIT CARDS:* None
SPECIALITIES: Alpines.   *MAP PAGE:* **9**

◆ **See also Display Advertisements**

NWea Weasdale Nurseries, Newbiggin-on-Lune, Kirkby Stephen, Cumbria, CA17 4LX
TEL: (01539) 623246 *FAX:* (01539) 623277 *E-MAIL:* sales@weasdale.com
WEB SITE: http://www.weasdale.com *CONTACT:* Andrew Forsyth
OPENING TIMES: 0900-1700 Mon-Fri. Closed w/ends, B/Hols, Xmas-New Year.
MIN. MAIL ORDER UK: No minimum charge *MIN. VALUE EC:* Nmc
CAT. COST: £1 (£1.50 by credit card) or 5 x 2nd or 4 x 1st class *W/SALE or RETAIL:* Retail
CREDIT CARDS: Visa, MasterCard, Switch, Delta, Access, Solo
SPECIALITIES: Hardy forest trees, hedging, broadleaved & conifers. Specimen Trees & Shrubs
grown at 850 feet. Mail Order a speciality. *MAP PAGE:* **9**

NWes Westwinds Perennial Plants, Filpoke Lane, High Hesleden, Hartlepool, Cleveland, TS27 4BT
TEL: (0191) 518 0225 *FAX:* (0191) 518 0225 *E-MAIL:* westwinds@btinternet.co.uk
CONTACT: Harry Blackwood
OPENING TIMES: Dawn until Dusk Sun & Mon and by appt.
MIN. MAIL ORDER UK: * *MIN. VALUE EC:* £20.00 + p&p
CAT. COST: 2 x 1st class *W/SALE or RETAIL:* Retail *CREDIT CARDS:* None
SPECIALITIES: Penstemon, Hosta, Geranium, Phygelius plus a range of specimen size Shrubs &
Climbers. NB Mail order for Hostas only. *MAP PAGE:* **9/10**

NWoo Woodlands Cottage Nursery, Summerbridge, Harrogate, North Yorkshire, HG3 4BT
TEL: (01423) 780765 *FAX:* (01423) 780765 *CONTACT:* Mrs Ann Stark
OPENING TIMES: 1100-1800 Mon, Wed, Fri, Sat & 1400-1700 Sun, mid Mar-end Sep.
No mail order
CAT. COST: 2 x 1st class *W/SALE or RETAIL:* Retail *CREDIT CARDS:* None
SPECIALITIES: Herbs, plants for Shade & Hardy Perennials. *MAP PAGE:* **9**

NYoL Yorkshire Lavender, Terrington, York, N Yorks, YO6 4QB
TEL: (01653) 648430 *CONTACT:* Nigel W B Goodwill
OPENING TIMES: By appt. only.
MIN. MAIL ORDER UK: No minimum charge *MIN. VALUE EC:* Nmc   *EXPORT:* Yes
CAT. COST: 2 x 1st class *W/SALE or RETAIL:* Both *CREDIT CARDS:* None
SPECIALITIES: Lavandula. *MAP PAGE:* **9**

NZep Zephyrwude Irises, 48 Blacker Lane, Crigglestone, Wakefield, West Yorkshire, WF4 3EW
TEL: (01924) 252101 *CONTACT:* Richard L Brook
OPENING TIMES: Viewing only 0900-dusk daily May-mid June, peak late May. Phone first,
0900-2300.
MIN. MAIL ORDER UK: £15.00 + p&p *MIN. VALUE EC:* £15.00 + p&p
CAT. COST: 1 x 1st class *W/SALE or RETAIL:* Retail *CREDIT CARDS:* None
SPECIALITIES: Bearded Iris, 1970s-80s hybrids only. Mainly 12" dwarf & intermediate, a few tall.
300 variety display garden. Cat. available Apr-Sep 15th. Delivery Aug-Oct only. *MAP PAGE:* **9**

SAga Agar's Nursery, Agars Lane, Hordle, Lymington, Hampshire, SO41 0FL
TEL: (01590) 683703 *CONTACT:* Mrs Diana Tombs
OPENING TIMES: 1000-1600 Fri-Wed 1st Feb-20th Dec.
No mail order
CAT. COST: None issued *W/SALE or RETAIL:* Retail *CREDIT CARDS:* None
SPECIALITIES: Penstemon & Salvia. Also wide range of Hardy plants inc. Shrubs & Climbers.
 MAP PAGE: **2**

SAll Allwood Bros, Mill Nursery, Hassocks, West Sussex, BN6 9NB
TEL: (01273) 844229 *FAX:* (01273) 846022 *CONTACT:* Sue James
OPENING TIMES: 0900-1600 Mon-Fri.
MIN. MAIL ORDER UK: No minimum charge *MIN. VALUE EC:* Nmc   *EXPORT:* SO
CAT. COST: 2 x 1st class *W/SALE or RETAIL:* Both *CREDIT CARDS:* Access, Visa
SPECIALITIES: Dianthus, incl Hardy Border Carnations, Pinks, Perpetual & Allwoodii, some
available as seed. See also SEED Index. *MAP PAGE:* **3**

Nursery ADDRESSES in BOLD do Mail Order to EU

SAPC **Architectural Plants (Chichester) Ltd, Lidsey Road Nursery, Westergate, Nr Chichester, West Sussex, PO20 6SU**

TEL: (01243) 545008 *FAX:* (01243) 545009 *CONTACT:* Christine Shaw
◆ *OPENING TIMES:* 1000-1600 every Sun; phone first on weekdays.
MIN. MAIL ORDER UK: No minimum charge *MIN. VALUE EC:* £150.00 + p&p *EXPORT:* Yes
CAT. COST: Free *W/SALE or RETAIL:* Both *CREDIT CARDS:* Visa, Access, EuroCard, Switch, Delta, Electron, JCB
SPECIALITIES: Architectural plants & hardy Exotics, esp. evergreen broadleaved trees, & seaside exotics. Note: second nursery near Horsham, Code SArc. *MAP PAGE:* 3

SApp **Apple Court, Hordle Lane, Hordle, Lymington, Hampshire, S041 0HU**

TEL: (01590) 642130 *FAX:* (01590) 644220 *E-MAIL:* applecourt@btinternet.com
WEB SITE: http://www.AppleCourt.com *CONTACT:* Diana Grenfell & Roger Grounds
◆ *OPENING TIMES:* Open daily (Closed 1300-1400) Jul-Aug. Thu-Mon Feb-Oct. Closed Nov-Jan.
MIN. MAIL ORDER UK: £15.00 + p&p *MIN. VALUE EC:* £50.00 + p&p
CAT. COST: 4 x 1st class *W/SALE or RETAIL:* Retail *CREDIT CARDS:* None
SPECIALITIES: Hosta, Grasses, Ferns, Hemerocallis. National Collection Woodwardia, Rohdea, & Hosta. *MAP PAGE:* 2

SApu **Apuldram Roses, Apuldram Lane, Dell Quay, Chichester, Sussex, PO20 7EF**

TEL: (01243) 785769 *FAX:* (01243) 536973 *E-MAIL:* d.sawday@virgin.net
WEB SITE: http://www.gardening-uk.com/apuldram/ *CONTACT:* Mrs Sawday
OPENING TIMES: 0900-1700 Mon-Sat, 1030-1630 Sun & Bank Hols. ex. Dec 23rd-Jan 5th.
MIN. MAIL ORDER UK: £4.50 + p&p *MIN. VALUE EC:* £4.50 + p&p
CAT. COST: 2 x 1st class *W/SALE or RETAIL:* Both *CREDIT CARDS:* Switch, MasterCard, Visa
SPECIALITIES: Roses. *MAP PAGE:* 2/3

SArc **Architectural Plants, Cooks Farm, Nuthurst, Horsham, West Sussex, RH13 6LH**

TEL: (01403) 891772 *FAX:* (01403) 891056 *CONTACT:* Sarah Chandler & Monique Gudgeon
◆ *OPENING TIMES:* 0900-1700 Mon-Sat.
MIN. MAIL ORDER UK: No minimum charge *MIN. VALUE EC:* £150.00 + p&p *EXPORT:* Yes
CAT. COST: Free *W/SALE or RETAIL:* Both *CREDIT CARDS:* Visa, Access, EuroCard, Switch, Delta, Electron, JCB
SPECIALITIES: Architectural plants & hardy Exotics. Note: second nursery near Chichester, Code SAPC. *MAP PAGE:* 3

SAsh **Ashenden Nursery, Cranbrook Road, Benenden, Cranbrook, Kent, TN17 4ET**

TEL: (01580) 241792 *CONTACT:* Kevin McGarry
OPENING TIMES: By appt. Please telephone.
No mail order
CAT. COST: Sae + 1 x 1st class *W/SALE or RETAIL:* Retail *CREDIT CARDS:* None
SPECIALITIES: Rock garden & perennials. *MAP PAGE:* 3

SAWi **Anthony Archer-Wills Ltd,** Broadford Bridge Road, West Chiltington, West Sussex, RH20 2LF

TEL: (01798) 813204 *FAX:* (01798) 815080 *CONTACT:* Anthony Archer-Wills
OPENING TIMES: By appt. only - please telephone.
MIN. MAIL ORDER UK: £15.00 + p&p *MIN. VALUE EC:*
CAT. COST: £1.00 + 2 x 2nd class *W/SALE or RETAIL:* Both *CREDIT CARDS:* None
SPECIALITIES: Ponds, Lakes & Water garden plants. *MAP PAGE:* 3

SAxl **Axletree Nursery, Starvecrow Lane, Peasmarsh, Rye, East Sussex, TN31 6XL**

TEL: (01797) 230470 *FAX:* (01797) 230470 *CONTACT:* D J Hibberd
OPENING TIMES: 1000-1700 Wed-Sat mid Mar-end Sep.
MIN. MAIL ORDER UK: No minimum charge *MIN. VALUE EC:* Nmc
CAT. COST: 4 x 1st class *W/SALE or RETAIL:* Retail *CREDIT CARDS:* MasterCard, Visa, AmEx, JCB, Switch, Delta
SPECIALITIES: Extensive range of Perennials, esp. Hardy Geraniums. *MAP PAGE:* 3

◆ **See also Display Advertisements**

SBai **Steven Bailey Ltd, Silver Street, Sway, Lymington, Hampshire, SO41 6ZA**
TEL: (01590) 682227 *FAX:* (01590) 683765 *CONTACT:* Fiona Whittles
OPENING TIMES: 1000-1300 & 1400-1630 Mon-Fri all year. 1000-1300 & 1400-1600 Sat Mar-Jun
ex Bank Hols.
MIN. MAIL ORDER UK: Quotation *MIN. VALUE EC:* Quotation   *EXPORT:* Yes
CAT. COST: 2 x 2nd class *W/SALE or RETAIL:* Both *CREDIT CARDS:* Visa, Access
SPECIALITIES: Carnations, Pinks & Alstroemeria. *MAP PAGE:* **2**

SBid **Biddenden Nursery at Garden Crafts, Sissinghurst Road, Biddenden, Kent, TN27 8EJ**
TEL: (01580) 292100 *FAX:* (01580) 292 097 *CONTACT:* Gerald Bedrich
♦ *OPENING TIMES:* 0900-1700 Mon-Fri, 1000-1700 Sat & Sun.
MIN. MAIL ORDER UK: No minimum charge *MIN. VALUE EC:* Nmc   *EXPORT:* Yes
CAT. COST: 3 x 1st class *W/SALE or RETAIL:* Both *CREDIT CARDS:* Visa, Access, AmEx,
Switch
SPECIALITIES: Wide range of unusual Shrubs, esp. Ceanothus, Hydrangea & Viburnum. Rare &
unusual Herbaceous. Comprehensive range of 'Sissinghurst' plants. *MAP PAGE:* **3**

SBir **Birchfleet Nursery, Nyewood, Petersfield, Hampshire, GU31 5JQ**
TEL: (01730) 821636 *FAX:* (01730) 821636 *E-MAIL:* gammoak@aol.com
CONTACT: John & Daphne Gammon
OPENING TIMES: By appt. only. Please telephone.
MIN. MAIL ORDER UK: £20.00 + p&p *MIN. VALUE EC:* £30.00 + p&p   *EXPORT:* Yes
CAT. COST: Sae *W/SALE or RETAIL:* Both *CREDIT CARDS:* None
SPECIALITIES: Oaks incl. many hybrids, and other rare trees. *MAP PAGE:* **2/3**

SBla **Blackthorn Nursery,** Kilmeston, Alresford, Hampshire, SO24 0NL
TEL: 01962 771796 *FAX:* 01962 771071 *CONTACT:* A R & S B White
OPENING TIMES: 0900-1700 Fri & Sat Mar-last weekend of June
No mail order
CAT. COST: 3 x 1st class *W/SALE or RETAIL:* Retail *CREDIT CARDS:* None
SPECIALITIES: Choice Perennials & Alpines, esp. Daphne, Epimedium & Helleborus.
MAP PAGE: **2**

SBod **Bodiam Nursery,** Ockham House, Bodiam, Robertsbridge, East Sussex, TN32 5RA
TEL: (01580) 830811/830649 *FAX:* (01580) 830071 *CONTACT:* Richard Biggs
OPENING TIMES: 0900-1800 or dusk.
MIN. MAIL ORDER UK: £30.00 + p&p *MIN. VALUE EC:*
CAT. COST: 4 x 1st class *W/SALE or RETAIL:* Both *CREDIT CARDS:* Visa, MasterCard,
EuroCard
SPECIALITIES: Heathers, herbaceous Perennials, Conifers, Azalea, Camellia & Climbers.
MAP PAGE: **3**

SBra **J Bradshaw & Son, Busheyfield Nursery, Herne, Herne Bay, Kent, CT6 7LJ**
TEL: (01227) 375415 *FAX:* (01227) 375415 *CONTACT:* D J Bradshaw
♦ *OPENING TIMES:* 1000-1700 Tue-Sat 1st Mar-31st Oct. Other times by appt. only.
MIN. MAIL ORDER UK: 2 plants + p&p* *MIN. VALUE EC:* 2 plants + p&p
CAT. COST: Sae + 2 x 1st class *W/SALE or RETAIL:* Both *CREDIT CARDS:* None
SPECIALITIES: Clematis, Climbers & Wall plants. NCCPG Collection of climbing Lonicera &
Clematis montana. *MAP PAGE:* **3**

SBre **Bressingham Plant Centre,** Borde Hill, Haywards Heath, West Sussex, RH16 1XP
TEL: (01379) 687464/688133 (Norfolk site temporarily)
FAX: (01379) 688034 (Norfolk site temporarily)
CONTACT: Nathan Berrisford (or Tony Fry by phone/fax at the Norfolk site)
♦ *OPENING TIMES:* 0900-1730 daily. (Direct retail Plant Centre.)
No mail order
CAT. COST: None issued *W/SALE or RETAIL:* Retail *CREDIT CARDS:* Delta, Switch,
MasterCard, Visa
SPECIALITIES: Very wide general range. Many own varieties. Focus on Hardy Ornamental plants
& Grasses. *MAP PAGE:* **3**

Nursery ADDRESSES in BOLD do Mail Order to EU

SBrw   **Broadwater Plants, Fairview Lane, Tunbridge Wells, Kent, TN3 9LU**
TEL: (01892) 534760 *FAX:* (01892) 534760 *E-MAIL:* broadwater@coblands.co.uk
CONTACT: John Moaby
OPENING TIMES: 0900-1630 Mon-Fri, 0900-1600 Sat 1st Mar-30th June.
MIN. MAIL ORDER UK: No minimum charge *MIN. VALUE EC:* Nmc   *EXPORT:* Yes
CAT. COST: 3 x 1st class *W/SALE or RETAIL:* Retail *CREDIT CARDS:* MasterCard, Visa
SPECIALITIES: Rhododendron, Camellia & Ericaceous plants incl. many unusual species.
MAP PAGE: **3**

SCha   **Chalkhill Nursery, Ballingdane, South Green, Sittingbourne, Kent, ME9 7RR**
TEL: (01622) 884602 *CONTACT:* Neal Pearson
OPENING TIMES: By appt. only. Please phone first.
MIN. MAIL ORDER UK: £10.00 + p&p *MIN. VALUE EC:* £15.00 + p&p
CAT. COST: 2 x 1st class *W/SALE or RETAIL:* Retail *CREDIT CARDS:* none
SPECIALITIES: Bamboos & Perennials. *MAP PAGE:* **3**

SChu   **Church Hill Cottage Gardens,** Charing Heath, Ashford, Kent, TN27 0BU
TEL: (01233) 712522 *FAX:* (01233) 712522 *CONTACT:* Mr M & J & Mrs M Metianu.
OPENING TIMES: 1000-1700 1st Feb-30th Nov Tue-Sun & Bank Hols Mon. Other times by appt.
MIN. MAIL ORDER UK: £10.00 + p&p *MIN. VALUE EC:*
CAT. COST: 3 x 1st class *W/SALE or RETAIL:* Retail *CREDIT CARDS:* None
SPECIALITIES: Unusual hardy plants, Dianthus, Hosta, Ferns & Viola. Alpines & Shrubs.
MAP PAGE: **3**

SCit   **The Citrus Centre, West Mare Lane, Marehill, Pulborough, West Sussex, RH20 2EA**
TEL: (01798) 872786 *FAX:* (01798) 874880 *E-MAIL:* chris_dennis@msn.com
CONTACT: Amanda & Chris Dennis
OPENING TIMES: 0930-1730 Wed-Sun & Bank Hols. Closed Xmas & Boxing Day.
MIN. MAIL ORDER UK: No minimum charge *MIN. VALUE EC:* Nmc   *EXPORT:* Yes
CAT. COST: Sae *W/SALE or RETAIL:* Both *CREDIT CARDS:* Visa, Access
SPECIALITIES: Citrus & Citrus relatives. *MAP PAGE:* **3**

SCob   **Coblands Nursery, (Off.) Trench Road, Tonbridge, Kent, TN10 3HQ**
TEL: (01732) 770999 *FAX:* (01732) 770271 *E-MAIL:* plants@coblands.co.uk
CONTACT: Nick Coslett
OPENING TIMES: 0830-1600 Mon-Fri.
MIN. MAIL ORDER UK: No minimum charge *MIN. VALUE EC:* Nmc   *EXPORT:* Yes
CAT. COST: W/Sale Cat only *W/SALE or RETAIL:* Both *CREDIT CARDS:* Visa, MasterCard
SPECIALITIES: General range, esp. Bamboos, Grasses & Ferns. NOTE:- Nursery at Back Lane,
Ightham, Sevenoaks. *MAP PAGE:* **3**

SCog   **Coghurst Nursery, Ivy House Lane, Near Three Oaks, Hastings, East Sussex, TN35
4NP**
TEL: (01424) 756228 *CONTACT:* J Farnfield & L A Edgar
OPENING TIMES: 1200-1630 Mon-Fri, 1000-1630 Sun.
MIN. MAIL ORDER UK: No minimum charge *MIN. VALUE EC:* Nmc
CAT. COST: 1 x 2nd class for availability list. *W/SALE or RETAIL:* Both *CREDIT
CARDS:* None
SPECIALITIES: Camellia & Eucryphia. *MAP PAGE:* **3**

SCoo   **Cooling's Nurseries Ltd,** Rushmore Hill, Knockholt, Sevenoaks, Kent, TN14 7NN
TEL: (01959) 532269 *FAX:* (01959) 534092 *CONTACT:* M Hooker
OPENING TIMES: 0900-1700 Mon-Sat & 1000-1630 Sun.
No mail order
CAT. COST: 3 x 1st class *W/SALE or RETAIL:* Retail *CREDIT CARDS:* Visa, Access, Switch,
Electron, Delta
SPECIALITIES: Large range of Perennials, Conifers & Bedding plants. Some unusual Shrubs.
MAP PAGE: **3**

◆ **See also Display Advertisements**

SCou **Coombland Gardens, Coombland, Coneyhurst, Billingshurst, West Sussex, RH14 9DG**

TEL: (01403) 741727 *FAX:* (01403) 741079 *CONTACT:* David Browne
OPENING TIMES: 1400-1600 Mon-Fri Mar-end Oct. Bank Hols & other times by appt. only.
MIN. MAIL ORDER UK: £20.00 + p&p* *MIN. VALUE EC:* 8 plants + p&p*   *EXPORT:* Yes
CAT. COST: 5 x 1st class *W/SALE or RETAIL:* Retail *CREDIT CARDS:* None
SPECIALITIES: Hardy Geranium (National Collection), Erodium & choice Herbaceous. *Note:
Hardy Geraniums only to EC. See also SEED Index. *MAP PAGE:* 3

SCro **Croftway Nursery, Yapton Road, Barnham, Bognor Regis, West Sussex, PO22 0BH**

TEL: (01243) 552121 *FAX:* (01243) 552125 *E-MAIL:* croftway@aol.com
WEB SITE: http://members.aol.com/croftway/ *CONTACT:* Graham Spencer
OPENING TIMES: 0900-1700 daily. Closed 1st Dec- 28th Feb except by appt.
MIN. MAIL ORDER UK: No minimum charge* *MIN. VALUE EC:* Nmc*
CAT. COST: 4 x 1st class *W/SALE or RETAIL:* Both *CREDIT CARDS:* Visa, Access, Switch
SPECIALITIES: Wide general range, emphasis on Perennials. Specialists in Iris & Hardy
Geranium. *Note: mail order for Iris & Geranium only. *MAP PAGE:* 3

SDad **J Dadswell**, 4 Marle Avenue, Burgess Hill, West Sussex, RH15 8JG

TEL: (01444) 232874 *CONTACT:* Judith Dadswell
OPENING TIMES: By appt. only
No mail order
CAT. COST: 3 x 1st class *W/SALE or RETAIL:* Retail *CREDIT CARDS:* None
SPECIALITIES: Geranium. *MAP PAGE:* 3

SDay **A La Carte Daylilies, Little Hermitage, St. Catherine's Down, Nr Ventnor, Isle of
Wight, PO38 2PD**

TEL: (01983) 730512 *CONTACT:* Jan & Andy Wyers
♦ *OPENING TIMES:* By appt. only
MIN. MAIL ORDER UK: No minimum charge *MIN. VALUE EC:* Nmc
CAT. COST: 3 x 1st class *W/SALE or RETAIL:* Retail *CREDIT CARDS:* None
SPECIALITIES: Hemerocallis *MAP PAGE:* 2

SDea **Deacon's Nursery, Moor View, Godshill, Isle of Wight, PO38 3HW**

TEL: (01983) 840750 (24 hrs), (01983) 522243 *FAX:* (01983) 523575
CONTACT: G D & B H W Deacon
♦ *OPENING TIMES:* 0800-1600 Mon-Fri May-Sep, 0800-1700 Mon-Fri 0800-1300 Sat Oct-Ap
MIN. MAIL ORDER UK: No minimum charge *MIN. VALUE EC:* Nmc*   *EXPORT:* Yes
CAT. COST: Stamp appreciated. *W/SALE or RETAIL:* Both *CREDIT CARDS:* Visa, Access
SPECIALITIES: Over 250 varieties of Apple, old & new. Pears, Plums, Gages, Damsons, Cherries
etc. Fruit & Nut trees, triple Peaches, Ballerinas. Modern Soft Fruit. Grapes, Hops. Family Trees -
Blueberries. *MAP PAGE:* 2

SDeJ **De Jager & Sons, The Nurseries, Marden, Kent, TN12 9BP**

TEL: (01622) 831235 *FAX:* (01622) 832416 *CONTACT:* Mr E Hotson
OPENING TIMES: 0900-1700 Mon-Fri.
MIN. MAIL ORDER UK: £15.00 + p&p *MIN. VALUE EC:* £15.00 + p&p   *EXPORT:* Yes
CAT. COST: Free *W/SALE or RETAIL:* Both *CREDIT CARDS:* Visa, Access   -
SPECIALITIES: Wide general range, esp. Bulbs. Lilium, Tulipa, Narcissus species &
miscellaneous. Large range of Perennials. *MAP PAGE:* 3

SDen **Denmead Geranium Nurseries, Hambledon Road, Denmead, Waterlooville,
Hampshire, PO7 6PS**

TEL: (01705) 240081 *CONTACT:* I H Chance
OPENING TIMES: 0800-1300 & 1400-1700 Mon-Fri, 0800-1230 Sat (ex Aug), 1400-1700 Sat
May-Jun. Closed Sun & B/Hol Mons.
MIN. MAIL ORDER UK: £10.00 + p&p *MIN. VALUE EC:* £10.00 + p&p
CAT. COST: 3 x 2nd class *W/SALE or RETAIL:* Both *CREDIT CARDS:* None
SPECIALITIES: Pelargoniums - Zonals, Ivy-leaved, Scented, Unique, Rosebud, Stellars,
Miniature, Dwarf, Swiss Balcony, Mini Cascade, Ornamental, Regals & Angels. *MAP PAGE:* 2

Nursery ADDRESSES in BOLD do Mail Order to EU

SDix   **Great Dixter Nurseries, Northiam, Rye, East Sussex, TN31 6PH**

TEL: (01797) 253107 *FAX:* (01797) 252879 *E-MAIL:* greatdixter@compuserve.com
WEB SITE: http://www.entertainnet.co.uk/greatdixter/index/html *CONTACT:* K Leighton
OPENING TIMES: 0900-1230 & 1330-1700 Mon-Fri, 0900-1200 Sat all year. Also 1400-1700 Sat,
Sun & Bank Hols Apr-Oct.
MIN. MAIL ORDER UK: £15.00 + p&p *MIN. VALUE EC:* £15.00 + p&p
CAT. COST: 4 x 1st class *W/SALE or RETAIL:* Retail *CREDIT CARDS:* Access, Switch, Visa
SPECIALITIES: Clematis, Shrubs and Plants. (Gardens open). *MAP PAGE:* 3

SDow   **Downderry Nursery, Pillar Box Lane, Hadlow, Nr Tonbridge, Kent, TN11 9SS**

TEL: (01732) 810081 *FAX:* (01732) 810081 *CONTACT:* Dr S J Charlesworth
OPENING TIMES: 1000-1700 Wed-Sat & 1100-1700 Sun 2nd May-1st Nov, and by appt.
MIN. MAIL ORDER UK: No minimum charge *MIN. VALUE EC:* Nmc   *EXPORT:* Yes
CAT. COST: 2 x 1st class *W/SALE or RETAIL:* Both *CREDIT CARDS:* Delta, MasterCard,
Switch, Visa
SPECIALITIES: Lavandula (NCCPG Collection Holder). *MAP PAGE:* 3

SDry   **Drysdale Garden Exotics, Bowerwood Road, Fordingbridge, Hampshire, SP6 1BN**

TEL: (01425) 653010 *CONTACT:* David Crampton
OPENING TIMES: 0930-1730 Wed-Fri, 1000-1730 Sun. Closed 24th Dec-2nd Jan incl.
MIN. MAIL ORDER UK: £10.00 + p&p *MIN. VALUE EC:* £15.00 + p&p
CAT. COST: 3 x 1st class *W/SALE or RETAIL:* Retail *CREDIT CARDS:* None
SPECIALITIES: Plants for exotic & foliage effect. Plants for Mediterranean gardens. National
Reference Collection of Bamboos. *MAP PAGE:* 2

SDys   **William T Dyson,** Great Comp Nursery, Comp Lane, Platt, Borough Green, Kent,
TN15 8QS

TEL: (01732) 886154 *CONTACT:* William Dyson
OPENING TIMES: 1100-1800 daily 1st Mar-31st Oct.
No mail order
CAT. COST: 2 x 1st class *W/SALE or RETAIL:* Retail *CREDIT CARDS:* none
SPECIALITIES: Perennials, Alpines, Sub-Shrubs, Sempervivum, Salvia, Geranium & uncommon
Heathers. *MAP PAGE:* 3

SEas   **Eastfield Plant Centre,** Paice Lane, Medstead, Alton, Hampshire, GU34 5PR

TEL: (01420) 563640 *FAX:* (01420) 563640 *CONTACT:* D M & P Barton
OPENING TIMES: 0900-1700 daily 1st Mar-20th Dec or by appt.
No mail order
CAT. COST: None issued *W/SALE or RETAIL:* Retail *CREDIT CARDS:* None
SPECIALITIES: General range. *MAP PAGE:* 2

SEND   **East Northdown Farm,** Margate, Kent, CT9 3TS

TEL: (01843) 862060 *FAX:* (01843) 860206 *CONTACT:* Louise & William Friend
OPENING TIMES: 0900-1700 Mon-Sat, 1000-1700 Sun all year. Closed Xmas week & Easter Sun.
No mail order
CAT. COST: 4 x 1st class *W/SALE or RETAIL:* Both *CREDIT CARDS:* Visa, Access, Switch
SPECIALITIES: Chalk & Coast-loving plants. *MAP PAGE:* 3

SExb   **Exbury Enterprises Ltd,** Exbury, Nr Southampton, Hampshire, SO45 1AZ

TEL: (01703) 898625 *FAX:* (01703) 243380 *CONTACT:*
OPENING TIMES: 0900-1700 Plant Centre seasonal.
MIN. MAIL ORDER UK: £15.00 + p&p *MIN. VALUE EC:*
CAT. COST: Sae *W/SALE or RETAIL:* Both *CREDIT CARDS:* Visa, Access
SPECIALITIES: Rhododendron, Azalea, Camellia & Pieris. *MAP PAGE:* 2

SFam   **Family Trees, Sandy Lane, Shedfield, Hampshire, SO32 2HQ**

TEL: (01329) 834812 *CONTACT:* Philip House
OPENING TIMES: 0930-1230 Wed & Sat mid Oct-mid Apr,
MIN. MAIL ORDER UK: No minimum charge *MIN. VALUE EC:* Nmc
CAT. COST: Free *W/SALE or RETAIL:* Retail *CREDIT CARDS:* None
SPECIALITIES: Fruit & Ornamental trees. Trained Fruit Tree specialists ie. standards, espaliers,
cordons etc. Also other Trees & Old Roses. *MAP PAGE:* 2

◆ **See also Display Advertisements**

SGre **Greenwood Plants, The Old Post House, Christchurch Road, Downton, Lymington, Hampshire, SO41 0LA**

TEL: (01590) 642409 *E-MAIL:* jgplants@aol.com *CONTACT:* Jeremy Greenwood
OPENING TIMES: 0900-1700 Sat & Sun Mar-June. Or by arrangement, please phone first.
MIN. MAIL ORDER UK: £10.00 + p&p *MIN. VALUE EC:* £20.00 + p&p
CAT. COST: 4 x 1st class *W/SALE or RETAIL:* Retail *CREDIT CARDS:* none
SPECIALITIES: Alpines esp. Saxifrages, uncommon Hardy Perennials many from wild collected seed, Conservatory plants. *MAP PAGE:* **2**

SHar **Hardy's Cottage Garden Plants, Freefolk Priors, Freefolk, Whitchurch, Hampshire, RG28 7NJ**

TEL: (01256) 896533 *FAX:* (01256) 896572 *CONTACT:* Rosy Hardy
OPENING TIMES: 0900-1730 daily 1st Mar-31st Oct.
MIN. MAIL ORDER UK: No minimum charge *MIN. VALUE EC:* No minimum charge
CAT. COST: 5 x 1st class. From May 1998. *W/SALE or RETAIL:* Both *CREDIT CARDS:* Visa, Access
SPECIALITIES: Hardy Geranium & other Herbaceous both old & new. *MAP PAGE:* **2**

SHay **Hayward's Carnations, The Chace Gardens, Stakes Road, Purbrook, Waterlooville, Hampshire, PO7 5PL**

TEL: (01705) 263047 *FAX:* (01705) 263047 *CONTACT:* A N Hayward
OPENING TIMES: 0930-1700 Mon-Fri.
MIN. MAIL ORDER UK: £10.00 + p&p *MIN. VALUE EC:* £50.00 + p&p
CAT. COST: 1 x 1st class *W/SALE or RETAIL:* Both *CREDIT CARDS:* None
SPECIALITIES: Hardy Pinks & Border Carnations. Greenhouse perpetual Carnations.
MAP PAGE: **2**

SHBN **High Banks Nurseries,** Slip Mill Road, Hawkhurst, Kent, TN18 5AD

TEL: (01580) 753031, (01580) 754492 *FAX:* (01580) 753031 *CONTACT:* Jeremy Homewood
OPENING TIMES: 0800-1700 daily
No mail order
CAT. COST: £1.50 (stamps) + A4 Sae *W/SALE or RETAIL:* Both *CREDIT CARDS:* Access, Visa
SPECIALITIES: Wide general range with many unusual plants. *MAP PAGE:* **3**

SHDw **Highdown Nursery, New Hall Lane, Small Dole, Nr Henfield, West Sussex, BN5 9YH**

TEL: (01273) 492976 *FAX:* (01273) 492976 *CONTACT:* A G & J H Shearing
OPENING TIMES: 0900-1700 daily
MIN. MAIL ORDER UK: £10.00 + p&p *MIN. VALUE EC:* £10.00 + p&p   *EXPORT:* Yes
CAT. COST: 3 x 1st class *W/SALE or RETAIL:* Both *CREDIT CARDS:* Visa, MasterCard, Delta, JCB, EuroCard
SPECIALITIES: Herbs. *MAP PAGE:* **3**

SHel **Hellyer's Garden Plants,** Orchards, off Wallage Lane*, Rowfant, Nr Crawley, Sussex, RH10 4NJ

TEL: (01342) 718280 *CONTACT:* Penelope Hellyer
◆ *OPENING TIMES:* 1000-1700 Wed-Sat Mar-Oct & by prior appt.
No mail order
CAT. COST: 3 x 1st + Sae A5 *W/SALE or RETAIL:* Retail *CREDIT CARDS:* None
SPECIALITIES: Unusual hardy plants for sun/shade. Small selection of Climbers & Shrubs. Over 100 varieties of hardy Geraniums. *Note: Wallage Lane is off the B2028 equidistant Crawley Down & Turners Hill. *MAP PAGE:* **3**

SHFr **Sue Hartfree,** 25 Crouch Hill Court, Lower Halstow, Nr Sittingbourne, Kent, ME9 7EJ

TEL: (01795) 842426 *CONTACT:* Sue Hartfree
OPENING TIMES: Any time by appt. Please phone first.
MIN. MAIL ORDER UK: £15.00 + p&p* *MIN. VALUE EC:*
CAT. COST: Sae + 1 x 1st class *W/SALE or RETAIL:* Both *CREDIT CARDS:* None
SPECIALITIES: Unusual & interesting Shrubs, Hardy & Half-hardy Perennials incl. Salvia, Lobelia & Lysimachia. All can be seen growing in the garden. *Note: mail order Oct-March, UK only. *MAP PAGE:* **3**

Nursery ADDRESSES in BOLD do Mail Order to EU

SHHo   Highfield Hollies, Highfield Farm, Hatch Lane, Liss, Hampshire, GU33 7NH

◆   *TEL:* (01730) 892372 *FAX:* (01730) 894853 *CONTACT:* Mrs Louise Bendall
OPENING TIMES: By appt.
MIN. MAIL ORDER UK: No minimum charge *MIN. VALUE EC:*
CAT. COST: 2 x 1st class *W/SALE or RETAIL:* Retail *CREDIT CARDS:* None
SPECIALITIES: Ilex. Over 70 species & cultivars incl. many specimen trees & topiary.
MAP PAGE: **2/3**

SHya   Brenda Hyatt, 1 Toddington Crescent, Bluebell Hill, Chatham, Kent, ME5 9QT

TEL: (01634) 863251 *CONTACT:* Mrs Brenda Hyatt
OPENING TIMES: Appt. only.
MIN. MAIL ORDER UK: No minimum charge *MIN. VALUE EC:* Nmc
CAT. COST: £1.00 *W/SALE or RETAIL:* Retail *CREDIT CARDS:* None
SPECIALITIES: Show Auricula. *MAP PAGE:* **3**

SIde   Iden Croft Herbs, Frittenden Road, Staplehurst, Kent, TN12 0DH

◆   *TEL:* (01580) 891432 *FAX:* (01580) 892416 *E-MAIL:* idencroft.herbs@dial.pipex.com
CONTACT: Rosemary & D Titterington
OPENING TIMES: 0900-1700 Mon-Sat all year. 1100-1700 Sun & Bank Hols 1st Mar- 30th Sep.
MIN. MAIL ORDER UK: No minimum charge *MIN. VALUE EC:* Nmc
CAT. COST: 4 x 1st class *W/SALE or RETAIL:* Retail *CREDIT CARDS:* Visa, Access, AmEx,
Delta, JCB, EuroCard, Switch
SPECIALITIES: Herbs, Aromatic & Wild flower plants & plants for bees & butterflies. National
Mentha & Origanum collection. *4x1st class for descriptive list. See also SEED index.
MAP PAGE: **3**

SIgm   Tim Ingram, Copton Ash, 105 Ashford Road, Faversham, Kent, ME13 8XW

TEL: (01795) 535919 *CONTACT:* Dr T J Ingram
OPENING TIMES: 1400-1800 Tue-Thur & Sat-Sun Mar-Oct. Nov-Feb by appt.
MIN. MAIL ORDER UK: £9.00 + p&p* *MIN. VALUE EC:*
CAT. COST: 4 x 1st class *W/SALE or RETAIL:* Retail *CREDIT CARDS:* None
SPECIALITIES: Unusual Perennials, alpines & plants from Mediterranean-type climates incl.
Lupins, Penstemons, Salvias & Umbellifers. Fruit & ornamental Trees. *NOTE: Only Fruit Trees
by Mail Order (Nov-Mar), ask for Fruit catalogue. *MAP PAGE:* **3**

SIng   W E Th. Ingwersen Ltd, Birch Farm Nursery, Gravetye, East Grinstead, West Sussex,
RH19 4LE

TEL: (01342) 810236 *CONTACT:* M P & M R Ingwersen
OPENING TIMES: 0900-1300 & 1330-1600 daily 1st Mar-30th Sep. 0900-1300 & 1330-1600
Mon-Fri Oct-Feb.
No mail order
CAT. COST: 2 x 1st class *W/SALE or RETAIL:* Retail *CREDIT CARDS:* None
SPECIALITIES: Very wide range of hardy plants mostly alpines. See also SEED Index.
MAP PAGE: **3**

SJus   Just Roses, Beales Lane, Northiam, Nr Rye, East Sussex, TN31 6QY

TEL: (01797) 252355 *FAX:* (01797) 252355 *CONTACT:* Mr J Banham
OPENING TIMES: 0900-1200 & 1300-1700 Tue-Fri & 0900-1200 & 1300-1600 Sat & Sun.
MIN. MAIL ORDER UK: 1 plant + p&p *MIN. VALUE EC:* No minimum charge
CAT. COST: Free *W/SALE or RETAIL:* Retail *CREDIT CARDS:* None
SPECIALITIES: Roses. *MAP PAGE:* **3**

SKee   Keepers Nursery, Gallants Court, Gallants Lane, East Farleigh, Maidstone, Kent,
ME15 0LE

◆   *TEL:* (01622) 726465 *FAX:* (01622) 726465 *CONTACT:* Hamid Habibi
OPENING TIMES: All reasonable hours by appt.
MIN. MAIL ORDER UK: £10.00 + p&p *MIN. VALUE EC:*
CAT. COST: 2 x 1st class *W/SALE or RETAIL:* Retail *CREDIT CARDS:* None
SPECIALITIES: Old & unusual Top Fruit varieties. Top Fruit propagated to order.
MAP PAGE: **3**

◆ **See also Display Advertisements**

SKen **Kent Street Nurseries,** Sedlescombe, Battle, East Sussex, TN33 0SF
TEL: (01424) 751134 *CONTACT:* Mrs D Downey
OPENING TIMES: 0900-1800 daily all year.
No mail order
CAT. COST: A5 Sae with 2 x 1st class* *W/SALE or RETAIL:* Both *CREDIT CARDS:* none
SPECIALITIES: Fuchsia, Pelargonium, Bedding & Perennials. *Note: Separate Fuchsia &
Pelargonium lists, please specify which required. *MAP PAGE:* 3

SLan **Langley Boxwood Nursery,** Rake, Nr Liss, Hampshire, GU33 7JL
TEL: (01730) 894467 *FAX:* (01730) 894703 *E-MAIL:* langbox@msn.com.uk
CONTACT: Elizabeth Braimbridge
◆ *OPENING TIMES:* Weekdays; Sat-please ring first. Please phone for directions.
MIN. MAIL ORDER UK: £20.00 + p&p *MIN. VALUE EC:* £100.00 + p&p   *EXPORT:* Yes
CAT. COST: 4 x 1st class *W/SALE or RETAIL:* Both *CREDIT CARDS:* None
SPECIALITIES: Buxus species, cultivars & hedging. Good range of topiary. Taxus.
MAP PAGE: 2/3

SLBF **Little Brook Fuchsias,** Ash Green Lane West, Ash Green, Nr Aldershot, Hampshire,
GU12 6HL
TEL: (01252) 329731 *CONTACT:* Carol Gubler
OPENING TIMES: 0900-1700 Wed-Sun 1st Jan-5th Jul.
No mail order
CAT. COST: 40p + Sae *W/SALE or RETAIL:* Both *CREDIT CARDS:* None
SPECIALITIES: Fuchsia old & new. *MAP PAGE:* 3

SLeo **Leonardslee Gardens Nurseries,** Market Garden, Lower Beeding, West Sussex, RH13
6PX
TEL: (01403) 891412 *FAX:* (01403) 891336 *E-MAIL:* christopher.loder@virgin.net
WEB SITE: http://www.gardening-UK *CONTACT:* Chris Loder
OPENING TIMES: Daily BY APPOINTMENT ONLY.
MIN. MAIL ORDER UK: No minimum charge *MIN. VALUE EC:* £100.00 + p&p *EXPORT:* Yes
CAT. COST: 2 x 1st class *W/SALE or RETAIL:* Both *CREDIT CARDS:* Visa, Access
SPECIALITIES: Rhododendron & Azalea in all sizes. *MAP PAGE:* 3

SLim **Lime Cross Nursery,** Herstmonceux, Hailsham, East Sussex, BN27 4RS
TEL: (01323) 833229 *FAX:* (01323) 833944 *CONTACT:* J A Tate, G Monk
◆ *OPENING TIMES:* 0830-1700 Mon-Sat & 0930-1700 Sun.
No mail order
CAT. COST: Free *W/SALE or RETAIL:* Both *CREDIT CARDS:* Visa, MasterCard, Delta,
Switch
SPECIALITIES: Conifers. *MAP PAGE:* 3

SLMG **Long Man Gardens,** Lewes Road, Wilmington, Polegate, East Sussex, BN26 5RS
TEL: (01323) 870816 *CONTACT:* O Menzel
OPENING TIMES: 0900-1700 (or dusk if sooner) Tue-Sun. Please check day before visit.
No mail order
CAT. COST: None issued *W/SALE or RETAIL:* Retail *CREDIT CARDS:* None
SPECIALITIES: Mainly Conservatory plants. *MAP PAGE:* 3

SLod **The Lodge Nursery,** Cottage Lane, Westfield, Nr Hastings, East Sussex, TN35 4RP
TEL: (01424) 870186 *CONTACT:* Mrs Sandra Worley
OPENING TIMES: 1030-1700 Wed-Sun mid Mar-end Oct, & all B/Hols.
MIN. MAIL ORDER UK: No minimum charge* *MIN. VALUE EC:*
CAT. COST: 4 x 1st class *W/SALE or RETAIL:* Retail *CREDIT CARDS:* None
SPECIALITIES: Small nursery with a wide variety of mainly Herbaceous Perennials. *Note: mail
order to UK only. *MAP PAGE:* 3

Nursery ADDRESSES in BOLD do Mail Order to EU

SLPl **Landscape Plants, Cattamount, Grafty Green, Maidstone, Kent, ME17 2AP**
TEL: 01622 850245 *FAX:* 01622 858063 *CONTACT:* Tom La Dell
OPENING TIMES: By appt. only.
MIN. MAIL ORDER UK: £100.00 + p&p *MIN. VALUE EC:* £200.00 + p&p   *EXPORT:* Yes
CAT. COST: 2 x 1st class *W/SALE or RETAIL:* Both *CREDIT CARDS:* None
SPECIALITIES: Low maintenance Shrubs. *MAP PAGE:* 3

SMac **MacGregors Plants,** Carters Clay Road, Lockerley, Romsey, Hampshire, SO51 0GL
TEL: (01794) 340256 *FAX:* (01794) 341828 *CONTACT:* Irene & Stuart Bowron
OPENING TIMES: 1000-1600 Fri-Sun & B/Hol Mons Mar-Oct & at other times by appt.
MIN. MAIL ORDER UK: £10.00 + p&p *MIN. VALUE EC:*
CAT. COST: 2 x 1st class *W/SALE or RETAIL:* Both *CREDIT CARDS:* None
SPECIALITIES: Phygelius (National Collection) and less common Shrubs & Perennials,
particularly for Shade. *MAP PAGE:* 2

SMad **Madrona Nursery, Pluckley Road, Bethersden, Kent, TN26 3DD**
TEL: (01233) 820100 *FAX:* (01233) 712734 *CONTACT:* Liam MacKenzie
OPENING TIMES: 1000-1700 Sat-Tue 21st Mar-3rd Nov. Closed 7th-21st Aug.
MIN. MAIL ORDER UK: No minimum charge *MIN. VALUE EC:* Nmc
CAT. COST: Free *W/SALE or RETAIL:* Retail *CREDIT CARDS:* Visa, MasterCard, AmEx,
JCB, Switch
SPECIALITIES: Unusual Shrubs, Conifers & Perennials. *MAP PAGE:* 3

SMer **Merryfield Nurseries (Canterbury) Ltd,** Stodmarsh Road, Canterbury, Kent, CT3 4AP
TEL: (01227) 462602 *CONTACT:* Mrs A Downs
OPENING TIMES: 1000-1600 Mon, 0900-1730 Tue-Sat, 1000-1700 Sun, & Bank Hol Mons.
MIN. MAIL ORDER UK: £10.00 + p&p* *MIN. VALUE EC:*
CAT. COST: 4 x 1st class *W/SALE or RETAIL:* Retail *CREDIT CARDS:* Access, Visa, Switch
SPECIALITIES: Herbaceous, Fuchsia & Conifers. *Note: mail order to UK only. *MAP PAGE:* 3

SMrm **Merriments Gardens,** Hawkhurst Road, Hurst Green, East Sussex, TN19 7RA
TEL: (01580) 860666 *FAX:* (01580) 860324 *E-MAIL:* merriments@msn.com
CONTACT: Mark & Amanda Buchele
OPENING TIMES: 1000-1730 daily.
No mail order
CAT. COST: £1.50 + 4 x 1st class *W/SALE or RETAIL:* Retail *CREDIT CARDS:* Visa, Access,
AmEx
SPECIALITIES: Unusual Shrubs. Tender & Hardy Perennials. *MAP PAGE:* 3

SMur **Murrells Plant & Garden Centre,** Broomers Hill Lane, Pulborough, West Sussex,
RH20 2DU
TEL: (01798) 875508 *FAX:* (01798) 872695 *CONTACT:* Clive Mellor
OPENING TIMES: 0900-1730 summer, 0900-1700 winter, 1000-1600 Sun.
No mail order
CAT. COST: 3 x 1st class *W/SALE or RETAIL:* Retail *CREDIT CARDS:* Switch, MasterCard,
Visa, Solo
SPECIALITIES: Shrubs, Trees & Herbaceous Plants incl. many rare & unusual varieties.
MAP PAGE: 3

SNut **Nutlin Nursery,** Crowborough Road, Nutley, Nr Uckfield, Sussex, TN22 3BG
TEL: (01825) 712670 *FAX:* (01825) 712670 *CONTACT:* Mrs Morven Cox
OPENING TIMES: Ring in the evening before visiting.
No mail order
CAT. COST: 2 x 1st class *W/SALE or RETAIL:* Retail *CREDIT CARDS:* None
SPECIALITIES: Hydrangea & Wisteria. *MAP PAGE:* 3

◆ **See also Display Advertisements**

SOkh   Oakhurst Nursery, Mardens Hill, Crowborough, East Sussex, TN6 1XL
TEL: (01892) 653273 *FAX:* (01892) 653273 *E-MAIL:* baileyp4@compuserve.com
CONTACT: Stephanie Colton
OPENING TIMES: 1100-1700 most days mid Apr-mid Sep. Other times and if travelling please
phone first, especially at weekends.
No mail order
CAT. COST: 2 x 1st class *W/SALE or RETAIL:* Retail *CREDIT CARDS:* None
SPECIALITIES: Common & uncommon Herbaceous Perennials. *MAP PAGE:* 3

SOWG The Old Walled Garden, Oxonhoath, Hadlow, Kent, TN11 9SS
TEL: (01732) 810012 *FAX:* (01732) 811257 *CONTACT:* John & Heather Angrave
OPENING TIMES: 0900-1700 Mon-Fri. Weekends by appt.
MIN. MAIL ORDER UK: £10.00* *MIN. VALUE EC:*
CAT. COST: 2 x 1st class *W/SALE or RETAIL:* Both *CREDIT CARDS:* None
SPECIALITIES: Many rare & unusual Shrubs. Wide range of Conservatory plants esp. Australian.
*Note: mail order within UK only. *MAP PAGE:* 3

SPan   Pandora Nursery, (Off.) 17 Quail Way, Horndean, Waterlooville, Hampshire, PO8
9YN
TEL: (01705) 597323, 0467 606053/54 mobile *CONTACT:* Paul & Amanda O'Carroll
OPENING TIMES: 1000-1600 Wed & Thur 1st Mar-31st Oct. Also by appt. Please ring
(answerphone) for shows list.
No mail order
CAT. COST: 5 x 2nd class *W/SALE or RETAIL:* Retail *CREDIT CARDS:* None
SPECIALITIES: Cistus & Euphorbias, plus expanding range of gardenworthy Shrubs & Climbers.
Note: nursery at The Walled Garden, Bury Lodge Estate, West Street, Hambledon, Hants.
MAP PAGE: 2

SPar   The Paradise Garden, The Courtyard at, Stable Antiques, 46 West Street, Storrington,
West Sussex, RH20 4EE
TEL: (01903) 744404 *FAX:* (01903) 740441 *CONTACT:* Clive Parker
♦   *OPENING TIMES:* 1000-1800 7 days British summer time, 1000-dusk Fri-Sun winter. Please phone
before visiting.
No mail order
CAT. COST: 2 x 1st class *W/SALE or RETAIL:* Retail *CREDIT CARDS:* Visa, MasterCard,
Access, AmEx, Switch, Delta
SPECIALITIES: Architectural & Foliage plants. *MAP PAGE:* 3

SPer   Perryhill Nurseries, Hartfield, East Sussex, TN7 4JP
TEL: (01892) 770377 *FAX:* (01892) 770929 *CONTACT:* P J Chapman (Manager)
OPENING TIMES: 0900-1700 daily March 1-Oct 31. 0900-1630 Nov 1-Feb 28.
No mail order
CAT. COST: £1.65 *W/SALE or RETAIL:* Retail *CREDIT CARDS:* Visa, Access, MasterCard,
EuroCard, Switch
SPECIALITIES: Wide range of Trees, Shrubs, Conifers, Rhododendron etc. Over 1300
Herbaceous varieties, over 500 varieties of Roses. *MAP PAGE:* 3

**SPil   Pilgrim House Herbs, Pilgrim House, Coles Dane, Stede Hill, Harrietsham, Maidstone,
Kent, ME17 1NP**
TEL: (01622) 859371 *FAX:* (01622) 859371 *CONTACT:* Diana Goss
OPENING TIMES: By appt. only.
MIN. MAIL ORDER UK: No minimum charge *MIN. VALUE EC:* Nmc
CAT. COST: 1 x 1st class *W/SALE or RETAIL:* Retail *CREDIT CARDS:* none
SPECIALITIES: Herbs incl. Digitalis, Mentha, Oenothera, Salvia, Tanacetum. *MAP PAGE:* 3

Nursery ADDRESSES in BOLD do Mail Order to EU

SPla **Plaxtol Nurseries, The Spoute, Plaxtol, Sevenoaks, Kent, TN15 0QR**
TEL: (01732) 810550 *FAX:* (01732) 810550 *CONTACT:* Tessa, Donald & Jenny Forbes
OPENING TIMES: 1000-1700 daily. Closed two weeks from Xmas eve.
MIN. MAIL ORDER UK: £10.00 + p&p* *MIN. VALUE EC:* £30.00 + p&p
CAT. COST: 2 x 1st class *W/SALE or RETAIL:* Retail *CREDIT CARDS:* Visa, AmEx,
MasterCard
SPECIALITIES: Hardy Shrubs & Herbaceous esp. for Flower Arranger. Old-fashioned Roses,
Ferns & Climbers. *Note: mail order Nov-Mar ONLY. *MAP PAGE:* **3**

SPop **Pops Plants, Greenfield Farm, North Gorley, Fordingbridge, Hampshire, SP6 2PL**
TEL: (01725) 511421 *CONTACT:* G Dawson
OPENING TIMES: Easter-mid Sept.
MIN. MAIL ORDER UK: No minimum charge *MIN. VALUE EC:* Nmc   *EXPORT:* Yes
CAT. COST: 1 x 1st class *W/SALE or RETAIL:* Both *CREDIT CARDS:* Visa
SPECIALITIES: Primula auricula. *MAP PAGE:* **2**

SRCN **Rose Cottage Nursery, Rose Cottage, Kingsley Common, Nr Bordon, Hampshire,
GU35 9NF**
TEL: (01420) 489071 *FAX:* (01420) 476629 *CONTACT:* Ian Elliot
◆ *OPENING TIMES:* Not open.
MIN. MAIL ORDER UK: No minimum charge *MIN. VALUE EC:* £20.00 + p&p
CAT. COST: 3 x 1st class *W/SALE or RETAIL:* Retail *CREDIT CARDS:* none
SPECIALITIES: Drought tolerant plants. *MAP PAGE:* **2/3**

SReu **G Reuthe Ltd, Crown Point Nursery, Sevenoaks Road, Ightham, Nr Sevenoaks, Kent,
TN15 0HB**
TEL: (01732) 810694 *FAX:* (01732) 862166 *CONTACT:* C Tomlin & P Kindley
OPENING TIMES: 0900-1630 Mon-Sat (1000-1630 Sun & Bank Hols during Apr & May ONLY.
Occasionally in June; please check.) Closed Aug.
MIN. MAIL ORDER UK: £25.00 + p&p *MIN. VALUE EC:* £500.00*   *EXPORT:* Yes
CAT. COST: £2.00 *W/SALE or RETAIL:* Retail *CREDIT CARDS:* Visa, Access
SPECIALITIES: Rhododendron, Azalea, Trees, Shrubs & Climbers. *Note: Certain plants only to
EC & Export. *MAP PAGE:* **3**

SRGP **Rosie's Garden Plants, Rochester Road, Aylesford, Kent, ME20 7EB**
TEL: (01622) 715777 *FAX:* (01622) 715777 *CONTACT:* J C A'violét
OPENING TIMES: By appt. only.
MIN. MAIL ORDER UK: No minimum charge *MIN. VALUE EC:* Nmc   *EXPORT:* Yes
CAT. COST: 2 x 1st class *W/SALE or RETAIL:* Retail *CREDIT CARDS:* Visa, MasterCard,
Switch
SPECIALITIES: Hardy Geranium. *MAP PAGE:* **3**

SRms **Rumsey Gardens, 117 Drift Road, Clanfield, Waterlooville, Hampshire, PO8 0PD**
TEL: (01705) 593367 *CONTACT:* Mr N R Giles
◆ *OPENING TIMES:* 0900-1700 Mon-Sat & 1000-1700 Sun & Bank Hols.
MIN. MAIL ORDER UK: No minimum charge *MIN. VALUE EC:* Nmc
CAT. COST: None issued *W/SALE or RETAIL:* Retail *CREDIT CARDS:* None
SPECIALITIES: Wide general range. National Collection of Cotoneaster. *MAP PAGE:* **2**

SRos **Rosewood Daylilies,** 70 Deansway Avenue, Sturry, Nr Canterbury, Kent, CT2 0NN
TEL: (01227) 711071 *CONTACT:* Chris Searle
OPENING TIMES: By appt. only. Please telephone.
MIN. MAIL ORDER UK: No minimum charge *MIN. VALUE EC:*
CAT. COST: 2 x 1st class *W/SALE or RETAIL:* Retail *CREDIT CARDS:* None
SPECIALITIES: Hemerocallis, mainly newer American varieties. *MAP PAGE:* **3**

◆ **See also Display Advertisements**

SRum **Rumwood Nurseries, Langley, Maidstone, Kent, ME17 3ND**
> *TEL:* (01622) 861477 *FAX:* (01622) 863123 *CONTACT:* Mr R Fermor or Mr J Fermor
> *OPENING TIMES:* 0900-1700 Mon-Sat 1000-1600 Sun.
> *MIN. MAIL ORDER UK:* No minimum charge *MIN. VALUE EC:* Nmc
> *CAT. COST:* 1 x 2nd class *W/SALE or RETAIL:* Both *CREDIT CARDS:* Visa, Access, AmEx, Switch
> *SPECIALITIES:* Roses & Trees. *MAP PAGE:* **3**

SSad **Mrs Jane Sadler,** Ingrams Cottage, Wisborough Green, Billingshurst, West Sussex, **RH14 0ER**
> *TEL:* (01403) 700234 *FAX:* (01403) 700234 *CONTACT:* Mrs Jane Sadler
> *OPENING TIMES:* Irregular. Please phone first.
> No mail order
> *CAT. COST:* Sae *W/SALE or RETAIL:* Retail *CREDIT CARDS:* None
> *SPECIALITIES:* Small nursery specialising in less common varieties, esp. Auriculas, Lavenders & Pelargoniums. *MAP PAGE:* **3**

SSca **Scalers Hill Nursery,** Scalers Hill, Cobham, Nr Gravesend, Kent, DA12 3BH
> *TEL:* (01474) 822856, (0468) 906770 *CONTACT:* Mrs Ann Booth
> *OPENING TIMES:* 1000-1600 Wed-Sat or by appt. Mid Mar-end Oct.
> No mail order
> *CAT. COST:* 2 x 1st class *W/SALE or RETAIL:* Retail *CREDIT CARDS:* None
> *SPECIALITIES:* Unusual Perennials & Alpines. *MAP PAGE:* **3**

SSea **Seale Nurseries,** Seale Lane, Seale, Farnham, Surrey, GU10 1LD
> *TEL:* (01252) 782410 *FAX:* (01252) 783038 *CONTACT:* David May
> *OPENING TIMES:* 0900-1700 daily
> No mail order
> *CAT. COST:* 2 x 2nd class *W/SALE or RETAIL:* Retail *CREDIT CARDS:* Visa, Switch, Access
> *SPECIALITIES:* Pelargonium, Fuchsia, Roses, Herbaceous. *MAP PAGE:* **3**

SSmi **Alan C Smith,** 127 Leaves Green Road, Keston, Kent, BR2 6DG
> *TEL:* (01959) 572531 *FAX:* (01959) 572531 *CONTACT:* Alan C Smith
> *OPENING TIMES:* Appt. only.
> *MIN. MAIL ORDER UK:* No minimum charge *MIN. VALUE EC:*
> *CAT. COST:* 50p *W/SALE or RETAIL:* Retail *CREDIT CARDS:* None
> *SPECIALITIES:* Sempervivum & Jovibarba. *MAP PAGE:* **3**

SSmt **Peter J Smith, Chanctonbury Nurseries, Rectory Lane, Ashington, Pulborough, Sussex, RH20 3AS**
> *TEL:* (01903) 892870 *FAX:* (01903) 893036 *CONTACT:* Sales Dept.
> *OPENING TIMES:* By appt. only
> *MIN. MAIL ORDER UK:* £6.00 + p&p *MIN. VALUE EC:* £30.00 + p&p
> *CAT. COST:* 1 x 1st class *W/SALE or RETAIL:* Both *CREDIT CARDS:* Visa, Access, MasterCard
> *SPECIALITIES:* The Princess & Little Princess range of hybrid Alstroemeria for conservatory & garden. Also hybrid Limonium & Freesias.

SSoC **Southcott Nursery,** Southcott, South Street, Lydd, Romney Marsh, Kent, TN29 9DQ
> *TEL:* (01797) 321848 *FAX:* (01797) 321848 *CONTACT:* Suzy Clark
> *OPENING TIMES:* 1000-1730 Tue-Sat Mar-Nov & Bank Hol w/ends.
> No mail order
> *CAT. COST:* 3 x 1st class *W/SALE or RETAIL:* Retail *CREDIT CARDS:* None
> *SPECIALITIES:* Unusual Hardy & Half Hardy Perennials & Shrubs. *MAP PAGE:* **3**

SSON **Stone Oak Nursery, Flood Street, Mersham, Nr Ashford, Kent, TN25 6NX**
> *TEL:* (01233) 720925 *FAX:* (01233) 720925 *CONTACT:* Mrs D E Saunders & Mr G M Saunders,
> *OPENING TIMES:* 1000-1700 Sat, Sun & B/Hols Feb-Nov. Other times by appt. only.
> *MIN. MAIL ORDER UK:* £10.00 +p&p *MIN. VALUE EC:* £25.00 +p&p *EXPORT:* Yes
> *CAT. COST:* 3 x 1st class *W/SALE or RETAIL:* Both *CREDIT CARDS:* none
> *SPECIALITIES:* Herbaceous & Woodland plants. *MAP PAGE:* **3**

Nursery ADDRESSES in BOLD do Mail Order to EU

SSpe   **Speldhurst Nurseries,** Langton Road, Speldhurst, Tunbridge Wells, Kent, TN3 0NR
TEL: (01892) 862682 *FAX:* (01892) 863338 *CONTACT:* Christine & Stephen Lee
OPENING TIMES: 1000-1700 Wed-Sat excl. Jan. 100-1600 Sun Mar-Jul & Sep-Oct.
No mail order
CAT. COST: 4 x 1st class for list. *W/SALE or RETAIL:* Retail *CREDIT CARDS:* MasterCard,
Visa, Switch, Delta, AmEx
SPECIALITIES: Herbaceous, Grasses. *MAP PAGE:* 3

SSpi   **Spinners Garden,** Boldre, Lymington, Hampshire, SO41 5QE
TEL: (01590) 673347 *CONTACT:* Peter Chappell & Kevin Hughes
OPENING TIMES: 1000-1700 Tue-Sat, Sun & Mon by appt. only.
No mail order
CAT. COST: 3 x 1st class *W/SALE or RETAIL:* Retail *CREDIT CARDS:* None
SPECIALITIES: Less common Trees and Shrubs esp. Acer, Magnolia, species & lace-cap
Hydrangea. Woodland & Bog Plants. NCCPG Trillium Collection. *MAP PAGE:* 2

SSpr   **Springbank Nurseries, Winford Road, Newchurch, Sandown, Isle of Wight, PO36 0JX**
TEL: (01983) 865444 *FAX:* (01983) 868688 *CONTACT:* K Hall
OPENING TIMES: Daily Sept & Oct. Collections by appt. Specific open days to be advertised.
MIN. MAIL ORDER UK: £10.00 + p&p *MIN. VALUE EC:* £25.00 + p&p   *EXPORT:* Yes
CAT. COST: £1.00 *W/SALE or RETAIL:* Retail *CREDIT CARDS:* None
SPECIALITIES: Nerine sarniensis hybrids (over 600 varieties), & some species. Interesting
reference collection. *MAP PAGE:* 2

SSta   **Starborough Nursery, Starborough Road, Marsh Green, Edenbridge, Kent, TN8 5RB**
TEL: (01732) 865614 *FAX:* (01732) 862166 *CONTACT:* C Tomlin & P Kindley
OPENING TIMES: 1000-1600 Mon-Sat. Closed Jan & Jul, & occasional Weds.
MIN. MAIL ORDER UK: £25.00 + p&p* *MIN. VALUE EC:* £500.00   *EXPORT:* Yes
CAT. COST: £2.00 *W/SALE or RETAIL:* Retail *CREDIT CARDS:* Visa, Access
SPECIALITIES: Rare and unusual Shrubs especially Daphne, Acer, Rhododendron, Azalea,
Magnolia & Hamamelis. *Note: certain plants only to EC & Export. *MAP PAGE:* 3

SSte   **Stenbury Nursery,** Smarts Cross, Southford, Nr Whitwell, Isle of Wight, PO38 2AG
TEL: (01983) 840115 *CONTACT:* Tony Bradford
OPENING TIMES: 0930-1700 Summer, 1000-1530 Winter Thu-Tue.
No mail order
CAT. COST: *W/SALE or RETAIL:* Retail *CREDIT CARDS:* None
SPECIALITIES: Hemerocallis, Geranium & Penstemon. *MAP PAGE:* 2

SSto   **Stone Cross Nurseries & Garden Centre,** Rattle Road, Pevensey, Sussex, BN24 5EB
TEL: (01323) 763250 *FAX:* (01323) 763195 *CONTACT:* Mr & Mrs G F Winwood
◆   *OPENING TIMES:* 0830-1730 Mon-Sat & 1000-1600 Sun & Bank Hols.
No mail order
CAT. COST: 50p refundable *W/SALE or RETAIL:* Both *CREDIT CARDS:* Visa, Access, Switch
SPECIALITIES: Hebe & Clematis, Evergreen Shrubs. Lime tolerant & coastal Shrubs & Plants.
MAP PAGE: 3

SSvw   **Southview Nurseries,** Chequers Lane, Eversley Cross, Hook, Hampshire, RG27 0NT
TEL: (0118) 9732206 *E-MAIL:* tink@sprynet.co.uk *CONTACT:* Mark & Elaine Trenear
◆   *OPENING TIMES:* 0900-1300 & 1400-1630 Thu-Sat 1st Feb-31st Oct. Nov-Jan by appt. only.
MIN. MAIL ORDER UK: No minimum charge* *MIN. VALUE EC:*
CAT. COST: Free *W/SALE or RETAIL:* Retail *CREDIT CARDS:* None
SPECIALITIES: Unusual Hardy plants, specialising in Old Fashioned Pinks & period plants.
NCCPG Collection of Old Pinks. *Note: mail order to UK only. *MAP PAGE:* 2/3

STil   **Tile Barn Nursery, Standen Street, Iden Green, Benenden, Kent, TN17 4LB**
TEL: (01580) 240221 *CONTACT:* Peter Moore
OPENING TIMES: 0900-1700 Wed-Sat.
MIN. MAIL ORDER UK: £10.00 + p&p *MIN. VALUE EC:* £25.00 + p&p   *EXPORT:* Yes
CAT. COST: Sae *W/SALE or RETAIL:* Both *CREDIT CARDS:* None
SPECIALITIES: Cyclamen species. *MAP PAGE:* 3

◆ **See also Display Advertisements**

STre   **Peter Trenear, Chantreyland, Chequers Lane, Eversley Cross, Hampshire, RG27 0NX**

♦
TEL: 0118 9732300   *CONTACT:* Peter Trenear
OPENING TIMES: 0900-1630 Mon-Sat.
MIN. MAIL ORDER UK: £5.00 + p&p   *MIN. VALUE EC:* £10.00 + p&p
CAT. COST: 1 x 1st class   *W/SALE or RETAIL:* Retail   *CREDIT CARDS:* None
SPECIALITIES: Trees, Shrubs, Conifers & Pinus.   *MAP PAGE:* 2/3

SUsu   **Usual & Unusual Plants,** Onslow House, Magham Down, Hailsham, East Sussex, BN27 1PL

TEL: (01323) 840967   *FAX:* (01323) 844725   *E-MAIL:* apel@cix.co.uk   *CONTACT:* Jennie Maillard
OPENING TIMES: 0930-1730 daily Mar-31st Oct. Closed Tues. Thu-Sun only during Aug.
No mail order
CAT. COST: 1 x 1st + Sae   *W/SALE or RETAIL:* Retail   *CREDIT CARDS:* None
SPECIALITIES: Small quantities of a wide variety of unusual perennials, esp. Diascia, Erysimum, Euphorbia, Hardy Geranium, Salvia & Grasses.   *MAP PAGE:* 3

SVen   **Ventnor Botanic Garden,** Undercliff Drive, Ventnor, Isle of Wight, PO38 1UL

TEL: (01983) 852198   *FAX:* (01983) 856154   *E-MAIL:* simon@vbg1.demon.co.uk
WEB SITE: http://botanic.co.uk   *CONTACT:* Simon Goodenough & Jan Wyers
OPENING TIMES: 1000-1700 7 days a week Mar-Oct.
MIN. MAIL ORDER UK: *MIN. VALUE EC:*
CAT. COST: n/a   *W/SALE or RETAIL:* Retail   *CREDIT CARDS:* MasterCard, Visa
SPECIALITIES: *MAP PAGE:* 2

SVil   **The Village Nurseries,** Sinnocks, West Chiltington, Pulborough, West Sussex, RH20 2JX

♦
TEL: (01798) 813040   *FAX:* (01798) 813040   *CONTACT:* Peter Manfield
OPENING TIMES: 0900-1800 or dusk, daily.
No mail order
CAT. COST: Free plant list   *W/SALE or RETAIL:* Retail   *CREDIT CARDS:* Visa, Delta, MasterCard
SPECIALITIES: Wide range of Shrubs & Perennials with many unusual plants.   *MAP PAGE:* 3

SWas   **Washfield Nursery,** Horn's Road (A229), Hawkhurst, Kent, TN18 4QU

TEL: (01580) 752522   *CONTACT:* Elizabeth Strangman
OPENING TIMES: 1000-1700 Wed-Sat. Closed December.
No mail order
CAT. COST: 5 x 1st class   *W/SALE or RETAIL:* Retail   *CREDIT CARDS:* none
SPECIALITIES: Alpine, Herbaceous & Woodland, many unusual & rare. Helleborus, Epimedium, Hardy Geranium.   *MAP PAGE:* 3

SWat   **Water Meadow Nursery, Cheriton, Nr Alresford, Hampshire, SO24 0QB**

TEL: (01962) 771895   *FAX:* (01962) 771895   *E-MAIL:* watermeadowplants@msn.com
CONTACT: Mrs Sandy Worth
OPENING TIMES: 0900-1700 Fri & Sat, 1400-1700 Sun, Mar-Oct.
MIN. MAIL ORDER UK: £10.00 + p&p   *MIN. VALUE EC:* £50.00 + p&p   *EXPORT:* Yes
CAT. COST: 3 x 1st class   *W/SALE or RETAIL:* Both   *CREDIT CARDS:* None
SPECIALITIES: Water Lilies, extensive Water Garden plants, unusual Herbaceous Perennials, aromatic & hardy Shrubs & Climbers.   *MAP PAGE:* 2

SWCr   **Wych Cross Nurseries,** Wych Cross, Forest Row, East Sussex, RH18 5JW

TEL: (01342) 822705   *FAX:* (01342) 825329   *E-MAIL:* wychcross@martex.co.uk
CONTACT: J Paisley
OPENING TIMES: 0900-1730 Mon-Sat.
No mail order
CAT. COST: Free list   *W/SALE or RETAIL:* Retail   *CREDIT CARDS:* Visa, MasterCard, Delta, Switch
SPECIALITIES: Roses.   *MAP PAGE:* 3

Nursery ADDRESSES in BOLD do Mail Order to EU

SWes   Westwood Nursery, 65 Yorkland Avenue, Welling, Kent, DA16 2LE

> *TEL:* (0181) 301 0886 *FAX:* (0181) 301 0886 *CONTACT:* Mr S Edwards
> *OPENING TIMES:* Not open.
> *MIN. MAIL ORDER UK:* No minimum charge *MIN. VALUE EC:* £50.00 + p&p
> *CAT. COST:* Sae *W/SALE or RETAIL:* Retail *CREDIT CARDS:* None
> *SPECIALITIES:* Pleiones & Hardy Orchids. Alpine House & Garden Orchids.

SWyc   Wychwood Waterlily & Carp Farm, Farnham Road, Odiham, Hook, Hampshire, RG29 1HS

> *TEL:* (01256) 702800 *FAX:* (01256) 701001 *E-MAIL:* cnhenley@aol.com
> *CONTACT:* Reg, Ann & Clair Henley
> *OPENING TIMES:* 1000-1800 daily
> *MIN. MAIL ORDER UK:* £1.00 + p&p *MIN. VALUE EC:* £1.00 + p&p   *EXPORT:* Yes
> *CAT. COST:* 2 x 1st class *W/SALE or RETAIL:* Retail *CREDIT CARDS:* Visa, Access, Switch
> *SPECIALITIES:* Aquatics. Nymphaea, Moisture loving, Marginals & Oxygenating plants. Moist & Water Iris inc. American ensata. *MAP PAGE:* 2/3

WAbb   Abbey Dore Court Gardens, Abbeydore, Nr Hereford, Herefordshire, HR2 0AD

> *TEL:* (01981) 240419 *FAX:* (01981) 240279 *CONTACT:* Mrs C Ward
> *OPENING TIMES:* 1100-1800 Thu-Tue from Mar-3rd Sun Oct.
> No mail order
> *CAT. COST:* None issued *W/SALE or RETAIL:* Retail *CREDIT CARDS:* None
> *SPECIALITIES:* Shrubs & hardy Perennials, many unusual, which may be seen growing in the garden. Some Seeds available from garden. *MAP PAGE:* 5

WAbe   Aberconwy Nursery, Graig, Glan Conwy, Colwyn Bay, Conwy, Wales, LL28 5TL

> *TEL:* (01492) 580875 *CONTACT:* Dr & Mrs K G Lever
> *OPENING TIMES:* 1000-1700 Tue-Sun.
> No mail order
> *CAT. COST:* 2 x 2nd class *W/SALE or RETAIL:* Retail *CREDIT CARDS:* Visa, MasterCard
> *SPECIALITIES:* Alpines, including specialist varieties, esp. Autumn Gentian, Saxifraga & dwarf ericaceous. Shrubs, Conifers & Woodland plants incl. Hellebores & Epimediums. *MAP PAGE:* 4

WAct   Acton Beauchamp Roses, Acton Beauchamp, Worcester, Hereford & Worcester, WR6 5AE

> *TEL:* (01531) 640433 *FAX:* (01531) 640802 *CONTACT:* Lindsay Bousfield
> *OPENING TIMES:* 1000-1800 Summer, 1000-1600 Winter Tue-Sat, B/Hol Mon, Sun June- July. Closed Aug & Jan.
> *MIN. MAIL ORDER UK:* No minimum charge *MIN. VALUE EC:* Nmc   *EXPORT:* Yes
> *CAT. COST:* 3 x 1st class appreciated. *W/SALE or RETAIL:* Retail *CREDIT CARDS:* Visa, MasterCard, EuroCard
> *SPECIALITIES:* Species Roses, Old Roses, modern shrub, English, climbers, ramblers & ground-cover Roses. *MAP PAGE:* 5

WAlt   Alternatives, The Brackens, Yorkley Wood, Nr Lydney, Gloucestershire, GL15 4TU

> *TEL:* (01594) 562457 *E-MAIL:* altern@lineone.net *CONTACT:* Mrs Rosemary Castle
> *OPENING TIMES:* 21st Apr-end Sep, by prior arrangement only.
> *MIN. MAIL ORDER UK:* £5.00 + p&p* *MIN. VALUE EC:*
> *CAT. COST:* 3 x 1st class *W/SALE or RETAIL:* Retail *CREDIT CARDS:* None
> *SPECIALITIES:* Unusual forms of British Native Plants. *Note: mail order to UK only. *MAP PAGE:* 5

WBay   Bayleys Garden Centre, Bayston Hill Nurseries, Shrewsbury, Shropshire, SY3 0DA

> *TEL:* (01743) 874261 *FAX:* (01743) 874208 *CONTACT:* Information Desk
> ♦ *OPENING TIMES:* 0830-1800 Mon-Sat all year, 1100-1700 Sun summer, 1030-1630 Sun winter.
> No mail order
> *CAT. COST:* Free plant list *W/SALE or RETAIL:* Retail *CREDIT CARDS:* Visa, Switch, MasterCard
> *SPECIALITIES:* Wide range of Trees, Shrubs, Herbaceous Perennials, Fruit, Climbing & Wall plants, Roses. *MAP PAGE:* 7

♦ **See also Display Advertisements**

WBcn   Beacon's Nurseries, Tewkesbury Road, Eckington, Nr Pershore, Worcestershire, WR10 3DE

TEL: (01386) 750359   *CONTACT:* Jonathan Beacon
♦   *OPENING TIMES:* 0900-1300 & 1400-1700 Mon-Sat & 1400-1700 Sun. (Closed 25th Dec-1st Jan.)
No mail order
CAT. COST: 4 x 1st class   *W/SALE or RETAIL:* Retail   *CREDIT CARDS:* None
SPECIALITIES: Shrubs, Camellias, Herbaceous, Aquatics, Conifers, Climbing Plants & Roses.
MAP PAGE: **5**

WBea   Beacons' Botanicals, Banc-y-Felin, Carregsawdde, Llangadog, Carmarthenshire, Wales, SA19 9DA

TEL: (01550) 777992   *CONTACT:* Mrs S H Williams
OPENING TIMES: Most weekdays, please telephone first.
MIN. MAIL ORDER UK: £10.00 + p&p*   *MIN. VALUE EC:*
CAT. COST: None issued   *W/SALE or RETAIL:* Retail   *CREDIT CARDS:* none
SPECIALITIES: Hardy Geranium, Aquilegia, Campanula, Persicaria, Veronica. Extensive range of rare & unusual Herbaceous plants. *Note: mail order to UK only.   *MAP PAGE:* **4**

WBod   Bodnant Garden Nursery Ltd, Tal-y-Cafn, Colwyn Bay, Clwyd, Wales, LL28 5RE

TEL: (01492) 650731   *FAX:* (01492) 650863   *E-MAIL:* ianshutes@enterprise.net
CONTACT: Mr Ian Shutes
OPENING TIMES: All year.
MIN. MAIL ORDER UK: No minimum charge   *MIN. VALUE EC:* Nmc   *EXPORT:* Yes
CAT. COST: 3 x 1st class   *W/SALE or RETAIL:* Retail   *CREDIT CARDS:* Visa, MasterCard, Switch, Connect
SPECIALITIES: Rhododendron, Camellia & Magnolia. Wide range of unusual Trees and Shrubs.
MAP PAGE: **4**

WBon   S & E Bond, (Off.) 10 Courtlands, Winforton, Herefordshire, HR3 6EA

TEL: (01544) 328422 after 1800   *CONTACT:* Miss S Bond
OPENING TIMES: 1000-1730 Thur-Sun & Bank Hol Mons 1st Mar-30th Sep.
MIN. MAIL ORDER UK: No minimum charge   *MIN. VALUE EC:*
CAT. COST: A5 Sae   *W/SALE or RETAIL:* Retail   *CREDIT CARDS:* None
SPECIALITIES: Shade plants. *Note: sales at Hay Castle, Hay on Wye.   *MAP PAGE:* **5**

WBor   Bordervale Plants, Nantyderi, Sandy Lane, Ystradowen, Cowbridge, Vale of Glamorgan, Wales, CF71 7SX

TEL: (01446) 774036   *CONTACT:* Claire E Jenkins
OPENING TIMES: 1000-1600 Thur-Fri, 1000-1700 Sat, Sun & B/Hols Apr-Oct. Other times by appt.
No mail order
CAT. COST: None issued.   *W/SALE or RETAIL:* Retail   *CREDIT CARDS:* none
SPECIALITIES: Wide selection of rare & unusual Herbaceous Perennials, many displayed in the garden.   *MAP PAGE:* **4**

WBou   Bouts Cottage Nurseries, Bouts Lane, Inkberrow, Worcestershire, WR7 4HP

TEL: (01386) 792923   *CONTACT:* M & S Roberts
OPENING TIMES: Not open to the public.
MIN. MAIL ORDER UK: No minimum charge   *MIN. VALUE EC:* Nmc
CAT. COST: Sae   *W/SALE or RETAIL:* Retail   *CREDIT CARDS:* None
SPECIALITIES: Viola.

WBrE   Bron Eifion Nursery, Bron Eifion, Criccleth, Gwynedd, LL52 0SA

TEL: (01766) 522890   *CONTACT:* Suzanne Evans
OPENING TIMES: 1000-dusk 7 days a week.
MIN. MAIL ORDER UK: £30.00 + p&p*   *MIN. VALUE EC:*
CAT. COST: 4 x 2nd class   *W/SALE or RETAIL:* Retail   *CREDIT CARDS:* none
SPECIALITIES: Kalmia, Embothrium, Plants for Coastal Regions & wide range of Hardy plants.
*Note: mail order to UK only.   *MAP PAGE:* **4**

Nursery ADDRESSES in BOLD do Mail Order to EU

WBro **Brook Farm Plants,** Boulsdon Lane, Newent, Gloucestershire, GL18 1JH

TEL: (01531) 822534 *CONTACT:* Mrs S E Keene
OPENING TIMES: 1000-1400 Tues & Thurs & 1400-1800 Sat, Apr-Oct. Most other times by appt.
MIN. MAIL ORDER UK: No minimum charge *MIN. VALUE EC:*
CAT. COST: 2 x 2nd class *W/SALE or RETAIL:* Retail *CREDIT CARDS:* None
SPECIALITIES: Digitalis, Papaver, Campanula & other unusual Perennials.   *MAP PAGE:* **5**

WByw **Byeways,** Daisy Lane, Whittington, Oswestry, Shropshire

TEL: (01691) 659539 *CONTACT:* Barbara Molesworth
OPENING TIMES: By appt. only. Please phone first.*
No mail order
CAT. COST: Sae + 1 x 2nd class *W/SALE or RETAIL:* Retail *CREDIT CARDS:* None
SPECIALITIES: Aster, Campanula, Hardy Geranium & Pulmonaria. *Note: Also at Newtown
Market on Tue. *MAP PAGE:* **7**

WCel **Celyn Vale Eucalyptus Nurseries, Carrog, Corwen, Clwyd, LL21 9LD**

TEL: (01490) 430671 *FAX:* (01490) 430671 *CONTACT:* Andrew McConnell
 ◆ *OPENING TIMES:* 0900-1600 Mon-Fri Mar-end Oct. Please telephone first outside these days.
MIN. MAIL ORDER UK: 3 Plants + p&p *MIN. VALUE EC:* 3 plants + p&p   *EXPORT:* Yes
CAT. COST: 2 x 1st class *W/SALE or RETAIL:* Both *CREDIT CARDS:* Visa, Access
SPECIALITIES: Hardy Eucalyptus & Acacia. *MAP PAGE:* **4**

WCer **Cerney House Gardens,** North Cerney, Cirencester, Gloucestershire, GL7 7BX

TEL: (01285) 831205 *FAX:* (01285) 831676 *CONTACT:* Barbara Johnson
OPENING TIMES: 1400-1800 Tue, Wed & Fri Apr-Sep.
No mail order
CAT. COST: A4 Sae + 6 x 1st class *W/SALE or RETAIL:* Retail *CREDIT CARDS:* None
SPECIALITIES: Herbs, Hardy Geraniums, Ajuga, Pulmonaria, Vinca, Tradescantia & Symphytum.
MAP PAGE: **5**

WCFE **Charles F Ellis,** (Off.) Barn House, Wormington, Nr Broadway, Worcestershire, WR12
7NL

TEL: (01386) 584077 (nursery) *CONTACT:* Charles Ellis
OPENING TIMES: 1000-1600 daily 1st Apr- 30th Sep.
No mail order
CAT. COST: None issued. *W/SALE or RETAIL:* Retail *CREDIT CARDS:* none
SPECIALITIES: Wide range of more unusual Shrubs, Conifers & Climbers. Note: Nursery is at
Oak Piece Farm Nursery, Stanton, Broadway, Worcs. *MAP PAGE:* **5**

WCGr **Carrob Growers,** The Old Post House, How Caple, Herefordshire, HR1 4TE

TEL: (01989) 740235 *CONTACT:* R & C Boyle
OPENING TIMES: Not open.
MIN. MAIL ORDER UK: No minimum charge *MIN. VALUE EC:*
CAT. COST: 1 x 1st class *W/SALE or RETAIL:* Retail *CREDIT CARDS:* none
SPECIALITIES: Old & modern varieties of Peonies of particular garden worthiness.

WCHb **The Cottage Herbery,** Mill House, Boraston, Nr Tenbury Wells, Worcestershire, WR15
8LZ

TEL: (01584) 781575 *FAX:* (01584) 781483 *CONTACT:* K & R Hurst
OPENING TIMES: 1000-1800 Sun and by appt, May-end July.
No mail order
CAT. COST: 4 x 2nd class *W/SALE or RETAIL:* Retail *CREDIT CARDS:* None
SPECIALITIES: Over 400 varieties of Herbs. Aromatic & scented foliage plants, esp. Symphytum,
Pulmonaria, Lamium, Monarda, Ajuga, Salvia, Lobelia & Crocosmia. See also SEED Index.
 MAP PAGE: **5**

WChe **Checkley Waterplants,** The Knoll House, Checkley, Herefordshire, HR1 4ND

TEL: (01432) 860672 *CONTACT:* Mrs M P Bennett
OPENING TIMES: By appt. only.
MIN. MAIL ORDER UK: No minimum charge *MIN. VALUE EC:*
CAT. COST: Sae *W/SALE or RETAIL:* Both *CREDIT CARDS:* None
SPECIALITIES: Pond, Bog and moisture loving plants. *MAP PAGE:* **5**

◆ **See also Display Advertisements**

WCla   **John Clayfield,** Llanbrook Alpine Nursery, Hopton Castle, Clunton, Shropshire, SY7 0QG
TEL: (01547) 530298   *CONTACT:* John Clayfield
OPENING TIMES: Daily - but please check first.
No mail order
CAT. COST: None issued   *W/SALE or RETAIL:* Both   *CREDIT CARDS:* None
SPECIALITIES: Alpines & Wildflowers. Cottage garden & Herbaceous plants.   *MAP PAGE:* **5/7**

WCoo   **Mrs Susan Cooper,** Firlands Cottage, Bishop Frome, Worcestershire, WR6 5BA
TEL: (01885) 490358   *CONTACT:* Mrs Susan Cooper
OPENING TIMES: Appt. only.
MIN. MAIL ORDER UK: £20.00 + p&p*   *MIN. VALUE EC:*
CAT. COST: Small Sae   *W/SALE or RETAIL:* Retail   *CREDIT CARDS:* None
SPECIALITIES: Rare & unusual Trees & Shrubs. Provenances on request at time of order. *Note: mail order to UK only.   *MAP PAGE:* **5**

WCot   **Cotswold Garden Flowers, 1 Waterside, Evesham, Worcestershire, WR11 6BS**
TEL: (01386) 47337 (Off.*)   *FAX:* (01386) 47337   *E-MAIL:* cgf@star.co.uk
WEB SITE: http://www.cgf.net   *CONTACT:* Bob Brown/Vicky Parkhouse/John McLeod
OPENING TIMES: 0800-1630 Mon-Fri all year. 1000-1800 Sat & Sun Mar-Sep, Sat & Sun Oct-Feb by appt.
MIN. MAIL ORDER UK: No minimum charge   *MIN. VALUE EC:* Nmc   *EXPORT:* Yes
CAT. COST: Free   *W/SALE or RETAIL:* Both   *CREDIT CARDS:* None
SPECIALITIES: Easy & unusual Perennials for the Flower Garden. *NOTE: Nursery at Sands Lane, Badsey. Tel: (01386) 833849.   *MAP PAGE:* **5**

WCru   **Crûg Farm Plants,** Griffith's Crossing, Nr Caernarfon, Gwynedd, Wales, LL55 1TU
TEL: (01248) 670232   *FAX:* (01248) 670232   *E-MAIL:* bleddyn&sue@crug-farm.demon.co.uk
WEB SITE: http://www.crug-farm.demon.co.uk   *CONTACT:* Mr B and Mrs S Wynn-Jones
◆   *OPENING TIMES:* 1000-1800 Thu-Sun last Sat Feb-last Sun Sept.
No mail order
CAT. COST: Sae + 2 x 2nd class   *W/SALE or RETAIL:* Both   *CREDIT CARDS:* Visa, Access, Delta, MasterCard
SPECIALITIES: Shade plants, climbers, Hardy Geranium, Pulmonaria, rare Shrubs, Tropaeolum, Herbaceous & bulbous incl. self-collected new introductions from the far East.   *MAP PAGE:* **4**

WCwm   **Cwmrhaiadr Nursery,** Glaspwll, Machynlleth, Powys, Wales, SY20 8UB
TEL: (01654) 702223   *CONTACT:* Glynne Jones
OPENING TIMES: By appt. only. Please 'phone.
No mail order
CAT. COST: 2 x 2nd class   *W/SALE or RETAIL:* Retail   *CREDIT CARDS:* none
SPECIALITIES: Rarer Conifer species & clones. Magnolias. Trees & shrubs for autumn colour. Increasing range of rarer trees & shrubs from seed.   *MAP PAGE:* **4**

WDib   **Dibley's Nurseries, Llanelidan, Ruthin, Clwyd, LL15 2LG**
TEL: (01978) 790677   *FAX:* (01978) 790668   *CONTACT:* R Dibley
◆   *OPENING TIMES:* 0900-1700 daily Apr-Sept.
MIN. MAIL ORDER UK: No minimum charge   *MIN. VALUE EC:* £20.00 + p&p
CAT. COST: Large (A4) Sae   *W/SALE or RETAIL:* Both   *CREDIT CARDS:* Visa, Access, Switch, Delta
SPECIALITIES: Streptocarpus, Columnea, Solenostemon & other Gesneriads & Begonia.   *MAP PAGE:* **4**

WDin   **Dingle Nurseries,** Welshpool, Powys, Wales, SY21 9JD
TEL: (01938) 555145   *FAX:* (01938) 555778   *CONTACT:* Kerry Hamer
OPENING TIMES: 0900-1700 Wed-Mon. (Wholesale Mon-Sat only).
No mail order
CAT. COST: Free plant list   *W/SALE or RETAIL:* Both   *CREDIT CARDS:* MasterCard, Switch, EuroCard, Delta, Visa
SPECIALITIES: Trees, Shrubs & Conifers. Herbaceous, Forestry & Hedging Trees.   *MAP PAGE:* **4/7**

Nursery ADDRESSES in BOLD do Mail Order to EU

WEas   Eastgrove Cottage Garden Nursery, Sankyns Green, Nr Shrawley, Little Witley, Worcestershire, WR6 6LQ

TEL: (01299) 896389 *WEB SITE:* http://www.hughesmedia.co.uk/eastgrove/
CONTACT: Malcolm & Carol Skinner
OPENING TIMES: 1400-1700 Thu-Mon 1st Apr-31st July. (Closed Aug.) 1400-1700 Thu, Fri & Sat 1st Sep-10th Oct. Also 1400-1700 Sun 27th Sept.
No mail order
CAT. COST: 5 x 2nd class *W/SALE or RETAIL:* Retail *CREDIT CARDS:* None
SPECIALITIES: Outstanding country flower garden from which exceedingly wide range of well grown hardy & half-hardy plants are produced. *MAP PAGE:* 5

WElm   The Garden at The Elms Nursery, Frenchlands Lane, Lower Broadheath, Worcestershire, WR2 6QU

TEL: (01905) 640841 *FAX:* (01905) 640675 *CONTACT:* Mrs E Stewart
OPENING TIMES: 1000-1700 Tue & Wed 1st Apr-30th Sept.
No mail order
CAT. COST: 3 x 1st class *W/SALE or RETAIL:* Retail *CREDIT CARDS:* None
SPECIALITIES: Unusual hardy plants & cottage garden favourites, most grown on the nursery from stock in an old farmhouse garden. *MAP PAGE:* 5

WFar   Farmyard Nurseries, Llandysul, Dyfed, Wales, SA44 4RL

TEL: (01559) 363389, (01267) 220259 *FAX:* (01559) 362200
E-MAIL: farmyard.nurseries@btinternet.com
WEB SITE: http://www.btinternet.com/~farmyard.nurseries *CONTACT:* Richard Bramley
◆   *OPENING TIMES:* 1000-1700 daily except Christmas, Boxing & New Years Day.
MIN. MAIL ORDER UK: No minimum charge *MIN. VALUE EC:* £50.00 + p&p *EXPORT:* Yes
CAT. COST: 4 x 1st class *W/SALE or RETAIL:* Both *CREDIT CARDS:* None
SPECIALITIES: Excellent general range, esp. Helleborus, Hosta, Tricyrtis & Herbaceous.
MAP PAGE: 4

WFib   Fibrex Nurseries Ltd, Honeybourne Road, Pebworth, Stratford-on-Avon, Warwickshire, CV37 8XT

TEL: (01789) 720788 *FAX:* (01789) 721162 *CONTACT:* H M D Key & R L Godard-Key
OPENING TIMES: 1200-1700 Mon-Fri Jan-Mar & Sept-Dec, Tue-Sun Apr-Aug, closed fortnight after Xmas. Office hours 0900-1700 Mon-Fri all year.**
MIN. MAIL ORDER UK: £10.00 + p&p* *MIN. VALUE EC:* £20.00 + p&p
CAT. COST: 2 x 2nd class *W/SALE or RETAIL:* Both *CREDIT CARDS:* MasterCard, Visa
SPECIALITIES: Ivies (Hedera), Ferns & Pelargonium & Helleborus. *Note: Hellebores not available by mail order. **Plant collections subject to time of year; please check by phone.
MAP PAGE: 5

WFoF   Flowers of the Field, Field Farm, Weobley, Herefordshire, HR4 8QJ

TEL: (01544) 318262 *FAX:* (01544) 318262 *CONTACT:* Kathy Davies
OPENING TIMES: 0900-1900 daily
No mail order
CAT. COST: 2 x 1st class *W/SALE or RETAIL:* Both *CREDIT CARDS:* None
SPECIALITIES: Traditional & unusual Perennials, Shrubs, Trees & Herbs. Summer & winter Bedding. Cut Flowers & Ornamental Grasses. *MAP PAGE:* 5

WFox   Foxbrush Gardens, Portdinorwic, Gwynedd, Wales, LL56 4JZ

TEL: (01248) 670463 *CONTACT:* Mrs J Osborne
OPENING TIMES: Apr-end Sep by prior arrangement only.
No mail order
CAT. COST: Sae *W/SALE or RETAIL:* Retail *CREDIT CARDS:* None
SPECIALITIES: Acer & Camellia. Conifers & hardy Perennials. *MAP PAGE:* 4

◆ **See also Display Advertisements**

WFro   **Fron Nursery, Fron Issa, Rhiwlas, Oswestry, Shropshire, SY10 7JH**
TEL: (01691) 600605 evenings *CONTACT:* Thoby Miller
OPENING TIMES: By appt. only. Please phone first.
MIN. MAIL ORDER UK: £20.00 + p&p *MIN. VALUE EC:* £50.00 + p&p   *EXPORT:* Yes
CAT. COST: 2 x 1st class *W/SALE or RETAIL:* Both *CREDIT CARDS:* None
SPECIALITIES: Rare and unusual Trees, Shrubs & Perennials. *MAP PAGE:* **4/7**

WGer   **Gerddi Fron Goch,** Pant Road, Llanfaglan, Caernarfon, Gwynedd, LL54 5RL
TEL: (01286) 672212 *FAX:* (01286) 678912 *CONTACT:* RA & Mrs V Williams
OPENING TIMES: 0900-1800 Mon-Sat all year round. 1000-1600 Sun.
No mail order
CAT. COST: None issued *W/SALE or RETAIL:* Retail *CREDIT CARDS:* MasterCard, Switch,
Visa
SPECIALITIES: Wide range of Trees, Shrubs, Conifers and Herbaceous Perennials, some Ferns &
Grasses; emphasis on plants for coastal & damp sites *MAP PAGE:* **4**

WGle   **Glebe Garden Nursery,** Kidnappers Lane, Leckhampton, Cheltenham, Gloucestershire,
GL53 0NR
TEL: (01242) 521001 *CONTACT:* Miss T K Budden
OPENING TIMES: 0900-1700 daily.
No mail order
CAT. COST: 1 x 2nd class *W/SALE or RETAIL:* Retail *CREDIT CARDS:* None
SPECIALITIES: Herbaceous, incl. unusual Hemerocallis, Liriope, Paeonia & Heuchera.
MAP PAGE: **5**

WGor   **Gordon's Nursery,** 1 Cefnpennar Cottages, Cefnpenner, Mountain Ash, Mid
Glamorgan, Wales, CF45 4EE
TEL: (01443) 474593 *FAX:* (01443) 475835 *E-MAIL:* 101716.2661@compuserve.com
CONTACT: D A Gordon
OPENING TIMES: 1000-1800 1st Mar-31st Oct daily. 1100-1600 1st Nov-28th Feb Sat & Sun only.
No mail order
CAT. COST: 3 x 1st class *W/SALE or RETAIL:* Retail *CREDIT CARDS:* Visa, MasterCard
SPECIALITIES: Conifers, Alpines especially Lewisias and perennials. *MAP PAGE:* **4**

WGwG   **Gwynfor Growers,** Gwynfor, Pontgarreg, Llangranog, Llandysul, Ceredigion, Wales,
SA44 6AU
TEL: (01239) 654151 *FAX:* (01239) 654152 *CONTACT:* Anne & Bob Seaman
OPENING TIMES: 1000-1600 Tues-Sun Winter, 1000-1800 7 days rest of the year.
MIN. MAIL ORDER UK: £30.00 + p&p* *MIN. VALUE EC:*
CAT. COST: 4 x 1st class *W/SALE or RETAIL:* Retail *CREDIT CARDS:* none
SPECIALITIES: Good general range specialising in Herbaceous plants, Fuchsia & Herbs. *Note:
mail order to UK only. *MAP PAGE:* **4**

WGWT   **Grafted Walnut Trees,** Bramley Cottage, Wyck Rissington, Cheltenham, Glos, GL54
2PN
TEL: (01451) 822098 *CONTACT:* George Latham
OPENING TIMES: Not open.
MIN. MAIL ORDER UK: No minimum charge *MIN. VALUE EC:*
CAT. COST: 3 x 1st class *W/SALE or RETAIL:* Both *CREDIT CARDS:* None
SPECIALITIES: Grafted Walnut Trees incl. nut bearing varieties of English Walnut, ornamental
forms of English & black Walnut, most minor Walnut species & hybrids. *MAP PAGE:* **5**

WGwy   **Gwydir Plants,** Plas Muriau, Betws-y-coed, North Wales, LL24 0HD
TEL: (01690) 710201 *FAX:* (01690) 750379 *CONTACT:* Mrs D Southgate & Mrs L Schärer
OPENING TIMES: 1000-1730 Tue-Sat & Bank Hols, 1400-1730 Sun, Mar-Oct.
No mail order
CAT. COST: 2 x 1st class *W/SALE or RETAIL:* Retail *CREDIT CARDS:* None
SPECIALITIES: Hardy Perennials, Wild flowers, Native Trees & Shrubs, Herbs; incl. many
noteworthy but hard-to-find plants. *MAP PAGE:* **4**

Nursery ADDRESSES in BOLD do Mail Order to EU

WHal **Hall Farm Nursery,** Vicarage Lane, Kinnerley, Nr Oswestry, Shropshire, SY10 8DH

TEL: (01691) 682135 *CONTACT:* Mrs C Ffoulkes-Jones
OPENING TIMES: For 1998: 1000-1700 Tue-Sat 3rd Mar-10th Oct. 1999 may differ.
No mail order
CAT. COST: 4 x 1st class *W/SALE or RETAIL:* Retail *CREDIT CARDS:* None
SPECIALITIES: Unusual Herbaceous plants incl. Hardy Geranium, Penstemon, Grasses & many others. *MAP PAGE:* 7

WHar **Harley Nursery,** Harley, Shropshire, SY5 6LP

TEL: (01952) 510241 *FAX:* (01952) 510222 *CONTACT:* Duncan Murphy
OPENING TIMES: 0900-1730 Mon-Sat, 1000-1750 Sun & Bank Hols.
No mail order
CAT. COST: 2 x 1st class *W/SALE or RETAIL:* Retail *CREDIT CARDS:* Visa, Access
SPECIALITIES: Wide range of own grown Shrubs, Climbing & Hedging plants. Many unusual varieties. *MAP PAGE:* 7

WHCG **Hunts Court Garden & Nursery,** North Nibley, Dursley, Gloucestershire, GL11 6DZ

TEL: (01453) 547440 *FAX:* (01453) 547440 *CONTACT:* T K & M M Marshall
◆   *OPENING TIMES:* Nursery & Garden 0900-1700 Tue-Sat ex Aug. Also by appt.*
No mail order
CAT. COST: 5 x 2nd class *W/SALE or RETAIL:* Retail *CREDIT CARDS:* None
SPECIALITIES: Old Rose species & climbers. Hardy Geraniums. Shrubby Potentilla, Penstemon & unusual shrubs. *See Display Advert for Charity openings. *MAP PAGE:* 5

WHCr **Hergest Croft Gardens,** Kington, Herefordshire, HR5 3EG

TEL: (01544) 230160 *FAX:* (01544) 230160 *CONTACT:* Stephen Lloyd
OPENING TIMES: 1330-1830 daily Apr-Oct.
No mail order
CAT. COST: None issued *W/SALE or RETAIL:* Retail *CREDIT CARDS:* None
SPECIALITIES: Acer, Betula & unusual woody plants. *MAP PAGE:* 5

WHen **Henllys Lodge Plants,** Henllys Lodge, Beaumaris, Anglesey, Gwynedd, Wales, LL58 8HU

TEL: (01248) 810106 *CONTACT:* Mrs E Lane
OPENING TIMES: 1100-1700 Mon, Wed, Fri, Sat, Sun & by appt. Apr-Oct.
No mail order
CAT. COST: 2 x 1st class *W/SALE or RETAIL:* Retail *CREDIT CARDS:* none
SPECIALITIES: Hardy Geranium, Ground cover & cottage style Perennials. See also SEED Index. *MAP PAGE:* 4

WHer **The Herb Garden & Historical Plant Nursery,** Capel Ulo, Pentre Berw, Gaerwen, Anglesey, Wales, LL60 6LF

TEL: CONTACT: Corinne & David Tremaine-Stevenson
OPENING TIMES: 0900-1700 daily exc. Tues. Open all Bank Hols.
MIN. MAIL ORDER UK: £15.00 + p&p *MIN. VALUE EC:*
CAT. COST: List £2.00 in stamps *W/SALE or RETAIL:* Retail *CREDIT CARDS:* None
SPECIALITIES: Wide range of Herbs, rare Natives & Wild flowers; rare & unusual Perennials, Scented Pelargoniums & Old Roses. *MAP PAGE:* 4

WHil **Hillview Hardy Plants, Worfield, Nr Bridgnorth, Shropshire, WV15 5NT**

TEL: (01746) 716454 *FAX:* (01746) 716454 *E-MAIL:* hillview_hardy_plants@compuserve.com
CONTACT: Ingrid Millington
OPENING TIMES: 0900-1700 Mon-Sat Mar-mid Oct. By appt. mid Oct-Feb.
MIN. MAIL ORDER UK: £10.00 + p&p *MIN. VALUE EC:* £10.00 + p&p   *EXPORT:* Yes
CAT. COST: 4 x 2nd class *W/SALE or RETAIL:* Both *CREDIT CARDS:* None
SPECIALITIES: Hardy Perennials & Alpines incl. Auriculas. Contract growing for Wholesale.
MAP PAGE: 7

◆ **See also Display Advertisements**

WHoo   Hoo House Nursery, Hoo House, Gloucester Road, Tewkesbury, Gloucestershire, GL20 7DA

TEL: (01684) 293389 *FAX:* (01684) 293389 *CONTACT:* Robin & Julie Ritchie
♦ *OPENING TIMES:* 1400-1700 Mon-Sat.
No mail order
CAT. COST: 3 x 1st class *W/SALE or RETAIL:* Both *CREDIT CARDS:* None
SPECIALITIES: Wide range of Herbaceous & Alpines - some unusual. *MAP PAGE:* 5

WHow   How Caple Court Gardens, How Caple Court, How Caple, Herefordshire, HR1 4SX

TEL: (01989) 740626 *FAX:* (01989) 740611 *CONTACT:* Mrs V Lee
OPENING TIMES: 0930-1730 all year. Closed Sats Oct-Feb.
No mail order
CAT. COST: 1 x 1st class *W/SALE or RETAIL:* Retail *CREDIT CARDS:* None
SPECIALITIES: English & old Rose varieties. Old Apples varieties. Herbaceous Perennials.
MAP PAGE: 5

WIvy   Ivycroft Plants, Upper Ivington, Leominster, Herefordshire, HR6 0JN

TEL: (01568) 720344 *CONTACT:* Roger Norman
OPENING TIMES: Please phone for opening times.
No mail order
CAT. COST: 2 x 1st class *W/SALE or RETAIL:* Retail *CREDIT CARDS:* None
SPECIALITIES: Cyclamen, Violas, Alpines and Herbaceous. *MAP PAGE:* 5

WJas   Paul Jasper - Fruit & Ornamental Trees, The Lighthouse, Bridge Street, Leominster, Herefordshire, HR6 8DU

TEL: FAX only for orders. *FAX:* (01568) 616499 *E-MAIL:* pjasper253@aol.com
CONTACT: Paul Jasper
OPENING TIMES: Not open for Retail sales.
MIN. MAIL ORDER UK: £20.00 + p&p *MIN. VALUE EC:* £50.00 + p&p
CAT. COST: 2 x 1st class *W/SALE or RETAIL:* Both *CREDIT CARDS:* None
SPECIALITIES: Full range of Fruit & Ornamental Trees. Over 100 modern and traditional apple varieties plus 120 other varieties all direct from the grower. *MAP PAGE:* 5

WJek   Jekka's Herb Farm, Rose Cottage, Shellards Lane, Alveston, Bristol, Avon, BS35 3SY

TEL: (01454) 418878 *FAX:* (01454) 411988 *CONTACT:* Jekka McVicar
OPENING TIMES: By appt. only
MIN. MAIL ORDER UK: No minimum charge *MIN. VALUE EC:* Nmc*   *EXPORT:* Yes
CAT. COST: 4 x 1st class *W/SALE or RETAIL:* Both *CREDIT CARDS:* None
SPECIALITIES: Culinary, Medicinal, Aromatic Decorative Herbs, Native Wild Flowers.
*Individual quotations for EC Sales. See also SEED Index. *MAP PAGE:* 5

WJun   Jungle Giants, Plough Farm, Wigmore, Herefordshire, HR6 9UW

TEL: (01568) 770708 *FAX:* (01568) 770383 *CONTACT:* Michael Brisbane & Paul Lickorish
OPENING TIMES: Daily - by appt. only please.
MIN. MAIL ORDER UK: £20.00 + p&p *MIN. VALUE EC:* £25.00 + p&p   *EXPORT:* Yes
CAT. COST: £5.75* *W/SALE or RETAIL:* Both *CREDIT CARDS:* None
SPECIALITIES: Bamboo. *Full descriptive information pack incl. p&p. *MAP PAGE:* 5

WKif   Kiftsgate Court Gardens, Kiftsgate Court, Chipping Camden, Gloucestershire, GL55 6LW

TEL: (01386) 438777 *FAX:* (01386) 438777 *CONTACT:* Mrs J Chambers
OPENING TIMES: 1400-1800 Wed, Thu & Sun Apr 1st-Sep 30th & Bank Hol Mons. Also Sats in Jun & Jul.
No mail order
CAT. COST: None issued *W/SALE or RETAIL:* Retail *CREDIT CARDS:* None
SPECIALITIES: Small range of unusual plants. *MAP PAGE:* 5

Nursery ADDRESSES in BOLD do Mail Order to EU

WKin Kingstone Cottage Plants, Weston-under-Penyard, Ross-on-Wye, Herefordshire, HR9 7NT

TEL: (01989) 565267 *E-MAIL:* kingstone@wyenet.co.uk *CONTACT:* Mr M Hughes
OPENING TIMES: By appt. and as under National Garden Scheme.
MIN. MAIL ORDER UK: No minimum charge *MIN. VALUE EC:* Nmc
CAT. COST: 2 x 1st class *W/SALE or RETAIL:* Retail *CREDIT CARDS:* none
SPECIALITIES: Dianthus - Nationial Collection Holders. *MAP PAGE:* 5

WLeb Leba Orchard - Green's Leaves, Lea Bailey, Nr Ross-on-Wye, Herefordshire, HR9 5TY

TEL: (01989) 750303 *CONTACT:* Paul Green
OPENING TIMES: By appt. only, weekends preferred.
MIN. MAIL ORDER UK: £10.00 + p&p *MIN. VALUE EC:*
CAT. COST: 2 x 2nd class *W/SALE or RETAIL:* Both *CREDIT CARDS:* None
SPECIALITIES: Ivies, ornamental Grasses & Sedges. Increasing range of rare & choice Shrubs, also some Perennials. *MAP PAGE:* 5

WLin Lingen Nursery and Garden, Lingen, Nr Bucknell, Shropshire, SY7 0DY

TEL: (01544) 267720 *FAX:* (01544) 267720 *CONTACT:* Kim W Davis
OPENING TIMES: 1000-1700 daily Feb-Oct. Fri-Sun Nov-Jan by appt.
MIN. MAIL ORDER UK: No minimum charge *MIN. VALUE EC:* £20.0 + p&p
CAT. COST: 3 x 1st class *W/SALE or RETAIL:* Both *CREDIT CARDS:* None
SPECIALITIES: Alpines, Rock Plants & Herbaceous esp. Androsace, Aquilegia, Campanula, Iris, Primula & Penstemon. *MAP PAGE:* 5

WLRN Little Rhyndaston Nurseries, Hayscastle, Haverfordwest, Pembrokeshire, SA62 5PT

TEL: (01437) 710656 *CONTACT:* D A & P Baster
OPENING TIMES: 0900-1700 Mon-Sat, 1100-1700 Sun. Closed August.
No mail order
CAT. COST: None issued *W/SALE or RETAIL:* Retail *CREDIT CARDS:* Visa, MasterCard, Switch
SPECIALITIES: Herbaceous Perennials, Conifers, Shrubs, Alpines, Climbers, Patio plants, many suitable for coastal locations. *MAP PAGE:* 4

WMal Marshall's Malmaison, 4 The Damsells, Tetbury, Gloucestershire, GL8 8JA

TEL: (01666) 502589 *CONTACT:* J M Marshall
OPENING TIMES: By appt. only.
MIN. MAIL ORDER UK: £16.50 incl. p&p *MIN. VALUE EC:* £16.50 incl p&p *EXPORT:* Yes
CAT. COST: 1st class Sae *W/SALE or RETAIL:* Both *CREDIT CARDS:* None
SPECIALITIES: Malmaison Carnations.

WMaN The Marches Nursery, Presteigne, Powys, Wales, LD8 2HG

TEL: (01544) 260474 *FAX:* (01544) 260474 *CONTACT:* Jane Cooke
OPENING TIMES: Mail Order only.
MIN. MAIL ORDER UK: No minimum charge *MIN. VALUE EC:* Nmc
CAT. COST: 2 x 1st class *W/SALE or RETAIL:* Retail *CREDIT CARDS:* None
SPECIALITIES: An increasing range of choice Perennials, many uncommon. See also SEED Index.

WMAq Merebrook Water Plants, Merebrook Farm, Hanley Swan, Worcester, Worcestershire, WR8 0DX

TEL: (01684) 310950 *FAX:* (01684) 310034 *E-MAIL:* lily@merebrk.demon.co.uk
CONTACT: Roger Kings
OPENING TIMES: 1000-1700 Thu-Tue Easter-Sep.
MIN. MAIL ORDER UK: No minimum charge *MIN. VALUE EC:*
CAT. COST: 1 x 2nd class *W/SALE or RETAIL:* Retail *CREDIT CARDS:* None
SPECIALITIES: Nymphaea (Water Lilies) & other Aquatic plants. *MAP PAGE:* 5

◆ **See also Display Advertisements**

WMer Merton Nurseries, Holyhead Road, Bicton, Shrewsbury, Shropshire, SY3 8EF

TEL: (01743) 850773 *FAX:* (01743) 850773 *CONTACT:* Jessica Pannett
OPENING TIMES: 0900-1730 daily ex. Christmas & New Year
No mail order
CAT. COST: 2 x 1st class *W/SALE or RETAIL:* Retail *CREDIT CARDS:* Access, Visa
SPECIALITIES: Hardy Perennials, Hosta & Clematis. *MAP PAGE:* **7**

WMEx Marston Exotics, Brampton Lane, Madley, Herefordshire, HR2 9LX

TEL: (01981) 251140 *FAX:* (01981) 251649
WEB SITE: http://freespace.virgin.net/carnivorous.connection/ *CONTACT:* Paul Gardner
OPENING TIMES: 0800-1630 Mon-Fri all year, 1300-1700 Sat & Sun Mar-Oct.
MIN. MAIL ORDER UK: See list for details *MIN. VALUE EC:* £50.00 + p&p   *EXPORT:* Yes
CAT. COST: List 3 x 1st class* *W/SALE or RETAIL:* Both *CREDIT CARDS:* Visa, MasterCard, Switch
SPECIALITIES: Carnivorous plants. Nursery holds the National Collection of Sarracenia. *Price list & Growers Guide £2.85. See also SEED Index. *MAP PAGE:* **5**

WMoo Moorland Cottage Plants, Rhyd-y-Groes, Brynberian, Crymych, Pembrokeshire, Wales, SA41 3TT

TEL: (01239) 891363 *CONTACT:* Jennifer Matthews
OPENING TIMES: Mail order & strictly by appt.
MIN. MAIL ORDER UK: See cat. for details.* *MIN. VALUE EC:*
CAT. COST: 4 x 1st class *W/SALE or RETAIL:* Retail *CREDIT CARDS:* none
SPECIALITIES: Traditional & Unusual Hardy Perennials, esp. Geranium, Campanula, Geum & colouful Ground Cover. *Note: mail order to UK only. *MAP PAGE:* **4**

WMou Mount Pleasant Trees, Rockhampton, Berkeley, Gloucestershire, GL13 9DU

TEL: 01454 260348 *CONTACT:* P & G Locke
OPENING TIMES: By appt. only.
No mail order
CAT. COST: 3 x 2nd class *W/SALE or RETAIL:* Both *CREDIT CARDS:* None
SPECIALITIES: Wide range of Trees for forestry, hedging, woodlands & gardens esp. Tilia, Populus & Sequoiadendron. *MAP PAGE:* **5**

WMow Mow Cottage Garden Plants, The Mow, Aston Rogers, Nr Westbury, Shropshire, SY5 9HQ

TEL: (01743) 891234 *CONTACT:* Tony Faulkner
OPENING TIMES: By appt. Please phone first.
MIN. MAIL ORDER UK: No minimum charge *MIN. VALUE EC:* £20.00 + p&p
CAT. COST: Large (A4) Sae *W/SALE or RETAIL:* Retail *CREDIT CARDS:* None
SPECIALITIES: Hardy herbaceous - Campanula, Geranium, Sidalcea, Potentilla etc.
MAP PAGE: **7**

WMul Mulu Nurseries, Burford House, Tenbury Wells, Worcestershire, WR15 8HQ

TEL: (01584) 811592 *FAX:* (01584) 810673 *E-MAIL:* mulu@burford.co.uk
CONTACT: Andrew Bateman
♦   *OPENING TIMES:* 1000-1800 or dusk if earlier 7 days. Phone first Nov-Mar.
MIN. MAIL ORDER UK: No minimum charge *MIN. VALUE EC:* £25.00 + p&p *EXPORT:* Yes
CAT. COST: 4 x 1st class *W/SALE or RETAIL:* Both *CREDIT CARDS:* none
SPECIALITIES: Rare & unusual Exotics for inside and out. *MAP PAGE:* **5**

WNor Norfields, Llangwm Arboretum, Usk, Monmouthshire, NP5 1NQ

TEL: (01291) 650306 *FAX:* (01291) 650306 *CONTACT:* Andrew Norfield
OPENING TIMES: Not open.
MIN. MAIL ORDER UK: £3.00 + p&p *MIN. VALUE EC:* £3.00 + p&p   *EXPORT:* Yes
CAT. COST: 1 x 1st class *W/SALE or RETAIL:* Retail *CREDIT CARDS:* None
SPECIALITIES: Wide range of Tree seedlings for growing on. Acer, Betula, Stewartia & pregerminated seed. See also SEED Index.

Nursery ADDRESSES in BOLD do Mail Order to EU

WOak **Oak Cottage Walled Herb Garden,** Uffington, Nr Shrewsbury, Shropshire, SY4 4TG

◆
TEL: (01939) 210219 *FAX:* (01939) 210219 *CONTACT:* Jane & Edward Bygott.
OPENING TIMES: 1100-1700 Fri, Sat & Sun from Easter to mid-Sept. Other times by appt. If making a special journey please phone first.
MIN. MAIL ORDER UK: No minimum charge* *MIN. VALUE EC:*
CAT. COST: 3 x 2nd class *W/SALE or RETAIL:* Retail *CREDIT CARDS:* none
SPECIALITIES: Herbs, Wild flowers, Cottage plants. Garden design. *Note: mail order to UK only. *MAP PAGE:* **7**

WOld **Old Court Nurseries, Colwall, Nr Malvern, Worcestershire, WR13 6QE**
TEL: (01684) 540416 *FAX:* (01684) 565314 *CONTACT:* Paul & Meriel Picton
OPENING TIMES: 1100-1730 Wed-Sun Apr-Oct. 2nd week Sep-2nd week Oct only 1100-1730 daily.
MIN. MAIL ORDER UK: No minimum charge* *MIN. VALUE EC:* Nmc
CAT. COST: £2.50. Price list free. *W/SALE or RETAIL:* Retail *CREDIT CARDS:* None
SPECIALITIES: National collection of Michaelmas Daisies. Herbaceous Perennials. *Note: mail order for Aster only. *MAP PAGE:* **5**

WOMN **The Old Manor Nursery,** Twyning, Gloucestershire, GL20 6DB
TEL: (01684) 293516 *FAX:* (01684) 293516 *CONTACT:* Mrs Joan Wilder
OPENING TIMES: 1400-1700, or dusk if earlier, Mons 1st Mar-31st Oct EXCEPT B/Hols. Winter visits by appt. Closed Sun.
No mail order
CAT. COST: 1 x 1st & 1 x 2nd class *W/SALE or RETAIL:* Retail *CREDIT CARDS:* none
SPECIALITIES: Predominantly Alpines, small supply of unusual & rare varieties of other Perennial plants incl. Trees, Shrubs & Bulbs. *MAP PAGE:* **5**

WOrn **Ornamental Tree Nurseries,** Broomy Hill Gardens, Cobnash, Kingsland, Herefordshire, HR6 9QZ
TEL: (01568) 708016 *FAX:* (01568) 709022 *CONTACT:* Russell Mills
OPENING TIMES: 0900-1700 Mon-Sat.
No mail order
CAT. COST: Sae *W/SALE or RETAIL:* Both *CREDIT CARDS:* None
SPECIALITIES: Ornamental Trees. *MAP PAGE:* **5**

WOve **Overcourt Garden Nursery,** Sutton St Nicholas, Hereford, HR1 3AY
TEL: (01432) 880845 *CONTACT:* Nicola Harper
OPENING TIMES: 0930-1630 Tues-Sat 1st Mar-31st Oct. If travelling please phone first.
No mail order
CAT. COST: 3 x 2nd class *W/SALE or RETAIL:* Retail *CREDIT CARDS:* None
SPECIALITIES: Hardy Perennials, many unusual. Garden open by appt. *MAP PAGE:* **5**

WOVN **The Old Vicarage Nursery,** Lucton, Leominster, Herefordshire, HR6 9PN
TEL: (01568) 780538 *FAX:* (01568) 780818 *CONTACT:* Mrs R M Flake
OPENING TIMES: 1000-1700 most days, but please telephone first to be sure.
MIN. MAIL ORDER UK: No minimum charge* *MIN. VALUE EC:*
CAT. COST: 2 x 1st class *W/SALE or RETAIL:* Retail *CREDIT CARDS:* None
SPECIALITIES: Roses - old roses, climbers & ramblers, species & ground cover. Euphorbia & half-hardy Salvia. *Note: mail order to UK only. *MAP PAGE:* **5**

WPat **Chris Pattison,** Brookend, Pendock, Gloucestershire, GL19 3PL
TEL: (01531) 650480 *FAX:* (01531) 650480 *CONTACT:* Chris Pattison
OPENING TIMES: 0900-1700 Mon-Fri. Weekends by appt. only.
No mail order
CAT. COST: 3 x 1st class *W/SALE or RETAIL:* Both *CREDIT CARDS:* None
SPECIALITIES: Choice & rare Shrubs and Alpines. Grafted Stock esp. Japanese Maples & Liquidambars. *MAP PAGE:* **5**

◆ **See also Display Advertisements**

WPbr   **Perrybrook Nursery,** Brook Cottage, Wykey, Ruyton XI Towns, Shropshire, SY4 1JA
TEL: (01939) 261120   *FAX:* (01939) 261120   *CONTACT:* Gayle Williams
OPENING TIMES: 1300-1800 1st Mar-30th Sept. Other times by appt.
No mail order
CAT. COST: 4 x 1st class   *W/SALE or RETAIL:* Retail   *CREDIT CARDS:* None
SPECIALITIES: Herbaceous Perennials. Many unusual varieties available in small numbers esp.
Tricyrtis, Epimedium, Centaurea & Tiarella.   *MAP PAGE:* **7**

WPeH   **Penhow Nurseries, St Brides Netherwent, Penhow, Nr Newport, Gwent, NP4 3AU**
TEL: (01633) 400419   *FAX:* (01633) 400419   *CONTACT:* David Jones
OPENING TIMES: 0900-1800 7 days.
MIN. MAIL ORDER UK: £16.00*   *MIN. VALUE EC:* £16.00*   *EXPORT:* Yes
CAT. COST: 1 x 1st class   *W/SALE or RETAIL:* Retail   *CREDIT CARDS:* none
SPECIALITIES: Diascia & Perennial Nemesia.   *MAP PAGE:* **5**

WPen   **Penpergwm Plants,** Penpergwm Lodge, Abergavenny, Gwent, Wales, NP7 9AS
TEL: (01873) 840422/840208   *FAX:* (01873) 840470/840208   *CONTACT:* Mrs J Kerr/Mrs S Boyle
OPENING TIMES: 26th Mar-4th Oct Thurs-Sun.
No mail order
CAT. COST: 2 x 1st class   *W/SALE or RETAIL:* Retail   *CREDIT CARDS:* None
SPECIALITIES: Hardy Perennials.   *MAP PAGE:* **5**

WPer   **Perhill Nurseries,** Worcester Road, Great Witley, Worcestershire, WR6 6JT
TEL: (01299) 896329   *FAX:* (01299) 896990   *CONTACT:* Duncan & Sarah Straw
OPENING TIMES: 0900-1700 Mon- Sat, 1000-1600 Sun, 1st Feb-15th Oct & by appt.
MIN. MAIL ORDER UK: No minimum charge*   *MIN. VALUE EC:*
CAT. COST: 6 x 2nd class   *W/SALE or RETAIL:* Both   *CREDIT CARDS:* None
SPECIALITIES: Over 2500 varieties of rare & unusual Alpines & Herbaceous Perennials incl.
Penstemon, Campanula, Salvia, Thyme, Herbs & Veronica. *Note: mail order to UK only.
MAP PAGE: **5**

WPGP   **Pan-Global Plants,** Spoonbed Nursery, Rococo Garden, Painswick, Glos, GL6 6TH
TEL: (01452) 814242   *FAX:* (01452) 813204   *CONTACT:* N Macer
OPENING TIMES: 1100-1700 Wed-Sun 2nd Wed in Jan-30th Nov. Daily July & Aug. Also Bank
Hols.
MIN. MAIL ORDER UK: £100.00 + p&p   *MIN. VALUE EC:*
CAT. COST: 3 x 1st class   *W/SALE or RETAIL:* Retail   *CREDIT CARDS:* None
SPECIALITIES: Rare, Unusual & hard to find Trees, Shrubs & Herbaceous esp. Paeonia sp.,
Hydrangea & Magnolia.   *MAP PAGE:* **5**

WPhl   **Just Phlomis, Sunningdale, Grange Court, Westbury-on-Severn, Gloucestershire, GL14
1PL**
TEL: (01452) 760268   *FAX:* (01452) 760268   *E-MAIL:* j.mann.taylor@clara.net
CONTACT: J Mann Taylor
OPENING TIMES: Appt. only.
MIN. MAIL ORDER UK: £7.50 + p&p   *MIN. VALUE EC:* £7.50 + p&p
CAT. COST: 2 x 2nd class   *W/SALE or RETAIL:* Retail   *CREDIT CARDS:* None
SPECIALITIES: Phlomis from the National Collection.   *MAP PAGE:* **5**

WPic   **The Picton Castle Trust Nursery,** Picton Castle, Haverfordwest, Pembrokeshire, SA62
4AS
TEL: (01437) 751326   *FAX:* (01437) 751326   *CONTACT:* D L Pryse Lloyd
OPENING TIMES: 1030-1700 daily except Mon Apr-Oct. Other times by arrangement.
No mail order
CAT. COST: 1 x 1st class   *W/SALE or RETAIL:* Both   *CREDIT CARDS:* none
SPECIALITIES: Woodland & unusual Shrubs.   *MAP PAGE:* **4**

Nursery ADDRESSES in BOLD do Mail Order to EU

WPnn **The Perennial Nursery,** Rhosygilwen, Llanrhian Road, Sr Davids, Pembrokeshire, SA62 6DB

TEL: (01437) 721954 *FAX:* (01437) 721954 *CONTACT:* Mrs Philipa Symons
OPENING TIMES: 0930-1730 Wed-Mon Mar-Oct. Nov-Apr by appt.
No mail order
CAT. COST: 1 x 1st class *W/SALE or RETAIL:* Retail *CREDIT CARDS:* None
SPECIALITIES: Herbaceous Perennials & Alpines, esp. Erodium. *MAP PAGE:* 4

WPnz **J Planitzer, 15 Ar-y-bryn, Pembrey, Carmarthenshire, SA16 0AX**

TEL: (01554) 832205 *CONTACT:* Mrs J Planitzer
OPENING TIMES: Not open.
MIN. MAIL ORDER UK: £12.00 + p&p *MIN. VALUE EC:* £12.00 + p&p *EXPORT:* Yes
CAT. COST: 1 x 2nd class *W/SALE or RETAIL:* Retail *CREDIT CARDS:* none
SPECIALITIES: Hellebores. Note: mail order dispatch in Jan-Mar & Sep-Oct only.

WPrP **Prime Perennials,** Llety Moel, Rhos-y-Garth, Llanilar, Nr Aberystwyth, Ceredigion, SY23 4SG

TEL: (01974) 241505 *CONTACT:* Elizabeth Powney
OPENING TIMES: Not open to public.
MIN. MAIL ORDER UK: £10.00 + p&p* *MIN. VALUE EC:*
CAT. COST: 4 x 1st class *W/SALE or RETAIL:* Retail *CREDIT CARDS:* none
SPECIALITIES: Unusual Perennials esp. Hardy Geraniums & Cottage Garden favourites. All grown on nursery. *MAP PAGE:* 4

WPyg **The Pygmy Pinetum,** Cannop Crossroads, Nr Coleford, Forest of Dean, Gloucestershire, GL15 7EQ

TEL: (01594) 833398 *FAX:* (01594) 810815 *CONTACT:* Keith Parker
OPENING TIMES: 0900-1800 daily all year.
No mail order
CAT. COST: 3 x 2nd class *W/SALE or RETAIL:* Retail *CREDIT CARDS:* Visa, MasterCard, Switch
SPECIALITIES: Unusual Shrubs, Alpines & Herbaceous. Wide range of Trees, Heathers, Ferns, Top Fruit, Water plants & Climbers. *MAP PAGE:* 5

WRha **Rhandirmwyn Plants,** (Off.) 8 Pannau Street, Rhandirmwyn, Nr Llandovery, Carmarthenshire, Wales, SA20 0NP

TEL: (01550) 760220 *CONTACT:* Sara Fox/Thomas Sheppard
OPENING TIMES: By appt. only.
No mail order
CAT. COST: None issued *W/SALE or RETAIL:* Both *CREDIT CARDS:* None
SPECIALITIES: Old-fashioned Cottage Garden plants, over 400 varieties. *Nursery is at Pwyllpriddog Farm, Rhandirmwyn. *MAP PAGE:* 4

WRHF **Red House Farm,** Flying Horse Lane, Bradley Green, Nr Redditch, Worcestershire, B96 6QT

TEL: (01527) 821269 *FAX:* (01527) 821674 *CONTACT:* Mrs Maureen Weaver
OPENING TIMES: 0900-1700 daily all year.
No mail order
CAT. COST: 2 x 1st class *W/SALE or RETAIL:* Retail *CREDIT CARDS:* None
SPECIALITIES: Cottage garden Perennials. *MAP PAGE:* 5

WRic **Rickard's Hardy Ferns, Kyre Park, Kyre, Tenbury Wells, Worcestershire, WR15 8RP**

TEL: (01885) 410282 *FAX:* (01885) 410398 *CONTACT:* Martin Rickard
OPENING TIMES: Wed-Mon all year but appt. advisable Nov-Feb.
MIN. MAIL ORDER UK: £20.00 + p&p *MIN. VALUE EC:* £50.00 + p&p
CAT. COST: 5 x 1st class* *W/SALE or RETAIL:* Retail *CREDIT CARDS:* none
SPECIALITIES: Ferns, hardy & half-hardy, Tree-ferns. National Reference Collection of Polypodium, Cystopteris & Thelypteroid ferns. *Descriptive list. *MAP PAGE:* 5

◆ **See also Display Advertisements**

WRus   **Rushfields of Ledbury,** Ross Road, Ledbury, Herefordshire, HR8 2LP

TEL: (01531) 632004 *FAX:* (01531) 632004 *E-MAIL:* rush01531@aol.com
CONTACT: B & J Homewood
OPENING TIMES: 1100-1700 Wed-Sat. Other times by appt.
No mail order
CAT. COST: A5 Sae 31p + £1.00 *W/SALE or RETAIL:* Both *CREDIT CARDS:* Visa, Access, AmEx
SPECIALITIES: Unusual Herbaceous, incl. Euphorbia, Hardy Geranium, Helleborus, Hosta, Osteospermum, Penstemon, Primroses & Grasses. *MAP PAGE:* 5

WSan   **Sandstones Cottage Garden Plants, 58 Bolas Heath, Great Bolas, Shropshire, TF6 6PS**

TEL: (01952) 541657 *FAX:* (01952) 541657 *E-MAIL:* pbrelsforth@mcmail.com
WEB SITE: http://www.sandstones.mcmail.com *CONTACT:* Joanne Brelsforth
OPENING TIMES: Tues & Wed May-Sept or by appt.
MIN. MAIL ORDER UK: £10.00 + p&p *MIN. VALUE EC:* £25.00 + p&p
CAT. COST: 4 x 1st class *W/SALE or RETAIL:* Retail *CREDIT CARDS:* None
SPECIALITIES: Unusual & interesting Hardy Perennials. Also large range of variegated varieties.
MAP PAGE: 7

WSel   **Selsley Herb Farm,** Waterlane, Selsley, Stroud, Gloucestershire, GL5 5LW

TEL: (01453) 766682 *FAX:* (01453) 753674 *CONTACT:* Rob Wimperis
OPENING TIMES: 1000-1700 Tue-Sat, 1400-1700 Sun & Bank Hols Apr-Sep.
No mail order
CAT. COST: None issued. *W/SALE or RETAIL:* Retail *CREDIT CARDS:* None
SPECIALITIES: Herbs - Lavandula, Penstemon & Rosemary. *MAP PAGE:* 5

WSHC **Stone House Cottage Nurseries,** Stone, Nr Kidderminster, Worcestershire, DY10 4BG

TEL: (01562) 69902 *FAX:* (01562) 69960 *CONTACT:* J F & L N Arbuthnott
OPENING TIMES: 1000-1730 Wed-Sat. For Sun opening see NGS 'Yellow Book'. Appt. only
mid-Oct-Mar.
No mail order
CAT. COST: Sae *W/SALE or RETAIL:* Retail *CREDIT CARDS:* None
SPECIALITIES: Small general range, especially wall Shrubs, Climbers and unusual plants.
MAP PAGE: 5

WShe   **Sherborne Gardens,** Sherborne, Cheltenham, Gloucestershire, GL54 3DW

TEL: (01451) 844522, (01451) 844248 *FAX:* (01451) 844695
E-MAIL: sherborne.gardens@dial.pipex.com *CONTACT:* John E.M. Hill
OPENING TIMES: 0800-1700 Mon-Sat Mar-Oct, & Mon-Fri Nov-Feb.
No mail order
CAT. COST: 2 x 1st class *W/SALE or RETAIL:* Both *CREDIT CARDS:* none
SPECIALITIES: *MAP PAGE:* 5

WShi   **John Shipton (Bulbs), Y Felin, Henllan Amgoed, Whitland, Dyfed, Wales, SA34 0SL**

TEL: (01994) 240125 *FAX:* (01994) 241180 *E-MAIL:* bluebell@zoo.co.uk
CONTACT: John Shipton
OPENING TIMES: By appt. only.
MIN. MAIL ORDER UK: No minimum charge *MIN. VALUE EC:* Nmc   *EXPORT:* Yes
CAT. COST: Sae *W/SALE or RETAIL:* Both *CREDIT CARDS:* None
SPECIALITIES: Native British Bulbs & Bulbs and Plants for naturalising. See also SEED Index.
MAP PAGE: 4

WSpi   **Spinneywell Nursery, Waterlane, Oakridge, Bisley, Glos, GL6 7PH**

TEL: (01452) 770092 *FAX:* (01452) 770151 *E-MAIL:* imminent-goto.nu-spinneywell
WEB SITE: http://www.imminent-goto.nu-spinneywell *CONTACT:* Wendy Asher
◆   *OPENING TIMES:* 1000-1700 summer, 1000-1600 winter daily Mar-Dec.
MIN. MAIL ORDER UK: £10.00 + p&p *MIN. VALUE EC:* £30.00 + p&p   *EXPORT:* Yes
CAT. COST: 6 x 1st class *W/SALE or RETAIL:* Both *CREDIT CARDS:* none
SPECIALITIES: Buxus, Taxus & Unusual Herbaceous & Shrubs. *MAP PAGE:* 5

Nursery ADDRESSES in BOLD do Mail Order to EU

WSPU   Specialist Plant Unit, Pershore Colleg of Hort., Avonbank, Pershore, Worcestershire, WR10 3JP

TEL: (01386) 561385   *FAX:* (01386) 555601   *CONTACT:* Julia Sanders
OPENING TIMES: 0900-1700 Mon-Sat, 1000-1600 Sun.
No mail order
CAT. COST: £1.00   *W/SALE or RETAIL:* Both   *CREDIT CARDS:* Visa, Access
SPECIALITIES: National Collection of Penstemon. Also South African plants.   *MAP PAGE:* 5

WStI   St Ishmael's Nurseries, Haverfordwest, Pembrokeshire, SA62 3SX

TEL: (01646) 636343   *FAX:* (01646) 636343   *CONTACT:* Mr D & Mrs H Phippen
OPENING TIMES: 0900-1730 daily Summer. 0900-1700 daily Winter.
No mail order
CAT. COST: None issued   *W/SALE or RETAIL:* Retail   *CREDIT CARDS:* Visa, Diners, Access, Switch, Delta, MasterCard, EuroCard
SPECIALITIES: Wide general range.   *MAP PAGE:* 4

WSuF   Sunnybank Vine Nursery, Sunnybank, Pontrilas, Herefordshire, HR2 0BX

TEL: (01981) 240256   *CONTACT:* B R Edwards
OPENING TIMES: Mail Order only.
MIN. MAIL ORDER UK: £5.00 incl. p&p   *MIN. VALUE EC:* £5.00*   *EXPORT:* Yes
CAT. COST: Sae   *W/SALE or RETAIL:* Both   *CREDIT CARDS:* None
SPECIALITIES: Vines. *EC sales by arrangement.

WThi   39 Steps, Grove Cottage, Forge Hill, Lydbrook, Gloucestershire, GL17 9QS

TEL: (01594) 860544   *CONTACT:* Graham Birkin
OPENING TIMES: By appt. only.
No mail order
CAT. COST: 3 x 1st class   *W/SALE or RETAIL:* Retail   *CREDIT CARDS:* None
SPECIALITIES: Shade lovers, Helleborus & Iris.   *MAP PAGE:* 5

WTin   Tinpenny Plants, Tinpenny Farm, Fiddington, Tewkesbury, Glos, GL20 7BJ

TEL: (01684) 292668   *CONTACT:* Elaine Horton
OPENING TIMES: 1200-1700 Wed, or by appt.
No mail order
CAT. COST: 2 x 1st class   *W/SALE or RETAIL:* Retail   *CREDIT CARDS:* None
SPECIALITIES: Wide range of Hardy garden worthy plants esp. Helleborus, Iris & Sempervivum.
MAP PAGE: 5

WTre   Treasures of Tenbury Ltd, Burford House Gardens, Tenbury Wells, Worcestershire, WR15 8HQ

TEL: (01584) 810777   *FAX:* (01584) 810673   *E-MAIL:* treasures@burford.co.uk
CONTACT: Mrs P A Cox & Mr Charles Chesshire
◆   *OPENING TIMES:* 1000-1800 daily. Until dusk in Winter
MIN. MAIL ORDER UK: No minimum charge   *MIN. VALUE EC:* Nmc
CAT. COST: Free Clematis list   *W/SALE or RETAIL:* Retail   *CREDIT CARDS:* Visa, Access, Switch
SPECIALITIES: Clematis and Herbaceous, Conservatory plants, Bamboos, Trees & Shrubs.
MAP PAGE: 5

WTro   Troed-y-Rhiw Trees & Shrubs, Abercregan, Cymmer, Port Talbot, West Glamorgan, SA13 3LG

TEL: (01639) 850503   *CONTACT:* F A Latham
OPENING TIMES: By arrangement.
MIN. MAIL ORDER UK: £10.00 + p&p*   *MIN. VALUE EC:*
CAT. COST: 2 x 1st class   *W/SALE or RETAIL:* Both   *CREDIT CARDS:* none
SPECIALITIES: Hardy Trees & Shrubs. *Note: mail order to UK only.   *MAP PAGE:* 4

◆ **See also Display Advertisements**

WTus   Martin Tustin, Bowers Hill Nursery, Willersey Road, Badsey, Nr Evesham, Worcestershire, WR11 5HG

TEL: (01386) 832124 *FAX:* (01386) 832124 *CONTACT:* Martin Tustin
OPENING TIMES: 0900-1800 daily ex Xmas week.
No mail order
CAT. COST: 2 x 1st class *W/SALE or RETAIL:* Both *CREDIT CARDS:* None
SPECIALITIES: Lavenders. *MAP PAGE:* 5

WUnd   Under the Greenwood Tree, Shrub & Wildflower Nursery, Chapel Cottage, Vernolds Common, Craven Arms, Shropshire, SY7 9LP

TEL: (01584) 823396 *CONTACT:* David Stoves
OPENING TIMES: Mail order only.
MIN. MAIL ORDER UK: No minimum charge *MIN. VALUE EC:* Nmc
CAT. COST: 1 x 1st class *W/SALE or RETAIL:* Both *CREDIT CARDS:* None
SPECIALITIES: Complete British Flora excl. legally protected plants. Plants & seeds of known British origin. *MAP PAGE:* 5,7

WUnu   Unusual Plants, Mork Road, St Briavels, Lydney, Gloucestershire

◆
TEL: (01594) 530561 *CONTACT:* Norman D Heath
OPENING TIMES: 1100-dusk Sat, Sun & B/Hols. Evenings by arrangement.
No mail order
CAT. COST: None issued *W/SALE or RETAIL:* Retail *CREDIT CARDS:* none
SPECIALITIES: Hardy Perennials, Alpines and Rockery Plants. *MAP PAGE:* 5

WViv   Viv Marsh Postal Plants, PO Box 115, Shrewsbury DO, Shropshire, SY4 2WD

◆
TEL: (01939) 291475 *FAX:* (01939) 290743 *CONTACT:* Mr Viv Marsh
OPENING TIMES: Not open to public.
MIN. MAIL ORDER UK: £5.00 + p&p *MIN. VALUE EC:* £10.00 + p&p
CAT. COST: 5 x 1st class *W/SALE or RETAIL:* Retail *CREDIT CARDS:* Visa, Access, MasterCard, Switch
SPECIALITIES: Rare & routine Herbaceous Perennials.

WWal   The Walled Garden at Pigeonsford, Llangranog, Llandysul, Ceredigion, Wales, SA44 6AF

TEL: (01239) 654360 *FAX:* (01239) 654360 *CONTACT:* David & Hilary Pritchard
OPENING TIMES: 1000-1800 Easter-end Oct. Please phone first.
No mail order
CAT. COST: 4 x 1st class *W/SALE or RETAIL:* Retail *CREDIT CARDS:* None
SPECIALITIES: Good general range specialising in Herbaceous plants esp. Hardy Geranium & Primula. *MAP PAGE:* 4

WWat   Waterwheel Nursery, Bully Hole Bottom, Usk Road, Shirenewton, Chepstow, Monmouthshire, Wales, NP6 6SA

◆
TEL: (01291) 641577 *FAX:* (01291) 641851 *CONTACT:* Desmond & Charlotte Evans
OPENING TIMES: 0900-1800 Tue-Sat incl. Best to phone first for directions. Also open Bank Hol Mons.
No mail order
CAT. COST: 2 x 1st class *W/SALE or RETAIL:* Retail *CREDIT CARDS:* none
SPECIALITIES: Unusual & more common 'Gardenworthy' plants, esp. Shrubs. Also Trees, Climbers, Perennials, Grasses etc. Over 1500 in all. *MAP PAGE:* 5

WWeb   Webbs of Wychbold, Wychbold, Droitwich, Worcestershire, WR9 0DG

◆
TEL: (01527) 861777 *FAX:* (01527) 861284 *CONTACT:* David Smith/Oliver Spencer
OPENING TIMES: 0900-1800 Mon-Fri Winter. 0900-2000 Mon-Fri Summer. 0900-1800 Sat & 1030-1630 Sun all year.
No mail order
CAT. COST: None issued *W/SALE or RETAIL:* Both *CREDIT CARDS:* Visa, Access, AmEx
SPECIALITIES: Hardy Trees & Shrubs, Climbers, Conifers, Alpines, Heathers, Herbaceous, Herbs, Roses, Fruit & Aquatics. *MAP PAGE:* 5

Nursery ADDRESSES in BOLD do Mail Order to EU

WWes   Westonbirt Arboretum, (Forest Enterprise), Tetbury, Gloucestershire, GL8 8QS

 TEL: (01666) 880544 *FAX:* (01666) 880386 *CONTACT:* Glyn R Toplis
 OPENING TIMES: 1000-1800 daily Summer, 1000-1700 Winter.
 MIN. MAIL ORDER UK: No minimum charge* *MIN. VALUE EC:*
 CAT. COST: None issued. *W/SALE or RETAIL:* Retail *CREDIT CARDS:* Visa, Access
 SPECIALITIES: Trees & Shrubs, many choice & rare. *Note: mail order Nov-Mar only.
 MAP PAGE: 5

WWhi   Whimble Nursery, Kinnerton, Presteigne, Powys, LD8 2PD

 TEL: (01547) 560413 *FAX:* (01547) 560413 *CONTACT:* Liz Taylor
 OPENING TIMES: Noon-1800 Wed-Fri mid Apr-end Sep (closed Aug). Other times by appt.
 No mail order
 CAT. COST: 6 x 1st class* *W/SALE or RETAIL:* Retail *CREDIT CARDS:* None
 SPECIALITIES: Mainly Herbaceous, some unusual; small collections of Achillea, Campanula,
 Dianthus, Geranium, Penstemon, Viola. * Send SAE for plant list (no descriptions).
 MAP PAGE: 5

WWin   Wintergreen Nurseries, Bringsty Common, Worcestershire, WR6 5UJ

 TEL: (01886) 821858 eves. *CONTACT:* S Dodd
 OPENING TIMES: 1000-1730 Wed-Sun 1st Mar-31st Oct & by appt.
 MIN. MAIL ORDER UK: £30.00 + p&p *MIN. VALUE EC:* £30.00 + p&p
 CAT. COST: 2 x 2nd class *W/SALE or RETAIL:* Retail *CREDIT CARDS:* None
 SPECIALITIES: General, especially Alpines & Herbaceous. *MAP PAGE:* 5

WWol   Woolmans Plants Ltd, The Plant Centre, Knowle Hill, Evesham, Worcestershire, WR11 5EN

 TEL: 01386 833022 *FAX:* 01386 832915 *E-MAIL:* woolman@compuserve.com
 CONTACT: John Woolman
 OPENING TIMES: 0900-1700 Mon-Sun.
 MIN. MAIL ORDER UK: No minimum charge *MIN. VALUE EC:* Nmc
 CAT. COST: Free *W/SALE or RETAIL:* Both *CREDIT CARDS:* MasterCard, Visa, Switch
 SPECIALITIES: Chrysanthemum, Hanging Basket & Patio Plants, Dahlias. *MAP PAGE:* 5

WWoo   Woodlands Nurseries, Woodlands View, Blakemere, Herefordshire, HR2 9PY

 TEL: (01981) 500306 *FAX:* (01981) 500184 *CONTACT:* Larry & Mal Lowther
 OPENING TIMES: By appt. only.
 No mail order
 CAT. COST: 2 x 1st class *W/SALE or RETAIL:* Both *CREDIT CARDS:* None
 SPECIALITIES: Common & unusual herbaceous Perennials. Shrubs, Ferns & Trees.
 MAP PAGE: 5

WWye   Wye Valley Plants, The Nurtons, Tintern, Chepstow, Gwent, Wales, NP6 7NX

 TEL: (01291) 689253 *FAX:* (01291) 689909 *CONTACT:* Adrian & Elsa Wood
◆ *OPENING TIMES:* 1030-1700 Wed-Mon (closed Tues) 1st Mar-mid Oct. Other times by appt.
 No mail order
 CAT. COST: 3 x 1st class *W/SALE or RETAIL:* Retail *CREDIT CARDS:* None
 SPECIALITIES: Wide range of unusual Perennials, Aromatic and Medicinal Herbs, Salvia,
 Origanum, Grasses & Sedges. *MAP PAGE:* 5

XFro   Frosch Exclusive Perennials, Am Brunnen 14, Kirchheim, Germany, 85551

 TEL: (0049-89) 9043190 *FAX:* (0049-89) 9037683 *E-MAIL:* michael_weinert@t-online.de
 CONTACT: Michael Weinert
 OPENING TIMES: Mail order only. 0700-2200.
 MIN. MAIL ORDER UK: £120.00 + p&p *MIN. VALUE EC:* £120.00 + p&p *EXPORT:* Yes
 CAT. COST: None issued. *W/SALE or RETAIL:* Both *CREDIT CARDS:* none
 SPECIALITIES: Cypripedium hybrids.

◆ **See also Display Advertisements**

Additional Nursery Index

Please note that all these nurseries are listed in ascending order of their numeric Codes.
All nurseries are listed in alphabetical order of their name in the **Nursery-Code Index** on page 731.
Addresses printed in **bold type** provide a Mail Order Service to the EU.

1   Foliage Scented & Herb Plants, Walton Poor Cottage, Crocknorth Road, Ranmore Common, Dorking, Surrey, RH5 6SX

TEL: (01483) 282273   *FAX:* (01483) 282273   *CONTACT:* Mrs Prudence Calvert
OPENING TIMES: 1000-1700 Wed-Sun Apr-Sep & Bank Hols. 1000-1700 Thu & Fri or by appt. remainder of year.
No mail order
CAT. COST: 3 x 2nd class   *W/SALE or RETAIL:* Retail   *CREDIT CARDS:* None
SPECIALITIES: Herbs, aromatic & scented plants.   *MAP PAGE:* 3

2   Jasmine Cottage Gardens, 26 Channel Road, Walton St. Mary, Clevedon, Somerset, BS21 7BY

TEL: (01275) 871850   *E-MAIL:* baron@bologrew.demon.co.uk   *CONTACT:* Mr & Mrs M Redgrave
OPENING TIMES: Thurdays & daily by appt.
No mail order
CAT. COST: None issued   *W/SALE or RETAIL:* Retail   *CREDIT CARDS:* None
SPECIALITIES: Rhodochiton, Asarina, Isotoma. See also SEED Index.   *MAP PAGE:* 2

3   Ballagan Nursery, Gartocharn Road, Nr Balloch, Alexandria, Strathclyde, G83 8NB

TEL: (01389) 752947   *FAX:* (01389) 711288   *CONTACT:* Mr G Stephenson
OPENING TIMES: 0900-1800 daily.
No mail order
CAT. COST: None issued   *W/SALE or RETAIL:* Retail   *CREDIT CARDS:* Visa, Access, Switch
SPECIALITIES: Home grown bedding and general nursery stock.   *MAP PAGE:* 10

4   Clonmel Garden Centre, Glenconnor House, Clonmel, Co. Tipperary, Rep. of Ireland,

TEL: 00 353 (0)5223294   *FAX:* 00 353 (0)5229196   *CONTACT:* C E & T Hanna
OPENING TIMES: 0900-1800 Mon-Sat, 1200-1800 Sun & Public Hols.
No mail order
CAT. COST: *W/SALE or RETAIL:* Both   *CREDIT CARDS:* Visa, Access, MasterCard, Laser
SPECIALITIES: Wide range of plants incl. many less common varieties. The Garden Centre is situated in the grounds of a Georgian Country House with extensive gardens.   *MAP PAGE:* 11

7   Liscahane Nursery, Ardfert, Tralee, Co. Kerry, Rep. of Ireland,

TEL: 00 353 (0)6634222   *FAX:* 00 353 (0)6634600   *CONTACT:* Dan Nolan/Bill Cooley
♦   *OPENING TIMES:* 0900-1800 Tue-Sat & 1400-1800 Sun Summer. 0830-1300 & 1400-1730 Winter. Closed Mon.
No mail order
CAT. COST: None issued   *W/SALE or RETAIL:* Retail   *CREDIT CARDS:* Visa, Access
SPECIALITIES: Coastal shelter plants, Eucalyptus & Pines.   *MAP PAGE:* 11

9   Bretby Nurseries, Bretby Lane, Burton-on-Trent, Staffordshire, DE15 0QS

TEL: (01283) 703355   *FAX:* (01283) 704035   *CONTACT:* Mr David Cartwright
♦   *OPENING TIMES:* 0900-1700 Mon-Sat, 1030-1630 Sun.
No mail order
CAT. COST: Info. on request   *W/SALE or RETAIL:* Both   *CREDIT CARDS:* Visa, AmEx, Diners, EuroCard, Switch, Delta, Electron
SPECIALITIES: Wide range of shrubs.   *MAP PAGE:* 7

10   Kingfisher Nurseries, Catshill, Bromsgrove, Worcestershire, B61 0BW

TEL: (01527) 835084   *FAX:* (01527) 578070   *CONTACT:* Gary Booker
OPENING TIMES: 0900-1730 Mon-Sat, (0900-2000 Wed), 1000-1700 Sun all year.
No mail order
CAT. COST: None issued   *W/SALE or RETAIL:* Retail   *CREDIT CARDS:* Visa, Access, Switch
SPECIALITIES: Half-hardy Perennials for Patio gardening. Annual flowering plants.
MAP PAGE: 5

See note on Mail Order, EC sales & Export on page 11

14 **Seaside Nursery, Claddaghduff, Co. Galway, Rep. of Ireland,**
TEL: 00 353 (0)954 4687 *FAX:* 00 353 (0)954 4761 *CONTACT:* Charles Dyck
OPENING TIMES: 0900-1300 & 1400-1800 Mon-Sat, 1400-1800 Sun.
MIN. MAIL ORDER UK: No minimum charge *MIN. VALUE EC:* Nmc *EXPORT:* Yes
CAT. COST: £2.00 *W/SALE or RETAIL:* Both *CREDIT CARDS:* Visa, AmEx
SPECIALITIES: Plants & Hedging suitable for seaside locations. Rare plants originating from
Australia & New Zealand, esp Phormium, Astelia. *MAP PAGE:* **11**

19 **Denmans Garden, (John Brookes Ltd),** Clock House, Denmans, Fontwell, Nr Arundel,
West Sussex, BN18 0SU
TEL: (01243) 542808 *FAX:* (01243) 544064 *CONTACT:* John Brookes
OPENING TIMES: 0900-1700 daily 4th Mar-31st Oct.
No mail order
CAT. COST: £2.50 *W/SALE or RETAIL:* Retail *CREDIT CARDS:* Visa, MasterCard
SPECIALITIES: Rare and unusual plants. *MAP PAGE:* **3**

22 **Elly Hill Herbs,** Elly Hill House, Barmpton, Darlington, Co. Durham, DL1 3JF
TEL: (01325) 464682 *CONTACT:* Mrs Nina Pagan
OPENING TIMES: By appt. only
No mail order
CAT. COST: 50p + large Sae *W/SALE or RETAIL:* Retail *CREDIT CARDS:* None
SPECIALITIES: Herbs. *MAP PAGE:* **9**

24 **Woodborough Garden Centre,** Nursery Farm, Woodborough, Nr Pewsey, Wiltshire, SN9
5PF
TEL: (01672) 851249 *FAX:* (01672) 851249 *CONTACT:* Els M Brewin
OPENING TIMES: 0900-1700 Mon-Sat, 1100-1700 Sun.
No mail order
CAT. COST: None issued *W/SALE or RETAIL:* Retail *CREDIT CARDS:* Access, Diners,
EuroCard, MasterCard, Switch, Visa
SPECIALITIES: Wide range of Shrubs, Trees, Herbaceous, Alpines & Herbs. Large selection of
Climbers, esp. Clematis, & spring Bulbs. *MAP PAGE:* **2**

26 **The Flower Centre,** 754 Howth Road, Raheny, Dublin 5, Rep. of Ireland,
TEL: 00 353-1-8327047 *FAX:* 00 353-1-8327251 *CONTACT:* Eugene Higgins
OPENING TIMES: 1000-1300 & 1430-1800 Summer, 1000-1300 & 1430-1700 Winter daily. Mon-Sat
only Jan & Feb.
No mail order
CAT. COST: None issued *W/SALE or RETAIL:* Retail *CREDIT CARDS:* Access, MasterCard,
Switch, Visa
SPECIALITIES: Impatiens, Universal pansies, Fuchsia & hanging baskets. Pottery. *MAP PAGE:* **11**

27 **Chennels Gate Gardens & Nursery,** Eardisley, Herefordshire, HR3 6LJ
TEL: (01544) 327288 *CONTACT:* Mark Dawson
OPENING TIMES: 1000-1700 daily Mar-Dec.
No mail order
CAT. COST: None issued *W/SALE or RETAIL:* Retail *CREDIT CARDS:* None
SPECIALITIES: Interesting & unusual Cottage Garden plants; Hedging & Shrubs. *MAP PAGE:* **5**

28 **Linda Gascoigne Wild Flowers, 17 Imperial Road, Kibworth Beauchamp, Leicestershire,**
LE8 0HR
TEL: 0116 2793959 *CONTACT:* Linda Gascoigne
OPENING TIMES: By appt. only.
MIN. MAIL ORDER UK: £5.00 + p&p *MIN. VALUE EC:* £10.00 + p&p
CAT. COST: 3 x 1st class *W/SALE or RETAIL:* Retail *CREDIT CARDS:* None
SPECIALITIES: Wide range of attractive Wild Flowers & Wildlife plants. No peat used.
MAP PAGE: **7**

◆ **See also Display Advertisements**

30   Nanney's Bridge Nursery, Church Minshull, Nantwich, Cheshire, CW5 6DY
   TEL: (01270) 522239 *FAX:* (01270) 522523 *CONTACT:* D Dickinson
   OPENING TIMES: By appt. only.
   No mail order
   CAT. COST: 3 x 1st class *W/SALE or RETAIL:* Both *CREDIT CARDS:* None
   SPECIALITIES: Erysimums, Geraniums, Penstemons, Salvias & Ornamental Grasses.
   MAP PAGE: **7**

31   Cold Harbour Nursery, (Off.) 19 Hilary Road, Poole, Dorset, BH17 7LZ
   TEL: 01202 696875 evenings *CONTACT:* Steve Saunders
   OPENING TIMES: 1000-1730 Tues-Fri & most weekends 1st Mar-end Oct.
   MIN. MAIL ORDER UK: £10.00 + p&p* *MIN. VALUE EC:*
   CAT. COST: 3 x 2nd class *W/SALE or RETAIL:* Retail *CREDIT CARDS:* None
   SPECIALITIES: Unusual Herbaceous Perennials, incl. hardy Geraniums & Grasses. NOTE: Nursery
   at Bere Road, (opp. Silent Woman Inn), Wareham, Dorset (no postal address). *Note: mail order to
   UK only. *MAP PAGE:* **2**

32   Grange Farm Nursery, Guarlford, Malvern, Worcestershire, WR13 6NY
   TEL: (01684) 562544 *FAX:* (01684) 562544 *CONTACT:* Mrs C Nicholls
 ◆ *OPENING TIMES:* 0900-1730 daily Summer. 0900-1700 daily Winter. ex Xmas & 2 weeks in Jan.
   No mail order
   CAT. COST: Free pamphlet *W/SALE or RETAIL:* Retail *CREDIT CARDS:* Visa, Access, Switch
   SPECIALITIES: Wide general range of container grown hardy Shrubs, Trees, Conifers, Heathers,
   Alpines & Herbaceous. Shrub, climbing & bush Roses. *MAP PAGE:* **5**

33   Birchwood Farm Nursery, Portway, Coxbench, Derbyshire, DE21 5BE
   TEL: (01332) 880685 *CONTACT:* Mr & Mrs S Crooks
 ◆ *OPENING TIMES:* 0900-1700 Mon, Tue, Thu, Fri, Sat Mar-Oct or by appt.
   No mail order
   CAT. COST: None issued *W/SALE or RETAIL:* Retail *CREDIT CARDS:* None
   SPECIALITIES: Unusual Hardy Perennials & Shrubs. *MAP PAGE:* **7**

34   Bradley Nursery and Gardens, Sled Lane, Wylam, Northumberland, NE41 8JL
   TEL: (01661) 852176 *E-MAIL:* yp@dial.pipex.com *CONTACT:* Chris Potter
   OPENING TIMES: 0900-1700 daily (closed Tues) Mar-Oct.
   No mail order
   CAT. COST: None issued *W/SALE or RETAIL:* Retail *CREDIT CARDS:* MasterCard, Visa
   SPECIALITIES: Herbs & Cottage Garden plants, Herbaceous Perennials & Shrubs, Wild Flowers.
   MAP PAGE: **10**

36   Herterton House Garden Nursery, Hartington, Cambo, Morpeth, Northumberland, NE61
   4BN
   TEL: (01670) 774278 *CONTACT:* Mrs M Lawley & Mr Frank Lawley
   OPENING TIMES: 1330-1730 Mon Wed Fri-Sun 1st April-end Sep. (Earlier or later in the year
   weather permitting).
   No mail order
   CAT. COST: None issued *W/SALE or RETAIL:* Retail *CREDIT CARDS:* None
   SPECIALITIES: Achillea, Aquilegia, Geum, Polemonium. *MAP PAGE:* **10**

40   Layham Nurseries, Lower Road, Staple, Canterbury, Kent, CT3 1LH
   TEL: (01304) 611380 (off.), (01304) 813267 (gdn. centre) *FAX:* (01304) 615349
   CONTACT: L W Wessel
   OPENING TIMES: 0900-1700 Mon-Sat 0900-1700 Sun.
   MIN. MAIL ORDER UK: £10.00 + p&p *MIN. VALUE EC:* £25.00 + p&p
   CAT. COST: Free *W/SALE or RETAIL:* Both *CREDIT CARDS:* Visa, AmEx, Switch
   SPECIALITIES: Roses, Herbaceous, Shrubs, Trees, Conifers, Liners & Whips. Aquatic plants,
   Hedging plants. *MAP PAGE:* **3**

See note on Mail Order, EC sales & Export on page 11

41 Littlewood Farm Nursery, Cheddleton, Nr Leek, Staffordshire, ST13 7LB

TEL: (01538) 360478 *CONTACT:* Nanette Bloore
OPENING TIMES: 1000-1800 Tue-Sun & Bank Hols Apr-Oct
No mail order
CAT. COST: 3 x 1st class *W/SALE or RETAIL:* Retail *CREDIT CARDS:* None
SPECIALITIES: Unusual Hardy Herbaceous plants, incl. Hardy Geranium, Campanula, Hosta & Pulmonaria. Also Grasses & Alpines. *MAP PAGE:* 7

43 Marle Place Plants & Gardens, Marle Place, Brenchley, Nr Tonbridge, Kent, TN12 7HS

TEL: (01892) 722304 *FAX:* (01892) 724099 *CONTACT:* Mrs L M Williams
OPENING TIMES: Easter-end Oct. Gardens open 1000-1730.
MIN. MAIL ORDER UK: No minimum charge *MIN. VALUE EC:* Nmc
CAT. COST: 1 x 1st class *W/SALE or RETAIL:* Retail *CREDIT CARDS:* None
SPECIALITIES: Herbs, Wild Flowers, Aromatics, Santolina & Calamintha. *MAP PAGE:* 3

46 Cilwern Plants, Cilwern, Talley, Llandeilo, Dyfed, Wales, SA19 7YH

TEL: (01558) 685526 *CONTACT:* Anne Knatchbull-Hugessen
OPENING TIMES: 1100-1800 daily Apr-Sept, 1100-dusk daily Oct-Mar.
No mail order
CAT. COST: Sae for list *W/SALE or RETAIL:* Retail *CREDIT CARDS:* None
SPECIALITIES: Hardy Perennials esp. Geranium. *MAP PAGE:* 4

47 Sue Robinson, 21 Bederic Close, Bury St Edmunds, Suffolk, IP32 7DN

TEL: (01284) 764310 *FAX:* (01284) 764310 *CONTACT:* Sue Robinson
OPENING TIMES: By appt. only.
No mail order
CAT. COST: None issued *W/SALE or RETAIL:* Retail *CREDIT CARDS:* None
SPECIALITIES: Variegated & Foliage plants. Garden open. Lectures at Clubs & Societies, group bookings welcome.

53 The Priory, Kemerton, Tewkesbury, Gloucestershire, GL20 7JN

TEL: (01386) 725258 *FAX:* (01386) 725258 *CONTACT:* Mrs P Healing
OPENING TIMES: 1400-1900 Thurs afternoons.
No mail order
CAT. COST: None issued *W/SALE or RETAIL:* Retail *CREDIT CARDS:* Visa, Access, AmEx, Diners
SPECIALITIES: Daturas, Rare & unusual plants. *MAP PAGE:* 5

54 Bucknell Nurseries, Bucknell, Shropshire, SY7 0EL

TEL: (01547) 530606 *FAX:* (01547) 530699 *CONTACT:* A N Coull
OPENING TIMES: 0800-1700 Mon-Fri & 1000-1300 Sat.
No mail order
CAT. COST: Free *W/SALE or RETAIL:* Both *CREDIT CARDS:* None
SPECIALITIES: Bare rooted hedging Conifers & forest Trees. *MAP PAGE:* 5

56 Ryans Nurseries, Lissivigeen, Killarney, Co. Kerry, Rep. of Ireland,

TEL: 00 353 (0)6433507 *FAX:* 00 353 (0)6437520 *CONTACT:* Mr T Ryan
OPENING TIMES: 0900-1800 Mon-Sat 1400-1800 Sun.
No mail order
CAT. COST: None issued *W/SALE or RETAIL:* Retail *CREDIT CARDS:* Visa
SPECIALITIES: Camellia, Pieris, Azalea, Acacia, Eucalyptus, Dicksonia & many tender & rare plants. *MAP PAGE:* 11

60 Muckross Garden Centre, Muckross, Killarney, Co. Kerry, Rep. of Ireland,

TEL: 00 353 (0)6434044 *FAX:* 00 353 (0)6431114 *CONTACT:* John R Fuller B.Ag.Sc.(Hort.)
OPENING TIMES: 1000-1800 Tue-Sat & 1415-1800 Sun. Jan & Feb please check first.
MIN. MAIL ORDER UK: IR£20.00 + p&p *MIN. VALUE EC:* IR£20.00 + p&p
CAT. COST: Please enquire *W/SALE or RETAIL:* Retail *CREDIT CARDS:* Visa, Access
SPECIALITIES: Many rare & unusual plants. Azalea, Hydrangea, Rhododendron & Camellia
MAP PAGE: 11

Additional Nursery Index

◆ **See also Display Advertisements**

61   Wards Nurseries (Sarratt) Ltd, Dawes Lane, Sarratt, Nr Rickmansworth, Hertfordshire, WD3 6BQ

TEL: (01923) 263237 *FAX:* (01923) 270930 *CONTACT:* M F Rawlins
OPENING TIMES: 0800-1700 Mon-Sat, 1030-1630 Summer Suns, 1000-1600 Winter Suns.
No mail order
CAT. COST: Sae* *W/SALE or RETAIL:* Both *CREDIT CARDS:* Visa, Access, AmEx
SPECIALITIES: Shrubs & Climbers, fragrant & aromatic plants. *State interest when asking for lists.
MAP PAGE: **6**

63   Kayes Garden Nursery, 1700 Melton Road, Rearsby, Leicestershire, LE7 4YR

TEL: (01664) 424578 *CONTACT:* Hazel Kaye
OPENING TIMES: 1000-1700 Tues-Sat & Bank Hols 1000-1200 Sun Mar-Oct. 1000-1600 Fri & Sat
Nov, Dec & Feb. Closed Jan.
No mail order
CAT. COST: 2 x 1st class *W/SALE or RETAIL:* Retail *CREDIT CARDS:* None
SPECIALITIES: Herbaceous, Climbers & Aquatic plants. *MAP PAGE:* **7**

73   Newton Hill Alpines, 335 Leeds Road, Newton Hill, Wakefield, Yorkshire, WF1 2JH

TEL: (01924) 377056 *CONTACT:* Sheena Vigors
OPENING TIMES: 0900-1700 Fri-Wed all year. Closed Thur. Please phone first.
No mail order
CAT. COST: 2 x 1st class *W/SALE or RETAIL:* Both *CREDIT CARDS:* None
SPECIALITIES: Alpines, esp. Saxifraga, also Erica, Conifers & dwarf Shrubs. *MAP PAGE:* **9**

77   The Old Mill Herbary, Helland Bridge, Bodmin, Cornwall, PL30 4QR

TEL: (01208) 841206 *FAX:* (01208) 841206 *CONTACT:* Mrs B Whurr
OPENING TIMES: 1000-1700 Thurs-Tues Apr-30th Sept.
No mail order
CAT. COST: 6 x 1st class *W/SALE or RETAIL:* Retail *CREDIT CARDS:* None
SPECIALITIES: Culinary, Medicinal & Aromatic Herbs, Shrubs, Climbing & Herbaceous plants.
MAP PAGE: **1**

84   Crocknafeola Nursery, Killybegs, Co. Donegal, Rep. of Ireland,

TEL: 00 353 (0)73 51018 *FAX:* 00 353 (0)73 51018 *CONTACT:* Andy McKenna
OPENING TIMES: 0900-2000 Mon-Sat & 1200-1800 Sun in Summer, until dusk in Winter; closed
Dec-Feb.
No mail order
CAT. COST: None issued *W/SALE or RETAIL:* Retail *CREDIT CARDS:* None
SPECIALITIES: Hardy Shrubs, Trees & Hedging suitable for exposed areas. *MAP PAGE:* **11**

99   Earlstone Nursery, Earlstone Manor Farm, Burghclere, Newbury, Berkshire, RG15 9NG

TEL: (01635) 278648 *FAX:* (01635) 278672 *E-MAIL:* ginsberg@dial.pipex.com
CONTACT: B C Ginsberg
OPENING TIMES: By appt.
MIN. MAIL ORDER UK: £30.00 + p&p* *MIN. VALUE EC:*
CAT. COST: Free *W/SALE or RETAIL:* Both *CREDIT CARDS:* None
SPECIALITIES: Buxus sempervirens. *Note: UK export only. *MAP PAGE:* **2**

100 Newington Nurseries, Newington, Wallingford, Oxfordshire, OX10 7AW

TEL: (01865) 400533 *FAX:* (01865) 891766 *E-MAIL:* newington.nurseries@btinternet.com
CONTACT: Mrs A T Hendry
OPENING TIMES: 1000-1700 Tues-Sun Mar-Oct, 1000-1600 Tues-Sun Nov-Feb.
MIN. MAIL ORDER UK: * *MIN. VALUE EC:*
CAT. COST: 4 x 1st class *W/SALE or RETAIL:* Retail *CREDIT CARDS:* Access, MasterCard,
Visa, Switch
SPECIALITIES: Unusual cottage garden plants, old-fashioned Roses, Conservatory Plants & Herbs.
*Note: mail order to UK only. *MAP PAGE:* **5**

See note on Mail Order, EC sales & Export on page 11

102 S & N Brackley, 117 Winslow Road, Wingrave, Aylesbury, Buckinghamshire, HP22 4QB

TEL: (01296) 681384 *CONTACT:* Mrs S Brackley/Mrs K Earwicker
OPENING TIMES: Please phone for appt.
MIN. MAIL ORDER UK: No minimum charge* *MIN. VALUE EC:* Nmc *EXPORT:* Yes
CAT. COST: 1st class Sae. *W/SALE or RETAIL:* Both *CREDIT CARDS:* MasterCard, Visa
SPECIALITIES: Sweet Pea Plants (for collection only). *Note: Onion & Leek Plants by mail order.
Seeds only by mail to EC. See also Seed Supplier Index. *MAP PAGE:* **5/6**

104 Eggesford Gardens, Eggesford, Chulmleigh, Devon, EX18 7QU

TEL: (01769) 580250 *FAX:* (01769) 581041 *CONTACT:* Jonathon Parish
OPENING TIMES: 0900-1800 every day exc. Christmas, Boxing & N.Year's Day. Boxing Day.
MIN. MAIL ORDER UK: £15.00 + p&p *MIN. VALUE EC:* £20.00 + p&p
CAT. COST: £3.00 in stamps *W/SALE or RETAIL:* Retail *CREDIT CARDS:* MasterCard, Visa,
Switch, Delta
SPECIALITIES: Wide General Range. Strong in Shrubs, Herbaceous, Roses, Clematis & Ivy.
MAP PAGE: **1**

107 MapleAsh Plants, Ashcombe Cottage, Ranmore Common, Dorking, Surrey, RH5 6SP

TEL: (01306) 881599 *CONTACT:* Beryl Davis
OPENING TIMES: Open most days but by appt. only. Also ring for directions.
No mail order
CAT. COST: None issued *W/SALE or RETAIL:* Retail *CREDIT CARDS:* None
SPECIALITIES: Less usual Hardy Perennials. Garden open to visitors & groups. *MAP PAGE:* **3**

113 Springfield Herb Nursery, 21 Queenside Close, Ipswich, Suffolk, IP1 4JZ

TEL: (01473) 463604 *CONTACT:* Mr M Perry
OPENING TIMES: Mail order only.
MIN. MAIL ORDER UK: No minimum charge *MIN. VALUE EC:* £25.00 + p&p
CAT. COST: Free *W/SALE or RETAIL:* Retail *CREDIT CARDS:* none
SPECIALITIES: Herbs, including wide range of Mints, Scented Pelargoniums & Thymes.
MAP PAGE: **6**

**114 Really Wild Flowers, H V Horticulture Ltd, The Shop, The Street, Sutton Waldron,
Blandford Forum, Dorset, DT11 8NZ**

TEL: (01747) 811778 *FAX:* (01747) 811499 *CONTACT:* Grahame Dixie
OPENING TIMES: Not open to public.
MIN. MAIL ORDER UK: £40.00 + p&p *MIN. VALUE EC:* £100.00 + p&p *EXPORT:* Yes
CAT. COST: 3 x 1st class *W/SALE or RETAIL:* Both *CREDIT CARDS:* none
SPECIALITIES: Wild flowers for Grasslands, Woodlands, Wetlands & Heaths.

115 Dave Spencer Dahlias, Field View, High Road, Fobbing, Essex, SS17 9HG

TEL: (01268) 558260 *CONTACT:* Dave Spencer
OPENING TIMES:
MIN. MAIL ORDER UK: £9.00 + p&p* *MIN. VALUE EC:*
CAT. COST: 1 x 1st class *W/SALE or RETAIL:* Retail *CREDIT CARDS:* None
SPECIALITIES: Dahlias. *Note: mail order to UK only. *MAP PAGE:* **3/6**

116 Betwys-Y-Coed Garden Nursery, Betwys-Y-Coed, Conwy, Wales,

TEL: (01690) 760395 *CONTACT:* John Thompson
OPENING TIMES: New nursery opening Apr 98. 1000-1700 Mon-Sat, 1000-1600 Sun.
No mail order
CAT. COST: None issued. *W/SALE or RETAIL:* Retail *CREDIT CARDS:* none
SPECIALITIES: Grasses, Perennials & some unusual hardy plants. *MAP PAGE:* **4**

117 The Water Gardens, Highcroft, Moorend, Wembworthy, Chulmleigh, Devon, EX18 7SG

TEL: (01837) 83566 *CONTACT:* J M Smith
OPENING TIMES: Garden open to the public 1000-1700 Fri, Sun & Mon incl. B/Hols April-Sept.
MIN. MAIL ORDER UK: *MIN. VALUE EC:*
CAT. COST: None issued *W/SALE or RETAIL:* Retail *CREDIT CARDS:* None
SPECIALITIES: Water/Bog/Perennials/Ferns for sale in the Garden. Entrance fee £2.00. (Nursery
closed.) *MAP PAGE:* **1**

♦ **See also Display Advertisements**

118 Balmer Grove Plants, Welshampton, Shropshire, SY12 0PP

TEL: (01948) 710403   *CONTACT:* Nick & Gill Eleftheriou
OPENING TIMES: 0930-1800 most days Mar-Oct, please phone to check times.
No mail order
CAT. COST: None issued   *W/SALE or RETAIL:* Retail   *CREDIT CARDS:* none
SPECIALITIES: Selected unusual hardy garden plants, mainly herbaceous perennials, all carefully home grown in loam-based compost.   *MAP PAGE:* **7**

119 Blacksmiths Cottage Nursery, Langmere Green Road, Langmere, Diss, Norfolk, IP21 4QA

TEL: (01379) 740982, Tel/Fax 741917 (nursery)   *FAX:* (01379) 741917   *CONTACT:* Ben Potterton
OPENING TIMES: 1000-1700 Fri-Sun all year, or by appt.
No mail order
CAT. COST: 2 x 1st class   *W/SALE or RETAIL:* Retail   *CREDIT CARDS:* none
SPECIALITIES: Hardy Geranium, Iris, Salvia & large selection of unusual herbaceous plants.
MAP PAGE: **6/8**

120 Plantiecrub Growers Ltd, Gott, Shetland, ZE2 9SH

TEL: (01595) 840600   *FAX:* (01595) 840600   *CONTACT:* Olaf Isbister
OPENING TIMES: 0830-1700
MIN. MAIL ORDER UK: No minimum charge   *MIN. VALUE EC:* Nmc
CAT. COST: 1 x 1st class   *W/SALE or RETAIL:* Both   *CREDIT CARDS:* none
SPECIALITIES: Bedding, Perennials, Basket & Patio Plants, Indoor Plants, Glasshouse Fruits & Salads.

121 Rosemary's Farmhouse Nursery, Llwyn-y-moel-gau, Llanfihangel, Llanfyllin, Powys, SY22 5JE

TEL: (01691) 648196   *FAX:* (01691) 648196   *CONTACT:* Rosemary Pryce
OPENING TIMES: 1000-1700 most days all year, but advisable to telephone to confirm.
No mail order
CAT. COST: None issued.   *W/SALE or RETAIL:* Retail   *CREDIT CARDS:* none
SPECIALITIES: Fuchsia paniculata, unusual Perennials & Cottage plants, Grasses & Herbs.
MAP PAGE: **4**

122 Hanging Gardens Nurseries Ltd, (Off.) 15 Further Meadow, Writtle, Chelmsford, Essex, CM1 3LE

TEL: (01245) 421020   *FAX:* (01245) 422293   *CONTACT:* Jim Drake & Louisa Drake
OPENING TIMES: 0900-1800 daily Apr-Nov, 0900-1700 daily Dec-Mar.
No mail order
CAT. COST: None issued   *W/SALE or RETAIL:* Retail   *CREDIT CARDS:* Access, AmEx, Delta, EuroCard, MasterCard, Switch, Visa
SPECIALITIES: Clematis, David Austin Roses, Basket & Patio plants, excellent range of hardy nursery stock. *Note: Nursery is at Ongar Road West, (A414) Writtle By Pass, Writtle, Chelmsford.
MAP PAGE: **6**

123 Oscroft's Dahlias, Woodside, Warwick Road, Chadwick End, Nr Solihull, West Midlands, B93 0BP

TEL: (01564) 782450   *CONTACT:* June & Fred Oscroft
OPENING TIMES: 0900-1700 daily.
MIN. MAIL ORDER UK: 6 plants or 2 tubers.   *MIN. VALUE EC:* Tubers only, Nmc.
CAT. COST: 1 x 1st class   *W/SALE or RETAIL:* Both   *CREDIT CARDS:* none
SPECIALITIES: Dahlias. Note: second nursery at Sprotborough Road, Doncaster, S.Yorks, DN5 8BE. Tel (01302) 785026.   *MAP PAGE:* **5**

125 Tartan Hill Nursery, Legerwood, Earlston, Berwickshire, Scotland, TD4 6AS

TEL: (01896) 849 354   *CONTACT:* Geoff Phillips
OPENING TIMES: 0830-1700 Wed-Sat Mar-Nov. Other times welcome by appt.
No mail order
CAT. COST: 1 x 2nd class   *W/SALE or RETAIL:* Both   *CREDIT CARDS:* none
SPECIALITIES: Hardy Climbers, Ornamental & Native Shrubs.   *MAP PAGE:* **10**

See note on Mail Order, EC sales & Export on page 11

126 Fen Lane Nursery, Fen Lane, Grainthorpe, Louth, Lincs, LN11 7JY

TEL: (01472) 388883, (01472) 388722 *CONTACT:* R Panter
OPENING TIMES: 1000-1700 Mon-Sat, 1000-1600 Sun all year exc. Christmas-New Year week.
MIN. MAIL ORDER UK: £20.00 + p&p *MIN. VALUE EC:* £20.00 + p&p
CAT. COST: 3 x 1st class *W/SALE or RETAIL:* Both *CREDIT CARDS:* none
SPECIALITIES: Hardy Geranium & Herbaceous Perennials, esp. old fashioned varieties.
MAP PAGE: **9**

127 Loch Leven Plants, The Grange, Leslie Road, Scotlandwell, Kinross, Scotland, KY13 7JE

TEL: (01592) 840220, (01592) 840220 *FAX:* (01592) 840220 *CONTACT:* Sandy or Sharon Fraser
OPENING TIMES: 1000-1600 Sun Jul-end Sep. Other times by appt.
No mail order
CAT. COST: None issued *W/SALE or RETAIL:* Retail *CREDIT CARDS:* none
SPECIALITIES: Southern hemisphere Shrubs & Climbers, Bamboos & Grasses, select range of
Perennials. *MAP PAGE:* **10**

128 Rotherview Nursery, Ivy House Lane, Three Oaks, Hastings, East Sussex, TN35 4NP

TEL: (01424) 717141 *FAX:* (01424) 428944 *CONTACT:* Ray Bates
OPENING TIMES: 1000-1700 daily Mar-Oct, 1000-1530 daily Nov-Feb.
MIN. MAIL ORDER UK: £10.00 + p&p *MIN. VALUE EC:* £20.00 + p&p
CAT. COST: 2 x 1st class *W/SALE or RETAIL:* Both *CREDIT CARDS:* none
SPECIALITIES: Alpines. *MAP PAGE:* **3**

129 Olde Walls Plants, Olde Walls, Fore Street, Grampound, Nr Truro, Cornwall, TR2 4SE

TEL: (01726) 883744 *FAX:* (01726) 883744 *E-MAIL:* dan.jacomb@virgin.net
CONTACT: Dudley Jaconib
OPENING TIMES: By appt.
MIN. MAIL ORDER UK: £10.00 + p&p *MIN. VALUE EC:* £25.00 + p&p *EXPORT:* Yes
CAT. COST: 1 x 1st class *W/SALE or RETAIL:* Both *CREDIT CARDS:* none
SPECIALITIES: Perennials, Palms - Ferns.

130 Aultan Nursery, Newton of Cairnhill, Cuminestown, Turriff, Aberdeenshire, Scotland,
AB53 5TN

TEL: (01888) 544702 *FAX:* (01888) 544702 *E-MAIL:* rlking@globalnet.co.uk
CONTACT: Richard King
OPENING TIMES: 1100-1600 Mon, 1330-1800 Sat, 1000-1800 Sun, Apr-Oct. Other times please
phone first.
No mail order
CAT. COST: 2 x 1st class *W/SALE or RETAIL:* Retail *CREDIT CARDS:* None
SPECIALITIES: Herbaceous Perennials & Shrubs, mostly grown in peat-free composts. A very wide
range including many unusual items. *MAP PAGE:* **10**

◆ **See also Display Advertisements**

Seed Suppliers

Agroforestry Research Trust, 46 Hunters Moon, Dartington, Totnes, Devon, TQ9 6JT
TEL: E-MAIL: agrorestr@aol.com *CONTACT:* Martin Crawford *CAT. COST:* 3 x 1st class
MIN. ORDER: No minimum charge *CREDIT CARDS:* None
SPECIALITIES: Trees, Shrubs & Perennials. See also in Nursery Index under Code 'CAgr'.

Allwood Bros, Hassocks, West Sussex, BN6 9NB
TEL: (01273) 844229 *FAX:* (01273) 846022 *CONTACT:* Sue James *CAT. COST:* 2 x 1st class
MIN. ORDER: No minimum charge *CREDIT CARDS:* MasterCard, Visa, Switch
SPECIALITIES: Carnations, Pinks & Dianthus. See also in Nursery Index under Code 'SAll'.

Ashwood Nurseries, Greensforge, Kingswinford, West Midlands, DY6 0AE
TEL: (01384) 401996 *FAX:* (01384) 401108 *CONTACT:* John Massey & Philip Baulk
CAT. COST: 4 x 1st class
MIN. ORDER: No minimum charge *CREDIT CARDS:* Visa, Access
SPECIALITIES: Lewisias, Cyclamen, Hellebores & Auriculas. See also in Nursery Index under Code 'MAsh'.

B & T World Seeds, Paguignan, 34210 Olonzac, France
TEL: 33 0468912963 *FAX:* 33 0468913039 *E-MAIL:* ralph@b-and-t-world-seeds.com
WEB SITE: http://www.b-and-t-world-seeds.com *CONTACT:* Lesley Sleigh & Ralph Wheatley
CAT. COST: £10 Europe, £14 elsewhere.
MIN. ORDER: £5.00 *CREDIT CARDS:* Visa, Access
SPECIALITIES: Master list contains over 37,000 items. 187 Sub-lists available. Lists to specification.

Bees of Chester, Freepost 980, Scaland Road, Chester, CH1 6ZT
TEL: (01945) 466660 *FAX:* (01945) 475255 *CONTACT:* Customer Services *CAT. COST:* Free
MIN. ORDER: No minimum charge* *CREDIT CARDS:* Access, Visa
SPECIALITIES: Spring Flowering Bulbs & Perennial Plants. *Note: mail order to UK only.

Blackmore & Langdon Ltd, Pensford, Bristol, Avon, BS39 4JL
TEL: (01275) 332300 *FAX:* (01275) 332300 *CONTACT:* J S Langdon *CAT. COST:* 1 x 1st class
MIN. ORDER: No minimum charge *CREDIT CARDS:* None
SPECIALITIES: Delphinium, Begonia. See also in Nursery Index under Code 'CBla'.

S & N Brackley, 117 Winslow Road, Wingrave, Aylesbury, Buckinghamshire, HP22 4QB
TEL: (01296) 681384 *CONTACT:* S Brackley & K Earwicker *CAT. COST:* 1st class Sae
MIN. ORDER: No minimum charge *CREDIT CARDS:* MasterCard, Visa
SPECIALITIES: Wholesale & Retail suppliers of Gold Medal Sweet Peas & Exhibition Vegetables. Seeds & plants. See also in Additional Nursery Index under Code 102.

Bush Green Cottage Nursery, Foxfield Road, Broughton-in-Furness, Cumbria, LA20 6BY
TEL: (01229) 716724 *CONTACT:* Jim Haunch *CAT. COST:* 2 x 2nd class
MIN. ORDER: No minimum charge *CREDIT CARDS:* None
SPECIALITIES: Hardy Geraniums and Perennials. See also in Nursery Index under Code 'NBus'.

Carters Seeds, Hele Road, Torquay, Devon, TQ2 7QJ
TEL: (01803) 616156 *FAX:* (01803) 615747 *CONTACT:* Customer Services *CAT. COST:* n/a
MIN. ORDER: CREDIT CARDS: None
SPECIALITIES: General range available from retail stockists.

Chadwell Seeds, 81 Parlaunt Road, Slough, Berkshire, SL3 8BE
TEL: (01753) 542823 *CONTACT:* Chris Chadwell *CAT. COST:* 3 x 2nd class
MIN. ORDER: No minimum charge *CREDIT CARDS:* none
SPECIALITIES: Seed collecting expedition to the Himalaya. Separate general Seed list of Japanese, N. America & Himalayan plants.

Chase Organics (GB) Ltd, Riverdene Estate, Molesey RoadAddlestone, Hersham, Surrey, KT12 4RG

TEL: (01932) 253666 *FAX:* (01932) 252707 *CONTACT:* M Hedges *CAT. COST:* Free
MIN. ORDER: 80p p&p under £14.00 *CREDIT CARDS:* Visa, Access, Switch
SPECIALITIES: 'The Organic Gardening Catalogue' offers Vegetable, Herb & Flower seeds & garden sundries especially for Organic gardeners.

Cheshire Herbs, Fourfields, Forest Road, Little Budworth, Cheshire, CW6 9ES

TEL: (01829) 760578 *FAX:* (01829) 760354 *CONTACT:* Mr & Mrs Ted Riddell
CAT. COST: 1 x 1st class
MIN. ORDER: No minimum charge *CREDIT CARDS:* Access, Visa, Switch
♦ SPECIALITIES: Herbs. See also in Nursery Index under Code 'MChe'.

Chiltern Seeds, Bortree Stile, Ulverston, Cumbria, LA12 7PB

TEL: (01229) 581137 *FAX:* (01229) 584549 *E-MAIL:* 101344.1340@compuserve.com *CONTACT:*
CAT. COST: 3 x 2nd class
MIN. ORDER: No minimum charge *CREDIT CARDS:* Visa, Access, AmEx, Switch, MasterCard, EuroCard
♦ SPECIALITIES: Almost 4,500 items of all kinds - Wild Flowers, Trees, Shrubs, Cacti, Annuals, Houseplants, Vegetables & Herbs.

Coombland Gardens, Coombland, Coneyhurst, Billingshurst, West Sussex, RH14 9DG

TEL: (01403) 741727 *FAX:* (01403) 741079 *CONTACT:* David Browne *CAT. COST:* £1.00
MIN. ORDER: £10.00 incl. p&p *CREDIT CARDS:* None
SPECIALITIES: Extensive list. See also in Code Nursery Index under 'SCou'.

The Cottage Herbary, Mill House, Boraston, Nr Tenbury Wells, Worcestershire, WR15 8LZ

TEL: (01584) 781575 *FAX:* (01584) 781483 *CONTACT:* K & R Hurst *CAT. COST:* List free
MIN. ORDER: No minimum charge *CREDIT CARDS:* None
SPECIALITIES: Herbs. See also in Nursery Index under Code 'WCHb'.

Craven's Nursery, 1 Foulds Terrace, Bingley, West Yorkshire, BD16 4LZ

TEL: (01274) 561412, (01274) 561412 *FAX:* (01274) 561412 *CONTACT:* S R & M Craven
CAT. COST: 4 x 1st class
MIN. ORDER: £5.00 *CREDIT CARDS:* None
SPECIALITIES: Seeds of Show Auriculas, Primulas, Pinks & Alpines. See also in Nursery Index under Code 'NCra'.

CTDA, 174 Cambridge Street, London, SW1V 4QE

TEL: (0171) 976 5115 *CONTACT:* Basil Smith *CAT. COST:* Free
MIN. ORDER: No minimum charge *CREDIT CARDS:* None
SPECIALITIES: Hardy Cyclamen & Hellebores. See also in Nursery Index under Code 'LCTD'.

Samuel Dobie & Sons, Broomhill Way, Torquay, Devon, TQ2 7QW

TEL: (01803) 616281 *FAX:* (01803) 615150 *CONTACT:* Customer Services *CAT. COST:* Free
MIN. ORDER: No minimum charge *CREDIT CARDS:* Visa, MasterCard
SPECIALITIES: Wide selection of popular Flower & Vegetable seeds. Also includes young Plants, summer flowering Bulbs & garden sundries.

Jack Drake, Inshriach Alpine Nursery, Aviemore, Invernesshire, Scotland, PH22 1QS

TEL: (01540) 651287 *FAX:* (01540) 651656 *CONTACT:* J C Lawson *CAT. COST:* £1.00
MIN. ORDER: No minimum charge *CREDIT CARDS:* None
SPECIALITIES: Rare & unusual Alpines & Rock Plants especially Primulas, Gentians & many others. See also in Nursery Index under Code 'GDra'.

John Drake, Hardwicke House, Fen Ditton, Cambridgeshire, CB5 8TF

TEL: (01223) 292246 *FAX:* (01223) 292246 *CONTACT:* John Drake *CAT. COST:* 70p*
MIN. ORDER: £12.50 *CREDIT CARDS:* None
SPECIALITIES: Aquilegia. *Note: Seed Catalogue available Aug.

♦ **See also Display Advertisements**

Elm House Nursery, Freepost, PO Box 25, Wisbech, Cambridgeshire, PE13 2BR
TEL: (01945) 581511 *FAX:* (01945) 588235 *CONTACT:* Customer Services *CAT. COST:* Free
MIN. ORDER: No minimum charge* *CREDIT CARDS:* Access, Visa
SPECIALITIES: Chrysanthemums & cutting raised plants. *Note: mail order to UK only.

Elm Tree Nursery, Court Farm, Sidbury, Sidmouth, Devon, EX10 0QG
TEL: (01395) 597790 *FAX:* (01395) 597790 *CONTACT:* M Saunders *CAT. COST:* 1 x 2nd class
MIN. ORDER: £4.50 + p&p* *CREDIT CARDS:* none
SPECIALITIES: Cyclamen species. See also in Nursery Index under Code 'CElm'. *Note: mail order to UK only.

Field House Nurseries, Leake Road, Gotham, Nottinghamshire, NG11 0JN
TEL: (0115) 9830278 *CONTACT:* Doug Lochhead & Valerie A Woolley
CAT. COST: 4 x 1st or 4 x IRCs
MIN. ORDER: 4 packets *CREDIT CARDS:* Visa, Access
SPECIALITIES: Primulas & Auriculas. See also in Nursery Index under Code 'MFie'.

Mr Fothergill's Seeds Ltd, Gazeley Road, Kentford, Newmarket, Suffolk, CB8 7QB
TEL: (01638) 751887 *FAX:* (01638) 751624 *WEB SITE:* http://www.oxalis.co.uk/bgol.html
CONTACT: Mail Order Dept. *CAT. COST:* Free
MIN. ORDER: No minimum charge *CREDIT CARDS:* Visa, Access, MasterCard, Switch
SPECIALITIES: Annuals, Biennials, Perennials, Herbs, Vegetables, plusPlants, Potatoes, Onion sets, soft Fruit and Garden Sundries. Overseas orders on application.

Glenhirst Cactus Nursery, Station Road, Swineshead, Nr Boston, Lincolnshire, PE20 3NX
TEL: (01205) 820314 *FAX:* (01205) 820614 *E-MAIL:* glenhirstcacti@lineone.com
WEB SITE: http://website.lineone.net/~glenhirstcacti *CONTACT:* N C & S A Bell
CAT. COST: 2 x 1st class
MIN. ORDER: No minimum charge *CREDIT CARDS:* none
SPECIALITIES: Extensive range of Cacti & Succulent seeds. Mail order all year. See also under Cactus & Succulent Specialists Index.

Elisabeth Goodwin Nurseries, Elm Tree Farm, 1 Beeches Road, West Row, Bury St. Edmunds, Suffolk, IP28 8NP
TEL: (01638) 713050 *CONTACT:* Elisabeth Goodwin *CAT. COST:* 50p coin/2x1st class
MIN. ORDER: No minimum charge *CREDIT CARDS:* None
SPECIALITIES: Drought tolerant plants. Seedlist includes cultivation instructions. Over 60 varieties stocked. See also in Nursery Index under Code 'EGoo'.

Peter Grayson (Sweet Pea Seedsman), 34 Glenthorne Close, Brampton, Chesterfield, Derbyshire, S40 3AR
TEL: (01246) 278503 *FAX:* (01246) 566918 *E-MAIL:* matthewfry@cableinet.co.uk
CONTACT: Peter Grayson *CAT. COST:* A5 Sae (20p stamp)
MIN. ORDER: No minimum charge *CREDIT CARDS:* None
SPECIALITIES: Lathyrus species & cultivars. World's largest collection of Old-Fashioned Sweet Peas.

Harvest Nurseries, Harvest Cottage, Boonshill Farm, Iden, Rye, E Sussex, TN31 7QA
TEL: (0181) 325 5420 *CONTACT:* D A Smith *CAT. COST:* 2 x 1st class
MIN. ORDER: No minimum charge *CREDIT CARDS:* None
SPECIALITIES: Epiphyllums & wide range of Succulents. Descriptive catalogue. See also under Cactus & Succulent Specialists Index.

James Henderson & Sons, Kingholm Quay, Dumfries, DG1 4SU
TEL: (01387) 252234 *FAX:* (01387) 262302 *CONTACT:* J H & R J Henderson
CAT. COST: 1 x 1st class Sae
MIN. ORDER: 3kgs *CREDIT CARDS:* None
♦ SPECIALITIES: Over 40 varieties of Scottish Seed Potatoes.

Henllys Lodge Plants, Henllys Lodge, Beaumaris, Anglesey, Gwynedd, Wales, LL58 8HU
TEL: (01248) 810106 *CONTACT:* Mrs E Lane *CAT. COST:* 2 x 2nd class
MIN. ORDER: No minimum charge *CREDIT CARDS:* none
SPECIALITIES: Small range of hardy Perennials, esp. hardy Geraniums. See also in Nursery Index under Code 'WHen'.

Holly Gate Cactus Nursery, Billingshurst Road, Ashington, West Sussex, RH20 3BA
TEL: (01903) 892 930 *WEB SITE:* http://www.yell.co.uk/sites/cactushg/ *CONTACT:* Mr T M Hewitt
CAT. COST: 2 x 1st class
MIN. ORDER: £2.00 + p&p *CREDIT CARDS:* None
SPECIALITIES: Cactus & Succulents.

Diana Hull, Fog Cottages, 178 Lower Street, Hillmorton, Rugby, Warwickshire, CV21 4NX
TEL: (01788) 536574 after 1600 *CONTACT:* Diana Hull *CAT. COST:* Sae or IRC for list
MIN. ORDER: No minimum charge *CREDIT CARDS:* None
SPECIALITIES: Pelargonium species. See also in Nursery Index under Code 'MHul'.

Iden Croft Herbs, Frittenden Road, Staplehurst, Kent, TH12 0DN
TEL: (01580) 891432 *FAX:* (01580) 892416 *E-MAIL:* idencroft.herbs@dial.pipex.com
CONTACT: Rosemary & D Titterington *CAT. COST:* A4 Sae for list
MIN. ORDER: No minimum charge *CREDIT CARDS:* Visa, Access, AmEx, Delta, JCB, EuroCard, Switch
♦ SPECIALITIES: Herbs - aromatic, wildflower, for bees/butterflies & hardy herbaceous. See also in Nursery Index under Code 'SIde'.

W E Th. Ingwersen Ltd, Birch Farm Nursery, Gravetye, E. Grinstead, West Sussex, RH19 4LE
TEL: (01342) 810236 *CONTACT:* M P & M R Ingwersen *CAT. COST:* Sae
MIN. ORDER: *CREDIT CARDS:* None
SPECIALITIES: Alpines & rock garden plants. See also in Nursery Index under Code 'SIng'.

Jasmine Cottage Gardens, 26 Channel Road, Walton St. Mary, Clevedon, Somerset, BS21 7BY
TEL: (01275) 871850 *E-MAIL:* baron@bologrew.demon.co.uk *CONTACT:* Mr & Mrs M Redgrave
CAT. COST: None issued
MIN. ORDER: No minimum charge *CREDIT CARDS:* none
SPECIALITIES: Rhodochiton, Asarina, Maurandya, Solenopsis/Isotoma/Laurentia. See also in Additional Nursery Index under Code 02.

Jekka's Herb Farm, Rose Cottage, Shellards Lane, Alveston, Bristol, Avon, BS35 3SY
TEL: (01454) 418878 *FAX:* (01454) 411988 *CONTACT:* Jekka McVicar *CAT. COST:* 4 x 1st class
MIN. ORDER: No minimum charge *CREDIT CARDS:* None
SPECIALITIES: Herb seed (NO wild flower seed). See also in Nursery Index under Code 'WJek'.

Landlife Wildflowers Ltd, National Wildflower Centre, Court Hey Park, Liverpool, Merseyside, L16 3NA
TEL: (0151) 737 1819 *FAX:* (0151) 737 1820 *E-MAIL:* info@landlife.u-net.com
WEB SITE: http://www.merseyworld.com/landlife *CONTACT:* Gillian Watson
CAT. COST: Sae + 2 x 2nd class
MIN. ORDER: No minimum charge *CREDIT CARDS:* Visa, AmEx
SPECIALITIES: Native Herbaceous plants. See also in Nursery Index under Code 'NLan'.

Lodge Lane Nursery & Gardens, Lodge Lane, Dutton, Nr Warrington, Cheshire, WA4 4HP
TEL: (01928) 713718 *CONTACT:* Rod or Diane Casey *CAT. COST:* 3 x 1st class
MIN. ORDER: £10.00 + p&p *CREDIT CARDS:* none
SPECIALITIES: Hardy Perennials. See also in Nursery Index under Code 'MLLN'.

Lydford Alpine Nursery, 2 Southern Cottages, Lydford, Okehampton, Devon, EX20 4BL
TEL: (01822) 820398 *CONTACT:* Julie & David Hatchett *CAT. COST:* Sae
MIN. ORDER: No minimum charge* *CREDIT CARDS:* none
SPECIALITIES: Allium, Auricula, Hardy Geranium, Sisyrinchium, & a wide range of Alpines. * Note: mail order to UK only. See also in Nursery Index under Code 'CLyd'.

♦ **See also Display Advertisements**

Seed Suppliers

The Marches Nursery, Presteigne, Powys, LD8 2HG

TEL: (01544) 260474 *FAX:* (01544) 260474 *CONTACT:* Jane Cooke *CAT. COST:* Sae
MIN. ORDER: No minimum charge *CREDIT CARDS:* None
SPECIALITIES: Hardy Perennials. See also in Nursery Index under Code 'WMaN'.

S E Marshall & Co Ltd., Regal Road, Wisbech, Cambridgeshire, PE13 2RF

TEL: (01945) 583407 (24 hours) *FAX:* (01945) 588235 *CONTACT:* Customer Services *CAT. COST:* Free
MIN. ORDER: No minimum charge *CREDIT CARDS:* Access, Visa
SPECIALITIES: Vegetables.

Marston Exotics, Brampton Lane, Madley, Hereforshire, HR2 9LX

TEL: (01981) 251140 *FAX:* (01981) 251649 *WEB SITE:* http://freespace.virgin.net/carnivorous.connection/
CONTACT: Paul Gardner *CAT. COST:* List 3 x 1st class
MIN. ORDER: See list for details *CREDIT CARDS:* MasterCard, Switch, Visa
SPECIALITIES: Carnivorous plants. Price list & Growers Guide £2.85. See also in Nursery Index under Code 'WMEx'.

S M McArd (Seeds), 39 West Road, Pointon, Sleaford, Lincolnshire, NG34 0NA

TEL: (01529) 240765 *FAX:* (01529) 240765 *CONTACT:* Susan McArd *CAT. COST:* 2 x 2nd class
MIN. ORDER: No minimum charge *CREDIT CARDS:* None
SPECIALITIES: Unusual & giant Vegetables. Seeds & Plants.

Mires Beck Nursery, Low Mill Lane, North Cave, Brough, North Humberside, HU15 2NR

TEL: (01430) 421543 *CONTACT:* Martin Rowland & Irene Tinklin *CAT. COST:* 3 x 1st class
MIN. ORDER: No minimum charge *CREDIT CARDS:* None
SPECIALITIES: Wild Flower Plants of Yorkshire Provenance. See also in Nursery Index under Code 'NMir'.

Monksilver Nursery, Oakington Road, Cottenham, Cambridgeshire, CB4 4TW

TEL: (01954) 251555 *E-MAIL:* monksilver@dial.pipex.com
WEB SITE: http://dialspace.dial.pipex.com/monksilver/ *CONTACT:* Joe Sharman & Alan Leslie
CAT. COST: 6 x 1st class
MIN. ORDER: £10.00 *CREDIT CARDS:* None
SPECIALITIES: Seed of some plants available. See also in Nursery Index under Code 'EMon'.

Monocot Nursery, Jacklands, Jacklands Bridge, Tickenham, Clevedon, Avon, BS21 6SG

TEL: (01275) 810394 *CONTACT:* M R Salmon *CAT. COST:* Sae
MIN. ORDER: No minimum charge *CREDIT CARDS:* None
SPECIALITIES: Rare & unusual Bulbous & Tuberous plants. See also in Nursery Index under Code 'CMon'.

Natural Selection, 1 Station Cottages, Hullavington, Chippenham, Wiltshire, SN14 6ET

TEL: (01666) 837369 *E-MAIL:* @worldmutation.demon.co.uk *CONTACT:* Martin Cragg-Barber
CAT. COST: Sae
MIN. ORDER: No minimum charge *CREDIT CARDS:* None
SPECIALITIES: Unusual British natives. See also in Nursery Index under Code 'CNat'.

Andrew Norfield Seeds, Llangwm Arboretum, Usk, Monmouthshire, NP5 1NQ

TEL: (01291) 650306 *FAX:* (01291) 650306 *CONTACT:* Andrew Norfield *CAT. COST:* 1 x 1st class
MIN. ORDER: No minimum charge *CREDIT CARDS:* None
SPECIALITIES: Germinated & pretreated Seed of hardy Trees, Shrubs, Herbaceous & House plants. See also in Nursery Index under Code 'WNor'.

North Green Seeds, 16 Wilton Lane, Little Plumstead, Norwich, Norfolk, NR13 5DL

TEL: (01603) 714661 *FAX:* (01603) 714661 *CONTACT:* John Morley & Richard Hobbs
CAT. COST: 4 x 1st class
MIN. ORDER: £5.00 + p&p *CREDIT CARDS:* None
SPECIALITIES: Small specialist range of Galanthus, Allium & Fritillaria Seed. See also in Nursery Index under Code 'EMor'.

Orchard Nurseries, Tow Lane, Foston, Grantham, Lincolnshire, NG32 2LE

TEL: (01400) 281354 *FAX:* (01400) 281354 *CONTACT:* Margaret Rose *CAT. COST:* Sae
MIN. ORDER: No minimum charge *CREDIT CARDS:* None
SPECIALITIES: Helleborus orientalis hybrids. See also in Nursery Index under Code 'EOrc'.

Paradise Centre, Twinstead Road, Lamarsh, Bures, Suffolk, CO8 5EX

TEL: (01787) 269449 *FAX:* (01787) 269449 *CONTACT:* Cees & Hedy Stapel-Valk
CAT. COST: 5 x 1st class
MIN. ORDER: £7.50 + p&p *CREDIT CARDS:* Visa, other
SPECIALITIES: Unusual bulbous & tuberous plants, incl. Bog & Shade species. See also in Nursery Index under Code 'EPar'. *NB Credit cards accepted for orders over £17.50.

Passiflora (National Collection), Lampley Road, Kingston Seymour, Clevedon, North Somerset, BS21 6XS

TEL: (01934) 833350 *FAX:* (01934) 877255 *E-MAIL:* passion@3wa.co.uk
CONTACT: John Vanderplank or Jane Lindsay *CAT. COST:* 3 x 1st class
MIN. ORDER: £6.00 *CREDIT CARDS:* Visa, Access, EuroCard
SPECIALITIES: Over 200 Passiflora. See also in Nursery Index under Code 'WGre'.

Phedar Nursery, Bunkers Hill, Romiley, Stockport, Cheshire, SK6 3DS

TEL: (0161) 430 3772 *FAX:* (0161) 430 3772 *CONTACT:* Will McLewin
CAT. COST: Separate Saes for lists.
MIN. ORDER: No minimum charge *CREDIT CARDS:* None
SPECIALITIES: Helleborus species seed wild collected & hybrids seed in categories; available Aug. Paeonia species seed wild coll. Nov. See also in Nursery Index under Code 'MPhe'.

Alan Phipps Cacti, 62 Samuel White Road, Hanham, Bristol, BS15 3LX

TEL: (0117) 960 7591 *CONTACT:* A Phipps *CAT. COST:* No catalogue
MIN. ORDER: £5.00 *CREDIT CARDS:* None
SPECIALITIES: See also in Cactus & Succulent Specialists Index. NB Minimum order is for mixed species or single genera.

Pinks & Carnations, 22 Chetwyn Avenue, Bromley Cross, Nr Bolton, Lancashire, BL7 9BN

TEL: (01204) 306273 *FAX:* (01204) 306273 *CONTACT:* Ruth & Tom Gillies *CAT. COST:* 1 x 1st class
MIN. ORDER: No minimum charge *CREDIT CARDS:* Visa, MasterCard
♦ SPECIALITIES: Perpetual Flowing Carnations, Border Carnations, Allwoodii Alpinus. See also in Nursery Index under Code 'NPin'.

Plant World Botanic Gardens, Seed Dept. (PF), St Marychurch Road, Newton Abbot, Devon, TQ12 4SE

TEL: (01803) 872939 *FAX:* (01803) 872939 *CONTACT:* Ray Brown
CAT. COST: 3 x 1st class/ $2/ 3 x IRC
MIN. ORDER: £8 UK, £20 o/s *CREDIT CARDS:* Visa, Access, MasterCard, EuroCard
♦ SPECIALITIES: Meconopsis, Gentiana, Primula, Aquilegia, Campanula, Viola, Geranium, Salvia, Eryngium. See also in Nursery Index under Code 'CPla'. No plants by Mail Order.

Pleasant View Nursery, Two Mile Oak, Nr Denbury, Newton Abbot, Devon, TQ12 6DG

TEL: Write with Sae *WEB SITE:* http://www.pview.demon.co.uk *CONTACT:* Mrs B D Yeo
CAT. COST: 2 x 2nd class or 2 IRC
MIN. ORDER: £10.00 + p&p *CREDIT CARDS:* None
SPECIALITIES: Salvia seed only. See also in Nursery Index under Code 'CPle'.

Potterton & Martin, Moortown Road, Nettleton, Caistor, Lincolnshire, LN7 6HX

TEL: (01472) 851714 *FAX:* (01472) 852580 *E-MAIL:* pottin01@globalnet.co.uk
WEB SITE: http://www.users.globalnet.co.uk/~pottin01 *CONTACT:* Mr or Mrs Potterton
CAT. COST: 50p in stamps only
MIN. ORDER: No minimum charge *CREDIT CARDS:* Visa, Access, MasterCard, EuroCard
SPECIALITIES: Alpines & dwarf Bulbs. Seed list sent out in November. See also in Nursery Index under Code 'EPot'.

♦ **See also Display Advertisements**

Poyntzfield Herb Nursery, Nr Balblair, Black Isle, Dingwall, Ross & Cromarty, Highland, Scotland, IV7 8LX
  TEL: (01381) 610352* *FAX:* (01381) 610352 *CONTACT:* Duncan Ross *CAT. COST:* 4 x 1st class
  MIN. ORDER: £5.00 + p&p *CREDIT CARDS:* None
  SPECIALITIES: *Note: Phone 1200-1300 & 1800-1900. See also in Nursery Index under Code 'GPoy'.

W Robinson & Sons Ltd, Sunny Bank, Forton, Nr Preston, Lancashire, PR3 0BN
  TEL: (01524) 791210 *FAX:* (01524) 791933 *CONTACT:* Miss Robinson *CAT. COST:* Free
  MIN. ORDER: No minimum charge *CREDIT CARDS:* Visa, Access, AmEx
  SPECIALITIES: Mammoth Vegetable seed. Onions, Leeks, Tomatoes & Beans.

R V Roger Ltd, The Nurseries, Pickering, North Yorkshire, YO18 7HG
  TEL: (01751) 472226 *FAX:* (01751) 476749 *E-MAIL:* ian@clivia.demon.co.uk
  CONTACT: J R Roger & A G & I M Roger *CAT. COST:* Sae
  MIN. ORDER: No minimum charge *CREDIT CARDS:* Visa, Access
  SPECIALITIES: Bulbs & Seed Potatoes. See also in Nursery Index under Code 'NRog'.

Roseland House Nursery, Chacewater, Truro, Cornwall, TR4 8QB
  TEL: (01872) 560451 *CONTACT:* Mr C. Pridham *CAT. COST:* 1 x 1st class
  MIN. ORDER: £5.00 + p&p *CREDIT CARDS:* Visa, Access
  SPECIALITIES: Herbaceous Perennials & Climbers. See also in Nursery Index under Code 'CRHN'.

Rougham Hall Nurseries, Ipswich Road, Rougham, Bury St Edmunds, Suffolk, IP30 9LZ
  TEL: (01359) 270577 *FAX:* (01359) 271149 *CONTACT:* A A & K G Harbutt *CAT. COST:* Sae
  MIN. ORDER: No minimum charge *CREDIT CARDS:* MasterCard, Visa
  SPECIALITIES: Delphinium mixed varieties & wide range of Hardy Perennials. See also in Nursery Index under Code 'ERou'.

Salley Gardens, 32 Lansdowne Drive, West Bridgford, Nottinghamshire, NG2 7FJ
  TEL: (0115) 9233878 evngs *CONTACT:* Richard Lewin *CAT. COST:* Sae
  MIN. ORDER: No minimum charge *CREDIT CARDS:* None
  SPECIALITIES: Wildflower & Medicinal Herbs. See also in Nursery Index under Code 'MSal'.

The Seed House, 9a Widley Road, Cosham, Portsmouth, PO6 2DS
  TEL: (01705) 325639 *CONTACT:* Mr R L Spearing *CAT. COST:* 4 x 1st class or 4 x IRA
  MIN. ORDER: £5.00 *CREDIT CARDS:* None
  SPECIALITIES: Australian seeds suitable for the European climate incl. Acacia, Banksia, Callistemon, & Eucalypts etc.

Seeds by Size, 45 Crouchfield, Boxmoor, Hemel Hempstead, Hertfordshire, HP1 1PA
  TEL: (01442) 251458 *E-MAIL:* john-robert-size@seeds-by-size.co.uk
  WEB SITE: http://www.seeds-by-size.co.uk *CONTACT:* Mr John Robert Size *CAT. COST:* Sae
  MIN. ORDER: No minimum charge *CREDIT CARDS:* None
  SPECIALITIES: Flowers & Vegetables. 1,400 varieties of Vegetable, (175 Cabbage, 99 Cauliflower, 70 Onion, 100 Tomatoes) & 4,900 flowers such as 291 varieties of Sweet Pea, 100 Herbs.

John Shipton (Bulbs), Y Felin, Henllan Amgoed, Whitland, Dyfed, Wales, SA34 0SL
  TEL: (01994) 240125 *FAX:* (01994) 241180 *E-MAIL:* bluebell@zoo.co.uk *CONTACT:* John Shipton
  CAT. COST: Sae
  MIN. ORDER: No minimum charge *CREDIT CARDS:* None
  SPECIALITIES: Species native to the British Isles. See also in Nursery Index under Code 'WShi'.

Sino-Himalayan Plant Association, 81 Parlaunt Road, Slough, Berkshire, SL3 8BR
  TEL: (01753) 542823 *FAX:* (01753) 542823 *CONTACT:* Chris Chadwell *CAT. COST:* None issued
  MIN. ORDER: *CREDIT CARDS:* none
  SPECIALITIES: Seed available for exchange to Members. Please apply for membership.

Siskin Plants, April House, Davey Lane, Charsfield, Woodbridge, Suffolk, IP13 7QG

TEL: (01473) 737567 *FAX:* (01473) 737567 *CONTACT:* Chris & Valerie Wheeler
CAT. COST: Sae for list.
MIN. ORDER: No minimum charge *CREDIT CARDS:* Access, Visa, MasterCard
SPECIALITIES: Alpines, small Perennials, dwarf Bulbs. See also in Nursery Index under Code 'ESis'.

Special Plants, Hill Farm Barn, Greenways Lane, Cold Ashton, Chippenham, Wiltshire, SN14 8LA

TEL: (01225) 891686 *E-MAIL:* derry@sclegg.demon.co.uk *CONTACT:* Derry Watkins
CAT. COST: Stamped Sae for list.
MIN. ORDER: £1.50 + p&p *CREDIT CARDS:* none
SPECIALITIES: Annuals, Biennials, short-lived & tender Perennials. See also in Nursery Index under Code 'CSpe'.

Stewart's (Nottingham) Ltd, 3 George Street, Nottingham, NG1 3BH

TEL: (0115) 9476338 *CONTACT:* Brenda Lochhead *CAT. COST:* 2 x 1st class
MIN. ORDER: No minimum charge *CREDIT CARDS:* Visa, MasterCard, Switch
SPECIALITIES: Large general range esp. Vegetables. Also seed Potatoes & Grasses.

Richard Stockwell, 64 Weardale Road, Sherwood, Nottingham, NG5 1DD

TEL: (0115) 969 1063 *FAX:* (0115) 969 1063 *CONTACT:* Richard Stockwell
CAT. COST: 4 x 2nd class or 2 x IRC
MIN. ORDER: £8.00 + p&p *CREDIT CARDS:* None
SPECIALITIES: Very rare climbing species, also dwarf species. See also in Nursery Index under Code 'MSto'.

Suttons Seeds, Hele Road, Torquay, Devon, TQ2 7QJ

TEL: (01803) 614455 *FAX:* (01803) 615747 *CONTACT:* Customer Services *CAT. COST:* Free
MIN. ORDER: No minimum charge *CREDIT CARDS:* Visa, MasterCard
SPECIALITIES: Wide general range of Flower & Vegetable Seed, plus young Plants & summer flowering Bulbs. See also in Nursery Index under Code 'CSut'.

Thompson & Morgan (UK) Ltd, Poplar Lane, Ipswich, Suffolk, IP8 3BU

TEL: (01473) 688821 *FAX:* (01473) 680199 *CONTACT:* Martin Thrower *CAT. COST:* Free
MIN. ORDER: No minimum charge *CREDIT CARDS:* Visa, Access, Switch
SPECIALITIES: Largest illustrated Seed catalogue in the world.

Town Farm Nursery, Whitton, Stillington, Stockton on Tees, Cleveland, TS21 1LQ

TEL: (01740) 631079 *CONTACT:* F D Baker *CAT. COST:* 1 x 1st class
MIN. ORDER: £5.00 + p&p *CREDIT CARDS:* none
♦ SPECIALITIES: Alpines & Perennials. See also Nursery Index under Code 'NTow'.

Edwin Tucker & Sons, Brewery Meadow, Stonepark, Ashburton, Newton Abbot, Devon, TQ13 7DG

TEL: (01364) 652403 *FAX:* (01364) 654300 *CONTACT:* Geoff Penton *CAT. COST:* Free
MIN. ORDER: No minimum charge *CREDIT CARDS:* Visa, Access
SPECIALITIES: Over 70 varieties of Seed Potatoes. Wide range of Vegetables, Flowers, Green Manures & sprouting seeds in packets. All not treated.

Unwins Seeds Ltd, Mail Order Dept., Histon, Cambridge, Cambridgeshire, CB4 4ZZ

TEL: (01945) 588522 *FAX:* (01945) 475255 *CONTACT:* Customer Services Dept. *CAT. COST:* Free
MIN. ORDER: No minimum charge *CREDIT CARDS:* Visa, Access
SPECIALITIES: Sweet Peas & wide general range.

Jill White, St. Davids', Recreation Way, Brightlingsea, Essex, CO7 ONJ

TEL: (01206) 303547 *CONTACT:* Jill White *CAT. COST:* Sae for England or 2 x IRC for overseas
MIN. ORDER: No minimum charge *CREDIT CARDS:* None
SPECIALITIES: Cyclamen. See also in Nursery Index under Code 'EJWh'.

♦ **See also Display Advertisements**

Woodfield Bros, Wood End, Clifford Chambers, Stratford-on-Avon, Warwickshire, CV37 8HR

TEL: (01789) 205618   *CONTACT:* B Woodfield   *CAT. COST:* Sae
MIN. ORDER: No minimum charge   *CREDIT CARDS:* None
SPECIALITIES: Lupin, Delphinium. See also in Nursery Index under Code 'MWoo'.

Y.S.J Seeds, Kingsfield Conservation, Broadenham Lane, Winsham, Chard, Somerset, TA20 4JF

TEL: (01460) 30070   *FAX:* (01460) 30070   *CONTACT:* Mrs M White   *CAT. COST:* 31p stamps
MIN. ORDER: No minimum charge   *CREDIT CARDS:* None
SPECIALITIES: British Wild Flowers seeds from native stock plants. See also in Nursery Index under Code 'CKin'.

Roy Young Seeds, 23 Westland Chase, West Winch, King's Lynn, Norfolk, PE33 0QH

TEL: (01553) 840867   *FAX:* (01553) 840867   *CONTACT:* Mr Roy Young
CAT. COST: UK 20p, o/s 3 x IRCs
MIN. ORDER: No minimum charge*   *CREDIT CARDS:* None
SPECIALITIES: Cactus & Succulent SEEDS only, for wholesale and retail purchase. 24pg Cat. listing app. 2,000 species, varieties & forms (Retail). 10 pg A4 listing (Wholesale). *£25 min Wholesale order charge.

Cactus & Succulent Suppliers

Bradley Batch Nursery, 64 Bath Road, Ashcott, Bridgwater, Somerset, TA7 9QJ
TEL: (01458) 210256 *CONTACT:* J E White
OPENING TIMES: 1000-1800 Tue-Sun. *W/SALE or RETAIL:* Both
No mail order *CAT. COST:* None issued *CREDIT CARDS:* None
SPECIALITIES: Echeveria, Haworthia, Lithops & Cacti.

Bridgemere Nurseries, Bridgemere, Nr Nantwich, Cheshire, CW5 7QB
TEL: (01270) 520381/520239 *FAX:* (01270) 520215 *CONTACT:* Carol Adams
OPENING TIMES: 0900-2000 Mon-Sat, 1000-2000 Sun, in summer, until 1700 winter.
W/SALE or RETAIL: Retail
No mail order *CAT. COST:* None issued *CREDIT CARDS:* Visa, Access, MasterCard, Switch
◆ *SPECIALITIES:* General range of Cacti & other Succulents incl. specimen plants. See also in ORCHID
Index and Nursery Index under Code 'MBri'.

Brookside Nursery, Elderberry Farm, Bognor Road, Rowhook, Horsham, West Sussex, RH12
3PS
TEL: (01403) 790996 *FAX:* (01403) 790195 *E-MAIL:* alanbutler1@compuserve.com
CONTACT: A J Butler
OPENING TIMES: 1000-1700 Thur-Sun; open Bank Hol Mons. Please phone first.
W/SALE or RETAIL: Both
MIN. VALUE: No minimum charge *CAT. COST:* 1 x 1st class *CREDIT CARDS:* None
SPECIALITIES: Cactus & Succulent plants.

Connoisseurs' Cacti, (Off.) 51 Chelsfield Lane, Orpington, Kent, BR5 4HG
TEL: (01689) 837781 *CONTACT:* John Pilbeam
OPENING TIMES: 1030-1430 but please phone first. *W/SALE or RETAIL:* Both
MIN. VALUE: No minimum charge *CAT. COST:* Sae or IRC *CREDIT CARDS:* None
SPECIALITIES: Mammillaria, Sulcorebutia, Gymnocalycium, Rebutia, Haworthia, Asclepiads etc. NOTE:
Nursery at Woodlands Farm, Shire Lane, Nr Farnborough, Kent.

Croston Cactus, 43 Southport Road, Eccleston, Chorley, Lancashire, PR7 6ET
TEL: (01257) 452555 *CONTACT:* John Henshaw
OPENING TIMES: 0930-1700 Wed-Sat & by appt. *W/SALE or RETAIL:* Retail
MIN. VALUE: No minimum charge *CAT. COST:* 2 x 1st or 2 x IRCs *CREDIT CARDS:* None
SPECIALITIES: Mexican Cacti, Echeveria hybrids & some Bromeliads & Tillandsia.

W G Geissler, Winsford, Kingston Road, Slimbridge, Gloucestershire, GL2 7BW
TEL: (01453) 890340 *FAX:* (01453) 890340 *CONTACT:* W G Geissler
OPENING TIMES: 0900-1700 (2000 in summer) Mar-Nov. *W/SALE or RETAIL:* Retail
No mail order *CAT. COST:* Sae *CREDIT CARDS:* None
SPECIALITIES: Hardy Cacti & Succulents & related books.

Glenhirst Cactus Nursery, Station Road, Swineshead, Nr Boston, Lincolnshire, PE20 3NX
TEL: (01205) 820314 *FAX:* (01205) 820614 *E-MAIL:* glenhirstcacti@lineone.com
WEB SITE: http://website.lineone.net/~glenhirstcacti *CONTACT:* N C & S A Bell
OPENING TIMES: 1000-1700 Thu, Fri, Sun & Bank Hols 1st Apr-30th Sep. Mail order all year.
W/SALE or RETAIL: Both
MIN. VALUE: No minimum charge *CAT. COST:* 2 x 1st class *CREDIT CARDS:* none
SPECIALITIES: Extensive range of Cacti & Succulent plants & seeds, inc. Christmas Cacti & Orchid
Cacti. Hardy & half-hardy desert plants. All stock fully described on lists.

Harvest Nurseries, Harvest Cottage, Boonshill Farm, Iden, Nr Rye, E Sussex, TN31 7QA
TEL: (0181) 325 5420 *CONTACT:* D A Smith
OPENING TIMES: Mail Order ONLY *W/SALE or RETAIL:* Retail
MIN. VALUE: No minimum charge *CAT. COST:* 2 x 1st class *CREDIT CARDS:* None
SPECIALITIES: Epiphyllums & wide range of Succulents. Descriptive catalogue. See also SEED index.

◆ **See also Display Advertisements**

Heldon Nurseries, Ashbourne Road, Spath, Uttoxeter, Staffordshire, ST14 5AD
TEL: (01889) 563377 *FAX:* (01889) 563377 *CONTACT:* Mrs J H Tate
OPENING TIMES: 1000-sunset daily. *W/SALE or RETAIL:* Retail
MIN. VALUE: £2.00 + p&p *CAT. COST:* Sae *CREDIT CARDS:* none
SPECIALITIES: Cactus & Succulents. See also in Nursery Index under Code 'MHel'.

Holly Gate Cactus Nursery, Billingshurst Road, Ashington, West Sussex, RH20 3BA
TEL: (01903) 892 930 *WEB SITE:* http://www.yell.co.uk/sites/cactushg/ *CONTACT:* Mr T M Hewitt
OPENING TIMES: 0900-1700 daily. *W/SALE or RETAIL:* Both
MIN. VALUE: £5.00 + p&p *CAT. COST:* 2 x 1st class *CREDIT CARDS:* Visa, Access, AmEx
SPECIALITIES: Cactus & Succulents.

Kent Cacti, (Off.) 35 Rutland Way, Orpington, Kent, BR5 4DY
TEL: (01689) 836249, 0467 881981 (mobile) *FAX:* (01689) 830157 *CONTACT:* Mr D Sizmur
OPENING TIMES: 1000-1700 most days. Please phone first. *W/SALE or RETAIL:* Retail
MIN. VALUE: No minimum charge *CAT. COST:* A5 Sae *CREDIT CARDS:* None
SPECIALITIES: Agave, Astrophytum, Conophytum, Crassula, Echeveria, small Opuntia, Mammillaria
etc. NOTE: Nursery at Woodlands Farm, Shire Lane, Farnborough, Kent.

Long Man Gardens, Lewes Road, Wilmington, Polgate, East Sussex, BN26 5RS
TEL: (01323) 870816 *CONTACT:* O Menzel
OPENING TIMES: 0900-1700 (or dusk if sooner) Tue-Sun. Please check before visiting.
W/SALE or RETAIL: Retail
No mail order *CAT. COST:* None issued *CREDIT CARDS:* None
SPECIALITIES: Agave, Echeveria, Euphorbia etc.

Oak Dene Nurseries, 10 Back Lane West, Royston, Barnsley, Yorkshire, S71 4SB
TEL: (01226) 722253 *CONTACT:* J Foster
OPENING TIMES: 1000-1600 1st Apr-30th Sep, 0900-1800 1st Oct-31st Mar. (Closed 12.30-13.30.)
W/SALE or RETAIL:
MIN. VALUE: Please phone for further info. *CAT. COST:* *CREDIT CARDS:* none
SPECIALITIES:

Pete & Ken Cactus Nursery, Saunders Lane, Ash, Nr Canterbury, Kent, CT3 2BX
TEL: (01304) 812170 *CONTACT:* Ken Burke
OPENING TIMES: 0900-1800 daily. *W/SALE or RETAIL:* Retail
MIN. VALUE: £3.00 + p&p *CAT. COST:* Sae for list *CREDIT CARDS:* None
SPECIALITIES: Cactus, Succulents, Lithops (Living stones).

Alan Phipps Cacti, 62 Samuel White Road, Hanham, Bristol, BS15 3LX
TEL: (0117) 9607591 *CONTACT:* A Phipps
OPENING TIMES: All times, but prior phone call ESSENTIAL to ensure a greeting.
W/SALE or RETAIL: Both
MIN. VALUE: £5.00 + p&p *CAT. COST:* Sae or 2 x IRC (EC) *CREDIT CARDS:* None
SPECIALITIES: Rebutia, Mammillaria & Astrophytum. See also SEED index.

The Plant Lovers, Candesby House, Candesby, Spilsby, Lincolnshire, PE23 5RU
TEL: (01754) 890256 *CONTACT:* Tim Wilson
OPENING TIMES: Daily - but please phone first. *W/SALE or RETAIL:* Both
No mail order *CAT. COST:* None issued *CREDIT CARDS:* None
SPECIALITIES: Sempervivum (Houseleeks) & wide range of Cacti and other Succulents. Brochure
available.

Southfield Nurseries, Bourne Road, Morton, Nr Bourne, Lincolnshire, PE10 0RH
TEL: (01778) 570168 *CONTACT:* Mr & Mrs B Goodey
OPENING TIMES: 1000-1230 & 1330-1600 daily except for Nov-Jan open by appt. only.
W/SALE or RETAIL: Both
MIN. VALUE: No minimum charge *CAT. COST:* 1 x 1st class *CREDIT CARDS:* None
SPECIALITIES: A wide range of Cacti & Succulents including some of the rarer varieties all grown on
our own nursery.

See note on Mail Order, EC sales & Export on page 11

Toobees Exotics, (Off.) 20 Inglewood, St Johns, Woking, Surrey, GU21 3HX

TEL: (01483) 797534 (nursery) *FAX:* (01483) 751995 *E-MAIL:* bbpotter@compuserve.com
WEB SITE: http://www.demon.uk/mace/toobees *CONTACT:* Bob Potter
OPENING TIMES: 1000-1700 Wed-Sun 1st Mar-30th Sept (incl. B/Hol Mons).
W/SALE or RETAIL: Retail
MIN. VALUE: No minimum charge   *CAT. COST:* Sae *CREDIT CARDS:* None
SPECIALITIES: South African & Madagascan Succulents. Many rare & unusual species. *Note: nursery is at Black Horse Road, Woking.

Westfield Cacti, Kennford, Exeter, Devon, EX6 7XD

TEL: (01392) 832921 *FAX:* (01392) 832921 *E-MAIL:* wescacti@aol.com
WEB SITE: http://members.aol.com/wescacti/page1.htm *CONTACT:* Ralph & Marina Northcott
OPENING TIMES: 1000-1700 daily. *W/SALE or RETAIL:* Both
MIN. VALUE: £5 + p&p   *CAT. COST:* 3 x 1st class *CREDIT CARDS:* Access, Visa, MasterCard, EuroCard
SPECIALITIES: Epiphytes.

Whitestone Gardens Ltd, The Cactus Houses, Sutton-under-Whitestonecliffe, Thirsk, Yorkshire, YO7 2PZ

TEL: (01845) 597467 *FAX:* (01845) 597035 *E-MAIL:* roy@whitestn.demon.co.uk
CONTACT: Roy Mottram
OPENING TIMES: Daylight hours Sat-Thu. *W/SALE or RETAIL:* Retail
MIN. VALUE: No minimum charge   *CAT. COST:* 4 x 2nd class *CREDIT CARDS:* Visa, MasterCard
SPECIALITIES: Cacti & other Succulents, Books & Sundries.

Howard & Sally Wills, Fernwood, Peters Marland, Torrington, Devon, EX38 8QG

TEL: (01805) 601446 *FAX:* (01805) 601446 *E-MAIL:* hjwills@aol.com *CONTACT:* H Wills
OPENING TIMES: By appt. only *W/SALE or RETAIL:* Retail
MIN. VALUE: £5.00 + p&p   *CAT. COST:* 3 x 1st class *CREDIT CARDS:* None
SPECIALITIES: Sempervivum, Jovibarba & Rosularia. See also in Nursery Index under Code CWil.

Roy Young Seeds, 23 Westland Chase, West Winch, King's Lynn, Norfolk, PE33 0QH

TEL: (01553) 840867 *FAX:* (01553) 840867 *CONTACT:* Mr Roy Young
OPENING TIMES: Not open. Mail Order ONLY. *W/SALE or RETAIL:* Both
MIN. VALUE: Nmc* *CAT. COST:* UK 20p, o/s 3 x IRC *CREDIT CARDS:* None
SPECIALITIES: Cactus & Succulent SEEDS only. 24pg cat. listing approx. 2000 species, varieties & forms (retail). 10pg A4 listing (wholesale). *Minimum Wholesale order £25.00

◆ **See also Display Advertisements**

Orchid Suppliers

Bridgemere Nurseries, Bridgemere, Nr Nantwich, Cheshire, CW5 7QB
> *TEL:* (01270) 520381/520239 *FAX:* (01270) 520215 *CONTACT:* Carol Adams
> *OPENING TIMES:* 0900-2000 Mon-Sat, 1000-2000 Sun in Summer, until 1700 in Winter.
> *W/SALE or RETAIL:* Retail
> No mail order *CAT. COST:* None issued *CREDIT CARDS:* Visa, Access, MasterCard, Switch
> ◆ SPECIALITIES: Cymbidium, Paphiopedilum, Phalaenopsis, Miltonia, Odontoglossum.

Burnham Nurseries, Forches Cross, Newton Abbot, Devon, TQ12 6PZ
> *TEL:* (01626) 352233 *FAX:* (01626) 362167 *CONTACT:* Brian Rittershausen
> *OPENING TIMES:* 0900-1700 Mon-Fri & 1000-1600 Sat & Sun. *W/SALE or RETAIL:* Both
> *MIN. VALUE:* No minimum charge *CAT. COST:* Large Sae + 31p stamp *CREDIT CARDS:* Visa,
> Access, Switch
> *SPECIALITIES:* All types of Orchid.

Equatorial Plant Co., 7 Gray Lane, Barnard Castle, Co. Durham, DL12 8PD
> *TEL:* (01833) 690519 *FAX:* (01833) 690519 *CONTACT:* Richard Warren PhD
> *OPENING TIMES:* By appt. only. *W/SALE or RETAIL:* Both
> *MIN. VALUE:* No minimum charge *CAT. COST:* Free *CREDIT CARDS:* Visa, Access
> *SPECIALITIES:* Laboratory raised Orchids only.

Flora Exotica, Pasadena, South-Green, Fingringhoe, Colchester, Essex, CO5 7DR
> *TEL:* (01206) 729414 *CONTACT:* J Beddoes
> *OPENING TIMES:* Not open to the public *W/SALE or RETAIL:* Both
> *MIN. VALUE:* No minimum charge *CAT. COST:* 6 x 1st class *CREDIT CARDS:* None
> *SPECIALITIES:* Insectivorous plants, esp. Pinguicula & rare & exotic Flora incl. Orchids. See also in
> Nursery Index under Code 'EFEx'.

Hardy Orchids Ltd, New Gate Farm, Scotchey Lane, Stour Provost, Gillingham, Dorset, SP8 5LT
> *TEL:* (01747) 838368 *FAX:* (01747) 838308 *CONTACT:* N J Heywood
> *OPENING TIMES:* 0800-1300 & 1400-1700 Mon-Fri, by appt. only. *W/SALE or RETAIL:* Both
> *MIN. VALUE:* £10.00 + p&p *CAT. COST:* 2 x 1st class *CREDIT CARDS:* none
> *SPECIALITIES:* Hardy Orchids.

Mansell & Hatcher Ltd, Cragg Wood Nurseries, Woodlands Drive, Rawdon, Leeds, LS19 6LQ
> *TEL:* (0113) 250 2016 *CONTACT:* Mr Allan Long
> *OPENING TIMES:* 0900-1700 Mon-Fri. *W/SALE or RETAIL:* Both
> *MIN. VALUE:* No minimum charge *CAT. COST:* 3 x 1st class *CREDIT CARDS:* Visa, Access
> *SPECIALITIES:* Odontoglossum, Masdevallia, Miltonia & Cattleya & species Orchids.

McBeans Orchids, Cooksbridge, Lewes, Sussex, BN8 4PR
> *TEL:* (01273) 400228 *FAX:* (01273) 401181 *CONTACT:* Jim Durrant
> *OPENING TIMES:* 1030-1600 daily ex. Xmas & Boxing day, New Year & Good Friday.
> *W/SALE or RETAIL:* Both
> *MIN. VALUE:* £50.00 + p&p *CAT. COST:* Free *CREDIT CARDS:* Visa, AmEx, Access
> *SPECIALITIES:* Orchids - Cymbidium, Odontoglossum, Phalaenopsis, Paphiopedilum, Miltonia, Cattleya
> & other genera.

Uzumara Orchids, 9 Port Henderson, Gairloch, Rosshire, Scotland, IV21 2AS
> *TEL:* (01445) 741228 *CONTACT:* Mrs I F La Croix
> *OPENING TIMES:* By appt ONLY. *W/SALE or RETAIL:* Retail
> *MIN. VALUE:* No minimum charge *CAT. COST:* Sae *CREDIT CARDS:* None
> *SPECIALITIES:* African & Madagascan Orchids.

Westwood Nursery, 65 Yorkland Avenue, Welling, Kent, DA16 2LE
> *TEL:* (0181) 301 0886 *FAX:* (0181) 301 0886 *CONTACT:* Mr S Edwards
> *OPENING TIMES:* Not open *W/SALE or RETAIL:* Retail
> *MIN. VALUE:* No minimum charge *CAT. COST:* Sae *CREDIT CARDS:* None
> *SPECIALITIES:* Pleione, Hardy Orchids & Australian Terrestrial Orchids.

Woodstock Orchids, Woodstock House, 50 Pound Hill, Great Brickhill, Buckinghamshire, MK17 9AS

TEL: (01525) 261352 *FAX:* (01525) 261724 *CONTACT:* Joan & Bill Gaskell
OPENING TIMES: STRICTLY by appt ONLY. *W/SALE or RETAIL:* Both
MIN. VALUE: See Cat. for details *CAT. COST:* Sae *CREDIT CARDS:* Visa, Access
SPECIALITIES: Orchids & Exotic House plants.

FRUIT AND VEGETABLE INDEX

Almond — See *Prunus dulcis*
Apple — See *Malus domestica*
Apple, Crab — See *Malus*
Apricot — See *Prunus armeniaca*
Artichoke, Globe — See *Cynara cardunculus* Scolymus Group
Artichoke, Jerusalem — See *Helianthus tuberosus*
Avocado — See *Persea*
Banana — See *Musa*
Blackberry — See *Rubus fruticosus*
Blackcurrant — See *Ribes nigrum*
Blueberry — See *Vaccinium corymbosum*
Boysenberry — See *Rubus* Boysenberry
Bullace — See *Prunus insititia*
Calamondin — See × *Citrofortunella*
Cape Gooseberry — See *Physalis*
Carambola — See *Averrhoa carambola*
Cardoon — See *Cynara cardunculus*
Cherry, Duke — See *Prunus* × *gondouinii*
Cherry, Sour or Morello — See *Prunus cerasus*
Cherry, Sweet — See *Prunus avium*
Chestnut, Sweet — See *Castanea*
Citron — See *Citrus medica*
Cobnut — See *Corylus avellana*
Coconut — See *Cocos nucifera*
Coffee — See *Coffea*
Cranberry — See *Vaccinium macrocarpon, V. oxycoccos*
Damson — See *Prunus insititia*
Date — See *Phoenix dactylifera*
Elderberry — See *Sambucus*
Fig — See *Ficus carica*
Filbert — See *Corylus maxima*
Gooseberry — See *Ribes uva-crispa* var. *reclinatum*
Granadilla — See *Passiflora*
Grape — See *Vitis*
Grapefruit — See *Citrus* × *paradisi*
Guava — See *Psidium*
Hazelnut — See *Corylus*
Hildaberry — See *Rubus* 'Hildaberry'
Jostaberry — See *Ribes* × *culverwellii* Jostaberry
Jujube — See *Ziziphus jujuba*
Kiwi Fruit — See *Actinidia deliciosa*
Kumquat — See *Fortunella*

Lemon — See *Citrus limon*
Lime — See *Citrus aurantiifolia*
Loganberry — See *Rubus* Loganberry
Loquat — See *Eriobotrya japonica*
Mandarin — See *Citrus reticulata*
Mango — See *Mangifera indica*
Medlar — See *Mespilus germanica*
Mulberry — See *Morus*
Nectarine — See *Prunus persica* var. *nectarina*
Nut, Cob — See *Corylus avellana*
Nut, Filbert — See *Corylus maxima*
Orange, Sour or Seville — See *Citrus aurantium*
Orange, Sweet — See *Citrus sinensis*
Passion Fruit — See *Passiflora*
Paw Paw — See *Carica papaya*
Peach — See *Prunus persica*
Pear — See *Pyrus communis*
Pear, Asian — See *Pyrus pyrifolia*
Pecan — See *Carya*
Pepino — See *Solanum muricatum*
Pinkcurrant — See *Ribes rubrum* (P)
Plum — See *Prunus domestica*
Pomegranate — See *Punica granatum*
Pummelo — See *Citrus maxima*
Rhubarb — See *Rheum* × *hybridum*
Quince — See *Cydonia*
Raspberry — See *Rubus idaeus*
Redcurrant — See *Ribes rubrum* (R)
Satsuma — See *Citrus unshiu*
Seakale — See *Crambe maritima*
Shaddock — See *Citrus maxima*
Strawberry — See *Fragaria*
Sunberry — See *Rubus* 'Sunberry'
Tamarind — See *Tamarindus indica*
Tangelo — See *Citrus* × *tangelo*
Tangerine — See *Citrus reticulata*
Tangor — See *Citrus* × *nobilis* Tangor Group
Tayberry — See *Rubus* Tayberry
Ugli — See *Citrus* × *tangelo* 'Ugli'
Walnut — See *Juglans*
Whitecurrant — See *Ribes rubrum* (W)
Wineberry — See *Rubus phoenicolasius*
Worcesterberry — See *Ribes divaricatum*
Youngberry — See *Rubus* 'Youngberry'

Fruit and Vegetable Index

REVERSE SYNONYMS

The following list of reverse synonyms is intended to help users find from which genus an unfamiliar plant name has been cross-referred. For a fuller explanation see page 10

Acacia - Racosperma
Acanthocalyx - Morina
Acca - Feijoa
× Achicodonia - Eucodonia
Achillea - Anthemis
Acinos - Calamintha
Acinos - Micromeria
Aethionema - Eunomia
Agapetes - Pentapterygium
Agarista - Leucothoe
Agastache - Cedronella
Aichryson - Aeonium
Ajania - Chrysanthemum
Ajania - Eupatorium
Albizia - Acacia
Alcea - Althaea
Allardia - Waldheimia
Allocasuarina - Casuarina
Aloysia - Lippia
Althaea - Malva
Alyogyne - Hibiscus
Alyssum - Ptilotrichum
× Amarygia - Amaryllis
Amaryllis - Brunsvigia
Amomyrtus - Myrtus
Amsonia - Rhazya
Anaphalis - Gnaphalium
Anchusa - Lycopsis
Androsace - Douglasia
Anemone - Eriocapitella
Anisodontea - Malvastrum
Anomatheca - Lapeirousia
Anredera - Boussingaultia
Antirrhinum - Asarina
Aphanes - Alchemilla
Arctanthemum - Chrysanthemum
Arctostaphylos - Arbutus
Arctotis - × Venidioarctotis
Arctotis - Venidium
Arenga - Didymosperma
Argyranthemum - Anthemis
Argyranthemum - Chrysanthemum
Armoracia - Cochlearia
Arundinaria - Pseudosasa
Asarina - Antirrhinum
Asclepias - Gomphocarpus
Asparagus - Smilax
Asperula - Galium
Asphodeline - Asphodelus
Asplenium - Camptosorus
Asplenium - Ceterach
Asplenium - Phyllitis
Asplenium - Scolopendrium

Aster - Crinitaria
Aster - Microglossa
Asteriscus - Pallenis
Astilboides - Rodgersia
Atropanthe - Scopolia
Aurinia - Alyssum
Austrocedrus - Libocedrus
Azorella - Bolax
Azorina - Campanula
Bambusa - Arundinaria
Bashania - Arundinaria
Bellevalia - Muscari
Bellis - Erigeron
Blechnum - Lomaria
Bolax - Azorella
Bolboschoenus - Scirpus
Borago - Anchusa
Borinda - Fargesia
Bothriochloa - Andropogon
Boykinia - Telesonix
Brachyglottis - Senecio
Bracteantha - Helichrysum
Brimeura - Hyacinthus
Brugmansia - Datura
Brunnera - Anchusa
Buglossoides - Lithospermum
Bulbine - Bulbinopsis
Buphthalmum - Inula
Cacalia - Adenostyles
Caiophora - Loasa
Caladium - Xanthosoma
Calamagrostis - Agrostis
Calamagrostis - Stipa
Calamintha - Clinopodium
Calliergon - Acrocladium
Callisia - Phyodina
Callisia - Tradescantia
Calocedrus - Libocedrus
Calocephalus - Leucophyta
Calomeria - Humea
Caloscordum - Nothoscordum
Calytrix - Lhotzkya
Camellia - Thea
Cardamine - Dentaria
Carpobrotus - Lampranthus
Cassiope - Harrimanella
Catapodium - Desmazeria
Cayratia - Parthenocissus
Centaurium - Erythraea
Centella - Hydrocotyle
Centranthus - Kentranthus
Centranthus - Valeriana
Cephalaria - Scabiosa
Ceratostigma - Plumbago
Cercestis - Rhektophyllum
Cestrum - Iochroma
Chaenomeles - Cydonia
Chaenorhinum - Linaria
Chamaecyparis - Cupressus

Chamaecytisus - Cytisus
Chamaedaphne - Cassandra
Chamaemelum - Anthemis
Chasmanthium - Uniola
Cheilanthes - Notholaena
Chiastophyllum - Cotyledon
Chimonobambusa - Arundinaria
Chimonobambusa - Gelidocalamus
Chimonobambusa - Quiongzhuea
Chionohebe - Pygmea
× Chionoscilla - Scilla
Chlorophytum - Diuranthera
Chondrosum - Bouteloua
Chrysanthemum - Dendranthema
Cicerbita - Lactuca
Cionura - Marsdenia
Cissus - Ampelopsis
Cissus - Parthenocissus
× Citrofortunella - Citrus
Citronella - Villaresia
Clarkia - Eucharidium
Clarkia - Godetia
Clavinodum - Arundinaria
Claytonia - Calandrinia
Claytonia - Montia
Clematis - Atragene
Cleyera - Eurya
Clinopodium - Acinos
Clinopodium - Calamintha
Clytostoma - Bignonia
Clytostoma - Pandorea
Cnicus - Carduus
Codonopsis - Campanumoea
Colobanthus - Arenaria
Consolida - Delphinium
Cordyline - Dracaena
Cornus - Chamaepericlymenum
Cornus - Dendrobenthamia
Coronilla - Securigera
Cortaderia - Gynerium
Corydalis - Fumaria
Corydalis - Pseudofumaria
Cosmos - Bidens
Cotinus - Rhus
Cotula - Leptinella
Crassula - Rochea
Crassula - Sedum
Crassula - Tillaea
Cremanthodium - Ligularia
Crinodendron - Tricuspidaria
Crocosmia - Antholyza
Crocosmia - Curtonus
Crocosmia - Montbretia
Cruciata - Galium
Ctenanthe - Calathea
Ctenanthe - Stromanthe
× Cupressocyparis - Chamaecyparis
Cyathodes - Leucopogon
Cyathodes - Styphelia

Cyclosorus - Pneumatopteris
Cymbalaria - Linaria
Cynara - Scolymus
Cyperus - Mariscus
Cypripedium - Criogenes
Cyrtanthus - Anoiganthus
Cyrtanthus - Vallota
Cyrtomium - Phanarophlebia
Cyrtomium - Polystichum
Cytisus - Argyrocytisus
Cytisus - Genista
Cytisus - Lembotropis
Cytisus - Spartocytisus
Daboecia - Menziesia
Dacrycarpus - Podocarpus
Dactylorhiza - Orchis
Danae - Ruscus
Darmera - Peltiphyllum
Dasypyrum - Haynaldia
Datura - Brugmansia
Datura - Datura
Davallia - Humata
Delairea - Senecio
Delosperma - Lampranthus
Delosperma - Mesembryanthemum
Dendrocalamus - Bambusa
Derwentia - Hebe
Desmodium - Lespedeza
Dichelostemma - Brodiaea
Dicliptera - Barleria
Dicliptera - Justicia
Diervilla - Weigela
Dietes - Moraea
Diplazium - Athyrium
Disporopsis - Polygonatum
Distictis - Phaedranthus
Distylium - Sycopsis
Dolichothrix - Helichrysum
Dracaena - Pleomele
Dracunculus - Arum
Dregea - Wattakaka
Drepanostachyum - Arundinaria
Drepanostachyum -
    Thamnocalamus
Drepanostachyum -
    Chimonobambusa
Drimys - Tasmannia
Duchesnea - Fragaria
Dunalia - Acnistus
Dypsis - Chrysalidocarpus
Dypsis - Neodypsis
Echeveria - Cotyledon
Echinacea - Rudbeckia
Edraianthus - Wahlenbergia
Egeria - Elodea
Elatostema - Pellionia
Eleutherococcus - Acanthopanax
Elliottia - Botryostege
Elliottia - Cladothamnus
Elymus - Agropyron
Elymus - Leymus
Ensete - Musa

Epilobium - Chamaenerion
Epipremnum - Philodendron
Epipremnum - Scindapsus
Episcia - Alsobia
Eranthis - Aconitum
Erigeron - Aster
Erigeron - Haplopappus
Erysimum - Cheiranthus
Eucodonia - Achimenes
Eupatorium - Ageratina
Eupatorium - Ajania
Eupatorium - Ayapana
Eupatorium - Bartlettina
Euphorbia - Poinsettia
Euryops - Senecio
Fallopia - Bilderdykia
Fallopia - Polygonum
Fallopia - Reynoutria
Farfugium - Ligularia
Fargesia - Arundinaria
Fargesia - Sinarundinaria
Fargesia - Thamnocalamus
Fatsia - Aralia
Felicia - Agathaea
Felicia - Aster
Fibigia - Farsetia
Filipendula - Spiraea
Foeniculum - Ferula
Fortunella - Citrus
Furcraea - Agave
Galium - Asperula
Galtonia - Hyacinthus
Gaultheria - Chiogenes
Gaultheria - × Gaulnettya
Gaultheria - Pernettya
Gelasine - Sisyrinchium
Genista - Chamaespartium
Genista - Cytisus
Genista - Echinospartum
Genista - Teline
Gentianopsis - Gentiana
Gladiolus - Acidanthera
Gladiolus - Homoglossum
Gladiolus - Petamenes
Glechoma - Nepeta
Gloxinia - Seemannia
Gomphocarpus - Asclepias
Goniolimon - Limonium
Graptopetalum - Sedum
Graptopetalum - Tacitus
Greenovia - Sempervivum
Gymnospermium - Leontice
Habranthus - Zephyranthes
Hacquetia - Dondia
× Halimiocistus - Cistus
× Halimiocistus - Halimium
Halimione - Atriplex
Halimium - Cistus
Halimium - × Halimiocistus
Halimium - Helianthemum
Halocarpus - Dacrydium
Hechtia - Dyckia

Hedychium - Brachychilum
Hedyscepe - Kentia
Helianthella - Helianthus
Helianthemum - Cistus
Helianthus - Heliopsis
Helichrysum - Gnaphalium
Helictotrichon - Avena
Helictotrichon - Avenula
Heliopsis - Helianthus
Hepatica - Anemone
Herbertia - Alophia
Hermodactylus - Iris
Heterocentron - Schizocentron
Heterotheca - Chrysopsis
Hibbertia - Candollea
Hieracium - Andryala
Himalayacalamus - Arundinaria
Himalayacalamus -
    Drepanostachyum
Hippocrepis - Coronilla
Hippolytia - Achillea
Hippolytia - Tanacetum
Hoheria - Plagianthus
Homalocladium - Muehlenbeckia
Howea - Kentia
Hyacinthoides - Endymion
Hyacinthoides - Scilla
Hymenocallis - Elisena
Hymenocallis - Ismene
Hyophorbe - Mascarena
Hypochaeris - Hieracium
Incarvillea - Amphicome
Indocalamus - Sasa
Ipheion - Tristagma
Ipheion - Triteleia
Ipomoea - Mina
Ipomoea - Pharbitis
Ipomopsis - Gilia
Ischyrolepis - Restio
Ismelia - Chrysanthemum
Isolepis - Scirpus
Jamesbrittenia - Sutera
Jeffersonia - Plagiorhegma
Jovibarba - Sempervivum
Juncus - Scirpus
Jurinea - Jurinella
Justicia - Beloperone
Justicia - Jacobinia
Justicia - Libonia
Kalanchoe - Bryophyllum
Kalanchoe - Kitchingia
Kalimeris - Aster
Kalimeris - Asteromoea
Kalimeris - Boltonia
Kalopanax - Eleutherococcus
Keckiella - Penstemon
Knautia - Scabiosa
Kniphofia - Tritoma
Kohleria - Isoloma
Kunzea - Leptospermum
Lablab - Dolichos
Lagarosiphon - Elodea

Lagarostrobos - Dacrydium
Lallemantia - Dracocephalum
Lamium - Galeobdolon
Lamium - Lamiastrum
Lampranthus -
    Mesembryanthemum
Lampranthus - Oscularia
Laurentia - Hippobroma
Lavatera - Malva
Ledebouria - Scilla
× Ledodendron - Rhododendron
Lepechinia - Sphacele
Lepidothamnus - Dacrydium
Leptinella - Cotula
Leptodactylon - Gilia
Leucanthemella - Chrysanthemum
Leucanthemella - Leucanthemum
Leucanthemopsis - Chrysanthemum
Leucanthemopsis - Tanacetum
Leucanthemum - Chrysanthemum
Leucochrysum - Helipterum
Leucophyta - Calocephalus
Leucopogon - Cyathodes
× Leucoraoulia - Raoulia
Leuzea - Centaurea
Leymus - Elymus
Ligularia - Senecio
Ligustrum - Parasyringa
Lilium - Nomocharis
Limonium - Statice
Linanthus - Linanthastrum
Lindelofia - Adelocaryum
Lindera - Parabenzoin
Liriope - Ophiopogon
Lithocarpus - Quercus
Lithodora - Lithospermum
Littorella - Plantago
Lophomyrtus - Myrtus
Lophomyrtus - Myrtus
Lophospermum - Asarina
Lophospermum - Maurandya
Lophostemon - Tristania
Lotus - Dorycnium
Lotus - Tetragonolobus
Ludwigia - Jussiaea
Luma - Myrtus
× Lycene - Lychnis
Lychnis - Agrostemma
Lychnis - Silene
Lychnis - Viscaria
Lycianthes - Solanum
Lytocaryum - Cocos
Lytocaryum - Microcoelum
Macfadyena - Bignonia
Macfadyena - Doxantha
Machaeranthera - Xylorhiza
Mackaya - Asystasia
Macleaya - Bocconia
Mahonia - Berberis
Mandevilla - Dipladenia
Mandragora - Atropa
Marrubium - Ballota

Matricaria - Chamomilla
Matricaria - Tripleurospermum
Maurandella - Asarina
Maurandella - Maurandya
Maurandya - Asarina
Melicytus - Hymenanthera
Melinis - Rhynchelytrum
Mentha - Preslia
Merremia - Ipomoea
Millettia - Wisteria
Mimulus - Diplacus
Minuartia - Arenaria
Modiolastrum - Malvastrum
Moltkia - Lithodora
Moltkia - Lithospermum
Morina - Acanthocalyx
Mukdenia - Aceriphyllum
Muscari - Hyacinthus
Muscari - Leopoldia
Muscari - Leopoldia
Muscari - Muscarimia
Muscari - Pseudomuscari
Myricaria - Tamarix
Myrteola - Myrtus
Naiocrene - Claytonia
Naiocrene - Montia
Nectaroscordum - Allium
Nematanthus - Hypocyrta
Nemesia - Diascia
Neopaxia - Claytonia
Neopaxia - Montia
Neoregelia - Guzmania
Neoregelia - Nidularium
Nepeta - Dracocephalum
Nepeta - Origanum
Nephrophyllidium - Fauria
Nertera - Coprosma
Nipponanthemum -
    Chrysanthemum
Nipponanthemum - Leucanthemum
Nymphoides - Villarsia
Oemleria - Osmaronia
Olearia - Pachystegia
Olsynium - Phaiophleps
Olsynium - Sisyrinchium
Onixotis - Dipidax
Ophiopogon - Convallaria
Orchis - Dactylorhiza
Oreopteris - Thelypteris
Orostachys - Sedum
Osmanthus - × Osmarea
Osmanthus - Phillyrea
Osteospermum - Dimorphotheca
Othonna - Hertia
Othonna - Othonnopsis
Ozothamnus - Helichrysum
Pachyphragma - Cardamine
Packera - Senecio
Paederota - Veronica
Papaver - Meconopsis
Parahebe - Derwentia
Parahebe - Hebe

Parahebe - Veronica
Paraserianthes - Albizia
Paris - Daiswa
Parthenocissus - Ampelopsis
Parthenocissus - Vitis
Passiflora - Tetrapathaea
Paxistima - Pachystema
Pecteilis - Habenaria
Pelargonium - Geranium
Peltoboykinia - Boykinia
Penstemon - Chelone
Pentaglottis - Anchusa
Pentalinon - Urechites
Pericallis - Senecio
Persea - Machilus
Persicaria - Aconogonon
Persicaria - Bistorta
Persicaria - Polygonum
Persicaria - Tovara
Petrocoptis - Lychnis
Petrophytum - Spiraea
Petrorhagia - Tunica
Petroselinum - Carum
Phegopteris - Thelypteris
Phoenicaulis - Parrya
Photinia - Heteromeles
Photinia - Stransvaesia
Photinia - × Stravinia
Phuopsis - Crucianella
Phyla - Lippia
Phymosia - Sphaeralcea
Physoplexis - Phyteuma
Physostegia - Dracocephalum
Pieris - Arcterica
Pilosella - Hieracium
Piper - Macropiper
Pisonia - Heimerliodendron
Plagiomnium - Mnium
Plecostachys - Helichrysum
Plectranthus - Solenostemon
Pleioblastus - Arundinaria
Pleioblastus - Sasa
Podranea - Tecoma
Polianthes - Bravoa
Polygonum - Persicaria
Polypodium - Phlebodium
Polystichum - Phanerophlebia
Poncirus - Aegle
Potentilla - Comarum
Pratia - Lobelia
Prumnopitys - Podocarpus
Prunus - Amygdalus
Pseudocydonia - Chaenomeles
Pseudopanax - Metapanax
Pseudopanax - Neopanax
Pseudopanax - Nothopanax
Pseudosasa - Arundinaria
Pseudotsuga - Tsuga
Pseudowintera - Drimys
Pterocephalus - Scabiosa
Ptilostemon - Cirsium
Pulicaria - Inula

Pulsatilla - Anemone
Pushkinia - Scilla
Pyrethropsis - Argyranthemum
Pyrethropsis - Chrysanthemum
Pyrethropsis - Leucanthemopsis
Pyrethropsis - Leucanthemum
Reineckea - Liriope
Retama - Genista
Rhapis - Chamaerops
Rhodanthe - Helipterum
Rhodanthemum - Chrysanthemopsis
Rhodanthemum - Chrysanthemum
Rhodanthemum -
   Leucanthemopsis
Rhodanthemum - Pyrethropsis
Rhodiola - Clementsia
Rhodiola - Rosularia
Rhodiola - Sedum
Rhododendron - Azalea
Rhododendron - Azaleodendron
Rhododendron - Rhodora
Rhodophiala - Hippeastrum
Rosularia - Cotyledon
Rosularia - Sempervivella
Rothmannia - Gardenia
Ruellia - Dipteracanthus
Ruschia - Mesembryanthemum
Rytidosperma - Merxmuellera
Saccharum - Erianthus
Sagina - Minuartia
Salvia - Salvia
Sanguisorba - Dendriopoterium
Sanguisorba - Poterium
Sasa - Arundinaria
Sasa - Pleioblastus
Sasaella - Arundinaria
Sasaella - Pleioblastus
Sasaella - Sasa
Sasamorpha - Sasa
Sauromatum - Arum
Saussurea - Jurinea
Scadoxus - Haemanthus
Schefflera - Brassaia
Schefflera - Dizygotheca
Schefflera - Heptapleurum
Schizachyrium - Andropogon
Schizostachyum - Arundinaria
Schizostachyum - Thamnocalamus
Schoenoplectus - Scirpus
Scirpoides - Scirpus
Scirpus - Eriophorum
Sedum - Hylotelephium
Sedum - Rhodiola
Sedum - Sedastrum
Sedum - Villadia
Semiaquilegia - Aquilegia
Semiaquilegia - Paraquilegia
Semiarundinaria - Arundinaria

Semiarundinaria - Oligostachyum
Senecio - Cineraria
Senecio - Kleinia
Senecio - Ligularia
Senna - Cassia
Seriphidium - Artemisia
Shortia - Schizocodon
Sibbaldiopsis - Potentilla
Sieversia - Geum
Silene - Lychnis
Silene - Melandrium
Silene - Saponaria
Sinacalia - Ligularia
Sinacalia - Senecio
Sinarundinaria - Semiarundinaria
Sinningia - Gesneria
Sinningia - Rechsteineria
Sisymbrium - Hesperis
Sisyrinchium - Phaiophleps
× Smithicodonia - × Achimenantha
Solanum - Lycianthes
Soleirolia - Helxine
Solenopsis, - Isotoma
Solenostemon, - Coleus
× Solidaster - Aster
× Solidaster - Solidago
Sorbaria - Spiraea
Sparaxis - Synnotia
Sphaeralcea - Iliamna
Sphaeromeria - Tanacetum
Spirodela - Lemna
Spraguea - Calyptridium
Stachys - Betonica
Steirodiscus - Gamolepis
Stenomesson - Urceolina
Stenotus - Haplopappus
Steptocarpus - Streptocarpella
Stewartia - Stuartia
Stipa - Achnatherum
Stipa - Lasiagrostis
Strobilanthes - Pteracanthus
Succisa - Scabiosa
Sutera - Bacopa
Syagrus - Arecastrum
Syagrus - Cocos
Tanacetum - Achillea
Tanacetum - Balsamita
Tanacetum - Chrysanthemum
Tanacetum - Matricaria
Tanacetum - Pyrethrum
Tanacetum - Spathipappus
Tanacetum - Sphaeromeria
Tecoma - Tecomaria
Tecomaria - Tecoma
Telekia - Buphthalmum
Tephroseris - Senecio
Tetradium - Euodia
Tetraneuris - Actinella

Tetraneuris - Hymenoxys
Tetrapanax - Fatsia
Thamnocalamus - Arundinaria
Thamnocalamus - Sinarundinaria
Thlaspi - Hutchinsia
Thlaspi - Noccaea
Thuja - Platycladus
Thuja - Thujopsis
Thymus - Origanum
Tonestus - Haplopappus
Toona - Cedrela
Trachelium - Diosphaera
Trachycarpus - Chamaerops
Tradescantia - Rhoeo
Tradescantia - Setcreasea
Tradescantia - Tradescantia
Tradescantia - Zebrina
Trichopetalum - Anthericum
Trichophorum - Scirpus
Tripetaleia - Elliottia
Tripleurospermum - Matricaria
Tripogandra - Tradescantia
Tristagma - Beauverdia
Tristaniopsis - Tristania
Triteleia - Brodiaea
Tritonia - Crocosmia
Tropaeolum - Nasturtium hort.
Tuberaria - Helianthemum
Tulipa - Amana
Tweedia - Oxypetalum
Ugni - Myrtus
Ursinia - Euryops
Uvularia - Oakesiella
Vaccinium - Oxycoccus
Verbascum - Celsia
Verbascum -
   × Celsioverbascum
Verbena - Glandularia
Verbena - Lippia
Veronicastrum - Veronica
Vigna - Phaseolus
Villadia - Sedum
Viola - Erpetion
Vitaliana - Androsace
Vitaliana - Douglasia
Weigela - Diervilla
Weigela - Macrodiervilla
Xanthophthalmum -
   Chrysanthemum
Xanthorhiza - Zanthorhiza
Yushania - Arundinaria
Yushania - Sinarundinaria
Yushania - Thamnocalamus
Zantedeschia - Calla
Zauschneria - Epilobium
Zephyranthes - × Cooperanthes
Zephyranthes - Cooper

Reverse Synonyms

Plant Deletions

Plants marked with '95', '96' or '97' were listed in the corresponding edition of the book (e.g. '95' = 1995/96 edition). **Earlier deletions are available as a supplementary list** (for a fuller explanation of Deletions, see page 10).
Back editions of *The RHS Plant Finder* may be obtained by writing to:
The Administrator, The RHS Plant Finder, RHS Gardens, Wisley, Woking, Surrey GU23 6QB
Price £6.00 each inclusive of p&p. Please make cheques payable to RHS Enterprises Ltd.

ABELIA
97 *graebneriana*
96 × *grandiflora* dwarf form

ABIES
96 *alba* 'Green Spiral'
96 – 'Pendula'
97 *borisii-regis*
96 *chensiensis*
96 *concolor* 'Argentea'
96 *delavayi*
97 – var. *delavayi*
95 *densa* S&L 5538
96 *kawakamii*
96 *koreana* 'Blauer Pfiff'
96 *lasiocarpa*
96 *nordmanniana* 'Reflexa'
95 *numidica* 'Lawrenceville'
97 *pinsapo* var. *marocana*
95 – 'Pendula'
95 *procera* 'Prostrata'
96 *recurvata* var. *ernestii*
97 *religiosa*
96 *spectabilis*
95 *vejarii*

ABRUS
97 *cantoniensis*
97 *precatorius*

ABUTILON
97 'Alpha Glory'
95 'Imp'
96 'Lemon Queen'
97 *megapotamicum* 'Wisley Red'
95 'Orange Glow' (v) ♀
95 'Orange Vein'
95 'Oxon Red'
95 × *suntense* 'White Charm'

ACACIA
95 *beckleri*
96 *boormanii*
95 *brachybotrya*
95 *burkittii*
95 *chlorophylla*
97 *dealbata* 'Gaulois Astier'
97 – 'Mirandole'
97 – 'Rêve d'Or'
97 *erioloba*
95 *extensa*
96 *gillii*
97 *tortilis*

ACAENA
95 *argentea*
97 *glabra*
97 *minor*
97 *sericea*
95 sp. RB 94004

ACANTHOLIMON
95 *acerosum* var. *acerosum*
95 *hypochaerum*
96 *litvinovii*

ACANTHUS
97 *caroli-alexandri*

ACER
96 *campestre* 'Autumn Red'
96 – 'Nanum'
95 – 'Queen Elizabeth'
96 – 'Rockhampton Red Stem'
96 – 'Weeping'
96 *cappadocicum* subsp. *sinicum* var. *tricaudatum*
97 *carnea* 'Variegatum'
96 *caudatum*
96 × *coriaceum*
96 × *dieckii*
96 *distylum*
96 *forrestii* TW 348
96 × *freemanii* 'Elegant'
97 *japonicum* 'O-taki'
96 – 'Viride'
96 *miyabei*
96 *nipponicum*
96 *palmatum* 'Crippsii'
96 – 'Mizu-kuguri'
96 – 'Monzukushi'
96 – 'Shichihenge'
96 – 'Tatsuta-gawa'
96 – 'Wada's Flame'
96 *pectinatum*
96 *platanoides* 'Reitenbachii'
97 *rubrum* 'Armstrong'
95 – 'Tridens'
95 *saccharum* 'Aureum'
97 *serrulatum* CC 1891
96 *sieboldianum* 'Kinugasayama'
97 sp. CC 1648
95 *stachyanthum*
97 *tenellum*

ACHILLEA
96 *ageratifolia* subsp. *ageratifolia* NS 692
97 'Crimson King'
97 'James Chapman'
97 *millefolium* 'Sweet Harmony'
95 'Moonbeam'
96 *nana*
95 'Obristii'
96 *odorata*
96 'Peach Queen'
95 'Theo Ploeger'
97 *umbellata* NS 390

ACHIMENES
97 'Aries'
96 'Margaret White'
96 'Mauve Queen'
95 'Miss Blue'
95 'Ruby'
97 *selloana*
96 'Violetta'

ACIPHYLLA
97 *aurea* CC 464

ACONITUM
97 *colensoi major*
97 *crosby-smithii*
97 *horrida*
95 *lamondii*
97 *monroi*
96 *procumbens*

ACONITUM
95 × *cammarum* 'Franz Marc'
96 *elliotii*
97 *falconeri*
97 *gymnandrum*
96 *hookeri*
95 *smithii*
97 *stapfianum* B&L 12038

ACTINIDIA
95 'Ananasnaya' (f)
96 *arguta* 'Stamford' (f)
96 *deliciosa* 'Boskoop'

ADENOCARPUS
96 *foliolosus*

ADENOPHORA
97 *axilliflora*
97 *coronopifolia*
97 *divaricata*
97 *pereskiifolia* 'Alba'
97 – var. *heterotricha*
97 – *uryuensis*
97 *potaninii* 'Alba'
97 – lilac
96 – 'Lilacina Flora Plena'
97 sp. Yunnan
97 *takedae*
97 *triphylla* var. *japonica*
97 – var. *puellaris*
97 *uehatae*

ADONIS
97 *aestivalis*

AECHMEA
96 *chantinii* ♀
97 Foster's Favorite Group ♀
97 *gamosepala*
96 'Grand Prix'
95 *nudicaulis* ♀
95 *orlandiana* ♀
96 'Romero'

AEGOPODIUM
97 *podagraria* 'Hullavington' (v)

AEONIUM
95 *arboreum* var. *rubrolineatum*

AESCHYNANTHUS
97 *rigidus*

AESCULUS
95 *hippocastanum* 'Memmingeri'
95 – 'Monstrosa'

AETHIONEMA
96 *caespitosum*
95 *glaucum*
97 *schistosum*

AGAPANTHUS
97 'Accebt'
97 *alboroseus*
96 'Apple Court'
96 'Ben Hope'
96 'Bicton Hybrid'
97 'Bleuet'
96 'Blue Star'
95 'Dawnstar'
96 'Kew White'
97 pale form
96 'Peter Pan' American
95 *praecox* subsp. *orientalis* 'Mount Thomas'
96 'Spode'
97 'Storm Cloud' (d)
96 'Super Star'
96 'White Giant'
96 'White Star'
96 'White Starlet'

AGASTACHE
96 *cana* variegated
96 *mexicana* 'Carminea'
95 *pallidiflora*
95 *palmeri*
96 *urticifolia* 'Alba Variegata'

AGATHOSMA
97 *ovata* 'Kleitijies Kraal'

AGAVE
95 *americana* 'Mediopicta Alba' ♀
96 *bovicornuta*
96 *ferdinandi-regis*
96 *franzosinii*
96 *potatorum* ♀
97 *schottii*
96 *sebastiana*
96 *shawii* subsp. *goldmaniana*
95 *striata rubra*
97 *utahensis* var. *discreta*
96 – var. *eborispina*
96 – subsp. *kaibabensis*

AGROSTIS
97 *stolonifera*

AINSLIAEA
95 *paucicapitata* B&SWJ 103

AIPHANES
95 *caryotifolia*

AJANIA
95 *pacifica* 'Hakai'

AJUGA
95 *genevensis* 'Pink Beauty'
97 *reptans* 'Carol'
96 – 'Cavalier'
97 – 'Harlequin' (v)
96 – 'Jungle Bronze'
97 – 'Pat's Selection'
96 – 'Silver Carpet'
95 – 'Tortoiseshell' (v)

ALCEA
96 *rosea* double white (d)
95 – Powder Puff Group
97 – single
96 – single white
97 *rugosa alba*
96 – 'Caucasian Yellow'

ALCHEMILLA
95 *falklandica*
96 *hoppeana* Della Torre
97 *robusta*

ALETRIS
96 *farinosa*

ALKANNA
97 *aucheriana*
97 *tinctoria*

ALLAMANDA
96 *blanchetii*
96 *cathartica* 'Stansill's Double' (d)

ALLARDIA
95 *tomentosa*
95 *tridactylites*

ALLIUM
95 *aflatunense* Fedtschenko
97 *anceps*
97 *canadense*
96 *carolinianum* CC 322
97 *cernuum album*
97 *cupanii* subsp. *hirtovaginatum*
97 *fimbriatum* var. *abramsii*
96 – var. *purdyi*
96 *fistulosum* red
97 – 'Streaker'
97 *haematochiton*
97 *jepsonii*
96 *libonicum*
95 *narcissiflorum* Villars pink
97 *peninsulare*
95 *rosenbachianum* 'Akbulak'
97 *roseum album*
96 – var. *carneum*
95 *rubrovittatum* CDB 292
97 *sarawschanicum*
96 *schoenoprasum* 'Shepherds Crooks'
97 *sikkimense* ACE 1363
96 sp. ACE 1745
97 *stellerianum* var. *kurilense*
97 *strictum*
96 *subhirsutum*
96 *thunbergii* 'Nanum'

ALLOCASUARINA
95 *distyla*

ALNUS
96 *formosana*
96 *jorullensis*
95 *oblongifolia*
95 *pendula*
95 *pinnatisecta*

ALOE
95 *bakeri* ♀
97 *cooperi*
97 *erinacea*
96 *melanacantha* ♀
96 *mitriformis*

---

97 *parvibracteata*
95 *rauhii* ♀
95 *somaliensis* ♀

ALOINOPSIS
97 *lueckhoffii*

ALONSOA
97 *acutifolia*
97 *meridionalis* 'Salmon Beauty'

ALOPECURUS
95 *arundinaceus*

ALPINIA
96 *purpurata*
96 *vittata* (v)
96 *zerumbet*

ALSTROEMERIA
96 *diluta*
95 aff. *exserens*
95 –
97 'Hatch Hybrid'
95 *hookeri* subsp. *cummingiana*
95 – subsp. *hookeri*
97 *ligtu* var. *ligtu*
96 *magnifica*
95 'Ohio'
97 *pallida* F&W 7241
96 – JJA 12497
96 *presliana*
96 Princess Margarita
96 'Purple Joy'
95 *revoluta*
96 'Rosy Wings'
95 'Saffier'
95 'Saxony'
97 'Solent Arrow'
97 'Solent Dawn'
97 'Solent Glow'
97 'Solent Mist'
97 'Solent Wings'
96 'Sovereign'
95 sp. Wr 8893
97 *spathulata*
97 Margaret = 'Stacova'
95 'Sunrise'
97 *umbellata*
96 'Vanitas'
96 *versicolor*
96 'White Knight'

ALYSSUM
96 *moellendorfianum*
95 *poderi*
97 *propinquum*
97 *repens*
95 *scardicum*
96 *sphacioticum*
96 *tenium*

× AMARINE
97 *tubergenii*

AMBROSIA
97 *mexicana*

AMELANCHIER
95 *asiatica*

AMMOCHARIS
97 *coranica*

AMOMUM
96 *compactum*

AMPELOPSIS
97 sp. Taiwan B&SWJ 1173

ANACYCLUS
97 *pyrethrum* var. *depressus* 'Silberkissen'

ANAGALLIS
96 *monellii* red

ANAPHALIS
96 *nepalensis*
97 – var. *monocephala* CC&McK 550

ANDROMEDA
95 *polifolia* 'Red King'

ANDROPOGON
97 *saccharoides*

ANDROSACE
96 *bisulca* var. *aurata* ACE 1750
96 *carnea* subsp. *brigantiaca* Myer's form
96 – subsp. *rosea* × *carnea* subsp. *laggeri*
97 *foliosa*
97 × *heeri*
96 *helvetica*
96 *lanuginosa* CC 1271
96 *lehmannii* EMAK 951
97 *muscoidea* f. *muscoidea*
95 × *pedemontana*
96 *rotundifolia* 'Elegans'
97 *sarmentosa* 'Brilliant'
96 – *monstrosa*
96 *septentrionalis* 'Stardust'
97 *spinulifera*
96 *strigillosa*
96 *tridentata*

ANEMONE
96 *blanda* 'Blue Star'
97 – 'Ingramii' CE&H 626
96 *caucasica*
96 *cernua*
96 *coronaria* 'Blue Moon'
97 – 'Creagh Castle'
97 *demissa*
96 × *hybrida* 'Alba Dura'
97 – 'Thomas Ahrens'
95 *nemorosa* 'Green Dream'
96 *raddeana*
97 *sherriffii*
96 *trifolia* pink

ANGELICA
96 *pinnata*
96 *triquinata*

ANIGOZANTHOS
96 *flavidus* green
96 *preissii*

ANISOTOME
97 *latifolia*

ANODA
95 *crenatiflora*
96 *cristata*

ANOMATHECA
96 *laxa* Blue Form
95 – *viridiflora*
96 *moisii*

ANTENNARIA
95 *dimorpha*
97 *microphylla* var. *rosea*

ANTHEMIS
97 *arvensis*
97 *tinctoria* 'Gold Mound'

ANTHRISCUS
97 *sylvestris*

ANTHYLLIS
96 *montana* 'Rubra Compacta'

ANTIRRHINUM
96 *barrellieri*
97 'White Monarch'

APHELANDRA
97 *alexandri*

APIUM
97 *nodiflorum*
97 *prostratum*

AQUILEGIA
96 *alpina* 'Carl Ziepke'
96 – German form
97 *caerulea* var. *pinetorum*
95 *chrysantha* double dark red (d)
97 'Dwarf Fairyland'
96 *flabellata* double white
97 – var. *pumila* 'Snowflakes'
97 *formosa* var. *formosa*
96 – × *longissima*
97 *fragrans* ex CC&MR 96
97 – ex KBE 48
96 *karelinii*
96 *kurdistanica*
96 Lowdham strain
96 × *maruyamana*
96 'Maxi Star'
97 *melange pygmaea*
96 *microphylla*
97 *moorcroftiana* CC 1414
95 *ottonis* subsp. *ottonis*
97 *rockii* CLD 0437
97 – KGB 176
97 'Rose Red'
96 sp. from Zigana Pass, Turkey
96 *vulgaris* 'Anne Calder'
96 – 'Belhaven Blue'
95 – var. *flore-pleno* green (d)
97 – – purple (d)
96 –
     from Brno, Czech Republic
96 – from Rize, Turkey
96 – 'Gisela Powell'
97 – 'Miss Coventry'
95 – subsp. *nevadensis*
96 – 'Ruth Steer'
96 – scented
96 – tall form
96 – 'Warwick'

ARABIS
97 *alpina* subsp. *caucasica* 'Corfe Castle'
95 – – 'Gillian Sharman' (v)
96 – – 'Snow White'
97 × *arendsii* 'La Fraicheur'
97 – 'Rose Frost'
97 *bryoides olympica*
95 *caerulea*
97 'Cloth of Gold'

95 *koehleri*
96 *microphylla*
96 'Pink Snow'
96 *soyeri*

ARACHNIODES
96 *simplicior* C&L 236
97 *standishii*

ARALIA
97 *continentalis* CC 1035
95 *decaisneana* CC 1925
96 *elata* 'Silver Umbrella'

ARBUTUS
97 *xalapensis*

ARCTOSTAPHYLOS
97 *nevadensis* var.
  coloradensis

ARCTOTIS
96 *grandiflora*
95 x *hybrida* 'Champagne'
95 – cream
96 – 'Harlequin'
96 – 'Irene'
97 – 'Midday Sun'
96 – orange
95 – 'Pollen'
97 – 'Tangerine'
95 – white
97 'Prostrate Raspberry'

ARENARIA
95 *fendleri*
97 *hookeri* var. *desertorum*
  NNS 93-53
97 *kingii*
96 *lithops*
95 *longifolia*
95 *procera*
95 *saxosonum*
95 sp. CC 1368
95 *tetraquetra* JJA 188.450

ARGYLIA
97 *adscendens*

ARGYRANTHEMUM
97 'Chelsea Princess'
96 double yellow (d)
97 *frutescens* subsp.
  frutescens
97 'Mini-star Yellow'
96 'Rosali' (d)
97 'Stydd Rose'
95 'Whiteknights' ♀

ARISAEMA
97 *consanguineum*
  CLD 1519
97 *flavum* subsp.
  intermedium
97 *fraternum*
96 *griffithii* var. *pradhanii*
96 *jacquemontii* SEP 263
95 *longilaminum*
97 *quinatum*
97 – *pusillum*
97 – *zebrinum*

ARISTIDA
97 *purpurea*

ARISTOTELIA
97 *peduncularis*

ARMERIA
96 *leucocephala*
97 sp. from Patagonia

ARNEBIA
97 *densiflora*

ARNICA
95 *angustifolia*
97 *cordifolia*
95 *louisiana*

ARTEMISIA
96 *campestris*
96 *rupestris*
96 sp. B&SWJ 088

ARTHROPODIUM
95 *cirratum* 'Three
  Knights'
95 – 'White Knights'

ARUM
97 *dioscoridis* var.
  dioscoridis
95 *euxinum*
97 *hygrophilum*
95 *italicum* subsp.
  italicum 'Tiny'
97 *orientale* subsp.
  sintenisii
96 *rupicola*
96 – var. *rupicola*
96 – var. *virescens*

ARUNCUS
96 *dioicus* var.
  kamtschaticus AGSJ 59
96 sp. CLD 718

ASCLEPIAS
95 *amplexicaulis*
95 *cryptoceras*
95 *exaltata*
96 *incarnata* 'Alba'
97 – 'White Superior'
95 *rubra*

ASPERULA
96 *perpusilla*
97 *purpurascens*
95 *taygetea* NS 758

ASPHODELINE
97 *brevicaulis*

ASPHODELUS
97 *albus* subsp. *albus*

ASPLENIUM
95 *marinum*
95 *onopteris*
95 *rhizophyllum*
95 *scolopendrium*
  (Crispum Group)
  'Horning'
95 – 'Crispum Variegatum
  Bolton'
97 – 'Spirale'
97 *septentrionale*
97 *trichomanes* 'Incisum
  Moule'
95 – subsp. *pachyrachis*

ASTER
95 *alpinus* 'Roseus'
95 *amellus* 'Praecox
  Junifreude'
96 *bellidiastrum*
97 *delavayi* CLD 0494
96 *ericoides* 'Blue Heaven'
97 – 'Dainty'
95 *flaccidus*
96 *foliaceus* var. *cusickii*
96 *himalaicus* BM&W 12

96 – EMAK 0952
97 *lateriflorus* 'Daisy
  Bush'
97 *maackii*
95 *nepaulensis*
95 *novae-angliae* 'Ernie
  Moss'
97 – 'Forncett Jewel'
95 – 'Lye End Companion'
96 *novi-belgii* 'Flamingo'
95 – 'Little Blue Baby'
97 – 'Mabel Reeves'
97 – 'Marie Ann Neil'
97 – 'Norton Fayre'
96 – 'Pink Buttons'
97 – 'Reitlinstal'
96 – 'Rembrandt'
97 – 'Sandford's Purple'
97 – 'Triumph'
95 *procumbens*
96 *shortii*
97 sp. CC&McK 145
97 *spathulifolius*
96 *yunnanensis*

ASTERISCUS
96 *spinosus*

ASTILBE
96 x *arendsii* 'Lilli Goos'
95 *biternata*
96 'Carmine King'
97 'Carnea'
  (*simplicifolia* hybrid)
97 'Darwin's Surprise'
96 'Möwe' (*japonica* hybrid)
95 'Nana'
  (*simplicifolia* hybrid)
97 x *rosea* 'Queen
  Alexandra'
95 'Saxosa' x *glaberrima*
96 *simplicifolia* 'Sheila
  Haxton'
95 sp. CLD 1559
97 'Sprite'

ASTRAGALUS
95 *amphioxys*
97 *arnotianus*
97 *odoratus*
96 *penduliflorus*
96 *purpureus*
95 *thompsoniae*
97 *whitneyi* var.
  lenophyllus NNS 93-98
95 – *leucophyllus*

ASTRANTHIUM
97 *beamanii*

ASYNEUMA
96 *limonifolium*
97 – subsp. *pestalozzae*

ATHAMANTA
96 *macedonica*

ATHYRIUM
97 *filix-femina* 'Rotstiel'
95 *frangulum*
96 *strigulosum*

AUBRIETA
96 'Alida Vahli'
97 'Blue Mist'
96 'Bonfire'
97 'Bonsul'
96 'Cumulus'
97 *deltoidea* 'Tauricola
  Variegata'

97 'Graeca'
97 'Hartswood Purple'
95 'Henslow Purple'
97 'Lilac Cascade'
97 'Pennine Glory'
97 'Pennine Heather'
97 'Red Carpet
  Variegated'
97 'Rosea Plena'

AUCUBA
97 *japonica* (f)
95 – 'Fructu Albo'
97 – 'Lance Leaf' (m/v)

AULAX
97 *cancellata*

AURINIA
96 *petraea*

AZARA
97 *alpina* SF 4583
97 *patagonica*

AZORELLA
95 Sydamerik form

BAMBUSA
97 *oldhamii*
97 *vulgaris*
97 – 'Vittata'
97 – 'Wamin'

BANKSIA
97 *burdettii*
97 *caleyi*
97 *media*

BAPTISIA
95 *alba*
97 *arachnifera*
97 *australis* dark blue form
97 *megacarpa*

BARLERIA
97 *cristata*
97 – *rosea*
97 *greenii*
97 *obtusa* pink
97 *repens* 'Blue Prince'
97 – 'Rosea'

BAUMEA
97 *rubiginosa* 'Variegata'

BECKMANNIA
97 *eruciformis*

BEGONIA
96 'Bertinii' (T)
97 *coccifera*
96 *fimbriata*
96 'Gloire de Lorraine'
95 'Sandersonii'
97 'Trout' (C)

BELLEVALIA
96 *forniculata* JCA 227.770

BELLIS
97 *perennis* 'Dawn Raider'
97 – 'Super Enorma'
95 – 'White Pearl'

BERBERIS
95 'Blenheim'
97 *concinna* B&SWJ 2124
96 x *hybridogagnepainii*
  'Robin Hood'
97 *koreana* 'Red Tears'
95 x *stenophylla*
  'Corallina'

96 *thunbergii* 'Vermilion'
97 *wallichiana* B&SWJ 2432

BERGENIA
95 *afghanica*
95 'Borodin'
95 'Croesus'
95 'Distinction'
96 'Eroica'
97 'Pugsley's Purple'
97 *purpurascens* hybrid
95 x *spathulata*
96 *stracheyi* red
95 'Summer Mountain'

BESSEYA
95 *wyomingensis*

BETA
96 *vulgaris* 'Bull's Blood'

BETULA
95 *delavayi*
97 – B&L 12260
97 *fontinalis*
97 *forrestii* Yu 10561
97 *glandulosa*
97 *globispica*
97 *litvinovii*
97 *medwedewii* 'Gold Bark'
97 *megrelica*
97 *papyrifera* var. *commutata*
95 – var. *minor*
95 *pendula arvii*
96 – var. *pendula* 'Dissecta'
97 *pubescens* subsp. *celtiberica*
97 *saposhnikovii*
95 sp. CLD 407
97 *utilis* CC 1409
97 – 'Gregory Birch'
97 – S&L 5380

BIARUM
95 *carratracense*
95 *dispar*
95 *tenuifolium* var. *abbreviatum*
95 – var. *zeleborii*

BIDENS
96 *ferulifolia* 'Golden Goddess'
97 *pilosa*
97 *triplinervia* var. *macrantha*

BILLARDIERA
97 *cordata*
97 *erubescens*

BLECHNUM
96 *auriculatum*

BLOOMERIA
96 *crocea* var. *aurea* JCA 13091

BOLUSANTHUS
97 *speciosus*

BOMAREA
95 *multiflora*
96 *sasilla*

BOOPHANE
97 *disticha*
97 *guttata*

BOSCIA
95 *albitrunca*

BOUGAINVILLEA
96 'Albo d'Ora'
95 'Indha' (*glabra* hybrid)
97 'Ninja Turtle' (v)
97 'Pearl'
97 'Poultonii Variegata'
97 'Ratana Orange'
97 'Ratana Red'
97 'Red Fantasy' (v)
95 'Royal Bengal Red' (v)
95 'Sea Foam'
95 *spectabilis* 'Royal Bengal Orange' (v)
97 – 'Variegata'
97 (Spectoperuviana Group) 'Makris'
96 'White Empress'

BOUVARDIA
96 x *domestica*
95 *scabrida*
95 *ternifolia*

BOYKINIA
96 *major*

BRACHYCHITON
97 *populneus*

BRACHYLAENA
97 *discolor*

BRACHYPODIUM
97 *phoenicoides*

BRACHYSCOME
95 'Lemon Drops'

BRACTEANTHA
95 *bracteata* 'Golden Beauty'

BRAYA
96 *alpina*

BRIGGSIA
97 *muscicola*

BRIZA
97 *media* Elatior Group
96 *minor*
97 *triloba*

BRODIAEA
97 *jolonensis*
97 *leptandra*
97 *minor*
97 *terrestris*
97 *volubilis*

BROMUS
95 *commutatus*
95 *unioloides*

BRUGMANSIA
97 x *candida* pink
97 *chlorantha*
97 hybrids
96 'La Fleur Lilas'
97 *sanguinea* 'Golden Queen'
96 *suaveolens* yellow

BRUNIA
97 *albiflora*

BRUNSVIGIA
97 *grandiflora*
97 *gregaria*
96 *herrei*

96 *natalensis*
95 *orientalis* 'Alba'

BRYANTHUS
96 *gmelinii*

BRYUM
96 *truncorum*

BUCHLOE
97 *dactyloides*

BUDDLEJA
96 *abbreviata*
96 *davidii* 'Calandrina'
97 – 'Golden Sunset'
97 – 'Royal Purple'
95 – 'Variegata'
97 – 'White Butterfly'
97 – 'White Perfection'
96 *lewisiana* x *asiatica*
97 sp. ACE 2522
97 sp. TS&BC 94062
97 sp. TS&BC 94287
97 sp. TS&BC 94408
95 'West Hill'

BULBINE
96 *alooides* S&SH 74
95 *annua*

BULBINELLA
97 *cauda-felis*

BUPLEURUM
96 *longifolium roseum*

BUXUS
95 *microphylla* 'Green China'
97 – var. *japonica* 'Aurea'
97 *sempervirens* clipped ball
97 – clipped pyramid
97 – 'Newport Blue'
96 – 'Tropical Garden'
97 *sinica* var. *insularis* 'Winter Beauty'

CAIOPHORA
96 *horrida*
96 *lateritia*

CALAMOVILFA
97 *longifolia*

CALANDRINIA
95 *caespitosa* P&W 6229
95 *ciliata* var. *menziesii*
96 *dianthoides*
95 *feltonii*
97 'Neon'
95 *rupestris*
95 *skottsbergii*
95 sp. JCA 12317

CALANTHE
95 *alismifolia*
95 *argenteostriata*
95 *cardioglossa*
97 g. *Hizen*
97 g. *Ishi-zuchi*
95 *kintaroi*
97 g. *Kozu*
95 *okinawensis*
97 g. *Satsuma*
95 *triplicata*

CALATHEA
96 *bella*
96 *burle-marxii*

CALCEOLARIA
96 *alba* RB 94025

97 *ericoides*
95 *integrifolia* 'Gaines' Yellow'
95 – 'Sunshine' ♀
95 *lanigera* RB 94026
95 *picta*

CALLICARPA
97 *americana* var. *lactea*
97 *cathayana*
95 x *shirasawana*

CALLIERGON
96 *giganteum*

CALLUNA
95 *vulgaris* 'Bronze Hamilton'
96 – 'Cape Wrath'
95 – 'Catherine'
97 – f. *hirsuta*
97 – 'Julie Gill'
95 – 'Kees Gouda'
97 – 'Nana'
95 – 'Red Hugh'
97 – 'Rosalind, Crastock Heath Variety'
96 – 'Roter Oktober'
97 – Saint Kilda Group
96 – 'Summer Gold'

CALOCEDRUS
95 *formosana*

CALOCHORTUS
96 *albus* J&JA 13053
96 *ambiguus*
97 *barbatus* var. *chihuahuaensis*
96 *exilis*
96 *kennedyi*
97 *monophyllus*
97 *obispoensis*
97 *striatus*
97 *umbellatus*
96 *venustus* Cuddy Valley reds
96 – J&JA 13288

CALOPOGON
96 *tuberosus*

CALPURNIA
97 *aurea*

CALTHA
97 *palustris* 'Wheatfen'
95 *polypetala* Hochst.

CALYDOREA
96 *xiphioides*

CALYPSO
97 *bulbosa*

CALYSTEGIA
97 *tuguriorum*

CAMELLIA
96 'Arbutus Gum' (*reticulata* x *japonica*)
97 'Autumnal White'
95 'Bellbird'
96 *caudata*
96 'Chandleri'
97 'China Lady' (*reticulata* x *granthamiana*)
95 'Cornish Pink'
96 'Debut' (*reticulata* x *japonica*)
95 'Doctor Louis Polizzi' (*saluensis* x *reticulata*)

96 'Dream Girl' (*sasanqua* X *reticulata*)
96 'Elizabeth Bolitho'
95 'Emmy'
95 'Fascination'
97 'First Flush' (*cuspidata* X *saluenensis*)
97 'Fishtail White'
96 'Flower Girl' (*sasanqua* X *reticulata*)
96 *fraterna*
96 'Grace Caple' (*pitardii* X *japonica*)
97 *granthamiana*
95 *hiemalis* 'Pink Snow'
97 'Howard Asper' (*reticulata* X *japonica*)
96 *japonica* 'Alex Blackadder'
97 – 'Ama-no-gawa'
97 – 'Arabella'
97 – 'Barbara Woodroof'
96 – 'Beau Harp'
96 – 'Belle of the Ball'
95 – 'Benten-kagura' (v)
97 – 'Berenice Perfection'
97 – 'Betty Sheffield Coral'
96 – 'Betty Sheffield Pink'
97 – 'Betty Sheffield White'
97 – 'Bienville'
95 – 'Bright Buoy'
96 – 'Bryan Wright'
96 – 'Burgundy Gem'
96 – 'Caleb Cope'
97 – 'Carolyn Tuttle'
97 – 'Cheerio'
96 – 'Clarissa'
97 – 'Colonial Dame'
97 – 'Conrad Hilton'
95 – 'Coronation'
97 – 'Daikagura'
96 – 'Daphne du Maurier'
96 – 'Dona Jane Andresson'
97 – 'Doutor Balthazar de Mello'
97 – 'Duc de Bretagne'
95 – Emmett Pfingstl® (v)
96 – 'Eugène Lizé'
97 – 'Faith'
97 – 'Faustina'
95 – 'Firebird'
95 – 'Flora'
97 – 'Flowerwood'
95 – 'Fran Homeyer'
96 – 'Funny Face Betty'
96 – 'Geisha Girl'
97 – 'Jean Lyne'
97 – 'Jovey Carlyon' (hybrid)
96 – 'Just Darling'
97 – 'K. Sawada'
97 – 'Lady McCulloch'
95 – 'Laura Walker'
97 – 'L'Avvenire'
97 – 'Look-away'
97 – 'Magic City'
95 – 'Magic Moments'
97 – 'Man Size'
96 – 'Margaret Short'
97 – 'Margarete Hertrich'
97 – 'Mariottii Rubra'
96 – 'Martha Brice'
95 – 'Melinda Hackett'
97 – 'Melody Lane'

95 – 'Mikado'
97 – 'Miss Frankie'
97 – 'Momiji-gari'
97 – 'Moonlight Bay'
96 – 'Moonlight Sonata'
95 – 'Nanbankô'
95 – 'Owen Henry'
97 – 'Painted Lady'
97 – 'Paolina'
95 – 'Paul Jones Supreme'
97 – 'Pauline Winchester'
97 – 'Pink Clouds'
97 – 'Pink Pagoda'
97 – 'Pirate's Gold' (v)
96 – 'Platipetala'
97 – 'Pompone'
95 – 'Press's Eclipse'
95 – 'Prince Eugène Napoléon'
95 – 'Priscilla Brooks'
97 – 'Professor Sargent'
95 – 'Red Cardinal'
97 – 'Red Ensign'
95 – 'Red Rogue'
97 – 'Reg Ragland'
95 – 'Rosa Perfecta'
97 – 'Sabrina'
96 – 'Sarah Frost'
96 – 'Sea Foam'
95 – 'Senator Duncan U. Fletcher'
97 – 'Sierra Spring'
97 – 'Silver Waves'
97 – 'Snow Goose'
95 – 'Speciosissima'
97 – 'Spring Sonnet'
97 – 'Strawberry Swirl'
95 – 'Sunset Glory'
96 – 'Sweet Delight'
97 – 'Sylva'
95 – 'Tama-ikari'
95 – 'Tarô'an'
97 – 'Teresa Ragland'
97 – 'The Pilgrim'
97 – 'Tickled Pink'
97 – 'Tomorrow Variegated'
97 – 'Tricolor Superba'
97 – 'Twilight'
95 – 'Winter Cheer'
97 – 'Woodville Red'
97 – 'Yukibotan'
97 'Lasca Beauty' (*reticulata* X *japonica*) ♀
96 'Marjorie Miller'
97 *nitidissima* var. *nitidissima*
96 *reticulata* 'Arch of Triumph' ♀
96 – 'Brilliant Butterfly'
97 – 'Nuccio's Ruby'
95 *rosiflora* 'Cascade'
97 *saluenensis* 'Baronesa de Soutelinho'
95 *sasanqua* 'Azuma-beni'
96 – 'Bert Jones'
96 – 'Fragrans'
96 – 'Momozono-nishiki'
95 – 'Yae-arare'
97 'Strawberry Parfait'
95 'Tiny Princess' (*japonica* X *fraterna*)
97 'Valley Knudsen' (*saluenensis* X *reticulata*)
97 X *williamsii* 'Bridal Gown'

97 – 'Charlean'
95 – 'Coral Delight'
96 – 'Dresden China'
97 – 'Empire Rose'
95 – 'Free Style'
97 – 'Joyful Bells'
95 – 'Jury's Sunglow'
95 – 'Lady's Maid'
97 – 'Little Lavender'
95 – 'Red Dahlia'
96 – 'Rose Holland'
95 – 'Shimna'
95 – 'Twinkle Star'

CAMPANULA

97 *adsurgens*
97 *aizoides*
96 *alpina* var. *bucegiensis*
97 *americana*
97 *andrewsii*
97 – subsp. *andrewsii*
95 – – NS 705
96 – subsp. *hirsutula*
95 – – NS 724
97 *atlantis*
97 *autraniana*
97 *baumgartenii*
97 *bertolae*
97 *betulifolia* X *trogerae*
97 *biebersteiniana*
97 *bornmuelleri*
97 *buseri*
97 *carpatica* 'Harvest Moon'
97 – 'Lavender'
97 – 'Mrs V. Frère'
96 – 'Queen of Sheba'
97 – 'Riverslea'
97 – var. *turbinata* 'Craven Bells'
97 – – 'Snowsprite'
97 *celsii*
96 – subsp. *carystea*
97 *cenisia*
97 *cervicaria*
97 *cespitosa*
95 *cochleariifolia* 'Annie Hall'
97 – 'R.B. Loder' (d)
96 *colorata*
97 *coriacea* JCA 253.800
97 *crispa* JCA 253.901
97 *divaricata*
97 *ephesia*
97 *erinus*
97 *fenestrellata* subsp. *fenestrellata*
97 – subsp. *istriaca*
97 *fragilis* 'Hirsuta'
97 *garganica* 'Major'
97 *gieseckiana*
96 *grossheimii*
97 *hagielia*
96 *hakkiarica*
97 *hemschinica*
97 *herminii*
97 *heterophylla*
97 *hierosolymitana*
97 *iconia*
96 *isophylla* X *fragilis*
95 – 'Pamela'
97 *justiniana*
97 *kladniana*
97 *latifolia* 'Roger Wood'
97 *longestyla*
97 *lyrata*

97 *medium* 'Calycanthema'
97 *mirabilis*
96 *modesta*
97 *mollis*
97 *oblongifolioides*
97 *orbelica*
97 *oreadum*
97 *orphanidea*
97 *pallida*
97 *parryi*
97 *patula* subsp. *abietina*
96 *persicifolia* 'China Blue'
96 – 'Grandiflora'
97 – 'Grandiflora Caerulea'
97 – 'Snowdrift'
97 *petraea*
95 *portenschlagiana* 'Bavarica'
97 *punctata* f. *impunctata*
97 – 'Nana'
97 – 'Pallida'
97 X *pyraversi*
97 *radchensis*
97 *raineri alba*
97 *ramosissima*
97 *reiseri*
97 *retrorsa*
97 *rigidipila*
96 *rotundifolia* 'Flore Pleno' (d)
95 *rupestris* NS 401
97 *rupicola*
95 – NS 798
97 *samarkandensis*
97 *saxatilis* ♀
97 – subsp. *saxatilis*
97 *scardica*
97 *sclerotricha*
97 *serrata*
97 *sibirica* subsp. *taurica*
97 *siegizmundii*
97 'Southern Seedling'
96 sp. ex Furze
97 sp. JCA 6872
97 sp. JCA 8363
97 sp. JJH 918638
97 *sparsa*
97 *spathulata*
97 – subsp. *spruneriana*
97 *speciosa*
97 *spicata*
95 *sporadum* K 92.162
97 *stevenii* subsp. *beauverdiana*
97 *sulphurea*
97 *topaliana* subsp. *cordifolia*
95 – subsp. *delphica* NS 829
97 *transsilvanica*
97 *trautvetteri*
97 *trichocalycina*
97 *uniflora*
97 *xylocarpa*

CAMPSIS

95 X *tagliabuana* 'Guilfoylei'

CANNA

96 'China Lady'
97 'Délibáb'
96 *flaccida*
96 *indica* X *generalis*
96 'La Bohème'
97 'Primrose Yellow'

97 'Salmon'

CARDAMINE
97 x *paxiana*
95 *pratensis* 'Improperly Dressed'

CARDIOSPERMUM
96 *halicacabum*

CARDUNCELLUS
96 *rhaponticoides*

CARDUUS
96 *nutans*

CAREX
97 *acutiformis*
97 *arenaria*
97 *aurea*
97 *crinata*
96 *cyperus*
97 *divulsa* subsp. *leersii*
97 *flagellifera* 'Rapunzel'
97 *fuscula*
97 *humilis* 'Hexe'
97 *paniculata*
96 *spicata*

CARLINA
97 *corymbosa*

CARMICHAELIA
97 *suteri*
97 *violacea*

CARPINUS
95 *betulus* 'Quercifolia'
95 – 'Variegata'
97 *caucasica*
97 x *schuschaensis*

CARPODETUS
97 *serratus*

CARYA
96 *aquatica*
96 *laciniosa*
96 *pallida*
96 *texana*
97 *tomentosa*

CASSIOPE
95 *fastigiata*
96 'Inverleith'
96 *lycopodioides* var. *crista-pilosa*
96 – var. *globularis*
96 – *minima*
96 *mertensiana* var. *californica*
96 *selaginoides*
96 – McB 1124

CASTANEA
97 'Marigoule'
97 *sativa* 'Corkscrew'
97 – 'Doré de Lyon'

CASUARINA
95 *muelleriana*

CATALPA
97 *bignonioides* 'Nana'

CATAPODIUM
97 *rigidum*

CAUTLEYA
97 *gracilis*

CEANOTHUS
97 'Blue Boy'
97 'Blue Mist'

97 'Burtonensis'
96 *coeruleus*
96 *depressus*
97 'Edward Stevens'
97 'Elan'
96 *fendleri*
97 'Gloire Porrectus'
96 *griseus* var. *horizontalis*
97 – 'Santa Ana'
97 *maritimus* 'Point Sierra'
97 'Mary Lake'
96 *papillosus* x *thyrsiflorus*
97 'Percy Picton'
97 'Picnic Day'
96 x *regius*
97 'Thundercloud'
97 'Tilden Park'

CEDRUS
97 *deodara* 'Albospica' (v)
97 – 'Aurea Pendula'
95 – 'Deep Cove'
97 – 'MacPenny's Seedling'
96 – 'Robusta'
97 – 'Verticillata Glauca'
96 *libani* subsp. *libani* 'De Creffe'

CELASTRUS
96 *loeseneri* (f)
96 – (m)
97 *orbiculatus* JLS 88018WI
96 *scandens* (f)
96 – (m)
96 sp. KR 1269

CELMISIA
96 *ceracophyllus*
96 *haastii*
96 *lindsayi*
96 *lyallii*
97 *ramulosa*
96 *spectabilis major*

CELTIS
96 *biondii*
96 *bungeana*
96 *caucasica*
96 *glabrata*
96 *jessoensis*
96 *laevigata*
96 *reticulata*
96 *tetrandra*

CENTAUREA
97 *cineraria* subsp. *cineraria* ♀
97 *drabifolia*
95 *montana purpurea*
95 *nigra* 'Breakaway' (v)
97 *rutifolia*
97 *seridis* subsp. *maritima*
95 *uniflora* subsp. *nervosa* JCA 287.000

CEPHALARIA
97 *dipsacoides*
97 *natalensis*

CEPHALOTAXUS
96 *fortunei* 'Prostrate Spreader'
96 *harringtonia* 'Nana'

CERATOSTIGMA
97 *minus*
96 – SF 95001

CERCIS
97 *chinensis* f. *alba*

CERCOCARPUS
95 *montanus*

CERINTHE
97 'Kiwi Blue'

CEROPEGIA
95 *sandersoniae*

CEROXYLON
97 *quindiuense*
97 *utile*

CESTRUM
96 *diurnum*
97 *parqui* 'Cretian Purple'
97 *violaceum* pale blue

CHAENOMELES
97 x *californica* 'Enchantress'
97 *japonica* f. *alba*
97 – 'Orange Beauty'
96 *speciosa* 'Phylis Moore' (d)
97 – 'Rosea Plena' (d)
97 x *superba* 'Yaegaki' (d)

CHAENORHINUM
95 *origanifolium* 'Blue Sceptre'

CHAMAEBATIARIA
96 *millefolium*

CHAMAECRISTA
96 *nictitans*

CHAMAECYPARIS
97 *lawsoniana* 'Bowleri'
95 – 'Dow's Gem'
95 – 'Drinkstone Gold'
95 – 'Erecta Argenteovariegata'
95 – 'Kilbogget Gold'
97 – 'Magnifica Aurea'
95 – 'Naberi'
96 – 'Nivea'
95 – 'Parsons'
97 – 'Reid's Own Number One'
95 – 'Snowgold'
96 – 'Summerford Spire'
97 *obtusa* 'Reis Dwarf'
96 – 'Verdon'
97 – 'Watchi'
95 *pisifera* 'Filifera Gracilis'
96 *thyoides*
95 – 'Heatherbun'

CHAMAECYTISUS
97 *glaber*

CHAMAEDOREA
97 *costaricana*

CHEILANTHES
96 *alabamensis*
96 *bonariensis*
96 *eatonii*
96 *hirta* var. *ellisiana*
96 *kaulfussii*
96 *lendigera*
96 *pulchella*

CHIMAPHILA
97 *maculata*
97 *umbellata*

CHIONOHEBE
95 x *petrimea* 'Margaret Pringle'

CHIRONIA
97 *baccifera*

CHOISYA
96 *mollis*

CHRYSANTHEMUM
95 'Abbygates' (25b)
97 'Aimee Jane' (24b)
97 'Alan Rowe' (5a)
97 'Alexis' (5a)
96 'Alfreton Cream' (5b)
97 'Aline' (29K)
97 'Allure' (22d)
97 'Amber Enbee Wedding' (29d) ♀
95 'Amber Yvonne Arnaud' (24b) ♀
97 'Ann Brook' (23b)
97 'Annapurna' (3b)
97 'Anne' (29K)
97 'Apricot Alexis' (5a)
96 'Apricot Cassandra' (5b)
96 'Apricot Enbee Wedding' (29d)
95 'Apricot Madeleine' (29c)
95 'Apricot Vedova' (6a)
96 'Arctic Beauty' (4b)
95 'Arthur Hawkins' (24b)
95 'Aucklander' (23b)
97 'Audrey Shoesmith' (3a)
96 'Aurora' (4a)
97 'Autumn Sonata'
97 'Baden Locke' (24b)
97 'Bertos'
95 'Bill Sands' (3a)
95 'Bob Dawsey' (25a)
95 'Bonigold' (25b)
95 'Bonnie Jean' (9d)
96 'Brendon' (9c)
95 'Bridget' (6b)
96 'Brierton Celebration' (7b)
95 'Brierton Festival' (7b)
96 'Bright Golden Princess Anne' (4b)
95 'Bronze Bridget' (6b)
97 'Bronze Elite' (29d)
95 'Bronze Fairweather' (3b)
97 'Bronze John Wingfield' (24b)
97 'Bronzetti'
97 'Buff Margaret' (29c)
97 'Butter Milk' (25c)
97 'Candlewick Limelight' (29d)
95 'Canopy' (24a)
96 'Cappa' (9a)
97 'Challenger' (25b)
95 'Charles Fraser' (25a)
97 'Charles Tandy' (5a)
97 'Charles Wood' (25a)
97 'Cherry Chessington' (25a)
96 'Cherry Dynasty' (14a)
96 'Christine' (28)
95 'Christmas Carol' (5a)
96 'Christmas Wine' (5a)
97 'Clare Dobson' (25b)

Plant Deletions

97 'Clare Louise' (24b)
95 'Cloudbank' (9a)
97 'Columbine' (29K)
95 'Connie Meyhew' (5a)
95 'Copeland' (14b)
95 'Coral Rynoon' (9d)
97 'Cottingham' (25a)
95 'Cream Allouise' (25b)
97 'Cream Pauline White' (15a)
96 'Cream Pennine Serene' (29d)
96 'Cream Pennine Thrill' (29)
97 'Cream West Bromwich' (14a)
96 'Cropthorne'
96 'Cygnet' (24b)
97 'Daphne'
96 'Dark Corfu'
96 'Deane Joy' (9a)
96 'Deane Snow' (9a)
97 'Debbie' (29K)
97 'Dee Pink' (29c)
96 'Diamond Wedding' (25a)
97 'Doris' (29K)
96 'Dorridge Gem' (24b)
97 'Duke of Kent' (1)
97 'Dulverton' (24c)
95 'East Riding' (25a)
95 'Eastleigh' (24b) ♀
95 'Edwin Painter' (7b)
96 'Elizabeth Burton' (5a)
97 'Embleton' (24a)
97 'Emily Peace' (25a)
95 'Epic' (6b)
95 'Ernie Lapworth' (25b)
96 'Formcast' (24a)
96 'Fortune' (24b)
96 'Frederick Thompson' (15b)
97 'Gala Princess' (24b)
97 'Gary Scothern' (25b)
97 'Gay Anne' (4b)
95 'Gladys Homer' (24a)
97 'Gloria' (25a)
97 'Gold Enbee Frill' (29d)
97 'Golden Allouise' (25b)
97 'Golden Anemone' (29K)
95 'Golden Fred Shoesmith' (5a)
95 'Golden Gigantic' (1)
96 'Golden Lady' (3b)
96 'Golden Orfe' (29c)
95 'Golden Pennine Pink' (29c)
95 'Golden Quill Elegance' (9f)
97 'Golden Taffeta' (9c)
97 'Goldmine' (22c) ♀
95 'Gordon Taylor' (7b)
95 'Grace Lovell' (25a)
95 'Green Chartreuse' (5b)
95 'Green Nightingale' (10)
97 'Halloween' (4b)
97 'Handford Pink' (29K)
97 'Happy Geel'
96 'Hardwick Bronze' (29c)
96 'Hardwick Lemon' (29c)
96 'Hardwick Primrose' (29c)

96 'Hardwick Yellow' (19b)
96 'Harry Gee' (1)
96 'Harry James' (25a)
96 'Harry Lawson'
95 'Harvest Bounty'
97 'Helen' (29K)
96 'Hesketh Crystal' (5b)
97 'Ian' (29K)
96 'Illusion'
95 'Inkberrow' (24b)
95 'Iris Coupland' (5a)
95 'Jan Okum' (24b)
95 'Jan Wardle' (5a)
97 'Janice' (7a)
96 *japonense* var. *ashizuriense*
97 'Jessica' (29c)
95 'John Austin' (25a)
95 'John Lewis' (24b)
96 'John Murray'
97 'John Riley' (14a)
95 'Joy Smith' (24b)
97 'June Wakley' (25b)
95 'Karen Riley' (25a)
96 'Kingfisher' (12a)
95 'Kismet' (4c)
96 'Lemon Blanket' (29K)
96 'Lemon Hawaii' (9c)
97 'Lilian Shoesmith' (5b)
96 'Lorraine' (24b)
95 'Louise Etheridge' (23a)
95 'Lucida' (29c)
95 'Mancetta Bride' (29a) ♀
96 'Margaret Patricia' (24b)
95 'Margaret Riley' (25b)
97 'Marie Brunton' (15a)
96 'Marlene Jones' (25b)
96 'Martina' (24b)
97 'Matthew Woolman' (4a)
96 'Maudie Hodgson' (24b)
97 'Maureen' (29K)
97 'Mauve Gem' (29K)
96 'Michael Woolman' (2)
96 'Michelle Walker' (24b)
97 'Mirage' (22b) ♀
97 'Moonlight' (29K)
97 'Mottram Barleycorn' (29d)
96 'Muriel Vipas' (25b)
97 'Myss Rosie' (29c)
97 'Myssy Angie' (29c) ♀
97 'Naomi' (22f)
95 'Nathalie' (19c) ♀
95 'New Stylist' (24b)
95 'Niederschlesien'
95 'Oakfield Bride' (24b)
96 'Ogmore Vale' (12a)
95 'Olga Patterson' (5b)
95 'Orange Fair Lady' (5a)
95 'Orange Pennine Pink' (29c)
96 'Orno' (29b) ♀
97 'Overbury'
97 'Packwell' (24b)
96 'Pat' (6b)
97 'Pat Addison' (24b)
96 'Patricia' (29c)
96 'Pavilion' (25a)
95 'Payton Glow' (29c)
97 'Payton Pixie' (29c)
95 'Payton Plenty' (29c)

95 'Payton Prince' (29c) ♀
95 'Payton Rose' (29c)
97 'Peggy' (28a)
95 'Pennine Amber' (29c)
95 'Pennine Brenda' (29d)
96 'Pennine Bride' (29c)
96 'Pennine Clarion' (29c)
95 'Pennine Crimson' (29c)
96 'Pennine Cupid' (29c)
95 'Pennine Dove' (29d)
97 'Pennine Fizz' (29d)
97 'Pennine Hannah' (29d)
95 'Pennine Harmony' (29f)
95 'Pennine Lace' (29f) ♀
95 'Pennine Mavis' (29f)
96 'Pennine Nectar' (29c)
96 'Pennine Pink' (29c)
97 'Pennine Pride' (29d)
97 'Pennine Punch' (29a)
97 'Pennine Ray' (29c)
97 'Pennine Ritz' (29d)
96 'Pennine Robe' (29c)
96 'Pennine Serene' (29d)
95 'Pennine Sergeant' (29c)
97 'Pennine Sparkle' (29f)
97 'Pennine Sprite' (29d)
95 'Pennine Sugar' (29)
96 'Pennine Sun' (29d) ♀
96 'Pennine Tango' (29d) ♀
96 'Pennine Thrill' (29d)
95 'Pennine Trill' (29c)
96 'Pennine Waltz' (29c)
96 'Pennine Wax' (29)
95 'Pennine White' (29c)
97 'Piecas'
96 'Pink Champagne' (4b)
96 'Pink Chempak Rose' (14b)
96 'Pink Gin' (9c) ♀
96 'Pink Sands' (9d)
96 'Pink Windermere' (24a)
97 'Pink World of Sport' (25a)
95 'Plessey Snowflake' (29d)
97 'Polaris' (9c)
97 'Pomander' (25b)
97 'Primrose Anemone' (29K)
96 'Primrose Dorridge Crystal' (24a)
95 'Primrose Muriel Vipas' (25b)
97 'Primrose Pennine Oriel' (29a)
96 'Primrose Sam Vinter' (5a)
96 'Primrose Tennis' (25b)
96 'Purple Gerrie Hoek'
95 'Purple Payton Lady' (29c)
97 'Purple Wessex Charm' (29d)
95 'Rachel Fairweather' (3a)
95 'Red Admiral' (6b)
97 'Red Chempak Rose' (14b)
97 'Red Claudia' (29c)
97 'Red Eye Level' (5a)
96 'Red Hoek' (29c)
95 'Red Keystone' (25a)

96 'Red Margaret'
97 'Red Payton Dale' (29c)
97 'Red Pheasant'
97 'Red Shoesmith Salmon' (4a)
96 'Red Windermere' (24a)
95 'Roblush' (9c)
97 'Rockwell' (14b)
97 'Romano Mauve'
95 'Ron James' (4a)
95 'Rose'
95 'Rose Payton Lady' (29c)
96 'Rose Windermere' (24a)
97 'Roy Coopland' (5b) ♀
96 'Royal Hawaii' (9c)
97 'Rozette'
97 'Ryflare' (9c)
96 'Ryred'
97 'Salmon Cassandra' (5b) ♀
96 'Salmon Nu Rosemary' (9d) ♀
97 'Salmon Pauline White' (15a)
95 'Salmon Payton Dale' (29c)
95 'Salmon Talbot Parade' (29c) ♀
97 'Salmon Venice' (24b)
96 'Salmon Woolley Pride' (24b)
97 'Salurose'
95 'Sam Oldham' (24a)
95 'Sandra Burch' (24b)
96 'Satin Pink Gin' (9c) ♀
95 'Sefton' (4a)
97 'Sheila' (29K)
97 'Shirley' (25b)
95 'Shirley Glorious' (24a)
95 'Shirley Model' (3a)
95 'Shirley Primrose' (1)
95 'Shoesmith's Salmon' (4a) ♀
95 'Silver Gigantic' (1)
95 'Silver Jubilee' (24a)
97 'Snowbound' (29K)
95 'Snowshine' (5a)
97 'Sonya' (29K)
96 'Southway Sacy' (29d)
96 'Southway Sovereign' (29d)
97 'Spartan Crest'
96 'Spartan Fire'
95 'Spartan Flame' (29c)
96 'Spartan Legend' (29c)
96 'Spartan Leo' (29c)
95 'Spartan Orange' (29d)
96 'Spartan Pearl'
96 'Spartan Royal'
96 'Spartan Sunrise' (29c)
96 'Spartan Sunset' (29d)
95 'Stan Addison' (5b)
95 'Star Centenary' (3b)
95 'Stoika' (9d)
96 'Stuart Lawson' (5b)
97 'Sun Spider' (29K)
97 'Sun Valley' (5a)
97 'Suncharm Bronze' (22a)
97 'Suncharm Pink' (22a)
97 'Suncharm Red' (22a)
96 'Suncharm White' (22a)

97 'Suncharm Yellow' (22a)
96 'Sunflash' (5b/12a)
95 'Sunny Margaret' (29c)
96 'Susan Dobson' (25b)
95 'Susan Riley' (23a)
96 'Sussex County' (15a)
95 'Swalwell' (25b) ♀
95 'Swansdown' (25b)
95 'Talbot Bouquet' (29a) ♀
95 'Talbot Jo' (29d)
97 'Tapis Blanc'
96 'Tennis' (25b)
96 'Terry Ball' (29c)
96 'Thacker's Joy' (24a)
97 'Tickled Pink' (29K)
96 'Tim Woolman' (25a)
97 'Topsy' (29K)
97 'Truro' (24a)
96 'Vedova' (6a)
97 'Veria'
97 'Virginia' (29K)
97 'Wendy Tench' (29d)
95 'Wessex Amber' (29d)
95 'Wessex Cream' (29d)
95 'Wessex Glory' (29d)
95 'Wessex Gold' (29d)
95 'Wessex Melody' (29d)
96 'Wessex Solo' (29d)
95 'Wessex Tang' (29d) ♀
97 'White Enbee Wedding' (29d)
96 'White Fiji' (9c)
97 'White Gem' (25b)
96 'White Gerrie Hoek' (29c)
95 'White Lilac Prince' (1)
95 'White Margaret Riley' (25b)
96 'Winchcombe' (29c)
96 'Woolley Pride' (14b)
96 'Woolman's Century' (1)
95 'Woolman's Giant'' (14a)
95 'Woolman's Glory' (7a)
95 'Woolman's Highlight' (3b)
97 'Woolman's Perfecta' (3a)
95 'Woolman's Queen' (24a)
97 'World of Sport' (25a)
97 'Yellow Alfreton Cream' (5b)
95 'Yellow Balcombe Perfection' (5a)
96 'Yellow Egret' (23b)
95 'Yellow Fairweather' (3b)
97 'Yellow Hammer' (12a)
97 'Yellow Margaret Riley' (25b)
96 'Yellow Pinocchio' (29c)
97 'Yellow Starlet' (29K)
95 'Yellow Tennis' (25b)
96 *zawadskii* var. *latilobum*

CHRYSOGONUM
97 *australe*

CHUNIOPHOENIX
95 *hainanensis*

CHUQUIRAGA
95 *straminea*

CIBOTIUM
96 *barometz*
96 *glaucum*
96 *schiedei*

CICHORIUM
96 'Rosso di Verona'
97 *spinosum*

CIRSIUM
95 *candelebrum*
95 *falconeri*
95 *japonicum*
95 – 'Snow Beauty'
96 – 'Strawberry Ripple'
95 – 'White Beauty'
95 – 'White Victory'
95 *mexicanum*
95 *spinosissimum*

CISTUS
97 × *platysepalus*

CITHAREXYLUM
95 *ilicifolium*

CITRONELLA
97 *gongonha*

CITRUS
97 × *latipes*
96 × *reticulata* Mandarin Group (F)
96 × *tangelo* 'Mapo' (F)

CLARKIA
96 *breweri*

CLAYTONIA
97 *caespitosa*

CLEMATIS
96 'Acton Pride'
95 'Ajisai' (LxJ)
96 *akebioides* CLD 0601/12
96 *alpina* 'Alba Belsay'
96 – 'Blush Queen'
95 – 'Inshriach'
96 – 'Linava'
95 – 'Maria'
96 – 'Ria'
96 *apiifolia* var. *biternata* GR 0008
95 *atrata*
97 'Benedictus' (P)
95 'Boskoop Glory'
95 *brevicaudata*
97 'Caerulea Luxurians'
97 *calanthe*
96 *campaniflora* × *viticella*
96 × *cartmanii* 'Joe' × 'Sharon'
97 'Cassiopeia' (PxL)
96 'Cherry Brandy'
97 *chrysantha*
96 *chrysocoma* B&L 12324
96 *cirrhosa* 'Ourika Valley'
96 'Darlene'
95 *delavayi* var. *spinescens* KGB 283
95 *denticulata* P&W 6287
96 'Dilly Dilly'
96 'Doctor Label'
96 'Donna'
95 *drummondii*
96 'East Sunset'
97 'Ellenbank White'

97 'Emajögi' (L)
96 'Farrago'
96 *fremontii*
97 'Georg' (A/d)
95 *grata* CC&McK 185
97 'Gravetye Seedling' (T)
95 'Green Parrot'
97 'Guernsey'
96 'Hainton Ruby' (P)
96 'Halina Nell' (Fl)
96 'Harlequin'
97 'Haru-no-hoshi'
96 'Heirloom'
95 *heracleifolia* B&SWJ 812
96 – CC 612
97 – 'Jaggards'
97 – 'Hint of Pink'
95 *hirsuta*
97 'Ilka' (P)
96 'Iola Fair' (P)
95 'Joan Baker' (Vt)
97 'Joanna' (Fo)
97 'Jubileinyi 70'
97 *macropetala* 'Alborosea' (A/d)
97 – 'Anders' (A/d)
96 – 'Rödklokke' (A/d)
97 – 'Rosea' (A/d)
97 – 'Salmonea' (A/d)
97 *marata* 'Temple Prince' (m)
97 – 'Temple Queen' (f)
95 'Marinka'
97 'Matthais' (PxL)
97 *montana* 'Snow'
96 'Morning Glory'
95 *occidentalis* subsp. *grosseserrata*
96 'Paala'
96 'Pat Ann'
96 *petriei* × *cartmanii* 'Joe' (Fo)
97 – × *parviflora*
95 'Princess'
95 'Radiant'
95 *reticulata*
97 'Sizaja Ptitsa' (I)
96 sp. B&L 12329
96 sp. B&SWJ 1423
96 sp. B&SWJ 1668
96 sp. B&SWJ 292
96 sp. B&SWJ 599
96 sp. CC&McK 1011
96 sp. CC&McK 1099
96 *tangutica* 'Warsaw'
97 'Tuczka' (J)
97 'Vivienne Lawson'
96 'Zato'

CLEOME
97 *arborea*

CLETHRA
95 *alnifolia* 'Fingle Dwarf'

CLEYERA
96 *japonica* 'Tricolor' (v)

CLITORIA
96 *mariana*
96 *ternatea*
96 – 'Blue Sails'

CLIVIA
97 *miniata* var. *citrina*

CNICUS
97 *diacantha*

COCOS
96 *nucifera* 'Dwarf Golden Malay'

CODONOPSIS
96 *benthamii*
95 *dahurica*
97 *dicentrifolia*
97 sp. ACE 1687
96 *viridiflora* CLD 156

COFFEA
97 *arabica*

COLCHICUM
96 *alpinum*
97 'Beaconsfield'
95 *boissieri* CE&H 628
96 *burttii*
97 *chalcedonicum*
97 *cilicicum* Bowles' form
95 *giganteum* AC&W 2337
96 'Jarka'
97 'Little Woods'
97 *micranthum* AB&S 4522
96 *psaridis*
96 *speciosum* 'Ordu'
97 *turcicum*

COLEONEMA
96 *aspalathoides*

COLLINSIA
97 *heterophylla*

COLLOMIA
97 *biflora*

COLOBANTHUS
97 *apetalus* var. *alpinus*
97 *muelleri*
96 *quitensis*

COLUTEA
95 *multiflora*

COLUTEOCARPUS
95 *vesicaria*

CONIUM
97 *maculatum* 'Golden Nemesis'

CONOCEPHALUM
96 *supradecompositum*

CONRADINA
95 *canescens*

CONVOLVULUS
97 *arvensis*
96 *assyricus*
96 *capensis*
96 *compactus*

COPROSMA
97 *foetidissima* Forster
97 *lucida* (m)
97 *pumila*
96 *quadrifida*
97 *rhamnoides*
97 'Tuffet' (f)

CORDYLINE
97 *baueri*
95 'Red Mountain'

COREOPSIS
97 *grandiflora* 'Rotkehlchen'
97 *lanceolata* 'Lichtstad'
97 *palmata*

CORETHROGYNE
96 *californica*

CORIANDRUM
96 *sativum* 'Morocco'

CORIARIA
96 'Pictons'
97 *terminalis fructu-rubro*

CORNUS
97 *chinensis*
96 *linifolia*
95 *paucinervis*
97 'Porlock' ♀
97 *stolonifera* Kelsey's
Gold = 'Roseo'
97 x *unalaschkensis*

CORTADERIA
95 *chathamica*

CORTUSA
95 *brotheri* C&R
96 – ex KBE 141
95 *turkestanica*

CORYDALIS
97 *aitchisonii* subsp.
aitchisonii
96 *atrata*
96 *aurea*
97 *bracteata alba*
95 *cava* subsp.
marschalliana
95 *decumbens*
95 *ecristata*
97 *ledebouriana*
96 *lindleyana*
97 *ludlowii*
97 *macrocentra*
96 *paczoskii* RS 12180
95 *pallida*
95 *petrophila* KGB 432
97 *rupestris*
95 *sempervirens* 'Cream
Beauty'
97 – 'Rock Harlequin'
97 aff. *smithiana* CLD 385
96 *solida* PJC 214
97 – subsp. *solida*
'Snowstorm'
97 – 'White King'
97 *speciosa*
96 *tashiroi*

CORYLOPSIS
97 sp. from Chollipo, South
Korea

CORYLUS
96 *colurna* variegated
97 *maxima* 'Annise
Summer Red'
97 – 'Tonne de Giffon' (F)

CORYMBIUM
96 *africanum*

COSTUS
96 *curvibracteatus*
97 *speciosus* tetraploid

COTONEASTER
95 *declinatus*
97 *frigidus* 'Sherpa'
97 *glaucophyllus* TW 332
95 *integerrimus*
Mac&W 5916
97 *lacteus* 'Golden Gate'
96 – 'Variegatus'

95 *nivalis*

COWANIA
97 *stanburyana*

CRAMBE
97 *abyssinica*

CRASPEDIA
96 *lanata*

CRASSULA
96 *exilis* subsp. *cooperi*
96 *milfordiae* 'Silver Stars'
95 *moschata*
95 *multicaulis*
97 *muscosa* 'Variegata'

+ CRATAEGOMESPILUS
96 'Jules d'Asnières'

CRATAEGUS
96 *laevigata* 'Masekii' (d)
96 *monogyna* 'Pendula
Rosea'
97 *succulenta* var.
macracantha

CRAWFURDIA
96 *crawfurdioides*
97 *speciosa*

CREMANTHODIUM
96 *pinnatifidum*
96 sp. ACE 1420

CREPIS
96 *paludosa*

CRISTARIA
95 *grandidentata* RB 94042

CROCOSMIA
96 x *crocosmiiflora* 'A.E.
Amos'
96 – 'Brightest and Best'
J.E. Fitt
97 'Golden Fleece'
M. Wickenden
97 'Lord Nelson'
96 *pottsii* CC 1077

CROCUS
97 *biflorus* subsp. *tauri*
97 – subsp. *weldenii*
97 *boryi* PJC 168
96 *carpetanus* B&S 399
97 *cartwrightianus*
CE&H 613
96 *caspius* PF 5036
97 *chrysanthus* 'Gladstone'
97 – 'Sunkist'
97 – 'Uschak Orange'
97 *cyprius*
97 *gargaricus* subsp.
herbertii
96 – *minor* JRM 3299/75
97 *hadriaticus* B&M 8039
96 – f. *hadriaticus*
97 x *jessoppiae*
97 *korolkowii* 'Agalik'
97 – 'Dytiscus'
97 – 'Mountain Glory'
97 – 'Varzob'
97 – 'Yellow Tiger'
97 *malyi* CE&H 519
96 *michelsonii*
97 *nevadensis* AB&S 4415
96 – SB&L 62
97 *niveus* blue
97 – PJC 164
97 *olivieri* subsp. *balansae*

97 *pulchellus albus*
97 – CE&H 558
97 *rujanensis*
96 *scardicus*
JCA Sar Planina 1985
97 *scharojanii* var. *flavus*
97 *serotinus* subsp.
salzmannii 'Albus'
97 *tommasinianus*
purple tips

CROTALARIA
97 *capensis*

CRYPTANTHA
95 *flava*
95 *johnstonii*
95 – NNS 93-178
95 *paradoxa*
95 – NNS 93-181

CRYPTOMERIA
97 *japonica* 'Airtaki'
95 – 'Aurea'
97 – 'Gracilis'
96 – 'Lobbii'
97 – 'Vilmorin Variegated'

CRYPTOSTEGIA
95 *grandiflora*

CUNNINGHAMIA
97 *lanceolata* Og 911101

CUNONIA
97 *capensis*

CUPHEA
96 x *purpurea*
96 *viscosissima*

x CUPRESSOCYPARIS
97 *leylandii* 'Golconda'
97 – 'Michellii'
97 – 'New Ornament'

CUPRESSUS
97 *chengiana*
97 *funebris*
96 *goveniana* var.
abramsiana
96 *macrocarpa* 'Gold
Spire'
95 *torulosa* CLD 1031

CURCUMA
97 *petiolata*

CUSSONIA
97 *spicata*

CYANANTHUS
96 *delavayi*
97 *incanus*
96 – ACE 1700
97 *integer* Wallich
97 *lobatus* var. *insignis*
97 *longiflorus* ACE 1963
96 sp. ACE 1813
97 *spathulifolius*
97 – CLD 1492

CYANELLA
95 *hyacinthoides*

CYATHEA
97 *albifrons*
96 *baileyana*
97 *celebica*
97 *cunninghamii*
97 *intermedia*
96 *nova-caledoniae*
97 *rebeccae*

97 *robertsiana*
96 *robusta*
97 *woollsiana*

CYCAS
97 *cairnsiana*
97 *papuana*

CYCLAMEN
97 *coum* BS 8927
97 – subsp. *coum* f. *coum*
Pewter Group white
96 – – magenta
97 *hederifolium*
arrow-head form
96 – var. *hederifolium* f.
albiflorum 'Cotswold
White'
95 – – f. *hederifolium*
'Elsie Thomas'
97 – – – 'Green Elf'
96 – – – 'Stargazer'
96 – 'San Marino Silver'
96 *intaminatum* 'E.K.
Balls'
96 – 'Silver Cloud'
97 *pseudibericum*
scented form
97 *purpurascens* form
97 'Super Puppet'
97 *trochopteranthum* 'Pink
Swirl'
97 – 'Red Devil'
96 – 'Speckles'

CYDONIA
97 *oblonga* 'Early Prolific'

CYMBALARIA
97 *aequitriloba*
96 *muralis* 'Rosea'

CYMBIDIUM
97 *kanran*

CYMOPTERUS
95 *terebinthinus*

CYNOGLOSSUM
96 *creticum*
97 *glochidiatum* CC 718
97 *hungaricum*
95 *nervosum roseum*

CYPERUS
97 *involucratus* 'Nanus'
95 – 'Variegatus'
97 *ustulatus*

CYPRIPEDIUM
97 *acaule*
97 *calceolus* var. *pubescens*
97 *flavum* var. *speciosum*
97 g. *Hank Small*
95 *hispidula*
97 *kentuckiense*

CYRTANTHUS
96 'Atalanta'
97 *breviflorus*
97 *clavatus*
97 *flanaganii* S&SH 11
95 *flavidus*
97 *montanus*
97 *obliquus*
97 *obrienii*
97 *ochroleucus*
97 *smithiae*
97 *spiralis*
97 *staadensis*

CYSTOPTERIS
97 *alpina*
96 *regia*

CYTISUS
96 'C.E. Pearson'
96 'College Girl'
97 'Eastern Queen'
95 'Enchantress'
96 'Luna' ♀
96 'Miki'
96 'Mrs Norman Henry'
95 'Newry Seedling'
96 'Radiance'
96 'Royal Standard'
96 *scoparius* f. *indefessus*
96 'Sunset'
96 'Sunshine'

DABOECIA
96 *cantabrica* 'Clifden'
96 – 'Hookstone Pink'

× DACTYLOGLOSSUM
95 sp. (*Dactylorhiza saccifera* ×
   Coeloglossum viride)

DACTYLORHIZA
95 g. *Aschersoniana*
   (*incarnata* subsp. *coccinea* ×
   majalis)
95 g. *Atlanta*
95 g. *Biskaya*
95 g. *Calibra* (*elata* (f) ×
   majalis (m))
95 *cordigera*
95 g. *Dutch Angel*
97 g. *Florina*
95 g. *Foliorella*
95 *foliosa* × *majalis*
96 – × *romana*
95 – × *saccifera*
96 *fuchsii* 'Bressingham
   Bonus'
95 g. *Glendora* (*elata* ×
   incarnata subsp. *coccinea*)
97 *incarnata* subsp.
   cruenta
96 – × *foliosa*
95 g. *Latirella*
97 *maculata* subsp.
   ericetorum
95 g. *Madonna*
96 *nieschalkiorum*
96 *pindica*
96 *praetermissa* subsp.
   junialis var. *junialis*
97 *triphylla*
95 *urvilleana*
95 g. *Wintonii*
   (*incarnata* subsp. *coccinea* ×
   praetermissa)

DAHLIA
95 'Abingdon Ace' (SD)
96 'Abridge Bertie'
   (MinD)
97 'Abridge Natalie'
   (SWL)
95 'Akita' (Misc)
95 'Alltami Apollo' (GS-c)
97 'Alltami Cherry' (SBa)
97 'Amaran Royale'
   (MinD)
96 'Amber Banker' (MC)
97 'Anaïs'
95 'Ann'

95 'Apricot Honeymoon
   Dress' (SD)
95 'Aylett's Dazzler'
   (MinD) ♀
96 'Banker' (MC)
95 'Barbarry Climax'
   (SBa)
96 'Barbarry Epic' (SD)
97 'Barbarry Gaiety'
   (MinD)
97 'Barbarry Gateway'
   (MinD)
96 'Barbarry Glamour'
   (SBa)
96 'Barbarry Lavender'
   (MinD)
96 'Barbarry Oracle' (SD)
97 'Barbarry Pinky' (SD)
95 'Barbarry Standard'
   (MinD)
96 'Barbarry Trend'
   (MinD)
95 'Betty Ann' (Pom)
97 'Bill Homberg' (GD)
96 'Bonanza' (LD)
95 'Border Triumph'
   (DwB)
97 'Burnished Bronze'
   (Misc/DwB) ♀
97 'Calgary' (SD)
95 'Camano Choice' (SD)
96 'Carstone Sunbeam'
   (SD)
95 'Catherine Ireland'
   (MinD)
96 'Charlie Kenwood'
   (MinD)
95 'Charmant' (MinBa)
95 'Chiltern Amber' (SD)
95 'Clarence' (S-c)
95 'Clint's Climax' (LD)
95 'Cloverdale' (SD)
95 *coccinea* var. *palmeri*
96 – – CD&R 1367
95 'Corton Bess' (SD)
97 'Cream Delight' (SS-c)
95 'Crichton Honey' (SBa)
95 'Daleko National' (MD)
97 'Dancing Queen' (S-c)
95 'Davar Donna' (MS-c)
   ♀
97 'Davenport Lesley'
   (MinD)
96 'Davenport Pride'
   (MS-c)
95 'Deepest Yellow'
   (MinBa)
95 'Diane Nelson' (SD)
95 'Doc van Horn' (LS-c)
96 'Duncan'
95 'Dusky Lilac' (SWL)
95 'Edna C' (MD)
95 'Emmental' (SD)
97 'Emory Paul' (LD)
96 'Evelyn Rumbold'
   (GD)
95 'Evening Mail' (GS-c)
   ♀
95 'Feu Céleste' (Col)
97 'Figaro White'
97 'Fluttering'
95 'Frank Holmes' (Pom)
96 'Freestyle' (SC)
95 'G.F. Hemerik' (Sin)
95 'Gateshead Galaxy'
   (DwB)

95 'Geerlings Queeny'
   (SC) ♀
95 'Gold Diable' (SS-c) ♀
96 'Golden Symbol'
   (MS-c)
97 'Good Hope' (MinD)
96 'Good Intent' (LD)
95 'Gordon Lockwood'
   (Pom)
97 'Hamari Fiesta' (SD)
97 'Hans Ricken' (SD)
97 'Hazel' (Sin/Lil)
97 'Highgate Gold' (MS-c)
97 'Hilda Clare' (Col)
95 'Hillcrest Blaze' (SS-c)
   ♀
96 'Hindu Star' (MinBa)
96 'Holland Festival' (GD)
95 'Ice Cream Beauty'
   (SWL) ♀
96 'Inland Dynasty' (GS-c)
95 'Jaldec Joker' (SC) ♀
95 'Jessica Crutchfield'
   (SWL) ♀
97 'Jill's Blush' (MS-c)
95 'Jo Anne' (MS-c)
96 'Kelvin Floodlight'
   (GD)
97 'Kenora Moonbeam'
   (MD)
97 'Kenora Petite'
   (MinS-c)
96 'Key West' (LD)
97 'Klondike' (LS-c)
97 'Kyoto'
97 'La Corbière' (DwBa)
95 'La Gioconda' (Col)
97 'Lady Kerkrade' (SC)
95 'Laura Marie' (MinBa)
95 'Lavender Symbol'
   (MS-c)
95 'Lavengro' (GD)
96 'Lemon Puff' (Anem)
95 'Life Size' (LD)
95 'Lilian Ingham' (SS-c)
95 'Lismore Peggy' (Pom)
95 'Little Laura' (MinBa)
97 'Mariner's Light' (SS-c)
   ♀
95 'Masons' (SWL)
97 'Maxine Bailey' (SD)
96 *merckii* gold-leaved
96 – 'Hadspen Star'
97 'Mistill Delight' (MinD)
95 'Nunton Harvest' (SD)
95 'Onslow Michelle' (SD)
95 'Orange Nugget'
   (MinBa)
97 'Park Fever'
95 'Paul Damp' (MS-c)
95 'Pensford Marion'
   (Pom)
95 'Phill's Pink' (SD) ♀
95 'Pink Cloud' (SS-c)
95 'Pink Honeymoon
   Dress' (SD)
95 'Pink Kerkrade' (SC)
95 'Pink Paul Chester'
   (SC) ♀
97 'Pink Silvia'
97 'Polventon' (SD)
95 'Pretty Little Princess'
   (SS-c) ♀
95 'Primrose Rustig' (MD)
95 'Red Sensation' (MD)
95 'Requiem' (SD)

95 'Reverend P. Holian'
   (GS-c)
95 'Rokesly Mini' (MinC)
   ♀
96 'Rosalie' (Pom)
95 'Rothesay Castle'
   (DwB)
95 'Rothesay Robin' (SD)
95 'Royal Blush' (MinD)
95 'Royal Ivory' (SWL)
95 'Ruskin Dynasty' (SD)
95 'Rustig' (MD)
97 'Ryedale Rebecca'
   (GS-c)
95 'Saint Moritz' (SS-c)
97 'Salmon Athalie' (SC)
95 'Scarlet Beauty' (SWL)
95 'Schweitzer's Kokarde'
   (MinD)
96 'Scottish Relation'
   (SS-c) ♀
97 'Shooting Star' (LS-c)
97 'Show and Tell'
95 'Sneezy' (Sin)
95 'Snowflake' (SWL)
95 'Suffolk Bride' (MS-c)
96 'Suffolk Spectacular'
   (MD)
95 'Sunray Glint' (MS-c)
95 'Sweet Content' (SD)
96 'Symbol' (MS-c)
95 'Trengrove Summer'
   (MD)
95 'Vantage' (GS-c)
95 'W.J.N.' (Pom)
97 'Walter James' (SD)
95 'Wandy' (Pom) ♀
97 'Warkton Willo' (Pom)
95 'Welcome Guest'
   (MS-c)
97 'Wendy's Place' (Pom)
95 'White Hornsey' (SD)
97 'White Kerkrade' (SC)
95 'White Rustig' (MD)
95 'William John' (Pom)
95 'Willo's Flecks' (Pom)
95 'Willo's Night' (Pom)
95 'Willo's Violet' (Pom)
95 'Winter Dawn' (SWL)
95 'Yellow Frank Hornsey'
   (SD)
97 'Yellow Spiky' (MS-c)

DAIS
97 *cotinifolia*

DALEA
96 *gattingeri*

DAPHNE
95 *caucasica* × *petraea*
95 *mezereum* var.
   autumnalis
95 *tangutica* 'Rajah'
96 'Warnford'

DAPHNIPHYLLUM
95 *humile* JR 902

DASYLIRION
97 *glaucophyllum*

DATURA
96 *ceratocaula*
97 *metel* black
97 – 'La Fleur Lilas'

DAVALLIA
95 *solida*

DECAISNEA
97 *fargesii* 'Harlequin' (v)

DELOSPERMA
97 *macei*
97 *mariae*
95 'Wilson'

DELPHINIUM
96 'After Midnight'
96 'Alie Duyvensteyn'
96 'Atholl'
97 'Barbara Nason'
96 *biternatum*
97 Blue Heaven Group
97 'Browne's Lavender'
97 'Celebration'
96 'Cream Cracker'
97 'Darling Sue'
96 'Diana Grenfell'
97 'Dora Larkan'
96 'Dorothy Ash'
97 'Dunsdon Green'
96 'Elisabeth Sahin'
96 'Evita'
96 'Florestan'
96 'Foxhill Eileen'
96 'Foxhill Lady'
97 'Foxhill Nina'
96 'Foxhill Oscar'
96 'Foxhill Pinta'
96 'Foxhill Roseanna'
95 'Giotto' ♀
96 *grandiflorum* 'White
   Butterfly'
97 'Honey Bee'
97 'Icecap'
96 'Iceman'
97 'Jill Curley'
97 'Kathleen Cooke' ♀
97 'Loch Katrine'
97 'Loch Nevis'
96 'Loch Torridon'
97 Pink Dream Group
97 'Princess Caroline'
96 'Rakker'
97 *requienii* variegated
96 'Romany'
97 'Rona'
97 Round Table Mixture
97 'Royal Velvet'
95 x *ruysii* 'Piccolo'
97 'Sandpiper' ♀
97 'Sarah Edwards'
97 'Sky Beauty'
96 Southern Countrymen
   Group ♀
96 Southern Noblemen
   Group
96 sp. CC&McK 123
97 'Thamesmead' ♀
96 Zeeland Series light blues
   ♀

DENDROCALAMUS
97 *giganteus*
97 *strictus*

DESCHAMPSIA
97 *cespitosa* var.
   parviflora
96 *flexuosa* 'Peter David'
97 *media*
97 – bronze
97 *setacea* bronze

DESMODIUM
97 *styracifolium*

DESMOSCHOENUS
95 *spiralis*

DEUTZIA
95 *discolor* 'Major'
95 x *magnifica* 'Nancy'
97 x *rosea* 'Floribunda'
96 *scabra* 'Watereri'
97 sp. CC 1231

DIANELLA
96 *revoluta* var. *revoluta*

DIANTHUS
96 'Albus'
95 'Alder House' (p)
95 'Aldersey Rose' (p)
95 'Alfred Galbally' (b)
95 'Alick Sparkes' (p)
97 'Allwood's Crimson'
   (pf)
95 *alpinus* 'Drake's Red'
95 – salmon
95 'Ann's Lass' (pf)
97 *anomala*
95 'Anthony' (p)
97 'Archfield'
97 'Bailey's Apricot' (pf)
95 'Bailey's Splendour' (p)
97 *barbatus*
96 – albus
97 – 'Wee Willie'
95 'Becky's Choice' (p)
95 'Betty Webber' (p)
97 'Bibby's Cerise' (pf)
97 'Bill Smith' (pf)
95 'Blaby Joy'
97 'Blue Hedgehog'
96 'Bridesmaid' (p)
96 'Brymos' (p)
97 'Bryony Lisa' (b) ♀
97 'Cannup's Pride' (pf)
97 'Carolyn Hardy' (pf)
95 'Christopher Tautz' (b)
   ♀
95 'Cindy' (p)
95 'Clara's Glow' (pf)
97 'Colin's Shot Salmon'
   (pf)
96 'Cornish Snow' (p)
97 'Crimson Chance'
97 'Crompton Wizard' (pf)
97 'Crowley's Pink Sim'
   (pf)
97 'Dainty Clove' (b)
96 'Dainty Dance'
95 'Daisy Hill Scarlet' (b)
95 'Dark Pierrot' (pf) ♀
97 'Debi's Choice' (p)
97 'Deep Purple' (pf)
97 *deltoides degenii*
96 – red
96 – 'Wisley Variety'
95 – 'Zwolle'
95 'Devon Blossom' (p) ♀
96 'Devon Pink Pearl'
95 'Dinkirk Spirit' (pf)
97 'Duchess of Fife' (p)
95 'Duke of Argyll'
96 'Edan Lady' (pf)
96 'Edith Johnson' (pf)
97 'Edward' (p)
95 'Elizabeth Anne' (pf)
95 'Eliza's Choice'
95 'Emma Sarah' (b)
96 'Esperance' (pf)

96 'Faith Raven' (p)
96 'Fascination' (b)
95 *ferrugineus*
96 'Firewitch'
95 'Fragrant Lace' (p)
97 *fragrantissimus*
97 'French'
97 'Frilly'
97 'G.W. Hayward' (b)
95 Gala (pf)
95 'Gertrude' (p)
95 'Gloriosa' (p)
96 'Gold Dust'
95 *gratianopolitanus*
   'Albus'
95 'Happiness' (b)
95 'Heath' (b)
95 'Henry of Essex' (p)
96 'Hollycroft Fragrance'
   (b)
96 'Iceberg' (p)
97 'Imperial Clove' (b)
97 'Inga Bowen' (p)
96 'Ipswich Crimson' (p)
95 'James' (pf)
97 'Janet Walker' (p)
97 'Jenny Spillers'
97 'Jewel'
97 'John Gray' (p)
97 'Joker' (pf)
97 'Little Diane' (p)
97 'Liz Rigby' (b)
97 'London Joy'
95 'Lord Chatham' (b)
96 'Lord Grey' (b)
97 *lusitanicus*
95 'Maggie' (p)
97 Manon® (pf)
97 'Martin Nest'
97 'Mary Jane Birrel' (pf)
97 'Michelangelo' (pf)
97 'Microchip' (p)
96 'Miss Sinkins' (p)
97 'Monarch' (pf)
95 *monspessulanus* subsp.
   sternbergii
96 'Muriel Wilson' (pf)
96 'Nancy Lindsay' (p)
95 'Nicola Jane Mannion'
   (pf)
95 'Nina' (p)
96 'Norman Hayward' (b)
95 'Oakfield Clove' (b)
95 'Oakwood Billy Boole'
   (p)
97 'Oakwood Erin
   Mitchell' (p)
97 'Old Crimson Clove'
   (b)
97 'Orchid Beauty' (pf)
97 'Patchwork'
96 'Picture' (b)
96 'Pink Devon Pearl'
97 'Pink Mist Sim' (pf)
97 'Purple Frosted' (pf)
95 'Queen's Reward' (pf)
97 'Raeden Pink' (p)
97 'Red Emperor' (p)
97 'Rembrandt' (p)
96 'Rhian's Choice' (p) ♀
96 'Robert Allwood' (pf)
97 'Rosalind Linda' (pf)
97 'Ruth' (p)
96 'Sabra' (pf)
97 Sammy
97 'Samuel Doby' (p)

97 'Sappho' (b)
95 'Scaynes Hill' (p)
95 'Sean Hitchcock' (b)
97 'Shaston Superstar' (b)
97 'Sir David Scott' (p)
96 'Solway Sovereign' (pf)
97 'Solway Splash' (pf)
97 'Spetchley'
96 'Spindrift' (b)
95 'Spinfield Happiness'
   (b) ♀
97 'Startler' (p)
95 'Tamsin Fifield' (b) ♀
97 'Tangerine Sim' (pf)
97 'Telstar' (pf)
97 'Tom Portman' (p)
95 'Tony Langford' (pf)
97 Van Gogh® (pf)
97 'Velvet and Lace'
97 'Violet Carson' (p)
95 'Wells-next-the-Sea' (p)
97 Whatfield pinks (p)
96 'Whatfield Polly Anne'
   (p)
97 'White Sim' (pf)
97 'Wild Velvet' (p)
97 'William Sim' (pf)
97 'Yellow Dusty Sim' (pf)
97 'Zodiac' (pf)
96 'Zoe's Choice' (p) ♀

DIARRHENA
97 *japonica*

DIASCIA
95 'Blue Mist'
95 'Christine'
96 'Coral Cloud'
96 *denticulata*
97 'Fiona'
97 'Lavender Bell'
97 'Pink Spires'
97 'Pitlochrie Pink'

DICENTRA
95 'Adrian Bloom
   Variegated'
96 'Cherub'
95 'Paramount'
95 *peregrina alba*
97 *torulosa*
96 – CLD 685
95 'Tsuneshige Rokujo'
96 *uniflora*

DICHELOSTEMMA
97 *multiflorum*

DICKSONIA
97 *brackenridgei*
97 *conjugata*
96 *herbertii*
97 *juxtaposita*
95 *lanata*
97 *neorosthornii*

DIEFFENBACHIA
95 'Camille' (v)
95 'Candida' (v)
95 'Compacta' (v)
95 'Jeanette' (v)
95 'Jupiter' (v)
95 'Mars' (v)
95 'Neptune' (v)
95 'Saturnus' (v)
95 'Schott Gitte' (v)
95 *seguine* 'Amoena' (v)
95 – 'Carina' (v)
95 – 'Katherine' (v)

95 – 'Tropic Snow' (v)
95 'Triumph' (v)
95 'Tropic Sun' (v)
95 'Tropic White' (v)
95 'Veerie' (v)

DIERAMA
96 *ambiguum*
96 'Coral Pink'
96 *luteoalbidum*
   CD&R 1025
95 *ochroleucum*
96 sp. CD&R 96

DIGITALIS
96 cream hybrids
97 'Frosty'
97 *grandiflora* 'Dropmore
   Yellow'
96 *nervosa*
96 *obscura* JCA 409.401
96 *purpurea* 'Campanulata'
97 – 'Danby Lodge'
97 – Excelsior Group
   (Suttons; Unwins) ♀
97 – Excelsior Group white
97 – peloric
95 *stewartii*
97 *thapsi* JCA 410.000
97 Vesuvius hybrids

DIONYSIA
97 *archibaldii*
97 'Nan Watson'
96 *tapetodes* 'Peter
   Edwards' (Hewer
   1164)

DIPCADI
97 *serotinum*

DIPLOTAXIS
97 *tenuifolia*

DISPORUM
95 *sessile*
95 *trachycarpum*

DISSOTIS
97 *canescens*

DISTYLIUM
95 *racemosum tutcheri*

DIURIS
96 *longifolia*

DODECADENIA
95 *grandiflora*

DODECATHEON
96 *alpinum* JCA 9542
96 *dentatum* subsp.
   dentatum
95 *hendersonii* 'Inverleith'
   ♀
97 *meadia* 'Goliath'
97 – red shades
96 – 'Rose Farben'
95 – 'Splendidum' ♀
97 *pulchellum album*
96 – subsp. *macrocarpum*

DODONAEA
97 *humilis* (f)
97 – (m)

DORONICUM
96 *catatactarum*
96 *orientale* 'Goldzwerg'
95 *plantagineum*

DRABA
97 *aizoides* 'Compacta'
95 *arabisans* var.
   canadensis
96 *breweri*
95 *bruniifolia* subsp.
   heterocoma var. *nana*
96 – subsp. *olympica*
96 *caucasica*
97 *haynaldii*
95 *hispanica* var.
   brevistyla
96 *igarishii*
96 *incerta*
96 *lasiocarpa* Compacta
   Group
96 sp. ACE 1382
97 sp. F&W 8173 from Peru
96 sp. from Mt Bross
96 sp. JHH 9309139
97 *talassica*
97 *yunnanensis* ex JJH 90856

DRACAENA
96 *cincta* 'Tricolor' (v)
96 *fragrans* Deremensis
   Group
95 *reflexa* 'Variegata' ♀
96 *surculosa* 'Florida
   Beauty' (v)
96 – 'Wit' (v)

DRACOCEPHALUM
97 *calophyllum* ACE 1611
96 aff. *forrestii* ACE 2465
97 aff. *paulsenii* JJH 9209334
96 sp. CLD 551

DRIMYS
95 *winteri* 'Glauca'

DROSANTHEMUM
97 *bicolor*

DROSERA
96 *dilatatopetiolaris*
95 *erythrogyne*
96 *falconeri*
97 *filiformis* var. *tracyi*
96 *fulva*
96 *indica*
96 *lanata*
95 *macrantha* subsp.
   eremaea
95 *macrophylla*
   marchantii
95 – *monantha*
97 *menziesii*
95 *neesii* subsp. *neesii*
96 *nitidula*
96 *ordensis*
97 *peltata* subsp.
   auriculata
97 *pulchella* giant form
96 *pygmaea*
95 *radicans*
97 *villosa*

DRYANDRA
97 *formosa*
97 *nivea*
97 *nobilis*
97 *praemorsa*

DRYAS
97 *grandis*

DRYOPTERIS
97 *affinis* 'Linearis
   Cristata'
96 – 'Revoluta'
96 *carthusiana* × *oreades*
97 *crispifolia*
96 *dilatata* 'Jimmy Dyce'
96 *filix-mas* 'Decomposita'
97 *fructosa*
95 *fuscipes*
97 *shiroumensis*

DRYPIS
96 *spinosa*

DUCHESNEA
97 *indica* 'Dingle
   Variegated'

DUDLEYA
96 *cymosa* JCA 11777
97 *pulverulenta*

DUMORTIERA
96 *hirsuta*

DYCKIA
96 *fosteriana*

EBENUS
97 *cretica*

ECHINACEA
95 *laevigata*
96 *purpurea*
   dark stemmed form
97 – 'The King'

ECHINOPS
96 *chantavicus*
96 *giganteus*
95 *humilis*
95 *niveus*
97 *ritro* 'Charlotte' Linnaeus
95 – Linnaeus ACL 149/75

ECHIUM
96 *pininana* × *wildpretii*
97 *simplex*

EDRAIANTHUS
95 *dalmaticus albus*
96 *graminifolius* NS 785
97 *parnassicus*
95 *tenuifolius*

ELAEAGNUS
97 × *ebbingei* 'Aurea'

ELATOSTEMA
95 *carneum*

ELEPHANTOPUS
97 *tomentosus*

ELYTROPUS
96 *chilensis*

EMINIUM
96 *rauwolffii*

EMPETRUM
96 *rubrum* 'Tomentosum'

ENCEPHALARTOS
95 *lebomboensis*

EPACRIS
97 *petrophila* Baw Baw form

EPHEDRA
96 aff. *glauca*
96 –
96 *intermedia*
95 sp. RB 94052

EPIDENDRUM
97 *criniferum*

EPILOBIUM
95 *brunnescens*
95 *caucasicum*
97 *tetragonum*

EPIMEDIUM
97 *perralderianum*
   'Weihenstephan'

EPIPACTIS
97 *gigantea* 'Enchantment'
97 – × *palustris*
g. *Lowland Legacy*
97 *veratrifolia* 'Jerusalem'

EPIPREMNUM
95 *pinnatum* 'Aztec' ♀

ERICA
96 *carnea* 'Kramer's
   Rubin'
96 – 'Winter Sports'
96 *ciliaris* 'Egdon Heath'
97 *cinerea* f. *alba*
97 – 'Atrococcinea'
95 *erigena* 'Mrs Parris'
   Red'
97 – 'Rubra Compacta'
96 × *hiemalis* 'Dusky
   Maid'
97 *laeta*
97 *patersonia*
95 *subdivaricata*
97 *vagans* 'Rubra
   Grandiflora'

ERIGERON
97 *aphanactis* NNS 93-249
97 *argentatus*
97 *atticus*
97 *bloomeri* NNS 92-108
96 *borealis* Arctic form
96 *compositus* JCA 8911
97 *daicus*
95 'Doctor Worth'
97 *epirocticus*
96 'Festivity'
97 'Gaiety'
95 *glabellus*
96 – *yukonensis*
97 *glaucus* 'Roger Raiche'
95 *hyssopifolius*
97 *peregrinus*
   callianthemus
96 'Profusion'
95 *pulchellus* 'Meadow
   Muffin'
95 *pumilus intermedius*
97 *roseus*
97 'Serenity'
97 'Sincerity'
96 'Snow Queen'
97 *strictus* from Ireland

ERIOGONUM
96 *argophyllum*
96 *breedlovei*
97 *croceum*
95 *latifolium*
97 *lobbii* var. *robustum*
96 *ovalifolium* var. *nivale*
97 *pauciflorum* subsp.
   nebraskense
97 *siskiyouense*
97 *thymoides*

95 *umbellatum* 'Kannah Creek'
97 – var. *subalpinum*
96 *wrightii*
95 – subsp. *wrightii* K 92.224

ERIOPHYLLUM
96 *lanatum achilleifolium*

ERITRICHIUM
96 *howardii*
97 *sibiricum*

ERODIUM
95 *chium* Guitt 88042202
95 *ciconium* Guitt 85051602
96 *corsicum* dark pink
97 *valentinum* 'Alicante'
95 × *variabile* dwarf white

ERYNGIUM
95 × *allionii*
96 *aquifolium*
97 *biebersteinianum* from Kashmir
95 *billardierei*
95 *humile* JCA 13912
97 × *tripartitum* 'Variegatum'
97 *umbelliferum*

ERYSIMUM
97 *amoenum*
95 'Changeling'
96 *cheiri* 'Chevithorne'
97 – 'Helen Louise'
97 'Clent Calcutt'
97 'Mayflower'
97 *pulchellum aurantiacum*
97 *semperflorens*
97 *witmannii*

ERYTHRINA
96 *corallodendron*
95 *herbacea*
96 *livingstoneana*
96 *variegata*

ERYTHRONIUM
97 *dens-canis* from Serbia, white
95 *hendersonii* × *citrinum*
95 *idahoense*
97 'Minnehaha' ♀
97 *moerheimii*
95 *montanum*
96 *revolutum* 'Rose Beauty'
96 *umbilicatum*

ESCALLONIA
96 'Compacta Coccinea'
95 'Donard Scarlet'
95 'Donard White'
95 'Glasnevin Hybrid'
95 'Lanarth Hybrid'
95 *pulverulenta*
95 'Rose Queen'
95 *rubra*
95 – 'Hybrida'
95 'Saint Keverne'
96 × *stricta* 'Harold Comber'

EUCALYPTUS
95 *barberi*
95 *globulus* subsp. *bicostata*

97 *haemastoma*
97 *kruseana*
97 *leucoxylon* subsp. *megalocarpa*
97 *macrocarpa*
97 *mannifera* subsp. *maculosa*
97 *polyanthemos*
97 *pulchella*
97 *radiata*
97 *remota*
97 *sideroxylon*
97 *sieberi*

EUCOMIS
95 *autumnalis* subsp. *autumnalis*
95 'Frank Lawley'

EUGENIA
97 *myrtifolia* 'Variegata'

EUONYMUS
97 *fimbriatus*
96 *fortunei*
95 – 'Dart's Cardinal'
97 – 'Emerald Carpet'
97 – 'Hort's Blaze'
96 – 'Variegatus' EM '85
97 *hamiltonianus* 'Fiesta'
95 – subsp. *sieboldianus* Semiexsertus Group
95 *japonicus* 'Viridivariegatus'
97 *latifolius* × *hamiltonianus*
97 *velutinus*

EUPATORIUM
97 *chinense*
95 *coelestinum* forms
97 *fistulosum*
96 *fortunei*
95 *glechonophyllum*
95 *hildalgense*
97 *hyssopifolium* 'Bubba'
97 *rotundifolium*
97 *rugosa* 'Braunlaub'

EUPHORBIA
95 *britzensis*
95 *characias* subsp. *characias* 'Little Court'
96 – 'Whistleberry Gold'
96 – 'Whistleberry Jade'
95 – subsp. *wulfenii* 'Jayne's Golden Giant'
97 – – 'Minuet'
96 – – 'Red House'
95 – – Ulverscroft form
96 *cyparissias* 'Ashfield'
97 *erubescens*
97 *hiemale*
95 *nereidum*
96 *palustris* 'Zauberflöte'
96 *polychroma* 'Vic's Purple'
97 'Welsh Dragon'

EURYOPS
97 *grandiflorus*
95 *speciosissimus*
97 *tenuissimus*

EUSTEPHIA
97 *jujuyensis*

EVOLVULUS
95 *pilosus*

FABIANA
96 *imbricata alba*

FAGUS
96 *sylvatica* Cuprea Group
95 – 'Nana'
95 – f. *tortuosa*

FELICIA
96 *amelloides* 'Santa Anita Variegated' ♀
95 *filifolia* blue
95 – pink
95 – white
97 *plena ensbergensis* (d)
97 'Snowmass'

FESTUCA
97 *alpina*
97 *amethystina* 'Bronzeglanz'
95 × *ampla*
97 *californica*
97 *dalmatica*
97 *dumetorum*
97 *elatior* 'Demeter'
97 *extremiorientalis*
97 *glacialis* 'Czakor'
97 *heterophylla*
97 *juncifolia*
97 *sclerophylla*

FICUS
96 *benjamina* 'Flandriana'
96 – 'Golden Princess'
96 – 'Green Gem'
97 *elastica*
96 – 'Zulu Shield'
96 *palmata*

FILIPENDULA
95 *multijuga* B&SWJ 789
95 sp. from Chirisan B&SWJ 605
95 sp. from Odesan B&SWJ 930

FITTONIA
96 *albivenis* Argyroneura Group ♀
95 – – 'Nana'
96 – Verschaffeltii Group

FOKIENIA
97 *hodginsii*

FORSYTHIA
96 × *intermedia* Goldzauber
97 *ovata* forms
97 *suspensa* 'Cynthia Barber' (v)
95 – 'Hewitt's Gold'

FRAGARIA
97 × *ananassa* 'Bounty' (F)
95 – 'Cambridge Rival' (F)
96 – 'Domanil' (F)
95 – 'Idil' (F)
96 – 'Pantagruella' (F)
96 – 'Talisman' (F)
96 – 'Tenira' (F)
97 *daltoniana* CC&McK 390
95 *nipponica*
97 *vesca* 'Semperflorens Alba' (F)

FRANKLINIA
97 *alatamaha*

FRAXINUS
96 *excelsior* 'Altena'
96 – 'Atlas'
97 – 'Aurea Pendula'
95 – 'Eureka'
97 – 'Stanway Gold'
97 – 'Stripey'
95 *lanuginosa* Koidz 0131
95 *latifolia*
96 *ornus* 'Fastigiata Pyramidalis'

FREESIA
96 'Ballerina'
96 'Melanie' (d)
96 'Oberon'
96 'Royal Blue'
96 'Royal Gold'

FRITILLARIA
95 *affinis* var. *tristulis*
95 *alfredae* subsp. *glaucoviridis*
95 *camschatcensis* green
95 *collina*
96 *epirotica*
97 *latakiensis*
95 *pontica* Pras 1276
95 *rhodocanakis* subsp. *argolica*
97 *stribrnyi*
95 *walujewii*

FUCHSIA
96 'Abbey Kilner'
96 'Achilles'
96 'Aladna's Rosy'
96 'Albert H'
96 'Alice Sweetapple'
97 'Alma Muir'
95 'Altmark'
96 'American Spirit'
97 'Anj'
95 'Ann Porter'
97 'Anna Douling'
97 'Annabelle Stubbs'
96 'Annie Johnson'
97 'Anthonetta'
97 'Art Nouveau'
96 'Ashwell'
97 'Atlantic Crossing'
95 'Baby Neerman'
96 'Bali Hi'
96 'Barbara Hallett'
96 'Barbara Hassey'
96 'Barnsdale'
97 'Barry Sheppard'
95 'Begame Kiekeboe'
95 'Bella'
96 'Belle de Lisse'
96 'Ben's Ruby'
95 'Berba's Trio'
95 'Billie Roe'
96 'Blackberry Ripple'
97 'Blue Halo'
95 'Bob Brown'
96 'Bohémienne'
96 'Brenda Megan Hill'
96 'Buena Maria'
96 'Buenos Aires'
97 'Buttons and Bows'
97 'Cable Car'
95 'Callaly Pink'
96 'Cannenburch Floriant'
96 'Carole Hardwick'
96 'Carole Scott'
96 'Chancellor'

95 'Chaos'
95 'Chartwell'
95 'Christine Truman'
96 Christmas Candy
95 'Churchtown'
96 'Claudine Sanford'
96 'Clifton Belle'
95 'Cloverdale Star'
96 'Col'
95 'Concorde'
97 'Coverdale Jewel'
96 'Croix d'Honneur'
96 'Danielle'
97 'Darreen Dawn'
95 'Dawn Redfern'
96 'Deben'
96 'Deborah'
96 'Dedham Vale'
96 'Delta's Drop'
95 'Delta's Flame'
97 'Delta's Paljas'
95 'Denis Bolton'
97 'Destiny'
97 'Diamond Wedding'
96 'Diann Goodwin'
96 'Doris Birchell'
96 'Doris Deaves'
96 'Dreamy Days'
95 'Drifter'
96 'Dunrobin Bedder'
96 'Edith of Kimbolton'
95 'Edna May'
96 'Elizabeth Anne'
96 'Elsstar'
97 'Emma Massey'
96 'Eric Cooper Taylor'
95 'Expo '86'
95 'Fan Tan'
96 'Feather Duster'
96 'Firecracker'
96 'First Lord'
96 'First Love'
96 'Flowerdream'
96 'Fondant Cream'
97 'Freeland Ballerina'
96 'Frosted Amethyst'
95 *fulgens* × *splendens*
96 'Gazebo'
97 'Gelre'
96 'Geoff Amos'
97 'Gerharda's Sophie'
97 'Giant Falls'
96 'Gladys Lorimer'
97 'Gold Leaf'
97 'Golden Drame'
96 'Golden Spring Classic'
97 'Golden Tolling Bell'
96 'Harry Lye'
96 'Hendrik Schwab'
95 'Henning Becker'
96 'Hungarton'
96 'Imagination'
96 'Ina Jo Marker'
95 'Jandel'
96 'Janice Revell'
95 'Jaunty'
96 'Javelin'
96 'Jayne Rowell'
96 'Jean Muir'
96 'Jessie Pearson'
95 'Jezebel'
96 'Jill Whitworth'
96 'Jim Dodge'
96 'John Yardell'
95 'Judith Coupland'
96 'Judith Mitchell'

96 'Kabibi'
95 'Kathleen Colville'
96 'Kathy Scott'
97 'Kegworth Delight'
97 'Kelly Rushton'
96 'Kevin Stals'
97 'Kleine Gärtnerin'
96 'Laing's Hybrid'
96 'Laleham'
95 'Lambaba'
97 'Lamme Goedzak'
96 'Lavender Cascade'
95 'Libra'
95 'Lilac Dainty'
97 'Linet'
95 'Linsey Brown'
97 'Long Distance'
96 'Lorna Hercherson'
96 'Love Knot'
97 'Loxhore Clarion'
96 'Lye's Favourite'
96 'Maddy'
96 *magellanica* var.
 molinae 'Enstone
 Gold'
96 'Magenta Flush'
96 'Mardale'
96 'Margaret Tebbit'
96 'Margarita'
95 'Marshside'
96 'Martha Brown'
97 'Martin's Catherina'
96 'Mary Ellen'
96 'Mary Rose'
95 'Mary Stilwell'
95 'Maureen Munro'
95 'Mazda'
96 'Medalist'
97 'Meike Meursing'
95 'Meols Cop'
96 *minutissima*
96 'Misty Morn'
96 'Moon Glow'
96 'Mother's Day'
96 'Mrs Minnie Pugh'
96 'Muirfield'
97 'Multa'
96 'My Beauty'
95 'Myra Baxendale'
97 'Night and Day'
95 'Nikki'
97 'Norman Greenhill'
95 'O Sole Mio'
96 'Oakham'
95 'Oldbury Delight'
97 'Olympic Sunset'
95 'Omeomy'
95 'Onna'
96 'Orange Bell'
95 'Oranje Boven'
96 'Orchid Princess'
96 'Orientalis'
96 'Oso Sweet'
96 'Ovation'
97 *paniculata* var.
 mixensis
96 'Pa's Princess'
95 'Passing Cloud'
97 'Paula Johnson'
96 'Pearly Gates'
96 'Pebble Mill'
95 'Piet Hein'
96 'Pink Campanella'
96 'Pink Galaxy'
95 'Pink Most'
96 'Pink Pineapple'

96 'Pink Snow'
96 'Pride and Joy'
96 'Purple Ann'
96 'Rahnee'
96 'Rainbow'
96 'Rebecca Williams'
95 'Reisken Boland'
95 'River Plate'
95 'Robert Bruce'
97 'Robin'
97 'Ron Venables'
96 'Rose Bower'
96 'Rosy Bows'
96 'Rothbury Beauty'
96 'Royal Mosaic'
95 'Rubens'
96 'Rutti Tutti'
96 'Sahara'
96 'Sally Gunnell'
96 'Santa Barbara'
95 'Sarah Ann'
96 'Sarah Louise'
95 'Scarlet Ribbons'
95 'Sensation'
96 'Shepard's Delight'
96 'Sherborne Las'
96 'Siobhan'
96 'Skylight'
97 'Snow Country'
96 'Spring Classic'
96 'Springtime'
96 'Stad Elburg'
95 'Stathern Surprise'
96 'Stephanie Morris'
96 'Strawberry Fizz'
96 'Student Prince'
96 'Sunny Skies'
96 'Sunsrise First'
96 'Supersport'
95 'Susan Daley'
96 'Susan Joy'
96 'Suzy'
96 'Swanland Candy'
95 'Sylvia Dyos'
96 'Tabatha'
96 'Tammy'
96 'Tartan'
95 'Texas Star'
95 'Thames Valley'
96 'The Red Arrows'
96 'The Spoiler'
96 'Top Score'
96 'Tosca'
96 'Tour Eiffel'
96 'Trabant'
96 'Tradewinds'
96 'Tranquility'
96 'Trish Dewey'
96 'Uncle Jinks'
96 'Uppingham Lass'
95 'Varty's Pride'
96 'Violacea'
95 'Walz Trompet'
96 'Washington
 Centennial'
96 'Water Baby'
97 'Wedding Bells'
96 'Wendy Brooks'
97 'White Marshmallow'
97 'Whiteknights Glister'
96 'William C. Dodson'
96 'Wm's Las'
95 'Zeeuwse Parel'

FUMANA
97 *procumbens*

FURCRAEA
96 *foetida*

GAGEA
97 *fibrosa*

GAILLARDIA
95 *aristata* Pursch JCA 11449
96 Kelway's hybrids
97 'Summer Fire'
96 'Summer Sun'

GALANTHUS
96 'April Fool'
95 *elwesii poculiformis*
96 'Ermine Street'
95 green-tipped Greatorex
96 *nivalis* 'Appleby One'
95 – 'Boyd's Double' (d)
96 – subsp. *imperati*
96 – 'Maximus'
97 –
 WM 9630 from C. Hungary
96 *plicatus* 'Upcher'

GALEGA
97 'Duchess of Bedford'

GALEOPSIS
97 *segetum*
97 *speciosa*

GALIUM
96 *arenarium*

GARDENIA
96 *augusta* 'Radicans
 Variegata'
97 – 'Veitchiana'
97 *thunbergia*

GAULTHERIA
95 *forrestii*
95 *myrsinoides* 'Geoffrey
 Herklots'
97 *yunnanensis*

GAYLUSSACIA
97 *ursinum*

GAZANIA
96 'Blackberry Split'
95 'Blaze of Fire'
97 'Brodick'
95 Flesh Tones Group
95 'Flore Pleno'
95 'Harlequin'
95 'Hazel'
97 *krebsiana*
95 'Michael' ♀
95 'Mini Star White'
97 'Patricia Morrow'
96 *rigens* 'Aureovariegata'
95 'Slate'
95 'Snuggle Bunny'
95 'Sunbeam'
97 'Sundance'

GEISSORHIZA
97 *splendidissima*
97 *tulbaghensis*

GENISTA
95 *albida*
96 *anglica*
97 – 'Cloth of Gold'
95 *involucrata* Spach
95 *pilosa* 'Superba'
97 'Porlock'
97 *subcapitata*
95 *tenera*

96 *tinctoria* 'Moesiaca'
96 – var. *virgata*

GENNARIA
96 *diphylla*

GENTIANA
97 *acaulis* Andorra form
96 – 'Harlin'
96 – 'Trotter's Variety'
96 *affinis*
96 *asclepiadea* 'Whitethroat'
97 *bavarica* var. *subacaulis*
96 *bisetaea*
96 *brachyphylla*
97 *clusii clusii*
95 – *rochelii*
96 'Coronation'
96 *fetisowii*
95 *gracilis*
97 *kauffmanniana*
96 *kolalowskyi*
95 *ligustica*
96 *macrophylla* 'Alba'
97 *makinoi alba*
96 *obconica* RH 61
96 *ornata*
96 'Orva'
95 *patula*
96 *platypetala*
96 *prolata* K 214
96 *punctata*
96 *rubicunda*
96 *sceptrum*
96 *septemfida* var. *lagodechiana* 'Latifolia'
96 *setigera*
96 *sikokiana*
95 *sino-ornata* 'Autumn Frolic'
95 sp. C 183
95 sp. C 201
95 sp. C 24
95 sp. C 77
97 *ternifolia* SBEC 1053
97 *thunbergii*
97 *trichotoma* ACE 1812
96 *trinervis*
96 'Veora'
96 *verna* subsp. *pontica* 'Alba'

GENTIANELLA
97 *hirculus* JCA 13880/93

GERANIUM
95 'Ann Folkard' × *psilostemon*
96 *antrorsum*
95 *argenteum*
97 *asphodeloides* subsp. *sintenisii*
97 'Crûg Dusk'
95 *dahuricum*
97 *donianum* CC 1074
96 'Eva'
97 *gracile* 'Blanche'
95 *grandistipulatum*
97 *kishtvariense* 'Blackthorn Garnet'
97 'Little David'
96 *macrostylum* JCA 6000
96 × *magnificum* 'Wisley Variety'
96 *magniflorum* S&SH 32

97 *molle album*
96 'Nora Bremner'
97 × *oxonianum* 'Mrs Charles Perrin'
97 – 'Rohina Moss'
97 – 'Thurstonianum Isherwood'
95 *palcaense* F&W 7851
96 *palustre* 'Plus'
97 *phaeum aureum*
96 – 'Joan Grey'
95 *pratense* 'Alboroseum'
96 – 'Catforth Cadense'
96 – CC 806
96 – 'Fiona'
97 – subsp. *stewartianum* ex CC 31
96 – 'Striatum Akaton'
96 'Priestley's Pink'
95 *renardii roseum*
97 *sanguineum* 'Elliott's Variety'
97 – var. *prostratum* hort.
97 – × *swatense*
96 'Scheherezade'
96 *schlechteri*
95 sp. from Central Asia
96 sp. from Chile
96 *subulatostipulatum*
96 *swatense* SEP 131
96 *traversii* 'Sugar Pink'
96 *versicolor* 'Bill Baker'
95 *weddellii* F&W 7890

GEUM
97 *aleppicum* CLD 610
96 – subsp. *strictum*
96 'Birkhead's Creamy Lemon'
96 *elatum* CC&McK 390
96 'Gordon Cooper'
96 × *heldreichii*
96 *leiospermum*
96 *macrophyllum* var. *sachalinense*
96 'Orangeman'
96 *pseudococcineum*
95 'Two Ladies'

GILIA
96 *caespitosa*

GINKGO
96 *biloba* 'Lakeview'
96 – 'Mayfield' (m)

GLADIOLUS
95 'Apricot Queen' (L)
95 'Blue Star'
95 'Charm Glow'
97 'Côte d'Azur' (G)
97 'Dancing Doll'
97 *ecklonii*
95 'Edward van Beinum' (L)
96 'Essex' (P/S)
95 'Firebird'
97 'Friendship' (L)
97 'Frosty Pink'
95 'Helene' (P/B)
97 'Her Majesty' (L)
95 'Jessica' (L)
96 'Jupiter'
95 'Liebelei'
95 'Marvinka' (M)
95 'Nicole'
95 'Ovation' (L)
95 'Pegasus' (P/Min)

95 'Picture' (P)
97 'Ramona'
95 'Red Beauty'
95 'Red Jewel' (P/S)
96 'Robin' (P)
95 'Rose Supreme' (G)
96 'Royal Dutch' (L)
96 'Sabu'
96 'Saxony' (P)
96 'Spic and Span' (L)
96 'Theresa'
97 'Violetta' (M)
95 'White Prosperity' (L)
96 'Wine and Roses' (L)
96 'Wise Cracks'

GLAUCIUM
97 *caucasicum*
96 *squamigerum*

GLOBBA
97 *marantina*

GLOBULARIA
96 *albiflora*

GLORIOSA
95 *caramii*
96 *superba* 'Carsonii'

GLOXINIA
97 *latifolia*

GLUMICALYX
96 aff. *goseloides* JJ&JH 9401347

GLYCERIA
97 *grandis*

GLYCYRRHIZA
96 *lepidota*

GNAPHALIUM
97 *norvegicum*

GOMPHOCARPUS
95 *physocarpus* S&SH 67

GONIOLIMON
96 *tataricum* 'Woodcreek'

GOODENIA
95 *humilis*

GOODYERA
97 *oblongifolia*

GRAPTOPETALUM
97 *bellus*

GREVILLEA
97 *aspleniifolia* 'Robyn Gordon'
95 *banksii* 'Albiflora'
d – f. *albiflora*
95 – var. *forsteri*

GREWIA
96 *biloba*

GRINDELIA
97 sp. G&K 4423

GRISELINIA
95 *racemosa*

GUNNERA
96 *magellanica* (f)
95 × *mixta*
95 *prorepens* small form

GYPSOPHILA
95 *nana*
96 *paniculata* 'Pink Star' (d)

HABERLEA
96 *rhodopensis austinii*

HABRANTHUS
97 *howardii*

HACQUETIA
97 *epipactis* 'Thor' (v)
96 – 'Variegata'

HAEMANTHUS
97 *crispus*
97 *deformis*
95 'König Albert'

HAKEA
97 *bucculenta*
96 *suaveolens*

HAMAMELIS
95 × *intermedia* 'Advent'
95 – 'Allgold'
97 – 'Fire Cracker'
95 – Hillier's clone
95 – 'Winter Beauty'
97 *mollis* 'Coombe Wood'
95 – Henry form
95 – 'James Wells'
95 – Renken form
97 *vernalis* 'Christmas Cheer'
97 – Compact form
95 – 'January Pride'
95 – 'Lombart's Weeping'
95 – 'New Year's Gold'
95 – 'Squib'

HANABUSAYA
97 *asiatica*

HAPLOPAPPUS
96 *foliosus*
97 *microcephalus* AJW 93/559
95 sp. P&W 6545
96 sp. RB 94063

HEBE
96 'Amethyst'
95 'April Joy'
97 *armstrongii* yellow
97 'Bracken Hills'
97 *buchananii* 'Minima'
97 *buxifolia patens* (Benth.) Ckn.& Allan
97 'Carnea'
97 'Colwall Blue'
97 *corstorphinensis*
97 'Craigpark'
97 'Cressit'
96 'Diamond'
96 'Diana'
97 *elliptica* 'Dwarf Blue'
97 'Evelyn'
97 × *franciscana* 'Red Gem'
97 *fruticeti*
97 'Gruninard's Seedling'
96 'Kewensis'
97 'Lavender Lady'
97 'Lavender Queen'
97 *leiophylla*
96 'Lewisii'
97 'Lilac Wand'
97 'Louise'
97 'Miss Lowe'
97 'Mont Blanc'
97 'Monticola'
95 'Mrs E. Tennant'

96 'Paula'
96 'Perry's Bluey'
96 'Pulchella'
96 *salicifolia* 'Variegata'
96 'Southlandii'
96 *speciosa* 'Kapiti'
96 *stricta* var. *macroura* 'Cookiana'
96 *subsimilis*
96 'Violet Queen'
96 'Violet Wand'
95 'White Spires'
97 'White Summer'
96 'Wootten'

HECHTIA
96 *argentea*
96 *montana*

HEDERA
97 *canariensis* Willdenow
96 *helix* 'Arborescens Variegata'
96 – 'Clouded Gold'
95 – 'Fiesta'
97 – 'Frosty' (v)
96 – 'Gold Knight'
96 – 'Limelight'
97 – 'Pedata Heron'
95 – 'Schäfer One' (v)
97 *nepalensis* CC&MR 460

HEDYCHIUM
95 *spicatum* CC 1215

HEDYSARUM
96 *coronarium* 'Album'
96 *nitidum*

HEDYSCEPE
95 *canterburyana*

HELENIUM
95 'Baronin Linden'
96 'Bressingham Gold'
95 'Goldlackzwerg'
97 'Indianersommer'

HELIANTHEMUM
97 'Bishopsthorpe'
97 'Brown Gold' (d)
96 'Gaiety'
95 'Gloiriette'
97 'Highdown Apricot'
97 'Rose Perfection'
97 'Salmon Bee'
97 'Snowball'
95 'Westfield Wonder'
97 'White Queen'

HELIANTHUS
97 *decapetalus* 'Kastle Kobena'
95 *divaricatus*
97 'First Light'
97 'Golden Pyramid'
97 'Summer Gold'

HELICHRYSUM
96 *aggregatum*
95 *arenarium* subsp. *aucheri*
97 *argyrophyllum*
96 *depressum*
97 *doerfleri*
96 *foetidum*
96 *gunnii*
95 *maginatum*
97 aff. *praecurrens*
97 × Raoulia 'Rivulet'

97 × Raoulia 'Silver Streams'

HELICONIA
96 *mariae*

HELICTOTRICHON
97 *filifolium*

HELIOPHILA
97 *longifolia*

HELIOPSIS
96 *helianthoides* 'Bressingham Doubloon' (d)
96 *orientalis*

HELIOTROPIUM
96 *arborescens* 'Album'
97 'Midnight'
97 'Mrs J.W. Lowther'

HELLEBORUS
96 *argutifolius* × *sternii*
97 *atrorubens*
    Waldst. & Kit. WM 9028 from Slovenia
97 – Waldst. & Kit. WM 9101 from Slovenia
97 *dumetorum*
    from Hungary WM 9307
95 – from Slovenia WM 9214/9301
95 *foetidus* compact form
96 – 'Melle'
95 – 'Pontarlier'
95 – scented form
96 – 'Tros-os-Montes'
96 – 'Yorkley'
96 *multifidus* subsp. *hercegovinus* WM 9011/9105
95 – subsp. *istriacus* WM 9092/9222
97 – – WM 9222
96 – – WM 9321/22/24
95 – subsp. *multifidus* WM 9010/9104
95 *niger* 'Higham's Variety'
97 – subsp. *macranthus*
95 – WM 9227
97 *orientalis* 'Albin Otto' hort.
95 – 'Amethyst' hort.
97 – 'Chartreuse' hort.
97 – Galaxy Group hort.
97 – subsp. *guttatus* hort. light purple
95 – 'Hercules' hort.
96 – ivory spotted
95 – 'Lavinia Ward' hort.
95 – 'Lilliwhite'
97 – 'Red Mountain'
97 *purpurascens* Hungary WM 9208
96 × *sternii* Ashfield strain
95 – dwarf form
97 *torquatus* WM 9003 from Bosnia
97 – WM 9111 from Bosnia
97 *viridis* from Germany
96 – from Spain

HELWINGIA
95 *himalaica*

HEMEROCALLIS
96 'Admiral'

97 'Amadeus'
95 × *andersonii* 'Nancy Saunders'
96 'Angel Flight'
96 'Ann Kelley'
96 'Antarctica'
96 'Apple Court Damson'
95 'Apple Tart'
95 'Atlanta Full House'
95 'Aurora'
95 'Azor'
97 'Aztec Furnace'
96 'Back Bay'
96 'Barbara Corsair'
96 'Battle Hymn'
97 'Bedarra Island'
97 'Beloved Returns' ♀
95 'Berlin Lemon' ♀
95 'Berlin Red Velvet' ♀
97 'Blushing Angel'
95 'Boulderbrook Serenity'
97 'Brand New Lover'
97 'Brass Buckles'
97 'Bruno Müller'
97 'Burlesque'
97 'Butterfly Charm'
96 'Button Box'
97 'Buttons'
95 'By Jove'
96 'Camden Ballerina'
96 'Captured Heart'
96 'Catherine Wheel'
96 'Caviar'
96 'Chestnut Lane'
95 'Child of Fortune'
97 'Chinese Imp'
97 'Christmas Candles'
95 'Claudine'
95 'Conspicua'
97 'Coreana Yellow'
96 'Corsican Bandit'
97 'Cynthia Mary'
96 'Dainty Dreamer'
96 'Daisy MacCarthy'
95 'Danity Dreamer'
96 'Dark Elf'
96 'Delightsome'
95 'Dorcas'
95 'Double Pink Treasure' (d)
95 'Down Town'
95 'Elf's Cap'
97 'Elizabeth Ann Hudson'
95 'Elsie Spalding'
97 'Enchanting Blessing'
97 'Erica Nichole Gonzales'
96 'Fairy Delight'
97 'Fairy Frosting'
96 'Fairy Jester'
97 'Fairy Wings'
97 'Feather Down'
96 'Feelings'
97 'Fire Music'
95 'Folklore'
96 *forrestii*
96 'French Porcelain'
95 'Fresh Air'
96 'Full Reward'
97 'Gateway'
97 'Giddy Go Round'
95 'Golden Chance'
97 'Golden Gate'
95 'Graceful Eye'
96 'Green Magic'

95 'Hadspen Samphire'
96 'Heartthrob'
97 'Heather Green'
97 'Helios'
95 'Helle Berlinerin' ♀
95 'High Time'
95 'Holiday Harvest'
95 'House of Lords'
96 'Ice Cool'
97 'Iron Gate Gnome'
96 'Journey's End'
96 'Jovial'
97 'Kelly's Girl'
96 'Killer Purple'
96 'Lady Inora Cubiles'
95 'Lady Limelight'
95 'Lemon Ice'
96 'Lilting Lady'
97 'Little Big Man'
97 'Little Bugger'
95 'Little Sally'
96 'Little Showoff'
97 'Look'
96 'Louis McHargue'
95 'Loving Memories'
96 'Lowenstine'
97 'Lukey Boy'
96 'Luna Danca'
97 'Matador Orange'
97 'Mauna Loa'
97 'Metaphor'
97 'Midnight Magic'
96 'Misty'
96 'Mokan Cindy'
96 'Mormon Spider'
97 'Mosel'
96 'Nile Plum'
97 'Nina Winegar'
96 'Nova' ♀
97 'Nutmeg Elf'
95 'Open Hearth'
95 'Peaceful'
95 'Peacock Maiden'
96 'Pink Snowflake'
97 'Prince Redbird'
96 'Pumpkin Face'
97 'Radiant'
96 'Rare China'
96 'Raspberry Sundae'
97 'Red Cup'
97 'Red Damask'
97 'Red Joy'
97 'Royal Heritage'
96 'Royal Ruby'
96 'Royal Saracen'
97 'Russian Rhapsody'
96 'Sari'
96 'Sariah'
95 'Seductress'
97 'Silent World'
97 'Siloam Baby Doll'
96 'Siloam Rose Queen'
96 'Silver Veil'
96 'Smoky Mountain Autumn'
95 'So Excited'
96 'Solano Bulls Eye'
96 'Solid Scarlet'
95 'Sound of Music'
96 'Spanish Gold'
96 'Sunset Pea'
97 'Sweet Refrain'
96 'Taffy Tot'
96 'Telstar'
96 'Thy True Love'
97 'Time Lord'

Plant Deletions

97 'Tiny Temptress'
96 'Tootsie'
96 'Twenty Third Psalm'
96 'Veiled Beauty'
97 'Virgin's Blush'
96 'War Paint'
97 'Wild Welcome'
95 'Windsong'
97 'Windsor Tan'
96 'World of Peace'

HEMIONITIS
97 *arifolia*

HEMIZYGIA
96 *obermeyerae*
97 *transvaalensis*

HEPATICA
95 *nobilis* 'Landquart Marble'
97 – 'Rubra Plena' (d)
97 *transsilvanica alba*
97 – 'Eisvogel'
97 – 'Loddon Blue'
95 – 'Nivea'

HERACLEUM
96 *nepalense* B&SWJ 2105
97 *sphondylium*

HERBERTIA
96 *pulchella*

HERMANNIA
95 *depressa* S&SH 12
96 *pinnata*

HESPERALOE
97 *parviflora* 'Rubra'

HESPERIS
97 *sylviniana*

HESPEROCHIRON
95 *californicus*

HEUCHERA
96 'Apple Blossom'
97 'Cherry Red'
97 'David'
96 'Dingle Amber'
96 'Dingle Mint Chocolate'
96 'Mary Rose'
96 'Moondrops'
97 'Mother of Pearl'
95 'Sparkler' (v)
97 *versicolor*

HEXAGLOTTIS
95 *longifolia*

HIBISCUS
96 *geranioides*
96 'Morning Glory'
96 *moscheutos* Southern Belle Group
96 *sinosyriacus* 'Red Centre'
97 *syriacus* 'Roseus Plenus' (d)
97 *trionum* 'Spirits Bay'

HIERACIUM
96 *alpinum*
96 *glabrum*
96 *mixtum*
95 *pannosum* NS 399

× HIPPEASPREKELIA
96 'Mystique'

HIPPEASTRUM
95 *gracile* 'Pamela'
96 'King of the Stripes'
96 'Lucky Strike'
96 'Rosy Queen'
96 'Spotty'
96 'Vera'
96 'White Snow'
96 'Wonderland'

HIRPICIUM
95 *armerioides* S&SH 6

HOMERIA
95 *comptonii*

HOMOGYNE
97 *alpina*

HOOKERIA
96 *lucens*

HORDEUM
96 *murinum*

HORKELIA
96 *fusca capitata*

HOSTA
95 'Apple Pie'
97 'Blue Lake'
95 *capitata*
96 'Chelsea Ore' (*plantaginea*) (v)
97 'Devon Giant'
97 'Elegans Alba' (*sieboldiana*)
95 'Emma Foster' (*montana*)
95 'Eunice Choice'
97 *fortunei* var. *albopicta* f. *aurea* dwarf form
95 'Gingee'
95 'Glauca' (*fortunei*)
95 'Golden Giboshi'
95 'Green Smash'
97 (Tardiana Group) 'Irische See'
97 'Kelly'
96 *kikutii* var. *pruinosa*
97 'Lady Isobel Barnett' (v)
96 'Lime Krinkles'
96 'Maculata'
96 'Midwest Gold'
96 *opipara*
95 'Parker Jervis Blue'
96 'Rosanne'
97 'Rough Waters'
97 (Tardiana Group) 'Serena'
97 *sieboldiana* var. *mira*
97 'Sweet Standard'
96 'Wheaten Gold'

HOVEA
97 *elliptica*

HOYA
96 *carnosa* 'Prolifica'
96 *crassicaulis*
96 *curtisii*
97 *fusca* 'Silver Knight'
96 *ischnopus*
96 *kenejiana*
96 *meredithii*
96 *obovata*
96 *parasitica* var. *citrina*
96 *pottsii*
96 *serpens*
96 *uncinata*

HUMULUS
96 *lupulus* (f)
96 – (m)
95 – 'Northdown'
95 – 'Target'

HYACINTHELLA
96 *acutiloba*

HYACINTHOIDES
97 *hispanica* 'Rose'
97 *italica vicentina alba*

HYACINTHUS
95 *orientalis* 'Chestnut Flower' (d)
96 – 'Pink Surprise'

HYDRANGEA
97 *anomala*
96 *cordifolia*
97 *heteromalla* 'Yalung Ridge'
95 *hirta*
97 *macrophylla* 'Belzonii' (L)
96 – 'Le Cygne' (H)
96 – 'Magic Light'
97 – 'Münster' (H)
97 – var. *normalis*
97 – 'Red Emperor' (H)
96 – 'Red Lacecap'
97 – 'Rex'
95 – 'Schadendorffs Perle'
97 – 'Seascape'
97 – 'Shower'
97 – 'Thomas Hogg' (H)
96 – 'Tödi' (H)
97 – 'Universal' (H)
97 – 'Ursula'
96 *paniculata* 'Touchard'
97 *serrata chinensis*

HYDROPHYLLUM
96 *appendiculatum*

HYMENOCALLIS
95 *amancaes*
97 *narcissiflora*

HYMENOSPORUM
95 *flavum*

HYMENOXYS
96 *lapidicola*
96 *torreyana*

HYOSCYAMUS
96 *aureus*
97 *niger* 'Capel Ulo'

HYPERICUM
97 *acmosepalum* SBEC 93
96 'Archibald'
97 *bellum* subsp. *latisepalum*
96 – pale form
97 *choisyanum* B&L 12469
95 *empetrifolium* subsp. *empetrifolium* NS 615
96 'Gemo'
95 *henryi* subsp. *hancockii* FSP 047
95 × *inodorum*
97 *lancasteri* L 750
95 *maclarenii*
96 *pseudohenryi*
97 – B&L 12009
97 *scouleri* subsp. *nortoniae*

97 sp. ACE 2321
97 sp. ACE 2524
96 *subsessile*
97 *uralum*
97 – CC 1225
97 *wilsonii*

HYPOCHAERIS
95 *tenuifolia odorata* F&W 7204

HYPOLEPIS
96 *punctata*

HYPOXIS
97 *argentea*
96 *krebsii*
97 *setosa*
97 *villosa*

HYSSOPUS
97 *officinalis decussatus*
95 *seravshanicus*

IBERIS
97 *sempervirens* 'Starkers'

ILEX
97 × *altaclerensis* 'Nigrescens' (m)
97 *aquifolium* 'Recurva' (m)
96 – 'Samuel Foster'
96 – 'Silver Wedding' (f/v)
96 *cassine* yellow-berried
95 *cornuta* Korean form
96 – 'Rotunda' (f)
96 *crenata* 'Bennett's Compact' (m)
96 – 'Green Dragon'
96 – 'Ivory Hall' (f)
96 – 'Rotundifolia'
96 – 'Sentinel' (f)
97 'Elegance' (f)
96 *hookeri*
96 *macrocarpa*
97 × *makinoi*
95 × *meserveae* 'Blue Boy' (m)
95 – 'Blue Girl' (f)
95 – 'Goliath' (f)
96 – 'Red Darling' (f)
96 *myrtifolia* yellow-berried
97 *nothofagifolia* C&H 424
95 *purpurea*

ILYSANTHES
95 *floribunda*

IMPATIENS
95 'Damask Rose'
97 'Dapper Dan' (v)
97 'Golden Surprise'
95 'Orange Delight'
97 *pseudoviola* 'Alba'

INCARVILLEA
95 *arguta* CC&McK 117
96 *compacta* CLD 0233
96 *mairei* pink
96 *sinensis*
97 'Snowcap'

INULA
96 *candida*
96 *ensifolia* 'Compacta'
97 *helianthus-aquaticus* CLD 658
96 *heterolepis*
95 *montbretiana*
97 'Oriental Star'

IOCHROMA
96 *coelestis*

IPOMOEA
96 *aculeata*
96 *costata*
95 *hederacea*
96 *leptotoma*
97 'Scarlett O'Hara'
96 *violacea* Linnaeus

IPOMOPSIS
97 *aggregata* subsp. *aggregata*
95 – subsp. *arizonica*
95 *rubra* K 92.249
95 *spicata* var. *orchidacea*
95 *stenothyrsa*

IRIS
95 *acutiloba*
96 *aitchisonii* var. *chrysantha*
97 'Alice Goodman' (TB)
96 'Alizes' (TB)
95 'All the Way' (AB)
95 'American Heritage' (TB)
96 'Amsterdam' (TB)
96 'Angel's Kiss' (SDB)
96 'Annikins' (IB) 🏆
96 'Antarctic' (TB)
96 'Antique Ivory' (TB)
96 'April Accent' (MDB)
96 'Apropos' (TB)
96 'Aquilifer' (AB)
96 'Arabic Night' (IB)
96 'Art Gallery' (TB)
95 'Banbury Velvet' (CH) 🏆
96 'Barbara's Kiss' (Spuria)
96 'Bedtime Story' (IB)
96 'Bel Azur' (IB)
96 'Belle Meade' (TB)
96 'Bengal Tiger' (TB)
96 'Benton Cordelia' (TB)
95 'Berry Rich' (BB)
97 'Best Bet'
97 'Betty my Love' (Spuria)
96 'Bewick Swan' (TB)
96 'Big Money' (TB) 🏆
96 'Big Wheel' (CH)
96 'Black Flag' (TB)
97 'Black Lady' (MTB)
96 'Blackberry Brandy' (BB)
96 'Blackfoot'
96 'Blockley' (SDB)
96 'Blue Asterisk' (IB)
95 'Blue Chip Pink' (TB)
96 'Blue Icing' (IB)
96 'Blue Mascara' (SDB)
96 'Blue Neon' (SDB)
96 'Blue Owl' (TB)
96 'Blue Sparks' (SDB)
96 'Bluebird in Flight' (IB)
96 'Blues Singer' (TB)
96 'Border Town' (Spuria)
97 'Breakers' (TB) 🏆
97 'Bright Chic' (SDB)
95 'Bronze Perfection' (Dutch)
96 'Brown Doll' (IB)
97 'Brown Trout' (TB)
97 'Brownstone' (Spuria)

96 'Bubbly Blue' (IB)
95 *bucharica* x *aucheri*
95 'Buckden Pike' (TB) 🏆
96 *bulleyana* ACE 1819
96 – ACE 1890
95 'Bunny Hop' (SDB)
97 'Burmese Dawn' (TB)
96 'Buttered Chocolate' (Spuria)
96 'Buttermilk'
96 'Cabaret Royale' (TB)
97 'Can Can Red' (TB)
95 'Canary Frills' (TB)
96 'Can't Stop' (SDB)
97 'Captain Gallant' (TB)
96 'Caress' (SDB)
95 'Carmel Mission' (CH)
96 'Carnival Glass' (BB)
97 'Celestial Glory' (TB)
95 'Center Ring' (TB)
96 'Champagne Music' (TB)
95 'Charter Member' (CH)
97 'Cherry Ripe' (TB)
96 'Chico Maid' (TB)
96 'Childsong' (AB)
97 *chrysographes* 'Kew Black'
96 'Circus Stripes' (TB)
95 'Cirrus' (TB)
95 'Classy Babe' (SDB)
96 'Clever Devil' (CH)
97 'Cold Cold Heart' (TB)
96 'Colonial Gold' (TB)
95 'Comma' (SDB)
96 'Concord Touch' (SDB)
96 'Confederate Soldier' (IB)
96 'Copper Pot' (TB)
96 'Cotati' (BB)
96 'Cranberry Crush' (TB)
95 'Crocus' (MDB)
96 'Curio' (MDB)
96 'Cycles' (TB)
97 'Dame Judy' (TB)
97 'Dappled Pony' (MTB)
96 'Dardanus' (Aril)
95 'Daring Eyes' (MDB)
96 'Deep Space' (TB)
95 'Deepening Shadows' (CH)
96 'Deltaplane' (TB)
97 'Depute Nomblot' (TB)
96 'Derry Down' (SDB)
96 'Diligence' (SDB) 🏆
96 'Disco Jewel' (MTB)
96 'Dragonsdawn' (AB)
96 'Edale' (TB) 🏆
95 'Elegans' (TB)
96 'Elisa Renee' (TB)
96 'Elizabeth of England' (TB)
96 'Encanto' (SDB)
96 'Enchanted Blue' (SDB)
96 'Encircle' (CH)
97 *ensata* 'Agrippine'
96 – 'Aoigata'
96 – 'Beni Renge'
95 – 'Benokohji'
97 – 'Blue Embers'
97 – 'Calamari'
97 – 'Chiyo-no-haru'
95 – 'Continuing Pleasure' 🏆
97 – 'Emotion' (I)

95 – 'Flying Tiger' 🏆
97 – 'Frilled Enchantment'
96 – 'Geisha Gown'
96 – 'Geisha Obi'
97 – 'Gei-sho-mi'
96 – 'Hoyden'
96 – 'Imperial Velvet'
97 – 'Kalamazo'
95 – 'Katy Mendez' 🏆
97 – 'Miss Coquette'
96 – 'Prairie Glory'
96 – 'Prairie Noble'
96 – 'Royal Banner'
96 – 'Royal Game'
95 – 'Sapphire Star'
96 – 'Sorceror's Triumph'
95 – 'Southern Son' 🏆
96 – 'White Chiffon'
95 – 'Winged Sprite'
96 – 'World's Delight' 🏆
97 'Etched Apricot' (TB)
96 'Ever After' (TB)
97 'Excelsior' (DB)
97 'Exotic Star' (TB)
96 'Fall Primrose' (TB)
97 'Fancy Tales' (TB)
96 'Fantasy World' (IB)
97 'Fashion Jewel' (TB)
97 'Femme Fatale' (TB)
95 'Fine Line' (CH) 🏆
96 'First Chapter' (AB)
96 'First Lilac' (IB)
96 'Flammenschwert' (TB)
97 'Flight of Cavalry' (IB)
96 'Foxcote' (IB)
97 'Foxtor' (TB)
96 'Fresno Calypso' (TB)
96 'Frosted Angel' (SDB)
96 'Frosty Crown' (SDB)
96 'Funny Face' (MDB)
96 'Gallant Moment' (TB)
95 'Gelee Royal' (AB)
97 *germanica* 'Amas'
97 – 'Mel Jope'
96 'Gleaming Gold' (SDB)
97 'Glen' (TB)
95 'Going West' (CH)
95 'Gold Intensity' (BB)
95 'Golden Hind' (TB)
96 'Goring Ace' (CH) 🏆
96 'Grape Orbit' (SDB)
97 'Green Little' (DB)
96 'Halo in Pink' (TB)
96 'Halo in Yellow' (TB)
95 'Hands On' (CH)
96 'Happy Mood' (IB) 🏆
97 'Happy Thought' (IB)
96 *hartwegii*
96 – subsp. *columbiana*
95 'Harvest Festival' (SDB)
96 'Heavenly Days' (TB)
96 'Hedge'
95 'Hildegarde' (Dutch)
97 'Hindenburg' (TB)
96 *histrioides*
95 'Holiday Flame' (IB)
97 'Hollywood Blonde' (TB)
97 'Holy Night' (TB)
96 'Honey Crunch' (TB)
96 'Honey Dip' (SDB)
96 'Hoodwink' (SDB)
96 'Hot Number' (CH)
97 'Howard Weed' (TB)
96 'Hugh Miller' (TB)

97 *iberica* subsp. *iberica*
95 'Ice Dancer' (TB) 🏆
96 'Ice White'
95 'Idylwild' (CH)
96 'Imperial Sun' (Spuria)
97 'Inaugural Ball' (TB)
96 'Indiscreet' (TB)
96 'Inferno' (TB)
97 'Irish Spring' (TB)
96 'Ivor Knowles' (CH)
95 'Jana White' (MTB)
95 'Jillaroo' (SDB)
95 'Jitterbug' (TB)
97 'Jo Jo' (TB)
96 'Joan Lay' (TB)
95 'Joanna' (TB)
97 'Joyce McBride' (SDB)
97 'Joyous Isle' (SDB)
97 'Juliet' (TB)
96 'Jungle Fires' (TB)
95 'Jungle Warrior' (SDB)
96 'Kashmir White' (TB)
97 *kashmiriana*
95 'Kate Izzard' (TB)
96 'Kildonan' (TB)
97 'Kirkstone' (TB)
95 *kirkwoodii*
97 *kopetdagensis*
95 'La Selva Beach' (CH)
96 'Lace Jabot' (TB)
97 *lactea* SULE 1
96 'Lady Ilse' (TB)
96 'Lady River' (TB)
96 'Lamorna' (TB)
95 'Langport Dawn' (IB)
96 'Langport Dolly' (IB)
97 'Langport Duke' (IB)
97 'Langport Fashion' (IB)
96 'Langport Finch' (IB)
97 'Langport Flash' (IB)
97 'Langport Hero' (IB)
96 'Langport Judy' (IB)
96 'Langport Kestrel' (IB)
96 'Langport Lady' (IB)
95 'Langport Pansy' (IB)
96 'Langport Secret' (IB)
96 'Langport Snow' (IB)
96 'Langport Tartan' (IB)
95 'Las Olas' (CH)
97 'Late Lilac' (TB)
97 'Laura' (TB)
96 'Lavender Royal' (CH) 🏆
97 'Lemon Brocade' (TB)
95 'Lenzschnee' (TB)
95 'Lighted Window' (TB)
96 'Likiang' (Chrysographes)
95 'Lilac Lulu' (SDB)
95 'Lincoln Imp' (CH) 🏆
96 'Lindis' (AB)
96 'Little Jewel' (DB)
95 'Little Miss' (BB)
97 'Little Sapphire' (SDB)
96 'Little Sir Echo' (MB)
95 'Little Tilgates' 🏆
96 'Little Vanessa' (SDB)
96 'Lollipop' (SDB)
96 'Lucinda' (TB)
97 'Lucky Devil' (Spuria)
97 'Lynwood Gold' (IB)
95 *maackii*
96 *macrosiphon*
97 'Magenta and Peach' (TB)
96 'Magharee' (TB)

95 'Maiden Blush' (TB)
96 'Main Sequence' (AB)
95 'Mama Hoohoo' (IB)
96 'Maori King' (TB)
95 'Mar Monte' (CH)
97 'Mariachi' (TB)
96 'Marmot' (MDB)
97 'Mary Randall' (TB)
96 'Meadow Moss' (SDB)
97 'Melbreak' (TB)
97 'Menton' (SDB)
97 'Merry Day' (IB)
96 'Merry Madrigal' (TB)
97 'Michael Paul' (SDB)
95 'Midas Kiss' (IB)
96 *milesii* CC&McK 357
96 'Mini Dynamo' (SDB)
95 'Mission Santa Cruz'
   (CH)
96 'Modern Classic' (TB)
97 'Moon's Delight' (TB)
97 'Murmuring Morn'
   (TB)
96 'Music Caper' (SDB)
96 'Mute Swan' (TB)
96 'Myra's Child' (SDB)
95 'Naranja' (TB)
96 'Navy Doll' (MDB)
96 'New Wave' (MTB)
97 *nicolai*
96 'Night Affair' (TB)
96 'Night Edition' (TB)
97 'Night Ruler' (TB)
95 'Night Shift' (TB)
97 'No-Name' (CH) ♀
95 'Norton Sunlight'
   (Spuria)
95 'Nuggets' (MDB)
95 *nusairiensis*
96 'Oktoberfest' (TB)
97 'Old Flame' (TB)
95 'Old Monterey' (CH)
96 'On Fire' (SDB)
95 'Orchid Flare' (MDB)
95 'Oroville' (Spuria)
96 'Ouija' (BB) ♀
96 'Outline' (AB)
96 'Outstep' (SDB)
96 'Painted Rose' (MTB)
97 'Palace Gossip' (TB)
96 *pallida* JCA 589.800
96 'Paradise Pink' (TB)
95 'Parakeet' (MTB)
97 'Patina' (TB)
97 'Peach Bisque' (TB)
96 'Peach Melba' (TB)
96 'Penny Bunker'
   (Spuria)
96 'Penny Candy' (MDB)
97 'Perfect Interlude' (TB)
95 'Petite Polka' (SDB)
95 'Phillida' (CH) ♀
95 'Pink Pleasure' (TB)
95 'Piper's Tune' (IB)
96 'Pippi Longstockings'
   (SDB)
96 'Pixie' (DB)
96 'Pixie Plum' (SDB)
96 *plicata*
97 *polakii* (Oncocyclus)
96 'Popinjay' (CH)
97 'Pot Luck' (IB)
95 'Prairie Warbler'
   (Chrysographes)
95 'Princess' (TB)
95 'Prodigy' (MDB)

96 'Prophetic Message'
   (AB)
96 'Proud Land' (TB)
96 *pseudacorus* 'Kimboshi'
   × *ensata*
96 – 'Tiger Brother'
97 *pseudopumila*
95 *pumila aequiloba*
96 *purdyi*
96 – × *tenuissima*
96 'Purple Dream' (CH)
95 'Quip' (MDB)
95 'Rainbow Connection'
   (CH)
95 'Raindance Kid' (IB)
95 'Raku' (CH)
97 'Rancho Grande' (TB)
97 'Ranger' (TB)
97 'Rapture in Blue' (TB)
97 'Raspberry Frills' (TB)
96 'Red Kite' (TB)
97 'Red Orchid' (IB)
97 'Red Tornado' (TB)
96 'Reflection'
96 'Rickshaw' (SDB)
96 'Ride Joy' (TB)
95 'Ring o'Roses' (CH) ♀
95 'Rio del Mar' (CH) ♀
95 'Roaring Camp' (CH)
97 'Robert J. Graves' (TB)
97 'Role Model' (TB)
96 'Rose Caress' (TB)
97 *rosenbachiana*
95 'Royal Blue'
   (Reticulata)
95 'Royal Elf' (SDB)
96 'Royal Eyelash' (SDB)
96 'Royal Ruffles' (TB)
95 'Royal Velours'
96 'Royal Viking' (TB)
97 'Royalist' (TB)
96 'Ruth Nies Cabeen'
   (Spuria)
96 'Safari Boy' (IB)
96 'Sailor's Dance' (TB)
95 'San Andreas' (CH)
96 'San Jose' (TB)
96 'Santa Clarita' (TB)
95 'Saturnus' (Dutch)
97 'Scarlet Ribbon' (TB)
97 'School Boy' (CH)
95 'Sea Gal' (CH)
96 'Sea Urchin' (SDB)
97 'Secret Melody' (TB)
95 *setosa major*
95 'Shaft of Gold' (TB)
95 'Sheer Class' (SDB)
95 'Sheik' (AB)
95 'Short Distance' (IB)
95 *sibirica* 'Ashfield
   Clementine'
95 – 'Berlin Ruffles' ♀
95 – 'Cleeton Double
   Chance' ♀
97 – 'Dark Lavender'
96 – 'Feathered Giant'
95 – 'Hubbard'
96 – 'Lavender Bonanza'
97 – 'Limelight'
96 – 'Marshmallow
   Frosting'
95 – 'Polly Dodge'
97 – 'Rebeboth Gem'
95 – 'Splash Down' ♀
97 – 'Welcome Return'

95 – 'Welfenprinz' ♀
95 – 'Zakopane' ♀
97 'Silhouette' (TB)
95 'Simply Wild' (CH)
97 'Sky and Snow' (SDB)
97 'Skyfire' (TB)
95 'Skylaser' (CH)
96 'Smiling Gold' (TB)
95 'Smoky Valley' (BB)
97 'Soft Caress' (TB)
95 'Solar Song' (SDB)
96 'Solid Gold' (TB)
96 'Song of Spring' (TB)
97 'Sooner Serenade' (TB)
96 'Sounder' (BB)
96 sp. CLD 1399
95 'Spanish Don' (CH)
96 'Spring Wine' (IB)
96 *spuria* subsp. *demetrii*
– subsp. *sogdiana*
97 'Spyglass Hill' (TB)
97 'Squeaky Clean' (SDB)
96 'Stability' (Spuria)
96 'Starlit River' (TB)
97 'Stellar Lights' (TB)
95 *stenophylla*
97 'Step by Step' (BB)
96 'Stepping Little' (BB)
97 'Sterling Prince' (TB)
96 *stolonifera* 'George
   Barr'
96 'Stylish' (DB)
96 'Sullom Voe' (TB)
96 'Sultry Sister' (TB)
96 'Sun Symbol' (SDB)
97 'Sunny Heart' (SDB)
96 'Sunny Side' (Spuria)
95 'Sunny Smile' (IB) ♀
96 'Sunset Fires' (TB)
96 'Sunset Sky' (TB)
96 'Sunset Trail' (AB)
95 'Surprise Sultan' (TB)
96 'Suspense' (Spuria)
96 'Svelte' (IB)
96 'Swahili' (TB)
97 'Sweertii'
96 'Symphony' (Dutch)
97 'Tarheel Elf' (SDB)
97 'Tease' (SDB)
97 *tectorum* Burma form
96 'Tequila Sunrise' (TB)
97 *thompsonii*
96 'Thrice Blessed' (SDB)
95 'Tid-bit' (DB)
96 'Tidle de Winks' (BB)
97 'Tiger Butter' (TB)
97 'Tinted Crystal' (TB)
96 'Tornado' (AB)
96 'Transcribe' (SDB)
96 'Treasure' (TB)
97 'Triffid' (TB)
96 'Tupelo Honey' (TB)
96 'Turkish Warrior' (AB)
95 'Twin Lakes' (CH)
97 *typhifolia*
97 'Unfurled Flag'
96 *unguicularis* JCA 600.412
97 'Ursula Vahl' (TB)
96 'Vague a l'Ame' (TB)
95 *variegata alba*
97 'Viking Princess' (TB)
96 'Vim' (SDB)
95 'Vinho Verde' (IB) ♀
95 'Violet Lulu' (SDB)
96 'Violet Zephyr' (Spuria)
96 'Violetta' (DB)

95 'Wampum' (IB)
97 'War Sails' (TB)
95 'Warl-sind' (Juno)
97 'Warrior King' (TB)
96 'Watchman' (AB)
97 'Well Endowed' (TB)
95 'Wensleydale' (TB) ♀
95 'Westerlies' (CH)
95 'Wharfedale' (TB) ♀
96 'White Superior'
   (Dutch)
97 'Wild West' (TB)
97 *willmottiana*
95 'Wirral Gold' ♀
96 'Woodling' (SDB)
95 'Yellow Apricot'
   (Chrysographes)
95 'Yellow Court'
   (Chrysographes)
96 'Zipper' (MDB)
97 'Zulu Chief' (Spuria)
97 'Zwanenburg Beauty'

ISOPOGON
97 *dubius*

ISOPYRUM
97 *nipponicum* var.
   sarmentosum

JABOROSA
96 *magellanica*

JASIONE
97 *amethystina*
96 sp. from Spain

JASMINUM
96 *humile* B&L 12086
95 – KR 709
95 × *stephanense*
   'Variegatum'

JATROPHA
97 *multifida*

JOVIBARBA
95 *arenaria* 'Opiz'
96 *heuffelii* 'Bronze King'
96 – 'Sundancer'

JUGLANS
96 *regia* 'Corne du
   Périgord' (F)
95 – 'Red Leaf'

JUNCUS
97 *concinnus*

JUNIPERUS
95 *chinensis* 'Iowa'
96 – 'Keteleeri'
95 – 'Mas'
96 *communis* 'Clywd'
96 – 'Mayer'
95 *excelsa* var. *polycarpos*
96 *procera*
96 *recurva*
95 *scopulorum*
96 – 'Silver Globe'
97 *virginiana* 'Pendula'
97 – 'Robusta Green'

JURINEA
96 *moschus* subsp.
   moschus

KALMIA
97 *cuneata*
97 *latifolia* 'Nipmuck'
97 – 'Pink Star'
96 – 'Pinwheel'

96 – 'Shooting Star'
96 *pygmaea*
95 × Rhododendron 'No
Suchianum'

KALMIOPSIS
97 *leachiana*
Cedar Park form
97 – Umpqua Valley form

KECKIELLA
97 *antirrhinoides*
96 – *antirrhinoides*
95 *ternata* JLS 86304LACA

KNIPHOFIA
96 *caulescens* BH 5020
96 'Cream Flame'
96 'Dr E.M. Mills'
97 'Early Yellow'
95 'Fireking'
97 'Limelight'
96 'Pencil'
95 sp. from Ethiopia
97 'Toasted Corn'
97 'Tubergeniana'
97 'Underway'

KNOWLTONIA
97 *bracteata*
97 *transvaalensis*

KOELERIA
97 *pyramidata*

LABLAB
96 *purpureus*

LABURNUM
95 *alpinum*
96 × *watereri* 'Alford's
Weeping'

LACHENALIA
96 *aloides* 'Nelsonii'
95 – 'Pearsonii'
97 hybrid Lac. 213
95 *mediana*
96 *reflexa*
95 × *regeliana*

LAGENOPHORA
96 *pinnatifida*

LAGERSTROEMIA
95 *chekiangensis*

LALLEMANTIA
95 *canescens*

LAMIUM
95 *album* 'Ashfield
Variegated'
96 *garganicum* 'Golden
Carpet' (v)
96 *maculatum* 'Silver
Dollar'

LAMPRANTHUS
96 *amoenus*
96 *falcatus*
96 *falciformis*
96 *primavernus*
96 *stayneri*
96 *zeyheri*

LARIX
97 *europaeus*
95 *kaempferi* 'Dervaes'
97 – 'Little Blue Star'

LASER
96 *trilobum*

LATHYRUS
95 *hookeri*
97 *laevigatus*
95 *latifolius* Rollinson's form
96 *macrocarpus* F&W 7737
95 *multiceps* F&W 7192
96 *odoratus* 'America' ♀
96 – 'Captain of the Blues'
96 – 'Countess Cadogan'
96 – 'Cupani'
96 – 'Quito'
96 – 'Violet Queen'
95 *roseus*
95 *sativus alboazureus*
96 – var. *albus*
95 *tingitanus* red and white
97 *undulatus*

LAURENTIA
97 *minuta*

LAVANDULA
97 *angustifolia* 'Arabian
Knight'
96 – 'Heacham Blue'
97 – 'Maillette'
96 – No. 9
97 *buchii* var. *buchii*
95 *dentata* forms
96 × *intermedia* 'Mitcham
Blue'
97 *latifolia* 'Alba'

LAVATERA
96 *arborea* 'Ile d'Hyères'
97 'Barnsley Perry's
Dwarf'
96 *tauricensis*

LEDEBOURIA
97 *pauciflora*

LEDUM
96 *glandulosum*

LEIOPHYLLUM
96 *buxifolium*
'Compactum'

LEMNA
97 *minuscula*

LEONTODON
97 *rigens*

LEONTOPODIUM
95 *hayachinense* AJS/J 111
95 *ochroleucum*
96 *souliei*

LEOPOLDIA
96 *brevipedicellata*

LEPIDIUM
97 *barnebyanum*

LEPTARRHENA
96 *pyrolifolia*

LEPTINELLA
96 *dendyi* forms
97 – 'Southley'

LEPTOPTERIS
97 *hymenophylloides*
97 *laxa*
97 *media*
96 *moorei*
97 *superba*
97 *wilkesiana*

LEPTOSPERMUM
97 *laevigatum*

97 *macrocarpum*
97 *scoparium* 'Bunting'
97 – 'Chiff Chaff'
97 – 'Firecrest'
95 – 'Gaiety Girl' (d)
95 – Jervis Bay form
97 – (Nanum Group)
'Kompakt'
95 – 'Nichollsii
Grandiflorum'
97 – 'Pink Champagne'
97 – 'Redstart'
97 – 'Ruby Wedding'
96 – 'Wiri Amy'

LESCHENAULTIA
95 *biloba*
96 *formosa*
96 – orange

LESQUERELLA
95 *arizonica*
95 *fendleri*
96 *kingii sherwoodii*

LEUCADENDRON
97 *discolor*

LEUCAENA
95 *latisiliqua*

LEUCANTHEMUM
95 *discoideum*
97 × *superbum* 'Annie
House'
95 – 'Flore Pleno' (d)
95 *vulgare* 'Corinne
Tremaine'

LEUCOCHRYSUM
97 *albicans* subsp.
albicans var. *incanum*

LEUCOCORYNE
97 'Andes'
97 'Caravelle'
97 *purpurea*

LEUCOGENES
96 *grandiceps* ×
Helichrysum
bellidioides

LEUCOJUM
95 *longifolium*
97 *vernum* 'Podpolozje'

LEUCOSCEPTRUM
96 *canum*

LEUCOSPERMUM
97 *cordifolium*

LEUCOTHOE
96 *axillaris*
97 *walteri* 'Red Pimpernel'
95 'Zebonard'

LEWISIA
96 *brachycalyx* pink
97 'Margaret Williams'
95 *oppositifolia*
ex JCA 11835
96 – 'Richeyi'
96 'Oxstalls Lane'

LIATRIS
96 *cylindracea*
96 *microcephala*
96 *scariosa* 'Alba'

LIBERTIA
97 *pulchella* Tasmanian form

96 sp. from New Zealand

LIGULARIA
96 *alpigena*
95 *jacquemoniana*

LIGUSTRUM
95 *lucidum*
'Aureovariegatum'
97 – 'Latifolium'
96 *obtusifolium* var.
regelianum

LILIUM
96 'Admiration' (Ia)
96 'Aladdin' (Ia)
96 'Allright' (VIIb/d)
97 'Annabelle' (Ia)
96 Aurelian hybrids (VIIa)
96 'Blitz' (Ia)
96 'Charmeur' (7c)
97 *concolor* var.
partheneion (IX)
96 'Connection' (Ia)
95 *davidii* (IX) ♀
96 'Domination'
97 *euxanthum* ACE 1268
97 – KGB 492
95 Everest Group (VIId)
96 'Fiesta Gitana' (Ia)
96 'Fire Star' (VIIc/d)
96 'Flamenco' (Ib)
96 'Gibraltar' (Ia)
97 'Golden Sunrise' (Ia)
95 'Green Dragon' (VIa)
♀
97 Green Magic Group
(VIa)
97 'Hannah North' (Ic)
95 'Harmony' (Ia)
96 'Her Grace' (Ia)
97 *humboldtii* (IX)
97 Imperial Gold Group
(VIIc)
95 'Jacques S. Dijt' (II)
95 Jamboree Group (VIId)
96 'Jazz' (Ia)
97 'Karen North' (Ic) ♀
97 'Kiwi Fanfare'
97 *lancifolium* var.
fortunei
95 *ledebourii* (IX)
96 *leichtlinii* 'Delta' (IX)
96 'Levant' (Ic)
96 'Little Girl' (VIIb)
96 *longiflorum* 'Casa
Rosa'
97 *lophophorum*
95 – CLD 1061 (IX)
95 'Make Up' (Ia)
97 'Marie North' (Ic)
95 'Marseille' (Ia)
96 *martagon* 'Inshriach'
(IX)
96 – pink
96 Moonlight Group (VIa)
96 'Mrs R.O. Backhouse'
(II) ♀
97 *nanum* CH&M
96 'Nivea' (I)
96 Paisley Group (II)
96 'Parisienne' (Ia)
97 *parvum*
96 'Passage' (VIIc)
96 'Peau Douce'
97 'Peggy North' (Ic)
96 'Picture' (VIId)

96 'Pink Beauty' (VIIc)
96 'Providence'
96 *pyrenaicum* subsp.
  carniolicum var.
  albanicum
96 – var. *pyrenaicum* (IX)
96 'Rosefire' (Ia)
96 'Sahara' (Ia)
96 'Shuksan' (IV)
96 'Silhouette' (Ia)
96 'Sorisso' (Ia)
96 'Sorrento' (Ia)
97 *souliei* ACE 1192
95 *speciosum* ♀
95 – 'Elite' (IX)
96 'Symphony' (Ib)
96 'Taptoe' (Ia)
96 'Ventoux' (Ia)
96 'White Star Gazer'
  (VII)
95 'Yellow Present'

LIMONIUM
96 *binervosum*
96 *dregeanum*
95 *perezii*
95 – 'Atlantis'
97 *platyphyllum* 'True
  Blue'
97 *rumicifolium*

LINANTHUS
97 *nuttallii*

LINARIA
96 *bipunctata*
96 'Blue Pygmy'
95 *lobata alba*
95 *purpurea* 'Dwarf Canon
  Went'
96 – Harbutt's hybrids
95 *tristis*

LINDERA
96 *megaphylla*

LINUM
97 *aretioides*
96 *hirsutum*
96 *mongolicum*
97 *perenne* subsp.
  anglicum
96 – 'Himmelszelt'
96 *spathulatum*

LIPPIA
96 sp. RB 94075

LIQUIDAMBAR
96 *styraciflua* 'Moraine'

LIRIOPE
97 *exiliflora* 'Silvery
  Sunproof'
97 *muscari* 'Ingwersen'
97 – 'Superba'

LITHOCARPUS
96 *pachyphyllus*

LITHODORA
97 *diffusa* 'Grace Farwell'

LIVISTONA
97 *saribus*

LLOYDIA
96 *flavonutans*

LOBELIA
97 'Bees Ridge'
95 *cardinalis* JLS 88010WI

96 – 'Shrimp Salad'
97 'Compliment Blue'
97 'Compliment Scarlet'
96 'Hadspen Royal Purple'
97 'Jack McMaster'
96 *kalmii*
97 'Kimbridge Beet' ♀
96 *linnaeoides* x Pratia
  macrodon
96 *longiflora* RB 94066
96 *oligodon*
96 'Pope's Velvet'
97 *pyramidalis* B&SWJ 316
95 *richardsonii* red
96 *roughii*
96 *siphilitica* 'Nana'
96 *surrepens*
97 'Wildwood Splendour'

LOBOSTEMON
97 *montanus*

LOISELEURIA
97 *procumbens* 'Saint
  Anton'

LOMATIUM
95 *canbyi*

LONICERA
95 *arizonica*
95 *glaucescens*
96 'Hidcote'
95 *hispidula*
96 *japonica* 'Soja'
96 *periclymenum clarkii*
96 – 'Cottage Beauty'
96 – 'Cream Cascade'
96 – var. *glaucohirta*
97 – 'Winchester'
97 – yellow
97 *praeflorens*
96 sp. CLD 1451
97 sp. CLD 315
96 sp. D.Fox 89251
97 *tatarica* 'Rosea'
97 – f. *sibirica*
95 *vesicaria*

LOPHOSPERMUM
97 *erubescens* 'Garnet'

LOTUS
97 *berthelotii* Kew form

LOXOSTYLIS
97 *alata*

LUDWIGIA
97 *palustris*

LUNARIA
95 *annua* 'Golden Spire'
97 – 'Ken Aslet'

LUPINUS
96 *albifrons* var. *douglasii*
97 *arboreus* cream
95 'Blushing Bride'
95 *breviscapus*
96 'Clifford Star'
96 'Daydream'
96 'Gold Dust'
96 *leucophyllus*
97 *microcarpus*
96 'Moonraker'
97 *oreophilus* F&W 7353
97 'Pink Fortune'
96 'Royal Parade' ♀
97 *sericatus*
97 'Sundown'

95 'Troop the Colour' ♀
96 'Walton Lad'

LUZULA
95 *alopecurus*
95 *alpinopilosa* subsp.
  candollei
95 *celata*
97 *plumosa*
97 *purpureosplendens*
95 *sibirica*
97 *sylvatica* 'Tatra Gold'

x LYCENE
95 *kubotae*

LYCHNIS
95 *alpina* subsp.
  americana
97 *chalcedonica* 'Valetta'
97 *flos-jovis* 'Alba'
95 *punctata* dwarf
97 sp. Andes
96 *viscaria* 'Splendens
  Rosea'

LYCIUM
97 *europaeum*

LYCOPUS
97 sp. JLS 88040

LYCORIS
95 *aurea*

LYGODIUM
97 *palmatum*

LYSIMACHIA
95 *congestiflora* 'Golden
  Falls'
97 – 'Silver Bird'
97 – 'Sunset Gold'
96 *mauritiana*
96 *nummularia nana*
97 *ovata*
97 *pseudohenryi*

LYTHRUM
97 'Croftway'
95 x *salmonea*

MACHAERANTHERA
97 *lagunensis*

MAGNOLIA
96 *acuminata* 'Golden
  Glow'
96 'Andre Harvey'
97 'Charles Coates'
97 'Cup Cake'
97 'Frank Gladney'
95 *fraseri*
96 *grandiflora* 'Charles
  Dickens'
96 'Kerr van Ann'
97 'Nimbus'
96 'Pickard's Charm'
97 'Pickard's Crystal'
97 'Pickard's Pink
  Diamond'
96 'Pickard's Stardust'
97 'Rouged Alabaster'
97 'Ruby'
95 *salicifolia* 'Jermyns'
96 x *soulangeana*
  'Coimbra'
96 – 'Just Jean'
97 *stellata* 'Massey'
97 'W.B. Clarke'

MAHONIA
97 *gracilipes*
97 'Gulf Tide'
96 *keiskei*
95 *napaulensis*
97 *pallida* T&K 553
97 *piperiana*
97 x *wagneri* 'Fireflame'

MAIANTHEMUM
96 *bifolium* British form

MAIHUENIA
97 *poeppigii* JCA 1253

MALLOTUS
97 *japonicus*

MALUS
96 x *adstringens* 'Almey'
96 – 'Purple Wave'
96 *baccata* 'Dolgo'
96 – 'Gracilis'
95 – var. *mandshurica*
96 *coronaria* 'Elk River'
97 *domestica* 'Acklam
  Russet' (D)
97 – 'Admiral' (D)
97 – 'Alderman' (C)
96 – 'Alford' (Cider)
96 – 'Ananas Reinette' (D)
96 – 'Andrew Johnson' (F)
96 – 'Anne-Marie' (C)
96 – 'Arthur W. Barnes'
  (C)
96 – 'Backwell Red'
  (Cider)
97 – 'Ballarat Seedling'
  (D)
96 – 'Baron Ward' (C)
97 – 'Beachamwell' (D)
96 – 'Beauty of Stoke' (C)
96 – 'Belle-fille Normande'
  (C)
96 – 'Belle-fleur de France'
  (C)
96 – 'Bulmer's Chisel
  Jersey' (Cider)
96 – 'Bulmer's Crimson
  King' (Cider)
96 – 'Bulmer's Fillbarrel'
  (Cider)
96 – 'Bulmer's Foxwhelp'
  (Cider)
96 – 'Buxted Favorite'
96 – 'Calagolden Elbee'
  (D)
97 – 'Calville des Femmes'
  (C)
97 – 'Captain Kidd' (D)
97 – 'Caroline' (D)
97 – 'Catherine' (C)
96 – 'Charles Eyre' (C)
97 – 'Close' (D)
97 – 'Cockpit' (C)
96 – 'Cortland' (C)
96 – 'Cox's Red Sport' (D)
96 – 'Crimson Bramley'
  (C)
96 – 'Crimson Peasgood'
  (C)
97 – 'Duck's Bill' (D)
97 – 'Early Crimson' (F)
96 – 'Edwin Beckett' (D)
97 – 'Eynsham Dumpling'
  (C)
97 – 'Fall Pippin' (D)

96 – 'Feltham Beauty' (D)
97 – 'Feuillemorte' (D)
97 – 'Fillingham Pippin' (C)
96 – 'First and Last' (D)
97 – 'Folkestone' (D)
97 – 'Foulden Pearmain' (D)
96 – 'Franklyn's Golden Pippin' (D)
96 – 'Frogmore Prolific' (C)
95 – 'Geneva'
95 – 'George Favers' (F)
97 – 'Gin' (Cider)
96 – 'Golden Nonpareil' (D)
96 – 'Grange's Pearmain' (C)
96 – 'Gulval Seedling' (D)
96 – 'Harry Master's Dove' (Cider)
97 – 'Hereford Cross' (D)
96 – 'Hormead Pearmain' (C)
97 – 'Houblon' (D)
96 – 'James Lawson' (D)
96 – 'John Broad' (F)
96 – Jubilee (Delbards) (F)
95 – 'Lady Bacon' (F)
97 – 'Lady Lambourne' (C/D)
97 – 'Lady Stanley' (D)
96 – 'Lady Williams' (D)
96 – 'Lady's Delight' (C)
96 – 'Laxton's Pearmain' (D)
96 – 'Laxton's Reward' (D)
96 – 'Leeder's Perfection' (F)
97 – 'Lobo' (D)
96 – 'Lodgemore Nonpareil' (D)
96 – 'Lord of the Isles' (F)
96 – 'Lord Rosebery' (D)
96 – 'Maiden's Blush' (D)
96 – 'Maidstone Favourite' (D)
96 – 'Mannington's Pearmain' (D)
96 – 'Marriage-maker' (D)
96 – 'Mead's Broading' (C)
96 – 'Mère de Ménage' (C)
96 – 'Merton Beauty' (D)
96 – 'Merton Charm' (D) ♀
96 – 'Merton Joy' (D)
96 – 'Monarch Advanced' (C)
96 – 'Mrs Crittenden' (D)
96 – 'Nehou' (Cider)
95 – 'New German' (D)
96 – 'Norman's Pippin' (D)
95 – 'Paroquet' (D)
95 – 'Patricia' (D)
97 – 'Polly Prosser' (D)
96 – 'Powell's Russet' (D)
96 – 'Puckrupp Pippin' (D)
96 – 'Queen Caroline' (C)
95 – 'Queenie' (D)
96 – 'Red Melba' (D)
96 – 'Red Newton Wonder' (C)
95 – 'Red Superb' (D)
97 – Reine des Reinettes

96 – 'Rosamund' (D)
97 – 'S.T. Wright' (C)
96 – 'Scarlet Crofton' (D)
96 – 'Scarlet Pimpernel' (D)
96 – 'Schweizer Orange' (F)
95 – 'Shortymac' (D)
96 – 'Starking Red Delicious' (D)
96 – 'Stark's Earliest' (D)
96 – 'Stembridge' (Cider)
97 – 'Summer Granny' (D)
96 – 'Summergold' (F)
96 – 'Taunton Cream' (F)
95 – 'Transparente de Bois Guillaume' (D)
96 – 'Tyler's Kernel' (C)
96 – 'Wellspur Delicious' (D)
97 – 'Wheeler's Russet' (D)
97 – 'Winter Majetin' (C)
96 – 'Yellowspur' (D)
97 – 'Yorkshire Greening' (C)
96 halliana
95 x hartwigii 'Katherine' ♀
96 mahonia
97 'Mamouth'
95 rufiensis
97 sp. CLD 417
95 'Stellata'
96 'Strathmore'
96 toringo 'Rosea'
95 – 'Wintergold'
96 x zumi 'Professor Sprenger'

MALVA
96 'Harry Hay'
96 robusta
95 sylvestris 'Cottenham Blue'
95 – Wallace Blues Group

MALVASTRUM
97 lateritium 'Eastgrove Silver' (v)
95 – 'Hopley's Variegated'

MANDEVILLA
96 'White Delite'

MARANTA
95 bicolor

MARCHANTIA
96 calcarea
96 palmatoides
96 sp. from Tristan da Cunha

MARRUBIUM
96 vulgare variegated

MASSONIA
97 echinata

MATTHIOLA
95 fruticulosa 'Alba'

MAURANDELLA
96 antirrhiniflora

MAURANDYA
96 wislizenii

MAYTENUS
95 boaria 'Worplesdon Fastigiate'

MECONOPSIS
97 betonicifolia
   Harlow Carr strain
96 grandis EMAK 473
96 latifolia
96 pseudointegrifolia subsp. robusta ACE 1732
96 x sheldonii 'Corrennie'
95 – 'Glen Tough'
97 – 'Miss Jebb'
96 sp. ACE 1875

MEEHANIA
97 cordata

MELALEUCA
97 pulchella

MELANTHIUM
96 virginicum

MELASTOMA
97 malabathricum

MELICA
97 altissima 'Alba'
97 ciliata bronze
97 – subsp. magnolii
97 – subsp. taurica
97 minima
97 picta
97 subulata

MELIOSMA
96 dilleniifolia subsp. flexuosa
95 – subsp. tenuis

MENTHA
97 diemenica var. koiscikoko
96 x piperita f. citrata orange
97 pycantheum pilosum

MENZIESIA
95 ciliicalyx
95 pentandra AGS J 317

MERTENSIA
95 pulmonarioides 'Alba'

MESEMBRYANTHEMUM
96 hispidum

METASEQUOIA
95 glyptostroboides 'Waasland'

METROSIDEROS
96 collinus
97 kermadecensis 'Radiant' (v)

MICHAUXIA
97 laevigata

MICHELIA
96 doltsopa 'Silver Cloud'

MICROMERIA
95 caerulea
95 varia

MIMULUS
96 aridus
95 aurantiacus red
96 'Burgess'
97 cardinalis 'Dark Throat'
95 longiflorus saccharatus
95 'Magnifique'

96 'Malibu Ivory'
96 moschatus 'Variegatus'
96 'Plymtree'
97 'Queen's Prize'
97 'Royal Velvet'
95 sp. C&W 5233
96 tilingii var. caespitosus
96 'Western Hills'
97 'Wine Red'
97 'Yellow Velvet'

MINUARTIA
97 recurva
95 verna subsp. verna

MISCANTHUS
97 nepalensis CLD 1314
97 sinensis dwarf form
96 – 'Hinjo'
96 – 'Rigoletto'
96 – 'Tiger Cub'

MITRASACME
95 pilosa

MITRIOSTIGMA
96 axillare

MOEHRINGIA
96 glaucovirens

MONARDA
97 didyma 'Red Explode'
96 – 'Variegata'
97 Libra
95 'Maiden's Pride'
95 'Meereswogen'
97 Pisces
97 Scorpio
97 stipitatoglandulosa
95 'Thundercloud'

MONARDELLA
97 viridis

MONOPSIS
97 unidentata

MORAEA
96 natalensis
96 papilionacea
96 ramosissima
96 schimperi
96 stricta
96 tripetala
96 vegeta

MORUS
96 alba 'Laciniata'

MUHLENBERGIA
96 dumosa
97 mexicana

MUSA
97 x paradisiaca

MUSCARI
97 armeniacum 'Cantab'
95 – 'New Creation'
96 azureum 'Amphibolis'
95 caucasicum
97 comosum 'Album'
97 'Sky Blue'
97 spreitzenhoferi
97 'White Beauty'

MUTISIA
95 ilicifolia RB 94087
96 subspinosa

MYOPORUM
97 tenuifolium

MYOSOTIS
95 *elderi*
96 *persicifolia* 'Coronata'
95 *petiolata* var. *pottsiana*
95 *suavis*
97 *traversii* AGS 90
97 *uniflora*

MYOSURUS
96 *minimus*

NANDINA
96 *domestica* 'Wood's Dwarf'

NARCISSUS
95 'Accolade' (3)
96 'Algarve' (2)
96 'Allafrill' (2)
96 'Arndilly' (2)
95 'Ashwell' (3)
96 'Badanloch' (3)
96 'Balvraid Lass' (2)
96 'Barnsdale Wood' (2)
97 'Bastion' (1)
95 'Beersheba' (1)
96 'Ben Bhraggie' (2)
96 'Ben Loyal' (2)
96 'Berry Gorse' (3)
96 'Big John' (1)
96 'Birichen' (2)
96 'Birthday Girl' (2)
97 'Biscayne' (1) ♀
96 'Brierglass' (2)
95 'Brilliant Star' (11)
96 'Buncrana' (2)
96 'Burning Heart' (11)
97 'Cantatrice' (1)
95 'Caruso' (2)
97 x *cazorlanus* (13)
96 'Celtic Song' (2)
96 'Chablis' (11)
96 'Chinese Sacred Lily' (8)
96 'Clashmore' (2)
96 'Cloud's Hill' (4)
96 'Colloggett' (2)
95 'Colston Bassett' (3)
96 'Como' (9)
97 'Connie Number 1'
97 'Coppins' (4)
96 'Coral Fair' (2)
96 'Cornish Cream' (12)
96 'Coverack Perfection' (2)
96 'Crenver' (3)
96 'Cushendall' (3)
97 'Dancer' (2)
96 'Darlow Dale' (2)
96 'Davochfin Lass' (1)
96 'Desert Orchid' (2)
96 'Drop o' Gold' (5)
96 'Edwalton' (2)
96 'Embo' (2)
96 'Eribol' (2)
96 'Eriskay' (4)
96 'Evelix' (2)
96 'Explosion' (8)
96 'Fairlight Glen' (2)
95 'Fairmile' (3)
95 'Faraway' (3)
96 'Fellowship' (2)
96 'Finchcocks' (2)
95 'Flowerdream'
96 'Fount' (2)
96 'Gay Challenger' (4)
96 'Gimli' (6)

96 'Glen Cassley' (3)
95 'Glencraig' (2)
96 'Glenmorangie' (2)
95 'Glorious' (8)
96 'Glory of Lisse' (9)
96 'Gold Medallion' (1)
97 'Golden Orchid' (11)
95 'Golden Ranger' (2)
96 'Golden Showers' (1)
97 'Gourmet' (1)
96 'Grapillon' (11)
96 'Great Expectations' (2)
96 'Green Howard' (3)
95 'Green Orchid'
95 'Greenvale' (2)
96 'Greeting' (2)
96 'Hazel Rutherford' (2)
96 'Hazel Winslow' (2)
96 'Holbeck' (4)
95 'Holly Berry' (2)
96 'Home Fires' (2)
95 'Howard's Way' (3)
97 'Ibberton' (3)
96 'Ibis' (6)
97 'Irish Minstrel' (2) ♀
96 'Jane France' (1)
96 'Jane MacLennan' (4)
96 'Jane van Kralingen' (3)
97 'Jessamy' (12)
96 'Juanito'
96 'Kathleen Munro' (2)
97 'Kilkenny' (1)
96 'Kitten' (6)
95 'La Riante' (3)
96 'Lalique' (3)
96 'Leading Light' (2)
96 'Lemon Candy' (2)
96 'Lemon Express' (1)
95 'Letty Green' (4)
96 'Little Jazz' (6)
95 'Loch Coire' (3)
95 'Loch Garvie' (2)
95 'Loch Owskeich' (2) ♀
96 'Loch Tarbert' (2)
95 'Loth Lorien' (3)
96 'Lydwells' (2)
96 'Madrigal' (2)
96 'Magic Maiden' (2)
96 'Maiden Over' (2)
96 'Mairead' (2)
96 'Majestic Gold' (1)
96 'Mary Schouten' (2)
95 'Mermaid's Spell' (2)
95 'Minikin' (3)
97 *minor* 'Cedric Morris'
96 – 'Douglasbank'
96 'Monksilver' (3)
96 'Montclair' (2)
96 'Moon Goddess' (1)
97 'Moon Jade' (3)
95 'Mountpleasant' (2)
97 'Muirfield' (1)
97 'Notable' (3)
96 'Oakham' (2)
97 'Old Satin' (2)
97 'Owen Roe' (1)
96 'Pennyghael' (2)
96 'Petsamo' (1)
95 'Pink Dawn' (2)
95 'Pink Mink' (2)
97 'Pink Panther' (2)
95 'Pink Whispers' (2)
96 'Piquant' (3)
96 'Polglass' (3)
96 'Primrose Beauty' (4)
96 'Printal' (11)

96 'Proska' (2)
95 x *pulchellus* (13)
95 'Queen of Bicolors' (1)
96 'Radical' (6)
95 'Rathgar' (2)
97 'Red Arrow' (1)
95 'Redlands' (2)
97 'Reprieve' (3)
96 'Ringmer' (3)
95 'Rival'
96 *romieuxii* AB&S 4656 (13)
95 'Royal Ballet' (2)
96 'Royal Dornoch' (1)
97 *rupicola* subsp. *marvieri* (13) ♀
97 'Rutland Water' (2)
95 'Ryan Son' (3)
96 'Saint Duthus' (1)
95 'Scoreline' (1)
95 'Scotney Castle' (1)
96 'Shepherd's Hey' (7)
96 'Shy Face' (2)
95 'Sigrid Undset' (3)
97 'Silver Princess' (3)
96 'Silvermere' (2)
96 'Silversmith' (2)
95 'Sinopel' (3)
96 'Sligachan' (1)
97 'Small Fry' (1)
96 'Snug' (1)
95 'Solferique' (2)
96 'Southease' (2)
95 'Stanley Park'
97 'Stockens Gib'
96 'Suilven' (3)
96 'Swallowcliffe' (6)
96 'Symphonette' (2)
95 'Syracuse' (3)
97 *tananicus* (13)
97 'Tara Rose' (2)
97 'Tinnell' (2)
95 'Tullycore' (2)
95 'Tullynakill' (2)
96 'Una Bremner' (2)
96 'Uncle Ben' (1)
96 'Upper Broughton' (2)
95 'Verdant' (1)
96 'Virgil' (9)
97 *viridiflorus* (13)
95 'Wahkeena' (2)
96 'War Dance' (9)
96 'Webster' (9)
96 'Westholme' (2)
95 'White Ermine' (2)
95 'Woolsthorpe' (2)
96 'Yellow Tresamble' (5)

NEILLIA
97 *rubiflora* CC&McK 18
96 *thyrsiflora*

NEMASTYLIS
97 *tenuis* subsp. *pringlei*

NEMESIA
96 'Hermione'

NEMOPHILA
97 *menziesii*

NEOLITSEA
95 *parviflora*

NEOPAXIA
97 *australasica* 'Great Lake'
97 – 'Lakeside'

NEPENTHES
96 *macfarlanei*

NEPETA
96 'Gottfried Kühn'
97 *mariae* JJH 948425
95 *nepetella* subsp. *amethystina*
96 'Pink Dawn'
97 'Thornbury'

NERINE
96 *breachiae*
97 'Camellia'
97 'Catkin'
97 'Christmas'
95 'Curiosity'
97 'Dover'
97 'Druid'
97 'Enchantress'
97 'Evening'
95 'Fairyland'
97 'Gaiety'
95 'Hera'
97 *hirsuta*
97 'Lindhurst'
95 'Miss Frances Clarke'
95 'Mrs Dent Brocklehurst'
97 'Solent Swan'

NERIUM
95 *oleander* double white (d)
96 – 'Oportum'

NIEREMBERGIA
96 *repens* 'Violet Queen'

NIVENIA
96 *stokoei*

NOLANA
96 *humifusa* 'Little Bells'

NOLINA
96 *bigelowii*
96 *humilis*
97 *longifolia*
96 *microcarpa*

NOMOCHARIS
96 *aperta* CLD 229
96 *pardanthina* CLD 1490

NOTELAEA
97 *ligustrina*

NOTHOFAGUS
95 *betuloides*
95 *fusca*
95 *truncata*

NUPHAR
95 *japonica*
96 *variegata*

NYMPHAEA
97 'Andréana'
95 'August Koch' (T/D)
95 *capensis* (T/D)
95 – var. *zanzibariensis* (T)
97 *cordata* 'Pink Pons'
97 'Laydekeri Rosea' Laydeker (H)
95 'Martin E. Randig'
97 'Perry's Red Sensation'
95 'Perry's Red Volunteers'
97 'Rio'
97 'Rosette'

95 'Trudy Slocum' (T)

NYSSA
96 *ogeche*

OENANTHE
97 *fluviatilis*
97 *pimpinelloides*

OENOTHERA
97 *acaulis* BC&W 4110
97 *brachycarpa*
97 *brevipes*
95 *californica*
97 *deltoides*
97 *fremontii*
96 *fruticosa* cream
95 – 'Cuthbertson'
97 *heterantha*
97 *laciniata*
97 *pallida* subsp.
   trichocalyx
97 *primiveris*
97 *serrulata*
95 – K 92.296
97 *speciosa* 'Siskiyou'
   variegated
95 *suaveolens*
97 *triloba*

OLEARIA
95 *ilicifolia* × *moschata*
97 *lepidophylla* green
95 'Talbot de Malahide'

OLSYNIUM
96 *biflorum*
96 *scirpoideum* F&W 776

OMPHALODES
97 *verna grandiflora*

OMPHALOGRAMMA
97 *delavayi*
96 – KGB 600
96 – KGB 800
96 *vinciflorum*

ONONIS
95 *cristata*
95 *natrix*
97 *spinosa* 'Alba'

ONOPORDUM
95 *argolicum*

ONOSMA
97 *echioides*
95 *montana*
97 *nana* Mac&W 5785
95 *pyramidalis*
97 *rutila*
96 *tornensis*

ONYCHIUM
96 *japonicum* L 1649

OPHIOPOGON
96 *intermedius*
   'Compactus'
97 *japonicus* B&SWJ 561
96 *planiscapus*
   'Silvershine'

ORIGANUM
95 *acutidens* JCA 735.000
97 *laevigatum* hybrids
97 *libanoticum* hybrids
96 'Pink Cloud'
96 'Purple Cloud'
96 'White Cloud'

ORNITHOGALUM
95 *woronowii*

OROSTACHYS
97 *chanetii*
95 *erubescens*

ORPHIUM
97 *frutescens*

ORTHOSIPHON
96 *labiatus*

OSBECKIA
95 *stellata*

OSMANTHUS
96 *heterophyllus* 'Latifolius
   Variegatus'
96 – 'Myrtifolius'

OSTEOSPERMUM
95 'Basutoland'
97 'Croftway Coconut-ice'
97 'Croftway Silverspoons'
95 'Croftway Snow'
97 *ecklonis* deep pink
95 'Hampton Court
   Purple'
97 *jucundum*
   'Jackarandum' ♀
97 'Kerdalo'
97 'Kriti'
96 Merriments Dark Seedling
96 'Mrs Reside's Purple'
95 'Prostrate Sparkler'

OURISIA
97 *modesta*
97 *racemosa*
95 *vulcanica*

OXALIS
95 *acetosella* var.
   subpurpurascens
97 *incarnata*
96 *japonica* 'Picta'
97 *lasiandra*
96 *ortgiesii*
96 'Royal Velvet'
97 *tetraphylla alba*

OXYLOBIUM
97 *ellipticum*
97 *lancelolatum*

OXYTROPIS
96 *chankaensis*
95 *persica*
96 *viscida*

OZOTHAMNUS
96 *selago* 'Major'

PACHYLAENA
95 *atriplicifolia* JCA 12522

PAEONIA
95 'Auten's Red'
96 *bakeri*
97 'Burma Ruby'
97 'Byzantine'
97 'Chocolate Soldier'
96 *cypria*
95 *delavayi* Potaninii
   Group (S)
95 – 'Yellow Queen'
95 'Early Windflower'
97 *kavachensis*
96 *lactiflora* 'Alice
   Graemes'
95 – 'Augustin d'Hour'

95 – 'Augustus John'
97 – 'Bahram'
95 – 'Balliol'
96 – 'Bridal Gown'
95 – 'Bright Era'
96 – 'Butter Ball'
96 – 'Canarie'
95 – 'Cecilia Kelway'
97 – 'Chocolate Soldier'
97 – 'Dragon'
95 – 'Duc de Wellington'
96 – 'Duchess of
   Marlborough'
95 – 'Elegant Lass'
95 – 'Empress of India'
95 – 'English Elegance'
97 – 'Eugénie Verdier'
97 – 'Fairy's Petticoat'
96 – 'Fire Flower'
95 – 'Full Moon'
95 – 'Gannymede'
96 – 'Globe of Light'
95 – 'His Majesty'
95 – 'John Howard Wigell'
95 – 'Kelway's Rosemary'
95 – 'Lady Mary
   Dashwood'
96 – 'Le Cygne'
97 – 'Le Jour'
95 – 'Limosel'
95 – 'Love Mist'
95 – 'Lowell Thomas'
95 – 'Mistral'
95 – 'Moon River'
96 – 'Octavie Demay'
95 – 'Persier'
95 – 'Pink Cream'
95 – 'Poetic'
95 – 'Queen of Hearts'
95 – 'Queen of Sheba'
95 – 'Queen Wilhelmina'
95 – 'R.W. Marsh'
96 – 'Raoul Dessert'
96 – 'Red Champion'
95 – 'Red Flag'
96 – 'Rhododendron'
96 – 'Rose of Silver'
96 – 'Ruigegno'
96 – 'Sante Fe'
95 – 'Snow Cloud'
95 – 'Souvenir d'A. Millet'
95 – 'Starlight'
95 – 'Suzette'
95 – 'The Moor'
97 – 'Toro-no-maki'
95 *mascula* 'Immaculata'
96 – subsp. *russoi*
95 *officinalis* 'Crimson
   Globe'
97 – 'James Crawford
   Weguelin'
95 – 'Paladin'
95 *peregrina* 'Fire King'
95 – 'Polindra'
95 – 'Postilion'
95 *suffruticosa* Great Gold
   Powder = 'Da-jin-fen'
   (S)
95 – False Kudzu Purple =
   'Jia-ge-jin-zi' (S)
97 – 'Kamada-nishiki' (S)
97 – 'Large Globe'
96 – Top Table Red =
   'Sho-an-hong' (S)
97 – 'Yoa-huang'

96 – Best-shaped Red =
   'Zhuan-yuan-hong' (S)
96 – Diamond Dust =
   'Zuan-fen' (S)

PANCRATIUM
97 *canariense*

PANICUM
97 *coloratum* 'Bambatsi'
97 *miliaceum* 'Violaceum'
97 *virgatum* 'Pathfinder'

PAPAVER
97 *dubium*
97 *julicum*
95 *orientale* 'Forncett
   Banner'
95 – 'Forncett Post'
95 – 'Forncett Summer'
96 – 'Garden Gnome'
97 – 'Midnight'
96 – 'Pink Chiffon'
97 – 'Redizelle'
95 *palaestinum*

PARAQUILEGIA
95 *anemonoides*
   Gothenburg Strain

PARDANTHOPSIS
97 *dichotoma*

PARIETARIA
97 *judaica* 'Corinne
   Tremaine'

PARIS
97 *incompleta*
97 *polyphylla yunnanensis
   alba*

PARKINSONIA
96 *aculeata*

PARNASSIA
97 *palustris palustris*

PAROCHETUS
97 *communis* 'Blue Gem'

PARTHENOCISSUS
97 *inserta*
96 sp. KR 708

PASITHEA
96 *caerulea*

PASPALUM
97 *quadrifarium*

PASSIFLORA
96 *adulterina*
96 *cissifolia*
97 *dioscoreifolia*
97 'Evatoria'
97 *exura*
97 *iralda*
96 *jamesonii*
96 'Lucia'
96 *luismanvelii*
97 *matthewsii*
96 *ornitheura*
96 *pilosa*
96 *quadriglandulosa*

PEDICULARIS
95 *verticillata*

PELARGONIUM
95 'Ade's Elf' (Z/St)
95 'Admiral Bouvant' (I)
95 'Aerosol Improved'
   (Min)

95 'Mrs Mavis Colley' (Z/v)
95 *multicaule* subsp. *multicaule*
97 'Muriel'
97 'Nan Greeves' (Z/v)
95 'Nanette' (Z)
95 'Nella' (Min)
95 'New Dawn Rose Form' (I)
97 'Nicola Gainford'
95 'Night and Day' (Dw)
95 'Nina West' (Z)
95 *oblongatum*
95 *ochroleucum*
96 'Oldbury Cascade' (I/v)
97 'Olive West'
97 'Orange Embers' (Dw)
97 'Orange Fizz' (Z/d)
95 'Orange Glow' (Dw/d)
95 'Orange Ruffy' (Min)
95 'Orwell' (Min)
95 'Otley' (Min)
95 'Oyster Maid' (Min)
95 'Paradise Moon' (Min/d)
97 'Partisan' (R)
95 'Peggy Franklin' (Min)
97 'Percival' (Dw/d)
97 'Perlenkette' (Z/d)
97 Perlenkette Weiss = 'Perlpenei'
96 'Persian Queen' (R)
96 'Phyllis Brooks' (R)
95 Picasso
95 'Picotee'
95 'Pier Head' (Z)
97 'Pink Bridal Veil' (Z/C)
97 'Pink Charm' (I)
97 'Pink Eggshell' (Dw)
95 'Pink Elizabeth Read' (Dw)
95 'Pink Floral Cascade' (Fr/d)
97 'Pink Lively Lady' (Dw/C)
95 'Pink Nosegay'
97 'Pink Parfait' (Z)
95 'Pink Profusion' (Min)
96 'Pink Slam' (R)
95 'Pink Splendour' (Min/d)
95 'Pink Startel' (Z/St)
95 *pinnatum*
95 'Pioneer'
95 'Pixie Glow' (Z/St)
95 'Pixie Prince' (Z/St)
95 'Playboy Blush' (Dw)
95 'Playboy Candy' (Dw)
95 'Playboy Cerise' (Dw)
95 'Playboy Coral' (Dw)
95 'Playboy Coral Orange' (Dw)
95 'Playboy Mauve' (Dw)
95 'Playboy Powder Pink' (Dw)
95 'Playboy Salmon' (Dw)
95 'Playboy Salmon Eyed' (Dw)
95 'Playboy Scarlet' (Dw)
95 'Playboy White' (Dw)
95 'Playford' (Dw)
95 'Polaris' (Min)
97 'Portsmouth' (R)
96 'Posey' (Min/d)
95 'Prudence' (Min)

95 *punctatum*
95 'Purple Gem' (Min)
95 'Purple Pat' (Min/d)
96 'Ragtime' (St)
96 'Ravensbeck'
96 'Rebecca' (R)
95 'Red Beauty' (Z/d)
96 'Red Brooks Barnes' (Dw/C)
95 'Red Comet' (Min)
95 'Red Devil' (Z/St)
95 'Red Dwarf' (Min/d)
95 'Red Elmsett' (Z/C/d)
95 'Red Grace Wells' (Min)
95 'Red Pearl' (Min)
96 'Red Streak' (Min/Ca)
95 'Red Sybil Holmes' (I)
95 'Reg 'Q'' (Z/C)
96 'Robinson Crusoe' (Dw/C)
95 'Roller's Pearly Lachs' (I)
95 'Ron's Elmsett' (Dw/C/d)
95 'Ron's Semer' (Min)
95 'Ron's Shelley' (Dw)
95 Rosais (I/d) ♀
95 'Rose Crousse' (I/d)
97 'Rose Startel' (Z/St)
97 'Rosebud Supreme' (Z/d)
97 'Rosita' (Dw/d) ♀
97 'Royal Blaze' (Z/v)
96 'Royal Parade' (R)
95 'Ruben' (I/d)
97 'Ruth Bessley'
97 'Ryan Dollery' (Z)
96 'Saint Catherine'
95 'Saint Malo'
97 'Salmon Comet' (Min)
96 'Salmon Grozser Garten' (Dw)
97 'Sante Fe' (Z/C)
95 'Sarah Mitchell' (Min)
95 'Sarkie' (Z/d)
96 'Saturn' (Z)
95 'Scarlet Crousse' (I/C)
96 'Scarlet Gem' (St)
95 'Scarlet Shelley' (Dw)
95 'Scarlett O'Hara' (Min)
97 'Seaview Star' (Z/St)
97 'Sensation' (Z)
95 'Shanks' (Z)
97 'Shaunough' (Min)
97 'Sheila Thorp' (Dw/d)
97 'Shocking' (Z/d)
95 'Silas Marner' (Dw)
97 'Single New Life' (Z)
95 'Snow Witch' (Z/St)
96 'Snowmite'
97 'Snowstar' (Z)
96 'Sofie Cascade' (I)
97 'Solent Star'
95 'Solent Sunrise' (Z/C)
96 'South American Delight' (R)
97 'Southampton' (Z)
95 'Sparkle' (Dw)
95 'Speckled Egg' (Dw)
95 'Speckled Hen' (Dw)
95 'Speckled Orange' (Dw)
96 'Splendour' (R) ♀
95 'Sporwen' (Min)
96 'Springfield Lilac' (R)
96 'Springfield Rose' (R)

97 'Sprite' (Min/v)
95 *staphysagrioides*
96 'Starbust'
95 'Stella May' (Dw)
97 'Stellar Orange' (Z/St)
96 'Stellar Snowflake' (Z/St)
97 'Stellar Telstar' (Z/St/d)
97 'Strasbourg'
97 'Strawberry Fayre'
95 'Sundance Orange Scarlet' ♀
95 'Sunset Marble' (I)
95 'Suntrap' (Z/C)
97 'Supernova' (Min/d)
96 'Susan' (Dw)
95 'Sussex Surprise' (Dw/v)
97 'Sweet Charlotte' (R)
95 'Swing' (Z)
96 'Sylvia' (R)
97 'Tami' (Min)
97 'Tamie D' (Min)
95 'Tanya' (Min)
95 'Tattoo' (Min)
96 'Ten of Hearts' (I)
95 'Terry' (I)
97 'The Prince' (Min)
97 'Thorley'
95 'Timmy Griffin' (Min)
95 'Tina Vernon' (Dw/C)
96 'Tiny Tim'
96 'Titan' (Z)
95 'Tom Tit' (Dw)
97 'Toni' (Min)
95 'Tracery' (Dw/St)
95 'Travira' (I)
97 'Treasure Trove' (Z/v)
95 'Trumps' (Min)
96 'Twist' (Z)
97 'Vagabond' (R)
97 'Valcandia' (Dw)
95 'Valerie' (Z/d)
96 'Valley Court' (I)
97 'Variegated Lorelei' (Z/d/v)
97 'Vectis Star'
96 'Vera Vernon' (Z/v)
96 'Vesuvius' (Z)
97 'Vibrant'
95 'Vida' (Min)
95 'Video Red' (Min)
95 'Video Rose' (Min)
95 'Video Salmon' (Min)
96 'Violetta' (Z/d)
95 *vitifolium*
95 'Vulcano Fire' (Dw)
97 'Wendy' (Min)
97 'West Priory'
95 'Westerfield' (Min)
95 'Weston Triumph' (Z/C/v)
95 'Wherstead' (Min)
96 'White Nosegay'
95 'White Roc' (Min/d)
95 'White Swaine' (Min)
95 'White Wooded Ivy'
95 'Wiener Blut'
95 'Wine Red'
95 'Wirral Moonglow'
95 'Wirral Supreme' (Z)
96 'Wordsworth'
95 'Yellow Snowball' (Z/C/d)
97 'Yours Truly' (Z)

PELLAEA
97 *paradoxa*
95 *ternifolia*

PELTARIA
97 *alliacea*

PENNISETUM
96 *alopecuroides* black

PENSTEMON
95 *angustifolius* K 92.3128
95 *barbatus* 'Rose Elf'
95 'Beverley'
95 'Blue King'
97 'Bridget's White'
97 *caespitosus albus*
97 *cardwellii* K 92.321
97 *caryi*
97 *clevelandii* var. *connatus*
97 *cyaneus*
96 'Delaware'
97 *digitalis* pink
97 *duchesnensis*
97 'Fanny's Blush'
96 from Broken Tops Mountain, USA
96 *globosus*
96 *grahamii*
96 *grandiflorus* 'Prairie Snow'
95 *grinnellii*
97 *heterophyllus* 'John D.'
96 – 'Perhill Purple'
97 'Hewitt's Pink'
96 'Heythrop Park'
97 'Hower Park'
97 'Mrs Golding'
96 'Old Silk'
96 'Park Garden'
95 *parryi*
96 *petiolatus*
95 pink and cream
97 'Raspberry Ripple'
97 *rattanii*
97 *rydbergii*
96 *subserratus*
96 *thompsoniae*
96 *virgatus* subsp. *asa-grayi*
– subsp. *virgatus*
95 *whippleanus* K 92.353

PENTALINON
96 *luteum*

PERESKIA
97 *corrugata*

PERICALLIS
96 *appendiculata*
95 *multiflora*

PERILLA
96 *frutescens* green

PERROTTETIA
95 *racemosa*

PERSEA
95 *ichangensis*
95 *indica*

PERSICARIA
95 *affinis* 'Hartswood'
96 – Kew form
95 *amplexicaulis* 'Clent Rose'
95 – 'Eggins Pink'

Plant Deletions

95 *regeliana*
96 sp. from Taiwan B&SWJ 1765

PETASITES
97 *hybridus* 'Variegatus'
96 *kablikianus*
AL&JS 90170YU

PETREA
96 *volubilis* 'Albiflora'

PETROCOSMEA
97 *kerrii*

PETRORHAGIA
96 *velutina*

PETROSELINUM
97 *crispum* var. *crispum*

PEUCEDANUM
97 *officinale*
97 *palustre*

PHACELIA
97 *tanacetifolia*

PHAEDRANASSA
97 *tunguraguae*

PHAENOCOMA
97 *prolifera*

PHAGNALON
96 *helichrysoides*

PHALARIS
97 *aquatica*
96 *canariensis*

PHELLODENDRON
95 *japonicum*

PHILADELPHUS
96 'Galahad'
96 *incanus*

PHILODENDRON
96 *erubescens* 'Valeria'

PHLEUM
97 *hirsutum*
95 *montanum*

PHLOMIS
97 *alpina*
97 *armeniaca*
97 *cashmeriana* CC&MR 31
95 *herba-venti* subsp. *pungens*
96 *purpurea* dark form
97 sp. B&SWJ 2210

PHLOX
96 *bifida* 'Onsted Gem'
96 *chonela* 'Nana'
96 *douglasii* 'Millstream Laura'
97 – × *multiflora* subsp. *depressa*
96 – 'Pink Chint'
96 – 'White Drift'
97 *maculata* 'Alba'
95 'Minima Colvin'
97 *missoulensis*
95 *multiflora*
95 *nana*
97 – subsp. *ensifolia*
96 – 'Manzano'
96 – 'Mary Maslin'
97 *nivalis* 'Jill Alexander'
97 *paniculata* 'Annie Laurie'

97 – 'Anthony Six'
95 – 'Elizabeth Campbell'
97 – 'Firefly'
96 – 'Gaiety'
97 – 'Jules Sandeau'
97 – 'Rheinländer'
97 – 'Sir John Falstaff'
97 – 'Snowball'
97 *stolonifera* 'Bruce's White'
97 *subulata* 'Nelsonii'
96 – 'Rose Mabel'
97 – 'Southcroft'
97 – 'White Swan'
96 – 'Winifred'

PHOEBE
95 *sheareri*

PHORMIUM
97 'Dusky Chief'
97 'Platt's Black'
95 'Purple Queen'
95 'Smiling Morn' (v)
97 *tenax* 'Yellow Queen'

PHYGELIUS
96 *aequalis* 'Apricot Trumpet'
95 × *rectus* 'Logan's Pink'

PHYLICA
96 *arborea* 'Superba'

× **PHYLLIOPSIS**
96 *hillieri*

PHYLLODOCE
96 *caerulea* Norwegian form

PHYLLOSTACHYS
95 *aurea* 'Albovariegata'
95 – *formosana*
95 *bambusoides* 'Slender Crookstem'
95 *nigra* 'Han-chiku'

PHYSALIS
95 *peruviana* (F)
97 *pubescens* (F)

PHYSOCARPUS
96 *bracteatus*
96 *capitatus*

PHYTEUMA
97 *globulariifolium*
97 *humile*
97 *japonicum*

PICEA
95 *abies* 'Pyramidata'
96 – 'Remontii'
96 – 'Saint Mary's Broom'
96 *alcockiana*
95 *asperata* 'Blue Sky'
96 *koraiensis* Beijing 176
95 *mariana*
96 × *mariorika* 'Gnom'
96 – 'Machala'
95 *meyeri*
96 *orientalis* 'Early Gold'
95 – 'Wittboldt'
96 *pungens* 'Blue Trinket'
97 – 'Drayer'
96 – 'Endtz'
96 – 'Oldenburg'
95 – 'Pendula'
96 *retroflexa*
96 *smithiana* CC&McK 363

PIERIS
96 *formosa* var. *forrestii* 'Charles Michael'
95 *japonica* 'Daisy Hill'
95 – pink
97 – 'Rosalinda'
95 – 'Rosamund'
96 – 'Silver Sword'

PILEA
95 *cadierei* 'Minima' ♀

PILOSELLA
96 *aurantiaca* subsp. *carpathicola*

PIMELEA
97 *sericeovillosa*
97 *suteri*

PIMPINELLA
97 *bicknellii*
95 *flahaultii*

PINGUICULA
96 'Ayantla'
96 *crassifolia*
95 'Fraser Beaut'
95 'George Sargent'
95 'Hamburg'
95 'Hameln'
97 *moranensis morelia*
95 *oblongiloba*
95 *rayonensis*
96 *rosea*
96 *santiago* 'Nuyoo Pass'
96 'Sargent'
95 'Tina'
96 'Vera Cruz'
96 *villosa*

PINUS
97 *armandii* TW 415
95 *banksiana* 'Uncle Fogy'
95 *cembra* 'Glauca'
95 *cembroides*
96 *engelmannii*
96 *flexilis* 'Vanderwolf's Pyramid'
95 *halepensis* subsp. *brutia*
96 *kesiya* TW 333
95 *lawsonii*
97 *nigra* 'Géant de Suisse'
96 – subsp. *salzmannii*
95 *oaxacana*
95 *parviflora* 'Gimborn's Pyramid'
96 – 'Janome'
96 *radiata* 'Nana'
96 *strobus* 'Contorta'
97 – 'Pendula'
97 *sylvestris* 'Hibernia'
97 – 'Scrubby'
97 *taeda*

PITTOSPORUM
95 *tenuifolium* 'Churchills'
97 – 'Green Thumb'

PLAGIANTHUS
96 *regius* var. *chathamicus*

PLAGIOMNIUM
96 *affine*

PLANTAGO
97 *alpina*
97 *argentea*
97 *gaudichaudii*
96 *major* B&L 12649

PLATANUS
95 'Augustine Henry'
95 × *hispanica* 'Bloodgood'
95 *orientalis* 'Autumn Glory'
95 – var. *insularis*

PLATYCODON
96 *grandiflorus* 'Axminster Streaked'
95 – blue
97 – 'Blue Pygmy'
97 – Purple Princess = 'Hime-murasaki'
97 – 'Purple Dwarf'

PLECTOCOLEA
96 *hyalina*

PLEIONE
97 *bulbocodioides* (Limprichtii Group) 'Primrose Peach'
97 g. *Etna* 'Bullfinch'
96 g. *Sajama*
95 g. *Shantung* 'Pixie'
95 – 'Silver Wedding'
96 g. *Tolima* 'Nightingale'
96 – 'Tufted Duck'
95 g. *Vesuvius* 'Linnet'

PLEUROCHAETE
96 *luteoalba*

PLEXIPUS
96 *cuneifolius*

PLUMBAGO
97 *zeylanica*

PLUMERIA
96 forms

POA
97 *abyssinica*
97 *araratica*
97 *badensis* 'Ingelkissen'
97 *fawcettiae*
97 *glauca*
97 *hothamensis*
97 *nemoralis*

PODALYRIA
97 *biflora*
97 *calyptrata*

PODOPHYLLUM
97 *hendersonii*
96 *hexandrum* ACE 1894

POLEMONIUM
96 *caeruleum* subsp. *amygdalinum*
96 – dwarf form
96 – 'Idylle'
97 *cashmerianum album*
97 – 'Daydawn'
96 *mexicanum*
97 *pulchellum* Willdenow
96 *reptans* 'Firmament'

POLIANTHES
97 *tuberosa* 'Marginata' (v)

POLYGONATUM
95 *hookeri* AGS/ES 523

POLYPODIUM
96 'Addison'
97 *aureum* ruffled form

97 *vulgare* 'Congestum
Cristatum'

POLYSTICHUM
96 *braunii* x *proliferum*
95 *discretum*
95 *fallax*
95 *interjectum*
96 *lonchitis*
96 *setiferum* Congestum
Cristatum Group
95 – Conspicuolobum
Group
96 – (Plumosodivisilobum
Group) 'Baldwinii'
96 *yunnanense*

PONERORCHIS
97 *taiwanensis*

POPULUS
97 *simonii*

POTENTILLA
95 *anserina* 'Ortie' (v)
95 – 'Variegata'
97 *argentea* 'Calabre'
97 – *glabra*
97 *clusiana*
95 *coriandrifolia*
97 *fruticosa* var. *arbuscula*
(D. Don) Maxim. KW 5774
96 – 'Donard Gold'
97 – 'Goldkugel'
96 – 'Goldrush'
97 – 'Hachmann's Gigant'
97 – 'Judith'
97 – 'Logan'
97 – 'Northman'
97 – 'Ochroleuca'
95 – 'Pastel Pink'
96 – 'Perryhill'
97 – 'Ruth'
97 – 'Sandved'
96 *gracilis* var.
pulcherrima
95 *lineata*
95 *millefolia klamathensis*
96 'Pheasant Eye'
97 *schillingii*
95 sp. CLD 286
97 *speciosa* var. *discolor*
97 'White Beauty'

PRATIA
97 *angulata* 'Ohau'
97 – 'Tim Rees'
97 *pedunculata* 'Clear
Skies'
97 – 'Kinsey'

PRIMULA
96 *allionii* 'Crystal'
KRW 425/69 (2)
96 – 'Jouster' (2)
97 – KRW 1971 (2)
96 – KRW 324/62 (2)
95 – 'Nymph' KRW 282/51
(2)
97 – 'Perkie'
97 – 'Phobos' (2)
96 – 'Pink Gin' (2)
95 – x *pubescens* (2)
96 – x *pubescens* 'Rosalie'
(2)
95 – R C E form (2)
95 – 'Superba'
97 *alpicola* hybrids (26)
96 *auricula* 'Alan' (A)

97 – 'Aviemore' (A)
95 – 'Avocet' (S)
95 – 'Balbithan' (B)
96 – 'Banana Split'
96 – 'Beckjay' (S)
96 – 'Bernard Smith' (d)
95 – 'Blue Garden'
95 – 'Blue Mist' (B)
96 – 'Blue Ridge' (A)
97 – 'Blue Wave' (d)
95 – 'Border Stripe' (B)
96 – 'Bramshill' (S)
97 – 'Bredon Hill' (S)
97 – 'Camilla' (A)
97 – 'Chamois' (B)
97 – 'Cherrypicker' (A)
95 – 'Coll' (A)
96 – 'Commander' (A)
97 – 'Creenagh Stripe' (A)
95 – 'Crimson Cavalier'
97 – 'Daphnis' (S)
97 – 'Dorothy' (S)
97 – 'E'
97 – E82 (S)
96 – 'Enismore'
96 – 'Envy' (S)
97 – 'Ethel'
96 – 'Eventide' (S)
96 – 'Faro' (S)
95 – 'Freda' (S)
96 – 'Gold Blaze' (S)
97 – 'Goldcrest' (S)
96 – 'Golden Gleam' (A)
96 – 'Goldilocks' (S)
97 – 'Goldthorn' (A)
96 – 'Gooseberries and
Cream'
96 – 'Grace' (S)
95 – 'Gracie' (A)
97 – 'Greenfinger' (S)
95 – 'Greenough Stripe'
97 – 'Haffner' (S)
97 – 'Harvest Moon' (S)
95 – 'Hermia'
96 – 'Hurstwood Majesty'
(S)
97 – 'Imber' (S)
95 – 'Joan Goalby' (d)
95 – 'John' (S)
97 – 'John Gledhill' (A)
97 – 'K.H.B.' (S)
97 – 'Lady Croft' (S)
97 – 'Larkhill' (A)
96 – 'Lime 'n' Lemon'
97 – 'Lisa's Red' (S)
95 – 'Lockyer's Gem'
(B/St)
96 – 'Lyn' (A)
96 – 'Magpie' (S)
95 – 'Mandan' (S)
95 – 'Marsco' (S)
96 – 'Matley' (S)
96 – 'Milkmaid' (A)
96 – 'Moonbeam' (S)
95 – 'Mrs Harris' (B)
95 – 'Nathan Silver' (A)
96 – 'New Baby' (A)
95 – 'Night Heron' (S)
96 – 'Norah' (A)
95 – 'Nordean'
95 – 'Nubian' (S)
95 – 'Old Pink Lace'
97 – 'Old Tawny' (B)
97 – 'Party Dress' (S)
96 – 'Pat Barnard'
96 – 'Paula Lewis'

95 – 'Purple Emperor' (A)
96 – 'Purple Frills'
96 – 'Quality Chase' (A)
96 – 'Radiance' (A)
96 – 'Ray Brown' (v)
97 – 'Rosanna' (S)
97 – 'Rosebud' (S)
97 – 'Rossiter's Grey' (S)
97 – 'Royal Purple' (S)
97 – 'Royalty' (S)
97 – 'Ruth Steed' (S)
97 – 'Salome' (A)
96 – 'Shergold' (A)
96 – 'Sir Robert Ewbank'
(d)
97 – 'Sonya' (A)
97 – 'Space Age' (S)
97 – 'Stoney Cross' (S)
97 – 'Stripey' (d)
97 – 'Tavistock' (S)
95 – 'Tomdown' (S)
97 – 'Upton Belle' (S)
97 – 'V.I. Hinney'
97 – 'Waincliffe Fancy' (S)
95 – 'Waincliffe Yellow'
(S)
97 – 'Watt's Purple' (d)
97 – 'Woodstock' (S)
95 – 'Wye Lemon' (S)
95 – 'Wye Orange' (S)
97 – 'Yelverton' (S)
95 – 'Young Rajah' (S)
96 *auriculata* (11)
95 'Belinda Red Shades'
(Belinda Series) ♀
95 'Belle Watling'
(dPrim)(30)
95 'Bon Accord Elegance'
(dPoly)(30)
95 'Bon Accord Gem'
(dPoly)(30)
95 'Bonfire' (Poly)(30)
97 'Bootheosa' (21)
96 *boothii* (21)
95 'Boudicca' (Prim)(30)
97 'Bronwyn' (30)
96 x *bulleesiana*
Asthore hybrids (4)
96 *bulleyana* ACE 2478 (4)
95 – CLD 920 (4)
95 *capitata* subsp. *capitata*
(5)
96 – KEKE 497 (5)
96 – subsp. *sphaerocephala*
ACE 2092 (5)
96 *carniolica* (2)
95 'Chevithorne Pink'
(Poly)(30)
97 *chionantha* subsp.
brevicaula ACE 1689
(18)
96 'Cluny'
95 *cockburniana* hybrids (4)
96 Cottage Mixed (Prim)(30)
97 x *crucis* (2)
96 'Dales Red'
97 *deflexa* ACE 2283 (17)
97 *deuteronana alba* (21)
96 'Doctor Lemon's White'
95 'E.R. Janes' (Prim)(30)
96 *elatior* JCA 785.150 (30)
97 – subsp. *meyeri* (30)
97 – subsp. *pallasii* (30)
96 – – JCA 786.500 (30)
95 – – JJH 9192145 (30)
97 *elliptica* (11)

97 'Ethel M. Dell'
(dPrim)(30)
96 *forrestii* ACE 1427* (3)
96 – CLD 1242 (3)
96 – CLD 738 (3)
97 'Frühlingszauber'
(Prim)(30)
97 Galligaskins Group
(Poly)(30)
97 'Gartenmeister Bartens'
(Prim)(30)
96 *glauca* ML form
97 'Gordon'
95 *gracilipes* 'Heathpool'
(21)
96 – L&S form (21)
97 – 'Masterton' (21)
97 'Graham'
97 'Granny Graham'
(Prim)(30)
96 *hirsuta nivea* (2)
96 *integrifolia* JCA 787.502
(2)
97 *ioessa* hybrids (26)
97 Jackanapes on
Horseback Group
(Poly)(30)
97 *jesoana* (7)
95 'Lambrook Yellow'
(Poly)(30)
96 'Lopen Red' (Poly)(30)
97 *marginata* 'Baldock's
Mauve' (2)
96 – 'Hurstwood' (2)
95 – KND seedling (2)
97 – 'Laciniata'
95 – 'Miss Savory' (2)
97 – 'Mrs Carter
Walmsley' (2)
95 – 'Shipton' (2)
97 – small flowered form (2)
97 'Mauvekissen'
97 *megaseifolia* (6)
96 *minima* JCA 788.900 (2)
95 *minkwitziae* (7)
97 *mistassinica alba* (11)
97 *modesta* (11)
97 *mollis* (7)
96 'Moulin Rouge'
(Prim)(30)
96 *nana* (21)
97 Pantaloons Group
(Poly)(30)
95 'Peggy Fell'
95 'Peter's Red'
95 'Peter's Violet'
97 *poissonii* ACE 1946 (4)
96 – ACE 2407 (4)
96 – CLD 1404 (4)
96 – CLD 485 (4)
96 x *pubescens* 'Gnome'
(2)
97 – mixed (2)
95 – 'Moonlight' (2)
97 – white (2)
96 x *pumila* (2)
97 'Raven'
95 *rosea* 'Micia Visser-de
Geer' (11)
97 – *splendens* (11)
96 *scapigera* (21)
96 *secundiflora* ACE 1518
(26)
96 – ACE 1820 (26)
95 – CLD 363/488 (26)

95 *sikkimensis* 'Phokphey' (26)
97 'Snowruffles'
96 sp. CLD 1217 (4)
95 sp. CLD 183
96 sp. CLD 487 (4)
96 Springtime Group (Prim)(30)
97 'Stradbrook Lilac Lustre' (2)
96 *stricta* (11)
96 Sunset Group
97 'Sylvia' (Prim)(30)
95 *takedana* (24)
96 'Techley Red' (Prim)(30)
95 x *truncata* (2)
97 *tschuktschorum* (18)
97 *veris* subsp. *canescens* JCA 789.600 (30)
96 Victorian shades (Poly)(30)
95 *vulgaris* double red (dPrim)(30)
97 – 'Double Sulphur' (dPrim)(30)
97 – subsp. *sibthorpii* HH&K 265 (Prim)(30)
97 – – HH&K 337 (30)
97 – – JCA 790.401 (Prim)(30)
97 – 'Viridis' semi-double (Prim)(30)
96 'Wisley Red' (Prim)(30)
97 'Zenobia'

PROBOSCIDEA
96 *fragrans*

PROSTANTHERA
96 'Poorinda Pixie'

PROTEA
97 *laurifolia*
97 *subvestita*
97 *venusta*

PRUNELLA
97 *grandiflora* purplish blue

PRUNUS
96 *avium* 'Alba'
97 – 'August Heart' (F)
97 – 'Black Elton' (F)
97 – 'Black Glory' (F)
96 – 'Black Heart' (F)
96 – 'Caroon' (F)
96 – 'Emperor Francis' (F)
96 – 'Frogmore Early' (F)
96 – 'Kent Bigarreau' (F)
96 – 'Merton Bigarreau' (F)
96 – 'Merton Bounty' (F)
96 – 'Merton Heart' (F)
97 – 'Merton Late' (F)
97 – 'Merton Marvel' (F)
96 – 'Nabella' (F)
97 – 'Noble' (F)
97 – 'Ronald's Heart' (F)
97 – 'Roundel Heart' (F)
97 – 'Smoky Dun' (F)
97 – 'Starking Hardy Giant' (F)
96 – 'Strawberry Heart' (F)
96 'Beni-higan'
96 *besseyi*
97 'Birch Bark'

97 *cerasifera* 'Pendula'
95 – 'Vesuvius'
97 *cerasus* 'Nabella' (F)
97 *domestica* 'Autumn Compote' (C)
96 – 'Black Prince' (C)
96 – 'Blaisdon Red' (C)
97 – 'Blue Imperatrice' (C/D)
95 – German Prune Group (C)
96 – 'Late Transparent Gage' (D)
96 – 'Laxton's Supreme' (C/D)
95 – 'Monsieur Hâtif' (C)
96 – 'Olympia' (C/D)
96 – 'Peach Plum' (D)
95 – 'Ruth Gerstetter' (C)
96 – 'Thames Cross' (D)
95 *dulcis* 'Praecox'
96 'Fudan-zakura'
95 *hirtipes* 'Semiplena'
96 'Hokusai'
96 'Horinji'
96 'Imose'
95 *incisa* 'Boten'
95 – 'Pendula'
95 *insititia* (F)
96 x *juddii*
97 *laurocerasus* 'Golden Splash'
95 – 'Herbergii'
96 *litigiosa*
96 'Ojôchin'
97 *padus* 'Dropmore'
96 *persica* 'Early Alexander' (F)
97 – 'Garden Silver'
97 – 'Melred'
96 – 'Miriam' (F)
95 – var. *nectarina* 'Fuzalode' (F)
97 – – 'Rivers Prolific' (F)
95 – 'Red Peachy' (F)
95 – 'White Peachy' (F)
96 *pseudocerasus* 'Cantabrigiensis'
97 *rufa* FK 40
96 *serrulata*
96 x *sieboldii* 'Caespitosa'
96 'Taki-nioi'
96 x *yedoensis* 'Moerheimii'

PSEUDOPANAX
97 *davidii*
97 *delavayi*

PSEUDOTSUGA
96 *menziesii* Pendula Group

PSILOSTROPHE
96 *tagentinae*

PTERIS
97 *bulbifera*

PTEROCEPHALUS
97 *perennis* subsp. *perennis*
97 *pinardii*

PTEROSTYLIS
95 *acuminata ingens*
96 *revoluta*

PTILOSTEMON
97 *afer*

PULMONARIA
97 'Botanic Hybrid'
97 'Buckland'
96 'Lambrook Silver'
97 *mollissima*
95 'Oxford Blue'
97 'Red Freckles'
95 'Regal Ruffles'
97 *rubra argentea*
97 *saccharata* 'Bofar Red'
97 – 'Snow Queen'

PULSATILLA
97 *halleri alba*
97 *patens* subsp. *trisecta*
97 *vulgaris* Czech Fringed hybrids

PUNICA
97 *granatum* 'Flore Pleno Luteo' (d)

PURSHIA
95 *tridentata*

PUSCHKINIA
96 *scilloides*
96 – var. *libanotica* S&L 113

PUYA
97 *conquimbensis*
96 *mitis*
96 sp. G&P 5036

PYCNANTHEMUM
97 *tenuifolium*

PYRACANTHA
95 *atalantioides* 'Nana'
95 *crenulata*
95 *fortuneana* B&L 12398
95 'Orange Cadence'
95 'Red Delight'

PYRUS
96 *communis* 'Abbé Fétel' (D)
96 – 'Admiral Gervais' (D)
96 – 'Alexandrina Bivort' (D)
96 – 'Bellissime d'Hiver' (C)
96 – 'Beurré Bachelier' (D)
96 – 'Beurré de Jonghe' (D)
96 – 'Beurré Diel' (D)
97 – 'Beurré Gris d'Hiver' (D)
96 – 'Beurré Jean van Geert' (D)
96 – 'Buckland' (F)
96 – 'Butt' (Perry)
96 – 'Charles Ernest' (D)
96 – 'Duchesse de Bordeaux' (D)
96 – 'English Caillot Rosat' (D)
97 – 'Fair Maid' (D)
96 – 'Fertility' (D)
96 – 'Hellen's Early' (Perry)
96 – 'Laxton's Early Market' (D)
95 – 'Longueville' (D)
96 – 'Louise Marillat' (F)
97 – 'Madame Treyve' (D)

95 – 'Marie Louise d'Uccle' (D)
97 – 'Martin Sec' (C/D)
96 – 'Muirfield Egg' (D)
96 – 'Nouvelle Fulvie' (D)
96 – 'Ovid' (D)
96 – 'Parsonage' (Perry)
96 – 'Précoce de Trévoux' (D)
96 – 'Red Pear' (Perry)
97 – 'Sucrée de Montluçon' (D)
96 – 'Taynton Squash' (Perry)
97 – 'Zéphirin Grégoire' (D)
96 *pyrifolia* 'Nijisseiki' (F)
95 – 'Shinko' (F)

QUERCUS
97 *baloot*
97 *chapmanii*
97 *durata*
95 *durifolia*
97 *geminata*
97 *gilva*
95 *graciliformis*
96 *macrocarpa* x *turbinella*
96 *mongolica*
97 *petraea* 'Columna'
95 *pyrenaica* 'Argenteomarginata'
97 *robur* 'Fastigiata Purpurea'
97 Quercus robur x macrocarpa x muehlenbergii
97 Quercus robur x macrocarpa x virginiana
97 – 'Salicifolia Fastigiata'
97 x *schuettei*

RACOPILUM
96 *robustum*

RANUNCULUS
95 *abnormis* JCA 809.500
96 x *arendsii*
97 *asiaticus* red
96 *brotherusii* CC&McK 745
95 *caucasicus* subsp. *caucasicus*
96 *eschscholtzii oxynotus*
96 – *trisectus*
95 *ficaria* double red (d)
96 x *flahaultii*
96 *glacialis*
97 *illyricus*
97 *muelleri* var. *brevicaulis*
97 sp. from Morocco

RAOULIA
96 *bryoides*
96 *hookeri* var. *apice-nigra*
96 *parkii*

RAUVOLFIA
97 *serpentina*
96 *verticillata*

REGELIA
97 *ciliata*

RESTIO
96 *tetraphyllus*

RETAMA
97 *monosperma*

RHAMNUS
97 *prinoides*

RHAPIS
95 *humilis*

RHEUM
96 *compactum*
95 *delavayi*
97 *forrestii* ACE 2286
96 *nobile*
97 *palmatum* var.
   tanguticum 'Rosa
   Auslese'
95 *reticulatum* JJH 9209375
97 *robertianum*
97 *spiciforme*

RHEXIA
97 *mariana*
97 – var. *purpurea*

RHODIOLA
96 *himalensis*
   (D. Don) Fu EMAK 331
95 sp. CLD 1329
95 sp. JJH 392
97 *yunnanensis*

RHODODENDRON
96 'Abbot' (EA)
95 *aberconwayi* dwarf form
96 – McLaren U35a
97 *acpunctum* SF 313
96 'Adamant'
96 Adelaide Group & cl.
95 'Ahren's Favourite'
96 'Airy Fairy'
96 *albertsenianum* F 14195
97 'Alex Hill'
96 'Alice Gilbert'
97 'Alpine Dew'
97 *alutaceum* var.
   russotinctum
   Triplonaevium Group
97 – – Tritifolium Group
   R 158*
95 *amagianum* ×
   reticulatum (A)
96 Amalfi Group & cl.
95 *ambiguum* dwarf form
95 – 'Keillour Castle'
97 'Amoenum Coccineum'
   (EA/d)
95 'Anah Kruschke'
95 'Anne's Delight'
96 *anthosphaerum*
   Eritimum Group
97 – F 17943
97 'Antje'
97 Antonio Group & cl.
95 'Antoon van Welie'
95 *aperantum* F 27020
97 'Apotheose' (EA)
97 'Apotrophia'
97 'Apricot Surprise'
97 'April Chimes'
96 Arblact Group
96 *arboreum* subsp.
   arboreum Sch 1111
97 – subsp. *cinnamomeum*
   var. *roseum crispum*
95 – subsp. *delavayi* var.
   peramoenum
96 – 'Goat Fell'

97 – TSS 26
96 *argipeplum* Eastern form
97 – KR 1231
97 *argyrophyllum* subsp.
   argyrophyllum
   W/A 1210
95 – 'Sichuan'
97 *arizelum* 'Brodick'
97 – F 21861
97 – KW 20922
97 'Arkle'
96 Armia Group
95 'Atalanta' (EA)
95 Atroflo Group
96 *augustinii* subsp.
   augustinii
   Vilmorinianum Group
97 – – W/A 1207
96 – subsp. *chasmanthum*
   white C&Cu 9407
96 – Dartington Form
96 – Reuthe's dark form
95 – subsp. *rubrum* F 25914
96 *auriculatum*
   compact form
97 – × *degronianum*
96 Avocet Group
96 'Ayton'
97 'Azurwolke'
95 'Bad Eilsen'
97 *balfourianum* F 16811
97 – F 29256*
97 *barbatum* B 235*
97 – KW 5659*
97 – LS&H 17512
97 – TSS 30
97 *basilicum* TW 368
96 'Basilisk' (K)
96 'Bastion'
96 'Beaulieu' (K)
97 'Beautiful Day'
97 *beesianum* R 176
97 'Belle of Tremeer'
95 'Ben Moseley'
95 'Benigasa' (EA)
96 Berryrose Group & cl.
96 'Bert's Own'
97 *bhutanense* KR 1753
96 Bibiani Group & cl.
96 Blanc-mange Group
   & cl.
96 'Blue Ensign'
96 'Blue Jay'
97 'Blue River'
96 'Blueshine Girl'
96 Boadicea Group
96 Bonito Group & cl.
97 'Bonnie Babe'
97 'Boulodes'
97 'Bounty'
97 *bracteatum* CH&M 2586
96 'Brookside'
96 Bulbul Group & cl.
97 *bureaui* EGM 141
96 Burning Bush Group
97 'Butter Brickle'
96 'C.B. van Nes' ♀
96 *caesium* F 26798
97 *callimorphum* var.
   myiagrum
97 *calophytum* var.
   calophytum W/A 4279
96 – Grieg's form
97 – W/V 1523
95 *calostrotum* subsp.
   riparioides

97 *camelliiflorum*
   Rump 5696A
97 *campanulatum album*
   SS&W
96 – SS&W 9108
95 – TSS 44
96 – TW 27
96 *campylocarpum* subsp.
   campylocarpum TSS 43
97 – TW 31*
96 *campylogynum* Celsum
   Group
96 – copper
95 – (Cremastum Group)
   'Thimble'
95 – 'New Pink'
95 – 'Plum Brandy'
95 'Canadian Beauty'
95 'Candida'
96 Cardinal Group & cl.
97 Carex Group & cl.
96 *carringtoniae* (V)
96 'Castle of Mey'
95 *catacosmum* F 21727
95 'Catalode'
96 *catawbiense* 'Powell
   Glass'
96 Cauapo Group
96 'Cavalcade'
95 *cephalanthum* subsp.
   cephalanthum
   Crebreflorum Group
   KW 8337
97 – – Crebreflorum
   Group Week's form
97 *cerasinum* KW 6923
97 – KW 8258
95 'Cheapside'
97 'Chipmunk' (E/d)
95 *ciliatum* BL&M 324
96 *ciliicalyx*
96 *cinnabarinum* Caerhays
   John Group
97 – subsp. *cinnabarinum*
   LS&H 21283
97 – SHE 638
96 – subsp. *xanthocodon*
   KW 6026
97 *clementinae* F 25917
96 *coelicum*
97 *coeloneuron* EGM 108
96 *collettianum*
97 'Commodore' (EA)
97 *concinnum*
   Benthamianum Group
97 'Coral Beauty'
95 'Coral Redwing' (EA)
95 'Coral Wing' (EA)
97 *coriaceum* F 16364
97 – F 21843
96 Cornsutch Group
96 Coronet Group
95 'Crater Lake'
96 'Crown Jewel' (EA/d)
97 'Crowthorne'
95 'Crushed Strawberry'
97 'Dagmar'
97 'Darkness' (EA)
97 'David Grant'
97 *davidsonianum*
   C&H 7023
97 – PA Cox 5007
97 – PA Cox 5091
96 'Dawn's Glory'
95 'Dayan'

97 *decorum* subsp.
   decorum SBEC 439
97 – X hybrid
97 – R 54021*
97 – TW 384
97 – TW 388
95 'Delectable' (K)
96 *dendricola* Taronense
   Group
97 'Denny's Rose' (A)
95 *denudatum*
96 'Diana Colville'
96 Dicharb Group
96 Diva Group & cl.
97 'Doctor Rieger'
97 'Dorothy Amateis'
95 'Dorothy Swift'
96 'Douglas McEwan'
95 Dusky Maid Group
96 'Early Gem'
95 'Eastertide' (EA/d)
97 *eclecteum* var.
   bellatulum
97 – – R 110*
97 – var. *eclecteum*
   'Kingdom Come'
   ex KW 6869
97 – – R 23512
97 *edgeworthii* Yu 17431
95 'Edith Bosley'
97 Edmondii Group
96 'Elegant Bouquet' (V)
97 'Elfenbein'
97 'Elizabeth Gable' (EA)
96 'Emanuela'
96 'Emma Williams'
97 'Exbury Lady
   Chamberlain'
97 *facetum* TW 360
97 *falconeri* subsp.
   falconeri EGM 55
96 Fandango Group
97 *fastigiatum* 'Harry
   White'
96 'Fawley' (K)
97 *ferrugineum* f. *album*
97 'Fidelio' (EA)
95 Fine Feathers Group
97 'First Love'
96 Flamingo Group
97 'Flare'
95 'Flautando'
97 'Flava Glendoick'
97 'Flavour'
96 aff. *flinckii* KR 1755
96 'Flirt'
97 *floccigerum* R 10
97 – USDAPQ 3966/ R18465
97 'Flora's Garden'
97 'Flora's Green'
97 'Florence Archer'
97 *floribundum* PA Cox 5090
95 – 'Swinhoe'
95 *formosum*
   Chamberlain 109
96 *fortunei* McLaren S146
97 'Frill'
97 'Frühlingszauber'
96 Full House Group
96 *fulvum* subsp. *fulvum*
   F 17636
97 – TW 379
97 *galactinum* CC&H 4023
96 'Garnet'
96 *genestierianum*
96 'Georg Arends'

97 'George Reynolds' (K)
96 Gibraltar Group
97 'Gigi'
96 Gipsy King Group
96 'Gleam'
96 'Gloriana'
95 'Golden Dream'
95 'Golden Orfe' ♀
96 'Golden Queen'
95 'Goldilocks'
95 'Goldstrike'
95 'Goldsworth Orange' x *insigne*
96 'Goldtopas' (K)
96 'Gossamer White' (V)
97 *gracilentum* (V)
95 'Graf Lennart'
96 'Grafton'
95 'Grand Pré'
97 *grande* EGM 58
96 'Green Eye'
97 'Grierdal'
97 Grierocaster Group
97 *griffithianum* EGM 101
96 'Grilse'
95 'Gumpo' x *nakaharae* (EA)
96 'Hachmann's Bananaflip'
96 *haematodes* subsp. *chaetomallum* KW 5431
97 – ex Hobbie
97 'Hakurakuten' (EA)
95 'Happy Occasion'
96 Hebe Group
97 'Heiwa' (EA)
96 *heliolepis* var. *brevistylum*
97 – Yu 7933*
95 Hermes Group
96 Hesperides Group
96 'Highland White Jade'
96 'Hill Ayah'
96 *hippophaeoides* var. *hippophaeoides* Fimbriatum Group
97 *hodgsonii* BL&M 232
97 aff. – EGM 81
97 – SU 323
96 *hookeri* 'Golden Gate'
95 'Hopeful' (EA)
97 'Horizon Dawn'
97 'Horizon Snowbird'
97 *huanum* EN 4028
95 'Hyde Park' (K)
96 'Hydon Snowflake'
97 *hyperythrum* subsp. *fauriei*
96 Icarus Group
95 'Ightham Pink'
97 *impeditum* 'Compactum'
97 – F 20454
97 *inconspicuum* (V)
96 Indiana Group
96 *indicum* 'Crispiflorum' (EA)
96 Iola Group
96 *irroratum* subsp. *kontumense* KR 3282
96 – KW 5002a
97 – subsp. *pogonostylum* KR 3121
97 – white
95 'Ivan D. Wood'
95 'J.G. Millais'

97 'Jack'
97 'Jack Skelton'
95 Jacquetta Group
96 Jaipur Group
95 'Janet Baker'
97 *javanicum* var. *teysmannii* (V)
97 Jean Group
97 'Jo Madden'
97 'Joe Paterno'
96 'John Keats'
95 'John Marchand'
97 'Johnson's Impeditum'
95 'Joseph Haydn' (EA)
96 'Joseph Whitworth'
95 'June Fire'
96 'Jungfrau'
96 *kaempferi* 'Eastern Fire' (EA)
95 – f. *latisepalum* (EA)
95 'Katsura-no-hana' (EA)
97 'Keija'
97 *keiskei* var. *ozawae* 'Yaku Fairy' x *campylogynum*
96 Keiskrac Group
96 'Kentucky Minstrel' (K)
96 'Keston Rose'
96 *kiusianum* 'Benichidori' (EA)
97 – var. *kiusianum* 'Mountain Gem' (EA)
96 – 'Mountain Pride' (EA)
97 – var. *sataense* (EA)
95 'Kumo-no-ito' (EA)
97 'Ladt Decis'
95 Lady Berry Group & cl.
96 Lady Jean Group
97 'Lady Malmesbury'
96 Lady Montagu Group & cl.
97 *lanatum* 716652
97 – C 2148
97 *lanigerum* 'Chapel Wood'
97 – KW 6258
97 'Le Havre'
97 'Lemon Ice'
95 'Lem's 121'
96 *lepidotum* CC&McK 530
97 – TW 40
96 *leptanthum* (V)
96 'Lewis Monarch'
95 'Lilacinum'
95 'Lillian Peste'
96 'Lincill'
97 'Linda R' (EA)
95 *lindleyi* 'Geordie Sherriff'
96 'Little Ginger' (V)
97 'Little Jessica'
97 'Littlest Angel' (V)
95 'Llenroc'
95 'Lobster Pot' (K)
97 'Lodestar'
97 *loranthiflorum* (V)
97 *luteiflorum* TW 390
95 *lutescens* 'Exbury'
96 – pink
95 *luteum* 'Batami Gold'
97 x *lysolepis* KW 4456
95 *macgregoriae* yellow (V)
97 *maculiferum* Guiz 148
96 *maddenii* pink
96 'Mademoiselle Masson'

96 'Magic Flute' (V)
96 Mai Group
95 *maius* Herklots
97 *mallotum* F 17853
97 – Farrer 815
96 Marie Antoinette Group
97 'Marion'
96 'Marmot' (EA)
96 Marshall Group
95 'Mary Belle'
97 'Master Mariner'
95 'Matsuyo' (EA)
97 *meddianum* var. *meddianum* F 24219
96 Medea Group
97 *mekongense* var. *mekongense* KW 21079
95 'Mephistopheles' (K)
96 Merops Group
95 Metis Group
96 *microgynum* Gymnocarpum Group
97 *microphyton*
96 'Mikado'
96 Mohamet Group & cl.
95 'Moira Pink' (EA)
95 'Molly Buckley'
95 'Molly Fordham'
96 'Monica Wellington'
96 'Moonstone Pink'
96 'Motherly Love'
96 'Mountain Dew'
96 'Mrs John Kelk'
95 'Mrs Peter Koster' (M)
96 *mucronulatum* 'Crater's Edge'
96 – var. *taquetii* 'Dwarf Cheju'
96 – 'Winter Brightness' ♀
96 *multicolor* (V)
95 *myrtifolium* 'Kotscaki'
96 'Mystic'
95 *nakaharae* Starborough form
96 'Nancy Buchanan' (K)
97 'Naomi Glow'
95 'Naomi Nautilus'
96 'Naomi Stella Maris'
95 Neda Group
96 *neriiflorum* subsp. *neriiflorum* 'Lamellen'
97 – – Phoenicodum Group
97 – subsp. *phaedropum* KR 1778
96 – – KW 6854
95 'Night Light' (K)
96 *nivale*
95 – subsp. *boreale*
97 – subsp. *nivale* Sch 2269
95 'Noble Fountain'
96 'Omurasaki' (EA)
97 'Optima' (EA)
96 'Orangeade' (K)
96 *orbiculare* x *decorum*
97 'Oregon Trail'
96 Orangio Group
97 *oreotrephes* 'Davidian's Favourite'
97 – R 96
96 – R/USDA 59593/ R11300
96 'Our Marcia' (V)
95 'P.G. Puddle'
97 *pachysanthum* x *morii*

95 *pachytrichum* var. *monosematum* 'Blackhills'
97 'Pamela-Louise'
95 Pandora Group
97 *paradoxum*
97 'Parisienne'
96 *pauciflorum* (V)
97 'Pearl Diver'
96 'Peekaboo'
96 'Pematit Oxford'
96 Penjerrick Group & cl.
96 'Pennywhistle' (V)
96 *pentaphyllum* (A)
96 *peregrinum* 'Wilson'
96 'Pettychaps' (EA)
96 *phaeochrysum* var. *phaeochrysum*
96 'Philomene'
96 'Pillar Box'
96 'Piquante'
97 (PJM Group) 'Checkmate'
97 x *planecostatum* (V)
97 *pleistanthum*
97 'Polycinn'
97 'Pratt's Hybrid'
95 'Princess Elizabeth'
95 'Princess Elizabeth' (M)
96 *pseudochrysanthum* AM 1956 form AM
97 – ETOT 162
97 – ETOT 164
96 *pubescens* 'Fine Bristles'
96 'Pucella' (G) ♀
96 'Purple Carpeter'
97 purple Glenn Dale
96 'Purple Lace'
96 *quadrasianum* var. *rosmarinifolium* (V)
95 'Queen Louise' (K)
95 'Queen's Wood'
97 *racemosum* TW 385
97 'Radistrotum'
97 *rarum* (V)
95 'Rasputin'
96 Red Cap Group
95 'Red Elf'
97 'Red Jack'
97 'Red Poll'
97 'Red Rum'
97 'Red Sunset' (EA/d)
96 Remus Group
96 'Rennie' (EA)
97 Rêve Rose Group & cl.
96 Review Order Group
97 'Rex' (EA)
97 *rex* subsp. *fictolacteum* TW 407
95 – subsp. *rex* 'Quartz' ♀
97 *rigidum* R 11288
96 *ririei* W 5254a
96 'Rivulet'
97 'Roberte'
97 'Robinette'
97 'Rose Bud'
95 'Rose Plenum' (G) (d)
96 'Rosevallon'
96 Royal Flush Group pink
96 Royal Flush Group yellow
95 Royalty Group
97 *rufum* Hummel 31
95 *russatum* 'Collingwood Ingram'
97 – Waterer form

96 Russautinii Group
96 'Russellianum'
95 'Sabina'
96 'Saint Kew'
96 'Saint Wenn'
96 'Salmon Trout'
97 'Sandling'
96 'Santa Claus'
96 *scabrifolium* var.
  spiciferum SBEC K 160
95 'Scarlatti' (K)
96 'Scarlet Pimpernel' (K)
97 Scarlett O'Hara Group
96 *schistocalyx* F 17637
96 *scopulorum*
  Magor's hardy form
97 *searsiae* W/A 1343
96 *selense* subsp. *selense*
  Probum Group
97 *setosum* TW 30
96 'Seville'
96 *sherriffii*
  AM 1966 clone ex L&S
  2751 AM
97 *sidereum* TW 345
97 – TW 350
96 'Silvetta'
96 *simiarum* SF 92304
96 *sinofalconeri* KR 1992*
97 *sinogrande* TW 341
97 – TW 383
97 Sir Frederick Moore
  Group & cl.
96 'Sir George Sansom'
96 'Sir John Tremayne'
96 'Sirius'
96 Smithii Group
95 'Spek's Brilliant' (M)
96 'Spellbinder'
96 *sphaeroblastum* F 17110
96 *spinuliferum* 'Jack
  Hext'
96 – TW 413
96 – TW 418
97 'Spinulosum'
96 'Spring Dawn'
95 'Spring Song'
96 'Springday'
97 'Starcross'
96 *stenosepalum* (A)
97 'Strategist'
97 *succothii* CH&M 3079
97 – CH&M 3105
97 – CH&M 3125
97 – LS&H 19850
97 'Suede'
97 'Sumatra'
95 'Sun Charm'
97 'Sundance'
97 'Sunny'
97 'Sunset over Harkwood'
96 'Sweet Beatrice' (V)
97 'Sweet Seraphim' (V)
96 'Sylvetta'
97 'Sylvia' (EA/d)
97 *taggianum*
95 – Headfortianum Group
97 'Tay' (K)
97 'Tender Heart' (K)
95 Thais Group
96 Thomdeton Group
95 'Tinsmith' (K)
97 'Tiny' (EA/d)
97 'Toff' (V)
97 'Tomba'
96 'Top Brass'

96 'Topaz'
96 'Tortoiseshell Biscuit'
97 *tosaense* (EA)
96 *trichanthum* W/A 1342
97 *tsariense* var. *tsariense*
  L&S 2766
95 'Valley Sunrise'
96 'Van Heka'
95 Vanguard Group
95 Varna Group
97 'Veldtstar'
97 *vernicosum* Yu 13961
97 – Yu 14694
96 'Vinecrest'
97 *virgatum*
97 *viscosum aemulans* (A)
97 'Vulcan's Flame'
97 *wallichii* KR 813*
97 – KR 882
97 – TW 32
97 *wardii* var. *puralbum*
  Yu 14757
97 – var. *wardii* KW 4170
97 – – R 18333
97 – – R 25391
97 – – SSNY 99
97 *wasonii* McLaren AD 106
96 'White Perfume'
96 'White Swan' (K)
95 'Whitney's Best Yellow'
97 *wightii* KR 877
97 'Wild Affair'
97 'Winter Green' (EA)
95 'Woodchat'
97 'Xenophile'
97 'Yachiyo Red'
97 *yakushimanum*
  'Beefeater'
95 – 'Snow Mountain'
97 – 'Torch'
96 – Tremeer tall form
97 'Yaya'
97 'Yellow by Trailer'
96 Yuncinn Group
96 *yunnanense* 'Diana
  Colville'
96 – Hormophorum Group
96 – 'Tower Court'
97 – TW 400
96 Yvonne Group
97 *zaleucum* TW 373

RHODOHYPOXIS
97 *baurii* forms
97 – x Hypoxis *parvula*
  , JJ's pink
97 'Betsy Carmine'
97 *milloides* giant form
96 'True'

RHODOMYRTUS
97 *tomentosa*

RHODOPHIALA
97 *advena* yellow form
97 *bakeri* F&W 7196

RHUS
95 *aromatica*
97 *glabra* 'Laciniata'
  Carrière
97 *incisa*
97 *leptodictya*
97 *punjabensis*

RIBES
95 *fasciculatum* var.
  chinense

96 *macabeanum*
96 *nigrum* 'Black Reward'
  (F)
97 – 'Blackdown' (F)
97 – 'Cascade' (F)
97 – 'Cherry' (F)
95 – 'Green's Black' (F)
95 – 'Loch Ness' (F)
97 – 'Seabrook's' (F)
96 *sanguineum* 'Elk River
  Red'
96 – 'Giant White'
97 – 'Splendens'
97 *uva-crispa* var.
  reclinatum 'Catherina'
  (C/D)

RIVINA
97 *humilis*

ROBINIA
96 x *ambigua* 'Bellarosea'
96 – 'Decaisneana'
95 *fertilis* 'Monument'
96 *luxurians*
97 *pseudoacacia*
  'Sandraudiga'

RODGERSIA
96 *pinnata* CLD 432
96 – 'Maurice Mason'

ROMANZOFFIA
97 *tracyi*

ROMULEA
97 *linaresii* var. *graeca*
97 *pratensis*
97 *tabularis*

ROSA
97 'Agathe Incarnata'
  (GxD)
97 'Allison' (F)
97 'Amatsu-otome' (HT)
95 'Amberlight' (F)
97 'Amelia Louise' (Min)
97 'Arizona Sunset' (Min)
95 *arkansana*
96 – x *moyesii*
96 Hotline = 'Aromikeh'®
  (MinMo)
97 'Arthur Scargill' (Min)
97 'Aunty Dora' (F)
97 Queen Nefertiti =
  'Ausap'® (S)
97 Dove = 'Ausdove'®(S)
95 Potter and Moore =
  'Auspot'®(S)
96 Wild Flower =
  'Auswing' (S)
96 'Avignon' (F)
95 'Bambino' (Min)
97 Arctic Sunrise =
  'Bararcsun' (Min/GC)
95 'Barbara Richards'
  (HT)
96 Beauty Queen (F)
97 Biddy = 'Benbid' (Min)
97 Black Jade =
  'Benblack'™ (Patio)
96 Old Glory = 'Benday'™
  (Min/Patio)
97 Figurine = 'Benfig'™
  (Min)
97 Gee Gee = 'Benjee'™
  (Min)
97 Jennifer = 'Benjen'™
  (Min)

97 Radiant = 'Benrad'™
  (Min)
96 Tiny Tot = 'Bentintot'
  (Min)
95 'Bharami' (Min)
95 'Born Free' (Min)
97 Tender Loving Care =
  'Bospeabay' (F)
95 'Brownie' (F)
97 *brunonii* CC 1235 (Ra)
97 – CC&McK 362 (Ra)
97 Carefree Beauty =
  'Bucbi'™ (S)
96 Canadian White Star®
  (HT)
97 Saint Helena =
  'Canlish' (F)
96 Lloyds of London =
  'Canlloyd' (F)
96 Prunella = 'Canplant'
  (F)
97 'Cardiff Bay' (HT)
95 *cerasocarpa* (Ra)
96 'Charlotte Elizabeth'
  (F)
96 Telford's Promise =
  'Chewoz' (GC/S)
97 'City of Cardiff' (HT)
97 'City of Gloucester'
  (HT)
97 'City of Worcester'
  (HT)
97 'Cliff Richard' (F)
97 'Climbing Spartan'
  (ClF)
97 Little Jewel = 'Cocabel'
  (Patio)
97 Sweet Nell =
  'Cocavoter' (F)
97 Little Prince =
  'Coccord' (F/Patio)
96 Clydebank Centenary =
  'Cocdazzle' (F/Min)
97 Claire Scotland =
  'Cocdimity'
  (Min/Patio)
97 Constance Fettes =
  'Cocnest' (F)
96 *colvillei*
95 Colwyn Bay (F)
96 'Commemoration'
97 'Conchita' (Poly)
96 Corso® (HT)
97 'Country Maid' (F)
96 'Creme' (S)
97 'Dame of Sark' (F)
97 'Danny Boy' (ClHT)
97 'Dave Hessayon' (HT)
96 Red Splendour =
  'Davona' (F)
96 *davurica*
97 'Debbie Thomas' (HT)
97 'Devon Maid' (Cl)
97 Yellow Ribbon =
  'Dicalow' (F)
97 Star Child =
  'Dicmadder'® (F)
95 'Dimples' (F)
96 Double Joy' (Min)
97 'Dream Time' (HT)
97 'Dream Waltz' (F)
97 'Dukat' (Cl)
96 'Egyptian Treasure' (F)
96 *elegantula* (S)
97 'Elsa' (HT)
97 'Emma May' (HT)

96 'Eurydice'
96 'Evelyn Taylor' (F)
97 'Evening Telegraph' (HT)
97 'Eyecatcher' (F)
97 'Fashion Flame' (Min)
96 Sea of Fire = 'Feuermeer' (F)
97 'Fire Princess' (Min)
97 Winter Magic = 'Foumagic'℗ (Min)
97 'Frank MacMillan' (HT)
97 'Frank Naylor' (S)
96 'Frau Eva Schubert' (Ru)
97 'Fred Gibson' (HT)
96 'Frohsinn'
97 The Observer = 'Frytango' (HT)
97 Good Morning = 'Fryyat' (F)
95 'Fyfield Princess' (F)
96 *gallica* 'Beckett's Single' (G)
96 'Gardener's Delight' (Ra)
97 'Gavotte' (HT)
95 'Gay Gordons' (HT)
95 'Geoff Boycott' (F)
95 'Geranium Red' (F)
96 'Geschwinds Orden'
96 'Geschwinds Schönste' (Ra)
96 'Ginsky' (F)
97 'Glenn Dale' (Cl)
95 'Gold Pin' (Min)
97 'Goldkrone' (HT)
96 Golden Treasure = 'Goldschatz' (F)
97 'Good News' (F)
95 'Gypsy Jewel' (Min)
96 'Gypsy Moth' (F)
96 Nevertheless = 'Hannev' (F)
97 Happy Wanderer® (F)
95 Caroline Davison = 'Harcester' (F)
97 Esther's Baby = 'Harkinder'® (Patio)
97 Sue Ryder = 'Harlino'® (F)
97 International Herald Tribune = 'Harquantum'® (F/Patio)
96 Hollie Roffey = 'Harramin' (Min)
96 Harkness Marigold = 'Hartoflex' (F)
97 Sheer Delight = 'Harwazzle' (Patio)
95 Harvest Home = 'Harwesi' (Ru)
96 Harold Macmillan = 'Harwestsun' (F)
97 Pandora = 'Harwinner'® (Min)
97 'Hazel Rose' (HT)
95 Super Dorothy = 'Heldoro'® (Ra)
95 Super Excelsa = 'Helexa'® (Ra)
97 'Hiawatha Recurrent' (Ra)
96 'High Noon' (ClHT)

96 'Himmelsauge' (Ra)
97 Friday's Child = 'Horabi' (HT)
96 Mary Campbell = 'Horlovequeen' (F)
97 Heather Honey = 'Horsilbee' (HT)
97 'Hutton Village' (HT)
96 *hypoleuca*
95 'Ideal' (Poly)
96 'Idylle'
96 'Inspiration' (Cl)
95 'Irish Brightness' (HT)
96 'Irish Mist' (F)
96 'Isobel' (HT)
97 'Jan Guest' (HT)
97 'Jason' (HT)
96 Emma Kate = 'Jayemm' (F)
97 'Jenny's Dream' (HT)
97 'Joan Bell' (HT)
97 'Joanna Lumley' (HT)
96 'Johanna Röpcke' (Ra)
97 'John Cabot' (S)
95 John Waterer® (HT)
95 'Joybells' (F)
97 'Kathleen O'Rourke' (HT)
96 'Kerrygold' (F)
97 'Kerryman' (F)
97 Fancy Pants = 'Kinfancy'℗ (Min)
97 'Kingig' (Min)
96 Tennessee = 'Kintenn'℗ (Min)
96 Clive Lloyd = 'Kirshow' (HT)
97 'Kitty Hawk' (Min)
97 Esther Ofarim = 'Korfarim'® (F)
95 Lichtkönigin Lucia = 'Korlillub'® (S)
96 Salita = 'Kormorlet'® (Cl)
96 Mary Hayley Bell = 'Korporalt' (S)
97 Woods of Windsor = 'Korprill' (HT)
95 Tatjana = 'Kortat'® (HT)
95 Zwergkönigin '82 = 'Korwerk'® (Min)
95 'La Plus Belle des Ponctuées' (G)
95 'Lady Helen' (HT)
97 'Lady Jane' (HT)
97 'Lady of Stifford' (F)
97 'Lady Seton' (HT)
97 Langford Light = 'Lannie' (Min/GC)
97 Laura (HT)
96 'Lavender Lace' (Min)
96 Green Snake = 'Lenwich'® (S/GC)
96 'Lily de Gerlache' (HT)
97 'Lily the Pink' (HT)
96 *longicuspis* Bertoloni B&L 12386 (Ra)
97 Loving Touch℗ (Min)
95 'Luis Brinas' (HT)
96 Olympiad = 'Macauck'® (HT)
97 Benson and Hedges Gold = 'Macgem'® (HT)

97 Longleat = 'Macinca' (Min)
96 Molly McGredy = 'Macmo' (HT)
96 Seaspray = 'Macnew' (Min/Patio)
95 *macrophylla* SF 16/131
96 'Mademoiselle Marie Dirvon' (Bb)
97 Young Venturer = 'Mattsun' (F)
96 *maximowicziana*
96 'May Woolley' (F)
97 Sarah Jo = 'Mehrex' (HT)
97 The Holt = 'Mehsherry' (F)
97 Charles Aznavour = 'Meibeausai'® (F)
97 Yorkshire Sunblaze = 'Meiblam'® (Min)
97 Pink Panther = 'Meicapinal'® (HT)
97 Air France = 'Meifinaro' (Min)
97 Matthias Meilland = 'Meifolio'® (F)
96 Petite Folie = 'Meiherode'® (Min)
95 Climbing Soraya = 'Meijenorsar' (ClHT)
97 Princess Margaret of England = 'Meilista' (HT)
95 Fantan = 'Meimex' (HT)
96 Scherzo = 'Meipuma'® (Min)
96 Rosy Gem = 'Meiradia' (Min)
96 Charleston '88 = 'Meiresty' (HT)
97 Minijet = 'Meirutego'® (Min)
97 Royal Brompton Rose = 'Meivildo' (HT)
97 Pierrine = 'Micpie'℗ (Min)
96 Orange Star = 'Minako'℗ (Min)
95 'Modern Times' (HT)
97 Anne Moore = 'Morberg' (Min)
96 Playtime = 'Morplati'℗ (F)
97 'Mrs Arthur Curtiss James' (ClHT)
96 *muriculata*
97 *nanothamnus*
97 *nitida* 'Defender'
96 'Non Plus Ultra' (Ra)
97 'Norma Major' (HT)
97 'Oakington Ruby' (MinCh)
96 'Octet' (S)
96 x *odorata* 'Bengal Crimson' (Ch)
97 Anusheh = 'Payable' (F)
96 The Daily Telegraph = 'Peahigh' (F)
96 Freddy = 'Peaproof' (F)
97 Charisma = 'Peatrophy' (F)
97 In the Pink = 'Peaverity' (F)

97 'Peggy Netherthorpe' (HT)
97 'Perla d'Alcañada' (Min)
97 'Perla de Montserrat' (Min)
97 'Pink Elizabeth Arden' (F)
96 'Pink Petticoat' (Min)
96 *pisocarpa*
95 Elfin = 'Poulfi'® (Min)
95 'Poulgold' (Min/Patio)
96 Sentimental = 'Poultal'® (HT)
96 *prattii*
95 'Pride of Park' (F)
96 'Primevère' (Cl)
96 'Princess Michiko' (F)
96 'Purezza' (Ra)
96 'Purity' (Cl)
97 New Daily Mail = 'Pussta' (S)
97 'Radway Sunrise' (S)
97 'Ravenswood Village' (HT)
96 'Red Beauty' (Min)
97 'Red Elf' (Min)
95 'Red Empress' (Cl)
96 'Rotkäppchen' (Poly)
97 'Ruby Pendant' (Min)
96 *rugosa* var. *ventenatiana* (Ru)
96 Flaming Rosamini = 'Ruiflami' (Min)
96 Rumba® (F)
96 *salictorum*
97 'Salmon' (ClMin)
97 Child's Play = 'Savachild'℗ (Min)
96 Dee Bennett = 'Savadee'℗ (Min)
97 Golden Halo = 'Savahalo'℗ (Min)
97 Minnie Pearl = 'Savahowdy'® (Min)
96 Rainbow's End = 'Savalife'℗ (Min)
95 High Spirits = 'Savaspir' (Min)
96 Royal Sunblaze = 'Schobitet'® (Min/Patio)
97 Albert Weedall = 'Scriveo' (HT)
96 Sea Foam® (S)
97 Portland Dawn = 'Seatip' (Min)
96 *sempervirens* (Ra)
97 *serafinoi*
96 'Serratipetala' (Ch)
96 'Sheldon'
96 'Silver Charm' (F)
95 'Soleil d'Or' (S)
96 sp. CDC 262
97 'Sparrieshoop' (CIS)
95 'Stacey Sue' (Min) ♀
95 'String of Pearls' (F)
97 'Surf Rider' (S)
97 'Swanland Gem' (F)
95 'Swedish Doll' (Min)
96 'Sweet Honesty' (Min)
95 'The Miller' (S)
97 Mother's Love = 'Tinlove' (Min)
95 'Toy Clown' (Min)

96 Joan Ball = 'Troball'
(Min)
95 Shell Beach =
'Trobeach' (Min)
96 Dollie B = 'Trobee'
(Min)
96 Paint-pot = 'Trobglow'
(Min)
95 Woodlands Lady =
'Trobsa' (Min/Patio)
95 Temptation = 'Tropat'
(F/Patio)
96 'Truly Yours' (HT)
96 'Turkestan'
96 *ultramontana*
95 'Vagabonde' (F)
96 'Vesuvius' (HT)
97 'Warley Jubilee' (F)
97 Fine Gold = 'Weegold'
(HT)
97 Heartbreaker =
'Weksibyl' (Min)
96 'Welcome Guest' (HT)
97 'Woodrow's Seedling'
(Cl)
96 *yainacensis*
97 'Yellow Pages' (HT)
97 'Zénobia' (Mo)

ROSCOEA
96 *cautleyoides* pink

ROSMARINUS
95 'Compactus Albus'
96 *officinalis* 'Alderney'
95 – *brevifolius*
96 – 'Eden'
95 – Israeli

ROSULARIA
96 *adenotricha* subsp.
adenotricha
96 *alpestris* CC 327
95 *globulariifolia*
96 *haussknechtii*
97 *hissarica* K 92.380
96 *sempervivum* subsp.
amanensis
96 *serrata*

ROTHMANNIA
97 *globosa*

RUBIA
97 *tinctoria*

RUBUS
96 *canadensis*
95 *deliciosus*
97 *fruticosus* 'Dart's
Robertville'
97 – 'Denver Thornless'
(F)
95 – 'Kotata'
97 *idaeus* 'Malling
Augusta'
97 *spectabilis* 'Gun Hildi'
97 *taiwanicola*
97 *treutleri*

RUDBECKIA
95 *grandiflora* var.
alismifolia
96 *nitida*
96 'Toto'
96 *viridis*

RUELLIA
97 *graecizans*

RUMEX
97 *rugosus*

RUMOHRA
96 *adiantiformis* ♀

RUSCHIA
96 *putterillii*

RUSPOLIA
97 *pseuderanthemoides*

SABAL
97 *mauritiiformis*

SAINTPAULIA
95 'Fancy Trail' ♀
95 'Granger's Wonderland'
♀
95 'Midget Valentine' ♀
95 'Moon Kissed' ♀
95 'Tomahawk' ♀
95 *velutina*

SALIX
96 *alba* 'Cardinalis' (f)
97 – 'Orange Spire'
95 *bicolor* Willdenow
96 *burjatica*
95 *candida*
97 *caprea* var. *variegata*
97 *capusii*
96 *cinerea* 'Variegata'
96 *japonica* Thunberg
97 *lanata* Kew form
96 x *laurina* (f)
97 'Onusta' (m)
95 *reinii*
95 *triandra* 'Rouge
d'Orléans'
96 *udensis*
97 *violescens*

SALVIA
96 *amgiana*
97 'Blue Bird'
95 *brandegeei*
96 *brevilabra*
96 *cadmica*
97 aff. *campanulata*
ACE 2379
96 *coccinea* 'Desert Blaze'
95 *dorrii*
95 *farinacea* 'Blue Victory'
♀
95 – 'White Victory' ♀
95 *guaranitica* 'Black
Knight'
96 *henryi*
95 *hirtella* JCA 13800
95 *huberi*
97 *jamensis* pink seedling
97 *jurisicii* 'Alba'
96 *lanigera*
97 *lavandulifolia* pink
96 *mexicana* var. *major*
96 *microphylla alba*
97 *munzii*
95 *napifolia*
95 *nemorosa* 'Brightness'
97 – 'Rose Queen'
97 *oresbia*
97 *patens* 'Oxford Blue'
96 'Peaches and Cream'
96 *pomifera*
97 *populifolia*
97 *potentillifolia*
97 *prostrata*
97 'San Antonio'

96 *sclarea* white-bracted
96 *scorodoniifolia*
97 sp. ACE 2172
96 *urticifolia*
97 *verticillata* HH&K 253
97 – HH&K 342

SAMBUCUS
95 *caerulea* var.
neomexicana
97 *canadensis*
95 *nigra* 'Bimble' (v)
96 – 'Golden Locks'
96 – 'Hadspen'
97 – 'Luteovariegata'
97 – mosaic virus
96 – 'Party Girl'
97 – 'Pygmy'
97 – 'Tenuifolia'
95 – f. *viridis*
95 sp. SF 92305

SANGUISORBA
96 *dodecandra*

SANICULA
96 *arctopoides*

SANSEVIERIA
95 *trifasciata* 'Bantel's
Sensation' ♀
95 – 'Craigii' ♀
96 – 'Gigantea' (v)
95 – 'Hahnii' ♀

SANTOLINA
97 *chamaecyparissus*
subsp. *squarrosa*
97 *elegans*

SAPINDUS
96 *drummondii*

SAPIUM
97 *japonicum*

SARCOCAPNOS
97 *enneaphylla*

SARRACENIA
96 x *ahlesii*
96 *alata* x *oreophila*
96 x *catesbyi* (x catesbyi x
flava)
96 x *catesbyi* x *popei*
96 – red
96 x *catesbyi* x *rubra*
96 x *comptonensis*
96 'Evendine'
96 x *excellens* x
wrigleyana
97 x *formosa*
96 x *formosa* x *excellens*
96 'Gulf Rubra'
96 *leucophylla* x *catesbyi*
96 – x *oreophila*
96 – x *popei*
96 *minor* x *wrigleyana*
96 x *moorei* 'Marston
Select'
96 x *moorei* (x moorei x
catesbyi)
96 x *moorei* x *readii*
96 *oreophila* x *minor*
96 x *popei* x *purpurea*
subsp. *venosa*
96 x *popoei* (x popei x
flava)
96 *purpurea* 'Louis Burke'
96 x *readii* x *excellens*

96 'Red Burgundy'
96 *rubra* x *excellens*
96 *willisii* x *flava*
96 – x *minor* 'Giant'

SASA
96 *chrysantha*

SASAELLA
95 *ramosa* 'Tsuyu-zasa'

SASAMORPHA
97 *borealis*

SATUREJA
95 *cuneifolia*

SAUSSUREA
96 *chionophylla*
96 *spathulifolia* ACE 1344

SAXIFRAGA
96 'Anagales Sunset'
96 *androsacea* (12)
96 'Aurantiaca' (x
luteopurpurea) (6)
96 'Backhouseana'
(*paniculata*) (7)
95 'Bornmuelleri' (8)
97 'Carnival' (12)
97 *carolinica*
95 *cherlerioides*
pseudoburseriana
95 'Claudia' (x *borisii*) (8)
95 'Cleo' (x *boydii*) (8)
97 *cortusifolia* dwarf form
(4)
95 *crispa* (4)
95 'Cwm Idwal' (*rosacea*)
(12)
96 'Dorothy Milne' (8)
95 'Eleanora Francini
Corti' (8)
97 *ferruginea*
95 *flagellaris*
96 – subsp. *crassiflagellata*
CC 298 (2)
95 *fortunei* var.
incisilobatum CDC 135
97 'Ganymede' (*burseriana*)
(8)
97 'Glowing Ember'
97 'Gold Leaf'
95 'Jan Palach' (x *krausii*)
(8)
96 *kotschyi* (8)
95 'Lemon Spires' (8)
95 *lowndesii*
95 x *luteopurpurea* (8)
96 *mutata* (7)
97 'Pandora' (*burseriana*) (8)
95 *pedemontana* (12)
95 – subsp. *cymosa* (12)
95 – – NS 674 (12)
95 *petraea*
95 'Planegg' (8)
96 *porophylla* x
sempervivum (8)
96 'Pseudopungens' (x
apiculata) (8)
97 'Pseudosalomonii' (x
salmonica) (8)
95 'Ronald Young' (8)
95 'Rosamunda' (8)
95 'Roy Clutterbuck' (8)
95 'Rubra' (*paniculata*)
96 x *salmonica*
95 *sempervivum* f.
sempervivum

96 'Skye' (*oppositifolia*) (9)
96 aff. **subsessiliflora** (8)
95 'Tábor' (X *schottii*) (8)
97 x *tazetta* (10x3)
95 *trifurcata*
97 'Walter Ingwersen' (*umbrosa* var. *primuloides*) (3)
95 'Wheatley Gem' (8)
97 'Winterfeuer' (*callosa*) (7)
97 'Wisley Variety' (*grisebachii*)
97 *zohlenschaferi*

SCABIOSA
97 *caucasica* 'Floral Queen'
96 – 'Moonstone'
97 – 'Penelope Harrison'
95 *cinerea* X Cephalaria alpina
95 *columbaria* var. *webbiana*
96 *cretica*
96 'Dingle Lilac'
96 *fischeri*
97 *graminifolia* 'Pinkushion'
96 *lacerifolia*
96 *mansenensis*
97 *maritima*
96 *olgae*
97 'Satchmo'
96 *vestita*

SCADOXUS
97 *membranaceus*
95 *multiflorus* subsp. *katherinae* ♀
97 – – 'King Albert'
96 *rigidus*

SCAEVOLA
97 *aemula* 'Alba'

SCHEFFLERA
97 *elegantissima* ♀

SCHISANDRA
96 *henryi*

SCHISTOSTEGA
96 *pennata*

SCHIVERECKIA
97 *doerfleri*
96 *podolica*

SCHIZANTHUS
97 *candidus*
95 *hookeri* JCA 12492

SCHIZOPETALON
96 *walkeri*

SCHIZOSTYLIS
97 *coccinea* 'Elburton Glow'
95 – 'Mary Barnard'
95 – 'Pink Ice'

SCILLA
97 *baurii*
96 *greilhuberi*
95 *haemorrhoidalis*
95 – MS 923
97 *liliohyacinthus* 'Alba'
97 *litardierei hoogiana*
95 *mischtschenkoana* 'Tubergeniana' ♀

95 – 'Zwanenburg'
97 *rosenii*

SCIRPOIDES
97 *holoschoenus*

SCLERANTHUS
96 *brockiei*

SCLEROCHITON
96 *harveyanus*

SCOPOLIA
96 *anomala*
96 *carniolica* from Slovenia

SCROPHULARIA
95 *coccinea*

SCUTELLARIA
95 *alpina* 'Alba'
96 *baicalensis* 'Coelestina'
97 *formosana*
97 *glandulosissima*
96 *repens*
96 *scordiifolia* 'Seoul Sapphire'
97 *serrata*

SEDUM
96 *acre* tetraploid
96 *beyrichianum* Masters
95 *cockerellii* K 92.401
96 *makinoi*
97 *obtusifolium* 'Variegatum'
96 *ochroleucum*
96 'Philip Houlbrook'
97 *rupestre* f. *purpureum*
96 *spathulifolium* var. *majus*
95 *spurium* 'Fool's Gold' (v)
96 *stevenianum*
97 *tatarinowii* K 92.405
95 *viviparum*

SELAGINELLA
95 *martensii* ♀
96 – 'Variegata'
97 *sanguinolenta*
95 *uncinata* ♀

SELINUM
96 *candollei*
97 *carvifolia*
96 sp. EMAK 886

SEMPERVIVUM
95 'Amtmann Fischer'
95 *arachnoideum* X *grandiflorum*
96 – 'Mole Harbord'
95 – X *montanum*
95 'Aymon Correvon'
95 *ballsii* from Kambeecho
95 'Banyan'
95 'Burgundy'
97 *calcareum* from Benz, Germany
96 – from Ceuze
96 *cantabricum* from Lago de Enol
95 'Carluke'
96 *ciliosum* from Alí Butús
97 'Coronet'
95 'Delta'
95 'Educator Wollaert'
95 *erythraeum* from Rila, Bulgaria
95 'Fat Jack'

95 'Fusilier'
97 'Gleam'
95 *grandiflorum* X *montanum*
97 'Haullauer's Seedling'
95 'Hayter's Red'
95 'Hekla'
95 'Hyacintha'
96 'Kerneri'
96 'Kimono'
95 'Mauvine'
95 'Merkur'
95 'Missouri Rose'
97 'Pam Wain'
96 'Pink Lemonade'
97 'Poldark'
95 'Pompeon'
95 x *praegeri*
97 'Query'
95 'Red Cap'
95 'Red Giant'
95 'Rotsand'
97 'Royal Mail'
97 'Rubikon Improved'
97 'Rubrum Ornatum'
95 'Smaragd'
95 sp. from Mont Cenis
95 'Strawberry Sundae'
95 'Sunkist'
95 *tectorum* 'Atrorubens'
96 – from Andorra
96 – from Mont Ventoux
95 'Verdo'
97 'Victorian'
95 'Zackenkrone'
97 'Zinaler Rothorn'

SENECIO
95 *amplectens holmii*
97 *cineraria* 'Alice'
97 – Sch 3129
95 – 'Sleights Hardy'
95 *crassulifolius*
97 *eminens*
95 *formosus*
97 *fuchsii* HH&K 293
96 *gilliesii* JJA 12379
97 *grandiflorus*
96 *incanus*
95 – subsp. *carniolicus*
95 *populnea*
97 *rodriguezii*
97 *squalidus*

SENNA
95 x *floribunda* ♀
95 *sturtii*

SESLERIA
97 *argentea*
97 *autumnalis*

SIBBALDIA
95 *cuneata*
97 *parviflora* NS 668
95 *procumbens*

SIBIRAEA
95 *laevigata* CLD 781

SIDALCEA
96 'Paramount'
96 'Puck'

SIDERITIS
95 *dasygnaphala*
97 *hyssopifolia*
95 *syriaca* NS 551

SIEVERSIA
97 *reptans*

SILENE
97 *acaulis* subsp. *bryoides*
96 – 'Correvoniana'
97 *andicola*
97 *andina*
95 *burchellii*
95 *californica*
97 *caryophylloides* subsp. *echinus*
97 *dioica alba*
96 *fortunei*
97 *hifacensis*
95 *keiskei* pale pink
97 *lerchenfeldiana*
97 *moorcroftiana*
97 *morrisonmontana*
96 *nigrescens*
97 aff. – ACE 1391
97 *parnassica*
95 *pygmaea*
97 *rotundifolia*
96 *rupestris*
96 *schafta* 'Brilliant'
96 sp. ACE 1320
95 sp. CDB 13013
95 *tatarica*
95 *virginica*
96 *wrightii*

SILPHIUM
96 *trifoliatum*

SILYBUM
96 *eburneum*

SISYRINCHIUM
96 *narcissiflorum*
96 *striatum* 'Rushfields'

SKIMMIA
96 *japonica* 'Stoneham Red'
95 – *viridis*
97 *laureola* 'Fragrant Cloud'
95 *mica*

SMELOWSKIA
96 *calycina* var. *americana*

SMILACINA
97 *racemosa* dwarf form

SOLANUM
95 *dulcamara* var. *album*
95 *muricatum* 'Pepino Gold' (F)
96 *pseudocapsicum* 'Thurino'
95 *umbelliferum*

SOLDANELLA
96 *pusilla alba*
95 'Tinkerbell'

SOLENOMELUS
96 *lechleri*
97 sp. RB 94117

SOLENOPSIS
95 sp. white

SOLENOSTEMON
96 'Jean Falmouth'
97 'Petunia Gem'

SOLIDAGO
95 *bicolor*
96 *canadensis* var. *scabra*

96 'Golden Falls'
95 'Leda'
96 'Lesden'
96 'Loddon'
96 'Mimosa'
96 *multiradiata* var.
scopulorum
97 *rugosa*
95 *spathulata*
96 *virgaurea* pale yellow

SONCHUS
95 *oleraceus*

SOPHORA
95 *alopecuroides*
96 *microphylla*
'Goldilocks'
95 *mollis*

SORBUS
97 *aucuparia* 'Cardinal
Royal'
97 – 'Rossica'
96 *cascadensis*
95 *cashmiriana* pink
96 *croceocarpa*
96 *dentata*
96 *glabrescens*
97 – 'Roseoalba'
97 *gonggashanica*
95 'Guardsman'
96 *kurzii* KR 1501
97 *matsumurana*
(Makino) Koehne
96 *microphylla*
95 *obtusa aureus*
96 *pogonopetala*
96 *poteriifolia* KW 6968
95 *reducta* B&L 12091
96 'Rowancroft'
96 sp. SEP 492
96 *vilmorinii* 'Pendula'

SPARAXIS
97 *fragrans* subsp.
grandiflora

SPATHIPHYLLUM
96 'Adagio'

SPERGULARIA
95 *marina*
97 *purpurea*

SPHAERALCEA
97 *grossulariifolia*
95 *parvifolia*

SPHAGNUM
96 *fuscum*
96 *magellanicum*
96 *pulchrum*

SPILANTHES
96 *acmella*
96 *oleracea*

SPIRAEA
97 *canescens*
96 'County Park'
97 'Dingle Apricot'
96 'Dingle Gold'
95 *japonica* 'Coccinea'
97 – 'Little Maid'
97 *latifolia*
97 sp. CLD 1389
97 *vacciniifolia*

SPOROBOLUS
97 *fertilis*

97 *wrightii*

STACHYS
95 *balansae*
96 *heraclea*
96 'Hopleys Variegated'
96 *macrantha* 'Rosea
Compacta'
97 *saxicola* subsp.
villosissima
96 *tmolea*

STACHYURUS
95 *salicifolius*

STAPHYLEA
96 *pringlei*

STEGNOGRAMMA
96 *pozoi*

STELLARIA
96 *ruscifolia*

STEMODIA
97 *tomentosa*

STENANTHIUM
95 *occidentale*

STENOGLOTTIS
96 *plicata*

STENOTUS
97 *acaulis*

STEPHANANDRA
95 *incisa* 'Dart's Horizon'

STERNBERGIA
97 *sicula* Dodona form
96 – 'John Marr'
ex JRM 3186/75

STIPA
97 *barbata* 'Silver Feather'
97 *comata*
97 *mollis*
97 *papposa*
95 *tirsa*

STOKESIA
97 *laevis* 'Wyoming'

STREPTOCARPUS
95 *baudertii*
95 'Blue Angel' ♀
97 'Blue Trumpets'
95 *buchananii*
95 *compressus*
96 'Constant Nymph'
seedling'
95 *cooperi*
95 *cyanandrus*
95 *daviesii*
95 *fanniniae*
95 *fasciatus*
95 *grandis*
95 'Holiday Blue' ♀
95 *johannis* ♀
95 *kungwensis*
95 *meyeri*
95 *parviflorus*
95 *pole-evansii*
95 *polyanthus*
95 *porphyrostachys*
95 *primulifolius*
95 'Royal Mixed' ♀
95 *saundersii*
95 *solenanthus*

STROMANTHE
95 *sanguinea* var.
spectabilis ♀

STYLIDIUM
95 *crassifolium* ♀

STYRAX
97 *japonicus* 'Pendulus'

SUTERA
95 *cordata* 'Eight Bells'
97 – mauve
97 – pale pink
97 *rosea* 'Plena'

SWAINSONA
96 *maccullochiana*

SWERTIA
95 *komarovii* JJH 93091003

SYMPHORICARPOS
97 *albus* 'Taff's White' (v)
96 – 'Turesson'

SYMPHYANDRA
95 *campanulata*
97 *cretica alba*
97 *ossetica* hybrids
97 *tianschanica*

SYMPLOCARPUS
97 *foetidus*

SYNGONIUM
96 'Jenny'

SYNTHYRIS
96 *pinnatifida laciniata*

SYRINGA
95 x *diversifolia* 'William
H. Judd'
95 'Fountain'
97 x *hyacinthiflora*
'Pocohontas'
97 x *josiflexa* 'Royalt'
97 *reticulata*
97 *vulgaris* 'Adelaide
Dunbar' (d)
95 – 'Aucubifolia'
97 – 'Charm'
95 – 'Dingle Variegated'
96 – 'Paul Deschanel' (d)
97 – 'Paul Thirion' (d)

TABERNAEMONTANA
96 *divaricata*

TALINUM
95 *spinescens*

TANACETUM
95 *coccineum* 'Alfred'
97 – 'Andromeda'
97 – 'Bees' Pink Delight'
97 – 'Phillipa'
97 – 'Pink Petite'
95 – 'Red Dwarf'
97 *corymbosum* subsp.
clusii
95 *griffithii*
95 *nuttallii*
97 *pseudachillea*

TAPEINOCHILOS
96 *ananassae*

TAXODIUM
95 *distichum* 'Pendens'
95 – 'Pendulum'

TAXUS
95 *baccata* f. *adpressa*
96 – 'Icicle'
96 – 'Judith'
97 – 'Rushmore'
95 *cuspidata*
'Luteobaccata'

TECOPHILAEA
97 *cyanocrocus* Storm
Cloud Group

TELLIMA
95 *grandiflora* Alba Group
95 – 'Perky' JLS 86282SCCA

TELOPEA
97 *mongaensis*

TETRACLINIS
95 *articulata*

TETRANEURIS
96 *acaulis* var. *caespitosa*
K 92.258

TETRATHECA
95 *hirsuta*

TEUCRIUM
97 *discolor*
96 *scorodonia* 'Cae Rhos
Lligwy' (v)

THALICTRUM
97 *delavayi* 'Sternhimmel'
95 *javanicum*
97 *pauciflorum*
96 sp. B&SWJ 2159
97 sp. B&SWJ 2520

THELYMITRA
96 *antennifera*

THEMEDA
97 *triandra* subsp.
australis
from Adaminaby
97 – – from Cooma
96 – subsp. *japonica*

THERMOPSIS
95 *barbata*
96 – ACE 2298

THLASPI
96 *alpestre*
97 *arvense*
96 *cepaeifolium* subsp.
cenisium
97 – subsp. *rotundifolium*
var. *limosellifolium*
96 *montanum*
96 *ochroleucum*

THUJA
95 *occidentalis* 'Baurmanii'
95 – 'Cristata
Argenteovariegata'
97 – 'Froebelii'
97 – 'Golden Gem'
95 – 'Perk Vlaanderen' (v)
96 – 'Smaragd Variegated'
96 *orientalis* 'Golden Ball'
97 – 'Golden Wonder'
95 *plicata* 'Brabant'
95 – 'Windsor Gold'

THYMUS
97 'Belle Orchard'
97 *praecox*

97 *serpyllum coccineus* × *zygis sylvestris*
96 'Valerie Finnis'
96 'Widecombe'

THYSANOTUS
96 *patersonii*
96 *tuberosus*

TIARELLA
95 'Maple Leaf'
96 *polyphylla* 'Axminster Variegated'

TIBOUCHINA
97 *granulosa*
97 *laxa* 'Skylab'

TIGRIDIA
96 *durangense*
95 – dwarf form

TILLANDSIA
95 *albida*
95 *gardneri*
95 *ionantha* var. *ionantha*
95 *lindenii* ♀
95 *melanocrater tricolor*
95 *pruinosa*
95 *stricta*
95 *usneoides*

TOFIELDIA
95 *glutinosa* var. *brevistyla*
96 *pusilla*

TOLPIS
97 *barbata*

TORTULA
96 *princeps*
96 *ruralis* subsp. *ruraliformis*

TOWNSENDIA
96 *eximia*
96 *glabella*
96 *jonesii* var. *tumulosa*

TRACHELIUM
97 *jacquinii*

TRACHYCARPUS
97 *sikkimensis*

TRADESCANTIA
95 *cerinthoides* 'Variegata'
95 *fluminensis* 'Tricolor Minima' ♀
95 *pallida* 'Purpurea' ♀
95 *spathacea* 'Vittata' ♀
97 'White Domino'

TRICHOCOLEA
96 *tomentella*

TRICYRTIS
97 'Citronella'
97 'Emily'
97 *macrocarpa*

TRIDENS
95 *flavus*

TRIENTALIS
96 *borealis*

TRIFOLIUM
97 *arvense*
97 *medium*
97 *stellatum*
96 *uniflorum*

TRILLIUM
96 *decumbens*
97 *erectum* 'Beige'
97 *grandiflorum* 'Snowbunting' (d)
96 'Hokkaido'
97 *ovatum* 'Wayne Roberts'
97 *rivale* 'Purple Heart'

TRINIA
97 *grandiflora*

TRIPETALEIA
97 *bracteata*

TRIPTEROSPERMUM
96 *cordifolium*
96 *lanceolatum*
96 *taiwanense*

TRITELEIA
97 *ixioides* subsp. *ixioides*
97 – var. *scabra*
97 *laxa* PJC 951

TRITONIA
95 *deusta*
95 *hyalina*
97 *lineata*
95 'Lynette'

TROCHOCARPA
96 *gunnii*

TROLLIUS
95 *riederianus*

TROPAEOLUM
96 *majus* 'Indian Chief'
97 – 'Variegatum'
95 × *tenuirostre*

TSUGA
97 *canadensis* 'Golden Splendor'
96 *mertensiana* dwarf form ,

TULIPA
95 'Amulet' (3)
95 'Anneke' (3)
95 'Bruno Walter' (3)
95 'Caland' (10)
95 'Capri' (4) ♀
95 'Cashmir' (5)
95 *clusiana* f. *clusianoides* (15)
95 'Coriolan' (3)
95 'Dover' (4) ♀
95 'Duke of Wellington' (5)
95 'Engadin' (14) ♀
95 'Esther' (5)
95 'Florosa' (8)
95 'Garanza' (2)
95 'Golden Eagle' (13)
95 'Goya' (2)
95 'Hadley' (1)
95 *hissarica* (15)
95 *humilis* 'Pallida' (15)
95 *iliensis* (15)
97 'Jacqueline' (6)
97 'Landseadel's Supreme' (5) ♀
97 'Love Song' (12)
97 'Madame Spoor' (3)
97 'Mirjoran' (3)
96 'Mrs John T. Scheepers' (5) ♀
95 'Murillo Maxima' (2)

95 'Orange Cassini' (3)
96 'Orange Toronto' (14)
95 'Orange Wonder' (3)
97 'Paris' (3)
95 'Paul Crampel' (2)
95 'Peer Gynt' (3)
97 'Prins Carnaval' (1)
97 'Prominence' (3)
97 'Red Sensation' (10)
95 'Red Surprise' (14) ♀
97 'Reforma' (3)
97 'Renown' (5)
97 'Rijnland' (3)
97 'Rockery Beauty' (13)
95 'Rockery Master' (14)
97 'Rockery Wonder' (14)
97 'Scarlet Cardinal' (2)
97 *sosnowskyi* (15)
97 'Success' (3)
97 'Tamara' (3)
97 'Teenager' (14)
95 'Teheran' (3)
97 'Topscore' (3)
97 'Trance' (3)
95 'Wallflower' (5)
97 'Yellow Dover' (4)
97 'Zwanenburg' (5)

TYPHA
96 *minima* var. *gracilis*

ULEX
95 *europaeus* 'Strictus'
96 *minor*

ULMUS
97 'Plantijn'
95 *procera*
95 'Regal'

UNCINIA
97 *clavata*
96 *divaricata*
95 *ferruginea*

URCEOLINA
97 *urceolata*

URTICA
97 *dioica*
96 *pilulifera dodartii*

UVULARIA
95 *caroliniana*

VACCARIA
96 *hispanica*

VACCINIUM
97 *alpinum*
95 *eriophyllum*
95 *griffithianum*
97 *nummularia* LS&H 17294
95 *ovalifolium*
96 *oxycoccos* var. *intermedium*
96 *parvifolium*

VALERIANELLA
97 *eriocarpa*

VANCOUVERIA
97 *planipetala*

VANIA
97 *campylophylla*

VELLA
95 *spinosa*

VERATRUM
97 *caudatum*

VERBASCUM
96 'Bold Queen'
97 (Cotswold Group) 'Boadicea'
95 – 'Bridal Bouquet'
96 – 'C.L. Adams'
97 – 'Cotswold Gem'
96 *elegantissimum*
95 *undulatum*
96 *virgatum*

VERBENA
97 'Artemis'
97 'Calcutta Cream'
97 'Cleopatra'
95 *litoralis*
95 'New Ophelia'
97 'Romance Silver'
95 Sandy Series ♀
95 *stricta* JLS 88008WI
97 'Texas Appleblossom'

VERNONIA
95 *baldwinii*
95 *nudiflora*

VERONICA
96 *austriaca* subsp. *teucrium* 'Blue Fountain'
97 *bombycina* subsp. *bolkardaghensis*
97 *caespitosa*
97 *incana* 'Candidissima'
95 *longifolia* 'Incarnata'
97 *nivalis nivea*
96 *orientalis*
97 – subsp. *carduchorum*
95 *schmidtiana* var. *bandaiana*
97 – 'Nana Rosea'
97 *serpyllifolia*
97 *spicata* 'Corali'
97 – hybrids
97 – 'Pavane'
96 *sumilensis*

VIBURNUM
95 *grandiflorum*
96 *lantana* 'Xanthocarpum'
97 *mullaha* CC 1241
95 *opulus* 'Summer Gold'
95 *purdomii*
97 *ribesifolium*
96 *trilobum*

VINCA
97 *herbacea*
96 *major* 'Sissinghurst'
96 – 'Starlight'

VIOLA
95 'Ann Robb' (ExVa)
97 *arvensis*
95 'Bates Green Purple'
95 'Benjie' (Va)
95 'Betty Grace' (Va)
95 'Blue Haze'
95 'Blue Lace' (Va)
95 'Blue Princess'
97 'Bruneau' (dVt)
95 *bubanii*
95 *canadensis*
97 'Catforth Suzanne'
95 'Chameleon'
97 'Charlotte'
96 Cornish indigenous mauve

96 *cornuta compacta*
96 'Coronation'
95 'Cream Sensation' (Va)
95 'Dulcie Rhoda' (Va)
95 'Ednaston Gem'
97 'Evelyn' (ExVa)
95 *eximia*
96 *flettii*
95 'Hazel Jean' (Va)
95 *incisa*
96 'Jack Simpson'
96 'Jodie' (Va)
95 'John Fielding' (Va)
96 'John Raddenbury' (Vt)
97 Joker Series (P) ♀
96 'June' (SP)
95 'Kadischa' (Va)
96 'Kathleen Hoyle'
  (ExVa)
97 *kusanoana*
97 *lactea*
95 'Lady Finnyoon' (Va)
96 'Lady Jane' (Vt)
95 'Lee' (Va)
97 'Little Johnny' (Va)
97 'Little Liz' (Va)
96 'Love Duet'
97 *lyallii*
96 'Macgregor's Moth'
  (Va)
95 *mandshurica* 'Bicolor'
96 'Mary Dawson' (Va)
97 'Merry Cheer' (C)
96 'Mother's Day'
97 'Mrs Pickett' (C)
96 'Mrs Pinehurst' (Vt)
95 'Nimrod' (Va)
96 'Noni' (Vt)
96 *odorata* 'Wellsiana'
  (Vt) ♀
97 'Opéra' (Vt)
96 'Orchid Pink' (Vt)
96 'Pam's Fancy' (ExVa)
97 'Penny Black' (Va)
95 'Piper' (Va)
96 'Princess Alexandra'
  (Vt)

97 'Princess Blue'
95 Princess Series ♀
96 'Quatre Saisons' (Vt)
96 'Rawson's White' (Vt)
97 'Rosine' (Vt)
96 *rupestris* blue
97 'Sandra Louise' (Va)
95 *schariensis* JCA 993.150
96 'Scottish Yellow' (Va)
97 *sieberiana*
96 'Sunshine' (Va)
96 'Susan' (SP)
97 *takedana* 'Variegata'
96 'Tina Whittaker' (Vt)
96 'Toulouse'
96 'Translucent Blue'
96 *tricolor* subsp.
  macedonica
96 'Tuscany' (Vt)
95 Ultima Series ♀
95 x *visseriana lutea*
96 'Wheatley White'
96 'White Czar' (Vt)
95 'Yellow Snowdon'
95 'Yoyo' (Va)

VITALIANA
95 *primuliflora* subsp.
  praetutiana compacta

VITIS
96 *coignetiae* Soja 457
95 'Espiran' (G)
96 *flexuosa*
95 *vinifera* 'Angers
  Frontignan' (G/O/B)
95 – 'Ascot Citronelle'
  (G/W)
95 – 'Auvergne
  Frontignan' (G/O/W)
95 – 'Black Prince' (G/B)
95 – 'Cote House Seedling'
  (O/W)
95 – 'Grizzley Frontignan'
  (G/R)
95 – 'Lucombe' (F)
95 – 'Madeira Frontignan'
  (G/R)

96 – 'Melon de Bourgogne'
  (O/W)
95 – 'Regner' (O/W)
95 – 'West's St Peter's'
  (G/B)

VRIESEA
95 *duvaliana* ♀
95 *psittacina* ♀

WACHENDORFIA
97 *paniculata*

WAHLENBERGIA
97 *albomarginata*
  white form
97 *albosericea*
97 *cartilaginea*
97 *ceracea*
97 *stricta*
97 *trichogyna*

WATSONIA
97 *coccinea* Herbert ex Baker
  dwarf form
96 'Indian Orange'
96 peach hybrid
96 sp. SH 89
97 *spectabilis*
97 'White Dazzler'
97 *wordsworthiana*

WEIGELA
96 'Abel Carrière Golden'
97 *coraeensis* 'Alba'
96 'Duet'
95 'Féerie'
95 'Fiesta' ♀
96 *florida* 'Magee'
96 – 'Pink Princess'
95 'Majestueux'

WESTRINGIA
97 *longifolia*

WISTERIA
97 *sinensis* 'Imp'
96 – 'Prematura Alba'

WOODSIA
96 *ilvensis*

WOODWARDIA
96 sp. from Emei Shan, China

XEROPHYLLUM
97 *tenax*

YUCCA
95 *flaccida* striated cultivar
97 *gloriosa* 'Tricolor'
97 *navajoa*
97 *recurvifolia* 'Marginata'
96 – 'Variegata'
97 *valida*
95 'Vomerensis'
96 *whipplei* var. *caespitosa*
95 – JLS 86188LACA

ZANTEDESCHIA
97 *aethiopica* pink

ZANTHOXYLUM
95 *ailanthoides*

ZAUSCHNERIA
96 *californica etteri*
96 – subsp. *latifolia*
  RMRF 93-0443

ZEPHYRANTHES
97 *atamasca*
97 'Capricorn'
97 *chlorosolen*
97 *grandiflora*
97 'Grandjax'
97 'La Buffa Rose'
97 *macrosiphon*
97 *morrisclintii*
96 'Panama Pink'
97 'Prairie Sunset'
97 *primulina*
97 *puertoricensis*
97 *pulchella*
97 *reginae*
97 *smallii*
96 *traubii*

ZIZANIA
97 *aquatica*

ZIZIA
96 *aptera*

Hardy Plant Society Search List

The following plants, for which no source is known in the British Isles, are being sought by the Hardy Plant Society for its members and for collections held by other societies and individuals. If anyone knows the whereabouts of any items, seed or plant, on this list, in the British Isles or overseas, would they please contact:-

Mrs Jean Sambrook, Garden Cottage, 214 Ruxley Lane, West Ewell, Surrey KT19 9EZ

ABRONIA
umbellata

ACAENA
caesiiglauca 'Frikart'

ACONITUM
delavayi
fletcherianum
pulchellum

ADONIS
dahurica 'Pleniflora' (d)

AESCULUS
× *carnea* 'O'Neill'
parviflora var. *serotina*
– – 'Rogers'
pavia var. *flavescens*
– 'Humilis'

AGAPANTHUS
'Dorothy Palmer'
praecox 'Aureovariegatus'
'Rosemary'
'Victoria'

AGERATUM
orientale 'Leichtlinii'
– 'Pallidum'

AJUGA
pyramidalis 'Metallica Crispa Purpurea'
– 'Metallica Crispa Rubra'
reptans 'Bronze Beauty'
– 'Burgundy Lace'
– 'Compacta'
– 'Cristata'
– 'Gaiety'
– 'Jungle Beauty Improved'
– 'Mini Crisp Red'
– 'Nana Compacta'
– 'Pink Beauty'
– 'Pink Silver'
– 'Royalty'
– 'Silver Beauty'

AKEBIA
quinata 'Alba'
– 'Rosea'
– 'Shirobana'
– 'Variegata'

ALLIUM
protensum

ALSTROEMERIA
'Afterglow'
'Ballerina'
caryophyllea 'Alba'
haemantha 'Parigo Charm'
'Sonata'

AMARYLLIS
belladonna 'Barberton'
– 'Cape Town'
– 'Elata'
– 'Jagersfontein'
– 'Maxima'
– 'Rosea'
– 'Rosea Perfecta'

– Spectabilis Tricolor = 'Spectabilis'

AMELANCHIER
× *grandiflora* 'Autumn Sunset'
– 'Cumulus'
– 'Prince Charles'
– 'Prince William'
– 'Princess Diana'

ANEMONE
glauciifolia
× *hybrida* 'Beauté Parfait'
– 'Brilliant'
– 'Collerette'
– 'Herbstrose'
– 'Herzblut'
– 'Lady Ardilaun'
– 'Lord Ardilaun'
– 'Magdalena Uhink'
– 'Magenta'
– 'Mignon'
– 'Stuttgard'
– 'Treasure'
– 'Turban'
– 'Vase d'Argent'
nemorosa 'Rubra Plena' (d)
tenuifolia

ANTHEMIS
tinctoria 'Moonlight'
– 'Perry's Variety'

ARISAEMA
angustina

ARISTOLOCHIA
moupinensis

ARMERIA
maritima white foliage

ARTEMISIA
ifranensis

ARUM
longispathum
orientale subsp. *danicum*

ASCLEPIAS
tuberosa 'Gerbe d'Or'

ASPARAGUS
tenuifolius

ASPHODELINE
amurensis 'Flore Pleno' (d)
lutea 'Flore Pleno' (d)

ASTER
amellus 'Bessie Chapman'
paternus
thomsonii 'Winchmore Hill'

ASTILBE
× *arendsii* 'Mars'
japonica 'Aureoreticulata'

ASYNEUMA
campanuloides

AUBRIETA
'Aileen'
'King of the Purples'

'Purple Splendour'

BAPTISIA
perfoliata

BELLIS
perennis 'Bunter Teppich'
– 'Chevreuse'
– 'Double Bells' (d)
– 'Eliza'
– 'Helichrysiflora'
– 'Lilliput Rose'
– 'Lutea'
– 'Madame Crousse'
– 'Mavourneen'
– 'Mount Etna'
– 'Pink Buttons'
– 'Rubriflora'
– 'Shrewley Gold' (v)
– 'String of Pearls'
– 'Tuberosa Monstrosa'
– 'Victoria'
sylvestris

BERGENIA
crassifolia 'Variegata'

BERKHEYA
macrophylla

BETA
vulgaris 'Variegata'

BOMAREA
andimarcana
carderi

BRASSICA
Four Seasons Cabbage

BRUNNERA
macrophylla 'Blaukuppel'

BULBINELLA
modesta

BUPLEURUM
ranunculoides 'Canalease'

CACCINIA
macrantha

CALCEOLARIA
integrifolia white

CALTHA
laeta var. *alpestris*
leptosepala 'Grandiflora'
– var. *leptosepala*
   blue flowered
novae-zelandiae
palustris Elata Group
– 'Pallida Plena' (d)
– 'Pleurisepala'
– 'Purpurascens'
– Silvestris Group

CALYSTEGIA
gigantea

CAMPANULA
'Fergusonii'
'Gremlin'
'Pamela'
persicifolia 'Spetchley'
– 'Profusion'
rapunculoides 'Plena' (d)

trachelium 'Versicolor'
'Woodstock'
zoysii f. *alba*

CANNA
'Feuerzauber'
× *generalis* 'America'
'Liebesglut'

CARDAMINE
nemorosa 'Plena' (d)

CARPINUS
betulus 'Albovariegata'
– 'Variegata'
caroliniana 'Pyramidalis'

CARYOPTERIS
× *clandonensis* 'Blue Mist'

CATANANCHE
caerulea 'Perry's White'

CENTAUREA
atropurpurea 'Alba'

CENTRANTHUS
ruber 'Bragg's Variety'

CERCIS
canadensis 'Appalachian Red'
– 'Pinkbud'
– 'Royal White'
– 'Silver Cloud'
– 'Wither's Pink Charm'

CHAEROPHYLLUM
hirsutum 'Rubriflorum'

CHASMANTHE
intermedia

CHELONE
obliqua 'Praecox Nana'

CHRYSANTHEMUM
'Anna Hay' (30)
'Ceres'
'Jean Harlowe'
'Tiny'

CIMICIFUGA
simplex 'Braunlaub'
   variegated form

CLEMATIS
recta 'Plena' (d)

CLETHRA
alnifolia 'Creel's Calico'

COCHLEARIA
officinalis 'Variegata'

COLCHICUM
callicymbium 'Danton'
guadarramense
'Mr Kerbert'
'President Coolidge'
triphyllum

CONVALLARIA
majalis 'Gigantea'
– 'Robusta'
– 'Rosea Plena' (d)

COREOPSIS
bigelovii

'Double Sunburst'
gigantea
grandiflora 'Perry's
   Variety'
lanceolata 'Mahogany'
maritima
pubescens
pulchra

CORNUS
mas 'Spring Glow'

CORTADERIA
selloana 'Bertini'

COSMOS
scabiosoides

COTINUS
coggygria 'Daydream'
– 'Nordine Red'

CRAMBE
pinnatifida

CRINUM
× *powellii* 'Krelagei'
– 'Variegatum'

CROCOSMIA
'Mephistopheles'

CROCUS
'Albidus'
chrysanthus 'Al Jolson'
– 'Andromeda'
– 'Atom'
– 'Aubade'
– 'Belle Jaune'
– 'Bloemfontein'
– 'Blue Beauty'
– 'Blue Bonnet'
– 'Blue Butterfly'
– 'Blue Jacket'
– 'Blue Jay'
– 'Blue Princess'
– 'Blue Rock'
– 'Blue Throat'
– 'Bullfinch'
– 'Bumble-bee'
– 'Buttercup'
– 'Constellation'
– 'Crescendo'
– 'Cum Laude'
– 'Cupido'
– 'Curlew'
– 'Dandy'
– 'Distinction'
– 'Golden Pheasant'
– 'Golden Plover'
– 'Goldene Sonne'
– 'Grand Gala'
– 'Grey Lady'
– 'Harlequin'
– 'Ivory Glory'
– 'Ivory Glow'
– 'Jester'
– 'Johan Cruyff'
– 'Khaki'
– 'Koh-i-Nor'
– 'Lemon Queen'
– 'Lentejuweel'
– 'Lilette'
– 'Lilliputaner'
– 'Magic'
– 'Mannequin'
– 'Mariette'
– 'Marion'
– 'Marlene'
– 'Morning Star'

– 'Mrs Moon'
– 'Mystic'
– 'Nanette'
– 'Olympiade'
– 'Opal'
– 'Palette'
– 'Parade'
– 'Paradiso'
– 'Plaisir'
– 'Reverence'
– 'Rising Sun'
– 'Ruby Gown'
– 'Shot'
– 'Siskin'
– 'Solfatare'
– 'Solo'
– 'Sorrento'
– 'Spotlight'
– 'Spring Song'
– 'Sulphur Glory'
– 'Sunset'
– 'Sunshine'
– 'Susie'
– 'Symphonia'
– 'Topolino'
– 'Trance'
– 'White Egret'
– 'White Splendour'
– 'Winter Gold'
– 'Yellow Gem'
– 'Yellow Hammer'
– 'Yellow Queen'
vernus 'Blue Ribbon'

CUNNINGHAMIA
lanceolata 'Chason's Gift'

CYPRIPEDIUM
arietinum
candidum
montanum
× *ventricosum*

DACTYLIS
glomerata 'Aurea'

DACTYLORHIZA
elata white
majalis 'Glasnevin'

DAHLIA
'Emperor Franz-Joseph'

DEINANTHE
caerulea f. *alba*

DELPHINIUM
brachycentrum

DIANTHUS
'Beverley Pink' (p)
'Black Prince' (p)
'Evelyn'
'Granado' (b)
'Lambrook Beauty' (p)
'Lincolnshire Lass' (p)
'Lucy Glendill' (b)
'Old Man's Head' (p)
'Ruth Fischer' (p)

DICENTRA
'Appleblossom'
'Queen of Hearts'

DISPORUM
menziesii

DORONICUM
pardalianches
   'Goldstrauss'

DRACOCEPHALUM
tanguticum

ECHINACEA
purpurea 'Abendsonne'

ECHINOPS
exaltatus f. *albus*

ENKIANTHUS
campanulatus 'Renoir'
– 'Showy Lantern'

EPILOBIUM
angustifolium var.
   variegatum

EPIMEDIUM
× *youngianum*
   Yenomoto form

EREMURUS
afghanicus
aitchisonii 'Dawn'
× *isabellinus* 'Highdown
   Dwarf'
– 'Highdown Gold'
kaufmannii
'Lady Falmouth'
'Primrose'
robustus var. *tardiflorus*
'Sunset'

ERIGERON
'Double Beauty' (d)
glaucus 'B. Ladhams'

ERYNGIUM
floribundum
lassauxii
× *zabelii* 'James Ivory'

ERYSIMUM
'Miss Massey' (d)

EUPATORIUM
fistulosum 'Gateway'
purpureum 'Album'

FRAGARIA
vesca 'Alpina Scarletta'

FRANCOA
rupestris

FRITILLARIA
imperialis 'Flore Pleno'
   (d)

GAILLARDIA
× *grandiflora* 'Ipswich
   Beauty'

GALANTHUS
'Allen's Perfection'
'Cupid'
'Jenny Wren'
'Rebecca'
'Romeo'
'Tomtit'
'Valentine'
'White Swan'

GALEGA
officinalis var. *compacta*

GENTIANA
asclepiadea 'Caelestina'
– 'Phaeina'
× *japonica*

GERANIUM
sanguineum double (d)

GEUM
× *ewenii*
pentapetalum 'Plenum' (d)

GLADIOLUS
× *brenchleyensis*

GLYCERIA
maxima 'Pallida'

HEDYCHIUM
'F.W. Moore'

HELENIUM
autumnale 'Aurantiacum'
'Baronin Linden'
'Brilliant'
'Chanctonbury'
'Flammenrad'
'Goldreif'
'Kugelsonne'
'September Gold'
'Spätrot'
'Tawny Dwarf'

HELIANTHUS
gracilentus
'Hallo'
hirsutus
longifolius
schweinitzii
simulans
tomentosus
'Zebulon'

HELIOPSIS
helianthoides 'Gigantea'
– 'Mid West Dream'
– var. *scabra* 'Desert King'
– – 'Patula'

HELLEBORUS
niger 'Mr Poë's Variety'

HEMEROCALLIS
'Aurantiaca Major'
'E.A. Bowles'
fulva var. *rosea*
'Gay Music'

HEUCHERA
'Baby's Breath'
'Crimson Cascade'
'Damask'
'Freedom'
'Gaiety'
'Gloriana'
'Honeybells'
'Ibis'
'June Bride'
'Lady Warwick'
'Montrose'
'Mount St Helens'
'Oakington Superba'
'Oxfordii'
'Rose Cavalier'
'Rufus'
'Scarlet Beauty'
'Tattletale'

HIDALGOA
wercklei

HYDRANGEA
macrophylla 'Merritt's
   Beauty'
– 'Pink 'n' Pretty'
– 'Red 'n' Pretty'
– 'Red Star'
– 'Revelation'
– 'Trophy'

quercifolia 'Alice'
– 'Alison'
– 'PeeWee'

HYPERICUM
olympicum f. *minus*
  'Schwefelperle'

IBERIS
sempervirens 'Plena' (d)

ILEX
vomitoria 'Folsom's
  Weeping' (f)
– 'Grey's Little Leaf'
– 'Jewel' (f)
– 'Nana'
– f. *pendula*
– 'Shadow's Female' (f)
– 'Straughn's'
– 'Wiggin's Yellow' (f)
– 'Will Fleming'
– 'Yellow Berry' (f)

ILLICIUM
floridanum 'Album'
– 'Halley's Comet'

IMPERATA
cylindrica 'Major'

INDIGOFERA
'Rose Carpet'

IRIS
'Barcarole' (Regeliocyclus)
'Camilla' (Regeliocyclus)
'Clara' (Regeliocyclus)
'Dorothea'
'Dress Circle' (Spuria)
'Emily Grey'
ensata 'Benibotan'
– 'Kegoromo'
– 'Kumazumi'
– 'Lady in Waiting'
– 'Reign of Glory'
– 'Sky Mist'
– 'Tinted Cloud'
– 'Warei Hotei'
'Ice Blue'
'Lutetas' (Regeliocyclus)
'Medea' (Regeliocyclus)
'Mercurius' (Regeliocyclus)
'Myddelton Blue'
orientalis 'Snowflake'
pseudacorus 'Gigantea'
sibirica 'Big Blue'
– 'Blue Reverie'
tectorum 'Lilacina'
  Tollong Group
  Toltec Group
unguicularis 'Bowles'
  White'
– 'Ellis's Variety'

ITEA
virginica 'Saturnalia'

JEFFERSONIA
dubia 'Flore Pleno' (d)

JUNIPERUS
horizontalis 'Argentea'
– 'Blue Horizon'
– 'Heidi'
– 'Lime Glow'
– 'Watnong'

KADSURA
japonica 'Chirimen' (v)
– 'Fukurin' (v)

KNIPHOFIA
'Adam'
'Amberlight'
'Bees' Orange'
'Bees' Yellow'
'Bressingham Glow'
'Bressingham Torch'
'Burnt Orange'
'Buttercrunch'
'Canary Bird'
'Chartreuse'
'Cleopatra'
'Cool Lemon'
'Enchantress'
'Florella'
'Green Lemon'
'Honeycomb'
'Hortulanus Laren'
'Indian'
leichtlinii 'Aurea'
'Lemon Queen'
'Maxima'
'Primulina' hort.
rogersii
'Russell's Gold'
'Slim Coral Red'
'Slim Orange'
'Snow Maiden'
'The Rocket'

KNOWLTONIA
capensis

LATHYRUS
latifolius violet
ornatus

LAVANDULA
'Backhouse Purple'
'Glasnevin Variety'

LEONTOPODIUM
haplophylloides

LEUCANTHEMUM
× *superbum* 'Beauté
  Anversoise'

LIATRIS
pycnostachya 'Alba'
scariosa 'White Spire'
spicata 'Picador'
– 'Silvertips'
– 'Snow Queen'

LIGULARIA
dentata 'Golden Queen'
– 'Moorblut'
persica
sibirica var. *racemosa*

LIGUSTICUM
mutellina

LILIUM
arboricola
brownii var. *australe*
candidum 'Peregrinum'
– purple-spotted flowers
× *maculatum* 'E.A.
  Bowles'
× *princeps* 'Myddelton
  House'

LIMONIUM
platyphyllum f. *roseum*

LINARIA
aeruginea 'Aureopurpurea'

LINUM
narbonense 'June Perfield'
– 'Six Hills'

LOBELIA
'Mrs Humbert'
× *speciosa* 'Anne'
'Twilight Time'

LONICERA
sempervirens 'Cedar Lane'

LUPINUS
'Betty Astell'
'Billy Wright'
'City of York'
'George Russell'
ornatus
'Pink Pearls'
polyphyllus 'Downer's
  Delight'
'Tom Reeves'

LYCHNIS
chalcedonica 'Alba Plena'
  (d)
coronata 'Speciosa'
flos-cuculi 'Adolph Muss'

LYSIMACHIA
leschenaultii

MAGNOLIA
grandiflora 'Bracken's
  Brown Beauty'
– 'Claudia Wannamaker'
– 'Gloriosa'
– 'Majestic Red'
– 'Ruff'
– 'Symmes Select'
virginiana 'Henry Hicks'

MATELEA
carolinensis

MECONOPSIS
× *cookei*
grandis 'Keillour Crimson'
– 'Miss Dickson'
× *sheldonii* 'Archie
  Campbell'
torquata

MELITTIS
melissophyllum 'Variegata'

MIMULUS
lewisii 'Albus'
– 'Sunset'

MISCANTHUS
floridulus 'Nippon
  Summer'
sinensis 'Autumn Red'
– 'Blondo'
– 'Gracillimus Nanus'
– 'Interstate'

MONARDA
'Falls of Hill's Creek'
'Gardenview Red'
'Gardenview Select'
'Gardenway Red'
'Magnifica'
'Ohio Glow'
'Raspberry Wine'
'Red Explosion'
'Souris'
'Stone's Throw Pink'
'Sunset'

MULGEDIUM
giganteum

MYOSOTIS
dissitiflora 'Elegantissima'
  (v)

NARCISSUS
'Alpha of Donard' (1)
'Astron' (2)
'Gog'
'Golden Miller' (1)
'Golden Thought'
'Green Mantle' (3)
'Lucinda'
'Magistrate' (1)
'Precentor' (1)
'Red Light' (2)
'Saint Dorothea' (1)
'Slieve Bernagh' (1)
'Slieve Donard' (1)
'Solid Gold' (1)

NEPETA
racemosa 'Blue Wonder'
– 'White Wonder'

OENOTHERA
fruticosa 'Best Red'

ORIGANUM
vulgare 'Bury Hill'

PAEONIA
'Archangel'
'Argosy'
'Black Douglas'
'Black Pirate'
'Chalice'
'Constance Spry'
'Daystar'
'Early Windflower'
'Good Cheer'
lactiflora 'Coral Charm'
– 'Doris Cooper'
– 'Jean Bockstoce'
– 'Sea Shell'
– 'Sword Dance'
'Legion of Honour'
'Little Dorrit'
mascula subsp. *arietina*
  'Hilda Milne'
officinalis 'Phyllis
  Prichard'
– 'Red Ensign'
– 'Splendens'
'Roman Gold'
suffruticosa 'Bijou de
  Chusan'
– 'Elizabeth'
'Sybil Stern'
'Victoria Lincoln'
'White Innocence'
wittmanniana var.
  nudicarpa

PANICUM
'Squaw'

PAPAVER
orientale 'Atrosanguineum
  Maximum'
– 'Australia's Orange'
– 'Barr's White'
– 'Blush Queen'
– 'Bobs'
– 'Border Beauty'
– 'Brightness'
– 'Burgundy'

- 'Cavalier'
- 'Cerise Bedder'
- 'Colonel Bowles'
- 'Countess of Stair'
- 'Crimped Beauty'
- 'Crimson Pompon'
- 'Curtis's Strain'
- 'Delicatum'
- 'Dengas'
- 'Duke of Teck'
- 'E.A. Bowles'
- 'Edna Perry'
- 'Enchantress'
- 'Enfield Beauty'
- 'Ethel Swete'
- 'Fire King'
- 'Fringed Beauty'
- 'Gibson's Salmon'
- 'Goldschmidt'
- 'Grenadier'
- 'Henri Cayeux Improved'
- 'Humphrey Bennett'
- 'Ida Brailsford'
- 'Immaculatum'
- 'Iris Perry'
- 'Ivy Perry'
- 'Jeannie Mawson'
- 'Joyce'
- 'Lady Haig'
- 'Lady Haskett'
- 'Lady Roscoe'
- 'Lavender Glory'
- 'Little Prince'
- 'Lovely'
- 'Magnificence'
- 'Mahony'
- 'Margherite'
- 'Marie Studholme'
- 'Masterpiece'
- 'Max Leichtlin'
- 'May Curtis'
- 'Medusa'
- 'Menelik'
- 'Minimum'
- 'Miss Julia'
- 'Mogul'
- 'Mrs Carl Skinner'
- 'Mrs John Harkness'
- 'Mrs Lockett Agnew'
- 'Mrs M. Bevan'
- 'Mrs Marsh'
- 'Orange Queen'
- 'Oriental King'
- 'Oriental Queen'
- 'Oriflamme'
- 'Pale Face'
- 'Parkmanii'
- 'Perry's Blush'
- 'Perry's Favorite'
- 'Perry's Pigmy'
- 'Perry's Unique'
- 'Persepolis'
- 'Peter Pan'
- 'Princess Ena'
- 'Princess Mary'
- 'Purity'
- 'Royal Prince'
- 'Royal Scarlet'
- 'Ruby Perry'
- 'Salmon Beauty'
- 'Salmon Perfection'
- 'Salmon Queen'
- 'Sass Pink'
- 'Semiplenum'
- 'Silberblick'
- 'Silver Queen'

- 'Silverblotch'
- 'Snoflame'
- 'Sonata'
- 'Souvenir'
- 'Splendens'
- 'Sungold'
- 'Surprise'
- 'The King'
- 'The Queen'
- 'Thora Perry'
- 'Tom Tit'
- 'Toreador'
- 'Van der Glotch'
- 'Vuurkogel'
- 'Winnie'
- 'Wurtemburgia'

PENSTEMON
'Prairie Dawn'

PHLEUM
pratense 'Aureum'

PHLOX
buckleyi
carolina forms
caryophylla
dolichantha
floridana
– subsp. *bella*
glaberrima
idahoensis
paniculata 'Antoine
  Mercier'
– 'Hochgesang'
x *procumbens* 'Pinstripe'
– 'Snowdrift'
– 'Vein Mountain'
stansburyi

PHORMIUM
'Aurora'
tenax 'Goliath'
– 'Purple Giant'

PHYTOLACCA
variegated forms

PIMPINELLA
saxifraga 'Rosea'

POLEMONIUM
carneum 'Rose Queen'
laxiflorum

POLYGONUM
coriaceum

POTENTILLA
alba 'Snow White'
'Arc-en-ciel'
'Congo'
'Hamlet'
ovalis

PRIMULA
'Donard Gem'

PRUNUS
persica var. *nectarina*
  'White Glory'
x *yedoensis* 'Afterglow'
– 'Pink Shell'
– 'Snow Fountains'

PULMONARIA
officinalis var. *immaculata*

RANUNCULUS
aconitifolius 'Luteus
  Plenus' (d)
alpestris 'Flore Pleno' (d)

parnassiifolius
  'Semiplenus'

RESEDA
odorata 'Parson's White'

RHEUM
'Dr Baillon'
palmatum
  'Atropurpureum
  Dissectum'

RHODODENDRON
prunifolium 'Cherry-bomb'
  (A)
– 'Coral Glow' (A)
– 'Lewis Shortt' (A)
– 'Peach Glow' (A)
– 'Pine' (A)

RIGIDELLA
flammea
orthantha

ROMNEYA
coulteri 'Butterfly'

ROSCOEA
cautleyoides 'Bees' Dwarf'

RUDBECKIA
laciniata 'Foliis Variegatis'
nitida 'Autumn Glory'
serotina

RUTA
graveolens 'Blue Beauty'

SACCHARUM
strictum

SALVIA
beckeri
ceratophylla
dichroa
eichleriana
formosa
'Glory of Stuttgart'
guaranitica 'Costa Rica'
– 'Indigo Blue'
– 'Purple Splendor'
ianthina
pinnata
teddii
valentina
yunnanensis

SANGUISORBA
officinalis 'Shiro-fukurin'

SAXIFRAGA
'Flore Pleno' (*virginiensis*)
  (d)

SCABIOSA
caucasica 'Blue Mountain'
– 'Constancy'
– 'Diamond'
– 'Loddon White'
– 'Mrs Isaac House'
– 'Penhill Blue'
– 'Rhinsburg Glory'

SENECIO
cineraria 'Hoar Frost'

SIDALCEA
'Donard Queen'
'H. Blanchard'
malviflora 'Pompadour'
'Scarlet Beauty'

SILPHIUM
'Carpenter's Cup'

TAMARIX
ramosissima 'Cheyenne
  Red'

TANACETUM
coccineum 'A.M. Kelway'
– 'Allurement'
– 'Avalanche'
– 'Beau Geste'
– 'Bishop of Salisbury'
– 'Bridal Pink'
– 'Bright Boy'
– 'Charming'
– 'China Rose'
– 'Comet'
– 'Countess Poulett'
– 'Duke of York'
– 'Kelway's Lovely'
– 'Kelway's Magnificent'
– 'Langport Scarlet'
– 'Lorna'
– 'Mrs Bateman Brown'
– 'Progression'
– 'Radiant'
– 'Somerset'
– 'White Madeleine'

TEUCRIUM
polium 'Album'

TIARELLA
cordifolia 'Montrose'

TILIA
americana 'Dakota'
– 'Douglas'
– 'Legend'
– 'Rosehill'
cordata 'DeGroot'
– 'Glenleven'
– 'Green Globe'
– 'Handsworth'
heterophylla 'Continental
  Appeal'
tomentosa 'Sterling'

TRILLIUM
catesbyi f. *album*
erectum var. *blandum*
– f. *cahnae*
– f. *polymerum*
gracile
japonicum
kamtschaticum 'Tsuzuki'
ovatum 'Edith'
– 'Kenmore'
– f. *roseum*
– 'Tillicum'
persistens
petiolatum
reliquum
rivale 'Del Norte'
– 'Verne Ahiers'
texanum
tschonoskii f. *violaceum*

TROLLIUS
asiaticus var. *aurantiacus*
'Miss Mary Russell'

ULMUS
alata 'Lace Parasol'

VERATRUM
stenophyllum
wilsonii
yunnanense

VERNONIA
angustifolia

HPS Search List

VERONICA
spicata 'Gina's Pale Blue'
VIOLA
'Red Giant'
VITEX
agnus-castus 'Rosea'
WISTERIA
floribunda 'Honey Bee
     Pink'
– 'Ivory Tower'
– 'Lawrence'
XEROPHYLLUM
asphodeloides
ZANTEDESCHIA
aethiopica 'Compacta'

THE NATIONAL COUNCIL FOR THE CONSERVATION OF PLANTS & GARDENS (NCCPG) COLLECTIONS

All or part of the following Genera are represented by a National Collection. Full details of these collections are contained in the National Plant Collections Directory 1998 available from: NCCPG, c/o RHS Garden, Wisley, Woking, Surrey GU23 6QP. Price £4.00 inclusive of post and packing.

Abelia	Buxus	Daboecia	Geum
Abies	Calamintha	Dahlia	Gladiolus
Abutilon	Calceolaria	Daphne	Grevillea
Acacia	Calluna	Davallia	Halimium
Acanthus	Caltha	Delphinium	Hamamelis
Acer	Camassia	Dendranthema	Haworthia
Achillea	Camellia	Dendrobium	Hebe
Actinidia	Campanula	Deutzia	Hedera
Adenophora	Canna	Dianthus	Hedychium
Adiantum	Cardamine	Diascia	Helenium
Aesculus	Carpinus	Dicentra	Helianthemum
Agapanthus	Carya	Dicksoniaceae	Helianthus
Alchemilla	Caryopteris	Diervilla	Helichrysum
Allium	Cassiope	Digitalis	Heliopsis
Alnus	Castanea	Dodecatheon	Helleborus
Alstroemeria	Catalpa	Doronicum	Hemerocallis
Amelanchier	Catasetum	Dracaena	Hepatica
Ampelopsis	Cattleya	Dryopteris	Hesperis
Anemone	Ceanothus	Echeveria	Heuchera
Anguloa	Celmisia	Echinacea	Hibiscus
× Angulocaste	Ceratostigma	Elaeagnus	Hillier Plants
Aquilegia	Cercidiphyllum	Embothrium	Hoheria
Arabis	Chamaecyparis	Encyclia	Hosta
Araceae	Chionodoxa	Enkianthus	Hyacinthus
Aralia	Chusquea	Epimedium	Hydrangea
Arbutus	Cimicifuga	Equisetum	Hypericum
Argyranthemum	Cistus	Erica	Ilex
Artemisia	Citrus	Erigeron	Inula
Aruncus	Clematis	Erodium	Iris
Arundinaria	Codiaeum	Eryngium	Jasminum
Asarum	Colchicum	Erysimum	Juglans
Asplenium	Coleus	Erythronium	Juniperus
Aster	Conifers	Eucalyptus	Kalmia
Astilbe	Conophytum	Eucryphia	Kniphofia
Astroloba	Convallaria	Euphorbia	Laburnum
Athyrium	Coprosma	Fagus	Lamium
Aubrieta	Coreopsis	Ferns	Lathyrus
Aucuba	Coriaria	Ficus	Lavandula
Azara	Cornus	Filipendula	Leptospermum
Bambuseae	Cortaderia	Fragaria	Leucanthemum
Barkeria	Corylopsis	Fraxinus	Leucojum
Begonia	Corylus	Fritillaria	Lewisia
Berberis	Cotoneaster	Fuchsia	Ligularia
Bergenia	Crocosmia	Galanthus	Ligustrum
Betula	Crocus	Garrya	Linum
Bletilla	× Cupressocyparis	Gasteria	Liquidambar
Borago	Cyclamen	Gaultheria	Liriodendron
Borzicactinae	Cymbidium	Gentiana	Lithocarpus
Brachyglottis	Cystopteris	Geranium	Lithops

Lobelia
Lonicera
Lupinus
Lycaste
Lychnis
Lysimachia
Magnolia
Mahonia
Malus
Meconopsis
Mentha
Monarda
Monsonia
Muscari
Narcissus
Nepeta
Nerine
Nerium
Nothofagus
Nymphaea
Oenothera
Olearia
Opuntia
Origanum
Osmunda
Osteospermum
Ourisia
Oxalis
Paeonia
Papaver
Paphiopedilum
Parahebe
Parthenocissus

Passiflora
Pelargonium
Penstemon
Pernettya
Philadelphus
Phlomis
Phlox
Phormium
Photinia
Phygelius
Phyllostachys
Picea
Pieris
Pinguicula
Pinus
Pittosporum
Pleioblastus
Platanus
Platycodon
Pleione
Pleurothallidinae
Polemonium
Polygonum
Polypodium
Polystichum
Populus
Potentilla
Primula
Prunus
Pseudopanax
Pulmonaria
Pyracantha
Pyrus

Quercus
Ranunculus
Rheum
Rhododendron
Ribes
Rodgersia
Rohdea
Rosa
Rosmarinus
Rubus
Rudbeckia
Ruscus
Salix
Salvia
Sambucus
Sansevieria
Santolina
Sarcocaulon
Sarcococca
Sarracenia
Sasa
Saxifraga
Scabiosa
Schizostylis
Scilla
Sedum
Semiaquilegia
Sempervivum
Sisyrinchium
Skimmia
Slieve Donard Plants
Sorbus
Spiraea

Sir Frederick Stern
Stewartia
Streptocarpus
Styracaceae
Symphyandra
Syringa
Tanacetum
Taxus
Thalictrum
Thelypteridaceae
Thuja
Thymus
Tilia
Trillium
Tropaeolum
Tulbaghia
Tulipa
Vaccinium
Variegated Plants
Verbascum
Veronica
Viburnum
Vinca
Viola
Vitis
Weigela
Wisteria
Woodwardia
Yucca
Zelkova

INTERNATIONAL PLANT FINDERS

Canada

Ashley, A. & P. (comp). (1996/97). *The Canadian Plant Source Book*. ISBN 0-9694566-2-X. 21,000 hardy plants available at retail and wholesale nurseries across Canada, including those who ship to US. English common names & English & French cross-indexes. Orders: 93 Fentiman Avenue, Ottawa, ON, Canada, K1S OT7. T (613) 730-0755. F (613) 730-2095. E-Mail apashley@cyberus.ca. $20 (Canadian or US) inc. p&p. Add $5 for airmail.

Germany

Erhardt, A. & W. (comp). (1997). 3rd ed. *PPP-Index*. ISBN-3-8001-6621-6. 80,000 plants from 1,200 European nurseries. CD-ROM included. Orders: Verlag Eugen Ulmer, PO Box 70 05 61, D-70574 Stuttgart. T (49) 711-4507-121. E-Mail info@ulmer.de. DM 58,00.

Italy

Feroni, F. C., & Volta, T. (comp) & Mondadori, G. (ed). (1996). *Il Cercapiante*. ISBN 88-374-1366-1. 15,000 plants from 400 nurseries including 100 specialist suppliers; 100 European nurseries; all Italian botanical and professional Associations, all Italian Garden Clubs, wide Bibliography. Orders: Via Andrea Ponti 10, 20143 Milano. T (02) 89166367. E-Mail edigmga@tal.it. L. 25,000.

Netherlands

Hart, S. (ed). (1997/98). *Plantenvinder voor de Lage Landen*. ISBN 90-6255-732-5. Approx. 45,000 plants and 140 nurseries. Orders: Uitgeverij TERRA, Postbus 188, 7200AD Zutphen. T (31) 575 525222. F (31) 575 525242. Dfl. 24,50.

New Zealand

Gaddum, M. (comp). (1997). *New Zealand Plant Finder*. ISBN 1- 86953-375-5. 22,000 plants (and seeds) listed from 160 nurseries with retail facilities. Comon names included and indexed. Searchable database including wholesale nurseries on internet. Orders: PO Box 2237, Gisborne. T (64 6) 862 3418. E-Mail meg@infogarden.co.nz. Website www.infogarden.co.nz. NZ$29.95 plus postage overseas.

United Kingdom

Pawsey, A. (ed). (1998). 16th ed. *Find That Rose!* Covers Autumn 1998 & Spring 1999 and lists approx. 2,800 varieties with basic type, colour and fragrance code plus full details of approx 70 growers. Orders: British Rose Growers Association, 303 Mile End Road, Colchester, Essex CO4 5EA. Website www.city2000com/sh/rose-growers. Sae for info. or £2.25.

Platt, K. (ed). (1997). 2nd ed. *The Seed Search*. ISBN 0-9528810-1-2. A directory of over 40,000 seeds, including over 5,900 vegetables, with details and essential information on suppliers from around the world. Lists seeds of trees, flowers, vegetables, herbs. Also lists English common names and hazardous plants, seeds. Orders: 35 Longfield Road, Crookes, Sheffield S10 1QW. T 0114 268 1700. E-Mail k@seedsearch.demon.co.uk. Website www.seedsearch.demon.co.uk. £10.99 plus £1.75 p&p.

USA

Isaacson, R. (comp). (1996). 4th ed. *The Andersenís Horticultural Libraryís Source List of Plants and Seeds*. Approx. 59,000 plants and seeds from 450 retail & wholesale outlets in the US & Canada. All are prepared to ship interstate. Does not include Orchids, Cacti or Succulents. Orders: Andersen Horticultural Library, Minnesota Landscape Arboretum, 3675 Arboretum Drive, Box 39, Chanhassen, MN 55317. US$only. 37.25. Surface rate outside USA.

Facciola, S. (ed). (1990). *Cornucopia - A Source Book of Edible Plants*. ISBN 0-9628087-0-9. A very substantial and comprehensive volume (678 pages) which documents 3,000 species of edible plants & 7,000 cultivars available in the US and abroad. MS Windows software version ISBN 0-9628087-1-7. Orders: Kampong Publications, 1870 Sunrise Drive, Vista, California 92084. T (760) 726-0990. US$40.00.

Barton, B. (comp). (1997). 5th ed. *Gardening by Mail*. ISBN 0-395-87770-9. A directory of mail order resources for gardeners in the USA and Canada, including seed companies, nurseries, suppliers of all garden necessaries and ornaments, horticultural and plant societies, magazines, libraries and books. E-mail & web addresses included. Orders: Houghton Miffin Co., 222 Berkeley Street, Boston, MA 02114. T (800) 597-6127. E-Mail tusker@ap.net. US$24.

New England Wild Flower Society. (1998). *Sources of Propagated Native Plants and Wildflowers*. Source list of US nurseries selling nursery propagated, North American native plants and seeds. 75 nurseries listed. Orders: Garden in the Woods, 180 Hemenway Road, Framingham, MA 01701-2699. E-Mail newfs.org. Website www.newfs.org. US$ 3.50 plus $1 postage.

Shank, D. (ed). (1998). Vol 9, Issues 1&2. *Hortus West: A Western North America Native Plant Directory & Journal*. Issn 1085 7095. Directory lists 2,500 western native species commercially available through 200 native plant vendors in 11 Western United States and two Canadian provinces. Orders: Hortus West Publications, PO Box 2870, Wilsonville, OR 97070-2870. US$ only. 12.00. (ex US add $3.00) for annual (2 issue) sub.

INDEX MAP

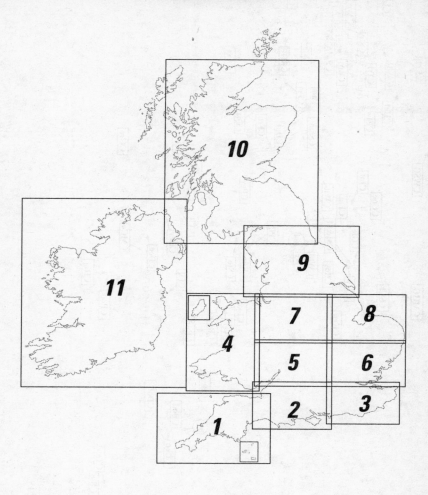

Motorways

Primary routes

Other 'A' roads

The maps on the following pages show the approximate location of the nurseries whose details are listed in this directory.

Details of nurseries with letter Codes in boxes are given in the CODE-NURSERY Index. CRow

Details of nurseries with number Codes in circles are given in the ADDITIONAL NURSERY Index.

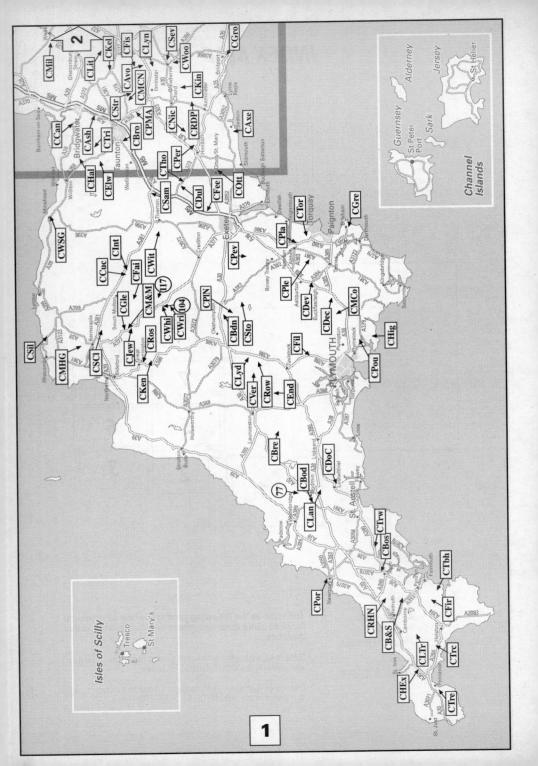

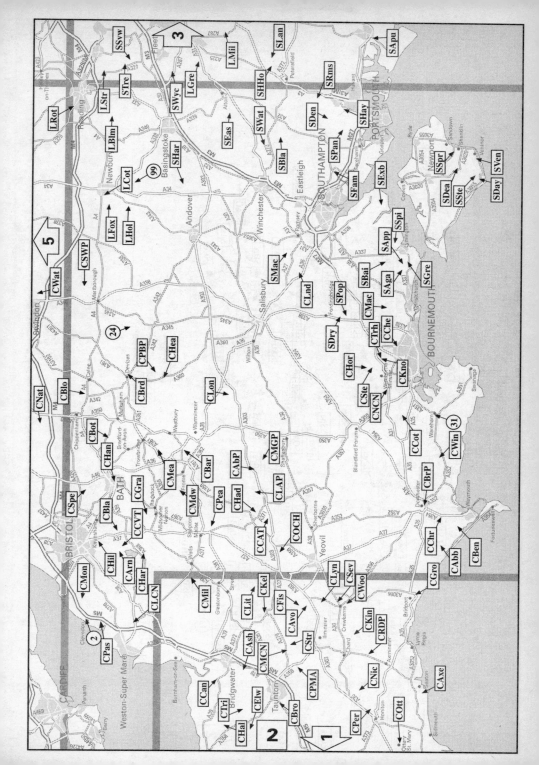

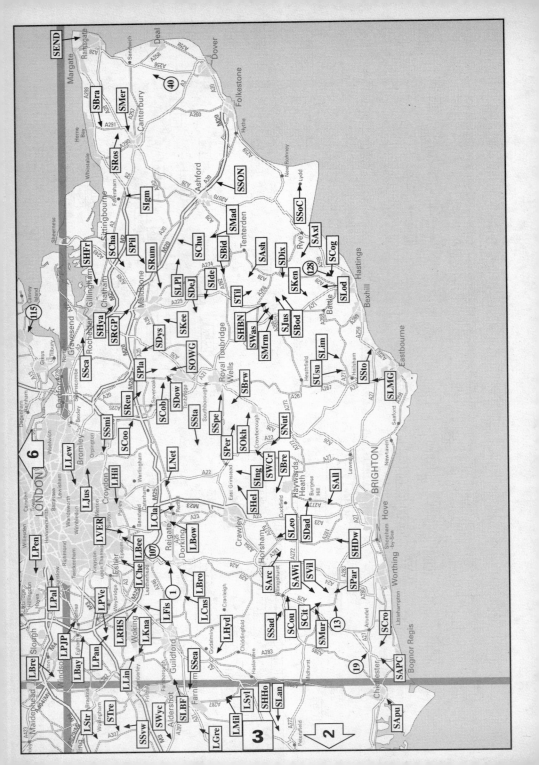

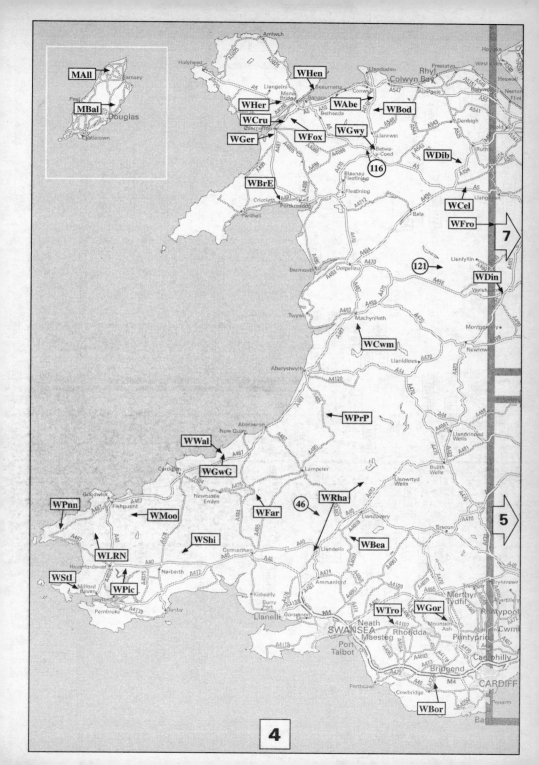

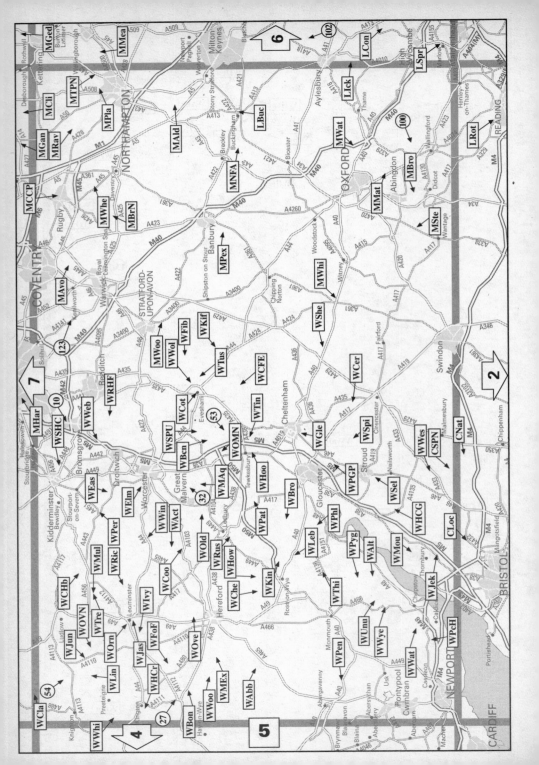

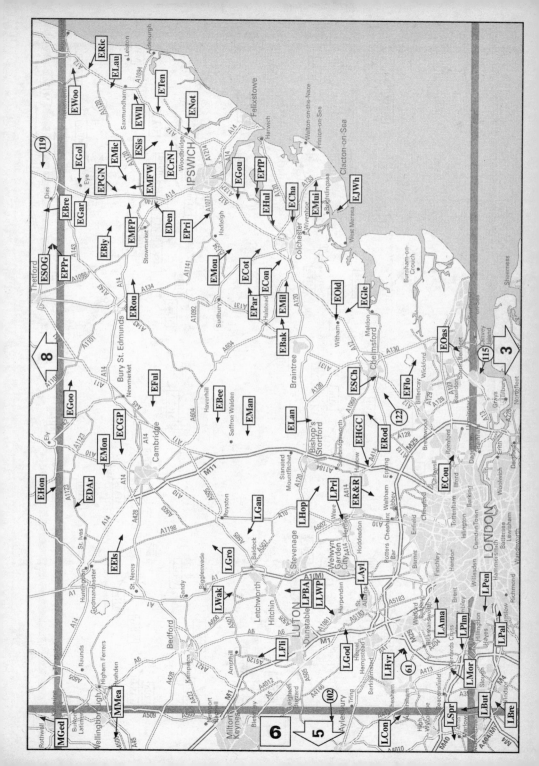

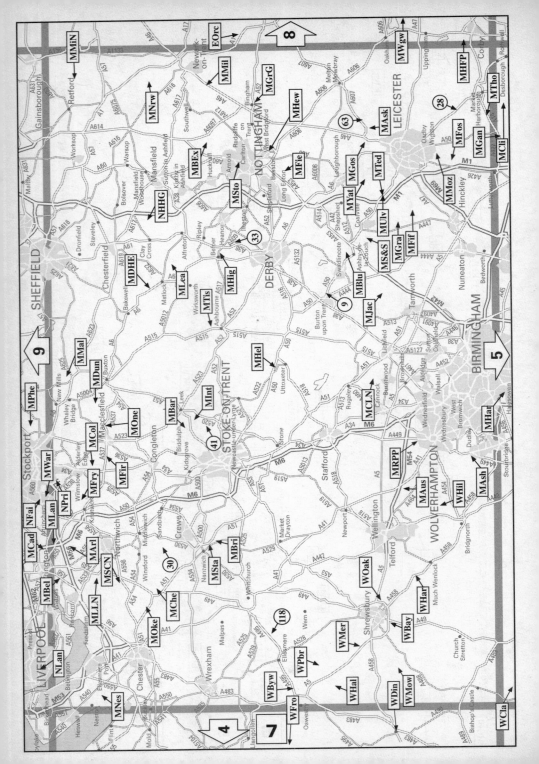

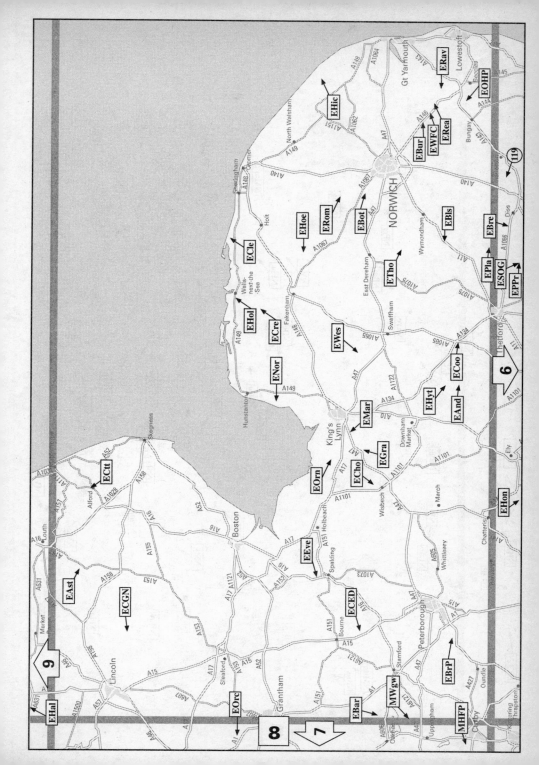

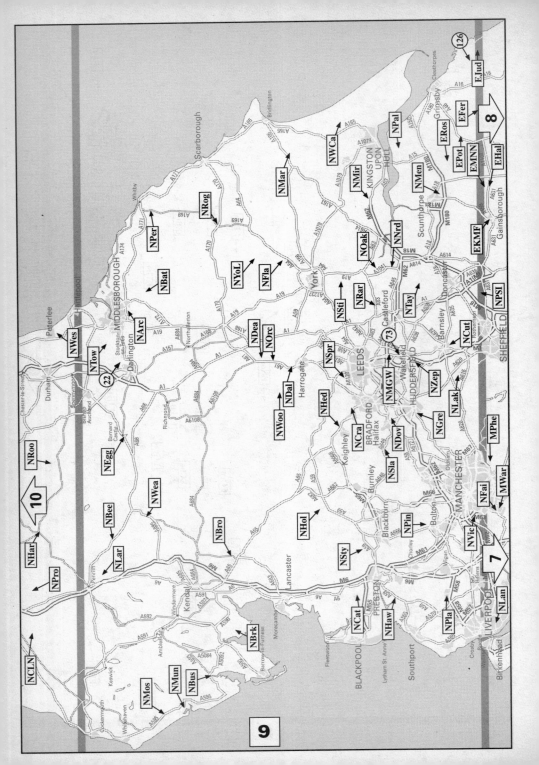

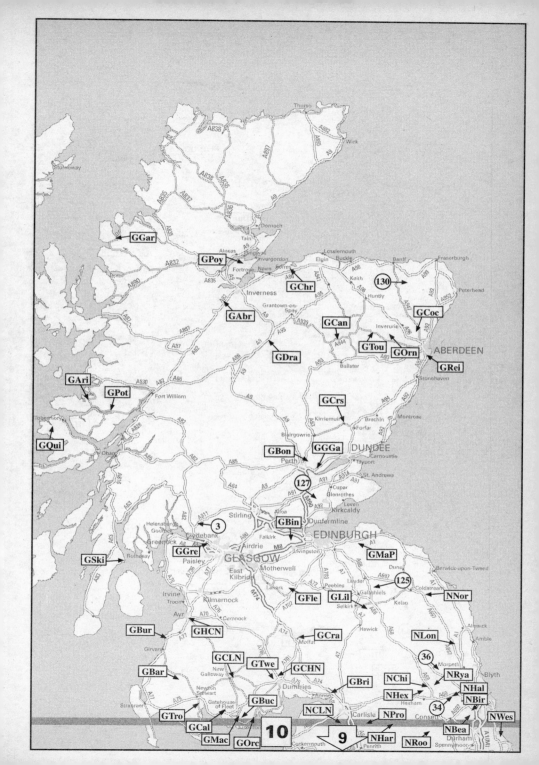

Your plant discoveries can work for you

At Bressingham we share your enthusiasm for new and unusual, hardy garden-worthy plants. Together we can bring your discoveries to gardeners worldwide.

Our New Plant Development Service gives you

Expert evaluation

Bressingham plantsmen and women are among the most knowledgeable and experienced. Where better to trial your plants than alongside our unique collection of rare, classic and unusual plants?

Commercial protection

Years as leaders in using the Plant Breeders' Rights system and US Plant Patents gives us unrivalled insight into the best way to protect your plants for the most income.

Market development

As brand leaders, our considerable marketing expertise is an indispensable asset to every serious plant launch and sales campaign.

International network

With our worldwide network we have considerable skill and experience introducing plants into key international markets.

Together we can realise your plants' full potential – successful, world–class varieties like *Astilbe Sprite AGM, Potentilla Red Ace, Fragaria Pink Panda, Hebe Margret* and *Polemonium Brise d'Anjou* say it all. Give us a ring – our 50 years' experience helping keen gardeners and growers to profit from their plant discoveries will stand you in good stead.

BLOOMS
of Bressingham

For further information contact
Paul Gooderham, or
Rodney Hall
tel 01379 687464 fax 01379 688034

IV

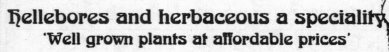

VI

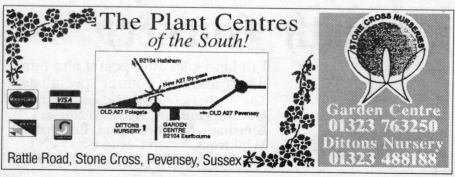

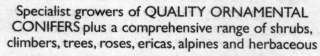

INDEX OF ADVERTISERS

THE HARDY PLANT SOCIETY

The Hardy Plant Society was formed to foster interest in hardy herbaceous plants on the widest possible scale. It aims to give its members information about the wealth of both well known and little known hardy plants, how to grow them to the best advantage and where they may be obtained. It also aims to ensure that all worthy hardy plants remain in cultivation and have the widest possible distribution.

Regional and Local Groups

Members may join any of the growing number of local groups organising many events in their own area including plant sales, garden visits, demonstrations and lectures. Most groups issue their own newsletter. the Groups form a basis for friendly exchange of information and plants and are an invaluable way of meeting other keen plantsmen locally. There is also a Correspondents Group for those not able to get out and about.

Genus and special Groups

Members may also join any of the specialised groups within the Society which will put them in touch with other members having similar interests. At present there are six such groups covering 'Variegated plants', 'Hardy Geraniums', 'Grasses', 'Paeony', 'Pulmonarias' and 'Half Hardy Plants'.

Publications and Slide Library

The Society's Journal 'The Hardy Plant' is currently issued twice a year containing major illustrated articles on a wide variety of plants and gardens. Regular newsletters keep members informed of current events. A central collection of slides is available for loan to members wishing to compile illustrated lectures.

Seed Distribution

Each year members are encouraged to collect seed from plants in their gardens for the seed Distribution which produces a printed list of all available seed, much of which comes from overseas. This currently lists over 2,500 varieties of seed, the majority of which is not available from commercial sources and, for a nominal sum members may select a number of packets from this.

Plant Sales and Shows

At organised meetings, both national and local, members bring interesting and unusual plants which are sold to aid the Society's funds. The Society puts on displays at the Royal Horticultural Society and other shows around the country and members can be involved by helping with the stands or by supplying plants to be shown.

Conservation

The Society is most concerned about the conservation of garden plants. Countless fine plants have totally disappeared from cultivation and remain but a memory. In close cooperation with the National Council for the Conservation of Plants and Gardens, the Society is making efforts to ensure that all worthy plants are kept in cultivation.

For further information or Membership Application Form please write to:

The Administrator
Mrs Pam Adams
Little Orchard
Great Comberton
Pershore
Worcs WR10 3DP

Tel No 01386 710317
Fax No 01386 710117

HARDY PLANT SOCIETY

MEMBERSHIP APPLICATION FOR 1998

The Annual Subscriptions are as follows:

Single Membership **£10.00**
Joint Membership (any two members living at the same address) **£12.00**

Subscriptions are renewable annually on **1 January**. Subscriptions of members joining after 1 October are valid until the end of the following year.

Overseas members are requested to remit by International Money Order in **Sterling** or by Credit Card. (Visa/Master Card/Eurocard/Access).

APPLICATION FORM

I/We wish to apply for membership for 1998

NAME/S ....

ADDRESS ....

....

.... POST CODE ....

TELEPHONE NUMBER ....

and would like to apply for the following type of membership

SINGLE	£10.00	....
JOINT (2 members at one address)	£12.00	....
Airmail postage (outside Europe)	£6.00	....
	TOTAL	....

I enclose a cheque in Pounds Sterling payable to **THE HARDY PLANT SOCIETY**.
(Please **DO NOT** send cheques in Foreign Currency)

OR
Please debit my Visa / Master Card / Eurocard / Access

CARD NUMBER ☐☐☐☐ ☐☐☐☐ ☐☐☐☐ ☐☐☐☐

EXPIRY DATE

☐☐☐☐

Your name as on Card ....

Signature .... Date ....

Please print name and address clearly, tear out page and send to:

**THE ADMINISTRATOR, Mrs Pam Adams,
Little Orchard, Great Comberton,
Pershore, Worcs. WR10 3DP. ENGLAND**
For further details of the Society please see previous page

The New Plantsman – essential reading if you have a passion for plants

Get the most out of your garden with the help of the RHS

Save £5

Whatever your gardening experience, there are times when having some expert advice would be very useful. Membership of the RHS is like having a panel of experts on hand whenever you need it. From practical advice in The Garden magazine to instructional model gardens and inspirational flower shows – there's something for every gardener. If you're already a member, then you'll know how much enjoyment you get from your membership, so why not give a gift of membership to a fellow garden lover.

Ten good reasons to join Britain's Gardening Charity today

- Save £5 by joining – or enrolling a friend – today
- Free monthly magazine *The Garden*
- Free unlimited access for you and a guest, to RHS Gardens Wisley, Rosemoor and Hyde Hall
- Free unlimited access for you to a further 24 beautiful gardens
- Reduced price tickets and members' only days to the Chelsea and Hampton Court Palace Flower Show,
- Reduced price tickets to BBC Gardeners' World Live, Scotland's National Gardening Show, Malvern Spring and Autumn Shows
- Free entry to monthly flower shows at Westminster
- Free gardening advice from Britain's experts
- Free seeds from RHS Garden Wisley
- Privileged access to over 250 talks and demonstrations

The RHS is not only the world's premier gardening organisation; it is your key to a world of gardening delights throughout the year. Simply complete the form below or make a copy and send it to us today to take advantage of this special price.

- -

The Plantfinder RHS membership offer

☐ **I would like to enjoy membership at the special reduced rate of £28 saving £5 (normal price of membership £33).**

☐ **I enclose a cheque made payable to The Royal Horticultural Society for £28.**

PLEASE COMPLETE IN BLOCK CAPITALS
YOUR DETAILS

Title ....Initials ....Surname...

Address..

....

Postcode...Daytime Tel. No. ....

Code 1154

Please return your completed form and cheque to : RHS Membership Department, 80 Vincent Square, London SW1P 2PE. Offer expires 31 October 1998. Please allow 28 days for delivery of your membership pack. Gift membership will be sent to you to pass on.